GEORGIA *continued*

GAU Atlanta University, Atlanta.
GAuA Augusta College, Augusta.
GColuC Columbus College, Columbus.
GCuA Andrews College, Cuthbert.
GDC Columbia Theological Seminary, Decatur.
GDS Agnes Scott College, Decatur.
GDecA* Agnes Scott College, Decatur.
GDecCT* Columbia Theological Seminary, Decatur.
GDoS South Georgia College, Douglas.
GEU Emory University, Atlanta.
GHi Georgia Historical Society, Savannah.
GMM Mercer University, Macon.
GMW Wesleyan College, Macon.
GMiW Woman's College of Georgia, Milledgeville.
GMilvC* Woman's College of Georgia, Milledgeville.
GOgU Oglethorpe University, Oglethorpe University.
GSDe* University of Georgia, DeRenne Library.
GU University of Georgia, Athens.
GU-De — DeRenne Georgia Library.
GU-Ex — Georgia State College of Business Administration Library, Atlanta.

HAWAII

HU University of Hawaii, Honolulu.
HU-EWC Center for Cultural and Technical Interchange between East and West, Honolulu.

ILLINOIS

I Illinois State Library, Springfield.
IC Chicago Public Library.
ICA Art Institute of Chicago, Chicago.
ICF Chicago Natural History Museum, Chicago.
ICF-A — Edward E. Ayer Ornithological Library.
ICHi Chicago Historical Society, Chicago.
ICIP Institute for Psychoanalysis, Chicago.
ICJ John Crerar Library, Chicago.
ICMILC* Center for Research Libraries, Chicago.
ICMcC McCormick Theological Seminary, Chicago.
ICN Newberry Library, Chicago.
ICRL Center for Research Libraries, Chicago.
ICU University of Chicago, Chicago.
ICarbS Southern Illinois University, Carbondale.
IEG Garrett Theological Seminary, Evanston.
IEN Northwestern University, Evanston.
IEdS Southern Illinois University, Edwardsville.
IGK Knox College, Galesburg.
IHi Illinois State Historical Library, Springfield.
ILS St. Procopius College, Lisle.
IMunS Saint Mary of the Lake Seminary, Mundelein.
INS Illinois State University, Normal.
IRA Augustana College Library, Rock Island.
IRivfR Rosary College, River Forest.
IU University of Illinois, Urbana.
IU-M — Medical Sciences Library, Chicago.
IU-U — Chicago Undergraduate Division, Chicago.

IOWA

IaAS Iowa State University of Science and Technology, Ames.
IaDL Luther College, Decorah.
IaDuC Loras College, Dubuque.
IaDuU University of Dubuque, Dubuque.
IaDuU-S — Theological Seminary Library.
IaDuW Wartburg Theological Seminary, Dubuque.
IaU University of Iowa, Iowa City.

IDAHO

IdB Boise Public Library.
IdPI Idaho State University, Pocatello.
IdPS* Idaho State University, Pocatello.
IdU University of Idaho, Moscow.

INDIANA

In Indiana State Library, Indianapolis.
InAndC Anderson College, Anderson.
InCollS* St. Joseph's College, Rensselaer.
InGo Goshen College Biblical Seminary Library, Goshen.
InHi Indiana Historical Society, Indianapolis.
InIB Butler University, Indianapolis.

INDIANA *continued*

InLP Purdue University, Lafayette.
InNd University of Notre Dame, Notre Dame.
InOlH* St. Leonard College Library, Dayton, Ohio.
InRE Earlham College, Richmond.
InRenS St. Joseph's College, Rensselaer.
InStme St. Meinrad's College & Seminary, St. Meinrad.
InU Indiana University, Bloomington.

KANSAS

K Kansas State Library, Topeka.
KAS St. Benedict's College, Atchison.
KAStB* St. Benedict's College, Atchison.
KHi Kansas State Historical Society, Topeka.
KKcB Central Baptist Theological Seminary, Kansas City.
KMK Kansas State University, Manhattan.
KStMC* St. Louis University, School of Divinity Library, St. Louis, Mo.
KU University of Kansas, Lawrence.
KU-M — Medical Center Library, Kansas City.
KWiU Wichita State University, Wichita.

KENTUCKY

Ky-LE Library Extension Division, Frankfort.
KyBgW Western Kentucky State College, Bowling Green
KyHi Kentucky Historical Society, Frankfort.
KyLo Louisville Free Public Library.
KyLoS Southern Baptist Theological Seminary, Louisville.
KyLoU University of Louisville, Louisville.
KyLx Lexington Public Library.
KyLxCB Lexington Theological Seminary, Lexington. (Formerly College of the Bible)
KyLxT Transylvania College, Lexington.
KyMoreT Morehead State College, Morehead.
KyU University of Kentucky, Lexington.
KyWA Asbury College Library, Wilmore.
KyWAT Asbury Theological Seminary, Wilmore.

LOUISIANA

L Louisiana State Library, Baton Rouge.
L-M Louisiana State Museum Library, New Orleans.
LCA Not a library symbol.
LCS Not a library symbol.
LHi Louisiana History Society, New Orleans.
LNHT Tulane University Library, New Orleans.
LNT-MA Tulane University, Latin American Library, New Orleans.
LU Louisiana State University, Baton Rouge.
LU-M — Medical Center Library, New Orleans.
LU-NO — Louisiana State University in New Orleans.

MASSACHUSETTS

M Massachusetts State Library, Boston.
MA Amherst College, Amherst.
MB Boston Public Library.
MBAt Boston Athenaeum, Boston.
MBBC* Boston College, Chestnut Hill.
MBCo Countway Library of Medicine. (Harvard-Boston Medical Libraries)
MBH Massachusetts Horticultural Society, Boston.
MBHo* Massachusetts Horticultural Society, Boston.
MBM* Countway Library of Medicine (Harvard-Boston Medical Libraries).
MBMu Museum of Fine Arts, Boston.
MBU Boston University.
MBdAF U.S. Air Force Cambridge Research Center, Bedford.
MBrZ Zion Research Library, Brookline.
MBrigStJ* St. John's Seminary, Brighton.
MBtS St. John's Seminary Library, Brighton.
MCM Massachusetts Institute of Technology, Cambridge.
MCR Radcliffe College, Cambridge.
MCSA Smithsonian Institution, Astrophysical Observatory, Cambridge.
MChB Boston College, Chestnut Hill.
MH Harvard University, Cambridge.
MH-A — Arnold Arboretum.
MH-AH — Andover-Harvard Theological Library.
MH-BA — Graduate School of Business Administration Library.
MH-FA — Fine Arts Library. (Formerly Fogg Art Museum)
MH-G — Gray Herbarium Library.
MH-HY — Harvard-Yenching Institute. (Chinese-Japanese Library)

MASSACHUSETTS *continued*

MH-L — Law School Library.
MH-P — Peabody Museum Library.
MH-PR — Physics Research Library.
MHi Massachusetts Historical Society, Boston.
MMeT Tufts University, Medford.
MNF Forbes Library, Northampton.
MNS Smith College, Northampton.
MNoeS Stonehill College Library, North Easton.
MNtcA Andover Newton Theological School, Newton Center.
MSaE Essex Institute, Salem.
MShM Mount Holyoke College, South Hadley.
MU University of Massachusetts, Amherst.
MWA American Antiquarian Society, Worcester.
MWAC Assumption College, Worcester.
MWC Clark University, Worcester.
MWH College of the Holy Cross, Worcester.
MWalB Brandeis University, Waltham.
MWelC Wellesley College, Wellesley.
MWhB Marine Biological Laboratory, Woods Hole.
MWiW Williams College, Williamstown.
MWiW-C — Chapin Library.

MARYLAND

MdAN U.S. Naval Academy, Annapolis.
MdBE Enoch Pratt Free Library, Baltimore.
MdBG Goucher College, Baltimore.
MdBJ Johns Hopkins University, Baltimore.
MdBJ-G — John Work Garrett Library.
MdBP Peabody Institute, Baltimore.
MdBWA Walters Art Gallery, Baltimore.
MdU University of Maryland, College Park.
MdW Woodstock College, Woodstock.

MAINE

MeB Bowdoin College, Brunswick.
MeBa Bangor Public Library.
MeU University of Maine, Orono.
MeWC Colby College, Waterville.
MeWaC* Colby College, Waterville.

MICHIGAN

Mi Michigan State Library, Lansing.
MiAC Alma College, Alma.
MiD Detroit Public Library.
MiD-B — Burton Historical Collection.
MiDA Detroit Institute of Arts, Detroit.
MiDU University of Detroit, Detroit.
MiDW Wayne State University, Detroit.
MiEM Michigan State University, East Lansing.
MiEalC* Michigan State University, East Lansing.
MiGr Grand Rapids Public Library.
MiH* Michigan College of Mining and Technology, Houghton.
MiHM Michigan College of Mining and Technology, Houghton.
MiU University of Michigan, Ann Arbor.
MiU-C — William L. Clements Library.

MINNESOTA

MnCS St. John's University, Collegeville.
MnH* Minnesota Historical Society, St. Paul.
MnHi Minnesota Historical Society, St. Paul.
MnRM Mayo Clinic and Foundation Library, Rochester.
MnSJ James Jerome Hill Reference Library, St. Paul.
MnSSC College of St. Catherine, St. Paul.
MnU University of Minnesota, Minneapolis.

MISSOURI

MoHi Missouri State Historical Society, Columbia
MoK Kansas City Public Library.
MoKL Linda Hall Library, Kansas City
MoKU University of Missouri at Kansas City, Kansas City.
MoS St. Louis Public Library.
MoSB Missouri Botanical Garden, St. Louis.
MoSC* Concordia Seminary Library, St. Louis.
MoSCS Concordia Seminary Library, St. Louis.
MoSM Mercantile Library Association, St. Louis.
MoSU St. Louis University, St. Louis.
MoSU-D — School of Divinity Library, St. Louis.
MoSW Washington University, St. Louis.
MoU University of Missouri, Columbia.

The National Union Catalog

Pre-1956 Imprints

The National Union Catalog

Pre-1956 Imprints

A cumulative author list representing Library of Congress printed cards and titles reported by other American libraries. Compiled and edited with the cooperation of the Library of Congress and the National Union Catalog Subcommittee of the Resources Committee of the Resources and Technical Services Division, American Library Association

Volume 300

KNAPP, JOHANN GEORG (DE S) -
KNOX, ROSE

Mansell 1973

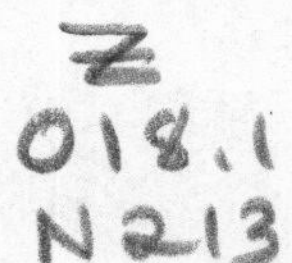

Mansell Information/Publishing Limited
3 Bloomsbury Place, London WC1

The American Library Association
50 East Huron Street, Chicago, Illinois 60611

The paper on which this catalog has been printed is supplied by P. F. Bingham Limited and has been specially manufactured by the Guard Bridge Paper Company Limited of Fife, Scotland. Based on requirements established by the late William J. Barrow for a permanent/durable book paper it is laboratory certified to meet or exceed the following values:

Substance 89 gsm
pH cold extract 9·4
Fold endurance (MIT ½kg. tension) 1200
Tear resistance (Elmendorf) 73 (or 67 × 3)
Opacity 90·3%

Library of Congress Card Number: 67–30001
SBN: 7201 0358 4

Printed by Balding & Mansell Limited, London and Wisbech, England
Bound by Bemrose & Sons Limited, Derby, England

American Library Association

Resources and Technical Services Division

RESOURCES COMMITTEE

SUBCOMMITTEE ON THE NATIONAL UNION CATALOG

Publisher's Note

Because of the large number of sources from which the information in the National Union Catalog has been collected over a long period of time an understanding of its scope and an acquaintance with its methods is necessary for the best use to be made of it. Users are therefore earnestly advised to make themselves familiar with the introductory matter in Volume 1. This fully defines the scope of the Catalog and sets out the basis on which the material reported to the National Union Catalog has been edited for publication in book form.

National Union Catalog Designation

Each main entry in the Catalog has been ascribed a unique identifying designation. This alphanumeric combination appears uniformly after the last line of the entry itself and consists of:

1 The letter N, signifying National Union Catalog.
2 The initial letter under which the entry is filed.
3 A number representing the position of the entry within the sequence under its initial letter.

This National Union Catalog designator is sufficient both to identify any main entry in the Catalog and to establish its position within the sequence of volumes. It is, however, recommended that when referring to titles by the National Union Catalog designation a checking element, such as the key word or initials of the title, be added.

Reported Locations

Alphabetic symbols which represent libraries in the United States and Canada follow the National Union Catalog designation. These groups of letters signify which libraries have reported holding copies of the work. The first library so represented usually is the one that provided the catalog information.

Printed on the end sheets of each volume is a list of most frequently used symbols, each followed by the full name of the library. *List of Symbols*, containing a comprehensive list of symbols used, is published as a separate volume with the Catalog. The Library of Congress has also issued *Symbols Used in the National Union Catalog of the Library of Congress*. In cases where a symbol is not identified in these lists the National Union Catalog Division of the Library of Congress will, on enquiry, attempt to identify the library concerned.

Other Developments

Under the terms of their agreement with the American Library Association, the publishers have undertaken to apply, as far as is practicable, new developments in library science and techniques which may have the effect of further enhancing the value of the Catalog. To this end, the publishers will be pleased to receive suggestions and enquiries relating to technical and production aspects of the Catalog and will be glad to consider proposals calculated to improve its utility and amenity. Mansell Information/Publishing Limited will be pleased also to advise libraries on possible applications of the methods and techniques developed for this and similar projects to their own requirements.

J.C.
London, *August 1968*

VOLUME 300

Knapp, Johann Georg, 1705-1771.
A30 ... De statu temporum Nato Christo et de
H2 singulari plane temporis nostri signo.
1755K Halae Magdeburgicae, 1755.

Programm - Halle.

NK 0196408 CtY

609.2 KNAPP, Johann Georg, 1705-1771
F829.9 Denkmal der schuldigen Hochachtung und
K67de Liebe gestiftet dem weiland Hochwürdigen
1770 und Hochgelarten Herrn D. Gotthilf August
Francken ... Nunmehr gesamlet und herausgegeben von D. Johann Georg Knapp ... Halle, in der Buchhandlung des Waisenhauses, 1770.
24p.l., 40, 60, 139, [1]p. front. (port.) 23.5cm.

NK 0196409 MH-AH IU PPLT CtY

Knapp, Johann Georg, 1705-1771, praeses
A31 Dispvtatio theologica de recto et genvino
K727 vsv argvmentorvm fidem hvmanam facientivm in
1757b probanda divina origine s. litteratvm. Halae Magdebvrgicae[1757]
Diss.-Halle(C.S.Baer, respondent)

NK 0196410 CtY

[Knapp, Johann Georg] 1705-1771, ed.
Neuere geschichte der evangelischen missionsanstalten zu bekehrung der heiden in Ostindien
see under title

---

621 KNAPP, Johann Georg, 1705-1771.
K67sa ... Samlung vermischter theologischer
1759 Abhandlungen ... Halle, in Verlegung des Waisenhauses, 1750-1760.
2v. in 1. 18cm.

At head of title: Johann Georg Knappens ...

NK 0196412 MH-AH

705.47 KNAPP, Johann Jacob
K67ła Gepruefter Widerspruch, welcher ver-
1745 mittelst Anfuehrung der heiligen Schrifft, Vernunft, LL. Symbolicorum, Kirchen=Historie, Friedens=Schluesse und anderer Reichs=Satzungen, wider die von den Hohenlohe Waldenburgischen evangelischen Pfarr=Gemeinden 1744. nach der evangelischen Reichs=Staenden gemeinsamlich abgefassten Verordnung celebrirte Oster=Feyer, in fuenf, theils academischen, theils Privat-Schrifften sich geaeusert,...[n.p., n.d]
423p. 18cm.

Bound with his: Lacrymae paschales hohenlohicae - ...

NK 0196414 MH-AH

705.47 KNAPP, Johann Jacob
K67ła Lacrymae paschales hohenlohicae oder
1745 historischer Bericht, von denen in der Graffschafft Hohenlohe Waldenburgischer Linie, Anno 1744. Bey Gelegenheit der Oster=Feyer=Discrepanz entstandenen Unruhen, aus denen Original-Actis gestellt. Gedruckt im Jahr Christi 1745.
9p.l., 412p. 18cm.

With this is bound his: Gepruefter Widerspruch...

NK 0196415 MH-AH

Knapp, Johann Jacob
Theologisch- und rechtliche Belehrungen die Gerechtsame derer protestantischen Kirchen unter cathol. Herrschafften im Römis. Reich, in Ansehung sowohl der Oster-Feyerlichen Discrepanz sonderheitlich, als auch anderer Vorfallenheiten betreffend, welchen eine Vor-Erinnerung von der Kirchen-Freyheit voran gesetzet hat Johann Jacob Knapp ... [Oehringen?] 1745.
17 p.l., 277 p. 16cm.

NK 0196416 MH-L

Knapp, Johann Martin
see Knapp, Martin, 1876-

Knapp, Johann Michael, 1793-1856, Denkmale der christlichen religion.

Bunsen, Christian Karl Josias, *freiherr* von, 1791-1860.
Die basiliken des christlichen Roms, nach ihrem zusammenhange mit idee und geschichte der kirchenbaukunst dargestellt von Christian Carl Josias Bunsen ... Auch, als erläuternder text zu dem kupfer-werke: Die basiliken des christlichen Roms (früher unter dem titel "Denkmale der christlichen religion &c. &c."), aufgenommen von ... J. G. Gutensohn und J. M. Knapp. München, Cotta [1843]

Avery
AA
363 Knapp, Johann Michael, 1793-1861.
R6 Monumenti dell'antico culto cristiano; o
B881 sia raccolta di tavole rappresentanti le sacre basiliche e chiese di Roma dal quarto sino al decimoterzo secolo. Delineate e pubblicate dall'architetto Giovanni Michele Knapp. Roma, 1840.
49 plates (incl. plans) 58cm.

Translation of Denkmale der christlichen Religion by Knapp and Johann Gutensohn.

NK 0196419 NNC

W 4 KNAPP, Johanna (Trautner) 1920-
M22 Über einige seltenere Suchten und die
1955 Beeinflussung ihrer Entziehungserscheinungen mit dem Phenothiazinderivat Megaphen. [Mainz] 1955.
49 ℓ.
Inaug.-Diss. - Mainz.
1. Mental disorders 2. Phenothiazine

NK 0196420 DNLM

Knapp, John.
The Two Bible Societies: being a Correspondence ... reprinted from "The Portsmouth Times." P., [1874]
16 p. 8°. [In College Pamphlets, v. 1471]
I. Bullinger, Ethelbert Wm.

NK 0196421 CtY

Knapp, John C.
Erstes deutsches systematisches lesebuch. Mit stoff zu anschauungs- und denkübungen von Johann C. Knapp ... Louisville, Ky., H. Knöfel; New York, E. Steiger [etc.] 1866.
2 v. $18\frac{1}{2}$cm.
On t.-p. of "2. lesebuch": Mit stoff zu sprach-, auschauungs- und denkübungen. Für die mittelklassen der deutsch-amerikanischen schulen bearb. von Knapp, Funke, Knöfel u. a.

1. Primers, German. 2. German language—Chrestomathies and readers. I. Funke, ———, joint author. II. Knoefel, Henry, joint author.

CA 17-3743 Unrev'd

Library of Congress PF3113.K65

NK 0196422 DLC MiU T

Knapp, John Francis, 1810-1830, defendant.
Most important testimony adduced on the trial of John Francis Knapp and Joseph Jenkins Knapp, jr. for the murder of Capt. Joseph White, of Salem ... April 6, 1830. Providence, 1830.
36 p. front. 21 cm.

NK 0196423 RPB

Knapp, John Francis, 1810-1830, *defendant.*
A report of the evidence and points of law, arising in the trial of John Francis Knapp, for the murder of Joseph White, esquire. Before the Supreme judicial court of the commonwealth of Massachusetts; together with the charge of His Honor Chief Justice Parker, to the grand jury, at the opening of the court. Salem, W. & S. B. Ives, 1830.
4 p. l., [3]-74 p. illus. (incl. plans) $21\frac{1}{2}$cm.
——— Copy 2. [Miscellaneous pamphlets, v. 1026, no. 6]
AC901.M5 vol. 1026

—— Appendix to the report of the trial of John Francis Knapp, on an indictment for murder. Containing the new evidence, the arguments of counsel, and the charge of His Honor Judge Putnam, to the jury, on the second trial. Salem ed. [Salem] 1830.
72 p. $21\frac{1}{2}$cm.
Arguments of Franklin Dexter, counsel for the prisoner, and Daniel Webster, counsel for the state.
1. White, Joseph, d. 1830. I. Parker, Isaac, 1768-1830. II. Dexter, Franklin, 1793-1857. III. Webster, Daniel, 1782-1852. IV. Putnam, Samuel, 1768-1853. V. Massachusetts. Supreme judicial court. VI. Title.

28-22030

Library of Congress

NK 0196425 DLC Vi PP ICN MnU-L CtY

Knapp, John Francis, 1810-1830, *defendant.*
Second trial of John Francis Knapp by a new jury, recommenced at Salem, August 14, 1830, for the murder of Capt. Joseph White, before the Supreme judicial court of the commonwealth of Massachusetts, at a special session, commenced at Salem, July 20, 1830. Reported for the publishers. Boston, Dutton and Wentworth, 1830.
28 p. illus. (incl. port., plans) $21\frac{1}{2}$cm.

1. White, Joseph, d. 1830. I. Massachusetts. Supreme judicial court. II. Title.

28-22028

NK 0196426 DLC MWA

Knapp, John Francis, 1810-1830, *defendant.*
The trial and conviction of John Francis Knapp for the murder of Joseph White, esq. of Salem, on the sixth of April, 1830. Boston, C. Ellms, 1830.
35, [1] p. incl. front. (ports.) $21\frac{1}{2}$cm.
Title vignette.
Second trial, August 14-20, 1830, in the Supreme judicial court.

1. White, Joseph, d. 1830. I. Massachusetts. Supreme judicial court. II. Title.

28-22029

NK 0196427 DLC MWA NN WaU-L

Knapp, John Francis, 1810-1830, *defendant.*
The trial in the case of the Commonwealth, *versus* John Francis Knapp, for the murder of Joseph White, esq. of Salem, Mass. at a special session of the S. J. court, holden at Salem on the third Tuesday in July, 1830. [n. p., 1830?]
1 p. l., [5]-36 p. 22cm.
Title vignette.

1. White, Joseph, d. 1830. I. Massachusetts. Supreme judicial court. II. Title.

28-22031

NK 0196428 DLC MWA NBuU CtY NN

VOLUME 300

Knapp, John Francis, 1810–1830, *defendant.*
Trial of George Crowninshield, J. J. Knapp, jun. and John Francis Knapp, for the murder of Capt. Joseph White, of Salem, on the night of the sixth of April, 1830. Reported by John W. Whitman, esq. Boston, Beals and Homer, and F. Ingraham, 1830.
104 p. 21½cm.
Trial of John Francis Knapp opened Aug. 3, 1830, at Salem, in the Supreme judicial court of Massachusetts and ended Aug. 13, 1830, the jury disagreeing. By order of the court, the government proceeded, the following morning, to try the case again.
Trials of George Crowninshield and J. J. Knapp are not included.
1. White, Joseph, d. 1830. I. Whitman, John Winslow, 1798–1833, reporter. II. Massachusetts. Supreme judicial court.
45-41296

NK 0196429 DLC ICU CtY PPB MH RPB WaU-L MB PP

Knapp, John Francis, 1810–1830, *defendant.*
Trial of John Francis Knapp as principal in the second degree for the murder of Capt. Joseph White, before the Supreme judicial court of the commonwealth of Massachusetts, at a special session, commenced at Salem, July 30, 1830. Reported for the publishers. Boston, Dutton and Wentworth, 1830.
60 p. illus. (incl. plans) 22½cm.
1. White, Joseph, d. 1830. I. Massachusetts. Supreme judicial court. II. Title.
28-22027

NK 0196430 DLC ICN MB NN MH

Knapp, John I 1825–
Illustrated history and biographical record of Lenawee County, Mich. ... By John I. Knapp and R. I. Bonner. Adrian, Mich., The Times printing company, 1903.
511 p. incl. front., illus., ports. 25½cm.
1. Lenawee Co., Mich.—Hist. 2. Lenawee Co., Mich.—Biog. I. Bonner, Richard I., 1838– joint author.
4-16330
Library of Congress F572.L5K6 Copyright

NK 0196431 DLC MiU NN

[Knapp, John Leonard] 1767–1845.
Country rambles in England; or, Journal of a naturalist; with notes and additions by the author of "Rural hours" [*i. e.* Susan Fenimore Cooper] ... Buffalo, Phinney & co., 1853.
3 p. l., [v]–x, [11]–336 p., 1 l. col. front., illus., 2 pl. 18½cm.
Added t.-p. in colors.
First pub. in 1829 under the title: The journal of a naturalist.
1. Natural history — England. 2. Natural history — Outdoor books. I. Cooper, Susan Fenimore, 1813–1894.
6-18046†
Library of Congress QH137.K6

NK 0196432 DLC PSt CoU OrP ViU PU NRU IU

Knapp, John Leonard, 1767–1845.
Gramina britannica; or, Representations of the British grasses with remarks and occasional descriptions. By J. L. Knapp ... London, Printed for the author, by T. Bensley, 1804.
3 p. l., 125 l. CXIX col. pl. 30½cm.
1. Grasses. [1. Gramineæ] 2. Botany—Gt. Brit. [2. Gt. Brit.—Botany]
Agr 6—908
U. S. Dept. of agr. Library for Library of Congress 452.3K722 [a40b1]

NK 0196433 DNAL MBH NIC

Knapp, John Leonard, 1767–1845.
Gramina britannica; or, Representations of the British grasses. With remarks and occasional descriptions. By L. J. Knapp ... 2d ed. London, Longman and co.; [etc., etc.] 1842.
127 l. 119 (*i. e.* 118) col. pl. 29½cm.
Plate 61 omitted in numbering.
1. Grasses—Gt. Brit.
6—40784
Library of Congress QK495.G74K7

NK 0196434 DLC MdBP NcD NIC WU MiU PPFr MdBP ICJ MH

Knapp, John Leonard, 1767-1845.
The journal of a naturalist. London, J. Murray, 1829.
xii, 403 p. 7 plates (part double, 1 fold.) 18.9 cm.
Subsequently published under title: Country rambles in England.
1. Natural history - England. 2. Natural history - Outdoor books. I. Title.

NK 0196435 CtU MH-A CtY

[**Knapp, John Leonard**] 1767–1845.
The journal of a naturalist. 2d ed. London, J. Murray, 1829.
1 p. l., [v]–xvi, 423 p. illus., VII pl. (4 double) 19½cm.
Title vignette.
Subsequently published under title: Country rambles in England.
1. Natural history—England. 2. Natural history—Outdoor books. I. Title.
6—18047
Library of Congress QH137.K5

NK 0196436 DLC CU OkU CaBVaU CtY PU-B ICJ OClW OU

[**Knapp, John Leonard**] 1767–1845.
The journal of a naturalist. 3d ed. London, J. Murray, 1830.
1 p. l., [v]–xvi, 440 p. illus., VII pl. (1 col., 4 double) 19½cm.
Title vignette.
Subsequently published under title: Country rambles in England.
1. Natural history—England. 2. Natural history—Outdoor books. I. Title.
35-33866
Library of Congress QH137.K5 1830

NK 0196437 DLC NcD CU OCl MH-A MdBP NN PPAN UU

[**Knapp, John Leonard**] 1767–1845.
The journal of a naturalist ... Philadelphia, Carey & Lea, 1831.
viii, [9]–286 p., 1 l. front., illus., pl. 18½cm.
Subsequently published under title: Country rambles in England.
1. Natural history — England. 2. Natural history — Outdoor books. I. Title.
6—18048
Library of Congress QH137.K5 1831

NK 0196438 DLC CU KyLx NjR KyU MeU ViU DI-GS NNBG IU PSC PP PPA MiU OO OClW AU MH MeB

[KNAPP, John Leonard], 1767-1845.
The journal of a naturalist. Philadelphia, G.W.Donahue, 1837.
Front.

NK 0196439 MH

[**Knapp, John Leonard**] 1767–1845.
The journal of a naturalist. 4th ed. London, J. Murray, 1838.
1 p. l., [v]–xvi, 440 p. illus., VII pl. (1 col., 4 double) 19½cm.
Title vignette.
Subsequently published under title: Country rambles in England.

NK 0196440 PSt CU MH MU OCU

QH 137 .K67 (Rare) [Knapp, John Leonard] 1767-1845.
The journal of a naturalist. Philadelphia, Gihon & Smith, 1846.
viii, 296 p. illus.
Subsequently published under title: Country rambles in England.
1. Natural history--England. 2. Natural history--Outdoor books. I. Title.

NK 0196441 ICU MH-Z PHi

[**Knapp, John Leonard**] 1767–1845.
The journal of a naturalist ... Philadelphia, J. & J. L. Gihon, 1850.
viii, [9]–286 p., 1 l. illus., 2 pl. incl. front. 19½cm.
Subsequently published under the title: Country rambles in England.
1. Natural history—England. 2. Natural history—Outdoor books. I. Title.
35-33865
Library of Congress QH137.K5 1850

NK 0196442 DLC PU CSmH

Knapp, John Matthew, *ed.*
The universities and the social problem, an account of the university settlements in East London; edited by John M. Knapp ... London, Rivington, Percival & co., 1895.
x, 235 p. 19½cm.
CONTENTS.—Introduction: "Settlements" in England and America [by] the Right Hon. Sir J. Gorst.—Working men's clubs [by] the Rev. A. F. Winnington-Ingram.—Hospitalities [by] the Rev. Canon S. A. Barnett.—The university settlement in relation to local administration [by] P. Alden.—The children's country holidays fund, and the settlements [by] C. Jackson.—Mayfield house (Cheltenham ladies' college settlement) by M. Corbett.—St. Margaret's house, Bethnal green (ladies' branch of the Oxford house) [by] M. Talbot.—The Repton club [by] H. Legge.—The Oxford house and the organization of charity [by] W. A. Bailward.—Shelters [by] the Rev. O. Jay.—Thrift and social intercourse [by] Mrs. Mace.—The clubs of the Club and institute union [by] T. S. Peppin.—The Federation of working men's social clubs: what it is and what it may be [by] G. Fiennes.
1. Social settlements. I. Gorst, Sir John Eldon, 1835–1916. II. Winnington-Ingram, Arthur Foley, bp. of London, 1858– III. Title.
E 10—867
U. S. Off. of educ. Library for Library of Congress HV4238.L7K7

NK 0196444 DHEW OrPR ICU PU PPL PBm MiU OClW DLC ICJ MdBP NN

Knapp, Josef Armin
see
Knapp, Jósef Armin.

Knapp, Joseph.
Gustav Friedrich Oehler; ein Lebensbild... Tübingen, J.J. Heckenhauer, 1876.
vi, 272 p. 23cm.
Bibliographical footnotes.
1 Oehler, Gustav Friedrich, 1812-1872

NK 0196446 NjPT MH-AH NcD CtY ICarbS PPLT

Knapp, Joseph.
Lebensbild von Albert Knapp. Eigene Aufzeichnungen ...
see under Knapp, Albert, 1798-1864.

VOLUME 300

Knapp, Joseph Burke.
... Fire-killed Douglas fir: a study of its rate of deterioration, usability, and strength. By Joseph Burke Knapp. Washington, Govt. print. off., 1912.
18 p. incl. tables, diagrs. 2 fold. diagr. 23cm. (U. S. Dept. of agriculture. Forest service. Bulletin 112. Forest products laboratory series)
1. Douglas fir. 2. Timber, Fire-killed.
Agr 12-1648
Library, U. S. Dept. of Agriculture 1F76B no. 112

NK 0196448 DNAL NcD Or OrU PPAmP PPAN MiU OO MH-A NN MB OrCS

KNAPP, Joseph Burke.
Montana's secondary wood-using industries. Compiled by U.S.forest service through J.B. Knapp. n.p.,[1912?].
4°. pp.(4).
"Reprinted from the Timberman,Portland,Oregon Nov.1912."

NK 0196449 MH-BA

Knapp, Joseph Burke, joint author.

SD11 .A2 no. 88

Cline, McGarvey.
... Properties and uses of Douglas fir. Part I. Mechanical properties. Part II. Commercial uses. By McGarvey Cline ... and J. B. Knapp ... Washington, Govt. print. off., 1911.

---

582 K67

Knapp,Joseph Burke,
...Western red cedar in the Pacific northwest,by Joseph Burke Knapp...& Alexander Grant Jackson...[no imprint]
cover-title,[24] p. illus. 23 cm.
Folded tables inserted.
At head of title:U.S.Dept.of Agriculture. Forest service.
Reprinted from the West coast lumberman, Feb.1,1914 & Mar.1,1914.
-- ---copies 2-3.

NK 0196451 MiU

Knapp, Joseph I
Catalogue of valuable paintings and sculpture belonging to the estates of the late J. F. Knapp and W. Sherburne, and several private collectors... Sold at unrestricted public sale...Jan... 1909, at Mendelssohn Hall... New York: Amer. Art Assoc., 1909. 48 l. 8°.
Priced.
1. Paintings.—Collections (Private): Knapp. 2. Paintings.—Collections (Private): Sherburne. 3. Sculpture.—Collections (Private): Knapp. 4. Sculpture.—Collections (Private): Sherburne. 5. Sherburne, Warren.
N. Y. P. L. May 14, 1914.

NK 0196452 NN

Knapp, Mrs. Joseph F
see Knapp, Phoebe (Palmer) 1839-1908.

Knapp, Joseph Gillett, 1805-
Ancient lakes of Wisconsin. By Hon. J. G. Knapp ...
(*In* Wisconsin academy of sciences, arts and letters. Transactions. Madison, Wis., 1872. 23cm. v. 1, p. 151-153)
1. Lakes—Wisconsin.
A 23-1200
Title from Wisconsin Univ. Printed by L. C.

NK 0196454 WU OCl MiU

Knapp, Joseph Gillett, 1805-
Coniferae of the Rocky Mountains. By J. G. Knapp ...
(*In* Wisconsin academy of sciences, arts and letters. Transactions. Madison, Wis., 1872. 23cm. v. 1, p. 117-123)
1. Coniferae.
A 23-1196
Title from Wisconsin Univ. Printed by L. C.

NK 0196455 WU MiU

Knapp, Joseph Gillett, 1805-1888.
Early reminiscences of Madison. By Judge J. G. Knapp. Read before the Society, July 12, 1866.
(*In* Wisconsin. State historical society. Report and collections ... 1869-1872. Madison, 1872. 23cm. v. 6, p. [366]-387)
1. Madison, Wis.
20-5284 Revised
Library of Congress F576.W81 vol. 6

NK 0196456 DLC MdBP

A280.29 K72

Knapp, Joseph Grant, 1900-
[Addresses, statements, etc.]
[Washington]

NK 0196457 DNAL

Knapp, Joseph Grant, 1900-
... Compra cooperativa de aperos y productos agrícolas, por Joseph G. Knapp ... Wáshington, D. C., Unión panamericana, Oficina de cooperación agrícola [1937]
2 p. l., 2-26 numb. l. 27½cm. ([Pan American union. Division of agricultural cooperation] Serie sobre cooperativas, no. 4, enero de 1937)
Reproduced from type-written copy.
Issued also in English.
1. Agricultural machinery—Trade and manufacture—U. S. 2. Agriculture, Cooperative—U. S. I. Title.
44-28337
Library of Congress HD2961.P28 no. 4
(334.6082) 334.62

NK 0196458 DLC DPU

Knapp, Joseph Grant, 1900-
... A compra cooperativa de fornecimentos para a agricultura, por Joseph G. Knapp ... Washington, D.C., União panamericana, Departamento de cooperação agricola [1937]
2 p. l., 2-22 numb. l. 27½cm. ([Pan American union. Division of agricultural cooperation] Serie sobre cooperativas, no. 4, junho de 1937)
Reproduced from type-written copy.
Issued also in English.
1. Agricultural machinery—Trade and manufacture—U. S. 2. Agriculture, Cooperative—U. S. I. Title.
44-28295
Library of Congress HD2961.P27 no. 4
(334.6082) 334.62

NK 0196459 DLC DPU

Knapp, Joseph Grant, 1900-
Cooperative farm supply purchasing in the British isles, by Joseph G. Knapp, principal agricultural economist. Farm credit administration, Cooperative research and service division, Washington, D. C. ... [Washington, U. S. Govt. print. off.] 1939.
vi, 86 p. incl. illus. (incl. maps) tables, diagrs. 23cm. ([U. S.] Farm credit administration. Bulletin, no. 31)
Running title: Cooperative purchasing in British isles.
Bibliography: p. 79-81.
1. Agricultural cooperative credit associations—Gt. Brit. I. Title. II. Title: Cooperative purchasing in British isles.
39-26915
Library of Congress HG2051.U5A574 no. 31

NK 0196460 DLC WaWW CaBVaU PPTU OU OClFRB

Knapp, Joseph Grant, 1900- joint author.

HD9433 .U4N6

Nourse, Edwin Griswold, 1883-
The co-operative marketing of livestock, by Edwin G. Nourse and Joseph G. Knapp. Washington, D. C., The Brookings institution, 1931.

Knapp, Joseph Grant, 1900-
... Cooperative purchasing of farm supplies, by Joseph G. Knapp ... Washington, D. C., Pan American union, Division of agricultural cooperation [1937]
2 p. l., 2-23 numb. l. 27cm. ([Pan American union. Division of agricultural cooperation] Series on cooperatives, no. 4, January, 1937)
Reproduced from type-written copy.
"This article is largely adapted from Cooperative purchasing of farm supplies, by Joseph G. Knapp and John H. Lister, Bull. no. 1 of the Cooperative division, Farm credit administration ... September, 1935."
1. Agricultural machinery—Trade and manufacture—U. S. 2. Agriculture, Cooperative—U. S. I. Title.
P A 37-22 Revised
Pan Amer. union. Library for Library of Congress HD2961.P26 no. 4
[r44d2] (334.6082) 334.62

NK 0196462 DPAHO MnHi PPT DLC

Knapp, Joseph Grant, 1900-
E. A. Stokdyk, architect of cooperation. Washington, American Institute of Cooperation [°1953]
ix, 229 p. illus., ports. 24 cm.
"Bibliography of [writings by] E. A. Stokdyk": p. 215-221.
1. Stokdyk, Ellis Adolph, 1897-1946. 2. Agriculture, Cooperative—U. S.
HD1491.U5S8 923.373 53-11613

NK 0196463 DLC DNAL MU PP PU PSt CU NIC IU MiD TU NN TxU OU OOxM OrCS IdU MtBC OrP

Knapp, Joseph Grant, 1900- joint author.

Froker, Rudolph Knugaard.
Farmers' purchasing associations in Wisconsin, by Rudolph K. Froker, associate professor, Department of agricultural economics, University of Wisconsin and Joseph G. Knapp, principal agricultural economist, Cooperative division, Farm credit administration. Wisconsin Agricultural experiment station in cooperation with Cooperative division, Farm credit administration ... October, 1937. [Washington, U. S. Govt. print. off., 1938]

Knapp, Joseph Grant, 1900-
... Handbook on major regional farm supply purchasing cooperatives, 1941 and 1942, by Joseph G. Knapp ... [Washington] 1943.
cover-title, 2 p.l., [3]-61 p. map, tables, diagrs. 27cm. (U. S. Farm credit administration. Cooperative research and service division. Miscellaneous report, no. 67)
1. Agriculture, Cooperative - U. S.
I. Title: Purchasing cooperatives.

NK 0196465 NNC PPTU

Knapp, Joseph Grant, 1900-
... Handbook on major regional farm supply purchasing cooperatives, 1942 and 1943, by Joseph G. Knapp. Cooperative research and service division ... [Washington] 1944.
2 p. l., 53 p. map, tables. (U. S. Farm credit administration. Cooperative research and service division. Miscellaneous report, no. 73)
At head of title: Farm credit administration. United States Department of agriculture. Washington, D. C.

NK 0196466 NNC PPT

VOLUME 300

Knapp, Joseph Grant, 1900-
Handbook on major regional farm supply purchasing cooperatives, 1945-46, by Joseph G. Knapp and Jane L. Scearce. ₍Washington₎ Cooperative research and service division, 1947.
45 p. maps, tables.

At head of title: Farm credit administration. United States Department of agriculture, Washington, D.C.

NK 0196467 NNC

Knapp, Joseph Grant, 1900-
The hard winter wheat pools; an experiment in agricultural marketing integration ₍by₎ Joseph G. Knapp ... Chicago, Ill., The University of Chicago press ₍1933₎
ix, 180 p. 21ᶜᵐ.
"An earlier and enlarged draft of this study ₍was submitted₎ as a doctoral dissertation ₍Stanford university₎ (1928)."—Pref.

1. Wheat trade—U. S. 2. Agriculture, Cooperative—U. S. 3. Wheat—U. S. I. Title. II. Title: Wheat pools. III. Title: Pools, Wheat.

Library of Congress HD9049.W5U445 1933 33-31665

338.1

OCl OU MB
NK 0196468 DLC OrP CaBVaU NcU NcRS NcD CU FMU MiU

1.955 C2K72 Jan.11 1943 Knapp, Joseph Grant, 1900-
Maintaining cooperative organization efficiency in wartime ... [Washington, 1943]
11 p. 27 cm.
Processed.
"Prepared from notes used in talk given at Managers' conference of Farm bureau cooperative association, inc., at Columbus, Ohio, on January 11, 1943."

NK 0196469 DNAL

1.955 C2K72 Apr. 30, 1942 Knapp, Joseph Grant, 1900-
The responsibilities of farmers' purchasing cooperatives in the war effort... ₍Washington, 1942₎
8 p. 27cm.

Processed.
"Prepared for conference celebrating the completion of the Reading plant of the Cooperative mills, inc., Cincinnati, Ohio, April 30, 1942."
Caption title.

NK 0196470 DNAL

1.955 C2K72 Jan.14/42 Knapp, Joseph Grant, 1900-
The rise of cooperative purchasing... ₍Washington, 1942₎
16 p. map. 27cm.

Processed.
"Prepared for American institute of cooperation, Atlanta, Georgia, January 14, 1942".

1. Consumers' cooperation. U.S. 2. Farmers' cooperative purchasing associations. U.S. I. Title.

NK 0196471 DNAL

166.3 M38 no.59 Knapp, Joseph Grant, 1900-
... Sideline merchandising operations of elevators affiliated with the Farmers' union grain terminal association, St.Paul,Minnesota ... ₍Kansas City, Mo.,1942₎
54 p. maps. 27cm. (U.S. Farm credit administration. Miscellaneous report no.59)

At head of title: Farm credit administration. United States Department of agriculture. Kansas City, Missouri.
Processed.

NK 0196472 DNAL

[Knapp, Joseph Grant] 1900- comp.
[Source materials on agricultural cooperation. Raleigh, N.C., 1934]
2 v.

NK 0196473 NcRS

630.62 qK67 Knapp, Joseph Grant, 1900-
Survey of National Co-operatives, inc. By Joseph G. Knapp, Cooperative Research and Service Division. ₍Washington, D.C.₎ 1941.
ii, 88, viii p. tables. 28 cm. (Special report no. 89)

Cover title.
At head of title: U.S. Dept. of Agriculture, Farm Credit Administration, Washington, D.C.
1. National Co-operatives, inc. I. Title.

NK 0196474 N

Knapp, Joseph Grant, 1900-
Using your purchasing association ₍by Joseph G. Knapp and Martin A. Abrahamsen. Rev. Washington, U. S. Govt. Print. Off., 1951₎
13, ₍1₎ p. illus. 24 cm. (U. S. Farm Credit Administration. Circular E-11)
"Some publications on purchasing cooperatives": p. ₍14₎

1. Farmers' cooperative purchasing associations—U. S. I. Abrahamsen, Martin Abraham, 1908- joint author. (Series)
[HG2051.U5A573 E-11] Agr 52-52

U. S. Dept. of Agr. Libr. for Library of Congress 166.2C4926 no.11 1951 ₍3*₎

NK 0196475 DNAL

1.955 C2K72 Oct.8, 1942 Knapp, Joseph Grant, 1900-
War crisis -- opportunity or calamity for farmers cooperative purchasing associations... ₍Washington, 1942₎
7 p. 27cm.

Processed.
"Presented at annual meeting of Consumers cooperative association, north Kansas city, Missouri, October 8, 1942."

1. Farmers' cooperative purchasing associations. I. Title.

NK 0196476 DNAL

Knapp, Joseph Jenkins, *defendant.*
Trials of Capt. Joseph J. Knapp, Jr., and George Crowninshield, Esq., for the murder of Capt. Joseph White, of Salem, on the night of the sixth of April, 1830. Boston, C. Ellms, 1830.
82 p. illus. 25 cm.

1. White, Joseph, d. 1830. I. Crowninshield, George, defendant. II. Title.

52-57101 ‡

NK 0196477 DLC OClWHi ICN CtY NN

Knapp, Joseph W 1861-
Store management and business organization, by J. W. Knapp ... New York, Alexander Hamilton institute ₍°1927₎
xx, 373 p. illus., diagrs. 22 cm. (*Added t.-p.:* Modern merchandising; a series of texts prepared as part of the modern merchandising course and service ... Alexander Hamilton institute. ₍v. 2₎)
Short series title on t.-p.

1. Retail trade. I. Alexander Hamilton institute, New York. II. Title.
HF5351.M77 vol. 2 27-5431

NK 0196478 DLC LU TU MtU MB MiU MH-BA OU

Knapp, Jozsef Armin, *d.* 1899.
Die bisher bekannten pflanzen Galiziens und der Bukowina, von Josef Armin Knapp. Wien, W. Braumüller, 1872.
xxxi, 520 p. 24ᶜᵐ.
"Verzeichniss der hierbei benützten schriften und erklärung der abkürzungen": p. ₍xxi₎-xxx.

1. Bukowina, Austria. Botany. 2. Galicia, Austria. Botany.

Agr 4-472

Library, U. S. Dept. of Agriculture 459K72

NK 0196479 DNAL InU MH-A

Knapp, Justina, *sister,* 1863-
Christian symbols and how to use them ₍by₎ Sister M. A. Justina Knapp, O. S. B. Milwaukee, The Bruce publishing company ₍°1935₎
xii, 164 p. incl. front., illus. 23½ᶜᵐ.
Part of the illustrations are numbered as plates.
Bibliography: p. 159-160.

1. Christian art and symbolism. I. Title.
₍*Secular name:* Theresia Knapp₎

35-6326

Library of Congress BV150.K6

246

OOxM OClh CaBVa OrAshS OrStbM
NK 0196480 DLC MiU IEG Or OrP WaT PP PPLas OCl MB

Knapp, K.B. Theodor
see Knapp, Theodor, 1854-

Knapp, Karl.
—— Rolník jako lesní hospodář. V Písku. 1902. 8°. pp. 87+. Illustr. (Lesnická knihovna, 13.)

NK 0196482 MH-A

Knapp, Karl Wilson, 1885-
Manual of fixed bridgework, by Karl W. Knapp ... New York, N. Y., New York university press book store ₍°1934₎
2 p. l., 167 p. diagrs. 23½ᶜᵐ.
Autographic reproduction of type-written copy.

1. Dentistry—Laboratory manuals.

36-17596

Library of Congress RK666.K55
Copyright AA 210865

617.69

NK 0196483 DLC DNLM NNC-M

Knapp, Karl Wilson, 1885-
A standardized inlay technic; being a brief resumé of the lectures delivered by Dr. K. W. Knapp, and illustrated from lantern slides used by him, before the national and other dental societies. K. W. Knapp, D. D. S. ₍Minneapolis, M. F. Patterson dental supply co., °1922₎
2 p. l., 29 p. 20½ᶜᵐ.

1. Dentistry. I. Title.

Library of Congress RK549.K6 22-21259

NK 0196484 DLC DNLM

[Knapp, Katharine] 1837- ed.
Arthur Mason Knapp, 1839-1898; a memorial ... Boston, Mass., 1899.
116 p. front. (port.) 19ᶜᵐ.
Signed, p. 24: K. K. *i. e.* Katharine Knapp₎
"Extracts from home letters": p. 25-62. "Tributes": p. 63-116.

Continued in next column

VOLUME 300

Continued from preceding column

1. Knapp, Arthur Mason, 1839-1898. I. Title.

13-26549

Library of Congress Z720.K7K

NK 0196485 DLC Nh NN MB ICJ

[**Knapp, Katherine**] 1837-

Emma A. Temple. A memorial read at the annual reunion of the Girls' high school association, May 9, 1888. Boston, Priv. print. [1888]

28 p., 1 l. 21cm.

Preface signed: K. K.

1. Temple, Emma A., d. 1887.

9-3141

NK 0196486 DLC MH

Knapp, Katherine, 1837- joint ed.

Knapp, Arthur Mason, 1839-1898.

The Knapp family in America. A genealogy of the descendants of William Knapp who settled in Watertown, Mass., in 1630. Including also a tabulated pedigree, paternal and maternal, of Hiram Knapp, by Arthur Mason Knapp ... Boston, Mass. [Fort Hill press] 1909.

Knapp, Kay, ed.

Directory for liberals; Kay Knapp, editor, David H. Scull, assistant editor. Washington, D. C., The Liberal survey, 1939.

Knapp, Klaus, 1902-

Das deutsche heimatschutzrecht. Greifswald, 1925.

Inaug.-Diss.

NK 0196489 ICRL

Knapp, Konstantin Konstantinovich.

Эксплуатация газового хозяйства жилого дома. Москва, Изд-во Министерства коммунального хозяйства РСФСР, 1953.

122 p. illus. 22 cm.

1. Gas appliances. 2. Gas distribution. I. Title.

Title transliterated: Ėkspluatafsiia gazovogo khoziaĭstva zhilogo doma.

TP758.K6 57-16849 rev ‡

NK 0196490 DLC

Knapp, Lawrence.

The history of What price glory. The play by Maxwell Anderson and Laurence Stallings as presented by Arthur Hopkins . . . at the Plymouth Theatre, New York.

= [New York.] 1925. 16 pp. Illus. Portraits. Illustrated title-page. Illustrated cover. 30 cm.

D7044 — What price glory. — Ana ,, Maxwell, 1888-. — Stallings, Laurence, 1894-

NK 0196491 MB

Knapp, Lebbeus J.

The origin of the constitution of the state of Washington, by Lebbeus J. Knapp... [Seattle,] 1910. 78, 8, 10 f. 4°.

Dissertation, Univ. of Washington.
Photostat reproduction of typewritten copy.
Bibliography, 1 f.
Includes: "Notes on the constitutional convention," by J. R. Kinnear, 8 f.; and "The constitution of the state and its effects upon public interests," by T. L. Stiles, 10 f.

255796A. 1. Constitutions—U. S.—Washington. 2. Kinnear, John R. 3. Stiles, Theodore L.
N. Y. P. L. September 10, 1926

NK 0196492 NN

Knapp, Lewis Mansfield.

The publication of Smollett's Complete history... and Continuation, by Lewis M. Knapp.

(*In* The Library. London, 1935. 22cm. Fourth ser., vol. XVI, no. 3, Dec. 1935, p. [295]-308)

"Transactions of the Bibliographical society, new ser., vol. XVI."

1. Smollett, Tobias George, 1721-1771. Compleat history of England.

A 36-555

Title from Cleveland Pub. Libr.
Library of Congress [Z671.L69 4th ser., vol. 16, no. 3]

NK 0196493 OCl MiU OU OCU

Knapp, Lewis Mansfield.

Ralph Griffiths, author and publisher, 1746-1750, by Lewis M. Knapp.

(*In* The Library. London, 1939. 22½cm. Fourth ser., vol. XX, no. 2, Sept. 1939, p. [197]-213)

"Transactions of the Bibliographical society. New ser., vol. XX, no. 2."

1. Griffiths, Ralph, 1720-1803.

A 40-1961

Cleveland. Public library
for Library of Congress [Z671.L69 4th ser., vol. 20, no. 2]
(010.5)

NK 0196494 OCl PU OCU OU

Knapp, Lewis Mansfield.

Smollett's works as printed by William Strahan, with an unpublished letter of Smollett to Strahan, by Lewis Mansfield Knapp.

(*In* The Library. London, 1933. 21½cm. Fourth ser., vol. XIII, no. 3, Dec. 1932, p. [282]-291)

"Transactions of the Bibliographical society. Second ser., vol. XIII."

1. Strahan, William, 1715-1785. 2. Smollett, Tobias George, 1721-1771.

A 33-1963

Title from Cleveland Pub. Libr.
Library of Congress [Z671.L69 4th ser., vol. 13, no. 3]

NK 0196495 OCl PU MiU OO

Knapp, Lewis Mansfield.

Tobias Smollett, doctor of men and manners. Princeton, Princeton Univ. Press, 1949.

xiii, 362 p. illus., ports. 24 cm.

Bibliography: p. 339-340. Bibliographical footnotes.

1. Smollett, Tobias George, 1721-1771.

PR3696.K5 928.2 49-7424 rev*

MB TxU Or OrCS OrPS OrSaW OrU WaE WaS WaSpG WaTC WaT IdU MtU KEmT MiU NcD-MC MeB CoU CtY OU DFo ViU ICU

NK 0196496 DLC OO PPT PPLas CaBVa OClW IdPI CaBVaU

Knapp, Lizzie Margaret.

An afternoon rehearsal, by Lizzie Margaret Knapp. Hartford, Conn., The United workers and woman's exchange, °1892.

1 p. l., 14 p. 16½cm.

I. Title.

12-34952

Library of Congress PS2196.K5A3 1892

NK 0196497 DLC PU CSt MH

Knapp, Lorenzo H

...Notes on the Le Conte families of New Rochelle, N. Y., by Lorenzo H. Knapp, White Plains, Westchester county historical soc., 1943. p. 21-33. illus. 23cm. (Westchester county historical society. Quarterly bulletin. v. 19, nos. 3-4.)

Title from mounted label.
"Authorities," p. 33.

1. Leconte family. I. Westchester county historical society, White Plains, N. Y.
N. Y. P. L. June 26, 1947

NK 0196498 NN

Knapp, Mrs. Louisa, ed.

The Ladies' home journal ... v. 1-
Dec. 1883-
Philadelphia [Curtis publishing company] 1883-

WY 18 K67o 1932

KNAPP, Louise.

The out-patient department in the education of the nurse; the demonstration of a plan for better utilizing the out-patient department in the education of the nurse under the auspices of the Subcommittee on Nursing in the Out-Patient Dept. of the Committee on Education, National League of Nursing Education. [New York, National League of Nursing Education] 1932.

73 p.

WY 18 K67o 1932

1. Nursing - Study & teaching
I. National League of Nursing Education. Committee on Education

NK 0196501 DNLM NNU-W PPT WU-M PU-Med

Knapp, Louise Allen.

A proposed type of American garden

see under Bird, Henry.

---

ar W 54560 no.14

Knapp, Ludwig.

Das gesetzliche Pfandrecht des Frachtführers. München, Buchdr. B. Wagner, 1928.

72 p. 22cm.

Inaug.-Diss.--Erlangen.

NK 0196503 NIC PU-L

Knapp, Ludwig, 1821-1858.

System der rechtsphilosophie, von Ludwig Knapp. Erlangen, F. Enke, 1857.

vi p., 1 l., 246, [2] p. 22½cm.

1. Law—Philosophy. I. Title.

42-42500

NK 0196504 DLC NcD MH-L

Knapp, Ludwig, 1868-

Allgemeine Rekonvaleszenten-Fürsorge; Vorschläge zu deren Ausgestaltung auf Grund der Erfahrungen mit den Militär-Rekonvaleszentenheimen, von Prof. Dr. Ludwig Knapp. Wien: F. Deuticke, 1919. 144 p. illus. (incl. map), tables. 8°.

Bibliography, p. 143-144.

1. Convalescents.—Care of. 2. Convalescents.—Homes for, Germany. 3. Disabled.—Rehabilitation, etc., Germany.
N. Y. P. L. April 15, 1921.

NK 0196505 NN PPCP MH

VOLUME 300

HM
WQ 215
K67b
1901
Knapp, Ludwig, 1868-
Beiträge zur geschichte der eklampsie. Berlin, Verlag, 1901.
47 p. 25 cm. (Sonder-abdruck aus der monatsschrift für geburtshülfe und gynaekologie, Bd. XIV)

In German.
References: p. 40-47.

1. Obstrectics. I. Title. II. Imprint date: 1901.

NK 0196506 KU-M

Knapp, Ludwig, 1868-
[Collected papers on gynecology and obstetrics.]

NK 0196507 ICJ

WQ
K67ge
1902
KNAPP, Ludwig, 1868-
Geburtshilfliche Diätetik und Therapie für Ärzte und Studierende. Prag, Tempsky, 1902.
xii, 316 p. illus.

NK 0196508 DNLM ICU

RG521
K5
Knapp, Ludwig, 1868-
Geburtshilfliche Propädeutik. Ein Leitfaden zur Einführung in das Studium der Geburtshilfe. Mit einem Vorworte von Alfons Edlen von Rosthorn. Wien, W.Braumüller, 1899.
289p. illus.(part fold.) 20cm.

1. Obstetrics. I. Title.

NK 0196509 IaU DNLM ICJ ICRL PPC ViU

Knapp (Ludwig) [1868-]. Der gegenwärtige Stand der Behandlung der Uterus-Myome. 21 pp. 8°. Berlin, Fischer, 1904.
Forms Heft 191 of Berl. Klinik.

NK 0196510 DNLM

Knapp, Ludwig, 1868-
——. Grundzüge der gynäkologischen Massagebehandlung. Ein Leitfaden für Studierende und Aerzte. 74 pp. 12°. Berlin, H. Kornfeld, 1909.

NK 0196511 DNLM

Knapp, Ludwig, 1868-
Leitfaden für Hebammen zur Erlernung und Einübung der äusseren sowie inneren Untersuchung Schwangerer und Gebärender. Prag, C. Bellmann, 1911.
41p. illus.

NK 0196512 ICRL DNLM

Knapp, Ludwig, 1868-
Die Prophylaxe und Therapie der Enteroptose. Für die ärztliche Praxis dargestellt von Prof. Ludwig Knapp, ... Berlin, [etc.], Urban & Schwarzenberg, 1921.
[8], 118 p. 26cm.

NK 0196513 ICJ PPC

WQ
K67sa
1901
KNAPP, Ludwig, 1868-
Sammlung stereoskopischer Aufnahmen als Behelf für theoretisch-praktischen Unterricht in der Geburtshilfe. München, Seitz & Schauer, 1901.
[4] p., 28 cards in case. illus.

NK 0196514 DNLM

WQ
K67sa
1911
KNAPP, Ludwig, 1868-
Sammlung stereoskopischer Aufnahmen als Behelf für den theoretisch-praktischen Unterricht in der Geburtshilfe. 2., erweiterte und verb. Aufl. München, Gmelin, 1911,
[4] p., 24 cards in case. illus.

NK 0196515 DNLM

Knapp, Ludwig, 1868-
Der Scheintod der Neugeborenen. Seine Geschichte, klinische und gerichtsärztliche Bedeutung. Von Dr. Ludwig Knapp. .... I.-[III.] Theil. Wien und Leipzig, W. Braumüller, 1898-1909.
3 vol. in 1. illus. 25½cm.
Vol. 2-3: "Herausgegeben mit Unterstützung der Gesellschaft zur Förderung deutscher Wissenschaft, Kunst und Literatur in Böhmen."
"Literatur," vol. 1, p. [151]-163; vol. 2, p. 171-179; vol. 3, p. 119-127.
Contents. — 1. Geschichtlicher Theil. 1898. iv, 163 p. 9 illus. — 2. Klinischer Theil. 1904. vi, [2], 179 p. 35 illus. — 3. Gerichtärztlicher Teil. 1909. viii, [4], 135 p. 20 illus.

NK 0196516 ICJ DNLM OCIW-H ICRL PPC

Knapp, Ludwig, 1868-
.... Theologie und Geburtshilfe. Nach F. E. Cangiamila's Sacra embryologia (editio latina, MDCCLXIV). Mit aktuellen Bemerkungen. Prag, C. Bellmann, 1908.
[4], xxxviii, 230, [2] p. 3 pl. 25cm.
At head of title: Prof. Dr. Ludwig Knapp.

NK 0196517 ICJ ICRL PPC DNLM

Knapp, Ludwig, 1868-
——. Ueber puerperale Eklampsie und deren Behandlung. 1 p. l., 50 pp. 8°. Berlin, S. Karger, 1900.

NK 0196518 DNLM

Knapp, Ludwig, 1868-
——. Ueber puerperale Infections-Erkrankungen und deren Behandlung. 67 pp. 8°. Berlin, H. Kornfeld, 1901.
Forms Hft. 61 of: Medicinische Wander-Vorträge. 1901.

NK 0196519 DNLM

Knapp, Lydia
see
Dickinson, Lydia (Knapp) "Mrs. D. S. Dickinson."

Knapp, M. A. Justina, *sister*
see
Knapp, Justina, *sister*, 1863-

Knapp, M Albert
see Knapp, Albert, 1798-1864.

Knapp, M Donald.
Instructions for field exercises in engineering III. Forest school, University of the Philipines. 1913-1914. [Manila, 1912]
17 p. 26.5 cm.
Typewritten manuscript.

NK 0196523 CtY

Knapp, M Donald.
Instructions for 1st semester field & laboratory exercises in forest management. Forest school, University of the Philipines. [Manila, 1912]
14 p. 26.5 cm.
Typewritten manuscript.

NK 0196524 CtY

KNAPP, M. Emma.
Lyrics of the past, and other poems. Saint John, N.B., J.& A.McMillan, 1872.
sq.16°.

NK 0196525 MH RPB

RC262
.N4
1950
Knapp, Margaret.
New York (*State*) *Dept. of Health.*
Cancer nursing; a manual for public health nurses [by Margaret Knapp] A joint project of the National Cancer Institute, Public Health Service, Federal Security Agency and the New York State Dept. of Health. [Albany, 1950.

3781
S78K
Knapp, Margaret Bates.
Natural inclination and moral obligation in Schiller's philosophical writings. [Stanford, Calif.] 1951.
v, 282 l.
Thesis (Ph.D.) - Dept. of German, Stanford University, 1951.
Bibliography: l. 268-282.

3.4
K
____ Another copy.

1.Schiller, Johann Christoph Friedrich von, 1759-1805.
Brief cataloging

NK 0196527 CSt

Knapp, Margaret F
Selected bibliography on practical nursing
see under
U.S. Office of Education. Division of Vocational Education.

Knapp, Margaret Lizzie, 1863-
But still a man, by Margaret L. Knapp ... Boston, Little, Brown, and company, 1909.
2 p. l., 376 p. 20cm. $1.50

9-4954

Library of Congress PZ3.K7258B
(Copyright 1909 A 230289)

NK 0196529 DLC

VOLUME 300

Knapp, Martha Winifred, 1876–
Select list of books in English about Scandinavia or by Scandinavians, compiled by Winifred Knapp ...
(*In* Bulletin of bibliography. Boston, 1915. 25½cm. v. 8, p. 187–192)

1. Scandinavia—Bibliography. 2. Scandinavian literature—Bibliography. 3. Scandinavian literature—Translations into English—Bibliography. 4. English literature—Translations from Scandinavian—Bibliography.

CD37-222
Library of Congress. Card div. Z1007.B94 vol. 8

NK 0196530 DLC OCl

Knapp, Martin.
Human liberty against ultra-temperance intolerance; or, Battle between innkeepers and ecclesiastics. Being the substance of a sledge-hammer lecture, delivered before a meeting called to express sympathy for certain innkeepers in Rockland county, who were indicted for not closing their houses on the Sabbath... By Martin Knapp... ⌊New York, 1853.⌋ 93 p. 8°.

BLACK TEMPERANCE COLL.
1. Sunday observance. 2. Temperance.—Addresses, essays, lectures.
N. Y. P. L. June 20, 1917.

NK 0196531 NN

Knapp, Martin, 1876–
Antiskia; ein Beitrag zum Wissen um die Präzession im Altertum, von Dr. Martin Knapp... Basel: Buchdruckerei zum Basler Berichthaus, 1927. 41 p. diagr. 4°.
Bibliography, p. 37–41.

412527A. 1. Equinoxes—Precession.
N. Y. P. L. June 3, 1929

NK 0196532 NN

NC
910
K67d
Knapp, Martin, 1876– ed.
Deutsche Schatten- und Scherenbilder aus drei Jahrhunderten. Mit 278 meist noch nicht veröffentlichten Bildern nach geschnitten Originalen. Dachau bei München, Der Gelbe Verlag ⌊1916⌋
119p. illus. 28cm.

1. Silhouettes. I. Title.

NK 0196533 NRU DAU

Knapp, Martin, 1876–
Pentagramma Veneris; eine historisch-astronomische Studie zum Verständnis alter astronomischer Symbole und ihrer Anwendung, von Dr. Martin Knapp... Basel: In Kommission bei Helbing & Lichtenhahn, 1934. 23 p. incl. tables. illus. (charts.) 30cm.

1. Venus (Planet), 1934. 2. Symbolism. I. Title.
N. Y. P. L. November 28, 1940

NK 0196534 NN

Knapp, Martin, 1876–
Zu Sebastian Muensters "astronomischen instrumenten." Basel, 1920.
Inaug.-Diss.

NK 0196535 ICRL PU MH CtY MiU CSdS

Knapp, Martin, 1883–
Albert Knapp als Dichter und Schriftsteller. Mit e. Anh. unveröff. Jugendgedichte. Leipzig 1912: Brandstetter. VIII, 56 S. 8° ¶(Vollst. b. Mohr, Tübingen.)
Straßburg, Phil. Diss. v. 1. Juli 1911, Ref. Henning
[Geb. 1. Sept. 83 Söhnstetten; Wohnort: Korntal; Staatsangeh.: Württemberg; Vorbildung: Friedrich-Eugens-Realsch. Stuttgart Reife Juli 03; Studium: Tübingen 4, Berlin 1, Bonn 2, Tübingen 2, Straßburg 3 S.] [U 12. 6750

NK 0196536 ICRL IU CtY PBm MH

3465
.107
.761
Knapp, Martin, 1883–
Albert Knapp als Dichter und Schriftsteller. Mit einem Anhang unveröffentlichter Jugendgedichte. Tübingen, Mohr, 1912
288 p. illus. 23 cm

Based on author's thesis, Strassburg
Bibliographical foot-notes

1. KNAPP, ALBERT, 1798–1864

NK 0196537 NjP

Knapp, Martin Augustine, 1843–1923.
Address by Hon. Martin A. Knapp ... before the eleventh annual convention of railroad commissioners, held at Denver, Colo., August 10, 1899. Pub. by the Interstate commerce commission. Washington, Govt. print. off., 1899.
10 p. 23cm.
Caption title: Personal influence in the administration of railway laws.

1. Railroads and state—U. S. I. U. S. Interstate commerce commission. II. Title: Personal influence in the administration of railway laws.

A 21—1167
Bur. of railway econ. Libr. for Library of Congress ⌊a41b1⌋

NK 0196538 DBRE OO

Knapp, Martin Augustine, 1843–
Address by Hon. Martin A. Knapp ... delivered at the annual dinner of the Railway business association, Waldorf-Astoria hotel, New York, November 22, 1910. ⌊New York, 1910⌋
13 p. 25½cm.
Issued also in the report of the "Second annual dinner" of the Association, 1910, p. 17–27.

1. Railroads and state—U. S. I. Railway business association, New York.

10-34011
Library of Congress HE2757.1910.K7

NK 0196539 DLC NN

Knapp, Martin Augustine, 1843–1923.
The advent of coöperation, an address delivered by Hon. Martin A. Knapp ... before the Law academy of Philadelphia, May 10, 1912 ... Philadelphia, Pa., International printing co. ⌊1912?⌋
35 p. front. (port.) 26½cm.

1. Cooperation. I. Title.
Library of Congress HM131.K6

41-41189
330.4

NK 0196540 DLC WaU-L PP

Knapp, Martin Augustine, 1843–1923.
Correspondence between Hon. Martin A. Knapp, chairman of Interstate commerce commission, and Joseph Nimmo, jr., relative to the provisions of the Cullom bill, S. 1439, 56th Congress, 1st session. June 11th to July 21st, 1900. ⌊Washington, 1900⌋
26 p. 23½cm.

1. Railroads—U. S.—Rates. I. Nimmo, Joseph, 1837–1909. II. Title.

A 17–1484
Title from Bureau of Library of Congress Railway Economics HE1843.K63

NK 0196541 DBRE IU CU MiU OU OClWHi

Knapp, Martin Augustine, 1843–1923.
U. S. *Interstate commerce commission.*
... Evidence taken by the Interstate commerce commission in the matter of proposed advances in freight rates by carriers. August to December, 1910 ... Washington, Govt. print. off., 1911.

Knapp, Martin Augustine, 1843–1923.
Government ownership of railroads.
(*In* American Academy of Political and Social Science, Philadelphia. Annals. Philadelphia, 1902. v. 19, no. 1, p. 61–73)

1. Railroads and state—U. S. I. Title.
H1.A4 vol. 19, no. 1 CD 17-88*
Library of Congress ⌊a48c1⌋†

NK 0196543 DLC NcD MiU OCl ICJ NN CaBVaU OrCS OrU

Knapp, Martin Augustine, 1843–
Government ownership of railroads, by Honorable Martin A. Knapp ... ⌊Washington, 1905⌋
15 p. 23½cm.
Reprinted from the Annals of the American academy of political and social science for January, 1902.

1. Railroads and state—U. S.

7—26940
Library of Congress HE1081.K7

NK 0196544 DLC

HE2712
.U5B44
Knapp, Martin Augustine, 1843–1923, defendant.
U. S. *District attorney (Missouri, Western district)*
In the Circuit court of the United States for the Western division of the Western district of Missouri. In equity. No. 3405. F. H. Peavey & company, Omaha elevator company, and Midland elevator company, complainants, v. Union Pacific railroad company and Martin A. Knapp ⌊et al.⌋ ... members composing the Interstate commerce commission, defendants. Answer of the Interstate commerce commission. Arba S. Van Valkenburgh, P. J. Farrell, solicitors for the Interstate commerce commission. ⌊Washington, Govt. print. off., 1908⌋

Knapp, Martin Augustine, 1843-
U. S. *Interstate commerce commission.*
... Increase in freight rates. Letter from the chairman of the Interstate commerce commission in response to Senate resolution of June 3, 1910, "directing the Interstate commerce commission to submit to the Senate a report concerning the proposed increases in freight rates under schedules recently filed." ⌊Washington, Govt. print. off., 1910⌋

Knapp, Martin Augustine, 1843–
... National regulation of railroads by Hon. Martin A. Knapp ... Reprinted from the Annals of the American academy of political and social science for November, 1905. Philadelphia, The American academy of political and social science, 1905.
cover-title, 16 p. 24cm. (American academy of political and social science, pub. no. 476)

1. Railroads—U. S.—Rates. 2. Railroads and state—U. S.

9-3092
Library of Congress HE1843.K65

NK 0196547 DLC MiU OO NN

VOLUME 300

Knapp, Martin Augustine, 1843–
Necessary changes in the inter-state commerce law, discussed by Martin A. Knapp ... Paul Morton ... before the National association of merchants and travelers, Monday evening, August 7th, 1899, at the Auditorium hotel, Chicago, Ill. [Chicago? 1899]
16 p. 21½cm.

1. Railroads—U. S.—Rates. 2. U. S. Interstate commerce commission. I. Morton, Paul, 1857–1911.
A 13-1548
Title from Bureau of Railway Economics. Printed by L. C.

NK 0196548 DBRE

Knapp, Martin Augustine, 1843–
Principles of railway legislation. By Hon. Martin A. Knapp ... Address before the Railway congress auxiliary of the World's Columbian exposition, June 23, 1893. Reprinted from the Railway review. Chicago, The Railway review, 1893.
cover-title, 16 p. 19cm.

1. Railroads and state—U. S.
8-15575* Cancel
Library of Congress HE2757.1893.K6

NK 0196549 DLC NcD-L

Knapp, Martin Augustine, 1843-1923.
... Railroad pooling, by Martin A. Knapp ... Philadelphia, American academy of political and social science [1896]
cover-title, 127-147 p. 23cm. (Publications of the American academy of political and social science, no. 179, August 11, 1896)

From The annals of the American academy of political and social science. Philadelphia, 1896. Vol. VIII, no. 1.
Volume of pamphlets.

NK 0196550 NNC NjP NN IU MH OOxM

TF630 .U6 1907
Knapp, Martin Augustine, 1843–1923.
U. S. *Interstate commerce commission.*
... Report of the Interstate commerce commission on block-signal systems and appliances for the automatic control of railway trains. Under Public joint resolution no. 46, approved June 30, 1906 ... Washington, Govt. print. off., 1907.

Knapp, Martin Augustine, 1843–1923.
Social effects of transportation.
(*In* **The annals of the American academy of political and social science. Philadelphia, 1902. vol. XX, no. 1, p. 1–15**)

1. Transportation. I. Title.
CD 17-106
Library of Congress Card Div. H1.A4

NK 0196552 OrU CaBVaU OrCS MiU OCU OCl ICJ MH NN

Knapp, Martin Augustine, 1843–1923.
Some observations on railroad pooling, and the conditions upon which pooling contracts should be authorized by law.
(*In* **The annals of the American academy of political and social science. Philadelphia, 1896. vol. VIII, no. 1, p. 127–147**)

1. Railroads—Rates. 2. Railroad law—U. S. I. Title: Railroad pooling, Some observations on.
CD 16—157
Library of Congress. Card div. H1.A4 vol. 8, no. 1

NK 0196553 NcD-L CaBVaU OrCS OrU MB MiU ICJ OCl OCU

Knapp, Martin Augustine, 1843–
Transportation and combination. The address of Judge Martin A. Knapp, of Washington, D. C., before the Virginia State bar association at the Hotel Chamberlin, Old Point, Va., August 6th, 7th, 8th, 1912. Richmond, Richmond press, inc. [1912]
cover-title, 20 p. 23cm.

1. Transportation—U. S. I. Title.
A 18-775
Title from Bureau of Railway Economics. Printed by L. C.

NK 0196554 DBRE

Knapp, M[artin] W[ells] 1853-1901.
Bible songs of salvation and victory for God's people of every land. Suitable for revivals, the church ... M. W. Knapp, ed. R. E. McNeil, musical ed. Cincinnati, O., n. d.
unp. front. (port.) 20 cm.

NK 0196555 RPB

Knapp, Martin Wells, 1853-1901.
Christ crowned within. 4th ed. 10th thousand. Cincinnati, Cranston & Stowe, 1889.
202 p. 18 cm.
1. Perfection. I. Title.

NK 0196556 IEG KyWA

Knapp, Martin Wells, 1853-1901.
The double cure. Cincinnati, O., Revivalist Office [1898?]
82 p. port. 20cm.

1. Christianity. 2. Spiritual life. I. Title.

NK 0196557 ViU IEG

Knapp, Martin Wells, 1853–1901.
Holiness triumphant; or, Pearls from Patmos, being the secret of Revelation revealed. Cincinnati, O., M. W. Knapp, 1900.
253 p. 12°.

I. Title.
0—4287

NK 0196558 DLC KyWAT

Knapp, Martin Wells, 1853-1901.
"Impressions". Kansas City, Mo., Nazarene publishing house, c.1892.

NK 0196559 MH OO OrU

Knapp, Martin Wells, 1853–1901.
"Impressions." By Martin Wells Knapp ... 7th thousand. Cincinnati, O., Revivalist publishing house [1900]
145 p. 18cm.

1. Conversion. 2. Christian life. I. Title.
0-1616 Revised
Library of Congress BX7990.H6K6

NK 0196559-1 DLC

BV4509.5 .K676 1887 1888
Knapp, Martin Wells, 1853-1901.
Out of Egypt into Canaan. Or, lessons in spiritual geography. Cincinnati, printed by Cranston & Stowe for the author 1888.
196p. illus. 20cm.

1. Christian life. I. Title. II. Title: Lessons in spiritual geography.

NK 0196559-2 IEG

Knapp, Martin Wells, 1853-1909.
Out of Egypt into Canaan; or, Lessons in spiritual geography ... 8th ed. ... Boston, McDonald, Gill & co.; Albion, Mich., The Revivalist pub. co., 1889.
196 p. front. (map) 19.5 cm.

NK 0196559-3 OrSaW

Knapp, Martin Wells, 1853-1901.
Out of Egypt into Canaan; or, lessons in spiritual geography. 16th ed. Cincinnati, The revivalist, 1894. [c1887]
196 p., frotn.

NK 0196559-4 OO MiU-H

Knapp, Martin Wells, 1853-1901.
Out of Egypt into Canaan, or lessons in Scriptural geography. Nashville, B. F. Hayes Pub. Co., c1897.

NK 0196559-5 KyWA

Knapp, Martin Wells, 1853-1901.
Out of Egypt into Canaan; or, Lessons in spiritual geography. Cincinati, Ohio, office of the Revivalist, Pentecostal holiness library, and Full salvation quarterly, 1900.

196 p.

NK 0196559-6 PPT

BV3797 .K67
Knapp, Martin Wells, 1853-1901.
Pentecostal aggressiveness; or, why I conducted the meetings of the Chesapeake Holiness Union at Bowens, Maryland. Cincinnati, Revivalist Office, 1899.

188 p. illus. 19 cm.

At head of title: Full salvation quarterly, v. 5, no. 4, October, 1899.

NK 0196559-7 IEG

Knapp, Martin Wells, 1853-1901.

Pentecostal messengers; Seth C. Rees, B. Carradine, W. B. Godbey, A. M. Hills, S. A. Keen, E. H. Dashiell, Abbie C. Morrow, F. S. Heath, M. W. Knapp. Cincinnati, O., M. W. Knapp, °1898.

VOLUME 300

M269
K67r

Knapp, Martin Wells, 1853-1901.
Revival kindlings, by Rev. Martin Wells Knapp. Albion, Mich., The Revivalist Publishing Co. [1890]
vi,336p. 20cm.

1.Evangelistic work-Michigan. 2.Revivals-Michigan. I.Title.

NK 0196559-8 Mi GEU CLamB InAndC

Knapp, Martin Wells, 1853-1901.
Revival tornadoes; or, Life and labors of Rev. Joseph H. Weber, evangelist, the converted Roman Catholic. By Rev. Martin Wells Knapp ... Boston, Mass., McDonald, Gill & co.; Albion, Mich., The Revivalist publishing co., 1889.
326 p. front. (port.) 20cm.
Hymns (with music): p. [8], [243]

1. Weber, Joseph Hulse, 1855- I. Title.

37-12171
Library of Congress BX8495.W33K5 ~~IU 7-63 Ki~~
Copyright 1889: 39325 922.773

NK 0196559-9 DLC TxU Mi IU

KNA P, MARTIN WELLS, 1853-1901.
R vival tornadoes; or, Life and labors of Rev. Joseph H. Weber, evangelist, the converted Roman Catholic. By Rev. Martin Wells Knapp... Third edition... Boston, Mass.: McDonald, Gill & Co., 1890. 326 p. front. (port.), illus. (music). 19½cm.

681403A. 1. Weber, Joseph Hulse, 1855-

NK 0196560 NN NRCR

Knapp, Rev. Martin Wells, 1853-1901.
Revival tornadoes...Cincinnati, Revivalist pub. co., 1899.
326 p. 19 1/2cm

NK 0196561 PPTU

Knapp, Mary Clay.
Whose soul have I now? A novel, by Mary Clay Knapp. Boston, Arena publishing company, 1896.
1 p. l., 242 p. 19½cm.

Library of Congress PZ3.K726W 7-14279†

NK 0196562 DLC NcD CU

Knapp, Mary Etta, 1902-
A checklist of verse by David Garrick. Charlottesville, University of Virginia Press for the Bibliographical Society of the University of Virginia, 1955.
69 p. 23 cm.
Errata slip tipped to p. [7]

1. Garrick, David, 1717-1779—Bibl.

Z8324.45.K6 A 55-9940
Virginia. State Library for Library of Congress [3]†

OO OU AAP FTaSU CaBViP
OrU IdPI TU PSt ViU OOxM OKentU MH PPT DCU LU
InU NcD OC1W OC1 OCU CU IEN NN PBm WaU CaBVaU Or
NK 0196563 Vi MB MeB ScU DLC NIC IaU ICU IU TxU

Knapp, Maud Lombard, 1897-
Democratic leadership in physical education, by Maud L. Knapp [and] Frances Todd. [Millbrae, Calif.] National Press [1952]
50 p. 22 cm.

1. Physical education and training. I. Title.

GV345.K6 371.732 52-28231 ‡

CaBVaU OrAshS OrCS
NK 0196564 DLC FU OC1 PU NcGU TxU TU KEmT OC1W OrU

Knapp, Miland Austin, 1868-
The Knapp system of teeth regulation for major protrusion; with instructions for the application and operation of the protrusion set "B," by Miland A. Knapp ... [Minneapolis?] °1905.
cover-title, 24 p. illus. 19 cm.

1. Orthodontia.

RK521.K66 7-8367

NK 0196565 DLC

Knapp, Miland Austin, 1868-
A new system of teeth regulation with finely made original devices ready for immediate operative application without soldering, by Miland A. Knapp ... Philadelphia, S. S. White dental manufacturing co. [1901?]
1 p. l., 20, [2] p. illus.

Cover-title: The Knapp system of teeth regulation for major protrusion.

NK 0196566 NNC

Knapp, Miland Austin, 1868-
Orthodontia practically treated; designed for the use of both practitioner and student, by Miland A. Knapp ... 1st ed., with five hundred and sixty-four illustrations. Minneapolis, Minn., Press of Harrison & Smith co., 1904.
1 p. l., [v]-viii, 406 p. incl illus., plates. 23 cm.

1. Orthodontia. I. Title.

RK521.K67 4-22872

NK 0196567 DLC ICRL PU-D DNLM ICJ

Knapp, Miland Austin, 1868-
Teeth regulation; with finely made original devices ready for immediate operative application without soldering ... By Miland A. Knapp, D. D. S. Philadelphia, Pa., The S. S. White dental manufacturing co., 1899.
58 p. illus. 23½cm.

1. Teeth—Abnormities and deformities. I. Title.

Library of Congress RK521.K68 99-2275

NK 0196568 DLC PU-D

Knapp, Miland Austin, 1868-
Teeth regulation; with finely made original devices ready for immediate operative application without soldering ... By Miland A. Knapp, D. D. S. 2d ed., rev. and enl. Philadelphia, Pa., The S. S. White dental manufacturing co., 1900.
78 p. illus. 23½cm.

1. Teeth—Abnormalities and deformities. I. Title.

Library of Congress RK521.K7 0-4066 Revised
Copyright 1900 A 16965 [r32e2]

NK 0196569 DLC PU-D MiU PPWD

Knapp, Miland Elbert, 1905-

Pohl, John Florian M 1903-
The Kenny concept of infantile paralysis and its treatment, by John F. Pohl ... in collaboration with Sister Elizabeth Kenny ... with a foreword by Frank R. Ober ... Minneapolis, Saint Paul, Bruce publishing company, 1943.

Knapp, Miland Elbert, 1905- joint author.

Cole, Wallace Hasbrouk, 1888-
The Kenny method of treatment for infantile paralysis, by Wallace H. Cole ... John F. Pohl ... [and] Miland E. Knapp ... Prepared under the auspices of its Committee on education and distributed by the National foundation for infantile paralysis, inc. New York city [1942]

[Knapp, Minna]
Explanation of the music chart. The face of the clock to illustrate the succession and relationship of all the major and minor keys ... San Francisco, Cal., M. Knapp [°1880]
2 l. 31cm.
Chart on t.-p.

1. Music—Charts, diagrams, etc.

CA 8-2709 Unrev'd
Library of Congress MT50.K676

NK 0196572 DLC

Knapp, Moses L 1799-1879

An | Address | Delivered at the Opening of the | Rock Island Medical School, | November 7, 1848, | by | M. L. Knapp, M.D., | President, and Professor of Materia Medica and Therapeutics. | [*Double rule*] | Chicago: | Campbell & Fuller, Printers, | 107 Lake Street. | [*Short rule*] | 1849.
14 x 23.5 cm. 20 p. Printed paper wrappers. Cover title, in decorative border, identical with above.
Library of Congress. Collection of Douglas C. McMurtrie.

NK 0196573 DLC MH-M ICJ KyU DNLM MiU-C IU

Knapp, Moses L., 1799-1879.
Address delivered to the graduating class of the Indiana Medical College, at the public commencement, Feb. 18, 1847, by M. L. Knapp ... Chicago, Printed at 128 corner of Lake and Clark streets, 1847.
22, [1] p. 23cm.
"Fee bill, adopted by members of the Medical Society of Illinois ... January 1840": p. [23]

NK 0196574 ICJ DNLM MHi DLC MB

Knapp, Moses L 1799-1879.
Astronomical etiology; or, An insight into coming troubles on the earth, from 1881 to 1885, as viewed from the standpoint of astronomy & astrology. By M. L. Knapp, M. D., and others. Chicago, T. Wilson [°1879]
64 p. fold. front., diagr. 19½cm.
On planetary attraction and its relation to epidemics.

1. Astrology. 2. Epidemics.

11-13454
Library of Congress BF1725.K6

NK 0196575 PPAN DLC DN-Ob

BF 1785
.H6 no. 1
Houdini
Coll.

Knapp, Moses L 1799-1879.
Astronomical etiology, or, An insight into coming troubles on the earth, from 1881 to 1885, as viewed from the standpoint of astronomy & astrology, by M.L. Knapp, M. D., and others. Chicago, T. Wilson [c1899]
72 p. fold. front. (diagr.) 19.5 cm.
Houdini pamphlets: prophecies, no. 1.
Cover-title: Astronomical etiology, or, Star prophecies, concerning coming disasters on the earth from 1881 to 1885 ... 3d ed.
Appendix, p. [63]-72, signed, Thomas Wilson.

NK 0196576 DLC

VOLUME 300

Knapp, Moses L., 1799-1879.
Coming disasters on the earth, 1881 to 1885, resulting from the perihelia of the planets. By M. L. Knapp, M.D., and others. Edinburgh. Somerville. 1881. 63 pp. Diagrams. Sm. 8°.

H231 — Astrology. — Predictions. — T.r. — Epidemics.

NK 0196577 MB

Knapp, Moses L.
Discovery of the cause, nature, cure and prevention of epidemic cholera: by M. L. Knapp ... Cincinnati, H. W. Derby, 1855.
48 p. 23cm.
Reprinted from the New York journal of medicine for January, 1855.

1. Cholera, Asiatic.
Library of Congress RC126.K67 7-30744†

NK 0196578 DLC PPHa PU PPL NN MB

RC126 .K67 1855a Toner coll. Knapp, Moses L , 1799-1879.
Discovery of the cause, nature, cure, and prevention of epidemic cholera; by M. L. Knapp ... New York, Holman, Gray & co., book and job printers, 1855.
27 p. 22 1/2cm.
"Reprinted from the New York journal of medicine for January, 1855."
1. Cholera, asiatic.

NK 0196579 DLC

Knapp, M[oses] L., 1799-1879.
Essay on cholera infantum: by M. L. Knapp ... Cincinnati, H. W. Derby, 1855.
96 p. 21½cm.

1. Cholera infantum.
Library of Congress RJ456.C5K6 6-42039†

NK 0196580 DLC ICJ WU-M OU DNLM PPL PU PPHa NN

RM666 C26 826K KNAPP, Moses L., 1799-1879.
An inaugural dissertation on the properties of the Apocynum cannabium, (Indian hemp;), submitted to the faculty of Jefferson Medical College. Philadelphia, R. Wright, 1826.
24p. illus. 22cm.
1. Cannabis indica
I. MS. Knapp, Moses L., 1799-1879
II. Short title

NK 0196581 CtY-M DNLM PPPH CtY

Knapp, Moses L 1799-1879.
Toner An inquiry into the cause and nature of nursing sore mouth: by M. L. Knapp ... Printed for the author. Philadelphia, Robb, Pile & M'Elroy, printers, 1856.
cover-title, 1 l., p. 163-312. 23cm.
First published in vol. I of the author's Researches on primary pathology, and the origin and laws of epidemics.
CONTENTS.—An inquiry into the nature of the nursing sore mouth affection.—Medical topography of the state of Illinois.—Etiological deductions—malaria.—Cases and deductions.
1. Stomatitis. 2. Medical geography—Illinois. 3. Epidemics—Illinois. I. Title. II. Title: Nursing sore mouth.
35-36461
Library of Congress RG871.S7K6

NK 0196582 DLC DNLM ICJ OU PPC

Knapp, Moses L 1799-1879.
Lectures on the science of life insurance ... By Moses L. Knapp ... 2d ed. Philadelphia, E. S. Jones & co.; Cincinnati, H. W. Derby & co., 1853.
x, [13]-242 p. 22cm.

1. Insurance, Life.
7-1089
Library of Congress HG8771.K67

NK 0196583 DLC NcD PPL PPCP PHi NN DeGE

Knapp, Moses L 1799-1879.
Properties of the apocynum cannabinum... 1826.
v. 5.

NK 0196584 NNNAM PU

Knapp, Moses L 1799-1879.
Researches on primary pathology, and the origin and laws of epidemics...By M. L. Knapp... Philadelphia, The author 1853.

NK 0196585 PPPH

Knapp, Moses L 1799-1879.
Researches on primary pathology, and the origin and laws of epidemics ... By M. L. Knapp ... Philadelphia, The author, 1858.
2 v. 22½cm.

1. Pathology. 2. Epidemics.
Library of Congress RB6.K67 6-42237

NK 0196586 DLC DNLM CtY PPL PU PPHa PPJ MiU ViU NN

Knapp, Moses L , 1799-1879.
Researches on primary pathology, and the origin and laws of epidemics; in two volumes. By M. L. Knapp, ... Second edition, enlarged. .... Philadelphia, The author, 1860.
187144 2 vol. in 1. 23½cm.

NK 0196587 ICJ OrU-M PU-D PP PPC DNLM

308t K65975 Knapp, Myron William, 1924-
Negative pions from neutron bombardment of deuterons. [Berkeley, 1955]
ii, 67 l. diagrs., illus., tables.
Thesis (Ph. D. in Physics) - Univ. of California, Jan. 1955.
Also issued as UCRL [i. e. University of California Radiation Laboratory] 2799.
Bibliography: leaves 66-67.

1. Collisions (Nuclear physics). 2. Deuterons. 3. Mesotrons.

NK 0196588 CU

Knapp, N B
Historical sermon preached...in the Third Presbyterian Church of Genoa, at five Corners, Cayuga Co., N. Y., July 2, 1876.

NK 0196589 PPPrHi

Graff 2348 KNAPP, N M
Historical sketch of Scott county, Illinois, by N.M. Knapp. Also, Response to a toast, by John Moses. Delivered at Winchester, Illinois July 4th, 1876. Winchester, Ill., Times Job Printing House, 1876.
36p. 21cm.

NK 0196590 ICN

Knapp, Nathaniel, 1736-1816.
The diary of Nathaniel Knap of Newbury, in the province of Massachusetts Bay in New England. Written at the second siege of Louisburg in 1758. Now first printed by the Society of colonial wars in ... Massachusetts. Boston, The Society, 1895.
42 p. 22½cm. [With Society of colonial wars. Massachusetts. Proceedings of the special courts and second general court, 1894. Boston, 1895. 23½cm.]
For an account of the writer, see Currier's "Ould Newbury," 1896, p. 484-491.
Subject entries: Louisburg—Siege, 1758.
2-19160
Library of Congress, no. E186.3.M34.

NK 0196591 DLC OClWHi MB NN PHi CaOTP

Wing ZW 883 .K 72 KNAPP, NATHANIEL C.
Knapp and Rightmyer's Commercial writing. McLees, engraver. New York, Knapp and Rightmyer, c1852.
36 pl. 18x28cm.

NK 0196592 ICN NN

Wing fZW 883 .K 7213 KNAPP, NATHANIEL C
Knapp & Rightmyer's German text and old English, containing a great variety of beautiful and highly embellished alphabets. Capital letters reduced to three principles; and small letters reduced to five ... New York, Published by Leavitt & Allen, c1853.
12l. 18x30cm.
69-1514 Cover title.
Imperfect: back cover wanting.

NK 0196593 ICN

Knapp, [Nathaniel C.],
Knapp & Rightmyer's original primary copy books. In 14 numbers. [no.] 3, 12-13. New York: Leavitt & Allen, cop. 1854. 3 nos. ob. 16°.

Titles from covers.

1. Handwriting.—Systems: Knapp's. 2. Rightmyer, Levi, jt. au.
N. Y. P. L. September 30, 1911.

NK 0196594 NN

Knapp, [Nathaniel C.],
A representation of German text & old English pens... New York: Knapp & Rightmyer [1852]. 12 pl. ob. 12°.
Bound with their: Knapp and Rightmyer's commercial writing. New York, cop. 1852. ob. 12°.

1. ~~Handwriting~~ Alphabet (German). 2. Rightmyer, Levi, jt. au.
N. Y. P. L. September 27, 1911.

NK 0196595 NN

Knapp, [Nathaniel C.],
Knapp & Rightmyer's system of ladie's (sic) epistolary penmanship. [Engraved by McLees] New York: Knapp & Rightmyer, cop. 1853. 12 pl. ob. 12°.
Bound with their: Knapp and Rightmyer's commercial writing. New York, cop. 1852. ob. 12°.

1. Handwriting.—Systems: Knapp's. 2. Rightmyer, Levi, jt. au. 3. McLees, A., engraver.
N. Y. P. L. September 26, 1911.

NK 0196596 NN

VOLUME 300

Knapp, ⌜Nathaniel C.⌝
Knapp & Rightmyer's system of ladie's epistolary penmanship. ⌜Engraved by⌝ McLees. New York: Leavitt & Allen, cop. 1853. 23 f., 1 l. ob. 48°.

Title from engraved cover.

1. Handwriting.—Systems: Knapp's. 2. Rightmyer, Levi, jt. au. 3. McLees, A., engraver.
N. Y. P. L. September 27, 1911.

NK 0196597 NN

Knapp, ⌜Nathaniel C.⌝
Knapp and Rightmyer's system of rapid off hand flourishing. New York: Knapp & Rightmyer, cop. 1852. 12 pl. ob. 12°.

Bound with their: Knapp and Rightmyer's commercial writing. New York, cop. 1852. ob. 12°.

1. Handwriting.—Flourishes. 2. Rightmyer, Levi, jt. au.
N. Y. P. L. September 27, 1911.

NK 0196598 NN

Knapp, Nathaniel P , d. 1854.

Select sermons; ed. by Wm. Johnson, with a brief sketch of the life of the Rev. Mr. Knapp during his connexion with the diocess of Alabama: by the editor. Philadelphia, H. Hooker, 1855.
502 p. port. 23cm.
1. Protestant Episcopal Church in the U. S. A.—Sermons. 2. Sermons, American. I. Johnson, William Bullien, 1782-1862, ed.

NK 0196599 ViU Vi TxU NcD

HM 281 .K5

Knapp, Newton Ben.
The psychology of ecstatic crowds; a paper read before the Contemporary Club, Davenport, Iowa, May 1, 1919. Davenport, Iowa, Contemporary Club, 1919.
19p. 24cm.

Author's autograph presentation copy.

1. Crowds. 2. Social psychology. I. Title.

NK 0196600 OrU

Knapp, O S
Grammar without a master, or Key to grammatical conversation. Boston, Dayton & Wentworth, 1854.

NK 0196601 MH

ND 497 .L4K5 1904

Knapp, Oswald Greenwaye, 1850–
An artist's love story, told in the letters of Sir Thomas Lawrence, Mrs. Siddons, and her daughters; ed. by Oswald G. Knapp ... London, G. Allen, 1904.

viii, 288 p., 1 l. front., ports., facsims. 22½ cm.
Printed in Great Britain.

NK 0196602 KyLoU LU MeB TU

Knapp, Oswald Greenwaye, 1859–
An artist's love story, told in the letters of Sir Thomas Lawrence, Mrs. Siddons, and her daughters; ed. by Oswald G. Knapp ... New York, Longmans, Green, and co.; London, G. Allen, 1904.
viii, 238 p., 1 l. front., ports., facsims. 22½cm.
Printed in Great Britain.

Continued in next column

Continued from preceding column

1. Artists—Correspondence, reminiscences, etc. I. Lawrence, Sir Thomas, 1769–1830. II. Siddons, Mrs. Sarah (Kemble) 1755–1831. III. Siddons, Sarah Martha, 1775–1803. IV. Siddons, Maria, 1779–1798. V. Title.

5–6037 Revised

Library of Congress ND497.L4K5

MB ViU
NK 0196603 DLC NcGU WaT WaS WaSp CaBVaU PPLas OCl

ND 497 .L4 K5 1905

Knapp, Oswald Greenwaye, 1859–
An artist's love story, told in the letters of Sir Thomas Lawrence, Mrs. Siddons, and her daughters; ed. by Oswald G. Knapp... ⌜2d ed.⌝ London, G. Allen, 1905.
viii, 288 p., 1 l. front., ports., facsims. 22½ cm.
Printed in Great Britain.

NK 0196604 OrU CtY CU

Knapp, Oswald Greenwaye, 1859–
A history of the chief English families bearing the name of Knapp. Comp. by Oswald Greenwaye Knapp ... Illustrated with portraits, views, etc. ⌜London⌝ Priv. print. for the author by the St. Catherine press, 1911.
2 p. l., x, 288 p. front., plates, ports. 29cm.
The American family: p. 189–234.

1. Knapp family.

13–10098

Library of Congress CS439.K75

NK 0196605 DLC MB NN

Knapp, Oswald Greenwaye, 1859–

Piozzi, Mrs. Hester Lynch (Salusbury) Thrale, 1741–1821.
The intimate letters of Hester Piozzi and Penelope Pennington, 1788–1821; ed. by Oswald G. Knapp, with thirty illustrations. London, John Lane; New York, John Lane company; ⌜etc., etc.⌝ 1914.

Knapp (Otto). Ueber die operative Behandlung irreponibler traumatischer Luxationen im Schultergelenk. 27 pp. 8°. *Tübingen, H. Laupp, jr.*, 1889.
Repr. from: Beitr. z. klin. Chir., Tübing., 1889, iv.

NK 0196607 DNLM

Knapp, Otto, 1874–
Die Ausbreitung des flektierten Genitivs auf -s im Mittelenglischen...von Otto Knapp... ⌜Heidelberg?⌝ 1902. 61 p. 8°.
Dissertation, Heidelberg.
Vita.
Bibliography, p. ⌜59–⌝61.

1. English language (Middle), ca. 1100–1580.—Grammar: Noun.
N. Y. P. L. April 23, 1923.

NK 0196608 NN ICRL CtY MH NjP PU NcD

834K727 Ok

Knapp, Otto, 1874-
Die kenner; lustspiel in einem akt ... Stuttgart, J. Hoffmann [c1913]
58p.

"Bühnen und vereinen gegenüber als manuskript gedruckt."

NK 0196609 IU MH NN ICRL

Knapp, Otto, 1874–

Stanton, Stephen Berrien.
Seele und welt, von St. B. Stanton. Stuttgart, J. Hoffmann ⌜°1912⌝

Knapp, Otto, 1874–

Montessori, Maria.
Selbsttätige erziehung im frühen kindesalter, nach den grundsätzen der wissenschaftlichen pädagogik methodisch dargelegt von dr. Maria Montessori. Stuttgart, J. Hoffmann ⌜°1913⌝

Knapp, Patricia B
The subject catalog in the college library; an investigation of terminology ... Chicago, 1943.
iv, 90 l. tables.

Microfilm copy.
"Dissertation submitted to the Faculty of the Graduate library school ⌞University of Chicago⌟ in candidacy for the degree of Master of arts."
Bibliography: leaves 89-90.
1. Subject headings. I. Title.

NK 0196612 NNC

W 047 .85 v.78

Knapp, Paul.
Heinrich Ludwigs leben... (in Ludwig, Heinrich. ...Ueber erziehung zur kunstuebung und zum kunstgenuss. 1907. p.[5]-35)

Half-title.

NK 0196613 ICN MB

Knapp, Paul
Die Kypseliden und die Kypseloslade... 1888.

NK 0196614 MiU

Knapp, Paul.
Nike in der vasenmalerei. Tübingen, F. Fues, 1876.
pp. (3), 101.

Vases-Greek

NK 0196615 MH OCU NN NjP PBm

Knapp, Paul.
Die Traditionen über die Stiftung der olympischen Spiele. Tübingen: F. Fues, 1881. 16 p. 8°.
Repr.: Corresp.-Bl. f. d. Gel.- & Realschulen. 1881, Heft 1 & 2.

1. Games (Olympic).
N. Y. P. L. March 6, 1911.

NK 0196616 NN MH

Knapp, Paul.
Ludwig, Heinrich, 1829–1897.
... Ueber erziehung zur kunstuebung und zum kunstgenuss. Mit einem lebensabriss des verfassers aus dem nachlass herausgegeben. Strassburg, J. H. E. Heitz, 1907.

VOLUME 300

Knapp, Paul.
Über Orpheusdarstellungen ... Tüb., 1895.
34 p. 26 cm.
Beilage zum Jahresbericht 1894/5 des Kgl. gymnasiums in Tübingen, 1895. Progr. nro. 606.

NK 0196618 CU NjP

Knapp, Paul
Zur frage der entstehungszeit des Herodotischen geschichtswerks. Von prof. dr. P. Knapp... [No imprint]
12 p.
Sonderabdruck aus dem neuen Korrespondenzblatt für die Gelehrten-u.realschulen Württembergs, 4. jahrgang, hft. 1,1897.

NK 0196619 MiU

Knapp, Paul, physician.
Diagnostisch-klinischer Leitfaden über den Zusammenhang von Augenleiden mit andern Erkrankungen für Studierende und Ärzte. Basel, Schwabe, 1920.
118 p.

NK 0196620 PPC

Knapp, Paul Stephan.
Lebensbild eines juenglings... Stuttgart, Steinkopf, 1858.
62p.

AC931 .H3 v.21 [Haverford-Bauer pamphlets, v. 21, no. 8]

NK 0196621 ICRL

KNAPP,Philip Coombs, 1858-1920.
Accidents from the electric current;a contribution to the study of the action of current of high potential upon the human organism.[Read before the Boston society for medical improvement,Feb.24,1890.] Boston,1890.
pp. 43. Diagrs. and fac-sim.
"Reprinted from the Boston medical and surgical journal of April 17 and 24, 1890."

NK 0196622 MB MH

Knapp, Philip Coombs, 1858-
The alleged reflex causes of nervous disease.
= [Philadelphia, 1895.] 9 pp. 8°.
From the American Journal of the Medical Sciences, new series, vol. 110, 1895 [*3736.1.n.s.110].

E6288 — Nervous system.

NK 0196623 MB

Knapp, Philip Coombs, 1858-
Anesthesia in diseases of the spinal cord.
= [Philadelphia, 1897.] 20 pp. Illus. 8°.
Reprinted from the Journal of Nervous and Mental Disease, new series, vol. 114, 1897 [*3736.1.n.s.114].

E6302 — Anaesthesia. — Spinal cord.

NK 0196624 MB

Knapp (Philip Coombs) [1858-]. A case of professional neurosis of co-ordination of unusual origin. 5 pp. 8°. [New York, 1887.]
Repr. from: J. Nerv. & Ment. Dis., N. Y., 1887, xiv.

NK 0196625 DNLM

KNAPP,Philip Coombs, 1858-
A case of retro-anterograde amnesia following gas poisoning. n.p.,[1915].
pp.(16).
"Reprinted from American journal of insanity, vol.LXXII,no.2,Oct,1915," pp.259-274.

NK 0196626 MBCo

KNAPP, Philip Coombs, 1858-
A case of tumor of the brain.
[Bost., 1889.] 43 pp. Illus. 8°.
From the Med. and surg. reports of the City hospital [*7720.4.4].

NK 0196627 MB

Knapp, Philip Coombs, M.D.
A case of tumor of the cerebellum, in which trephining was done for the relief of increased intra-cranial pressure. n. t.-p. [New York, 1892.] 10 p. 8°.
Repr.: Jour. of nervous and mental disease. Feb., 1892.

1. Brain.—Tumors.
N. Y. P. L. February 3, 1913.

NK 0196628 NN

Knapp, Philip Coombs, M.D.
A contribution from brain surgery to the study of the localization of the sensory centres in the cerebral cortex. Boston: Damrell & Upham, 1891. 12 p. illus. 16°.
Repr.: Boston medical and surgical journal. October, 1891.

1. Brain.—Localization of functions.
N. Y. P. L. December 7, 1912.

NK 0196629 NN

KNAPP,Philip Coombs, 1858-
Criminal responsibility;read before the Boston Society of Psychiatry and Neurology, Feb.18,1915,and before the American Association of Jurisprudence,May 22,1915. n.p., [1915].
Pamphlet.
"Reprinted from the Journal of criminal law and criminology,Vol.VI,no.4,Nov.1915".

NK 0196630 MH

KNAPP,Philip Coombs,1858-
The insanity of doubt. [Baltimore,1890.]
pp.23.
"Bibliography," pp.22-23.
"Reprint from the American journal of psychology,Jan.1890."

NK 0196631 MH

Knapp, Philip Coombs, 1858-
Landry's paralysis.
= [Philadelphia? 1900.] 18 pp. 8°.

E6306 — Paralysis, Landry's. — Jt. auth.

NK 0196632 MH

Knapp, Philip Coombs, 1858-
A list of works relating to Dante printed in the United States of America.
(In Dante Society, Cambridge, Mass. Annual report, 3d, 1884. Pp. 15-27. Cambridge. 1884.)
The author's name appears on page 11.

This card was printed at the Boston Public Library, January 14, 1919.
L5917 — Dante Alighieri. Bibl.

NK 0196633 MB

KNAPP, Philip Coombs, 1858-
Methods of examination in medico-legal cases involving suits for damages for real or supposed injuries to the brain or spinal cord.
Bost. Damrell & U. 1889. 24 pp. 16°.
From the Bost. med. and surg. journ. [*5476.1.121].

NK 0196634 MB

Knapp, Philip Coombs, 1858-
The nature of neurasthenia, and its relation to morbid fears and imperative ideas.
= Boston. Damrell & Upham. 1896. 12 pp. 16°.
Reprinted from the Boston Medical and Surgical Journal, vol. 135, 1896 [*5746.1.135].
The title is on the cover.

E6288 — Nervous system.

NK 0196635 MB

KNAPP, Philip Coombs, 1858-
Nervous affections following injury.
Bost. Cupples & H. 1888. 35 pp. 12°.
From the Boston med. and surg. journ., Nov., 1888 [*7774.5.119].

NK 0196636 MB

Knapp, Philip Coombs, 1858-
The nervous and mental sequelæ of influenza.
= [Boston, 1892.] 17 pp. 8°.
Reprinted from the Medical Communications of the Massachusetts Medical Society, vol. 15, 1892 [*7737.10.15].
References, pp. 16, 17.

E6118 — Influenza. — Nervous system.

NK 0196637 MB

Knapp, Philip Coombs, 1858-1920.
.... The pathology, diagnosis and treatment of intra-cranial growths. By Philip Coombs Knapp. .... Boston, Press of Rockwell and Churchill, 1891.
viii, 165 p. illus. 23½cm. (Fiske Fund prize dissertation, no. XLI.)
"References," p. [163]-165.

NK 0196638 ICJ RP CtY-M MiU ICU IU-M MH IaU PPC DNLM

VOLUME 300

Knapp, Philip Coombs.
President's address delivered at the 21st annual meeting of the American Neurological Association, Boston, June 5, 1895.
= Boston. Damrell & Upham. 1895. 8 pp. 16°.
Reprinted from the Boston Medical and Surgical Journal, vol. 132, 1895 [*5746.1.132].
The title is on the cover.

E6289 — American Neurological Association.

NK 0196639 MB

Knapp, Philip Coombs, 1858-1920.
The problem of Boston's insane.
= Boston. Damrell & Upham. 1900. 9 pp. 16°.
Reprinted from the Boston Medical and Surgical Journal, vol. 142, 1900 [*5746.1.142].
The title is on the cover.

E6306 — Boston. Med. — Insanity.

NK 0196640 MB

KNAPP, Philip Coombs.
Pulmonary complications of apoplexy. n.p., [1915].

1.8°. pp.(5).
"Reprinted from the Journal of nervous and mental disease, vol.42, no.3, Mar.1915,"pp.150-154.

NK 0196641 MBCo

Knapp, Philip Coombs.
Recurrent oculo-motor paralysis. Report of a case with recurrent anæsthesia in the distribution of the fifth nerve.
= Boston. Damrell & Upham. 1894. 19 pp. Table. 16
Reprinted from the Boston Medical and Surgical Journal, vol. 131, 1894 [*5746.1.131].
The title is on the cover.
Bibliography, pp. 16-19.

E6318 — Eye. — Paralysis.

NK 0196642 MB

Knapp, Philip Coombs, 1858-
Simulation in traumatic nervous diseases.
= Boston. Damrell & Upham. 1893. 14 pp. 16°.
Reprinted from the Boston Medical and Surgical Journal, vol. 129, 1893 [*5746.1.129].
The title is on the cover.

E6306 — Nervous system. — Simulation.

NK 0196643 MB

Knapp, Philip Coombs.
Spinal concussion. — Traumatic spinal sclerosis.
= Boston. Damrell & Upham. 1894. 18 pp. 16°.
Reprinted from the Boston Medical and Surgical Journal, vol. 133, 1894 [*5746.1.133].
The title is on the cover.

E6280 — Spine.

NK 0196644 MB

Knapp, Philip Coombs, 1858-
Sudden death from affections of the nervous system.
= Boston. Damrell & Upham. 1892. 8 pp. 16°.
Reprinted from the Boston Medical and Surgical Journal, vol. 126, 1892 [*5746.1.126].
The title is on the cover

E6307 — Death. Physiologically considered. — Nervous system.

NK 0196645 MB

Knapp, Philip Coombs, 1858- joint tr.

FOR OTHER EDITIONS SEE MAIN ENTRY

Strümpell, Adolf von, 1853-1925.
A text-book of medicine for students and practitioners, by Dr. Adolf Strümpell ... 3d American ed., tr. by permission from the 13th German ed., by Herman F. Vickery ... and Philip Coombs Knapp ... With editorial notes by Frederick C. Shattuck ... With one hundred and eighty-five illustrations in the text, and one plate. New York, D. Appleton and company, 1901.

Knapp, Philip Coombs, 1858-
Three cases of general paralysis preceded by optic atrophy.
= Boston. Damrell & Upham. 1899. 22 pp. 16°.
Reprinted from the Boston Medical and Surgical Journal, vol. 140, 1899 [*5746.1.140].
The title is on the cover.

E6609 — Paralysis.

NK 0196647 MB

Knapp, Philip Coombs, 1858-
Traumatic nervous affections. An attempt at their classification based on a study of ninety cases.
= [Philadelphia, 1892.] 15 pp. 8°.
From the American Journal of the Medical Sciences, new series, vol. 104, 1892 [*3736.1.n.s. 104].

E6289 — Nervous system.

NK 0196648 MB

Knapp, Philip Coombs, 1858-
Traumatic neurasthenia and hysteria.
= [London, 1897.] 385-408 pp. 8°.
Cut from Brain, vol. 20, 1897 [*3802.103.20].

E9077 — Hysteria. — Nervous system.

NK 0196649 MB

KNAPP, Philip Coombs, 1858-
The treatment of cases of mental disorder in general hospitals. Boston, W.M.Leonard, 1914.

pp.18.
"Reprinted from the Boston medical and surgical journal, vol.clxx, no.17, pp.637-642, Apr. 23, 1914."

NK 0196650 MBCo

Knapp, Philip Coombs, 1858-
The treatment of cerebral tumors.
= Boston. Damrell & Upham. 1899. 13 pp. 4°.
Reprinted from the Boston Medical and Surgical Journal vol. 141, 1899 [*5746.1.141].
The title is on the cover.

E6307 — Brain. — Tumors.

NK 0196651 MB

Knapp, Philip Coombs.
The treatment of chorea, with especial reference to the use of quinine.
= Boston. Damrell & Upham. 1895. 8 pp. 16°.
Reprinted from the Boston Medical and Surgical Journal, vol. 132, 1895 [*5746.1.132].
The title is on the cover.

E6307 — Quinine. — Saint Vitus' dance.

NK 0196652 MB

KNAPP, Philip Coombs, 1858-
The treatment of paresis by intraventricular injections of diarsenolized serum, with presentation of cases. [Boston, Jamaica printing co., 1916].

pp.6.
"Reprinted from the Boston medical and surgical journal, vol.clxxv, no.1, pp.24,25, July 6, 1916."

NK 0196653 MBCo

KNAPP, Philip Coombs, 1858-
Two cases of removal of extra-dural tumor of the spinal cord. n.p., [1914?].

1.8°. pp.15.
"Reprinted from the Journal of nervous and mental disease, vol.4, no.1, Jan.1914."

NK 0196654 MBCo

Knapp, Philip Coombs, 1858-1920.
Two cases of trephining for traumatic epilepsy. Boston: Damrell & Upham, 1892. 20 p. 16°.

Repr.: Boston medical and surgical jour. 1892.
Title from cover.

1. Epilepsy. 2. Post, Abner, M.D., jt. au.
N. Y. P. L. February 4, 1913.

NK 0196655 NN MB

Knapp, Philip Coombs, 1858-1920
The unity of the acute psychoses.
= Boston. Damrell & Upham. 1900. 18 pp. 16°.
Reprinted from the Boston Medical and Surgical Journal, vol. 142, 1900 [*5746.1.142].

E6289 — Insanity.

NK 0196656 MB

VM 2193 K 67b 1873 KNAPP, Mrs. PHOEBE (PALMER) 1839-1908, comp.
Bible school songs, for the use of Sunday-schools. Prepared by Mrs. J.F.Knapp and J.H.Vincent... New York, Nelson & Phillips [c1873]
64p.

NK 0196657 ICN MWA RPB

VM 2193 K 67n KNAPP, Mrs. PHOEBE (PALMER) 1839-1908, comp.
Notes of joy, for the Sabbath school, the social meeting and the hour of prayer... New York, Palmer [c1869]
176p.

NK 0196658 ICN N RPB DLC MH-AH NNUT IU NIC

VOLUME 300

Knapp, Phoebe (Palmer) 1839-1908.
Open the gates of the temple [sacred song] New York, Wm A. Pond & co. [c1892]
7 p. 35 1/2 cm.
Mezzo-soprano or baritone.

NK 0196659 OrU

Knapp, Phoebe (Palmer) 1839-1908.
Open the gates of the temple, words by Fanny Crosby. Pond, c1903.
Copies for high and medium voice.

NK 0196659-1 OrP

Knapp, Phoebe (Palmer) 1839-1908.
Open the gates of the temple. Words by Fanny Crosby. Music by Mrs. Joseph F. Knapp. New York, Robbins music corp. [c1951]

Song with piano accompaniment.

1. Sacred songs, U.S. 2. Songs, Sacred--1870- I. Crosby, Fanny.

NK 0196659-2 NN

Knapp, Phoebe (Palmer) 1839-1908.
A ray of sunshine. Words by Thomas MacKellar. n.p. [c1903]
[3] p.

NK 0196659-3 IU

Knapp, Reinhart.
So liest man den Wirtschaftsteil der Zeitung. Stuttgart, C. E. Poeschel, 1953.
122 p. 19 cm.

1. Economics—Study and teaching. I. Title.

New York Univ. for Library of Congress Libraries H62 A 57-21

NK 0196659-4 NNU

Knapp, Robert, 1804-
see Knapp, Aug. Theod. Robert, 1804-

Knapp, Robert B ed.
Orientation to America for foreign exchangees; report of a conference held under the auspices of the American Council on Education, Washington, D. C., June 19-21, 1952. Washington, 1952.
viii, 74 p. 23 cm. (American Council on Education. Studies. Series 1: Reports of committees and conferences, no. 54)
Bibliography: p. 70-71.

1. U. S.—Civilization—Study and teaching. 2. Educational exchanges. I. Title. (Series)

L13.A383 no. 54 378.3 52-14038

PU-Penn
NK 0196659-5 DLC WaWW OrPR IdPI NIC TxU ViU NcD

Knapp, Robert Hampden, 1915-
Origins of American scientists; a study made under the direction of a committee of the faculty of Wesleyan University, by R. H. Knapp and H. B. Goodrich. [Chicago] University of Chicago Press for Wesleyan University, Middletown, Conn. [1952]
xiv, 450 p. illus. 25 cm.

1. Scientists, American. 2. Science as a profession. I. Goodrich, Hubert Baker, joint author. II. Wesleyan University, Middletown, Conn. Committee on the Education of Scientists. III. Title.

Q127.U6K55 507.1173 52-14611

OrCS MtBC NjN PV MiU PSt NcU OU CaBVaU OrPS OrP OrU IdU Wa WaTC MtBuM OrHi Or NIC PP OCU OC1W WaWW DNAL ICRL NN CoBBS OrPR
NK 0196659-6 DLC GAT DSI LU TU CU MB ICJ TxU NN

Knapp, Robert Hampden, 1915-
The younger American scholar: his collegiate origins, by Robert H. Knapp and Joseph J. Greenbaum. [Chicago] University of Chicago Press and the Wesleyan University Press for Wesleyan University, Middletown, Conn.; distributed by the University of Chicago Press [1953]
xiii, 122 p. illus. 25 cm.

1. Universities and colleges — U. S. 2. U. S. — Intellectual life. 3. Learning and scholarship—U. S. I. Greenbaum, Joseph J., joint author. II. Title.

LB2321.K53 378.73 53-8206

OrCS MtBC WaWW WaSpG WaS Wa OKentC PRosC OrPR WaTC OrU OrLgE AU CaBVaU MtU PPEB NcD OO OC1W NN TxU NSyL IaAS MB ViU OC1W
NK 0196659-7 DLC KEmT CoFS TU PSt PPPL PRosC PPT

Knapp, Robert Henry.
Practical guidance methods for counselors, teachers, and administrators. New York, McGraw-Hill, 1953.
320 p. illus. 24 cm.

1. Personnel service in education. I. Title.

LB1027.5.K585 371.42 52-13008 ‡

OrCS CtY-M CaBVaU Wa IdPI IdU Or OrPS OrU WaS WaTC NcRS NcD TxU OOxM ViU OU PP MB PU PSt PBL PRosC ODW
NK 0196659-8 DLC OC1W MiU WaU KEmT KMK OCU PPT PPPL

Knapp, Robert Henry.
A survey of practices and trends in administrative provisions for individual differences, 1928-1938, by Robert H. Knapp ... [Lincoln? Neb., 1940]
4 p. l., 215 numb. l. 27cm.
Thesis (PH. D.)—University of Nebraska, 1939.
Mimeographed.
Bibliography: leaves 204-215.

1. Education of children. 2. Children, Abnormal and backward.

Library of Congress LC3981.K55 1939 40-13074
Univ. of Nebraska Libr. 371.90973

MB ViU
NK 0196659-9 NbU MtU PPPL CU NIC IdU OrU NcU PPT OU

BF 431 .K57 Knapp, Robert S.
Statistical analysis and evaluation of the entrance test battery of Kent State University for the academic year, 1945-1946. Kent, 1949.
ix, 125 l. tables, charts. 28 cm. (Kent State University. Graduate School. Masters theses. Department of Psychology)
Bibliography and bibliographical footnotes.
Non-circulating copy in Archives.

1. Ability--Testing. I. Title II. Series

NK 0196660 OKentU

Knapp, Robert W
Home and peace; poems by Robert W. Knapp. New York, William-Frederick press, 1946. 29 p. 21cm. (The William-Frederick poets. no. 25.)

NK 0196661 NN RPB

Knapp, Roy A., joint author.

Hunter, George William, 1873-
Mastery tests in general science. Set Y. [By] George W. Hunter ... and Roy A. Knapp ... New York, Cincinnati [etc.] American book company [c1934]

---

q789.1 K72fu Knapp, Roy C 1891-
Fundamental rudiments of mallet technique and tympani tuning. Excerpts from lesson studies. [Chicago, Ludwig & Ludwig, 1939]
[4]p. illus., music. 31cm.

Caption title.

1. Kettle drum--Instruction & study.

NK 0196663 IU

---

q789.1 K72f Knapp, Roy C 1891-
The fundamentals of modern drumming. Excerpts from his lesson studies. [Chicago, Ludwig & Ludwig, 193-]
[6]p. illus., music. 31cm.

Caption title.

1 Drum--Instruction & study.

NK 0196664 IU

Knapp, Royce Henderson, 1913-

Christensen, Chris Lauriths, 1894-
... Agriculture; teaching youth about the problems of the farmer and rural America; analysis by Chris L. Christensen ... and Noble Clark ... Teaching aids by Royce H. Knapp ... Washington, D. C., National council for the social studies, National association of secondary-school principals, departments of the National education association [1942]

Knapp, Royce Henderson, 1913-
American regionalism and social education, a study of the implications of American regionalism for the social-studies programs in New England schools, by Royce H. Knapp ... Cambridge, Harvard university press, 1947.
x p., 1 l., 156 p. illus. (maps) 22½cm. (Half-title: Harvard studies in education, published under the direction of the Graduate school of education, v. 30)
Includes bibliographies.
1. Social sciences—Study and teaching. 2. Regionalism—U. S. I. Title.
H62.K6 307 47-3607
© 5May47; President and Fellows of Harvard college, Cambridge, Mass.; A12659.

TxU DNAL
NK 0196666 DLC Or NIC LU ViU DAU MtBC OrU ICU MB MH

Knapp, Royce Henderson, 1913-
A bibliography on the New England region, selected and annotated for teachers of the social studies, and a list of unit titles suggested as possibilities for social studies units on New England; prepared by Royce H. Knapp, under the guidance and direction of Professor Howard E. Wilson, in the Social studies workshop. [Cambridge] Graduate school of education, Harvard university [1941]
1 p. l., 16 numb. l. 28 x 21½cm.
Reproduced from type-written copy.

1. New England—Bibl. I. Harvard university. Graduate school of education.

Library of Congress Z1251.E1K5 [3] 43-1744 016.9174

NK 0196667 DLC

VOLUME 300

Knapp, Royce Henderson, 1913–
Citizenship education for secondary schools, by Royce H. Knapp and ⌜others⌝ Lincoln, Nebraska Citizenship Education Project, Teachers College, University of Nebraska ⌜1953⌝
91 p. 28 cm.

1. Civics—Study and teaching. I. Title.

H62.K62 307.12 58–62671 ‡

NK 0196668 DLC

Knapp, Royce Henderson, 1913–
The Nebraska citizenship education project: a three-year report, by Royce H. Knapp. ⌜Lincoln, University of Nebraska, Teachers College⌝ 1953.
31 p. 23 cm. (⌜Nebraska. University. Extension Division⌝ Contributions to education, no. 30)
University of Nebraska. ⌜Extension Division⌝ Publication no. 188.
"Resources for citizenship education": p. 24–31.

1. Civics—Study and teaching. I. Title. (Series)

LB1584.K57 64–64113

NK 0196669 DLC CU ICU MiU WaU MoU FTaSU TxU

Knapp, Royce Henderson, 1913–
A resource handbook for secondary-school social studies. ⌜Lincoln, University of Nebraska Teachers College⌝ 1950.
40 p. 23 cm. (Contributions to education, no. 27)
University of Nebraska publication no. 174.

1. Social sciences—Bibl. I. Title. (Series: Nebraska. University. Extension Division. Contributions to education, no. 27. Series: Nebraska. University. Extension Division. Publication no. 174)

Z7161.K68 016.30712 51–62379

NK 0196669-1 DLC CU MoU ViU TxU

Knapp, Royce Henderson, 1913–
Teaching the social-studies problems course in selected senior high schools. ⌜Lincoln⌝ Extension Division, University of Nebraska, 1948.
26 p. 23 cm. (Contributions to education, 25)
University of Nebraska publication no. 164.
"Outstanding teaching resources": p. 18–25. Bibliography: p. 26.

1. Social problems—Study and teaching. I. Title. (Series: Nebraska. University. Extension Division. Contributions to education, 25. Series: Nebraska. University. Extension Division. Publication no. 164)

HN29.K58 301.153 49–47208*

NK 0196669-2 DLC CU MB MoU PPT OOxM CaBViP ViU TxU

Knapp, Royce Henderson, 1913– *ed.*
UNESCO and Nebraska secondary school youth. Foreword by R. G. Gustavson. ⌜Lincoln, Univ. of Nebraska Teachers College⌝ 1947.
39 p. 23 cm. (⌜Nebraska. University. Extension Division⌝ Contributions to education, no. 24)
University of Nebraska publication no. 160.
"Resources and teaching aids": p. 33–39.

1. United Nations Educational, Scientific and Cultural Organization. 2. ⌜International education⌝ I. Title. (Series. Series: Nebraska. University. Extension Division. University of Nebraska publication no. 160)

AS4.U83K6 060 E 48–10*
U. S. Office of Education. Library
for Library of Congress ⌜2⌝†

NK 0196669-3 DHEW CU PP OOxM PU-Penn MH TxU DLC ViU

Knapp, Rüdiger, 1917–
Angewandte Pflanzensoziologie. Stuttgart, E. Ulmer, 1949.
132 p. illus., maps. 21 cm. (*His* Einführung in die Pflanzensoziologie, Heft 3)

1. Phytosociology. 2. Botany, Economic. I. Title. (Series)

QK911.K55 52–15188

NK 0196669-4 DLC MnU WU MoU NcD

Knapp, Rüdiger, 1917–
Arbeitsmethoden der Pflanzensoziologie und Eigenschaften der Pflanzengesellschaften. Stuttgart, E. Ulmer ⌜1948⌝
100 p. maps, diagrs. 21 cm. (*His* Einführung in die Pflanzensoziologie, Heft 1)
Bibliography: p. 96.

1. Botany—Ecology. 2. Botany—Methodology. I. Title.

QK901.K63 51–32653

NK 0196669-5 DLC MnU

Knapp, Rüdiger, 1917–

S599
.G4H4

Schönhals, Ernst, 1909–
Die Böden Hessens und ihre Nutzung; mit einem Beitrag von R. Knapp. Hrsg. von der Direktion des Hessischen Landesamtes für Bodenforschung. Wiesbaden, 1954.

QK901
K63
Biology
Library

Knapp, Rüdiger, 1917–
Einführung in die Pflanzensoziologie.
Stuttgart, E. Ulmer ⌜1948–49⌝
3 no.in 1 v. illus.,maps,diagrs.

Includes bibliographies.

Contents.- Heft 1. Arbeitsmethoden der Pflanzensoziologie und Eigenschaften der Pflanzengesellschaften.- Heft 2. Die Pflanzengesellschaften Mitteleuropas.- Heft 3. Angewandte Pflanzensoziologie.

NK 0196669-6 CU OrCS NIC MnU IU DNAL

Knapp, Rüdiger, 1917–
Experimentelle Soziologie der höheren Pflanzen. Stuttgart, E. Ulmer, 1954–
v. illus. 22 cm.
Includes bibliographies.
Contents.—1. Bd. Einwirkung der Pflanzen aufeinander. Soziologie der Keimung und des aufwachsenden Bestandes.

1. Phytosociology. 2. Germination. I. Title.

QK911.K57 57–266 ‡

NK 0196669-7 ICU OkU NIC NcD DCU DNAL DLC PSt TNJ TxU OrCS AU MiU CtY IU

Knapp, Rüdiger, 1917–
Die Pflanzengesellschaften Mitteleuropas. Stuttgart, E. Ulmer ⌜1948⌝
94 p. illus. 21 cm. (*His* Einführung in die Pflanzensoziologie, 2)

1. Botany—Ecology—Europe. I. Title.

QK955.K59 A 51–1454
Harvard Univ. Library
for Library of Congress ⌜a53b1⌝†

NK 0196669-8 MH DNAL DLC

Knapp, Rüdiger, 1917–
Studien zur Vegetation und pflanzengeographischen Gliederung Nordwest-Italiens und der Süd-Schweiz. Köln, Selbstverlag des Geographischen Instituts der Universität, 1953.
59 p. map, diagrs. 21 cm. (Kölner geographische Arbeiten, Heft 4)
Bibliography: p. 55–59.

1. Botany—Italy. 2. Botany—Switzerland. 3. Botany—Ecology.

QK956.I 8K6 55–21923

NK 0196669-9 DLC NN

Knapp, Rüdiger, 1917-
„Über Pflanzengesellschaften der Wiesen im Vogelsberge. Über den Einfluss der Höhenlage und des Klimas auf die Artenzusammensetzung von Wiesen im mittleren Deutschland. Lauterbach, Hessen, Lauterbacher Hohhausmuseum, 1951
18 p. illus. (Lauterbacher Sammlungen, 6)

NK 0196670 MH DNAL

Knapp, Russell S jt. auth.
Accounting periods and accounting methods

see under

Blattmachr, George G

Knapp, Russell S
Forms of business organization and the federal tax laws, by Russell S. Knapp and William C. Warren. Revised to February 1, 1951. ⌜New York⌝ Practising Law Institute, c1951.
105 p. (American Bar Association. Section of Taxation. Current problems in federal taxation, no. 13, rev. 1951)

Bibliographical footnotes.
Earlier ed. by Charles D. Hamel and others.

NK 0196672 NNC NcD-L NBuU-L ViU

Knapp, Russell S
Forms of business organization and the Federal tax laws, by Russell S. Knapp and William C. Warren. Revised to February 1954. ⌜New York⌝ Practising Law Institute, c1954.
120 p. (American Bar Association. Section of Taxation. Current problems in Federal taxation, no. 13, rev. 1954)

A previous ed. was by C. D. Hamel and others.

NK 0196673 NNC PPT-L ViU-L NcU NcD-L

Knapp, Ruth Whitney.
... If you are a child, by Ruth Whitney Knapp and Elizabeth Jane Merrill. ⌜Pasadena, Calif., Esto publishing company, °1935⌝
cover-title, 16 p. illus. 15cm. (Enjoy your museum. VII B)

1. Art—Study and teaching. 2. Art criticism. I. Merrill, Elizabeth Jane, joint author. II. Title.

Library of Congress N7435.K55 42–8797

NK 0196674 DLC NcD

Knapp, Sally Elizabeth, 1918–
Eleanor Roosevelt, a biography. New York, Crowell Co. ⌜1949⌝
185 p. port. 21 cm.

1. Roosevelt, Eleanor (Roosevelt) 1884–

E807.1.R57 920.7 49–11201*

NK 0196675 DLC PP IdB Or TU OrAshS OrU WaSp WaT

Knapp, Sally Elizabeth, 1918–
New wings for women ⌜by⌝ Sally Knapp. New York, Thomas Y. Crowell company ⌜1946⌝
x p., 1 l., 179 p. ports. 21cm.
Contents.—Teddy Kenyon.—Pauline Gower.—Lois Coots Tonkin.—Nancy Love.—Maxine Miles.—Ellen Church.—Helen Harrison.—Caroline Iverson.—Ethel Colwell.—Valentina Grizodubova.—Helen Montgomery.—Phoebe Omlie.—Isabel Ebel.

Continued in next column

VOLUME 300

Continued from preceding column

1. Women in aeronautics. I. Title.

Library of Congress TL553.K58 46-6736 331.482913

NK 0196676 DLC ViU PP PU PWcS Or OrU WaE DSI

Knapp, Sally Elizabeth, 1918–
Sink the basket; illustrated by Dorothy Bayley Morse. New York, Crowell [1953]
186 p. illus. 21 cm.

I. Title.

PZ7.K73Si 52—8853 ‡

NK 0196677 DLC Or OrP WaS WaSp PP OO OOxM WaT

Knapp, Sally Elizabeth, 1918–
Women doctors today. New York, Crowell [1947]
184 p. ports. 21 cm.

CONTENTS.—Katherine Li.—Vesta Rogers.—Edith Summerskill.—Lena Edwards.—Ida Scudder.—Lauretta Bender.—Emily Van Loon.—Katharine Elsom.—Sophie Rabinoff.—Hanna Hirszfeld.—Barbara Stimson.—Rita Finkler.

1. Women as physicians. [1. Women in medicine] I. [Title]

R134.K55 926.1 Med 47-2494

U. S. Army Medical Library for Library of Congress [W1041K67w 1947]

Copyright [4]†

NK 0196678 NIC Wa WaS MB OU ICJ DLC OrU-M WaSp WaT DNLM CaBVa IdU Or OrU NcGU NcC OKentU

RS
73
K7274 Knapp, Samuel A
Pentecostal sanctification. [n.p., c1897]
99 p. 18 cm.

80586 Imperfect: title-page wanting; replaced by type-written title-page.

1. Sanctification. I. Title.

NK 0196679 KyWAT

Knapp, Samuel Lorenzo, 1783-1838.
Address before the New England Society, Dec. 22, 1829. N. Y., 1830.
22 p.

NK 0196680 PHi

Knapp, Samuel Lorenzo, 1783–1838.
An address delivered in Chauncey place church, before the young men of Boston, August 2, 1826, in commemoration of the death of Adams and Jefferson. By Samuel L. Knapp. Boston, Ingraham and Hewes, printers, 1826.
31 p. 21½cm.

1. Adams, John, pres. U. S., 1735-1826. 2. Jefferson, Thomas, pres. U. S., 1743-1826.

Library of Congress E322.K5 43-22112

NK 0196681 Vi MH RPB ICU CtY PHi PPAmP MB ViU ICRL DLC ICN MeWC OU PSt TxU ViU MdBP CSmH NN MB

---

*
PS2196
.K53A4
1832 Knapp, Samuel Lorenzo, 1783-1838.
Advice in the pursuits of literature, containing historical, biographical, and critical remarks. By Samuel L. Knapp. New-York, J. K. Porter, 1832.
2 p. l., [v]-x, [7]-296 p. 18½cm.
Inscribed "Edwin S. Child no. 10" and "Edward S. Child no 4 1835."

1. English literature—Hist. & crit. 2. Books and reading. I. Title.

NK 0196682 ViU KyLx KyU PU NNU MH IU RPB OClW NN

PR99
K5 Knapp, Samuel Lorenzo, 1783-1838.
Advice in the pursuits of literature, containing historical, biographical, and critical remarks. 2d ed. New York, J.K. Porter, 1832.
296p. 19cm.

1. English literature - Hist. & crit. 2. Books and reading.

NK 0196683 IaU ICN NN CtY

Knapp, Samuel Lorenzo, 1784–1838.
Advice in the pursuits of literature; containing historical, biographical, and critical remarks; by Samuel L. Knapp. Middletown, N. J., G. H. Evans, 1837.
x, 7-296 p. 19cm.

1. Books and reading. 2. Literature.

A 10-549

Title from Brown Univ. Printed by L. C.

NK 0196684 RPB ViU NcU TxU NjP OU

Micro
Film
D50
reel
370
no.5 Knapp, Samuel Lorenzo, 1783-1838
Advice in the pursuits of literature; containing historical, biographical, and critical remarks; by Samuel L. Knapp. Middletown, N.J., G.H. Evans, 1837.
(On American culture series, reel 370, no.5)
Microfilm (positive). 35mm. Ann Arbor, Mich., University Microfilms, 1968.
Collation of the original: x,7-296p. 19cm.

1. Books and reading. 2. Literature. I. Title.

NK 0196685 PSt

Knapp, Samuel Lorenzo, 1783–1838.
Advice in the pursuits of literature, containing historical, biographical, and critical remarks. By Samuel L. Knapp ... New York, C. S. Francis; Boston, J. H. Francis, 1841.
x, [7]-296 p. 18½cm.

1. English literature—Hist. & crit. 2. Books and reading.

15-8684

Library of Congress PR99.K5

NK 0196686 DLC NcD TxU OCU NN

---

*
PS2196
.K53A4
1833 Knapp, Samuel Lorenzo, 1783–1838.
American biography, by Samuel L. Knapp: forming part VI of The treasury of knowledge, and library of reference. New York, Conner & Cooke, 1833.
2 p. l., [5]-408 p. 18cm.
Author's inscription "Samuel L Knapp".

1. U. S.—Biog. I. The treasury of knowledge and the library of reference. II. Title.

NK 0196687 ViU

Knapp, Samuel Lorenzo, 1783-1838.
American biography; or, Original biographical sketches of distinguished Americans, by Samuel L. Knapp... New York: J. W. Bell, 1855. 412 p. 8°. (In: The treasury of knowledge and library of reference, 1855. v. 3.)

269175A. 1. United States—Biog.
N. Y. P. L. June 30, 1927

NK 0196688 NN

[Knapp, Samuel Lorenzo] 1783-1838, ed.
American history: containing: Belknap's biographies of the early discoverers; Robertson's History of South America; Graham's History of North America, and the North American colonies; Ramsey's History of the United States, continued to the present time; the history of three judges of Charles I. who fled to America and were concealed in Massachusetts and Connecticut for near thirty years; and Hubbard's History of the Indian wars in New England ... New York, Leavitt and Allen [1835?]
2 v. in 1. plates 29 cm.

NK 0196690 CtY-L

JGN
E
18
.A5 Knapp, Samuel Lorenzo, 1783-1838, ed.
American history; containing Belknap's Biographies of the early discoverers; Robertson's History of South America; Graham's History of North America and the North American colonies; Ramsey's History of the United States, continued to the present time; the History of three judges of Charles I...and Hubbard's History of the Indian Wars in New England; giving to the reader a full view of the history of America, from the earliest discovery to the present day.

New York, Leavitt and Allen [1855]
2 v. in 1. illus.
Vol. 2 has title Library of American history.

#America--Hist.
#America--Disc. & explor.
#Explorers.
#Indians of North America--Wars--1600-1750.
Knapp, Samuel Lorenzo, 1783-1838, ed.
a/t Library American history.

NK 0196692 OClWHi ViU NN PPULC IU MoU NBuG NjR MnHi MiD PU PHi NcD CtY

Knapp, Samuel L[orenzo] *ed.*
The American library: being a weekly publication devoted to American history. Ed. by Samuel L. Knapp. no. 1-16. New York, Lohman, Irwin & Hall, 1834-35.
1 v. 30½ x 24½cm.
Reprinted under title: Library of American history: a reprint of standard works.

Subject entries: 1. U. S.—Hist. 2. America—Discovery & exploration. 3. America—Hist.

2-17187

Library of Congress, no. E173.K66.

NK 0196693 DLC

Knapp, Samuel Lorenzo, 1783-1838.
At a numerous and respectable meeting of Federal Republicans
see under Federal party. Massachusetts.

Knapp, Samuel Lorenzo, 1783-1838.
The bachelors, and other tales, founded on American incidents and character. New-York, J. and W. Sandford, 1836.
216 p. 20 cm.

Continued in next column

VOLUME 300

Continued from preceding column

I. Title.

PZ3.K727Bac 49-32963*

PU ICN MB CSmH IU TxU MH NNC
NK 0196695 DLC MB ViLxW ViU NcD CU KEmT InU CtY ICU

Knapp, Samuel Lorenzo, 1783-1838.
Biographical sketches of eminent lawyers, statesmen, and men of letters ... By Samuel L. Knapp. Boston, Richardson and Lord, 1821.
iv, [5]-360 p. 22 cm.
[Waterman pamphlets, v. 41, no. 1]
On p. 360: End of volume I. No more published.
——— [Another issue]
Verso of 2d leaf numbered v instead of iv.
F36.K62
1. Massachusetts—Biog.
F63.K61 5-37658

MWA OrU WaU-L
OClWHi MdBP PP PU PPC PPL ViU-L I NjP NN MH Nh WaS
NK 0196696 DLC MiU-L NIC IaU MeB TU ViU KyU NcD OClW

Knapp, Samuel Lorenzo, 1784-1838.
Boston monthly magazine. v. I, v. 2, no. 1-2; June 1825-July 1826. [Boston, 1825-26]

Microfilm 01104 no. 74 AP
Knapp, Samuel Lorenzo, 1783-1838. ed.
Boston monthly magazine. v. 1-2, no. 2; June 1825-July 1826. [Boston]

Knapp, Samuel Lorenzo, 1783-1838.
A discourse on the life and character of DeWitt Clinton, delivered before the Grand chapter and Grand lodge of the District of Columbia, the Grand chapter of Maryland, the Blue lodges of Washington, Georgetown and Alexandria, and other masons of the vicinity, and the brethren sojourners in the city of Washington, on the 29th of March, 1828. By Samuel L. Knapp. Washington, Printed by W. Greer, 1828.
36 p. 21½cm.
1. Clinton, DeWitt, 1769-1828.
18-12675
Library of Congress E340.C65K6

NK 0196699 DLC ViU PHi PPL MWA

Knapp, Samuel Lorenzo, 1783-1838.
Eulogy delivered in Christ-church, Boston, at the request of Saint John's lodge, June 8, 1819, on the character of their brother and past master, Shubael Bell, esq. By Samuel L. Knapp ... Boston, Printed by J. T. Buckingham [1819]
19 p. 21½cm.
1. Bell, Shubael, 1767-1819. I. Freemasons. Boston. St. John's lodge. II. Title.
21-8113
Library of Congress HS511.B5K6

NK 0196700 DLC MB MH MWA

[**Knapp, Samuel Lorenzo**] 1783-1838.
Extracts from a journal of travels in North America, consisting of an account of Boston and its vicinity. By Ali Bey, &c. [*pseud.*] Translated from the original manuscript... Boston: Printed by Thomas Badger, Jun. 1818.
124 p. 19cm.
1. Boston—Soc. life & cust. 2. Harvard university. I. Title.
1-12266
Library of Congress F73.44.K67

MShM MWA MnU
NK 0196701 DLC N NcD ViU MiU-C GEU InU CU MeB PU NjP

[**Knapp, Samuel Lorenzo**] 1783-1838.
Extracts from the journal of Marshal Soult (*pseud.*) addressed to a friend: how obtained, and by whom translated is not a subject of enquiry ... Newburyport, W. B. Allen & co., 1817.
143 p. 19 cm.
1. Massachusetts—Soc. life & cust. 2. Essex Co., Mass. I. Title.
F69.K67 10-8719

NK 0196702 DLC MWA RP InU PU LU PMA ViU CU

Knapp, Samuel Lorenzo, 1783-1838.
Female biography; containing notices of distinguished women, in different nations and ages. By Samuel L. Knapp ... Philadelphia, Leary & Getz [n.d.]
xii, [13]-501, [1] p. 19.5 cm.

NK 0196703 NcGW

Knapp, Samuel Lorenzo, 1783-1838.
Female biography; containing notices of distinguished women, in different nations and ages. By Samuel L. Knapp ... Stereotyped by Francis F. Ripley. New York, published by J. Carpenter; Baltimore, Phoenix, Wood & co., 1834.
xii, [13], 501, [3] p. 19.5 cm.

NK 0196704 NcD OO ICN MB RPB MiEM OClWHi OClW

Knapp, Samuel Lorenzo, 1783-1838.
Female biography. Biography of remarkable females. From a late London edition. With portraits from steel plates. Philadelphia, J. J. Woodward, 1835.
513 p. 23 cm.

NK 0196705 PV

Knapp, Samuel Lorenzo, 1783-1838.
Female biography; containing notices of distinguished women, in different nations and ages. By Samuel L. Knapp ... Stereotyped by Francis F. Ripley. Philadelphia, T. Wardle, 1836.
xii, [13]-501, [3] p. 20cm.

NK 0196706 ViU LU CSt

Knapp, Samuel Lorenzo, 1783-1838.
Female biography; containing notices of distinguished women, in different nations and ages. By Samuel L. Knapp ... Stereotyped by Francis F. Ripley. Philadelphia, T. Wardle, 1842.
xii, [13], 501, [3] p. 20cm.
1. Woman—Biog. I. Title.
19-6544
Library of Congress CT3202.K6 1842

NK 0196707 DLC TU PSC-Hi

Knapp, Samuel Lorenzo, 1783-1838.
Female biography; containing notices of distinguished women, in different nations and ages. By Samuel L. Knapp... Stereotyped by Francis F. Ripley. Philadelphia, T. Wardle, 1843.
xii, [13], 501, [3] p.

NK 0196708 PMA MH PRosC

CT3202 .K6 1868
Knapp, Samuel Lorenzo, 1783-1838.
Female biography; containing notices of distinguished women in different ages and nations. Philadelphia, Sower, Barnes & Potts, 1868.
.12. 501p. illus. 19cm.

1.Women - Biography. I.Title.
67-5-4 BBmh 6

NK 0196709 NcU ViU PPL

Knapp, Samuel Lorenzo, 1784-1838.
The genius of masonry, or A defence of the order, containing some remarks on the origin and history; the uses and abuses of the science, with some notices of other secret societies in the United States, in three lectures. By Samuel L. Knapp ... Providence, Cranston & Marshall, printers, 1828.
ix, [11]-107 p. 18½cm.
1. Freemasons.
9-26894†
Library of Congress HS527.K67

NK 0196710 DLC MB ViU OU MWA ICU PPL NN

Knapp, Samuel Lorenzo, 1783-1838,
FOR OTHER EDITIONS SEE MAIN ENTRY
Hinton, John Howard, 1791-1873.
The history and topography of the United States of North America, brought down from the earliest period ... by John Howard Hinton, A. M., assisted by several literary gentlemen in England and America. With additions and corrections, by Samuel L. Knapp, esq.; and a continuation to the present time by John Overton Choules, D. D. ... Boston, S. Walker, 1854-56.

Knapp, Samuel Lorenzo, 1783-1838,
Hinton, John Howard, 1791-1873.
History of the United States, from the earliest period. By John Howard Hinton, A. M. With additions by Samuel L. Knapp, esq., and John Overton Choules, D. D. A new edition, brought down to the present time. To which are added Biographies of the signers of the Declaration of independence by W. A. Crafts. Boston, Walker and Virtue, 1861.

Knapp, Samuel Lorenzo, 1783-1838.
Lectures on American literature, with remarks on some passages of American history. N. Y., E. Bliss, 1827.
300 p.

NK 0196713 PPM

Knapp, Samuel Lorenzo, 1783-1838.
Lectures on American literature, with remarks on some passages of American history. By Samuel L. Knapp ... [New York] E. Bliss, 1829.
300 p. 21½cm.
1. American literature—Hist. & crit. 2. U. S.—Hist.
17-21576
Library of Congress. PS85.K6

MnHi ViU ICRL KyLx
CtY MiU MnU ViU MB IU ODW MeB NjP MWA KEmT ICRL TU
NK 0196714 DLC PSt NWM NcU NcD PPA PPT PPL PU OCl Nh

VOLUME 300

[Knapp, Samuel Lorenzo] 1783–1838.
Letters of Shahcoolen, a Hindu philosopher, residing in Philadelphia; to his friend El Hassan, an inhabitant of Delhi. Boston, Printed by Russell and Cutler. (Proprietors of the work.) 1802.
152 p. 18½cm.
"Originally published in the New-York 'Commercial advertiser'."—p. [7]
CONTENTS.—General account of the new philosophy.—Mary Woolstonecraft.—Practical influence of her writings upon the women of the United States.—State of the female sex in the United States.—State of American poetry; American poets, extracts from their writings.—Scenes of nature in America; calculated to excite poetical enthusiasm; comparison of them with those of Hindustan.—Selections from Hindu poetry; remarks.—Poetry of the Scriptures; Solomon's song; resemblance between it and the Gitogavinda of Jayadeva.—Solomon's song considered as a poem; selections from it.—Attachment of the writer to poetry; selections from the Gitagovinda.—Dialogue with a modern philosopher.
I. Title.
Library of Congress AC8.K8 32–10880 081

PU IU ICU NjP MB MH MWA CSmH MnU ViU PMA MH IEN MiU
NK 0196716 DLC MnHi NIC InU ViU WU MiU-C PU NcD PPL

Knapp, Samuel Lorenzo, 1784–1838, *ed.*
Library of American history: a reprint of standard works: connected by editorial remarks, abounding with copious notes, biographical sketches, and miscellaneous matter, intended to give the reader a full view of American history, colonial and national. Ed. by Samuel L. Knapp ... New York, J. H. Turney, 1835
v. front. (port.) 28½ x 22½cm.
Originally pub. in weekly numbers, under title: The American library.
CONTENTS.—I. Biographies of the early discoverers, by Jeremy Belknap. The history of South America, by William Robertson. The history of North America, by James Grahame. The history of the United States (by David Ramsay)
1. U. S.—Hist. 2. America—Disc. & explor. 3. America—Hist. I. Title.
Library of Congress E173.K67 2-5694

NK 0196717 DLC MiU-C OClWHi

Knapp, Samuel Lorenzo, 1784–1838, editor.
Library of American history: a reprint of standard works: connected by editorial remarks, abounding with copious notes, biographical sketches, and miscellaneous matter, intended to give the reader a full view of American history, from the earliest discovery to the present time... Edited by Samuel L. Knapp... New York: C. H. Jackson & Co., 1836–37. 2 v. in 1. Map, pl., port. 4°.
v. 2 has imprint: A. Neal & Co.
Published originally in weekly numbers under title: The American library.
The editor states that Grahame's history in v. 1 and Ramsay's history in v. 1–2 have been continued from "authorities of accredited correctness."
v. 1. Biographies of the early discoverers, by J. Belknap. History of South America, by W. Robertson. History of North America, by J. Grahame. History of the United States, by D. Ramsay.
v. 2. History of the United States, by D. Ramsay. History of three of the judges of King Charles I, by E. Stiles. History and character of the Indians: A narrative of the Indian wars in New England, by W. Hubbard; The entertaining history of King Philip's war, by B. Church, with some account of Col. Benjamin Church, by T. Church.
1. U. S.—History. 2. America.—Discovery. 3. America.—History. 4. Indians. 5. Title.
August 4, 1919.

NK 0196719 NN OClW

Knapp, Samuel Lorenzo, 1784–1838, editor.
Library of American history: a reprint of standard works connected by editorial remarks, abounding with copious notes, biographical sketches, and miscellaneous matter, intended to give the reader a full view of American history, from the earliest discovery to the present time... Edited by Samuel L. Knapp... New York: J. C. Riker, 1839. 2 v. in 1. facsim., front., plates. 2. ed. 4°.
1. U. S.—History. 2. America.—Discovery. 3. America.—History. 4. Indians.
N. Y. P. L. January 12, 1921.

NK 0196720 NN KAS NIC MnU MH DSI-W PHi

Knapp, Samuel Lorenzo, 1783–1838.
The life of Aaron Burr. By Samuel L. Knapp ... New-York, Wiley & Long, 1835.
x, [11]–290 p. 17½cm.

Continued in next column

Continued from preceding column

1. Burr, Aaron, 1756–1836.
Library of Congress E302.6.B9K6 7—14877
[a39b1]

MWA MdBP NjN MiU-C AU ViU TU LU OOxM MeB ViU
NK 0196721 DLC NcD MU IaU NIC PHi OO IC NjP DAU NN

Knapp, Samuel Lorenzo, 1783–1838.
Life of Lord Timothy Dexter; embracing sketches of the eccentric characters that composed his associates: including "Dexter's pickle for the knowing ones". By Samuel L. Knapp. Newburyport, J. G. Tilton; Boston, W. J. Reynolds & co., 1848.
viii, [9]–107, [1], 36 p. incl. front., illus. 16cm.
"A pickle for the knowing ones" has special t.-p. and separate pagination.
1. Dexter, Timothy, 1747–1806.
Library of Congress N55.D482 4—20032

PBm MB MiU-C
NK 0196722 DLC OClW ViU OU OClWHi MH CtY PHC PPPrHi

Knapp, Samuel Lorenzo, 1783–1838.
Life of Lord Timothy Dexter; embracing sketches of the eccentric characters that composed his associates: including "Dexter's pickle for the knowing ones". By Samuel L. Knapp. Newburyport, J. G. Tilton; Boston, W. J. Reynolds & co., 1852.
viii, [9]–107, [1], 36 p. incl. front., illus. 16cm.
"A pickle for the knowing ones" has special t.-p. and separate pagination.

NK 0196723 MiU-C ViU

Ch32
380c
Knapp, Samuel Lorenzo, 1783–1838.
Life of Lord Timothy Dexter; with sketches of the eccentric characters that composed his associates; including his own writings, "Dexter's pickle for the knowing ones", &c., &c. By Samuel L.Knapp; an introduction by "Cymon" ... Boston,J.E.Tilton and company,1858
158p. incl.front.,illus. 18cm.

PU MoU MB
NK 0196724 CtY MiU-C RPB MWA OCl NBu ICN MH TU PHi

Knapp, Samuel Lorenzo, 1783–1838.
The life of Thomas Eddy; comprising an extensive correspondence with many of the most distinguished philosophers and philanthropists of this and other countries. By Samuel L. Knapp ... New York, Conner & Cooke, 1834.
394 p. front. (port.) 20½cm.
The Appendix (p. [351]–394) contains: Memoir of William Roscoe, by Dr. Thomas Stewart Traile, and memoirs of General Schuyler, John Murray, jun., Ambrose Spencer, and John Howard.
1. Eddy, Thomas, 1758–1827. 2. Philanthropists.
Library of Congress HV8978.E3K6 15—126

OO MWA OClW NN MB Nh OU
NK 0196725 DLC NcGuG NBu CtY PHi PSC PP PU PSC-Hi

Knapp, Samuel Lorenzo, 1784–1838.
The life of Thomas Eddy, comprising an extensive correspondence with many of the most distinguished philosophers and philanthropists of this and other countries. By Samuel L. Knapp ... London: E. Fry and Son, 1836. 264 p., front. (port.) 8°.
1. Eddy, Thomas, 1758–1827. 2. Indians (N. A.).—Iroquois.
N. Y. P. L. November 1, 1915.

NK 0196726 NN MnU PP PHi PHC NjP NjR

Knapp, Samuel Lorenzo, 1783–1838.
Life of Timothy Dexter; embracing sketches of the eccentric characters that composed his associates. By Samuel Knapp ... Boston, G. N. Thomson, 1838.
viii, [9]–108 p. incl. front., illus. 15½cm.
Pages 107–108, advertising matter.
1. Dexter, Timothy, 1747–1806.
Library of Congress F74.N55D48 13—18455

CU MB MWH
NK 0196727 DLC MeB MiU-C MH MWA PPL DSI NcD ScU CtY

Knapp, Samuel Lorenzo, 1783–1838.
A memoir of the life of Daniel Webster. By Samuel L. Knapp. Boston, Stimpson and Clapp, 1831.
1 p. l., 234 p. front. (port.) 18½cm.
1. Webster, Daniel, 1782–1852.
Library of Congress E340.W4K6 14—767

MB MWA CLU NIC TU OU WaWW
NK 0196728 DLC AU PPA MdBP Nh PPL PNt PHi OClWHi OO

Micro
Film
D50
reel
272
no.5
Knapp, Samuel Lorenzo, 1783–1838
A memoir of the life of Daniel Webster. By Samuel L. Knapp. Boston, Stimpson and Clapp, 1831.
1 reel. 35mm. (American culture series, reel 272, no.5)
Microfilm (positive) made in 1964 by University Microfilms, Ann Arbor, Mich.
Collation of the original: 1p.l.,234p. front. (port.)
1. Webster, Daniel, 1782–1852. I. Title.
oap

NK 0196729 PSt KEmT ICRL

Knapp, Samuel Lorenzo, 1784–1838.
A memoir of the life of Daniel Webster. By Samuel L. Knapp ... 2d ed. Rev. and brought down to the present time. New York, J. S. Redfield, 1835.
108 p. 19½cm.
1. Webster, Daniel, 1782–1852.
Library of Congress E340.W4K62 13-25501

NK 0196730 DLC

*KNAPP,SAMUEL LORENZO,1783–1838
Mémoire justificatif de Monsieur le Maréchal Soult *pseud.* duc de Dalmatie. Paris, Le Normant, 1815.
1 p.l., 33 p. 8vo

NK 0196731 InU

[Knapp, Samuel Lorenzo] 1783–1838.
Memoirs of General Lafayette. With an account of his visit to America, and of his reception by the people of the United States; from his arrival, August 15th, to the celebration at Yorktown, October 19th, 1824. Boston, E. G. House, 1824.
v, [7]–264 p. front. (port.) 19cm.
1. Lafayette, Marie Joseph Paul Yves Roch Gilbert du Motier, marquis de, 1757–1834.
Library of Congress E207.L2K6 10—21807

NK 0196732 DLC TU OU ViU MWA MiD-B PHi MH MB

VOLUME 300

[Knapp, Samuel Lorenzo] 1783–1838.
Memoirs of General Lafayette, with an account of his tour through the United States; and a description of the ceremonies in laying the corner stone of the Bunker Hill monument. [Boston, 1825]
cover-title, [3]–24 p. front. (port.) 20cm.
Taken in part from author's earlier work "Memoirs of General Lafayette. With an account of his visit to America ... Boston, 1824."
1. Lafayette, Marie Joseph Paul Yves Roch Gilbert du Motier, marquis de, 1757–1834.
Library of Congress E207.L2K7 10—21818

NK 0196733 DLC MWA NjP MB

[Knapp, Samuel Lorenzo] 1783-1838.
Memoirs of General Lafayette, embracing details of his public & private life, sketches of the Amer. revolution, the French revolution, the downfall of Bonaparte, & the restoration of the Bourbons. With biographical notices of individuals who have been distinguished actors in these events. N.Y., Robins, 1825.
455p., port.
Cop. 3: Hartford, Barber.

NK 0196734 OClW CtY ViW PU MiU-C

KD 1820 K5
Knapp, Samuel Lorenzo, 1783-1838.
An oration, delivered at Dedham, June 24, A.D.1820, at the request of Constellation Lodge... Dedham, Printed by H. & W.H.Mann, 1820.
18 p. 22cm.
Shoemaker 1875.
1.Freemasons - Addresses, essays, lectures.

NK 0196735 CSt TU MWA MB

Knapp, Samuel Lorenzo, 1783–1838.
An oration, delivered at Newburyport, on the Fourth day of July 1810. By Samuel L. Knapp ... Newburyport [Mass.] From the press of Ephraim W. Allen [1810]
16 p. 21cm.
1. Fourth of July orations.
Library of Congress E286.N567 1810 18-6136

NK 0196736 DLC CtY PHi CU-S ICN RPB MH MWA IU

Knapp, Samuel Lorenzo, 1783–1838.
An oration delivered before "The associated disciples of Washington," on the 22d of February, 1812. The first anniversary of the institution. By Samuel L. Knapp, esq. Newburyport: From the press of E. W. Allen. 1812.
23 p. 21cm.
1. U. S.—Pol. & govt.—1789–1811. 2. Washington, George, pres. U. S., 1732–1799. I. The associated disciples of Washington.
Library of Congress E341.K67 9–28879 Revised

NK 0196737 DLC CSt NN CLU PPL MH MWA

Knapp, Samuel Lorenzo, 1783–1838.
An oration delivered before the ... masters and brethren of the lodges of St. Peter and St. Mark, on the festival of St. John the Baptist. By Brother Samuel L. Knapp, P. M. Newburyport: From the press of Brother E. W. Allen. 5811 [1811]
23 p. 20½cm.

Continued in next column

Continued from preceding column

1. Freemasons—Addresses, essays, lectures.
Library of Congress HS397.K6 22–14031

NK 0196738 DLC CSt ViU MWA

Knapp, Samuel Lorenzo, 1784–1838.
An oration delivered before the Merrimack humane society, on their anniversary, September 3, 1811. By Samuel L. Knapp. Newburyport: From the press of E. W. Allen. 1811. 22 p. 24cm.
List of officers of the society and treasurer's report, p. [23]
1. Humanitarianism. I. Merrimack humane society, Newburyport, Mass.
N. Y. P. L. April 1, 1940

NK 0196739 NN InU NjP MH NcU DLC RPB TU

KNAPP, SAMUEL LORENZO, 1784-1838.
An oration, pronounced before the Society of phi beta kappa, at Dartmouth college, Aug.19,1824. Published by request of the society. Boston, Commercial Gazette press, 1824. 32 p. 22cm.
1. United States--Civilization--Addresses, essays, lectures.

NK 0196740 NN MiD-B MWA NNU-W PPL CSmH IU MH Nh RPB

Knapp, Samuel Lorenzo, 1783–1838.
The picturesque beauties of the Hudson river and its vicinity; illustrated in a series of views, from original drawings, taken expressly for this work, and engraved on steel, by distinguished artists. With historical and descriptive illustrations, by Samuel L. Knapp, esq. [pt. I–II] New-York, J. Disturnell, 1835–36.
2 v. in 1. illus., 6 pl. 35 cm. (v. 2: 27 cm)
Added t.-p., engr.
Paged continuously.
No more published. cf. British museum Catalogue.
1. Hudson valley—Views. I. Title.
F127.H8K6 1—14122

NK 0196741 DLC CtY NIC PPL

[Knapp, Samuel Lorenzo] 1783-1838, supposed author.
The Polish chiefs; an historical romance
see under title

[Knapp, Samuel Lorenzo] 1783–1838.
Sketches of public characters. Drawn from the living and the dead. With notices of other matters. By Ignatius Loyola Robertson ... [pseud.] New York, E. Bliss, 1830.
viii, [5]–259, [1] p. 18cm.
1. U. S.—Biog. 2. Washington, D. C. I. Title.
Library of Congress E339.K68 5—37659

NK 0196743 DLC NcU AAP TU AU NcD PPA PPL PHi ViU OU OOxM MB MWA MiU-C

[Knapp, Samuel Lorenzo] 1783-1838.
State of American poetry: American poets extracts from their writings.
(In [Knapp, S. L.] Letters of Shahcoolen. 1802)

NK 0196744 RPB

Knapp, Samuel Lorenzo, 1784–1838.
Tales of the garden of Kosciusko. By Samuel L. Knapp ... New York, Printed by West & Trow, 1834.
216 p. 18cm.
I. Title.
Library of Congress PZ3.K727T 7—14280

NK 0196745 DLC N CU ViU InU CSmH PU NN ODW OO TxU MB

---

*
PS2196 .K53T35 1839
Knapp, Samuel Lorenzo, 1783-1838.
Tales of the garden of Kosciuszko. By Samuel L. Knapp. New York, Levison & Brother, 1839.
2 p. l., [5]-216 p. 18cm.
Inscribed "A. C. Bradstreet."

NK 0196746 ViU

---

*
PS2196 .K53T6 1824
Knapp, Samuel Lorenzo, 1783-1838.
To the Federal Republicans of Massachusetts. [Boston? Mass., 1824?]
[2] l. 25½cm.
Caption title.
"At a numerous and respectable meeting of Federal Republicans, at the Supreme Court Room, convened by a notice in the newspapers, last evening (18th Oct. inst.) the following Preamble and Resolutions were adopted Unanimously:"
Inscribed "Nathan Belton Esq."
1. Republican Party—Mass. I. Title.

NK 0196747 ViU

Knapp, Samuel Lorenzo. 1783-1838.
The travels of Ali Bey, in Morocco, Tripoli, Cyprus, Egypt, Arabia, Syria, and Turkey, between 1803 and 1807. Written by himself. 1st American edition.
Philadelphia. Carey. 1816. 2 v. Plates. 8°.
Two of the plates are missing.
[This work is kept on the Special Libraries Floor.]
F188 — T.r. — Barbary States. Geog. — Levant, The. Geog.

NK 0196748 MB

Knapp, Samuel Lorenz, 1784-1838, ed.
The two Americas. Their complete history ...
see under title

Knapp, Seaman Asahel, 1833–
Agricultural education for the rural districts. <A synopsis>
(In National education association of the United States. Journal of proceedings and addresses, 1909. p. 954-959)
1. Agriculture—Teaching—Rural schools.
Library, U. S. Bur. of Education E 10-766

NK 0196750 DHEW OU

Knapp, Seaman Asahel, 1833-1911.
U. S. Office of experiment stations.
... Agricultural resources and capabilities of Porto Rico. Message from the President of the United States, transmitting a report on investigations of the agricultural resources and capabilities of Porto Rico with special reference to the establishment of an agricultural experiment station in that island. December 11, 1900.—Message and accompanying papers ordered printed and referred to the Committee on insular affairs. [Washington, Gov't print. off., 1900]

VOLUME 300

Knapp, Seaman Asahel, 1833-1911.

U. S. *Dept. of agriculture. Bureau of plant industry.*
... Boys' demonstration work: the corn clubs. [Washington, Govt. print. off.] 1911.

Knapp, Seaman Asahel, 1833-1911.
Causes of southern rural conditions and the small farm as an important remedy.
(*In* U. S. Dept. of agriculture. Yearbook, 1908, p. 311-320. 23 cm. Washington, 1909)

1. Agriculture—Southern states. 2. Farms, Small.
Agr 9—2031
U. S. Dept. of Agr. Libr. for Library of Congress 1Ag84Y 1908 [a48b½]

NK 0196753 DNAL DL MiU OCl OU

Knapp, Seaman Asahel, 1833-

U. S. *Congress. Senate. Committee on agriculture and forestry.*
... The cotton boll weevil. Hearing before the Committee on agriculture and forestry, United States Senate, on the bill H. R. 18162, a bill making appropriations for the Department of agriculture for the fiscal year ending June 30, 1911. Statements of Dr. Seaman A. Knapp ... and Hon. William A. Dickson ... [February 23, 1910] Washington, Govt. print. off., 1910.

[Knapp, Seaman Asahel] 1833 -
... Cotton, the greatest of cash crops. [Washington, Govt. print. off., 1910]
10 p. 23ᶜᵐ. (U. S. Dept. of agriculture. Office of the secretary. Circular no. 32)
"Address of Dr. Seaman A. Knapp ... on the present outlook for cotton production in boll-weevil territory, delivered at Greenville, Miss., Jan. 17, 1910."
1. Cotton.
Agr 10-429
Library, U. S. Dept. of Agriculture 1Ag86C no. 32

NK 0196755 DNAL PP NN

[Knapp, Seaman Asahel] 1833-1911.
... Deep fall plowing and the seed bed. [Washington, Gov't print. off., 1908]
7 p. illus. 23ᶜᵐ.
At head of title: United States Department of agriculture, Bureau of plant industry.
Signed: S. A. Knapp.

1. Plowing.
Agr 8-891
U. S. Dept. of agr. Library for Library of Congress [a45b1]

NK 0196756 DNAL

Knapp, Seaman Asahel, 1833-1911.
... Demonstration work in cooperation with southern farmers. By S. A. Knapp ... Washington, Govt. print. off., 1908.
22, [1] p. 23ᶜᵐ. (U. S. Dept. of agriculture. Farmers' bulletin 319)

1. [Demonstration work in agriculture]
Agr 8-415 Revised
Library, U. S. Dept. of Agriculture

NK 0196757 DNAL CaBVaU WaS PPAmP PBa OCl OU OO MB NN

Knapp, Seaman Asahel, 1833-1911.
... Demonstration work on southern farms. By S. A. Knapp ... Washington, Govt. print. off., 1910.
19 p. illus. 23ᶜᵐ. (U. S. Dept. of agriculture. Farmers' bulletin 422)

1. [Demonstration work in agriculture]
Agr 10-1706 Revised
Library, U. S. Dept. of Agriculture 1Ag84F no. 422

NK 0196758 DNAL CaBVaU WaS PP PPFr PBa OCl OU MB NN

[KNAPP, Seaman Asahel.]
Experiment stations. n.p., [19-].
pp. 7.
Without title-page. Caption title.
Signed: S.A.Knapp, Pres.Iowa Agricultural College.

NK 0196759 MH

Knapp, Seaman Asahel, 1833-.
The farmers' cooperative demonstration work.
(*In* U. S. Dept. of agriculture. Yearbook, 1909, p. 153-160. pl. I-IV. 23ᶜᵐ. Washington, 1910)
1. Demonstration work in agriculture.
Agr 10-744
Library, U. S. Dept. of Agriculture 1Ag84Y 1909

NK 0196760 DNAL MiU OU

Knapp, Seaman Asahel, 1833-
... Farmers' cooperative demonstration work in its relation to rural improvement. By S. A. Knapp ... Washington, Govt. print. off., 1908.
20 p. 23ᶜᵐ. (U. S. Dept. of agriculture. Bureau of plant industry. Circular 21)
1. Demonstration work in agriculture.
Agr 8-1114
Library, U. S. Dept. of Agriculture

NK 0196761 DNAL MB PPAmP MH-A

Knapp, Seaman Asahel, 1833-
"Let us enlarge the domain of industrial knowledge", an address delivered at the Miss. agricultural and mechanical college, June 20, 1894. Starkville, n.d.

NK 0196762 Nh OU

Knapp, Seaman Asahel. 1833 -
... The mission of cooperative demonstration work in the South. [Washington, Govt. print. off.] 1910.
8 p. 23ᶜᵐ. (U. S. Dept. of agriculture. Office of the secretary. Circular no. 33)
1. Demonstration work in agriculture.
Agr 10-1707
Library, U. S. Dept. of Agriculture 1Ag86C no. 33

NK 0196763 DNAL NN OO

Knapp, Seaman Asahel. 1833 -
... The present status of rice culture in the United States. By S. A. Knapp. Washington, Govt. print. off., 1899.
56 p. III pl. 23ᶜᵐ. (U. S. Dept. of agriculture. Division of botany. Bulletin no. 22)

1. Rice—Culture.
Agr 9-509
Library, U. S. Dept. of Agriculture

NK 0196764 DNAL PU PPD PP MBHo MiU OCl DPU OO MB Nh

---

630 Knapp, Seaman Asahel, 1833 -
K72p The production of cotton under boll-weevil conditions. Washington, 1911.
8p. (U.S. Bureau of plant industry. Farmers' cooperative demonstration work)

NK 0196765 IU

Knapp, Seaman Asahel, 1833-1911.
... Recent foreign explorations, as bearing on the agricultural development of the southern states. By S. A. Knapp ... Washington, Govt. print. off., 1903.
44 p. VI pl., 2 diagr. 20ᶜᵐ. (U. S. Bureau of plant industry. Bulletin no. 35)
At head of title: U. S. Department of agriculture. Bureau of plant industry ...
1. Agriculture—Southern states. 2. Agriculture—China. 3. Agriculture—India. 4. Agriculture—Japan. 5. Agriculture—Ceylon. 6. Agriculture—Philippine islands. 7. Rice and rice culture. [7. Rice—Culture] I. Title.
Agr 9-161 Revised
U. S. Dept. of agr. Library for Library of Congress 1P69B no. 35 [QK1.U45 no. 35]
——— Copy 2. [S406.K67] [r37b1-]

NK 0196766 DNAL PPAN PPAmP PU PP OCl OO MB

Knapp, Seaman Asahel, 1833-1911.

U. S. *Dept. of agriculture. Bureau of plant industry. Farmers' cooperative demonstration work.*
... Results of boys' demonstration work in corn clubs in 1910-1911. [Washington, Govt. print. off.] 1911-12.

Knapp, Seaman Asahel, 1833 -
... Rice culture. By S. A. Knapp ... Washington, Govt. print. off., 1910.
30 p. 23ᶜᵐ. (U. S. Dept. of agriculture. Farmers' bulletin 417)
1. Rice—Culture.
Agr 10-1518
Library, U. S. Dept. of Agriculture 1Ag84F no. 417

NK 0196768 DNAL CaBVaU WaS PP PPFr PBa MBH OCl OO OU MB NN

Knapp, Seaman Asahel, 1833 -
... Rice culture in the United States. By Dr. S. A. Knapp. Washington, Gov't print. off., 1900.
28 p. 23ᶜᵐ. (U. S. Dept. of agriculture. Farmers' bulletin 110)

1. Rice.
Agr 7-187
Library, U. S. Dept. of Agriculture

NK 0196769 DNAL CaBVaU PP PPAmP NN

Knapp, Seaman Asahel, 1833-1911, ed.

Rice journal and Gulf coast farmer, devoted to the rice industry in particular, in all its branches, and to Gulf coast agricultue in general.

Crowley, La. [The Signal printing company, limited]

VOLUME 300

Knapp, Seaman Asahel, 1833 –
... Seed selection for southern farms. [Washington, Gov't print. off.] 1908.
8 p. illus. 23cm.
At head of title: United States Department of agriculture. Bureau of plant industry.
Signed by S. A. Knapp and D. N. Barrow.
1. Seed selection. I. Barrow, David Nicholas, joint author.
Library, U. S. Dept. of Agriculture Agr 8-794

NK 0196771 DNAL

Knapp, Seaman Asahel, 1833-1911.
Select quotations
see under
Texas. Agricultural and Mechanical College, College Station. Extension Service.

Knapp, Seaman Asahel, 1833-1911.
The work of the community demonstration farm at Terrell, Tex.
(*In* U. S. Dept. of agriculture. Bureau of plant industry. Bulletin no. 31, p. 9-14. 23cm. Washington, 1903)
1. [Terrell, Tex. Porter demonstration farm] 2. [Demonstration farms]
Library, U. S. Dept. of Agriculture Agr 9-179 Revised

NK 0196773 DNAL OCl OO OU PPAmP

KNAPP, Sheldon.
Towards a new era in healing. London, The C.W.Daniel Co., [1926].
nar.16°. pp.62.

NK 0196774 MH

Knapp, Sheldon L
Laws and history of the financial legislation of the United States, by Sheldon L. Knapp. Historically and legally considered. Aurora, Ill., C. B. Phillips, 1895.
3 p. l., [5]-327 p. 22 cm.
1. Finance, Public—U. S. 2. Currency question—U. S.
HG529.K6 6—36870

NK 0196775 DLC

Knapp, Shepherd, *ed.*
America's army, edited by Shepherd Knapp; cover illustration by Herbert Rudeen, research and inside illustrations by George Moll. Chicago, Rand McNally & company, ©1942.
1 p. l., [5]-70 p. illus. (part col., incl. ports.) 14cm.
1. U. S.—Army. 2. World war, 1939- —U. S. I. Title.
Library of Congress UA25.K65 42-24217
355.0973

NK 0196776 DLC PBa

Knapp, Shepherd, *ed.*
America's navy, edited by Shepherd Knapp; cover illustration by Herbert Rudeen, research and inside illustrations by George Moll. Chicago, Rand McNally & company, ©1942.
1 p. l., [5]-70 p. illus. (part col., incl. ports.) 14cm.

Continued in next column

Continued from preceding column

1. U. S.—Navy. 2. World war, 1939- —Naval operations. I. Title.
Library of Congress VA58.K53 42-24216
359.0973

NK 0196777 DLC PBa

Knapp, Mrs. Shepherd.
See
Knapp, Emma (Benedict), 1847-1907.

Knapp, Shepherd, 1795-1875.
Letter to the stockholders of the Mechanics' bank, from Shepherd Knapp, in reply to the Defence of Francis W. Edmonds, their late cashier. New York, H. Anstice & co., stationers, 1855.
11 p. 21½cm. [*With, as issued:* Edmonds, F. W. Defence of Francis W. Edmonds ... against the charges preferred against him ... New York, 1855]
I. Edmonds, Francis William, 1806-1863. Defence. II. Mechanics and metals national bank, New York.
Library of Congress HG2613.N54M36 46-32206

NK 0196779 DLC MH

Knapp, Shepherd, 1873-1946.
Christianity and war, a sermon, by Shepherd Knapp. Worcester, Mass., The W. B. Crombie company, 1917.
11 p. 23cm.
1. European war, 1914- —Addresses, sermons, etc. I. Title.
Library of Congress D524.K6 17-16543

NK 0196780 DLC

Knapp, Shepherd, 1873-1946.
Family memories, by Shepherd Knapp. [Worcester? Mass.] Priv. print., 1946.
1 p. l., 78 p. fold. geneal. tab. 29 x 22½cm.
Errata slips inserted.
1. Knapp family.
CS71.K675 1946 47-15735

NK 0196781 DLC NN

Knapp, Shepherd, 1873-1946, ed.
Knapp, Gideon Lee, 1822?-1875.
Gideon Lee Knapp and Augusta Murray Spring, his wife: extracts from letter & journal, ed. by one of their grandsons. [n. p.] Priv. print., 1909.

Knapp, Shepherd, 1873- comp. and ed.
Knapp, Emma (Benedict) "*Mrs.* Shepherd Knapp," 1847-1907.
Hic habitat felicitas, a volume of recollections and letters, by Mrs. Shepherd Knapp (Emma Benedict) comp. and ed. by her children ... Boston, W. B. Clarke co., 1910.

Knapp, Shepherd, 1873-1946.
A history of the Brick Presbyterian church in the city of New York, by Shepherd Knapp ... New York, Trustees of the Brick Presbyterian church, 1909.
xxii, 566 p. front., plates, ports., plans, facsim. 24 cm.
Bibliography: p. [495]-510.
1. New York. Brick Presbyterian church.
Library of Congress F128.62.B8K6 9—4285

NK 0196784 DLC MH ICMcC PPPrHi OClWHi OO MWA NN NIC NjNbS

Knapp, Shepherd, 1873-1946, ed.
Letters to Emma Benedict from her parents and sisters, 1866-71. Edited by her son.
[n.p.], 1911.
36 p. 8°

NK 0196785 MWA

Knapp, Shepherd, 1873- *comp.*
The liberated Bible, the Old Testament, compiled by Shepherd Knapp. New York, London [etc.] Fleming H. Revell company [©1941]
286 p. 23½cm.
1. Bible. O. T.—Indexes, Topical. 2. Bible—Indexes, Topical—O. T. I. Title.
Library of Congress BS432.K55 41-23094
[4] 221.2

NK 0196786 DLC PPWe NjPT OCl

Knapp, Shepherd, 1873-
Phelps, Edward John, 1822-1900.
Miller & Knapp, trustees, &c., *vs.* the Rut. & Wash. R. R. co., and others. Vermont Supreme court, Nov. gen. term, 1862. Additional brief for def't trustees. E. J. Phelps, counsel. [Burlington, Free press print, 1863]

Knapp, Shepherd, 1873-
Old Joe, and other vesper stories, by Shepherd Knapp. New York, Cincinnati. The Abingdon press [©1922]
297 p. 19cm.
CONTENTS.—Old Joe.—Repentance for a purpose.—The nurse.—Monsieur le curé.—The head of the firm.—The garden.—The field.—The art of knowing how.—The mountain pass.—Doors.—The gift.—A successful experiment.—Goblins and fairies.—The waiter.—His conquerors.—The manger—a Christmas legend.
I. Title.
Library of Congress PZ3.K728Ol 22-11789

NK 0196788 DLC MB

Knapp, Shepherd, 1873-
On the edge of the storm; the story of a year in France, by Shepherd Knapp. Worcester, Mass., Commonwealth press [©1921]
3 p. l., 79 p. 23cm.
1. European war, 1914- —Personal narratives. I. Title.
Library of Congress D570.9.K6 21-21706

NK 0196789 DLC MWA

Knapp, Shepherd, 1873-1946, ed.
New York. Brick Presbyterian church.
Personal records of the Brick Presbyterian church in the city of New York, 1809-1908, including births, baptisms, marriages, admissions to membership, dismissions, deaths, etc., arranged in alphabetical order; ed. by Shepherd Knapp. New York, Trustees of the Brick Presbyterian church, 1909.

VOLUME 300

Knapp, Shepherd, 1873–
The war's need of Christ; a Palm Sunday sermon, by Shepherd Knapp. Worcester, Mass., The W. B. Crombie company, 1917.
10 p. 23cm.

1. European war, 1914– —Addresses, sermons, etc. I. Title.
17-16542
Library of Congress D524.K65

NK 0196791 DLC

Knapp, Shepherd, 1873-1946.
A Worcester epic. Read by Shepherd Knapp at the complimentary dinner given to Dr. Homer Gage in Worcester, on Dec. 19, 1931. [Worcester, 1931?]
[7 p.] 16 cm.
Cover title.

NK 0196792 RPB

Knapp, Thad Johnson, 1876–
Educational insurance. Stopping the failures; or, Making education certain by the fixing of desirable habits, by Thad Johnson Knapp ... Boston, Mass., The Stratford company [c1930]
3 p. l., viii p., 1 l., 131 p. fold. pl., forms (part double) 19½cm.
"References": p. 129-131.

1. Teaching. 2. Educational psychology. 3. Habit. I. Title.
30-24213
Library of Congress LB1027.K55
——— Copy 2.
Copyright A 27371 371.3

NK 0196793 DLC PPPL PU-Penn MiU OCl OU

Knapp, Thad Johnson, 1876–
Merit promotion of teachers.
(*In* **National education association of the United States. Addresses and proceedings, 1921. p. 820–822**)

[1. Teachers—U. S.—Salaries; [2. Teachers—Promotions—U. S.]
1, 2. Teachers—U. S.—Salaries, pensions, etc. I. Title.
E 22—237
U. S. Off. of educ. Library for Library of Congress [a41d1]

NK 0196794 DHEW

Knapp, Theodor, 1854 -
Abriss der Geschichte der Bauernentlastung in Württemberg, von Rektor Dr. Knapp... Stuttgart: W. Kohlhammer, 1908. 20 p. 4°.
Cover-title.
Beilage zu den Nachrichten über das Gymnasium zu Tübingen vom Schuljahr 1907–08.
Repr.: Württembergische Jahrbücher für Statistik und Landeskunde. Jahrg. 1907.

1. Serfdom.—History, Germany: Württemberg.
N. Y. P. L. April 25, 1924.

NK 0196795 NN PU

Knapp, Theodor, 1854-
Der Bauer im heutigen Württemberg, nach seinen Rechtsverhältnissen vom 16. bis 19. Jahrhundert. Stuttgart, D. Gundert, 1902.
104 p.
(Württembergische Neujahrsblätter, n. F., Blatt 7)

4K Ger. 2645

NK 0196796 DLC-P4 PU MH

K 347 .468 **KNAPP, THEODOR**, 1854-
Der Bauer im heutigen Württemberg. Verfassung, Recht und Wirtschaft vom Ausgang des Mittelalters bis zur Bauernentlastung des 19. Jahrhunderts. 2. völlig umgearbeitete Ausgabe. (Zugleich Band 1 der Neuen Beiträge zur Rechts- und Wirtschaftsgeschichte des württembergischen Bauernstandes) Tübingen, H. Laupp, 1919.
vii, 210p. 25cm.

NK 0196797 ICN MB

Knapp, Theodor, 1854-
Tübingen. Universität.
Die feier des 450jährigen bestehens der Eberhard-Karls-universität, Tübingen, vom 24. bis 26. juli 1927. Stuttgart, W. Kohlhammer, 1928.

Knapp, Theodor, 1854–
Gesammelte beiträge zur rechts- und wirtschaftsgeschichte vornehmlich des deutschen bauernstandes. Von Theodor Knapp ... Tübingen, H. Laupp, 1902.
xii, 485 p. 24cm.
Bibliography: p. ix–xi.

1. Law—Germany—Hist. & crit. 2. Germany—Economics. 3. Peasantry—Germany.
3—19956
Library of Congress [a40c1]

NK 0196799 DLC CtY NN ICJ OCU CSt

Knapp, Theodor, 1854 -
Gesammelte beitraege zur rechts- und wirtschaftsgeschichte vornehmlich des deutschen bauernstandes. Tuebingen, Laupp, 1908.
485 p.

NK 0196800 PU

Knapp, Theodor, 1854-
Grenzrecht und grenzzeichen...
see under title

Knapp, Theodor, 1854 -
Neue beiträge zur rechts- und wirtschaftsgeschichte des württembergischen bauernstandes. Von Theodor Knapp. Tübingen, H. Laupp, 1919.
2 v. 24½cm.
"Verzeichnis der abgekürzten titel und sonstigen abkürzungen": v. 2, p. v–x.
CONTENTS.—1. bd. Darstellung.—2. bd. Nachweise und ergänzungen.

1. Law—Württemberg—Hist. & crit. 2. Württemberg—Econ. condit. 3. Peasantry—Württemberg. I. Germany. Laws, statutes, etc. II. Title.
27-377

NK 0196802 DLC NN MoKU MB IU

Knapp, Theodor, 1854–
Die Universität Tübingen, ihre institute und einrichtungen, herausgegeben von dr. Th. Knapp und Hans Kohler. 78 lichtbilder. Düsseldorf, F. Lindner [1928]
123 p. incl. illus., plates. front., 2 pl. 31cm.
Advertising matter: p. 79–123.

1. Tübingen. Universität. I. Kohler, Hans, joint ed.
CA 31-305 Unrev'd
Library of Congress LF3147.K6 378.43

NK 0196803 DLC MH CU MoSCS PU IU CtY

Knapp, Theodor, 1882- Rechtsanw.: Die Beseitigung einer ungerechtfertigten Verurteilung nach dem Tode des Verurteilten. Neuenbürg: Meeh [1911]. 74 S. 8°
Tübingen, Jur. Diss. v. 20. Dez. 1911, Ref. Beling
[Geb. 23. Juni 82 Kirchheim u. T.; Wohnort: Neuenbürg, Württ.; Staatsangeh.: Württemberg; Vorbildung: Karls-Gymn. Stuttgart Reife Juli 00; Studium: Tübingen 3, Leipzig 2, Tübingen 3 S.; Rig. 25. Nov. 11.] [U 12.4392

NK 0196804 ICRL MH-L

Knapp, Theodor, 1889-
Untersuchungen zur Frage der krebsigen "Entartung" adenomatöser Geschwülste der Brustdrüse ... Leipzig, 1913.
Inaug.-Diss. - Tübingen.
Lebenslauf.
"Sonderdruck asu 'Arbeiten auf dem Gebiete der pathologischen Anatomie und Bakteriologie aus dem pathologisch-anatomischen Institut zu Tübingen', Bd. VIII, p. 272-287."
"Literaturverzeichnis": p. 286-287.

NK 0196805 CtY

H 252.7 K72o 1859 Knapp, Theodore Judson
An ordination sermon, preached at the ordination of Joseph A. Daniels, in the Hertford Baptish Church, February 3rd, 1859. By Elder Theodore Judson Knapp... Published by request of the church. New York: Thomas Holman, printer... 1859.
26p. 23cm.

NK 0196806 ViHarEM

Knapp (Theodorus [Otto Henricus]) [1822–].
*De febre traumatica pyæmica. 28 pp., 2 l. 8°. *Berolini, G. Schade*, [1846].

NK 0196807 DNLM

QD391 .K63 Knapp, Theophil.
Studien aus der naphtalinreihe.
Basel, 1898.
48p.
Inaug. diss. Basel.

NK 0196808 DLC PU

Knapp, Theresia
see Knapp, Justina, sister, 1863-

Knapp, Topsy, *pseud.*
see
Knapp, Estelle M.

Knapp, Valentine.
"Blewe" clothes of Christ's Hospital, with the simple story of "John I'th' Hospitall" ("Blewe John").
= Kingston-upon-Thames. Knapp, Drewett & Sons, Ltd. 1928. (2). 23 pp. Plates. Facsimiles. 24.5 cm.
Description and history of the blue uniform worn at Christ's Hospital, London.

E1266 — T.r. — Christ's Hospital, London.

NK 0196811 MB

VOLUME 300

Knapp, Viktor.
... Národní správa a vracení majetku z národní správy
see under Czechoslovak republic. Laws, statutes, etc.

Czech 46 K727n
Knapp, Viktor ed.
Osidlovací právo hmotné. Praha, Orbis, 1949.
293p. 8cm. (Právnické příručky a rozpravy. Československé právo, řada II, sv.10)
Bibliography: p.281-287.
1.Game laws - Czechoslovak Republic. 2.Ser: Československé pravo, řada II, sv.10.

NK 0196813 CtY-L

Law
Knapp, Viktor, ed.
Czechoslovak Republic. *Laws, statutes, etc.*
Přiděl živností a rodinných domků. Sestavil a výkladem opatřil Viktor Knapp. [Vyd. 1.] V Praze, V. Linhart, 1948.

Knapp, Viktor.
Problém nacistické právní filosofie. [Vyd. 1.] Praha, V. Linhart, 1947.
281 p. 21 cm. (Knihovna právní prakse, sv. 4)
Bibliography: p. 217-223.
1. Law—Philosophy. 2. National socialism.
51-23384

NK 0196815 DLC InU

Knapp, Viktor.
Собственность в странах народной демократии; правовой режим собственности в Чехословацкой Республике. Перевод с чешского Л. Ф. Жуковой и Ю. А. Юдина, под ред. и с предисл. С. Н. Братуся. Москва, Изд-во иностранной лит-ры, 1954.
445 p. 23 cm.
Errata slip inserted.
Translation of Vlastnictví v lidové demokracii.
1. Property. 2. Socialism. I. Title.
Title transliterated: Sobstvennost' v stranakh narodnoĭ demokratii.
HB701.K538 55-22083
Library of Congress

NK 0196816 DLC MiU

Knapp, Viktor.
Splnění závazků a jiné způsoby jejich zániku. [1. vyd.] Praha, Nakl. Československé akademie věd, 1955.
327 p. 25 cm.
On leaf preceding t. p.: Československá akademie věd. Sekce ekonomie a práva.
Summary in Russian.
Bibliography: p. 322-323.
1. Performance (Law)—Czechoslovak Republic. 2. Extinguishment of debts—Czechoslovak Republic. I. Title.
59-35744

NK 0196817 DLC IU CtY-L InU MH-L NN

Law
Knapp, Viktor, ed.
FOR OTHER EDITIONS SEE MAIN ENTRY
Czechoslovak Republic. *Ministerstvo spravedlnosti. Právnický ústav.*
Učebnice občanského a rodinného práva. [Autory: Bedřich Andres et al.] Za hlavní red. Viktora Knappa. 2., přepracované a doplněné vyd. Praha, Orbis, 1955.

Knapp, Viktor.
Vlastnictví v lidové demokracii; právní, úprava vlastnictví v Československe republice. [1. vyd.] Praha, Orbis, 1952.
510 p. 22 cm. (Knižnice Socialistické právo)
At head of title: Právnicky ústay Ministerstva spravedlnosti.
1. Property. 2. Socialism. I. Title.
HB701.K53 53-36979 ‡

NK 0196819 DLC NN MH-L

Knapp, Viktor, comp.
Czechoslovak Republic. *Laws, statutes, etc.*
Vrácení majetku pozbytého za okupace, Restituční zákon; výklad zákona č 128/1946 Sb. o neplatnosti některých majetkoprávních jednání z doby nesvobody a o nárocích z této neplatnosti ... Sestavili a výkladem opatřili Viktor Knapp [a] Tomáš Berman. Předmluvu napsal Radim N. Foustka. [Vyd. 1.] V Praze, V. Linhart, 1946.

Knapp, Victor, 1899-
The principles and practice of medical nursing, by Victor Knapp ... New York, G. P. Putnam's sons, 1938.
xx p., 1 l., 366 p. illus., diagrs. 21cm.
Bibliography: p. 341-346.
1. Pathology. 2. Nurses and nursing. I. Title: Medical nursing, The principles and practice of.
Library of Congress RT65.K6 38-32832
——— ——— Copy 2.
Copyright A 121472 610.73

NK 0196821 DLC ViU OU

1.914 A28el
Knapp, Virginia.
The Seaman A. Knapp silver cup. [Washington] 1953.
sheet.
Issued May 1953.
1. Knapp, Seaman Asahel, 1833-1911. I. U.S. Dept. of Agriculture. Office of Information.

NK 0196822 DNAL

F1203 M8 v.11;5 x
Knapp, W Augustus
Memorial y demanda de W. Augustus Knapp y S. Heber Wood, a la Comisión Mixta Americana y Mexicana. [n. p., 187-]
13 p. 27cm. [Mugarrieta collection, v.11, no.5]
Cover title.
1. Knapp, W Augustus - Claims vs. Mexico. 2. Wood, S Heber - Claims vs. Mexico. I. United States and Mexican Claims Commission, 1869-1876. II. Title. (Series)

NK 0196823 CU-B

---

17 1861a
Knapp, Rev. W.C.
Funeral services: being a collection and arrangement of the scriptures suitable for funerals, with appropriate hymns and tunes. Peoria, [Ill.], Franks and sons, 1874.
168 p. 16°.

NK 0196824 DLC

Knapp, Walter.
Die eisenkonstruktionen des hochbaues, von baurat professor Walter Knapp, mit 473 abbildungen im text und zahlreichen tabellen. Leipzig, C. Scholtze [1911]
vii, 199, [1] p. illus. 26½cm.
"Literatur-nachweis": [1] p. at end.
1. Building, Iron and steel.
12-26258
Library of Congress TA684.K6

NK 0196825 DLC ICJ

624.2 K72s
Knapp, Walter
Statik der Hochbaukonstruktionen. Leipzig, C. Scholtze c1910.
viii, 213p. diagrs., tables. 27cm.
1. Structures, Theory of. 2. Statics. 3. Building.

NK 0196826 IU ICJ NN CU NNU

---

ar W 54734 no.1
Knapp, Walter, writer on law
Die rechtliche Natur des Dividendennachbezugsrechts und seine Gestaltung bei dem Bestehen eines Pfandrechts und eines Niessbrauchs. Coburg, Druckerei des Coburger Tageblatt, 1928.
viii, 67 p. 23cm.
Inaug.-Diss.--Erlangen.

NK 0196827 NIC PU

NA8204 .W4
Knapp, Werner, 1903- joint ed.
Weicken, Otto, *ed.*
Bauernhöfe; [hrsg. von O. Weicken und W. Knapp] Stuttgart, K. Krämer [1943]

Knapp, Werner, 1903-
... Deutsche dorfplanung ... von Werner Knapp. Stuttgart, K. Krämer [1942-
v. illus. (incl. map, plans) 30cm. (Bauen und planen der gegenwart. 1-
CONTENTS.—[1. t.] Gestalterische grundlagen.
1. Cities and towns—Planning—Germany. I. Title.
45-13410
Library of Congress NA9199.K6
711.4

NK 0196829 DLC MH

Knapp, Werner, 1903-
Landbaukunst; weg zu bewusstem gestalten. Stuttgart, K. Krämer verlag [1951]
62p., illus., 30.5cm.

NK 0196830 RU OOxM

Knapp, Werner, 1903-
Neubildung politischer Mittelpunkte I. Stuttgart, K. Krämer [1941]
64 p. illus. 30 cm. (Architektur Wettbewerbe, Schriftenreihe für richtungweisendes bauen, Heft 7)
No more published?
1. Germany—Public buildings. 2. Architecture—Competitions. I. Title.
NA4299.K5 55-51493 ‡

NK 0196831 DLC NNC

VOLUME 300

KNAPP, WERNER, 1903-
"O du lieber Weissensee;" ein Heimatbuch erwandert und erlauscht von Werner und Sigrid Knapp. [Illus. von Sigrid Ipsen-Knapp] [n.p.] Selbstverlag der Verfasser [1953] 116 p. illus. (part col.) 20cm.

1. Weissensee, Austria—Descr. and trav. I. Knapp, Sigrid, joint author. II. Title.

NK 0196832 NN

Knapp, Werner, 1903-
... Rathäuser, von ... Werner Knapp ... Stuttgart, Karl Krämer, [1940]
64, iv p. illus. incl. plans. 29cm. (Architektur wettbewerbe; schriftenreihe für richtungweisendes bauen ... hft. 5)

"Gute neuerscheinungen und neuauflagen"; p. iv and p. [3] of cover.
1. City halls.

NK 0196833 NNC

Knapp, Wilhelm
Photographischer verlag von Wilhelm Knapp in Halle a. S. ... [Halle a. S., Knapp, 1892?] cover-title, 3 p. l., 68 p. 15½cm.

1. Photography - Bibliography.

NK 0196834 NNC

Knapp, Wilhelm.
Raumlehre und Werken; Arbeitshilfe in Unterrichtseinheiten. Frankfurt am Main, M. Diesterweg, 1953.
66 p. illus. 30 cm.

1. Geometrical drawing. 2. Design. 3. Geometry—Problems, exercises, etc. I. Title.
A 54-1994
Illinois. Univ. Library for Library of Congress

NK 0196835 IU

Knapp, Wilhelm, 1912-
Statistisches und empirisches über das gesetz zur verhütung erbkranken nachwuchses. ... Bonn, 1934. 39 p.
Inaug. Diss. - Bonn, 1934.
Lebenslauf.
Bibliography.

NK 0196836 CtY DNLM

TA681 .K4
Knapp, Willard Alfred, 1885-
[Kelly, Joe Wallace] 1895-
... How to avoid faulty concrete in small structures, prepared by the staffs of the Engineering extension department and the School of civil engineering. Lafayette, Ind., Purdue university, 1932.

Knapp, Willard Alfred, 1885- ed.

Indiana fire school, *Purdue university, Lafayette, Ind.*
... Selected papers from 19
Indiana fire schools held at Purdue university ... Lafayette, Ind., Purdue university, 19

Knapp, Willem Hendrik Christiaan.
Botercontrôle in Nederland, de geschiedenis van de Nederlandsche botercontrôle in verband met de boterwetgeving en handel ... Schiedam, Coöperatieve drukkerij "De Eendracht", 1927.
xv, 551 p. diagrs. 24cm.
Proefschrift—Wageningen.
"Stellingen" (2 leaves) laid in.

1. Butter—[Legislation]
Agr 28-609
Library, U. S. Dept. of Agriculture 44K72

NK 0196839 DNAL CtY

Knapp, Willem Hendrik Christiaan.
Nederland's ondergang of redding? Verstaat het Nederlandsche volk de teekenen des tijds? Door Dr. Ir. W. H. C. Knapp. Den Haag: W. P. van Stockum & Zoon, 1932. 78 p. 22½cm.

655937A. 1. Agriculture—Netherlands. September 19, 1933
N. Y. P. L.

NK 0196840 NN

Knapp, Willem Hendrik Christiaan.
Wereldontwrichting en wereldherstel, het economisch wereldgebeuren getoetst aan den landbouw. Utrecht, Drukkerij L. E. Bosch, 1931.
288 p. 23 cm.

1. Agriculture—Economic aspects. 2. Economic policy. 3. Economic conditions—1918-1945. I. Title.
HD1411.K54 1931 48-44054*

NK 0196841 DLC NN

Knapp, Willem Hendrik Christiaan.
Wereld ontwrichting en wereldherstel, het economisch wereldgebeuren getoetst aan den landbouw. 2., omgewerkte druk. Amsterdam, Scheltema & Holkema [1933]
243 p. 24 cm.

1. Agriculture—Economic aspects. 2. Economic policy. 3. Econ. condit.—1918-1945. I. Title.
HD1411.K54 1933 48-41233*

NK 0196842 DLC

Knapp, Willem Hendrik Christiaan.
World dislocation and world recovery; agriculture as the touchstone of the economic world events, by Dr. Ir. W. H. C. Knapp. London, P. S. King & son, ltd., 1935.
vii p., 1 l., 203 p. 22½cm.
Translated by S. W. Fleming. cf. Foreword.

1. Agriculture—Economic aspects. 2. Economic policy. 3. Economic conditions—1918- I. Fleming, S. W., tr. II. Title.
35-12965
Library of Congress HD1411.K55
338.1

NK 0196843 DLC OrPR WaTC CU OCU OU OO NN

ML552 .K66
Knapp, Willem Hendrik Christiaan, *engineer.*
Het orgel. Amsterdam, G. J. A. Ruys, 1952.
x, 332 p. illus., ports. 25 cm.
"Literatuur": p. [317]

1. Organ. 2. Organ—Construction. I. Title.
A 52-5707
Oregon. Univ. Libr. for Library of Congress

NK 0196844 OrU OU DLC NN NjR LNHT

---

*AO6 M4208 Zz723v
Knapp, William, d.1688.
Abraham's image in one of his sonnes: or, The picture of a good old man, represented in a sermon upon the third of November, anno Dom. 1657. in West-Newton, at the funeral of John Dethick esquire, father to the late Lord mayor that was of London in the year 1655. By William Knapp master of arts, of Katherine-hall, now rector of VVest-Newton in Cambridge in Norfolk ...
London, Printed by Peter Cole, printer and bookseller, and are to be sold at the sign of the Printing-Press in Cornhill, neer the Royal Exchange. 1658.
3p.ℓ.,34p. 19.5cm.
No.15 in a volume of tracts from the Mather family library.

NK 0196846 MH MWA

-VM 2082 K 67n 1751
KNAPP, WILLIAM, 1698-1768.
New church melody; being a set of anthems, psalms, hymns, &c. in four parts, on various occasions. With a great variety of other anthems, psalms, hymns, &c. composed after a method entirely new, and never printed before. [Wit]h an anthem on Psalm cxxvii. by one of the greatest [ma]sters in Europe. Together with four excellent [hym]ns and an anthem for the Nativity. To which is added, [an im]ploration to the King of Kings. [Wrote by Kin]g Charles I. during his captivity in [Carisbrook] Castle, Isle of Wight, Anno Dom. 1648. Together with [an anthem for t]he martyrdom of that blessed prince. London [Printed for R.Baldwi]n, the author[1753]
vii,[1]p.,score(193p.),[1]ℓ. 20cm.

First edition? Title varies slightly from 1st ed. listed in British union-catalogue of early music.

Imperfect: piece torn from t.-p., with loss of text (including imprint date?); part of title supplied from 4th ed. Portrait wanting?

NK 0196849 ICN TxW CtHC DNC

M783.9 K72n 1756
Knapp, William, 1698-1768.
New church melody: being a set of anthems, psalms, hymns, &c. on various occasions. In four parts. With a great variety of other anthems, psalms, hymns, &c. composed after a method entirely new, and never printed before. With an anthem on Psalm cxxvii. by one of the greatest masters in Europe. Together with four excellent hymns, and an anthem for the nativity. To which is added, an imploration to the King of Kings. Wrote by King Charles I. during his captivity in Carisbrook Castle, in the Isle of Wight, Anno Dom. 1648. Together with an anthem for the martyrdom of that blessed prince. 3d ed. London, R. Baldwin, 1756.
v, [3], 193p. port. 20cm.
Error in binding: p.112 followed by p.115-116, 113-114, 119-120, 117-118.
Top of p.[2]-[3], which apparently bore a signature, has been cut off.
Autograph on t.-p.: Francis Hopkinson's 1761.

NK 0196851 IU

-VM 2082 K 67n
KNAPP, WILLIAM, 1698-1768.
New church melody: being a set of anthems, psalms, hymns, &c. on various occasions. In four parts. With a great variety of other anthems, psalms, hymns, &c. composed after a method entirely new, and never printed before... To which is added, An imploration to the King of kings. Wrote by King Charles I. during his captivity in Carisbrook castle...1648. Together with an anthem for the martyrdom of that blessed prince. The 4th edition. London, 1761.
193p.
Autograph of Saml. Bass.
[27261

NK 0196852 ICN NjPT ICN MWA MH

VOLUME 300

Knapp, William, 1698-
New church melody: being a set of anthems, psalms, hymns, &c. on various occasions...5th edition. London, printed for R. Baldwin and S. Crowder, 1764.
193p. 19.5cm.

NK 0196853 NhHi CtY

M 2136 .A2K67 Knapp, William, 1698-1768.
A set of new psalms and anthems, in four parts: on various occasions ... The seventh edition. London, Printed for J. Newberry ...

NK 0196854 DLC

M2082.4 .K67 Knapp, William, 1698-1768.
A sett of new psalm-tunes and anthems, in four parts: on various occasions... 2d ed. corr. With an additional number of several new anthems and psalm-tunes... and an introduction to psalmody... London, Printed by J. Leake, 1741.
[1] l., [4], 200 p. 21 cm.
p. [34-35] consists of 1 folded sheet of music.
1. Choruses, Sacred (Mixed voices, 4 pts), Unaccompanied-- To 1800. 2. Psalters.

NK 0196855 IEG

Knapp, William, 1698-
A set of new psalms and anthems in four parts on various occasions, and an introduction to psalmody, ... by William Knapp. The fifth edition corrected and improved to which is added, an anthem in six parts by a very eminent master also an anthem composed by King Henry the seventh London, Printed by Robert Brown, for Thomas Astley 1752. 8° BUC

1. Vocal - anthems. 2. Vocal - psalms.

NK 0196856 TxWB

SC Mx82 K72a Knapp, William, 1698-1768.
A set of new psalms and anthems, in four parts; on various occasions, and an introduction to psalmody, after a plain and familiar manner. 8th ed. London, G. Bigg, 1770.
210 p. 21 cm.

1. Church of England—Hymns. 2. Hymns, English. I. Title. NUC 2s.

NK 0196857 CtY-Mus

Knapp, Mrs. William D.
Chronicles of the Great Falls high school delivered by Mrs. Wm. D. Knapp, at the first annual reunion of the high school graduates, town hall, September fifth, 1877. 1877.

NK 0196858 NhDo Nh

Knapp, William A
The Department for the Deaf of F. Knapp's Institute. Baltimore, Maryland, 1877-1893. Washington, Gibson Bros., 1893.
13 p. 1 port., illus. 8°. (Volta Bureau)

NK 0196859 NN

Knapp, William Daniel.
Somersworth. An historical sketch.
(In Somersworth, N.H. Municipal government. 1st annual report. p. iii-lxxxviii. Somersworth, 1894)

NK 0196860 MB Nh NhDo

308t K6598 Knapp, William Eugene, 1925-
Perceptual certainty and rigidity. [Berkeley, 1954]
vii,99 l. tables.

Thesis (Ph.D. in Psychology) - Univ. of California, Sept. 1954.
Bibliography: leaves 96-99.

NK 0196861 CU

Knapp, William Franklin, 1874- ed.

Noel, Napoleon, 1853-1932.
... The history of the Brethren, by Napoleon Noel; edited by William F. Knapp. Denver, Col., W. F. Knapp, 1936.

Knapp, William Gerard, 1920-
Reflux redistribution and vapor concentration gradient in a fibrous glass packed column ... 1949.
98 numb. l.
Thesis (PH.D.) - Ohio state university, 1949.

NK 0196863 OU

Knapp, William Hackett.
A study of the quality of slowness of two groups of psychotic patients as demonstrated by performance on the Revised Beta examination.
105 l., tables.
Thesis. - Ph.D. degree. - Western Reserve University. - Dept. of Psychology. - Jan. 30, 1952.

NK 0196864 OCIW

[Knapp, William Henry] b. 1812.
An autobiography. In three parts. With essays. Boston, A. Williams and company, 1873.
vi p., 1 l., 307 p. 18½cm.
Portions of this autobiography have appeared in the Religious magazine. cf. p. v.

I. Title.

Library of Congress BX9869.K6A3 37-10029
Copyright 1872: 13001 922.8173

NK 0196865 DLC FMU RPB MH-AH MWA MB

Knapp, William Henry, b. 1812.
An AUTOBIOGRAPHY in three parts. With essays. 2d ed. Boston, A. Williams and company, 1873.

NK 0196866 MH

Knapp, William Henry
A discourse of demand and supply in church and state. Boston, William V. Spencer, 1869.
17p.

NK 0196867 ICRL

Knapp, William Henry.
Reformers fellow-laborers of Christ; a sermon to the Second Congregational society at Nantucket, May 26, 1844. Boston, 1844.
20 p. nar O.

NK 0196868 RPB

Knapp, W[illiam] H[enry].
Resistance to evil. A discourse delivered to the Barton-Square Society at Salem, Sept. 6, 1863. Boston, J. Wilson & son, 1863.
13 p. 12°.
Contains author's autograph.

NK 0196869 NN

[Knapp, William Ireland] 1835-1908.
Biblioteca escogida de literatura española. Madrid, Impr. de M. Ginesta, 1875[-76]
99 p. 17cm.
Signed: William I. Knapp.
"Apéndice A" (p. [73]-99) dated: Octubre 1876. "Apéndice B", 2 p. in manuscript following p. 99.

1. Spanish literature—Bibl. I. Title.

29-24106

Library of Congress Z2691.K68

NK 0196870 DLC MB CtY

Knapp, William Ireland, 1835-1908.

Boileau-Despréaux, Nicolas, 1636-1711.
Choix d'extraits des œuvres de Boileau Despréaux, disposé avec notes à l'usage des classes de français au collège de Yale, par William I. Knapp ... New Haven, H. H. Peck, 1879.

Knapp, William Ireland, 1835-1908.
Chrestomathie française. A French reading book: containing I. Selections from the best French writers ... II. The masterpieces of Molière, Racine, Boileau, and Voltaire. With ... notes, biographical notices, and a vocabulary. By William I. Knapp ... New York, Harper & brothers, 1863.
1 p. l., 480 p. 19½cm.
Binder's title: Knapp's French reading book.

1. French language—Chrestomathies and readers. I. Title.

F-1875

Library of Congress PC2117.K6

NK 0196872 DLC RPB MiU OO NN

Knapp, William Ireland, 1834-1908.
Chrestomathie francaise; a French reading book ...with...vocabulary. 2d ed. rev. & enl. N. Y., Harper, 1868. c1863.
482 p.

NK 0196873 PP

Knapp, William Ireland, 1835-1908.
Chrestomathie française; a French reading book... 2d ed., revised and enlarged. New York, Harper & brothers, 1870.

NK 0196874 MH

VOLUME 300

Knapp, William Ireland, 1835-1908.
Chrestomathie française. A French reading book ... With notes & a vocabulary. 2d ed. New York, 1872.
12°.

NK 0196875 CtY

Knapp, William Ireland, 1835–1908.
Class readings.—Spanish. No. 1. **Lecturas de clase escojidas de autores españoles que hoy viven, coleccionadas y anotadas, por D. Guillermo I. Knapp. New Haven,** H. H. Peck; New York, F. W. Christern, 1880.
120 p. 18½cm.

1. Spanish language—Chrestomathies and readers.

Library of Congress PC4117.K6 10-30317†

NK 0196876 DLC

Knapp, William Ireland, 1835–
... Concise bibliography of Spanish grammars and dictionaries, from the earliest period to the definitive edition of the Academy's dictionary. 1490–1780. By William I. Knapp ... Republished from the Bulletin of the Boston public library, October, 1884. Boston, By order of the Trustees, 1884.
8 p. 28cm. (Boston public library. Bibliographies of special subjects, originally published in the Bulletins of the library. no. 2)
Series t.-p. added.
1. Spanish language—Dictionaries—Bibl. 2. Spanish language—Grammar—Bibl. 3-1588

Library of Congress Z2695.G7K6

NK 0196877 DLC MH-AH MB CU OO NN ICJ

Knapp, William Ireland, 1835-1908.
George Borrow. [Meadville, Pa., 1887]
1 p.l., 9 p. 23.5 cm.
Extracted from "The Chautauquan", November 1887.

NK 0196878 CtY

Knapp, William Ireland, 1835–1908.
A grammar of the modern Spanish language as now written and spoken in the capital of Spain. By William I. Knapp ... Boston, Ginn, Heath & co., 1882.
x, 486 p. 19cm.

1. Spanish language—Grammar—1870–

Library of Congress PC4111.K5 1882 10—30471

NK 0196879 DLC ICU CtY PPD PPL MiU OCIW OCI MB MH

Knapp, William Ireland, 1835-1908.
A grammar of the modern Spanish language as now written and spoken in the capital of Spain. By William I. Knapp...2d ed., carefully revised by the author. Boston, Ginn & company, 1884.
1 p.

NK 0196880 PSC

Knapp, William Ireland, 1835-1908.
A grammar of the modern Spanish language, as now written and spoken in the capital of Spain. 2d ed., carefully revised by the author. Boston, Ginn & co., 1885.

NK 0196881 MH NjP

Knapp, William Ireland, 1835–1908.
A grammar of the modern Spanish language as now written and spoken in the capital of Spain. By William I. Knapp ... 2d ed., carefully revised by the author. Boston, Ginn & company, 1890.
1 p. l., [v]–x, 488 p. 19cm.

NK 0196882 ViU PSC MH

Knapp, William Ireland,1835-1908.
Grammar of the modern Spanish language... Ed. 2. Boston., Ginn, 1891, c82.
488 p.

NK 0196883 PPD NcRS

Knapp, Wm. Ireland.
Grammar of the modern Spanish language...
Bost. 1892.

NK 0196884 ODW

KNAPP,William Ireland.
A grammar of the modern Spanish language as now written and spoken in the capital of Spain. 2d ed.,carefully revised by the author. Boston, Ginn & Co.,1896.

NK 0196885 MH ICJ MB

Knapp, William Ireland, 1835–1908.
A grammar of the modern Spanish language as now written and spoken in the capital of Spain. By William I. Knapp ... 2d ed., carefully revised by the author. Boston, Ginn & company, 1898.
1 p. l., [v]–x, 488 p. 19cm.

1. Spanish language—Grammar—1870–

33–39080

Library of Congress PC4111.K5 1898 465

NK 0196886 DLC PU NcU NN

Knapp, William Ireland, 1835-1908.
A grammar of the modern Spanish language; as now written and spoken in the capital of Spain. 2d ed., carefully revised by the author. Boston, Ginn & co., 1900.

NK 0196887 MH CU

Knapp, William Ireland, 1835-1908.
A grammar of the modern Spanish language as now written and spoken in the capital of Spain 2d ed. carefully rev. Boston, Ginn, 1901, c1882.
488 p. D.

NK 0196888 PP

Knapp, William Ireland, 1835–1908.
A grammar of the modern Spanish language as now written and spoken in the capital of Spain. By William I. Knapp ... 2d ed. carefully rev. by the author. Boston, Ginn & company, 1902.
x, 488 p. 19 cm.

1. Spanish language—Grammar. 4—13155

Library of Congress PC4111.K5 1902
[a49b½] 465

NK 0196889 DLC NcD OCl

Knapp, William Ireland, 1835–1908.
A grammar of the modern Spanish language, by William I. Knapp ... 2d ed. carefully revised by the author. Supplemented by The new system of written accentuation prescribed by the Royal academy of Spain, by Captain Henry R. Lemly ... Boston, London [etc.] Ginn and company [1910]
1 p. l., [v]–x, 444, 15 p. 18 cm.
Cover-title: Spanish grammar.
Supplement has separate t.-p.: The new system of written accentuation ... Boston, London [etc.] Ginn & company [°1890]
1. Spanish language—Grammar—1870– I. Lemly, Henry Rowan, 1851–1925. II. Title.

A 14—2989

Enoch Pratt Free Libr. for Library of Congress [a61e½]

NK 0196890 MdBE OCl OClW MB NcU

Knapp, William Ireland, 1835–1908.
... Historical and personal reminiscences of the Spanish Revolution. By Professor W. I. Knapp... [New Haven, 1881.]
1 p.l., [137–]172 p. 8°.
Repr: New Englander. March, 1881.

1. Spain—Hist., 19th cent.
N. Y. P. L. December 15, 1925

NK 0196891 NN MH

Knapp, William Ireland, 1835-1908, ed.

Borrow, George Henry, 1803–1881.
Lavengro, the scholar, the Gypsy, the priest, by George Borrow. A new edition containing the unaltered text of the original issue; some suppressed episodes; ms. variorum, vocabulary and notes by the author of the Life of George Borrow. London, J. Murray, 1907.

Knapp, William I[reland].
Life, writings, and correspondence of George Borrow; derived from official and other authentic sources. London: John Murray, 1899. 2 v. fac. (1 folded), illus., map, pl. (1 folded), port. 8°.
Chronological bibliography, v. 2, p. 355-388.

CENTRAL CIRCULATION.

1. Borrow, George.
N. Y. P. L. May 9, 1911.

NK 0196893 NN CSmH MB NjP

Knapp, William Ireland, 1835–1908.
Life, writings and correspondence of George Borrow (1803–1881) ... based on official and other authentic sources, by William I. Knapp ... New York, G. P. Putnam's sons; London, J. Murray, 1899.
2 v. fronts. (v. 1, port.) illus., plates, facsims. (1 fold.) plans, map. 23cm.
"Chronological bibliography (1823–1874)": v. 2, p. 341–375.
1. Borrow, George Henry, 1803–1881.
Library of Congress PR4156.K5 99—946

OrP IaU
ICarbS WaS WaT ICN MH PSt PSC PP PBm MiU OCl OCU ODW
NK 0196894 DLC NcU MeB TU NN NIC DAU CaBVaU TxU KyLx

Knapp, William Ireland, 1835–1908, *ed.*
Modern French readings, ed. by William I. Knapp ... Boston, Ginn, Heath, & co., 1883.
v, [1], 457 p. 19cm.

1. French language—Chrestomathies and readers.

Library of Congress PC2117.K65 12-36017

NK 0196895 DLC MtU NcD MiU OO

VOLUME 300

Knapp, William Ireland, 1835-1908, ed.
Modern French readings, ed. by William I. Knapp ... 2d ed. Boston, Ginn, Heath & co., 1883.
v p., 2 l., 457 p. 19cm.

1. French language - Chrestomathies and readers.

NK 0196896 NNC MH

Knapp, William Ireland, 1835-1908, ed.
Modern French readings. 2nd ed. Boston, Ginn, 1888.

457 p.

NK 0196897 PP PU

Knapp, William I
Modern French readings ... 2d ed. Bost., Ginn, 1891.
457 p.

NK 0196898 PPEB

Knapp, William I
Modern French readings ... 2d ed. Boston, Ginn, 1891.
457 p.

NK 0196899 PPEB

Knapp, William Ireland, 1835–1908.
Modern Spanish readings, embracing text, notes and an etymological vocabulary. By William I. Knapp ... Boston, Ginn, Heath, & co., 1883.
vii, [1], 449, [1] p. 19cm.

1. Spanish language—Chrestomathies and readers.
11—33549
Library of Congress PC4117.K62

NK 0196900 DLC NcRS NcD PPL MiU ODW OO MH

Knapp, William Ireland, 1835–1908.
Modern Spanish readings; embracing text, notes, and an etymological vocabulary. By William I. Knapp... Boston: Ginn & Co., 1885. vii, 449 p. 12°.
Vocabulary, p. 233–449.

500939A. 1. Spanish language—Exercises and readers.
N. Y. P. L. November 11, 1930

NK 0196901 NN MH

Knapp, William Ireland, 1835-1908.
Modern Spanish readings, embracing text, notes, and an etymological vocabulary. Boston, Ginn & co., 1887.

NK 0196902 MH NjP

---

ar V
3994

Knapp, William Ireland, 1835-1908.
Modern Spanish readings, embracing text, notes, and an etymological vocabulary. Boston, Ginn, 1891 [c1883]
vii, 449 p. 19cm.

1. Spanish language--Chrestomathies and readers.

NK 0196903 NIC ViU

Knapp, William Ireland, 1835-1908.
Modern Spanish readings, embracing text, notes, and an etymological vocabulary. Boston, Ginn & co., 1893.

NK 0196904 MH

Knapp, William Ireland, 1835-1908.
Modern Spanish readings, embracing text, notes and an etymological vocabulary. Boston, Ginn & co., 1895.

NK 0196905 MH PP OCU OCLW

Knapp, William Ireland, 1835-1908, ed.

Hurtado de Mendoza, Diego, 1503–1575.
Obras poéticas de d. Diego Hurtado de Mendoza. Primera edicion completa. Madrid, Impr. de M. Ginesta, 1877.

Knapp, William Ireland, 1835–1908.
Official editions and reprints of the Index librorum prohibitorum issued in the sixteenth century. By William I. Knapp... New-York: F. Hart & Co., printers, 1880. 8 p. 8°.
Autograph letters etc. of the author laid in.

1. Index librorum prohibitorum—Bibl.
N. Y. P. L. December 15, 1925

NK 0196907 NN MB MH CtY

Knapp, William Ireland, *1835-1908.*
Ormsby's Don Quixote.
(*Cut from* Semi-Weekly Evening Post, New York. Dec. 22, 1885, Jan. 1, 1886. New York. 1885, 86.)
A review of John Ormsby's translation.

N136 — Cervantes Saavedra, Miguel de, 1547-1616. Don Quixote. English. Ormsby's translation.

NK 0196908 MB

Knapp, William Ireland, 1835-1908, ed.

Pardo Bazán, Emilia, *condesa* de, 1852–1921.
Pascual Lopez; autobiografía de un estudiante de medicina, por doña Emilia Pardo Bazán; ed. with English notes and a vocabulary, by Professor W. I. Knapp ... Boston, London [etc.] Ginn & company [°1905]

There are no cards for numbers
NK 0196910 to NK 0196919

Knapp, William Ireland, 1835-1908.
... Personal reminiscences of the Spanish revolution ... [New Haven, 1881]
[687]-709 p. 23 cm.
Caption title.
From the New Englander for November, 1881.

NK 0196920 CtY MB

Knapp, William Ireland, 1835–1908.
A practical grammar of the French language. Containing a grammar, exercises, reading lessons, and a complete pronouncing vocabulary. By William I. Knapp ... New York, Harper & brothers, 1864.
xii, [13]-502 p. 19½cm.

1. French language—Composition and exercises. 2. French language—Grammar—1800-1870.
10-24393†
Library of Congress PC2109.K6

NK 0196921 DLC ViU

Knapp, William Ireland, 1835–1908.
A practical grammar of the French language. Containing a grammar, exercises, reading lessons and a complete pronouncing vocabulary. By William I. Knapp ... New York, Harper & brothers, 1868.
xii, [13]-502 p. 19½cm.

1. French language—Composition and exercises. 2. French language—Grammar—1800-1870.
17-10473
Library of Congress PC2111.K65

NK 0196922 DLC MiU

Knapp, William Ireland, 1835-1903.
A practical grammar of the French language, containing a grammar, exercises, reading lessons, and a complete pronouncing vocabulary. New York, Harper & brothers, 1869.

NK 0196923 MH

Knapp, William Ireland, 1835-1908.
A practical grammar of the French language, containing a grammar, exercises, reading lessons, and a complete pronouncing vocabulary. New York, Harper & bros., 1870.

NK 0196924 MH

Knapp, William Ireland, 1835-1908.
A practical grammar of the French language. Containing a grammar, exercises, reading lessons, and a complete pronouncing vocabulary ...
New York, 1876.
19.5 cm.

NK 0196925 CtY

Knapp, William I[reland].
A practical grammar of the French language, containing a grammar, exercises, reading lessons, and a complete pronouncing vocabulary. New York: Harper & Brothers, 1879. xii, (1)14-502 p. 12°.

1. French language.—Grammar.
N. Y. P. L. May 20, 1912.

NK 0196926 NN

VOLUME 300

Knapp, William Ireland, 1835-1908, ed.
FOR OTHER EDITIONS SEE MAIN ENTRY
Borrow, George Henry, 1803-1881.
The Romany rye; a sequel to "Lavengro", by George Borrow. A new edition containing the unaltered text of the original issue, with notes, etc., by the author of "The life of George Borrow". London, J. Murray, 1914.

KNAPP, William Ireland, 1835-1908.
The Ticknor Spanish library.
= [New Haven, 1880.] 385-397 pp. 8°.
From the New Englander for May, 1880 [*7444.1.1880].

NK 0196928 MB

[Knapp, William L]
"I die a true American." The true life of William Pool giving a correct history of his grandparents and his parents, with a full account of the terrible affray at Stanwix hall... Containing also, an authentic account of his life from the age of eighteen months, the various kinds of business he followed, with the official report of the coroner's investigation, and verdict of the jury. New York, W. L. Knapp, 1855. 80 p. 22cm.
Introduction signed: W. L. Knapp.

1. Pool, William, d. 1855.
N. Y. P. L. June 17, 1947

NK 0196929 NN CtY PP TxU

Knapp, Winifred.
Select list of books in English about Scandinavia or by Scandinavians.
(In Bulletin of Bibliography. Vol. 8, pp. 187-192. Boston. 1915.)

L8008 — Scandinavia. Bibl.

NK 0196930 MB IU

Knapp, Z H
... Mezi nebem a mořem; zápisky radiotelegrafisty... Praha, Naše vojsko, 1946. 101 p. illus. 22cm. (Boj a odboj. sv. 4)

1. World war, 1939-1945—Aerial operations. 2. World war, 1939-1945—Personal narratives, Czecho-Slovakian.
N. Y. P. L. April 26, 1950

NK 0196931 NN

Knapp-Fisher, Arthur Bedford, 1888-
The future of church building. London, Incorporated Church Building Society, 1951
8 p. illus., plans

NK 0196932 MH NNC

BX5131 .K67
Knapp-Fisher, Edward George
The churchman's heritage; a study in the ethos of the English church. London, A. and C. Black [1952]
96 p.
Bibliographical footnotes.

1. Church of England. I. Title.

NK 0196933 ICU PPPD NcD PPEB CtY KyLxCB

Knapp-Fisher, Edward George
The churchman's heritage; a study in the ethos of the English Church. Greenwich, Conn., Seabury Press [1954]
96 p. 21 cm.

1. Church of England. I. Title.
BX5131.K64 283 54-14529 ‡

NK 0196934 DLC PSt

Knapp-Fisher, Hubert Clinton, 1899-
...Furness and Cartmel... London, Saint Catherine press [1948] viii, 72 p.. illus., map. 14cm. (Footpath guides. no. 46)
1. ed.

1. Furness, Eng.—Guidebooks, 1948. 2. Cartmel, Eng. —Guidebooks, 1948. I. Ser.

NK 0196935 NN

Knapp-Fisher, Hubert Clinton, 1899-
Man and his creatures, by H. C. Knapp-Fisher. With 44 illustrations by Joan Harrison. London, G. Routledge & sons, ltd. [1940]
viii, 236 p. illus., diagr. 21cm.
"First published 1940."
CONTENTS.—Introduction: The creatures and man.—The creatures of man.—Animals in sport.—Animals in fancy and in fact.—Animals in war.—Conclusion: Man and his creatures.

1. Domestic animals. 2. Hunting. 3. Animals, Legends and stories of. 4. Animals, War use of. I. Title.
A 41-1739
Harvard univ. Library for Library of Congress GT5880.K6
636

NK 0196936 MH NcD PPD CtY

Knapp-Fisher, Hubert Clinton, 1899-
Man and his creatures, by H. C. Knapp-Fisher, with 44 illustrations by Joan Harrison. New York, E. P. Dutton and company, inc., 1942.
viii, 236 p. illus., diagr. 20½cm.
"First edition."

1. Domestic animals. 2. Hunting. 3. Animals, Legends and stories of. 4. Animals, War use of. I. Title.
42-8655
Library of Congress GT5880.K6 1942
636

NK 0196937 DLC WaT Or OrP NcC OCl OEac

Knapp-Fisher, Hubert Clinton, 1899-
The modern world: a junior survey. London: Victor Gollancz Ltd., 1933. 447 p. maps. 12°.

1. Government. 2. International relations. 3. Title.
N. Y. P. L. May 22, 1934

NK 0196938 NN

Knapp-Fisher, Hubert Clinton, 1899-
... The modern world: a pageant of today. New York, E. P. Dutton & co., inc. [c1934]
447 p. illus. (incl. maps) diagrs. 19½cm.
At head of title: H. C. Knapp-Fisher.
"First edition."

1. History, Modern — 20th cent. — Juvenile literature. 2. Political science—Juvenile literature. 3. Civilization—Hist.—Juvenile literature. I. Title.
34-1240
Library of Congress D422.K6
——— Copy 2.
Copyright A 67965
940.5

NK 0196939 DLC NN OClh OCl PSC NcC PPGi WaSp Or MB

Knapp-Fisher, Hubert Clinton, 1899-
Outline of world history for boys and girls. London, Routledge, 1931.
illus.

NK 0196940 WaSp

Knapp-Fisher, Hubert Clinton, 1899-
Outline of world history for boys and girls, by H. C. Knapp-Fisher; with 81 illustrations. New York, E. P. Dutton & co., inc. [c1932]
ix, 445 p. illus. 23cm.
"First edition."

1. History, Universal—Juvenile literature. I. Title.
32-24269
Library of Congress D21.K6
——— Copy 2.
Copyright A 53561
909

NK 0196941 DLC Or PWcT PPGi PPD PP MB OCl

Knapp-Fisher, Hubert Clinton, 1899-
The world of nature, by H. C. Knapp-Fisher; with an introduction by E. W. MacBride ... and illustrations of more than 500 forms of life by Joan Harrison. London, V. Gollancz, ltd., 1935.
2 p. l., 512 p. illus. 19cm.

1. Natural history. I. Title.
35-13533
Library of Congress QH45.K5 1935
Copyright A ad int. 20443
574

NK 0196942 DLC FMU OClW

KNAPP, BURRELL & COMPANY.
Office of the Agricultural Warehouses of | Knapp, Burrell & Co., | Portland, Oregon, April 20, 1866. | Dear Sir:— | We beg leave to call particular attention to the fact that we have imported for the present season a | large stock of | Extras and Repairs, | for the leading Farm Machines sold by us the last four years.
[343b]
Broadside. 19.3 x 25.3 cm.

NK 0196943 OrHi

KNAPP FAMILY ASSOCIATION.
[Announcement of the organization of the Knapp Family Association] [New York, 1936] 1 v. 29cm.
Loose-leaf.
Mounted clippings.

871794A. 1. Knapp family.

NK 0196944 NN

Knapp family association.
... Bulletin. v. 1- March 1937-
[New York?] 1937-
v. 23cm.
Caption title.
Editor: 1937- Mrs. F. K. Dickinson.

1. Knapp family. I. Dickinson, Mrs. Flora (Knapp) ed.
37-16846
Library of Congress CS71.K675 1937

NK 0196945 DLC Or KyU OClWHi PHi WHi

VOLUME 300

Bb38
2
K727 Knapp family history. [n.p.,n.d.]
A prospectus of a proposed history of the English families of the name of Knapp.

1. Genealogy - Knapp. 2. Knapp family.

NK 0196946 CtY

[KNAPP family records. v.p., 1933-60] 6 pieces in 1 v. mounted photos 23-30cm.

CONTENTS.--A brief genealogy of one branch of the Knapp family; being a family record of the descendants of Alanson and Harriet Knapp, by [Flora Knapp Dickinson]--Knapp; first generation in America, by John McSweeny.--Knapp family data, by Elizabeth Horton.--George Knapp, of England, and some of his descendants in America. Job Knapp and some of his descendants. Ancestral lines of Mary Lenore Knapp, extending back to Adam, by Alfred Averill Knapp.

1. Knapp family. I. Dickinson, Flora Knapp. II. McSweeny, John. III. Horton, Elizabeth. IV. Knapp, Alfred Averill, 1868-

NK 0196948 NN

Knapp & son, *Chicago.*
The invalid's friend and health instructor, by Drs. Knapp & son ... [Chicago] Chicago printing company [°1868]
78 p. 22½cm.

Library of Congress RM671.K6 CA 10-1869 Unrev'd

NK 0196949 DLC

Knapp & Spencer company, *Sioux City, Ia.*
General catalog
Sioux City, Ia., °19
v. illus., plates (col. mounted samples) 29cm.
On cover, 19 : Wholesale hardware.

1. Hardware—Catalogs.

41-35124

Library of Congress TS405.K5
——— Copy 2.
671.085

NK 0196950 DLC

The Knapp company, inc., New York.
The Knapp pricer. Calendars, Stuyvesant prints, blotters, fans, etc. HF6146 .C2K5
[New York, c 1913.

NK 0196951 DLC

Knapp company, inc., *New York.*
The Knapp way ... a contribution of specialized experience in advertising and selling, from the members of the Knapp staff to our brother workers on the road ... New York, The Knapp company, inc., °1912.
105 p. 1 illus. 19cm.

1. Calendars. 2. Salesmen and salesmanship. I. Title.

13-2598

Library of Congress HF5444.K7

NK 0196952 DLC

Knapp Dovetailing Machine Co.
Knapp Dovetailing Machine. Northampton, 1876.

4 p.

NK 0196953 PPF

Knapp-Sparks Producing Co., Rushville, Ill.
"Monkey-Bizness." A comedy in three acts. Rushville, Ill., c1930.
[18 p.] 1 l. 21 x 36 cm.
Mimeographed copy.

NK 0196954 RPB

The Knapp pricer
see under The Knapp company, inc., New York.

The Knapp way ...
see under Knapp company, inc., New York.

398
K72k2 Knappe, Adolf.
Die Kiesewälder spinnstube in dramatischer form, nebst einer sammlung alter spinnlieder, alter tänze und mundartlicher gedichte ... Hirschberg i. Rsgb., H. Springer [1930]
39, [1]p. plates.

Second edition.
Contains music.

NK 0196957 IU

PT1205
.R55K6 KNAPPE, ADOLF, comp.
Die volkslieder und volkstänze des Riesen- und Isergebirges, gesammelt von Adolf Knappe... Hirschberg i. Schles., H. Springer [1912]
[3]-119 p. 19½cm.
With music.

1. Folk-songs, German--Riesengebirge. 2. Folk-songs, German--Isergebirge.

NK 0196958 ICU

Knappe, Alfred.
Die luftfahrt im naturkundlichen unterricht der volksschule; eine einführung an hand zahlreicher versuche mit einfachen mitteln, von Alfred Knappe. Leipzig, Quelle & Meyer, 1936.
134 p. illus., diagrs. 22½cm.

1. Aeronautics—Study and teaching. I. Title.

39-13944

Library of Congress TL560.K55
629.13

NK 0196959 DLC WaS NcD NN

Knappe, Alfred.
Die neue volksschulphysik; ein handbuch für lehrer, von Alfred Knappe. Mit 170 abbildungen. Leipzig, Quelle & Meyer, 1939.
240 p. illus., diagrs. 23½cm.
Bibliographical foot-notes.

Continued in next column

Continued from preceding column

1. Physics. I. Title.

41-16304

Library of Congress QC23.K6
[2] 530

NK 0196960 DLC ICRL NNC ICU

Knappe (Carl [Ferdinand]) [1854-]. *Zur Statistik der Tuberculose der Hirnsubstanz. 30 pp., 1 l. 8°. *Berlin, G. Schade,* [1877].

NK 0196961 DNLM ICRL

Knappe, Carolus Christianus
see Knappe, Charles Christian, 1852-

Knappe, Charles Christian, 1852-
De Tibulli libri quarti elegiis inde ab altera usque ad duodeciman disputatio: dissertatio inauguralis quam ... scripsit Carolus Christianus Knappe. Duderstadt, Wagner, 1880.
44 p. O. (Tibullus. Pamphlets, no. 1)

NK 0196963 NcD NjP CU ICRL MiU

KNAPPE, CHR.
Ist die 21. Rede des hl. Gaudentius (Oratio B. Gaudentii episcopi de vita et obitu B. Filastrii episcopi praedecessoris sui) echt? Zugleich ein Beitrag zur Latinität des Gaudentius. Osnabrück, 1908.

66 p.
"Jahresbericht des Königl. Gym. Carolinum. 1908. No. 408."

NK 0196964 DDO NjP

Knappe, Emil, 1853-
see Knappe, Erdmann Bruno, Emil, 1853-

Knappe, Erdmann Bruno Emil, 1853–
Das Bidder'sche Organ. Ein Beitrag zur Kenntnis der Anatomie, Histologie und Entwicklungsgeschichte der Geschlechtswerkzeuge einiger Amphibien, besonders der einheimischen Bufoniden. Inaugural-Dissertation . . . Leipzig . . .
Leipzig. Engelmann. 1886. vi, 64, (1) pp. Plates. 22½ cm., in 8s.
Separat-Abdruck aus Morphol. Jahrbuch. 11. Band.
Verzeichnis der benutzten Litteratur, pp. 61, 62.

L4340 — Bidder's organ. — Amphibia. — Toad.

NK 0196966 MB NjP ICRL

Knappe, Erichs.
Kartupeļu schķirņu apraksti. [Pēc] agr. E. Knappe. [Rīgā] Latw. lauks. b-bas preekuļu selekzijas stazija, 1934. 27 p. 17cm.

857833A. 1. Potato—Varieties.
N. Y. P. L. December 2, 1936

NK 0196967 NN

VOLUME 300

Knappe, F.
D. Bekker'sche paraphrast d. Ilias ... bedeutung für d. textkritik. n.p., 1892.

NK 0196968 NjP

Knappe, Ferdinand: Über klinische Erfahrungen mit dem Extractum Apocyni cannabini fluidum und dem Bariumchlorid. [Maschinenschrift.] 48 S. 4°. — Auszug: Berlin (1921): Ebering. 2 Bl. 8°
Berlin, Med. Diss. v. 1. Nov. 1921 [1922] [U 22. 349

NK 0196969 ICRL

Knappe, Ferdinand, 1864-
see Knappe, Joh. Ferdinand, 1864-

Knappe, Franz.
Am Lindenbaum [T. T. B. B.]. Op. 8, No. 1.
Cöln. Tonger. [188-?] 3 pp. [Deutsche Männerchor. 2.] L. 8°.

E2766 — T.r. — Part songs.

NK 0196971 MB

Knappe, Franz.
Bilder aus Schiller's „Glocke," für Männerchor, Solostimmen und Orchester oder Klavier componirt von Franz Knappe. Op. 9. Klavierauszug.
Köln a/Rh. Tonger. [188-?] 43 pp. L. 8°.

E2766 — Cantatas. Male voices. — Schiller.

NK 0196972 MB

Knappe, Fritz Alfred, 1881- ed.
FOR OTHER EDITIONS SEE MAIN ENTRY
De rebus in Oriente mirabilibus.
Das angelsächsische prosastück Die wunder des Ostens. Überlieferung, quellen, sprache und text nach beiden handschriften ... Von Fritz Knappe ... Berlin, Druck von G. Bernstein, 1906.

Knappe, Georg, d. 1942.

Müller, Otto Max.
Roscado y Cálculo de las ruedas para roscar, por Otto Müller [y] Georg Knappe. Con 164 grabados. 3. ed. Barcelona, Editorial Labor, 1943.

Knappe, Georg, d 1942
...Wechselräderberechnung für Drehbänke unter Berücksichtigung der schwierigen Steigungen, von Georg Knappe... Berlin: J. Springer, 1921. 77 p. incl. diagrs., tables. 8°. (Werkstattbuecher für Betriebsbeamte, Vor- und Facharbeiter. Heft 4.)

1. Lathes. 2. Series.
N. Y. P. L. January 13, 1922.

NK 0196975 NN

Knappe, Georg, d. 1942.
... Wechselräderberechnung für drehbänke unter berücksichtigung der schwierigen steigungen, von Georg Knappe ... 4., verb. aufl. (25. bis 30. tausend) Mit 10 abbildungen im text und 7 zahlentafeln. Berlin, J. Springer, 1940.

64 p. diagrs. 23cm. (Werkstattbücher für betriebsbeamte, konstrukteure und facharbeiter. Herausgeber: dr.-ing. H. Haake ... Hft. 4)

1. Screw-cutting machines. I. Title.

TJ1222.K56 1940 621.94 46-44099

NK 0196976 DLC

Knappe, Georg, d. 1942.

TJ1222
.M32

Mayer, Emil, *engineer.*
... Wechselräderberechnung für drehbänke under berücksichtigung der schwierigen steigungen, von ing. Emil Mayer ... 5., verb. aufl. des zuerst von Georg Knappe verfassten heftes (31. bis 36. tausend) Mit 10 abbildungen im text und 7 tabellen. Berlin, Springer, 1943.

JA
44
G59
v.8

Knappe, Hans Joachim.
Das Problem der überholenden Kausalität. Die Bedeutung eines nachträglichen hypothetischen Schadensereignisses im Recht der Schadenshaftung. Göttingen, O. Schwartz, 1954.
124 p. 23cm. (Göttinger rechtswissenschaftliche Studien, Hft. 8)

1. Damages. I. Series.

NK 0196978 NIC CtY-L MH-L NNC MiU-L IU MdBJ

Knappe, Heinrich.
... Friedrich Klose; eine studie. München, Drei masken verlag, 1921.

3 p. l., 3-142 p. illus. (music) port. 20cm. (*Added t.-p.:* Zeitgenössische komponisten ... hrsg. von H. W. v. Waltershausen. III)
"Verzeichnis der werke von Friedrich Klose": p. 138-140.

1. Klose, Friedrich, 1862-

25-4275

Library of Congress ML410.K56K6

NK 0196979 DLC IaU MiU MH IEN TxU PPGi NN

Knappe, Heinrich, arr.

M2003
.K68S6

Klose, Friedrich, 1862-1942.
[Der Sonne-Geist. Piano-vocal score. German]

Der Sonne-Geist; Dichtung von Alfred Mombert in Musik gesetzt für Soli, Chöre, Orchester und Orgel. Klavier-Auszug von Heinrich Knappe. Wien, Universal-Edition, °1918.

Knappe, Herbert: Haftungs- und Regreßbeziehungen beim Frachtvertrage mit mehreren selbständigen Frachtführern. (Mit Ausschluß des Eisenbahnfrachtrechtes.) Borna-Leipzig 1914: Noske. VIII, 59 S. 8°
Breslau, Jur. Diss. v. 22. Juni 1914, Ref. H. Meyer, Schott
[Geb. 28. Jan. 91 Lewin; Wohnort: Görlitz; Staatsangeh.: Preußen; Vorbildung: Matthias-G. Breslau Reife 10; Studium: Breslau 7 S.; Rig. 6. Febr. 14.] [U 14. 222

NK 0196981 ICRL

Knappe (Joh. Ferdinand) [1864-]. *Ueber die Wirkung des Calomels bei gleichzeitiger Anwendung von Jodpräparaten. 27 pp., 1 l. 8°. Berlin, O. Francke, 1888.

NK 0196982 DNLM ICRL

Knappe, Karl Adolf, 1884-
Das Gesetz heisst Wand, der Ausweg: Plastik. Gedanken zur Kunst unserer Zeit, nach Briefen zusammengestellt und hrsg. von Helmut Beck. [Stuttgart, Stuttgarter Verlag, 1950.
112 p. plates. 30 cm.

1. Sculpture. 2. Art, Modern—20th cent. I. Beck, Helmut, ed.

NB198.K6 51-32032 rev

NK 0196983 DLC TxU TU NNC

Knappe, [Karl] Christian.
Grundzüge der aristotelischen lehre von der endämonie. [Progr.] Wittenberg, B.H. Rübener, 1864.
16 p. 4°.

NK 0196984 MH PU PBm NjP

Knappe, Karl Christian, 1852-
see Knappe, Charles Christian, 1852-

KNAPPE, KARL FRIEDRICH.
Original drawings of Pallas' Flora rossica, with four unedited drawings. [n.p., 17-] 1 v. 47cm.

Title in manuscript.
Includes 104 drawings in pencil, ink and wash, 74 colored, from which plates for the Flora rossica were made and colored. With 2 proof plates and a colored drawing for the added illustrated title lettered in Russian.
I. Pallas, Peter Simon. Flora rossica.

NK 0196986 NN

Knappe, Max, 1883-
... Über einen fall von schussverletzung der harnblase ... Neisse, Bär, 1914.
30, [2] p. fold. diagr.

Inaug.-diss., Greifswald, 1914.
Lebenslauf.
"Literatur": p. [31]

1. Bladder - Wounds and injuries. 2. Gunshot wounds.

NK 0196987 NNC CtY

Knappe, Otto.
Die bilanzen der aktien-gesellschaften vom standpunkte der buchhaltung, rechtswissenschaft und der steuergesetze. Für die gerichtliche und geschäftliche praxis bearb. von dr. jur. Otto Knappe. Hannover [etc.] C. Meyer (G. Prior) 1903.
vi, [2], 122 p., 1 l. 24½cm.
"Hauptsächlich benutzte literatur": 2d p. following p. vi.

1. Corporations — Accounting. 2. Stock companies. 3. Commercial law—Germany.

8—26409

Library of Congress HG4028.B2K6

NK 0196988 DLC ICJ

Knappe, Otto.
Die bilanzen der aktiengesellschaften vom standpunkte der buchhaltung, rechtswissenschaft und der steuergesetze. Für die gerichtliche und geschäftliche praxis bearb. von dr. jur. Otto Knappe. 2. verb. aufl. Hannover-List [etc.] C. Meyer (G. Prior) 1909.
vi, [2], 129 p. 25½cm.
"Hauptsächlich benutzte literatur": 2d p. following p. vi.

Continued in next column

VOLUME 300

Continued from preceding column

1. Corporations—Accounting. 2. Stock companies. 3. Commercial law—Germany.
11-26243
Library of Congress HG4028.B2K6 1909

NK 0196989 DLC NIC CU ICJ

Knappe, Otto.
Die gesellschaft mit beschränkter haftung, ihre gründung, geschäftsführung, buchhaltung, ihre steuern und anderen abgaben, mit vollständigem, kommentiertem gesetzestexte, mustern und formularen, von dr. jur. Otto Knappe ... Mit alphabetischem sachregister ... Hannover-List, Berlin, C. Meyer, 1910.
x, 160 p. 25ᶜᵐ.
"Hauptsächlich benutzte literatur": p. [vi]
1. Private companies—Germany. I. Germany. Laws, statutes, etc.
12-15188 Revised
Library of Congress HD2858.K6

NK 0196990 DLC ICJ

Knappe, Otto.
Grundriss der römischen rechtsgeschichte, umfassend das gesamte private und öffentliche römische recht in seiner geschichtlichen entwicklung. Berlin, P. Nitschmann, 1904.
pp. xii, 420.

Roman law-Hist.||AcS 232706 HCL 23-1511

NK 0196991 MH

Knappe, Otto.
Die weltweisheit des schlichten menschen (richtlinien) von dr. jur. Otto Knappe. Berlin-Wilmersdorf, Knappe [°1927]
110 p. 18ᶜᵐ.

1. Philosophy. 2. Spiritualism. I. Title.
28-7056
Library of Congress BD41.K6

NK 0196992 DLC

W 4 M96 1948
KNAPPE, Paul, 1921-
Anatomische, physiologische und klinische Untersuchungen an Arbeitern einer Münchner Schuhfabrik hinsichtlich ihres Ernährungs- und Leistungszustandes. Günzburg, 1948.
70 p. illus.
Cover title.
Inaug.-Diss. - Munich.
1. Nutrition 2. Work

NK 0196993 DNLM

W 4 B51 1941
Knappe, Werner, 1909-
Ein Beitrag zur Frage der Uteruslipome. Berlin, Linke [1941?]
15 p.

Inaug.-Diss. - Berlin.
Bibliography: p. 15

NK 0196994 DNLM

Knappe, Wilhelm, 1855-
Deutsche kulturbestrebungen in China; vortrag gehalten von geh. legationsrat dr. Knappe. Berlin, H. Paetel, 1906.
2 p. l., 28 p. 23ᶜᵐ. (Added t.-p.: Schriften der Deutsch-asiatischen gesellschaft ... 3. hft.)
Cover-title: Deutsche kulturaufgaben in China.

1. Education—China. 2. Germans in China. 3. Missions—China. I. Title.
25-2594
Library of Congress LA1131.K6

NK 0196995 DLC CU ICJ NN

1885-
Knappe, Wilhelm, appr. Arzt: Die Generationspsychosen in der Provinzial Heil- und Pflegeanstalt zu Osnabrück. Osnabrück 1913: Osnabr. Volkszeitung. 38 S. 8°
Greifswald, Med. Diss. v. 22. Mai 1913, Ref. Schröder
[Geb. 5. Nov. 85 Osnabrück; Wohnort: Osnabrück; Staatsangeh.: Preußen; Vorbildung: G. Carolinum Osnabrück Reife 04; Studium: Freiburg 2, Marburg 4, Göttingen 2, Greifswald 6 S.; Coll. 1. Aug. 11; Approb. 1. Okt. 12.]
[U 13. 2006

NK 0196996 ICRL DNLM NN

1886-
Knappe, Wilhelm: Wolf Dietrich von Maxlrain und die Reformation in der Herrschaft Hohenwaldeck. Ein Beitrag zur Geschichte der deutschen Reformation und Gegenreformation. Erlangen 1919: Jacob. VI, 152 S. 8° ¶Soll m. 2 Beil. u. Reg. vollst. ersch. als: Quellen u. Forschungen z. bayer. Kirchengesch. Bd 4.
Erlangen, Phil. Diss. v. 9. März 1920, Ref. Beckmann
[Geb. 25. Nov. 86 Thuisbrunn; Wohnort: Erlangen; Staatsangeh.: Bayern; Vorbildung: G. Regensburg Reife 06; Studium: Erlangen 3, Leipzig 2, Rostock 1, Erlangen 2 S.; Rig. 11. Juli 19.] [U 20. 3486

(Nur in beschränkter Anzahl für den Austausch)

NK 0196997 ICRL NN CtY

BR857 B3Q4 v.4
Knappe, Wilhelm, 1886-
Wolf Dietrich von Maxlrain und die Reformation in der Herrschaft Hohenwaldeck. Ein Beitrag zur Geschichte der deutschen Reformation und Gegenreformation. Leipzig, A. Deichertsche Verlagsbuchhandlung dr. W. Scholl, 1920.
156 p. maps. (Quellen und Forschungen zur bayerischen Kirchengeschichte. Bd. 4)

1. Maxlrain, Wolf Dietrich, Herr von Hohenwaldeck, 1523 or 24-1561. 2. Hohenwaldeck, Ger. - Church history. 3. Reformation - Germany - Hohenwaldeck.

NK 0196998 CU OU NcD CaBVaU IaU InU NjPT PPStch

Knappe, Wilhelm C.
see Knappe, Wilhelm, 1855-

Knappek, L'udevít.
Obsadzovanie uhorských biskupstiev od x. do konca xiv. storočia so zvláštnym zreteľom na pápežské zásahy a na postavenie uhorských kráľov. V Bratislavě, Nákl. Právnickéj fakulty Univerzity Komenského; v komisii F. Řivnáča v Prahe, 1934.
265 p. 25 cm. (Knihovňa Právnickej fakulty Univerzity Komenského v Bratislave, sv. 42)
Summary in French.
Bibliography: p. [245]-260.
1. Bishops—Hungary. 2. Investiture. 3. Church and state in Hungary. I. Title. (Series: Knihovňa Fakulty právnickéj Univerzity Komenského v Bratislave, sv. 42)
51-49479

NK 0197000 DLC IU OCl

Knappen, Ashmun A.
[In memoriam] ... to our father, Reverend Ashmun A. Knappen
see under title

KNAPPEN, D M
Aion and aionios. [Boston, 1847]
24p.

Signed: D.M.K.
Caption title.
Reprinted from the Universalist quarterly, v.4, 1847.
Facts and opinions relating to these words in answer to the opponents of Universalism.

NK 0197002 ICN

Knappen, Laurence Stevens, 1898-
Revenue bonds and the investor, by Laurence S. Knappen ... New York, Prentice-Hall, inc., 1939.
xiii, 329 p. incl. forms. 23½ᶜᵐ.
Thesis (PH. D.)—Columbia university, 1940.
Without thesis note.
"First printing October, 1939."
Bibliography: p. [297]-304.

1. Bonds—U. S. I. Title.
40-1398 Revised
Library of Congress HG4936.K55 1940
[r43l3] 332.66

NK 0197003 DLC IdU OrP TU CU PPD PPT PU NcD OCl ODW OClW MtU OCU CoU NN

Knappen, Marshall Mason, 1901-
And call it peace. Chicago, University of Chicago Press [1947]
viii, 218 p. 21 cm.

1. Germany—Hist.—Allied occupation, 1945- 2. Denazification. I. Title.
D802.G3K6 940.5343 47—11542*

NK 0197004 DLC OrU OrP IdU MB ICU TxU DS ViU NcD AU MiU WaS WaT OrCS WaU

Knappen, Marshall Mason, 1901-
Constitutional and legal history of England [by] M. M. Knappen ... New York, Harcourt, Brace and company, 1942.
x p., 3 l., 3-607 p. front., illus. (maps) plates, ports., diagrs. 22ᶜᵐ.
"Chronological chart of chapters and subtopics" on lining-papers.

1. Gt. Brit.—Constitutional history. 2. Law—Gt. Brit.—Hist. & crit. I. Title.
42-8549
Library of Congress JN121.K55
[6] 342.4209

NK 0197005 DLC TxU TU PSC PBm PU OCl OCU OO ODW ViU-L NcD CaBVaU OrPR WaU-L OrSaW OrU CaBVa OrPS WaTC NBuC NcU MiU KyU-A KyU AU

Knappen, Marshall Mason, 1901-

Chicago. University. *University extension division. Home-study dept.*
... History 261; English history to 1660, by Marshall M. Knappen. [Chicago] The University of Chicago, °1934.

Knappen, Marshall Mason, 1901-

Chicago. University. *University extension division. Home-study dept.*
... History 262; English history from 1660 to 1935, by Marshall M. Knappen [and] Louise D. Walker. [Chicago] The University of Chicago, °1936.

DA32 .7 .C453
Knappen, Marshall Mason, 1901-

Chicago. University. *University extension division. Home-study dept.*
... History 263 (English history, 1714-1943) by Marshall M. Knappen [and] Frances E. Gillespie. [Chicago] The University of Chicago, °1943.

VOLUME 300

Knappen, Marshall Mason, 1901-
The Marshall plan. East Lansing [1947]
10 p. 23 cm. (Michigan. State College, East Lansing. Extension Service. Current issues pamphlet 1)

1. Reconstruction (1939-)—Europe. I. Title. II. Series: Michigan. State College of Agriculture and Applied Science, East Lansing. Extension Division. Current issues pamphlet 1.

HC240.K65 330.94 48-45025*

NK 0197009 DLC Or PP

Knappen, Marshall Mason.
Richard Greenham and the practical Puritans under Elizabeth. Ithaca, N. Y., 1927.
266 l. 28cm.

Thesis (Ph. D.)--Cornell University, 1927.

NK 0197010 NIC

Film N2585 Knappen, Marshall Mason.
Richard Greenham and the practical Puritans under Elizabeth. Ithaca, N. Y., 1927.
266 l. 28cm.
Thesis (Ph. D.)--Cornell University, 1927. Microfilm (negative) Ithaca, N. Y., Photo Science, Cornell University, 1969. 1 reel. 35mm.

NK 0197011 NIC

microfm BX 371 Knappen, Marshall Mason, 1901-
Richard Greenham and the practical Puritans under Elizabeth. Ithaca, N.Y., 1927.
Positive.
Thesis--Cornell University.

1. Greenham, Richard, 1535?-1594? 2. Puritans--England.

NK 0197012 ICU

Knappen, Marshall Mason.
Robert II of Flanders in the first crusade. (In: The Crusades and other historical essays. New York, 1928. 8°. p. 79-100.)
Caption-title.
Signed: M. M. Knappen.

359322A. 1. Robert II, count of Flanders, d. 1111. 2. Crusades, First, 1096-1099.
N. Y. P. L. July 5, 1928

NK 0197013 NN OCl OU

Knappen, Marshall Mason, 1901-
Tudor puritanism, a chapter in the history of idealism, by M. M. Knappen ... Chicago, The University of Chicago press [1939]
xii, 555 p. 24½cm.
"Select bibliography": p. [521]-531.

1. Puritans. 2. Idealism. I. Title. 39-10082
Library of Congress BX9334.K5
——— Copy 2.
Copyright A 126669 [12] 285.942

NcRS Wa OrU IdU ViU WaWW WaS CaBVaU PV PHC PPT OCl ODW OCU OU ICN NN WaTC OrPR OrSaW
NK 0197014 DLC KyWAT NRCR NcD MtU OrCS MiU NbU PU

Knappen, Marshall Mason, 1901- *ed.*
Two Elizabethan Puritan diaries, by Richard Rogers and Samuel Ward, edited, with an introduction, by M. M. Knappen ... Chicago, The American society of church history [°1933]
xiii, 148 p. illus. (map) 2 port. (incl. front.) facsims. 24½cm. (*Half-title: Studies in church history. vol. II*)
CONTENTS.—The Puritan character as seen in the diaries.—The life of Richard Rogers.—The life of Samuel Ward.—The diary of Richard Rogers.—The diary of Samuel Ward.—Historical notes from Ward's ms. "Adversaria".—Selected bibliography (p. 137-140)

1. Puritans. I. Rogers, Richard, 1550?-1618. II. Ward, Samuel, d. 1643. III. Title. 34-853
Library of Congress BX9339.R6K6
——— Copy 2.
Copyright A 68111 [5] 285.9

PPT NRCR PPWe PU OCU OO OU MB ViU WaU
NK 0197015 DLC UU TxU NcD CaBVaU DAU OrU PPPrHi

Knappen, Russell Stafford, 1892-
... Geology and mineral resources of the Dixon quadrangle, by Russell Stafford Knappen ... Printed by authority of the state of Illinois. Urbana, Ill., 1926.
141 p. illus., v fold. maps (2 in pocket) 25 cm. ([Illinois. State geological survey] Bulletin no. 49)
Contributions from the Department of geology and mineralogy, Columbia university, v. 36, no. 1.
At head of title: State of Illinois. Department of registration and education ... Division of the State geological survey.
Thesis (PH. D.)—Columbia university, 1927.
Vita.
Published also without thesis note.
1. Geology—Illinois—Lee co. 2. Geology—Illinois—Ogle co. 3. Mines and mineral resources—Illinois—Lee co. 4. Mines and mineral resources—Illinois—Ogle co. I. Title: Dixon quadrangle, Geology and mineral resources of the.
QE1.C7 vol. 36, no. 1 28-27755

NNC PSt MiU OU MB ICJ OCl CU CoDGS
NK 0197016 DLC DI-GS WaS MtBuM PPAmP PPAN NIC NcRS

Knappen, Russell Stafford, *1892-* , and Gail Francis Moulton, *1898-*
Geology and mineral resources of parts of Carbon Big Horn, Yellowstone, and Stillwater counties, Montana.
(*In* United States. Geological Survey. Contributions to economic geology (short papers and preliminary reports). Part 2, pp. 1-70. Illus. Plates. Folded chart. Tables. Washington. 1931.)

D1034 — Montana. Geol. & paleon. — Montana. Mineralogy. — Jt. auth.

NK 0197017 MB DLC MtBC

Knappen, Russell Stafford, 1892-
Influence of geology on engineering problems of the Second army area. [By] R. S. Knappen ...
(*In* The Military engineer. Washington, 1922. 30cm. vol. XIV, no. 76, p. 219-222, 254 incl. map)

1. [Military geology] I. Title. II. Title: Geology, Influence of, on engineering problems.
E S 23-177
Title from U. S. Engineer School Libr. Printed by L. C.

NK 0197018 DES OU

Knappen, Theodore Macfarlane, 1871-1938, joint author
Day, Frank A.
John Albert Johnson's lifsgärning, tre gänger guvernör öfver Minnesota, af Frank A. Day och Theodore M. Knappen. St. Paul, Day & Knappen, 1910.

Knappen, Theodore Macfarlane, 1871-1938, joint author
Day, Frank A.
Life of John Albert Johnson, three times governor of Minnesota, by Frank A. Day and Theodore M. Knappen. Chicago, Forbes & company, 1910.

Knappen, Theodore Macfarlane, 1871-1938.
Wings of war; an account of the important contribution of the United States to aircraft invention, engineering, development and production during the world war, by Theodore Macfarlane Knappen, with an introduction by Rear-Admiral D. W. Taylor ... With 43 illustrations. New York and London, G. P. Putnam's sons, 1920.
xv, 289 p. front., plates. 21cm.

1. European war, 1914-1918—Aerial operations. 2. European war, 1914-1918—U. S. 3. Aeronautics, Military—U. S. I. Title.
20-15470
D606.K6

OClh OCl OEac MB NN Ok IdU OrU MtBC WaS
NK 0197021 DLC MtU WaE WHi NcC DN DAL PPLas MiU

Knappen Engineering Company
see
Tippetts-Abbett-McCarthy-Stratton.

Knappen-Tippetts-Abbett-McCarthy
see
Tippetts-Abbett-McCarthy-Stratton.

Knappenberger, George L
Down there in Oklahoma ... Compiled from data selected from annual report of Oklahoma's governor to Interior Department, Washington, D.C. Issued by Geo. L. Knappenberger, immigration agent, Atchison, Topeka & Santa Fe Railway System. Shawnee, Okla., McGill-Peyton Printing Co., [1905?]
cover-title, 60 p. illus.(incl. port.) 24 cm.
Zc41 905kn

Zc41 905kn Devoted largely to the town of Shawnee.

1. Shawnee, Okla. 2. Walz, H W - Presentation inscription. I. Atchison, Topeka and Santa Fe Railway Company. II. Title.

NK 0197025 CtY

Knappenberger, J William.
The descendants of Elisha Harvey from 1719 to 1914, comp. and arranged by Rev. J. Wm. Knappenberger ... [n. p., 1914]
44 p. front. (coat of arms) pl., ports. 23cm.

1. Harvey family (Elisha Harvey, 1719-1800) I. Title.
14-14323
Library of Congress CS71.H341 1914

NK 0197026 DLC MWA MB

Knappenberger, James Buchanan, 1856-
Christian science unmasked; sermons delivered at the Wesleyan Methodist church, Syracuse, N. Y., by the pastor, Rev. J. B. Knappenberger ... [Syracuse, N. Y., J. C. McBride, °1918]
1 p. l., 60, [2] p. 17cm.

I. Title. 18-7734
Library of Congress BX6955.K55

NK 0197027 DLC WHi

Knappenberger, James Buchanan, 1856-
Exposition of the book of Revelation, by J. B. Knappenberger ... Syracuse, N. Y., The author, 1908.
200 p. front. (port.) 20½cm.

Continued in next column

VOLUME 300

Continued from preceding column

1. Bible. N. T. Revelation—Commentaries.
8-16399
Library of Congress BS2825.K6
[a44b1]

NK 0197028 DLC PPLT

17
1874a
Knappenberger, James Buchanan, 1856-
A sermon. The old and the new Sabbath. Middlefield, O.A.R. Woolsey, 1886.
1 p.l., 22 p. 12°.

NK 0197029 DLC

Knappenberger, Philip.
An inquiry into the deity of Jesus Christ, with an exhortation to all to read and understand the Bible, and not be led from party to party, or from sect to sect, and end in having their pockets picked. To which is added an answer to the question, who was God speaking to, when he said, "Let us make man in Our own image" ... By Philip Knappenberger. Strasburg, O., 1856.
64 p. 18cm.

1. Christianity—Controversial literature. I. Title.
38-33132
Library of Congress BL2775.K57
[2]

NK 0197030 DLC PPPrHi

Knappenberger, Philip.
An Inquiry into the Rights of holding Negroes a. Slaves, proven from Natural Facts and the Bible. Strawsbury, O., 1864.
11 p.

NK 0197031 MH

Knappen-Musikkapelle, Häring.
140 [i. e. Hundertvierzig] Jahre Knappen-Musikkapelle Häring; Fest-Schrift anlässlich der ... Festveranstaltungen am 17. und 18. Juli 1954. Häring, 1954.
47 p. illus. 23 cm.

I. Title.
ML246.8.H3K6 60-19067 ‡

NK 0197032 DLC

513
K72l3
Knapper, C
Leerboek der meetkunde ... 3. herziene en vermeerderde druk. Arnhem, 1885.
v. diagrs.

NK 0197033 IU

Knapper,
Leerboek van het handelsrekenen. 7.herziene en vermeerderde druk. Arnhem, J.Rinkes jr. [1907]

2 v.

NK 0197034 MH

KNAPPER, C.
Waartoe Multatuli zoo al dient. Arnhem, J. Rinkes, 1890.

pp.40.
Cover-title.

NK 0197035 MH

QM691
.K67
Knapper, Christiaan.
Over hemiacardie ... Amsterdam, Universitets-boekhandel [1925]
146, [2] p. illus., III pl. 24cm.
Proefschrift—Amsterdam.
"Geraadpleegde werken": p. [142]-146.

1. Monsters.

NK 0197036 ICU DNLM MiU

Knapper (Nicolaas), Czn. *Die Schnittführung bei der Oberkieferresection, mit specieller Berücksichtigung der intrabuccalen Methode. [Freiburg.] 160 pp., 1 l. 8°. *Arnhem, J. Rinkes jr.*, 1895.

NK 0197037 DNLM

Knappert, Artur.
Vom Bäckerlehrling zum Bäckmeister, in Frage und Antwort; zur Vorbereitung auf die Gesellen- und Meisterprüfung, hrsg. von Artur Knappert...und August Späh... 2. Aufl. Stuttgart, H. Matthaes [c1949] 126 p. 20cm.

531117B. 1. Baking. 2. Bread making. I. Späh, August, jt. comp.

NK 0197038 NN

Knappert, Bastiaan.
Bijdragen tot de ontwikkelings-geschiedenis der zoetwater-planariën, door Dr. B. Knappert ... Utrecht, C. van der Post jr., 1865.
5 p. l., 39 p. II pl. 29 x 23cm. (Added t.-p.: Natuurkundige verhandelingen uitg. door het Provinciaal Utrechtsch genootschap van kunsten en wetenschappen. nieuwe reeks, 1. deel, 4. stuk)
"Eene door het Provinciaal Utrechtsch genootschap van kunsten en wetenschappen bekroonde prijsverhandeling."

1. Turbellaria.
Library of Congress AS244.U8335 22-4706

NK 0197039 DLC

Knappert (Bastiaan). *Over aangeboren hartgebreken. 4 p.l., 70 pp. 8°. *Leiden, S. van Doesberg*, 1861.

NK 0197040 DNLM PPC

RG125
.K7
Knappert, Jan.
Pituitrine-injecties bij de baring... Leiden, Gebr.van der Hoek, 1915.
[7], 107 p. 24½cm.

Proefschrift-Leiden.

1.Obstetrics. 2.Pituitary extract.

NK 0197041 ICU DNLM

Knappert, Jan, 1836-1893
The religion of Israel, a manual; tr. from the Dutch by Richard A. Armstrong. viii, 231p. London [etc.] Williams and Norgate, 1877.

From the library of the Rev. Geo. A. Thayer.

NK 0197042 OCl PU PPDrop OO MH NN WU NjPT

Knappert, Jan, 1836-1893.
The religion of Israel, a manual; translated from the Dutch of J. Knappert ... by Richard A. Armstrong, B.A. Boston, Roberts brothers, 1878.
viii, 283 p. 17cm.

1. Jews—Religion. I. Armstrong, Richard Acland, 1843-1905, tr. II. Title.

MH NcD OClW CtY
NK 0197043 ViU CU NcU NIC PPPD PPDrop MiU OCH ICU

OE25
K727b
Knappert, Laurentius, 1863-1943.
De beteekenis van de wetenschap van het folklore voor de godsdienstgeschiedenis onderzocht en aan de holda-mythen getoetst. Amsterdam, D.B. Centen, 1887.
xvi, 272 p. 22 cm.

Akademisch proefschrift - Amsterdam.
Bibliographical footnotes.

NK 0197044 CtY-D MH ICU CU

BL
870
H9
K57
Knappert, Laurentius.
De beteekenis van de wetenschap van het folklore voor de godsdienstgeschiedenis onderzocht en aan de Holda-Mythen gestoetst door Dr. L. Knappert. Amsterdam, D. B. Centen, 1887.
xi, 272 p. 23cm.

1. Huldar saga. 2. Folk-lore. 3. Religion, Primitive. 4. Mythology.

NK 0197045 NIC

AGA
K727b
Knappert, Laurentius, 1863-1943.
Bibliografische inleiding tot de theologie; een beredeneerde boekenlijst samengesteld ten dienste van predikanten, theologische studenten, openbare leeszalen en bibliotheken. Leiden, A.W. Sijthoff [1924]
149 p. 25 cm.

1. Theology - Bibl. 2. Bibliography - Theology.

NK 0197046 CtY-D WaU

LL56
K727g
Knappert, Laurentius, 1863-1943.
De Gereformeerde kerk aan den arbeid 1657-1672. Leiden, E.J. Brill, 1913.
72 p. 25 cm.

Bibliographical footnotes.

1. Nederlandse Hervormde Kerk. 2. Netherlands - Church history.

NK 0197047 CtY-D

VOLUME 300

Knappert, Laurentius, 1863-
Geschiedenis der hervormde kerk onder de republiek en het koningrijk der Nederlanden ... door prof. dr. L. Knappert. Amsterdam, Meulenhoff & co., 1911-12.
2 v. fronts., ports. 24½cm.
Each vol. has also special t.-p.
"Geillustreerd onder toezicht van E. W. Moes."
CONTENTS.—Vol. I. Geschiedenis der Nederlandsche hervormde kerk gedurende de 16e en 17e eeuw.—Vol. II. Geschiedenis der Nederlandsche hervormde kerk gedurende de 18e en 19e eeuw.
1. Nederlandsche hervormde kerk—Hist. 2. Netherlands—Church hist.

ICN NN
NK 0197048 MiU ICMcC MH NjPT MH-AH CBPac CU CtY-D

4F 290 Knappert, Laurentius, 1863-
Geschiedenis van de Nederlandsche Bovenwindsche eilanden in de 18de eeuw. 's-Gravenhage, M. Nijhoff, 1932.
308 p.

NK 0197049 DLC-P4 NN NNC CU IEN FU ICU CtY-D

Knappert, Laurentius, 1863-1943
Godsdienstig Nederland, door L.Knappert. Huis ter Heide, N.V.Uitgevers-mij.De Wachttoren, 1928
228 p. (Het handboek; bibliotheek van wetenschappelijke geschriften over den godsdienst)
1. Netherlands - Religion

NK 0197050 MH

Knappert, Laurentius, 1863- joint ed.

Molhuysen, Philip Christiaan, 1870- *ed.*
Nieuw Nederlandsch biografisch woordenboek onder redactie van dr. P. C. Molhuysen ... en prof. dr. P. J. Blok ... met medewerking van tal van geleerden ...
Leiden, A. W. Sijthoff, 1911-

LL52 K727o Knappert, Laurentius, 1863-1943.
Het ontstaan en de vestiging van het Protestantisme in de Nederlanden. Door L. Knappert. Utrecht, A. Oosthoek, 1924.
450 p. 24 cm.
Bibliographical footnotes.
1. Protestantism in the Netherlands. 2. Netherlands - Church history. 3. Sects, Medieval. 4. Reformation - Netherlands. I. Title.
1/18/68 KBB

NjNbS PSC-Hi
NK 0197052 CtY-D PU-W ICMcC CU CtY WU NcD NjPT ICU

Knappert,Laurentius,1863-
De opkomst van het Protestantisme in eene Noord-Nederlandsch stad. Geschiedenis van de hervorming binnen Leiden van den aanvang tot op het beleg,door dr.L.Knappert ,.. Met bijlage,kaart en platen. Leiden, S.C.van Doesburgh, 1908.
4 p.l.,290 p. 2 pl.,fold.map. 25cm.
"Het boek ... is ontstaan uit eenige artikelen in het Theologisch tijdschrift van 1906 en 1907."
Bibliographical foot-notes.
1.Reformation--Netherlands. 2.Leyden--Church history.

NK 0197053 MiU ViHarEM CU NjPT NcD CtY ICU MH-AH

---

946 K67p **KNAPPERT, Laurentius, 1863-1943.**
Protestantsche heldenvereering. Hillegom Uitgeversmij "Editio" [1923]
83p. illus. 16cm.

NK 0197054 MH-AH

DJ411 L5 K53 Knappert, Laurentius, 1863-1943.
De ramp van Leiden, 12 Januari 1807; na honderd jaar herdacht, door L. Knappert. Schoonhoven, S. & W. N. van Nooten, 1906.
165 p. illus., map. 22 cm.
1. Leyden - Hist. I. Title (1)

NK 0197055 CtY MH-AH

Knappert, Laurentius, 1863-
Saul, koning in Israël; treurspel in 4 bedrijven, door Dr. L. Knappert. Utrecht: W. de Haan [1920]. 71 p. 12°.
1. Saul, king of Israel.—Drama. 2. Drama (Dutch). 3. Title.
N. Y. P. L. June 28, 1922.

NK 0197056 NN

Knappert, Laurentius, 1863-

Theologisch tijdschrift ... 1.-53. jaarg.; 1867-1919. Amsterdam, Loman & Verster; [etc.] 1867-72; Leiden, S. C. van Doesbrugh, 1873-1919.

[KNAPPERT, LAURENTIUS] 1863-
Uit de geschiedenis der Groote of Latijnsche school te Leiden. [Leiden, 1903] p. [93]-139. 19cm.
Caption-title.
Signed: L. Knappert.
1. Education—Netherlands—Leiden. I. Title.

NK 0197058 NN

---

943 Ref Box 1 [KNAPPERT, Laurentius, 1863-1943.
Uit de Geschiedenis der Hervorming te Antwerpen [Brussel, Evangelisatie-Drukkerij, 1926?]
16p. 21.5cm.
Toespraak te Antwerpen op 27 Mei 1926. De Ned. Gustaaf-Adolf-Vereeniging en het Wezen van het Protestantsch geloof, by H.M. van Nes: pp.12-16.

NK 0197059 MH-AH

Knappert, Laurentius, 1863-
...Uit het Leidsche volksleven in den anvang der 16de eeuw...Leiden, E. J. Brill, 1905.
1 p. l., 26 p. 25cm.

NK 0197060 PSC-Hi

---

943 Menn. Box 5 KNAPPERT, Laurentius, 1863-1943.
Van der vaderen lijdensmoed. Amsterdam, de Bussy [193-?]
16p. illus. 21.5cm. (Doopsgezinden in de verstrooiing, Geschriftjes, 56)
Cover title.
"2e uitgave van no. 23."

NK 0197061 MH-AH

GT 3254 .K67 KNAPPERT,LAURENTIUS
Van sterven en begraven. [Baarn, Hollandia-Drukkerij, 1909]
47 p. (Uit onzen bloeitijd; schetsen van het leven onzer vaderen in de 17e eeuw, serie I, no. 3)
1. Funeral rites and ceremonies--Netherlands. I. Title.

NK 0197062 InU

923.1492 W699K Knappert, Laurentius, 1863-
Willem I, prins van Oranje, een vader des vaderlands. Haarlem, H. D. Tjeenk Willink, 1933.
90 p. port. 22 cm.
Bibliographical footnotes.
1. Willem I, prince of Orange, 1533-1584.

NK 0197063 NcD

Knappert, Laurentius, 1863-1943
Het zedelijk leven onzer vaderen in de achttiende eeuw. Haarlem, Tjeenk Willink, 1910
159 p.

NK 0197064 MH

Knappertsbusch, W Gustav, 1886-
Die Knappertsbusch und ihre Vorfahren. Elberfeld, 1943
385 p. illus.

NK 0197065 MH

Knappett, Rachel.
... A pullet on the midden. London, M. Joseph ltd. [1946]
212 p. front. (port.) 21cm.
"First published 1946."
1. Country life — England — Lancashire. 2. Agriculture — England — Lancashire. I. Title.
46-18006
Library of Congress S521.K56
[3] 630.1

NK 0197066 DLC

Knappett, Rachel.
A pullet on the midden. London, M. Joseph ltd. [1946, 1953]
191 p. 20 cm. (Mermaid books)
"First published 1946."

NK 0197067 LU

VOLUME 300

Knappett, Rachel.
Wait now! London, Joseph [1952]
208 p. illus. 21 cm.

1. Ireland—Descr. & trav. I. Title.

DA977.K55 52-31382 ‡

NK 0197068 DLC MH NN

Knappich (Franz). * Historische Skizze über die Influenz. 16 pp. 8°. *München, J. G. Weiss,* 1854.

NK 0197069 DNLM

Knappich, Jacob.
40155 Die Herstellung, Aufbewahrung und Verwendung von Acetylengas und Lagerung von Carbid. Erläuterungen zur Kgl. bayerischen allerhöchsten Verordnung vom 22. Juni 1901, G. und V. Bl. 30 vom 26. Juni 1901. Von Jacob Knappich .... Halle a. S., C. Marhold., 1902.
vi, 129, v p. 20 illus. 24cm.

NK 0197070 ICJ

Knappich, Sigmund, gepr. Rechtsprakt.: Wandelung und Minderung beim Werkvertrag. Erlangen 1912: Jacob. VII, 152 S. 8°
Erlangen, Jur. Diss. v. 11. März 1912, Ref. Siber
[Geb. 2. Febr. 83 Traunstein; Wohnort: München; Staatsangeh.: Bayern; Vorbildung: Gymn. Freising Reife Juli 03; Studium: Freising Lyz. 1, München 5, Erlangen 2 S.; Rig. 18. Dez. 11.] [U 12. 863

NK 0197071 ICRL NN NIC

Knappich, Wilhelm.
...Die Astrologie im Weltbild der Gegenwart; eine kritische Untersuchung. Villach, M. Stadler, 1948. 107 p. 21cm.

Bibliography, p. 99-107.

1. Astrology.

NK 0197072 NN

Knappich, Wilhelm.
Der Mensch im Horoskop; Versuch einer Charakter- und Lebenslaufdeutung auf Grund der symbolischen Astrologie. Villach, M. Stadler [1951]
215 p. illus. 20 cm.
Bibliography: p. 191-192.

1. Astrology.

A 53-8611

Harvard Univ. Library for Library of Congress [2]

NK 0197073 MH

Knappitsch, H., ed.

Verein der ärzte in Steiermark, *Gratz.*
Mittheilungen des Vereines der ärzte in Steiermark ...

Graz. 18

Knappius, Georg Christian
see Knapp, Georg Christian, 1753-1825.

Knappmann, Arthur
Ein beitrag zum morphinismus. ... (Auszug)
Inaug. Diss. - Kiel, 1925.

NK 0197076 ICRL

Knapp's family record ...
see under Knapp, Albert Eaton, 1810-

Knapp's liberator. v. 1, no. 1. Boston, 1842.
[4] p. 46 cm.
Editor: Isaac Knapp.
No more published?

NK 0197078 RPB

Knappschafts-berufsgenossenschaft.
Bericht über die verwaltung der Knappschafts-berufsgenossenschaft ...
Berlin,
v. tables (part fold.) diagrs. (part col.) 29cm. (Beilage zu "Der Kompass" ... jahrg. Organ der Knappschafts-berufsgenossenschaft für das Deutsche Reich)

I. Der Kompass. Supplement.

16-17011

Library of Congress HD7177.M6A2

NK 0197079 DLC

KNAPPSCHAFTS-BERUFSGENOSSENSCHAFT.
Die rechtsverhältnisse der ausländer in der reichsgesetzlichen unfallversicherung. I. Die rechtsverhältnisse der ausländer in der reichsgesetzlichen unfallversicherung. II. Die besonderen rechtsverhältnisse bei den Saarländern. III. Die fürsorge des Reichs für versicherte aus den abgetrennten gebieten. Bochum, 1936.
pp.14+151. Tables, forms.

NK 0197080 MH-L

Knappschafts-Berufsgenossenschaft
49767
Statistik der Knappschafts-Berufsgenossenschaft für das Deutsche Reich über die in der Zeit vom 1. Oktober 1885 bis 1. Januar 1895 vorgekommenen 31679 entschädigungspflichtigen Betriebsunfälle. Bearbeitet im Centralbureau der Knappschafts-Berufsgenossenschaft zu Berlin. Herausgegeben vom Genossenschaftsvorstande. Mit 1 geographischen Karte und 4 Tafeln im Anhange, sowie 8 graphischen Darstellungen im Text. Berlin, 1897.
[4], 160 p. diagrs., v pl. (fold. map, diagrs.) 29½ x 22½cm.
Slip pasted over imprint reads: C. Heymanns Verlag.

NK 0197081 ICJ MH

Knappschafts-verein der königlichen saline zu Dürrenberg.
FOR OTHER EDITIONS SEE MAIN ENTRY

Prussia. *Oberbergamt in Halle.*
Statistische uebersicht über die 13 knappschaftsvereine im oberbergamtsbezirk Halle a/Saale für die jahre 1867–1874. [Halle a/S.? 1875]

Knappstein (H. L.) Special-Geschäft in Projectirung und Ausführung von Warmwasser-Heizungs-Anlagen für Gewächshäuser, Kirchen, Wohnhäuser, etc. 36 pp. 8°. *Bochum, Märx,* [1882].

NK 0197083 DNLM

JF1525 .P8I5

Knappstein, Karl Heinrich.

Institut zur Förderung Öffentlicher Angelegenheiten.
Die Beziehungen zwischen Presse und Behörden; Bericht über eine Arbeitstagung. Mit Referaten von Karl Heinrich Knappstein, Fritz Sänger [und] Theodor Eschenburg. Frankfurt am Main, 1950.

KNAPS, Fritz.
Der strafschutz des deutschen volkes vor ehrenkränkenden gedankenäusserungen. Würzburg, R.Mayr, 1937.
pp.(8)+70+(1). 8°.
Inaug.-diss. --- München.

NK 0197085 MH-L

The **Knapsack** ... no. 1–7; Dec. 14–21, 1863. **Boston, C. D. Palmer & S. S. Preston, 1863.**
1 v. 41cm. daily (except Sunday)
"Devoted to the interests of the New England sanitary commission fair."
No more published.

1. Boston. New England sanitary commission fair, 1863. I. United States sanitary commission.

Library of Congress E632.B78 27-14521

NK 0197086 DLC MB

The **Knapsack**...
v. 1

Cincinnati [etc.] Boys' brigade press, 1892– 23 – 40cm.
v. illus. (incl. music.)
Weekly (slightly irregular), Dec. 10, 1892 – July 29, 1893; monthly (irregular), Aug. 1893 –
Vol. 5, no. 11 (Dec., 1896), incorrectly called no. 12; v. 6, no. 4 (April, 1897), incorrectly called v. 7.

Published for the United boys' brigades of America (Dec. 10, 1892 – Sept., 1894, Boys' brigades of the United States <Jan. 13–21, 1893, adds: and Dominion of Canada>; Oct., 1894 – Feb., 1896, Boys' brigades of America).
Absorbed the Boys' brigade bulletin in Oct., 1893; the Boys' brigade standard, Baptist b. b. sentinel and Connecticut picket in Oct., 1894.
Title varies: v. 1–3, no. 9 (Dec. 10, 1892 – Sept., 1894, Boys' brigade courier; v. 3, no. 10 – v. 7, no. 6 (Oct., 1894 – The Knapsack.

NK 0197088 NN

E 172 K 65

The Knapsack. v. 1, no. 1; June 1928
v. 1, no. 3-[5]; Aug. - Oct. 1928.
[Madison, Wisconsin, 1928-
1 v. illus. 26 cm.
"A monthly bulletin issued by the Patriotic commission, G.A.R. rooms, the capitol, Madison, Wisconsin."
Vol.1, no. 5 erroneously called no. 4.

NK 0197089 DLC

The Knapsack.

[Koppke, Georgenia Josephine Luke]
The jolly raftsman on the Wisconsin, by George Nye [pseud.] The Knapsack ed. Madison, Wis., Mayer printing company [°1929]

Cc3 0412p

The Knapsack.
New Haven, Conn.
illus. 29½cm.

Caption title.
Published for one week before and on each day of the Fair week, under the auspices of the General committee of citizens and members of the Grand army, Admiral Foote post, no.17, New Haven, Conn.
"The Fair is given for the benefit of the poor and disabled veterans of the late war."

NK 0197091 CtY

VOLUME 300

q606.1 N48NAk The Knapsack; a daily journal of the Seventh regiment new armory fair. v.1, no.1-18; Nov. 17-Dec.6,1879. New York, 1879.
1v. illus.

Vol.1 [no.16] erroneously called v.1,no.15.
No more published.

1. Exhibitions--Period. I. New York. Seventh regiment new armory fair.

NK 0197092 IU CU-A ICRL CSmH DLC CSmH NN RPB OClWHi OCf

KNAPSACK. Oakland, Cal. Contra Costa Hills Club.

NK 0197093 NhD

The **Knapsack.** no. I-II; Oct. 24-Nov. 4, 1865. [Philadelphia, 1865.
66, [2] p. 30cm. daily except Sunday. [With Our daily fare. Philadelphia, 1864-65]

Journal of the Soldiers' and sailors' home fair.
R. Fitzgerald, editor.
No more published.

I. Philadelphia. Soldiers' and sailors' home fair, 1865. II. Fitzgerald, Riter, ed.

1—27278

Library of Congress E632.P65 [a41b1]

NK 0197094 DLC NcD IHi PU PPL P NhD PU NN MB PP MH MB N

The Knapsack; a collection of original short stories
see under Fire underwriters' association of the Pacific.

Rare Book Room Uzn10 K62 The Knapsack: the field, the farm, the garden, the turf, hunting, coursing, archery ... Illustrated in gallitype. v.1, no.1-6; July-Dec. 1859. [London] "The Review office" [1859] 1v. plates. 22½cm. monthly.

Cover-title.
The section "Turf register for 1859" has separate pagination.
No more published?

NK 0197096 CtY

Knapsack and rifle; or, Life in the Grand Army ...
see under [Patrick, Robert W.]

K726 The knapsack full of fun; or, 1000 rations of laughter. Illustrated with over 500 comic engravings. New York, Dick & Fitzgerald [187-?]
64 p. illus. 28cm.

1. American wit and humor.

NK 0197098 NNC

Knapsack guide for travellers in Italy
see under Murray, John, publisher, London

Knapsack guide to Norway
see under Murray, John, publisher, London.

Bonaparte Collection No. 12,848 Knapski, Grzegorz, 1564-1638

Słownik polsko-łacinski... Przez... Benedykta Woronowskiego pomnozony. W Kaliszu,1787. 3v.

NK 0197101 ICN

Bonaparte Collection No. 12,815 Knapski, Grzegorz, 1564-1638

Synonima; sev, Dictionarivm polonolatinvm. In gratiam & vsum studiosæ iuuentutis polonæ, ex Thesauro Gregorii Cnapii...collectum. 5.ed., multis vocabulis correctum & auctum... Cracoviæ, 1662.

NK 0197102 ICN

Bonaparte Collection No. 12,816 Knapski, Grzegorz, 1564-1638

Synonyma; seu, Dictionarium polonolatinum. In gratiam & usum studiosæ iuventutis polonæ. Ex Thesauro Gregorii Cnapii... Secundo collectum & recusum. Calissi,1698.

NK 0197103 ICN

KNAPSKI, GRZEGORZ, 1564-1638.
Synonyma seu Dictionarium polono-latinum in gratiam & usum studiosae iuventutis polonae, nuper correctum & multis vocabulis auctum. Cracoviae, Typis academicis, 1722. 420 p. 17cm.

1. Polish language-- Dictionaries, Latin. I. Title.

NK 0197104 NN

Bonaparte Collection No. 12,817 Knapski, Grzegorz, 1564-1639

...Thesaurus latino-polono-germanicus, novo synonymorum et phrasium poeticarum apparatu auctus; nec non innumeris latinis, polonicis ac germanicis vocabulis locupletatus per admodum R. P. Paulum Kollacz... Varsaviæ,1780.

NK 0197105 ICN

PG7124 .K67 Rare Bk Knapski, Grzegorz, 1564-1638.
Thesauri Polono-Latino-Graeci Gregorii Cnapii ... Tomus tertius. Continens Adagia Polonica selecta et sententias morales ac dicteria faceta, honesta, Latine et Graece reddita, quibus, praesertim obscurioribus, addita est lux et interpretatio ex varijs auctoribus, ac multiplex eruditio passim inspersa... Cracoviae, Typis F. Caesarij, 1632.
1388 p. 21 cm.
Imperfect: t.p. and all after p.1370 wanting; title supplied from Estreicher, K. Bibl. polska, t.19, p.337.
1. Proverbs, Polish.

NK 0197106 ICU NjP MH

Bonaparte Colle. No.1670 Knapski, GREGORIUS, 1564-1638.
Thesavrvs Polonolatinogræcvs, sev, Promptvarivm lingvæ latinæ et graecæ, in tres tomos diuisum. Polonorum, Roxolanorum, Sclauonum, Boëmorum vsui accomodatum... Editio secunda... Accessit index latinus...plenissimus... Tertia pars adagia continebat... [Tomus I] Cracoviae,Typis & sumptu F.Caesarij,1643.
1465p.

NK 0197107 ICN

Knapstein, Adam

——. Sind Atropin und Morphin Antidote? Neue Versuche, nebst einer Abfertigung der Angriffe des Herrn Dr. Hans Heubuch. 28 pp. 8°. *Bonn, E. Tschiersky*, 1879.

NK 0197108 DNLM

Knapstein (Adam). *Ueber die gleichzeitige Wirkung von Atropin und Morphium. 51 pp. 8°. *Bonn, J. F. Carthaus*, [1878].

NK 0197109 DNLM

Knapton, Ernest John.
France since Versailles. New York, Holt [1952]
120 p. 19 cm. (Berkshire studies in European history)

1. France—Hist.—20th cent. I. Title.

DC389.K5 944.08 52—7016 ‡

NK 0197110 DLC MeB CoU CaBVaU CaBViP OCU MiU ScU ViU NN TxU PSt PU MiHM ScCleA TU NIC MtBC MtU OrPS

KNAPTON,Ernest John.
The Holy Alliance: a retrospect. n.p., [1941].

25 cm. pp.(12).
"Offprint from Queen's Quarterly,vol.XLVIII, no.2,1941."

NK 0197111 MH

Knapton, Ernest John.
The lady of the Holy alliance; the life of Julie de Krüdener, by Ernest John Knapton. New York, Columbia university press, 1939.
ix p., 3 l., [3]-262 p. front., plates, ports. 24cm.
Bibliography: p. [231]-250.

1. Krüdener, Barbara Juliane (von Vietinghoff) freifrau von, 1764-1824. 2. Holy alliance. I. Title.

39-14081

Library of Congress CT1218.K7K6
——— Copy 2.
Copyright A 129513 [4] 920.7

NK 0197112 DLC MtU IdU OrU OOxM PU PPT PSC MU OO OClW OU ViU MtU WaSp MeB NIC MsU TU CU WaSpG WaU

Case Y 135 .T 188 KNAPTON, JAMES, d.1738.
Books printed for James Knapton, at the Crown in St. Paul's Church-Yard. [London, 1704]
[2]l. 23cm.

In: Taverner, William. The faithful bride of Granada ... 1704.

205290

NK 0197113 ICN

VOLUME 300

W.C.L. Knapton, Philip, 1788-1833.
M780.88
E58I Caller herring; a favorite Scotch air. Arr. with variations as a duet for the harp
no.18 & piano forte. London, Printed by Goulding, D'Almaine, Potter & Co. [ca. 1810]
parts. 34 cm.
[No.18] in a collection of harp and piano music with binder's title: Music.

1. Harp and piano music. 2. Music, Scottish. I. Title.

NK 0197114 NcD

KNAPTON, PHILIP, 1788-1833.

Caller Herring, a favorite Scotch air; arranged with variations as a duet for the harp & piano forte. London, Goulding, D'Almaine, Potter [ca. 1818] 5 p. 33cm.

Part for harp only.

1. Folk songs, Scottish (Instrumental settings). I. Title.

NK 0197115 NN

KNAPTON, PHILIP, 1788-1833.

Four songs and two duets; the poetry by Major Aldington the melodies compos'd by an amateur. Arranged with symphonies and an accompaniment for the piano forte, by Philip Knapton. London, Goulding [181-?] 19 p. 32cm.

"Publish 'd for the benefit of the York charity schools."

CONTENTS.--Great Britain.--May.--The merry toned horn (duet)--The soldier's farewell.--Morning.--Music (duet)

1. Songs, English. 2. Vocal duos, Secular (Women)--Keyboard acc. 3. Vocal duos, Secular (Mixed)--Keyboard acc. I. Aldington, Maj. II. An amateur.

NK 0197117 NN

Knapton, Philip, 1788–1833.
Mrs. Macdonald. A favorite Scotch air, with variations & an introduction, composed... by Philip Knapton... London: Goulding, D'Almaine, Potter & C°. [ca. 1820.] 7p. f°.

1. Piano.—Variations.
N. Y. P. L. November 10, 1921.

NK 0197118 NN

Knapton, Philip, 1788-
Mrs. Macdonald; a Scotch air with variations and an introduction. Philadelphia, G. E. Blake. [between 1823 and 1826]
9 p. 34 cm.
Cover title.
For piano.

1. Variations (Piano) 2. Folk-songs, Scottish (Instrumental settings) I. Title.
M1.A13K 72-216528
[M27] [M1747] [M5120]

NK 0197119 DLC NcD MB

KNAPTON, PHILIP, 1788-1833.

Swiss air with variations, for the harp & piano forte. London, Chappell [ca. 1816] Pl. no. 725. 7 p. 33cm.

Part for harp only.

1. Folk songs, Swiss (Instrumental settings). I. Title.

NK 0197120 NN

Knaresborough, Henry Meysey Meysey-Thompson, 1st baron, 1845–
Address, by Sir Henry M. Meysey-Thompson, bart., at the bimetallic conference, Manchester, 4th April, 1888. Manchester: The Bimetallic League, 1888. 11 p. 8°.

Cover-title.

1. Bimetallism.
N. Y. P. L. November 20, 1922.

NK 0197121 NN

Knaresborough, Henry Meysey Meysey-Thompson, 1st baron, 1845–
Bimetallism. Speech, by Sir Henry M. Meysey-Thompson, bart., at the conference of the Bimetallic League, held at Manchester, 4th and 5th April, 1888. Manchester: Guardian Prtg. Works, 1888. 12 p. 8°.

1. Bimetallism.
N. Y. P. L. November 22, 1922.

NK 0197122 NN CtY

Knaresborough, Henry Meysey Meysey-Thompson, *1st baron,* 1845–
... Bi-metallism. Speech by Sir H. Meysey-Thompson ... in moving a resolution urging the re-assembly of the International monetary conference ... 28th February, 1893. Extracted from "The Parliamentary debates, authorised ed." London, Eyre and Spottiswoode [1893]
16 p. 25cm.

1. Bimetallism. 2. International monetary conference, Brussels, 1892.
6—43203
Library of Congress HG942.K6

NK 0197123 DLC CtY MH-BA NN ICJ

Knaresborough, Henry Meysey Meysey-Thompson, *1st baron,* 1845–
Catalogue of the valuable library of Sir Henry & Lady Meysey-Thompson, collected almost entirely by the late Colonel Shipperdson, of Durham, comprising romances of chivalry; ancient Spanish, French and European chronicles; early histories; voyages and travels; rare & early editions of the Greek & Latin classics; English county histories; and works of general interest. Which will be sold by auction, by Messrs. Sotheby, Wilkinson & Hodge ... 28th of April, 1887, and four following days ... London, J. Davy and sons [1887]
1 p. l., 121 p. 22½cm.
1785 lots.
I. Shipperdson, ——.
Library of Congress Z997.K698 10-3460

NK 0197124 DLC MH

Knaresborough, Henry Meysey-Thompson, 1st baron, 1845–
In memoriam. The late Sir Harry Stephen Meysey-Thompson
see under title

Knaresborough, Henry Meysey Meysey-Thompson, *1st baron,* 1845–
Letter (with appendix), addressed to the members of the International monetary conference, by Sir Henry Meysey-Thompson, 1892. York, Printed by the Yorkshire herald newspaper compy., limited, 1892.
13 p. 23cm.

1. Bimetallism. 2. Currency question. 3. International monetary conference, Brussels, 1892.
10-8608
Library of Congress HG405.K6

NK 0197126 DLC CtY

Knaresborough, Henry Meysey Meysey-Thompson, *1st baron,* 1845–
The silver question. Inquiry to British trade and manufactures. The paper by George Jamieson ... which won the bimetallic prize offered by Sir Henry M. Meysey-Thompson in 1894; together with two other papers on the same subject, by Thomas Holyoake Box ... and David Octavius Croal ... Also a preface and sequel by Sir Henry M. Meysey-Thompson ... London, E. Wilson, 1895.
2 p. l., v, 75 p. 24cm.
1. Bimetallism. 2. Currency question—Gt. Brit. I. Jamieson, George. II. Box, Thomas Holyoake. III. Croal, David Octavius. IV. Title.
6—43202
Library of Congress HG941.K6

NK 0197127 DLC IEN CU-S NjP MeWC

Knaresborough, Henry Meysey Mensey- Thompson, 1st baron, 1845-
The Transvaal crisis: remarks on the present condition of affairs, together with a reprint of an article by him...on the "Real grievances of the Uitlanders London, 1898.

NK 0197128 PPL

Knaresborough, Henry Meysey Meysey-Thompson, 1st baron, 1845–
The Transvaal crisis. By Sir Henry Meysey-Thompson, bart... Remarks on the present condition of affairs. Together with a reprint of an article by him in the "Nineteenth century" review on the "Real grievances of the Uitlanders." London: S. Low, Marston & Co., 1899. 30 p. 4°.

1. Transvaal.—History, 1899.
N. Y. P. L. November 20, 1922.

NK 0197129 NN MH

Knaresborough, Lucius Smith, bp. of
see Smith, Lucius, bp. of Knaresborough, 1860-

Knaresborough, Philip Albert Inman, *baron Inman of*
see **Inman, Philip Albert Inman,** *baron,* 1892–

Knaresborough (*Honor*)
Wills & administrations from the Knaresborough court rolls. Durham, Published for the Society by Andrews & co.; [etc., etc.] 1902–05.
2 v. 23cm. (*Half-title:* The publications of the Surtees society ... vol. CIV, CX)
T.-p. of v. 2: ... With index to original wills, &c., at Somerset house. Ed. by Francis Collins, M. D.

1. Wills—Knaresborough, Eng. I. Collins, Francis, ed.
5—41908
Library of Congress DA20.S9

NK 0197129-1 DLC OU MH-L WaU-L PP PBm PU NN MB MH PPPD

Knaresborough, Eng. (Parish)
The Catholic registers of Knaresborough, 1765–1840. Contributed by T. G. Cummins, G. F. Engelbach and J. S. Hansom. Historical notes by the Rt. Rev. Abbot Cummins, O.S.B. (*In* Catholic Record Society. Publications. Vol. 22. Miscellanea, 12, pp. 220–275. London. 1921.)

This card was printed at the Boston Public Library, February 4, 19—.
M3463 — Hansom, Joseph Stanislaus, comp. — Engelbach, George Frederick, comp. — Cummins, John Ildefonsus, abbot, O.S.B., ed. — Registers. Parish. Knaresborough, Yorkshire, England.— Cummins, Thomas George, comp.

NK 0197129-2 MB

VOLUME 300

Knaresborough, Eng. (Parish)

Harrogate, *Eng.*
Records of Harrogate, including the register of Christ church (1748–1812), with supplementary extracts from Knaresborough (1560–1753), notes on the pre-reformation chantry & the early history of the waters, early inhabitants, and extracts from the parish accounts of Pannal, Knaresborough and Clint, and from court rolls, quarter sessions rolls and muster rolls, transcribed, ed. and indexed by Walter J. Kaye ... with six illustrations. Leeds, F. J. Walker; [etc., etc.] 1922.

Knaresbrough, Eng. (Parish) -9 -28
Select portions of Psalms, for the use of the parish church of Knaresbrough. Knaresbrough, 1823
see under Bible. O. T. Psalms. English. Paraphrases. 1823.

Knarf, Elivas, pseud.
See
Savile, Frank Mackenzie.

Knarr, Carl, bacc. iur.: Der Namensschutz nach § 12 B.G.B. Boxhagen-Rummelsburg 1909: Herrgott. 59 S. 8°
Leipzig, Jur. Diss. v. 13. April 1910
[Geb. 25. Juli 80 Spandau; Wohnort: Spandau; Staatsangeh.: Preußen; Vorbildung: Gymn. Spandau Reife O. 01; Studium: Berlin 4, Göttingen 2, Berlin 1 S.; Rig. 20. Okt. 06.] [U 10. 2764

NK 0197129-3 ICRL

WB 13983 **Knarr, Peter**
Im goldige Ochse; Mundartkomödie in 3 Akten Schweizerdeutsche Bearbeitung von T. J. Felix. Aarau, A. Breuninger [.d.]

NK 0197129-4 CtY

Knatchbull, Sir Edward, 1781-1849.
The speech of Sir E. Knatchbull, bart. ... to which is added the speech of H. Bankes ... in defence of the Protestant constitution. London, 1829.
16 p.
No. 4 of a volume of pamphlets.
I. Bankes, Henry, 1757-1834.

NK 0197129-5 NjP

1659 Knatchbull, Sir Norton, Bart., 1602-1685.
ANIMADVERSIONES./ IN LIBROS/ NOVI TESTAMENTI/ Paradoxae Orthodoxae./ AUTHORE/ D. Nortono Knatchbull/ Eq. & Bar./ LONDINI,/ Typis GUIL GODBID in vico vulgo/ vocato Little Brittain, apud quem/ prostant venales. M.DC.LIX./
[6]331[5]333-385 p. 18 x 12 cm.
Wing: K668.
Provenance: Maryland Diocesan Library.
1. Bible. N.T. Commentaries. I. Title.

NK 0197130 NNG NNUT-Mc NjNbS

Rare Book Room Mhc9 K729 A7 1672 [Knatchbull, Sir Norton] 1602-1685.
Animadversiones in libros Novi Testamenti. Jam recens editae secunda cura avthoris. Londini, Typis Guil. Godbid, in vico vulgo vocato Little-Brittain, apud quem prostant venales. 1672.
3p.ℓ., 167, [1]p. 16cm.
Signatures: [A]^4([A]$_1$ blank)B-L^{8}M^4.

NK 0197131 CtY

Knatchbull, Sir Norton, bart., 1602–1685.
Animadversiones in libros Novi Testamenti jam tertiâ curâ auctæ & emendatæ. Authore D. Nortono Knatchbull, Eq. & Bar. Oxoniæ: Excudebat Henric. Hall, 1677. 3 p.l., 191 p. 8°.
With this are bound: A philosophicall essay for the reunion of the langvages. Oxford, 1675. Shelton, T. Tachygraphy. London, 1671. [Lobo, J.] A short relation of the river Nile. London, 1673.

HOWARD SHORTHAND COLL.
225449A. 1. Bible. N. T.—Commentaries. N. Y. P. L. February 5, 1926

NK 0197132 NN CLU-C CtY RPB

Knatchbull, Sir Norton, 1602-1685.
Animadversiones in libros Novi Testamenti. Per Nortonum Knatchbull ... Jam pluribus locis auctæ & emendatæ tertiâ curâ authoris. Francofurti ad Moenum, typis & impensis J.P. Andreæ, 1701.
157p. 17cm. [Bound with Varenius, Augustus. Paulus ... Epistolæ ad Romanos, analysi et exegesi. Hamburgi, 1696]

NK 0197133 NNUT

WILLIAM ANDREWS CLARK MEMORIAL LIBRARY
Knatchbull, Sir Norton, bart., 1602-1685.
Annotations upon some difficult texts in all the books of the New Testament. By Sr Norton Knatchbull kt & bart. Cambridge, Printed by J. Hayes ... for W. Graves ... 1693.
8 p.l., 320 p. 20cm.
Signatures: A-X^8 (A6, verso, advertisements)
Page 253 incorrectly numbered 153.
Title within double line border.
Translation of the author's Animadversiones in libris Novis Testamenti.
Bound in half calf.

NK 0197134 CLU-C CtY PPL ICU CU IU DLC MdBJ CU-A FU TxDaM

B 1827 491* Knatchbull, Sir Norton, bart., 1602-1685.
The library of Sir Norton Knatchbull ... To which is annex'd, an appendix of antient and modern manuscripts, Italian and French prints, pieces of fine writing and medals. Collected by another gentleman. All which will be sold by auction at Tom's coffee house, adjoyning to Ludgate. The sale to begin on Wednesday the 22d of this instant June, at three afternoon. By J. Bullord ...
[London, 1698]
4°. 2p.ℓ., 20, 17-30p., 1ℓ., 13p. 23cm.

NK 0197135 MH

PJ7696 .H3M8 1820 **Knatchbull, Wyndham, 1786–1868 ed. and tr.**

al-Hārith ibn Ḥillizah, *6th cent.*
Harethi Moallakah, cum scholiis Zouzenii, e codice manuscripto Arabico edidit, vertit et illustravit Wyndham Knatchbull. Oxonii, E Typographeo Clarendoniano, 1820.

Knatchbull, Wyndham, 1786-1868, tr.
Kalila and Dimna, or, The fables of Bidpaī see under Bīdpāī.

Knatchbull-Hugessen, Adrian
see
Hugessen, Adrian Knatchbull, 1891–

Knatchbull-Hugessen, Cecil Marcus, *4th baron Brabourne*
see
Brabourne, Cecil Marcus Knatchbull-Hugessen, *4th baron*, 1863–

Knatchbull-Hugessen, Edward Hugessen, *1st baron Brabourne*
see
Brabourne, Edward Hugessen Knatchbull-Hugessen, *1st baron*, 1829-1893.

Knatchbull - Hugessen, Eva Mary, 1861 - 1895
A hit and a miss...London, 1893.

NK 0197141 PPL

Knatchbull-Hugessen, Eva Mary. 1861—.
Newnham College from within. 14 pp. (*Nineteenth Cent.* v. 21, 1887, p. 843.)

NK 0197142 MdBP

PZ7 .K725 Sat **Knatchbull-Hugessen, Eva Mary, 1861-1895**
The satellite and other stories, by the Hon. Eva Knatchbull-Hugessen. London, A. D. Innes and co., 1894.
315, [1] p. front. 17 1/2cm.
Contents:—The satellite.—The story of the 'Smite-them-hip-and-thigh.—Geof.—Fräulein Schmitt.
I. Title.

NK 0197143 MB

Knatchbull-Hugessen, Sir Hughe Montgomery
see **Hugessen, Sir Hughe Montgomery Knatchbull**, 1886–

Knatchbull-Hugessen, Kenneth Wyndham
see
Hugessen, Kenneth Wyndham Knatchbull, 1925–1942.

Knatchbull - Hugessen, Wyndham Wentworth, *3d baron Brabourne*
see
Brabourne, Wyndham Wentworth Knatchbull-Hugessen, *3d baron*, 1885–1915.

Knaths, Charlotte: Der Magnetismus einiger Nickelsalze in verdünnten Lösungen. Halle a. S. 1913: Kaemmerer. 68 S., 4 Taf. 8°
Halle, Phil. Diss. v. 28. Juli 1913, Ref. Dorn
[Geb. 15. Sept. 83 Leopoldshall; Wohnort: Halle a. S.; Staatsangeh.: Preußen; Vorbildung: RG. Halberstadt Reife 09; Studium: Berlin 1, Halle 1, Berlin 2, Halle 2 S.; Rig. 17. Febr. 13.] [U 13. 3608

NK 0197147 ICRL PU MH CtY

VOLUME 300

Knaths, Erwin, 1904-
Die entwicklung des Berliner droschkenführwesens unter besonderer beruecksichtigung seiner motorisierung.
Inaug. diss. Marburg, 1929.
Bibl.

NK 0197148 ICRL CtY PU MH

Knattspyrnufélag Reykjavíkur. Félagsblað. Ritstjóri og ábyrgðarmaður: Kristján L. Gestsson. 1. árg., 1. tbl. Febrúar 1932. Reykjavík. 4°. +IcN9K671

NK 0197149 NIC

Ic N9 K672 [Knattspyrnufélag Reykjavíkur]
KR 50 ára. 1899-1949. Reykjavík, Knattspyrnufélag Reykjavíkur, 1949.
96 p. illus. 25cm. (Félags-blað KR. 10. árg., Marz 1949, Afmælisútgáfa)
Cover title.

NK 0197150 NIC

Knattspyrnulög gefin út af Íþróttafjelagi Reykjavíkur. Reykjavík, 1907. 12°. pp. 23. IcL4K672
Covertitle.

NK 0197151 NIC

Knattspyrnulög
Gefin út af Íþróttasambandi Íslands. Með 22 myndum af rangstöðu- og réttstöðureglunum. 1. útgáfa. Reykjavík, 1916. 8°. pp. 56 + (2). IcL4K673
This translation from the edition of June 13, 1914, of The International Board's rules, is made by Ben. G. Waage.

NK 0197152 NIC

N7765 .P36K7 Knatz, Friedrich Heinrich Karl, 1868-
Qvomodo Persei fabvlam artifices Graeci et Romani tractaverint ... Bonnae, typis C. Georgi, 1893.
63, [2] p. 21cm.
Inaug.-diss.—Bonn.
Vita.

1. Perseus. 2. Art, Greco-Roman.

NK 0197153 ICU PU CU MH NN NjP MiU

LK74.1 K67 Knatz, Jean
Vaudois et Taborites; essai sur leurs rapports ... Genève, Impr.M.Richter, 1889.
98p.,1l. 24cm.
Thèse - Faculté de théologie protestante de Montauban, 1889.

NK 0197154 NNUT

Knatz (Karl Heinrich). *Ueber Doppelmissbildungen. 26 pp., 1 pl. 8°. Marburg, C. L. Pfeil, 1856.

NK 0197155 DNLM

Knatz, Karlernst, 1882- comp.
Aus Goethes Sonnentagen...
see under Goethe, Johann Wolfgang von, 1749-1832.
Poems.

Knatz, Karlernst, 1882-
Der polterabend im hause Soeter, kriminal-roman von Karlernst Knatz. Stuttgart, J. Engelhorns nachf., 1924.
143, [1] p. 18cm.

I. Title.
Library of Congress PT2621.N3P6 1924 25-18606
Copyright A—Foreign 28408
[2]

NK 0197157 DLC

Knatz, Thomas, 1906-
Die kammern für handelssachen, auf geschichtlicher und rechtsvergleichender grundlage dargestellt ... 1932. 106 p.
Inaug. Diss. -Freiburg i. Br., 1932.
Lebenslauf.
Bibliography.

NK 0197158 ICRL

Knau, Hugo, 1912-
Die erweiterung der restitutionsgründe. ... Giessen, 1938. 48 p.
Inaug. Diss. - Giessen, 1938.
Lebenslauf.
Schrifttumsverzeichnis.

NK 0197159 DLC

Knaub, André, 1892-
... Les abus et les inconvénients des injections d'huile camphrée ... Valence, 1920.
25.5 cm.
Thèse - Univ. de Lyon.

NK 0197160 CtY

KNAUBER, Alma Jordan.
Christmas decorations. Rev.ed.
[Cincinnati. Tri-state offset co.] 1946,c45-46. unp. illus.

NK 0197161 WaS

---

*C.U. B01 K67 Knauber, Alma Jordan.
The Knauber art ability test; examiners manual, by Alma Jordan Knauber ... Cincinnati, c1935.
2 v. illus. 28cm.
"Published through funds provided by the Carnegie corporation of New York in cooperation with the American federation of arts committee for research in art."
1.Art - Study and teaching. 2.Ability Testing. 3.Cincinnati. University - Publications of faculty - General. ~~Cincinnati. Univ.~~

NK 0197162 OCU OCIMA MdBJ

LB 1695 .A4 K6 Knauber, Alma Jordan.
The Knauber art ability test for junior and senior high schools, colleges, universities, and art schools, devised by Alma Jordan Knauber ... [n.p.] c1932.
Caption title.

NK 0197163 ICJ OCIMA

Knauber, Aloys, 1911-
Die unveräusserlichkeit und unbelastbarkeit des erbhofes. ... Düsseldorf, 1936. 52 p.
Inaug. Diss. - Bonn, 1936.
Lebenslauf.
Verzeichnis des schrifttums.

NK 0197164 ICRL CtY

W 4 H461 1939 Knauber, Walter, 1914-
Experimentelle Untersuchungen über die etwaige ernüchternde Wirkung von Coca-Cola. Homburg, Ermer, 1939.
29 p. illus.
Inaug.-Diss. - Heidelberg.
Bibliography: p. 24-27.

NK 0197165 DNLM

Knaudt, Franc. Philippus, respondent.
De haemorrhoidibus hodie
see under Detharding, Georg Christoph, 1699-1784, praeses.

TC439 R6K5 Knaudt, Julio.
Anotaciones sobre el Río Rocha, por Julio Knaudt. La Paz, Impr. Artística de C. Diez de Medina, 1909.
28 p. illus.
Cover title.
1. Rocha River Floods. 2. Floods control--Bolivia--Cochabamba. 3. Flood damage prevention--Bolivia--Cochabamba. I. Title.

NK 0197167 PPiU

Knaudt, M.
Des Universums Werdegang. Eine philosophisch-naturalistische Studie. Berlin: C. Wigand, 1910. 45 p. 12°.

1. Universe.
N. Y. P. L. N. Y. PUBLIC LIBRARY December 29, 1910.

NK 0197168 NN

Knauer, ------ von.
Prussia. K. Landesaufnahme. Trigonometrische abteilung.
Astronomische ortsbestimmung für die zwecke der Trigonometrischen abteilung der Landesaufnahme ... Berlin, 1909-10.

Knauer, Adalbert.
Die sieben Hauptsünden auf dem Kreuzwege Christi; kurze Betrachtungen über die vierzehn Kreuzweg-Stationen für Fastenzeit, Wallfahrt, Kreuzwegübungen, heilige Messe usw.
Mainz, Druckerei Lehrlingshaus [1908].
xxiv, 324 p. 19 cm.

NK 0197170 PLatS

Knauer, Adolf.
Erbe und Erbschaft. Berlin, Deutscher Rechtsverlag, 1939.
108 p. 21 cm. (Rechtspflege und Verwaltung, Schriftenreihe für Ausbildung und Praxis. II. Deutsche Rechtspflege, Heft 13)

1. Inheritance and succession—Germany. I. Title. (Series)
50-44864

NK 0197171 DLC MH

VOLUME 300

Knauer, Adolf.
Sippe. Berlin, Deutscher Rechtsverlag [1942]
155 p. 21 cm. (Rechtspflege und Verwaltung; Schriftenreihe für Ausbildung und Praxis. II. Deutsche Rechtspflege, Heft 12)

1. Domestic relations—Germany. I. Title.

54-51536 ‡

NK 0197172 DLC MH-L IEN CtY NNC MnU

Knauer, Adolf, 1891–
Der normative Aspekt in der pädagogischen Psychologie... von Adolf Knauer... Schramberg, Württ.: Gatzer & Hahn, 1933.
65 p. 21cm.

Inaugural-Dissertation — Tübingen, 1932.
Lebenslauf.
"Literaturnachweis," 1 p. at end.

830931A. 1. Education—Psychology.
N. Y. P. L. July 1, 1936

NK 0197173 NN PU CtY ICRL

KNAUER, Albert.
Verfügungsbeschränkungen im Grundbuchrecht. Inaug.-diss., Würzburg. Strassburg i.E., Goeller, 1911.

NK 0197174 MH-L ICRL

Knauer, Alexander.
Die höhere Gewalt im Reichsrecht. Berlin, Struppe & Winckler, 1901.
iv, 166 p. 23 cm.
Bibliographical footnotes.

1. Vis major (Civil law)—Germany. I. Title.

68-39029

NK 0197175 DLC CtY MH-L ICRL

Knauer, Alois.
Fischarts und Bernhard Schmidts anteil an der dichtung "Peter von Stauffenberg" 1588, von dr. Alois Knauer ... Reichenberg i. B., F. Kraus, 1925.
6 p. l., 71 p. 25cm. (Added t.-p.: Prager deutsche studien ... 31. hft.)
Title of the poem: Ernewerte beschreibung, der wolgedenckwürdigen alten vnd warhafften verwunderlichen geschicht. Vom herren Peter von Stauffenberg genant Diemringer, auss der Ortenau bei Rein, rittern: Was wunders jhme mit einer Meervein oder Mörfähe seie begegnet ... Strassburg, Bei Bernhard Jobin, 1588.
The author's inaugural dissertation, Prague.
"Gedruckt mit unterstützung des Ministeriums für schulwesen und volkskultur."
"Benützte bücher": prelim. leaf 5.
1. Fischart, Johann, 1550 (ca.)–1590? Peter von Stauffenberg. 2. Schmidt, Bernhard, 1535–1592. I. Title. II. Title: Peter von Stauffenberg.

26-7970

Library of Congress PD25.P7 31. hft.
[2]

NK 0197176 DLC PBm CU OCU

Knauer, Alwin
see Knauer, Erich Alwin, 1878-

Knauer (Andreas) [1874-]. *Ein Fall von Myelitis chronica. 34 pp., 1 l. 8°. München, Kastner & Lossen, 1901.

NK 0197178 DNLM

Knauer, Carl.
Beiträge zum Ausdruck von Abstraktem im Französischen.
(In Romanische Forschungen. Band 44, pp. 185-254. Erlangen. 1930.)
Verwendete Literatur, pp. 186-188.

D.9999 — Semasiology. — Abstract, The. — France. Lang. Etym.

NK 0197179 MB

Knauer, Berthe, 1910–
... Contribution à l'étude du traitement de l'abcès du poumon par la méthode de Landau ... Nimes, 1936.
Thèse - Univ. de Montpellier.
"Bibliographie": p. [28]-29.

NK 0197180 CtY

Knauer, Carl, 1909–
... Zwei Fälle von Coeliakie bei angeborener cystischer Pancreasfibromatose und congenitalen Bronchiektasien ... Zürich, 1935.
Inaug.-Diss. - Zürich.
Curriculum vitae.
"Literatur": p. 46-48.

NK 0197181 CtY

KNAUER, Charles.
Ulfila, sa vie et sa doctrine. Thèse. Strasbourg, J.H.E.Heitz, 1872.

At head of title: Faculté de théologie protestante de Strasbourg.

NK 0197182 MH

W 4
T91
1939

KNAUER, Eberhard, 1911-
Zur Frage der Verdaubarkeit von Zellen durch Trypsin. Tübingen, Bölzle, 1939.
15 p.
Cover title.
Inaug.-Diss. - Tübingen.
1. Enzymes

NK 0197183 DNLM

Knauer, Emil, 1867–
[Collected papers chiefly on gynecology and nervous diseases.]
183889

NK 0197184 ICJ

Knauer, Emil, 1867–
Der plötzliche Tod in Schwangerschaft, Geburt und Wochenbett. Von Hofrat Prof. Dr. Emil Knauer ...
(In Biologie und Pathologie des Weibes. Berlin, [etc.], 1927. 27cm. VIII. Band, 1. Teil, p. [993]-1060.)
"Literatur," p. 1055-1060.

NK 0197185 ICJ

W 4
M961
1954

KNAUER, Erich, 1925-
Verhalten des Plasma-Kaliums nach Glukose- und Fruktose-Belastungen. München, 1954.
48 l. illus.
Inaug.-Diss. - Munich.
1. Blood - Chemistry 2. Potassium

NK 0197186 DNLM

Knauer, Erich Alwin, 1878–
... Kann der dünndarm sterinsauren kalk resorbieren? ... Altenburg, S.-A., Piererersche hofbuchdruckerei S. Geibel & co., 1904.
24 p., 1 l., [2] p. 23cm.
Inaug.-diss.—Bonn.
Lebenslauf.
"Literatur": 1 p. at end.

1. Absorption. 2. Calcium stearate.

8-6007

Library of Congress QP165.K6

NK 0197187 DLC ICRL

PK3157
.G7
1884

Knauer, Fedor Ivanovich, ed. and tr.
Gobhila.
Das Gobhilagṛhyasūtra, herausgegeben und übersetzt von dr. Friedrich Knauer ... Dorpat, Gedruckt bei C. Mattiesen; Leipzig, Simmel & co., 1884–86.

Knauer, Fedor Ivanovich, ed.
Manu.
... Das Mānava-çrauta-sūtra, hrsg. von dr. Friedrich Knauer ...
St.-Pétersburg, Commissionnaires de l'Académie impériale des sciences: I. Glasounof; M. Eggers & cie.; [etc., etc.] 1900–

Knauer, Fedor Ivanovich.
Ueber die Betonung der Composita mit a privativum im Sanskrit ... Dorpat, 1882.
Abhandlung - Dorpat.

NK 0197190 CtY

Knauer, Fedor Ivanovich
Ueber die betonung der composita mit a privatim im Sanskit. 68 pp. (Zeits. f. vergleich. sprachforsch. v. 27, 1885, p. 1.)

NK 0197191 MdBP

Knauer, Ferdinand
Die rübe das wichtigste curtur-gewachs der gemässigten zone. Ein handbuch für praktische landwirthe, insbesondere für rubenbauer und rubenzuckerfabrikanten. Mit 12 eingedruckten holzschnitten. Lpz., L. Wiedemann, 1861.
183 p. illus.

NK 0197192 OU PPF

Knauer, Ferdinand,
Rübenbau. Für landwirthe und zuckerfabrikanten bearbeitet. 4te vermehrte und verbesserte aufl. Berlin. Wiegandt, Hempel & Parey, 1876.
143 p.

NK 0197193 PPF

Knauer, Ferdinand,
Rübenbau. Für landwirthe und zuckerfabrikanter 5te vermehrte und verbesserte aufl. Berlin, Parey, 1882.
152 p.

NK 0197194 PPF

VOLUME 300

Knauer, Ferdinand.
Der Rübenbau. Für Landwirte und Zuckerfabrikanten bearbeitet
183825 von Ferdinand Knauer, ... Sechste, verbesserte und vermehrte Auflage. Mit 29 Textabbildungen. Berlin, P. Parey, 1886.
[4], 186 p. incl. illus., tables. 19cm. (*On cover:* Thaer-Bibliothek.)

NK 0197195 ICJ PPF OU

Knauer, Ferdinand.
Der Rübenbau; für Landwirte und Zuckerfabrikanten, bearbeitet von F. Knauer. Siebente Auflage, herausgegeben von Dr. Titus Knauer ... Berlin, P. Parey, 1894.
viii, 204 p. incl. illus., tables. front. (port.) 19cm. (*On cover:* Thaer-Bibliothek. Bd. 19)

NK 0197196 ICJ PPF

Knauer, Ferdinand,
Rübenbau. Für landwirte und zuckerfabrikanten. Achte aufl. neuarbeitet von M. Hollrung. Berlin. Psrey, 1901.
152 p.

NK 0197197 PPF

SB221 K7 1906 Knauer, Ferdinand
Der Rübenbau für Landwirte und Zuckerfabrikanten. 9.Aufl. neubearb. von Prof. Dr. M. Hollrung ... Berlin, P. Parey, 1906.
viii,174 p. illus. (Thaer-Bibliothek, Bd.19)

1. Beets and beet sugar.

NK 0197198 CU

Knauer, Ferdinand
F. Knauers Rübenbau. Für landwirte und zuckerfabrikauten. ii. aufl. neubear. und ergänzt von Dr Paul Holdefleiss ... Berlin, P. Parey, 1917.
vii, 190 p. illus. 19 cm.

NK 0197199 CaBVaU

---

ar W 32444 Knauer, Ferdinand.
Die sociale Frage auf dem platten Lande. Ein mittel/gegen den Arbeitermangel und gegen die Entsittlichung der ländlichen Arbeiter. Berlin, Wiegandt, Hempel & Barey, 1873.
v, 264 p. 24cm.

1. Agricultural laborers--Germany. 2. Germany--Rural condit. I. Title.

NK 0197200 NIC WU

Knauer, Ferdinand.
Ueber contractliche Verhältnisse zwischen Arbeitgeber und Arbeitnehmer auf dem platten Lande, event. über den Bruch dieser Verträge (Contractbruch). Gutachten.
(In Verein fuer Socialpolitik. Schriften. 7. Pp. 1–18. Leipzig, 1874.)

Dec. 4, 1901
E2494 — Germany. Labor. — Employers and employed.

NK 0197201 MB

Knauer, Ferdinand.
Über rübensamenzucht. Gröbers, provinz Sachsen im herbst 1883. Ferdinand Knauer. Bunzlau, Druck von L. Fernbach [1884?]
cover-title, 9, [1] p. illus., col. pl. 22½cm.

1. Sugar beet seed.

Agr 9-1334

Library, U. S. Dept. of Agriculture 66K72R

NK 0197202 DNAL

Knauer, Ferdinand.
Das Zukunfts-Schaf Norddeutschlands. Von Ferdinand Knauer,
184297 .... Zweite verbesserte und vermehrte Auflage. Halle, C. E. M. Pfeffer, 1869.
vi, 50 p. 23½cm.

NK 0197203 ICJ

Knauer (Friedrich). Luft und Licht als Heilfaktoren. 16 pp. 8°. Tachau, H. Holub [1910.]

NK 0197204 DNLM

Knauer, Friedrich.
—— Die Sauermilch als ein Mittel zur Erhaltung der Gesundheit und Verlängerung des Lebens. 26 pp. 8°. Tachau [n. d.]

NK 0197205 DNLM

Knauer, Friedrich, of Dorpat and Kief
see Knauer, Fedor Ivanovich, 1849-1917.

RE121 K72 **Knauer, Friedrich,** of Wiesbaden.
Ueber ptosis und deren therapie mit besonderer berücksichtigung der Pagenstecher'schen fadenoperation ... Wiesbaden, Schollenberg, 1891.
33 p. plate.

Inaug.-diss., Würzburg.

1. Eyelids - Diseases. 2. Eyelids - Surgery.

NK 0197207 NNC DNLM

Knauer, Friedrich, 1886- **a. Frankfurt a. M.: Der Erlos aus einem Pfandverkauf ohne gültiges Pfandrecht, der nach § 1244 BGB. wirksam ist. Borna-Leipzig 1913: Noske. VIII, 77 S. 8°**
Marburg, Jur. Diss. v. 16. Sept. 1913, Ref. Leonhard
[Geb. 21. Juli 86 Offenbach a. M.; Wohnort: Eltville; Staatsangeh.: Preußen; Vorbildung: Goethe-G. Frankfurt a. M. Reife 05; Studium: München 1, Genf 1, Leipzig 1, Marburg 3 S.; Rig. 1. Aug. 13.] [U 13. 1115

NK 0197208 ICRL

Knauer, Friedrich Ivanovic
see Knauer, Fedor Ivanovich.

Knauer, Friedrich Karl, 1850-1926.
Die alte Grenzscheide zwichen Thier-und Pflanzenwelt und deren Umsturz durch die moderne Naturwissenschaft; eine anatomisch-physiologische Abhandlung. Wein, A. Hölder, 1876.
[4], 38 p. 22 cm.

NK 0197210 OkU MH

Knauer, Friedrich Karl, 1850-
... Die ameisen, von dr. Friedrich Knauer ... Leipzig, B. G. Teubner, 1906.
2 p. l., 156 p. illus. 19½cm. (Aus natur und geisteswelt, sammlung wissenschaftlich-gemeinverständlicher darstellungen. 94. bändchen)

1. Ants.

Agr 6-1915 Revised

Library, U. S. Dept. of Agriculture 426K72

NK 0197211 DNAL OOxM ICJ

Knauer, Friedrich Karl, 1850-
Amphibien und Reptilienzucht. Wien, 1875.
56 p. 5 tables. 8°.

NK 0197212 MH-Z PPAN

Knauer, Friedrich Karl, 1850-
Aus der Thierwelt. Schilderungen und allgemeine Umblicke.
188782 Ein naturhistorisches Lesebuch für Schüler der Mittelschulen und für jeden Naturfreund. Von Friedrich K. Knauer, ... Mit vielen Abbildungen. Freiburg im Breisgau, [etc.], Herdersche Verlagshandlung, 1886.
[4], 186 p. illus. 23½cm.

NK 0197213 ICJ CU

Knauer, Friedrich Karl, 1850-
Beobachtungen an reptilien und amphibien in der gefangenschaft. Ein kleiner beitrag zur näheren kenntnisse des lebens dieser thiere, von Friedrich K. Knauer. Wien, A. Hölder, 1875.
54, [2] p., 1 l. 24cm.
"Literatur": [2] p.

1. Reptiles. 2. Batrachia. I. Title.

22-10655

Library of Congress QL669.K7

NK 0197214 DLC PPAN

Knauer, Friedrich Karl, 1850-1926.
Deutschlands und Österreichs amphibien. Für den naturfreund beschrieben und nach ihrem leben geschildert, von dr. Friedrich K. Knauer. Wien, Verlag von A. Pichler's witwe & sohn [1877]
2 p.l., 76 p. front. 15 cm. (On cover: Volks- und jugend-bibliothek ...)
1. Batrachia - Germany. 2. Reptiles - Germany. 3. Batrachia - Austria. 4. Reptiles - Austria.

NK 0197215 CU

Zool.Mus.

Knauer, Friedrich Karl, 1850-
Fang der Amphibien und Reptilien. Wien, 1875.
20 p. 8°.

NK 0197216 MH-Z PPAN

VOLUME 300

Knauer, Friedrich Karl, 1850–
70043 Die Fauna und Flora des Meeres, von Dr. Friedrich Knauer. Mit 1 Vollbild und 47 Illustrationen im Text. Berlin und Leipzig, H. Hillger, 1906.
136 p. illus. 22^{cm}. (*Half-title:* Einzeldarstellungen aus den Naturwissenschaften. II.)

NK 0197217 ICJ

Knauer, Friedrich Karl, 1850–
Handwörterbuch der zoologie. Unter mitwirkung von prof. dr. von Dalla Torre ... bearb. von dr. Friedrich Knauer ... Stuttgart, F. Enke, 1887.
2 p. l., [iii]–xiv, 828 p. IX pl. 25^{cm}.
"Die zoologische literatur": p. [v]–xiii.

1. Zoology—Dictionaries. I. Dalla Torre, Karl Wilhelm von, 1850– II. Title.

Agr 26-821

Library, U. S. Dept. of Agriculture 411K72

OCU IU PPAN
NK 0197218 DNAL PBL CU DLC DSI CSt DNLM PHC CtY-M

Knauer, Friedrich Karl, 1850-1926.
Illustrirte Naturgeschichte der Kriechthiere und Lurche.
[In Martin, P.L. Illustrirte Naturgeschichte der Thiere. Bd. 2, Abth. 1]

NK 0197219 CtY

Knauer, Friedrich Karl, 1850-1926.
... Die Kakteen ... Berlin, Leipzig, H. Hillger Verlag [1906]
94 p., 1 l. illus. (Hillgers illustrierte Volksbücher, Band 65)

NK 0197220 CtY

Knauer, Friedrich Karl, 1850–
61204 Das Leben unserer heimischen Lurche und Kriechtiere im Kreislaufe eines Jahres. Von Dr. Friedrich K. Knauer. Dresden, H. Schultze, 1905.
208 p. illus., 10 pl. 22^{cm}.

NK 0197221 ICJ

Knauer, Friedrich Karl, 1850–
Menschenaffen, ihr Frei- und Gefangenleben, von Dr. Friedrich Knauer... Leipzig: Deutsche naturwissenschaftliche Gesellschaft[, 1915]. 96 p. illus. 21cm.

624675A. 1. Ape, Anthropoid. October 21, 1933
N. Y. P. L.

NK 0197222 NN PPAN DNLM

Knauer, Friedrich Karl, 1850–

Ornithologischer verein in Wien.
Mittheilungen ... 1.–21. jahrg.; 1877–97. Wien [1877–97]

Knauer, Friedrich Karl, 1850-
Naturgeschichte der Lurche. (Amphibiologie). Eine umfassendere Darlegung unserer Kenntnisse von dem anatomischen Bau, der Entwicklung und systematischen Eintheilung der Amphibien etc. Wien, 1878.

340 p. 4 maps, 2 tables, 120 wdcts. 8°.

NK 0197224 MH-Z PPAN NNC CU CtY

Knauer Friedrich Karl, 1850-
Die Reptilien und Amphibien Nieder-Oesterreichs Eine faunistische Skizze. Wien, 1878.

42 p. 8°.

NK 0197225 MH-Z

Knauer, Friedrich Karl, 1850–
67225 Das Süsswasser-Aquarium. Seine Herstellung, Einrichtung, Besetzung und Instandhaltung. Von Dr. Friedrich Knauer. Mit 88 Illustrationen. Regensburg, Verlagsanstalt vorm. G. J. Manz, 1907.
iv, 331 p. 88 illus. $19\frac{1}{2}^{cm}$.

NK 0197226 ICJ CU

Knauer, Friedrich Karl, 1850–
Tierwanderungen und ihre ursachen, von dr. Friedrich Knauer; mit 80 abbildungen und einer karte. Köln, J. P. Bachem, 1909.
xi, 288 p. illus. 23^{cm}. M. 3.50

1. Animals, Habits and behavior of. 2. Zoology—Geographical distribution. I. Title.

Library of Congress QL751.K6 9-27441 Revised

NK 0197227 DLC CU ICJ MiU

KNAUER, Friedrich Karl, 1850–
Unsere kenntnisse von der entstehung und dem baue des chlorophyll's und dessen rolle im pflanzenleben. Wien, 1875.

ff.(2), pp.52.

NK 0197228 MH

Knauer, Friedrich, 1850–
Vogelschutz und Federnindustrie; eine Streitfrage der Zeit, von Dr. Friedrich Knauer... Wien: W. Braumüller, 1914. 159(1) p. illus. 8°.

1. Birds.—Protection. 2. Feathers.—Trade and statistics. 3. Title.
N. Y. P. L. August 6, 1915.

NK 0197229 NN

KNAUER, Friedrich [Karl], 1850–
Der zoologische garten; entwicklungsgang, anlage, und betrieb unserer tiergärten, und deren erzieh[l]ische, belehrende, und wissenschaftliche aufgaben. Leipzig, Deutsche naturwissenschaftliche gesellschaft, [191-?].

pp.250. Illustr.
(Der naturborscher.)
"Literatur über tiergärten", pp.241-244.

NK 0197230 MH

Knauer, Friedrich Karl, 1850–1926.
... Zwiegestalt der geschlechter in der tierwelt (dimorphismus) von dr. Friedrich Knauer, mit 37 abbildungen im text. Leipzig, B. G. Teubner, 1907.
2 p. l., 126 p. illus. $18\frac{1}{2}^{cm}$. (Aus natur und geisteswelt; sammlung wissenschaftlich-gemeinverständlicher darstellungen. 148. bdchen.)

1. Dimorphism (Animals) I. Title.

43-45875

Library of Congress QL799.K55

NK 0197231 DLC CU ICJ

Knauer, Friedrich Peter, 1922–
Kalkulationsformen im Stahlbau. Mannheim, 1954.
150 p. illus. 24 cm.
Inaug.-Diss.—Wirtschaftshochschule Mannheim.
Vita.
Bibliography: p. 149–150.

1. Building, Iron and steel. 2. Building—Estimates. I. Title.

TA684.K65 58-23468

NK 0197232 DLC

Knauer, Fritz: Ueber Echinokokkus im weiblichen Becken. Im Anschl. an e. an d. chir. Abt. d. Städt. Krankenh. zu Chemnitz beobacht. Fall. Leipzig 1913: Lehmann. 39 S. 8°
Leipzig, Med. Diss. v. 26. Febr. 1913, Ref. Payr
[Geb. 4. Nov. 87 München; Wohnort: Chemnitz i. Sa.; Staatsangeh.: Bayern; Vorbildung: Theresien-G. München Reife 06; Studium: München 10 S.; Coll. 26. Febr. 13; Approb. 9. Febr. 13.] [U 13. 2338

NK 0197233 ICRL DNLM CtY

Knauer, Georg
Ueber die deckung grosser hautdefekte mittels der Thiersch'schen transplantationsmethode ... Würzburg, Bonitas-Bauer, 1889.
38 p., 1 l.

Inaug.-diss., Würzburg.
"Benutzte litteratur": p. [39]

1. Skin-grafting.

NK 0197234 NNC DNLM

Knauer, Georg.
Winke für den ärztlichen Weg aus zwanzigjähriger Erfahrung. Wiesbaden, J. F. Bergmann, 1912.
105p.

NK 0197235 ICRL DNLM ICJ

Knauer, Georg Andreas, 1900-
Ueber anregung der milchsekretion.
Inaug. diss. - Freiburg, 1926. (Hamburg)
Bibl.

NK 0197236 ICRL CtY

Knauer, Georg Nicolaus.
Psalmenzitate in Augustins Konfessionen. Göttingen, Vandenhoeck und Ruprecht, 1955.
215 p. 25 cm.
Issued also as thesis, Hamburg.
Bibliography: p. 7–17.

1. Augustinus, Aurelius, Saint, Bp. of Hippo. Confessiones. 2. Bible. O. T. Psalms—Commentaries. I. Title.

A 56–3935

Harvard Univ. Library
for Library of Congress [1]

NK 0197237 MH CtY IU IEG PV DDO NcD NjPT CtY-D

Knauer (Guido). * Diss. exhibens nonnulla in pupillam arte formandam. 16 pp., 1 l. 4°. *Jenæ, typ. Schlotterianis,* [1829].

NK 0197238 DNLM

VOLUME 300

Knauer, Gustav, 1832-
Contrar und contradictorisch (nebst convergirenden lehrstücken) festgestellt und Kants kategorientafel berichtigt. Eine philosophische monographie von Gustav Knauer ... Halle, C.E. M.Pfeffer, 1868.
xviii p.,1 l.,157 p. 23cm.

1.Logic. 2.Kant,Immanuel,1724-1804.

NK 0197239 MiU MdBP

KNAUER, Gustav, 1832-
Das facit aus E.v.Hartmann's philosophie des unbewussten. Berl., 1873.
ff.(2),pp.63.

NK 0197240 MH MiU

Knauer, Gustav, 1832- Reflexion und reflexionsbegriffe. 27 pp. (Zeits. f. philos. v. 90, 1887, p. 248.)

NK 0197241 MdBP

Knauer, Gustav, 1832-
Die reflexionsbegriffe ... Zum centenarium der "Kritik der reinen vernunft" ... Leipzig, Druck von Bockwitz & Webel, 1881.
iv, 58 p. double tab. 21 cm. [With Pflüger, W. Untersuchungen über die ... aesthetik Kants. 1867]
Inaug.-diss. - Jena.
1. Kant, Immanuel, 1724-1804. Kritik der reinen vernunft.

NK 0197242 CU NjP RPB

Knauer, H
.... Der Eisenbahnbau. I.-[II.] Teil. ... . Bearbeitet von Ingenieur H. Knauer, ... Strelitz in Mecklenburg, M. Hittenkofer, [1909].
2 vol. illus., tables. 26½cm. (Unterrichtswerke für Selbstunterricht, Schule und Bureau.)
Contents.—I. Tl. Die Anlagen der freien Strecke. Weichen- u. Gleisverbindungen. x, 206 p. 2 diagr.—2. Tl. Bahnhofsanlagen nebst Signal- und Sicherungswesen. vii, 132 p. 5 diagr. (partly fold.)

NK 0197243 ICJ NN

Knauer, H.
Eisenbahnhochbauten. Nach amtlichem Material bearbeitet. Strelitz in Mecklenburg: M. Hittenkofer [1912]. 88 p., 14 pl. 4°.

1. Railways.—Stations. 2. Locomotives.—Roundhouses.
N. Y. P. L. November 25, 1912.

NK 0197244 NN IU

Knauer, H.
Meliorationen (bodenverbesserungen) Mit 3 tafeln und 166 abbildungen. Von H. Knauer ... Strelitz in Mecklenburg, M. Hittenkofer [1912]
2 p. l., [iii]-vi, 183, [1] p. illus., diagrs. (2 fold.) 26½cm.
Katalog nr. 214.

1. Reclamation of land. 2. Drainage. 3. Irrigation.

12-27454

Library of Congress S605.K6

NK 0197245 DLC DNAL ICJ

Knauer, H
... Der städtische Tiefbau. [I.]-IV. Teil ... . Bearbeitet von Ingenieur H. Knauer, ... Strelitz in Mecklenburg, M. Hittenkofer, [1910]-1911.
4 vol. illus., diagrs. 26½cm. (Vol. 1-2: Werke für Studium & Bureau.)
Contents.—I. Teil. Der städtische Strassenbau. [1910.] 103 p.—2. Teil. Die Wasserversorgung der Städte. [1910.] 188 p. v pl.—3. Teil. Die Entwässerung der Städte (Kanalisation). [1911.] vii, 198 p. XII pl., IX (i.e. 9) tables (incl. diagrs., part fold.)—4. Teil. Abwasserreinigung. 1911. iv, 57 p.

NK 0197246 ICJ CU NN MH-GM

Knauer, Hans.
see
Knauer, Johannes, 1895-

Knauer, Hans von.
El servicio de mediciones de la artillería, por Hans von Knauer ... Santiago de Chile, Instituto geográfico militar, 1933.
5 p. l., 123 p. fold. plates, fold. map, diagrs. (part fold.) 26cm.
"Anexos" (tables (part fold.) fold. map) in pocket.

1. Range-finding. I. Chile. Instituto geográfico militar. II. Title: Mediciones de la artillería.

46-47440

Library of Congress UF850.A2K55

NK 0197248 DLC

Knauer, Heinrich, editor.
Schule für Trommel, besonders zum Selbstunterricht, bearbeitet von Heinrich Knauer... Leipzig: M. Biering, [1927]. Publ. pl. no. M. B. 10. illus., tables. 55 p. obl. 16°.

Juilliard Foundation Fund.

1. Drum.
N. Y. P. L. April 12, 1928

NK 0197249 NN

Knauer (Heinrich) [1854-]. *Ueber den Einfluss des Aufenthalts in verdünnter Luft auf die Form der Pulscurve. 30 pp., 1 l., 1 ch. 8°. Berlin, G. Schade, 1878.

NK 0197250 DNLM

Knauer, Heinrich, 1885-
Der Bergbau zu Amberg in der Oberpfalz; ein Beitrag zur vaterländischen Wirtschaftsgeschichte...von Heinrich Knauer ... Amberg: H. Böes, 1913. vii, 77 p. incl. tables. 8°.
Dissertation, Erlangen, 1913.
Lebenslauf.
Bibliography, p. iv.

1. Iron—Mines and mining—Germany—Amberg.
N. Y. P. L. April 8, 1926

NK 0197251 NN CtY PU MH NIC ICRL

Knauer, Helmut, 1907-
Die klagerücknahme und ihre prozessrechtlichen wirkungen. ... Quakenbrück i. H., 1934.
Inaug. Diss. - Göttingen, 1934.
Lebenslauf.
Schrifttum.

NK 0197252 ICRL

Knauer, Helmut, 1909-
Magnetochemische untersuchungen an komplexen eisensalzen. ... 75 p.
Inaug. Diss. - Techn. Hochschule Dresden, [1939]
Lebenslauf.

NK 0197253 ICRL

Knauer, Hennie.
Mad - ABC, af Hennie Knauer og Merete Wandall. Med forord af E.Herløv-Müller. København, P. Haase, 1952.
142 p.

NK 0197254 InLP

Knauer, Henry.
Tests for railway material and equipment, by Henry Knauer ... a book for all railroad men who, in any way, are called on to test or pass upon the merits of railway materials and appliances ... New York, N. Y., Chicago [etc.] Simmons-Boardman publishing company [°1925]
ix, 11-257 p. illus., diagrs. 19½cm. (Railwaymen's handbook series)

1. Railroads—Equipment and supplies. I. Title.

Library of Congress TF361.K5 25-8670

NK 0197255 DLC WaS CU NcD ICRL OCl MB NN

A-12879
C_R t.C

Knauer, Hermann.
Eine Amerikafahrt und die Welt-Ausstellung in St. Louis. Berlin, F. Dümmler, 1903.
133p. illus.

NK 0197256 ICRL ICJ

Knauer, Hermann.
Deutschland am Mississippi. Neue eindrücke und erlebnisse von Hermann Knauer. Berlin, L. Oehmigke's verlag (R. Appelius) 1904.
vi p., 1 l., 184 p. illus. 23½cm.
Illustrated cover.

1. U. S.—Descr. & trav. 2. St. Louis. Louisiana purchase exposition, 1904—Germany. I. Title.

5-5137

Library of Congress E168.K67

NK 0197257 DLC ICRL TxU MsU MoU ICJ MB NN

[Knauer, Hermann]
Guide to the German and Tyrolean Alps, World's fair, St. Louis, 1904. [St. Louis, 1904]
45, [1] p. 22cm.

1. St. Louis. Louisiana purchase exposition, 1904. I. Title.

5-32318

Library of Congress T860.L1K6
[a42b1]

NK 0197258 DLC

Knauer, Hermann.
St. Louis and its World's fair. Impressions and experiences of Hermann Knauer. Berlin [G. Bernstein, printer] 1904.
43, [1] p. 19cm.

1. St. Louis. Louisiana purchase exposition, 1904.

Library of Congress T860.B1K6 5-30717

NK 0197259 DLC

VOLUME 300

Knauer, Hermann, of Munich
Die stellung der rinderhaltung in der oberfränkischen bauernwirtschaft. Das wirken der bayreuther herdbuchgesellschaft. ... München, 1931.
Inaug. Diss. Techn. Hochsch. München, 1931.
Bibliography.

NK 0197260 ICRL

KNAUER, Hermann, writer on law
Ueber den strafrechtlichen notstand und die grenzen der selbsthilfe nach reichsstrafrecht. Breslau, 1902.

pp.70.

NK 0197261 MH

W 6 KNAUER, Ilse
P3 The feeding of children. London, New Knowledge Books [1951?]
36 p.
Reprinted from Natura.
"[It] is intended here ... to rationalise the subject of nutrition with the help of the results of spiritual science ... or anthroposophy." - p. 36.
1. Children - Nutrition
2. Infants - Nutrition

NK 0197262 DNLM

Knauer, Indra Devi (Petersen) 1899–
Forever young, forever healthy, by Indra Devi. New York, Prentice-Hall [1953]
174 p. illus. 21 cm.

1. Yoga, Haṭha. I. Title.

B132.Y6K55 181.45 53-10933 rev ‡

NK 0197263 IdB IdPI Or OrP WaE Wa WaS WaT WaSp DLC TU PP NcC MB NN ViU CtY-M OKentU

Knauer, Indra Devi (Petersen) 1899–
Yoga, the technique of health and happiness, by Eugenie Strakaty (Indira Devi) Foreword by G. V. Deshmukh. Allahabad, Kitabistan [1948]
133 p. illus., plates, port. 22 cm.
Bibliography: p. 132-133.

1. Yoga. I. Title.

B132.Y6K56 181.45 59-51895

NK 0197264 DLC

Knauer, Irmgard, 1921-
Frauenzeichnung und Frauenpsychologie bei Franz Grillparzer. [Munich, 1947]
154 l.

Microfilm of typewritten copy.
Inaug.-diss.--Munich.
"Literaturverzeichnis": l. 150-154.
On reel with: Herding, Gertrud. Theodor Fontane. [1946]

NK 0197265 NNC

Knauer, J.
Sectional map of the Territory of Minnesota, exhibiting the official surveys.
New York. Colton. 1853. Size, 23⅜ × 25¾ inches. Scale (computed), 6 miles to 1 inch. Folded.

F2127 — Minnesota. Geog. Maps.

NK 0197266 MB

Knauer, Johannes: Ein Beitrag zur Frage der Salaamkrämpfe. [Maschinenschrift.] 23 S. 4°. — Auszug: Breslau 1923: Bresl. Genoss.-Buchdr. 2 Bl. 8°
Breslau, Med. Diss. v. 30. Juni 1923 [U 23. 1279

NK 0197267 ICRL

Knauer, Johann, 1885- Arzt: Über Aetiologie, Prophylaxe und Therapie bei Tetanus und über Spätfälle nach Tetanusinfektion. Strassburg i. E. 1915: Els.-Lothr. Dr. 59 S. 8°
Straßburg, Med. Diss. v. 1. Juli 1915, Ref. Madelung
[Geb. 4. Aug. 85 Haag a. d. Amper; Wohnort: Hönheim; Staatsangeh.: Bayern; Vorbildung: G. Eichstätt Reife 07; Studium: München 6, Erlangen 5 S.; Coll. 10. Juni 15; Approb. 1. Aug. 14.] [U 15. 1311

NK 0197268 ICRL MH CtY DNLM

Knauer, Johannes, 1895–
... Die bluttransfusion im kindesalter, von prof. dr. Hans Knauer ... Stuttgart, F. Enke, 1936.
33 p. 25½cm. (Beihefte zum Archiv für kinderheilkunde. 7. hft.)

1. Blood—Transfusion. 2. Children—Diseases.
A C 37-2496

John Crerar library for Library of Congress [4]

NK 0197269 ICJ ViU

Knauer, Johannes, 1895–
... Ergebnisse der lipoidstoffwechselforschung mit besonderer berücksichtigung der verhältnisse im kindesalter, von dr. Hans Knauer ... Mit 1 abbildung und 22 tabellen im text. Berlin, S. Karger, 1928.
iv, 164 p. incl. illus., tables. 26cm. (Abhandlungen aus der kinderheilkunde und ihren grenzgebieten ... hft. 22)
"Literaturverzeichnis": p. 136-145.

1. Metabolism. 2. Lipoids.
A C 33-2426

Title from John Crerar Libr Printed by L. C.

NK 0197270 ICJ PPC OC1W MiU OU CtY

Knauer, Johannes, 1895–
Varizellen, von Prof. Dr. Hans Knauer ...
(In Neue deutsche Klinik. Berlin, 1938. 26cm. Bd. 15 (Erg. Bd. 5) p. [617]-648. illus.)

NK 0197271 ICJ

Knauer, Joseph, 1880-
... Die ablagerungen der älteren Würm-eiszeit (Vorrückungsphase) im süddeutschen und norddeutschen vereisungsgebiet, von Joseph Knauer. Mit 1 kartentafel und 29 figuren auf 9 tafeln. München, Hrsg. vom Bayerischen oberbergamt [Universitätsbuchdruckerei dr. C. Wolf & sohn] 1935.
65 p. 10 pl. (incl. maps, profile) 24cm. (Bavaria. Bayerisches oberbergamt. Geologische landesuntersuchung. Abhandlungen hft. 21)
Map and profile in pocket.
Plate 1 accompanied by descriptive guard-sheet.
"Schriftenverzeichnis": p. 65.
1. Geology, Stratigraphic—Pleistocene. 2. Geology—Germany. 3. Glacial epoch. I. Title.
G S 35-218

Library, U. S. Geological Survey (530.2) Ab hft. 21
Library of Congress [QE269.B hft. 21]
[2]

NK 0197272 DI-GS

Knauer, Joseph, 1880–
Diluviale Talverschüttung und Epigenese im südlichen Bayern. München, 1952.
32 p. illus. 24 cm. (Geologica Bavarica, Nr. 11)
"Schriftenverzeichnis": p. [31]-32.

1. Geology—Bavaria. 2. Geology, Stratigraphic—Pleistocene. 3. Valleys. (Series)
QE269.G36 Nr. 11 G S 52-287
U. S. Geol. Survey. Libr. for Library of Congress [2]†

NK 0197273 DI-GS TxU CoU DLC

Knauer, Joseph, 1880-
Die gehangerutsche (Blattanbrüche) bei Garmisch-Partenkirchen. (Ein beispiel für die erodierende kraft des Hagels) Von Joseph Knauer.
(In Bavaria. Oberbergamt. Geologische landesuntersuchung. Abhandlungen. München, 1933. 24cm. hft. 11, p. 47-55. 2 pl.)
"Angeführte schriften": p. 55.

1. Landslides—Bavaria—Garmisch-Partenkirchen. 2. Hail.
G S 33-192
Library, U. S. Geological Survey (530.2) Ab hft. 11 [QE269.B hft.11]
[2] (554.33) 551.35094336

NK 0197274 DI-GS

Knauer, Joseph, 1880-
Die geologischen ergebnisse beim bau der Bayerischen Zugspitzbahn, von Josef Knauer.
(In Bavaria. Oberbergamt. Geologische landesuntersuchung. Abhandlungen. München, 1933. 23½cm. hft. 10, p. [23]-50 incl. plan, diagr. III pl., fold. map)
"Schriftenverzeichnis": p. 50.

1. Geology—Bavaria—Zugspitze. 2. Geology—Tyrol.
G S 33-188
Library, U. S. Geological Survey (530.2) Ab hft. 10 [QE269.B hft. 10]
[2] (554.33) 554.336

NK 0197275 DI-GS

Knauer, Joseph, 1880–
Die herkunft der blei- und zinkerze im Rauschenberg-gebiet bei Inzell, von Joseph Knauer.
(In Bavaria. Oberbergamt. Geologische landesuntersuchung. Abhandlungen. München, 1938. 24cm. hft. 30, p. 3-15. illus., diagr.)
"Schriftenverzeichnis": p. 15.

1. Lead ores—Bavaria. 2. Zinc ores—Bavaria. I. Title.
G S 38-257
U. S. Geol. survey. Library for Library of Congress (530.2) Ab hft. 30 [QE269.A19B hft. 30]
[3]

NK 0197276 DI-GS

Knauer, Joseph, 1880–
Die Mindel-eiszeit, die zeit grösster diluvialer vergletscherung in Suddeutschland, von Joseph Knauer.
(In Bavaria. Oberbergamt. Geologische landesuntersuchung. Abhandlungen. München, 1938. 24cm. hft. 29, p. [35]-45. illus., III pl.)
"Schrifttum": p. 45.

1. Geology, Stratigraphic—Pleistocene. 2. Geology—Bavaria. 3. Glacial epoch. I. Title.
G S 38-258
U. S. Geol. survey. Library for Library of Congress (530.2) Ab hft. 29 [QE269.A19B hft. 29]

NK 0197277 DI-GS

Knauer, Joseph, 1880–
Über das alter der moränen der Zürich-phase im Linthgletscher-gebiet, von Joseph Knauer.
(In Bavaria. Bayerische oberbergamt. Geologische landesuntersuchung. Abhandlungen. München, 1938. 24cm. hft. 33, p. [3]-29 incl. illus., tab., diagrs., VII pl. (incl. fold. map))
"Schriftenverzeichnis": p. 29.

1. Moraines. 2. Glacial epoch. 3. Geology—Bavaria.
G S 40-22
U. S. Geol. survey. Library for Library of Congress (530.2) Ab hft. 33 [QE269.A19B hft. 33]
[2] (554.33)

NK 0197278 DI-GS

VOLUME 300

Knauer, Joseph, 1880-
Überzählige schichtablagerung und scheintektonik, von Jos. Knauer; mit 2 abbildungen und 3 tafeln.
(In Bavaria. Oberbergamt. Geologische landesuntersuchung. Abhandlungen. München, 1935. 24cm. hft. 17, p. [47]-55. illus., 3 pl.)
"Schriftenverzeichnis": p. 55.
1. Geology—Bavaria. 2. Geology, Structural—Bavaria. I. Title.
G S 35-136
Library, U. S. Geological Survey (530.2) Ab hft. 17
Library of Congress [QE269.B hft. 17]
[2]

NK 0197279 DI-GS

KNAUER, Karl, 1883-
Studien zur Geschichte der Farbenbestimmung im Französischen von den Anfängen bis gegen Ende des 18. Jahrhunderts. Geneve, etc., L.S. Olschki, 1933.
28 cm. pp.58.
"Estratto dall'Archivum Romanicum, Vol. XVII, Nr.2, aprile-giugno 1933."

NK 0197280 MH

Knauer, Karl, 1886- Referendar: Das Erfolgsdelikt unter besonderer Berücksichtigung des Versuchs im Reichsstrafgesetzbuch und im Vorentwurf von 1909. Strassburg i. E. 1911: Goeller. 73 S. 8°
Würzburg, Jur. Diss. v. 21. April 1911, Ref. Oetker
[Geb. 6. Aug. 86 Oberbronn; Wohnort: Straßburg; Staatsangeh.: Elsaß-Lothringen; Vorbildung: Gymn. Buchsweiler Reife M. 05; Studium: Straßburg 4, München 1, Berlin 1 S.; Rig. 15. Juni 10.] [U 11. 4504

NK 0197281 ICRL MH

P 123 K67g Knauer, Karl, 1906-
Grenzen der Wissenschaft vom Wort. Wiesbaden, Verlag der Akademie der Wissenschaften und der Literatur in Mainz in Kommission bei F. Steiner [1950]
19p. diagrs. 26cm. (Akademie der Wissenschaften und der Literatur. Abhandlungen der Geistes- und Sozialwissenschaftlichen Klasse. Jahrg. 1950, Nr.13)
Pages also numbered [1077]-1093, continuing the paging of the preceding no.
Bibliographical footnotes.
1. Language and languages.

NK 0197282 NRU NBuU MoSW MU TxDaM NIC CSt CtY IU

PQ2005 .Z5K65 KNAUER, KARL, 1906-
... Ein künstler poetischer prosa in der französischen vorromantik: Jean-François Marmontel... Bochum-Langendreer, Druck: H. Pöppinghaus, 1936.
vi, 158, [1]p. 2 fold. diagr. 23½cm.
Habilitationsschrift--Münster.
1. Marmontel, Jean François, 1723-1799.

NK 0197283 ICU OrU NcU NNC InU

Knauer, Karl, 1906-
Künstlerisches Schaffen im Dienste der nationalen Gemeinschaft und der politischen Propaganda Frankreichs im Zeitalter der nationalen Festigung, von Franz I bis Ludwig XIV. Stuttgart, Kohlhammer, 1944

NK 0197284 MH

838 K72s KNAUER, Karl, 1906-
Steppenblumen; Heiteres und Ernstes in Schwäbischer und hochdeutscher Sprache ays dem Leben der Deutchen in Bessarabien. Stuttgart, Karl Knauer, c1954.
270p.

NK 0197285 WaWW

Knauer, Karl, 1906-
Vulgärfranzösisch. Charakterzüge und Tendenzen des gegenwärtigen französischen Wortschatzes. München, M. Hueber, 1954.
91 p. 21 cm.
Bibliography: p. 60-61.
1. French language—Etymology. I. Title.
A 54-5460
Illinois. Univ. Library for Library of Congress [1]

NK 0197286 IU OU PSt NN OCU NcU CtY

Knauer, Karl, Hermann Philipp: Karls des Kahlen Kaiserkrönung und seine Schenkung an die römische Kurie. Coburg 1909: Roßteutscher. 74 S. 8°
Leipzig, Phil. Diss. v. 19. April 1909, Ref. Seeliger, Lamprecht
[Geb. 28. April 83 Neuses b. Koburg; Wohnort: Neuses; Staatsangeh.: Sachsen-Koburg-Gotha; Vorbildung: Gymn. Koburg Reife O. 03; Studium: Jena 3, Leipzig 7 S.; Rig. 16. Febr. 09.] [U 09. 3002

NK 0197287 ICRL PU MH CtY

Knauer, Moritz
Hundertjähriger Kalender des Herrn Abtes Moriz Knauer, für das jetzige Jahrhundert bis 1899. 4. verb. Aufl. München, G. Jaquet, 1835.
116p. illus. 18cm.
1. Calendar. I. Title.

NK 0197288 CSdS

KNAUER, Moritz.
Immerwährender curieuser hauskalender. n.p., [18- ?].
sm.8°. Wdcts.

NK 0197289 MH

Knauer, Moritz.
Oekonomisch-praktischer hundertjähriger hauskalender, von 1803 bis 1915, von Moritz Knauer ... Zum gebrauch für jedermann besonders für das landvolk eingerichtet, nebst einem bewährten und sehr deutlichen menschen- und vieharzney-büchlein ... Neu verbesserte und vermehrte aufl. Grätz, Im verlage bey F.X. Miller, 1806.
viii, [9]-156 p., 1 l. incl. front., illus. 2 fold. tab. 16½cm.
"Vieharzneybüchlein": p.104-152.
1. Almanacs, German. I. Title.

NK 0197290 MiU

Knauer, Moritz.
Oekonomisch-praktischer hundertjähriger Hauskalender, von 1803 bis 1915, von Moritz Knauer... Nebst einem bewährten und sehr deutlichen Menschen- und Vieharzney-Büchlein... Neu verb. und verm. Aufl. Grätz, F. X. Miller [1856] viii, 9-157 p. illus. 17cm.
604935B. 1. Almanacs—Austria. I. Title: Hundertjähriger Hauskalender.
N. Y. P. L. December 20, 1951

NK 0197291 NN

Knauer, Oswald, ed.
Branberger, Friedrich.
Das österreichische Gewerberecht. 2. Aufl. bearb. von Oswald Knauer. Wien, Manzsche Verlags- und Universitätsbuchhandlung, 1955.

Knauer, Oswald
Beitrag zur casuistik der mediastinaltumoren. Inaug. Diss. Wuerzburg, 1883
Bibl.

NK 0197293 ICRL DNLM

Knauer, Oswald, psychiatrist
Über puerperale Psychosen. Für practische Ärzte, von Dr. Oswald Knauer, ... Mit einem Vorwort, von Prof. Dr. A. Martin, ... Berlin, S. Karger, 1897.
109000
54 p. incl. tables. 24cm.
"Litteratur," p. 54.

NK 0197294 ICJ PPC ICRL DNLM

BF K67v 1899 KNAUER, Oswald, psychiatrist
Die Vision im Lichte der Kulturgeschichte und der Dämon des Sokrates; eine kulturgeschichtlich-psychiatrische Studie. Leipzig, Friedrich, [1899]
vi, 222 p.
1. Socrates.

NK 0197295 DNLM

[Knauer, Otto]
... Beiträge zur Kenntniss der französischen Sprache des XIV. Jahrhunderts. [Leipzig, 1867]
p. 14-44. 23.5 cm.
Caption title.
From Jahrbuch für romanische und englische Literatur, VIII, 1.

NK 0197296 CtY

Knauer, Otto,
...Zur altfranzösischen lautlehre...Leipzig, A. Edelmann, 1876.
46 p.

NK 0197297 PHC PU NjP

Knauer, Otto, 1910- ed.
Die Epigramme des Asklepiades v. Samos...
see under Asclepiades, of Samos.

Knauer, Paul: Aus d. chirurg. Klinik d. Tierärztl. Hochsch. zu Berlin (Vorstand: Eberlein). Beitrag zur Statik und Mechanik des Hufbeins. Mit 2 Taf. und 1 Textfig. Berlin 1909: Schumacher. 28 S. 8° ¶(Aus: Archiv. f. wissensch. u. prakt. Tierheilkunde. Bd 35.)
Gießen, Veterinär-Med. Diss. v. 23. Juli 1909, Ref. Martin
[Geb. 25. Okt. 74 Königsberg i. P.; Wohnort: Tilsit; Staatsangeh.: Preußen; Vorbildung: Realgymn. Königsberg i. P. Reife M. 94; Studium: Berlin Militärveterinär-Akad. 8 S.; Rig. 30. Okt. 08.] [U 09. 1155

NK 0197299 ICRL DNLM OU MH

VOLUME 300

Knauer, Paul.
Ernst Moritz Arndt, der grosse Erzieher der Deutschen. Stuttgart, K. Gutbrod, 1935.
165 p. 19 cm. (Gestalten und Urkunden deutschen Glaubens, 2)
"Arndts wichtigste Schriften in zeitlicher Aufeinanderfolge": p. 160–161.
Bibliography: p. 162–163.

1. Arndt, Ernst Moritz, 1769–1860.

DD86.7.A8K6 51–48528

NK 0197300 DLC IaU NcD CtY

809.8
K729
Knauer, Paul, 1890-
Der ursprung der Marien-wallfahrt zu Wartha in Schlesien; eine quellenkritische untersuchung... von Paul Knauer ... Breslau, R. Nischkowsky, 1917.
3 p. l.,90 p., 1 l. 22½cm.

Bibliography: p. l.:3.
Thesis, Breslau.
1. Mary, Virgin - Legend. 2. Mary, Virgin - Ar 3. Wartha, Ger. Church. 4. Balbinus, Bohuslaus Aloysius, 1621-168 8. Diva Wartensis.

NK 0197301 NNC CtY PU ICRL

Knauer, R
Der Graf von Gleichen
see under Doerstling, Gustav Robert, b.1821.

RX72
833K
KNAUER, Robert
Das Verbot des Selbstdispensirens der homöopatischen Aerzte, als nothwendiges allgemeines Staatsbedürfniss; mit besonderer Beziehung auf das Herzogthum Sachsen-Gotha. Ein W t zu seiner Zeit, geschrieben für Gesundheitspolizei-Beamte, Aerzte und Laien. Arnstadt,Mirus,1833.
88p. 23cm.
1.Homeopathy 2.Medical laws and legislation
I.Title

NK 0197303 CtY-M

QD299
.A7K6
Knauer, Robert Wilhelm Ferdinand, 1877-
Ueber die einwirkung von freiem hydroxylamin auf ungesaettigte sauren.
Greifswald, 1903.
49p.
Inaug. diss. Greifswald.

NK 0197304 DLC NN PU

Phil 3010.10
Knauer, Rudolf, 1870-
Der Voluntarismus; ein Beitrag zu seiner Geschicht und Kritik mit besonderer Berücksichtigung des 19.Jahrhunderts. Berlin, 1907

Diss. - Giessen

NK 0197305 MH ICRL NN PU NjP

Knauer, Tilly, and K. (V.) Stieger.
Handweberei, von Tilly Knauer und Käte Stieger-Voelkel ... Dritte, durchgesehene und erweiterte Auflage. Berlin [etc.] W. Vobach & Co. [1937] viii, 107 p. illus., 24 pl. on 12 l. 26½cm. (On cover: Vobachs Handarbeitsbuch. Bd. 5.)

907611A. 1. Weaving. I. Stieger, Käte (Voelkel), jt. au. II. Ser.
N. Y. P. L. March 10, 1938

NK 0197306 NN

KNAUER,Titus.
Untersuchungen über den marktpreis des heues und dessen verwendbarkeit zu landwirtschaftlichen veranschlagungen. Inaug.-diss. Jena, 1889.

pp.(2),52. Tables

NK 0197307 MH PU ICRL CU

Knauer, Vincenz, 1828-1894
Geschichte der Philosophie, mit besonderer Berücksichtigung der Neuzeit. Wien, W. Braumüller, 1876.
x, 387 p. 24cm.

Includes a section on Spinoza (p. [134]-138)

NK 0197308 NNC MH

KNAUER,Vincenz.
Geschichte der philosophie mit besonderer berücksichtigung der neuzeit. 2.verbesserte aufl. Wien,W.Braumüller,1882.

NK 0197309 MH

Knauer, Vincenz, 1828–1894.
Grundlinien zur aristotelisch-thomistischen psychologie. Von d[r.] Vincenz Knauer ... Wien, C. Konegen, 1885.
4 p. l., [vii]–viii, 283 p. 23 cm.

1. Aristoteles. 2. Thomas Aquinas, Saint—Psychology. 3. Psychology—Hist.
Full name: Vincenz Andreas Knauer.

B491.P8K5 39—14875

NK 0197310 DLC NBuU PU NjP NNUT MiU

B
82
K67
Knauer, Vincenz, 1828-1894.
Die Hauptprobleme der Philosophie in ihrer Entwicklung und Theilweisen Lösung von Thales bis Robert Hamerling. Wien W. Braumüller, 1892.
xviii, 408 p. 25cm.

"Vorlesungen gehalten an der K. K. Wiener Universität."

1. Philosophy--Hist. I. Title.

NK 0197311 NIC MB CtY NNC OCH OCIW NRU MH

Knauer, Vincenz, 1828–1894.

Die könige Shakespeares. Ein beitrag zur rechtsphilosophie. (Ursprünglich als festgabe zu dr. Anton Günthers 79. geburtstag bestimmt.) Von Vinzenz Knauer ... Wien, K. Gorischek, 1863.

NK 0197312 PU-F MB

PR
3001
.K67
Knauer,Vincenz,1828-1894.
William Shakespeare,der philosoph der sittlichen weltordnung. Von dr.Vincenz Knauer ... Innsbruck, Wagner, 1879.
x,370 p.,1 l. 21cm.

1.Shakespeare,William--Philosophy.
[Full name: Vincenz Andreas Knauer]

NK 0197313 MiU OU MH PU-F IU MB

Knauer, Vincenz

Anacreon.
... Die lieder des Anakreon in sinngetreuer nachdichtung, mit einer besprechung Rudolf Steiners aus dem jahre 1888 als geleitwort. Stuttgart [etc.] Orient-Occident-verlag, 1928.

Knauer, Vincenz Andreas
see Knauer, Vincenz, 1828-1894.

812
K72c
Knauer, Virginia Dare.
A crafty crook, a comedy ... Dayton, O., Paine publishing company [c1927]
14p. (On cover: Paine's popular plays)

NK 0197316 IU RPB

Knauer, Walter, *Diplomgärtner.*
... Der beitrag des gemüsebaues zu der ernährung des deutschen volkes, von diplomgärtner W. Knauer ... Mit einem vorwort von prof. dr. J. Reinhold ... Berlin, P. Parey, 1938.
116 p. incl. map, diagrs. 26 cm. (*On cover:* [Germany] Reichsministerium für ernährung und landwirtschaft. Berichte über landwirtschaft ... n. f. 141. sonderheft)
At head of title: Aus der Reichsarbeitsgemeinschaft "Agrarpolitik und betriebslehre" des Forschungsdienstes. Arbeit aus der Staatlichen versuchs- und forschungsanstalt für gartenbau zu Pillnitz a. d. Elbe. Direktor: prof. dr. J. Reinhold.
Summaries in German, English, French and Spanish.

"Schrifttum": p. 113–116.

1. Food supply—Germany. [1. Germany—Food supply] 2. Vegetables. (Series: Germany (Federal Republic, 1949–) Bundesministerium für Ernährung, Landwirtschaft und Forsten. Berichte über Landwirtschaft. Sonderheft 141)
[HD1951.A3 sonderheft 141] Agr 40–606 rev

U. S. Nat'l Agr. Libr. 18G31A sonderheft 141
for Library of Congress [r68c2]

NK 0197318 DNAL MoU MU

Knauer, Wilhelm.
..."Die freiheitskämpfe der Germanen unter Vespasian" im lateinischen unterrichte der prima... Gleiwitz, 1910.

NK 0197319 MdBJ

480
K72g
Knauer, Wilhelm.
Geschichte des klassischphilologischen vereins zu Halle a.S., von 1877-1902. Halle, 1902.
21p.

NK 0197320 IU

Knauer, Wilhelm, 1879–
De Luciano Menippeo ... Halis Saxonum, typis Wischani et Burkhardti, 1904.
3 p. l., 66 p., 1 l. 23cm.
Inaug.-diss.—Halle.
Vita.
Bibliography: p. 3.

Library of Congress 5-34363

NK 0197321 DLC NjP PU NIC CU CtY

VOLUME 300

583.951 K72a
Knauer, Wilhelm, 1909-
Anatomie und entwicklungsgeschichte der "rauhschaligen" rizinussamen und der nachweis von rizinus in futtermitteln... Hamburg [Hansischen Universität zu Hamburg] 1940.
pp.[125]-182. diagrs. 25cm.
Schrifttum: p. 178-182.
"Sonderdruck aus "Zeitschrift für tierernährung und futtermittelkunde", bd. 4, heft 2.
Inaug.-diss.-- Hamburg.
Lebenslauf.

NK 0197322 LU

Knauer-Groebers, Ferdinand.
Contra Delbrück; oder, Finanzzöllner gegen Frethändler und Schutzzöllner in Beziehung auf den Getreidezoll. Berlin, J. Bohne, 1879.
16 p. 8°.
n.t.-p.
In: TK p.v. 49, no. 4.
Title from cover.

NK 0197323 NN

Knauerhase, Edgar, 1911-
... Die Zähne als Ursache von Mandelentzündungen ... Greifswald, 1935.
Inaug.-Diss. - Greifswald.
Lebenslauf.
"Literaturangabe": p. 15-16.
[Full name: Edgar Gustav Eugen Knauerhase]

NK 0197324 CtY

Knauerhase, Gottfried, 1905-
... Ueber die Brauchbarkeit der Kahn-Reaktion zur serologischen Luesdiagnostik ... Bonn, 1930.
Inaug.-Diss. - Bonn.
Lebenslauf.
"Literaturverzeichnis": p. 30-32.

NK 0197325 CtY

Knauers Lexikon ...
see Knaurs Lexikon ...

Knauer's manufacturers of the United States...
New York, 1887-

Direct.
DK.16

NK 0197327 DLC MB ICJ OCl

Knauf, Albert Ensign, 1904-
The stereochemistry of diisoduryl disulfonic acid and certain N-phenyl triazoles, by Albert Ensign Knauf ... Urbana, Ill., 1933.
8 p., 1 l. 23½cm.
Abstract of thesis (PH. D.)—University of Illinois, 1933.
Vita.

1. Diphenyl compounds. 2. Triazoles. 3. Stereochemistry.
34-1783
Library of Congress QD341.H9K73 1933
Univ. of Illinois Libr.
——— Copy 2. [2] 547.27

NK 0197328 IU OU DLC

Knauf, Alfred, 1876-
... Die geographische verbreitung der gattung Cluytia ... Breslau, Buchdruckerei H. Fleischmann, 1903.
54, [2] p. 22cm.
Inaug.-dis.—Breslau.
At head of title: Aus dem Königl. Botanischen garten der Universität Breslau.

Subject entries: Cluytia.
Agr 4-89
Library, U. S. Dept. of Agriculture, no. 452.3K72

NK 0197329 DNAL CU MH-A CtY

Knauf, Erich, ed.
Das blaue Auge
see under title

Knauf, Erich.
... Ça ira! Reportage-roman aus dem Kapp-putsch. Berlin, Büchergilde Gutenberg, 1930.
3 p. l., 9-190, [1] p. illus. 24cm.

1. Germany—Hist.—Kapp putsch, 1920—Fiction. I. Title.
31-21563
Library of Congress PT2621.N33C2 1930
[a44c1] 833.91

NK 0197331 DLC CtY NcD NN MH

Knauf, Erich.
... Daumier. Berlin, Büchergilde Gutenberg, 1931.
3 p. l., 9-204, [2] p. illus. 24cm.

1. Daumier, Honoré Victorin, 1808-1879.
31-32696
Library of Congress NC1499.D3K6
Copyright A—Foreign 13635
[2] 927.4

NK 0197332 DLC CSt

Knauf, Erich.
... Empörung und gestaltung; künstlerprofile von Daumier bis Kollwitz. Berlin, Büchergilde Gutenberg, 1928.
2 p. l., 9-222 p., 1 l. illus., pl. 24cm.
CONTENTS.—Das gelächter von Paris. Honoré Daumier.—Der pflüger am morgen. Jean François Millet.—Ein vergessener. Alexandre Théophile Steinlen.—Der singende hammer. Constantin Meunier.—Der mensch steht auf. Frans Masereel.—Ein volkslied. Hans Thoma.—Der irrtum Wilhelm Leibls.—Der tumult des fleisches. Lovis Corinth.—Lebendige vergangenheit. Max Liebermann.—Im land der schönen träume. Ludwig von Hofmann.—Lachen, um nicht zu weinen. Heinrich Zille.—Rückkehr zur werkstatt. Emil Orlik.—Der einsame. Ernst Barlach.—Zwischen traum und leben. Alfred Kubin.—Es werde! Max Pechstein.—Die naturgewalt Nolde.—Bewegte landschaft. Fritz Winkler.—Die rote bulldogge. Th. Th. Heine.—In der feuerlinie. George Grosz.—Die nackte wahrheit. Otto Dix und Kurt Günther.—Die mutter erhebt sich. Käthe Kollwitz.

1. Artists. 2. Artists, French. 3. Artists, German. 4. Art—Hist.—19th cent. 5. Art—Hist.—20th cent. I. Title.
29-22956
Library of Congress N6450.K5

NK 0197334 DLC GU IEN MH OCl

Knauf (Ernst). *Ueber Fracturen des äusseren Gehörganges. [Wurtzburg.] 22 pp. 8°. *Leipsig, Hesse & Becker*, 1886.

NK 0197335 DNLM

G332.45 K729e
KNAUF, FRANCISCO I
Exchange tables; tablas de cambio de libras esterlinas a pesos y centavos y vice versa calculadas por octavos de peniques a los cambios de 10 peniques hasta 30 7/8 peniques, por Francisco I. Knauf ... Santiago de Chile, Imprenta Estrella de Chile, 1891.
90p. 27cm.

1. Foreign exchange - Tables, etc.

599521

NK 0197336 TxU

Knauf (Georg) [1877-]. *Ueber einen Fall von Bauch-Blasen-Genitalspalte. 36 pp., 2 pl., 1 l. 8°. München, C. Wolf & Sohn, 1904.

NK 0197337 DNLM

Knauf (Karl) [1893-]. *Ein Beitrag zur Kenntnis der Explosionsverletzungen des Auges durch Pulver und Dynamit. [Giessen.] 22 pp. 8°. Neuwied, J. Meincke, 1920.

NK 0197338 DNLM ICRL

KNAUF, Max.
Die operative behandlung der ankylosen des kniegelenkes. Jena, 1884.

NK 0197339 MBCo ICRL DNLM

Knauf, Richard.
Erläuterungen zum Kontenrahmen für mittlere und kleinere Betriebe der privaten Wirtschaft. Berlin, Deutscher Zentralverlag [1954]
62 p. 21 cm. (Schriftenreihe zum Abgabenrecht, Heft 6)

1. Accounting. I. Title.
HF5645.K59 66-93784

NK 0197340 DLC

Knauf, Walter: Über Mirion. [Maschinenschrift.] 21 S. 4° [Lag nicht vor.] — Auszug: Hanau a. M. 1922: Oppenheim. 2 Bl. 8°
Gießen, Med. Diss. v. 24. März 1923 [U 23. 3444

NK 0197341 ICRL

Knauff, Carl Gustave Bruno, 1867-
Refurbishing the home, by Carl G. B. Knauff; illustrations by the author. [New York] Whittlesey house, McGraw-Hill book company, inc. [°1938]
xviii, 337 p. incl. front., illus. 23½cm.

1. House decoration. I. Title.
38-27650
Library of Congress NK2110.K55
[a42z2] 747

OCl OLak OOxM WaT Or OrU CaBVaU WaSp
NK 0197342 DLC NcC NcD WaS IdU MU NcD PP PPD PPGi

VOLUME 300

Knauff, Christopher Wilkinson, 1838–1911.
... Doctor Tucker, priest-musician; a sketch which concerns the doings and thinkings of the Rev. John Ireland Tucker, s. t. d., including a brief converse about the rise and progress of church music in America; by Christopher W. Knauff, m. a. New York, A. D. F. Randolph company, 1897.
ix, 351 p. pl., 2 port. (incl. front.) 20½cm.

1. Tucker, John Ireland, 1819–1895.

Library of Congress ML410.T89 5-20194 Revised

NK 0197343 DLC IU MeB PPL PP OCl OO MWA NN NNUT

Knauff, Christopher Wilkinson, 1838–1911.
A sermon by the Rev. Christopher W. Knauff, m. a., preached upon the occasion of the benediction of an organ a. d. 1890. Philada, New York, Theo. C. Knauff co. [©1890]
14, [1] p. illus. 13¾ x 17½cm.
Cover-title: De organis.

1. Music in churches. 2. Organ. i. Title: De organis.

Library of Congress ML3001.K6 24-31343
Copyright 1890: 1958?

NK 0197344 DLC

Knauff, Christopher Wilkinson, 1838-1911
Te Deum laudamus. Benedictus. [In C. Accomp. for organ.]
(In Parish Choir, The. No. 151, pp. 601-607. Medford, 1881.)

May 9, 1902
E3959 — T.r. (2). — Church music. Anthems. &c.

NK 0197345 MB

Knauff, Claus Heinrich, 1858-

Polbahnen, deren roulette ein kreis ist... Marburg, 1889

Thesis--Marburg
Lebenslauf.

1. Mathematics--Dissertations--Marburg

NK 0197346 RPB CU MH

Knauff, Elisabet.
Frau und Pferd. Berlin, Krüger [c1953]
126 p. illus.

NK 0197347 MoU

Knauff, Ellen (Raphael) 1915–
The Ellen Knauff story. [1st ed.] New York, W. W. Norton [1952]
xvi, 242, [2] p. facsims. 22 cm.

1. Emigration and immigration law—U. S.

JV6507.K56 325.73 52-8208

NK 0197348 DLC WaT WaS WaE CaBVa OrP Or OCH NN TxU MB

QC7
K6
1900
Knauff, Franz

Die Physik des Heron von Alexandria. Berlin, 1900.
23p. diagrs. 25 cm.

Beilage zum Jahresbericht des Sophien-Gymnasiums zu Berlin. Ostern 1900.
Bibliographical footnotes.

1. Physics--History. 2. Hero, of Alexandria.

NK 0197349 RPB MH DDO

WX
K67n
1879
Knauff, Friedrich.
Das neue academische Krankenhaus in Heidelberg. Im auftrage der academischen Krankenhaus-Commission. München, F. Basserman, 1879.
66 p. and atlas.
Text inserted in atlas.
1. Heidelberg. Universität. Akademisches Hospital.
I. Title

NK 0197350 DNLM MiDA PBL MB

Knauff (Fritz) [1880–]. *Zwei Fälle von Aneurysma der Bauchaorta. 30 pp. 8°. München, C. Wolf & Sohn, 1905.

NK 0197351 DNLM

814.8
X2
K67hu
1745
[KNAUFF, Georg]
Huelff in der Noth, das ist: S. Franciscus Xaverius S. J. der Indianer Apostel, in schwaeren Anligen bey dem gecreutzigten Jesu Wunder-Thaetiger Noth-Helffer durch Zehen-Freytaegige Andacht, zum Geist- und leiblichen Trost aller Noth-Leydenden von Einem auss der Gesellschafft Jesu vorgestelt. Coelln, bey Servatii Noethen Seel. Erben unter goelden Wwagen, 1745 ...
3p.l.,184, [4]p. front.(port.) 14cm.

NK 0197352 MH-AH

---

*
M1
.S444
v.148
no.59
Knauff, George P

Jacksons cotillion. Baltimore, Geo. Willig, ©1839.
[1] p. 33cm. [Sheet music collection, v. 148, no. 59]
Caption title.
Gillingham.

1. Cotillions (Piano).

NK 0197353 ViU

---

*
M1
.S444
v.82
no.23
Knauff, George P

Mount Elba waltz, composed & dedicated to Miss Virginia A. B. Shields. Baltimore, F. D. Benteen & Co. [185-] Pl. no. 2400.
[1] p. 36cm. [Sheet music collection, v. 82, no. 23]
Caption title.

1. Waltzes (Piano) I. Title.

NK 0197354 ViU

---

*
M1
.S444
v.122
no.13
Knauff, George P.

Virginia quick march. Baltimore, Geo. Willig, Jr ©1839.
[1] p. 33cm. [Sheet music collection, v. 122, no. 13]
Caption title.
E. Gillingham.

Continued in next column

Continued from preceding column

1. Marches (Piano). I. Title.

NK 0197355 ViU

Knauff, George P *comp. and arr.*
Virginia reels; selected and arranged for the piano forte. 37 cts net. Published by Geo. Willig, Baltimore. [18—] Pl. no. 1535, 1536.
2 v. 36 cm.

1. Country-dances (Piano) I. Title.

M1.A13K M 56-313 rev

NK 0197356 DLC NcD ViU

W.C.L.
M780.88
A512P
no.31-34
Knauff, George P compiler and arr.

Virginia reels. Baltimore, F. D. Benteen [ca. 1850]
4 v. 33 cm.
For piano.
[No. 31-34] in a vol. of piano music collected by H. H. Alexander.

1. Country-dances (Piano) I. Title.

NK 0197357 NcD ViU

---

fM1
A13C6
no.27
Knauff, George P

Wait for the wagon. Ethiopian song, for the piano forte. By Geo. P.Knauff. Baltimore, Miller & Beacham, successors to F.D.Benteen [1851]
5p. 34cm. (In [Collection of songs published in the U.S. 1840-1860, no.27])

For voice and piano with choral refrain for S.A.T.B.
1. Vocal quartets with piano. I. Title.

NK 0197358 IaU NcD MB

Knauff, Günther, 1903-
Studien über Balantidium Coli. ... Würzburg, 1935.
Inaug. Diss. - Berlin, 1935.
Lebenslauf.

NK 0197359 ICRL CtY

Knauff, Gustav, 1860–
Studien über Sir David Lyndsay. I. ... Von Gustav Knauff ... Berlin, Buchdruckerei von G. Schade (O. Francke) [1885?]
2 p. l., 91, [1] p. 22½cm.
Inaug.-diss.—Berlin.
Vita.

1. Lindsay, Sir David, fl. 1490–1555.

Library of Congress PR2296.L8K6 42-42844

NK 0197360 DLC NIC NcD ICRL CtY MiU MH NN NjP

32
10102
Knauff, H.W., ed.
Music of the Service adapted to the Church Book for the use of Evangelical Lutheran congregations. No. 1 and 2. Philadelphia, [H. Knauff and son, 1871]
16 p. 12°.

NK 0197361 DLC

VOLUME 300

Knauff, M.
. Entwurf zur Kanalisation der Residenzstadt Potsdam nach dem Shone-System, nebst Vorschlägen zur Reinigung der Spüljauche. Aufgestellt im Auftrage des Magistrats der Stadt Potsdam. 1 p. l., 90 pp. roy. 8°. 6 ch. fol. folded in 8°. *Berlin, A. Leydel*, 1885.

NK 0197362 DNLM

K
TD
655
H68
Knauff, M
Die Mängel der Schwemmkanalisation gegenüber dem Shone-System mit Hinblick auf die Kanalisation der Stadt Berlin; Beiträge zur Beurtheilung des gegenwärtigen Standes der Kanalisations- und Berieselungsfrage. Eingabe an den Magistrat zu Berlin, von M. Knauff. Berlin, Polytechnische Buchhandlung A. Seydel, 1884.
59 p. fold. chart. 25cm.

Bound with Hobrecht, James. Beiträge zur Beurtheilung des gegenwärtigen Standes der Kanalisations- und Berieselungs-Frage. Berlin, 1883.

1. Berlin--Sewerage. 2. Sewerage. I. Title.

NK 0197364 NIC

Knauff (M.) The sewage of Steglitz on the Shone system. Transl. from a lecture given by . . ., with an introduction by Edwin Chadwick. 20 pp. 8°. *London*, [1888].
Repr. from: San. Engin., Lond., 1888. xiii.

NK 0197365 DNLM

Knauff (M.) Der Torf als Filtrationsmittel für Kanaljauchen. 24 pp. 8°. *Berlin, A. Leydel*, 1884.

NK 0197366 DNLM

Knauff, M., writer of fiction.
Auf dem Holzwege! Schwank in vier Aufzügen. Berlin, F. Bloch, 1887.
82 p., 1 l. 8°.

NK 0197367 NN

Z5814
.C9K6
(Ed)
Knauff, Mary E
The elementary school curriculum; an annotated bibliography. Prepared by Mary E. Knauff, Alfred R. Marsh and Arline F. Pickett. Irvington, N.J., 1950.
ii, 52 l.

1. Education—Curricula—Bibl.

NK 0197368 ICU MnU

Knauff, Max, & Weyl, Th.
Asyle, niedere Herbergen, Volksküchen u. s. w. 1895. (*In* Handbuch der Hygiene, vol. 6. p. 141-177. 18 il. Jena 1897.)

NK 0197369 ICJ NN MB

KNAUFF, Maximilian, 1864-
Ueber die anatomie der Beckenregion beim Braunfisch. Inaug.-diss., Breslau. Jena, 1905.
64 p

NK 0197370 MH DNLM CtY PU NN

Knauff, Raymond Eugene, 1925-
Thiamine deprivation and the utilization of certain keto acids by the rat. Ann Arbor, University Microfilms, 1951 [i. e. 1953]
([University Microfilms, Ann Arbor, Mich.] Publication no. 5060)
Microfilm copy of typescript. Positive.
Collation of the original: vi, 141 l. illus., tables.
Thesis—University of Michigan.
Abstracted in Dissertation abstracts, v. 13 (1953) no. 3, p. 304-305.
Bibliography: leaves 135-141.
1. Thiamine. 2. Acids, Organic. 3. Metabolism.
Microfilm AC-1 no. 5060 Mic A 53-541

Michigan. Univ. Libr.
for Library of Congress [1]†

NK 0197371 MiU DLC

D
765.2
.D3
K5
Knauff, Stanisław
Wojna zaczęła się w Gdańsku. Warszawa, Państwowe Zakłady Wydawn. Szkolnych, 1946.
46 p. 25 cm. (Biblioteka ziem odzyskanych)

1. World War, 1939-1945 - Danzig. 2. World War, 1939-1945 - Causes. 3. Danzig - Hist. I. Title.

1907

NK 0197372 WU NN

Knauff, Theodore Christian, 1847-
Aladdin the Second, by Theo. C. Knauff... New York, J. S. Tait & sons, 1894. 279 p. illus. 19cm.

NK 0197373 NN

Knauff, Theodore Christian, 1847-
Athletics for physical culture. By Theo. C. Knauff. New York, J. S. Tait & sons [1894]
1 p. l., 9-422 p. front., illus., 46 pl. 19cm.

1. Athletics. 2. Physical education and training. 3. Sports.

Library of Congress GV701.K67 5-29259

NK 0197374 DLC PP PPM PHC PU OClW MB NN

Knauff, Theodore Christian, 1847-
An experiment in training for the useful and the beautiful, a history, by Theodore C. Knauff. [Philadelphia] Philadelphia school of design for women, 1922.
100 p. fold. front., illus. (incl. ports., facsims.) 17½cm.

1. Philadelphia school of design for women. I. Title.

Library of Congress N330.P52 1922 23-3589

NK 0197375 DLC PPTU PHi PPL PPFr

Knauff, Theodore Christian, 1847-
Glances at our history. Read before Union Lodge, No. 121, F. and A. M., jurisdiction of Pennsylvania, on its 75th anniversary. Phila., 1886.
46 p.

NK 0197376 PHi PPL

Knauff, Theodore Christian, 1847-
A history of the Society of the sons of Saint George, established at Philadelphia, for the advice and assistance of Englishmen in distress, on Saint George's day, April 23, 1772, with the several charters of the society, the first and the present by-laws, complete alphabetical list of members from 1772 to 1923, a list of the present members, a full list of the officers for the one hundred and fifty-one years, the complete story of the Sully portrait of Queen Victoria, and "The impressions of a steward", concerning the work of the society in its most important connection, which was the end and object for which it was formed, by Theodore C. Knauff. [Philadelphia] 1923.
256 p. front., plates, ports., facsims. 24cm.

1. Society of the sons of St. George, Philadelphia.

Library of Congress HS1804.P5S64 1923 24-3547

NK 0197378 DLC PP PHi PPL PHC PU TU

[**Knauff, Theodore Christian**] 1847-
Other sheep I have, by Theodore Christian [*pseud.*]; The proceedings of the celestial commission on church unity ... New York and London, G. P. Putnam's sons, 1911.
vi p., 1 l., 385 p. 22cm. $2.00

"Opinions expressed by imaginary characters in the work are really the opinions of learned authorities in the churches."

Library of Congress 12-387

NK 0197379 DLC OrP OKentU KyWAT NRCR PU PPL PP OO

Knauff, Theo[dore] Christian, 1847-
The people's friend. An address ... at Meadville, Pa., October 20, 1896, opposing the re-election of Hon. Jos. C. Sibley to congress. n.p., 1896.
44 p. 24°.

NK 0197380 NN PU PHi

Knauff, Theodore Christian, 1847-
Richard Vaux. An address delivered at the unveiling of the second painting of Brother Vaux, October 11, 1917. Phila., 1917.
20 p.

NK 0197381 PHi

Knauff, Theodore Christian, 1847-
The silver question in a nutshell, by Theo. C. Knauff. Philadelphia[, cop. 1895]. 48 p. illus. 24°. (Sound Money League of Pennsylvania. [Document no. 9.])

1. Bimetallism. 2. Ser.
N. Y. P. L. May 9, 1927

NK 0197382 NN PU

VOLUME 300

Knaufft, Ernest, 1864-
The Art student, an illustrated monthly for the home study of drawing and illustrating, and the Limner, art school news and art school literature.
New York ₍18

Knaufft, Ernest, 1864–
Drawing for printers. A practical treatise on the art of designing and illustrating in connection with typography. Containing complete instruction, fully illustrated, concerning the art of drawing, for the beginner as well as the more advanced student. By Ernest Knaufft. Chicago, The Inland printer company, 1899.
246 p. illus. 19cm.

1. Drawing. 2. Illustration of books. 3. Lettering. 4. Wood-engraving.
A 10-2536
Title from St. Paul Pub. Libr. Printed by L. C.

NK 0197384 PSt PP OCl OO OU ViU ICJ MB MnS

[KNAUFFT, ERNEST] 1864–
The early art training of B.R. at Purdue University. [New York: Press of the Woolly Whale, privately printed, 1935] 6 l. illus. (incl. facsim.) 22½cm.

Caption-title.
Signed: Ernest Knaufft.

798898A. 1. Rogers, Bruce, 1870– . I. Title.

NK 0197385 NN NBu

W 4 M96 1951
KNAUL, Eckart, 1921-
Das Felsenbeinspitzen-Syndrom, Gradenigo. ₍München₎ 1951.
37 *l.*
Cover title.
Inaug.-Diss. - Munich.
Typewritten copy.
1. Otitis media

NK 0197386 DNLM

Knaul, Peter.
Der Kesselschmied, lehr- und nachschlagebuch für lehrlinge, gesellen, vorzeichner und meister. Berlin, Verlag der Deutschen arbeitsfront «1943»
103p. illus.

NK 0197387 ICRL

Knaul, Peter.
Das kesselschmied, lehr- und nachschlagenbuch für lehrlinge, gesellen, vorzeichner und meister, von Peter Knaul. Berlin, Verlag der Deutschen arbeitsfront ₍1943₎
103 p. incl. illus., tables, diagrs. 21 cm.
"2. auflage."
"Zahlentafeln": p. 77–103.

1. Steam-boilers—Design. 2. Sheet-metal work—Pattern-making.
TJ290.K67 1943 621.1845 A F 47–5239
Brown univ. Library for Library of Congress ₍2₎†

NK 0197388 RPB DLC

W 4 F821 1939
KNAUP, Richard, 1912-
Dauerschlagprüfung von Halbkronenanzern mit und ohne Verschraubung im Dentin. Seligenstadt, Sprey, 1939.
16 p. illus.
Inaug.-Diss. - Frankfurt am Main.

NK 0197389 DNLM

W 4 W95 1954
KNAUP, Rudolf, 1919-
Über die Schlatter-Osgood'sche Erkrankung und ihre Behandlung. Würzburg, 1954.
36 p. illus.
Inaug.-Diss. - Würzburg.
1. Osteochondritis

NK 0197390 DNLM

Knaupp, A.
Die jong Van der Byls, deur A. Knaupp ⟨Tieras⟩ Tekenings deur J. B. Montgomery. Pretoria, J. L. van Schaik, bepk., 1939.
150 p. incl. front., illus. 20½cm.

I. Title.
42-9258
Library of Congress PZ13.K55

NK 0197391 DLC

Knaupp, Oskar, Tierarzt in Aichstetten ⟨i. Allgäu⟩: Arbeiten aus d. med. Veter.-Klinik d. Univ. Giessen. ₍Klinische u. experimentelle Studien über die Wirkung des Spiritus auf die Mägen der Wiederkäuer. Mit 19 Tab., 19 Kurventaf., u. 2 schwarzen Figurentaf. München 1911: Leopold-Buchdr. 76 S., 1 Taf. 8°
Gießen, Veterinär-Med. Diss. v. 19. April 1911, Ref. Gmeiner
[Geb. 7. Dez. 86 Deggingen; Wohnort: Gießen; Staatsangeh.: Württemberg; Vorbildung: Realgymn. Ulm Reife M. 05; Studium: Tierärztl. Hochschulen Stuttgart 4, Berlin 1, Stuttgart 3 S.; Rig. 3. Febr. 11.] [U 11. 1297

NK 0197392 ICRL PU MH DNLM CtY

Knaur, Friedrich Karl, 1850-
see Knauer, Friedrich Karl, 1850-

Knaur, Fritz.
Johannisbad im Riesengebirge, Böhmen. Mit 14 Zinkogravuren. Von Dr. Fritz Knaur, ... Wien, Selbstverlag des Verfassers, 1897.
[4], 59, [1], lxiii, [1] p. incl. tables. plates. 19cm.

NK 0197394 DNLM ICJ

Knaur, Käthe, 1915–
Schöne Hunde ₍von₎ Käthe Knaur ₍und₎ Marga Ruperti. 88 Kunstdrucktafeln nach Originalaufnahmen von Käthe Knaur, mit erläuternden Texten von Marga Ruperti. Rüschlikon-Zürich, A. Müller ₍1953₎
116 p. illus. 26 cm.

1. Dog breeds. I. Ruperti, Marga, 1918– joint author. II. Title.
SF427.K48 636.71 53–35765 ‡

NK 0197395 DLC InLP

Knaur, Käthe, 1915–
Schöne Hunde ₍von₎ Käthe Knaur ₍und₎ Marga Ruperti. Neue Folge. 80 Kunstdrucktafeln nach Originalaufnahmen von Käthe Knaur, mit erläuternden Texten von Marga Ruperti. Rüschlikon-Zürich, A. Müller ₍1954₎
128 p. illus. 26 cm.

1. Dog breeds. I. Ruperti, Marga, 1918– joint author. II. Title.
SF427.K482 54–44034 ‡

NK 0197396 DLC NIC DNAL InLP

Knaur, Thomas.
Selectus instrumentorum chirurgicorum in usum discentium et practicorum tabulis exaratus. Cum usus declaratione edidit Thomas Knaur, ... Cum indice tabularum et instrumentorum trilingui latino, germanico, gallico. Viennae, Apud viduam Alberti, 1796.
[12], xvi, 48, [2] p. xxv pl. (part fold.) 34cm.
Latin and German text in parallel columns.

NK 0197397 ICJ PPPH CtY-M DNLM PPC PU

Knaurs Buch der Schwänke
see under
Penzoldt, Ernst, 1892- comp.

Knaurs gesundheits-lexikon; ein führer ...
see under Hiron, Peter.

Knaurs Gesundheits-Lexikon; ein Handbuch ...
see under Löbel, Josef, 1882-

Knaurs Gesundheits-Lexikon; ein Nachschlagewerk ...
see under Hiron, Peter.

Knaurs Heilpflanzenbuch; ein Hausbuch der Naturheilkunde
see under Hertwig, Hugo.

Knaurs konversations-lexikon, A-Z: 35000 stichwörter, 2600 illustrationen, 70 einfarbige und bunte tafeln und geographische karten, 20 übersichten, 115 statistische schaubilder im text. Verlag von Th. Knaur Nachf., c. 1931.
1875 p.
1. German language - Dictionaries.

NK 0197403 GAT

Knaurs konversations-lexikon, A–Z; 35000 stichwörter, 2600 illustrationen, 70 einfarbige und bunte tafeln und geographische karten, 18 übersichten, 115 statistische schaubilder im text. Berlin, T. Knaur nachf., 1932.
3 p. l., 1876 col. illus. (incl. ports.) plates (part col.) fold. maps, diagrs. 18½cm.
In double columns.
"Vorwort des herausgebers" signed: Dr. Richard Friedenthal.

1. Encyclopedias and dictionaries, German. I. Friedenthal, Richard, ed.
Library of Congress AG27.K65 32-1858
Copyright A—Foreign 14551
₍3₎ 033

NK 0197404 DLC WaS CBM MB

Knaurs konversations-lexikon, A–Z; 37000 stichwörte 2600 illustrationen, 75 einfarbige und bunte tafeln u geographische karten, 50 übersichten, 100 statistisc schaubilder im text. Berlin, T. Knaur nachf., 1934.
ix p., 1900 col. illus. (incl. ports.) plates (part col.) maps (part fold.) diagrs. 18½cm.
In double columns.

1. Encyclopedias and dictionaries, German.
Library of Congress AG27.K65 1934 34-4826
Copyright A—Foreign 22954
₍3₎ 033

NK 0197405 DLC NcU PSC CtY

VOLUME 300

Knaurs konversations-lexikon, A-Z; 37000 stichwörter, 2600 illustrationen, 75 einfarbige und bunte tafeln und geographische karten, 50 übersichten, 100 statistische schaubilder im text. Berlin, T. Knaur nachf., 1936.
ix p., 1900 col. illus. (incl. ports.) plates (part col.) maps (part fold.) diagrs. 18cm.
Two columns to the page.

1. Encyclopedias and dictionaries, German.
36-3837
Library of Congress AG27.K65 1936
Copyright A—Foreign 30044
[2] 033

NK 0197406 DLC WaU NN MH OOxM

Knaurs lexikon, A-Z; 37000 stichwörter, 2600 illustrationen, 75 einfarbige und bunte tafeln und geographische karten, 50 übersichten, 100 statistische schaubilder im text. Berlin, T. Knaur nachf., 1938.
ix, 1900 col. illus. (incl. ports.) plates (part col.) maps (part fold.) diagrs. 18½cm.
In double columns.

1. Encyclopedias and dictionaries, German.
38-30932
Library of Congress AG27.K65 1938
Copyright A—Foreign 38335
[2] 033

NK 0197407 DLC NN

Knaurs lexikon, A-Z; 37000 stichwörter, 2650 illustrationen, 75 einfarbige und bunte tafeln und geographische karten, 120 übersichten und statistische schaubilder im text. Berlin, T. Knaur nachf., 1939.
ix p., 1900 col. illus. (incl. ports.) plates (part col.) fold. maps, diagrs. 18½cm.
In double columns.

1. Encyclopedias and dictionaries, German.
41-10247
Library of Congress AG27.K65 1939
[a2] 033

NK 0197408 DLC

Knaurs lexikon, A-Z; 37000 stichwörter, 2650 illustrationen, 75 einfarbige und bunte tafeln und geographische karten, 120 übersichten und statistische schaubilder im text. Nachtrag. Berlin, Th. Knaur nachf., 1939.
ix p., 1900 col. illus. (incl. ports.) plates (part col.) maps (part fold.) diagrs. 18½cm.
Two columns to the page.

1. Encyclopedias and dictionaries, German.
46-32382
Library of Congress AG27.K65 1939 a
[2] 033

NK 0197409 DLC ViU NSyU NcU MH

Knaurs Lexikon, A-Z. München, Droemersche Verlagsanstalt, 1950.
2086 columns. illus. (part col.) ports., maps (part fold., part col.) 19 cm.

1. Encyclopedias and dictionaries, German.
AG27.K65 1950 033 50-29539
[7]

NK 0197410 DLC DNLM

Knaurs Lexikon, A-Z. [Herausgeber: Paul Zöckler] München, Droemersche Verlagsanstalt, 1950/51.
vi p., 1996 columns. illus. (part col.) ports., maps (part fold., part col.) 19 cm.

1. Encyclopedias and dictionaries, German.
AG27.K65 1950a 033 51-22852

NK 0197411 DLC MtBC NcD DS

Knaurs Lexikon, A-Z. [Herausgeber: Paul Zöckler] München, Droemersche Verlagsanstalt, 1951/52 [c1952]
v p., 1996 columns. illus. (part col.) ports., maps (part fold., part col.) 19 cm.

1. Encyclopedias and dictionaries, German.
AG27.K65 1952 033 53-23831

NK 0197412 DLC

Knaurs Lexikon, A-Z. [Herausgeber: Fritz Bolle] München, T. Knaur Nachf. [c1954]
v p., 1994 columns. illus. (part col.) ports., maps (part fold., part col.) 19 cm.
Originally published under title: Knaurs Konversations-Lexikon.

1. Encyclopedias and dictionaries, German.
AG27.K65 1954 57-19991
[4]

NK 0197413 DLC OU OCl NN

Knaurs Lexikon moderner Kunst. 321 meist farbige Abbildungen. [Bearb. und hrsg. von L. G. Buchheim] München, T. Knaur Nachf. [1955]
336 p. illus. (part col.) 22 cm.
Based on Dictionnaire de la peinture moderne (Paris, 1954)

1. Art—Dictionaries—German. 2. Painting—Dictionaries—German. I. Buchheim, Lothar Günther, ed. II. Dictionnaire de la peinture moderne.
ND30.K58 A 56-1069
Harvard Univ. Library for Library of Congress [a56b1]†

NK 0197414 TNJ NcD MdU MH DLC NN CU OClW ICU NcU NjP CLU KEmT

Knaurs welt-atlas; 40 farbige haupt- und nebenkarten, und 90 statistische und spezialkarten, diagramme und zahlreiche tabellen mit ausführlichem geo-politischen text und vollständigem alphabetischen verzeichnis von über 20,000 geographischen namen; herausgegeben von dr. Johannes Riedel. Berlin, Th. Knaur nachf. [1928]
410, [1] p. incl. 107 maps (part col.) tables, diagrs. 20cm.

1. Atlases. I. Riedel, Johannes, ed.
Map 40-96
Library of Congress. Div. of maps
[2]

NK 0197415 DLC NcU OU CtY

912
K729
1931
Knaurs Welt-atlas. 40 farbige Haupt- und Nebenkarten und 90 statistische und Spezialkarten, Diagramme und zahlreiche Tabellen mit ausführlichem geo-politischen Text und vollständigen alphabetischen Verzeichnis von über 20,000 geographischen Namen. Hrsg. von Johannes Riedel. Vollständig neue Ausg. 1932. Berlin, Knaur [1931]
416p. maps(part col.) 20cm.

1. Geography. 2. Atlases. I. Riedel, Johannes, cartographer, ed.

NK 0197416 IU ICU MH

Knaurs welt-atlas; 53 farbige haupt- und nebenkarten, 100 statistische schaubilder, zahlreiche spezialkarten, diagramme und tabellen, ausführlicher geographischer, bevölkerungs- und wirtschaftsstatistischer text, alphabetisches verzeichnis von über 29000 geographischen namen; herausgegeben von dr. Johannes Riedel. Vollständig neue ausg. 1936. Berlin, T. Knaur nachf. [1935]
591 p. incl. illus., double maps, diagrs. 20cm.

1. Geography. 2. Atlases. I. Riedel, Johannes, ed.
37-16918
Library of Congress
Copyright A—Foreign 30045
[2] 912

NK 0197417 DLC WaU PSC

Knaurs welt-atlas; 130 farbige und schwarze haupt- und nebenkarten, ausführlicher geographischer, bevölkerungs- und wirtschaftspolitischer text mit vielen spezialkarten, tabellen und schaubildern. Register mit 29000 stichworten. Vollständig neue ausg. Berlin, T. Knaur nachf., 1938.
272, 175, [1] p. illus., 40 double maps. 20cm.

1. Geography. 2. Atlases.
38-22911
Library of Congress
Copyright A—Foreign 38333
[2] 912

NK 0197418 DLC NcD

Knaurs welt-atlas; 130 farbige und schwarze haupt- und nebenkarten. Ausführlicher geographischer, bevölkerungs- und wirtschaftspolitischer text mit vielen spezialkarten, tabellen und schaubildern. Register mit 29000 stichworten. Vollständig neue ausg. Berlin, T. Knaur nachf., 1939.
272, 175, [1] p. illus., 40 double maps, diagrs. 20cm.

1. Geography. 2. Atlases.
41-13102
Library of Congress [2] 912

NK 0197419 DLC

Knaurs Welt-Atlas; 119 farbige und schwarze Haupt- und Nebenkarten. Ausführlicher geographischer, bevölkerungs- und wirtschaftspolitischer Text mit vielen Spezialkarten, Tabellen und Schaubildern. Register mit 23,000 Stichwörtern. Vollständig neu bearb. von Günter Pahl. München, Droemer, 1951/52 [c1950]
304 p., 51 col. maps (part fold.) 159 p. maps, diagrs., tables. 20 cm.

1. Geography. 2. Atlases, German. I. Pahl, Günter, 1910– ed.
G1019.K57 1951 Map 52-1188

NK 0197420 DLC

G1019
.K57
1955
Map
Knaurs Welt-Atlas; 186 farbige Haupt- und Nebenkarten. Ausführlicher geographischer, bevölkerungs- und wirtschaftspolitischer Text mit vielen Spezialkarten, Tabellen und Schaubildern. München, Th. Knaur Nachf. [1955]
226, 176, 135 p. illus., col. maps. 25 cm.
"In einer völlig neu gestalteten Ausgabe."—Book jacket.

Geography. 2. Atlases, German.
G1019.K57 1955 A 56-1879
Harvard Univ. Library for Library of Congress [1]

NK 0197421 MH CU-SB IaU DLC

Knaurs weltgeschichte von der urzeit bis zur gegenwart
see under Müller, Karl Alexander von, 1882- ed.

Knaus, A.
...La guerre hors la loi. Paris: "Éditions Spes," 1929. 264 p. incl. tables. 8°.

547006A. 1. European federation. 2. War and peace, 1914.
N. Y. P. L. October 22, 1931

NK 0197423 NN DS CtY

Knaus (Albert). *Ueber nervöse Affektionen im sekundären Stadium der Syphilis. 28 pp. 8°. Bern, Haller, 1894.

NK 0197424 DNLM

VOLUME 300

Knaus, Albrecht, 1913- ed.

PT2100 .M8A3 1950 **Müller, Friedrich von,** 1779-1849.
Goethes Unterhaltungen mit dem Kanzler Friedrich von Müller. ⌜Hrsg. von Albrecht Knaus⌝ München, R. Piper ⌜1950⌝

Knaus, Albrecht, 1913- ed.

ML410 .M5A285 **Mendelssohn-Bartholdy, Felix,** 1809-1847.
Reisebriefe. ⌜Hrsg. von Albrecht Knaus⌝ München, R. Piper ⌜°1947⌝

Knaus (Antonius). * De rheumatismo. 11, 6 pp. sm. 4°. *Monachii, C. Wolf,* 1828.

NK 0197427 DNLM

HD 1491 .G3 K67 Knaus, Carl Christian, 1801-1884.
Der flurzwang in seinen folgen und wirkungen und die mittel zu dessen beseitigung. Von dr. Carl Christ. Knaus ... Stuttgart und Tübingen, J. G. Cotta'scher verlag, 1843.
vi, ⌜7⌝-48 p., 1 ℓ. VII fold. plans (part col.) 22½ cm.

1. Agriculture, Cooperative - Germany. I. Title.

NK 0197428 MiU

Knaus, Carl Christian, 1801-1884.
Ueber die mittel, um die waldstreu für die landwirthschaft möglichst entbehrlich zu machen. Amorbach, 1839.
"Für die verhältnisse der Odenwälder abtheilung des Grossherzoglich badischen landwirthschaftlichen bezirksvereins buchen."
No. 7 in volume lettered: Pamphlets. Agriculture. v. 3.

NK 0197429 MiU

Knaus, Carl Christian, 1801-1884.
Vortrag über mobilisirung des grundeigenthums oder bodenzerstücklung. Stuttgart, 1842.
"Gehalten in der zweiten allgemeinen sitzung der sechsten Versammlung deutsche land- und forstwirthe zu Stuttgart den 22. september 1842."
No. 7 in volume lettered: Pamphlets. Agriculture. v. 4.

NK 0197430 MiU CtY

Knaus, Cassian, 1899-
Ueber den einfluess der konstitution auf bildungsgeschwindigkeit ... Basel, 1923.
Inaug.-diss.

NK 0197431 ICRL CtY MH PU

Knaus, Edward William, 1912-
Composite and pattern statements; preparation and use, using shirt industry as the sample. ⌜New York, Credit Research Foundation, 1952⌝
61 p. illus. 28 cm.
"Submitted in fulfillment of the requirements for the Executive award and for graduation from the Graduate School of Credit and Financial Management sponsored by Credit Research Foundation ... ⌜and others⌝"

1. Financial statements. 2. Shirts, Men's. I. Title.

HF5681.B2K57 *657.3 52-4370 ‡

NK 0197432 DLC

Knaus, Frank J
How to paint with air, by Frank J. Knaus. For artists, illustrators, cartoonists, designers, photographers and architects. Chicago, Paasche airbrush co., c1947. 92 p. illus. 25cm.

475921B. 1. Air brush. 2. Advertising—Art.
N. Y. P. L. June 24, 1949

NK 0197433 NN KEmT DCU PSt MiD Or WaS NcGW MiU

751.49 K729h 1947 Engin Lib'y **Knaus, Frank J**
How to paint with air; for artists, illustrators, cartoonists, designers, photographers and architects. 3d. ed. Chicago, Paasche Airbrush Co., c1947.
95p. illus., ports. 26cm.

1009192 1. Airbrush art. I. Title.

NK 0197434 TxU

⌜Knaus, Henry⌝
Judicial usurpation. An open letter to Congress showing this in the injunctions in labor disputes ... Chicago, °1908.
⌜16⌝ p. 24cm.
Signed: Henry Knaus.

1. Injunctions. 2. Labor laws and legislation—U. S.

8-9022

Library of Congress HD7819.U5K6
(Copyright 1908 A 199824)

NK 0197435 DLC ICJ DL

Knaus, Hermann, 1892-
The fertile and infertile days of women and their definite calculation; a book of enlightenment for all women, dealing with the rhythm of the creative power in their bodies and its application toward a natural sex life with full control of reproduction. ⌜Translated from the German by Gideon Horowitz⌝ Hackensack, N. J., Rhythm Consultation Bureau, a division of the H. E. Budek Co. ⌜1951⌝
50 p. illus. 23 cm.

1. Fecundity. 2. Conception—Prevention. 3. Birth control. 4. Menstruation. I. Title.

QP251.K683 612.62 51-6518 ‡
⌜2⌝

NK 0197436 DLC DNLM

WP 630 K67f 1951a KNAUS, Hermann, 1892
Die fruchtbaren und unfruchtbaren Tage der Frau und deren sichere Berechnung. 11.-15. Aufl. Wien, Maudrich, 1951.
58 p. illus.
"Über die Notwendigkeit kalendermässiger Aufschreibung des Eintrittes der Regelblutungen. 13. 17. Aufl.:" (⌜8⌝ p., 12 ℓ.) has cover title: Menstruations kalender. The calendar is in pocket.

Continued in next column

Continued from preceding column

1. Birth control 2. Fecundity 3. Menstrual cycle

NK 0197438 DNLM PPC

W 6 P3 KNAUS, Hermann, 1892-
Die fruchtbaren und unfruchtbaren Tage der Frau und deren richtige Berechnung. 16.-20. Aufl. Wien, Maudrich, 1953.
viii, 62 p. illus.
"Über die Notwendigkeit kalendermässiger Aufschreibung des Eintrittes der Regelblutungen. 18.-22. Aufl." (⌜30⌝ p.) has cover title: Menstruations-Kalender.

The calendar is in pocket.
1. Birth control 2. Fecundity 3. Menstrual cycle

NK 0197440 DNLM

Knaus, Hermann, 1892-

O'Brien, John Anthony, 1893-
Lawful birth control, according to nature's law, in harmony with Catholic morality, by the Rev. John A. O'Brien ... with the assistance of Dr. Herman Knaus ... Dr. Raoul de Guchteneere ... ⌜and⌝ Dr. Henry Schmitz ... Fort Wayne, Ind., Courtney company, 1934.

Knaus, Hermann, 1892-

O'Brien, John Anthony, 1893-
Natural birth control without contraceptives, according to nature's law, in harmony with Catholic morality, by John A. O'Brien ... with the assistance of Dr. Herman Knaus ... Dr. Raoul de Guchteneere ... ⌜and⌝ Dr. Henry Schmitz ... Champaign, Ill., The Newman company ⌜°1938⌝

Knaus, Hermann, 1892-
Periodic fertility and sterility in woman, a natural method of birth control, by Professor Hermann Knaus ... with a foreword by F. H. A. Marshall ... Authorized English translation by D. H. Kitchin ... and Kathleen Kitchin ... with 64 illustrations and 12 tables. Vienna, W. Maudrich, 1934.
vi p., 2 l., 162 p. illus., tables (part fold.) diagrs. 24½cm.
"First English edition November 1934."
Bibliography: p. ⌜149⌝-162.

1. Fecundity. 2. Sterility. 3. Birth control. 4. Conception—Prevention. 5. Menstruation. I. Kitchin, Derek Harcourt, tr. II. Kitchin, Mrs. Kathleen (Lander) joint tr. III. Title.

35-14527

Library of Congress QP251.K72
⌜3⌝ 612.63

NK 0197443 DLC ICJ NIC NcD NcD-MC PPC DNAL OOxM NN

Knaus, Hermann, 1892-
Die periodische fruchtbarkeit und unfruchtbarkeit des weibes; der weg zur natürlichen geburtenregelung, von professor dr. Hermann Knaus ... mit 64 abbildungen und 12 tabellen. Wien, W. Maudrich, 1934.
8 p. l., 147 p. illus., tables (part fold.) diagrs. 24½cm.
"Über die notwendigkeit kalendermässiger aufschreibung des eintrittes der regelblutungen; von professor dr. Hermann Knaus": (⌜6⌝ p. 41 forms. 15cm) has cover-title: "Menstruations-kalender". The calendar is in pocket.
"Literatur": p. ⌜137⌝-147.

1. Fecundity. 2. Sterility. 3. Birth control. 4. Conception—Prevention. 5. Menstruation. I. Title.

34-36760

Library of Congress QP251.K7
Copyright A—Foreign 25699
⌜2⌝ 612.63

NK 0197444 DLC NcD DNLM NcD-MC ICJ

WQ 205 K67p 1950 **KNAUS, Hermann, 1892-**
Die Physiologie der Zeugung des Menschen. 3. vollständig neubearb. Aufl. Wien, Maudrich, 1950.
vi, 485 p. illus.
Earlier editions have title: Die periodische Fruchtbarkeit und Unfruchtbarkeit des Weibes.
1. Birth control 2. Fecundity 3. Menstrual cycle Title

NK 0197445 DNLM PPC ICJ NIC NNC-M

VOLUME 300

QP251 K6 1953
Knaus, Hermann, 1892-
Die Physiologie der Zeugung des Menschen. 4. gegenüber der 3. unveränderte Aufl. Wien-Dusseldorf, Verlag für Medizinische Wissenschaften, W. Maudrich, 1953.
485 p. (1 fold.) illus. 25cm.
1st and 2d ed. appeared with title: Die periodische Fruchtbarkeit und Unfruchtbarkeit des Weibes.
"Literatur": p.[241]-481.
1. Physiology. 2. Reproduction. I. Title.

NK 0197446 OrCS

WP 510 K67u 1943
KNAUS, Hermann, 1892-
Über die Notwendigkeit kalendermässiger aufschreibung des Eintrittes der Regelblutungen. 4.-5. Aufl. Wien, Maudrich, 1943.
[6] p. illus.
Cover title: Menstruations-Kalender
Calendar generally appears in pocket of the editions of the author's Die periodische Fruchtbarkeit und Unfruchtbarkeit des Weibes, 1934.
1. Menstrual cycle

NK 0197448 DNLM

WP 510 K67u 1948
KNAUS, Hermann, 1892-
Über die Notwendigkeit kalendermässiger Aufschreibung des Eintrittes der Regelblutungen. 6. u. 7. Aufl. Wien, Maudrich, 1948.
[6] p. illus.
Cover title: Menstruations-Kalender
Calendar generally appears in pocket of the editions of the author's Die periodische Fruchtbarkeit und Unfruchtbarkeit des Weibes.
1. Menstrual cycle

NK 0197449 DNLM

WP 510 K67u 1954
KNAUS, Hermann, 1892-
Über die Notwendigkeit kalendermässiger Aufschreibung des Eintrittes der Regelblutungen. 23. Aufl. München, Urban & Schwarzenberg, 1954.
[15] p.
Cover title: Menstruations-Kalender
1. Menstrual cycle

NK 0197450 DNLM

RM799 .M8
Knaus, Hermann, 1892-
Mühlbock, Otto, 1906-
Die weiblichen Sexualhormone in der Pharmakotherapie, bearb. von O. Mühlbock, H. Knaus [und] E. Tscherne. Bern, H. Huber [1948]

Knaus, Hermann, 1907-
Die königlichen forstprivilegien für die Abtei Fulda. ... Giessen, 1938.
Inaug. Diss. - Giessen, 1938.
Lebenslauf.

NK 0197452 ICRL CtY

KNAUS, HERWIG.
Franz Mathias Techelmann, 1649-1714; kaiserlicher Hoforganist in Wien. (IN: Denkmäler der Tonkunst in Österreich. Studien zur Musikwissenschaft; Beihefte der Denkmäler der Tonkunst in Österreich. Graz. 24cm. Bd. 27 (1966) p. [186]-199)
1. Techelmann, Franz Mathias, ca. 1649-1714.

NK 0197453 NN

Knaus, J M.
Die beweise für die unsterblichkeit im Platonischen Phädon, kritisch beleuchtet ... [Bern, 1870]
23 p. 26½cm.
Programm—Kantonsschule, Bern.
1. Plato. Phaedo. 2. Immortality.
CA 10-2152 Unrev'd
Library of Congress LF5045.B5K3

NK 0197454 DLC NjP

Knaus, Karl.
Beginnings of bilateral technical aid in Pakistan agriculture. [Washington] Foreign Agricultural Service, U. S. Dept. of Agriculture, 1953.
74 p. illus. 27 cm.
1. Agriculture — Pakistan. 2. Technical assistance, American — Pakistan. I. Title.
S471.P25K55 54-60289

NK 0197455 DLC OrCS DNAL

Knaus, Karl.
Outlined summary of lectures, discussions and reports in Course ED 208
see under Colorado. State University, Fort Collins. Extension Service.

1.913 A2P253
Knaus, Karl.
The part of the supervisor in an extension marketing program. [Washington?] 1946.
2 p.
1. Market extension work. 2. Supervisors. I. U.S. Extension service.

NK 0197457 DNAL

1.913 A2Su324
Knaus, Karl.
A suggested training program for extension workers in the central states. Washington, 1946.
8 p.
Issued Apr. 1946.

NK 0197458 DNAL

Knaus, Karl.
System in the county extension office. [Washington, U. S. Govt. Print. Off.] 1951.
24 p. illus. 24 cm. (U. S. Dept. of Agriculture. Agriculture information bulletin no. 28)
1. County agricultural agents. 2. Office management. I. Title. (Series)
[S21.A74 no. 28] 630.82 Agr 51-306
U. S. Dept. of Agr. Libr. for Library of Congress 1Ag84Ab no. 28 [5*]

NK 0197459 DNAL NNC

[Knaus, Ludwig,] 1829-1910.
Album. Photographien nach Original-Gemälden moderner Meister. München: F. Hanfstaengl[, 189-?]. 12 mounted pl. f°.
477004A. 1. Paintings, German. I. Title.
N. Y. P. L. April 30, 1930

NK 0197460 NN ICN

Knaus, Ludwig, 1829-1910.
Ludwig Knaus, acht farbige wiedergaben nach bildern und skizzen, mit errinerungen an Ludwig Knaus [von E.T. Andrews] Leipzig, [1915]
[8] p. 8 mounted col. plates. 32 cm.
(E.A. Seemanns künstlermappen, 12)
Portrait on t.p.

NK 0197461 RPB MdBP NIC OCl MiDA

Knaus, Ludwig, 1829-1910.
Ludwig Knaus: eine Kunstgabe für das deutsche Volk
see under Freie Lehrervereinigung für Kunstpflege, Berlin. [Supplement]

Knaus, Mathias, 1850-
Die sogenannten verträge zu gunsten dritter nach römischem rechte ... von Math. Knaus ... Köln, Buchdr. der Rheinischen eisenbahngesellschaft, 1875.
2 p. l., 31, [1] p., 1 l. 21cm.
Inaug.-diss.—Bonn.
Vita.
"Einleitung" contains bibliography.
1. Third parties (Roman law) 2. Contracts (Roman law) I. Title.
33-35043 Revised

NK 0197463 DLC CU-AL NNC MH

Knaus (Philippus Theophilus). * Diss. sistens annotationes quasdam circa morbum bilioso-mucosum. xxxvi pp. 4°. *Stuttgardiæ*, [1786].

NK 0197464 DNLM

Knaus, Segismundo.
... La lucha por los rios y la guerra de montaña, por el general Segismundo Knaus ... Conferencias dictadas en el Círculo militar. Buenos Aires, República Argentina [1936] 2 v. front. (port.), maps, plates, tables. 20cm. (Biblioteca del oficial. v. 217-218.)
CONTENTS.—[v. 1] Text.—[v. 2] Maps.
882836-7A. 1. European war, 1914-1918—Campaigns—Serbia. 2. European war, 1914-1918—Campaigns—Causasus. 3. European war, 1914-1918—Campaigns—Galicia. 4. European war, 1914-1918—Campaigns, Austro-Italian. 5. European war, 1914-1918—Mountain warfare. 6. Stream crossing, Military. I. Title. II. Ser.
N. Y. P. L. December 21, 1937

NK 0197465 NN

Knaus, Warren, ed.
Horn, Walther, 1871-1939.
Letters of a traveling entomologist, by Walther Horn ... McPherson, Kans., Press of Democrat-Opinion, 1919.

Knauschner, Franz.
... Der trotz. Wesen, arten, entstehung, behandlung, prophylaxe. 2., unveränderte aufl. Von Franz Knauschner. Prag, Staatliche verlagsanstalt, 1936.
52 p. 21cm. (Bücherei für die elternvereinigungen ... 3. bd.)
"Verzeichnis der benützten literatur": p. 49-51.
1. Child study. I. Title.
38-9017
Library of Congress BF723.C45K6 1936
[2] [159.92272] 136.72

NK 0197467 DLC

VOLUME 300

Knausenberger, Emil
Über verzerrungsfragen bei der gleichrichtung. ... 75 p.
Inaug. Diss. - Techn. Hochschule Dresden, [1937]
Literatur.

NK 0197468 ICRL

Knausenberger, Winfried, *ed.*
Beiträge zur Geschichte Lahrs. Festschrift zum hundertfünfzigjährigen Bestehen des humanistischen Gymnasiums in Lahr. Hrsg. von Winfried Knausenberger, Oskar Längle ⌊und⌋ Theodor Uhrig. ⌊Lahr/Baden⌋ 1954.
144 p. illus., maps, ports. 22 cm.

1. Lahr, Ger.—Hist. 2. Lahr, Ger. Scheffel-Gymnasium. I. Title. II. Title: Festschrift zum hundertfünfzigjährigen Bestehen des humanistischen Gymnasiums.

DD901.L23K6 65-57474

NK 0197469 DLC NN MH CtY

Knauser, Ernst, 1911-
... Die jugendliche monostotische Ostitis fribrosa ... Quakenbrück, 1934.
Inaug.-Diss. - Münster.
Lebenslauf.

NK 0197470 CtY

Knauss, Archibald C., joint author.

Heim, Arthur Lloyd.
... Internal stresses in laminated construction, by A. L. Heim, A. C. Knauss, and Louis Seutter. Washington, Govt. print. off., 1922.

KNAUSS, Archibald C
Utilization of mill residues in the timber products mills of the Lakeview working circle. Portland, 1953.
14p. (U.S. Forest service. Pacific Northwest forest and range experiment station. Research paper no.6)

NK 0197472 WaWW

Knauss, B. J., joint author.

⌊Stephens, James Albert⌋ 1873-
Munson shorthand ... Chicago, Metropolitan text book co. ⌊©1914⌋

Knauss, Bernhard, 1896-
Das künstlerideal des klassizismus und der romantik, von dr. Bernhard Knauss. Reutlingen, Gryphius-verlag, 1925.
125 p. 22cm. (*Half-title:* Tübinger forschungen zur archäologie und kunstgeschichte ... bd. IV)
"Literaturverzeichnis": p. 120-123.

1. Art—Germany—History. 2. Classicism. 3. Romanticism in art.
A C 33-1355
Title from Princeton Univ. Printed by L. C.

NK 0197474 NjP

Knauss, Bernhard, 1896-
Leidenschaft und Mass, Aufsätze zur Antike. Augsburg, W. Beyschlag ⌊©1947⌋
74 p. 22 cm.

1. Philosophy, Ancient—Addresses, essays, lectures. I. Title.

B165.K6 913.8 49-13540*
⌊1⌋

NK 0197475 DLC CU

Knauss, Bernhard, 1896-
...Staat und Mensch in Hellas. Berlin ⌊etc.⌋ C. Habel ⌊1949⌋
314 p. 19cm.
2. unveränderte Aufl.

591772B. 1. Greece—Govt. 2. Greece—Civilization. I. Title.
N. Y. P. L. November 19, 1951

NK 0197476 NN NNC NjP MH

Knauss, Calvin Ambrose, 1899-
... The action of bromine on unsaturated fatty acids, by Calvin A. Knauss ... and Judson G. Smull ... Bethlehem, Pa., Lehigh university ⌊1928⌋
cover-title, p. ⌊2808⌋-2815. tables. 23½cm. (⌊Lehigh university⌋ The Institute of research. Circular no. 19. Science and technology, no. 14)
At head of title: Lehigh university publication. vol. II, no. 9, Sept. 1928.
Reprinted from the Journal of the American chemical society, v. 49, 1927.

1. Bromine. 2. Acids, Fatty. I. Smull, Judson Gray, 1882- joint author. II. Title.
A 33-205
Title from Lehigh Univ. Library of Congress [QD305.A2K665]
⌊2⌋

NK 0197477 PBL OrCS PPTU MiU OCU OU ViU

Knauss, Calvin Ambrose, 1899- joint author.

Long, James Scott, 1892-
... I. Rate of molecular weight increase in boiling linseed and China wood oils, by James Scott Long ... and Graham Wentz ... II. Rate of molecular weight increase in the boiling of linseed oil, by James Scott Long, PH. D., and William J. Arner ... III. Studies in boiling linseed oil, by James Scott Long, PH. D., Calvin A. Knauss ... and Judson G. Smull ... Bethlehem, Pa. ⌊1927⌋

Knauss, D S
.... A suggested extension of the Dewey decimal system of classification to gas engineering. Written for the Accounting Section of the ninth annual meeting of the American Gas Institute, October, 1914, by D. S. Knauss, ... [New York?, 1914.]
108726
128 p. 23cm.
Caption title.

NK 0197479 ICJ WaS NNC MiD NIC

Knauss, Elizabeth.
The conflict; a narrative based on the fundamentalist movement, by Elizabeth Knauss. ⌊Los Angeles⌋ Bible institute of Los Angeles, ©1923.
225 p. 18½cm.

I. Title.
23-10694
Library of Congress PZ3.K729Co

NK 0197480 DLC

Knauss, Elizabeth.
The rising tide; a novel dealing with the spread of bolshevism and atheism throughout America, by Elizabeth Knauss. New York, N. Y., The Christian alliance publishing company ⌊©1927⌋
248 p. 19½cm.

1. Communism—U. S.—1917- I. Title. 27-20343
Library of Congress PZ3.K729Ri
⌊2⌋

NK 0197481 DLC WHi IaU

Knauss, Emma.
Wide open windows. A pageant for High school Girl reserves. Written by Emma Knauss and Frances Perry ...
Bd. with- Carr, M.L. The world circle. N.Y., [c1925] 18 cm. p. [13]-29.

NK 0197482 RPB

Knauss, Gerhard, 1928-
Gegenstand und Umgreifendes. Basel, Verlag für Recht und Gesellschaft, 1954.
xi, 124 p. 23 cm. (Philosophische Forschungen. N. F., v. 3 (der ganzen Ser. v. 12))
Bibliography: p. ix-xi.

1. Logic. 2. Paradox. I. Title. (Series: Philosophische Forschungen. N. F., v. 3)
A 54-3355
Harvard Univ. Library for Library of Congress ⌊2⌋

NK 0197483 MH OrCS CaBVaU NNC DLC-P4 CtY NN ICU

W 4 KNAUSS, Hans, 1912-
T91 Liquorbefunde bei endogenen Psychosen.
1938 ⌊Bad Mergentheim⌋ 1938.
29 p.
Cover title.
Inaug.-Diss. - Tübingen.
1. Cerebrospinal fluid - Examination 2. Schizophrenia

NK 0197484 DNLM

Knauss, Harold Paul, 1900-
Band spectra in the extreme ultra-violet excited by active nitrogen, by Harold P. Knauss ... [Berkeley, 1928]
1 p.l., 18 numb. l., 2 l. diagrs. (part mounted) 28 cm.
Thesis (Ph.D.) - Univ. of California, May 1928.
References: last leaf.
1. Spectrum, Ultra violet. 2. Nitrogen. I. Title.

NK 0197485 CU

Knauss, Harold Paul, 1900-
Discovering physics; illustrated by Harold F. Lindergreen. Cambridge, Mass., Addison-Wesley Press, 1951.
443 p. illus. 25 cm. (Addison-Wesley physics series)

1. Physics. I. Title.
QC23.K62 530 51-12183 ‡

NK 0197486 CU TxU IdU AAP FTaSU OrCS WaS WaSpG DLC MtU IdU KEmT MiEM GU KMK TU MB NN NcU

Knauss, Heinz, 1907-
Studien zum stil von Grimmelshausens Simplizissimus ... Würzburg, K.Triltsch, 1934.
3 p.l.,88 p.,1 l. 22½cm.
Inaug.-diss.--Giessen.
Lebenslauf.
"Giessen,1935" stamped above imprint,in which the date "1934" has been cancelled.
"Literaturverzeichnis": p.88.

1.Grimmelshausen,Hans Jacob Christoffel von,1625-1676. Simplizissimus.

NK 0197487 MiU CtY NjP ICRL PBm WaU NIC TxU

Knauss, James Owen, 1885-
Christopher Saur the Third, by James O. Knauss.
(*In* American antiquarian society, Worcester, Mass. Proceedings. Worcester, Mass., 1932. 25cm. n. s., v. 41, p. 235-253)
Bibliographical foot-notes.

1. Sower, Christopher, 1754-1799.
A 34-2208
Newberry library for Library of Congress [E172.A35 vol. 41]

NK 0197488 ICN DLC

VOLUME 300

Knauss, James Owen, 1885–
The first fifty years; a history of Western Michigan College of Education, 1903–1953. Kalamazoo, Western Michigan College of Education, 1953.
214 p. illus. 22 cm.

1. Michigan. Western Michigan College of Education, Kalamazoo. I. Title.
LB1891.K42K57 370.73774 54–34338 ‡

NK 0197489 DLC MsU NcD CU MiD-B OClW OOxM PBL PSt

Knauss, James Owen, 1840–
History and genealogy of the Knauss family in America, tracing back the records to Ludwig Knauss to the year 1723, comp. and arranged by James Owen Knauss ... and Tilghman John Knauss ... Emaus, Pa., Knauss family association, inc., 1915.
242 p. front., plates, ports., col. coat of arms. 24cm. $1.50

1. Knauss family (Ludwig Knauss, fl. 1723) 2. Knauss family. I. Knauss, Tilghman John, 1869– joint comp. II. Knauss family association, inc.
15-18261
CS71.K678 1915

NK 0197490 DLC C-S PHi MWA PNorthHi

Knauss, James Owen, 1885–
Golden anniversary edition

see under

Western Michigan College News Magazine.

LB1891 .K22K68 Knauss,James Owen,1885–
...History of the participation of Western Michigan college of education in the Cooperative teacher education study. Summary report by James O.Knauss... ₍Kalamazoo,Mich.,1942₎
47 numb. l. 28cm.
Mimeographed.

1.Michigan. State teachers college,Kalamazoo.
2.Michigan cooperative teacher education study.

NK 0197492 ICU

Knauss, James Owen, 1885–
History of Western state teachers college, 1904–1929, by James O. Knauss ... Kalamazoo, Mich., Western state teachers college ₍°1929₎
156 p. incl. front., illus., ports. 22½cm.
"List of printed and written sources": p. 112–114; "Publications of the faculty": p. 115–132.

1. Michigan. State teachers college, Kalamazoo.
Library of Congress LB1891.K42K6 29-15496
——— Copy 2.
Copyright A 10193 ₍2₎

NK 0197493 DLC PP PU

Knauss, James Owen, 1885–
Social conditions among the Pennsylvania Germans in the eighteenth century, as revealed in the German newspapers published in America, by James Owen Knauss ... Lancaster, Pa. ₍Press of the New era printing company₎ 1922.
x, 217 p. 25½cm. (*Added t.-p.:* Pennsylvania: the German influence in its settlement and development ... pt. xxx)
In Pennsylvania-German society. Proceedings and addresses ... Oct. 2, 1918. 1922. v. 29.
Published also as thesis (PH. D.) Cornell university, 1918.
"Table of German-American newspapers of the eighteenth century": p. 169–211.
Bibliography: p. 212–217.
1. Germans in Pennsylvania. 2. Pennsylvania—Soc. life & cust. 3. American newspapers—Pennsylvania.
Library of Congress F146.P23 vol. 29 24—23946

PPAmP PU MiU OCl OU MdBP NIC NcD
NK 0197494 DLC Vi PBm PPCS MoU ViU CU MWA PPLT PHi

Z 1297 K67 **Knauss,James Owen,1885–**
Syllabus of Michigan history for schools and colleges,by Prof.James O. Knauss ... ₍Lansing,Mich., 1932₎
₍464₎–486 p. 22½cm.
Caption title.
Extracted from Michigan history magazine,v.16,autumn number.
An "outline with ... attached bibliography".

1.Michigan--Hist.--Outlines,syllabi,etc
2.Michigan--Hist.--Bibl.

NK 0197495 MiU

Knauss, James Owen, 1885–
Territorial Florida journalism, by James Owen Knauss ... Deland, The Florida state historical society, 1926.
x p., 3 l., ₍3₎–250 p., 1 l. front., ports. 25½cm. (*Added t.-p.:* Publications of the Florida state historical society, no. 6)
"Facsimiles of first pages of Florida newspapers" (6 in pocket)
"Three hundred and sixty copies of this book have been printed for the Florida state historical society by the Yale university press."
"Bibliographical list of works consulted": p. ₍227₎–231.

1. Journalism—Florida. I. Title. 27-2343
Library of Congress F306.F75 no. 6
Copy 2. PN4897.F7K5

OU ViU MWA MB MiU-C
NK 0197496 DLC MoU NcD MU TU LNHT NcD WaS PU OCl OCU

Knauss (Karl) [1865–1902]. * Ueber Xanthoma multiplex. 30 pp. 8°. *Würzburg, J. B. Fleischmann,* [1889].

NK 0197497 DNLM

---

ar W 54486 no.12 Knauss, Karl, 1888–
Über einen eigenartigen Fall von Schleimbeutelhaematombildung am Oberschenkel. Erlangen, Druck von E. T. Jacob, 1916.
25 p. plates. 23cm.

Inaug.-Diss.--Erlangen.

NK 0197498 NIC CtY DNLM ICRL

NA9108 .A3 1930 **Knauss, Norman L.**

U. S. ***National bureau of standards. Division of building and housing.***
... Survey of zoning laws and ordinances adopted during 1930, by Norman L. Knauss, Division of building and housing, Bureau of standards. Washington, 1931.

NA9108 .A3 1931b **Knauss, Norman L.**

U. S. ***National bureau of standards. Division of building and housing.***
... Zoned municipalities in the United States, by Norman L. Knauss. Division of building and housing, Bureau of standards. Washington, 1931.

NA9050 .U6 1930 **Knauss, Norman L., comp.**

U. S. ***National bureau of standards. Division of building and housing.***
... Zoning progress in the United States. Zoning legislation in the United States. Comp. by Norman L. Knauss. Division of building and housing. Bureau of standards. Washington, 1930.

Knauss, Norman L.

Bassett, Edward Murray, 1863–1948.
Zoning progress in the United States: pt. 1. Zoning and the courts, by Edward M. Bassett. pt. 2. Report on zoning laws and ordinances, by the Division of Building and Housing. Washington, 1926.

Knauss, Oscar Penrose, 1959–
Millerstown, founded in 1776, since 1875 borough of Macungie; dates, landmarks, institutions, incidents, character sketches, anecdotes, by O. P. Knauss. ₍Macungie, Pa.₎ 1932. 46 p. 21cm.

1. Macungie, Pa.—Hist.
N. Y. P. L. September 10, 1941

NK 0197503 NN

Knauss, Oscar Penrose, 1859–
Millerstown, founded in 1776, since 1875, borough of Macungie; dates, landmarks, institutions, incidents, character sketches, anecdotes by O. P. Knauss. 2d ed. ₍Macungie? Pa.₎ 1943.
73 p. 23½cm.

1. Macungie, Pa. 44-11537
Library of Congress F159.M3K6 1943
₍3₎ 974.827

NK 0197504 DLC

Knauss, Otto, 1914–
Die Entstehung der Grünberger Familiennamen. Giessen, 1940.
107 p. 24 cm.
Inaug.-Diss.—Giessen.
"Sonderdruck aus den 'Giessener Beiträgen zur deutschen Philologie.'"
Vita.
Bibliography: p. 96–101.

1. Names, Personal—Germany—Grünberg (Hesse) 2. German language—Etymology—Names.
PF3576.K6 1940 54-49911

NK 0197505 DLC

Knauss, Otto, 1914–
... Die entstehung der Grünberger familiennamen, von Otto Knauss. Giessen, von Münchowsche universitäts-druckerei Otto Kindt gmbh, 1940.
107 p. 24½cm. (Giessener beiträge zur deutschen philologie ... 74)
"Verzeichnis der quellen und darstellungen": p. 96–101.

1. Names, Personal — Germany — Grünberg (Hesse) 2. German language—Etymology—Names.
A C 40-1919
Chicago. Univ. Library for Library of Congress PF3025.G5 no. 74 ₍2₎

MnU CtY
NK 0197506 ICU MoU INS PBm PU NjP WU NNC MH PU NN

H35 .P6 hft.42 **Knauss, Robert.**
Die armee in der Demokratie ₍von₎ Robert Knauss. Der wiederaufbau Österreichs ₍von₎ Julius Raab. München, Isar verlag, 1953.
60 p. illus. (Politische studien, hft. 42)

1. Germany (Dem. Rep.) - Armed forces. 2. Austria-Reconstruction (1939-1951) 3. Reconstruct/ (1939-1951)-Austria. I. Title. II. Raab, Julius. Der wiederaufbau Osterreichs.
agr-dm 9-8-61

NK 0197507 DS

Knauss, Robert.
Die deutsche, englische und französische kriegsfinanzierung, von dr. Robert Knauss. Berlin und Leipzig, W. de Gruyter & co., 1923.
4 p. l., ₍7₎–194 p. 24cm. (*Added t.-p.:* Sozialwissenschaftliche forschungen, hrsg. von der Sozialwissenschaftlichen arbeitsgemeinschaft. Abt. v, hft. 1)
"Literaturverzeichnis": p. ₍7₎–11.

1. European war, 1914–1918—Finance—Germany. 2. European war, 1914–1918—Finance—Gt. Brit. 3. European war, 1914–1918—Finance—France.
25-9158
Library of Congress D635.K5

NK 0197508 DLC PU CU NjP NN ICU IU

VOLUME 300

of Tübingen
Knauss (Robert) *Ueber metallisch-klingende, von der Herzbewegung abhängende Geräusche bei Lungen-Cavernen. 30 pp. 8°. *Tübingen, H. Laupp,* 1867.

NK 0197509 DNLM PU

Knauss, Robert, 1892–
Im grossflugzeug nach Peking; der erste weltflug der Deutschen luft hansa, von dr. Robert Knauss; mit 46 abbildungen und 2 karten. Berlin, Union deutsche verlagsgesellschaft [1927]
176 p. front. (port.) illus., fold. map. $21\frac{1}{2}$ cm.
Account of the flight of D901 and D903, piloted by A. Doldi and K. Schnäbele, from Berlin to Peking and back, July–September, 1926.
1. Aeronautics—Flights. 2. Siberia—Descr. & trav. 3. China—Descr. & trav. 4. Deutsche luft hansa a. g. 5. Doldi, Adolf, 1891– 6. Schnäbele, Karl, 1896– I. Title.
Library of Congress TL721.D4K6 33-12998
[2] [915] 629.1333431

NK 0197510 DLC

Knauss, Robert, 1892–
Im Grossflugzeug nach Peking, der erste Weltflug der deutschen Luft Hansa, von Dr. Robert Knauss... Berlin: Union Deutsche Verlagsgesellschaft, Abt. Luftfahrtverlag, G.m. b.H.[, cop. 1927.] 176 p. diagr., front. (port.), illus. (incl. facsim.), map. 2. ed. 8°.

343756A. 1. Aeronautics—Ascensions, flights, etc., 1926. 2. China—Descr. and trav., 1910–
N. Y. P. L. January 20, 1928

NK 0197511 NN

DS6 Knauss, Robert, 1892–
.K85 Im grossflugzeug nach Peking; der erste weltflug der Deut-
(Ge) schen luft hansa, von dr. Robert Knauss ... 3. aufl. Berlin, Union deutsche verlagsgesellschaft, abt. Luftfahrtverlag [1927]
176 p. front. (port.) illus., maps (1 fold.) $21\frac{1}{2}$ cm.

1. Asia—Descr. & trav. 2. Aeronautics—Voyages.

NK 0197512 ICU

[Knauss, Robert, 1892–
Luftkrieg 1936; die zertrümmerung von Paris, von major Helders [*pseud.*] Berlin, W. Kolk, 1932.
2 p. l., 9–150 p. 21 cm.
Pages 149–150, advertising matter.

1. Imaginary wars and battles. 2. Aeronautics, Military. I. Title.
32-35666 Revised
Library of Congress U313.K5
[r43c2] 833.91

NK 0197513 DLC DLC-P4 CoD MH CtY NN

[Knauss, Robert] 1892– 1955.
... Воздушная война 1936 года; разрушение Парижа. Перевод с немецкого А. Зелениной, с предисловием А. Лапчинского и с приложением "Полемических вариантов" П. Павленко. Изд. 2. Москва, Государственное военное издательство, 1934.
160 p. illus. (maps, 1 double) diagrs. 20 cm.
Author's pseud., Гельдерс, at head of title.
"В переводе опущены места, не имеющие прямого отношения к военным вопросам, в том числе и вся романическая часть."
1. Aeronautics, Military. 2. Imaginary wars and battles. I. Zelenina, A., tr. II. Lapchinskii, Aleksandr Nikolaevich, 1882– III. Pavlenko, Petr Andreevich, 1899– IV. Title. *Title transliterated:* Vozdushnaia voina 1936 goda.
43-31552
Library of Congress UG630.K58 1934 DDT 15 Je 42
[3]

NK 0197514 DLC

[Knauss, Robert] 1892–
The war in the air, 1936, by Major Helders [*pseud.*] Translated from the German by Claud W. Sykes. London, J. Hamilton [1932]
254 p. plates, fold. map. 19 cm.

1. Imaginary wars and battles. 2. Aeronautics, Military. I. Sykes, Claud Walter, 1883– tr. II. Title.
33-17954 Revised
Library of Congress U313.K52
[r44c2] 833.91

NK 0197515 DLC MH DAL NN

U
313
.H413
1935
Knauss, Robert, 1892- 1955.
War in the air, by Major Helders. Translated from the German by Claud W. Sykes. London, J. Hamilton [1935.
222p. illus. 19 cm ("Ace" series)

1. Imaginary wars and battles. 2. Aeronautics, Military. I. Title.

NK 0197516 KU DNW

Knauss, Robert, 1892– 1955.
Die Welt des Fliegers; das Buch der Weltluftfahrt. [1. Aufl.] Stuttgart, Franckh [1950]
184 p. illus. 26 cm.

1. Aeronautics—Popular works.
TL546.7.K6 629.13 51-35921 ‡

NK 0197517 DLC MH

Knauss, Rudolf, 1901-
Die Vorschläge Adickes zur Justizreform (1906) und ihre Verwirklichung in der deutschen Gesetzgebung ... von Rudolf Knauss ... [Schönberg, Lehmann & Bernhard, 1928]
100 p., 2 l. $22\frac{1}{2}$ cm.
Inaug.-Diss. - Freiburg i. B.
"Lebenslauf": p. [101]
"Verzeichnis der benützten Literatur": p. [96]-100.

NK 0197518 MH-L ICRL CtY

Knauss, Tilghman John, 1869- joint comp.

Knauss, James Owen, 1840–
History and genealogy of the Knauss family in America, tracing back the records to Ludwig Knauss to the year 1723, comp. and arranged by James Owen Knauss ... and Tilghman John Knauss ... Emaus, Pa., Knauss family association, inc., 1915.

KNAUSS, WILHELM.
Die Gedanken sind frei; ein heiteres Spiel für Mädchen. München, V. Höfling [n.d.] 24 p. 17cm. (Spiele des bunten Wagens. Heft 103)

I. Series. II. Title.

NK 0197520 NN

KNAUSS, WILHELM.
Der Wohnungstausch; ein übermütiges Spiel für Burschen nach einer chinesischen Fabel. München, V. Höfling [n.d.] 35 p. 17cm. (Spiele des bunten Wagens. Heft 113)

I. Series. II. Title.

NK 0197521 NN

Knauss, Wilhelm, 1883 De Stephani Byzantii Ethnicorum exemplo Eustathiano. Bonnae 1910: Georgi. 114 S. 8°
Bonn, Phil. Diss. v. 10. Aug. 1910, Ref. Brinkmann
[Geb. 3. Aug. 83 Ehrenbreitstein; Wohnort: Ehrenbreitstein; Staatsangeh.: Preußen; Vorbildung: Gymn. Koblenz Reife O. 03; Studium: Münster 2, München 1, Berlin 1, Bonn 8 S.; Rig. 28. Juli 09.] [U 11. 488

NK 0197522 ICRL PU IU MH DDO CtY NjP

Knauss, William H.
The story of Camp Chase; a history of the prison and its cemetery, together with other cemeteries where Confederate prisoners are buried, etc. By William H. Knauss. Nashville, Tenn. and Dallas, Tex., Publishing house of the Methodist Episcopal church, South, Smith & Lamar, agents, 1906.
xx, 407 p. incl. front., illus., plates, ports. fold. tab. 24 cm.
Plates printed on both sides.
1. Chase, Camp, O. 2. Johnson's island, Lake Erie. 3. U. S.—Hist.—Civil war—Prisoners and prisons.
6-22869
Library of Congress E616.C4K67

NK 0197523 DLC NcD FTaSU Vi NIC OClWHi MB NjP ViU

Knauss family association, inc.

Knauss, James Owen, 1840–
History and genealogy of the Knauss family in America, tracing back the records to Ludwig Knauss to the year 1723, comp. and arranged by James Owen Knauss ... and Tilghman John Knauss ... Emaus, Pa., Knauss family association, inc., 1915.

Knaust, Heinrich, 1540-1577, ed. and tr.

Phreisleben, Christoph, *fl.* 1544.
Erotemata latino-germanica, e / divi Ivstiniani imperatoris Institutionibus, in legalis militiæ tyronum vsum, per d. Christophorum Phreislebium Lincensem, collecta. Lateinische / vnd dargegen teutsche frage vnd antwort / auss des keysers Justiniani Institutionibus zu nutz vund gebrauch der edlen jugent / so in den keyserlichen rechten studiret / vnd kriegsvbung treibet / vor etlichen zeitē von dem hochgelerten herrn Christoff Phreissleben lateinisch zusamen gebracht / jetzt aber zu mehrem nutz der jugent / in die teutsche spraach / gegen einander zu conferirn / gesetzet vund mit fleiss vbersehen. Durch herrn Heinrich Knausten ... [Franckfurt am Meyn, Getruckt bey C. Egenolffs erben] 1569.

TJ1350
.A815
Knaust, Herbert, 1904- joint author.

Aumund, Heinrich, 1873–
Hebe- und Förderanlagen; ein Lehrbuch für Studierende und Ingenieure, von H. Aumund und H. Knaust. 3., neubearb. Aufl. Berlin, Springer, 1950.

Knaust, Herbert, 1904-
Die treibscheibenförderung mit aussenantrieb. ... n.p., 1932. 46 p.
Inaug. Diss. Techn. Hochsch. Berlin, 1932.
Lebenslauf.

NK 0197526 ICRL

VOLUME 300

Knaust, Walter, 1905-
Ueber sole von eisenhydroxyd und manganhydroxyd in ihrer beziehung zur bildung der sogenannten schutzrinden und dos laterits.
Inaug. diss. Jena, 1930.

NK 0197527 ICRL CtY

Knaut (Æmilius). * De vitali quæ pulmonum contractilitate, nervis vagis irritatis. 37 pp. 8°. *Dorpat, typ. H. Laakmanni*, 1859.

NK 0197528 DNLM

---

von Knaut (Arthur). * Innervation des Magens seitens des Rückenmarks in Hinsicht auf den Brechakt. 61 pp., 1 l. 8°. *Dorpat, H. Laakmann* 1886

NK 0197529 DNLM PPC

---

von Knaut (Arthur). Tabellen zur Bestimmung der Trinkwasserbakterien. 99 pp. 8°. Strassburg i. E. & Leipzig, J. Singer, 1911.

NK 0197530 DNLM

Knaut (Augustus Christianus). * De efficacia dierum criticorum in vulneribus de lethalitate dubiis. 44 pp. 4°. *Jenæ, lit. Krebsianis*, [1712].

NK 0197531 DNLM PPC

Knaut (Bernhard) [1872-]. * Ueber die durch Speiseröhrenkrebs bedingten Perforationen der benachbarten Blutbahnen, nebst einer Beobachtung von primärer Oesophagusdilatation und von Leukoplakia oesophagi. 34 pp. 8°. *Berlin, Vogt*, 1896.

NK 0197532 DNLM CtY

---

ar X 1148 no.18 **Knaut, C**
Hadrian als Regent und als Character. Nordhausen, C. Kirchner, 1871.
43 p. 26cm.
"Realschule erster Ordnung zu Nordhausen. ⌜Programm⌝"
No. 18 in a vol. with binder's title: Programmes: Roman history. II.
1. Hadrianus, Emperor of Rome, 76-138.

NK 0197533 NIC

Knaut, Carl Friedrich, 1868-
Ueber die Metrik Robert Greene's...von Carl Knaut... Halle a. S.: M. Hoffmann, 1890. 63 p. 8°.
Dissertation, Halle-Wittenberg.
Vita.

1. Greene, Robert, 1560?-1592.
N. Y. P. L. September 20, 1927

NK 0197534 NN IEN MH MB MiU PPiU NcD NjP

Knaut, Christian, 1654–1716.
Methodus plantarum genuina, qva notae characteristicæ seu differentiæ genericæ tam summæ, qvam subalternæ ordine digeruntur et per tabulas, qvas vocant, synopticas perspicue delineantur; in gratiam studiosæ juventutis adornata atqve edita a Christiano Knaut ... Lipsiæ et Halæ, prostat in officina A. Sellii, 1716.
2 p. l., 267, ⌜13⌝ p. fold. tables. 17cm.

Continued in next column

Continued from preceding column

1. Botany, Systematic.
Agr 5-1077
Library, U. S. Dept. of Agriculture 452K72.

NK 0197535 DNAL NNBG MoSB

Knaut, Eva, 1911-
... Untersuchungen über gruppenspezifische Eigenschaften der Zähne ... Halle (Saale) 1934.
Inaug.-Diss. - Halle-Wittenberg.
Lebenslauf.
"Literaturverzeichnis": p. 18-[20]

NK 0197536 CtY

Law **Knaut, Heinrich, ed.**

Germany. *Laws, statutes, etc.*
Die wichtigsten grundlegenden Preisgesetze sowie die Preisstrafrechts-Verordnung vom 3. Juni 1939 in der Fassung vom 26. Oktober 1944 mit Einführung und kurzem Überblick unter Berücksichtigung der Bedürfnisse der unteren Preisbehörden; hrsg. von Heinrich Knaut. Stuttgart, Kohlhammer, 1946.

Knaut, Hermann.
Louis Harms, ein Lebensbild des Begründers der Hemannsburger Mission, auf Grund seiner eignen Schriften und zeitgenössischer Quellen, mit einem statistischen Anhange, zum 50jähr. Jubiläum des Hermannsburger Missionswerkes... Göttingen, Vandenhoeck & Ruprecht, 1899.
⌜vi⌝, 90 p. 21cm.
"Litteratur": p. ⌜vi⌝
1 Harms, Louis, 1808-1865

NK 0197538 NjPT OO CtY

KNAUT, Karl, of Magdeburg.
Observationes criticae in Taciti qui fertur Dialogum de oratóribus. Magdeburg, [1879].
4°. pp.1-28.
(Progr.d.pädagogiums zum kloster unser lieben frauen. "1879.nr.200.").

NK 0197539 MH NjP CtY OCU

Knaut, Karl Friedrich.
see Knaut, Carl Friedrich, 1868-

Knaut, Karl Friedrich Ernst, 1844-
De Luciano libelli qui inscribitur Lucius sive Asinus auctore ... Lipsiae, 1868.
59 p. 21 cm.
Inaug.-Diss. - Leipzig.
Vita.

NK 0197541 CtY MiU NjP

Knaut, Ulrich, 1909-
Die internationale rechtsordnung der eisenbahnen ... Berlin, 1934.
Inaug. Diss. - Göttingen, 1934.
Lebenslauf.
Literatur.

NK 0197542 ICRL CtY

Knaut, Walter, 1914-
Treu und Glauben im Verwaltungsrecht unter Berücksichtigung der Zivilrechtlichen Entwicklung. Düsseldorf, Nolte, 1937.
97 p.
Thesis - Göttingen.
Vita.
Bibliography: p. 95-97.

NK 0197543 NNC NIC

Knauth, Adalbert: Johannes Reinke als Naturphilosoph. Darstellung und Würdigung. Regensburg 1912: Manz. XVI, 207 S. 8° ¶ (Im Buchh. ebd.)
Würzburg, Phil. Diss. v. 21. Juni 1912, Ref. Stölzle
[Geb. 6. Jan. 83 Neubrunn, B. A. Marktheidenfeld; Wohnort: Würzburg; Staatsangeh.: Bayern; Vorbildung: Altes Gymn. Bamberg Reife Juli 03; Studium: Würzburg 8 S.; Rig. 24. Mai 11.] [U 12. 4703

NK 0197544 ICRL PU MH CtY ICJ CaBVaU

Knauth, Andreas, joint author.
Die Erdbeere
see under
Thiele, Karl Paul.

Knauth, Arnold Whitman, 1890-
Air carriers' liability in comparative law: Europe and the United States ⌜by⌝ Arnold W. Knauth. Latin America ⌜by⌝ David E. Grant ... New York, N. Y., New York university law quarterly review, 1937.

Knauth, Arnold Whitman, 1890-
Alien seamen's rights and the war, by Arnold W. Knauth ...
(*In* American journal of international law. Concord, N. H., 1943. 26cm. v. 37, p. 74-80)

1. Aliens. 2. World war, 1939- —⌜Aliens⌝ 3. Seamen.
A 43-1196
Carnegie endow. int. peace. Library for Library of Congress [JX1.A6 vol. 37]
⌜3⌝ ($41.05)

NK 0197547 NNCE DS

Knauth, Arnold Whitman, 1890-
The American law of ocean bills of lading; the American carriage of goods by sea act, 1936; the Canadian water carriage of goods act, 1936; the Newfoundland carriage of goods by sea act, 1932; the Convention for the unification of certain rules relating to ocean bills of lading, Brussels, 1924, known as the Hague rules; the Uniform North Atlantic bill of lading, 1937; the Liverpool cotton agreement, 1907–1911. Complete texts, with tables of foreign legislation, ratifications and adherences, a historical statement, and a commentary. By Arnold W. Knauth ... 1937. Baltimore, Md., American maritime cases, inc. ⌜°1938⌝
4 p. l., 203 (*i. e.* 201) p. 23cm.
Cover-title: Knauth on ocean bills of lading, the American and Canadian law, 1937.
Irregular paging.
"Table of cases": p. 193–199.
1. Bills of lading—U. S. 2. Bills of lading—Canada. 3. Maritime law—U. S. 4. Maritime law—Canada. 5. Commerce. I. U. S. Laws, statutes, etc. II. Gt. Brit. Laws, statutes, etc. III. Title. IV. Title: Ocean bills of lading
38-9033
Library of Congress HE596.K57
—— —— Copy 2.
Copyright A 114294 ⌜5⌝ 347.7

NK 0197549 DLC CaBVa MoU CU-AL PU-L ViU-L CaBVaU

Knauth, Arnold Whitman, 1890-
The American law of ocean bills of lading ... Complete texts, with tables of foreign legislation, ratifications and adherences, a historical statement, and a commentary. By Arnold W. Knauth ... 2d printing, rev., 1941. Baltimore, Md., American maritime cases, inc. ⌜1941⌝
x, 268 p. 23½cm.

Continued in next column

VOLUME 300

Continued from preceding column

1. Bills of lading—U. S. 2. Bills of lading—Canada. 3. Maritime law—U. S. 4. Maritime law—Canada. 5. Commerce. I. U. S. Laws, statutes, etc. II. Canada. Laws, statutes, etc. III. Title. IV. Title: Ocean bills of lading.

Library of Congress HE596.K57 1941 41-10552 [6] 347.7

NK 0197550 DLC CaBVaU WaU-L OrU NcD DS PPT ViU-L

Knauth, Arnold Whitman, 1890–
The American law of ocean bills of lading ... Complete texts, with tables of foreign legislation, ratifications and adherences, historical statement, and commentary. 3d ed. Baltimore, American Maritime Cases, 1947 [i. e. 1948]
xi, 307 p. 24 cm.
Cover title: Ocean bills of lading, 1947.
1. Bills of lading—U. S. 2. Bills of lading—Canada. 3. Maritime law—U. S. 4. Maritime law—Canada. 5. Commerce. I. U. S. Laws, statutes, etc. II. Canada. Laws, statutes, etc. III. Title. IV. Title: Ocean bills of lading.
HE596.K57 1948 347.7 48-14763*

NK 0197551 DLC CaBVaU WaU-L CaBVaU OU OrU-L

Knauth, Arnold Whitman, 1890–
The American law of ocean bills of lading ... 4th ed., rev. and enl. Baltimore, American Maritime Cases, 1953.
538 p. 24 cm.
Includes bibliography.
1. Bills of lading—U. S. 2. Bills of lading—Canada. 3. Bills of lading. I. Title. II. Title: Ocean bills of lading.
658.78825 53—20882 ‡

NK 0197552 TU CaBVaU DLC ViU-L CU-AL NBuU-L N OClW PU-L TxU

Knauth, Arnold Whitman, 1890-1960, ed. FOR OTHER EDITIONS SEE MAIN ENTRY
American maritime cases, published under the auspices of the Maritime law association of the United States. v. 1– Jan. 1923–
Baltimore, American maritime cases, inc. [1923]–

Knauth, Arnold Whitman, 1890-1960 joint ed.
American maritime cases.
First- 5-year digest of American maritime cases, 1923/27- A. M. C. ... Baltimore, American maritime cases, inc., 1928–

Knauth, Arnold Whitman, 1890–
Aviation and salvage, the convention of 1938, and the pending bill, S. 7; address by Arnold W. Knauth at a round table conference conducted by the Section on insurance law of the American bar association, at Indianapolis, September 29, 1941. [New York, The Hecla press, 1941]
cover-title, 32 p. 22½ᶜᵐ.
1. Salvage. 2. Aeronautics—Laws and regulations. I. American bar association. Section of insurance law. II. Title.
Library of Congress JX5771.K6 42-22622 [2]

NK 0197555 DLC

KNAUTH, ARNOLD WHITMAN, 1890–
Aviation and shipping, by Arnold Knauth... [New York? 1930?] 426-438 p. 25½cm.
Cover-title.
Bibliographical footnotes.
"Reprinted from Air law review. v. 1, no. 4. November, 1930."
731766A. 1. Aeronautics—Jurisp.—U.S. 2. Navigation—Jurisp.—U.S.

NK 0197556 NN MH-L WaU-L

Knauth, Arnold Whitman, 1890–
The Aviation salvage at sea convention of 1938, by Arnold W. Knauth ... New York, N. Y., New York university law quarterly review, 1939.
1 p. l., 23 p. 25½ᶜᵐ. (New York university School of law Contemporary law pamphlets. Ser. 1, no. 18)
1. Aviation salvage at sea convention, 1938. 2. Life-saving. 3. Salvage. 4. Aeronautics—Accidents. 5. Maritime law.
Library of Congress JX4436.K6 43-2062

NK 0197557 DLC NBuU-L WaU-L MH-BA DS CU NcD NNC

HE970 .A8 **Knauth, Arnold Whitman, 1890–**
Audouin, Émile.
... General average. York-Antwerp rules, 1924. An account of the Stockholm conference, 1924, and a study of the 1924 rules, by mm. Audouin, Gervais and Lieury ... Translation edited by Arnold W. Knauth ... Baltimore, American maritime cases, inc., 1925.

HE965 .U5 1942 c **Knauth, Arnold Whitman, 1890–**
U. S. *War shipping administration.*
... Insurance policies, charter-parties, bills of lading. Forms, orders and bulletins. November, 1942 ... Arnold W. Knauth—Emory H. Niles, editors. Baltimore, Md. [American maritime cases, inc., 1942]

Law **Knauth, Arnold Whitman, 1890-1960 ed.**
Benedict, Erastus Cornelius, 1800–1880.
Knauth's Benedict on admiralty. 7th ed., by Arnold Whitman Knauth. Mount Kisco, N. Y., Baker, Voorhis [°195

Knauth, Arnold Whitman, 1890–
Law **Benedict, Erastus Cornelius,** 1800–1880.
The law of American admiralty, its jurisdiction and practice; with forms and directions. 6th ed., rev. and enl. in scope by Arnold Whitman Knauth. New York, M. Bender, 1940-41.

Knauth, Arnold Whitman, 1890-1960 joint ed.
Pilot's manual of air law ...
Baltimore, U. S. aviation reports, inc., 1929–

209ª 177 Knauth, Arnold Whitman, 1890-1960.
Renvoi and some related problems ... [by] Arnold W. Knauth ... [New York, Hecla press] 1948.
1 p.l., 24 p. 22cm.
"A paper prepared for the meeting of the International bar association at the Hague, August 1948".

NK 0197560 MH-L

Law **Knauth, Arnold Whitman, 1890–**
United States aviation reports. 1928– New York.

Knauth, Carl.
Viel Lärmen um Nichts
see under Thomas, F.G.

Knauth, Christian, 1706-1784
Derer Oberlausitzer Sorberwenden umständliche kirchengeschichte. Von Christian Knauthen. Görlitz, J. F. Fickelscherer, 1767.
pp. (16), 455 +.
Lusatia||AcS 22265

NK 0197560-1 MH NjPT ICN

KNAUTH, Christian, 1706-1784.
Dissertatio philologica qva consensv amplissimae facvltatis philosophicae veram vocis [] etymologiam et significatvm ex intimo hebrais[] adserit vindicatqve. Lips., [17[]]
4°. pp.(6),34.

NK 0197560-2 MH

Knauth, Christian, 1706–1784.
Christian Knauthes ... Kurze beschreibung eines modells des tempels Salomonis, welches nach anleitung Heiliger Schrift und anderer bewährten scribenten, von Michael Dieneln, einem der tischlerarbeit ergebenen jungen menschen ... aus seinem holze, sauber und accurat, mit grossem fleiss, mühe und arbeit, in jahresfrist 1765, gefertiget. Görlitz, Gedruckt bey J. F. Fickelscherer [1766]
24 p. 19 x 15½ᶜᵐ.
1. Jerusalem. Temple.
Library of Congress BM655.K6 38-31687

NK 0197560-3 DLC MH

Knauth, Christian Friedrich, respondent. [1720-44]
... Commentatio iuridica, De iniuria conditional
see under Horn, Caspar Heinrich, 1657-1718, praeses.

Knauth, Christian Friedrich, respondent. [1720-48]
... De inivria conditionali
see under Horn, Caspar Heinrich, 1657-1718, praeses.

Knauth, Christian Maximilian Wilhelm, 1736–1829.
... Spanisches kriegstagebuch, feldzug in Katalonien 1810, herausgegeben von dr. O. Bessenrodt. Gotha, Engelhard-Reyher-verlag, 1937.
63, [1] p. 18½ᶜᵐ.
At head of title: Major C. M. W. Knauth.
"Schrifttum": p. 60.
1. Peninsular war, 1807–1814—Personal narratives. I. Bessenrodt, Otto, 1897– ed. II. Title.
Library of Congress DC231.K7 38-35395 [2] 946.06

NK 0197560-4 DLC

Knauth (Christoph) [1638-94] *De phthisi. 27 pp. 4°. Jenæ, typ. S. Krebsii, 1664.

NK 0197560-5 DNLM

Knauth, Christoph, 1638–1694.
Enumeratio plantarum circa Halam Saxonum et in ejus vicinia, ad trium fere milliarium spatium, sponte provenientium, cum earum synonymiis, locis natalibus, ubi proveniunt, et tempore, qvo florent, additis characteribus generum summorum atqve subalternorum, & indice copioso, in botanophilorum gratiam methodice consignata, studio Christophori Knauths ... Lipsiæ, sumpt. hæred. F. Lanckisch, 1687.
4 p. l., 187, [27] p., 1 l. 16½ cm.
1. Botany—Germany—Halle. [1. Halle—Botany] 2. [Botany—Pre-Linnean works]
Agr 25—87
U. S. Nat'l Agr. Libr. for Library of Congress 459.3K72 [a66b½]

NK 0197560-6 DNAL NNBG

VOLUME 300

RBR
QK314 Knauth, Christoph, 1638-1694.
.K5515 Herbarium Hallense; sive, Plantarum quae circa Halam Saxonum et in ejus vicinia, ad trium fere milliarium spatium, sponte proveniunt, methodica enumeratio. Cum earum synonymiis, locis natalibus ubi proveniunt, & tempore quo florent, additis characteribus generum summorum atq. subalternorum & indice copioso... Halae Saxonum, Typis C. Salfeldi, 1689.
4 p. *l.*, 216, [14] p. 17 cm.
4740 Pritzel.
1. Botany - Germany - Halle area. 2. Botany - Pre-Linnean works. i.t.

NK 0197560-7 NNBG

378.1 **Knauth, Ernest Frederic,** 1902–
K67c The college business manager. New York, New York University Press, 1955.
xiv, 166 p. 29 cm.
Revision of thesis, New York University, issued in microfilm form under title: The role of the business manager in the independent liberal arts college.
Bibliography: p. 163–166.

1. Universities and colleges—Administration. I. Title.

LB2341.K6 378.1 55–9897

KEmT OrCS
NcD MH IU PPD PBL OrU Wa OrLgE MiU OU MsU MB ICU
NK 0197560-8 DLC FTaSU LU MB PPT CU TxU NN OOxM ViU

LD3907
.E3 Knauth, Ernest Frederic, 1902-
1954 The role of the business manager in the
.K5 independent liberal arts college; a study of the duties, background, and education-related activities of the chief business officer of the independent liberal arts college of moderate size.
376p. tables, forms.
Thesis (Ph.D.) - N.Y.U., School of Education, 1954.
Bibliography: p.370-376.

NK 0197561 NNUT

Knauth, Ernest Frederic, 1902–
The role of the business manager in the independent liberal arts college; a study of the duties, background, and education-related activities of the chief business officer of the independent liberal arts college of moderate size. Ann Arbor, University Microfilms [1955]
([University Microfilms, Ann Arbor, Mich.] Publication no. 10,639)
Microfilm copy of typescript. Positive.
Collation of the original: 2, xv, 376 l. illus.
Thesis—New York University.
Bibliography: leaves 370–376.
1. Universities and colleges—Administration. I. Title.

Microfilm AC–1 no. 10,639 Mic 55–15

[1]

NK 0197561-1 DLC

PE1111
.K5 Knauth, Ernest Frederic, 1902-
Selected principles of English grammar. New York, Author, 1953.
84p. 27cm.

1. English language - Grammar.

NK 0197561-2 NNU

Knauth, Franz, 1822-1893 (*Ed.*) Alldeutschland. Dichtergruesze am auferstehungsmorgen des geeinigten Deutschlands im hochsommer des jahres 1870. Langensalza, 1870. 2 v. in 1, 16°.

NK 0197561-3 MdBP

Knauth, Franz, 1822-1893.
Auswahl deutscher gedichte. Halle, 1890.

352 p.

NK 0197561-4 PHC

438.2 Knauth, Franz, 1822-1893.
K72f Fibel für den ersten unterricht im schreiben und lesen, nach der schreiblesemethode bearb. und hrsg. Halle, Buchhandlung des Waisenhauses, 1851.
[26], 8p. illus.

1. Primers, German.
[Full name: Christoph Gottlieb Franz Knauth]

NK 0197561-5 IU

265.2 Knauth, Franz, 1822-1893, comp.
K72g Geleitworte für confirmanden und confirmandinnen beim austritt aus der schule. Eine sammlung von entlassungsreden, gehalten von schulinspectoren und schulrectoren. Zusammengestellt von Franz Knauth ... Braunschweig, H. Bruhn, 1876.
86p.

1. Confirmation.

NK 0197562 IU

832N39 Knauth, Franz, 1822-1893
DK72 Georg Neumark nach leben und dichten. Zur feier der zweihundertsten wiederkehr des todestages des dichters am 8.juli 1681 dem deutschen volke und dessen reiferer jugend, dargeboten von Franz Knauth ... Langensasza, H. Beyer & söhne, 1881.
75p. front.(port.)

Includes music.

1. Neumark, Georg, 1621-1681.

NK 0197563 IU OClW OO NNC

Knauth, Franz, 1822-1893
Philipp Melanchthon. 2ᵉ vermehrte aufl. Berlin, J. A. Wohlgemuth, [vorwort, 1865].
24°. pp. 143. Front.

Melanchthon||AcS 22266

NK 0197564 MH

Knauth, Franz, 1822-1893, ed.
Sieben bücher deutscher dichtungen
see under Bernhardt, Gustav.

Knauth, Franz, 1822-1893
Der Vertrag zu Passau, vom 2. August 1552; ein gedenkblatt zu dritten säcularfeier Deutschlands evangelischer jugend gewidmet. Halle, Waisenhaus, 1852.

19 p.

NK 0197566 PPLT

Knauth, Günter, 1914-
Grundlagen eines Reichswasserrechts. Eine Vorarbeit ... von Günter Knauth ... Forchheim, Otto Mauser, 1939.
xv, 165 p. 21cm.
Inaug.-Diss. - Halle-Wittenberg.
Errata leaf laid in.
"Lebenslauf": p. 165.
"Verzeichnis der benutzten Schriften": p. v-xi.

NK 0197567 MH-L NIC

SD196
S6K53 Knauth, Hans
Die Aufforstung der Laubholz-Krüppelbestände im Spessart, mitgeteilt von Hans Knauth. München, Druck von Joh. Naderer, 1889.
30 p. 22cm.

1. Reforestation - Germany - Spessart Mountains. 2. Afforestation - Germany - Spessart Mountains. 3. Forests and forestry - Germany - Spessart Mountains. I. Title.

NK 0197568 GU

Knauth, Hans. Waldwegbau und terrainstudien im keupergebiete, mit besonderer berücksichtigung der verhältnisse im staatswalddistrikt "Bruderwald," Königl. forstamts Bamberg-West. Frankfurt am Main. 1896. 8°. pp. [2], 56. 9 plans.

NK 0197569 MH-A

Knauth (Heinrich). *Die Einleitung der künstlichen Frühgeburt durch die Tamponade des Cervix mit Jodoformgaze. 34 pp. 8°. *Würzburg, P. Scheiner,* 1889.

NK 0197570 DNLM

Knauth, Hermann,
Quaestiones Propertioanae. Halle, 1878.

NK 0197571 PU CU

Knauth, Hermann.
Übungsstücke zum überstzen in das lateinische für abiturienten. ... 1. teil: Deutscher text. 2. teil: Lateinische übersetzung. 4. auflage ... Lpz., G. Freytag, 1902.
iv, 76p.
1. Latin language - Composition & exercises. I. Ti.

NK 0197572 OCU

Knauth, Jon.
Friederich, Karl.
Die steinbearbeitung in ihrer entwicklung vom 11. bis zum 18. jahrhundert, von Karl Friederich ... Augsburg, B. Filser verlag, g. m. b. h., 1932.

Knauth, Joh.
Das Strassburger münster und die Cheopspyramide, rätsel der baukunst, von dombaumeister J. Knauth-Strassburg. Strassburg i. E., C. A. Vomhoff, 1908.
2 p. l., 48, [2] p. illus., diagrs. 33ᶜᵐ.
"Sonderdruck der Illustrirten elsässischen rundschau, heft I-III, 1907."

1. Strassburg. Cathedral. 2. Pyramids.

13-25423

Library of Congress NA5586.S7K5

NK 0197574 DLC

VOLUME 300

PA 8577 .S425K5 Knauth, Johann Christian
Exemplis illustrata analecta styli, quae ex ore divi Conradi Samuelis Schurtzfleischii, polyhistoris incomparabilis, vitembergae quondam calamo excepta, nunc vero in usum studiosae juventutis sunt exhibita. Dresdae, In Officina Librar. Hekeliana, 1725.
G39027 337 p.

NK 0197575 MoU

KNAUTH, Johann Christian editor.
Pythagorae carmen aureum, Graece & Latine cum analysi critica et ethica. Casp. Barlaei Orationes ii patheticae, Miscella quaedam, carmina &c. Dresdae, sumptibus J.C. Zimmermauni & J. N. Gerlachii, 1720.

nar. 12°. Front.

NK 0197576 MH

[Knauth, Johann Conrad]
Misniae illustrandae prodromus; oder, Einleitung zu des edlen hochlöblichen und hochbegabten Marggraffthumbs Meissen; Landes- und Geschicht-Beschreibung ... Dresden, J. Riedeln, 1692.
13.5 cm.
Added engr. t.-p.: Misnia illustrata authore Io: Conradô Knauthen. A.O.R. CIƆIƆCXCI.

NK 0197577 CtY

HV687 .T55 **Knauth, Marjorie (Strauss) 1897- joint author.**
Thornton, Janet.
The social component in medical care; a study of one hundred cases from the Presbyterian hospital in the city of New York, by Janet Thornton ... in collaboration with Marjorie Strauss Knauth ... New York, Columbia university press, 1937.

Knauth, Oswald Whitman, 1887-
Distribution of income by states in 1919, by Oswald W. Knauth ... New York, Harcourt, Brace and company, 1922.
v, 30 p. incl. tables. 24½cm. (*Half-title:* Publications of the National bureau of economic research, incorporated, no. 3)

1. Income. 2. U. S.—Econ. condit.—1918- I. Title.
22—17295
Library of Congress HB601.K66

OrU MtBC OrPR Or CaBVaU WaTC ICJ CU MiU NSyU
NK 0197579 DLC ViU PBm PHC PU PPT OCl ODW ICJ OCU OrP

Knauth, Oswald Whitman, 1887-
Distribution of income by states in 1919, by Oswald W. Knauth ... 2d ed. New York, National bureau of economic research, inc., 1923.
v, 30 p. incl. tables. 24cm. (*Half-title:* Publications of the National bureau of economic research, incorporated, no. 3)

1. Income. 2. U. S.—Econ. condit.—1918- I. Title.
29-14951
Library of Congress HB601.K66 1923

MB
NK 0197580 DLC CU OU NBuC PSC PU-W PPCuP IdU WaS Vil

Knauth, Oswald Whitman, 1887-
National bureau of economic research.
Income in the United States, its amount and distribution, 1909–1919, by the staff of the National bureau of economic research, incorporated: Wesley C. Mitchell, Willford I. King, Frederick R. Macaulay, Oswald W. Knauth ... New York, Harcourt, Brace and company, 1921–22.

Knauth, Oswald Whitman, 1887-
Managerial enterprise, its growth and methods of operation. [1st ed.] New York, W. W. Norton [1948]
224 p. 21 cm.
Bibliography: p. 214–215.

1. Industry. 2. U. S.—Indus. I. Title.
HD31.K56 338.8 48-6692*

ICU MB WaTC PU PV MiU PPF WaS IdPI NcC OrU OrP
NK 0197582 DLC OrCS IdU ScU MiU FU CU CoU TU OU TxU

Knauth, Oswald Whitman, 1887-
The policy of the United States towards industrial monopoly, by Oswald Whitman Knauth ... New York, 1913.
2 p. l., 7–235 p. 25cm.
Thesis (PH. D.)—Columbia university.
Vita.

1. Trusts, Industrial. 2. Trusts, Industrial—Law. 3. Monopolies—U. S.
14-2575
Library of Congress HD2785.K6
Columbia Univ. Libr. 338.8

NK 0197583 DLC NNC IdU PU CLSU CU NIC WaU-L ViU OOxM

Knauth, Oswald Whitman, 1887-
... The policy of the United States towards industrial monopoly, by Oswald Whitman Knauth ... New York, Columbia university; [etc., etc.] 1914.
233 p. 24cm. (Studies in history, economics and public law, ed. by the Faculty of political science of Columbia university. vol. LVI, no. 2; whole no. 138)
Published also as thesis (PH. D.) Columbia university, 1914.

1. Trusts, Industrial—U. S. I. Title.
14—6034
Library of Congress H31.C7 vol. 56
——— Copy 2. HD2785.K5

PU-L ViU MiU OCU OU ICJ ICN MB NjP NN
NK 0197584 DLC ViU-L IdPI CaBVaU WaS OrP PBm PSC OO

Knauth, Paul, 1856-
Goethes sprache und stil im alter. Von dr. Paul Knauth ... Leipzig, E. Avenarius, 1898.
ix p., 1 l., 156 p. 23cm.
"Meine im jahre 1894 erschienene dissertation 'Von Goethes sprache und stil im alter' habe ich unterdes erweitert und zu einem selbständigen buche herausgearbeitet."—Vorwort.

1. Goethe, Johann Wolfgang von—Language. 2. Goethe, Johann Wolfgang von—Style. I. Title.
33-8189
Library of Congress PT2226.A4K6 832.62

NK 0197585 DLC TxU NcD CU CoU CtY PU PBm MH NIC

Knauth, Paul, 1856-
Ortsnamenkunde des östlichen Erzgebirges, von dr. Paul Knauth. Freiberg, Sa., E. Mauckisch, 1927.
2 p. l., iii, 161 p. map. 23½cm.

1. Names, Geographical—Erzgebirge. I. Title.
30-1849
Library of Congress DD801.S54K5

NK 0197586 DLC MH NN ICU

833G55 DK72 Knauth, Paul, 1856-
Von Goethes sprache und stil im alter ... Leipzig, 1894.
46p.

Inaug.-diss.--Leipzig.
Vita.
Bibliographical foot-notes.

NK 0197587 IU ICU CU MA OClW ICRL MiU PSC

Knauth, Paul Heinrich
see Knauth, Paul, 1856-

Knauth, Percy, 1914-
Germany in defeat, by Percy Knauth. New York, A. A. Knopf, 1946.
ix p., 2 l., 3–233 p., 1 l. 22cm.
"First edition."

1. Germany—Hist.—Allied occupation, 1945- I. Title.
46-3053
Library of Congress DD256.K6
[40] 943.086

WaSp WaT OrPR
PPGi PSt ViU MB OCl TxU OCU Or OKentU GU OrP OrU Wa
NK 0197589 DLC AU DAU NIC MeB CaBViP CaBVa KU PP DS

KNAUTH, Rudolf, 1879-
Die bedeutung des eigenbesitzer nach dem Bürgerlichen gesetzbuche. Inaug.-diss., Jena. Weimar, 1906.

NK 0197590 MH-L ICRL NN

4K GER. 2658 Knauth, Rudolf, 1884-
Die Gesetzgebung über die Verwaltungsrechtspflege in Thüringen. Berlin, C. Heymann, 1914.
360 p.

NK 0197591 DLC-P4

Knauth, Rudolf, 1884- *ed.*
Landesverwaltungsordnung für Thüringen vom 10. juni 1926, erläutert von dr. jur. Rudolf Knauth ... [und] Kurt Wagner ... Weimar, Weimarischer verlag g. m. b. h., 1927.
395, [1] p. 21½cm. (Thüringische verwaltungsgesetze)

1. Administrative law—Thuringia. I. Wagner, Kurt, joint ed. II. Thuringia (1919-) Laws, statutes, etc. III. Title.
30-18627

NK 0197592 DLC

Knauth, Rudolf: 1887- Henry Taylor's Leben und Werke nebst einer Untersuchung der Quellen seiner Tragödie 'Philip Van Artevelde'. Straßburg 1912: DuMont Schauberg. VII, 99 S. 8° ¶ (Soll vollst. im Buchh. ersch.)
Straßburg, Phil. Diss. v. 16. Dez. 1911, Ref. Koeppel
[Geb. 22. Okt. 87 Trier; Wohnort: Trier; Staatsangeh.: Preußen; Vorbildung: Kaiser-Wilhelms-Gymn. Trier Reife O. 07; Studium: Straßburg 3, Marburg 1, Straßburg 4 S.] [U 12. 4343

NK 0197593 ICRL OU MH CtY PU PBm NN

---

* BV5080 .A75 1702 Knauth, Theodor.
Unterthänige Vorstellung an das hochlöbliche Consistorium des Hertzogthums Magdeburg, nebst beygefügtem Send-Schreiben, betressend der so genannten neuen Propheten ihren auszerordentlichen Zustand. [pref. Halle] 1714.
40 p. 17cm. [With Arnold, Gottfried. Historia et descriptio theologiae mysticae. Francofurti, 1702]

1. Lutheran church—Doctrinal and controversial works. I. Title.

NK 0197594 ViU

Knauth, Theodore Whitman, tr.
Foertsch, Hermann.
The art of modern warfare, by Hermann Foertsch ... with an introduction by Major George Fielding Eliot. New York, Veritas press, 1940.

VOLUME 300

Knauth, Victor W.
Bolshevik propaganda at home and abroad, an address delivered at the second annual Institute of statesmanship at Rollins college, Winter Park, Florida, by Victor W. Knauth. New York, N. Y., Keen, Simons and Knauth [°1930]
21 p. 22cm.

1. Propaganda, Russian. 2. Russia—Pol. & govt.—1917- 3. Soviet. I. Institute of statesmanship, Rollins college. II. Title.
30-7310
Library of Congress DK270.K55

NK 0197596 DLC NcD MH

[Knauth, Victor W]
Mayan motifs. New York: Restaurant Mayan [193-?] 23 p. illus. 22½ x 18cm.
"Text by Victor W. Knauth and drawings by Cardwell S. Higgins."
Maps on p. [2]-[3] of covers.

1. Art, Indian-American—Maya. I. New York (City). Restaurant Mayan. II. Title.
N. Y. P. L. June 9, 1939

NK 0197597 NN

Knauth, Walter, Dipl.-Ing.: Das Kaliumzinkferrocyanid. Die elektrometrische Bestimmung des Zinks. Borna-Leipzig 1915: Noske. 53 S., 1 Taf. 8°
Dresden TeH., Diss. v. 12. März 1915, Ref. Förster, Hempel
[Geb. 4. Dez. 89 Dresden; Wohnort: Dresden; Staatsangeh.: Sachsen; Vorbildung: Gewerbeak. Chemnitz Reife 10; Studium: Dresden 7 S.; Dipl.: Chem. 8. Mai 14; Dr.-Prüf. 12. März 15.] [U 15. 2537

NK 0197598 ICRL

Knauth, Wilhelm Rudolf
see Knauth, Rudolf, 1887-

Knauth brothers, *New York.*
Catalogue of surgical instruments and physicians' supplies ... Knauth brothers ... New York, Knauth brothers [°1892]
cover-title, 1 p. l., 100, 41 p. illus. 28½cm.

1. Surgical instruments and apparatus—Catalogs.
7-2643†
Library of Congress RD76.K67

NK 0197600 DLC

Knauth, Nachod & Kühne, firm, New York.
American finance in war time. Developments of a noteworthy twelve months' period. Course of financial markets before and after American participation in the world war... New York: Knauth, Nachod & Kuhne [1918]. 24 p. 8°.

1. European war, 1914- .—Finance. U. S. 2. European war, 1914- Economic aspects. U. S. 3. Title.
N. Y. P. L. July 2, 1918.

NK 0197601 NN

Knauth, Nachod and Kühne, firm, New York.
Circular letters of credit for travelers.
[New York], [c1896]
20 p. illus. 15 cm.

NK 0197602 RPB

631.5 Knauth, Nachod & Kühne, firm, New York
K72c The conquest of the desert; an illustrated description of irrigation in the West and its results. New York, [c1910]
unp. illus.

NK 0197603 IU

Knauth, Nachod & Kühne, New York.
Knauth, Nachod & Kühne's descriptions of railroad and industrial securities of the United States.
New York, c 1906

HG8921
.K6

NK 0197604 DLC

BTZE p.v.482, no.4
Knauth, Nachod & Kuhne, firm, New York.
The first year of reconstruction, 1919. Chief incidents in the development of world trade and financial expansion during a critical period... New York: Knauth, Nachod & Kuhne [1920?]. 23 p. incl. table. 8°.

1. European war, 1914- .—Reconstruction (Economic), U. S. 2. Economic history, U. S.
N. Y. P. L. September 16, 1920.

NK 0197605 NN MH

Knauth, Nachod & Kuhne, firm, N.Y.
The last year of world war 1918; important developments in world trade & finance during an unusual period ... (1919?)
24p.

NK 0197606 OClFRB

Knauthe, Erhart.
Der Finanzplan des volkseigenen Industriebetriebes. Berlin, Verlag Die Wirtschaft, 1955.
129 p. illus. 21 cm. (Diskussionsbeiträge zu Wirtschaftsfragen Heft 21)

1. Germany (Democratic Republic, 1949-)—Indus. I. Title.
HC287.A2K6 57-31955 ‡

NK 0197607 DLC NN DS

Knauthe, Fritz.
Die erzieherische behandlung der psychopathischen konstitutionen. Vortrag, gehalten auf der versammlung der leiter der erziehungsanstalten der provinz Sachsen in Halle a. S. am 29. april, 1920, von anstaltsdirektor Fr. Knauthe. Langensalza, H. Beyer & söhne, 1920.
16 p. 24½cm. (*Added t.-p.:* Beiträge zur kinderforschung und heilerziehung. hft. 176)

1. Defective and delinquent classes—Germany. 2. Children, Abnormal and backward. [2. Backward children—Germany] I. Title.
E 22-434
Library, U. S. Bur. of Education LC4696.G3K7
[2]

NK 0197608 DHEW MH

Knauthe, Fritz.
Die pädagogik im heilerziehungsheim. Von Fr. Knauthe ... Langensalza, H. Beyer & söhne, 1919.
33 p. 24½cm. (*Added t.-p.:* Beiträge zur kinderforschung und heilerziehung. hft. 159)
"Literatur": p. 31-33.

1. Physical education [and training] I. Title.
E 26-93
Library, U. S. Bur. of Education GV361.K7

NK 0197609 DHEW NN

Knauthe, Fritz.
Sonder-katalog für die gruppe jugendfürsorge der Internationalen hygieneausstellung Dresden 1911
see under Dresden. Internationale hygiene-ausstellung, 1911. [Supplement]

QL Knauthe, Karl, ed.
638 Die karpfenzucht. Anleitung zum prak-
C94 tischen betriebe unter berücksichtigung
K67 der neuesten wissenschaftlichen erfahrungen. Unter mitwirkung der herren ... dr.C. Apstein ... geheimsekretär Bertnelmann ... Fr.Borcherding ... [u.a.] zusammengestellt und herausg.von Karl Knauthe ... mit 53 abbildungen. Neudamm, J.Neumann, 1901.
vii, 389, [1] p. illus. (incl. plans) 21cm.
1. Carp. 2. Fish-culture.

NK 0197611 MiU MH NjP ICJ

Knauthe, Karl.
Das süsswasser, chemische, biologische und bakteriologische untersuchungsmethoden unter besonderer berücksichtigung der biologie und der fischereiwirtschaftlichen praxis, von Karl Knauthe ... Neudamm, J. Neumann, 1907.
v p., 1 l., 663, [1] p. illus. 21cm.

1. Pisciculture. 2. Water.
Agr 11-654
Library, U. S. Dept. of Agriculture 278K72

NK 0197612 DNAL ICJ PPAN ICRL

Knauthe, Karl.
Two fertile cyprinoid hybrids. By Karl Knauthe. [Washington, Govt. print. off., 1894]
p. 29-30. 27cm. [U. S. Commission of fish and fisheries. Doc. 234]
Caption title.
"Tr. from the German: Zoologischer anzeiger. v. 16 ..."
Extracted from the bulletin of the United States fish commission for 1894.

1. Hybridization.
F 12-180
Library, U. S. Bur. of Fisheries

NK 0197613 DI CaBVaU

Knauthe, Theodor Hermann, 1837-1895.
61312 Arzneitaschenbuch zur oesterreichischen Pharmakopoe. Von Dr. Theodor Knauthe. Wien, W. Braumüller, 1877.
viii, [2], 159 p. 15½cm.
With Dillnberger, E. Therapeutisches Recept-Taschenbuch für Frauen- und Kinderkrankheiten. 1878.

NK 0197614 ICJ

Knauthe (Theodor [Hermann]) [1837-]. Handbuch der pneumatischen Therapie. Für praktische Aerzte und Studirende der Medicin bearbeitet. x, 306 pp. 8°. *Leipzig, O. Wigand,* 1876.

NK 0197615 DNLM

Knauthe (Theodor Hermann) [1837-1895] * Ueber Astigmatismus. 14 pp., 1 l. 8°. *Leipzig, L. Schnauss,* [1863].

NK 0197616 DNLM ICRL PPC

VOLUME 300

Theodor Hermann, 1837-1895

Knauthe, Die Weintraube in historischer, chemischer, physiologischer, therapeutischer Beziehung und in ihrer Anwendung zu Traubenkuren, nebst Beschreibung sämmtlicher bekannteren Traubenkurorte. 1 p. l., 84 pp. 12°. *Leipzig, O. Wigand,* 1874.

NK 0197617 DNLM

Knauthe, Theodor Hermann, 1837-1895

—. Wie die Alten die Lungenschwindsucht behandelten. 2 l. 8°. *Wien, Genossenschafts-Buchdruckerei.* [n. d.]

NK 0197618 DNLM

Knautz, Günther, 1909-
Studien zur Aesthetik und psychologie der schauspielkunst. ... Essen, 1934. 190 p.
Inaug. Diss. - Kiel, 1934.
Lebenslauf.
Bibliography.

NK 0197619 ICRL OrU CtY MH PU

Knautz, Harry Armel, joint author.

FOR OTHER EDITIONS SEE MAIN ENTRY

Langer, Charles Heinrichs, 1876–
Walton federal income tax accounting and procedure, 1941 [by] Charles H. Langer ... and Harry A. Knautz ... Chicago, Ill., Walton publishing company [°1941]

943.91
K729
Knauz, Nándor, 1831-1898.
Buda ostromához. Budapest [Franklin-Társulat] 1886.
128 p. facsims.

1. Hungary - History - 1526-1683.
2. Hungary - History - 1683-1848.

NK 0197621 NNC

Knauz, Nándor. 1831-1898
Bq80 Codex diplomaticus primatialis ecclesiae
Es8 Strigoniensis. Strigonii, Horák, 1863-66.
863K 2v. in 1. 23cm.
Added t.p. in Hungarian: "Az Esztergomi föegyháznak okmánytára".

NK 0197622 CtY MH

Knauz, Nándor, 1831-98
A Garan-melletti Szent-Benedeki Apátság; a templom felszenteltetésének emlékére. Kiadja az Esztergomi Fokaptalan. 1. köt. Budapest, 1890

250 p. illus.
No more published

NK 0197623 MH ViU NNC

4CE
30
Knauz, Nándor, 1831-
Kortan, hazai történelmünkhöz alkalmazva. Budapest, Akademia Könyvkiadó -Hivatala, 1876
589 p.

NK 0197624 DLC-P4 MH CtY

Z
6620
.H9
K5
Knauz, Nándor, 1831-1898, comp.
Libri missales ac breviaria Ecclesiae Hungaricae ad receptionem usque ritus Romani. Collegit Ferdinandus Knauz. Strigonii, Typis Aegidii Horák, 1870.
111 p. 25 cm.

Cover title: A magyar egyház régi mise- és zsolozsma-könyvei.
"Különnyomat a Magyar Sion VII. évfolyamából."
Bibliographical footnotes.

NK 0197625 NNC

BX
1521
E8K67+
Knauz, Nándor, 1831-1898, ed.
Monumenta ecclesiae Stringoniensis, jussu et sumptu eminentissimi et reverendissimi domini Joannis Cardinalis Simor ... Stringonii, Typis descripsit Aegydius Horák, 1874-
v. 30cm.

Vol. 3 edited by C. L. Dedek.

Contents.--t.1. Ab a. 979. ad a. 1273. --t.2. Ab a. 1273 ad a. 1321.--t.3. Ab a. 1321 ad a. 1349.

1. Esztergom (Archdiocese)--Hist.--Sources. I. Dedek, Crescens Lajos, 1862- ed. II. Title.

NK 0197627 NIC NNC MH

Knauz, Nándor, 1831-1898.
Az országos tanács és országgyűlések története, **1445–**1452. A. M. Akademiában székfoglalólag előadta **Knauz** Nándor. Pest, Eggenberger F., 1854.

175 p. illus. 24 cm.

Includes bibliographical references.

1. Hungary. Országgyűlés—History. 2. László V, King of Hungary and Bohemia, 1440–1457. 3. Hunyadi, János, d. 1456. I. Title.

DB930.7.K58 76–256324

NK 0197628 DLC

JN2124
1445
K5
Knauz, Nándor, 1831-1898.
Az Országos Tanács és országgyűlések története, 1445-1452. Pest, Eggenberger F., 1859.
175 p. illus.

M. Akadémiai székfoglaló.
Hungarian, Latin or German.
Includes bibliographies.

1. Hungary. Országgyűlés. 2. Hungary. Országos Tanács. 3. Hungary - Pol. & govt.

NK 0197629 CU NNC MH-L CtY

BX
1521 Knauz, Nándor, 1831-1893.
.B73 Válaszul Pinely Károly Adalékjára. Budapest,
K53 Knoll Károly, 1881.
150 p. 23 cm.

"Különnyomat az 'Uj Magyar Sion' 1881. évi folyamából."
Errata slip inserted.
Bibliographical footnotes.

NK 0197630 NNC

Knave, Ernst Bengtsson
Über die bandenspektren einiger metallhydride. ... Uppsala, 1932.
Inaug. Diss. -Stockholm, 1932.
Bibliography.

NK 0197631 ICRL

Knave, Ernst Bengtsson.
...Über die Bandenspektren einiger Metallhydride, von Ernst Bengtsson Knave... Uppsala: Almqvist & Wiksells boktryckeri-a.-b., 1932. 98 p. incl. diagrs., tables. illus. (incl. charts), pl. 29cm. (Kungliga vetenskaps-societeten i Upsala. Nova acta. ser. 4, v. 8, no. 4.)

"Literaturverzeichnis," at end of each chapter.

1. Spectra, Band. 2. Metals—Spectra.
N. Y. P. L. June 12, 1934

NK 0197632 NN NIC CtY ICJ OO

The **knave** in graine, new vampt. A witty comedy, acted at the Fortune many dayes together with great applause. Written by J. D., gent. London, Printed by J. O. and are to be sold by John Nicholson at his shop under St. Martins church neare Ludgate. 1640.
[88] p. 18 cm.
Signatures: 2 leaves unsigned: B–L^4, M^2.
Bound in morocco, tooled in gilt.
Tentatively ascribed to John Day by Halkett & Laing, and others.
I. Day, John, 1574–1640? supposed author. II. D., J.

PR2411.K75 1640 18–10621 rev*
Copy 2. [Longe, F. Collection of plays. v. 83, no. 3]
PR1241.L6 vol. 83, no. 3

NjP CtY CSmH MWiW-C MB
NK 0197633 DLC DFo NN NIC OKentU MB TxU ICN OU MiU

FILM
S-8
reel
1170
The Knave in graine, new vampt. A witty comedy, acted at the Fortune many dayes together with great applause. Written by J.D.Gent. London, Printed by J.Okes, 1640.
Tentatively ascribed to John Day by Halkett and Laing, and others.
Short-title catalogue no.6174 (carton 1170)
Microfilm

I.Day, John, 1574-1640? supposed author.

NK 0197634 MiU ViU

MICPT Knave in grain [or, New vampt by] J. D.
822.08 London, 1640.
(In Three centuries of drama: English, 1512-1641)

Microprint.

I. D., J. II. Title: New vampt.

NK 0197635 MoU

Wh
A100 The KNAVE of clubs. Otherwise called, A game
643k2 at cards, and clubs trump. Doe you not see the knave turn'd up? Rub and lose cards ...
London, Shuffled, cut, and dealt faire, by Stysichorus, Anno Dom. 1643. 1p.ℓ., 6p. 22cm.
Woodcut illus. on t.-p.
Attributed to George Wither in the Wrenn catalogue.

NK 0197636 TxU CSmH NcD

The knave of clubbs. Tis merry when knaues meete
see under [Rowlands, Samuel] 1570?-1630?

VOLUME 300

Knave of harts. Haile fellow, well met
see under [Rowlands, Samuel] 1570?-1630?

The knave of hearts; a novel ...
see under [Diehl, Alice (Mangold)]
1844-1912.

British Tracts 1679 K72 The knave uncloak'd: or, The jesuit in his colours. Being an answer ... to a late seditious pamphlet, called, The cloak in its colours; or, The presbyterian unmasked. Wherein is ... discovered the treacherous designs of the popish party ... By a Son of the Church of England. London,T.Parkhurst,1679.

11p. 21cm.

1. The cloak in its colours. I. Son of the Church of England. cdu chronology card

NK 0197640 CtY IU NNUT-Mc

Knavery in all trades: or, The coffee-house. A comedy. As it was acted in the Christmas holidays by several apprentices with great applause. With license. London, Printed by J. B. for W. Gilbertson, and H. Marsh; and are to be sold at the Royal Exchange, Fleet-Street, and Westminster-Hall, 1664.

[40] p. 22cm.

Collation: 2 leaves unsigned (t.-p., Persons named); text: B-E[4], F[2].
Ascribed by some authorities to John Tatham, but not conclusively.
Trimmed to 16½ x 11cm inset in paper 21½ x 16cm.
The Kemble-Devonshire copy, with Kemble's notation on t.-p. "First edition" and "Collated & Perfect. J. P. K. 1798."
Bound in calf by Rivière & son.

I. Tatham, John, fl. 1632-1664. 21-3185

Library of Congress PR2411.K8 1664

NK 0197641 DLC KU MH CtY

The Knavery of astrology discover'd ...
see under Tell-Troth, Tim., pseud.

Knavery unmasked
see under Ali, Mahamed, dacoit.

1648 K72 Knaves and fooles in folio. Discovered, and then advised, that once at the last they will grow both wise and honest. Or, A meanes to undeceive, and so to beget a right understanding and judgement throughout the three kingdomes, hitherto deluded by the aforesaids ... London,Printed by M.Simmons for R.H.1648.

3p.ℓ.,36[i.e.37],[1]p. 18cm.
Preface signed: S.H.

NK 0197644 CtY CSmH

Knave's calendar; or, A step towards the duty of a legislator. [London, 1799]
62 p. il. 22 cm.

NK 0197645 RPB

Knayer, Christian, 1876-

Leichte Kinderstücke ohne Oktaven. Easy children pieces without octaves ... Für Klavier zu zwei Händen. Op. 17. Leipzig, Breitkopf & Härtel [1920]

15 p. 31 cm. (Edition Breitkopf, Nr. 5147)

For piano.

1. Piano music, Juvenile. I. Title. II. Title: Easy children pieces without octaves.

M1380.K 49-30850*

NK 0197646 DLC

Knayer, Lydia Friederike, 1883-

Durch Gesang zu Gesundheit und Schönheit; die günstigen Einwirkungen der Gesangstudien auf Körper, Seele und Geist, dargestellt von Lydia Knayer... Stuttgart: H. Fink[, 1930]. 78 p. front. (port.) 8°.

517623A. 1. Singing—Study and teaching. I. Title.
N. Y. P. L. April 14, 1931

NK 0197647 NN

Knayer, Lydia Friederike, 1883-

... Das tüchtige alleinmädchen; den jungen mädchen ein ratgeber, den hausfrauen eine hilfe beim einlernen, von Lydia Knayer. Stuttgart, K. Thienemann [°1930]

126 p. 21cm. (Neue hauswirtschaft-bücher)

1. Servants. 2. Domestic economy. I. Title.

30-25604

Library of Congress HD8039.D52G35
Copyright A—Foreign 8367
[2] 647.25

NK 0197648 DLC

Knaysi, Georges Abdallah, 1898-

Elements of bacterial cytology, by Georges Knaysi ... Ithaca, N. Y., Comstock publishing company, inc., 1944.

xii, 209 p. illus., diagrs. 24cm.
Bibliography: p. 190-198.

1. Bacteria. 2. Cells. I. Title: Bacterial cytology.

44-7030

Library of Congress QR75.K58
[10] 589.95

DNAL OrSaW DAU NNBG CaBVaU
ViU OOxM NcD PPF TxU OrU NcGU IdPI NcD-MC OrU-M
NK 0197649 DLC MtBC CU PSC PSt PPC PU-B TU OCU OU

Knaysi, Georges Abdallah, 1898-

Elements of bacterial cytology. 2d ed. Ithaca, N. Y., Comstock Pub. Co., 1951.

xviii, 375 p. illus. 25 cm.
Bibliography: p. [345]-360.

1. Bacteria. 2. Cells. I. Title: Bacterial cytology.

QR75.K58 1951 589.95 51-521

NNBG PPC OC1W DNLM MtBC DNAL MtU OrCS OrU WaSpG OrU-M
NK 0197650 DLC IdU CaBVaU MB CU NcU ICU ICJ TU TxU

Knaysi, Georges, Abdallah, 1898-

Some factors other than bacteria that influence the body of artificial buttermilk.

(*In* U. S. Dept. of agriculture. Journal of agricultural research. v. 34, no. 8, April 15, 1927, p. 771-784. diagr. 23½cm. Washington, 1927)

Contribution from Cornell agricultural experiment station (N. Y. (Cornell)—9)
Published June 17, 1927.
"Literature cited": p. 784.

1. Dairy products. [1. Buttermilk]

Agr 27-497

Library, U. S. Dept. of Agriculture 1Ag84J vol. 34

NK 0197651 DNAL

99.76 K722 Knězovický, Július.
Prerezávky a prebierky. [Vyd. 1.
Bratislava] Oráč [1952]
133 p. (Nové lesy, v. 9)

1. Lumbering. Czechoslovak Republic.
2. Selective logging. I. Nové lesy, v. 9.

NK 0197652 DNAL

Knczynski, Arnold.
Verzeichnisz einer Sammlung von nahezu 3000 Flugschriften Luthers. Leipzig, 1870.
262 + 79 p.

NK 0197653 PPeSchw NRCR

Kneale, Albert H 1872-

Indian agent. [An autobiographical sketch] Caldwell, Idaho, Caxton Printers, 1950.

429 p. illus., ports., maps. 24 cm.

Half title: Indians and the Indian Bureau.

1. Indians of North America—Government relations. I. Title.

E93.K6 970.5 50-9648

OrMonO OrP WaE WaS WaT CaBViPA IdU CaBVaU
NK 0197654 DLC TxU GU CU-B ICU OFH DI MB MtBC MtU Or

Kneale, Nigel.

Tomato Cain; and other stories; with a foreword by Elizabeth Bowen. London, Collins, 1949.

256 p. 21 cm.

I. Title.

Full name: Thomas Nigel Kneale.

PZ3.K7284To 50-22913

NK 0197655 DLC ViU MH IU

Kneale, Nigel.

Tomato Cain, and other stories; with a foreword by Elizabeth Bowen. [1st American ed.] New York, Knopf, 1950.

xvi, 300 p. 20 cm.

I. Title.

PZ3.K7284To 2 50-12595

NK 0197656 DLC Or KMK ICU OrU IU OC1W OrP WaE OkU

Kneale, R. D.

Measurement of water. n. t.-p. [Bozeman, 1913.] 133 p. illus. 8°. (Montana. Agricultural Experiment Station. Circular 24.)

1. Water.—Measurement.
N. Y. P. L. December 30, 1913.

NK 0197657 NN

Kneale, Samuel George.
Axially symmetric Stokes flows.

Thesis - Harvard, 1953

NK 0197658 MH

Kneale, Thomas Nigel
see **Kneale, Nigel.**

Kneale, William Calvert.

The idea of invention.

(*In* British Academy, London (Founded 1901) Proceedings, 1955. London. 26 cm. v. 41 (1956) p. [85]-108)

Philosophical lecture, read 16 Feb. 1955.
Bibliographical footnotes.

Continued in next column

VOLUME 300

Continued from preceding column

1. Inventions. I. Title. (Series: British Academy, London (Founded 1901) Annual philosophical lecture, Henriette Hertz Trust, 1955)

AS122.L5 vol. 41 A 56—6162

Wisconsin. Univ. Libr. for Library of Congress [58r57e2]†

CaBVaU
NK 0197660 WU IdU MB OU NcD MiU LU CLSU NN DLC DCU

Kneale, William Calvert.
Probability and induction. Oxford, Clarendon Press, 1949.
viii, 264 p. diagrs. 23 cm.

1. Probabilities. 2. Logic. I. Title.

BC141.K55 519 49-9123*

MtBC MtU NcD PPLas MiEM CaBVaU
TxU OrP IdU OrPR WaWW PSt PPF MiU TxU PP PSC ScU AU
NK 0197661 DLC OkU OU NcU OCU NN CtY ICU MH NcU MB

Kneale, William Calvert.
Probability and induction. Oxford, Clarendon Press, [1952]
viii, 264 p. diagrs. 23 cm.

NK 0197662 ViU WaU IaU MiU OO NBC MH PHC CaBVa OU

Kneale's Guide to the Isle of Man, comprising an account of the island, historical, physical, archæological, & topographical, and all the information desirable for visitors and tourists. To which is added a collection of entertaining Manx legends. Douglas, W. Kneale, [1860]. 8°. pp. 224, *map and pls.*
IcB43K679

NK 0197663 NIC MWA

Knease, Tacie Mary, 1889–
An Italian word list from literary sources, compiled by Tacie Mary Knease ... [Toronto] The University of Toronto press, 1933.
70 p. 22cm.
Thesis (PH. D.)—University of Iowa, 1931.
Thesis note on label mounted on t.-p.
"List of authors and their works": p. 8-10.
Bibliography: p. [6]

1. Italian language—Glossaries, vocabularies, etc. I. Title.

33-32893

Library of Congress PC1691.K6 1931
Univ. of Iowa Libr.
———Copy 2. [2] 453

MdBJ MH
NK 0197664 IaU NcD NN CU OO PBm OOxM CaBVaU DLC

Kneass, Horn Riley, 1812-1861, comp.
Election laws of the commonwealth of Pennsylvania
see under Pennsylvania. Laws, statutes, etc.

[Kneass, Horn Riley] 1812-1861.
Contested election between Horn R. Kneass and William B. Reed for the office of district attorney of the county of Philadelphia; petitions, evidence, speeches, opinions, etc. JK2246 .P4K6
Philadelphia? 1851

NK 0197666 DLC PHi

Kneass, Horn Riley, 1812-1861.
Proceedings of the celebration of the anniversary of the glorious battle of New Orleans, by "the personal and political friends" of George Mifflin Dallas, containing the regular toasts, the volunteer sentiments, replies to invitations, and the oration pronounced on the occasion by Horn R. Kneas [!], esquire, with an appendix, containing very interesting letters, written by Vice-President Dallas in the year 1845. Philadelphia, Printed and pub. at the office of the "Daily keystone", 1846.

Kneass, Nelson, d. 1869.
...Ben Bolt; or, Oh! dont you remember. Ballad sung by Miss Clara Bruce. Composed by Nelson Kneass... Baltimore: W. C. Peters, cop. 1848. Publ. pl. no. 1138. 5 p. 2. ed. f°.

English words; music for 1 voice with piano acc.
Words by Thomas Dunn English.

1. Songs, American. 2. English, Thomas Dunn, 1819–1902. 3. Title.
4. Title: Oh! don't you remember.
N. Y. P. L. March 13, 1929

NK 0197668 NN ViU MiU-C

M1619
S69
v.665

Kneass, Nelson.
[Ben Bolt; acc. piano]
Ben Bolt; [or] Oh! don't you remember. 3d ed. Baltimore, W.C.Peters [1848] Pl.no.1138.
6 p. 35cm.
No. 3 in a vol. lettered:Songs, v.665.

1. Songs. I. Title. II. Title: Oh! don't you remember.

NK 0197669 CSt ViU

Kneass, Nelson.
Ben Bolt: ballad. [With accompaniment for pianoforte.] Composed by Nelson Kneass. [Words by Thomas Dunn English.] 10th edition.
Louisville. Peters, Webb & Co. [1848.] 6 pp. 33 cm. 8051.318

L1140 — Double main card. — Kneass, Nelson. (M1) — English, Thomas Dunn. (M2) — T.r. (1, 2) — Songs. With music. (1)

NK 0197670 MB ViU NcD

KNEASS, NELSON, arranger?
...Ben Bolt; ballad composed by Nelson Kneass... Cincinnati,W.C.Peters & sons[c1848]
[6]p. 34cm.

Vocal solo.
At head of cover-title: Tenth edition; at head of caption title: Twenty-seventh edition.
"German air, arr. by N.Kneass. Words by T.D.English."—Sears. Song index.
Caption title: Ben Bolt. Or, "Oh! don't you remember?"

NK 0197671 ICN MH MB ViU MiU-C NcD

W.C.L. **Kneass, Nelson**
M780.88
A512CT
no.7

Ben Bolt; [or,] Oh! don't you remember. 15th ed. Cincinnati, W. C. Peters [c1848]
6 p. 33 cm.
For voice and piano.
[No. 7] in an album with binder's title: Music collected by Emily B. Jones, ca. 1850]

1. Songs (Medium voice) with piano.
I. Title. II. Title: Oh! don't you remember.

NK 0197672 NcD

M1
.S444
v.103
no.28

Kneass, Nelson.
Ben Bolt; or, Oh! don't you remember. Sung by Miss Clara Bruce. Composed by Nelson Kneass. 20th ed. 38 cts. nett. Cincinnati, W. C. Peters & Sons; Louisville, Peters, Webb & Co.; St. Louis, Balmer & Weber [c1848] Pl. no. 1138-5.
6 p. 35cm. [Sheet music collection, v. 103, no. 28]
E. H. Andrews, Printer.
1. Songs with piano. I. Title.

NK 0197673 ViU

M1
.S444
v.78
no.1

Kneass, Nelson.
Ben Bolt. Oh! don't you remember. Sung by Miss Clara Bruce. Composed by Nelson Kneass. 10th ed. 38 cts. net. Baltimore, W. C. Peters; Cincinnati, Peters & Field; Louisville, Peters, Webb & Co. [185-?] Pl. no. 1138.
6 p. 35cm. [Sheet music collection, v. 78, no. 1]
Stamped in gold on cover: Anna M. Preston.
1. Songs with piano. I. Title.

NK 0197674 ViU

M1642
.E54B4
1860

Kneass, Nelson.
Ben Bolt [or, Oh! don't you remember. By] N. Kneass. Augusta, Ga., Blackmar & Bro.; Richmond, Va., West & Johnston, J. W. Randolph, P. H. Taylor; B. Duncan, Lith., Columbia, S. C. [186-?]
[3] p. 30cm.

NK 0197675 ViU

M1619
S69
v.228

Kneass, Nelson.
[Ben Bolt; acc.piano]
Ben Bolt, part song for mixed voices; arr.by J.C.Macy. [Words by Thomas Dunn English. Boston] O.Ditson, c1903. Pl.no.4-97-64245-7.
8 p. 28cm. (Oliver Ditson Company's secular selections, 57th ser., no.11, 151)
Caption title.
Vol. 228 in a set lettered:Songs.

1.Part-songs, Secular. I.Macy, James Cartwright, 1845-1918. arr. II.English, Thomas Dunn, 1819-1902. III.Title.

NK 0197676 CSt

Kneass, Nelson. No. 41 in **M.450.170
Gently down the stream. [Song with accompaniment for the pianoforte.]
— New York. Berry & Gordon. 1854. 5 pp. [Songs composed by & for Geo. Christy and Wood's Minstrels. No. 1.] 34 cm.

D8726 — T.r. — Christy's Minstrels. — Negro minstrels.

NK 0197677 MB

VM
1
F 91
no.289

KNEASS, NELSON.
...I hear the hoofs; or, The lost child... New York,Firth,Pond & co.,c1849.
5p. 34cm. (Melodies of the New Orleans serenaders... [no.3])

Vocal solo with piano accompaniment.
Plate no.: 393.

NK 0197678 ICN

VOLUME 300

Kneass, Nelson. No. 17 in **M.450.170
Ne'er fear, boys, cheer. [Song and chorus with accompaniment for the pianoforte.]
New York. Berry & Gordon. 1854. 5 pp. [Songs composed by & for Geo. Christy and Wood's Minstrels.] 34 cm.

D8726 — T.r. — Christy's Minstrels. — Negro minstrels.

NK 0197679 MB

Kneass, Nelson. No. 63 in 8050a.23.
Old Aunty Brown [Song. Altered from a melody by Nelson Kneass]. Arranged by Wm Cumming. Guitar accompt.
= Cincinnati. Peters & Field. [184-?] 5 pp. F°.

G3338 — T.r. — Songs. With music. — Cumming, William, ed.

NK 0197680 MB

W.C.L. Kneass, Nelson
M780.88
A512VS The old veteran. Words by T. H. Bayly. Baltimore, W. C. Peters [c1848]
no.35 5 p. 34 cm.

For voice and piano.
[No. 35] in a vol. of songs collected by Sallie M. Pennypacker.
1. Songs (Medium voice) with piano. I. Bayly, Thomas Haynes, 1797-1839. The old veteran. II. Title.

NK 0197681 NcD

Und41 Kneass, Samuel H
+1 Report of an examination of the coal mines, lands and estate of the Lykens Valley Coal Company ... By Samuel H.Kneass ... [Philadelphia,1844]
L98 28p. 22½cm.
Cover-title.
Pamphlet

1. Lykens Valley Coal Company. 2. Coal mines and mining - Pennsylvania.

NK 0197682 CtY PPAN PHi

Kneass, Samuel H.
Report of the survey of a line of rail road, from the borough of Marietta, to intersect the Columbia & Philadelphia railroad, near the Little Conestogo, by Samuel H. Kneass ... Lancaster [Pa.] J. Reynolds, printer, 1832.
11 p. 20½cm.

1. Railroads—Pennsylvania—Early works. 2. Philadelphia and Columbia railroad.

A 22-1690

Title from Bureau of Railway Economics. Printed by L. C.

NK 0197683 DBRE MWA MiU-T P NN

Kneass, Samuel H.
Report on drainage and sewerage, made to the select and common councils of Philadelphia: May 9, 1853. Phila. 1853.

22 p.

NK 0197684 PHi

Kneass, Strickland, 1821-1884
The new bridge over the river Schuylkill at Chestnut street, Philadelphia. n.p., n.d.

8 p.

NK 0197685 PPF

Kneass, Strickland, 1821–1884.
Report on the eastern terminus of the Pennsylvania railroad. By Strickland Kneass ... Philadelphia, Crissy & Markley, printers, 1859.
15 p. 23cm.

1. Pennsylvania railroad.

A 15—1756

Bur. of railway econ. Libr. for Library of Congress TF25.P4K6

NK 0197686 DBRE PPL

Kneass, Strickland, 1821-1884.
Widening of Delaware Avenue: Letter to Councils. By Strickland Kneass, et al. Phila., 1877.

7 p.

NK 0197687 PHi

[Kneass, Strickland Landis] 1861–
Handbook of injectors and the improved self-acting injector. 9th ed., 55 thousand. Philadelphia, Pa., W. Sellers & co., inc., Injector department [1911]
88 p. illus., tables. 13cm.
p. 87-88 left blank for "notes."

1. Injectors.

Library of Congress TJ387.K67 11-24366

NK 0197688 DLC

Kneass, Strickland Landis, 1861–
Practice and theory of the injector. By Strickland L. Kneass ... New York, J. Wiley & sons, 1894.
2 p. l., 132 p. illus. 23½cm.

TJ387.K68

——— 2d ed. Rev. and enl. 1st thousand. New York, J. Wiley & sons; [etc., etc.] 1898.
iv, 161 p. illus. 23½cm.

1. Injectors.

6-33912-3

Library of Congress TJ387.K69

MtBC ICJ
NK 0197689 DLC MB MiHM PP PPD PSC PP MiU ICJ MtU

Kneass, Strickland Landis, 1861-
Practice & theory of the injector. 2d. ed. rev. enl. N.Y., 1899

NK 0197690 OC1W OCU CU

Kneass, Strickland Landis, 1861–
Practice and theory of the injector. By Strickland L. Kneass ... 3d ed. Rev. and enl. 1st thousand. New York, J. Wiley & sons; [etc., etc.] 1910.
v, 175 p. incl. illus., tables, diagrs. 23½cm. $1.50

1. Injectors.

Library of Congress TJ387.K7 10—7466

NK 0197691 DLC CU IdU NcRS TxU PU-Sc MiU OC1 NN

KNEAZJESKIJ,B.
Bolgarernes skikke og overtro. Efter det russiske ved E.M.Thorson. Kjøb.,1855.

16°. pp.(2),39.

NK 0197692 MH

Knebel, Aaron G 1874–
Four decades with men and boys, by A. G. Knebel; with a foreword by C. V. Thomas. New York, Association press, 1936.
vi p., 2 l., 244 p. front. (port.) 21cm.

1. Young men's Christian associations. I. Title.

37-21815

Library of Congress BV1085.K5A3
——— ——— Copy 2.
Copyright A 108852 [3] 922

NK 0197693 DLC PCC OC1 OC1U OrSaW

Knebel, Aaron G 1874–
Hit by a flivver; letters from Rudolph to Heinie Oskar, arranged and edited by A. G. Knebel. New York, Association press, 1926.
2 p. l., 59 p. illus. 21cm.

I. Title.

Library of Congress PN6231.D6K6 27-2202

NK 0197694 DLC OC1U

4UD-37 Knebel, Aladár, Ritter von Treuenschwert.
Der Infanterieangriff im Lichte des russisch-japanischen Krieges. Das Zusammenwirken mit den anderen Waffen, Maschinengewehre, technische Hilfsmittel, Verwundungen, Bekleidung, Ausrüstung etc. Wien, L.W. Seidel, 1906.
116 p.

NK 0197695 DLC-P4 CLU DNW

Knebel, Aladár, *Ritter* von Treuenschwert. 355.053 7 V.2
47174 Lose Gedanken über den Infanterieangriff. Von Aladár Knebel Ritter v. Treuenschwert .... Wien, L. W. Seidel & Sohn, 1904.
[4], 69 p. 24½cm. (*In* Militärische Essays, Heft 2.)

NK 0197696 ICJ

Knebel, Aladár, *Ritter* von Treuenschwert. 355.04 K73
49396 Nächtliche Unternehmungen. Märsche, Vorposten, Gefechte in der Nacht, Ausnützung der Nacht beim planmässigen Angriffe etc. Von Aladár Knebel Ritter von Treuenschwert, ... Mit einer Figurentafel. Wien, L. W. Seidel & Sohn, 1905.
[4], 125 p. 1 fold. map. 24½cm.
"Benützte Quellen," p. [2].

NK 0197697 ICJ

Knebel,Carl Ludwig von.

see

Knebel,Karl Ludwig von,1744-1834.

VOLUME 300

Knebel, Curt, 1871–
Phyllocactus. Compiled by Werner Engelhardt, edited by Gertrude W. Beahm. Pasadena, Calif., Abbey Garden Press, ©1949.
63 p. illus. 21 cm.

1. Phyllocactus. I. Engelhardt, Werner, comp. II. Beahm, Gertrude W., ed.
SB413.C12K5 635.933471 Agr 50-29
U. S. Dept. of Agr. Libr. for Library of Congress 96.31K73 [3]†

NK 0197699 DNAL CU ICU DLC Or CaBVaU

SB 413 C12 K68
Knebel, Curt, 1871-
Phyllokakteen; ein Buch von Züchtung und Pflege schöner Blumen. Bearb. und hrsg. von Werner Engelhardt, Potsdam, E. Stichnote, 1951.
90 p. col. plates. 21 cm.

1. Phyllocactus. I. Engelhardt, Werner.

NK 0197700 NIC

KNEBEL, Eduard.
Die vinkulierung der inhaberschuldverschreibungen. Inaug.-diss., Würzburg. Rothenburg, 1906.

NK 0197701 MH-L ICRL

Knebel, Emerich Carl. *9330.436.35
Der Wucher im preussischen Saargebiete.
(In Verein fuer Socialpolitik. Schriften. 35. Pp. 121-149. Leipzig, 1887.)

Dec. 9, 1901
E2407 — Prussia. Soc. sci. — Usury.

NK 0197702 MB

Knebel, Emil.
Mittheilungen aus dem staedtischen krankenhause zu Wiesbaden ueber die daselbst waehrend der epidemie im sommer 1885 behandelten faeelle von typhus abdominalis.
Inaug. diss. Wuerzburg, 1886. (Muenchen).

NK 0197703 ICRL

Knebel (Ernst). *Die Bestandteile der Kolanuss. [Erlangen.] 28 pp. 8°. [*Frankfurt a. M., Baier & Lewalter*, 1892.]

NK 0197704 DNLM ICRL

Knebel, Georg Konrad, 1856-
see Knebel, Konrad, 1856-

Knebel, Gerh. von
Hund und Katze; ein praktischer Ratgeber für das Halten und Pflegen unserer vierbeinigen Hausfreunde. Berlin, Grüne Post [1937]
100 [1] p., illus.

NK 0197706 MiD

Knebel, Gottfried, 1908-
Monographie der algenreihe der prasiolales, insbesondere von prasiola crispa ... Dresden, 1935.
Inaug. Diss. - Berlin, 1935.
Lebenslauf.
Wichtigste literatur.

NK 0197707 ICRL CtY

Knebel, Hans, 1909-
Der begriff der eisenbahnhoheit und seine entwicklungsstufen im Deutschen reich bis zur gegenwart ... von Hans Knebel ... München, Gerber [1934?]
32 p.

Thesis, Freiburg i. Br.
"Literaturverzeichnis": p. 5-6.

1.Railroads - Germany.

NK 0197708 NNC ICRL PU CtY

PC2109 K65
Knebel, Heinrich.
Französische schulgrammatik für gymnasien und progymnasien, von dr. Heinrich Knebel ... Fünfte verbesserte und vermehrte auflage. Koblenz, Karl Bädeker, 1848.
viii, 97, [1] p. 22cm.

1. French language.-Grammar.-1800-1870.

NK 0197709 NBuG

Knebel, Heinrich.
Französische schulgrammatik für gymnasien und progymnasien, von dr. Heinrich Knebel ... 7. verb und verm. aufl. Koblenz, K. Bädeker, 1854.
xii, 172 p. 21½cm.

1. French language—Grammar—1800–1870.
10-24394†
Library of Congress PC2109.K65

NK 0197710 DLC

Knebel, Heinrich
Französisches lesebuch für die mittleren klassen der gymnasien und die progymnasien. ...Ein anhang to dessen französischer schulgrammatik. 2, stark verm. aufl. Koblenz, Karl Bädecker, 1841.
iv, 107 p. 20 cm.

NK 0197711 PLatS

LF 3195 C6K5
Knebel, Heinrich.
Jahresbericht über den Zustand des Königlichen Friedrich-Wilhelms-Gymnasiums zu Köln während des Schuljahres 1845-46, erstattet von Heinrich Knebel. Köln, M. DuMont-Schauberg, 1846.
32 p. 26cm.
Preceded by Schraut, J.: Ueber die Bildung des Futurums in den romanischen Sprachen.

1. Cologne. K. Friedrich-Wilhelms-Gymnasium. 2. Romance philology. 3. Grammar, Comparative and general - Tense. I. Schraut, J
Ueber die Bildung des Futurums in den romanischen Sprac hen

NK 0197713 CoU

Knebel, Heinrich, 1900-
Die verwendbarkeit der senkungsgeschwindigkeit, der resistenzbestimmung der erythrocyten und des blutbildes bei der diagnose der carcinome des intestinaltractus.
Inaug. Diss. Berlin, 1927
Bibl.

NK 0197714 ICRL CtY

Knebel (Immanuel Gottlieb) [1772–1809]. *Diss. sistens hydrothoracem, inprimis ejus diagnosin. 36 pp. sm. 4°. *Vitebergæ, lit. A. C. Charisii*, [1795].

NK 0197715 DNLM PPC

WQ K69g 1803
KNEBEL, Immanuel Gottlieb, 1772-1809
Grundriss der polizeilich-gerichtlichen Entbindungskunde. Breslau, Korn, 1801-[03]
xx, 535 p.
Issued in parts.

NK 0197716 DNLM ICU

Knebel, Immanuel Gottlieb, 1772-1809
——. Grundriss zu einer Zeichenlehre der gesammten Entbindungswissenschaft. Zum Gebrauch für angehende Geburtshelfer. xxiv, 592 pp. 8°. *Bresslau, J. F. Korn*, 1798.

NK 0197717 DNLM

WI K68g 1801
KNEBEL, Immanuel Gottlieb, 1772-1809
Grundsätze zur Kenntniss der Wassersucht im Allgemeinen. Breslau, Korn, 1801.
180 p. WI K68g

NK 0197718 DNLM

WCK K68t 1805
KNEBEL, Immanuel Gottlieb, 1772-1809
Theoretischer Versuch über den Charakter, einige Erscheinungen und die Heilart des gelben Fiebers in Briefen an einen Arzt.. Nebst einer historisch-kritischen Übersicht der gesammten Literatur dieser Krankheit. Görliz, Anton, 1805.
354 p.
Contains signature of Greenville Dowell, M. D.

NK 0197719 DNLM

Knebel, Immanuel Gottlieb, 1772-1809.
——. Versuch einer chronologischen Uebersicht der Literargeschichte der Arzneiwissenschaft zur Beförderung und Erleichterung des Studiums derselben. xxxiv, 377 pp. 8°. *Breslau, Hirschberg u. Lissa*, 1799.

NK 0197720 DNLM PPC

Knebel, J.

Brandes, Jan Laurens Andries, 1857–1905.
... Beschrijving van de ruïne bij de desa Toempang, genaamd Tjandi Djago, in de residentie Pasoeroean; samengesteld naar de gegevens verstrekt door H. L. Leydie Melville en J. Knebel, onder leiding van Dr. J. L. A. Brandes. Met 104 platen, 24 bouwkundige teekeningen, en 1 kaart ... 's-Gravenhage, M. Nijhoff; Batavia, Albrecht & co., 1904.

VOLUME 300

DS646 .22 .A8 vol. 2 Knebel, J.

Brandes, Jan Laurens Andries, 1857–1905.
... Beschrijving van Tjandi Singasari; en de wolkentooneelen van Panataran. Samengesteld naar de gegevens verstrekt door H. L. Leydie Melville en J. Knebel, onder leiding van wijlen dr. J. L. A. Brandes. Benevens eene herdenking van dr. J. L. A. Brandes ... door G. P. Rouffaer. Met 113 platen, 19 bouwkundige teekeningen, en 2 kaarten ... 's-Gravenhage, M. Nijhoff; [etc., etc.] 1909.

Knebel (Joannes Godofredus). *De opio. 32 pp. 8°. Traj. ad Viadr., e typog. Apitziano, [1794].

NK 0197723 DNLM

Knebel, Johannes, fl. 1473-1479.
Diarium ... Sept. 1473-Juli 1479. [Herausgegeben durch W. Vischer und H. Boos] Latin. [In Basel, Switzerland- Historische und antiquarische Gesellschaft. Basler Chroniken, 1880-87, v. 2,3]

NK 0197724 CtY

DC 611 B775K68 1851 Knebel, Johannes, Cistercian monk, 16th cent.
Chronik aus den Zeiten des Burgunderkriegs [hrsg. von K. Buxtorf-Falkeisen] Basel, C. Detloff, 1851-55.
3 v. 22cm.

1. Burgundy--Hist. I. Buxtorf-Falkeisen, Karl, ed.

NK 0197725 NIC MH PBm LN

Knebel, Johannes, *Cistercian monk, 16th cent.*
Die chronik des klosters Kaisheim, verfasst vom Cistercienser Johann Knebel im jahre 1531. Hrsg. von Franz Hüttner ... Tübingen, Litterarischer verein in Stuttgart, 1902.
2 p. l., 625 p. 21½cm. (*Added t.-p.:* Bibliothek des Litterarischen vereins in Stuttgart. [bd.] CCXXVI)
Übersicht über das 51. verwaltungsjahr des Litterarischen vereins (1900-1901): p. 624-625.

1. Kaisheim, Ger. (Cistercian abbey) I. Hüttner, Franz, ed.

4-17462

Library of Congress PT1101.L5 vol. 226

NK 0197726 DLC MoU NcD CtY PBm MiU OCl OCU NjP MH MB NN PLatS

PT 2433 M17 Z74 Knebel, Karl, 1885-
Nikolaus Meyer als Freund Goethes und Förderer des geistigen Lebens in Westfalen, ein Beitrag zur Geschichte des westfälischen Zeitungswesens. Münster, Regensberg, 1908.
103 [4] p.

Inaug.-Diss. - Münster.
Vita.
Bibliography: p.[5]-6.

NK 0197727 WaU NjP CSt MH ICRL

KNEBEL, Karl Heinrich.
Dissertatio theologica de miraculoso linguarum dono, etc. Tubingae, [1749].

NK 0197728 MH-AH

PT2383 .K3Z8A2 Knebel, Karl Ludwig von, 1744-1834.
Aus Karl Ludwig von Knebels briefwechsel mit seiner schwester Henriette (1774-1813). Ein beitrag zur deutschen hof- und litteraturgeschichte. Hrsg. von Heinrich Düntzer. Jena, F. Mauke, 1858.
[3],652 p. 22cm.

I. Knebel, Henriette i.e. Magdalene Henriette von, 1755-1813. II. Düntzer, Heinrich i.e. Johann Heinrich Josef, 1813-1901, ed.

NK 0197729 MB OCIW CU NIC DLC

Knebel, Karl Ludwig von, 1744-1834,

Schiller, Charlotte (von Lengefeld) von, 1766-1826.
Briefe von Schiller's gattin an einem vertrauten freund. Hrsg. von Heinrich Düntzer. Leipzig, F. A. Brockhaus, 1856.

Knebel, Karl Ludwig von, 1744-1834.
Briefwechsel zwischen Goethe und Knebel, 1774-1832.
see under Goethe, Johann Wolfgang von, 1749-1832. Correspondence.

Yb K66 820 [Knebel, Karl Ludwig von] 1744-1834, supposed author.
Dem verehrten Jubelgreise, Herrn Geheimen-Rath von Einsiedel, bey Ueberreichung eines Lorbeerkranzes am 2. May 1820. [n.p.,1820] broadside. 16x13½cm.
"by ?Knebel" written in pencil after title.

1. Einsiedel, Friedrich Hildebrand Freiherr von, 1750-1828. I. Title.

NK 0197732 CtY

Zgl8 K731 815s **Knebel, Karl Ludwig von, 1744-1834**
Jahresblüthen von und für Knebel. Gedruckt als Manuscript für Freunde und Freundinnen zur Feyer des 30. Novembers 1825. Weimar, 1825.
[21]p. 25cm. [With his Sammlung kleiner Gedichte. Leipzig, 1815]
Includes poems by Goethe, Riemer, Eckermann and Peuzer as well as Knebel.

NK 0197733 CtY

PT2383 .K3A17 **Knebel, Karl Ludwig von,** 1744-1834.
K. L. von Knebel's literarischer nachlass und briefwechsel. Hrsg. von K. A. Varnhagen von Ense und Th. Mundt ... Leipzig, Gebrüder Reichenbach, 1835-36.
3 v. in 2. fronts. (ports.) 22cm.
"K. L. von Knebel's leben von Th. Mundt": v. 1, p. [i]-lxi.

NK 0197734 ICU RPB GEU CtY PU CaBVaU MiU CU NcD InU PU NjP RPB

PT 2383 K3A6 1840 Knebel, Karl Ludwig von, 1744-1834.
Literarischer Nachlass und Briefwechsel; hrsg. von K. A. Varnhagen von Ense und Th. Mundt. 2. unveränderte Ausg. Leipzig, Reichenbach, 1840.
3 v. ports. 22cm.

I. Varnhagen von Ense, Karl August Ludwig Philli pp, 1785-1853. II. Mundt, Theodor, 1808-1861. ed.

NK 0197735 NIC CU PHC RPB OCIW MdBP MH PSt TNJ TxU IU

Zgl8 K731 815s **Knebel, Karl Ludwig von, 1744-1834**
Sammlung kleiner Gedichte ... Leipzig, Georg Joachim Göschen, 1815.
1v,82p. 25cm.
Author's presentation copy, signed: K.L.v. Knebel.

NK 0197736 CtY CU CU-W PBm

PT 2383 K3B8 1858a Knebel, Karl Ludwig von, 1744-1834.
Zur deutschen Literatur und Geschichte. Ungedruckte Brief aus Knebels Nachlass; hrsg. von Heinrich Düntzer. Nürnberg, Bauer und Raspe, 1858.
2 v. in 1. 19cm.

NK 0197737 NIC CU MH

Knebel, Konrad, 1856-
Geschichte der Stadt Dippoldiswalde bis zum Jahre 1918. Im Auftrage der städtischen Behörden verfasst. Dippoldiswalde, Jehne [1920]

499 p. illus.
Kriegs=Chronik der kirchgemeinde Dippoldiswalde, 1914-1918 [von] J. Nosen, 32 p., inserted

NK 0197738 MH

Knebel, Konrad, i.e. Georg Konrad, 1856- ed.

Freiberger altertumsverein.
Mitteilungen des Freiberger altertumsvereins, mit bildern aus Freibergs vergangenheit ... 1.- hft.; 1862-
Freiberg, Gerlach'sche buchdr., 1862-19[ ].

Knebel, Ludwig von
see
Knebel, Karl Ludwig von, 1744-1834.

Knebel, Max: Beiträge zur bakteriologischen Diagnose und Statistik der Diphtherie. (Aus d. städt. hygien. Inst. zu Frankfurt a. M. Dir. Neisser.) Berlin 1912: Hause. 41 S. 8°
Gießen, Med. Diss. v. 20. Aug. 1912, Ref. Neumann
[Geb. 1. März 87 Frankfurt a. M.-Bockenheim; Wohnort: Frankfurt; Staatsangeh.: Preußen; Vorbildung: Realgymn. Mustersch. Frankfurt Reife O. 06; Studium: Marburg 1, München 2, Freiburg i. B. 2, München 3, Straßburg 1, München 1 S.; Coll. 29. Juli 12; Approb. 30. Juni 12.] [U 12. 5278

NK 0197741 ICRL DNLM MBCo

PF 645 .H8 K5 Knebel, Miklós.
Nederlandsch-Hongaarsch, samengesteld door Knebel Miklós.. [N.p.] Ned. R.K. Huisvestings-Comité [1922]
62 p.

1. Dutch language - Dictionaries Hungarian. 2. Hungarian language - Dictionar - Dutch. I. Title.

NK 0197742 DGU

KNEBEL, Oskar.
Die reichsbahn-personentarife und ihre wirtschaftliche bedeutung... 2.aufl.... Berlin, Verlag der verkehrswissenschaftlichen lehrmittel, gesellschaft m.b.h., 1931.

pp.239. Tables, charts.

NK 0197743 MH-BA

VOLUME 300

Knebel, Rudolf: Zur Statistik der Augenverletzungen vom 1. April 1910 bis 1. April 1914. [Maschinenschrift.] 25 Bl. 4° [Lag nicht vor.] — Auszug: Giessen 1922: Meyer. 4 S. 8°
Gießen, Med. Diss. v. 30. Dez. 1922 [U 22. 3072

NK 0197744 ICRL

QV 740 GG4 K68a 1941
KNEBEL, Rudolf, 1910-
Arzneiverordnungen für den Truppenarzt von Rudolf Knebel und Willi Willecke. 2. Aufl. Leipzig, Hirzel, 1941.
51 p.
1. Formularies 2. Pharmacy - Military - Germany I. Willecke, Willi

NK 0197745 DNLM

QV 740 GG4 K68a 1944
KNEBEL, Rudolf, 1910-
Arzneiverordnungen für den Truppenarzt, von Rudolf Knebel und Willi Willecke. 5. Aufl. Leipzig, Hirzel, 1944.
55 p.
1. Formularies 2. Pharmacy - Military - Germany I. Willecke, Willi

NK 0197746 DNLM

Knebel, Rudolf, 1910–
Arzneiverordnungen für den Truppenarzt, von Rudolf Knebel und Willi Willecke. 6. Aufl. Leipzig, S. Hirzel, 1945 [°1940]
55 p. 17 cm.

1. Medicine, Military. 2. Pharmacy, Military. I. Willecke, Willi, joint author. II. Title.
UH445.G4K6 1945 615 A 48-7371*
New York. Public Libr. for Library of Congress [1]†

NK 0197747 NN NcD MH CoD DLC

Knebel, Rudolf, 1910- , ed
Fortschritte der Diagnostik und Therapie
see under title

Knebel, Rudolf, 1910-
...Über die arteriellen Blutdruckschwankungen bei der oberflächlichen Atmung... München, 1936.
Inaug.-Diss. - München.
Lebenslauf.

NK 0197749 CtY

Knebel, R[udolf] J[ulius] W[ilhelm] 1862-
Ueber abkömmlinge des "salols"...
Leipzig, 1891.
QD341 .A2K684
Inaug.- diss- Leipzig.
Vita.

NK 0197750 DLC

Knebel, Theodor, 1897-
Das Prüfungsrecht der eingetragenen Genossenschaft. Die Grundsätze ordnungsmässiger Prüfung von Genossenschaften ... von Theodor Knebel ... [Berlin, Theodor Abb] 1941.
vi p., 1 l., 207, [1] p. 21cm.
Inaug.-Diss. - Halle-Wittenberg.
"Lebenslauf": p. [208]
"Schrifttumverzeichnis": p. [205]-207.

NK 0197751 MH-L NIC

4K Ger 895
Knebel, Theodor, 1897-
Das Prüfungsrecht der eingetragenen Genossenschaft. Die Grundsätze ordnungsmässiger Prüfung von Genossenschaften. [Berlin] 1941.
207 p.

NK 0197752 DLC-P4

Knebel, Walther von, 1880- 1907.
Beiträge zur kenntniss der ueberschiebungen am vulkanischen ries von Nördlingen ... von Walther von Knebel ... Berlin, J. F. Starcke, 1902.
1 p. l., [5]-84 p., 1 l. illus., 3 double pl. (1 col.) 21cm.
Lebenslauf.
Inaug.-diss.—Berlin, 1902.

1. Volcanoes.

NK 0197753 MiU ICRL NN CtY PU MH

Knebel, Walther von, 1880–1907.
Höhlenkunde mit berücksichtigung der karstphänomene, von Walther von Knebel ... mit 42 abbildungen im text und auf 4 tafeln. Braunschweig, F. Vieweg und sohn, 1906.
xvi, 222 p. illus., 4 pl. 22½ cm. (*Added t.-p.:* Die wissenschaft. Sammlung naturwissenschaftlicher und mathematischer monographien. 15. hft.)

1. Speleology. 2. Karst.
GB601.K6 7—16500

NK 0197754 DLC PPAN PU MiU ICJ NN MB

Knebel, Walther von, 1880–1907.
Island. Eine naturwissenschaftliche studie, von dr. W. von Knebel †. Nach einem begonnenen manuskript, notizen und bildern des verstorbenen bearb., fortgeführt und hrsg. von dr. Hans Reck. Stuttgart, E. Schweizerbart, 1912.
1 p. l., v, [4], [7]-290 p. illus., XXVIII pl. (part col., incl. front.) fold. map. 24½cm.
"Literaturnachweis": p. [272]-275.
1. Iceland. 2. Natural history—Iceland. I. Reck, Hans, ed.
Library of Congress DL313.K6 13—7732

NK 0197755 DLC PBm PPAN NIC MiU ICJ NN

Knebel, Walter von, 1880-1907.
—— Lavaspalten und Kraterrillen auf Island. *Extr. fr.* Gaea. XLIII. Jahrg. Heft 9. 1907, pp. 547-561, 1 *pl., illustr.*
IcC13P211

NK 0197756 NIC

Knebel, Walter von, 1880-1907.
—— **Der Nachweis verschiedener Eiszeiten in den Hochflächen des inneren Islands.** (Vorläufige Mitteilung.) Stuttgart, E. Schweizerbart'sche Buchhandlung, 1905. 8°. pp. 546-553, *figs.*
IcC13P212
"Separat-Abdruck aus dem Centralblatt für Mineralogie, Geologie und Paläontologie. Jahrg. 1905. No. 17-18." Covertitle.

NK 0197757 NIC

Knebel, Walter von, 1880-1907.
—— Studien in den Thermengebieten Islands. (Originalmitteilung.) Braunschweig, 1906. 8°. pp. 15. IcC13P212
"Sonder-Abdruck aus der 'Naturwissenschaftlichen Rundschau,' Jahrg. XXI, 1906. Nr. 12." Covertitle.

NK 0197758 NIC

Knebel, Walter von, 1880-1907.
—— Vorläufige Mitteilung über die Lagerungsverhältnisse glazialer Bildungen auf Island und deren Bedeutung zur Kenntnis der diluvialen Vergletscherungen. Stuttgart, E. Schweizerbart'sche Verlagsbuchhandlung, 1905. 8°. pp. 535-546, *figs.* IcC13P212
"Separat-Abdruck aus dem Centralblatt für Mineralogie, Geologie und Paläontologie. Jahrg. 1905. No. 17-18." Covertitle.

NK 0197759 NIC

Knebel, Walther von, 1880-1907. 5869a.32
Der Vulkanismus.
Osterwieck. Zickfeldt. [1908.] (4), 128 pp. Illus. Plates. Map. [Die Natur. Eine Sammlung naturwissenschaftlicher Monographien. Band 3.] 19 cm., in 8s.
Literatur, pp. 122-125.
Some of the plates are colored.

H860 — Volcanoes. — S.r.

NK 0197760 MB

Knebel, Walter von, 1880-1907.
—— Zur Frage der diluvialen Vergletscherungen auf der Insel Island. (Entgegnung an Helgi Pjetursson.) Stuttgart, E. Schweizerbart'sche Buchhandlung, 1906. 8°. pp. 232-237. IcC13P212
"Separat-Abdruck aus dem Centralblatt für Mineralogie, Geologie und Paläontologie. Jahrg. 1906. No. 8." Covertitle.

NK 0197761 NIC

Knebel, Werner, 1909-
... Studien zur Geschichte der Orthodontie und den kommenden Aufgaben der Kinderzahnpflege ... Heidelberg, [1937]
Inaug.-Diss. - Heidelberg.
Lebenslauf.
"Literaturverzeichnis": p. [22]

NK 0197762 CtY

Knebel, Wilhelm, 1879–
Kaiser Friedrich II. und papst...
Inaug. diss. Muenster, 1905.

NK 0197763 ICRL MH PU

VOLUME 300

Knebel-Doeberitz, Bernd von.
Allgemeine grundzuege des handelskaufes. Leipzig, 1908.
Inaug.-Diss. - Leipzig.
Bibl.

NK 0197764 ICRL

Knebel-Doeberitz, Edgar von

914.3
K68S

Streifzüge eines modernen Junkers ... I. Vom Rhein nach Pommern. II. Erlebtes und Erschautes auf einer Reise nach Italien ⌊2. Aufl.⌋ Berlin, Friedrich Luckhardt ⌊1885⌋
238 p. 19½cm.

1. Germany. Description and travel. 2. Germany. Social life and customs. 3. Italy. Description and travel. I. Title.

NK 0197765 NcD

Knebel-Doeberitz, Hugo von.
Besteht für Deutschland eine amerikanische gefahr? Von Hugo von Knebel Doeberitz. Berlin, E. S. Mittler und sohn, 1904.
viii, 88 p. 24½cm.

I. Title.

4-33572

Library of Congress HC106.K68

NK 0197766 DLC CtY ICJ MB NN

Knebel-Doeberitz, Hugo von.
Karl Ludwig von Knebel. Ein lebensbild von Hugo von Knebel-Doeberitz ... Weimar, H. Böhlau, 1890.
xi p., 1 l., 183 p. front. (port.) 21½cm.

1. Knebel, Karl Ludwig von, 1744-1834.

NK 0197767 MiU NIC TNJ CU IU MH NjP ICU

Knebel-Doeberitz, Hugo von, joint ed.

Gerhard, Stephan, *ed.*
Kommentar zum deutschen reichsgesetz über den versicherungs-vertrag; von Stephan Gerhard ... Otto Hagen ... Hugo v. Knebel Doeberitz ... Hermann Broecker ... ⌊und⌋ Alfred Manes ... Berlin, E. S. Mittler und sohn, 1908.

Knebel-Doeberitz, Hugo von.
Das private versicherungswesen in Preussen. Von Hugo von Knebel Doeberitz ... und Dr. Hermann Broecker ... Berlin, "Zeitschrift für versicherungswesen," 1902.
v. tables (1 fold.) 22cm.

CONTENTS.—
v. 2. Das sterbekassenwesen in Preussen. Von Hugo von Knebel Doeberitz und Dr. Hermann Broecker ... 2. aufl.

I. Broecker, Hermann, 1857–

6-6939

NK 0197769 DLC

Knebel Doeberitz, Hugo von.
Das sparkassenwesen in Preussen, von Hugo v. Knebel Doeberitz ... Berlin, E. S. Mittler und sohn, 1907.
xii, 228 p. 23cm.

Continued in next column

Continued from preceding column

1. Savings-banks—Prussia. I. Title.

16-7314

Library of Congress HG1939.G4P5

NK 0197770 DLC

Knebel-Doeberitz, Rudolf von.
Genehmigungsbedürftigkeit landwirtschaftlicher Bodenrechtsgeschäfte auf Grund des Kontrollratsgesetzes Nr. 45. Bearbeitung in Verbindung mit der Ausführungsverordnung Nr. 166 zum Kontrollratsgesetz Nr. 45 für Württemberg-Baden vom 16. Juli 1947. ⌊Heidelberg⌋ 1948.
84 l. 29 cm.
Typescript (carbon)
Inaug.-Diss.—Heidelberg.
Bibliography: leaf 83.

1. Land tenure—Germany (Federal Republic, 1949–) 2. Entail—Germany. 3. Land titles—Registration and transfer—Germany (Federal Republic, 1949–) I. Title.

55-31294

NK 0197771 DLC

Knebel von Treuenschwert, Aladár
see Knebel, Aladár, Ritter von Treuenschwert.

Knebelman, Morris Samuel, 1891–
Collineations and motions in generalized spaces ... by M. S. Knebelman. Princeton, 1928.
1 p. l., p. 527-564. 25cm.
Thesis (PH. D.)—Princeton university, 1928.
"Reprinted from the American journal of mathematics, vol. LI, number 4."

1. Collineation. 2. Hyperspace.

30-3362

Library of Congress QA601.K75 1928
Princeton Univ. Libr.

NK 0197773 NjP DLC MH OU

Knebelman, Morris Samuel, 1891–
Principles of college algebra, by Morris S. Knebelman ... and Tracy Y. Thomas ... New York, Prentice-Hall, inc., 1942.
x p., 1 l., 380 p. diagrs. 23½cm.
"Answers to exercises": p. 363-375.

1. Algebra. I. Thomas, Tracy Yerkes, 1899– joint author.

42-23721

Library of Congress QA154.K58
⌊7⌋ 512

WaT NNC CaBVaU OrU-M
NK 0197774 DLC NcRS NcD IU CU PPD PSC PSt OCU OU

Knebelmann (Abraham) [1887–]. *Ein Fall von Meningitis luetica mit Gefäss-Erkrankung bei einem zweijährigen heredosyphilitischen Mädchen mit Bericht über einige Fälle aus der Literatur. 1 p. l., 21 pp., 1 l. 8°. München, M. Steinebach, 1912.

NK 0197775 DNLM

Knebelmann, Jacques, 1893–
... Sur un cas de gros abcès amibien du foie d'origine autochtone ... Montpellier, 1921.
25 cm.
Thèse - Univ. de Montpellier.

NK 0197776 CtY

Knebelsberger, Leopold, 1814–1869.
...Andreas Hofer. (Text von Julius Mosen.) Tiroler Volkslied, zum Konzertvortrag bearbeitet von Eugen Thomas... Partitur. Wien: Universal-Edition, A. G.⌋, 1913.⌋ Publ. pl. no. U. E. *2726.* 6 p. 4°.

German words precede and accompany score; music for 4 mixed voices.
At head of title: Ausgabe des "Wiener a cappella-Chor." Österreichische Volksweisen .. No. 47.

1. Hofer, Andreas, 1767-1810. 2. Folk songs, German—Austria. 3. Choruses, Unaccompanied. 4. Mosen, Julius, 1803-1867. 5. Thomas, Eugen, 1863-1922, editor. 6. Wiener a cappella-Chor. 7. Title.
N. Y. P. L. March 31, 1939

NK 0197777 NN

Kneberg, Madeline Dorothy
see
Lewis, Madeline Kneberg, 1903–

Kneblewski, Lucjan M.
Nie taki murzyn czarny; wspomnienia z Afryki (Z Nigeryskiego pułku królewskich Zachodnio-Afrykańskich sił granicznych) Edin., Składnica księgarska, 1946.
282 ⌊1⌋ p.

NK 0197779 MiD

Knebusch
Die Spannung im Pferde und die Mittel sie zu beseitigen. Stuttgart, Schickhardt & Ebner, 1911.
31p. (Unsere Pferde, 43. Heft)

NK 0197780 ICRL

Knebusch, Ernst, 1911-
Das Mecklenburg-Schweriner bergbaurecht in materieller hinsicht, verglichen mit dem bergwerkseigentum des preussischen rechts. ... Rostock, 1934.
Inaug. Diss. - Rostock, 1934.
Lebenslauf.
Benutztes schrifttum.

NK 0197781 ICRL

Knebusch, Magnus.
Die Krankenversicherung der Landarbeiter. Wismar: Willgeroth & Wenzel Nachflg., 1913. 1 p.l., 168 p. 8°.

1. Insurance (Sickness), Germany.
N. Y. P. L. November 19, 1913.

NK 0197782 NN

WP
K68v
1860

KNEBUSCH, Theodor
Vollständiges Taschenbuch bewährter Heilmethoden und Heilformeln für Frauen- und Kinderkrankheiten, nebst einem Compendium der Pharmakodynamik für die Kinderkrankheiten. Erlangen, Enke, 1860.
iv, 461 p.

NK 0197783 DNLM PPC NIC

VOLUME 300

K RM 88 K68 1866
Knebusch, Theodor
Vollständiges Taschenbuch bewährter Heilmethoden und Heilformeln für innere Krankheiten. 2. ganz umgearb. und durch die neuern Erfahrungen in der Therapie bereicherte Aufl. Erlangen, F. Enke, 1866.
viii,520 p. 17cm.

1. Therapeutics. I. Title.

NK 0197784 NIC PPC

WP K68v 1872
KNEBUSCH, Theodor
Vollständiges Taschenbuch bewährter Heilmethoden und Heilformeln für äussere Krankheiten einschliesslich der Augen-, Ohren- und Zahnkrankheinten. 2. ganz umgearb. und durch die neueren Erfahrungen in der chirurg. Therapie bereicherte Aufl. Erlangen, Enke, 1872.
vi, 516 p.

NK 0197785 DNLM

Knebworth, Edward Anthony James Lytton, *viscount*, 1903–1933.
Antony (Viscount Knebworth) A record of youth by his father, the Earl of Lytton; with a foreword by J. M. Barrie ... London, P. Davies [1935]
xv, 368 p. plates, ports. 22cm.
This record consists chiefly of letters which passed between Viscount Knebworth and his parents.

I. Lytton, Victor Alexander George Robert Bulwer-Lytton, 2d earl of, 1876– II. Title.
36-7775
Library of Congress DA566.9.K58A3 1935
Copyright A ad int. 21062 [3] 923.242

NK 0197786 DLC WaTC MU NcD CtY OClh OClW MH NN

Knebworth, Edward Anthony James Lytton, *viscount*, 1903–1933.
Antony (Viscount Knebworth) A record of youth by his father, the Earl of Lytton; with a foreword by J. M. Barrie ... New York, C. Scribner's sons, 1936.
xv, 368 p. front., plates, ports. 22cm.
This record consists chiefly of letters which passed between Viscount Knebworth and his parents.

I. Lytton, Victor Alexander George Robert Bulwer-Lytton, 2d earl of, 1876– II. Title.
36-8066
Library of Congress DA566.9.K58A3 1936
——— Copy 2.
Copyright A 92403 [5] 923.242

TU WaS MiU
PBa NN ViU MB ICU Or NNU OrCS NcU WaTC PU OrU WaT
NK 0197787 DLC CaBVaU OrP TNJ OrU CoFS InU PPGi PBm

B K68a 1937
Knebworth, Edward Anthony James Lytton, viscount, 1903-
Antony (Viscount Knebworth) A record of youth by his father, the Earl of Lytton; with a foreword by J. M. Barrie... London, P. Davies [1937]
xv,368p. plates,ports. 22cm.
This record consists chiefly of letters which passed between Viscount Knebworth and his parents.

NK 0197788 KU

Knebworth, Edward Anthony James Lytton, viscount, 1903-1933.
Antony (Viscount Knebworth) A record of youth by his father, by Earl of Lytton; with a foreword by J.M. Barrie ... London, P. Davies [1947]
xv, 368 p. front., (port.) 20.5 cm.
This record consists chiefly of letters whict passed between Viscount Knebworth and his parents.

NK 0197789 OU

Knebworth, Edward Anthony James Lytton, *viscount*, 1903–1933.
... Boxing; a guide to modern methods, by Viscount Knebworth, with a contribution by W. Childs ... with over fifty illustrations. London, Seeley, Service & co. ltd., 1931.
287 p. illus., 50 pl. (incl. front., ports.) diagrs. 22cm. (The Lonsdale library. vol. XI)

1. Boxing.
32-7580
Library of Congress GV1133.K6
[a36c1] 796.83

NK 0197790 DLC PPGi NN OLak MB Wa OrP ODaU

Knebworth, Edward Anthony James Lytton, *viscount*, 1903–1933.
... Boxing; a guide to modern methods, by Viscount Knebworth, with a contribution by W. Childs ... with over fifty illustrations. London, Seeley, Service & co. ltd. c1943.
287 p. illus., 50 pl. (incl. front., ports.) diagrs. 22 cm. (The Lonsdale library. vol. XI)

NK 0197791 OU WaPS OCl OClW

Knebworth, Edward Anthony James Lytton, viscount, 1903-1933.
Lytton, *Hon.* **Neville Stephen,** 1879– *ed.*
... Winter sports, by Viscount Knebworth, Captain S. Duff-Taylor, Lt.-Col. J. T. C. Moore-Brabazon, Hubert Martineau, Alexander Lorimer, M. S. Madden. Edited by the Hon. Neville Lytton. With sixty-seven illustrations. London, Seeley, Service & co. ltd., 1930.

Knecht, Adolf Emil, 1846-
——. Die Irrenstation bei der Strafanstalt Waldheim. 17 pp. 8°. *Berlin*, [1880].
Repr. from: Allg. Ztschr. f. Psychiat. [etc.], Berl., 1880, xxxvii.

NK 0197793 DNLM

Knecht, Adolf Emil, 1846– .
Uber [!] gehirnkrebs und einige damit zu verwechselnde gehirngeschwülste ... Leipzig, Druck von C. G. Naumann [1869]
1 p. l., 14 p., 1 l. 21½cm.
Inaug.-diss.—Leipzig.
Vita.

1. Brain—Cancer.
7-35819†
Library of Congress RC261.K68

NK 0197794 DLC DNLM

KNECHT, Adolf Emil, 1846-
Ueber die unterbringung irrer verbrecher. n.t.p.
18 p.

NK 0197795 MH-L

Knecht, Arthur.
Musical dreamer; narration based on Stephen Foster's life and songs [with orchestral score] [Cincinnati, c1953]
20 p. 38 cm.
"This condensed musical biography ... was written at the request of Thor Johnson, musical director of the Cincinnati Symphony Orchestra, for presentation at his Young people's concerts in March 1933."

NK 0197796 OCU

Knecht, August, 1866–1932 .
... Derecho matrimonial católico; traducción de T. Gómez Pinán [!] ... Madrid, Editorial Revista de derecho privado [1932]
2 p. l., 644 p. diagrs. 23½cm.
At head of title: A. Knecht.
With special reference to German civil marriage law, and notes on Spanish and Spanish-American civil marriage laws.
"Bibliografía": p. 26-31.

1. Marriage (Canon law) 2. Catholic church. Codex juris canonici. 3. Marriage law—Germany. 4. Marriage law—Spain. 5. Marriage law—Spanish America. 6. Catholic church—Discipline. I. Gómez Piñán, Tomás, tr. II. Title. *Translation of* Handbuch des katholischen eherechts.
35-29708
Library of Congress HQ1024.K65
[3] 173.1

NK 0197797 DLC CtY

Knecht, August, 1866–1932.
Die Ehescheidung in Religion und Recht, von Dr. August Knecht... Augsburg: Haas & Grabherr, 1926. 40 p. 8°. (Politik und Kultur. Heft 2.)

549062A. 1. Divorce. I. Ser.
N. Y. P. L. October 6, 1931

NK 0197798 NN ICU

Knecht, August, 1866–1932.
Grundriss des Eherechts, bearb. auf Grund des Codex iuris canonici. Freiburg im Breisgau, Herder, 1918.
vii, 207 p. 18 cm.
Bibliographical footnotes.

1. Marriage (Canon law)
A 49-2068*
Catholic Univ. of America. Library for Library of Congress [1]

NK 0197799 DCU PPPD

Knecht, August, 1866–1932.
Handbuch des katholischen Eherechts, auf Grund des Codex iuris canonici und unter Berücksichtigung des bürgerlichen Eherechts des Deutschen Reiches, Österreichs, Ungarns, der Tschechoslowakei und der Schweiz. Freiburg im Breisgau, Herder, 1928.
xi, 812 p. diagrs. 24 cm.
Bibliographical footnotes.

1. Marriage (Canon law) 2. Marriage law—Germany.
A 49-2076*
Catholic Univ. of America. Library for Library of Congress [1]

NK 0197800 DCU OrStbM

Knecht, August, 1866–1932.
Das neue kirchliche Gesetzbuch, Codex juris canonici; seine Geschichte und Eigenart. Mit einem Anhang: Sammlung einschlägiger Aktenstücke. Strassburg, K. J. Trübner, 1918.
71 p. 26 cm. (Schriften der Wissenschaftlichen Gesellschaft in Strassburg, 35. Heft)

1. Catholic Church. Codex juris canonici. I. Title. (Series: Strassburger Wissenschaftliche Gesellschaft. Schriften, 35. Heft)
52-50182

NK 0197801 DLC MH NN

Knecht, August, 1866-1932, ed.
Catholic church. *Pope, 1903–1914 (Pius X) Ne temere (2 Aug. 1907)*
... Die neuen eherechtlichen dekrete "Ne temere" (v. 2. august 1907) und "Provida" (v. 18. januar 1906) Dargestellt und kanonistisch erläutert von dr. theol. et iur. utr. August Knecht ... Köln, I. P. Bachem, 1907.

VOLUME 300

Knecht, August, 1866-1932.
Die Religions-Politik Kaiser Justinians I... Würzburg, A. Göbel, 1896.
vi, 148 p., 23cm.

Inaug.-Diss.
Bibliographical footnotes.

NK 0197803 NjPT DDO CU NjP MH ICRL

Knecht, August, 1866–1932.
System des justinianischen kirchenvermögensrechtes. Von August Knecht ... Stuttgart, F. Enke, 1905.

xii, 141 p. 22½cm. (*Added t.-p.:* Kirchenrechtliche abhandlungen. Hrsg. von dr. Ulrich Stutz ... 22. hft.)

Issued also in part as the author's dissertation, Munich, 1905.
"Verzeichnis der hauptsächlich benützten quellen und literatur": p. [vii]-xii.

1. Church property (Canon law, Orthodox Eastern) 2. Ecclesiastical law—Byzantine empire.

A C 38-4216

Chicago. Univ. Library for Library of Congress BV759.A1K6 vol.22 [2]

NK 0197804 ICU CU-L CSaT DDO CtY MH NNC

Knecht, Bruno, 1925–
Beiträge zur Aufklärung des Substituenteneinflusses auf die dehydrogenatische Wirkung von Isatin-Derivaten. [Freiburg im Breisgau, 1955]

60 p. illus. 21 cm.
Inaug.-Diss.—Fribourg.
Vita.
Bibliography: p. 59-60.

1. Isatin. 2. Hydrogenation.

QD401.K722 57-49739

NK 0197805 DLC NIC NN CtY MH

Knecht (Carl). *Beitrag zur Histologie der Epuliden. 24 pp. 8°. *Würzburg, J. M. Richter,* 1892.

NK 0197806 DNLM

Knecht, D respondent.
Vindiciae juris divini...
see under Andreae, Samuel, 1640-1699, praeses.

Knecht, Ed.
...Nouveau manuel complet du dessinateur et de l'imprimeur lithographe. Nouvelle édition, entièrement refondue, mise au courant de l'industrie actuelle, et augmentée de plusieurs procédés nouveaux concernant la lithographie mécanique, la chromolithographie, la lithophotographie, la zincographie et traitant des papiers de sûreté. Par M. Knecht. Ouvrage accompagné d'un atlas. Paris: Librairie encyclopédique de Roret, 1867. xx, 403 p. and atlas of 7 p., 16 pl. (1 col'd; incl. map, port.) in 1 v. 16cm. (Manuels-Roret.)

The atlas has separate t.-p.

80179B. 1. Lithography—Technique. I. Ser.
N. Y. P. L. January 27, 1941

NK 0197808 NN IU DSI CtY

Wing W 835 .465 Knecht, Ed.

Le petit manuel du lithographe; ou, Abrégé des meilleurs procédés pour dessiner, graver et imprimer sur pierre. Par.1832. O.
40p.
Cover-title.
Title-page reads: Bureau d'autographie tenu par A.Gaynon dans l'etablissement lithographique de Mmrs. Knecht de Rois- sy.

NK 0197809 ICN

Knecht, Edmund.
Die Entwicklung der pfälzischen Gemeindeverfassung seit 1869...von Edmund Knecht... Kaiserslautern: P. Schneider, 1928. 55 p. 8°.

Dissertation, Erlangen.
Bibliography, p. [4.]

538630A. 1. Government, Local— Germany—Palatinate.
N. Y. P. L. July 23, 1931

NK 0197810 NN PU DLC CtY

TP914 .B4 1889 Knecht, Edmund, 1861-1925, ed. and tr.

Benedikt, Rudolf, 1852–1896. FOR OTHER EDITIONS SEE MAIN ENTRY
... The chemistry of the coal-tar colours. Tr. from the German of Dr. R. Benedikt, and ed., with additions, by E. Knecht ... 2d ed., rev. and enl. London, G. Bell and sons, 1889.

Knecht, Edmund, 1861-1925,

Society of dyers and colourists, *Bradford, Eng.* (*Yorkshire*)
The journal of the Society of dyers and colourists, for all interested in the use or manufacture of colours, and in calico printing, bleaching, etc. v. 1– 1885 [*i. e.* Nov. 1884]– Bradford, Yorks. [1884–19

Knecht, Edmund, 1861–1925.
A manual of dyeing: for the use of practical dyers, manufacturers, students, and all interested in the art of dyeing. By Edmund Knecht ... Christopher Rawson ... and Richard Loewenthal ... With numerous illustrations and specimens of dyed fabrics ... London, C. Griffin & company, limited, 1893.

2 v. illus., tables, diagrs. *and* 1 vol. of 144 col. patterns mounted on 24 l. 23½cm.

1. Dyes and dyeing. I. Dawson, Christopher, joint author. II. Loewenthal, Richard, joint author.

1—18632

Library of Congress TP897.K68

NK 0197813 DLC PPF MB OkU MiU ICJ OC1W PPPTe

Knecht, Edmund, 1861–1925.
A manual of dyeing: for the use of practical dyers, manufacturers, students, and all interested in the art of dyeing. By Edmund Knecht ... Christopher Rawson ... and Richard Loewenthal ... 2d ed. London, C. Griffin and company, limited, 1910.

2 v. illus., v pl., fold. tables. 23½ cm.
Paged continuously.

1. Dyes and dyeing. I. Loewenthal, Richard, joint author. II. Rawson, Christopher, joint author.

TP897.K68 1910 Agr 10–1131

U. S. Dept. of Agr. Libr 392K73
for Library of Congress [a52b½]†

NK 0197814 DLC DNAL PSC PPF OrP PPPTe OC1 ICJ NN NcRS

Knecht, Edmund, 1861–1925.
A manual of dyeing: for the use of practical dyers, manufacturers, students, and all interested in the art of dyeing. By Edmund Knecht ... Christopher Rawson ... [and] Richard Loewenthal ... 3d ed. ... London, C. Griffin, 1916.

2 v. illus., v pl., fold. tables. 23cm.
Paged continuously.

1. Dyes and dyeing. I. Loewenthal, Richard, joint author. II. Rawson, Christopher, joint author.

Agr 17—534

U. S. Dept. of agr. Library 306K73
for Library of Congress [a40b1]

NK 0197815 DNAL PP MiU OC1

Knecht, Edmund, 1861–1925.
A manual of dyeing: for the use of practical dyers, manufacturers, students, and all interested in the art of dyeing. By Edmund Knecht ... Christopher Rawson ... and Richard Loewenthal ... 4th ed. ... London, C. Griffin & co., ltd., 1917.

2 v. illus., v pl., fold. tables. 23cm.
Paged continuously.

1. Dyes and dyeing. I. Loewenthal, Richard, joint author. II. Rawson, Christopher, joint author.

Agr 19—132

U. S. Dept. of agr. Library 306K73
for Library of Congress [a40b1]

NK 0197816 DNAL ViU PPEFH

KNECHT, Edmund, 1861-1925.
A manual of dying. By Edmund Knecht, Christopher Rawson, and Richard Loewenthal. Vol.I. 5th ed. London, 1919.

NK 0197817 MH

Knecht, Edmund, 1861-1925
A manual of dyeing; for the use of practical dyers, manufacturers, students, and all interested in the art of dyeing, by Edmund Knecht, Christopher Rawson, and Richard Loewenthal. London: Charles Griffin and Co., Ltd., 1920. 2 v. diagr., illus., pl., tables (some fold.). 6. ed. 8°.

NK 0197818 NN MH

Knecht, Edmund, 1861-1925.
A manual of dyeing: for the use of practical dyers, manufacturers, students, and all interested in the art of dyeing. By Edmund Knecht ... Christopher Rawson ... and Richard Loewenthal ... 7th ed. ... London, C. Griffin & co., ltd., 1922.
2 v. illus., v pl., fold. tables. 23 cm.
Paged continuously.
1. Loewenthal, Richard, joint author. II. Rawson, Christopher, joint author.

NK 0197819 CtY

Knecht, Edmund, 1861-1925.
A manual of dyeing; for The use of practical dyers, manufacturers, students, and all interested in the art of dyeing, by Edmund Knecht, Christopher Rawson, and Richard Loewenthal. London: Charles Griffin and Co., Ltd., 1925. 2 v. diagr., illus., pl., tables (some fold.). 8. ed. 8°.

Paged continuously.

NK 0197820 NN WaS PPF PSC NN DNAL OC1W MiEM NcRS MH

Knecht, Edmund, 1861-1925.
A manual of dyeing: for the use of practical dyers, manufacturers, students, and all interested in the art of dyeing. By Edmund Knecht ... Christopher Rawson ... and Richard Loewenthal ... 9th ed. ... London, C. Griffin & co., ltd., 1933.

2 v. illus., v pl., fold. tables. 23cm.
Paged continuously.

1. Dyes and dyeing. I. Loewenthal, Richard, joint author. II. Rawson, Christopher, joint author.

NK 0197821 NcU PPF

Knecht, Edmund, 1861–1925.
New reduction methods in volumetric analysis. A monograph by Edmund Knecht ... and Eva Hibbert ... London, New York [etc.] Longmans, Green and co., 1910.

x, 108 p. illus. 19cm.
"Literature": p. 105.

1. Chemistry, Analytic. I. Hibbert, Eva, joint author.

A 11—20

Cincinnati. Public library for Library of Congress [a41e1]

NK 0197822 WaS ICRL CU OC NcRS OCU PPPTe NjP ICJ NN MiHM MiU OO

VOLUME 300

Knecht, Edmund, 1861-1925.
New reduction methods in volumetric analysis. A monograph, by Edmund Knecht ... and Eva Hibbert ... Reissue with additions. London, New York [etc.] Longmans, Green and co., 1918.
2 p. l., iii-viii, 135, [1] p. illus. 19cm.

1. Volumetric analysis. I. Hibbert, Eva, joint author.

Agr 19—506

U. S. Dept. of agr. Library for Library of Congress 387K73 [a40h1]

NK 0197823 DNAL PPF MiU DBS NjP OCl OClW OrP MtBC

Knecht, Edmund, 1861-1925.
New reduction methods in volumetric analysis; a monograph, by Edmund Knecht and Eva Hibbert. 2d ed. London,Longmans,Green,1925.
x,134p. illus. 23cm.

NK 0197824 CU CtY-M TU MB IU IaU MH PSC ICJ OU ODW OCl

Knecht, Edmund, 1861-
The principles and practice of textile printing. By Edmund Knecht ... and James Best Fothergill ... with 13 plates, many patterns, and 80 illustrations in the text. London, C. Griffin & company, limited, 1912.
xvi, 615 p. illus., XIII pl. (part col., part fold.) 23cm.
Part of the illustrations are mounted samples.

1. Textile printing. I. Fothergill, James Best, joint author.

14—8985

Library of Congress TP930.K6

NK 0197825 DLC WaS MB PPF ICJ MB NN

Knecht, Edmund, 1861- , and J. B. Fothergill.
The principles and practice of textile printing. By Edmund Knecht...and James Best Fothergill... Second edition, revised throughout by James Best Fothergill. London: C. Griffin & Co., Ltd., 1924. xix, 731 p. incl. diagrs., tables. illus. (part col'd and mounted), plates. 8°.
Colored illustrations consist of samples of textile printing.

NK 0197826 NN PPPTe OCl DBS MH ICJ NcRS DLC-P4

Knecht, Edmund, 1861-1925.
The principles and practice of textile printing. By Edmund Knecht ... and James Best Fothergill ... With 19 plates, 221 patterns, and 90 illustrations in the text. 3d ed., revised throughout by James Best Fothergill. London, C. Griffin & company, limited, 1936.
xxiii, 1048 p. illus., XIX pl. (1 fold.) diagrs. 23cm.
Part of the illustrations are mounted samples.

1. Textile printing. I. Fothergill, James Best, joint author.

37-8389

Library of Congress TP930.K6 1936 [3] 667.2

NK 0197827 DLC NcU PPPTe CtY OCl OCU OU ICJ

Knecht, Edmund, 1861-1925.
The principles and practice of textile printing [by] Edmund Knecht and James Best Fothergill. 4th ed., with emendments and additional notes by J. G. Hurst. London, Griffin [1952]
xxiv, 1064 p. illus., ports., mounted samples. 23 cm.

1. Textile printing. I. Fothergill, James Best, joint author.

TP930.K6 1952 *667.3 667.2 53-23670

NK 0197828 FU ScCleU WaU DLC PPMoI PP PPPTe MB NN NcC PU-Sc NcGA

RD544 K73 1902
Knecht, Ernst, 1877-
Zur operation des prolapsus ani et recti. Greifswald, Abel, 1902.
32 p.

Inaug.-diss., Greifswald.
"Litteraturangabe": p. [33]

1. Rectum - Surgery. 2. Rectum - Diseases. 3. Anus - Surgery. 4. Anus - Diseases.

NK 0197829 NNC-M DNLM ICRL

Knecht, Ernst, 1884-
Die sozial-pädagogik, von J. G. Fichte nebst einem anhang, enthaltend einen vergleich der philosophischen und sozialpädagogischen gedanken von J. G. Fichte und P. Natorp ... M. Gladbach, Buchdr. W. Hütter, g. m. b. h., 1912.
4 p. l., vi, 95 p., 1 l. 22½cm.
Inaug.-diss.—Münster.
Lebenslauf.
"Literaturverzeichnis": 4th prelim. leaf.

1. Fichte, Johann Gottlieb, 1762-1814. 2. Natorp, Paul Gerhard, 1854- 3. Education. I. Title.

E 13-430

Library, U. S. Bur. of Education LB675.F43K7

NK 0197830 DHEW CtY PU MiU MH

Knecht, Ernst, 1886-
Studien ueber anthrachinonthioxanthone.
Inaug. diss. Zuerich, 1911

NK 0197831 ICRL NN

W 4 B29 1948
KNECHT, Fridolin
Untersuchungen über Witterungseinflüsse auf die nicht akuten Glaukomformen. Basel, Karger, 1948.
p. [21]-38.
Inaug.-Diss. - Basel.
Reprinted from Ophthalmologica, v. 116, Nr. 1.
Summary in German, English and French.
1. Glaucoma 2. Weather - Physiological & psychological effects

NK 0197832 DNLM CtY

PT2296 .Z5K7
Knecht, Frieda, 1895-
Die frau im leben und in der dichtung Friedr. Hebbels ... Zürich, Buchdr. Neue Zürcher zeitung, 1919.
84 p. 22cm.
Inaug.-diss.—Zürich.
Vita.
"Literaturverzeichnis": p. 81-83.

1. Hebbel, Friedrich *i. e.* Christian Friedrich, 1813-1863. 2. Women in literature and art.

NK 0197833 ICU MiDW ICRL OCU

Knecht, Frieda, 1895-
Die frau im leben und in der dichtung Friedr. Hebbels ... Zürich, Rascher & co., 1920.
84p. 21½cm.
"Literaturverzeichnis": p.81-83.

1. Hebbel, Friedrich. 2. Women in literature and art. I. Title.

NK 0197834 NRU PBm CU MH CLSU NIC OrU MiU OCU IU NcU

Knecht, Friedrich Justus, bp., 1839-1921.
Biblische Geschichte fuer Schule und Haus. Freiburg im Breisgau, Herder [1945]
240 p.

NK 0197835 DCU CtY

BS551 .K68
KNECHT,FRIEDRICH JUSTUS,bp.,1839-1921.
The child's Bible history. Adapted from the works of J.Schuster and G.Mey. By the Right Rev.Bishop F. J.Knecht,D.D. Tr.from the German... American ed. St.Louis,B.Herder book co.;[etc.,etc.]1930.
104 p.incl.front.,illus. 16½cm.

1.Bible--History of Biblical events.

NK 0197836 ICU OClStM

Knecht, Friedrich Justus, bp., 1839-1921.
Compendio de historia sagrada para uso de los niños que frecuentan las escuelas católicas. Por el ilmo. Sr. dr. D. Federico Justo Knecht... Edición araucana de P. Félix José de Augusta ... Friburgo de Brisgovia (Alemania): Tip. pontificia de B. Herder, 1903. x, 92 p. illus. 16cm.
Added t.-p. in Araucanian.

984281A. 1. American languages—Araucanian—Texts and translations. I. Félix José de Augusta, fray, tr.
N. Y. P. L. December 22, 1939

NK 0197837 NN

Knecht, Friedrich Justus, Bp., 1839-1921.
Der ehrwürdige Johann Baptist de Lasalle und das Institut der Brüder der christlichen Schulen. Ein beitrag zur geschichte der pädagogik. Freiburg im Br., Herder, 1879.

xii, 266 p. 18 cm. (Half title: Sammlung historischer Bildnisse, 4 Serie, VI).

1. John Baptist de la Salle, Saint, 1651-1719.
2. Brothers of the Christian school.
3. Catholic education.

NK 0197838 PLatS

Knecht, Friedrich Justus, bp., 1839-1921, ed.

Schuster, Ignaz, 1813-1869.
Kurze Biblische geschichte für die unteren schuljahre der katholischen volksschule. Mit 46 bildern. Nach der Biblischen geschichte von Schuster-Mey bearbeitet von dr. Friedrich Justus Knecht ... Saint Louis, Mo., B. Herder, 1911.

BX2152 .K57
Knecht, Friedrich Justus, bp., 1839-1921.
Manna der jugend. Ein gebet- und lehrbuechlein fur schulpflichtige knaben und maedchen. Einsiedeln [etc.] Benziger & co., 1888 [1887]
1 p.l., 240 p. front. 24°.

NK 0197840 DLC

BS 491 .K68 E5
Knecht, Friedrich Justus, Bp., 1839-1921.
A practical commentary on Holy Scripture for the use of catechists and teachers, by Frederick Justus Knecht ... Tr. from the 10th German ed. Preface by Rev. Michael F. Glancey ... St. Louis, B. Herder [1894]
2 v. illus., maps. 20cm.

1. Bible - History of Biblical events.
2. Bible - Commentaries. I. Title.

NK 0197841 DCU OClJC MnCS

VOLUME 300

Knecht, Friedrich Justus, Bp., 1839-1921.
A practical commentary on Holy Scripture for the use of those who teach Bible history; translated and adapted from the 16th German edition. Pref. by Rev. Michael F. Glancey. 2d Endligh ed. rev. Freiburg i.B., St. Louis, Herder, 1901
2 v. in 1, illus., col. maps, 23 cm.

1. Bible - History of Biblical events. I. Glancey, Michael F., 1854-

NK 0197842 DCU MB PPCCH

KNECHT, Friedrich Justus, bp., 1839-1921
A practical commentary on Holy Scripture. For the use of those who teach Bible History. Translated and adapted from the sixteenth German edition. Preface by Very Rev. Canon M.F. Glancey Third English edition revised containing 100 illustrations and four coloured maps. London, B. Herder, 1910.
xxxii, 839 p. illus., maps, fronts. 23cm.

1. Bible—Commentaries. 2. Bible—History of Biblical events.

NK 0197843 MBtS CU

Knecht, Friedrich Justus, *bp.*, 1839-1921.
A practical commentary on Holy Scripture for the use of those who teach Bible history, by Frederick Justus Knecht ... Translated and adapted from the 16th German ed. Preface by Very Rev. Canon M. F. Glancey ... 4th English ed., containing hundred illustrations and four coloured maps. London, St. Louis, Mo., B. Herder, 1923.
xxxii, 839 p. front., illus., maps (1 double) 22cm.

1. Bible—History of Biblical events. 2. Bible—Commentaries.

Library of Congress BS491.K6 1923 26-13111

NK 0197844 DLC ICRL OrStbM WaSpG OClUr OCX

Knecht, Friedrich Justus, bp., 1839-1921.
A practical commentary on Holy Scripture for the use of those who teach Bible hist., Tr. & adapted from the 16th German ed. Preface by Very Rev. Canon M. F. Glancey ... 5th Eng. ed., containing hundred illus., & four coloured maps. Lond., St. Louis, Mo., B. Herder [1923.] 1930.
839 p.

NK 0197845 OCl

Knecht, Friedrich Justus, bp., 1839-1921.
Praktischer kommentar zur biblischen geschichte mit einer anweisung zur erteilung des biblischen geschichts-unterrichtes und einer konkordanz der biblischen geschichte und des katechismus. Im anschlusse an die von G.Mey neu bearbeitete Schustersche biblische geschichte für die katholischen religionslehrer an volksschulen herausgegeben von Friedrich Justus Knecht. 5 verb. aufl. Freiburg im Br., Herder, 1886.
xv, 771 p. fold. plans 20 cm.
Copy 2: 9 verb. und verm. aufl. 1889.

NK 0197846 PLatS OCX

Knecht, Friedrich Justus, Bp., 1839-1921.
Praktischer Kommentar zur Biblischen Geschichte; mit einer Anweisung zur Erteilung des biblischen Geschichtsunterrichtes... 14., unveränderte Auflage. Freiburg i.B., Herder 1894.
xiv, 796p. fold. map, fold. tables, 21cm.

NK 0197847 PLatS

Knecht, Friedrich Justus, bp., 1839-1921
Die Staatserziehung ist im Princip verwerflich. Den Freunden der christlichen Jugendbildung gewidmet. Freiburg im Breisgau, Herder, 1880.
37p. 23cm.
On spine: Canisiusverein Broschüren.

1. Education and state - Germany. 2. Public schools - Germany. 3. Education (Works published 1800-1900) I. Title.

NK 0197848 InStmeS

Knecht, Friedrich Justus, Bp., 1838-1921
Die Staatserziehung ist in ihren Folgen verderblich. Den Freunden der christlichen Jugendbildung gewidmet. Freiburg im Breisgau, Herder, 1880.
98p. 23cm.
(Bound with the author's work - Die Staatserziehung ist im Princip verwerflich. Freiburg 1880)

1. Education and state - Germany. 2. Public schools - Germany. 3. Education (Works published 1800-1900) I. Title.

NK 0197849 InStmeS

[Knecht, Friedrich Justus.] bp., 1839-1921. 2234.140
Toreñöb in Bibel in oniñ. [Kurze Biblische geschichte; in die sprache der Nauru-insel (Marshallinseln) übersetzt von Friedrich Gründl.] Freiburg im Breisgau, Herder, 1905.
pp. v, 86. Illus.

Oceanic lang.-Marshall Islands

NK 0197850 MH

Knecht, Günther, 1909-
Handeln unter fremdem namen. ... 1935.
Inaug. Diss. - Giessen, 1935.
Lebenslauf.
Bibliography.

NK 0197851 ICRL

Knecht, Gustav, manufacturing co., *Chicago.*
... Price list and barber's reference book of Gustav Knecht ... [New rev. list, 1885-1886] Chicago [J. Morris company, printers, 1885]
78, [2] p. illus. 23cm.
Advertising matter interspersed.

1. Barbers' supplies—Catalogs. CA 10-2608 Unrev'd

Library of Congress TT979.K68 1884

NK 0197852 DLC

Knecht, Gustav, manufacturing co., *Chicago.*
... Price list and barbers' reference book of Gust. Knecht m'f'g co. ... 1888-1889. Chicago, Ill. [Goes & Quensel, °1888]
100 p. illus. 23½cm.
Advertising matter interspersed.

1. Barbers' supplies—Catalogs. CA 10-2606 Unrev'd

Library of Congress TT979.K68 1888

NK 0197853 DLC

Knecht, Gustav, manufacturing co., *Chicago.*
... Price list and barbers' reference book of Gust. Knecht m'f'g co. ... 1889-1890. Chicago [McCluer printing co., °1889]
106 p. illus. 22½cm.
Advertising matter interspersed.

1. Barbers' supplies—Catalogs. CA 10-2607 Unrev'd

Library of Congress TT979.K68 1889

NK 0197854 DLC

Knecht, Gustav, manufacturing co., *Chicago.*
... Price list, and barbers' reference book of Gust. Knecht manufacturing co. ... [Chicago, J. Morris company, printers and mnfg. stationers] 1890.
64 p. illus. 23 x 30½cm.

1. Barbers' supplies—Catalogs. CA 10-2605 Unrev'd

Library of Congress TT979.K68 1890
© 1890: 12431

NK 0197855 DLC

Knecht, H 1898-
Die Klippengruppe Buochserhorn-Musenalp und ihre Unterlage. Basel, 1925.
352 p.

NK 0197856 DLC-P4 CtY TxU ICRL

Knecht, Hans.
Strasse ohne Ende. Zürich, Scheuch [1949]
296 p. plates, ports. 22 cm.

1. Cycling. I. Title.

GV1051.K6A3 796.6 50-26348

NK 0197857 DLC NN

Knecht, Hans, 1904-
Über die beziehungen zwischen katalaseaktivität und vitalität im ruhenden samen. ... Dresden, 1931.
Inaug. Diss. - Landwirtschaftlichen Hochschule Hohenheim, 1930.
Lebenslauf.
Schriftenverzeichnis.

NK 0197858 ICRL

Knecht, Heinz.
Die Abänderungsklagen. Aarau [1954]
118 p. 23 cm.
Diss.—Zürich.
Vita.
Published also as Zürcher Beiträge zur Rechtswissenschaft, n. F., Heft 194)
Bibliography: p. [9]-10.

1. New trials—Switzerland. 2. Annuities—Switzerland. I. Title.

58-41888

NK 0197859 DLC MH-L

VOLUME 300

Knecht, Heinz.
Die Abänderungsklagen. Aarau, H. R. Sauerländer, 1954.
118 p. 23 cm. (Zürcher Beiträge zur Rechtswissenschaft, n. F., Heft 194)
Published also as thesis, Zürich.
Bibliography: p. [9]-10.

1. New trials—Switzerland. 2. Annuities—Switzerland. I. Title. (Series)

57-16115

NK 0197860 DLC MH-L IU

Knecht, Henri, 1904-
Contribution a l'etude de la myomectomie en dehors et au cours de la grossesse.
Inaug. diss. Strasbourg, 1930.
Bibl.

NK 0197861 ICRL CtY

W.C.L. M780.88 M987C no.7
Knecht, Henry.
Fairy waltz. Baltimore, F. D. Benteen [ca. 1839, Pl. no. 248.
3 p. 34 cm.
Caption title.
For piano.
[No. 7] in a volume of songs and piano music, 1822-1855 with binder's title: Music.

1. Waltzes (Piano) I. Title.

NK 0197862 NcD

M1 .S444 v.43 no.26
Knecht, Henry.
Fairy waltz, composed & respectfully dedicated to Miss Mary Morton Clark of Petersburg Va. Baltimore, F. D. Benteen [184- or 185-?] Pl. no. 1362.
3 p. 34cm. [Sheet music collection, v. 43, no. 26]
Caption title.
"L. W. Webb [Eng.]

1. Waltzes (Piano) I. Title.

NK 0197863 ViU

KNECHT, Henry. 80;
Mobile grand march. [For the pianoforte.]
New York. Hewitt & Jaques. [184-?] (2) pp. F°.

NK 0197864 MB

W.C.L. M780.88 M987 no.52
Knecht, Henry.
Mobile grand march. Baltimore, Published by F. D. Benteen [ca. 1850] Pl. no. 646.
[2 p.] 34 cm.
Caption title.
[No. 52] in a volume of music, ca. 1845-60 with binder's title: Music.

1. Marches (Piano) I. Title.

NK 0197865 NcD

* M32 .K54R5 18—
Knecht, Henry.
The Richmond waltz, arranged for the piano forte and respectfully dedicated to Miss Virginia Heath (of Petersburg Va.) Baltimore, Geo. Willig, Jr. [not after 1867] Pl. no. 1363.
[2] p. 35cm.
Caption title.
L. W. Webb, Lith. (p. [2])
1. Waltzes (Piano). I. Title.

NK 0197866 ViU

M1 .S444 v.145 no.23
Knecht, Henry.
Sonnet to beauty, brilliant waltz, composed & respectfully dedicated to Miss P. W. Goodwyn (of Petersburg, Va.) by Henry A. Knecht. Baltimore, F. D. Benteen, ©1847. Pl. no. 1023.
3 p. 35cm. [Sheet music collection, v. 145, no. 23]
Webb.
Stamped: Gaines, Riches & Co., Petersburg.

1. Waltzes (Piano) I. Title.

NK 0197867 ViU

M1 .S444 v.145 no.24
Knecht, Henry.
Sonnet to youth, brilliant waltz for the piano forte. Composed & respectfully dedicated to Miss Ann E. McIlvaine (of Petersburg, Va.) by Henry A. Knecht. [Price] 25 cts. net. Baltimore, Frederick D. Benteen [©1846] Pl. no. 967.
5 p. 35cm. [Sheet music collection, v. 145, no.24]
Webb.
Stamped: Gaines, Riches & Co., Petersburg.
1. Waltzes (Piano) I. Title.

NK 0197868 ViU

M1 .S444 v.156 no.19
Knecht, Henry.
The Virginia gallopade. Composed & respectfully dedicated to Miss Susanna Parrish (of Petersburg, Va.) by Henry Knecht. Baltimore, F. D. Benteen [after 1829?] Pl. no. 1360.
[2] p. 33cm. [Sheet music collection, v. 156, no. 19]
L. W. Webb.

1. Galops (Piano) I. Title.

NK 0197869 ViU

Knecht (Hermine). *Ueber Encephalopathia saturnina. [Zürich.] 24 pp. 8°. Wien, A. Holzhausen, 1922.

NK 0197870 DNLM CtY

Knecht, Hugo: Randständige Hornhautgeschwüre und [Ausz.: in] Rosacea. [Maschinenschrift.] 27 S. 4° [Lag nicht vor.] — Auszug: (Rostock 1922). 1 Bl. 8°
Rostock, Med. Diss. v. 25. Okt. 1922 [1925] [U 25. 7830

NK 0197871 ICRL

Knecht, J.
Die wallonische Gemeinde zu Otterberg. Magdeburg: Heinrichshofen, 1892. 21 p. 8°. (Deutscher Hugenotten-Verein. Geschichtsblätter. Heft 7.)
Signed: J. Knecht.

1. Walloon church.—History, Germany: Otterberg.
N. Y. P. L. September 4, 1918.

NK 0197872 NN

Knecht, Jacob.
... Die kongruenz zwischen subjekt und prädikat und die 3. person pluralis präsentis auf -s im elisabethanischen englisch, von dr. Jacob Knecht. Heidelberg, C. Winter, 1911.
xiii, [1], 152 p. 22½cm. (Anglistische forschungen ... hft. 33)
"Der erste teil der vorliegenden arbeit (über die kongruenz) ist als Tübinger dissertation erschienen."—Vorwort.
"Literatur": p. [ix]-xiii.

1. English language—Early modern (1500-1700)—Verb. 2. English language—Verb. 3. English language—Number.

11—32319

Library of Congress PE25.A5

NK 0197873 MoSU PU CtY PU-F MH IU ICRL TNJ FTaSU DLC NcD PU-F PBm MiU OCU OU NjP NN MoU

Knecht (Jean). *De la fréquence de l'oxyure vermiculaire dans l'appendice; étude basée sur l'examen de 4,260 appendices. 30 pp., 2 pl. 8°. Lausanne, Pache-Varidel & Bron, 1922.

NK 0197874 DNLM

Knecht (Joh. Rodolphus). *De asthmate. 12 l. sm. 4°. *Basileæ, lit. J. Brandmylleri*, 1704.

NK 0197875 DNLM

30.2 K73 Ed.5-6
Knecht, Johannes.
Das Jahr des jungen Landwirts; ein Lehr- und Handbuch für den landwirtschaftlichen Berufsschüler und Landwirtschaftslehrling. 5./6. erweiterte Aufl. Stuttgart, Ulmer, 1951.
287 p.

1. Agriculture. Text-books. 2. Germany. Agriculture.

NK 0197876 DNAL

Knecht, John.
In memory of John Knecht
see under title

KNECHT, JOSEPH.
Spring and love. Words by M. E. Wood. Music by Joseph Knecht. Boston, O. Ditson co., c1896.

Song with piano accompaniment.
First line: Comes fair spring, and soft the falling show'r.
1. Songs, U.S. 2. Songs, Secular--1870- 3. Spring. I. Wood, M. E.

NK 0197878 NN

VMT 6 K 68a
KNECHT, JUSTIN HEINRICH, 1752-1817.
Allgemeiner Katechismus; oder, Kurzer Inbegriff der allgemeinen Musiklehre zum Behufe der Musiklehrer und ihrer Zöglinge. Wien, S.A. Steiner und Comp.[1814?]
6iii[i.e.viii],120p. illus.,2 plates(1 fold.) 21cm.

NK 0197879 ICN

Knecht, Justin Heinrich, 1752-1817.
Knechts Allgemeiner musikalischer katechismus, oder: Kurzer inbegriff der allgemeinen musiklehre zum behufe der musiklehrer und ihre zöglinge. Biberach, Gebrüder Knecht, 1803.
viii, 120 p. 20cm.

1. Music—Manuals, text-books, etc.

10-9344

Library of Congress MT6.K63

NK 0197880 DLC CtY

VOLUME 300

MT6 K57 1816 Music Library

Knecht, Justin Heinrich, 1752-1817.
Knechts allgemeiner musikalischer Katechismus, oder: kurzer Inbegriff der allgemeinen Musiklehre zum Behufe der Musiklehrer und ihrer Zöglinge. 4. verb. und verm. Ausg. Freiburg, in der Herderschen Universitäts-Buchhandlung, 1816.
x, 114 p. music.

1. Music - Manuals, text-books, etc.

NK 0197881 CU MH

-VMT 40 P 924w

KNECHT, JUSTIN HEINRICH, 1752-1817.
Allgemeiner musikalischer Katechismus; oder, Kurzer Inbegriff der allgemeinen Musiklehre; zum Behufe der Musiklehrer, und ihrer Zöglinge. Neueste, verb. und verm. Ausg. Wien, In Commissiom bey T. Haslinger [1822?]
107p. music. 21cm. (with Preindl, Joseph. Wiener-Tonschule ... [1827])

NK 0197882 ICN MB CU

Knecht, Justin Heinrich, 1752-1817.
Bewährtes methodenbuch beim ersten klavierunterricht, mit 50 notentafeln ... verfasst von Justin Heinrich Knecht. Freiburg, Herder [1825]
36, 52 p. 24 x 21cm.

1. Pianoforte—Instruction and study.

11-30498

Library of Congress MT222.K74

NK 0197883 DLC CtY

Knecht, Justin Heinrich, 1752-1817 (2)
Variations, keyboard
XII variations pour le clavecin ou pianoforte. Leipsic, Schwickert [ca. 1785]
Score (6 p.)

NK 0197884 MH

---

fMT50 K57 1814

Knecht, Justin Heinrich, 1752-1817.
Elementarwerk der Harmonie, als Einleitung in die Begleitungs- und Tonsetzkunst, wie auch in die Tonwissenschaft. Nach drei Lehrkursen geordnet, für Anfänger und Geübtere. 2. ganz umgearb. und verm. Ausgabe. Munchen, Falter, 1814.
2 v. in 1.

fMT50 K57 1814 suppl.

--- LX Notentafeln zu Knechts Elementarwerk der Harmonie. München, Falter [1814?]
2 v. in 1. (98 p.) music. 28x36cm.

NK 0197885 CU CtY

Knecht, Justin Heinrich, 1752–1817.
Erklärung einiger von einem der R. G. B. in Erlangen angetasteten, aber missverstandenen grundsätze aus der Voglerschen theorie ... von Justin Heinrich Knecht ... Nebst angehängten Anmerkungen über herrn Lôhleins einleitung in den zweyten theil seiner Clavierschule. Ulm, Gedruckt bey C. U. Wagner, 1785.
35 p. 22 x 18cm.
Head and tail pieces.
Written in reply to Johann Michael Weissbeck's "Protestationsschrift, oder Exemplarische widerlegung einiger stellen ... der kapellmeister Voglerischen Tonwissenschaft und tonsetzkunst."

1. Weissbeck, Johann Michael, 1756–1808. Protestationsschrift. 2. Lôhlein, Georg Simon, 1727–1781. Clavier-schule. 3. Vogler, Georg Joseph, abt, 1749–1814.

9–14269

Library of Congress MT40.A2K6

NK 0197886 DLC CtY

Knecht, Justin Heinrich, 1752–1817.
Gemeinnützliches Elementarwerk der Harmonie und des Generalbasses. Das ist: wahre Art, die Begleitungskunst in Verbindung mit einer vollkommenen Kenntnis aller Harmonien nach Voglerschen Grundsätzen zu lehren und zu lernen, mit ... harmonischen Tabellen und praktischen Notenbeispielen begleitet ... von Justin Heinrich Knecht. Erste[-vierte] Abtheilung ... Augsburg: Gedruckt bei J. W. Hamm, d. jung., 1792–97. 4 v. in 1. 21 x 17½cm.

Paged continuously.
"Notentafeln" in each volume wanting.
Imprint varies: Abt. 2–4, Gedruckt bei den Gebrüdern Mäntler, Stuttgart, 1793–97.

649744A. 1. Harmony. 2. Thorough-bass. I. Title.
N. Y. P. L. August 22, 1933

NK 0197888 DLC PU CtY NRU-Mus NN

Knecht, Justin Heinrich, 1752–1817.
Kleine theoretische klavierschule für die ersten anfänger, worin die anfangsgründe sowohl der musik überhaupt, als des klavierspielens ins besondere auf eine fassliche weise gelehret werden. Von J. H. Knecht ... München, In der Falterischen musikhandlung [1800–02]
2 v. in 1. illus. (music) 24 x 21cm.
Musical exercises: abt. 2, p. 92–130.

1. Pianoforte—Instruction and study. 2. Music—Manuals, text-books, etc.

25-13381

Library of Congress MT222.K741

NK 0197889 DLC

Knecht, Justin Heinrich, 1752–1817.
Kleines alphabetisches wörterbuch der vornehmsten und interessantesten artikel aus der musikalischen theorie. Verfasst von Justin Heinrich Knecht. Ulm, In der Wohlerschen buchhandlung, 1795.
viii, 117 p., 1 l. 20 cm.

1. Music—Terminology.

ML108.K5 8-16359

NK 0197890 DLC NRU-Mus

M 2020 .K68 P4

Knecht, Justin Heinrich, 1752-1817.
[Psalm 23. German]
Neue Kirchenmusik, bestehend in dem Drey und zwanzigsten Psalm, mit vier Singestimmen, Orgel und einer willkührlichen Begleitung von verschiedenen Instrumenten. Leipzig, Im Schwickertschen Verlage [1783]
2 p.l., score (54 p.) 28 x 32 cm.
For soloists (SATB) chorus (SATB) and continuo (organ) with 2 horns, 2 flutes, 2 bassoons, and strings ad libitum.
Sign. O_2 lacking (blank?)
1. Choruses, Sacred (Mixed voices, 4 pts.) with orchestra--To 1800--Scores. 2. Psalms (Music)--23d Psalm.

NK 0197891 MiU ICN DLC

M 22 .K68

Knecht, Justin Heinrich, 1752-1817.
Neue vollstaendige Sammlung aller Arten von Vor u. Nachspielen, Fantasien, Versetten, Fugetten u. Fugen für geübtere und ungeübtere Klavier- und Orgelspieler. [1]-[7] Heft ... Speier, Bei Bossler [1790-95] Pl. no. 198-
7 v. in 4. 25 x 32 cm.
Hefte 1 and 3-6 bound together.
Each Heft numbered in manuscript. Heft 6 unnumbered and bound out of order.
Gerber lists 8 Hefte, Heft 8 (1800) having a different place of publication.
1. Piano music--To 1800. 2. Organ music--To 1800.

NK 0197892 MiU MB ICN

KNECHT, JUSTIN HEINRICH, 1752-1817.
Neue vollständige Sammlung aller Arten von Vor- und Nachspielen, Fantasien, Versetten, Fugetten und Fugen für geübtere und ungeübtere Klavier und Orgel Spieler. 2. verb. Aufl. Mainz, B. Schott [1812-17?] Pl. nos. 563/986. 6 nos. in 1 v. 25 x 34cm.

For organ or piano.
First published 1790-99? in 8 parts: part 1-7 by Bossler, Speier (1790-95); part 8 by Falter, Munich (1799?)

1. Organ—To 1800. 2. Piano—To 1800. 3. Organ—Studies and exercises.

NK 0197893 NN CU

Knecht, Justin Heinrich, *1752-1817.* No. 15 in **M.201.37
O send out Thy light. Quartett. [Accomp. for pianoforte.]
(In Hasse, C. F. Sacred Music. Pp. 81-86. Leeds. [1829.])

E2766 — T.r. — Church music. Anthems, &c.

NK 0197894 MB

VMT 182 C 87b

KNECHT, JUSTIN HEINRICH, 1752-1817.
Orgelstücke für anfänger und geübtere... 1. heft. Leipzig, Breitkopf und Härtel [n.d.]
38p. 24x29½cm. (with Couturier, N.M. Breve metodo per suonare l'organo... [n.d.])

Binder's title: Organ music.

NK 0197895 ICN IU

Knecht, Justin Heinrich, 1752–1817.
Le portrait musical de la nature; ou, Grande symphonie à deux violons, alte & basse, avec deux flûttes [sic] traversières, deux hautbois, fagotts, cors, trompettes & timbales ad libitum... Par Iustin Henri Knecht. Spire: Bossler [1784]. Publ. pl. no. 40. 15 parts. f°.

Separate parts for violin I and II, viola, bass, flute I and II, oboe I and II, bassoon I and II, horn I and II, trumpet I and II, and kettledrums.

BEETHOVEN ASSOCIATION FUND.

1. Orchestra (Full)—Symphonies. 2. Title.
N. Y. P. L. October 21, 1924

NK 0197896 NN

Film 1872

Knecht, Justin Heinrich, 1752-1817.
Le portrait musical de la nature; ou, grande symphonie à deux violons, alte & basse, avec deux fluttes traversières, deux hautbois, fagotts, cors, trompettes & timbales ad libitum. Spire, Bossler [1784]
15 parts.
Microfilm. New York, New York Public Library, n.d. 1 reel.
1. Symphonies--To 1800--Parts. I. Title.

NK 0197897 NSyU

VMT 222 K 68t

KNECHT, JUSTIN HEINRICH, 1752-1817.
Theoretisch praktische Generalbassschule, welche in neunzig Notentafeln nebst allen Intervallen, alle mögliche Bewegung Arten der Töne, Uebungen aller vorkommenden Akkorde, die verschiedenen Uebergänge und das Ineinanderweben der Töne durch alle gebräuchlichen Dur- und Moll-Tonarten enthält. Freiburg, Herder [1815?]
score (92p.) [8], 60p. 25cm.

"Einleitung. Vom Generalbass überhaupt": 60p.

NK 0197898 ICN

VOLUME 300

Knecht, Justin Heinrich, 1752–1817.
Theoretisch praktische generalbassschule, welche in neunzig notentafeln, nebst allen intervallen, alle mögliche bewegungs arten der töne, uebungen aller vorkommenden akkorde, die verschiedenen übergänge und das ineinanderweben der töne durch alle gebräuchlichen dur- und moll-tonarten enthält. Von Justin Heinrich Knecht. Freiburg, Herder [1825]
2 p. l., 60, [8], 3-92 p. 24 x 21cm. [*With his* Bewährtes methodenbuch beim ersten klavierunterricht. Freiburg [1825]]
1. Thorough-bass.
Library of Congress MT222.K74 11-30499

NK 0197899 DLC CtY

Knecht, Justin Heinrich, 1752-1817.
Die treuen Köhler; eine Operette in zwey Aufzügen, von Herrn Heerman in Weimar. In Musik gesetzt von Herrn Musikdirektor Knecht in Biberach. Wird den 29 Juni auch 2ten und 4ten Julii 1789 allhier zu Kaufbeuren auf dem gewöhnlichen Theater der burgerlichen Agenten A. C. aufgeführt. [Kaufbeuren] gedruckt bey Dorn [1789]
1v. (unpaged)
Microcard edition

NK 0197900 ICRL

Knecht, Justin Heinrich, 1752–1817.
Vollständige orgelschule für anfänger und geübtere, hrsg. von Justin Heinrich Knecht ... Leipzig, In der Breitkopfischen musikhandlung [1795–98]
3 v. 31 x 24cm.
Vol. 3: In der Breitkopf- und Härtelschen musikhandlung.
Of the six parts announced in the preface of v. 3 only the first three were published.
CONTENTS.—1. abth. Die anfangsgründe der orgelspielkunst.—2. abth. Die kenntnis der vornehmsten orgelregister.—3. abth. Eine theoretisch-praktische abhandlung über das choralspiel auf der orgel.
1. Organ—Methods.
Library of Congress MT182.K58 9-31205

NK 0197901 DLC CSt NNU MB MnU NcWsMM

Film 15554
Knecht, Justin Heinrich, 1752-1817.
Vollständige Orgelschule für Anfänger und Geübtere, hrsg. von Justin Heinrich Knecht. Leipzig, In der Breitkopfischen Musikhandlung [1795-98]
3v. music. 31 x 24cm.
Vols.3: In der Breitkopf- und Hartelschen Musikhandlung.
Of the six parts announced in the preface of v.3 only the first three were published.
Contents.- 1.Abth. Die Anfangsgrunde der Orgelspielkunst.- 2. Abth. Die Kenntnis der Vornehmsten Orgelregister.- 3.Abth. Eine theoretischpraktische Abhandlung über das Choralspiel auf der Orgel
Microfilm (negative). Ann Arbor, Mich., University of Michigan Photoduplication Service, 1972. 1 reel.
1. Organ - Instruction and study. I. Title.

NK 0197903 IaU

Knecht, Justin Heinrich, 1752-1817.
M2138 .W95V6 Case
Württembergisches choralbuch.
Vollständige sammlung, theils ganz neu componirter, theils verbesserter, vierstimmiger choralmelodien für das Neue Wirtembergische landgesangbuch. Zum orgelspielen und vorsingen in allen vaterländischen kirchen und schulen ausschliessend, gnädigst verordnet. Nebst einer zwekmässigen einleitung; in zehen rubriken eingetheiltem register; u. einem mit diesem werke eng verbundnen anhange. Herausgegeben von Christmann und Knecht ... Stuttgart, Gebrüder Mäntler, 1799 [*i. e.* 1806?]

7Q 113
KNECHT, JUSTIN HEINRICH, 1752-1817.
Wechselgesang der Mirjam und Debora, aus dem zehnten Gesange der Klopstockischen Messiade, in Musik gesetzt ... von Justin Heinrich Knecht. Leipzig, Im Schwickertschen Verlage[1781]
score(18p.) 29cm.
For 2 sopranos and keyboard instrument.

NK 0197905 ICN DLC

Knecht, Karl Kae.
Drawing pictures by radio; a method for making drawings when directions are broadcasted over a radio, by Karl Kae Knecht ... [Evansville, Ind.] ©1926.
cover-title, 4 l. illus. 28 x 17cm.
Text runs parallel with back of cover.
I. Title. II. Title: Radio, Drawing pictures by.
Library of Congress NC620.K55 CA 26-452 Unrev'd

NK 0197906 DLC

Knecht, Karl Oskar, 1914-
Über m-Phenylen-di-glykol. Basel, E.Birkhäuser & Cie., A.G., 1944.
Verkürzte Fassung der Inaugural-Dissertation - Basel.
"Separatabdruck aus Helvetica chimica acta, Vol.XXVII, Fasciculus quintus, 1944", p. [1108]-1115.
"Curriculum vitae" at end.

NK 0197907 MH CtY

Knecht, Klara E.
Animal-book, by Klara E. Knecht ... paintings by Diana Thorne. Akron, O., The Saalfield pub. co., 1933.
[24] p. col. illus. 32cm.
1. Animals, Legends and stories of. 2. Animal pictures. I. Thorne, Diana, illus. II. Title.
Library of Congress PZ10.3.K732An [3] 33-38211

NK 0197908 DLC Or OCIh OLak

Knecht, Klara E.
Big animals. Akron, Ohio, Sallfield publishing company, c1937.
17 p. 32cm.

NK 0197909 PPT

Knecht, Klara E.
The circus, by Klara E. Knecht; contributing photographers, Karl K. Knecht, Century photos, H. A. Atwell studio, Lentz studio and Charles L. Franck. Akron, O., New York, The Saalfield publishing company, ©1934.
[32] p. illus. (1 double) 30½cm.
"No. 2098."
1. Circus.
Library of Congress GV1821.H3K55 34-36799
Copyright AA 157860 [2] 791.3

NK 0197910 DLC PBa OCl

Knecht, Klara E.
The circus book, by Klara E. Knecht, educational director of Hagenbeck-Wallace circus ... photography by Karl K. Knecht, Century photos, H. A. Atwell studio, Lentz studio and Charles L. Franck. Akron, O., New York, The Saalfield publishing company, ©1934.
[30] p. illus. (1 double) 31 x 25cm.
On cover: No. 371.
Published also in the same year under title: The circus.
1. Circus.
Library of Congress GV1821.H3K55 1934 a [2] 35-20467 791.3

NK 0197911 DLC

Knecht, Klara E.
Wild animals as I know them, by Klara E. Knecht ... twelve color illustrations by Diana Thorne. Akron, O., New York, The Saalfield publishing company [©1933]
90 p. incl. col. front. col. plates. 30½cm.
Descriptive letterpress on verso of each plate.
Head-pieces.
1. Zoology—Juvenile literature. I. Thorne, Diana, illus. II. Title.
Library of Congress QL49.K6 [3] 33-19069
Copyright A 64432 591.5

NK 0197912 DLC WaSp OrMonO OCl

Knecht, Lucien, 1902-
... Contribution à l'étude expérimentale de la di-phényl-hydantoïne. ... Paris, R. Foulon, 1943.
76 p.
Thèse.

NK 0197913 DNLM MnU

Knecht, Ludwig, 1893-
Das Chasseurlied, Roman. Berlin, Aufwärts-Verlag [19—]
182 p. 19 cm.
I. Title.
PT2621.N35C5 [1] 49-33542*‡

NK 0197914 DLC

Knecht, Ludwig, 1893–
Das chasseurlied, roman, von Lutz Knecht. Berlin, Vier falken verlag [©1937]
347, [1] p. 19cm.
I. Title.
Library of Congress PT2621.N35C5 1937 38-21406
Copyright A—Foreign 39102 [2] 833.91

NK 0197915 DLC

Knecht, Ludwig, 1893–
Feuerzeichen, eine Erzählung aus der pfälzischen Separatistenzeit 1923 bis 1924. Berlin, Aufwärts-Verlag [19—]
38 p. illus. 22 cm. (Aufwärts-Jugend-Bücherei, Heft 11)
I. Title.
PZ35.K552 52-21206

NK 0197916 DLC

VOLUME 300

Knecht, Ludwig, 1893 –
Eine Handvoll Männer & ein Mann, Roman. Wien, Speidel, 1932.
248 s.

NK 0197917 PPG NcD

Knecht, Ludwig, 1893–
Eine Handvoll Männer und ein Mann, Roman. Wien, F. Speidel [1937]
254 p. 20 cm.

I. Title.
PT2621.N35H3 1937 52-47168

NK 0197918 DLC

Knecht, Ludwig, 1893–
Spiel an der Donau; roman von Lutz Knecht. Berlin, Vier falken verlag [°1938]
295 p. 19cm.

I. Title.
39-3500
Library of Congress PT2621.N35S7 1938

NK 0197919 DLC

Knecht, Ludwig, 1893–
Die verschlossenen gärten, roman von Lutz Knecht. Berlin, Vier falken verlag [°1939]
332, [1] p. 19cm.
Sequel to Das chasseurlied.

I. Title.
40-38051
Library of Congress PT2621.N35V4 1939
Copyright A—Foreign 45235
[2] 833.91

NK 0197920 DLC

4PT Ger.-5174
Knecht, Ludwig, 1893-
Die verschlossenen Gärten, Roman. [Erweiterte Neuaufl. des zweibändigen Romans: I. Das Chasseurlied, II. Die verschlossenen Gärten] Ulm, Aegis-Verlag [1949]
501 p.

NK 0197921 DLC-P4

Knecht, Lutz
see Knecht, Ludwig, 1893–

Knecht, Marcel.
Proceedings on the occasion of the presentation to Mr. Charles W. Ames of the cross of the Legion of honor, by Dr. Marcel Knecht ... representing Ambassador Jules J. Jusserand, at Saint Paul, Minnesota, November the twelfth, 1919. [Saint Paul, 1919]

Knecht (Matthæus). *De habenda climatis ratione in conservanda militum valetudine. 36 pp. 4°. *Halæ Magdeb., lit. Hendelianis,* [1758].

NK 0197924 DNLM PPC

Knecht, Max.
Das institut der staatsanwaltschaft nach zürcherischem recht ... von Max Knecht ... Männedorf, Buchdruckerei E. Meyer. 1914.
110 p. 22½cm.
Inaug.-diss.—Zürich.
"Literatur-verzeichnis": p. [107]–108.

1. Public prosecutors—Zürich (Canton) I. Title.
42-32302

NK 0197925 DLC ICRL

Knecht, N M
Dramatische dichtungen. 1.bd. Würzburg, Stahel, 1879.
199p.
Contents: 1) Johanna die Erste von Kastilien. 2) Johanna die Zweite von Kastilien.

NK 0197926 OClW

Knecht, Norbert F., joint author.

JA37 .W3 no. 102
Vogel, Joshua Holmes, 1889–
Parking of motor vehicles in cities (with illustrative ordinances) by Joshua H. Vogel and Norbert F. Knecht. Seattle, Bureau of Governmental Research and Services, University of Washington in cooperation with Association of Washington Cities, 1949.

Knecht, Oskar.
Zur kenntnis der nitrophenolsulfosaeuren.
Inaug. diss. Zuerich, 1906 (Basel).
48p.

NK 0197928 ICRL

Knecht, Otto
... Experimentelle Untersuchungen über das Verhalten der Eiweisskörper am Kaninchenherzmuskel nach Verabreichung von Vitamin D und Cholesterin ... Bern,1941.
Inaug.-Diss. - Bern.

NK 0197929 CtY

Knecht, Otto, 1909-
Die beweisverträge im zivilprozess. ...
Freiburg i. Br., 1937. 119 p.
Inaug. Diss. - Freiburg i. Br., 1937.
Lebenslauf.
Literatur.

NK 0197930 ICRL

Knecht, Peter
Die Voraussetzungen der Entmündigung von Geisteskranken und moralisch Minderwertigen. Egnach, Schwitter & Co. [1954]
xi, 115 p.

Thesis - Bern.
Bibliography : p. viii-xi.

NK 0197931 NNC-L CU-L MH-L

KNECHT, Roger.
Des conflits des coutumes matrimoniales de Paris et de Normandie à partir du seizième siècle. Thèse, Univ. de Paris. Paris, 1909.

NK 0197932 MH-L

Knecht, Sylvain.
Nuages, quelques photographies. Tours, Arrault, 1944.
1 v. (plates) 27 cm.

1. Photography of clouds. I. Title.
TR660.K55 54-52763

NK 0197933 DLC NNC MH NN

Knecht, Sylvain.
Saint Martin de Tours
see under
Sadoux, Jacques.

Knecht, Theodor.
Das eisenbahnstrafrecht...
Inaug. diss. Zuerich, 1908
Bibl.

NK 0197935 ICRL NN

KNECHT, Theodor.
Siedlungsgeographie des Berchtesgadener Landes (Bezirksamt Berchtesgaden). Inaug.-diss., München. Bad Reichenhall, Zugschwerdt, (1913).
"Literatur", pp. 31-34.

NK 0197936 MH CtY PU MiU

Knecht, Theodor, 1919–
Geschichte der griechischen Komposita vom Typ τερψίμβροτος. [Teildruck] Biel, Graphische Anstalt Schüler, 1946.
51 p. 24 cm.
Thesis—Zürich.
"Das Manuskript der vollständigen Arbeit befindet sich in der Handschriftensammlung der Zürcher Zentralbibliothek."
Lebenslauf.
"Bibliographie": p. 1–2.

1. Greek language—Compound words.
PA287.K5 485.1 47–27387*

NK 0197937 DLC WaU PBm IU

Knecht, Theodoro.
... Jazida de magnetita do Morro do Serrote, por Theodoro Knecht e Jesuino Felicissimo Junior. São Paulo, 1939.
29 p. 4 pl., fold. map, fold. profile. 23cm. ([São Paulo (State)] Instituto geografico e geologico. Boletim nº. 23)
At head of title: Secretaria da agricultura, industria e comercio do estado de São Paulo ... Instituto geografico e geologico ...

1. Magnetite. 2. Iron ores—Brazil—São Paulo (State) I. Junior, Jesuino Felicissimo, joint author.
G S 40-24
U. S. Geol. survey. Library for Library of Congress (410) Sa3b no. 23 [TN404.B6]

NK 0197938 DI-GS NN

VOLUME 300

Knecht, Theodoro.
... Os mineraes e minerios do estado de São Paulo (com uma planta dos recursos mineraes da parte sudoeste do estado) por Theodoro Knecht ... São Paulo [Typographia Brasil, Rothchild & co.] 1935.
93 p. fold. map. 23cm.
At head of title: Secretaria da agricultura, industria e commercio do estado de São Paulo. Directoria de publicidade agricola.
"Do 'Boletim de agricultura' n.º unico, 1934."
1. Mines and mineral resources—Brazil.
G S 41-154
U. S. Geol. survey. Library for Library of Congress [2]

NK 0197939 DLC OrCS

TN42 .S3K59
Knecht, Theodoro.
... Os minérios não metálicos do estado de São Paulo, por Theodoro Knecht, com a colaboração dos engenheiros Estevão Alves Pinto e Jesuino Felicissimo Jr., e dos quimicos Antonio Furia, Fernando Galha e Antonio Marques Soares. São Paulo [Papelaria Riachuelo] 1940.
cover-title, 291 p. plates, maps, tables. 23½cm. (São Paulo, Brazil (State) Instituto geografico e geologico. Boletim no. 27)
At head of title: Secretaria da agricultura, industria e comercio do estado de São Paulo ...
Part of the illustrative material is folded.
"Bibliografia": p. 108, 177.
1. Mines and mineral resources—Brazil—São Paulo (State) I. Alves Pinto, Estevam.
G S 45-47
U. S. Geol. survey. Library for Library of Congress [3]

NK 0197940 DI-GS DLC

Knecht, Theodoro.
... I. As ocorrencias de minerios de ferro e pirita no estado de São Paulo, por Theodoro Knecht. II. Gondito no estado de São Paulo, por Jesuino Felicissimo Junior. São Paulo, 1939.
cover-title, 127 p. incl. illus., maps, tables, diagrs. 23½cm. (São Paulo, Brazil (State) Instituto geografico e geologico. Boletim no. 25)
At head of title: Secretaria da agricultura, industria e comercio do estado de São Paulo ... Instituto geografico e geologico ...
1. Iron mines and mining—Brazil—São Paulo (State) 2. Pyrites. 3. Manganese ores—Brazil—São Paulo (State) I. Felicissimo, Jesuino. II. Title: Gondito no estado de São Paulo.
G S 45-105
U. S. Geol. survey. Library for Library of Congress [a2]

NK 0197941 DI-GS

Knecht, Theodoro.
Ocorrências minerais do Estado de São Paulo. Desenhos e cartografia por Otto Bendix. São Paulo, Secretaria da Agricultura, 1950–
v. illus., col. port., col. maps (part fold.) tables. 23 x 32 cm.
At head of title: Instituto Geográfico e Geológico.
Includes bibliographies.
CONTENTS.—v. 1. Municípios de S. Paulo, Santana de Parnaíba, Barueri, Franco da Rocha, Guarulhos, Mogi das Cruzes, Suzano e Poá.
1. Mines and mineral resources — Brazil — São Paulo (State) I. Bendix, Otto. II. São Paulo, Brazil (State) Instituto Geografico e Geologico. III. Title.
TN42.S3K58 G S 52-251
U. S. Geol. Survey. Libr for Library of Congress [2]†

NK 0197942 DI-GS CU NSyU GEU NN DI DLC

Knecht, Theodoro.
... Ouro no estado de São Paulo, por Theodoro Knecht. São Paulo [Papelaria Riachuelo] 1939.
cover-title, 4 l., [7]-97 p. illus. (incl. maps) 23½cm. (São Paulo, Brazil (State) Instituto geografico e geologico. Boletim no. 26)
At head of title: Secretaria da agricultura, industria e comercio do estado de São Paulo ... Instituto geografico e geologico ...
1. Gold mines and mining—Brazil—São Paulo (State)
G S 45-94
U. S. Geol. survey. Library for Library of Congress [2]

NK 0197943 DI-GS

Knecht, Theodoro.
... Sobre algumas novas occorrencias de mineraes no estado de S. Paulo, por Theodoro Knecht ... São Paulo [Typographia Brasil, Rothschild & cia.] 1937.
25 p. illus., diagrs. 23cm.
At head of title: Secretaria da agricultura, industria e commercio do estado de São Paulo. Directoria de publicidade agricola.
"Do 'Boletim de agricultura' n.º unico, 1936."
1. Mines and mineral resources—Brazil—São Paulo (State) I. Title.
G S 41-155 Revised
U. S. Geol. survey. Library for Library of Congress TN42.S3K6

NK 0197944 DI-GS DLC

QK999 Knecht, Violet Clara.
Effects of molybdenum deficiency and excess on plants. 1947.
22 l.
Typewritten.
Essay (S.M.)--Univ. of Chicago.

NK 0197945 ICU

Knecht, Vladimir.
Seltsimees Reene. Tallinn, RK "Ilukirjandus ja kunst," 1946.
167 p. 20cm.
1. Fiction, Esthonian.

NK 0197946 NN

Knecht, Volker.
Terminwesen und Lagerhaltung in der Massenfertigung. Rechnerische Unterlagen und Verfahren zur Betriebsüberwachung. 2. verb. Aufl. Berlin, Springer-Verlag, 1951.
88 p. diagrs. 23 cm.
1. Industrial management. 2. Factory management. I. Title.
HD35.K57 658.5 52-66294 ‡

NK 0197947 DLC NN

Knecht, Walter, 1909-
Das kombinierte licht und elektronenmikroskop, seine eigenschaften und seine anwendung. ...Leipzig 1934.
Inaug. Diss. - Techn. Hochsch. Berlin, 1934.
Lebenslauf.
(Sonderdruck aus "Annalen der physik" 5. folge, Band 20, Heft 2, 1934.)

NK 0197948 ICRL

W 4 M31 1937
KNECHT, Werner, 1913-
Ueber einige biologische Wirkungen der Salzschlirfer Trink- und Badekur; Beeinflussung der Blutbakterizidie und des Blutharnsäurespiegels. Marburg, Koch, 1937.
17 p.
Cover title.
Inaug.-Diss. - Marburg.
1. Hydrotherapy

NK 0197949 DNLM

Knecht, Wilhelm, 1872–
Auswahl von kohlehydraten durch verschiedene hefen bei der alkoholischen gärung ... Jena, G. Fischer, 1901.
2 p. l., 20 p., 1 l. 23½cm.
Inaug.-diss.—Erlangen.
Lebenslauf.
Reprinted from Centralblatt für bakteriologie. 2. abt., no. 7, 1901, p. 161–167, 215–228.
1. Fermentation.
8-12607†
Library of Congress QR151.K6

NK 0197950 DLC PU NIC

Knecht-Castièl, Nina, 1919-
Beim winterkönig, märchen von Nina Castièl. Zeichnungen von Willi Hessel. Stuttgart/Tübingen, Bodensee-verlag.
40 p.

NK 0197951 DLC

Knecht-Castièl, Nina, 1919–
Die Königsblume und andere indische Märchen. Illus. von Annemarie Gramberg. [1. Aufl.] Stuttgart, Bodensee-Verlag [1946]
79 p. illus. 21 cm.
I. Title.
PZ34.K62 55-39079 ‡

NK 0197952 DLC PU ICU

Knecht et Roissy, Paris.
Le petit manuel du lithographe
see under Knecht, Ed.

Knecht G. m. b. H.
Knecht Filter Lexikon. [1. Aufl. Stuttgart, 1955]
251 p. illus. 11 cm.
1. Automobiles—Motors—Oil filters. I. Title.
A 59-945
Detroit. Public Library for Library of Congress [3]

NK 0197954 MiD

Knechtel, Abraham.
... The Dominion forest reserves, by A. Knechtel ... [Ottawa, 1908?]
19 p. plates. 23cm. (Dept. of the interior, Canada. Forestry branch ... Bulletin no. 3)
Reprinted from Canadian forestry journal. v. 5.
1. Canada. Forest reservations.
Agr 11-288
Library, U. S. Dept. of Agriculture 99.9C16B no. 3

NK 0197955 DNAL MB NcD CU MH-A CaBVaU OrCS

Knechtel, Abraham.
New York (*State*) *Forest, fish and game commission.*
... Making a woodlot from seed. By A. Knechtel, forester. Albany, J. B. Lyon company, state printers, 1907.

VOLUME 300

SD555 K5 Knechtel, Abraham.
Methods of estimating and measuring standing timber. By A. Knechtel ... (New York, 1900) p. 67-86. plates(1 col.) 26cm.

Caption title.
Running title: Report of the Forest, fish and game commission.
An excerpt from the sixth annual report of the Forest, fish and game commission of the state of New York, 1899-1900.

1. Forests and forestry- Mensuration. I. Title.

NK 0197957 CU

Knechtel, Abraham.
... Planting and care of a forest of evergreens, by A. Knechtel ... Ottawa, Printed for Government printing bureau, 1908.
cover-title, 8 p. illus. 22cm. (Dept. of the interior, Canada. Forestry branch ... Bulletin no. 2)

1. Evergreens. 2. Sylviculture.

Agr 11-287

Library, U. S. Dept. of Agriculture 99.9C16B no. 2

NK 0197958 DNAL OrCS MH-A NcD CaBVaU MBH

Knechtel, Maxwell McMichael, 1897–
Bentonite deposits of the Yellowtail district, Montana and Wyoming, by M. M. Knechtel and S. H. Patterson. Washington, 1952.
7 p. maps (2 in pocket) fold. table (in pocket) 27 cm. (Geological Survey circular 150)
"References cited": p. 7.

1. Bentonite. I. Patterson, Sam H., 1918– joint author. (Series: U. S. Geological Survey. Circular no. 150)
[QE75.C5 no. 150] G S 52-94

U. S. Geol. Survey. Libr. for Library of Congress [3]

NK 0197959 DI-GS WaTC

Knechtel, Maxwell McMichael, 1897– joint author.

Collier, Arthur James, 1866–1939.
... The coal resources of McCone county, Montana, by A. J. Collier and M. M. Knechtel ... Washington, U. S. Govt. print. off., 1939.

Knechtel, Maxwell McMichael, 1897–
Geology and coal and natural gas resources of northern Le Flore County, Oklahoma. Norman, 1949.
76 p. illus., 2 fold. maps (in pocket) 5 fold. diagrs. (in pocket) 23 cm. (Oklahoma. Geological Survey. Bulletin 68)
Investigation conducted under cooperative agreement between the Oklahoma Geological Survey and the Geological Survey of the United States Department of the Interior.
Bibliographical footnotes.

1. Geology—Oklahoma—Le Flore Co. 2. Coal—Oklahoma—Le Flore Co. 3. Gas, Natural—Oklahoma—Le Flore Co. (Series)
QE153.A2 no. 68 553.2 G S 50-104
——— Copy 2. QE154.L4K5
U. S. Geol. Survey. Libr. for Library of Congress [3]†

NK 0197961 DI-GS WaS MoU CU UU OU TxU DI DLC

Knechtel, Maxwell McMichael, 1897– joint author.

Hendricks, Thomas Andrews, 1907–
... Geology and fuel resources of the southern part of Oklahoma coal field, by T. A. Hendricks, M. M. Knechtel, C. H. Dane, H. E. Rothrock, and J. S. Williams. Washington, U. S. Govt. print. off. [1937]–39.

GB705 .A6K6 Knechtel, Maxwell M.
...Geology and ground water resources of the valley of Gila river and San Simon creek, Graham county, Arisona...
Washington,1938
p.181-222 23 cm.
(U.S. Geol. surv. Water-supply paper [Separate 796-F)

NK 0197963 DLC

Knechtel, Maxwell McMichael, 1897– joint author.

QE153 .A2 no. 67 Oakes, Malcolm Christie, 1899–
Geology and mineral resources of Haskell County, Oklahoma, by Malcolm C. Oakes and M. M. Knechtel. Prepared in cooperation between the Oklahoma Geological Survey and the Geological Survey, United States Department of the Interior. Norman, 1948.

Knechtel, Maxwell McMichael, 1897-
... Manganese deposits of the Lyndhurst-Vesuvius district, Augusta and Rockbridge counties, Virginia, by Maxwell M. Knechtel ... Washington, U. S. Govt. print. off., 1943.
iv, 163-198 p. maps (part fold.) tables, diagrs. 23 cm. (U. S. Geological survey. Bulletin 940-F)
At head of title: U. S. Dept. of the interior Harold L. Ickes, secretary. Geological survey. W. E. Wrather, director ...
Reproduced from type-written copy.

Two of folded maps are in pocket on p. [3] of cover.
"Strategic minerals investigations, 1943 (Pages 163-198)"
Bibliographical foot-notes.
1. Manganese. 2. Mines and mineral resources Virginia - Augusta co. 3. Mines and mineral resources - Virginia Rockbridge co. I. Title. II. Title: Lyndhurst-Vesuvius district.

NK 0197966 Vi

Knechtel, Maxwell McMichael, 1897–
Mesozoic fossils of the Peruvian Andes, by Maxwell M. Knechtel, Edward F. Richards and Mary V. [i. e. J.] Rathbun. Ellsworth Expedition publication. Baltimore, Johns Hopkins Press, 1947.
150 p. illus., plates. 25 cm. (The Johns Hopkins University studies in geology, no. 15)
Bibliography: p. 135–139.
1. Paleontology—Mesozoic. 2. Paleontology—Peru. 3. Geology—Andes. I. Richards, Edward Franklin, 1903– II. Rathbun, Mary Jane, 1860–1943. III. Johns Hopkins University. Ellsworth Expedition to the Peruvian Andes, 1924. IV. Series.
QE731.K55 562 47-11254*

NK 0197967 DLC TxU OU NIC CU

Knechtel (O.) Uebungsbuch der freiwilligen Sanitäts-Colonnen der Krieger-Vereine, Samariter-Vereine, etc., für Wiederholungs-Kurse den Leitern und Führern, sowie zum Selbstgebrauch, zusammengestellt von ... vi, 40 pp. 12°. Leipzig, F. C. W. Vogel, 1891.

NK 0197968 DNLM

Knechtel, Paul, joint author.

TJ175 .J352 Jahr, Willy.
Grundzüge der Getriebelehre, von Willy Jahr und Paul Knechtel. 4., verb. und erweiterte Aufl. Leipzig, Fachbuchverlag, 1955–56.

TJ175 .J35 Knechtel, Paul.

Jahr, Willy.
Grundzüge der getriebelehre, auf anregung des Ausschusses für wirtschaftliche fertigung dargestellt von dipl.-ing. dr. Willy Jahr und dipl.-ing. Paul Knechtel ... Leipzig, M. Jänecke, 1930–1943.

Knechtel, Ried, 1908–
Universal's fundamental method for the cello, a graded elementary course by Ried Knechtel, edited by Milton James. [New York] Universal music publishers [1942]
cover-title, 52 p. illus. 30½cm.
Publisher's plate no.: U108-48.

1. Violoncello—Methods. I. James, Milton, ed.
[Full name: Christian Ried Knechtel]
43-10824
Library of Congress MT302.K6U6
[2] 787.3

NK 0197971 DLC OO

Knechtel, Ried, 1908–
Universal's fundamental method for the viola, a graded elementary course, by Ried Knechtel ... Edited by Milton James. [New York] Universal music publishers [°1942]
cover-title, 52 p. illus. 31cm.
Publisher's plate no.: U 107-46.

1. Viola—Methods. I. James, Milton, ed.
[Full name: Christian Ried Knechtel]
43-7635
Library of Congress MT282.K53U5
[2] 787.2

NK 0197972 DLC

Knechtel, Ried, 1908–
Universal's Fundamental method for the violin; a graded elementary course, by Ried Knechtel ... [New York city] Universal music publishers [°1940]
cover-title, 52 p. illus. 30½ x 23cm.

1. Violin—Methods. I. Title.
[Full name: Christian Ried Knechtel]
42-2694
Library of Congress MT262.K72U7
[2] 787.1

NK 0197973 DLC

QL 591 R8 K68 Knechtel, Wilhelm.
Oekologisch-zoogeographisches Studium an Coleopteren des rumänischen Faunengebietes, von Wilhelm K. Knechtel und Sergius A. Panin. Bucuresti, Imprimeria natională, 1944.
219 p. fold. map. 25 cm. (Académie Roumaine. Études et recherches. 15)

1. Beetles - Rumania. I. Title. II. Panin, Sergius A. III. Series: Academia Romănă, Bucharest. Études et recherches. no. 15.

NK 0197974 NIC NN CU MH NNM

422.59 B85 v.8 no.1 Knechtel, Wilhelm.
Thysanoptera. [Bucureşti, 1951.
259 p. illus. (Bucharest. Academia Republicii Populare Române. Fauna Republicii Populare Române. Insecta. v.8, no.1) (07)

NK 0197975 DNAL

VOLUME 300

Knechtl, Bohumir,
Třicet let našeho zápasu v Olomouci. V Olomouci, Nákladem Vydavatelstva deníku "Pozor", 1923.
291 p.

1. Olomouc, Moravia - History. 2. Bohemia - Nationality.

NK 0197976 NNC

Knechtl, Fritz Ch., ed.

Sozialversicherungsrechtliche entscheidungen ...

Wien, F. C. Knechtl ,19

Knechtli, Ernst.
Die hypothekarverschuldung im kanton Appenzell a.-Rh., unter besonderer berücksichtigung der landwirtschaftlichen bodenverschuldung ... von Ernst Knechtli ... Zürich, E. Lang, 1941.
107 p. fold. tables. 21cm.
Inaug.-diss.—Bern.
"Literaturverzeichnis": p. 106-107.

1. Mortgages—Appenzell Ausserrhoden (Canton) 2. Real property—Appenzell Ausserrhoden (Canton) I. Title.
44-30498
Library of Congress HG2051.S9K6

NK 0197978 DLC NN

Knechtli, Pierre
see Domec, Pierre, 1920-

Knechtli, Ronald Charles, 1927-
Microwave reactance tubes. Princeton, N. J., RCA Laboratories, 1955.
iv, 121 p. diagrs. 28 cm.
Thesis—Swiss Federal Institute of Technology, Zurich.
Vita.
Bibliography: p. 119-120.
Includes bibliography.

1. Microwave tubes. I. Title.
TK7872.V3K55 62-46349

NK 0197980 DLC CtY NN NNC

Knedel, Franz.
Die versicherungsbedingungen der in Österreich-Ungarn operierenden lebensversicherungsgesellschaften in vergleichender übersicht, hrsg. von Franz Knedel ... [5. aufl.] Wien, In kommission bei Gerold & comp., 1904.
187 p. incl. tables (part fold.) 22½cm.

1. Insurance, Life—Policies.
5—34204
Library of Congress HG8861.K6

NK 0197981 DLC ICJ

Knedler, John Warren, 1901- ed.
Masterworks of science; digests of 13 great classics, edited by John Warren Knedler, jr. Garden City, N. Y., Doubleday & company, inc., 1947.
ix, 637 p. illus. (incl. maps) diagrs. 22cm. [Masterworks series]
"First edition."
CONTENTS.—The elements, by Euclid.—On floating bodies, and other propositions, by Archimedes.—On the revolution of the heavenly spheres, by Nikolaus Copernicus.—Dialogues concerning two new sciences, by Galileo.—Principia, by Isaac Newton.—The atomic theory, by John Dalton.—Principles of geology, by Charles Lyell.—The origin of species, by Charles Darwin.—Experimental researches of electricity, by Michael Faraday.—Experiments in plant-hybridization, by G. J. Mendel.—The periodic law, by D. I. Mendeleyev.—Radioactivity, by Marie Curie.—Relativity: the special and general theory, by Albert Einstein.
1. Science—Collected works. I. Title.
Q111.K47 508 47-3691

OrU WaT MiU CU WaSpG
OrCS WaE WaS WaSp OrPS NcGU GAT NcRS MeB NcD NcU
NK 0197982 DLC OKentU CaBVa MtBuM MiHM MB ICU Wa

Knee, Ernest.
Mexico: Laredo to Guadalajara. New York, Hastings House [1951]
96 p. (chiefly illus.) map (on lining paper) 23 cm.

1. Mexico—Descr. & trav.—Views.
F1215.K7 917.2 51-5662

NK 0197983 DLC TxU IU CU-B AAP OkU NN MH

Knee, Ernest.
Santa Fe, New Mexico, by Ernest Knee. New York, Hastings house [1942]
101 p. front., illus. (incl. ports.) 21 x 16cm.
Illustrations: p. 4-101.

1. Santa Fé, N. M.—Descr.—Views. 42-22056
Library of Congress F804.S2K6
[10] 917.89

OO OLak
NK 0197984 DLC WaS Or WaT TxU NIC CU-B MoU OCl OU

Knee, Gina.
Monkey in the mirror, a satirical comedy in one act, by Gina Knee ... New York, N. Y., Los Angeles, Calif., S. French; [etc., etc.] °1941.
35, [1] p. plates, diagr. 18½cm.

I. Title. 41-25640
Library of Congress PS3521.N35M6 1941
[3] 812.5

NK 0197985 DLC

LD 2668 R4 1955 K68

Knee, Loren Billy.
Metal spinning practice and problems.
49 l. (K.S.U. Master's Report, 1955)

NK 0197986 KMK

Knee, Ruth I., ed.

HV689 .A54 1954

American Association of Psychiatric Social Workers.
Better social services for mentally ill patients; proceedings of [the] institute on social work in psychiatric hospitals, Lake Forest Academy, Lake Forest, Illinois, June 12-18, 1954. Sponsored by American Association of Psychiatric Social Workers, assisted by a grant from the National Institute of Mental Health, National Institutes of Health, Public Health Service [and] Department of Health, Education, and Welfare. Ruth I. Knee, editor. [New York, 1955]

The knee: anatomy, injuries, treatment
see under [Boughton, Lloyd L

Kneebone, Leon Russell.
An investigation of basidiospore germination in the Hymenomycetes, especially in the Agaricaceae. Ann Arbor, University Microfilms, 1950.
([University Microfilms, Ann Arbor, Mich.] Publication no. 2249)
Microfilm copy of typescript. Positive.
Collation of the original, as determined from the film: 109 l. illus.
Thesis—Pennsylvania State College.
Bibliography: leaves 103-109.

1. Agaricaceae. 2. Germination. 3. Spores (Botany)
Microfilm AC-1 no. 2249 Mic 51-374

NK 0197989 DLC NIC DNAL

Kneebone, Peter, 1923-
Look before you elope. [L] Longmans [1952]

[94 p.] illus.

NK 0197990 MH

Kneebusch, *Karl, d. 1902.*
Fuehrer durch das Sauerland, Ruhr- und Lennethal, von Dr. Kneebusch... Dortmund: O. Uhlig, 1885. viii, 60 p. map. 2. ed., rev. 16°.

1. Ruhr valley—Guide books, 1885. 2. Sauerland, Germany—Guide books, 1885.
N. Y. P. L. September 9, 1926

NK 0197991 NN

Kneebusch, Karl, *d.* 1902.
Führer durch das Sauerland, Siegerland, Wittgensteiner Land, Bergische und Ober-bergische Land, Waldeck und das Gebiet der unteren Ruhr, vereinigt mit Krachts "Sauerländischem Wanderbuch." Bearb. von Hugo Kracht. Wintersport in Sauerlande. 23. Aufl. Iserlohn, Sauerland-Verlag, 1950.
448 p. (p. 417-448 advertising matter) illus., maps (1 fold. col. in pocket) 16 cm. (Grosser amtlicher Führer des Sauerländischen Gebirgs-Vereins)
Bibliography: p. 47-48.
1. Sauerland—Descr. & trav.—Guide-books. 2. Bergisches Land—Descr. & trav.—Guide-books. I. Kracht, Hugo. Sauerlandisches Wanderbuch. (Series: Sauerländischer Gebirgs-Verein, Iserlohn. Grosser amtlicher Führer)
DD491.W5K6 1950 54-30671

NK 0197992 DLC

Kneece, Eunice E
From a radio program to a city-wide project [by] Eunice E. Kneece... [Chapel Hill, 1939] p. [176]-182. illus. 25cm.
Caption-title.
Excerpt: The High school journal. vol. XXII, no. 5. May, 1939.

1. Radio in education—U. S.
N. Y. P. L. October 22, 1948

NK 0198001 NN

Kneece, Eunice E.
. . . Report on radio education, by Eunice Kneece . . . [Greensboro, N. C., 1937] 11 f. 28cm.

1. Radio in education.
N. Y. P. L. May 7, 1947

NK 0198002 NN

Kneece, Mrs. J. F.
See
Kneece, Mattie (Crouch)

Kneece, *Mrs.* Mattie (Crouch)
The contributions of C. G. Memminger to the cause of education, by Mattie Crouch Kneece (Mrs. J. F. Kneece) [Columbia, S. C.] University extension division, University of South Carolina, 1926.
84 p. front. (port.) illus. 23cm. (*On cover:* Bulletin of the University of South Carolina ... no. 177. Feb. 15, 1926)
Bibliography: p. 83-84.

1. Memminger, Christopher Gustavus, 1803-1888. 2. Education—South Carolina—Hist.
26-27345
Library of Congress LA2317.M4K6

NK 0198004 DLC OrU FTaSU NcU ViU PU OCU

VOLUME 300

Kneedler, Grace M

Legislative councils and commissions. ₍Berkeley, Calif.₎ 1939.
34 l. 28cm. (Bureau of Public Administration, University of California. 1939 Legislative problems, no. 12)
Mimeographed.
Bibliographical foot-notes.
"Selected reading list": leaves 29-31.

1. Legislation—California. 2. Legislative councils. 3. California. Legislature—Committees. I. Ser.

NK 0198005 ViU ICU MH ViU-L MiU

Kneedler, Grace M

Severance taxation. ₍Berkeley, Calif.₎ 1939.
58 l. 28cm. (Bureau of Public Administration, University of California. 1939 Legislative problems, no. 11)
Mimeographed.
Bibliographical foot-notes.
Bibliography: leaves 56-58.

1. Taxation—California. I. Title. II. Ser.

NK 0198006 ViU ICU PP OrU

Kneedler, H S.

The coast country of Texas; a general study of the region, together with a brief outline of its history, its agricultural and historical possibilities, its socal conditions and inducements to home-seekers. By H. S. Kneedler. Cincinnati, O., The A. H. Pugh printing company, 1896.
2 p. l., ₍3₎-76 p. illus. (incl. map) 23½cm.
Printed seal of Southern Pacific railroad company on cover.
1. Texas—Descr. & trav. I. Southern Pacific company.
9—1958
Library of Congress F391.K68

NK 0198007 DLC NcD OO MB MWA

F868 M7K5 Kneedler, H S
Monterey County, California. San Francisco, Sunset Magazine Homeseekers' Bureau [1909?]
31 p. illus. 18cm.
Cover title.

1. Monterey Co., Calif. - Description and travel.

NK 0198008 CU-B

Kneedler, H.S.

Hoover, John F.
Souvenir and annual for 1881-82, containing ... brief biographies of the faculties of the State university of Iowa and of prominent citizens of Iowa City and Johnson county ... also, sketches of orders and societies of the city ... Comp., ed., and pub. by J. F. Hoover, H. S. Kneedler and C. J. Faust. Iowa City ₍Printed at Republican steam printing house, ᶜ1882₎

Kneedler, H S
Through storyland to sunset seas; what four people saw on a journey through the southwest to the Pacific coast. Cinn., 1893.
205 p., illus. O.

NK 0198010 TxH CSmH

Kneedler, H S.

Through storyland to sunset seas; what four people saw on a journey through the Southwest to the Pacific coast. By H. S. Kneedler ... Chicago, Knight, Leonard & co., printers, 1895.
2 p. l., ₍3₎-205 p. illus. 23½cm.

1. Southwest, New—Descr. & trav. 2. Southwest, Old—Descr. & trav. I. Title.

Library of Congress F786.K68 Rc—549

ICJ Nh
NK 0198011 DLC OrHi NIC CtY TxU OC1W OC1WHi MWA MB

Kneedler, H S
Through storyland to sunset seas; what four people saw on a journey through the Southwest to the Pacific coast. Cin. Pugh, 1896.

NK 0198012 OC1 PPF

Kneedler, H S.
Through storyland to sunset seas; what four people saw on a journey through the Southwest to the Pacific coast. By H. S. Kneedler ... Cincinnati, A. H. Pugh Print. Co., 1898.
2 p. l., ₍3₎-205 p. illus. 23½cm.

NK 0198013 CU-B

Kneedler, H S
Through storyland to sunset seas; what four people saw on a journey through the Southwest to the Pacific coast. By H. S. Kneedler ... Cincinnati, Pugh, 1900.
[3]-205[3]p.illus.23cm.

Title-page (cover title?) lacking.

1. Southwest, New--Descr. & trav. 2. Southwest, Old--Descr. & trav. I. Title.

NK 0198014 OC

Kneedler, Harry Lane,
Charles Thomson, by Harry Lane Kneedler. ₑPhiladelphia, Pa.ₒ 1940.

iv. 114p. 28 1/2cm.

NK 0198015 PPT

Law Kneedler, Henry S., complainant.

Pennsylvania. *Supreme court.*
Opinions of the judges of the Supreme court of Pennsylvania, on the constitutionality of the Act of Congress of March 3, 1863, "For enrolling and calling out the national forces, and for other purposes." Philadelphia, Kay & brother, 1864.

WZ 100 qK681 KNEEDLER, William L 1856-

A collection of miscellaneous bio-bibliographical material on this person, together with abstracts, résumés, etc. of his works, may be found on the shelves under the above call number.

NK 0198017 DNLM

Kneeland, Abner, 1774-1844.
The American definition spelling book: in which the words are not only rationally divided into syllables, accurately accented, the various sounds of the vowels, represented by figures, and their parts of speech properly distinguished, but the definition or signification affixed to each word; upon a plan agreeable to Mr. Noah Webster's easy standard. Designed for the use of schools. By Abner Kneeland, school-master. 1st ed. ... Keene, New-hampshire, Printed by John Prentiss, for the author, 1802.
vi, ₍7₎-179, ₍1₎ p. 18½cm.
1. Spellers. I. Title.
CA 17-3018 Unrev'd
Library of Congress PE1144.K68

NK 0198018 DLC

Kneeland, Abner, 1774-1844.
The American definition spelling-book; in which the words are not only rationally divided into syllables, accurately accented, the various sounds or the vowels represented by figures, and their parts of speech properly distinguished, but the definition or signification affixed to each word; upon a plan agreeable to Mr. Noah Webster's easy standard. Designed for the use of schools. By Abner Kneeland ... Kingsbery & Blake's 1st ed., with many corrections and improvements, by the author ... Windsor, (Vermont,) Printed by Nahum Mower, 1804.
vii, ₍1₎, 9-249, ₍3₎ p. 17cm.
1. Spellers. I. Title.
CA 17-3017 Unrev'd
Library of Congress PE1144.K7

NK 0198019 DLC PU MH MiU

Kneeland, Abner, 1774-1844.
American definition spelling book...upon a plan agreeable to Mr. Noah Webster's Easy standard...Concord, Hough, 1809.

211 p.

NK 0198020 PU-Penn Nh PU

LT PE1144 .K67 Kneeland, Abner, 1774-1844.
The American definition spelling book ... the definition or signification affixed to each word. Carefully rev. and compared with the most approved authorities. Designed for the use of schools. ... Hough's 4th ed. Concord, G. Hough ₍c1813₎
168 p.

NK 0198021 ICU

Kneeland, Abner, 1774-1844.
The American definition spelling book: in which the words are not only rationally divided into syllables, accurately accented, the various sounds of the vowels represented by figures, and their parts of speech properly distinguished, but the definition or signification affixed to each word: carefully revised and compared with the most approved authorities. Designed for the use of schools. By Abner Kneeland. Hough's second edition. Concord: G. Hough, 1814. 213 p. 16½cm.
Imperfect: p. 209-212 wanting; p. 213 mutilated.

928292A. 1. English language—Spelling books, American.
N. Y. P. L. June 9, 1938

NK 0198022 NN MH MB IU NcD

428.1 K68 Kneeland, Rev. Abner, 1774-1844.
The American definition spelling book ... Hough's 2d ed. Concord: Printed and published by George Hough. Sold at his book-store, wholesale and retail. Sold also by D. Cooledge, and I. & W. R. Hill, Concord; ₑetc., etc.ₒ 1814.
213p. 18cm.

1. Spellers. I. Title.

NK 0198023 N

VOLUME 300

Kneeland, Abner, 1774-1844.
The American definition spelling book: in which the words are not only rationally divided into syllables, accurately accented ... but the definition or signifacation affixed to each word: carefully rev. and compared with the use of schools. By Abner Kneeland. Hough's 3d ed. Concord, N. H. [etc.] G. Hough, and Nathan Burrill, 1820.
189 p. 17.5cm.

First ed., 1802.

NK 0198024 NNC

Kneeland, Abner, 1774-1844.
The American definition spelling book: in which the words are not only rationally divided into syllables, accurately accented ... but the definition or signification affixed to each word. Carefully rev. and compared with the most approved authorities. Designed for the use of schools. By Abner Kneeland. Hough's 4th ed. Concord [N. H.] Printed and published by G. Hough, 1826.
168 p. 17.5cm.

First ed., 1802

NK 0198025 NNC

Kneeland, Abner, 1774-1844.
The American pronouncing spelling book; or, Sure guide to the true pronunciation of the English language ... By Abner Kneeland ... Philadelphia, The Author, 1825.
xi, [7], [15]-168 p. 18cm.

1. English language—Orthography and spelling. 2. Spellers.

NK 0198026 MB MeWC PPM PU

230.91 K68 Kneeland, Abner, 1774-1844.
Ancient universalism, as taught by Christ and his apostles; in reply to a pamphlet, entitled "Remarks on the distinguishing doctrine of modern universalism ... By Adam Empie ..." New-York: Printed at the office of the Gospel herald, no. 67 Chrystie-street. 1825.
64p. 22cm.

1. Universalism. 2. Empie, Adam, 1785-1860. Remarks on the distinguishing doctrine of modern universalism.

NK 0198027 N LU NCaS CSmH PPL MB ICN

Kneeland, Abner, 1774-1844, comp.
Appendix to a Selection of sacred poetry, consisting of psalms and hymns, from Watts, Doddridge, Merrick, Scott, Cowper, Barbauld, Steele and others. Philadelphia, R. H. Small, 1828.
vi, [7]-52 p. 15 cm.
Contains hymns 607-646.
Manuscript annotations.

NK 0198028 NNUT

Kneeland, Abner, 1774–1844.
A brief sketch of a new system of orthography, delineated in an orthographical chart, containing the alphabet and scheme of the New orthographer. In which the most serious objections against the system are fairly stated and fully answered. To which is added a specimen of the new orthography, reduced to practice. By Abner Kneeland... Walpole, N. H.: Nichols & Hale, 1807. 23 p. plate. 16°.

534202A. 1. English language—Spelling. June 22, 1931
N. Y. P. L.

NK 0198029 NN CtY NNC MWA MH PPAmP

Micro-film PE 19 Kneeland, Abner, 1774-1844.
A brief sketch of a new system of orthography, delineated in an orthographical chart, containing the alphabet and scheme of the New orthographer ... To which is added a specimen of the new orthography, reduced to practice. Walpole, N.H., Printed for the author by Nichols and Hale, 1807.

Negative; original in Columbia Univ. Library.

NK 0198030 ICU

252.091 K68 Kneeland, Abner, 1774-1844.
A charity sermon on the late fire at Savannah; delivered in the First independent church of Christ called Universalist, in Lombard street .. Philadelphia, Published for the Author, Adam Waldie, printed, 1820.

NK 0198031 NCaS

Kneeland, Abner, 1774-1844.
The child's scriptural catechism. For the use of families and schools. By Abner Kneeland, pastor of the first Universalist church and society in Charlestown, Mass. ... Charlestown: Mass. Printed by W.S. & H.Spear. For the author. For sale by Munroe & Francis, Cornhill, Boston [etc., etc.] Price 8 cents single, 80 cents a dozen, 2 dollars 67 cents a half hundred and 5 dollars a hundred. 1812.
36, [4] p. 13.5cm.
"Books sold by Abner Kneeland ..." [4] p. at end.

Based on Hosea Ballou's Child's scriptural catechism, published in 1810.-cf. Preface.

1. Catechisms. 2. Children's literature. I. t. II. Ptr.

NK 0198033 MiU-C

Kneeland, Abner, 1774–1844.
The child's spelling book: containing easy words, from one to four syllables. Intermixed with lessons of easy words ... Comp. for the use of schools and small children. By Abner Kneeland ... Keene, Newhampshire, Printed by John Prentiss for the author, 1802.
64 p. 14cm.

1. Spellers. I. Title.

CA 17-3016 Unrev'd

Library of Congress PE1144.K73

NK 0198034 DLC

BX9901 .C55 Kneeland, Abner, 1774-1844, ed.
The Christian messenger, devoted to doctrine, religion, and morality. v. 1-2, no. 51; Aug. 7, 1819-July 21, 1821. Philadelphia.

Kneeland, Abner, 1774-1844, *ed.*
The Columbian miscellany; containing a variety of important, instructive, and entertaining matter, chiefly selected out of the Philadelphia magazines, published in London in the years 1788 and 1789, calculated to promote true religion and virtue. Compiled for the use and benefit of the followers of Christ. By Abner Kneeland ... Keene, Newhampshire. Printed by John Prentiss, for the editor. 1804.
xix, [20]-408 p. 18cm.

1. The Philadelphia magazine. II. Title.

28-3074

Library of Congress BX9913.K5

NK 0198036 DLC MH Nh MB NN MiU-C PPL OClWHi MWA NNUT PMA MnU

KNEELAND, Abner, 1774-1844, comp.
The Columbian miscellany; containing a variety of matter, chiefly selected out of the Philadelphian magazines, published in London, in 1788 and 1789. Keene, Newhampshire, 1805.

12°.

NK 0198037 MH-AH

Kneeland, Abner, 1774-1844.
The eleven sermons...
see under Ballou, Hosea, 1771-1852.

289.1 K68 F Kneeland, Abner, 1774-1844.
Five words spoken with the understanding in Two Discourses, delivered at Langdon, New-Hampshire, July 22d. 1805... Walpole, N. Y., Published by the author, 1805. Charter & Hale printers.
32p.

NK 0198039 NCaS

Kneeland, Abner, 1774–1844.
A funeral sermon on the death of Captain Abijah Harding, who was killed by the fall of a tree, in Barre, Mass., February 23, 1826; aged 84 years: delivered...in the First Universalist church, in the city of New-York...March 12, 1826. By Abner Kneeland... New York: Fingh, 1826. 16 p. 20cm.

1. Harding, Abijah, d. 1826. December 30, 1943
N. Y. P. L.

NK 0198040 NN RPB DLC

BX9901 .G3 Kneeland, Abner, 1774-1844, ed.
The Gazetteer. v. 1; Jan. 7-Dec. 29, 1824. [Philadelphia]

Kneeland, Abner, 1774-1844, ed.
The Gospel visitant. Being principally original tracts on moral and religious subjects: in which an illustration of the gospel of God Our Saviour is attempted by arguments drawn from Scripture and reason. The whole directed to the promotion of piety and morality. By the Gloucester conference ... v. 1- June 1811-
Charlestown: Printed by William S. & Henry Spear, 1812-

BV450 .A3 1810 Rare bk. Coll. Kneeland, Abner, 1774-1844.
Universalist church of America.
Hymns, composed by different authors, at the request of the General convention of Universalists of the New England states and others ... 2d ed. Charlestown (Mass.), Printed for the committee, by Samuel T. Armstrong. Sold by A. Brown and W. Hovey, Charlestown; C. Steele, Salem; Charles Tappan, Portsmouth, N. H.; and by the booksellers, in general, in town and country. 1810.

BV450 .A3 1808 Rare bk. Coll. Kneeland, Abner, 1774-1844.
Universalist church of America.
Hymns, composed by different authors, by order of the General convention of Universalists of the New-England states and others. Adapted to public and private devotion ... Walpole, N. H., Printed for the Committee. By George W. Nichols. 1808.

VOLUME 300

K 684 .467 KNEELAND, ABNER, 1774-1844.
An introduction to the defence of Abner Kneeland, charged with blasphemy; before the Municipal court, in Boston, Mass., at the January term, in 1834. By Abner Kneeland, the defendant. Boston,1834.
43p.

Binder's title: Defence of Abner Kneeland.

ViU-L
NK 0198045 ICN IU MH NNU-W MiU TxDaM PPL PPB MiU-L

Kneeland, Abner, 1774-1844, ed.
Hē Kainē Diathēkē
see under Bible. N. T. Greek. 1822. (also 1823)

Kneeland, Abner, 1774-1844. **H.99c.66
Kneeland's Key to the new orthography.
— New York. Published and sold by the author . . . 1827. 96 pp. Illus. 32°.

E8380 — Orthography.

NK 0198047 MB

Micro-film PE 22 Kneeland, Abner, 1774-1844.
A key to the new system of orthography ...
New York, The author, 1827.

Negative; original in Boston Public Library.

NK 0198048 ICU

289.1 K68 Kneeland, Abner, 1774-1844.
A letter to Rev. Jeremiah Higbee, containing a few remarks upon his sermon delivered at Des S. Kingsbery's, Alstead, N. H., January 15, 1807. At the funeral of Mr. Benton. By Abner Kneeland Pastor of the Universalist Church of Christ in Langdon..... Walpole, N. H., From The Observatory Press, Charter & Hale, printers, 1807.
12p. 12 x 19 cm.

NK 0198049 NCaS

Kneeland, Abner, 1774-1844.
Letters in defence of divine revelation...
see under Ballou, Hosea, 1771-1852.

Kneeland, Abner, 1774-1844.
Minutes of a discussion on the question, "Is the punishment of the wicked absolutely eternal?" Between Rev. Abner Kneeland and Rev. W. L. M'Calla, which commenced at the First independent church of Christ called Universalist, in Lombard Street, Philadelphia, July 13th and concluded on the Friday following. Taken in shorthand by R. L. Jennings. [n.p.] 1824.
336p.

NK 0198051 ICRL NjNbS MWA NcRS OOC PPL DLC MiU-C

BX9943 A1 S4 Kneeland, Abner, 1774-1844
The mystery of Revelation unfolded; in a sermon delivered before the First Universalist Church in Philadelphia... in February, 1823... Also, A sermon delivered before the First Universalist Society in Cambridge (Mass.) ... in February, 1823, by Thomas Whittemore... Philadelphia, A. Kneeland, 1823.
30 p. 23cm.

In [Sermons and orations, chiefly by Universalist ministers. New York, etc. 1817-30]

NK 0198052 RPB

BV459 .K6 1832 Kneeland, Abner, 1774-1844.
National hymns, original and selected; for the use of those who are "slaves to no sect." Boston, Office of the Investigator, 1832.
iv, 140 p. 15cm.

1. Hymns, American. I. Title.

NK 0198053 ViU NNUT RPB

BV399 .F7K6 Kneeland, Abner,1774-1844.
National hymns, original and selected.
Boston,1834.

NK 0198054 DLC RPB

Kneeland, Abner, 1774-1844.
National hymns, original and selected; for the use of those who are "slaves to no sect." By Abner Kneeland. Stereotype ed. Boston, Office of the Boston investigator, 1836.
2 p. l., 140 p. 14cm.
Without music.

1. Hymns, English. I. Title. 20—1578

Library of Congress BV459.K6

NK 0198055 DLC NNUT

Kneeland, Abner, 1.74-1844, comp.
National hymns, original and selected; for the use of those who are "slaves to no sect." By Abner Kneeland. Stereotype edition. Boston, J.P. Mendum, 1870, [c.1834]
1 p.l., 140 p. 17 cm.
123 hymns; 17 doxologies; hymns numbered 124-169.
Book arranged in four divisions called Numbers 1-4.

NK 0198056 NNUT

Kneeland, Abner, 1774-1844, tr.
The New Testament; being the English only of the Greek-and-English Testament ...
see under Bible. N.T. English. 1822. Kneeland. (Also 1823)

Kneeland, Abner, 1774-1844, ed.
The Olive branch and Christian inquirer, devoted to science, religion and morality. Pub. weekly: by Rev. Abner Kneeland. v. 1, no. 1-26; May 17-Dec. 27, 1828. New-York, A. Kneeland, 1828.

Kneeland, Abner, 1774-1844.
An oration, delivered July 4, 1826, being the semicentural anniversary of the independence of the United States of America: before the societies assembled to celebrate the day. By Abner Kneeland, pastor of the First Universalist church in the city of New-York. New-York, Printed by J. Finch, 1826.
34 p. 21½cm.

1. Fourth of July orations.

Library of Congress E286.N6 1826 19-19571

NK 0198059 DLC NjNbS N PPL NN OClWHi

Kneeland, Abner, 1774-1884, comp.
The Philadelphia hymn book...
see under title

Microfilm 01104 no. 187 AP Kneeland, Abner, 1774-1844, ed.
The Philadelphia Universalist magazine and Christian messenger, devoted to doctrine, religion, and morality. v. 1-2; Aug. 1821-July 1823. Philadelphia, J. Young, printer.

Kneeland, Abner, 1774-1844.
Voltaire, François Marie Arouet de, 1694-1778.
A philosophical dictionary; from the French of m. de Voltaire. With additional notes, both critical and argumentative, by Abner Kneeland ... 1st American stereotyped ed. Boston, J. Q. Adams, 1836.

---

205 A505 Kneeland, Abner, 1774-1844.
Presbyterianism versus Presbyterianism, or a candid review of "An essay on the inability of sinners, by a Presbyterian," also A Pamphlet, entitled "Natural Ability consistent with Moral Inability: being remarks on 'An essay on the Inability of Sinners by a Presbyterian,' by a Christian." By Abner Kneeland... Second edition Philadelphia, Printed for the author, Adam Waldie, printer, 1817.
24p.

Bound with: American Baptist Magazine and Missionary Intelligencer, 1817 (n. s. v.1)

1. Universalism - Doctrinal and controversial works. I. An essay on the inability of sinners by a Presbyterian. II. Natural ability consistent with moral inability... III. Title

NK 0198064 NCaS

Kneeland, Abner, 1774-1844.
Presbyterianism versus Presbyterianism; or, A candid review of "An essay on the inability of sinners, by a Presbyterian", also a pamphlet, entitled "Natural ability consistent with moral inability: being remarks on 'An essay on the inability of sinners, by a Presbyterian', by a Christian", by Abner Kneeland ... Philadelphia, Printed for the author. Adam Waldie, printer, 1819.
24 p. 21 cm.

NK 0198065 ICU

Kneeland, Abner, 1774-1844.
Presbyterianism versus Presbyterianism; or, A candid review of "An essay on the inability of sinners, by a Presbyterian", also a pamphlet, entitled "Natural ability consistent with moral inability: being remarks on 'An essay on the inability of sinners, by a Presbyterian', by a Christian", by Abner Kneeland ... Second edition. Philadelphia, Printed for the author. Adam Waldie, printer, 1819.
24 p. 20cm.

1. Free will and determinism. 2. An essay on the inability of sinners. 3. Wilson, James Patriot, 1809-1889. Natural ability consistent with moral inability. I. Title. A 32-2178

Title from Portland, Me., Pub. Libr. Printed by L. C.

NK 0198066 MeP NcD PHa PPL PU PPAmP PPPrHi NN MB PU

VOLUME 300

BX9946 .B5 Kneeland, Abner, 1774-1844.

Bishop, Garry.

A public controversy, upon fair investigation of doctrines; or, Universalism weighed in the balance and found wanting; being the substance of a public debate, held at the Commissioners' hall, Northern liberties, Philadelphia; between the author and the Rev. Mr. A. Kneeland ... upon the important question whether the Scriptures teach us to believe in a punishment, or condemnation after death. By G. Bishop. Philadelphia, Printed for the author, 1822.

Kneeland, Abner, 1774-1844.

A refutation of the unmerciful doctrin [!] of endless misery; or A candid examination of certain equivocal terms on which the said doctrin[!] is supposed to rest ... To which is prefixed, a general epistle to the churches. By Abner Kneeland ... Manlius [N. Y.] Printed by L. Kellogg, 1816.

57, [3] p. 16 1|2 cm.

1. Future punishment. I. Title.

NK 0198068 CSmH MWA Nh

Kneeland, Abner, 1774-1844.

Remarks on pamphlet entitled A review, of an anonymous publication styled strictures, on a pamphlet entitled "A religious tract," Published by the Genesee missionary society ... By Jabez Chadwick, minister of the Gospel in Pompey. By Abnor Kneeland ... Manlius [N.Y.] Printed by Kellogg & Clark, 1817.

16 p. 17cm.

1. Chadwick, Jabez, b. 1779. A review of an anonymous publication styled "Strictures" I. Title.

NK 0198069 CSmH MWA

Kneeland, Abner, 1774-1844, defendant.

[Parker, Samuel Dunn] 1780-1873.

Report of the arguments of the attorney of the commonwealth, at the trials of Abner Kneeland, for blasphemy, in the Municipal and Supreme courts, in Boston, January and May, 1834. (Collected and published at the request of some Christians of various denominations.) ... [Boston] Printed by Beals, Homer & co., 1834.

Kneeland, Abner, 1774-1844.

A review of the evidences of Christianity: delivered in New York, 1829. N. Y., 1829. 12°

NK 0198071 NNUT OClWHi

Kneeland, Abner, 1774-1844.

Review of the evidences of christianity; in a series of lectures, delivered in New York, August 1829. Ed. 2. New York, 1830.

NK 0198072 PPWa

Kneeland, Abner, 1774-1844.

A review of the evidences of Christianity; in a series of lectures, delivered in Broadway hall, New-York, August, 1829. To which is prefixed, an extract from Wyttenbach's Opuscula, on the ancient notices of the Jewish nation previous to the time of Alexander the Great. By Abner Kneeland ... 3d ed. Boston, Office of the Investigator, 1831.

204 p. 19½cm.

1. Christianity—Controversial literature. 2. Free thought. I. Wyttenbach, Daniel Albert, 1746-1820. Opuscula. II. Title.

Library of Congress BL2775.K6 1831 38-37844
[2] 211

NK 0198073 DLC MWA ICRL

Kneeland, Abner, 1774-1844.

A review of the evidences of Christianity; in a series of lectures delivered in Broadway hall, N.Y. August, 1829. To which is prefixed an extract from Wyttenbach's Opuscula on the ancient notices of the Jewish nation previous to the time of Akexander the Great. 3d ed. Boston, Investigator, 1831.

204p.

NK 0198074 ICRL

BL2775 .K68 **Kneeland, Abner, 1774-1844.**

A review of the evidences of Christianity; in a series of lectures, delivered in Broadway Hall, New York, August, 1829. To which is prefixed an extract from Wyttenbach's Opuscula, on the ancient notices of the Jewish nation previous to the time of Alexander the Great. 5th ed. Boston, Published and sold at the office of the Investigator, 1833.

204p. 19cm.

1. Christianity. Controversial literature. 2. Free thought. I. Wyttenbach, Daniel Albert, 1746-1820. Opuscu

NK 0198075 IEG MH

Kneeland, Abner, 1774-1844.

A review of the evidences of Christianity; in a series of lectures, delivered in Broadway hall, New-York, August, 1829. To which is prefixed, an extract from Wyttenbach's Opuscula, on the ancient notices of the Jewish nation previous to the time of Alexander the Great. By Abner Kneeland ... 6th ed. Boston, Office of the Investigator, 1835.

204 p. 20cm.

1. Christianity—Controversial literature. 2. Free thought. I. Wyttenbach, Daniel Albert, 1746-1820. Opuscula. II. Title.

Library of Congress BL2775.K6 1835 38-37843
[2] 211

NK 0198076 DLC ICU

Kneeland, Abner, 1774-1844.

A review of the evidences of Christianity; in a series of lectures, delivered in Broadway hall, New York, August, 1829. To which is prefixed, an extract from Wyttenbach's Opuscula, on the ancient notices of the Jewish nation previous to the time of Alexander the Great. By Abner Kneeland ... 6th ed. Boston, Office of the Investigator [1835?]

204 p. 19cm.

1. Christianity—Controversial literature. 2. Free thought. I. Wyttenbach, Daniel Albert, 1746-1820. Opuscula. II. Title.

Library of Congress BL2775.K6 1835 a 38-37829
[2] 211

NK 0198077 DLC MoU ICN MH

Kneeland, Abner, 1774-1844.

A review of the trial, conviction, and final imprisonment in the common jail of the county of Suffolk, of Abner Kneeland, for the alleged crime of blasphemy. Written by himself. Boston, G. A. Chapman, 1838.

132 p. 19cm.

Library of Congress BL2790.K6A3 24-19741

NK 0198078 DLC PP PPB PPL PPT-L NN

BX 9943 .K55 **Kneeland, Abner, 1774-1844.**

A series of lectures on the doctrine of universal benevolence; delivered in the Universalist Church in Lombard Street, Philadelphia in the autumn of 1818. Philadelphia, Printed for the author by Clark & Raser, 1818.

204 p. front. (port.) 18 cm.

1. Universalism--Addresses, essays, etc. 2. Universalist Church of America. I. T.

NK 0198079 MH-AH IaU NCaS DLC OOC MWA MH PP PHi MH

BX 9943 .K55 1824 **Kneeland, Abner, 1774-1844.**

A series of lectures on the doctrine of universal benevolence; delivered in the Universalist Church in Lombard Street, Philadelphia in the autumn of 1818. 2d ed., with additional notes. Philadelphia, Printed for the author by Atkinson & Alexander, 1824.

232 p. 18 cm.

1. Universalism--Addresses, essays, etc. 2. Universalist Church of America. I. T.

NK 0198080 MH-AH CSmH PHi MH

Kneeland, Abner, 1774-1844.

A series of letters in defence of divine revelation...

see under Ballou, Hosea, 1771-1852.

---

*AC8 K7335 807s Kneeland, Abner, 1774-1844.

A sermon delivered before the Northern association of Universalists, convened at Bridport, Vt. on the second Wednesday and Thursday in June, 1807, upon the two covenants. By Abner Kneeland ... Walpole, N.H. Printed by Nichols & Hale. 1807.

22p. 22cm.

NK 0198082 MH NNUT

Kneeland, Abner. 1774-1844. 4346.11

A sermon, occasioned by the death of Mrs. Hastings . . . (In Hastings, Susanna. [A] narrative of the captivity of Mrs. Johnson . . . Pp. 113-127. Lowell. 1834.)

NK 0198083 MB

Kneeland, Abner, 1774-1844, defendant.

Dunlap, Andrew, 1794-1835.

A speech delivered before the Municipal court of the city of Boston, in defence of Abner Kneeland, on an indictment for blasphemy. January term, 1834. By Andrew Dunlap. Boston, Printed for the publisher, 1834.

Kneeland, Abner, 1774-1844, defendant.

Speech of Abner Kneeland, delivered before the Supreme court of the city of Boston, in his own defence, on an indictment for blasphemy. November term, 1834. Boston, J. Q. Adams, 1834.

32p. 21cm.

No.3 in pamphlet vol. [Kneeland defence]

NK 0198085 MiU-L NNU-W TxDaM ViU-L CtY PP PHi MH PBL ICN

Kneeland, Abner, 1774-1844.

Speech of Abner Kneeland, delivered before the full bench of judges of the Supreme court, in his own defence, for the alleged crime of blasphemy. Law term, March 8, 1836. Boston, J. Q. Adams, 1836.

viii, [9]-44 p. 21½cm.

6-24687†

NK 0198086 MnU DLC OU TxDaM PPL OClWHi NNU-W MB NN ICN

VOLUME 300

Kneeland, Abner, 1774-1844.
Strictures on strictures, in a letter to the Rev. Dr. Benjamin Farnham, containing an answer to his reply to the remarks of the author on the Rev. Jeremiah Higbee's sermon, delivered at the funeral of Mr. Benton, at Alstead, N. H. By Abner Kneeland, ... Walpole, N. H. Printed for the author, by G. W. Nichols. 1808.
21 p. 16 1|2 cm.

1. Farnham, Benjamin. I. Title.

NK 0198087 CSmH

C 6592 .916 KNEELAND, ABNER, 1774-1844.
The substance of a sermon, on the doctrine of atonement; delivered in the Universalist church, Prince-street, New-York, on the evening of the 27th of Nov. 1825... New-York, Gospel herald, 1826.
16p. 23cm.

Binder's title: Universalist pamphlets.

NK 0198088 ICN MH-AH LU DLC

---

230 K68t Kneeland, Abner, 1774-1844.
Three sermons; delivered in the First Universalist Church, in the city of New-York, on Easter Sunday, March 26, 1826, in which is embodied a brief portraiture of Christian theology. New-York, J. Finch, printer, 1826.
iv, 42 p. 23 cm.

1. God. 2. Jesus Christ. Resurrection.

NK 0198089 N MiU-C DLC

Kneeland, Bertha Louise (Junkins), and F. E. Kneeland, comps.
The Kneeland miscellany; a heterogeneous collection consisting of father's and mother's songs, genealogical notes of the Crockett and Heagan families and incidents of family history, together with extracts from the first census, historical notes regarding the Porter district, &c., compiled by Bertha J. and Frank E. Kneeland, 1914–17. [Brooklyn, N. Y., 1917] vii, 392 f. 28½cm.

Typewritten.

802193A. 1. Kneeland family. 2. Crockett family. 3. Heagan family. 4. Poetry, American—Collections. I. Kneeland, Frank Elmer, 1870– , jt. comp.
N. Y. P. L. April 17, 1936

NK 0198090 NN

Kneeland, Clarissa Abia, 1878–
Smugglers' Island and the devil fires of San Moros, by Clarissa A. Kneeland; with illustrations by Wallace Goldsmith. Boston and New York, Houghton Mifflin company, 1915.
3 p. l., 356, [2] p. front., illus. 20½cm. $1.25

I. Title.
Library of Congress PZ7.K733S 15—24857

NK 0198091 DLC MB NN PP

Kneeland, Clarissa Abia, 1878–
... Smugglers' Island and the devil fires of San Moros, by Clarissa A. Kneeland, with illustrations by F. C. Yohn and Wallace Goldsmith. Boston and New York, Houghton Mifflin company, 1928.
4 p. l., 354, [1] p. col. front., illus., col. plates. 22cm. (Riverside bookshelf)

I. Title.
Library of Congress PZ7.K733S 9 28-22134

NK 0198092 DLC OClh OEac OLak MB WaS

Kneeland, Frank E.

Webster, F. S., company.
Catalogue of the F. S. Webster company; typewriters of all kinds, and our galaxy of stars ... By Frank E. Kneeland ... Boston, New York [etc., F. S. Webster company, 1898]

Kneeland, Frank Elmer, 1870–
A Colombian diary; a description of a trip to and life in Colombia's capital during the troublous times of a typical South American revolution, with much "inside history" concerning the same, by Frank Elmer Kneeland. [n. p., cop. 1909] vii, 421 f., 10 l. 29cm., and album of photographs. 26 x 31½cm.

Typewritten.
Photograph (port.) inserted as front.

802449-50A. 1. Colombia—Descr. and trav., 1900– 2. Bogota, Colombia—Descr. 3. Colombia—Views. I. Title.
N. Y. P. L. March 4, 1936

NK 0198094 NN

[KNEELAND, FRANK ELMER,] 1870–
A Mexican diary; an intimate relation of a composite year's experiences in Mexico, by Frank Elmer [pseud.] New York, 1916. 462 f. 28½cm.

Reproduced from typewritten copy.

802448A. 1. Mexico—Descr. and trav., 1910– . I. Title.

NK 0198095 NN

Kneeland, Frank H *comp.*
... Getting out the coal; stripping—underground mining—loading machines—roof support, compiled by Frank H. Kneeland ... 1st ed. New York [etc.] McGraw-Hill book company, inc., 1926.
vii, 403 p. illus., diagrs. 21cm. (Practical coal production) $3.00

1. Coal mines and mining. I. Title.
Library of Congress TN802.K55 26-9797

NK 0198096 DLC Wa CaBVaU ViU PP PPGi NN OCl OU MB ICJ MiHM

Kneeland, Frank H.
... Mine transportation and market preparation; mine transportation—hoisting and hoisting equipment—coal preparation, compiled by Frank H. Kneeland ... 1st ed. New York [etc.] McGraw-Hill book company, inc., 1926.
vii, 354 p. illus., diagrs. 21cm. (Practical coal production) $3.00

1. Coal mines and mining. I. Title.
Library of Congress TN331.K5 26-13178

NK 0198097 DLC PP OCl OU ICJ MB MiHM OrP WaS CaBVaU

Kneeland, Frank H *comp.*
Mining equipment and mine organization and safety, comp. and written by Frank H. Kneeland ... Ventilating equipment, by W. M. Weigel ... Erecting work, comp. and written by Hubert E. Collins ... New York [etc.] McGraw-Hill book company, inc. [°1915]
[288] p. illus., diagrs. 22cm. (*Half-title:* Library of coal mining and engineering)
Various paging.

1. Mining engineering. 2. Coal mines and mining. 3. Mine ventilation. 4. Machinery—Erecting work. I. Weigel, William Melvin, 1878– II. Collins, Hubert Edwin, 1872–
Library of Congress TN145.K6 15—19987

NK 0198098 DLC PP ICJ

Kneeland, Frank H.
Practical coal production. New York, (etc.) 1926.

NK 0198099 DN

Kneeland, Frank H.
... Preliminaries of coal mining; prospecting—explosives—development—drainage—ventilation, compiled by Frank H. Kneeland ... 1st ed. New York [etc.] McGraw-Hill book company, inc., 1926.
vii, 419 p. illus., diagrs. 21cm. (Practical coal production) $3.00

1. Coal mines and mining. I. Title.
Library of Congress TN802.K6 1926 26-1377

NK 0198100 DLC PP PPGi OCl OClW OU DN ICJ MB MiHM Wa MtBuM

M780 M62 no.26 Vault Kneeland, Fred
Shriners' march to Mecca; two step, composed by Fred Kneeland. Arranged for band and orchestra by Frank Thompson. Detroit, Mich., Central Music Pub. Co. [c1896]
5p. 36cm. ([Michigan sheet music collection] no. 26)
For voice and piano.
"Dedicated to the Shriners of the United States by Noble A.F.R. Arndt."
1.Ancient Arabic Order of the Nobles of the Mystic Shrine for North America-Songs and music. I.Thompson, Frank. II.Arndt, A.F.R.

NK 0198101 Mi

Kneeland, Frederick Newton.
Drives in Northampton and vicinity ... by F. N. Kneeland. Northampton, Mass., Gazette printing co., 1888.
1 p. l., iv, [5]-61 p. illus., fold. maps. 24 x 12cm.

1. Northampton, Mass.—Descr. 2. Hampshire co., Mass.—Descr. & trav.
Library of Congress F74.N86K6 1-11544 rev.

NK 0198102 DLC NcD OClWHi

[Kneeland, Frederick Newton]
Northampton, the meadow city; over two hundred and fifty illustrations. Northampton, Mass., F. N. Kneeland and L. P. Bryant [°1894]
107, [1] p. incl. front., illus. 31½ x 24cm.
Includes contributions by various writers.

1. Northampton, Mass. I. Title.
Library of Congress F74.N86K7 1-11545

NK 0198103 DLC MnHi CLSU MiU ICN

Kneeland, Frederick Newton.
White mountain glimpses, by Frederick N. Kneeland ... [Florence, Mass., The Bryant printing co.] Pub. by the author, 1896.
56 p. incl. front., illus. 16 x 24cm.

1. White mountains.
Library of Congress F41.5.K68 1-8825 Revised

NK 0198104 DLC

VOLUME 300

Kneeland, George Jackson, 1872–
... Commercialized prostitution in New York city, by George J. Kneeland; with a supplementary chapter by Katharine Bement Davis ... introduction by John D. Rockefeller, jr. ... New York, The Century co., 1913.
xii, 334 p. tables, diagrs. 21cm. (Publications of the Bureau of social hygiene)
"The first of four studies dealing with various aspects of the problem of prostitution."—Introd.

1. Prostitution—New York (City) I. Davis, Katharine Bement.
13—11647
Library of Congress HQ146.N7K5

NK 0198105 DLC Or FMU DNLM TxU PBm PPULC PPC NcD ICJ MB NjP NN ViU MH GU CU WU-M CaBViP IdB

Kneeland, George Jackson, 1872–
... Commercialized prostitution in New York city, by George J. Kneeland, with a supplementary chapter by Katharine Bement Davis ... introduction by John D. Rockefeller, jr. ... New ed. rev. to date. New York, The Century co., 1917.
xii, 344 p. diagrs. 21cm. (Publications of the Bureau of social hygiene) $1.30

1. Prostitution—New York (City) I. Davis, Katharine Bement.
17—10889
Library of Congress HQ146.N7K5 1917

NK 0198106 DLC ViU ICRL PPRCl MiU OCU OCl OClW MtU

Kneeland, George Jackson, 1872-

New York. Committee of fourteen.
The social evil in New York city; a study of law enforcement by the Research committee of the Committee of fourteen. New York, A. H. Kellogg co., 1910.

KNEELAND, GERTRUDE A.
Let no man; a modern comedy-drama in three acts, by Gertrude A.Kneeland. Milwaukee, Wis., U.S.A.: The Catholic dramatic movement, 1935. 88 p. 18½cm. [Library of Catholic plays]

1. Drama, American. I. Title. II. Ser.

NK 0198108 NN DLC KAS

KNEELAND, GERTRUDE A.
Retribution; a comedy-drama in three acts, by Gertrude A. Kneeland. Milwaukee, Wis., U.S.A.: The Catholic Dramatic Movement, 1934. 83 p. 18½cm. ([Library of Catholic plays])

807106A. 1. Drama, American. I. Title. II. Ser.

NK 0198109 NN DLC RPB

F
02844
.466
KNEELAND, HARRIET I.
Some old Northampton homes... Northampton, 1909.
27p. 21½cm.

"Written for Betty Allen chapter of the D.A.R."

NK 0198110 ICN

Kneeland, Henry T
A plan for clearances of stocks and securities, and differences between dealers, on the New York stock exchange, by Henry T. Kneeland ... New York, P. F. McBreen, printer, 1885.
22 p. 22½cm.

1. New York Stock-exchange. 2. Clearing-house.
7-777
Library of Congress HG4631.K6

NK 0198111 DLC

PS1918
.A65
1923
Kneeland, Henry Tracy.

Lafcadio Hearn's brother.
(In The Atlantic monthly. Boston. 25cm. v. 131, no. 1 (Jan. 1923) p. 20-27)
Letters from Lafcadio Hearn to his brother James Daniel Hearn.

I. Hearn, Lafcadio, 1850-1904. II. Hearn, James Daniel, 1854-

NK 0198112 ViU NNC

Kneeland, Henry Tracy.
Paintings in Hartford collections
see under Wadsworth atheneum, Hartford.

Kneeland, Hildegarde, 1889-

U. S. *National resources committee. Industrial committee.*
Consumer expenditures in the United States; estimates for 1935-36. National resources committee. Washington, U. S. Govt. print. off., 1939.

Kneeland, Hildegarde, 1889-

U. S. *National resources committee. Industrial committee.*
Consumer incomes in the United States: their distribution in 1935-36. National resources committee. Washington, U. S. Govt. print. off., 1938.

Kneeland, Hildegarde, 1889-

U. S. *National resources committee.*
Family expenditures in the United States. Statistical tables and appendixes. A National resources committee publication released by the National resources planning board. Washington, U. S. Govt. print. off., 1941.

Kneeland, Hildegarde, 1889 -
... The feeding of children, by Hildegarde Kneeland ... Columbia, Mo., University of Missouri, 1917.
12 p. 23cm. (The University of Missouri bulletin. v. 18, no. 8. Extension ser. 23)
Bibliography: p. 12.

1. Children—Nutrition.
18-27210
Library of Congress RJ206.K6

NK 0198117 DLC PU OrU

BT309
K6
Kneeland, Ira Sprague, 1859-

Congenial hearts; holiday greeting by Rev. I. S. Kneeland. Buffalo, N. Y., The Hammond press, 1911.

[30]p. 21½cm.in23cm.

I. Title. 1. Imprints (in books)-Buffalo, N. Y.

NK 0198118 NBuG NRAB

Kneeland, Ira Sprague, 1859-
Rev, J. H. Miller; a hero of faith; a memorial prepared at the request of the Buffalo Baptist ministers' conference...Holland, N. Y., The Holland guide, 1918.
24 p.

NK 0198119 NRCR

Kneeland, John, ed.

Masterpieces of American literature; Franklin: Irving: Bryant: Webster: Everett: Longfellow: Hawthorne: Whittier: Emerson: Holmes: Lowell: Thoreau: O'Reilly; with biographical sketches. Boston and New York, Houghton, Mifflin and company, 1891.

Kneeland, Katharine Priscilla, 1906- joint author.
Huffaker, Carl L 1885–
... The elementary school teacher of Oregon, by C. L. Huffaker ... and Katharine P. Kneeland ... Eugene, The University [1929]

Kneeland, Louise Wenzel, 1859–
Sunlight and shadow, by Louise W. Kneeland. Boston, Sherman, French & company, 1914.
4 p. l., 93 p. 19½cm. $1.00
Poems.

I. Title.
14-14131
Library of Congress PS3521.N4S8 1914

NK 0198122 DLC NNUT PSC

BX9225
K58A3
Kneeland, Martin Dwelle, 1848-
Eighty-one years young. Introductions by Bishop S. G. Babcock, Rev. A. Z. Conrad [and] Hon. Robert Luce. Bangor, Me., Jordan-Frost Print. Co., 1930.
xiv, 191 p. port. 22 cm.

NK 0198123 MeB MA CtY-D NjP MB

Kneeland, Martin Dwelle, 1848–
Life begins at seventy, by Rev. Martin Dwelle Kneeland ... Claremont, Calif. [Printed at the Saunders studio press] 1937.
xi, 94 p. front., ports. 23cm.
"Second impression."

1. Old age. I. Title.
39-24846
Library of Congress BJ1691.K6 1937 a
——— Copy 2.
Copyright A 132024 [3] 179

NK 0198124 DLC NN

VOLUME 300

Kneeland, Martin Dwelle, 1848–
Ten reasons why in the beginning of the twentieth century a day of weekly rest & worship is peculiarly necessary. Address, N.Y., Woman's Natl. Sabbath Alliance, 1901. 2p. S.

NK 0198125 OO

Kneeland, Natalie, 1892–
Aprons and house dresses, by Natalie Kneeland ... Chicago & New York, A. W. Shaw company; [etc., etc.] 1925.
xxi, 141 p. illus. 21½cm. (*Half-title:* Merchandise manuals for retail salespeople, W. W. Charters, editor)
Contains "References".

1. Clothing and dress. 2. Salesmen and salesmanship. I. Title.
25—9782
Library of Congress HF5439.C6K5

MH-BA Or
NK 0198126 DLC NcRS PPD PPT MiU OCl OClCC ICJ MB

Kneeland, Natalie, 1892– ed.
HF5438 .K54
... The case method for teaching retail selling; a collection of cases on selling service, for the use of teachers and students of retail selling. Pittsburgh, Pa., 1923.

NK 0198127 DLC

Kneeland, Natalie, 1892–
Cases in retail salesmanship, by Natalie Kneeland ... Chicago & New York, A. W. Shaw company; [etc., etc.] 1924.
xv, 189 p. 21½cm. (*Half-title:* Merchandise manuals for retail salespeople, W. W. Charters, editor)
Contains "References."

1. Salesmen and salesmanship. I. Title.
24—32116
Library of Congress HF5438.K543

NN ICJ
NK 0198128 DLC MtU Or IdU NcRS NcD CU MiU OCl OCU

Kneeland, Natalie, 1892– 5639-547
Cases in retail salesmanship.
— Chicago. A. W. Shaw Co. 1926. xv, 189 pp. [Merchandise manuals for retail salespeople.] 20½ cm.
In the form of questions and answers.

NK 0198129 MB

Kneeland, Natalie, 1892–
Hoisery, knit underwear, and gloves, by Natalie Kneeland ... Chicago & New York, A. W. Shaw company; [etc., etc.] 1924.
xx, 126 p. illus. 21½cm. (*Half-title:* Merchandise manuals for retail salespeople, W. W. Charters, editor)

1. Hosiery. 2. Underwear. 3. Gloves. 4. Knit goods. 5. Salesmen and salesmanship.
24—32119
Library of Congress HF5439.H6K6

NN ICJ MB MtBC Or OrU
NK 0198130 DLC WaS CU NcRS PP PPD PPT MiU OCl ODW

Kneeland, Natalie.
Infants' and children's wear, by Natalie Kneeland ... Chicago & New York, A. W. Shaw company; [etc., etc.] 1925.
xxi, 187 p. illus. 21½cm. (*Half-title:* Merchandise manuals for retail salespeople, W. W. Charters, editor)
"References" at end of some of the chapters.

1. Infants—Clothing. 2. Clothing and dress. 3. Salesmen and salesmanship. I. Title. II. Title: Children's wear.
25—11195
Library of Congress HF5439.I 5K6

NK 0198130-1 DLC NN Or PP PPD PPT MiU OCl ODW MB ICJ

Kneeland, Natalie, 1892–
Millinery, by Natalie Kneeland ... Chicago & New York, A. W. Shaw company; [etc., etc.] 1925.
xviii, 145 p. illus. 21½cm. (*Half-title:* Merchandise manuals for retail salespeople, W. W. Charters, editor)

1. Millinery. 2. Salesmen and salesmanship.
25—8522
Library of Congress HF5439.M5K5

Or ICJ NN MB
NK 0198131 DLC WaT IdU AAP PPD PPT NcRS MiU OCl ODW

Kneeland, Natalie, 1892–
Negligees, by Natalie Kneeland ... Chicago & New York, A. W. Shaw company; [etc., etc.] 1925.
xxii, 156 p. illus. 21½cm. (*Half-title:* Merchandise manuals for retail salespeople, W. W. Charters, editor)
"References" at end of some of the chapters.

1. Clothing and dress. 2. Salesmen and salesmanship. I. Title.
25—11193
Library of Congress HF5439.N35K6

NK 0198132 DLC PP PPD PPT MiU OClW ICJ MB

Kneeland, Natalie, 1892–
Self-estimates of improvement in repeated tasks, by Natalie Kneeland ... New York, 1934.
76 p. diagrs. 24½cm.
Thesis (PH. D.)—Columbia university, 1934.
Vita.
Published also as Archives of psychology, no. 163.
Bibliography: p. 75.

1. Psychology, Physiological. I. Title.
34-30521
Library of Congress LB1131.K62 1934
Columbia Univ. Libr. [2] [159.94373] 158.433

NK 0198133 NNC MiU OCl ODW WaTC DLC

Kneeland, Natalie, 1892–
Self-estimates of improvement in repeated tasks, by Natalie Kneeland ... New York, 1934.
75 p. diagrs. 25cm. (Archives of psychology ... no. 163)
Issued also as thesis (PH. D.) Columbia university.
Bibliography: p. 75.

1. Psychology, Physiological. I. Title.
34-30520
Library of Congress BF21.A7 no. 163
[(159.9082)] [2] (150.82) [159.94373] 158.433

NK 0198134 DLC PBm PU ViU

Kneeland, Natalie, 1892–
Selling to today's customer, by Natalie Kneeland ... Louise Bernard ... and Gerald B. Tallman ... illustrated by Fred Cooper. Boston, New York [etc.] Ginn and company [1942]
vii, 412, [1] p. illus., plates, diagrs. 24cm.
Illustrated title on two leaves.
"Books for further reading": p. 407–408.
HF5438.K543
———— Teacher's key and manual ... Boston, New York [etc.] Ginn and company [1942]
1 p. l., 42 p. 28½cm.
Reproduced from type-written copy.
1. Salesmen and salesmanship. I. Bernard, Louise, joint author. II. Tallman, Gerald Bruce, joint author. III. Title.
42-5245 Revised
Library of Congress HF5438.K543 k [r43x4] 658.8

OEac ViU WaS FTaSU
NK 0198135 DLC OrCS Or OOxM PPD PPT PU PSt OCl OU

Kneeland, Natalie, 1892–
Sweaters and bathing suits, by Natalie Kneeland ... Chicago & New York, A. W. Shaw company; [etc., etc.] 1925.
xxi, 144 p. illus. 21½cm. (*Half-title:* Merchandise manuals for retail salespeople, W. W. Charters, editor)
"References" at end of some of the chapters.

1. Knit goods. 2. Clothing and dress. 3. Salesmen and salesmanship. I. Title. II. Title: Bathing suits.
25—11191
Library of Congress HF5439.S96K6

NK 0198136 DLC WaS PP PPD PPT MiU OCl ICJ MB

Kneeland, Natalie, 1892– ed.
Technique of job analysis for executive and supervisory personnel in distributive occupations; leader's manual. Prepared by Natalie Kneeland cooperating with Texas Education Agency, Vocational Division, Distributive Education Service. [Austin? 195–?]
iv, 45, [29] l. 28 cm.
Bibliography: leaf [28] at end.

1. Job analysis.
HF5549.5.J6K6 658.386 54-62068

NK 0198137 DLC NBuG

Kneeland, Natalie, 1892–
Waists, by Natalie Kneeland ... Chicago & New York, A. W. Shaw company; [etc., etc.] 1924.
xxi, 149 p. illus. 21½cm. (*Half-title:* Merchandise manuals for retail salespeople, W. W. Charters. editor)
Contains "References".

1. Clothing and dress. 2. Salesmen and salesmanship. I. Title.
24—32114
Library of Congress HF5439.C6K6

NK 0198138 DLC CU PP PPD PPT MiU OCl ICJ MB NN Or WaS

Kneeland, Paul Dwelle. Hardwood dimension stock, a synopsis of a paper presented at the Hartford meeting [of the Society of American foresters, New England section], Jan. 31, 1929. [Hartford. 1929.] nar. f°. ff. 3. Mimeograph.

NK 0198139 MH-A

Kneeland, Paul Dwelle. FOR OTHER EDITIONS SEE MAIN ENTRY
Massachusetts. *State forester.*
Instructions for making improvement thinnings and the management of moth-infested woodlands, by H. O. Cook, M. F., assistant forester, and P. D. Kneeland, M. F., forester, Moth division, under the direction of F. W. Rane, state forester. Boston, Wright & Potter printing co., state printers, 1914.

Kneeland, Paul Dwelle.
Massachusetts. *State forester.*
The utilization of forest products in Massachusetts as affected by the war; by Paul D. Kneeland, M. F., assistant forester. Under the direction of F. W. Rane, B. AGR., M. S., Massachusetts, state forester. Boston, Wright & Potter printing company, state printers, 1918.

Kneeland, Paul Dwelle.
Wood fuel; a bulletin to stimulate the production and use of wood as fuel for patriotic and economic reasons as a war measure ... by Paul D. Kneeland ... assistant forester ... [Boston, 1917?] 11 p. 8°.

1. Fuel (Wood), U. S. 2. Wood, U. S., 1917. 3. Massachusetts. Forest Service.
N. Y. P. L. January 30, 1920.

NK 0198142 NN MBH OU MH-A MH

Kneeland, Samuel, 1821–1888.
An American in Iceland. An account of its scenery, people, and history. With a description of its millennial celebration in August, 1874; with notes on the Orkney, Shetland, and Faroe islands, and the great eruption of 1875. By Samuel Kneeland ... Boston, Lockwood, Brooks, and company, 1876.
viii, 326 p. front. (ports.) illus., plates, fold. map. 19½cm.

1. Iceland—Descr. & trav. 2. Volcanoes—Iceland.
4—6203
Library of Congress DL312.K68

MB ViU MdBP NIC MBCo DI-GS NcU DAU OKentU
NK 0198143 DLC PPA PPFr PPL MiU OCl OClW MWA ICJ NN

VOLUME 300

Kneeland, Samuel, 1821-1888.
An American in Iceland. An account of its scenery, people, and history. With a description of its millennial celebration in August, 1874; with notes on the Orkney, Shetland, and Faroe islands, and the great eruption of 1875. By Samuel Kneeland. New York, Worthington co., 1888.
viii, 326 p. front. (ports.) illus. 19cm
"Copyright ... 1875."

NK 0198144 NcD

Kneeland, Samuel, 1821-1888, ed.
Annual of scientific discovery: or, Year-book of facts in science and art, for [1850]-71, exhibiting the most important discoveries and improvements in mechanics, useful arts, natural philosophy, chemistry, astronomy, geology, biology, botany, mineralogy, meteorology, geography, antiquities, etc., together with notes on the progress of science ... a list of recent scientific publications; obituaries of eminent scientific men, etc. ... Boston, Gould and Lincoln; [etc., etc.] 1850-71.

Kneeland, Samuel, 1821-1888, ed.
[Schubert, Gotthilf Heinrich von] 1780-1860.
Explanatory text to S. R. Urbino's charts of the animal kingdom. Rev. and cor. by Samuel Kneeland ... Boston, S. R. Urbino, 1869.

Kneeland, Samuel. 1821-88. Manilla and its surroundings. 9 pp. (Harper's Mag. v. 80. 1890, p. 621.)

NK 0198147 MdBP

Kneeland, Samuel, 1821-1888.
Smith, Charles Hamilton, 1776-1859.
The natural history of the human species: its typical forms, primeval distribution, filiations, and migrations ... By Lieut.-Col. Chas. Hamilton Smith ... With a preliminary abstract of the views of Blumenbach, Prichard, Bachman, Agassiz, and other authors of repute on the subject. By S. Kneeland, jr., M. D. Boston, Gould and Lincoln, 1851.

Kneeland, Samuel, 1821-1888.
On economy of fuel, and the consumption of smoke, as effected by "Amory's improved patent furnace", with an investigation of the principles involved. By Samuel Kneeland ... Boston, J. E. Farwell & co., printers, 1866.
39, [3] p. illus. 21cm.

1. Furnaces. 2. Smoke prevention.

Library of Congress TK320.K7 6-33082

NK 0198149 DLC MB

Kneeland (Samuel) [1821-1888]. On the contagiousness of puerperal fever, and its connection with epidemic erysipelas. 42 pp. 8°. Philadelphia, Lea & Blanchard, 1846.
Repr. from: Am. J. M. Sc., Phila., 1846, n. s., xi.

NK 0198150 DNLM PPC

Kneeland, Samuel, 1821-1888. On the Santhals, a semi-barbarous tribe of northeastern Bengal. [Salem, Mass. 1888.] 8°. pp. 24. Wdcts. PM.
"From the Bulletin of the Essex institute, vol. xix. nos. 7-9."

NK 0198151 MH

Kneeland (S[amuel]) [1821-1888]. On the skeleton of the great chimpanzee, Troglodytes gorilla. pp. 336-348. 8°. Boston, 1852. [P., v. 1466.]
Cutting from: Bost. Soc. Nat. Hist., 1852.

NK 0198152 DNLM PPAN

Kneeland, Samuel, 1821- 1888.
The Philippine Islands. Their physical characters, customs of the people, products, earthquake phenomena and savage tribes. By Samuel Kneeland,
[n.p., 188-]

DS656
.K5

NK 0198153 DLC

Kneeland, Samuel, 1821-1888. L991.4 0300
The Philippine Islands. Their physical characters, customs of the people, products, earthquake phenomena, and savage tribes. 73-100 p. il. Q. (American Geographical Society. Bulletin. [Journal, vol. 15, no. 2.]) New York 1883.
Published with this: Antisell, T. The currents of the Pacific Ocean. 101-132 p.
No title-page. Title taken from inside cover.

NK 0198154 ICJ MWA MdBP MH

KNEELAND, Samuel, 1821-1888.
Report on idiotic crania, idiocy, and cretinism Read before the Boston society for medical improvement, Jan. 13, 1851. [Phil., etc.] [1851.]

Pam.

NK 0198155 MH-P

KNEELAND, Samuel, 1821-1888.
The subsidence theory of earthquakes.
[Bost. 1884.] 8 pp. 8°.

NK 0198156 MB Nh NN MH CU

Kneeland, Samuel, 1821-1888
Travels in Iceland; an account of its scenery, people, and history, with a description of its millennial celebration in August, 1874. New York, A. L. Burt [1875]
viii, [3]-326p.

YA26320

NK 0198157 OCl PP MH DLC

DL
312
.K68
1900

Kneeland, Samuel, 1821-1888.
Travels in Iceland; an account of its scenery, people and history, with a description of its millenial celebration in August, 1874. New York, A.L. Burt c1900?]
326p. 19cm.

A reprint of the author's An American in Iceland ..., Boston, 1876.

1. Iceland. Descr. & trav. 2. Volcanoes. Iceland. I. Kneeland, Samuel, 1821-1888. // An American in Iceland. II. Title.

NK 0198158 OrU

Kneeland, Samuel, 1821-1888.
Travels in Iceland. An account of its scenery, people and history, with a description of its millennial celebration in August, 1874. By Samuel Kneeland ... New York, A. L. Burt company [1901]
viii, [3]-326 p. illus. (incl. music. port.) 19½cm.
Running title: An American in Iceland. Also published under this title.

1. Iceland—Descr. & trav. 2. Volcanoes—Iceland.

NK 0198159 ViU

Kneeland, Samuel, 1821-1888.
Volcanoes and earthquakes. A popular account of their nature, causes, effects and geographical distribution, from personal observation in the Hawaiian and Philippine islands, Japan, Iceland, the Mediterranean basin, Spain and the United States, by Samuel Kneeland ... Boston, D. Lothrop co. [1888]
3 p. l., v-viii, [9]-220 p. incl. 12 pl. front., illus. 23cm.

1. Volcanoes. 2. Earthquakes.

G S 10-151

Library, U. S. Geol. survey 220 K73v

NK 0198160 DI-GS PPA PPL PPGi OCl OClW MH ICJ KAS WaWW OKentU

Kneeland, Samuel, 1821-1888.
The wonders of the Yosemite Valley, and of California. [By] Prof. Samuel Kneeland ... With original photographic illustrations, by John P. Soule. Boston, A. Moore, 1871.
2 p. l., ix-xii, 13-71 p. front., illus., plates. 27cm.

1. California—Descr. & trav. 2. Yosemite Valley. I. Title.

Rc-630

Library of Congress F868.Y6K6

NK 0198161 DLC CU-A CU OU PHi MWA MB NN WaS

F868
Y6K6
1872a
x

Kneeland, Samuel, 1821-1888.
The wonders of the Yosemite Valley, and of California. With original photographic illustrations by John P. Soule. Boston, A. Moore, Lee & Shepard, 1872.
79 p. illus., maps. 27cm.

NK 0198162 CU-B MH CU

Kneeland, Samuel, 1821-1888.
The wonders of the Yosemite Valley, and of California. By Samuel Kneeland ... With original photographic illustrations, by John P. Soule. 3d ed., rev. and enl. Boston, A Moore [etc.]; New York, Lee, Shepard & Dillingham, 1872.
3 p. l., xi-xii, 13-98 p. incl. illus., map. photos. (incl. front.) 27cm.

1. California—Descr. & trav. 2. Yosemite Valley.

22-2868

Library of Congress F868.Y6K62

NK 0198163 DLC OrU NNC MH OCU CLU MiU OCl ODW NjP ICJ CU-B CU-S

Kneeland, Stillman Foster, 1845-1926.
The commercial law register, a manual of the international merchants' protective law association... Albany, N.Y., Parker & Herrick, 1873.
557p.

NK 0198164 ICRL MH NN DLC

VOLUME 300

Kneeland, S[tillman] F[oster] 1845-1926.
The commercial law register, a manual of the International Law Association, compiled by S. F. Kneeland. Containing a list of the law members...and a...synopsis of the state laws of the United States, and Dominion of Canada, relating to commerce... New York: McDivitt, Campbell & Co., 1876. 6 p., 2 l., (1)10-573 p. 8°.

1. Commerce.—Jurisprudence, U. S.
N. Y. P. L. March 21, 1911.

NK 0198165 NN ViW

Kneeland, Stillman Foster, 1845-1926.
The commercial law register, a manual of the International law association, containing a list of the law members of the association, with their home testimonials, and a complete synopis of the state laws of the United States, and dominion of Canada, relating to commerce, and other matters of interest to merchants, manufacturers, and the legal profession. New York, J.R. McDivitt & co., 1878.
6 p., 2 l., [9]-573 p. 23.5 cm.
Contains autograph of W.W. Corlett.
On binding: Third edition, 1878-'9.

NK 0198166 CtY

Kneeland, Stillman Foster, 1845-1926.
Law, lawyers and lambs, by Stillman F. Kneeland ... New York, The Banks law publishing co., 1910.
vii, 124 p. incl. front. 24 cm.

I. Title.
11—660
Library of Congress PN6268.L4K5

NK 0198167 DLC NcD PP-C PPB PU-L ViU-L NN CU-AL OrU OKentU

Kneeland, Stillman Foster, 1845-
On free exhibition day and evening at the Lihou Art Galleries ... Catalogue of the private collections of modern paintings belonging to S.F. Kneeland and J. de Lamare ... auction ... October ... [189-?]
70 p. 12°.

NK 0198168 NN

Kneeland, Stillman Foster, 1845-
Random reveries of a busy barrister, by Stillman Foster Kneeland ... New York, Broadway publishing co. [°1914]
167 p. front. (port.) 19½cm. $1.50
Part of the pages blank.
Poems.

I. Title.
15-1074
Library of Congress PS3521.N43R3 1914

NK 0198169 DLC FMU Or

Kneeland, Stillman Foster, 1845-1926.
Seven centuries in the Kneeland family. By Stillman Foster Kneeland ... New York, The author, 1897.
583 p. front., plates, ports., coats of arms. 23cm.

1. Kneeland family (John Kneeland, fl. 1630) 2. Kneeland family (Edward Kneeland, fl. 1630) 3. Kneeland family.
9—11450
Library of Congress CS71.K68 1897

NK 0198170 DLC MB C PHi MB MWA Nh OClWHi

KNEELAND, STILLMAN FOSTER, 1845-1926.
Seven centuries in the Kneeland family. New York, 1897. 583 p. illus.

Microfilm (master negative).

NK 0198171 NN

Kneeland, Stillman Foster, 1845-1926.
A treatise on the law of attachments in civil cases: together with the leading statutory provisions of the several states and territories of the United States in relation to suits by attachment, and a collection of forms. By S. F. Kneeland ... New York, G. S. Diossy, 1884.
2 p. l., vii-xxvii, 722 p. 24cm.

1. Attachment and garnishment—U. S. 2. Forms (Law)—U. S.
32-2091
Library of Congress

NK 0198172 DLC PPB OClW CtY

Kneeland, Stillman Foster, 1845-1926.
A treatise upon the principles governing the acquisition and enforcement of mechanic's liens. By S. F. Kneeland ... New York, McDivitt, Campbell & co., 1876.
xl, [7]-522 p., 1 l. 23cm.
Lettered on cover: Mechanics liens with forms.

1. Mechanics' liens—New York (State) 2. Forms (Law)—New York (State)
32-2081
Library of Congress

NK 0198173 DLC FU

Kneeland, Stillman Foster, 1845-1926.
A treatise upon the principles governing the acquisition and enforcement of mechanic's liens. By S. F. Kneeland ... 2d ed. New York, S. S. Peloubet & company, 1882.
vi p., 1 l., [vii]-xv, [7]-486 p. 24cm.

1. Mechanics' liens—New York (State) 2. Forms (Law)—New York (State)
32-2080
Library of Congress

NK 0198174 DLC PPB WaU-L NcD OU

Kneeland, Yale, jr.
Art, science, and responsibility. [Address to the incoming first year class, College of Physicians and Surgeons, Columbia University] [New York, 1952]
10 l.

1. Medicine - Addresses, essays, lectures.

NK 0198175 NNC-M

Kneelands' Troy directory, 1847/8-
vol. 1-
Troy, J. C. Kneeland & co., 1847-
v. front. (fold. map) 19cm.

1. Troy, N. Y.—Direct.
16-4793
Library of Congress F129.T8A18

NK 0198176 DLC

Kneen, Alice Shepherd
A hist. of the family of James & Mary Shepherd & their children 1815-1915.
Cleveland, O. Gurney bros., co., 1916.
27 p.

NK 0198177 OClWHi

Kneen, E W
CS71 G855K6
The Griswold family of Vermont, compiled by Mr. E. W. Kneen, of Cleveland. Ohio. No imprint [1920?]

3 l.(folded) 25½cm.

1. Griswold family.

NK 0198178 NBuG

Kneen, Eleanor G.
Into unknown seas, and other period plays, by Eleanor G. Kneen... London: Sidgwick & Jackson, Ltd[, 1933]. vii, 96 p. illus. (plans.) 19cm.

CONTENTS.—Into unknown seas.—False dawn.—At sunset.

678099A. 1. Drama, English. I. Title. II. Title: False dawn. III. Title: At sunset.
N. Y. P. L. December 11, 1933

NK 0198179 NN

Kneen, Eleanor G.
Lordless, by E. G. Kneen. London, Sidgwick & Jackson, ltd., 1936.
4 p. l., 3-339, [1] p. 19cm.

I. Title.
36-11966
Library of Congress PZ3.K7286Lo

NK 0198180 DLC

Kneen, Eleanor G.
Lordless, by E. G. Kneen. New York, G. P. Putnam's sons, 1936.
4 p. l., 300 p. 19½cm.

I. Title.
36-19247
Library of Congress PZ3.K7286Lo 2

NK 0198181 DLC

Kneen, Eric, 1909-
... Carbohydrate metabolism and winter hardiness of wheat, by Eric Kneen ... and M. J. Blish ...
(*In* U. S. Dept. of agriculture. Journal of agricultural research. Washington, 1941. 23cm. v. 62, no. 1, Jan. 1, 1941, p. 1-26 incl. 1 illus., tables, diagrs.)
Contribution from Nebraska Agricultural experiment station (Nebr.—19)
Paper no. 262, Journal series, Nebraska Agricultural experiment station.
Published April 10, 1941.
"Literature cited": p. 24-26.
1. Wheat—[Hardiness] I. Blish, Morris Joslin, 1889- joint author. II. Title.
Agr 41-587
U. S. Dept. of agr. Library for Library of Congress 1Ag84J vol. 62, no. 1 [S21.A75 vol. 62, no. 1] [4°] (630.72)

NK 0198182 DNAL OU

Kneen, Herbert Luther.
The sea serpent, by Herbert L. Kneen. East Haven, Conn., H. L. Kneen [°1934]
1 p. l., 12 p. 23½cm.

I. Title.
34-18840
Library of Congress PZ3.K7292Se

NK 0198183 DLC

Law
Kneen, J. G., comp.

Basutoland. *Laws, statutes, etc.*
Revised edition of the laws of Basutoland in force on the 1st day of January, 1949. Compiled by J. G. Kneen and H. C. Juta. London, Waterlow, Govt. printer, 1950.

VOLUME 300

Kneen, John Joseph, 1873-
English-Manx pronouncing dictionary, by J. J. Kneen. Douglas, Isle of Man, Clucas & Fargher 1938.
viii, 86 p. front. (port.)

At head of title: "Mona's Herald".

1. Manx language - Dictionaries - English. 2. English language - Dialects - Man, Isle of - Dictionaries.

NK 0198185 NNC NNU CU NN ViU

KNEEN, JOHN JOSEPH, 1873-
English-Manx pronouncing dictionary. Revised and reprinted and published by Mona's Herald. Douglas, Isle of Man, 1953. viii, 96 p. 21cm.

1. English language--Dictionaries, Manx. I. Mona's Herald, Douglas, Isle of Man.

NK 0198186 NN C NcD ICU

Kneen, John Joseph, 1873-
Lessons in Manx (Part 2), based on "First lessons in Manx" by the late Edmund Goodwin, with additional exercises by J. J. Kneen. Douglas, Yn Cheshaght Ghailckagh, 1936.
80 p. (Beginning Manx Gaelic)

Bound with Douglas, Mona. A Manx primer. 1940.

1. Manx language - Grammar. 2. Manx language - Conversation and phrase books. I. Goodwin, Edmund First lessons in Manx.

NK 0198187 NNC MH

PB1867 .K7I31
Kneen, John Joseph, 1873-
Illiam Dhone. A Manx historical drama which won the Cruinnaght Gold Medal, 1924. Douglas [Isle of Man] S. K. Broadbent, 1926.
19 p. (Yn Cruinnaght Vanninagh Ashoonagh. Publication, 1)
Text in English.

1. Christian, William, 1608-1663--Drama. Man, Isle of--Hist.--Drama.

NK 0198188 ICU NcD NN ICN MH

Kneen, John Joseph, 1873–
A grammar of the Manx language, by J. J. Kneen ... published under the auspices of Tynwald by the Manx museum and ancient monuments trustees. London, Oxford university press, H. Milford, 1931.
xi, [1], 209 p., 1 l. 23cm.
"List of publications in the Manx language": p. 10–14.

1. Manx language—Grammar. I. Man, Isle of. Tynwald court. II. Manx museum and ancient monuments trustees.
33–4383
Library of Congress PB1811.K6
[3] 491.645

NK 0198189 DLC NN MB ViU CLSU PBm PU CtY ICN MH

[KNEEN, John Joseph] 1873-
Lessons in the Manx language; the Acts of the apostles, The lament of the mother tongue, with other lessons in prose and verse. Douglas, etc., [Isle of Man], S.K. Broadbent & Co., [preface 1901].

pp. (3), 90.
Manx and English title and text.

NK 0198190 MH

Kneen, John Joseph, 1873–
The personal names of the Isle of Man, by J. J. Kneen ... Published under the auspices of Tynwald by the Manx museum and ancient monuments trustees. London, Oxford university press, H. Milford, 1937.
lx, 295, [1] p. 23cm.
Cover-title: Manx personal names.
Bibliography: p. [lviii]–lx.

1. Names, Personal—Manx. I. Man, Isle of. Tynwald court. II. Manx museum and ancient monuments trustees. III. Title. IV. Title: Manx personal names.
38–24383
Library of Congress CS2509.I 8K6
[5] 929.4

NK 0198191 DLC NcD ICU

Kneen, John Joseph, 1873–
The place-names of the Isle of Man with their origin and history, by J. J. Kneen. Douglas, Yn Cheshaght Ghailckagh (The Manx society) 1925–
6 v. fold. maps. 23cm.
Paged continuously.

1. Names, Geographical—Man, Isle of.
26–27627
Library of Congress DA670.M2K5

NK 0198192 DLC NcD ICN NRU CtY OCl MB NN

KNEEN, John Joseph, 1873 -
Yn saase jeeragh (the direct method); the most approved system of teaching languages, applied to the Manx language, etc. [Douglas], Yn cheshagt ghailckagh, 1911.

"Reprinted from the Isle of Man examiner, 1911."

NK 0198193 MH

---

pY 829 .69
KNEEN, LILIAN.
Mr Quilliam decides, a sketch in Manx dialect by Lilian and Eva Kneen. Birkenhead [n.d.]
8p. 22cm.

"A tribute to Manx friends at home and abroad."

NK 0198194 ICN

Kneen, Orville Hayter, 1889–
Everyman's book of flying, by Orville H. Kneen ... with a foreword by Professor Roland H. Spaulding ... profusely illustrated and with an index. New York, Frederick A. Stokes company, 1930.
xxvi p., 1 l., 406 p. incl. front., illus., plates, diagrs. maps (1 fold.) tables. 21cm.

1. Aeronautics. 2. Aeroplanes. I. Title.
30–16366
Library of Congress TL545.K65
——— Copy 2.
Copyright A 23949 [5] 629.13

OEac OC1h MB ICJ NN
NK 0198195 DLC DAL Wa Or WaS NcC PPGi PP PU OCl

Kneen, Orville Hayter, 1889–
Flying for everybody ... by Orville H. Kneen ... in collaboration with Augustus Post and members of the staff of Aero mechanics ...
New York, Experimenter publications, inc. [1929]–
v. illus., diagrs. 29½cm.
"Aviation books": v. 1, no. 1, p. 95–96.

1. Aeronautics. 2. Aeroplanes. I. Post, Augustus, 1873– joint author. II. Title.
30–5875
Library of Congress TL547.K6

NK 0198196 DLC WaS

Kneen, Orville Hayter, 1889–
Young pioneers on western trails, young explorers' own stories of adventure in the unknown West, by Orville H. Kneen, with a frontispiece and a map. New York, Frederick A. Stokes company, 1929.
viii, 311 p. front. 19½cm.
Map on lining-papers.
Bibliography: p. 311.
CONTENTS.—Samuel Hearne. First overland to the Arctic.—Alexander Mackenzie. First overland to the Pacific.—Zebulon Montgomery Pike. First into the great Southwest.—James Ohio Pattie. From Yellowstone to Mexico City.—Kit Carson. Master scout of the West.
1. Pioneers—U. S. 2. Frontier and pioneer life—The West. I. Hearne, Samuel, 1745–1792. II. Mackenzie, Sir Alexander, 1763–1820. III. Pike, Zebulon Montgomery, 1779–1813. IV. Pattie, James Ohio, b. 1804? V. Carson, Christopher, 1809–1868. VI. Title.
Library of Congress F592.K68 29–17879 Revised

MB NN
NK 0198197 DLC IU Or Wa WaS OrLgE OrMonO CaBViPA

Kneen, William
The love of God; brief outline of sermon preached in Manx and English on Sunday evening, July 3rd., 1897, at the Town and Seamen's Bethel Mission, Circular Road, Douglas, Isle of Man, by W. Kneen (town missionary). [Douglas, printed at the Manxman office, 1897?]

8 p.
Text in English & Manx

NK 0198198 MH

Kneer, August, 1867–
Die Denkmalpflege in Deutschland, mit besonderer Berücksichtigung der Rechtsverhältnisse, von . . . Aug. Kneer . . . M. Gladbach: Volksvereins-Verlag, G. m. b. H., 1915. 1 p.l., (1)8–249 p. 8°.

Bibliography, p. 12–16.

1. Monuments.—Preservation, Germany.
N. Y. P. L. March 10, 1916.

NK 0198199 NN

Kneer, August, 1867–
Die deutsche Rechtsanwaltschaft, von Rechtsanwalt Dr. phil. August Kneer. M. Gladbach: Volksvereins-Verlag, G.m.b.H., 1917. 72 p. 12°. (Staatsbürger-Bibliothek. Heft 77.)

1. Lawyers, Germany. 2. Series.
N. Y. P. L. October 27, 1923.

NK 0198200 NN

Kneer, August, 1867–
Die entstehung der konziliaren theorie. Zur geschichte des schismas und der kirchenpolitischen schriftsteller Konrad von Gelnhausen († 1390) und Heinrich von Langenstein († 1397) von dr. August Kneer. Roma, Tip. di F. Cuggiani, 1893.
1 p. l., [5]–145 p. 24cm. (*On cover:* Römische quartalschrift für christl alterthumskunde und für kirchengeschichte. 1. supplementheft)

1. Councils and synods. 2. Schism, The great western, 1378–1417. I. Konrad von Gelnhausen, 1324 (ca.)–1390. II. Heinrich von Langenstein. 1325 (ca.)–1397. III. Title.
35–28530
Library of Congress BX820.K6 262.4

NK 0198201 DLC PU DDO MiU MH

Kneer, August, 1867–
Heimat und Recht; die Heimatpflege (Denkmalpflege und Heimatschutz) im Rechtsleben der Gegenwart, von Rechtsanwalt Dr. phil. August Kneer . . . M. Gladbach: Volksvereins-Verlag, 1922. 31 p. 1. ed. 8°. (Staatsbürger-Bibliothek. Heft 106.)

1. Monuments.—Preservation of, Germany. 2. Scenery.—Preservation of, Germany. 3. Series.
N. Y. P. L. October 10, 1923.

NK 0198202 NN

VOLUME 300

Kneer, August, 1867-
Kardinal Zabarella (Franciscus de Zabarellis, cardinalis Florentinus) 1360-1417. Ein Beitrag zur Geschichte des grossen abendländischen Schismas. Erster Teil ... Münster, Druck der Theissing'schen Buchdruckerei, 1891.

Thesis, Münster.

NK 0198203 ICRL PPPD PSt CU

Kneer, August, 1867-
Kardinal Zabarella (Franciscus de Zabarellis, cardinalis Florentinus) 1360-1417. Ein Beitrag zur Geschichte des grossen abendländischen Schismas. Erster Teil ... Münster, Druck der Theissing'schen Buchdruckerei, 1891.

Microfilm of copy at Yarnell Library of Theology, S. Clements church. Negative.
Thesis, Münster.

NK 0198204 NNC

Kneer, August, 1867-
Der rechtsanwalt; ein kulturgeschichtliche studie, von August Kneer, mit sechs abbildungen. M(ünchen) Gladbach, Volksvereins-verlag, 1928.
3 p. l., (11)-130 p. front., illus. 27cm.

1. Lawyers. 2. Lawyers—Germany. I. Title.
Library of Congress 29-12185

NK 0198205 DLC GEU CtY

Kneer, August, 1867-
Das uneheliche kind; eine alte menschheitsfrage als gegenwartsproblem, von dr. phil. August Kneer ... M(ünchen) Gladbach, Volkvereins-verlag, 1926.
3 p. l., (9)-83 p. 24½cm.

1. Illegitimacy.
Library of Congress HQ998.K6 27-14041

NK 0198206 DLC

Kneer, Fritz
Über 32 traumatische hüftgelenks-luxationen ... Tübingen, Laupp, 1889.
28 p.

Inaug.-diss., Tübingen.
"Sonderabzug aus Beiträge zur klinischen chirurgie, IV. band, III. heft."

1. Hip-joint - Dislocation.

NK 0198207 NNC PPC DNLM

Kneer, Georg, 1901-
Das familienproblem in Emile Zola's Rougon-Macquart. ...
Inaug. Diss. - Würzburg, [1934].
Lebenslauf.
Bibliography.

NK 0198208 ICRL PU MiU CtY MH

Kneer, Hans, 1925-
Die Wettbewerbsfähigkeit der deutschen Silberwarenindustrie auf dem Weltmarkt nach dem zweiten Weltkrieg. München, 1950.
227 l. mounted illus. 30 cm.
Typescript (carbon copy)
Inaug.-Diss.—Munich.
Vita.
Bibliography: leaves 224-227.

1. Silversmithing—Germany. I. Title.

HD9536.G42K5 56-24519

NK 0198209 DLC

Kneer, Marian, ed.
Selected softball articles
see under American Association for Health Physical Education and Recreation. Division for girls and women's sports.

Kneer, Marian.
Softball; instructor's guide
see under Athletic Institute.

DC 73 A2K68 Kneer, Martin.
Die Urkunde über die Heiligsprechung Karls d. Gr. v. 8. Januar 1166 und ihr Verfasser in der Kanzlei Kaiser Friedrichs I. Erlangen, Palm & Enke, 1930.
vii, 80 p. 25cm. (Erlanger Abhandlungen zur mittleren und neueren Geschichte, Bd. VI)

1. Charlemagne, 768-814. I. Series.

NK 0198211 NIC CU MH NN CtY

WP 520 K68s 1951 KNEER, Max
Die Sexualhormone, klinische Bedeutung und therapeutische Anwendung in der Frauenheilkunde und Geburtshilfe. Stuttgart, Enke, 1951.
xii, 155 p. illus.
1. Gynecology 2. Hormones - Sex - Therapeutic use 3. Obstetrics

NK 0198212 DNLM

Kneer, Max,
Strahlenbehandlung des mammakarzinoms. Inaugural dissertation, Universität zu München, 1933.

NK 0198213 PPWI CtY

Knees, Joseph.
*pGB8 V6755R 5.23.48 Ehre dem Ehre gebührt! oder auch ein Wort zur Vertheidigung der Wiener=Studenten.
[Wien]Gedruckt bei M.Lell.[1848]

broadside. 48x60.5cm.
Dated & signed: Wien, den 23. Mai 1848. Joseph Knees, Nationalgardist.

NK 0198214 MH

Knees, Joseph.
*pGB8 V6755R 5.23.48 Ehre dem Ehre gebührt! oder auch ein Wort zur Vertheidigung der Wiener=Studenten. Zweite Auflage.
[Wien]Gedruckt bei M.Lell.[1848]

broadside. 47.5x57.5cm.
Dated & signed: Wien, den 23. Mai 1848. Joseph Knees, Nationalgardist.
Printed on 1 side of a folio sheet; on the other side is printed B. Knöpfelmacher's Das Verbrüderungs=Fest im Odeon.

NK 0198215 MH

Kneese, Ed., d. 1813.
Unterricht über das gliederreissen. Pirna, 1804.
8°

NK 0198216 NN

Kneeshaw, J.W.
Conscription and motherhood, by J.W. Kneeshaw ... Manchester and London, The National labour press, limited [1916?]
11 p. 23 cm.

NK 0198217 CSt-H

Kneeshaw, J W
HD4905.5 K66 Conscription enters the workshops, by J. W. Kneeshaw (parliamentary candidate for West Birmingham)... Manchester and London, The National labour press limited [1916?]
14 p. 21½cm.
Illustrated cover.

1.Service, Compulsory non-military. 2.Military service, Compulsory. 3.European war, 1914-1918 Labor - Gt.Brit. 4.Trade unions - Gt. Brit.

NK 0198218 CSt

Kneeshaw, J W
HD4905.5 K67 Conscription or trade unionism! By J. W. Kneeshaw (parliamentary candidate for West Birmingham) ... Manchester and London, The National labour press, ltd. [1916?]

10 [1] p. 21cm.

1.Service, Compulsory non-military. 2.European war, 1914-1918 - Labor - Gt. Brit. 3. Trade unions - Gt. Brit. I.Title.

NK 0198219 CSt-H

Kneeshaw, J W
HD4905.5 K68 How conscription works! By J.W.Kneeshaw (parliamentary candidate for West Birmingham) ... Manchester and London, The National labour press limited [1917?]
12 p. 21½cm.
Advertising matter: p.12.

1.Military service, Compulsory. 2.Service, Compulsory non-military. 3.European war, 1914-1918 - Labor - Gt. Brit. I.Title.

NK 0198220 CSt-H

Kneeshaw, J W
329.942 I38 no.3 The politics of Christ. Manchester, National Labour Press [n.d.]
13, [1] p. 21 cm.

[No.3] in a volume with binder's title: I.L.P. report and pamphlets.

1. Jesus Christ. Teachings 2. Poverty I. Title

NK 0198221 NcD

VOLUME 300

Kneeshaw, J
Profits and patriotism ... Manchester, The National labour press, ltd. [1916]
cover-title, 15 p. 21cm.

NK 0198222 NcD

Kneeshaw, J.W.
Profits and patriotism, by J.W. Kneeshaw ... Manchester and London, The National labour press, ltd. [1917]
10, [1] p. 23 cm.
Illustrated t.-p.

NK 0198223 CSt-H

Kneeshaw, J. W.
What socialism means, by J. W. Kneeshaw... London: I. L. P. Publ. Dept.[, 1926.] 15 p. illus. 8°.

1. Socialism—Pro. 2. Independent Labour Party (Gt. Br.). Publication Department.
N. Y. P. L. December 22, 1926

NK 0198224 NN

WA 10308
Kneeshaw, W S
Sea fishing on the North Wales coast. Bangor, Jarvis & Foster[pref. 1918]
61p. illus.

1. Fishing - Wales.

NK 0198225 CtY NN

Kneeshaw, W S
Sea fishing on the north Wales coast. Bangor, Jarvis, 1922.
66 p. illus. 18½ cm.

NK 0198226 NjP MH

Knef, Hildegard
see
Neff, Hildegarde, 1925-

Knefel, Conrad Ernst.
Commentatio de Horatii Epod. 2. [Gymnasium-Programm] Herfordiae 1828.
8 p. 30.5 cm.

NK 0198228 CtY

Gnh6 yl K73
Knefel, Conrad Ernst
... Quaestiunculae duae de Horatii carminibus. Herfordiae, 1832.
Pamphlet
Programm - Herford, Germany.

NK 0198229 CtY NjP ICU

Knefeli, K
Ausfuhr und Umsatzsteuer; Leitfaden für Exporteure. Erläuterungen der gesetzlichen Bestimmungen, Gesetzestext, Beispiele und Formulare. Wiesbaden, T. Gabler [1951]
92 p. forms. 21 cm. (Fachbücher für die Wirtschaft)

1. Germany—Comm. 2. Sales tax—Germany. I. Title.
A 53-39
New York Univ. Wash. Sq. Library HF3566.K58
for Library of Congress

NK 0198230 NNU-W

Knefeli, Wilhelm, 1912-
Die haftung bei sportverletzungen. ...Dresden, 1937. 67 p.
Inaug. Diss. - Jena, 1937.
Lebenslauf.
Literatur-Verzeichnis.

NK 0198231 ICRL CtY MH

Knefeli, Wilhelm, 1912 –
Die haftung bei sportverletzungen, von dr. jur. Wilhelm Knefeli. Dresden, M. Dittert & co., 1937.
67 p. 21cm.
Issued also as inaugural dissertation, Jena.
"Literatur-verzeichnis": p. 7-8.

1. Sports—Accidents and injuries. 2. Torts—Germany. I. Title.
42-6260

NK 0198232 DLC

Knefler, Frederick, *1834-* *"20th".75.5
Missionary Ridge. Portrait.
(*In* Military Order of the Loyal Legion of the United States. Indiana Commandery. War papers . . . Pp. 178-206. Indianapolis. 1898.)

D7300 — United States. Hist. Civil \ Pers. narr. — Missionary Ridge, Battle of. 1863.

NK 0198233 MB

Knégévitch (Velimir). *Inégalité pupillaire chez les tuberculeux. 15 pp. 8°. Genève, A. Renaud. 1921

NK 0198234 DNLM

GV722 1948 .B47
Knegjens, Peter, joint author.
Berg, Henk van den.
Van Athene naar Londen [door] Henk van den Berg [en] Peter Knegjens, ingeleid door C. F. Pahud de Mortanges. Amsterdam, Het Wereldvenster [1948]

Knegt, D
Smalfilmers! Ideeën! Met illustraties van Wim van Overbeek. Bloemendaal, Focus [1947]
324 p. illus. 23 cm.

1. Moving-picture plays. 2. Moving-pictures—Plots, themes, etc. 3. Moving-pictures—Netherlands. I. Title.
PN1995.8.K6 54-42508 ‡

NK 0198236 DLC WU

Knegt, D
Zó is filmen. Een nieuwe reeks suggesties voor beginnende en gevorderde amateur-filmers, met voorbeelden van film-scenario's. Bloemendaal, Focus [1951]
244 p. illus. 20 cm.
On cover: Nieuwe scenario's voor smalfilmers.

1. Moving-pictures. 2. Moving-picture plays. I. Title.
PN1994.K47 A 52-339 rev
Southern Calif., Univ. of. Library
for Library of Congress [r52b½]†

NK 0198237 CLSU DLC WU NN

W 4 G87 1948
KNEGTEL, Aloysius Petrus Cornelis Henricus
Een clinisch en experimenteel onderzoek naar de pathogenese van de coeliakie. Tilburg [1948]
155 p.
Proefschrift - Groningen.
Summary in Dutch, English, and French.
1. Celiac disease

NK 0198238 DNLM ICU

Knehr, Charles Anthony, 1910-
The effects of monocular vision on measures of reading efficiency and perceptual span, by Charles Anthony Knehr ... [Lancaster, Pa., Lancaster press, inc., 1941]
cover-title, 133-154 p. incl. tables, diagrs. 24cm.
Thesis (PH. D.)—Columbia university, 1941.
"Reprinted from the Journal of experimental psychology, vol. 29, no. 2, August, 1941."
Vita: p. [2] of cover.
Bibliographical foot-notes.

1. Eye—Movements. 2. Perception. 3. Reading, Psychology of. I. Title. II. Title: Monocular vision.
A 42-926
Columbia univ. Libraries
for Library of Congress ,F456.R2K55
[3]† [159.9464] 158.84

NK 0198239 NNC DLC

30.61 K73
Knehr, Hermann.
Wirtschaftsbeschreibung, Betriebserfolg und Voranschläge. [Stuttgart, Ulmer, 1955]
39 p.

1. Farm records. 2. Agriculture. Accounting (Account books)

NK 0198239-1 DNAL

Kneib, Philipp, 1870-1915.
Die beweise für die unsterblichkeit der seele aus allgemeinen psychologischen tatsachen neu geprüft von Dr. Philipp Kneib ... Freiburg im Breisgau, St. Louis, Mo. [etc.] Herder, 1903.
3 p. l., 106 p. 23cm. (*Added t.-p.:* Strassburger theologische studien. 5. bd., 2. hft.)

1. Immortality. 2. Soul.
3-21474
Library of Congress BR45.S7 bd. 5, hft. 2

NK 0198239-2 DLC

Kneib, Philipp, 1870-1915.
Handbuch der apologetik als der wissenschaftlichen begründung einer gläubigen weltanschauung, von dr. Philipp Kneib ... Paderborn, F. Schöningh, 1912.
xiii, 850 p. 23cm. (*Added t.-p.:* Wissenschaftliche handbibliothek. 1. reihe. Theologische lehrbücher. XXXII) M.9

13-421
Library of Congress

NK 0198239-3 DLC

VOLUME 300

Kneib, Philipp, 1870-1915.
Die "heteronomie" der christlichen moral; eine apologetisch-moraltheologische studie von dr. Philipp Kneib ... Wien, Mayer & co., 1903.
vi p., 1 l., 70 p., 1 l. 23½cm. (Added t.-p.: Theologische studien der Leo-gesellschaft, hrsg. von dr. A. Ehrhard ... und dr. F. M. Schindler ... 7)

1. Christian ethics—Catholic authors. 2. Salvation.
6-23292
Library of Congress BR45.T5 vol. 7

NK 0198239-4 DLC

BJ1238 S3 K59 1906
Kneib, Philipp, 1870-1915.
Die "Jenseitsmoral" im Kampfe um ihre Grundlagen. Freiburg i. Br., Herder, 1906.
viii, 282 p. 24 cm.

1. Christian ethics. 2. Salvation. I. Title.

NK 0198239-5 CaBVaU

Kneib, Philipp, 1870-1915.
Die "lohnsucht" der christlichen moral; ein beitrag zur apologie der christlichen sittenlehre von Dr. Philipp Kneib ... Wien, Mayer & co., 1904.
4 p. l., 66 p. 23½cm. (Added t.-p.: Theologische studien der Leo-gesellschaft hrsg. von Dr. A. Ehrhard ... und Dr. F. M. Schindler ... 11)

6-23289

NK 0198239-6 DLC

232.9 K68m Theol.
Kneib, Philipp, 1870-1915
Moderne Leben-Jesu-Forschung unter dem Einflusse der Psychiatrie. Eine kritische Darstellung für Gebildete aller Stände. Mainz, Kirchheim & co., 1908.
76p. 24cm.

1. Jesus Christ--Psychiatry. I. Title.

NK 0198239-7 TxDaM CtY ODW

Kneib, Philipp, 1870-1915.
Ein theoretischer Beweis für die Tatsächlichkeit der Freiheit des menschlichen Willens. (Festschrift Georg von Hertling zum siebzigsten Geburtstage am 31. Aug. 1913 dargebracht. Kempten, 1913. f°. p. 421-425.)

1. Will, The.
N. Y. P. L. January 8, 1914.

NK 0198239-8 NN

Kneib, Philipp, 1870-1915.
Die willensfreiheit und die innere verantwortlichkeit. Mainz, F. Kirchheim, 1898.
xii, 73 p. 8°.
Inaug.-diss.—Würzburg.
Bibliography: p. viii.

G—2403

NK 0198239-9 DLC MH CU NjP CU

Kneib, Philipp, 1870-1915.
Wissen und bedeutung der enzyklika gegen den modernismus ... Mainz, 1908.

NK 0198240 ODW

KNEIB, Philipp, 1870-1915.
Wissen und glauben. Ein wort zur klarstellung und verständigung. 2e vermehrte aufl. Mainz, Kirchheim & co, 1905.

NK 0198240-1 MH

Kneibler, A. R.
Making your ledger produce, by A. R. Kneibler ... [Benton Harbor, Mich.?] 1915. 51 p. illus. 4°.

1. Bookkeeping.
N. Y. P. L. November 7, 1923.

NK 0198241 NN

Kneiding, Erich, 1901-
Die zwangsvollstreckung in das handelsgeschäft. ... Göttingen, 1932. 39 p.
Inaug. Diss. -Göttingen, 1932.
Lebenslauf.
Bibliography.

NK 0198242 ICRL

W 4 M961 1955
KNEIDINGER, Gustav, 1915-
Die Zahnmedizin bei Oswald Gäbelkover; Untersuchungen über ihre Abhängigkeit von den älteren zahnmedizinischen Schriften und ihren Einfluss auf spätere, mit mehreren Texten aus alten Drucken und Handschriften. München, 1955.
123 l.
Inaug.-Diss. - Munich.
1. Gabelkover, Oswald, 1539-1616

NK 0198243 DNLM

LA 689 .K25 K6
KNEIDL, FRANTIŠEK.
Dějiny karlínského školství za první půlstoletí jeho trvání od r. 1841 do r. 1891. V Karlíně, Nakladem Obce karlínské, 1891.
82 p.

1. Education--Czechoslovak Republic--Karlin.

NK 0198244 InU

La15 A96 898K
Kneidl, František, comp.
Paměti škol okresu Karlínského. Soudní okresy: Karlín a Brandýs n. L. Od nejstarších časů, zvláště však od r. 1848 až do r. 1898. V Praze, Nákl. c.k. Okresní Školní Rady v Karlíně[1898]
675 p. illus., facsims., plans, tables. (2 fold. in pocket) 27 cm.

1. Schools - Prague-Karlin. 2. Schools - Brandýs nad Labem, Czechoslovakia.

NK 0198245 CtY NNC

4Z 874
Kneidl, Max
Verzeichnis der bayerischen heimat- und volkskundlichen Zeitungsbeilagen, zusammengestellt von Max Kneidl und Hedwig Magin. München, Herausgeber: Landesverband für nationale Volkserziehung, 1938.
48 p.

NK 0198246 DLC-P4

Kneier, Charles Mayard, 1898-
City government in the United States, by Charles M. Kneier ... New York and London, Harper & brothers, 1934.
vii p., 1 l., 482 p. 22cm.
"First edition."
"Suggested readings" at end of each chapter.

1. Municipal government—U. S. I. Title.
Library of Congress JS331.K6 34-21291 rev.
——— Copy 2.
Copyright A 74155 [r35k2] 352.073

ViU CaBVaU OrPR OrU
Or IdU MtU OrP OOxM PPT PSC PHC PU OCl OO OU ViU-L
NK 0198247 DLC WaS IdU-SB WaWW NcRS TxU MB NcD KMK

Kneier, Charles Mayard, 1898-
City government in the United States. Rev. ed. New York, Harper [1947]
viii, 727 p. 22 cm.
Includes "Suggested readings."

1. Municipal government—U. S. I. Title.
JS331.K6 1947 352.073 47-31187*

ICU TxU OrCS OrP OrPR OrSaW Wa WaSp OrPS OrMonO
NK 0198248 DLC IdB MtBC MtU PSt MiHM MiU Or MB ViU

Kneier, Charles Mayard, 1898- joint author.

Fairlie, John Archibald, 1872-
County government and administration, by John A. Fairlie ... and Charles Maynard Kneier ... New York, The Century co. [c1930]

Kneier, Charles Mayard, 1898-
Illustrative materials in municipal government and administration, by Charles M. Kneier ... New York, London, Harper & brothers [c1939]
xix p., 2 l., 3-632 p. 22cm.
"First edition."

1. Municipal government—U. S. I. Title.
Library of Congress JS308.K6 39-3430
——— Copy 2.
Copyright A 125822 [5] 352.073

ViU WaWW Or OrU OrCS Wa IdPI PSt PP OU ICRL WaTC
NK 0198250 DLC OrP NcRS NcD PPT PU-W PSC OCl OO OClW

Kneier, Charles Mayard, 1898- ed.
Readings in municipal government and administration, by Charles M. Kneier and Guy Fox. New York, Rinehart [1953]
486 p. illus. 22 cm.

1. Municipal government—U. S. 2. Municipal corporations—U. S. I. Fox, Guy, 1908- joint ed. II. Title.
JS308.K63 352.073 52-14015 ‡

Wa WaS WaTC
PU-FA PSt MB ODW PPT PPLas ViU TxU TU ScU LU OrP
NK 0198251 DLC PLF OrLgE OrCS CaBVaU MoU Or OO MiU

353.9 K73s
Kneier, Charles Maynard, 1898-
Some legal aspects of the governor's power to remove local officers. [University, Va., 1931]
16p.

"Reprinted from Virginia law review, volume xvii, no.4, February 1931."

NK 0198252 IU

VOLUME 300

Kneier, Charles Mayard, 1898–
State regulation of public utilities in Illinois, by Charles Mayard Kneier ... [Urbana, Ill., 1927]
3 p. l., 9-226 p., 1 l. 24½ cm.
Thesis (PH. D.)—University of Illinois, 1927.
Vita.
"Reprinted from the University of Illinois studies in the social sciences, vol. XIV, no. 1."
Bibliography: p. 208-215.
1. Public service commissions—Illinois. 2. Public utilities—Illinois. I. Title.
HD2767.I 54K6 1927 27—23843
Illinois. Univ. Library for Library of Congress [a66d½]†

NK 0198253 IU DLC

45.903 **Kneier, Charles Mayard, 1898-**
I3 State regulation of public utilities
K734 in Illinois, by Charles Mayard Kneier. Urbana, Ill., University of Illinois [c1927]
3 p. l., 9-226 p. 25 cm.
Thesis (Ph.D.) -- University of Illinois, 1927.
Without thesis statement.
"Reprinted from the University of Illinois studies in the social sciences, vol. XIV, no.1."
Bibliography: p. 208-215.

NK 0198254 NBuU-L

Kneier, Charles Mayard.
State regulation of public utilities in Illinois, by Charles Mayard Kneier ... Urbana, The University of Illinois [*1927]
226 p. incl. tables. 24½cm. (Added t.-p.: University of Illinois studies in the social sciences, vol. XIV, no. 1)
Bibliography: p. 208-215.
1. Public service commissions—Illinois. 2. Public utilities—Illinois. I. Title.
27-21917
Library of Congress H31.I 4 vol. XIV, no. 1
——— Copy 2. HD2767.I 54K6

ICJ CoU PU PPUG
NK 0198255 DLC OrP IU PU PBm PPT MiU OC1 OU ODW Vi

Kneier, Gerold.
Zur kasuistik der schussverletzungen... (Auszug) Breslau, 1920.
Inaug.-diss. Breslau.

NK 0198256 ICRL

KNEIFEL, Artur, 1901– *Sprünge im Dentin bei abgekauten Zähnen. 44p. 8°. Bresl., 1930.

NK 0198257 DNLM CtY

DK412 **Kneifel, Eduard, joint ed.**
.K37
Kargel, Adolf, *ed.*
Deutschtum im Aufbruch; vom Volkstumskampf der Deutschen im östlichen Wartheland [von] Adolf Kargel [und] Eduard Kneifel. Leipzig, S. Hirzel, 1942.

942.55 KNEIFEL, Eduard
K14z Die evangelisch-augsburgischen Gemeinden
K68e der Kalischer Dioezese. Plauen im Vogtland, Guenther Wolff, 1937.
284p. illus., map, tabs. 23.5cm. (Deutsche Gaue im Osten, 10)(Forschungen zur Geschichte der evangelisch-augsburgischen Kirche in Polen, 1)

NK 0198259 MH-AH NN

KNEIFF (C. A.) G. m. b. H.
100 [Hundert] Jahre C. A. Kneiff G. m. b. H., Nordhausen, 1827-1927. [Magdeburg, 1927]
27 p. illus. 17 x 24cm.

NK 0198260 NN

Kneiff, Elisabeth, 1899-
Bedeutung des Registers und des guten Glaubens in einem künftigen deutschen Gesetz über das Registerpfandrecht ... von Elisabeth Kneiff ... Berlin, P. Funk, 1930.
71 p. 21cm.
Inaug.-Diss. - Halle-Wittenberg.
"Lebenslauf": p. 71.
"Literaturverzeichnis": p.65-70.

NK 0198261 MH-L ICRL

Kneiff, J.
's Lieserl. Berlin, Bloch, n.d.
39p. 17 1/2cm.

NK 0198262 PPT

PR2303 **Kneile, Karl,** 1888–
.K7 Die formenlehre bei John Lyly ... Heidelberg, C. Winter, 1914.
xii, 89, [1] p. 22cm.
Inaug.-diss.—Tübingen.
Lebenslauf.
"Literatur": p. [ix]-xii.

NK 0198263 ICU PU ICRL CtY MH

Knein, Joannes, 1833-
De cerebri commotione et contusione...
Inaug. Diss. Greifswald, 1862

NK 0198264 ICRL DNLM

Kneip, Alexander, 1887– Apotheker u. Nahrungsmittelchemiker: Beiträge zur Kenntnis der Derivate des Hydroperoxydes. Frankfurt a. M. 1915: Voigt & Gleiber. 87 S. 8°
Rostock, Phil. Diss. v. 1915 (1. Aug. 1914), Ref. Michaelis
[Geb. 15. März 87 Wittlich; Wohnort: Eppstein i. Taunus; Staatsangeh.: Preußen; Vorbildung: Friedrich-Wilhelm-G. Trier bis 02; Studium: Darmstadt TeH. 6, Rostock 2 S.; Rig. 29. Juli 14.] [U 15. 2331

NK 0198265 ICRL PU MiU MH CtY

Kneip (August Adolph Christian). *De ossificatione pathologica. 2 p. l., 38 pp., 1 pl. 8°. *Gripswaldiæ, F. G. Kunike,* [1841]. [*Also, in:* P., v. 146.]

NK 0198266 DNLM

Kneip (Curt. Carol. Adolph.) [–1842]. *Degeneratio et amputatio penis. 1 p. l., 56 pp., 1 l., 1 pl. 12°. *Gryphiæ, F. G. Kunike,* 1838.

NK 0198267 DNLM PPC

Kneip, Günter, 1909-
... Grosser angeborener linksseitiger Zwerchfell[]bruch mit durchgebrochenem Magengeschwür .. [Schwäb. Gmünd, 1935]
Inaug.-Diss. - München.
Lebenslauf.
Full name: Günter Hugo Nikolaus Kneip.

NK 0198268 CtY

Kneip, Gustav.
[Tuba mirum. Libretto. German]
"Tuba mirum ..." Eine heitere Angelegenheit von Ernst Falkner. Köln, 1928.
15 p. 16 cm.
One-act opera.
[1. Operas—Librettos; I. Falkner, Ernst. Tuba mirum. II. Title.
ML50.K667T8 1928 50-54287

NK 0198269 DLC

Kneip, Gustav Wilhelm, 1881- joint ed.
Law FOR OTHER EDITIONS SEE MAIN ENTRY
Baath, Peter August, 1872– *ed.*
Fürsorgepflicht nach der Verordnung vom 13. februar 1924 einschl. der für voraussetzung, art und mass der öffentlichen fürsorge geltenden reichsgrundsätze und der nebengesetze sowie der einschlägigen landesrechtlichen vorschriften, herausgegeben von P. A. Baath ... und dr. G. W. Kneip ... 12. aufl. Berlin, F. Vahlen, 1939.

Kneip, Gustav Wilhelm, 1881–
Das schicksal der lebensversicherungssumme bei den verschiedenen gueterstaenden des B.G.B.
Inaug. Diss. Freiburg, 1906
Bibl.

NK 0198271 ICRL MH

Kneip, Gustav Wilhelm, 1881- joint ed.
FOR OTHER EDITIONS SEE MAIN ENTRY
Baath, Peter August, 1872– *ed.*
Verordnung über die fürsorgepflicht vom 13. februar 1924 einschl. der für voraussetzung, art und mass der öffentlichen fürsorge geltenden reichsgrundsätze und der nebengesetze, sowie der einschlägigen landesrechtlichen vorschriften, herausgegeben von P. A. Baath ... und dr. Kneip ... 11. aufl. Berlin, F. Vahlen, 1937.

Kneip, Jakob, 1881-
831.91
K68A An Frankreich. Köln, Gonski, 1922.
47 p. 21 cm.
1. Germany. Relations (general) with France. 2. France. Relations (general) with Germany. I. Title.

NK 0198273 NcD NN

Kneip, Jakob, 1881-
Retzlaff, Erich.
Das antlitz des alters, photographische bildnisse von Erich Retzlaff, einleitung von Jakob Kneip. Düsseldorf, Pädagogischer verlag g. m. b. h., 1930.

VOLUME 300

Kneip, Jakob, 1881–
Der Apostel, Roman. München, P. List [1955]
270 p. 20 cm.

I. Title.

PT2621.N36A7 55–57013 ‡

NK 0198275 DLC NN CtY NjN

Kneip, Jakob, 1881–
... Bauernbrot; neue gedichte. Leipzig, P. List [°1934]
135, [1] p. 19cm.

I. Title.

35–3944
Library of Congress PT2621.N36B3 1934
Copyright A—Foreign 27246
[2] 831.91

NK 0198276 DLC

Kneip, Jakob, 1881–
... Bekenntnis. Berlin-Grunewald, Horen-verlag, 1927.
173, [1] p., 1 l. 19½cm.
"Zweite vermehrte auflage."
Poems.

I. Title.
Library of Congress PT2621.N36B4 1927 29–1329

NK 0198277 DLC WU NBuU

Kneip, Jakob, 1881–
... Bergweihnacht, erzählungen. Leipzig, P. List [°1937]
2 p. l., 7–80 p. illus. 20½cm.
CONTENTS.—Im schlitten fuhren wir.—Weihnachten im Hunsrückdorf.—Das gestohlene Christkind.—Der Leyenhannes.—Der schäfer Mattes und der Burrisbauer.—Rutenstreiche.—Der versehgang.—Weihnachtsbrief eines abgewanderten an die daheim.—Gang zur mette.

1. Christmas stories. I. Title.
38–21593
Library of Congress PT2621.N36B46 1937
Copyright A—Foreign 38730
[2] 833.91

NK 0198278 DLC

KNEIP, JAKOB, 1881-
Bergweihnacht. [Erweiterte Ausg.] München, P. List [1949, c1937] 140 p. 20cm.

NK 0198279 NN DLC

Kneip, Jakob, 1881–
Ein deutsches Testament, Stimmen der Toten. Köln, Staufen-Verlag [1934]
41 p. 21 cm.
Poems.

I. Title.

PT2621.N36D4 52–47407

NK 0198280 DLC CtY

Hky
K726
D48
Kneip, Jakob,1881-
Ein deutsches Testament; Stimmen der Toten
Leipzig,P.List[c1938]
41p. 21cm.
Poems.

NK 0198281 CtY

PT
1175
K677d
Kneip, Jakob, 1881- comp.
Dichter unserer tage ... Köln a.Rh., H.Schaffstein [1923?]
64,[1]p. 17cm. (On cover: Schaffsteins blaue bändchen 160)
"Quellenangabe": p.[65]

1. German poetry - 20th century

NK 0198282 NRU

Kneip, Jakob, 1881–
Die Eifel
see under title

Kneip, Jakob, 1881–
... Feuer vom himmel; roman. Leipzig, P. List [°1936]
445, [1] p. 19cm.
Sequel to Porta nigra.

I. Title.
37–11811
Library of Congress PT2621.N36F4 1936
Copyright A—Foreign 34894
[2] 833.91

NK 0198284 DLC

Kneip, Jakob, 1881-
... Feuer vom himmel; roman. Leipzig,P.List [1943]
346p. 19cm.
6.-13.Aufl.
Sequel to Porta nigra.

NK 0198285 CtY

4PT
Ger.-1471
Kneip, Jakob, 1881-
Frau Regine; Roman. Leipzig, P. List [c1942]
348 p.

NK 0198286 DLC-P4

Kneip, Jakob, 1881–
... Fülle des lebens; verserzählungen und gedichte. Leipzig, P. List [1935]
61, [1] p. 19cm. [Lebendiges wort. 4]

I. Title.
36–36208
Library of Congress PT2621.N36F8 1935
Copyright A—Foreign 31030
[2] 831.91

NK 0198287 DLC PBm OO

Kneip, Jakob, 1881- ed.
Der gefährte; deutsche dichtung aus zweihundert jahren, von Jakob Kneip. Frankfurt am Main, M. Diesterweg, 1924.
2 p. l., 441 p. (Half-title: Diesterwegs deutschkunde)

1. German poetry. I. Title.

NK 0198288 NNC

KNEIP, JAKOB, 1881- , ed.
Der Gefährte; deutsche Dichtung aus zweihundert Jahren. 2. Aufl. Frankfurt a.M., M. Diesterweg, 1925. 485 p. 22cm. (Diesterwegs Deutschkunde)

1. Poetry, German—Collections. I. Title.

NK 0198289 NN

6908.27
Kneip, Jakob, 1881– compiler.
Der Gefährte. Deutsche Dichtung aus zweihundert Jahren. 3. Auflage.
— Frankfurt a.M. Diesterweg. 1926. (2), 485 pp. [Diesterwegs Deutschkunde.] 21 cm., in 8s.

D4491 — T.r. — S.r. — Germanv. Lit. Poetry. Colls.

NK 0198290 MB

Kneip, Jakob, 1881-
Der Gefährte. Deutsche Dichtung aus zweihundert Jahren. 4.unveränderte Aufl. Frankfurt a.M., Diesterweg, 1928
485 p.

NK 0198291 MH

PT 1171
.K68
1933
KNEIP,JAKOB,1881- ,ed.
Der Gefährte; deutsche Dichtung aus zweihundert Jahren, von Jakob Kneip. Frankfurt am Main, M. Diesterweg, 1933.
485 p.

NK 0198292 InU

831.08
K68G
Kneip, Jakob, 1881- ed.
Der gefährte; deutsche dichtung aus zweihundert jahren, herausgegeben von Jakob Kneip. 10., neubearbeitete aufl., unter mitwirkung von Friedrich Brock. Frankfurt am Main, M. Diesterweg, 1937.
xv, 432 p. 21½cm.
"Bei der neubearbeitung dieser auflage hat studienassessor Friedrich Brock die auswahl und zusammenstellung der jüngeren dichtung ("Rufe in die zeit") mitbesorgt."
"Quellen": p. 431-432.

NK 0198294 NcD

Kneip, Jakob, 1881– *ed.*
Der gefährte; deutsche dichtung aus zweihundert jahren, herausgegeben von Jakob Kneip. 12. aufl. Frankfurt am Main, M. Diesterweg, 1940.
xv, 432 p. 21½cm.
"Bei der neubearbeitung des 'Gefährten' hat Friedrich Brock die auswahl und zusammenstellung der jüngeren dichtung ('Rufe in die zeit') mitbesorgt."
"Quellen": p. 431–432.

1. German poetry—18th cent. 2. German poetry—19th cent. 3. German poetry—20th cent. I. Brock, Friedrich. II. Title.
45–46973
Library of Congress PT1171.K6 1940
[2] 831.082

NK 0198295 DLC CtY

VOLUME 300

PT 1171
K6
1951
Kneip, Jakob, 1881- ed.
Der Gefährte; deutsche Dichtung aus dreihundert Jahren, ausgewählt von Jakob Kneip. 14. Aufl. Frankfurt am Main, M. Diesterweg, 1951.
416 p. 21 cm.

NK 0198296 OU

Kneip, Jakob, 1881-
Gesänge an Gott
see under Haas, Joseph, 1879-1960.

Kneip, Jakob, 1881-
Gesammelte Gedichte. Köln, Greven Verlag [1953]
253 p. 20 cm.

PT2621.N36A17 1953 54-24678 ‡

NK 0198298 DLC NcD CtY NN

Kneip, Jakob, 1881-
... Hampit der jäger, ein fröhlicher roman. Berlin-Grunewald, Horen-verlag, 1927.
286, [1] p., 2 l. 19cm.
"Erstes bis drittes tausend."

I. Title.
Library of Congress PT2621.N36H3 1927 27-24147

NK 0198299 DLC PPG PPT

Kneip, Jakob, 1881-
... Hampit der jäger, ein fröhlicher roman. Leipzig, P. List [194-]
283, [1] p., 1 l. 19cm.
"83.-94. auflage der gesamtausgabe."

I. Title.
Library of Congress PT2621.N36H3 46-40671
[2] 833.91

NK 0198300 DLC CtY

Kneip, Jakob, 1881-
...Hunsrückweihnacht; erzählungen. Köln, Staufen-verlag [1934]
80 p. illus. 20½cm.
"Holzschnitte von Maria Braun."

NK 0198301 CSt NRU WU

Kneip, Jakob, 1881-
Jakob Kneip. M[ünchen]-Gladbach, Orplid-Verlag [1926]
54p. 24cm. (Wege nach Orplid, 21. Bändchen)
Excerpt from the novel Hampit, der Jäger, and poems.

I. Kneip, Jakob, 1881- Hampit, der Jäger. II. Title: Hampit, der Jäger.

NK 0198302 IEN MH PPT

Hky
K736
J6
Kneip, Jakob, 1881-
Johanna; eine Tochter unserer Zeit. Köln, Greven Verlag [c1954]
176p. 19cm.

NK 0198303 CtY NN

PT2621
Kn36L4
Kneip, Jakob, 1881-
Der lebendige Gott; Erscheinungen, Wallfahrten und Wunder. Jena, E. Diederichs, 1919.
114 p. (Nyland Werke, 4)
Poems.

NK 0198304 CU RPB MH InU NjP WU

Kneip, Jakob, 1881-
... Der lebendige Gott: erscheinungen und wunder. Berlin-Grunewald, Horen-verlag, 1927.
126 p., 2 l. 19½cm.
Poems.
"Zweite veränderte auflage."

I. Title.
Library of Congress PT2621.N36L4 1927 31-19610
831.91

NK 0198305 DLC CtY

Kneip, Jakob, 1881-
Licht in der Finsternis. Köln, B. Pick, 1949.
161 p. 20 cm.
Novel.

I. Title.
PT2621.N36L5 A 51-10531
Rochester. Univ. Libr. for Library of Congress [2]†

NK 0198306 NRU DLC

Kneip, Jakob, 1881-
Die Mosel. Königstein im Taunus, K. R. Langewiesche [195-?]
55 p. illus. 21 cm.

1. Moselle Valley—Descr. & trav.—Views. I. Title.
DD801.M7K59 59-24769 ‡

NK 0198307 DLC NN

Kneip, Jakob, 1881-
... Porta nigra; oder, Die berufung des Martin Krimkorn, roman. Leipzig, P. List [c1932]
429, [1] p. 19cm.

I. Title. II. Title: Die berufung des Martin Krimkorn.
Library of Congress PT2621.N36P6 1932 33-14180
Copyright A—Foreign 20345
[2] 833.91

NK 0198308 DLC NN WU

Kneip, Jakob, 1881-
Porta Nigra; Roman. München, P. List [1941]
330p. 20cm.

NK 0198309 ICarbS

Kneip, Jakob, 1881-
Porta Nigra, Roman unserer Zeit. Leipzig, P. List [1946, °1941]
585 p. 22 cm.

I. Title.
PT2621.N36P6 1946 48-27706*‡

NK 0198310 DLC CtY CU

Kneip, Jakob, 1881-
Das reich Christi, von Jakob Kneip. Köln, Staufen-verlag [1935]
80 p. 20½cm.

1. Jesus Christ—Kingdom. I. Title.
Library of Congress BT94.K6 35-11677
231.7

NK 0198311 DLC WU

Kneip, Jakob, 1881-
Das Siebengebirge, mit 12 farbigen Bild-Tafeln nach Aquarellen von F. M. Jansen. Köln, R. Malzkorn [1941]
46 p. illus., 12 col. plates. 22 cm.

1. Siebengebirge.
DD491.R517K6 50-42083

NK 0198312 DLC

PT2609
.N67V4
1937
Kneip, Jakob, 1881- ed.
Engelke, Gerrit, 1890-1918.
... Vermächtnis; aus dem nachlass herausgegeben von Jakob Kneip. Leipzig, P. List [1937]

Kneip, Jacob, 1881-
Weltentscheidung des Geistes am Rhein. Köln, Greven Verlag [1953]
34 p. 19 cm.
1. Ethics. 2. Christian life.

NK 0198314 ICarbS MH NN

Kneip, Karl, 1911-
... Die Bedeutung zahnärztlicher Fürsorge und Frühbehandlung nach einem Fall typischer Gebissverkrüppelung ... Frankfurt a.M. [1934]
Inaug.-Diss. - Frankfurt a.M.
Lebenslauf.
"Literaturverzeichnis": p. 19-20.

NK 0198315 CtY

17
1185
Kneip, Nikolaus.
Grosse biblische geschichte fuer die obere klasse. 3 te aufl. Freiburg im Breisgau, Herder, 1887.
204 p. front., 1 map. 16°.

NK 0198316 DLC

VOLUME 300

Kneip, Theodore Joseph, 1926–
A study of the electroreduction and adsorption of N,N-dimethyl-p-phenylazoaniline at a mercury surface. Ann Arbor, University Microfilms [1955]
([University Microfilms, Ann Arbor, Mich.] Publication no. 10,497)
Microfilm copy of typescript. Positive.
Collation of the original: vi, 54 l. diagrs., tables.
Thesis—University of Illinois.
Abstracted in Dissertation abstracts, v. 15 (1955) no. 1, p. 35–36.
Vita.
Bibliography: leaves 51–53.
1. Aniline. 2. Adsorption. 3. Reduction, Electrolytic.
Microfilm AC–1 no. 10,497 Mic A 55–54
Illinois. Univ. Library
for Library of Congress [1]†

NK 0198317 IU DLC

Kneipp, E.H. Sebastian
see Kneipp, Sebastian, 1821-1897.

Kneipp, Leon Frederick.
The national forests as a form of federal aid to the states. [By L. F. Kneipp] From "A national plan for American forestry". A report prepared by the Forest service, U. S. Department of agriculture, in response to S. Res. 175 (72d Congress) ... Washington, U. S. Govt. print. off., 1933.
ii, 1095–1124 p. diagrs. 23cm. ([U. S. 73d Cong., 1st sess.] Senate. Doc. 12—Separate no. 12)
1. Forest reserves. I. Title. Agr 34–106
Library, U. S. Dept. of Agriculture 1F76Naa no. 12
Library of Congress [SD11]

NK 0198319 DNAL

Kneipp, Leon Frederick.
Public acquisition of private lands as an aid to private forestry. [By L. F. Kneipp] From "A national plan for American forestry". A report prepared by the Forest service, U. S. Department of agriculture, in response to S. Res. 175 (72d Congress) ... Washington, U. S. Govt. print. off., 1933.
ii, 1147–1176 p. 23cm. ([U. S. 73d Cong., 1st sess.] Senate. Doc. 12—Separate no. 14)
[1. Forest lands] [2. Forestry—Government aid] 1. 2. Forests and forestry—U. S. I. Title. Agr 34–108
Library, U. S. Dept. of Agriculture 1F76Naa no. 14
Library of Congress [SD11]

NK 0198320 DNAL

Kneipp, Otto, 1884–
Die landwirtschaft im kreise Giessen, ihre grundlagen, ihr derzeitiger stand nebst massnahmen zu ihrer hebung; zugleich einsicht in einzelne betriebe ... Giessen [Druckerei Zeuner & co., Bad Homburg] 1924.
39 p. 22½cm.
Inaug.-diss.—Giessen.
Lebenslauf.
"Auszug aus der dissertation ..."
"Benutzte literatur": p. 38.
1. Agriculture—Hesse—Giessen. 2. Cattle—Hesse—Giessen. 3. Agricultural laws and legislation—Hesse. I. Title.
28-14974
Library of Congress S466.H5K6

NK 0198321 DLC ICRL

RM 700 K54 1898
Kneipp, Sebastian, 1821-1897.
Allerhand nützliches für Wasser-Kur und Lebensweise; gesammelte Aufsätze aus den sieben ersten Jahrgängen (1891-1897) des illustrierten Wörishofener Kneipp-Kalenders. Kempten, J. Rösel, 1898.
xiii,550p. illus.
1. Therapeutics, Physiological. 2. Hygiene. 3. Hydrotherapy.

NK 0198322 UU

Kneipp, Sebastian, 1821-1897, ed.
Almanach-Kneipp
see under title

Kneipp, Sebastian, 1821–1897.
... Baby's Kneipp cure; or, The care of children in health and disease. [Popular American ed.] By Monsignore Sebastian Kneipp ... New York city, The Kneipp publishing company [°1897]
2 p. l., vii–xvii, 159 p. illus. 19cm.
1. Hydrotherapy. I. Title.
7—39749
Library of Congress RM817.K7

NK 0198324 DLC ICJ

WS 80 K67k 1897
KNEIPP, Sebastian, 1821-1897
The care of children in sickness and in health. London, Grevel, 1897.
xvi, 261 p. illus.
Translation of Kinderpflege in gesunden und kranken Tagen.

NK 0198325 DNLM MB NN

RM817 K8 897K
Kneipp, Sebastian, 1821-1897.
The codicel to "My will" for the healthy and the sick ... Kempten(Bavaria)J. Koesel, 1897.
1p.ℓ., vi, 429p. illus., plates(part col.) 20cm.
Head and tail pieces.
1. Kneipp cure. I. Title. II. Title: My will.

NK 0198326 CtY-M MB

Unclass.
Kneipp, Sebastian, 1821-1897.
The codicil to "my will" for the healthy and the sick ... Second edition. Kempten (Bavaria),Jos Koesel, Publisher, 1906.
v, 429 p. 19 cm.

NK 0198327 DLC

Kneipp, Sebastian, 1821-1897.
Codizill zu meinem Testament für Gesunde & Kranke. Aufl. 3. 376 S. ill. Bilder, 12. Kempten, Kosel, 1897.

NK 0198328 PPG

Kneipp, Sebastian, 1821-1897.
Codizill zu meinem Testamente für Gesunde und Kranke. 4. Aufl. Kempten, Kosel, 1897.
376 p.

NK 0198329 PPC

WB 520 K68s 1892
KNEIPP, Sebastian, 1821-1897
Comment il faut vivre; avertissements et conseils s'adressant aux malades et aux gens bien portants pour vivre d'après une hygiène simple et raisonnable et une thérapeutique conforme à la nature. 4. éd. Kempten, Kösel, 1892.
xii, 385 p. illus., port.
Translation of So sollt ihr leben!

NK 0198330 DNLM MiU

WB 520 K68s 1897
KNEIPP, Sebastian, 1821-1897
Como habéis de vivir! Avisos y consejos para sanos y enfermos, ó reglas para vivir conforme a la sana razón y curar las enfermedades según los preceptos de la naturaleza. Versión española de la 17. ed. alemana por Francisco G. Ayuso. 4. ed. Kempten, Kösel, 1897.
xvi, 420 p. illus.
Translation of So sollt ihr leben!

NK 0198331 DNLM

Kneipp, Sebastian, 1821-1897.
El cuidado de los niños; avisos y consejos para tratarlos en el estado de salud y en las enfermedades. Vertido de la 6a. edicion alemana por F. G. Ayuso. México: E. Rodriguez, 1895. viii, 259 p. 12°.
1. Children.—Care and hygiene. 2. García Ayuso, Francisco, translator.
N. Y. P. L. January 8, 1914.

NK 0198332 NN

SLOVENIAN 615 K736d
Kneipp, Sebastian, 1821-1897
Domači zdravnik; po naukih in izkušnjah župnika Kneippa. Priredil Valentin Podgorc. Šesti, popravljeni natis. V Celovcu, Družba Sv. Mohorja [n.d.]
312 p. illus.

NK 0198333 MiD OCl

Kneipp, Sebastian, 1821-1897
Domači zdravnik po naukih in izkusnjah. 6., popravljeni in pomnozeni natis. [240p.] illus. Mohorja na Preveljah, 1924.

NK 0198334 OCl

Kneipp, Sebastian, 1821-1897.
Das grosse Kneippbuch. Ein Volksbuch für Gesunde und Kranke... bearbeitet und hrsg. von Bonifaz Reile... Kempten und München, J. Kösel, 1913.
xxiv, 1314, xxp. illus. (part col.) 24cm.
1. Therapeutics, Physiological. 2. Hygiene. 3. Materia medica, vegetable. I. Reile, Bonifaz, ed.

NK 0198335 KAS

Kneipp, Sebastian, 1821-1897
Das grosse Kneippbuch, ein volksbuch für gesunde und kranke. Nach dem tode des verfassers in dessen auftrag bearbeitet und herausgegeben von Bonifaz Reile... München, Kösel & Pustet, 1922.
1418 p., illus. (part col. port.)
English translation has title: My water-cure.
I. Reile, Bonifaz, ed.

NK 0198336 MiD

Kneipp, Sebastian, 1821-1897.
Das grosse Kneippbuch; ein Volksbuch für Gesunde und Kranke. Nach dem Tode des Verfassers in dessen Auftrag bearb. u. hrsg. von Bonifaz Reile. München, J. Kösel & F. Pustet, 1928.
1060 p. illus., plates (part col.) 24 cm.

NK 0198337 PLatS

VOLUME 300

Kneipp, Sebastian, 1821–1897.
Das grosse Kneippbuch; lehr- und hausbuch der gesamten naturgemässen lebens- u. heilweise, von Sebastian Kneipp und Bonifaz Reile; neu bearbeitet und erweitert von dr. med. Christian Fey ... 76.–95. tausend. München, Kösel-Pustet [1939]
2 p. l., xvi, 662 p. front. (port.) illus., xxvi pl. (part col.) on 13 l., diagrs. 25cm.
1. Therapeutics, Physiological. 2. Hygiene. 3. Materia medica, Vegetable. I. Reile, Bonifaz, ed. II. Fey, Christian, 1901– III. Title.
41-314
Library of Congress RM700.K55 1939
Copyright A—Foreign 44981
[2] 615.8

NK 0198338 DLC OrStbM ICJ

Kneipp, Sebastian, 1821-1897.
——. Jaarboekje bevattende de verschillende begietingen, baden enz. Korte verhandeling over de gezondheidsleer, levensregelen, verpleging van oogen, tanden, haren enz. Velerlei nieuwe genezingen met opgaaf der aangewende middelen. Verschillende nuttige wenken. Voorschriften tegen cholera, influenza, verschillende ziekten, die in de 4 jaargetijden voorkomen enz. 159 pp. 12°. *'s Bosch, G. Mosmans Senior*, 1892.

NK 0198339 DNLM

Slavic-American Imprints Coll. 420.35 G4 K54
Kneipp, Sebastian, 1821-1897.
Jak žíti; rady a pokyny zdravým i nemocným, aby prostě, rozumně žili a přirozeně se léčili. 2. vyd. americké. Milwaukee, A. Novák [1889?]
344 p. 20 cm.
English translation of title: Thus shalt thou live; hints and advice for the healthy and the sick on a simple and rational mode of life and a natural method of cure.

NK 0198340 IEdS MnHi

Kneipp, Sebastian
Jak žiti; rady a pokyny zdravym i nemocným, aby prosté, rozumné žili a přirozené se léčili;...přel. J. Ježek. [324p.] Kemptenu, Koesla, 1897.

NK 0198341 OCl

Kneipp, Sebastian, 1821–1897.
Kinderpflege in gesunden und kranken tagen. Ratschläge von msgr. Sebastian Kneipp ... 3. aufl. Donauwörth, L. Auer, 1890.
208 p. 18cm.

NK 0198342 CLU

Kneipp, Sebastian, 1821-1897.
Kinderpflege in gesunden und kranken Tagen... 8. Aufl. Donauwörth, Auer, 1890.
208 p.

NK 0198343 PPC

Kneipp, Sebastian, 1821–1897.
Kinderpflege in gesunden und kranken tagen. Ratschläge von msgr. Sebastian Kneipp ... 13. aufl. Donauwörth, L. Auer [189–?]
208 p. 18cm.
1. Children—Care and hygiene. 2. Children—Diseases. I. Title.
40-22465
Library of Congress RJ61.K68

NK 0198344 DLC

Kneipp, Sebastian, 1821–1897.
Kinderpflege in gesunden und kranken Tagen. Ratschläge von Pfarrer Sebastian Kneipp. Donauwörth, L. Auer [1891]
208 p. 18½cm.
Portrait vignette.

NK 0198345 ICJ NNU-W

WBF K68k 1905
KNEIPP, Sebastian, 1821-1897
Das kleine Kneipp-Buch. Meine Lebensregeln für Gesunde und meine Heilmittel für Kranke, in alphabetischer Form aus meinen gesammelten Schriften der gebrechlichen Menschheit dargeboten... Nach dem Tode des Verfassers und in dessen Auftrag hrsg. von Bonifaz Reile. 3. Aufl. Kempten, Kosel, 1905.
v, 655 p.
I. Reile, Bonifaz, ed.

NK 0198346 DNLM

RM817 .K6
Kneipp, Sebastian, 1821-1897.
The Kneipp cure; an absolutely verbal and literal translation of "Meine Wasserkur" (My water cure) Complete American ed. Milwaukee, Wis., C. N. Caspar Co. [pref. 1896]
xvi, 451 p. illus., ports. 20cm.
Translator's pref. signed: St. D.
Imprint from label.
1. Hydrotherapy. I. Title.

NK 0198347 MB

Kneipp, Sebastian, 1821–1897.
... The Kneipp cure; an absolutely verbal and literal translation of "Meine wasserkur" (My water cure) by Sebastian Kneipp ... With 200 illustrations and a portrait of the author. [Complete American ed.] New York city, The Benedict Lust publishing company [1896]
xvi, 451 p. incl. front. (ports.) illus. 20cm.
Translator's preface signed: St. D.
(In orig. paper wraps)

NK 0198348 KU-M

Kneipp, Sebastian, 1821–1897.
... The Kneipp cure; an absolutely verbal and literal translation of "Meine wasserkur" (My water cure) by Sebastian Kneipp ... With 200 illustrations and a portrait of the author. [Complete American ed.] New York city, The Kneipp cure publishing company [1897]
xvi, 451 p. incl. front. (ports.) illus. 20cm.
Translator's preface signed: St. D.
6-28457
Library of Congress RM817.K6

NK 0198349 DLC DNLM

RM817 K8 949K
Kneipp, Sebastian, 1821-1897.
... The Kneipp cure; an absolutely verbal and literal translation of "Meine Wasserkur" (My water cure) ... [New York, The Nature Cure publishing company, 1949]
xvi, 451p. illus., port. 20cm.

NK 0198350 CtY-M WU-M OWorP

WB 520 K68m 1890
KNEIPP, Sebastian, 1821-1897
Ma cure d'eau; ou, Hygiène et médication pour la guérison des maladies et la conservation de la santé. 2. éd. Strasbourg, Le Roux, 1890.
xii, 560 p. illus.
Translation of Meine Wasserkur.

NK 0198351 DNLM

Kneipp, Sebastian, 1821-1897.
Ma cure d'eau, trad. 25th ed.
12 560p. Paris 1892 Retaux

NK 0198352 MiU

WB 520 K68m 1892b
KNEIPP, Sebastian, 1821-1897
Ma cure d'eau; ou, Hygiène et médication pour la guérison des maladies et la conservation de la santé. 30. éd. Strasbourg, Le Roux, 1892.
xii, 560 p. illus.
Translation of Meine Wasserkur.

NK 0198353 DNLM

---

ar V 11055
Kneipp, Sebastian, 1821-1897.
Ma cure d'eau; ou, Hygiène et médication pour la guérison des maladies et la conservation de la santé ... Seule traduction française autorisée par l'auteur. 38. éd. Strasbourg, Le Roux, 1893.
560 p. illus. 18cm.
Translation of Meine Wasserkur.
1. Hydrotherapy. I. Title. II. Kneipp, Sebastian, 1821- 1897. [Meine Wasserkur--French.

NK 0198354 NIC

YA16479
Kneipp, Sébastian, 1821-1897.
Ma Cure d'Eau, ou Hygiène et Médication pour la Guérison des Maladies et la conversation de la Santé. Strasbourg, F.-X. Le Roux & Co., 1895.
52me édition.

NK 0198355 DLC

Kneipp, Sebastian, 1821-1897.
Mano gydymas vandeniu sulig 40-metiniu patirimu...iš vokiečiu kalbos verté Aguenaitis. [224 p. il] Ryga, Maciejausko, 1909.

NK 0198356 OCl

WZ 100 K68m 1949
KNEIPP, Sebastian, 1821-1897
Mein Leben. Regensburg, Von Gott [1949]
28 p. illus., ports.

NK 0198357 DNLM

Kneipp, Sebastian, 1821-1897
Mein Testament für Gesunde und Kranke. 4. Aufl. Kempten, Kosel, 1894.
340 p.

NK 0198358 PPC

Kneipp, Sebastian, 1821–1897.
Mein testament für gesunde und kranke. Von Msgr. Sebastian Kneipp ... 6. aufl. Kempten (Bayern) J. Kösel, 1895.
xii, 340 p. front. (2 port.) illus., plates. 19cm.
CONTENTS. — Allgemeines. — Die abhärtung. — Wasseranwendungen. — Krankheiten. — Die bereitung der thee, pulver, tinkturen etc. — Uebungsschule. Praktische unterweisung zur genauen anwendung meiner güsse, dämpfe und wickel.
1. Hydrotherapy. 2. Medicine,-Popular.
8-18860†
Library of Congress RM817.K47

NK 0198359 DLC KU-M DNLM

VOLUME 300

Kneipp, Sebastian, 1821-1897.
Mein Testament für Gesunde und Kranke. 10. Aufl. Kempten, J. Kösel, 1896.
xii, 340 p. plates. 19 cm.

NK 0198360 PLatS

Kneipp, Sebastian, 1821-1897.
Mein Testament für Gesunde und Kranke ... 18. Aufl. Kempten (Bayern) J. Kösel, 1903.
xii, 340 p. front. (port) illus., plates.

1. Hyrdotherapy. 2. Medicine, Popular. I. Title.

NK 0198361 TxHU

Kneipp, Sebastian, 1821-1897.
Mein Testament und Codizill; neu hrsg. und bearb. von Christian Fey. München, Ehrenwirth [1955]
276 p. illus., map (on lining paper) 21 cm.

1. Hydrotherapy. 2. Medicine, Popular. I. Fey, Christian, 1901- ed. II. Title.

RM817.K48 64-53804

NK 0198362 DLC OCl DNLM

RM817 .K8K6 Kneipp, Sebastian, 1821-1897.
Meine wasser-kur, durch mehr als 30 jahre erprobt und geschrieben zur heilung der krankheiten und erhaltung der gesundheit. St. Paul, Druckerei des Wanderer [1886?]
424 p. illus. 20cm.

NK 0198363 MnHi

WB 520 K68m 1887 **KNEIPP**, Sebastian, 1821-1897
Meine Wasser-Kur, durch mehr als 30 Jahre erprobt und geschrieben zur Heilung der Krankheiten und Erhaltung der Gesundheit. 2., verm. Aufl. Kempten, Kösel, 1887.
vi, 338 p. illus., port.

NK 0198364 DNLM

WBF K68me 1888 KNEIPP, Sebastian, 1821-1897
Meine Wasser-Kur, durch mehr als 30 Jahre erprobt und geschrieben zur Heilung der Krankheiten und Erhaltung der Gesundheit. 5. verm. und berichtigte Aufl. Kempten, Kösel, 1888.
v, 360 p. illus., port.

NK 0198365 DNLM

4RM-12 Kneipp, Sebastian, 1821-1897.
Meine Wasser-Kur, durch mehr als 30 Jahre erprobt und geschrieben zur Heilung der Krankheiten und Erhaltung der Gesundheit. Kempten, J. Kösel, 1889.
368 p.

NK 0198366 DLC-P4

KNEIPP, Sebastian, 1821-1897.
Meine wasser-kur. 9e aufl. Kempten, 1889.
sm.8°.

NK 0198367 MH

Kneipp, Sebastian, 1821-1897. 615.853 O900
Meine Wasser-Kur, durch mehr als 30 Jahre erprobt und geschrieben zur Heilung der Krankheiten und Erhaltung der Gesundheit von Sebastian Kneipp, ... Mit dem autotypischen Bildnisse des Verfassers. (Neueste photographische Aufnahme von 1889.) Elfte Auflage. Kempten, J. Kösel'sche Buchhandlung, 1889.
iv, [4], 368 p. front. (port.), 24 illus. 18½cm.

NK 0198368 ICJ

Kneipp, Sebastian, 1821-1897.
Meine Wasser-Kur, durch mehr als 30 Jahre erprobt und geschrieben zur Heilung der Krankheiten und Erhaltung der Gesundheit. 15. Aufl. Kempten, Kösel, 1890.
368 p.

NK 0198369 PPC

Kneipp, Sebastian, 1821-1897.
Meine Wasser-Kur, durch mehr als 30 Jahre erprobt und geschrieben zur Heilung der Krankheiten und Erhaltung der Gesundheit, von Sebastian Kneipp... Kempten: J. Kösel, 1890. vii(i), 368 p. front. (port.) 16. ed. 12°.

1. Water cure. January 7, 1920.

NK 0198370 NN

Kneipp, Sebastian, 1821-1897.
Meine Wasser-Kur, durch mehr als 30 Jahre erprobt und geschreiben zur Heilung der Krankheiten und Erhaltung der Gesundheit. 17. Aufl. Kempten, Kosel, 1890.
368 p.

NK 0198371 PPC

WB 520 K68m 1891 **KNEIPP**, Sebastian, 1821-1897
Meine Wasser-Kur, durch mehr als 30 Jahre erprobt und geschrieben zur Heilung der Krankheiten und Erhaltung der Gesundheit. 25. Aufl. Kempton, Kösel, 1891.
vii, 368 p. illus., port.

NK 0198372 DNLM DLC

Kneipp, Sebastian, 1821-1897.
Meine Wasser-Kur, durch mehr als 30 Jahre erprobt und geschreiben zur Heisung der Krankheiten und Erhaltung der Gesundheit. 28. Aufl. Kompten, Jos. Kösel'schen Buchhandlung, 1891.
368p. illus.

NK 0198373 ICRL NN MiU

Kneipp, Sebastian, 1821-1897.
Meine wasserkur, durch mehr als 35 jahre erprobt und geschrieben zur heilung der krankheiten und erhaltung der gesundheit, von Sebastian Kneipp. 34. aufl. Kempten (Bayern), J. Kösel, 1891.
vii, 376 p. illus. 19cm.

1. Hydrotherapy. I. Title.

NK 0198374 KAS

RM 817 .K49 1893 Science Kneipp, Sebastian, 1821-1897.
Meine Wasser-Kur, durch mehr als 35 jahre erprobt und geschrieben zur heilung der krankheiten und erhaltung der gesundheit, von Sebastian Kneipp. Mit dem bildnisse des Verfassers. 42. Aufl. Kempten, Rösel'schen, 1893.
vii,376p. illus.,port. 19cm.

1. Hydrotherapy. II. Title.

NK 0198375 KU

Kneipp, Sebastian, 1821-1897.
Meine Wasser-Kur...Aufl. 53. Bildnis, 12. Kempten, Kösel, 1894.
376 S. ill.

NK 0198376 PPG

615.853 K68m54 Kneipp, Sebastian, 1821-1897.
Meine wasser-kur, durch mehr als 35 jahre erprobt und geschrieben zur heilung der krankheiten und erhaltung der gesundheit ... 54.aufl. Kempten (Bayern) J. Kösel, 1894.
376p. front.(port.) illus.

1. Hyrdrotherapy.

NK 0198377 IU-M ICRL

RM817 K5 1895 Kneipp, Sebastian, 1821-1897.
Meine wasser-kur, durch mehr als 35 jahre erprobt und geschrieben zur heilung der krankheiten und erhaltung der gesundheit, von Msgr. Sebastian Kneipp ... Mit dem bildnisse des verfassers. (Neueste photographische aufnahme von 1894) Sechsundfünfzigste auflage. Kempten (Bayern) Jof. Kösel, 1895.
vii,[1],376p. front.(port.)illus. 18½cm.

1. Hydrotherapy I. Title.

NK 0198378 NBuG

RM817 .K49 1895 Kneipp, Sebastian, 1821-1897.
Meine Wasser Kur, durch mehr als 35 Jahre erprobt und geschrieben zur Heilung der Krankheiten und Erhaltung der Gesundheit... 57. Aufl. Kempten, J. Rösel, 1895.
376 p. illus. 19 cm.

1. Hydrotherapy. I. Title.

NK 0198379 TU

Kneipp, Sebastian, 1821-1897. 7809.78
Meine Wasser — Kur, durch mehr als 40 Jahre erprobt, und geschrieben. Zur Heilung der Krankheiten und Erhaltung der Gesundheit. 60. Auflage.
= Kempten. Kösel. 1896. viii, (1), 376 pp. Illus. Portrait. 16°.

NK 0198380 MB

VOLUME 300

Kneipp, Sebastian, 1821-1897.
Meine Wasser-Kur, durch mehr als 40 Jahre erprobt und geschrieben zur Heilung der Krankheiten und Erhaltung der Gesundheit. 62.Aufl. Kempten, Bayern, J.Kösel, 1897.
376 p. illus., port.
Contents.-1 Wasser-Anwendungen.-2 Apotheke.-3 Krankheiten.

NK 0198381 ICJ

Kneipp, Sebastian, 1821-1897.
Meine Wasser-Kur, durch mehr als 40 Jahre erprobt und geschrieben zur Heilung der Krankheiten und Erhaltung der Gesundheit. 63.Aufl. Kempten (Bayern) Verlag der J.Kösel'schen Buchhandlung, 1897.

NK 0198382 MH

Kneipp, Sebastian, 1821-1897.
Meine Wasserkur, durch mehr als vierzig Jahre erprobt und geschrieben zur Heilung der Krankheiten und Erhaltung der Gesundheit. 69. Aufl. Kempten, Jos. Kösel'schen Buchhandlung, 1901.
vii, 376 p.

NK 0198383 WaU

Kneipp, Sebastian, 1821-1897.
Meine Wasser-Kur, durch mehr als 40 Jahre erprobt und geschrieben zur Heilung der Krankheiten und Erhaltung der Gesundheit ... 71. Aufl. Kempten (Bayern) J. Kösel, 1902.
vii, 376 p. front. (port.) illus.

1. Hydrotherapy. I. Title.

NK 0198384 TxHU

Kneipp, Sebastian, 1821-1897.
Meine Wasser-kur durch mehr als 40 Jahre erprobt und geschrieben zur Heilung der Krankheiten und Erhaltung der Gesundheit. 104-108. Aufl. München, Josef Kösel & Friedrich Pustet, 1928.
376p. illus.

NK 0198385 ICRL

Kneipp, Sebastian, 1821-1897.
Meine wasserkur, durch mehr als vierzig jahre erprobt und geschrieben zur heilung der krankheiten und erhaltung der gesundheit, von Sebastian Kneipp. Herausgegeben und neubearbeitet von dr. med. Christian Fey. 581.-600. tausend, mit 22 neuen abbildungen. München, Kösel-Pustet, 1939.
350, ⌊2⌋ p. front. (port.) x pl. on 5 l. 20cm.

1. Hydrotherapy. I. Frey, Christian, 1901- ed. II. Title.
39-33033
Library of Congress RM817.K49 1939
Copyright A—Foreign 43744
⌊2⌋ 615.853

NK 0198386 DLC OKentU

WB 520 K68m 1954

KNEIPP, Sebastian, 1821-1897.
Meine Wasserkur durch mehr als vierzig Jahre erprobt und geschrieben zur Heilung der Krankheiten und Erhaltung der Gesundheit. Neu hrsg. und bearb. von Christian Fey. München, Ehrenwirth ⌊1954⌋
292 p. illus.
1. Hydrotherapy I. Fey, Christian, 1901- ed.

NK 0198387 DNLM OCl

RM817 K8 892Kc

Kneipp, Sebastian, 1821-1897.
Mi cura de agua; ó Higiene y medicina para la cración de las enfermedades y la conservación de la salud. Versión Castellana, con una carta-prólogo de D. Francisco Serrano de la Pedrosa. Madrid, Calle de Eguilaz, 1892.
237p., 3l. port. 19cm.

1. Kneipp cure. I. Serrano, Franciso, de la Pedrosa. tr.

NK 0198388 CtY-M

WB 520 K68m 1892a

KNEIPP, Sebastian, 1821-1897
Mijne waterkuur, sinds 30 jaren toegepast en goed bevonden, geschreven tot genezing der ziekten en tot behoud der gezondheid. Naar de 23ste uitg. het Duitsch vertaald. 's-Gravenhage, Van der Straaten, 1892.
viii, 329, xviii p. illus.
Translation of Meine Wasserkur.

NK 0198389 DNLM

WB 520 K68m 1890a

KNEIPP, Sebastian, 1821-1897
Moje léczenie woda, na podstawie przeszło 35-letniego doświadczenia, dla leczenia chorób i utrzymania zdrowia. Z 33. powiększonego i oprac. na nowo wyd. przetłómaczył J. A. Łukaszkiewicz. Chicago ⌊Polish American Pub. Co., 1890⌋ xvi, 420 p. illus., port.
Translation of Meine Wasserkur.

NK 0198390 DNLM

Slavic-American Imprints Coll. 420.35 34 K584

Kneipp, Sebastian, 1821-1897.
Moje závěť neboli poslední vůle. Zdravým a nemocným zanechává autorisovaný překlad pořídil J. Ježek. Chicago, August Geringer [1894]
314 p. illus. 20 cm.

English translation of title: My testament or last will. To healthy and sick people, dedicated by Sebastian Kneipp.

NK 0198391 IEdS

Kneipp, Sebastian, 1821-1897. 615.853 O901
.... My water-cure as tested through more than thirty years
107912 and described for the healing of diseases and the preservation of health, by Sebastian Kneipp, ... With illustrations. Translated from the thirtieth German edition by A. de F. Edinburgh and London, W. Blackwood and Sons, 1891.
xxv, 272 p. front. (port.), 25 illus. 19cm.

NK 0198392 ICJ CtY PPC OClW-H IU-M PPL DNLM

Kneipp, Sebastian, 1821-1897.
My water-cure tested for more than 40 years and published for the cure of diseases and preservation of health. Translated from the 62nd German edition. Kempton, Kosel, 1891.
395 p.

NK 0198393 PPC

Kneipp, Sebastian, 1821-1897.
... My water-cure. Tested for more than 35 years and published for the cure of diseases and the preservation of health by Sebastian Kneipp ... ⌊The only authorized and complete English ed.⌋ Tr. from his 36th German ed. ... Kempten, Bavaria, J. Kœsel, 1892.
xvi, 395, ⌊1⌋ p. front. (port.) illus. 20½cm.

1. Hydrotherapy. I. Title. 7—40153
Library of Congress RM817.K5

NK 0198394 DLC OrStbM DNLM ICJ PPJ OCX OClJC NN

Kneipp, Sebastian, 1821-1897.
My water-cure as tested through more than thirty years and described for the healing of diseases and the preservation of health. Transl. by A. de F. 2d ed., with an appendix, containing the latest developments of Pfarrer Kneipp's system, and a pref. by E. Gerard. Edinburgh, W. Blackwood, 1893.
xxxiii, 282p. (+ 32p.advertisements) front., illus. 19cm.
At head of title: Only authorised English translation.

NK 0198394-1 KU-M PPC NN

Kneipp, Sebastian, 1821-1897
.. My water-cure. Tested for more than 35 years & published for the cure of diseases & the preservation of health by Sebastian Kneipp ... [The only authorized & complete Eng. ed.] Tr. from his 36th German ed. ... Kempten, Bavaria, J. Koesel, 1894. 3d ed.
395 p. illus.

NK 0198395 OU MiU PPWa

Kneipp, Sebastian,
My water cure...published for the cure of diseases & the preservation of health, tr. from 62nd German ed. Kempten, (Bavaria) Koesel, 1897.
319 p.

NK 0198396 PCC

B615.853 K736E 1897

Kneipp, Sebastian, 1821-1897
My water-cure, tested for more than 40 years and published for the cure of diseases and the preservation of health. Kempten, Bavaria, Koesel, [1897]
395 p. illus., port. 19 cm.
Translated from the 62th German edition of Meine wasserkur.
At head of title: The only authorized and original edition, Popular edition for America.
I.Title.

NK 0198397 MnU-B

Kneipp, Sebastian, 1821-1897.
... My water-cure as tested through more than thirty years and described for the healing of diseases and the preservation of health, by Sebastian Kneipp ... Translated by A. de F. 6th ed., with an appendix, containing the latest developments of Pfarrer Kneipp's system, and a preface, by E. Gerard. Edinburgh and London, W. Blackwood and sons ltd. ⌊1935⌋
4 p. l., ⌊vii⌋-xxxiii, 282 p. illus. 19cm.
At head of title: Only authorised English translation.

1. Hydrotherapy. I. Ferro-Gerard, Anne de, tr. II. Title.
36-8902
Library of Congre RM817.K6 1935
⌊3⌋ 615.853

NK 0198398 DLC CaBVaU

RM 871 K8K68

Kneipp, Sebastian, 1821-1897.
My will; a legacy to the healthy and the sick. Translated from the 12d ⌊!⌋ German ed. Kempten, Bavaria, J. Koesel ⌊pref. 1894⌋
xii, 380 p. illus. 19cm.

Cover imprint: New York, J. Schäfer.
Translation of Mein Testament für Gesunde und Kranke.

NK 0198399 NIC

VOLUME 300

KNEIPP, Sebastian, 1821-1897. 7807.15
My will. A legacy to the healthy and the sick. Trans. from the 9th German ed.
— London. Grevel & co. 1896. xii, (1), 380 pp. Illus. Portrs Pls. Sm. 8°

NK 0198400 MB

RM 817 .K68 1899 Kneipp, Sebastian, 1821-1897.
My will; a legacy to the healthy and the sick. Translated from the 14th German edition. 2nd ed. Kempten, J. Koesel, 1899.
xii, 380 p. illus., plates 20 cm.

1. Hydrotherapy. 2. Medicine, Popular.

NK 0198401 DCU OClJC PPC

Kneipp, Sebastian, 1821-1897.
Pflanzen-Atlas zu Seb. Kneipp's "Wasser-Kur", enthaltend die Beschreibung und naturgetreue bildliche Darstellung von sämmtlichen in dem genannten Buche besprochenen, sowie noch einigen anderen vom Volke vielgebrauchten Heil-Pflanzen. Ausgabe II (Farben-Lichtdruck). Kempten, Jos. Kösel, 1890.
iv p. 41 col. plates (69 illus.) 19 cm.
Each plate is accompanied with a page of explanation prepared by O. von Kolb.

NK 0198402 PLatS

Kneipp, Sebastian, 1821–1897. 581.63 P20
Pflanzen-Atlas zu Seb. Kneipp's "Wasser-Kur", enthaltend die Beschreibung und naturgetreue bildliche Darstellung von sämmtlichen in dem genannten Buche besprochenen, sowie noch einigen anderen vom Volke vielgebrauchten Heil-Pflanzen. Ausgabe II. (Farben-Lichtdruck.) Dritte Auflage. Kempten (Bayern), J. Kösel'sche Buchhandlung, 1892.
xvii, [88] p. XLI col. pl. 19cm.

NK 0198402-1 ICJ IMunS

Knipp, Sebastian, 1821-1897.
Rathgeber für Gesunde & Kranke. Aufl. 3. 296 S. 12. Donauworth, Auer, K. D.

NK 0198403 PPG

Kneipp, Sebastian, 1821-1897.
Rathgeber für Gesunde und Kranke ... 5. Aufl. Donauwörth, L. Auer [1891]
iv, 296, vi p. (Donauwörther kathol. Zeitschriften)

1. Hygiene. 2. Hydrotherapy. 3. Children - Care and hygiene. 4. Woman - Health and hygiene.

NK 0198404 TxHU WaU

Kneipp, Sebastian, 1821-1897.
So Sollt ihr Leben. Kempten, 1889.

NK 0198405 OClStM

WB 520 K68s 1890 KNEIPP, Sebastian, 1821-1897
So sollt ihr Leben! Winke und Rathschläge für Gesunde und Kranke zu einer einfachen, vernünftigen Lebensweise und einer naturgemässen Heilmethode. 10. Aufl. Kempten, Kösel, 1890.
xii. 364 p.

NK 0198406 DNLM PPC OClStM NN

Kneipp, Sebastian. 7809.109
So sollt ihr leben! Winke und Rathschläge für Gesunde und Kranke zu einer einfachen, vernünftigen Lebensweise und einer naturgemässen Heilmethode. 20. Auflage.
= Kempten. Kösel. 1894. xii, 364 pp. 18 cm., in 8s.
On water-cure.

NK 0198407 MB

Kneipp, Sebastian, 1821-1897
So sollt ihr leben. Winke und Rathschlage fur Gesunde und Kranke zu einer einfachen, vernunftigen Lebensweise und einer naturgemassen Heilmethode. 21. Aufl. Kempten, Kosel, 1895.
364 p.

NK 0198408 PPC

Kneipp, Sebastian, 1821-1897.
So sollt ihr Leben! Winke und Rathschläge für Gesunde und Kranke zu einer einfachen, vernünftigen Lebensweise und einer naturgemässen Heilmethode ... 22. Aufl. Kempten (Bayern) J. Kösel, 1896.
xii, 364 p. illus.

1. Hygiene. 2. Hydrotherapy. I. Title.

NK 0198409 TxHU

615.853 K73s 1897 Kneipp, Sebastian, 1821-1897.
So sollt ihr leben! Winke und Ratschläge für Gesunde und Kranke zu einer einfachen, vernunftigen Lebensweise und einer naturgemassen Heilmethode. 24. Aufl. Kempten, Jos. Kosel'schen Buchhandlung, 1897.
364 p.

1. Hygiene. 2. Hydrotherapy. II. Title.

NK 0198410 WaU MB

Kneipp, Sebastian, 1821–1897.
So sollt ihr leben! Winke und ratschläge für gesunde und kranke zu einer einfachen, vernünftigen lebensweise und einer naturgemässen heilmethode, von Sebastian Kneipp. Neu herausgegeben und bearbeitet von dr. med. Christian Fey. 191.–200. tausend. München, Kösel-Pustet [1938]
367 p. 20cm.

1. Hygiene. 2. Hydrotherapy. I. Fey, Christian, 1901– ed. II. Title.
39-18265
Library of Congress RM817.K73 1938
Copyright A—Foreign 42577
[2] 615.853

NK 0198411 DLC

WB 520 K68s 1953 KNEIPP, Sebastian, 1821-1897
So sollt ihr leben! Winke und Ratschläge für Gesunde und Kranke zu einer einfachen, vernünftigen Lebensweise und einer naturgemässen Heilmethode, neu hrsg. und bearb. von Christian Fey. München, Ehrenwirth [1953]
310 p.
1. Hygiene 2. Hydrotherapy
I. Fey, Christian, 1901- ed.

NK 0198412 DNLM

WS 80 K67k 1892a **KNEIPP, Sebastian, 1821-1897**
Soins à donner aux enfants dans l'état de santé et dans l'état de maladie; ou, Conseils sur l'hygiène et la médecine de l'enfance. Seule traduction française autorisée par l'auteur. Paris, Lethielleux, 1892.
312 p. port.
Translation of Kinderpflege in gesunden und kranken Tagen.

NK 0198413 DNLM

Kneipp, Sebastian, 1821–1897.
... Thus shalt thou live; hints and advice for the healthy and the sick on a simple and rational mode of life and a natural method of cure, by Sebastian Kneipp ... Tr. from the 19th German ed. Kempten (Bavaria) J. Kœsel, 1894.
xv p., 2 l., [3]–389 p. front., illus. 20cm.
At head of title: The only authorized English edition.

1. Hygiene. 2. Hydrotherapy. I. Title.
12-36081
Library of Congress RM817.K75

NK 0198414 DLC MB

WS 80 K67k 1892 **KNEIPP, Sebastian, 1821-1897**
De verzorging van het kind in gezonde en zieke dagen. Vrij vertaald uit het Duitsch door eenen dankbaren kurgast. s'Gravenhage, Voogd van der Straaten, 1892.
146, v p.
Translation of Kinderpflege in gesunden und kranken Tagen.

NK 0198415 DNLM

WBF K68s 1891 KNEIPP, Sebastian, 1821-1897
Vivez ainsi; ou, Avis et conseils pratiques pour vivre en bonne santé et guérir les maladies. Seule traduction française autorisée par l'auteur. Strasbourg, Le Roux, 1891.
xvi, 544 p.
Translation of So sollt ihr leben!

NK 0198416 DNLM

YA16491 Kneipp, Sébastian, 1821-1897.
Vivez Ainsi, ou Avis et Conseils Pratiques pour Vivre en Bonne Santé et Guérir les Maladies. 24th ed. Strasbourg, F.-X. Le Roux & Co., 1895.

NK 0198417 DLC

Kneipp, Sebastian, 1821-1897. 7809.75
Vivez ainsi; ou, l'art de vivre en bonne santé et de guérir les malades. Traduction française [par J. Bechtold].
Paris. Retaux. 1898. xvi, 459 pp. 16°.

NK 0198418 MB

Film 861 no. 3 KNEIPP, Sebastian, 1821-1897
Pfarrer Kneipp's volkstümliche Vorträge über seine Güsse, Wickel, Räder und Waschungen. Mit Genehmigung des Autors, hrsg. von H. Hartmann. Nebst einer allgemein verständlichen, zur richtigen Ausführung der Güsse u. notwendigen Anleitung, bearb. nach den neuesten Vorschriften des hochw. Mons Seb. Kneipp und auf Grund mehrjähriger, in eigener Kneipp-scher Wasserheilanstalt

Continued in next column

VOLUME 300

Continued from preceding column

in Wörishofen gemachter praktischer Erfahrungen von Simpert Kreuzer. 5. verb. und verm. Aufl. Wörishofen, Hartmann [1894]
112 p. illus.
Film copy.

I. Hartmann, H ed.
II. Kreuzer, Simpert

NK 0198421 DNLM

WB K68v 1892 KNEIPP, Sebastian, 1821-1897
Voordrachten van Pastoor Sebastian Kneipp over ziekten en geneeskruiden. Op den 70sten verjaardag van Pastoor Kneipp voor gezonden en zieken bijeenverzameld en uitg. door Friedrich Mayer. Amsterdam, Seyffardt [1892?]
2 v. in 1. (Gezondheids-Bibliotheek, no. 38-39)
I. Mayer, Friedrich, ed.

NK 0198422 DNLM

WB 520 K68s 1892a KNEIPP, Sebastian, 1821-1897
Zoó zult gij leven! Wenken en raadgevingen aan gezonden en zieken voor eene eenvoudige, verstandige levenswijze en eene natuurlijke geneesmethode. Naar de 8. uitgave uit het Duitsch vertaald. 's-Gravenhage, De Voogd van der Straaten, 1892.
xii, 347 p.
Translation of So sollt ihr leben!

NK 0198423 DNLM

W 1 KN586 KNEIPP Blätter; Monatsschrift für die Kneippsche naturgemässe Lebens- und Heilweise.
Jahrg. 1- 1891-
Bad Wörishofen.
v. illus., ports.

Organ of the Kneipp-Bundes e. V.
1. Hydrotherapy - period.
2. Naturopathy - period. I. Kneipp-Bund, Wörishofen, Ger.

NK 0198424 DNLM

W 1 NA845 The KNEIPP water cure monthly and herald of health. v. 1-2; Jan. 1900-Dec. 1901. New York.
2 v. in 1. illus., ports.
Issued Jan.-Dec. 1900 with title: The Kneipp water cure monthly.
Continued by the Naturopath and herald of health.
Issued also in German with title: Amerikanische Kneipp-Blätter und Gesundheits-Rathgeber (varies slightly)

NK 0198425 DNLM

W 6 P3 KNEIPPÄRZTEBUND, Bad Wörishofen
Bad Wörishofener Diätbüchlein. [Bad Wörishofen, 1955]
46 p.
1. Diet - popular works

NK 0198426 DNLM

W 1 KN587 KNEIPP-JOURNAL. année 1-13; 15 jan. 1892-déc. 1904. Bruxelles.
13 v. in illus.

Part of title on microfilm.
French ed. of Kneipp Blätter.

NK 0198427 DNLM

W 1 AL967 KNEIPP-KALENDER. 1.- Jahrg.; 1891-
Stuttgart.
v. illus., port.
Publication suspended 1943-49.
Yearbook of Kneipp-Bund e. V., Bad Wörishofen.
French translation issued under title: Almanach-Kneipp.
1. Hydrotherapy I. Kneipp-Bund, Wörishofen, Ger.

NK 0198428 DNLM

Film S174 KNEIPP'S jaarboekje. s'Bosch [1892?]
v. illus.
Film copy.
Translation of Kneipp-Kalender.

NK 0198429 DNLM

Die Kneippsche Naturheilkunde und ihre Grenzgebiete in Lehre und Beispiel
see under Fey, Christian, 1901- ed.

Kneise, August Martin Otto
see Kneise, Otto, 1875-

Kneise, G Chr
Das Wissenswertheste für den geographischen Unterricht. Reichenbach, Schumanm. Co., 1838.
124 w.

NK 0198432 PPG

Kneise, Otto, 1875–
Die bakterienflora der mundhöhle des neugeborenen vom momente der geburt an und ihre beziehungen zur ätiologie der mastitis ... [Von] Otto Kneise ... Leipzig, A. Georgi, 1901.
33, [1] p. incl. tables. 24cm.
Inaug.-diss.—Halle.
Lebenslauf.
Bibliographical foot-notes.

1. Breast—Diseases. 2. Mouth—Bacteriology.
[Full name: August Martin Otto Kneise]
11-5105 Revised
Library of Congress QR201.M4K6

NK 0198433 DLC DNLM

WJ 17 qK68h 1908 KNEISE, Otto, 1875-
Handatlas der Cystoskopie. Halle, Gebauer-Schwetschke, 1908.
96 p. (chiefly illus.)

NK 0198434 DNLM IU-M ICJ PPC MiU

WJ 17 qK68h 1926 KNEISE, Otto, 1875-
Handatlas der Cystoskopie. 2. völlig umgearb. und verm. Aufl. Leipzig, Thieme, 1926.
119 p. (chiefly illus.)
3d ed. has title: Handatlas der Cystoskopie und Urethrocystoskopie.
1. Cystoscopy 2. Urology - Atlases

NK 0198435 DNLM ICJ PPC TxHMC

WJ 17 qK68h 1953 KNEISE, Otto, 1875-
Handatlas der Cystoskopie und Urethrocystoskopie, von O. Kneise und M. Stolze. 3. umgearb. und verm. Aufl. Leipzig, Thieme, 1953.
xvi, 110 p. (chiefly illus.)
Earlier eds. have title: Handatlas der Cystoskopie.
1. Cystoscopy 2. Urology - Atlases
I. Stolze, Martin.

NK 0198436 DNLM ICJ

WJ 17 qK68h 1955 KNEISE, Otto, 1875-
Handatlas der Cystoskopie und Urethrocystoskopie, von O. Kneise und M. Stolze. 4. umgearb. und verm. Aufl. Leipzig, Thieme, 1955.
xx, 112 p. (chiefly illus.)
1. Cystoscopy 2. Urology - Atlases
I. Stolze, Martin

NK 0198436-1 DNLM

WJ 141 qK68r 1941 KNEISE, Otto, 1875-
Die Röntgenuntersuchung der Harnorgane; Lehrbuch, von O. Kneise und K. L. Schober. Leipzig, Thieme, 1941.
226 p. illus.
1. Urinary organs - Radiography
I. Schober, Karl Ludwig, 1912-

NK 0198437 DNLM

WJ 141 qK68r 1943 KNEISE, Otto, 1875-
Die Röntgenuntersuchung der Harnorgane; Lehrbuch, von O. Kneise und K. L. Schober. 2., umgearb. und verm. Aufl. Leipzig, Thieme, 1943.
246 p. illus.
1. Urinary organs - Radiography
I. Schober, Karl Ludwig, 1912-

NK 0198438 DNLM

RC78 946K Kneise, Otto, 1875-
Die Röntgenuntersuchung der Harnorgane; lehrbuch von dr. med. O. Kneise und dr. med. K. L. Schober. 3. umgearb. und vermehrte Aufl., mit 288 farbigen Abbildungen. Leipzig, Thieme, 1946.
250p. illus. (pt. col.) 27cm.
1. Radiography. 2. Genito-urinary organs - Diagnosis. I. Schober, K. L. jt. auth.

NK 0198439 CtY-M DNLM

WJ 141 qK68r 1952 KNEISE, Otto, 1875-
Die Röntgenuntersuchung der Harnorgane; Lehrbuch, von O. Kneise und K. L. Schober. 4., umgearb. und verm. Aufl. Leipzig, Thieme, 1952.
279 p. illus.
1. Urinary organs - Radiography
I. Schober, Karl Ludwig, 1912-

NK 0198440 DNLM

VOLUME 300

WJ 141 K68t 1924 **KNEISE**, Otto, 1875-
Technik der Blasenspiegeluntersuchung, Cystoskopie, und der Nierenfunktionsprüfung, sonderlich unter Zuhilfenahme des Ureterenkatheterismus, funktionelle Nierendiagnostik. Berlin, Urban & Schwarzenberg, 1924.
vi, 144 p. illus.
Published simultaneously in Abderhalden, Handbuch der biologischen Arbeitsmethoden, Abt. 4, T. 5.

NK 0198441 DNLM PPC

Kneise, Otto, 1875–
Technik der blasenspiegeluntersuchung (cystoskopie) und der nierenfunktionsprüfung, sonderlich unter zuhilfenahme des ureterenkatheterismus (funktionelle nierendiagnostik). Von O. Kneise ...
(*In* Abderhalden, Emil, ed. Handbuch der biologischen arbeitsmethoden ... Berlin, 1920– 25cm. abt. IV, Angewandte chemische und physikalische methoden. t. 5, 2. hälfte (1929) p. ₍1₎–142. illus.)
Bibliographical foot-notes.
1. Bladder—Exploration. 2. Kidneys.
₍*Full name:* August Martin Otto Kneise₎
A C 36-2661
Title from Ohio State Univ. Library of Congress [QH324.A3 1920 abt. 4, t. 5] ₍2₎ (574.072)

NK 0198442 OU

PA3879 .K68 Kneisel, A B
Aristophanes, ein Spiegel unserer Zeit. Cöthen-Anhalt, P. Schettlers Erben, 1913.
78 p.
Contents.--Eine Verspottung der radikalen Demokratie im Altertum. Die Ritter.--Wider den Naturalismus. Die Frösche.--Wider den Atheismus. Die Wolken.

1. Aristophanes.

NK 0198442-1 ICU MH CU NcD

Kneisel, Adolf, 1884–
Das mystère 'La passion de Jesu-Christ en rime franchoise,' handschrift no. 421 der Städtischen bibliothek zu Valenciennes. Teil I: Analyse, varianten, gegenüberstellungen, textproben von journée 1–10 ... von Adolf Kneisel. Greifswald, F. W. Kunike, 1906.
2 p. l., 83 p. 23cm.
Inaug.-diss.—Greifswald.
Lebenslauf.
No more published?
"Litteratur": p. 1–2.
1. Valenciennes passion-play, 1549–50. I. Title.
43-41051
Library of Congress PQ1365.V33K5

NK 0198443 DLC MH ICRL LU NcD NIC

GR8 K737b Kneisel, Bruno
Beiträge aus Erasmus' Colloquien für die Kulturgeschichte des 16. Jahrhunderts. ₍Naumburg a/S.?₎ 1897.
16 p. 25 cm.
"Beilage zum Jahresbericht des Domgymnasiums zu Naumburg a/S."
Bibliographical footnotes.
1. Erasmus, Desiderius, d.1536. Colloquia.

NK 0198444 CtY-D

KNEISEL, Bruno. 2231.1
Kulturzustand der indogermanischen Völker vor ihrer Trennung. (*In* Domgymnasium, *Naumburg*. Zu der öffentlichen Prüfung sämmtlicher Klassen, April 1867. Pp. 1-24. Naumburg a/S., 1867.)

NK 0198445 MB NjP

G 141 K68 **Kneisel,** Bruno.
Leitfaden der historischen Geographie. **Berlin,** Weidmann, 1874-79.
v. 22cm.
Contents: I. Zur alten Geschichte.--II. Zur Geschichte des Mittelalters.--III. Zur Geschichte der Neuzeit.
1. Geography, Historical. 2. Classical geography. I. Title.

NK 0198446 NIC

---

ar W 38370 Kneisel, Bruno.
Sturz des Baiernherzogs Tassilo. Naumburg a. S., H. Sieling, 1875.
40 p. 24cm.
1. Tassilo III, Duke of Bavaria, 8th cent.

NK 0198447 NIC

KNEISEL,Bruno.
Ueber den kulturzustand der indogermanischen völker vor ihrer trennung,mit besonderer rücksicht auf die Gräco-Italiker. [Progr.] Naumburg,1867.
4°. pp.1-24.

NK 0198449 MH

Kneisel, Ernst.
Administrative politics and the AAA.
Honors thesis - Harvard, 1947.

NK 0198450 MH

Kneisel, Frank, 1907- ed.

M219 .N9 op. 11 **Notman, Howard,** 1881–
₍Sonata, violin & piano, op. 11, C major₎
Sonata in C, for violin and piano. Fingering and bowing for violin by Frank Kneisel. Dongan Hills, N. Y. ₍1945₎

KNEISEL, FRANZ, 1865-1926.
Advanced exercises for the violin. New York, G. Schirmer [c1912] 1 v. 31cm.
Pt. 1.
1. Violin--Studies and exercises.

NK 0198452 NN

Kneisel, Franz, 1865-1926.
Cadenza to the violin concerto in D ...
see under Brahms, Johannes, 1833-1897.

Kneisel, Franz, 1865–1926.
Facsimiles collected by the late Franz Kneisel. ₍v. p., 184–?₎
11 facsims. (in portfolio) 45 cm.
Title in ms. on portfolio.
Facsimiles of music and signatures, principally of composers, chiefly extracted from or issued as supplements to various periodicals.
1. Music—Facsimiles.
ML96.4.K6 52-47469

NK 0198454 DLC

Kneisel, Franz, 1865-1926.
Kneisel collection for violin & piano; selection from the masters, old & new. Cincinnati, Church, 1908.
3 v. in 6.

NK 0198455 PP OrP

MT267 K6 **Kneisel, Franz,** 1865-1926.
Principles of bowing and phrasing; hints to serious violin students... New York, C. Fischer ₍1925₎
31p. illus., music. 23cm.
"Dedicated to Felix E.Kohn."
"Written for the Minnesota Music Teacher's Assn."
1. Violin - Instruction and study. 2. Stringed instruments, Bowed - Bow.

NK 0198456 IaU IU MB OCl OU NN MiU

Kneisel, Friedrich Christoph, 1797-1883
see Kneisel, Johann Friedrich Christoph, 1797-1883.

Kneisel, Fritz Rudolf Richard
see Kneisel, Rudolf, 1881-

Kneisel, Gotthold.
Volkhafte Dichtung in Österreich, junge Dichtung als Spiegelbild inneren Volkstumes. Graz, Leuschner & Lubensky, 1937.
50, ₍1₎ p. 23 cm.
Bibliographical references included in "Anmerkungen": p. ₍51₎
1. German poetry—Austrian authors—Hist. & crit. 2. German poetry—20th cent.—Hist. & crit. I. Title.
PT3820.K6 52-47699

NK 0198459 DLC CtY MH

Kneisel, Jessie (Hoskam) 1908–
Mörike and music. ₍New York?₎ 1949.
xiii, 236 p. music. 22 cm.
Thesis—Columbia University.
Vita.
"Composers of Mörike and their compositions": p. ₍170₎–189. "Poems which were set to music": p. ₍190₎–207. Bibliography: p. ₍211₎–220.
1. Mörike, Eduard Friedrich, 1804–1875. Gedichte. 2. Songs, German—Hist. & crit.
PT2434.Z5K6 831.79 A 50-655
Columbia Univ. Libraries for Library of Congress ₍1₎†

NK 0198460 NNC ViU DLC

Kneisel, Jessie (Hoskam) 1908–
Mörike and music. ₍New York?₎ 1949.
xiii, 236 p. music. 22 cm.
Thesis—Columbia University.
Vita.
"Composers of Mörike and their compositions": p. ₍170₎–189. "Poems which were set to music": p. ₍190₎–207. Bibliography: p. ₍211₎–220.
Microfilm (negative) Original in the Columbia University Library.

NK 0198461 ICU

VOLUME 300

WU K71s 1836 KNEISEL, Johann Friedrich Christoph, 1797-1883.
Position irrégulière des dents; ses causes, et la manière d'y remédier d'après une méthode nouvelle, sûre et sans douleur. Berlin, Mittler, 1836.
22 p.
Bound with his Der Schiefstand der Zähne. Berlin, 1836.
Translation of Der Schiefstand der Zähne.

NK 0198462 DNLM

WU K71s 1836 KNEISEL, Johann Friedrich Christoph, 1797-1883.
Der Schiefstand der Zähne; dessen Ursachen und Abhülfe nach einer neuen, sichern und schmerzlosen Heilmethode. Berlin, Mittler, 1836.
22 p. illus.
Bound with his Position irrégulière des dents. Berlin, 1836.

NK 0198463 DNLM PU-D MiU

KNEISEL, Rudolf, 1832-1899. No. 3 in 4896.50.3
Chemie fürs Heiraten. Originalschwank. 16°.
Leipz. Reclam. [1894.] 84 pp. [Universal-Bibliothek. 3305.]

NK 0198464 MB

Kneisel, Rudolf, 1832-1899.
Fingerhut, dramatischew Märchen...71 S. B. Hamburg, K.D.

NK 0198465 PPG

Kneisel, Rudolf, 1832-1899.
De gevolgen van een leugen. Blijspel in vier bedrijven, naar het Duitsch. 2.ed. Zaandijk, J. Heijnis, 1904.
84 p. 12°.

NK 0198466 NN

Kneisel, Rudolf, 1832-1899.
Das Haus der Wahrheit. Schwank in vier Aufzügen ... Berlin, [R. Boll] 1882.
83 p. 12°.

NK 0198467 NN

KNEISEL, Rudolf, 1832-1899.
Die lehre von der seelenwanderung. Leipzig, Mutze, 1889.

NK 0198468 MH OClW

Kneisel, Rudolf, 1832-1899.
König Georg; grosse romantische Oper
see under Ehrlich, Friedrich Christian, 1807-1887.

Kneisel, Rudolf, 1832-1899.
Der liebe Onkel. Schwank in 4 Aufzügen, von Rudolph Kneisel ... 3. Auflage. Berlin: Kühling & Güttner [1876?] 48 p. 23cm. (Volks-Schaubühne. Nr. 12.)

831698A. 1. Drama, German. I. Title. July 8, 1936
N. Y. P. L.

NK 0198470 NN

Kneisel, Rudolf, 1832-1899.
Der liebe Onkel; Schwank in 4 Aufzügen. Berlin, Kühling & Güttner [1876]
52p.
Microcard edition.

NK 0198471 ICRL

Kneisel, Rudolf, 1832-1899.
Die Lieder des Musikanten; Volksstück mit Gesang in 5 Akten, von Rudolf Kneisel. Musik von Richard Thiele. Fünfte Auflage. Berlin: E. Bloch, [190-?]. 56 p. 22cm. (Eduard Blochs Volks-Theater. Nr. 14.)
Without music.

706847A. 1. Drama, German. I. Title. May 17, 1934
N. Y. P. L.

NK 0198472 NN

Kneisel, Rudolf, 1832-1899.
Papageno; Posse in vier Akten, von Rudolf Kneisel. Dritte Auflage. Berlin: Kühling & Güttner [1889?] 63 p. 22½cm. (Volks-Schaubühne. Nr. 73.)

831698A. 1. Drama, German. I. Title. July 8, 1936
N. Y. P. L.

NK 0198473 NN

Kneisel, Rudolf, 1832-1899.
Schmerle's Geheimniss. Schwank in vier. Akten. Berlin, F. Bloch, 1887.
91 p. 8°.

NK 0198474 NN

Kneisel, Rudolf, 1832-1899.
Sie weiss etwas!! Schwank in vier Akten. Berlin, F. Bloch, 1885.
72 p. 8°.

NK 0198475 NN

Kneisel, Rudolf, 1832-1899.
Sie weiss etwas. Schwank. Leipz., Reclam, [1894]
76 p. 16°. [Universal-Bibliothek]

NK 0198476 MB

Kneisel, Rudolf, 1832-1899.
Sie weiss etwas! Schwank in vier Aufzügen. Leipzig, Reclam [n.d.]
76p.
Microcard edition.

NK 0198477 ICRL

Kneisel, Rudolf, 1832-1899.
Unschuldige Männer. Original-Schwank in vier Akten. Berlin, F. Bloch Erben, 1890.
78 p., 1 l. 8°.
In: NGB p.v. 17, no. 10.

NK 0198478 NN

Kneisel, Rudolf, 1832-1899.
Wo ist die Frau? Original-Lustspiel in vier Akten. Berlin, [R. Boll] 1885.
91, (1) p. 12°.

NK 0198479 NN

KNEISEL, Rudolf, 1832-1899. No. 3 in 4896.50
Wo ist die Frau? Lustspiel. 16°.
Leipz. Reclam. [1895.] 96 pp. [Universal-Bibliothek. 3348.]

NK 0198480 MB

Kneisel, Rudolf, 1832-1899.
Wo ist die Frau? Lustspiel in vier Aufzügen. Leipzig, Reclam [n.d.]
96p.
Microcard edition.

NK 0198481 ICRL

WG 34169 Kneisel, Rudolf, 1881-
Polymerisation des γ-Chlor- und γ-Brom-propylpiperidins. Jena, 1907.
28 p.
Inaug.-Diss. - Jena.

NK 0198482 CtY ICRL MH PU PPAmP

Kneisel, Walter
Rückfall und Gewohnheitsverbrecher nach geltendem Recht und den Entwürfen Deutschlands, Österreichs und der Schweiz ... von Walter Kneisel ... Bonn, Verein Studentenwohl, 1929.
1 p.l., x, 96 p. 21cm.
Inaug.-diss. - Bonn.
"Literaturverzeichnis": p. ii-x.

NK 0198483 MH-L ICRL

Kneisel Quartet, Boston. **M.304.6
Programmes and notices, compiled [with indexes] by Allen A. Brown. Seasons, 1885-1902.
= [Boston, 1885-1902.] 2 v. Photograph. 8°.

E9382 — Concerts. Programmes. — Chamber music. Programmes. — Brown, Allen Augustus, comp.

NK 0198484 MB

Kneisl, Ludwig Scheer-
see
Scheer, Ludwig, 1876-

Kneisley, Joseph Wayne, 1917-
Organic chemical manufacturers
see under Illinois. University. Dept. of chemistry.

VOLUME 300

Kneisley, Joseph Wayne, 1917–
Part one: The structure of isodurylphenylvinyl alcohol. Part two: The coupling action of the Grignard reagent. By Joseph Wayne Kneisley ... Urbana, Ill., 1943.
6 p., 1 l. 22½cm.
Abstract of thesis (PH. D.)—University of Illinois, 1943.
Vita.
Bibliography: p. 5, 6.
1. Alcohols. 2. Grignard reagents. A 43-2572
Illinois. Univ. Library for Library of Congress QD305.A4K63
NK 0198487 IU DLC

Kneisly, Harry Loren, 1888–
Kneisly genealogy, copyright ... by Harry Loren Kneisly ... Including the names of 685 descendants, and relatives of the earliest residents in America of whom records have been obtained, and references to 150 others believed to be related ... ⌊Reading, Pa., Miller printing and lithographing co., °1932⌋
46 p. 23cm.
1. Kneisly family. 32-10157
Library of Congress CS71.K69 1932
NK 0198488 DLC PHi OClWHi

Kneisly, Kay, comp.
List of general line automotive and replacement parts jobbers ...
see under Irving-Cloud pub. co.

Kneisner, Friedrich. 366.1 R200
Geschichte der deutschen Freimaurerei in ihren Grundzügen dargestellt von Friedrich Kneisner. Im Auftrage des Vereins Deutscher Freimaurer. Berlin, A. Unger, 1912.
xii, 292 p. incl. tables. 21½cm.
NK 0198490 ICJ NIC

Kneisner, Friedrich, 1890– , Referendar: Verfügungen des Gemeinschuldners nach der Konkurseröffnung und § 15 der Konkursordnung. Borna-Leipzig 1916: Noske. VIII, 42 S. 8°
Jena, Jur. Diss. v. 16. Nov. 1916, Ref. Gerland
[Geb. 21. Juli 90 Hamburg; Wohnort: Hamburg; Staatsangeh.: Hamburg; Vorbildung: Wilhelms-G. Hamburg Reife 09; Studium: Würzburg 4, Jena 3 S.; Rig. 27. Sept. 16.] [U 16. 478
NK 0198491 ICRL

Kneiss, Gilbert H.
Bonanza railroads, by Gilbert H. Kneiss. Stanford University, Calif., Stanford university press ⌊°1941⌋
xvi, 148 p., 1 l. incl. front., illus. plates. 26cm.
Map on lining-papers.
"References": p. 141-145.
1. Railroads—California. 2. Railroads—Nevada. I. Title.
Library of Congress HE2771.C2K56 41-25972
⌊15⌋ 385.09793
NK 0198492 DLC Or OrPR NIC NcD PPF PSt PU PPT OCU OU MiHM WaWW WaS CaBViP OrP FMU CU OrU OCf

Kneiss, Gilbert H
Bonanza railroads, by Gilbert H. Kneiss. Stanford University, Calif., Stanford university press ⌊1943⌋
xvi, 148 p., 1 l. incl. col. front., illus. plates. 26cm.
Map on lining-papers.
"Second edition."
"References": p. 141-145.
1. Railroads—California. 2. Railroads—Nevada. I. Title. 43-14912
Library of Congress HE2771.C2K56 1943
⌊2⌋ 385
NK 0198493 DLC CaBViPA OrSaW MtHi ICJ

Kneiss, Gilbert H
Bonanza railroads, by Gilbert H. Kneiss. Stanford University, Calif., Stanford university press [1944]
xvi, 148 p., 1 l. col. front., illus. plates. 26 cm.
Map on lining-papers.
"Second edition, June 1943; third printing, Nov. 1944."
"References": p. 141-145.
NK 0198494 CU

Kneiss, Gilbert H 1899–
Bonanza railroads. ⌊3d ed.⌋ Stanford University, Stanford Univ. Press ⌊1947⌋
xviii, 187 p. illus., ports., map (on lining-papers) 27 cm.
"References": p. 179-184.
1. Railroads—California. 2. Railroads—Nevada. I. Title.
HE2771.C2K56 1947 385 47-11046*
NK 0198495 DLC IU IdU OrPR FMU CoU ICJ TxU OrCS NN CU

Kneiss, Gilbert H 1899–
Bonanza railroads. ⌊4th ed.⌋ Stanford, Stanford University Press ⌊1954⌋
187 p. illus. 27 cm.
1. Railroads—California. 2. Railroads—Nevada. I. Title.
HE2771.C2K56 1954 385 54-4721 ‡
NK 0198496 DLC WaS Wa OClJC NcD CU-B TxU NcD ODW PU PBm MB OrP CaBVaU

HE2791 W526K6
Kneiss, Gilbert H 1899–
Fifty candles for Western Pacific. ⌊San Francisco? 1953⌋
40 p. illus., ports., map. 20cm.
Caption title.
"Reprinted from Mileposts for March, 1953, in observance of the fiftieth anniversary of Western Pacific."
1. Western Pacific Railroad Company.
NK 0198497 CSt OClWHi OrP

Kneiss, Gilbert H., 1899–
It happened between trains, a play in one act, with sound effects, by Gilbert H. Kneiss ... San Francisco, Calif., Cincinnati, O., Banner play bureau, inc., °1936.
11 p. 19½cm.
I. Title.
37-33549
Library of Congress PN6120.A5K66
Copyright D pub. 41525 ⌊3⌋ 812.5
NK 0198498 DLC Or

Kneiss, Joachim, 1906–
... Aktinomykose; ihre Klinik, Behandlung und Unfallbegutachtung auf Grund der Beobachtung an 159 Fällen der Greifswalder Chirurgischen Universitäts-Klinik ... Greifswald, 1934.
Inaug.-Diss. - Greifswald.
Lebenslauf.
"Literaturverzeichnis": p. 28-30.
NK 0198499 CtY

Kneisser, Hippolyt, 1831-1883
see Kneissler, Hippolyt, 1831-1883.

Kneissl, Hans, ed.
Czechoslovak republic. *Laws, statutes, etc.*
... Das Handelsgesetzbuch vom 17. dezember 1862, R. G. Bl. 1 für 1863 samt anderen einschlägigen gesetzen und verordnungen sowie entscheidungen des Obersten gerichtshofes in Brünn. II. aufl. bearb. von dr. Hans Kneissl ... Reichenberg, Gebrüder Stiepel, 1926.

W 4 M961 1955
KNEISSL, Josef, 1930–
Untersuchungen über die Ausscheidungen von Steroiden im Harn bei Polyarthritikern unter ACTH- und Cortisonbelastung und bei Patienten nach grossen Operationen. München, 1955.
21 l. illus.
Inaug.-Diss. - Munich.
1. Adrenocorticotropic hormones 2. Arthritis - Treatment 3. Cortisone 4. Steroids
NK 0198502 DNLM

Kneissl, Karl, ed.
Czechoslovak Republic. *Laws, statutes, etc.*
... Das Strafgesetz vom 27. mai 1852, R.-g.-bl. nr. 117, samt allen bis juni 1927 ergangenen nebengesetzen. Bearb. und mit den bis ende 1926 veröffentlichten entscheidungen des Obersten gerichtes in Brünn sowie mit wichtigen entscheidungen des ehemaligen Obersten gerichts- und kassationshofes in Wien versehen von dr. Karl Kneissl ... Reichenberg, Gebrüder Stiepel gesellschaft m. b. h., 1927.

Kneissl, Karl.
... Strafgesetzgebung in den historischen ländern ...
see under Czechoslovak Republic. Laws, statutes, etc.

Kneissl, Karl, joint ed.
Czechoslovak republic. *Laws, statutes, etc.*
... Die Strafprozessordnung vom 23. mai 1873, Rgbl. nr. 119, mit nebengesetzen, verordnungen und erlässen sowie den oberstgerichtlichen entscheidungen. Bearb. von dr. Edgar M. Foltin ... ⌊und⌋ dr. Karl Kneissl ... Reichenberg, Gebrüder Stiepel, 1935.

Kneissl, Max, 1907–
Anschauliche Einführung in den geometrischen Teil der höheren Geodäsie, nach einer Vorlesung von Sebastian Finsterwalder, bearb. von Max Kneissl. Berlin, Verlag des Reichsamts für Landesaufnahme, 1944.
78 p. illus. 24 cm. (Nachrichten aus dem Reichsvermessungsdienst, Mitteilungen des Reichsamts für Landesaufnahme, Sonderheft 27)
1. Geodesy. I. Finsterwalder, Sebastian, 1862–
QB321.K56 64-58614 ‡
NK 0198506 DLC MH

Kneissl, Max.
Die Bildung eines einheitlichen europäischen Nivellementsnetzes. Stuttgart, K. Wittwer, 1955.
20 p. 25 cm.
Two fold. maps inserted.
Bibliographical footnotes.
1. Geodesy—Europe. 2. Levelling. I. Title.
QB296.E9K55 59-30733
NK 0198507 DLC CU

VOLUME 300

Kneissl, Max
Entwicklung und Stand der bayerischen Katasterkartographie. München [194-?]
28 p. (B[avaria]. Landesvermessungsamt. Lehrbrief, 3)

NK 0198508 MH

Kneissl, Max
Entwicklung und Stand der bayerischen Katasterkartographie [von] M.Kneissl und W. Scherrer. München, 1954
21 p. (B[avaria]. Landesvermessungsamt. Ausbildungsvortrag, 4)

NK 0198509 MH

Kneissl, Max.
Die Genauigkeit der Winkel und astronomischen Azimute im Zentraleuropäischen Hauptnetz. München, Hrsg. von dem Deutschen geodätischen Forschungsinstitut, Abt. I, 1953. ix, 106 p. tables,maps. 30cm. (Deutsche geodätische Kommission. Veröffentlichung. Reihe A: Höhere Geodäsie. Nr. 2)
Bibliography, p. 103-106.

1. Triangulation—Europe, Central. 2. Azimuth—Europe, Central, 1953. I. Series. t.1953.

NK 0198511 NN

Kneissl, Max, *ed.*
Internationale Streckenmesskurse in München. Ausgewählte Vorträge über neuere Entwicklungen geodätischer Instrumente und Fortschritte in der optischen Streckenmessung. Goslar, M. Wittke, 1955.
221 p. illus. 22 cm.
Bibliography : p. 210-211.

1. Surveying—Instruments. 2. Area measurements. 3. Optical measurements. I. Title.
TA562.K6 A 57-6950
Illinois. Univ. Library for Library of Congress [a58b½]†

NK 0198512 IU DLC

Kneissl, Max.
Nachweis systematischer Fehler beim Feinnivellement. Vorgelegt am 4. Februar 1955. München, Verlag der Bayerischen Akademie der Wissenschaften; in Kommission bei Beck, 1955.
54 p. (p. 32-54 tables) 29 cm. (Abhandlungen der Bayerischen Akademie der Wissenschaften. Mathematisch-Naturwissenschaftliche Klasse, n. F., Heft 68, 1955)
1. Leveling. I. Title. (Series: Akademie der Wissenschaften, Munich. Mathematisch-Naturwissenschaftliche Abteilung. Abhandlungen, n. F., Heft 68, 1955)
AS182.M817 n. F., Heft 68 56-34962

NK 0198513 DLC PU OU ICU OCU NIC

Kneissl, Max, 1907-
Versteifung eines geodätisch ausgeglichenen dreiecksnetzes durch die rechnerische einbeziehung astronomischer beobachtungen. ...
Inaug. Diss. - Techn. Hochschule München, [1936]
Lebenslauf.
Literatur.

NK 0198514 ICRL

Kneissl, Max, 1907- ed.
Wissenschaftliche Referate [gehalten auf der Vollsitzung der Deutschen geodätischen Kommission
see under Akademie der Wissenschaften Munich. Deutsche geodätische Kommission.

Kneissler (Guilelmus). *De angina membranacea. 22 pp. 8°. *Vindobonæ, A. Pichler,* 1825.

NK 0198516 DLNM

[Kneissler, Hippolyt] 1831-1883.
...Brennende Herzen. Lustspiel in einem Aufzuge. Mit freier Benützung einer französischen Idee. Von Erik Nessl [pseud.]... Wien: Wallishausser, 1871. 16 p. 22cm. (Wiener Theater-Repertoir. Lief. 245.)
Cover-title.

1. Drama, German. I. Title.
N. Y. P. L. May 28, 1937

NK 0198517 NN

*GB8 V6755R 3.32.48
[Kneissler, Hippolyt, 1831-1883]
Das edle, treue Oesterreich!!
[Wien]Gedruckt bei Carl Gerold.[1848]
[2]p. 22.5x14.5cm.
Not recorded by Helfert (Wiener Parnass).
Caption title; imprint on p.[2].
Dated & signed at end: Wien, 1848. Im Monat März. Hippolyt Kneissler, Poet am akademischen Gymnasium.

NK 0198518 MH

[Kneissler, Hippolyt] 1831-1883.
...Mein Onkel Hammelmeier. Schwank in einem Aufzuge (frei nach einer französischen Idee) von Erik Nessl [pseud.]... Wien: Verlag der Wallishausser'schen Buchhandlung, 1871. 16 p. 24cm. (Wiener Theater-Repertoir. Lief. 255.)
Cover-title.

532892. 1. Drama, German. I. Title. II. Ser. *Revised*
N. Y. P. L. March 2, 1937

NK 0198519 NN

[Kneissler, Hippolyt] 1831-1883.
...Ein Schwiegervater für Alles. Schwank in einem Aufzuge. Mit theilweiser Benützung einer französischen Idee, von Erik Nessl [pseud.]... Wien: Verlag der Wallishausser'schen Buchhandlung, 1870. 15 p. 22½cm. (Wiener Theater-Repertoir. Lief. 240.)
Cover-title.

486682. 1. Drama, German. I. Title. II. Ser. *Revised*
N. Y. P. L. March 2, 1937

NK 0198520 NN

[Kneissler, Hippolyt] 1831-1883.
...Vaterfreude. Lustspiel in einem Aufzuge. Mit freier Benutzung einer französischen Idee, von Erik Nessl [pseud.]... Wien: Verlag der Wallishausser'schen Buchhandlung, 1871. 16 p. 24cm. (Wiener Theater-Repertoir. Lief. 247.)
Cover-title.

532892. 1. Drama, German. I. Title. II. Ser. *Revised*
N. Y. P. L. June 14, 1937

NK 0198521 NN

Kneissler, Leodegar.
Der Weg aus der Wirtschaftskrise, von Dr. Leodegar Kneissler. Wietzendorf, St. Pölten: Im Selbstverlag des Verfassers, 1932. 30 p. 23cm.

675379A. 1. Crises and panics, 1929-1932.
N. Y. P. L. October 17, 1933

NK 0198522 NN

Lfj 954K
Kneissler, Leonhard.
Das humanistische Gymnasium im Zeitalter der Technik. Wien,A.Sexl,1954.
14p. 21cm. (Verein der Freunde des humanistischen Gymnasiums. Veröffentlichung)

1. Education, Humanistic. I. Ser.

NK 0198523 CtY

Kneissler, Leonhard.
Die Maxwellsche Theorie in veränderter Formulierung. Wien, Springer, 1949.
viii, 51 p. 22 cm.

1. Electromagnetic theory. I. Title.
QC670.K55 50-56162

NK 0198524 DLC TxU

KNEIST, Giambattista, compiler.
Fatti guerrieri, dedicati ai giovani militi acciocchè per gli esempî eroici della gloriosa armata austriaca s'inspirino ai sentimenti di valore, di giustizia e d'umanità. Venezia, tip.di Sante Martinengo, 1857.

NK 0198525 MH

Kneisz (Walther Gustav) [1874-]. *Ueber Appendicitis. 25 pp., 1 l. 8°. *Halle a. S., C. A. Kaemmerer & Co.* 1901

NK 0198526 DLNM MH ICRL

Kneitschel, Víctor.
Catálogo de los sellos postales de la República argentina y sus derivados [por] Víctor Kneitschel ... Buenos Aires, 1943.
404 p. illus., col. plates. 18½ cm.

1. Postage-stamps—Argentine republic. 2. Postage-stamps—Catalogs.
44-18673
Library of Congress HE6185.A6K6
[3] 383.22

NK 0198527 DLC DSI

HE6185 .P37 K64
Kneitschel, Victor.
Catalogo de los sellos postales de la Republica del Paraguay y sus derivados. Buenos Aires, 1947.
188p. illus. (part col.)

1. Postage-stamps - Paraguay - Catalogs.

NK 0198528 NcU

VOLUME 300

Arg HE 6185 .C3 1939
Kneitschel, Victor.
... Catálogo de sus sellos postales y derivados. Buenos Aires, Víctor Kneitschel, 1939.
194 p. incl. illus. 19 cm.
Four folded plates in pocket.

NK 0198529 DPU

Kneitz, Otto.
Albrecht Alcibiades, Markgraf von Kulmbach, 1522–1557. ⌊Hrsg. im Auftrage des Vereins "Freunde der Plassenburg e. V." durch Georg Fischer. Kulmbach, E. C. Baumann, 1951⌋
162 p. illus., port. 21 cm. (Die Plassenburg; Blätter für Heimatkunde und Kulturpflege in Ostfranken, Heft 2)
Bibliography: p. 149–150.

1. Albrecht Alcibiades von Brandenburg, Margrave of Kulmbach, 1522–1557. (Series)
DD370.K6 54–28194

NK 0198530 DLC CU NN PP

R PG1376 K68
Knéjévitch, Lazare R.
Dictionnaire français-serbe, par Lazare R. Knéjévitch. Belgrade, Imprimerie Makarié, 1927.
xii, 938p. 19cm.
Title-page also in Serbian.

1. French language--Dictionaries--Serbian.

NK 0198531 PPiU OCl

Knekht, Vladimir Alekseevich.
Добрая Надежда; из цикла "Закон." Ленинград, Художественная литература, 1936.
207 p. 20 cm.

I. Title. *Title transliterated:* Dobraia Nadezhda.
PG3476.K55D6 54–45685 ‡

NK 0198532 DLC

Knekht, Vladimir Alekseevich.
Штурм; из цикла "Закон." Ленинград, "Художественная литература," 1937.
426, ⌊2⌋ p. 21 cm.

I. Title. *Title transliterated:* Shturm.
PG3476.K55S47 49–34404

NK 0198533 DLC

Knekht, Vladimir Alekseevich.
Страна на замке. Ленинград, Худож. лит-ра, 1940.
292 p. illus. 17 cm.

I. Title. *Title transliterated:* Strana na zamke.
PG7158.K54S7 64–31222

NK 0198534 DLC

Knelb, Philip H.
The narratives of an old traveller; containing the perils and hair-breadth escapes from shipwreck, famine, wild beasts, savages, etc., of travellers in every part of the world. From the German of Dr. Ph. H. Knelb, by a lady. Philadelphia, W.P. Hazard, 1854.
192 p. plates 21cm.
Added t.-p., engr.
Lettered: Encyclopedia of perils and adventures of travellers, hunters, sailors, &c.
Bound with this is the author's Perilous incidents in the lives of sailors and travellers. Philadelphia, 1854.
1. Shipwrecks.

NK 0198535 CtNlCG ICU NN CtY

Knelb, Philip H.
Perilous incidents in the lives of sailors and travellers. Translated from the German of Dr. Ph. H. Knelb, by a lady. Philadelphia: W. P. Hazard, 1854. 192 p. front., plates. 8°.

Bound with his: The narratives of an old traveller. Philadelphia, 1854. 8°.
Contents: Pirate life. Captivity among the Japanese. A sea-fight on the Cuban coast. A winter in the frozen ocean. The shipwreck. Voyage to the East Indies. Home-sickness of a Siberian.

261667A. 1. Fiction, Adventure. 2. A lady, translator. 3. Title.
N. Y. P. L. April 22, 1927

NK 0198536 NN MH CtY

Knell, A.
The phonic reader, for common schools. Number one. Prepared on the objective plan. By A. Knell & J. H. Jones. Cincinnati, Wilson, Hinkle & co.; ⌊etc., etc.⌋ 1868.
xi, ⌊13⌋–112 p. incl. front., illus. 17cm.

1. Readers and speakers—1800–1870. I. Jones, J. H.
12-6853
Library of Congress PE1119.A1K6

NK 0198537 DLC OClWHi

Knell, A.
The phonic reader, for common schools. Number one. Prepared on the objective plan. By A. Knell & J. H. Jones. New York, ⌊etc.⌋ American book co., ⌊c1868⌋
xi, ⌊13⌋–112 p. incl. front., illus. 17cm.

NK 0198538 OCl MiU

Knell, August.
Aus zwei welten. Winterthur, Steiner, 1882.
316 p.

NK 0198539 PU

Knell, August Karl
Die Pollenkörner als Diagnostikum in Drogenpulvern (Blüten, Kräutern und Blättern). Würzburg, Druck der Kgl. Universitätsdruckerei H. Stürtz, 1914.
52 p.
Inaug.-Diss.- Kgl. Bayer. Julius-Maximilians-Universität Würzburg.

NK 0198540 MH-A ICRL MH CtY

Music dept.
Knell, Benj[amin] F., comp.
Daily exercises for the mandolin. Phila., Stewart & Bauer, 1899.
17 p. sm. fol.

NK 0198541 DLC

Knell, Benjamin F.
Mandolin technic: 38 graduated exercises and studies from 1st to 6th positions for the mandolin to strengthen and develop the left hand, arranged by Benj. F. Knell. Philadelphia, Fischer music house, 1901.
15 p. fol.

Library of Congress 1—315 Music div.

NK 0198542 DLC

---

821 K738a
Knell, Betty.
As the story goes. Sydney, New Century Press, 1929.
46p. 23cm.
Poems.
With author's autograph.

NK 0198543 TxU MH

Knell, Charles E.
Duke university; a collection of 25 photographs by Charles E. Knell of the exterior and interior of Duke university. Durham, N. C., n.d.
25 pl. F

NK 0198544 PP

Knell, Elfriede, 1903-
Klinische Studien über die Wirkung von Arsen auf den Grundumsatz, den Reststickstoff und die Reticulozyten im Blute des Menschen ... Giessen, 1936.
Inaug.-Diss. - Giessen.
Lebenslauf.
Published also in Archiv für experimentelle Pathologie und Pharmakologie. Bd. 181.

NK 0198545 CtY

Knell, Étienne.
La Bosnie et l'Herzégovine (étude d'histoire politique et économique) par Étienne Knell ... Paris, A. Rousseau, 1900.
xv, 204, ⌊2⌋ p. 25cm.
"Bibliographie": p. ⌊v⌋–ix.

1. Bosnia and Herzegovina—Descr. & trav.
1-F-3400
Library of Congress DB245.K68

NK 0198546 DLC NN

Knell (Franciscus). *Asthma theoretice et practice perlustratum. 16 pp. 4°. *Argentorati, typ. J. H. Heitzii,* [1785].

NK 0198547 DNLM

Knell, Marianne, 1904–
... Charles Péguy und seine bedeutung für die geistige erneuerung Frankreichs, von dr. Marianne Knell. Münster, Selbstverlag des Romanischen seminars; ⌊etc., etc.⌋ 1934.
3 p. l., 93 p. 23½cm. (Arbeiten zur romanischen philologie, hrsg. von Eugen Lerch, nr. 22)
"Die vorliegende abhandlung (nr. 22) wurde als dissertation der Philosophischen ... fakultät der Universität Münster vorgelegt."
"Literatur-verzeichnis": p. 92–93.

1. Péguy, Charles Pierre, 1873–1914.
42-11908
Library of Congress PQ2631.E25Z63

NK 0198548 DLC CtY NIC ICU NN

VOLUME 300

Knell, Marlise, 1908- Beeinflusst das spezifische Hormon des Corpus luteum den Blutcholesteringehalt? (gleichzeitig ein Beitrag zur Physiologie des Blutcholesteringehaltes beim Kaninchen) p.176–85. 8° Berl., 1933.

NK 0198549 DNLM CtY

Knell, Martin, 1920-
I. Preparation of mercaptans and sulfides. II. Reactions and structure of a sultone from styrene. Evanston, 1950.
89l. tables. 28cm.

Thesis - Northwestern Univ.
Vita.
Bibliography: leaves [86]-89.

1. Petroleum. Refining. 2. Mercaptans. 3. Sulphides. 4. Styrene.

NK 0198550 IEN

QE105 .A45 no. 136

Knell, Martin, joint author.
(1920-

Finger, Glenn Charles, 1905–
Some trisubstituted benzotrifluorides, by G. C. Finger and Martin Knell. Some factors in the synthesis of 3, 5-dinitrobenzotrifluoride, by O. F. Williams and G. C. Finger. Urbana, 1947.

Knell, Paul, 1615?-1664.

Five seasonable sermons. As they were preached before eminent auditories, upon several arguments ... London, 1660.
188 p. 17½cm.

Each sermon has special title-page.
From the library of Charles II, to whom the book was dedicated, with the royal coat of arms stamped in gold on cover.

Wing K-678

NK 0198552 CLU-C DGU

Knell, Paul, 1615?–1664.
Israel & England parallel'd: in a sermon preached before the Honourable Society of Grayes-Inn, upon Sunday in the afternoon, April the 16th, 1648. Being now very seasonable and useful for all such as retain the principles of the people in those times. By Paul Knell... London: Printed in the year 1648. And now reprinted for a caution to all those that are given to change. Sold by R. Tayler and R. Stephens, 1681. 16 p. 18cm.

712592A. 1. Great Britain—Hist.— Charles I, 1625–1649—Pamphlets.
N. Y. P. L. October 2, 1934

NK 0198553 NN PPL NjPT

---

*EC65 K7383 648id

Knell, Paul, 1615?-1664.
Israel and England paralelled, in a sermon preached before the Honourable society of Grayes-Inn, upon Sunday in the afternoon, April 16. 1648. By Paul Knell, master in arts of Clare-hall in Cambridge ...
London, Printed in the year of our Lord, 1648. And now reprinted (at the request of some friends) anno, 1695.
2p.l., 19p. 18.5cm.
Originally in support of Charles I, evidently reprinted for the Jacobite cause.

NK 0198554 MH MnU DFo CU-A CLU-C ICN CU NNUT-Mc

Knell, Paul, 1615?–1664.
Israel and England parallell'd. A sermon preach'd before the Honourable Society of Grays-Inn, on Sunday April 16, 1648 ... By Paul Knell. London: printed, 1648, reprinted 1711. 2 p.l., 29 p. 4. ed. 12°.

In: *Cp. v. 1663, no. 9.

1. Great Britain.—History, Charles I, 1625–49: Pamphlets.
N. Y. P. L. October 13, 1920.

NK 0198555 NN

---

*EC65 K7383 648l

Knell, Paul, 1615?-1664.
The life-guard of a loyall Christian, described in a sermon, preached at St Peters Corn-hill, upon Sunday in the afternoone, May 7. 1648. by Paul Knell, master in arts of Clare-hall in Cambridge ...
London, Printed in the yeare 1648.
2p.l., 19p. 19cm.

NK 0198556 MH MnU CtY NNUT-Mc CSmH ICN

British Tracts 1648 K73

Knell, Paul, 1615?-1664
A looking-glasse for levellers: held out in a sermon, preached at St. Peters Pauls-Wharfe ... Sept. 24. 1648 ... London, Printed in the year 1648.
1p.l., 20p. 18cm.

NK 0198557 CtY DFo CSmH TxDaM NNUT-Mc

Knell, Thomas, fl. 1560-1581.
An A B C to the christen congregation or a pathe way to the heauenly habitacion. London, by Rycharde Kele [1560?]
Broadside.
Laid no. (49) in same volume with: Awdelay or Awdeley, John. Ecclesi. XX. 1569.
Britwell Sale, November 1919, no. 16 (49)

NK 0198558 CSmH

Knell, Thomas, fl. 1560-1581.
An A B C to the christen congregacion; or, A pathe way to the heauenly habitacion. [London, 1550?]
Film reproduction, position 2.
Colophon: Imprynted at London by Rycharde Kele ...
Caption title.
Signed: Thomas Knell.
Dict.nat.biog.gives date of publication as 1560?
University microfilms no.2483 (case 23, carton 134)
Short-title catalogue no.15029.

1. Christian life. I. Title.

NK 0198559 MiU

[Knell, Thomas] fl. 1560–1581.
An answer at large, to a most hereticall, trayterous, and Papisticall Byll, in English verse, which was cast abrode in the streetes of Northamton, and brought before the Judges at the last Assises there. 1570. Imprinted at London by John Awdelye.

(In Tracts ... relating to Northamptonshire. Northampton, 1881. 21cm. [no. 14] 25 p.)

"An answer to a Romish ballad ridiculing the marriage of the English clergy."—Dict. nat. biog.

1. Catholic church—Clergy. 2. Celibacy. I. Title.
23-1820
Library of Congress DA670.N7T7 no. 14
—— —— Copy 2, detached. [Hazlitt tracts, v. 29, no. 12]
AC911.H3 vol. 29, no. 12

NK 0198560 DLC NN CtY

Knell, Thomas, fl. 1560-1581.
An answer to a Papisticall Byll, cast in the streetes of Northampton, and brought before the Iudges at the last Syses. 1570. The Papistes bill. London, by Iohn Awdely, 1570.
Broadside.
Laid no. (50) in same vol. with: Awdelay or Awdeley, John. Ecclesi. XX. 1569.
Britwell Sale, November 1919, no. 16 (50)

NK 0198561 CSmH

Knell, Thomas, fl. 1560-1581.
An answer to a papisticall byll, cast in the streetes of Northampton, and brought before the iudges at the last syses. 1570 ... Jmpzynted at London by Iohn Awdely ... 1570.
By Thomas Knell. cf. Christie Miller Sale Cat., 5:15:50; Dict.nat.biog.
Broadside.
In verse.
University microfilms no.14946 (case 65, carton 385)
Short-title catalogue no.15030.

1. Catholic church--Clergy. 2. Celibacy. I. Title.

NK 0198562 MiU DFo ViU

FILM

Knell, Thomas, fl.1560-1581.
An epitaph, or rather a short discourse made vpon the life & death of D.Boner sometimes vnworthy Bishop of London, whiche dyed the v. of September in the Marshalsie. London, Imprinted by J.Allde, 1569.
In verse.
Short-title catalogue no.15033 (carton 803)
With this is filmed: A commemoration or dirige of bastarde Edmonde Boner, alias Sauage, vsurped Bisshoppe of London. Compiled by Lemeke Auale.

[London] Imprinted by P.O., 1569 (Short-title catalogue no.977) already cataloged on carton 375 as MiU F51-698)

1. Bonner, Edmund, Bp. of London, 1500?-1569.

NK 0198564 MiU

Knell, Thomas, fl. 1560–1581.
An epitaph, or rather a short discourse, made vpon the life and death of Dr. Bonner, sometime vnworthy bishop of London; whiche dyed the fifth of September in the Marshalsie. Imprinted at London, at the long shop adjoyning vnto S. Mildreds church in the Pultrie, by John Allde, an. Dom. 1569. Sept. 14.

(In The Harleian miscellany. London, 1808–13. 30½cm. vol. I (1808) p. 612–617)

Signed: T. Knell, ju.
Verse.

1. Bonner, Edmund, bp. of London. 1500?–1569.
A C 40-1472
Hamilton college. Library for Library of Congress [DA300.H vol. 1]
[2] (942.0082)

NK 0198565 NCH MnHi OCl NBuG RPB MdBJ ICN IEN ViU

PR 1121 .C68 v.1

Knell, Thomas, fl.1560-1581.
A piththy note to papists all and some that ioy in Feltons martirdome. Desiring them to read this, and to iudge, & and in spite of simple truth to grudge. Set foorth by one that knew his life, and was with him at the houre of his death, which was viii of August. Anno.1570. at the west end of Paules Churche ... Imprinted at London ... by John Allde [1570. Reprinted, London, 1863]
ii p., reprint: 20 p. 21 cm. (In Collier, J.P., ed. Illustrations of early English popular literature. London, 1863-64. v.1)
ii p. (editor's Introd.) follow the t.p. which is part of the reprint.
In verse.

1. Felton, John, d.1570. I. Collier, John Payne, 1789- 1883, ed. II. Title.

NK 0198567 MiU MH CtY OU

VOLUME 300

Knell (Wilhelm) [1876–]. *Ueber die Kombinationswirkung von Morphium muriaticum und Chloralhydrat bei gleichzeitiger intravenöser Application. 28 pp., 1 l. 8°. Geissen, O. Kindt, 1907.

NK 0198568 DNLM ICRL

M2 .O78 reihe 4, hft. 2, 5, 7

Kneller, Andreas, 1649-1724.

[Seiffert, Max, 1868– ed.]
[Orgelmeister ... hrsg. v. M. Seiffert] Leipzig, F. Kistner & C. F. W. Siegel [1925–

Kneller, C M
Traffic accident investigation procedure by C.M. Kneller and Arnold F. Nelius. Prepared for use in connection with the California peace officers' training program. Sacramento, California State Dept. of Education, Bureau of Industrial Education, 1954.
35 p. 28 cm. (California peace officers' training publication no. 68)

1. Traffic accident investigation. I. Nelius, Arnold F. II. California. Bureau of Industrial Education.

NK 0198570 N WaU-L N CLSU

TS2301 .P3A4

Kneller, Cy, ed.

Radio and television weekly.

New York [Phonograph Publications Co.]

Kneller, Friedrich
Städtebau. Stuttgart, Karl Krämer [1952] 72, I-IV p. illus., plans. 30cm. (Architektur-wettbewerbe; schriftenreihe für richtungweisendes bauen, heft 12/13)

"Besprechung richtungweisender städtebauliteratur": p. I-II.
"Weitere literatur über stätebau und landesplanung": p. II.

NK 0198572 NNC-A MH

Kneller, George Frederick.
The education of the Mexican Nation. New York, Columbia University Press, 1951.
xi, 258 p. illus. 25 cm.
Bibliography: p. [229]-241.

1. Education—Mexico. I. Title.

LA422.K6 370.972 51-9931

TxU KEmT CU-B MiU OrSaW CaBVaU
NK 0198573 DLC Or OrU Wa WaS MB NN DPU ICU NNC ViU

Kneller, George Frederick.
The educational philosophy of national socialism, by George Frederick Kneller. New Haven, Pub. for the Department of education in Yale university by the Yale university press; London, H. Milford, Oxford university press, 1941.
viii, 299 p. 24½ cm.
"The material for this book in its original form was presented in partial fulfillment of the requirements for the degree of doctor of philosophy in Yale university [1940]"—Acknowledgment.
Bibliography: p. [257]-284.
1. Nationalism and education—Germany. I. Title.

LA722.K62 370.10943 41-6385

IaU
WaSp NcD PBL NIC KEmT NBuC MU OrCS WaE CaBVa CaBVaU
NK 0198574 DLC Or OCl OCU OU OO PU PPT DS OrU Wa

Kneller, George Frederick.
The educational philosophy of national socialism, by George Frederick Kneller. New Haven, Pub. for the Department of education in Yale university by the Yale university press; London, H. Milford, Oxford university press, [1942]
viii, 299 p. 24½ cm.
"The material for this book in its original form was presented in partial fulfillment of the requirements for the degree of doctor of philosophy in Yale university."—Acknowledgment.
Bibliography: p. [257]-284.
"Second printing, March, 1942."

NK 0198575 ViU MH MiHM PSC PBm

Kneller, George Frederick.
Higher learning in Britain. Berkeley, University of California Press, 1955.
xii, 301 p. 23 cm.
Bibliography: p. 279-287.

1. Education, Higher. 2. Universities and colleges—Gt. Brit. I. Title.

A 55—8707

California. Univ. Libr. for Library of Congress [58x5]

OrPR OrU Wa CaBVaU PHC PSt PCM CaBVa WaWW WaS NN TxU TU NcD IdPI IdU OClW OO ODW OOxM OU OCl OrP OrPS MeB MtU PLF PPT PP PPD NNC ICarbS MB
NK 0198576 CU KEmT IU ViU MiU OKentU Or OrCS

Kneller, Sir Godfrey, bart., 1646-1723, illus.

Gosse, *Sir* Edmund William, 1849-1928.
British portrait painters and engravers of the eighteenth century, Kneller to Reynolds; with an introductory essay and biographical notes by Edmund Gosse, LL. D. Paris, London, New York, Berlin, Goupil & co., Manzi, Joyant & co., successors, 1906.

Kneller, Sir Godfrey, bart., 1646-1723, illus.
Stukeley, William, 1687-1765.
The family memoirs of the Rev. William Stukeley, M. D., and the antiquarian and other correspondence of William Stukeley, Roger & Samuel Gale, etc. Durham [Eng.] Pub. for the society by Andrews & co.; [etc., etc.] 1882-87.

Kneller, *Sir* Godfrey, *bart.*, 1646-1723.
The Kit-Cat club, done from the original paintings of Sr Godfrey Kneller by Mr Faber. [London] Sold by J. Tonson & J. Faber, 1735.
2 p. l., 43 (*i. e.* 47) port. (1 double) 45cm.
Engraved t.-p.

1. Kit-Cat club, London. 2. Gt. Brit.—Biog.—Portraits. I. Faber, John, 1695?-1756, engr.

46-42113

Library of Congress ND497.K47F3

NK 0198579 DLC MH ICN NcU MiU CLU-C InU FU CSmH

Kneller, Sir Godfrey, bart., 1646-1723.

[Caulfield, James] 1764-1826.
Memoirs of the celebrated persons composing the Kit-Cat club; with a prefatory account of the origin of the association: illustrated with forty-eight portraits from the original paintings by Sir Godfrey Kneller ... London, Hurst, Robinson, and company, 1821.

Kneller, Heinz, 1888-
Das Kundeneffektengeschäft des Bankiers in seiner rechtlichen Beleuchtung mit besonderer Berücksichtigung des Kommissionsgeschäfts ... von Heinz Kneller. Berlin, Druck von der Buch- und Kunstdruckerei für Handel und Industrie, 1912.
156 p., 1 l. 22cm.
Inaug.-diss. - Heidelberg.
"Lebenslauf": leaf at end.
"Literatur": p. [7]

NK 0198581 MH-L CtY ICRL

SF463 .A1C34

Kneller, Helen, ed.

Canary-budgie world. v. 1– June 1943–
Lecanto, Fla. [etc.]

.K59

Kneller, ÎU V
Эксплуатация трактора ХТЗ-7. Москва, Гос. изд-во сельхоз. лит-ры, 1955.
138, [4] p. illus. 20 cm.
Bibliography: p. [140]

1. Tractors. I. Title.
Title transliterated: Ėkspluatatsiia traktora KhTZ-7.

S711.K59 55-40918

NK 0198583 DLC

Kneller, John W joint author.
Introduction à la poesie française

see under

Grubbs, Henry Alexander, 1904-

Kneller, Karl Alois, 1857-
Das christentum und die vertreter der neueren naturwissenschaft. Ein beitrag zur kulturgeschichte des 19. jahrhunderts. Von Karl Alois Kneller, S. J. ... Freiburg im Breisgau, Herder, 1903.
2 p. l., 266 p. 23½cm. (Ergänzungshefte zu den "Stimmen aus Maria-Laach."—84 u. 85)

1. Religion and science. I. Title.

CA 8—880 Unrev'd

Library of Congress AP30.S7 suppl.

NK 0198585 DLC PLatS

Kneller, Karl Alois, S.J., 1857-
Das Christentum und die Vertreter der neueren Naturwissenschaft; ein Beitrag zur Kulturgeschichte des 19. Jahrhunderts. 3. u. 4., verb. u. verm. Aufl. Freiburg i.B., Herder, 1912.
523 p. 20 cm.

NK 0198586 PLatS CaBVaU

Kneller, Karl Alois, 1857-
Christianity and the leaders of modern science: a contribution to the history of culture in the nineteenth century, by Karl Alois Kneller, S. J. Translated from the 2d German ed. by T. M. Kettle ... with an introduction by Rev. T. A. Finlay ... Freiburg im Breisgau, St. Louis, Mo., [etc.] B. Herder, 1911.
vii p., 1 l., 403 p. 20cm.
Bibliographical foot-notes.

1. Religion and science—1900– I. Kettle, Thomas Michael, 1880-1916, tr. II. Title.

CA 14—277 D

Library of Congress BL240.K55 [a37e1] 215

NK 0198587 DLC OrStbM CoU PPCCH PV

Kneller, Karl Alois, 1857-
Christianity and the leaders of modern science. A contribution to the history of culture in the nineteenth century by Karl Alois Kneller, S. J. Tr. from the 2d German ed. by T. M. Kettle ... with an introduction by Rev. T. A. Finley, S. J., M. A. With the approbation of the Most Rev. Archbishop of Freiburg. London, St. Louis, Mo. [etc.] B. Herder, 1911.
vii p., 1 l., 403 p. 20cm.

1. Christianity. 2. Culture. I. Kettle, Thomas Michael, 1880- tr.

A 11-1343

Title from Union Theol. Sem. Printed by L. C.

NK 0198588 NNUT PPCCH OClND OClJC OCX MB CU

VOLUME 300

Kneller, Karl Alois, 1857–
Des Richard Löwenherz deutsche gefangenschaft (1192–1194). Von Karl Alois Kneller, s. J. ... Freiburg im Breisgau, St. Louis, Mo. [etc.] Herder, 1893.
2 p. l., 128 p. 22cm. (Ergänzungshefte zu den "Stimmen aus Maria-Laach." 59)

1. Richard I, king of England, 1157–1199.

A 14-438

Title from Harvard Univ. Printed by L. C.

NK 0198589 MH PU PLatS OCl

AP 30 S85 suppl. no.98 Kneller, Karl Alois, 1857–
Geschichte der Kreuzwegandacht von den Anfängen bis zur völligen Ausbildung. Freiburg i.Br., Herder, 1908.
ix, 216 p. 23 cm. (Ergänzungsheft zu den "Stimmen aus Maria-Laach", 98)

NK 0198590 NIC MnCS PLatS

Kneller, Karl Alois, S.J., 1857–
Der hl. Cyprian und das Kennzeichen der Kirche. Freiburg i.B., Herder, 1914.
[3]–71 p. 24 cm. (Ergänzungshefte zu den "Stimmen aus Maria-Laach," 115)

NK 0198591 PLatS

BL240 K616 Kneller, Karl Alois, 1857–
A kereszténység és a modern természettudomány úttörői; adatok a XIX. század művelődéstörténetéhez, írta Kneller Károly Alajos. A német eredetinek 2. jav. és bőv. kiadása után fordította és kiadta a Budapesti Papnövendékek Magyar Egyházirodalmi Iskolája. Budapest, Stephaneum Nyomda, 1908.
xxxii, 527 p.

Translation of Das Christentum und die Vertreter der neueren Naturwissenschaft.
Bibliographical footnotes.

1. Religion and science - 1900-1925.

NK 0198592 CU

Kneller, Karl Alois, 1857–

Pesch, Christian, 1853–
Zur neuern literatur über Nestorius, von Christian Pesch, s. J. Der hl. Cyprian und das kennzeichen der kirche, von Karl Alois Kneller ... Freiburg im Breisgau, St Louis, Mo. [etc.] Herder, 1914.

Kneller, Ludwig, 1889–
Die rechtliche Stellung der stellvertretenden Vorstandsmitglieder einer Aktiengesellschaft ... von Ludwig Kneller. Zürich, Gebr. Leemann & Co., 1913.
2 p.l., [3]-91, [1] p. 22cm.
Inaug.-diss. - Heidelberg.
"Lebenslauf": p.[92]
"Literaturverzeichnis": p.[5]-8.

NK 0198594 MH-L PU ICRL

Kneller, Robert, 1898–
Die bilanzierung der unverbrieften forderungen mit heimischer währung ... von dipl.-kfm. Robert Kneller ... Bergisch Gladbach, Buchdruckerei J. Heider, 1926.
xi, 125 p., 1 l. incl. tables. 22cm.
Inaug.-diss.—Cologne.
Lebenslauf.
"Literatur": p. viii–ix.

1. Accounting. 2. Financial statements.

42-49625

Library of Congress HF5645.K6

NK 0198595 DLC IU

Knelles, Adolf. 625.1 R004
Die Berechnung von Gleis- und Weichenanlagen vorzugsweise für Strassen- und Kleinbahnen. Von Adolf Knelles, ... Mit 44 Figuren im Text und auf einer Tafel. Berlin, J. Springer, 1910.
iv, 83, [1] p. incl. illus., 4 tables. 1 fold. diagr. 24½cm.

NK 0198596 ICJ

PT 1741 K63 1693 Cage Knellinger, Balthasar, 1635-1696.
Caesar Caccabensis ludio ludo suo immortuus. Auss Schimpff wird Ernst... Caesar Caccabensis auff offentlichem Schau-Platz mit gaehem Todt gestrafft ... Ynnsprugg, Bey Benedict Carl Reisacher [1693].
[4] l. 4to.

NK 0198597 DFo

Knellinger, Balthasar, S.J., 1635-1696.
Lait-und Schreck-Stern. Das ist: Geschicht-Predigen. In sich haltend: Theils Folg-Theils Hass-Würdige Lebens-Thaten. Hervorgegeben und in sieben Theil abgesonderet von R.P. Balthasore Knellinger der Gesellschafft Jesu Priestern. Augsburg, In verlag des Martin Veith, 1737.
368 p. 306 p. 156 p.

NK 0198598 MoSU-D

Knellinger, Balthasar, 1635-1696. Ott 401.15
Predigen zu zeit dess Türken-kriegs von anno 1683. In welchen das christen volk zur buss und andacht dann auch zu lob- und danksprechung auffgemahnet worden. München, J. H. von Gelder, 1687–90.
3 vol. sm. 4°.
Vol. 2 has half-title only.

NK 0198599 MH

Knellwolf, Arnold.
Der weltliche reformator Ulrich von Hutten; eine charakterzeichnung, von Arnold Knellwolf ... [Zürich, Beer & cie., 1917]
31 p. incl. front. (port.) 23 cm.
1. Hutten, Ulrich von, 1488-1523.

NK 0198600 CU

Knellwolf, Arthur, 1912–
Das preisschleudern mit markenartikeln nach schweizerischem privatrecht in rechtsvergleichender darstellung von Arthur Knellwolf ... [Altstätten, "Rheinthaler"-druckerei a. g., 1938]
3 p. l., 141 p. 23cm.
Inaug.-diss.—Zürich.
Curriculum vitae.
"Verzeichnis der verwendeten literatur": p. 133–140.

1. Price maintenance. 2. Price maintenance—Switzerland. 3. Competition, Unfair—Switzerland. 4. Competition, Unfair. 5. Comparative law. I. Title.

41-18532

Library of Congress HF5417.K6
[a44c1] 338.509494

NK 0198601 DLC ICRL CtY

FILM 532.5 K73s **Knelman, F H**
A study of the mechanism of liquid entrainment as affecting the design of dephlegmators, evaporators, absorbers. London, 1953.
Microfilm copy (negative) of typescript, made in 1965 by the Photographic Dept., University of London Library.
Collation of the original: 120, [3] l. illus.
Thesis--University of London.
Bibliography: leaves [121]-[123]

NK 0198602 IU

Knemeyer, Ludwig: Aus d. Prov.-Irrenanst. Dziekanka b. Gnesen. Dir.: Kayser. Die körperlichen Symptome der Dementia praecox. Königsberg i. Pr. 1915: Kümmel. 89 S. 8°
Königsberg, Med. Diss. v. 5. Jan. 1916, Ref. E. Meyer
[Geb. 9. Mai 83 Kasum; Wohnort: Eekloo; Staatsangeh.: Preußen; Vorbildung: G. Gütersloh Reife 04; Studium: Bonn 6, Kiel 1, Berlin 1, Kiel 2 S.; Coll. 16. Nov. 15; Approb. 20. Okt. 13.] [U 16. 1115

NK 0198603 ICRL DNLM CtY

Knepflé, G A
In naam der menschheid; de wereld spreekt vonnis over Nazi-Duitschland. Neurenberg 1945-1946. Amsterdam, Buyten en Schipperheyn [1947]
359 p. illus. 23 cm.

1. Nuremberg Trial of Major German War Criminals, 1945-1946. I. Title.

55-37421 ‡

NK 0198604 DLC NN MH

Knepler, Abraham Eleazer.
Education in the Cherokee nation, by Abraham Eleazer Knepler.
(*In* Chronicles of Oklahoma. Oklahoma City, 1943. 25cm. vol. XXI, p. 378–401)
Thesis (PH. D.)—Yale university, 1939.
Without thesis note.
Bibliographical foot-notes.

1. Cherokee Indians. 2. Indians of North America—Education.

A 44-3837

Yale univ. Library for Library of Congress F691.C55 vol. 21
——— Detached copy. E99.C5K55
[3]† (976.6) 371.975

NK 0198605 CtY DLC

KNEPLER, Albert.
Beitrag zur frage der psychopathologischen heredität. Inaugural-dissertation. Basel, buchdr. Brin & cie, 1911.
4 tables.
"Literaturangaben", 2 pp. at end.

NK 0198606 MH CtY DNLM

Knepler, Georg
Die geistigen Arbeiter und die Kommunisten. [Wien, 1947?]

NK 0198607 MH

PR635 .M35K7 Knepler, Henry William, 1922–
Mary Stuart on the stage in England and America. 1950.
205 l.
Thesis--Univ. of Chicago.

1. Mary Stuart, Queen of the Scots, 1542-1587--Drama.

NK 0198608 ICU

KNEPLER, Hermann.
Der prozess Goldmark aktenmässig dargestellt. Wien, 1868.

NK 0198609 MH-L OCH

VOLUME 300

Knepler, Hugo.
... O, diese künstler! Indiskretionen eines managers. Mit achtundzwanzig ganzseitigen bildern. Wien-Leipzig, Fiba-verlag [°1931]
198, [1] p. illus. (incl. facsims., music) plates, ports. 16½cm.

1. Musicians — Correspondence, reminiscences, etc. 2. Impresarios. 3. Music—Austria—Vienna. 4. Music—Anecdotes, facetiae, satire, etc. 5. Children as musicians. I. Title.
Library of Congress ML429.K6 31-21069
Copyright A—Foreign 10897
[3] 927.8

NK 0198610 DLC NN

Knepler, Paul. Giuditta.

Lehár, Ferenc, 1870–
... Giuditta. Leipzig, New York [etc.] W. Karczag [°1933]

PT1268 .Z9K55 Knepler, Paul.
Die lockende flamme...Regiebuch.
Berlin, 1934.
1 v. 12°

NK 0198612 DLC

Knepler, Paul.

ML50 .S9M8 1948

FOR OTHER EDITIONS SEE MAIN ENTRY

Straus, Oscar, 1870–
[Die Musik kommt. Libretto. German]
Die Musik kommt; eine Komödie in Musik, zwei Akte, 10 Bilder, von Paul Knepler und Armin L. Robinson. Gesangstexte von Robert Gilbert. Regiebuch nach der Zürcher Uraufführung eingerichtet von Oberregisseur Fritz Schulz. Zürich, Musikverlag und Bühnenvertrieb Zürich [1948]

M1503 .L518P3 1936

Knepler, Paul. Paganini.

Lehár, Ferenc, 1870–1948.
[Paganini. Piano-vocal score. German]
Paganini; Operette in drei Akten von Paul Knepler und Bela Jenbach. Musik von Franz Lehár. Klavierauszug mit Text. Wien, Glocken-Verlag, °1936.

Knepp, L'udovít.
Prúdové pole. Podl'a prednášok Ludovíta Kneppu spracoval C. Lad. Cesnak. [V Bratislave, Rektorát Slovenskej vysokej školy technickej, 1951]
34 p. diagrs. 31 cm. (*His* Teoretická a experimentálna elektrotechnika, 1)

1. Electromagnetic theory. I. Title.
QC670.K57 55-17854

NK 0198615 DLC

Knepp, Ľudovít.
Striedavé prúdy. Bratislava, Vydavateľstvo Slovenskej akadémie vied, 1954.
351 p. illus. 24 cm.
Includes bibliography.

1. Electric currents, Alternating. I. Title.
TK1141.K55 62-35464 ‡

NK 0198616 DLC CU NN MiU

TK 7872 .M3 K68 Knepp, L'udovít.
Základy teórie transduktorov. [V Bratislave, Vydavatel'stvo Slovenskej akádemie vied, 1954.
147 p. diagrs,tables. 26 cm.
Bibliography: 130-147.

1.Magnetic amplifiers.

NK 0198617 MiU CU NN

612.6 K68h **Knepp, Thomas H**
The human reproductive system; a text-booklet for high school students. Dubuque, Iowa, W. C. Brown [1950]
v,50 p. illus. 22cm.

1. Reproduction. I. Title.

NK 0198618 IEN

4PT Ger. 494 Kneppeck, Paul.
Sarre, 1934; Roman. München-Pullach, K. Knippel.
174 p.

NK 0198619 DLC-P4

QZ K68S 1805 Kneppelhout, Cornelius Johannes
... Sectiones cadaverum pathologicae. Lugduni Batavorum, Apud Haak et socios, 1805.
[2] l., 67 p. ii fold. plates. 24 cm.
Bibliographical footnotes.
"Ex dono Gulielmi Thomson."

1. Pathology. I. Title.

NK 0198620 WU-M DNLM

W 4 L68 v.3 no.40 KNEPPELHOUT, Joannes
Dissertatio medica inauguralis de aphthis ... Lugduni Batavorum, Apud Johannem van Abkoude, 1733.
23 p. 23 cm.
Diss. - Leyden.

NK 0198621 DNLM

Kneppelhout, Johannes, 1814-1885.
Een beroemde knaap. Ter herinnering aan Jan de Graan, geboren te Amsterdam 10 September 1852, overleden te 's Gravenhage 8 Januarij 1874, door J. Kneppelhout ... 's Gravenhage, M. Nijhoff, 1875.
viii, 123 p., 1 l. 20cm.

1. Graan, Jan de, 1852-1874.
Library of Congress ML418.D3K7 11-3529

NK 0198622 DLC

Kneppelhout, Johannes, 1814–1885.
Catalogue de la bibliothèque de feu m.-J. Kneppelhout ... dont la vente publique aura lieu du 15 au 22 mai 1920 dans la salle de vente de Van Stockum's antiquariaat ... La Haye, Van Stockum's antiquariaat, 1920.
cover-title, 163 p. fold. pl. 21½cm.
3032 entries.

Library of Congress Z997.K699 41-42033
[2] 018.2

NK 0198623 DLC

Kneppelhout, J[ohannes] 1814-1885.
Lamartine. Amsterdam, P.N. van Kampen, 1848.
44 p. 12°.
In: *C. p.v. 1274.

NK 0198624 NN

Kneppelhout, Johannes, 1814–1885.
... Politiek kritiek. Leiden, [Gedrukt bij J. G. La Lau], 1855.
[10, 3]–143, [1] p. 24cm.
At head of title: J. Kneppelhout.
Contents.—Landgenooten.—Onder welke voorteekenen Willem I de grondwet der Vereenigde Nederlanden bezwoer.—Ons verzoekschrift.—12 Augustus 1842.—En regard du portrait de Guizot.—Het laatste vlugschrift.—Iets over eene beoordeeling.—Een leesboek over de grondwet.—Eene nieuwe ster aan de kim.—Over den volksdichter.—Een dichter uit den burgerstand.

NK 0198625 ICJ

Kneppelhout, Johannes, 1814–1885.
De studenten en hun aanhang, door Klikspaan [pseud.] Leyden, H. W. Hazenberg [1843]
118 p. 25 cm.
Bound with the author's Een tusschenspel. Leyden [184–]
Cover title.
Issued in parts.
Published later under title: De studenten en hun bijloop.

1. Students—Netherlands. I. Title.
PT5850.K5T8 55-54654

NK 0198626 DLC

Kneppelhout, Johannes, 1814–1885.
De studenten en hun bijloop, door Klikspaan [pseud.] December 1840–Maart 1844. Leyden, H. W. Hazenberg, 1844.
1 v. (various pagings) 23 cm.
Published earlier under title: De studenten en hun aanhang.
Contents.—De studenten en hun bijloop.—Ophelderingen.—Klikspaan redekavelt over den almanak. — De studenten-almanak, eene microscopische uitspanning.—Aan de commissie voor de redactie van den studenten-almanak. — Een tusschenspel. — Ophelderingen. — Bijvoegsel.—Naschrift.

1. Students—Netherlands. I. Title.
PT5850.K5S67 1844 55-54602

NK 0198627 DLC

Kneppelhout, Johannes, 1814–1885.
Studentenleven, door Klikspaan [pseud.] Met platen van O. Veralby. Augustus 1841–Februarij 1844. Leyden, H. W. Hazenberg, 1844.
xx, 6, 820 p. illus. 25 cm.
Issued in 16 parts.

1. Students—Netherlands. I. Title.
PT5850.K5S8 1844 55-53038

NK 0198628 DLC

[Kneppelhout, Johannes] 1814–1885.
... Studentenleven, Augustus 1841–Februari 1844 ... 3. druk. Leiden, A. W. Sijthoff [1873]
2 v. 20½cm.
Author's pseud., Klikspaan, at head of title.
Preceded by his Studenten-typen, December 1839–Mei 1841.

1. Students—Netherlands. I. Title.
Library of Congress PT5850.K5S8 18-646

NK 0198629 DLC

Kneppelhout, Johannes, 1814-85
Studentenleven, door Klikspaan [pseud.] Met photogravures naar teekeningen van J.Braakensiek. Leiden, Sijthoff, [1899]

NK 0198630 MH

VOLUME 300

Kneppelhout, Johannes, 1814–1885.
Studenten-typen, door Klikspaan [pseud.] met platen van O. Veralby December 1839–Mey 1841. Leiden, H. W. Hazenberg, 1841.
xx, 386 p. plates. 25 cm.
Bound with the author's Een tusschenspel. Leyden [184–]
Issued in parts.

1. Students—Netherlands. I. Title.
PT5850.K5T8 55-54653

NK 0198631 DLC OCl

[Kneppelhout, Johannes] 1814–1885.
... Studenten-typen, December 1839–Mei 1841. 3. druk. Leiden, A. W. Sijthoff [1872]
xxii, 212 p., 2 l. 20½cm.
Author's pseud., Klikspaan, at head of title.
Followed by his Studentenleven, Augustus 1841–Februari 1844.

1. Students—Netherlands. I. Title.
18-547
Library of Congress PT5850.K5S7

NK 0198632 DLC

PT 5850 .K5 S3 KNEPPELHOUT, JOHANNES, 1814-1885
Studenten-typen en -leven [door] Klikspaan [pseud.] 4. druk. Leiden, A. W. Sijthoff [1885.
1 v. (various pagings) illus.

NK 0198633 InU

839.38 K68st 1898 Kneppelhout, Johannes, 1814-1885.
Studenten-typen [door] Klikspaan. Geïllustreerd door Johan Braakensiek. 7.druk. Leiden, A.W. Sijthoff [1898]
287 p. illus.

1.Students--Netherlands. I.Title.

NK 0198634 MiU

[Kneppelhout, Johannes] 1814-1885.
Studenten-typen. [By Klikspaan, pseud.] Geillustreerd door Johan Braakensiek. Leiden: A. W. Sijthoff [1904]. 3 p.l., 287(1) p. 8. ed. 8°.
Introduction by Jan ten Brink.
At head of title: Klikspaan.

1. Fiction (Dutch). 2. Student life, Netherlands: Leyden. 3. Braakensiek, Johan, 1858- , illustrator. 4. Brink, Jan ten, 1834-1901.
N. Y. P. L. December 21, 1914.

NK 0198635 NN

KNEPPELHOUT, JOHANNES, 1814-1885.
Studenten-typen. [By] Klikspaan [pseud.] Geïllustreerd door Johan Braakensiek. Leiden, A.W. Sijthoff [1904] 287 p. 21cm.
Microfiche (neg.) 6 sheets. 11 x 15cm. (NYPL FSN-3205)

1. Fiction, Dutch. 2. Leiden. Rijksuniversiteit--Fiction.

NK 0198636 NN

Kneppelhout, Johannes, 1814–1885.
Een tusschenspel, van Klikspaan [pseud.] Leyden, H. W. Hazenberg [184–]
36 p. plate. 25 cm.
Cover title.
Bound with the author's De studenten en hun aanhang. Leyden, 1843 and Studenten-typen. Leiden, 1841.

I. Title.
PT5850.K5T8 55-54655

NK 0198637 DLC

Kneppelhout, Johannes, 1814–1885.
Verhalen. 's Gravenhage, J. L. van der Vliet, 1846.
vi, 313 p. 23 cm.

PT5850.K5V4 49-35497*

NK 0198638 DLC

Kneppelhout van Sterkenburg, Karel Jan Frederik Cornelis, 1818-1885.
De gedenkteekenen in de Pieters-Kerk te Leyden, verzameld en beschreven door Mr. K. J. F. C. Kneppelhout van Sterkenburg. Leyden, P. H. van den Heuvell, 1864-[71]
2 p.l., 90 p. front., 47 plates. 34 cm.
Issued in parts.

NK 0198639 CtY MH

Kneppen, Theodore M.
1925's weather forecast indicates unusual business year...1924.
p. 921-922; 978-979. diagr. port. 29 cm.
44586

NK 0198640 DAS

Knepper, Adrian W
Obadiah Rich: bibliopole.
[19] p.
"Separate from the Papers of the Bibliographical Society of America, v. 49, 2d quarter, 1955." p. 112-130.

NK 0198641 OClW

Knepper, David Wilbur, 1899–
The municipal assessor; some aspects of municipal finance in Iowa, by David W. Knepper ... [Iowa City?] 1930.
cover-title, 1 p. l., p. 379-416, 567-576. 22½cm.
Thesis (PH. D.)—University of Iowa, 1927.
"Reprinted from Municipal government and administration in Iowa, volume I."

1. Municipal finance—Iowa. 2. Taxation—Iowa.
30-15690
Library of Congress HJ9237.7.K6 1927
Univ. of Iowa Libr.
——— Copy 2. [3] 352.109777

NK 0198642 IaU DLC

Knepper, Edwin Garfield, 1886–
History of business education in United States, by Edwin G. Knepper ... Bowling Green, O. [Ann Arbor, Mich., Edwards brothers, inc., lithoprinters] 1941.
iii p., 1 l., 221 p. 23½cm.

1. Business education—U. S.
41-10169
Library of Congress HF1131.K55
[2] 650.7

NK 0198643 NN OrCS DLC OrU TU PPPL PSt PU ScU OCU OCl OU ICJ

Knepper, Edwin Garfield, 1886–
School arts, a graded course, by Edwin G. Knepper ... [and] Verne C. Knepper ... Oklahoma City, Fort Worth [etc.] The Economy co., °1933.
8 v. illus. (part col.) 26½cm.

1. Art—Study and teaching. 2. Drawing—Instruction. I. Knepper, Verne Cullen, 1890– joint author. II. Title.
33-15937
Library of Congress N350.K57
Copyright AA 122674 [2] [707.13] 372.52

NK 0198644 DLC Or OrU

Knepper, Edwin Garfield, 1886–
School arts, a graded course, by Edwin G. Knepper ... [and] Verne C. Knepper ... Oklahoma City, Fort Worth [etc.] The Economy co., °1934.
8 v. illus. (part col.) 26½cm.

1. Art—Study and teaching. 2. Drawing—Instruction. I. Knepper, Verne Cullen, 1890– joint author. II. Title.
35-8199
Library of Congress N350.K57 1934
Copyright AA 174832 [3] [707.13] 372.52

NK 0198645 DLC

Knepper, Ewald Heinrich, 1863-
... Über oesophagotomie bei stenose des oesophagus ... von Ew. Heinr. Knepper ... Köln, Quos [1889]
29 p.

Inaug.-diss., Bonn, 1889.
Vita.

1. Esophagus - Surgery.

NK 0198646 NNC DNLM CU PPC

Knepper, Ferdinand.
Die Fabrikation und Berechnung der modernen Metalldrahtglühlampen einschliesslich der Spiraldraht- und Halb-Watt-Füllungslampen, von F. Knepper. Leipzig: Hachmeister & Thal, 1922. iv, 160 p. incl. tables, illus. 4°.

NK 0198647 NN OCIL ICJ DP

Knepper, Ferdinand.
Die fabrikation und berechnung der modernen metalldrahtglühlampen, einschliesslich der spiraldraht- und halb-wattfüllungslampen, von F. Knepper ... Mit 292 abbildungen und 32 tabellen. Zweite, verbesserte auflage. Leipzig, Hachmeister & Thal, 1926.
vi p., 1 l., 205 p. incl. illus., tables, diagrs. 26½cm.
"Verzeichnis der die glühlampenindustrie betr. patente ...": p. [191]-205.

1. Electric lamps, Incandescent. I. Title.
P O 32-59
Library, U. S. Patent Office TK4352.K68

NK 0198648 DP

Knepper, Ferdinand.
Die fabrikation von wolframdrähten für elektrische glühlampen und radioröhren, von ingenieur F. Knepper. Mit 51 abbildungen und 7 tabellen. Leipzig, Hachmeister & Thal, 1930.
viii, 111 p. incl. illus., tables, diagrs. 20cm.
"Advertising matter": p. 106-111.

1. Wire. 2. Tungsten. 3. Tungsten lamp. I. Title.
P O 32-44
Library, U. S. Patent Office TS270.K68

NK 0198649 DP NN

VOLUME 300

Knepper, Flavius J.
The farmers' veterinary; a treatise on the horse and his diseases, by F. J. Knepper ... [Vancouver? Wash., 1904]
25, [3] p. 19½cm.

1. Horse—Diseases.
Library of Congress SF951.K68 17-15720

NK 0198650 DLC

PS3521 .N44E3 1932
Knepper, Florence.
The Easter message "Lest we forget," by Florence Knepper. [Clayton, Mo., Watchman-advocate, c1932]
4 p.l., 11-57, [1] p. illus. 15.5 cm.

NK 0198651 DLC

PZ3 .K7293 Pe
Knepper, Florence.
The perfect gift, a Christmas story, by Florence Knepper, with illustrations by the author. [n.p., c1932]
47 p. illus., pl. 15 cm.

NK 0198652 DLC

---

x811 K73f
Knepper, George D
First fruits. [n.p., 1952]
48p. 19cm.

Cover title.

NK 0198653 IU

---

x811 K73w
Knepper, George D
What's Hecuba to him, or he to Hecuba? Poems. Fostoria, Ohio, Gray Print. Co. [1955]
44p. 19cm.

NK 0198654 IU

Knepper, George W., 1926–
The Convention army, 1777–1783. Ann Arbor, University Microfilms [1954]
([University Microfilms, Ann Arbor, Mich.] Publication no. 8326)
Microfilm copy of typescript. Positive.
Collation of the original: iv, 282 l.
Thesis—University of Michigan.
Abstracted in Dissertation abstracts, v. 14 (1954) no. 7, p. 1067.
Bibliography: leaves 275–282.

1. Burgoyne's Invasion, 1777. I. Title.
Microfilm AC-1 no. 8326 Mic A 55-3335
Michigan. Univ. Libr. for Library of Congress [1]†

NK 0198655 MiU UU DLC

Knepper, Hans Dietrich, 1908-
Geldschuld und girozahlung nach deutschem bürgerlichem recht. ... Würzburg, 1934. 67 p.
Inaug. Diss. - Würzburg, 1934.
Lebenslauf.
Bibliography.

NK 0198656 ICRL

Knepper, Joseph, 1864–1906.
Jakob Wimpfeling (1450–1528) Sein leben und seine werke nach den quellen dargestellt von dr. Joseph Knepper ... Freiburg im Breisgau; [etc., etc.] St. Louis, Mo., Herder, 1902.
xx, 375 p. 23½cm. (*Added t.-p.:* Erläuterungen und ergänzungen zu Janssens Geschichte des deutschen volkes. Hrsg. von L. Pastor. III. bd., 2.–4. hft.)
"Ausgaben-verzeichnis der schriften Wimpfelings": p. [xi]–xiv.
"Handschriften-verzeichnis": p. [xv]–xvi.
"Litteratur-verzeichnis": p. [xvii]–xx.
1. Wimpfeling, Jakob, 1450–1528.
4—30627
Library of Congress DD176.J26

NK 0198657 DLC NSyU PU NcD IEG MH MB

Knepper, Joseph, 1864–1906.
Nationaler gedanke und kaiseridee bei den elsässischen humanisten. Ein beitrag zur geschichte des deutschthums und der politischen ideen im Reichslande. Von dr. Joseph Knepper ... Freiburg im Breisgau; [etc., etc.] St. Louis, Mo., Herder, 1898.
xv, 207 p. 23cm. (*Added t.p.:* Erläuterungen und ergänzungen zu Janssens Geschichte des deutschen volkes. Hrsg. von L. Pastor. I. bd., 2.–3. hft.)
"Ausgaben der schriften der humanisten, auf welche sich die citate der abhandlung beziehen": p. [xi]–xv.
1. Alsace—Nationality. 2. Nationalism and nationality. 3. Humanism. 4. Holy Roman empire. 5. Kings and rulers—Duties.
4—30635
Library of Congress DD176.J26

NK 0198658 DLC CSt MH MB

Knepper, Joseph, 1864–1906.
Das schul- und unterrichtswesen im Elsass von den anfängen bis gegen das jahr 1530, von dr. Joseph Knepper ... Mit 12 abbildungen. Strassburg, J. H. E. Heitz (Heitz & Mündel) 1905.
xvi, 459 p. illus. 23½cm.
"Häufiger und abgekürzt angeführte schriften": p. [xiii]–xvi.

1. Education—Alsace-Lorraine.
6—42934
Library of Congress LA770.A42K5

NK 0198659 DLC PU CSt NIC CtY CU ICJ

857v K68
Knepper, Joseph, 1864-1906.
Tempora und modi bei Walther von der Vogelweide ... Lingen, Druck von R.van Acken, 1889.
92,[2]p.,1 l. 24cm.

Inaug.-diss. - Münster.
Lebenslauf.
Bibliography: p.6.

NK 0198660 CU MiU ICRL

Knepper, Kurt, 1911–
Hauptintervention und Drittwiderspruchsklage; eine prozessökonomische Studie. Würzburg, 1941.
79 p. 21 cm.
Inaug.-Diss.—Köln.
Vita.
Bibliography: p. 77–79.

1. Intervention (Civil procedure)—Germany. I. Title.
50-47948

NK 0198661 DLC

KNEPPER, LAURA M comp.
Knepper families in Pennsylvania. 1820 Kearny Ave., San Diego, 1950.
53 ℓ.

Mimeographed.

NK 0198662 Or

Knepper, M., joint author.

T26 .R9H3
Haack, W
Eisen, Kohle und Öl in Sowjet-Russland. Ergebnisse [und Tagesberichte] einer von Mai bis Juli 1931 ausgeführten Reise durch den Ural, Westsibirien, das Donezbecken und den Kaukasus, zusammengestellt von W. Haack und M. Knepper. [n. p., Vereinigte Stahlwerke Aktien-Gesellschaft, 1931?]

Knepper, Mamie C
Life is a mirror, by Mamie C. Knepper. Columbus, O., The F. J. Heer printing company [1944]
64 p. 23cm.
Poems.

I. Title.
45-161
Library of Congress ° PS3521.N443L5
[2] 811.5

NK 0198664 DLC

CS71 .K69 1911
Knepper, Margaret comp.
Genealogy of the Knepper family in the United States, 1681 - 1911. Compiled and arranged by Margaret Knepper, Highland, Kansas, 1906. Revised by Ethel Knepper. Forsyth, Mo., 1911.
1 v.(various pagings) ports. 22 cm.

Contents.-pt.1. Descendants of John Knepper.-pt.2. Descendants of Godfrey Knepper.-pt.3. Descendants of William Knepper.-pt.4. Historical notes and biographical sketches.-pt.5. Descendants of Jacob Knepper ... & Elizabeth Flick ... pt.6. Families whose connection is not known.

NK 0198665 T MiD

Knepper, Max.
Sodom and Gomorrah; the story of Hollywood, by Max Knepper. First printing. Los Angeles, Calif. [°1935]
236 p. 20 cm.
"Sponsored by End poverty league."

1. Hollywood, Calif. 2. Moving-pictures—Moral and religious aspects. 3. Actors. I. Title.
PN1993.5.U65K6 791.4 35—8981

NK 0198666 DLC CLSU

KNEPPER, MAX.
Sodom and Gomorrah; the story of Hollywood. Los Angeles, Calif. [c1935] 236 p. 20cm.
Film reproduction. Positive.
Imperfect: p. 227-236 wanting.
"Sponsored by End poverty league."
1. Hollywood, Calif. 2. Moving pictures--Moral and religious aspects.

NK 0198667 NN

Knepper, Verne Cullen, 1890- joint author
FOR OTHER EDITIONS SEE MAIN ENTRY
Knepper, Edwin Garfield, 1886–
School arts, a graded course, by Edwin G. Knepper ... [and] Verne C. Knepper ... Oklahoma City, Fort Worth [etc.] The Economy co., °1933.

Knepper, Walter, joint author.

Bartels, Martin.
... Das augenzittern der bergleute; seine soziale bedeutung, ursache, häufigkeit und die durch das zittern bedingten beschwerden, von prof. dr. M. Bartels ... und dr. med. W. Knepper ... Mit 19 abbildungen ... Berlin, J. Springer, 1930.

VOLUME 300

Knepper, Walter.
Ueber encephalitis epidemica. (Auszug)
Inaug. diss. Kiel, 1924.

NK 0198670 ICRL

Knepper, Willi, 1911-
... Untersuchungen über gemischte Sulfidsysteme (Ag_2S H_2, Ag_2S-Sb_2S_3-H_2, Ag_2S-PbS-H_2, Sb_2S_3-PbS-H_2) nebst Beobachtungen über thermische Gasentmischung ... Bottrop i. W., 1936.
Inaug.-Diss. - Münster.
Lebenslauf.
"Literatur": p. 41.

NK 0198671 CtY

Kneppers, G C
Bouwen in baksteen, handleiding voor het samenstellen en uitvoeren van metselwerken ten dienste van metselaars, bouwkundigen, studerenden, enz. Onder redactie van A. Rauwerda. Haarlem, V/h A. Kemperman [1949]
111 p. illus. 24 cm.

1. Masonry. 2. Building, Brick.

TH1301.K6 50-16194

NK 0198672 DLC IU

Kneppers, G C
Steigers en stutwerk in het bouwvak. Handleiding ten dienste van het nijverheidsonderwijs, studerenden, metselaars, timmerlieden, opzichters, uitvoerders, enz. Onder redactie van A. Rauwerda. Haarlem, A. Kemperman [1950?]
175 p. illus. 24 cm.

1. Scaffolding. 2. Shoring and underpinning. I. Title.
A 51-1061

Illinois. Univ. Library for Library of Congress [1]

NK 0198673 IU

Kneppert, François Pierre, 1906-
... Contribution à l'étude des formes phantastique et confabulante de la paraphrénie ... Strasbourg, 1932.
Thèse - Univ. de Strasbourg.
"Bibliographie": p. [67]-68.

NK 0198674 CtY

Kneppert, Jean.
... De la propriété apparente en matière de droits d'enregistrement ... Paris, Impr. du Montparnasse et de Persan-Beaumont, 1928.
4 p.l., [5]-273, [2] p. 25 cm.
Thèse - Faculté de droit de Paris.
"Bibliographie": p. [271]-273.

NK 0198675 CtY-L

NK5199
K68 Kneppert, P., Paris.
Album spécial des vaporisateurs a pompe et a balle: "Le Select" - "Le Moscovite". Paris, A. Nachmann [1890?] 8 plates (part col.) 22 x 31 cm.

Sales catalogue.

5106. 1. Glassware--Sales catalogues. I. Title: Vaporisateurs a pompe et a balle: "Le Select" - "Le Moscovite".

NK 0198676 NCorniC

Knepple, Rudolf, 1908-
Über Strahlungsmessungen im Sonnenvertikal ... [Leipzig, 1933]
Pamphlet.
Inaug.-Diss. - Frankfurt a. M.
Lebenslauf.
"Sonderabdruck aus 'Gerlands Beiträge zur Geophysik,' Band 39, Heft 4, 1933."

NK 0198677 CtY

Kneppo, L'udovit
see
Knepp , L'udovit.

Knepscher, Walther.
... Die Appretur der Seiden-, Halbseiden- und Samtgewebe, von Walther Knepscher ... Zweite Auflage. Leipzig: Dr. M. Jänecke [192-?] 39 p. illus. 21½cm. (Handbuch der gesamten Textilindustrie. Bd. 8.)
On cover: Bibl. d. ges. Technik 204.

1. Silk—Manufacture. 2. Textile finishing. I. Ser. II. Ser.: Bibliothek der gesamten Technik.
N. Y. P. L. May 17, 1940

NK 0198679 NN

Kner, Emerich
see Kner, Imre, 1893-

4PT
Ger.-4278 Kner, Hermann.
Wie lustig frei spazieren die Gedanken. Gera, P. E. Blank, 1948.
83 p.

NK 0198681 DLC-P4

Kner, Imre, 1893-1944?
... Die elemente des typographischen stils. [Gyoma, Isidor Kner, 1934]
81-96 p., 1 l. illus. 30cm.

Caption title.
At head of title: Emerich Kner...
"Hergestellt in 200 exemplaren..."
"Sonderabdruck aus dem zum sechzigsten geburtstag Carl Ernst Poeschels erschienenen buche."
1. Printing, Practical.

NK 0198682 NNC ICN IU

308
Z
Box 891
Kner, Imre, 1893-1944?
Das Gebetbuch des Generals Gyulai; ein seltenes Denkmal alter ungarischer Druckkunst, hrsg. von Emerich Kner. Gyoma, Isidor Kner, 1926.
7 p. facsims.

With facsimile of t.-p. and of three pages of the text of the original Hungarian text published in 1783.

NK 0198683 NNC

Z
232
.K738
1926
K73 Kner, Imre, 1893-1944? ed.
Gyulai Generális imádságos Könyve; a régi magyar tipográfia egy ritka emléke. Gyoma, Kner Izidor, 1926.
7 p., facsim: [5] p. 20cm.

200 copies printed.
Title of the prayer-book reads: Lelki paraditsom könyvböl ... 1783.

NK 0198684 NNC

GRAPHIC ARTS
Z137
K738
1912 Kner, Imre, 1893-1944?
Könyv a könyvről. Gyoma, Kner Izidor, 1912.
80 p. illus. (part col.) ports. (part col.) 31cm.

1. Books - History - Hungary. 2. Printing - History - Hungary.

NK 0198685 NNC

KNER, IMRE, 1893-1944? *I p.v.149
...Zeitfragen des typographischen Stils. [Gyoma, Ungarn: Buchdr. I. Kner, 1937?] 15 p. 21½cm.

At head of title: Emerich Kner.
"Vorgetragen am 5. Internationalen Buchdruckerkongress in Budapest, am 25. August 1937."

1. Printing—Hist., 19th-20th cent.

NK 0198686 NN ICN

PH
3281
K738A25 Kner, Izidor, 1860-1935.
Aforizmái. Vadász Miklós rajzaival. Gyoma, 1917.
167 p. illus., port.

NK 0198687 CLU

Kner, Izidor, 1860-1935
Agyafurt alakjai. Csicseri Bors (Ágai Adolf) és Molnár Jenő előszavával, Ber Dezső [et al.] ketszázötvenhárom eredeti rajzaival. 3., tetemesem bőv. kiad. Gyoma, 1926
367 p. illus.

NK 0198688 MH NNC

Kner, Izidor, 1860-1935
Apró lurkóságok, tizenkét képpel. [83p.]
Gyoma, Kner Izidor kiadasa, 1933.

NK 0198689 OCl

Kner, Izidor, b. 1860.
Ein halbes Jahrhundert im Dienste der Buchdruckerkunst; Auszug aus einer ungarischen Selbstbiographie, den Freunden der Buchdruckerkunst überreicht. Gyoma, Druck und Verlag des Autors, 1931.
31 p. 21cm.

NK 0198690 NNC

VOLUME 300

Kner, Izidor, 1860-1935.
...Félévszázad mesgyéjén, 1882-1932. Gyoma: Kner I., 1931. 176 p. front. (port.) 21cm.

668039A. 1. Publishers and publishing—Hungary. January 27, 1934
N. Y. P. L.

NK 0198691 NN OCl MH

Kner Izidor, 1860-1935, comp.
Kalászok és kévék; modern anthologia. Gyomán, 1902
98 p.

NK 0198692 MH

Kner, Izidor, 1860-1935
Keserves kenyér; tréfa két felvonásban Garay Ákos rajzaival. Gyoma, Kner Izidor, 1928
41 p. illus.

NK 0198693 MH

Kner, Rudolf, 1810-1869.
Fische. Wien, 1865-67.
14 cards. 7.5 x 12.5 cm. (Reise der österreichischen Fregatte Novara um die Erde in dem Jahren 1857, 1858, 1859, unter den Befehlen des Commodore B. von Wüllerstorf-Urbair. Zoologischer Theil)
Micro-opaque.
Collation of original: Abt. 1, p. 1-109, plates I-V; Abt. 2, p. 111-272, plates VI-XI; Abt. 3, p. 273-433, plates XII-XVI.

NK 0198694 OrCS

fQL615 .K5
Kner, Rudolf.
Fische. [Vienna, 1867]
3 v. in 1 (433 p.) 16 plates. 32 cm.
Novara-Expedition. Aoologischer Theil.
1. Fishes. I. Title. II. Novara-Expedition.

NK 0198694-1 AAP

Kner, Rudolf, 1810 1869.
Fische. Abth.1-3. Wien, 1869.
433 p. 16 plates. 4°.
Novara-Exped. Zool.Theil, 1869. 1. no.5.

NK 0198695 MH-Z CSt MB MdBP

13545 Y v.24
Kner, Rudolf, 1810-1869.
Fische aus dem Naturhistorischen Museum der Hrn. J.C. Godeffroy & Sohn in Hamburg. [Wien, K.K. Hof- und Staatsdruckerei, 1865]
12 p. 4 plates. 29cm. (Akademie der Wissenschaften, Vienna. Mathematisch-naturwissenschaftliche Klasse. Denkschriften, Bd. 24, 1. Abth.)
1. Fishes--Classification.

NK 0198696 NIC

13545 Y v.7
Kner, Rudolf, 1810-1869.
Die Hypostomiden. Zweite Hauptgruppe der Familie der Panzerfische. (Loricata vel Goniodontes). [Wien, K.K. Hof- und Staatsdruckerei, 1854]
251-286 p. plates. 29cm. (Akademie der Wissenschaften, Vienna. Mathematisch-naturwissenschaftliche Klasse. Denkschriften, Bd. 7, 1. Abth.)
1. Coffer- fish.

NK 0198697 NIC

Kner, Rudolf, 1810-1869
Lehrbuch der zoologie zum gebrauche für höhere lehranstalten ... 2d. aufl. Wien, L.W. Seidel, 1855.
xxiv, 656 p. 22½ cm.
Bibliographical footnotes.

NK 0198698 PPAN InU

Kner, Rudolf, 1810-1869. 550.2 L163
Leitfaden zum Studium der Geologie mit Inbegriff der Palaeontologie. Zum Gebrauche für Studirende an Ober-Gymnasien und technischen Lehranstalten. Von Rudolf Kner ... Mit vielen Holzschnitten. Wien, L. W. Seidel, 1851.
[8], 173, [3] p. illus. 22½cm.

NK 0198699 ICJ

Kner, Rudolf, 1810-1869.
Leitfaden zum Studium der Geologie mit Inbegriff der Palaeontologie. Ed.2. Vienna, 1855.
vi, (1), 181 p. 8°.

NK 0198700 MH-Z

Kner, Rudolf, 1810-1869
Heckel, [Johann] Jacob, 1790-1857.
Neue beiträge zur kenntniss der fossilen fische Österreichs. Begonnen von ... Jackob Heckel, beendet von Rudolf Kner. (Mit zehn tafeln in farbendruck) ... Wien, In commission bei K. Gerold's sohn, 1861.

13545 Y v.21
Kner, Rudolf, 1810-1869.
Neue Beiträge zur Kenntniss der fossilen Fische Österreichs, von Rudolf Kner und Franz Steindachner. [Wien, K.K. Hof- und Staatsdruckerei, 1863]
17-36 p. 7 plates. 29cm. (Akademie der Wissenschaften, Vienna. Mathematisch-naturwissenschaftliche Klasse. Denkschriften, Bd. 21, 1. Abth.)
1. Fishes, Fossil. I. Steindachner, Franz, 1834- 1919, joint author.

NK 0198702 NIC

13545 Y v.3
Kner, Rudolf, 1810-1869.
Neue Beiträge zur Kenntnis der Kreideversteinerungen von Ost-Galizien. [Wien, K.K. Hof- und Staatsdruckerei, 1852]
293-334 p. plates. 37cm. (Akademie der Wissenschaften, Vienna. Mathematisch-naturwissenschaftliche Klasse. Denkschriften, Bd. 3)
1. Paleontology--Austria.

NK 0198703 NIC MH

Kner, Rudolf, 1810-1869.
Neue fische aus dem museum der Herren J.C. Godeffroy & sohn ... [Wien, 1867]

NK 0198704 NjP

Kner, Rudolf, 1810-1869.
Neue gattungen und arten von fischen aus Central-Amerika; gesammelt von prof. Moritz Wagner, beschrieben von prof. Rudolf Kner und dr. Franz Steindachner ... Mit sechs tafeln abbildungen. [München, Franz, 1865]
61 p. vi pl. 28½cm.
Found also in Königlich-bayerische akademie der wissenschaften. Abhandlungen. bd. x.
1. Fishes—Central America. I. Steindachner, Franz, 1834- joint author.
F 11—84
U. S. Bur. of fish. Library for Library of Congress [a41b1]

NK 0198705 DI NIC

13545 Y v.6
Kner, Rudolf, 1810-1869.
Die Panzerwelse des K.K. Hof-Naturalien-Cabinetes zu Wien. I. Abtheilung: Loricarinae. [Wien, K.K. Hof- und Staatsdruckerei, 1854]
65-98 p. plates. 29cm. (Akademie der Wissenschaften, Vienna. Mathematisch-naturwissenschaftliche Klasse. Denkschriften, Bd. 6)
1. Lorica riidae.

NK 0198706 NIC

Sw3.2 1
Kner, Rudolf, 1810-1869.
... Über den Flossenbau der Fische ... [Wien, 1860-61]
p.[807]-824,232-260,759-786,[123]-152,[49]-80. illus. 22½cm
Caption titles.
"Sonder-Abdruck aus dem XLI. [-XLIV] Bde. d. Sitzungsb. der kais. Akademie d. Wissenschaften."
[Binder's title: Fishes]

NK 0198707 CtY

Kner, Rudolf, 1810-1869.
Über einige fossile Fische aus den Kreide - und Tertiärschichten von Comen und Podsused. Wien, 1863.

NK 0198708 NjP

Kner, Rudolf, 1810-1869, joint author.
Steindachner, Franz, 1834-
... Über einige pleuronectiden, salmoniden, gadoiden und blenniiden aus der Decastris-Bay und von Viti-Levu. Von Dr. Franz Steindachner ... und weil. Prof. Dr. Rudolph Kner ... (Vorgelegt in der sitzung am 21. april 1870.) [Wien, Aus der K. K. Hof- und staatsdruckerei, 1870]

fQE755 P7K55 Earth Sciences Library
Kner, Rudolf, 1810-1869.
Versteinerungen des Kreidemergels von Lemberg und seiner Umgebung, von Rudolph Kner. [Wien, Braumüller und Seidel, 1847?]
42 p. 5 tables. 35x27cm. (Naturwissenschaftliche Abhandlungen, 3.Bd., 2.Abth.)
Caption title.
"Mitgeheilt am 3. September, 1847 in einer Versammlung von Freunden der Naturwissenschaften in Wien."
1. Paleontology - Poland - Lemberg. 2. Mollusks, Fossil - Poland - Lemberg.

NK 0198710 CU

VOLUME 300

13545 **Kner, Rudolf, 1810-1869.**
Y Zur Familie der Characinen. 3. Folge:
v.17 Die ichthyologischen Beiträge. ⌐Wien, K. K. Hof- und Staatsdruckerei, 1859⌐
137-182 p. 9 plates. 29cm. (Akademie der Wissenschaften, Vienna. Mathematisch-naturwissenschaftliche Klasse. Denkschriften, Bd. 17, 1. Abth.)

1. Characinidae.

NK 0198711 NIC

13545 **Kner, Rudolf, 1810-1869.**
Y Zur Familie der Characinen. 3. Folge: Die
v.18 ichthyologischen Beiträge. 2. Abth. ⌐Wien, K.K. Hof- und Staatsdruckerei, 1860⌐
9-62 p. 8 plates. 29cm. (Akademie der Wissenschaften, Vienna. Mathematisch-naturwissenschaftliche Klasse. Denkschriften, Bd. 18, 1. Abth.)

1. Characinidae.

NK 0198712 NIC

Z
232
.K738 Kner-klasszikusok. ⌐Szerk. Király György, a
1921 könyvdíszeket tervezte Kozma Lajos⌐ Gyoma,
K73 Kner Izidor, 1921.
12 v. 20cm.

Decorations.

NK 0198713 NNC

Knerr, Arthur Frank, joint comp.

⌐Deutschmeister, Abraham⌐ *comp.*
Uncle Sam's teasers and chronicles of the revolution; a liberal education in American history. New York, The Oak press ⌐1927⌐

Knerr, Arthur Frank, joint comp.

Deutschmeister, Abraham, *comp.*
Uncle Sam's teasers, from the discovery to the present day; a liberal education in American history, being a series of questions and answers compiled and arranged by Abraham Deutschmeister, Charles Taylor Wandres, Arthur Frank Knerr. New York, The Oak press ⌐1927⌐

Knerr, Calvin Brobst, 1847- joint ed.

Hering, Constantin, 1800-1880.
The guiding symptoms of our materia medica, by C. Hering ... Philadelphia, The American homœopathic publishing society, 1879-

---

Knerr, Calvin Brobst, 1847-
Life of Hering; the conversation, life and times of Constantine Hering, founder of the Allentown academy of homoeopathic medicine, Hahnemann hospital, Hahnemann college, American institute of homoeopathy, author of the leading works in homoeopathic literature, homoeopathic practitioner. By Calvin B. Knerr, M. D. Philadelphia, The Magee press, 1940.
xi p., 2 l., 347 p. front., pl., ports., facsim. 22cm.
"First edition."
"Literary production": p. ⌐181⌐-194.
1. Hering, Constantin, 1800-1880. 2. Homeopathy.

40-30665

Library of Congress RX66.H4K55
—— —— Copy 2.
Copyright ⌐2⌐ 926.1

NK 0198717 DLC PPHa PPFr PPG PHi

Knerr, Calvin Brobst, 1847-

Hering, Constantin, 1800-1880.
A repertory of Hering's guiding symptoms of our materia medica, by Calvin B. Knerr, M. D. Philadelphia, F. A. Davis co., for the estate of C. Hering, 1896.

Knerr, E. B.
Special report on mineral waters...
see under Bailey, Edgar Henry Summerfield, 1848-

973.7L63 **Knerr, H O**
H2K73ℓ Lincoln, man of destiny. ⌐n.p., n.d.⌐
1 fold.ℓ. 21x28cm.

A poem.

1. Lincoln, Abraham, Pres. U.S.—Poetry.

NK 0198720 IU

Knerr, Henry William, 1905-
The electric spectrum of liquid water from five to twenty centimeters, by Henry W. Knerr ... ⌐New York, 1937⌐
1 p. l., p. 1054-1067. diagrs. 26½ x 20cm.
"Taken from a dissertation submitted ... for the degree of doctor of philosophy in the University of Michigan ⌐1937⌐"
"Reprinted from the Physical review, vol. 52, no. 10, November 15, 1937."
Bibliographical foot-notes.

1. Spectrum analysis. 2. Refractive index. 3. Electric waves. 4. Water. I. Title.

38-21469

Library of Congress QC454.K557 1937
Univ. of Michigan Libr. ⌐3⌐ 535.84

NK 0198721 MiU DLC OCU

Knerr, Horace Calvin, 1888-
Heat treament ⌐!⌐ and metallography of steel; elements of physical metallurgy, by Horace C. Knerr ... 2d ed. ... ⌐Philadelphia⌐ ©1935.
cover-title, 161 (*i. e.* 167) numb. l. illus., diagrs. 28cm.
Includes six extra numbered leaves.
"Made by the photo-offset process."—Foreword.
"This work was first published serially in Forging, stamping and heat treating magazine."—Foreword.

1. Steel—Metallurgy. 2. Steel—Metallography.

CA 35-223 Unrev'd

Library of Congress TN730.K6 1935
Copyright AA 173043 669.1

PPEFH
NK 0198722 DLC PBL WaS NcRS CU PSC PU OCl OEac IU

L669.1 Knerr, Horace Calvin, 1888-
K68h Heat treatment and metallography of steel; elements of physical metallurgy. 2d ed. [Philadelphia] 1946.
161p. illus., diagrs. 28cm.

"Made by the photo-offset process."
"This work was first published serially in Forging, stamping and heat treating magazine."

1. Steel. Metallurgy. 2. Steel. Metallography. I. Title.

NK 0198723 IEN

Knerr, Horace Calvin, 1888-

American society for testing materials.
Symposium on aircraft materials, held at the thirty-third annual meeting of the American society for testing materials, Atlantic City, N. J., June 23 to 27, 1930 ... ⌐Philadelphia, 1930?⌐

Knerr, Hugh J 1887-
The student pilot's training primer ⌐by⌐ Hugh J. Knerr ... Illustrations by S. F. Knerr. New York, D. Van Nostrand company, inc., 1941.
ix, 172 p. incl. front. (port.) illus., diagrs. 23½ cm.
—— —— Question book ... New York, D. Van Nostrand company, inc. ⌐1942⌐
40 p. illus. 23 cm.
TL710.K55a
—— —— Answer book, including true-false quizzes ... New York, D. Van Nostrand company, inc. ⌐1942⌐
23 p. 23 cm.
TL710.K55b
1. Aeroplanes—Piloting. I. Title.

TL710.K55 629.1325 41-7736 rev 2

OClW OU PPGi
NK 0198725 DLC CaBVa Or WaS OCl PP NcC NcD KEmT CU

629.1 Knerr, Hugh J 1887-
K738s The student pilot's training primer ... Illus-
1942 trations by S. F. Knerr. Third printing. New York, D. Van Nostrand company, inc. [1942]
172p.

"First published April 1941; reprinted ... September 1942."

1. Aeroplanes--Piloting. I. Title.

NK 0198726 IU

L194
.B52
no. 331F **Knerr, Michael W**
Metal forming as an area of industrial arts instruction in Pennsylvania public schools. Harrisburg, 1953.
x, 63 p. illus. 23 cm. (Pennsylvania. Dept. of Public Instruction. Bulletin ⌐new ser.⌐ 331F)
"Supplements Industrial arts in Pennsylvania, Bulletin 331, published in ... 1951."
"Instructional aids: books, magazines, films": p. 37-44.
1. Metal-work. I. Pennsylvania. Dept. of Public Instruction. Industrial arts in Pennsylvania. II. Title. (Series)

[L194.B52 no. 331F] A 54-9443

Pennsylvania. State University. Library
for Library of Congress ⌐1⌐

NK 0198727 PU DLC MtU PPS PSt PV PP

Knerr, Sylvester Buck.
Fruit from the garden of spices, together with Rescued from a miner's grave. By S. B. Knerr. ⌐Reading? Pa., ©1900⌐
106 p. front. (port.) illus. 15cm.

I. Title.

0-5992 Revised

Library of Congress BR125.K598

NK 0198728 DLC

Knerr, Valerie Catherine (Hiatt) 1929-
Elihu Stout, Indiana's first printer. Rochester, N. Y., University of Rochester Press for the Association of College and Reference Libraries, 1955.
2 cards. 7½ x 12½ cm. (ACRL microcard series, no. 48)
Microprint copy of typescript.
Collation of the original: iii, 44 l. 28 cm.
Thesis (M. A.)—Indiana University.
Bibliography: leaves 41-44.

1. Stout, Elihu, 1782 or 3-1860. (Series: Association of College and Reference Libraries. ACRL microcard series, no. 48)

Microcard Z232 Micp 55-51

Library of Congress ⌐1⌐

N NIC InU OU DCU OClW
NK 0198729 DLC MiU NBuU ICN CaBVaU OrU LU ViU IU NNC

Knesch, Heinrich, *ed. and tr.*
... Lesebuch für landwirtschaftliche schulen, zusammengestellt von prof. Heinrich Knesch. Mit 7 abbildungen. 2. verb. aufl. ... Prag, Tschechoslowakische akademie der landwirtschaft, 1932.
316 p. illus. 25½cm. (Lehrbücher für landwirtschaftliche schulen, bd. 18)
CONTENTS.—Aus den werken deutscher dichter, von Gellert bis zur gegenwart.—Stimmen der heimat.—Aus der tschechischen literatur.—Geschichte.—Bauerntum.—Volkswirtschaft, naturwissenschaften, landwirtschaft u. a. m.
1. German language—Chrestomathies and readers. 2. German literature (Selections: Extracts, etc.) 3. Bohemian literature—Translations into German. 4. German literature—Translation from Bohemian. 5. German literature—Bohemia.

34-15393

Library of Congress PF3117.K62 1932
⌐2⌐ 830.822

NK 0198730 DLC

VOLUME 300

Kneschaurek, Francesco.
Der schweizerische Konjunkturverlauf und seine Bestimmungsfaktoren; dargestellt auf Grund der Periode 1929 bis 1939. Zürich, Polygraphischer Verlag, 1952.
xvi, 256 p. diagrs. 21 cm. (Veröffentlichungen der Handels-Hochschule St. Gallen, Reihe A, Heft 30)
"Unveränderter Abdruck meiner der Handels-Hochschule St. Gallen eingereichten Dissertation."
Bibliography: p. 250-254.
1. Switzerland—Comm. 2. Switzerland—Economic policy. (Series: St. Gall, Switzerland. Handelshochschule. Veröffentlichungen, Reihe A, Heft 30)
New York Univ. for Library of Congress Libraries HF3706 [3] A 56-1440

NK 0198731 NNU MH NN NIC

4PF Ger.-100 **Kneschaurek, Franz.**
Deutsches Lesebuch für gewerbliche Lehranstalten zunächst für Werkmeisterschulen, gewerbliche Fach- und Fortbildungsschulen und Handwerkerschulen. 3., verb. Aufl. Wien, K. Graeser, 1909.
384 p.

NK 0198732 DLC-P4

Kneschke, Abraham. Compendium Theologico-Vandalicum per Quaestiones & Responsiones . . . Autore Abrahamo Kneschkio. typis et sumptibus Jo. Jac. Lubenae Böllmanni 1727. 13 cm.
Wendischer Titel: To Wusnasche teje Wernoscizi k'Bohgabojasnaszi, . . . Schischzane Lübine, 1727.

NK 0198733 CU

517.37 K739a **Kneschke, Alfred,** 1902-
Anwendung der theorie der integralgleichungen auf das durch schlagsproblem von festen isolatoren. Berlin, 1927.
p.[195]-210.
Inaug.-diss.--Sächsischen technischen hochschule zu Dresden.
"Sonderabdruck aus 'Zeitschrift für physik', bd.41, heft 2/3."

NK 0198734 IU

PT 1173 K68 **Kneschke, Emil, 1835- , ed.**
Anthologie deutscher Lyriker seit 1850; hrsg. mit literarhistorischer Einleitung und biographisch-kritischen Notizen von Emil Kneschke. Leipzig, C. H. Lorck, 1865.
xii, 568 p. 20cm.
1. German poetry (Collections) 2.German poetry--19th cent.

NK 0198735 NIC InU

Kneschke, Emil, 1835-
Das Conservatorium der musik in Leipzig. Seine geschichte, seine lehrer und zöglinge. Festgabe zum 25jährigen jubiläum am 2. april 1868, von dr. Emil Kneschke. Leipzig, Breitkopf und Härtel [1868]
70 p. 23½cm.
1. Leipzig. Landeskonservatorium der musik.
[Full name: Julius Emil Kneschke]
Library of Congress MT5.L5L257 10-9345 Revised

NK 0198736 DLC

Kneschke, Emil, 1835-
Das deutsche lustspiel in vergangenheit und gegenwart. Kritische beiträge zur literaturgeschichte unseres volkes, von dr. Emil Kneschke. Leipzig, Veit & comp., 1861.
3 p. l., [v]-vi, 469, [1] p. 19cm.
1. German drama (Comedy)—Hist. & crit.
[Full name: Julius Emil Kneschke]
Library of Congress PT676.K6 12-23024

NK 0198737 DLC CU CaBVaU NjP NN

Kneschke, Emil, 1835-
Deutsche Lyriker seit 1850. Mit literarhistorischer Einleitung und biographisch-kritischen Notizen. 2. verb. und verm. Aufl. Leipzig, 1868
xxii, 679 p. port.
1. German poetry (9) - 19th cent. - Coll.

NK 0198738 MH PU

Kneschke, Emil, 1835- and **Moltke,** Max.
Deutsche lyriker seit 1850. Mit literarhistorischer einleitung und biographisch-kritischen notizen. Vierte bedeutend vermehrte und verbesserte auflage. Leipzig, 1874. 12°.

NK 0198739 MdBP

Kneschke, Emil, 1835- ed.
Deutsche Lyriker seit 1850; mit einer litterar-historischen Einleitung und biographisch-kritischen Notizen. Mit Emanuel Geibel's Porträt in Stahlstich, gestochen von A. Weger. 6. Aufl. Leipzig, T. Knaur, 1886.
816 p. illus. 18 cm.
1. German poetry—19th cent. I. Title.
Full name: Julius Emil Kneschke.
PT1173.K5 1886 54-50494 ‡

NK 0198740 DLC

Kneschke, Emil, 1835- ed.
Deutsche lyriker seit 1850, mit einer litterar-historischen einleitung und biographisch-kritischen notizen. 7 aufl. Leipzig, 1887.
816 p.

NK 0198741 PHC MiU

Kneschke, Emil, 1835-
Deutsche lyriker seit 1850; mit einer litterar-historischen einleitung und biographisch-kritischen notizen, hrsg. von dr. Emil Kneschke. Mit den bildnissen unserer beliebtesten dichter und Emanuel Geibel's portrait in stahlstich, gestochen von A. Weger. 7. aufl. Leipzig, Th. Knaur, 1889.
2 p. l., [iii]-viii, 816 p. front., ports. 18cm.
Title-page to 5th ed., 1883, inserted.

NK 0198742 NNC

Kneschke, Emil, 1835-
Deutsche Lyriker seit 1850. Mit einer litterar-historischen Einleitung und biographisch-kritischen Notizen. Hrsg. von Dr. Emil Kneschke. Mit den Bildnissen unserer beliebtesten Dichter und Emanuel Geibel's Portrait in Stahlstich, gestochen von A. Weger... Leipzig: T. Knaur, 1899. viii, 816 p. front., ports. 7. ed. 12°.
With bookplate of P. W. Shedd.
255815A. 1. Poetry, German—Collections. N. Y. P. L. December 10, 1926

NK 0198743 NN

92 D51441k Kneschke, Emil, 1835-
Emil Devrient, biographisch-kritische Studie zur deutschen Bühnengeschichte. Festgabe zum 1. Mai 1868, dem Tage des letzen öffentlichen Auftretens Devrients. Dresden, C.C. Meinhold [1868]
50p. port. 24cm.
1. Devrient, Emil, 1803-1872.

NK 0198744 CLSU MH

KNESCHKE, EMIL, 1835-
Göthe und Schiller in ihren Beziehungen zur Frauenwelt. Dargestellt in zwei Abschnitten nebst Zusätzen und Anhängen. Nürnberg, Bauer & Raspe, 1858.
xvi, 394 p. 19cm.
Bibliographical footnotes.
1. Goethe, Johann Wolfgang von--Relations with women. 2. Schiller, J. C. F. von

NK 0198745 NN MH MiU

Kneschke, Emil, 1835-
... Die hundertundfünfzigjährige geschichte der Leipziger Gewandhaus-concerte 1743-1893. Von dr. Emil Kneschke ... 4. tausend. Leipzig und New-York, Internationale verlags- und kunstanstalt (J. Laurencic) [1893]
159, [1] p. incl. front., illus. (ports.) 17½cm. (Universal-bibliothek für musiklitteratur ... [nº 1-3])
On cover: Zürich, Internationale verlags- und kunst-anstalt, vorm. (A. von Hagen & co.) Direktor: J. Laurencic.
1. Leipzig. Gewandhaus. 2. Leipzig. Konzerthaus. 3. Music—Germany—Leipzig.
[Full name: Julius Emil Kneschke]
Library of Congress ML280.8.L3K6 9-31206 Revised 2

NK 0198746 DLC MB

Kneschke, Emil, 1835-
... Das Königliche conservatorium der musik zu Leipzig 1843-1893. Von dr. Emil Kneschke ... 3. tausend. Leipzig und New-York, Internationale verlags- und kunstanstalt (A. Laurencic) [1893]
86 p. incl. front., illus. 18cm. (Universal-bibliothek für musiklitteratur ... no. 4-5)
Label mounted over imprint on cover: Berlin-Leipzig ... Schulz & co.
1. Leipzig. Landeskonservatorium der musik.
[Full name: Julius Emil Kneschke]
Library of Congress MT5.L5L259 10-9346 Revised

NK 0198747 DLC

DD 901 L58 K68 1868 Kneschke, Emil, 1835-
Leipzig seit 100 Jahren; Säcularchronik einer werdenden Grossstadt; ein Beitrag zur Localgeschichte seiner Heimath. 2. verm. und revidirte Aufl. Leipzig, Verfassers, 1868.
505 p. 22cm.
1. Leipzig--Hist.

NK 0198748 NIC PPG

Kneschke, Emil, 1835-
Leipzig seit 100 Jahren; Säcularchronik einer werdenden Grossstadt. Ein Beitrag zur Localgeschichte seiner Heimath von Emil Kneschke. 2., verm. und revid. Aufl. Leipzig, J.F. Hartknoch, 1870.
505 p. 23 cm.
1. Leipzig - History. I. Title.

NK 0198749 CaBVaU MH

VOLUME 300

Kneschke, Emil. 1835- Nationalgalerie in Berlin. 26 pp. (*Unsere Zeit*, 1877, v. 2, p. 241.)

NK 0198750 MdBP

Kneschke, Emil, 1835-
Zur geschichte des theaters und der musik in Leipzig. Von dr. Emil Kneschke. Leipzig, F. Fleischer, 1864.
vi, 330 p. 20cm.

1. Theater—Leipzig. 2. Music—Germany—Leipzig.

10-9347

Library of Congress ML280.8.L3K63

NK 0198751 DLC NcU CtY

Kneschke, Ernst Heinrich, 1798-1869. *De hydrothorace. 34 pp. 4°. *Lipsiæ, lit. Staritzii,* [1828].

NK 0198752 DNLM

CS618
.K5
Kneschke, Ernst Heinrich, 1798-1869.
Deutsche Grafen-Haeuser der Gegenwart in heraldischer, historischer und genealogischer Beziehung. Leipzig, T. O. Weigel, 1852-54.
3 v. illus. 22cm.

CONTENTS.--1. Bd. A-K.--2. Bd. L-Z.--3. Bd. A-Z.

1. Germany--Nobility. 2. Heraldry--Germany. 3. Germany--Genealogy. I. Title.

NK 0198753 ViU MH NN NIC

Kneschke, Ernst Heinrich, 1798–1869.
Neues allgemeines deutsches adels-lexicon, im vereine mit mehreren historikern, hrsg. von prof. dr. Ernst Heinrich Kneschke ... Leipzig, F. Voigt, 1859–70.
9 v. 23cm.

1. Germany—Nobility. 2. Heraldry—Germany. I. Title.

22-2411

Library of Congress CS617.K6

NK 0198754 DLC NN IU MdBP CtY NcU NIC

Kneschke, Ernest Heinrich, 1798-1869, respondent.
[Pr.] de usu hydrargyri ... XII
see under Haase, Wilhelm Andreas, 1784-1837.

Kneschke, Ernst Heinrich, 1798-1869.
Die Wappen der deutschen freihenlichen und adeligen Familien in genauer, ...
see under title

Kneschke, Heinz.
Das ruhen des verfahrens nach der revidierten ZPI. Inaug. diss. Leipzig, 1927. (Loebau in Sachsen) Bibl.

NK 0198757 ICRL

027.5
Z82Zk
Kneschke, Johann Gottfried, 1766-1825.
Geschichte und merkwürdigkeiten der Rathsbibliothek in Zittau, beschrieben von m. Johann Gottfried Kneschke ... Zittau, J.D.Schöps, 1811.
3p.ℓ., viiip., 1ℓ., 164p. 20cm.

1. Zittau. Rathsbibliothek.

NK 0198758 IEN

Kneschke, Johann Gottfried, 1766-1825.
Geschichte und Merkwürdigkeiten der Rathsbibliothek in Zittau, beschrieben von M. Johann Gottfried Kneschke. Zittau und Leipzig, In Commission bey I. D. Schöps' und Gedruckt in Görlitz bey C. G. Schirach, 1811.
viii, 164 p.

Microfilm of copy in Harvard Library.

NK 0198759 NNC

Kneschke, Julius Emil
see
Kneschke, Emil, 1835-

Kneschke, Karl.
Wem sollen wir treue halten? Geschrieben für Mitglieder der "Treuegemeinschaft sudetendeutscher Sozialdemokraten," von Karl Kneschke. London, "Einheit," 1944. 31 p. 15cm.

1. Germans in Czecho-Slovakia. 2. Socialism—Czecho-Slovakia.
N. Y. P. L. February 19, 1948

NK 0198761 NN

KNESCHKE, Frau Martha, 1866-
Auf den spuren der weissen frau. Berlin, etc., W. Vobach & co., [1909].

pp.53. Illustr.
On cover:-Zur erinnerung an burg Lauenstein in Oberfranken.

NK 0198762 MH

Kneschke, *Frau* **Martha,** 1866–
... Mutter Königen, ein märchen für kleine und grosse von M. Kneschke-Schönau [*pseud.*] ... Beppo, der geiger, erzählung von J. Utecht ... Der zimmermann von Saardam, erzählung von G. Nieritz. Neu bearb. von R. Thiele ... Mit einem buntdruckbild und drei textbildern ... Dresden, R. H. Dietrich [1911]
228 p. col. front., 3 pl. 19cm. (Dietrichs bibliothek für die reifere jugend und deren freunde. [13. bd.]) M. 1.50

I. Utecht, J. II. Nieritz, Karl Gustav, 1795–1876. III. Thiele, R.

11-20906

Library of Congress

NK 0198763 DLC

PT2621
.N4356
Kneschke, Frau Martha, 1866-
Spätsommerglück; roman einer zweiten liebe von M. Kneschke-Schönau. Leipzig, [1912].

NK 0198764 DLC

Kneschke, Rudolf: Georg von Stein. Versuch einer Biographie. Weida i. Th. 1913: Thomas & Hubert. IX, 133 S. 8°
Leipzig, Phil. Diss. v. 18. Nov. 1913, Ref. Seeliger, Brandenburg
[Geb. 11. April 89 Bischofswerda; Wohnort: Leipzig; Staatsangeh.: Sachsen; Vorbildung: G. Bautzen Reife 09; Studium: München 3, Berlin 1, Leipzig 4 S.; Rig. 24. Juli 13.] [U 13. 4089

NK 0198765 ICRL CtY PU MH

Kneschke-Schoenau, M.
see
Kneschke, Martha, 1866-

Kneschkius, Abrahamus
see Kneschke, Abraham.

Knese, Adolf.
Die Majestätsbeleidigung des Reichsstrafgesetzbuchs unter besonderer Berücksichtigung der Novelle vom 17. Februar, 1908. Göttingen: W. F. Kaestner. 1909. x, 58 p. 8°.
Dissertation, Göttingen. Bibliography, p. vii-x.

1. Lèse majesté, Germany.
N. Y. P. L. February 23, 1911.

NK 0198768 NN MH-L

Knese, Karl Heinrich, 1914-
... Das Kopfgelenk der aquatilen Säugetiere ... Berlin, 1936.
Inaug.-Diss. - Berlin.
Lebenslauf.
"Diese Arbeit erschien gleichzeitig in 'Morphologisches Jahrbuch', [Bd.] 78."

NK 0198769 CtY

Knesebeck, von dem, supposed author.
Drottning Fredrika af Sverige
see under title

Knesebeck, A von dem
Aus dem Leben der Vorfahren vom Schlosse zu Tylsen in der Altmark. Berlin, Druck von W. Bürenstein, 1875
242 p.

NK 0198771 MH

Knesebeck, Frau Adolphine (von Klitzing) von dem, b. 1772.
Kleist, Heinrich von, 1777–1811.
Zwei briefe Heinrich von Kleists an Adolphine von Werdeck. Mit 2 faksimilenachbildungen. Nachwort von Herbert Wünsch. [n. p., 1935]

Knesebeck, Bodo von dem, 1851-1911.
Die deutsche freiwillige Kriegskrankenpflege im Kriegsjahre 1870-71. Gedächtnissrede gehalten am 8. Mai 1896 im Weissen Saale des königlichen Schlosses. Hrsg. vom Central-Comité der Deutschen Vereine vom Rothen Kreuz. Berlin, 1896.
35 p. 4°.

NK 0198773 DNLM

VOLUME 300

Hist RA644 +T7K54 1905 KNESEBECK, Bodo von dem, 1851-1911.
Das Deutsche Rote Kreuz und die Tuberkulose-Bekämpfung. La Croix Rouge allemande et la lutte contre la tuberculose. The German Red Cross and the fight against tuberculosis. Denkschrift für den Internationalen Tuberkulose-Kongress, Paris, 2-7. Okt. 1905, gewidmet vom Volksheilstätten-Verein vom Roten Kreuz. Herausgeber: B. von dem Knesebeck [und] Dr. Pannwitz. Berlin, Verlag: Das Rote Kreuz, 1905.
219p. illus., ports. 29cm.

1. Tuberculosis - Prevention 2. Tuberculosis - Germany 3. Red Cross. Germany. Deutsches Rotes Kreuz I. Pannwitz, Gotthold II. International Congress on Tuberculosis, 4th, Paris, 1905 III. Red Cross, Germany. Volksheilstätten-Verein vom Roten Kreuz. IV. Title V. Title: La Croix Rouge allemande et la lutte contre la tuberculose VI. Title: The German Red Cross and the fight against tuberculosis

NK 0198776 CtY-M

Hist RA644 +T7K541 1908 KNESEBECK, Bodo von dem, 1851-1911.
Das Deutsche Rote Kreuz und die Tuberkulose-Bekämpfung. La Croix Rouge allemande et la lutte contre la tuberculose. The German Red Cross and the fight against tuberculosis. Denkschrift für den Internationalen Tuberkulose-Kongress, Washington, 21. Sept. bis 12. Okt. 1908, gewidmet vom Volksheilstätten-Verein vom Roten Kreuz. Herausgeber: B. von dem Knesebeck [und] Dr. Pannwitz. Berlin, Verlag: Das Rote Kreuz, 1908.

viii, 230p. illus., ports. 29cm.

1. Tuberculosis - Prevention 2. Tuberculosis - Germany 3. Red Cross. Germany. Deutsches Rotes Kreuz I. Pannwitz, Gotthold II. International Congress on Tuberculosis, 6th, Washington, 1908 III. Red Cross. Germany. Volksheilstätten-Verein vom Roten Kreuz IV. Title V. Title: La Croix Rouge allemande et la lutte contre la tuberculose. VI. Title: The German Red Cross and the fight against tuberculosis ACK

NK 0198779 CtY-M PPC

Knesebeck, Bodo von dem, 1851–1911.
... Das Deutsche Rote kreuz und die tuberkulose-bekämpfung. / La Croix rouge allemande et la lutte contre la tuberculose. The German Red cross and the fight against tuberculosis. Denkschrift für den Internationalen tuberkulose-kongress, Rom 1912 und die Internationale Rote-kreuz-konferenz, Washington 1912 ... Im auftrage des Volksheilstätten-vereins vom Roten kreuz. 4. aufl. hrsg. von generalarzt z. d. dr. Werner ... [und] prof. dr. Pannwitz ... Berlin-Charlottenburg, Das Rote kreuz, 1912.

4 p. l., 213, [4] p. illus., ports. 28½cm.

At head of title: Von dem Knesebeck und Pannwitz.
German, French, and English.

1. Tuberculosis—Prevention. 2. Tuberculosis—Germany. 3. Red cross. I. Pannwitz, Gotthold, 1861–1926. II. Werner, Otto B. III. Red cross. Germany. Deutsches Rotes kreuz. Volksheilstätten-verein vom Roten kreuz.

13–33521

Library of Congress RA644.T7K6

NK 0198781 DLC

Knesebeck, Carl Friedrich von dem
see Knesebeck, Karl Friedrich von dem, 1768-1848.

Knesebeck, Christian Matthaeus
Prodromus juris publici universalis, magna eruditorum exspectatione diu desiderati, contenentis praetensiones illustres imperatoris & imperii, regum, principum ac rerumpublicarum totius Europae, majori operi praemissus ad vindicanda S.R.J. jura adversus Mezeraeum, Hadr. Valesium, David, Blondellum, aliosq; veluti primipilares jurium et rerum gallicarum scriptores,

qvorum lapsus ea, qva par est, modestia detegutur, rationibus ex historia, jure naturali et gentium petitis confutantur, cunctaq; diplomatibus non unis ex archivis depromtis, Limnaeo et Conringio nunqvam visis, demonstrantur ac corroborantur, autore Christiano

Matthaeo Knesebeck. Rodopoli, G. Libezeit, 1700.
[76] p. 18cm.

NK 0198785 MH-L

Knesebeck, Ernst von dem, ed. and tr.
Ferdinand, herzog zu Braunschweig und Lüneburg, während des siebenjährigen krieges
see under Ferdinand, duke of Brunswick-Luneburg, 1721-1775.

Knesebeck, Ernst von dem.
Geschichte der churhannoverschen Truppen in Gibraltar, Minorca und Ostindien. Hannover, Im Verlage der Helwingschen Hof-Buchhandlung, 1845.
189 p. 2 fold. plans, 1 fold. table. 23cm.

1. Hanoverian mercenaries.

NK 0198787 NN MH MB

KNESEBECK, Ernst von dem.
Geschichte der churhannoverschen Truppen in Gibraltar, Minorca und Ostindien. Hannover, Im Verlage der Helwingschen Hof-Buchhandlung, 1845.
189 p. 2 fold., plans, 1 fold. table. 23cm.

Microfilm (master negative).

NK 0198788 NN

4DD-1261 Knesebeck, Ernst von dem.
Leben des Freiherrn Hugh von Halkett, K. hannover'scher General der Infanterie, nach dessen hinterlassenen Papieren und andern Quellen entworfen. Stuttgart, E. Hallberger, 1865.
70 p.

NK 0198789 DLC-P4 CtY

Knesebeck, F W B F , Freiherr von dem
Archiv für Geschichte und Genealogie. Hannover, Hahn'schen Hofbuchhandlung, 1842-
v.

NK 0198790 MH

Knesebeck, F W B F
Freiherr von dem
Bb17 20 Historisches Taschenbuch des Adels im Königreich Hannover. Von F.W.B.F. Freih. von dem Knesebeck ... Hannover, In der Hahn'schen Hofbuchhandlung, 1840.
xi, [1], 444p. 17½cm.

1. Hanover - Nobility. 2. Genealogy - Hanover. 3. Hanover - Geneal.

NK 0198791 CtY NNC

[Knesebeck, Franz Julius von dem] fl. 17th cent.
Dreiständige Sinnbilder zu fruchtbringendem Nutze, und beliebender Ergetzlichkeit, ausgefertiget durch den Geheimen [pseud.] Braunschweig, Bei C. Buno, Kunst- und Kupffersteckern, 1643.
Microfilm copy (negative) of original in the Bodleian Library, Oxford University.
Collation of the original as determined from the film: a-z, aa-pp p. 60 plates, ports.

NK 0198792 IU

Knesebeck, Hertha von dem.
Das arme Mariechen; verse von Hertha v. d. Knesebeck, bilder von Else Wenz-Viëtor. Oldenburg i. O., G. Stalling, ©1930.

[16] p. col. illus. 29½cm.
Illustrated t.-p. in colors.

I. Wenz-Viëtor, Else, illus. II. Title. 31–765
Library of Congress PZ34.3.K57
Copyright A—Foreign 9381
[2] 831.9.

NK 0198793 DLC NN

Knesebeck, Hertha von dem.
Das englein auf dem maskenball; neue kindergedichte von Hertha v. d. Knesebeck, mit zeichnungen von Louise Staudt-Zoerb. Oldenburg i. O., G. Stalling a. g., ©1929.

[16] p. col. illus. 28½cm.

I. Staudt-Zoerb, Louise, illus. II. Title. 30–14836
Library of Congress PZ34.3.K6

NK 0198794 DLC

Knesebeck, Hertha von dem.
Weihnachten; verse von Hertha v. d. Knesebeck, bilder von Else Wenz-Viëtor. Oldenburg i. O., G. Stalling, ©1932.

[16] p. col. illus. 28½cm.
Illustrated t.-p. in colors.

I. Wenz-Viëtor, Else, illus. II. Title. 33–12433
Library of Congress PZ34.3.K63
Copyright A—Foreign 18342
[2] 831.91

NK 0198795 DLC NN OrP WaS

Knesebeck, J R
freiherr von dem
Deutschlands erlauchten souverainen. Bei dem sturz der dynastie Karls X. königs von Frankreich ... [von] J.R. frhrn F. v. d. K. in G. n.p., 1830.
18 p. 17cm.

NK 0198796 MH-L

Knesebeck, Karl Friedrich, Freiherr von dem, 1768-1848.
Abhandlungen über Goethe, Schiller, Bürger und einige ihrer Freunde ...
see under Pröhle, Heinrich Christoph Ferdinand, 1822-1895.

VOLUME 300

F 4762 .466 [KNESEBECK, KARL FRIEDRICH VON DEM] 1768-1848.
[Betrachtung über den jetzigen Krieg, und die Ursachen seiner falschen Beurtheilung. Ein Beytrag zur richtigen Kenntniss desselben. Von einem Schweizer bei der alliirten Armee am Oberrhein. [n.p.] 1794.
115p. 18cm.

NK 0198798 ICN CSt

[Knesebeck, Karl Friedrich, Freiherr von dem] 1768-1848.
Kurze uebersicht des feldzuges im jahr 1793 zwischen dem Rhein und der Saar, von einem unpartheiischen beobachter ... Frankfurt und Leipzig, 1793-94.
2 v. in 1. 17 cm.
"Aus dem tagebuch eines bey der alliirten armee befindlichen englischen officiers frey übersetzt."
1. France - Hist. - 1793 (Revolution) 2. Germany - Hist. - 1789-1900. I. Title.

NK 0198799 CU ICN

Knesebeck, Ludolf Gottschalk von dem.
Die Wahrheit über den Propagandafeldzug und Deutschlands Zusammenbruch, der Kampf der Publizistik im Weltkriege. Im Anhang: 20 unveröffentlichte Briefe Ludendorffs aus dem Weltkrieg, und die wahrscheinliche Denkschrift Bethmanns zu Falkenhayns Entlassung. München, Selbstverlag des Verfassers, Auslieferung: Fortschrittliche Buchhandlung, München [©1927]
168 p. 23 cm.
Bibliography: p. 11-14.
1. European War, 1914-1918—Propaganda. I. Title.
D639.P6K55 52-53292

NK 0198800 DLC NjP IU MnU CSt-H

Knesebeck, Thomas von, respondent.
... De proportione arithmetica in poenis irrogandis ...
see under Arnisaeus, Henning, d. 1636?, praeses.

Wisdom *AC9 W8327 LZ999 Knesebeck, Paridam von dem.
... Thomas Wolfe, die Legende seines Lebens. (In Deutsche Beiträge. München, 1939. 22.5cm. in file box. Jahrg.III, Hft.3, p.220-234)
At head of title: Paridam von dem Knesebeck.

NK 0198802 MH

Knesebeck, Wilhelm Friedrich von dem, respondent.
... De advocatis et ivre magni advocati in dvcatv Cellensi s. Lvnebvrgico ... Goettingae, litteris Pockwitzii et Barmeieri, 1757.
2 p.l., 136 p. 22 cm.
Diss.-inaug. - Göttingen.

NK 0198803 CtY-L

Knesebeck, Willi.
Des fussballspielers trainingsbuch, von Willi Knesebeck ... Mit 73 abbildungen. Berlin, G. Hackebeil a.-g., 1925.
139 p. incl. front., illus., diagrs. 18cm.
1. Foot-ball.
Library of Congress GV959.K6 25-27880

NK 0198804 DLC

DD 247 H5 K55 Knesebeck-Fischer, Alfred.
Adolf Hitler's Werdegang [bis zum Reichskanzler mit Liederanhang. Verfasst von A. Knesebeck-Fischer. 6. Aufl. Berln [P. Schmidt, 1934?]
31p. 16cm.
1. Hitler, Adolf, 1889-1945 2. National-sozialistische Deutsche Arbeiter-Partei - Songs and music

NK 0198805 WU

Knesebeck-Fischer, Alfred.
Hermann Göring's werdegang bis zum staatsmann, von A. Knesebeck-Fischer ... [Berlin, N.S. verlagsanstalt pg. P. Schmidt, 1933?]
15, [1] p. illus. 23 cm. (Nationalsozialistische bücherserie nr. 2)
1. Göring, Hermann, 1893-1946. 2. National socialism. I. Title.

NK 0198806 CSt-H

Kneser, Adolf, 1862-1930.
Bemerkungen über die Anzahl der Extreme der Krümmung auf geschlossenen Kurven und über verwandte Fragen in einer nicht-euklidischen Geometrie. (In: Festschrift Heinrich Weber ... gewidmet... Leipzig, 1912. 4°. p. 170-180.)
1. Geometry (Non-Euclidean). 2. Curves. September 14, 1912.
N. Y. P. L.

NK 0198807 NN

Kneser, Adolf, 1862-1930.
Lecat, Maurice Marie Albert, 1884–
Calcul des variations; exposé d'après les articles allemands de A. Kneser ... E. Zermelo ... et H. Hahn ... par M. Lecat ... [1913-1916]
(In Encyclopédie des sciences mathématiques. Paris [1913-1916] 25cm. t. 2, v. 6- fasc. 1-2, p. 1-288)

Kneser, Adolf, 1862-1930.
... Festschrift zur feier des 200. geburtstages Leonhard Eulers. Herausgegeben vom vorstande der Berliner mathematischen gesellschaft. Mit 2 bildnissen Eulers. Leipzig und Berlin, B. G. Teubner. 1907.

Kneser, Adolf, 1862-1930.
Die integralgleichungen und ihre anwendungen in der mathematischen physik, vorlesungen an der universität zu Breslau gehalten von Adolf Kneser. Braunschweig, F. Vieweg und sohn, 1911.
viii, 243 p. 23½ cm.
"Literarische notizen": p. [240]-243.
1. Integral equations. 2. Mathematical physics.
QA431.K6 11—9955

NK 0198810 DLC NcRS OrPR OrCS PBm NBuU MoU CU NcU CtY PU PHC NjP MB ViU ICJ OU OCU MiU

Kneser, Adolf, 1862-1930. 517.3 S200
Die Integralgleichungen und ihre Anwendungen in der mathematischen Physik. Vorlesungen von Adolf Kneser ... Zweite umgearbeitete Auflage. Braunschweig, F. Vieweg & Sohn, 1922.
viii, 292 p. 22½cm.
"Anmerkungen," p. [286]-292.

NK 0198811 ICJ NcU CU-S CU NcD MiU OCU OClW MH NjP TU CtY PU-Math PPTU

Kneser, Adolf, 1862-1930.
Irreduktibilitaet und monodromiegruppe algebraischer gleichungen.
Inaug. Diss. Berlin, 1884

NK 0198812 ICRL PU RPB CtY NjP

Kneser, Adolf, 1862-1930.
Lehrbuch der variationsrechnung, von Adolf Kneser ... Mit 24 eingedruckten abbildungen. Braunschweig, F. Vieweg und sohn, 1900.
xiv p., 1 l., 311, [1] p., 1 l. diagr. 23cm.
"Literaturverzeichnis": p. [307]-311.
1. Calculus of variations.
Library of Congress QA315.K7 3—5853

NK 0198813 DLC PU-Math OrCS CU PSC CtY MiU OClW NBC ICJ NjP ViU

Kneser, Adolf, 1862-1930.
Lehrbuch der variationsrechnung, von Adolf Kneser ... 2. umgearb. aufl., mit 13 abbildungen. Braunschweig, F. Vieweg & sohn akt.-ges., 1925.
vii, 397 p. diagrs. 23cm.
"Anmerkungen" (p. 389-397) includes bibliography.
1. Calculus of variations.
Library of Congress QA315.K7 1925 28—1809

NK 0198814 DLC PU-Math CtY MiU OCU NjP ICJ OU NBuU IaU NcU CLSU NcD MoU

Kneser, Adolf, 1862-1930.
Mathematik und natur: rede zum antritt des rektorats der Breslauer Universität in der aula Leopoldina am 15. Oktober 1911. 2. abdruck. Breslau, 1913.
18 p.

NK 0198815 IU

Kneser, Adolf, 1862-1930.
Das prinzip der kleinsten wirkung von Leibniz bis zur gegenwart, von Adolf Kneser. Leipzig und Berlin, B. G. Teubner, 1928.
2 p. l., 70 p. 23½cm. (Added t.-p.: Wissenschaftliche grundfragen ... IX)
1. Teleology. I. Title.
Library of Congress BD543.K6 32-30917
[2] 124

NK 0198816 DLC NN OO ICU NjP MH ViU

QA343 .J3 Kneser, Adolf, 1862-1930, ed.
Jacobi, Karl Gustav Jakob, 1804-1851.
Theorie der elliptischen funktionen aus den eigenschaften der thetareihen abgeleitet, von C. G. J. Jacobi; hrsg. von Adolf Kneser. Leipzig, Akademische verlagsgesellschaft m. b. h., 1927.

Kneser, Adolf, 1862-1930.
Über einige fundamentalsätze aus der theorie der algebraischen funktionen von mehreren variabeln ... Marburg, Universitäts-buchdruckerei (R. Friedrich) 1884.
25 p. 21½cm.
Zur erlangung der venia docendi—Marburg.
1. Functions, Algebraic.
Library of Congress QA341.K68 5-31341†

NK 0198818 DLC PU

VOLUME 300

Kneser, Adolf, 1862-1930.
Variationsrechnung, von Adolf Kneser ... [1900]
(*In* Encyklopädie der mathematischen wissenschaften. Leipzig [1899-] 25cm. bd. II—1, hft. 3, p. 571-625)
"Lehrbücher": p. 572.

1. Calculus of variations.

A 13-55
Title from Brown Univ. Library of Congress QA36.E56

NK 0198819 RPB ICRL CU MiU ODW

Kneser, Hans Otto.
Der aktive stickstoff. Von H. O. Kneser ... Mit 12 abbildungen.
(*In* Ergebnisse der exakten naturwissenschaften. Hrsg. von der schriftleitung der "Naturwissenschaften". Berlin, 1922- 24cm. 8. bd. (1929) p. [229]-257. illus., diagrs.)
"Literaturverzeichnis": p. 255-257.

1. Nitrogen. I. Title.
A C 36-4646
Title from Ohio State Univ. Library of Congress [Q111.E7 bd. 8]
[2] (508)

NK 0198820 OU OCU

Kneser, Hans Otto.
Molekulare Schallabsorption und -Dispersion.
(*In* Ergebnisse der exakten Naturwissenschaften. Berlin. 24 cm. v. 22 (1949) p. 121-185)
"Literaturverzeichnis": p. 182-185.

1. Supersonic waves. I. Title.
[Q111.E7 vol. 22] A 50-4591
Ohio State Univ. Libr. for Library of Congress [1]

NK 0198821 OU

Kneser, J C Christoph Adolf
see Kneser, Adolf, 1862-

Knespeln, Jacob.
Neu-bereitetes herzen-opfer; oder, Achtfache bet buss- beicht- und communion-zellen ... von Jacob Knespeln ... mit einer neuen vorrede und allen hiesiges orts üblichen alt- und neuen communionliedern vermehret ... Nürnberg, Felseckerische erben, 1694.
10 p. l., 599, [12], 117, [3] p. plates. 16 cm.
Added t.-p. engr.
Second part has title: Buss-ächzende auch lob- und lieb-jauchzende Sulamithin.

NK 0198823 CU

KNESSL, LOTHAR.
Motetto I, per il Natale. Für achtstimmigen Chor a cappella [1953] Wien, Universal Edition, c1959. score (40 p.) 26cm. (Universal-Edition. Nr. 13096)
For chorus (SSAATTBB); German words.
First line: In unter dunklen Zeit wir das Christkind suchen.
1. Christmas music--Motets. 2. Choral music, Sacred (Mixed, 8 pt.)--Unacc.

NK 0198824 NN

Kneszet Bné Akiba b'Hungária
Oszef tárbuti. [2.kiad. Arad] Hahánhágá Hárásit sel Kneszet Bné Akiba b'Hungária [1946?]
118 p. illus.
Title also in Hebrew alphabet; text in Hungarian

1. Bnai Akiba. 2. Zionism. I. Title

NK 0198825 MH

Knetsch, Alfons
Der begriff der notwehr nach der peinlichen gerichtsordnung Karls V. und dem strafgesetzbuch für das deutsche reich. Dogmatisch-historische studie von dr. iur. Alfons Knetsch ... Berlin, Wilhelm Pilz, 1906.
88 p. 24cm.
Bibliography: p. [86]-88.

NK 0198826 MH-L ICRL

Knetsch, Alfons, 1903-
Zur solitaren ausschaelbaren haematocele. Inaug. diss. Breslau, 1927 (Leipzig) Bibl.

NK 0198827 ICRL

Knetsch, Alfons Wilhelm. 664.3 R900
Die Rohfettwirtschaft, von Dr. A. W. Knetsch. 1.-6. Tausend. Berlin, Druck von Liebheit & Thiesen, 1919.
cover-title, 240 p. incl. tables. 22cm.

NK 0198828 ICJ

Knetsch, Berthold, 1855 -
...Allgemeine Musiklehre, von Berthold Knetsch... Berlin: H. Hillger[, 1909]. 87 p. illus. (music.) 16°. (Hillgers illustrierte Volksbücher. Bd. 130.)

307455A. 1. Music—Instruction and study. 2. Ser. July 1, 1927
N. Y. P. L.

NK 0198829 NN

Knetsch, Berthold, 1855 -
...Die Grundlagen für das Verständnis des musikalischen Kunstwerkes, von Berthold Knetsch... Berlin: H. Hillger Verlag[, 1911]. 124 p. illus. (music.) 17½cm. (Bücher des Wissens. Bd. 151.)

652384A. 1. Musical form. I. Title. August 7, 1933
N. Y. P. L.

NK 0198830 NN OU

Knetsch, Berthold, 1855-
Stettin. Riemann-conservatorium.
Organisation des unterrichtes im Riemann-conservatorium zu Stettin. Stettin, Gedruckt bei H. Saran, 1903.

Knetsch, Carl
see
Knetsch, Karl Gustav Philipp, 1874-1938.

W 4 M31 1935
KNETSCH, Eberhard, 1909-
Über Gelenkchondromatose. Marburg, Fischer, 1935.
42 p.
Cover title.
Inaug.-Diss. - Marburg.
1. Chondroma 2. Joints - Neoplasms

NK 0198833 DNLM

QE320 .B4
Knetsch, Georg, 1904-
Behrend, Fritz, 1885- *ed.*
... Der geologische bau, die nutzbaren lagerstätten und die bergwirtschaft Afrikas, von dr. Werner Beetz ... prof. dr. Fritz Behrend ... dr. phil. habil. Fritz-Erdmann Klingner ... [und] dozent dr. phil. habil. Georg Knetsch ... unter der schriftleitung von prof. dr. Fritz Behrend ... Berlin, W. de Gruyter & co., 1942-

---

Knetsch, Gustav: Die landständische Verfassung im Kurstaate Trier, vornehmlich im XVI. Jahrhundert. Berlin 1909: Ebering. 103 S. 8° ¶(Ersch. vollst. u. d. T.: Die landständ. Verfassung u. reichsritterschaftl. Bewegung im Kurstaate Trier, vornehml. im XVI. Jh., als: Histor. Studien. H. 75.)
Bonn, Phil. Diss. v. 15. Okt. 1909, Ref. v. Bezold
[Geb. 2. Febr. 85 Straelen; Wohnort: Ratingen; Staatsangeh.: Preußen; Vorbildung: Gymn. Koblenz Reife O. 04; Studium: Bonn 2, Freiburg i. B. 2, Bonn 6 S.; Rig. 26. Mai 09.] [U 10. 395

NK 0198835 ICRL MiU CU NN MH CtY OU PU DLC

Knetsch, Karl Gustav Philipp, 1874-1938.
Ahnentafel Johann Wolfgang Goethes, bearb., von dr. Carl[Knetsch... Leipzig, Zentralle für deutsche personen- und familiengeschichte e. v., 1932.
16 p. port. 34 cm. (On cover: Ahnentafeln berühmter Deutschen; hrsg., von der Zentralstelle für deutsche person- und familiengeschichte; schriftleitung: Peter von Gebhardt und dr. Johannes Hohlfeld; neue folge. 1.)

1.Goethe, Johann Wolfgang von, 1749-1832 - Biography - Ancestry.

NK 0198836 IU NNC OCIW

4DD 3360
Knetsch, Karl Gustav Philipp, 1874-1938.
Elisabeth Charlotte von der Pfalz und ihre Beziehungen zu Hessen. Marburg, N. G. Elwert, 1925.
116 p.

NK 0198837 DLC-P4

Knetsch, Karl [Gustav Philipp] 1874-1938.
Die erwerbung der herrschaft Schmalkalden durch Hessen ... Marburg, Druck von L. Döll in Cassel, 1897 [*i. e.* 1898]
2 p. l., 56, [4] p. 20½cm.
Inaug.-diss.—Marburg.
Lebenslauf.
"Quellen": 2 p. following p. 56.

1. Hesse—Hist. 2. Schmalkalden—Hist.
G-2404
Library of Congress DD491.H66K5

NK 0198838 DLC CtY PU

VOLUME 300

Knetsch, Karl Gustav Philipp, 1874–1938.
Goethes ahnen, von dr. Carl Knetsch. Leipzig, Klinkhardt & Biermann, 1908.
2 p. l., 93, [1] p. xxx geneal. tab. (1 fold.) 24cm.
Most of the tables are printed on both sides.

1. Goethe, Johann Wolfgang von, 1749–1832. 2. Goethe family.
12-643 Revised
Library of Congress PT2075.K6

NK 0198839 DLC CU TxU IU NBuU CtY OClW NjP NN

KNETSCH, Karl Gustav Philipp, 1874-1938.
Das haus Brabant; genealogie der herzoge von Brabant und der landgrafen von Hessen. [Teil I,II,1,2]. Darmstadt,im selbstverlag des Historischen vereins für das grossherzogtum Hessen,[1918-28].
4°, plates and geneal.tables.
"Literatur",pp.74-78.

NK 0198840 MH

Knetsch, Karl Gustav Philipp, 1874–1938.
Das haus Brabant, genealogie der herzoge von Brabant und der landgrafen von Hessen, von dr. C. Knetsch. Darmstadt, Selbstverlag des Historischen vereins für das grossherzogtum Hessen [1931]
524, [2] p. incl. coats of arms. front., coats of arms (part col.) fold. geneal. tables. 31cm.
Title vignette: col. coat of arms.
Issued in parts.
"Vorwort" dated 1917.
"Verzeichnis der benutzten literatur": p. 74–78.

1. Brabant, Dukes of. 2. Brabant—Nobility. 3. Hesse—Kings and rulers.
31-31984
Library of Congress DH801.B76K6
[2] 929.793

NK 0198841 DLC

Knetsch, Karl Gustav Philipp, 1874-1938, ed.

Mechtel, Johannes, 1562–1653.
Die Limburger chronik des Johannes Mechtel. Hrsg. von Carl Knetsch. Wiesbaden, J. F. Bergmann, 1909.

Knetsch, Otto, 1914-
Die täterpersönlichkeit bei Franz von Liszt und im kommenden strafrecht.. Giessen, Glagow, 1936.
55 p. 22½ cm.
Inaug.-diss. - Giessen.
Lebenslauf.
"Schrifttum": p.[7]-8.
1.Liszt,Franz von,1851-1919. 2. Criminal law.

NK 0198843 NjP DLC MH CtY

KNETSCH,W.Alfons.
Das staats- und verwaltungsrecht von Sachsen-Weimar-Eisenach,nebst revidiertem grundgesetz für das Grossherzogtum Sachsen-Weimar-Eisenach vom 15.oktober,1850. Hannover,1909.
16°.
"BIBLIOTHEK des öffentlichen rechts",14.

NK 0198844 MH-L

Knetschke, ———, supposed author.

Lezte stunden und leichenbegängniss Friedrichs des Zweiten, königs von Preussen. Potsdam, C. C. Horvath, 1786.

Knetschowsky, Kurt: Die innere Sekretion und ihre Beziehungen zu Kiefer und Zähnen. [Maschinenschrift.] 45, 11 S. 4°. — Auszug: Breslau 1922: Bresl. Genoss.-Buchdr. 2 Bl. 8°
Breslau, Med. Diss. v. 1. Aug. 1922 [U 22. 1444

NK 0198846 ICRL

Knett, J
Das Erdbeben am Böhmischen Pfahl, 26. November 1902. Wien, C. Gerold's Sohn, 1903.
2 p.l., 22 p. 1 map, 1 tab. 8°. (Kaiserliche Akademie der Wissenschaften in Wien. Erdbeben Commission. Mittheilungen. N.F. no. 18)

NK 0198847 NN

RA887 T72 902K
Knett, J
Die geologisch-balneotechnischen Verhältnisse von Trencsin-Teplicz. Trencsin, F. X. Starnitzl, 1902.
42p. illus., plate, col. map. 22cm.
Separatabdruck aus dem 1900/1901. Jahrbuch des Trencsiner Naturwissenschaftlichen Vereines, Bd. 23-24.

1. Physical medicine - Hydrotherapy - Trentschin.

NK 0198848 CtY-M

Knett, J
Vorläufiger Bericht über das erzgebirgische Schwarmbeben 1903 vom 13. Februar bis 25. März ... Wien, C. Gerold's Sohn, 1903.
2 p.l., 27 p. 1 map. 8°. (Kaiserliche Akademie der Wissenschaften in Wien. Erdbeben Commission. Mittheilungen. N.F. no. 16)

NK 0198849 NN

Kneubuehler, Emil,
Ueber verschiedene einfluesse auf die sporenresistenz... Zuerich,1906.
In. Diss.

NK 0198850 ICRL

Kneucker, A W
Richtlinien einer Philosophie der Medizin. Wien, W. Maudrich, 1949.
vii, 197 p. 25 cm.

1. Medicine—Philosophy. I. Title.
R723.K5 610.1 49-22763*

NK 0198851 DLC DNLM ICJ

KNEUCKER,J. A. ed.
Mitteilungen aus pflanzenwelt des nordwestlichen Deutschland./Festschrift.. Karlsruhe i.B.G.Braunschen hofbuchdruckerie, 1916.
I. Title.

NK 0198852 MH

KNEUCKER,Johann Jacob, 1840-1909.
Die anfänge des römischen Christentums. Karlsruhe,Reuther,1881.

NK 0198853 MH-AH

Kneucker, Johann Jacob, 1840-1909.
Das buch Baruch. Geschichte und kritik, übersetzung und erklärung auf grund des wiederhergestellten hebräischen urtextes. Mit einem anhang über den pseud-epigraphischen Baruch. Von lic. theol. J. J. Kneucker ... Leipzig, F. A. Brockhaus, 1879.
2 p. l., [vii]-x, 361, [1] p. 21cm.
"Urtext des buches Baruch": p. [351]-361.
1. Bible. O. T. Apocrypha. Baruch—Commentaries. 2. Bible. O. T. Apocryphal books. Apocalypse of Baruch—Criticism, interpretation, etc. I. Bible. O. T. Apocrypha. Baruch. Hebrew. 1879. II. Bible. O. T. Apocrypha. Baruch. German. 1879. Kneucker.
24-17621
Library of Congress BS1775.K6

NK 0198854 DLC DDO CtY-D CSaT CU PU ViU DCU-H

Kneucker, Johann Jacob, 1840-1909.
Die Gleichberechtigung des kirchlichen Liberalismus mit der Kirchlichen Rechtglaeubigkeit im Lichte des biblischen Christentums, der reformatorischen Grundsaetze und des badischen Bekenntnisstandes. Gegen unevangelische Verdunkelungen nachgewiesen von D. J. J. Kneucker. Heidelberg, Druck und Verlag von J. Hoerning, 1898.
63 p. 23 cm.

NK 0198855 MH-AH

Kneucker, Johann Jacob, 1840-1909.
Vorlesungen ueber biblische theologie und messianische weissagungen des Alten Testaments
see under Hitzig, Ferdinand, 1807-1875.

Kneucker, Rudolf, 1909-
... Die Harnstainkrankheit an der Freiburger chirurgischen Universitätsklinik von 1928 bis 1936 (September) ... Freiburg i. Br., 1937.
Inaug.-Diss. - Freiburg i. Br.
Lebenslauf.
"Literatur": p. 32-33.

NK 0198857 CtY

Kneuer, Alfred, 1899-
Zur kenntnis des lupanins. Lupanidin, ein neues lupinenalkaloid. ...Freiburg,1929. (Leipzig) 54 p.
Inaug. Diss. Freiburg i. Br., 1929.
Lebenslauf.

NK 0198858 ICRL CtY

Kneuer (Balthasar). *Ueber die Karies. 36 pp. 8°. *Würzburg, C. W. Becker,* 1838.

NK 0198859 DNLM

KNEUER,Heinrich, 1887-
Die allgemeinen grundlagen der beweislast des zivilprozesses und die folgerungen hieraus fur die beweislast fur bedingungen bei rechtsgeschaften. Inaug.-diss.,Würzburg. Tirschenreuth;1920.

NK 0198860 MH-L ICRL

VOLUME 300

Kneuer, Heinrich, 1887-
Das Bayerische Gemeinderecht und Stiftungsrechts, Handbuch des Bayerischen Verwaltungsrechts. 1.-3. Aufl. Leipzig, C. L. Hirschfeld, 1930.
111 p. (Grundriss des privaten und öffentlichen Rechts sowie der Volkswirtschaftslehre. 30 Bd., 2. T. C.)

NK 0198861 DLC

Kneuer, Heinrich, 1887-
... Kurzes handbuch des bayerischen verwaltungsrechts ... von dr. H. Kneuer ... 1.-2. aufl. Leipzig, C. L. Hirschfeld, 1928.
v. 21½cm. (Grundriss des privaten und öffentlichen rechts sowie der volkswirtschaftslehre. 30. bd., 2. t., A
"Literatur": p. [1]

1. Administrative law—Bavaria. I. Bavaria. Laws, statutes, etc. II. Title.
35-16692

NK 0198862 DLC MH

---

ar W 13690 Kneuer, Karl, 1862-
Die Sprichwörter Hendyngs; Nachweis ähnlicher Sprichwörter in den germanischen und romanischen Sprachen. Weilheim [Ger.] 1901.
v, 93 p. 23cm.
Diss.--Leipzig.
1. Proverbs of Hendyng.

NK 0198863 NIC NcD CtY NjP MH OCl ODW MnU PU ICRL

Kneust, Ra
see Knevet, Ralph, 1600-1671.

Kneuker, Harold J 1905-
A study of partial or progress payments under Government prime or sub-contracts. [Bergenfield? N. J.] 1954.
83 l. 28 cm.

1. Public contracts—U. S. I. Title: Partial or progress payments under Government prime or sub-contracts.
HD3858.K55 *336.39 351.71 54-27620 ‡

NK 0198865 DLC

621.436 qK68 Kneule, Friedrich.
Beitrag zur Erforschung des Verbrennungsvorganges im schnellaufenden Dieselmotor. Berlin, VDI-Verlag [1938]
20 p. illus. 30 cm. (Deutsche Kraftfahrforschung im Auftrag des Reichs-Verkehrsministeriums. Heft 5)
Includes bibliography.
1. Diesel motor I. Title. Series.

NK 0198866 N

Kneusel-Herdliczka, Emil.
Beschreibung der an dem K.K.Hydrographischen amte (Marinesternwarte) zu Pola in verwendung stehenden meteorologischen instrumente. Zusammengestellt von...Emil Kneusel-Herdliczka und Leonidas Piehl... Pola, Hydrographisches amt, 1882.
24 p.
"Beilage zu den 'Mitteilungen aus dem gebiete des seew esens,' n.vii & viii, 1882.

NK 0198867 MiU

Kneusel-Herdliczka, Emil.
Resultate aus den meteorologischen beobachtungen an dem K.K.Hydrographischen amte (Marinesternwarte) zu Pola vom Aug., 1864 bis ende Dec., 1881. Zusammengestellt von ... Emil Kneusel-Herdliczka und Hermann Mirosevic...Pola, Hydorgraphisches amt, 1882.
51 p.
"Beilage zu den 'Mitt.aus dem gebiete des seewesens,hft xix, 1882'".

NK 0198868 MiU

Kneussel (Christophorus Fridericus). *De hæmorrhagia uterina matronæ abortientis, vulgo von dem angegangenen Hertzgeblüt ex praxi clinica desumpta. 24 pp. 4°. Gissæ-Hassorum, typ. Mülleri, [1698].

NK 0198869 DNLM

Kneussel, Christophorus Fridericus
——. De ipecuanha novo gallorum antidysenterico. 24 pp. 4°. Gissæ-Hassorum, typ. H. Mülleri. 1698.

NK 0198870 DNLM

4PT Ger.-3608 Kneussl, August.
Iskender; Tragödie. Braunschweig, E. Appelhans, 1949.
93 p.

NK 0198871 DLC-P4

KNEUSSL, Paul.
Geschichte des K.bayer.2.(vormals 3.)Jäger-Bataillons nebst einer kurzgefassten darstellung der geschichte seiner stammabteilungen,1753-1898. Würzburg,Kgl.Universitätsdruckerei,1899.
Port.,tables,and portfolio of plates and maps

NK 0198872 MH

Kneustub, John, 1544-1624
see Knewstub, John, 1544-1624.

Kneuttinger, A.
Über d. modi d. gr. u. lat. sprache im einfachen satze. Mün., 1841.

NK 0198874 NjP

WH K68z 1865 KNEUTTINGER, Georg Anton Maria
Zur Histiologie des Blutes. Würzburg, Stahel, 1865.
iv, 62 p.
"Eine von der medizinischen Fakultät der k. Universität in München einstimmig gekrönte Preisschrift."

NK 0198875 DNLM CtY

Kneutz, Peter.
... Einsteigen zum Flug! Leipzig: R. Voigtländer [1938] 80 p. incl. diagrs., tables. illus. (charts), plates. 25½cm.

990940A. 1. Aeronautics, Commercial, 1938. I. Title.

NK 0198876 NN

Knevelkamp, Walter, 1907-
... Untersuchungen über den Acetonkörper-, Kreatin- und Kreatiningehalt im Blute Otosklerosekranker. (Ein ergänzender Beitrag zum Blutchemismus bei Otosklerose) ... Günzburg/Donau, 1935.
Inaug.-Diss. - München.
Lebenslauf.

NK 0198877 CtY

[Knevels, Mrs. D. C.]
Geoffrey the Lollard. By Frances Eastwood [pseud.]... New York: Dodd, Mead & Co.[, cop. 1870.] 342 p. front., illus. 16°.

451286A. 1. Fiction, American. 2. Lollards—Fiction. I. Title.
N. Y. P. L. April 24, 1930

NK 0198878 NN NRCR MB ViU NGenoU OU NNC MH

PS 2196 K55 M3 1870 Knevels, Mrs. D C
Marcella: the fearless Christian maiden; a tale of the early church, by Frances Eastwood. New York, Dodd, Mead [c1870]
329 p. 19 cm.

NK 0198879 OU TxDaM-P MnU

[Knevels, Mrs. D. C.]
Marcella: the fearless Christian maiden. A tale of the early church. By Frances Eastwood [pseud.]... New York: Dodd, Mead & Co.[, cop. 1872.] 329 p. front., pl. 16°.

490002. 1. Fiction, American. I. Title.
N. Y. P. L. October 27, 1930

NK 0198880 NN

[Knevels, Mrs. D. C.]
Marcella: the fearless Christian maiden; a tale of the early Church, by Frances Eastwood [pseud.] New York, Dodd, Mead [1876]
329 p. 19cm.

NK 0198881 ViU

Knevels, Mrs. D.C.
My godmother's pomander.
7 p. (Harper's Mag. v. 45, 1872, p. 208)

NK 0198882 MdBP

Knevels, Gertrude, 1881 -
Smith, Grace E.
The arrow-maker's daughter; a camp fire play adapted from Longfellow's poem of Hiawatha, by Grace E. Smith and Gertrude Knevels ... New York, S. French; [etc., etc.] 1913.

Knevels, Gertrude, 1881 -
By candle-light, by Gertrude Knevels ... New York and London, D. Appleton and company, 1926.
4 p. l., 315, [1] p. 19½cm.

I. Title.
Library of Congress PZ3.K7294By 26-15734

NK 0198884 DLC OU PPL MB OCl OClh

VOLUME 300

Knevels, Gertrude, 1881–
David, a Biblical play, by Gertrude Knevels. Philadelphia, The Penn publishing company [°1937]
23 p. diagr. 18½cm.

1. David, king of Israel—Drama. I. Title.
Library of Congress PN6120.R4K55 38-19677
——— Copy 2.
Copyright D pub. 53546 [2] 812.5

NK 0198885 DLC

Knevels, Gertrude, 1881–
Death on the Clock, by Gertrude Knevels. New York, Pub. for the Crime club by Doubleday, Doran and co., inc., 1940.
4 p. l., vii–viii p., 1 l., 278 p. 19½cm.
"First edition."

I. Title.
Library of Congress PZ3.K7294De 40-30402

NK 0198886 DLC

Knevels, Gertrude, 1881–
The diamond rose mystery, by Gertrude Knevels. New York, London, D. Appleton and company, 1928.
4 p. l., 304, [1] p. 19½cm.

I. Title.
Library of Congress PZ3.K7294Di 28-19240

NK 0198887 DLC PU MB

Knevels, Gertrude, 1881–
Don't count your chickens, a black-face comedy in one act, by Gertrude Knevels. Philadelphia, The Penn publishing company [°1936]
17 p. diagr. 18cm.

I. Title.
Library of Congress PN6120.N4K6 37-33551
——— Copy 2.
Copyright D pub. 46005 [3] 792.2

NK 0198888 DLC

Knevels, Gertrude, 1881–
Dragon's glory; a Chinese comedy in four scenes, by Gertrude Knevels. New York, London, D. Appleton and company, 1924.
53, [1] p. 19cm. (*Half-title:* Appleton's short plays, no. 2)

I. Title.
Library of Congress PS3521.N45D7 1924 24-25137

NK 0198889 DLC OCl

Knevels, Gertrude, 1881–
The fairies' child, by Gertrude Knevels. Philadelphia, The Penn publishing company, 1915.
13 p. diagr. 18cm.

I. Title.
Library of Congress PS3521.N45F3 1915 33-32474
Copyright D 40323 812.5

NK 0198890 DLC PU

Knevels, Gertrude, 1881–
A little excitement, a play for girls in three acts; by Gertrude Knevels ... New York, S. French; London, S. French, ltd., °1921.
1 p. l., 5–34 p. 19cm.

I. Title.
Library of Congress PS3521.N45L5 1921 33-32475
Copyright D 57260 812.5

NK 0198891 DLC OCl

Knevels, Gertrude, 1881–
Lovers' luck [by] Gertrude Knevels ... Philadelphia, The Penn publishing company [°1935]
314 p. 19½cm.

I. Title.
Library of Congress PZ3.K7294Lo 35-4526

NK 0198892 DLC OU

HS3353 .G5K6 Knevels, Gertrude, 1881–
Minnetoska's dream; a play in one act, with tableaux, songs and dances written by Gertrude Knevels; music and dances arranged by Grace E. Smith ... [New York, c1905]

NK 0198893 DLC

Knevels, Gertrude, 1881–
Minnetoska's dream; a play in one act with tableaux, songs and dances ... New York, c1915.
28 p. 18 cm.

NK 0198894 RPB PU

Knevels, Gertrude, 1881–
Molly Moonshine, by Gertrude Knevels. New York, London, D. Appleton and company, 1930.
viii p., 1 l., 328, [1] p. 19½cm.

I. Title.
Library of Congress PZ3.K7294Mo 30-12301

NK 0198895 DLC MB

Knevels, Gertrude, 1881–
No, Mr. Brown [by] Gertrude Knevels. Philadelphia, The Penn publishing company [°1938]
2 p. l., [7]–322 p. 20cm.

I. Title.
Library of Congress PZ3.K7294No 38-6018

NK 0198896 DLC PP

PS 3521 N45 O2 1925a Knevels, Gertrude, 1881–
Octagon house. New York, A. L. Burt [c1925]
viii, 308 p. 20 cm.

NK 0198897 OU

Knevels, Gertrude, 1881–
Octagon house, by Gertrude Knevels. New York, London, D. Appleton and company, 1925.
viii p., 1 l., 308 p. 19½cm.

I. Title.
Library of Congress PZ3.K7294Oc 25-15983

NK 0198898 DLC PPL OClh OO PPSCl

Knevels, Gertrude, 1881–
Of love beware [by] Gertrude Knevels. Philadelphia, The Penn publishing company [°1936]
320 p. 19½cm.

I. Title.
Library of Congress PZ3.K7294Of 36-9859

NK 0198899 DLC MB

Knevels, Gertrude, 1881–
Out of the dark [by] Gertrude Knevels. Philadelphia, The Penn publishing company [°1932]
viii, 9–312 p. 19½cm.

I. Title.
Library of Congress PZ3.K7294Ou 32-28828

NK 0198900 DLC MB

Knevels, Gertrude, 1881–
The peddler of hearts, a play for young people; by Gertrude Knevels ... Boston, W. H. Baker & co., 1917.
35 p. 19cm. (*On cover:* Baker's edition of plays)

I. Title.
Library of Congress PS3521.N45P4 1917 33-32476
Copyright D 46381 [2] 812.5

NK 0198901 DLC MH OCl

Knevels, Gertrude, 1881–
Skyboy, a play for little boys and girls with instructions for costumes and dances, by Gertrude Knevels ... New York, The Camp fire outfitting co. [°1915]
12 p. 18cm.

1. Children's plays. I. Title.
Library of Congress PS3521.N45S5 1915 33-32477
Copyright D 41975 812.5

NK 0198902 DLC PU

Knevels, Gertrude, 1881–
Twelfth night at Moulderby hall, by Gertrude Knevels and Marie Norton Van Doren. Boston, Mass. and Los Angeles, Cal. [Walter H. Baker company, °1936]
14 p. 19cm. (*On cover:* Baker's plays for amateurs)

I. Van Doren, Marie Norton, joint author. II. Title.
Library of Congress PN6120.A5K67 37-30306
——— Copy 2.
Copyright D pub. 42896 [2] 812.5

NK 0198903 DLC

VOLUME 300

Knevels, Gertrude, 1881-
The wonderful bed, by Gertrude Knevels; with illustrations by Emily Hall Chamberlin. Indianapolis, The Bobbs-Merrill company [1912]
4 p. l., 228, [1] p. col. front., illus., col. plates. 21cm. $1.00

1. Title.
12-21605
Library of Congress PZ8.K35W

NK 0198904 DLC

BX7435 .E5K7 **KNEVELS, JOHANN WERNER.**
Geheimnis der bosheit der ellerianischen secte zu Ronsdorff im herzogtum Berg, worinnen derselben irrtümer, ursprung, wachstum und verfall entdecket werden. Nebst zweien responsis theologicis wegen zauberei, der apologie des verfassers, und einigen protocollen... Ans licht gebracht von Johann Werner Knevels... Marburg, P.C.Müllern, 1751.
[14], xii, 701, [1], 80, 96 p. 17½cm.
Title vignette.

"Apologia, oder, Entdeckte unschuld gegen die falsche beschuldigung einer ehr-raubenden ... rotte zu Ronsdorf...": 80 p.
"Actum Ronsdorff den 8ten jan. 1750": 96 p.

1. Ellerians.

NK 0198906 ICU IU

Knevels, Wilhelm, 1897- *ed.*
Brücken zum Ewigen, die religiöse Dichtung der Gegenwart. 8. Aufl. Braunschweig, H. Wollermann [19—]
286 p. 20 cm.
Bibliography: p. 269-[280]

1. Religious poetry, German. 2. German poetry—20th cent. I. Title.
PT1229.K6 52-21809
[2]

NK 0198907 DLC NcU

Knevels, Wilhelm, 1897-
Brücken zum ewigen; die religiöse dichtung der gegenwart. Herausgegeben von Wilhelm Knevels. 7. aufl. Braunschweig, Wollermann, 1928.
286, [1] p.
"Die dichter und ihre werke": p. 269-[280]
No subject.

NK 0198908 NNC

Knevels, Wilhelm, 1897-
Brücken zum ewigen; die religiöse dichtung der gegenwart. Herausgegeben von Wilhelm Knevels. Neuntes bis elftes tausend. Braunschweig, Hellmuth Wollermann verlagsbuchhandlung (W. Maus) [1935]
287, [1] p. 19½cm.
"Quellen": p. 277-279.

1. German poetry—19th century. 2. German poetry—20th century. 3. Religious poetry, German. I. Title.
A C 36-1175
Title from Columbia Univ. Printed by L. C.

NK 0198909 NNC

Div.S. 274.3 F646 no.3 Knevels, Wilhelm, 1897-
Deutsches Wesen und christlicher Glaube. Frankfurt a. M., H. L. Brönner [c1933]
14 p. 24 cm. (Deutschtum und Christentum, 1. Heft)

No. [3] in a vol. with binder's title: Flugschriften.
1. Christianity. Germany. 2. Religious thought. Germany. I. Title.

NK 0198910 NcD

PT 553 K5 **Knevels, Wilhelm, 1897-**
Expressionismus und Religion; gezeigt an der neuesten deutschen expressionistischen Lyrik. Tübingen, J. C. B. Mohr, 1927.
40p. 24cm. (Sammlung gemeinverständlicher Vorträge und Schriften aus dem Gebiet der Theologie und Religionsgeschichte, Heft 123)
Includes bibliography.
1. German poetry - 20th cent. - Hist. & crit. 2. Expressionism 3. Religion in literature I. Title

NK 0198911 WU IU MU RPB CU IEN NcD

Knevels, Wilhelm, 1897-
Fritz Philippi als religiöser Dichter. Leipzig, A. Klein, 1929.
98 p. 18 cm.
"Gedichte von Fritz Philippi": p. 79-98.

1. Philippi, Fritz, 1869-
PT2631.H56Z75 52-47400

NK 0198912 DLC

4PT Ger. 162 **Knevels, Wilhelm, 1897-**
Funken aus Gottes Brand, Lyrik der Gegenwart. Heilbronn, E. Salzer, 1935.
79 p.

NK 0198913 DLC-P4

Knevels, Wilhelm, 1897-
...Das moderne drama; gesicht unserer zeit; darstellung, deutung, wertung. Braunschweig, H. Wollermann [1930?]
320p. 20½cm.

1. German drama. History and criticism.

NK 0198914 NRU CtW CLSU ICU PBm PU OCl OClW OO NN PU

Knevels, Wilhelm, 1897-
... Das moderne drama, gesicht unserer zeit; darstellung, deutung, wertung. 2. aufl. Braunschweig, H. Wollermann verlagsbuchhandlung (W. Maus) [1933?]
320 p. 20½cm.

1. German drama—20th cent.—Hist. & crit.

NK 0198915 MiU MH

Knevels, Wilhelm, 1897-
... Das moderne drama; gesicht unserer zeit, darstellung, deutung, wertung. 3. aufl. Braunschweig, H. Wollermann (W. Maus) [1936?]
320 p. 20½cm.
First edition appeared in 1930.
"Die dichter": p. 317-318.

1. German drama—20th cent.—Hist. & crit. I. Title. 39-11604
Library of Congress PT666.K5 1936
[2] 832.9109

NK 0198916 DLC NcD PSt OCU

DD253 K649 Knevels, Wilhelm, 1897-
Der Nationalsozialismus am Scheidewege [von] Wilh. Knevels. Dresden, C. L. Ungelenk, 1932.
[8], -120 p. 24cm.

Cover title.
"Christentum und Wissenschaft, März heft - Jahrg. 1932."

NK 0198917 GU

Knevels, Wilhelm, 1897-
... Die Offenbarung des Johannes, praktisch erklärt von Wilhelm Knevels ... Frankfurt am Main, H. L. Brönner, 1935.
102 p. 21cm. (Praktisch-theologische hilfsbücher (homiletische hilfsbücher) ... hrsg. von Wilhelm Knevels ... nr. 13)
"Die erklärung der kapitel 7-22 ist in der von mir herausgegebenen zeitschrift "Christentum und leben", september 1933 bis februar 1935, erschienen."—p. [3]

1. Bible. N. T. Revelation — Commentaries. 2. Bible — Commentaries—N. T. Revelation.
35-34784
Library of Congress BS2825.K65
[2] 228

NK 0198918 DLC

Me21 Au7 8 Knevels, Wilhelm, 1897-
Das Religiöse in der neuesten lyrischen Dichtung. Giessen, A. Töpelmann, 1927.
94 p. 20 cm. (Aus der Welt der Religion. Praktisch-theologische Reihe, Heft 5)
Bibliography: p. 89-91.

1. Religious poetry, German - Hist. & crit.
2. German poetry - 20th cent. - Hist. & crit.

NK 0198919 CtY NcU TxU PPT LU

KNEVELS, Wilhelm, 1897-
Simmels religionstheorie; ein beitrag zum religiösen problem der gegenwart. Leipzig, J.C.Hinrichs, 1920.

NK 0198920 MH OCH OU CtY

FILM 11462 PR Knevet, Ralph, 1600-1671.
An edition of Ralph Knevett's Supplement to the Faerie queene (1635), by Andrew Lavender ... [New York] 1955.
2 v. on 1 reel (1246 ℓ.) On film (Positive)
Microfilm. Original in New York Univ. Library.
Thesis - New York Univ.

I. Lavender, Andrew, ed. II. Title: Supplement to the Faerie queene. III. Spenser, Edmund, 1552? -1599./ The faerie queene.

NK 0198921 CU

Knevet, Ralph, 1600-1671.
An edition of Ralph Knevett's Supplement to the Faerie queene
see also his A supplement of the Faery Queene.

VOLUME 300

Knevet, Ralph, 1600-1671.

M1614
.F45F3
Finzi, Gerald, 1901-
[Farewell to arms. Piano-vocal score. English]

Farewell to arms, introduction & aria for tenor voice and small orchestra or strings. Words by Ralph Knevet [and] George Peele. London, New York, Boosey & Hawkes [c1945]

FILM
Knevet,Ralph,1600-1671.
Funerall elegies consecrated to the immortall memory of the Right Honorable the Lady Katherine Paston,late wife to the truely noble,and heroicke William Paston of Oxned,esquire./ London, Printed by T.Cotes,for A.Crooke, 1637.
In verse.
Dedication signed: Ra.Knevet.
University Microfilms no.20365 (carton 762)
Short-title catalogue no.15035.
1.Paston,Katherine (Bertie) Lady,d.1636.

NK 0198924 MiU

821
K739g
1954
Knevet, Ralph, 1600-1671.
A gallery to the temple; lyrical poems upon sacred occasions. Testo, introduzione, note, a cura di Giuliano Pellegrini. Pisa, Libreria Goliardica editrice, 1954.
xxiii, 171p. 25cm. (Studi e testi, 6)

I. Pellegrini, Giuliano, ed. II. Title.

NK 0198925 IU CaBVaU ViU MH NIC NN LU NcU NhU

---

*XG
.3973
.20
[Knevet, Ralph] 1600-1671.
Rhodon and Iris. A pastorall, as it was presented at the Florists Feast in Norwich, May 3. 1631 ...
London: Printed for Michael Sparke, at the blew Bible in Greene-Arbour. 1631.
[74] p. 18.5cm.
Title vignette.
Signatures: A^2, a^4, B-I^4.
Dedication signed (A2v): Ra. Knevet.

STC 15036.
Imperfect: I4, blank, wanting.
Ex libris (armorial bookplate): William Holgate.

NK 0198927 MB NjR DFo ICN CSmH IU CtY

FILM
Knevet,Ralph,1600-1671.
Rhodon and Iris. A pastorall as it vvas presented at the Florists Feast in Norwich,May 3. 1631. London, Printed for M.Sparke, 1631.
Dedication signed: Ra.Knevet.
University Microfilms no.20366 (carton 762)
Short-title catalogue no.15036.

NK 0198928 MiU MoU

STCA
15037
[Knevet, Ralph, 1600-1671]
Στρατιωτικον. Or A discourse of militarie discipline. Shewing the necessitie therof according to these perillous times ...
[London]Printed[by M.Flesher].1628.
4°. 70ℓ. 22cm.
Photostat reproduction (positive) of the Huntington library copy.
Collation of the original as determined from the photostat: A-I^4 (I4 blank, wanting); [70]p.
Dedication signed: Ra. Kneuet.

Armorial device on t.-p. (lion rampant, holding sword & heart, motto "Pro aris et focis").
In verse.

NK 0198930 MH CSmH

[Knevet, Ralph] 1600-1671.
A supplement of the Faery Queene, in three bookes; wherein are allegorically described affairs both military and civill of these times. [A reproduction of ms. Ee.iii. 53 in the Cambridge University Library]
Negative copy made by University Microfilms.

NK 0198931 NcU

Knevet, Ralph, 1600-1671.
A supplement of the Faery Queene ...
see also his An edition of Ralph Knevett's supplement to the Faerie queene.

Knevet, Thomas
see **Knyvett, Thomas,** 1596-1658.

Knevett, Ralph
see Knevet, Ralph, 1600-1671.

Knewitz, Fritz, 1885-
Die landwirtschaftlichen betriebsverhältnisse in den holsteinischen marschen ... Giessen, Hof- und universitätsdr. O. Kindt, 1911.
130 p., 1 l. 23cm.
Inaug.-diss.—Giessen.
Lebenslauf.

1. Holstein, Ger. Agriculture. 2. Marshes.

Agr 12-2077

Library, U. S. Dept. of Agriculture 33K73

NK 0198935 DNAL CtY MH PU CU ICRL

STC
15038
Knewstub, John, 1544-1624.
An aunsweare vnto certayne assertions, tending to maintaine the Church of Rome, to be the true and catholique church. By Iohn Knewstub.
Printed in London at the three Cranes in the Vintree,by Thomas Dawson for Richard Sergier. 1579.
[224]p. 15cm.
Signatures: $*^4$,A-N^8,O^4.
A made-up copy; O^4 inserted from another copy.

NK 0198936 MH DFo NNUT-MC

FILM
Knewstub,John,1544-1624.
An aunsweare vnto certayne assertions,tending to maintaine the Church of Rome,to be the true and catholique church. London, Printed by T. Dawson for R.Sergier, 1579.
University microfilms no.16205 (carton 712)
Short-title catalogue no.15038.

1.Catholic Church--Doctrinal and controversial works--Protestant authors.

NK 0198937 MiU

Case
C
6504
.466
KNEWSTUB, JOHN, 1544-1624.
A confutation of monstrous and horrible heresies, taught by H.N. [i.e. Hendrik Niclaes] and embraced of a number, who call themselues the Familie of Loue... London, Imprinted by T.Dawson, for R.Sergier,1579.
[16],94,[28]ℓ. 19cm.
Title within ornamental border; initials.
Printer's device on verso of ℓ.92.
STC 15040.
"A sermon preached at Paules Crosse the Fryday before Easter... in the yeere...1576. By Iohn Knewstub": [28]ℓ. at end.

NK 0198938 ICN CtY DFo CSmH WU ViHarEM NNUT-MC

FILM
Knewstub,John,1544-1624.
A confutation of monstrous and horrible heresies,taught by H.N.and embraced of a number, who call themselues the familie of loue. By I. Knewstub ... Imprinted in London ... by Thomas Dawson,for Richard Sergier. 1579.
An answer to Hendrik Niclaes' Evangelium regni,translation of a part of which is included. cf.Dict.nat. biog.
Contains also "A confutation of the doctrine of Dauid George,and H.N. ... By M.Martyn Micronius", "A confutation of the doctrine of Dauid George,and H.N. ... By M.Nicholas Charinaeus","The iudgement of another godly learned man touching the same matter",and "A sermon preached at Paules Crosse the Fryday before Easter ... 1576. By Iohn Knewstub."
University microfilms no.14947 (case 43,carton 253)
Short-title catalogue no.15040.

1.Niclaes,Hendrik,1502?-1580? Evangelium regni. 2. Familists. I.Micronius,Marten,d.1559. II.Carineus, Nicolaas,d.1563. III.Title.

NK 0198940 MiU

Knewstub, John, 1544-1624.
The Lectvres of Iohn Knewstub, vpon the twentith Chapter of Exodus, and certeine other places of Scripture. Seene and allowed according to the Queenes Maiesties Iniunctions. [London] Imprinted by Lucas Harrison, 1578. 10 p.l., 299 p. 18cm. (4°.)

STC 15043.
Prelim. leaf 8 blank.
Includes commentaries on I Corinthians xiii, Galatians iii:10, John iii:16 and Matthew vi:9-13.
Bound by Rivière in blue morocco, gilt.

1. Bible. O.T. Exodus XX— Commentaries. *Card revised* August 30, 1943
N. Y. P. L.

NK 0198941 NN CtY CSmH NNUT-Mc

Knewstub,John,1544-1624.
The lectvres of Iohn Knewstub,vpon the twentieth chapter of Exodus,and certeine other places of Scripture ... [London] Imprinted by Lucas Harrison ... 1578.
University microfilms no.14948 (case 43,carton 253)
Short-title catalogue no.15043.

1.Bible. O.T. Exodus XX--Commentaries. 2.Bible. N.T.--Commentaries.

NK 0198942 MiU

STC
15044
Copy 1
Knewstub, John, 1544-1624.
The lectures ... vpon the twentith [ˈ] chapter of Exodus, and certeine other places of Scripture ... [London] Imprinted for Thomas Woodcocke, 1579.
A-V^8, X^2. 4to.
Exodus 20 incorporates the Ten Commandments.
Six of the lectures are on books in the N.T.

NK 0198943 DFo

Knewstub, John, 1544-1624.
1584
THE/ LECTVRES/ of Iohn Knewstub,/ vpon the twentith Chap-/ ter of Exodus, and cer-/teine other places of/Scripture./ Seene and allowed accor-/ ding to the Queenes Ma-/ iesties Iniunctions./ IMPRINTED FOR/ Thomas Woodcocke,/ ANNO, 1584./
308 p. 18 x 13 cm.
Title within woodcut border: McKerrow & Ferguson, no. 133, lower border shaved. Fragments of old printing & mss. used as end papers. Chapter initials. On front blank flyleaf is signature:"Robt.Fernly His Book 1758", and on recto of end blank flyleaf:"Thomas Okes his booke,1619" and below that,"it is 1620", & on verso "Robert Fernly His Book Oct 26 -1752."
STC: 15045.

1. Bible. O.T. Exodus 20 - Commentaries. I. Title.

NK 0198945 NNG DFo MH

VOLUME 300

[Knewstub, John, 1544-1624]
STC 15046 [A sermon preached at Paules crosse the Fryday before Easter, commonly called good Friday, in the yeere of our Lorde. 1579. By Iohn Knewstub.]
[Printed in London at the three Cranes in the Vintree, by Thomas Dawson for Richard Sergier.1579.]
48 numb.ℓ. 14.5cm.
Imperfect: t.-p. and leaf 8 wanting; supplied in positive photostats from the Folger copy.

NK 0198946 MH DFo MWA

Knewstub, John, 1544-1624.
A sermon [on Titus II,11-15] preached at Paules Crosse the Fryday before Easter, commonly called Good Friday, in the yeere of Our Lorde. 1579. [i.e.1576] London, Printed by T.Dawson for R.Sergier, 1579.
Short-title catalogue no.15046 (carton 994)

NK 0198947 MiU

Knewstubb-Rothenstein, Sir John Maurice.
See
Rothenstein, Sir John Knewstub Maurice, 1901-

Kneyber, Johanna Maria van Voorn-
see
Voorn-Kneyber, Johanna Maria van.

Kneysl, Johann August,
Dissertatio de retractu conventionali legali et gentilitio... Bohemus Goslaviensis, Pruscha, 1754.
2 v.

NK 0198950 PU

Knez, Jože, joint ed.

HD9765 .A93S67

Turk, Zdravko, *ed.*
O gospodarjenju z lesom v LR Sloveniji; referat in razprava na posvetovanju v Celju 23–24 januarja 1954. [Uredila: Zdravko Turk in Jože Knez] Ljubljana [Izdalo Društvo inženirjev in tehnikov gozdarstva in lesne industrije; zarožila Nova proizvodnja] 1954.

Knez Mihailo i zajednička radnja balkanskih naroda
see under Piročanac, Milan S., 1837-1897.

Knězek, Libor.
Fraňo Kráľ. [1. vyd.] Praha, Československý spisovatel, 1953. 87 p. 22cm. (Postavy a dílo. Malá řada, sv. 5)
Bibliography, p. 81–82.

1. Kráľ, Fraňo, 1903– I. Postavy a dílo. Malá řada.

NK 0198953 NN IU MH

Knězek, Zdeněk.
Rusko-český a česko-ruský sklářský slovník. [Vyd. 1.] V Praze, Státní nakl. technické literatury, 1954.
293 p. 18 cm.
Added t. p. in Russian.
"Slovník obsahuje asi 7000 hesel rusko-českých a 5000 hesel česko-ruských, která zahrnují sklářské suroviny, technologii, stroje a nomenklaturu skla a skleněných výrobků."
Bibliography: p. [12]

1. Glass manufacture—Dictionaries—Russian. 2. Russian language—Dictionaries—Czech. 3. Glass manufacture—Dictionaries—Czech. 4. Czech language—Dictionaries—Russian. I. Title.

TP788.K6 55–58363

NK 0198954 DLC

Knežević, Antun.
Praktična slovnica njemačkog jezika za porabu samoucima i hrvatskim školama. Sastavio Tone Knežević... Praktische Grammatik der deutschen Sprache für Kroaten. Zum Selbstunterricht und für kroatische Schulen. Von Anton Knežević... Wien: A. Hartleben[, 1915]. viii, 184 p. 2. enl. ed. 17½cm. (Die Kunst der Polyglottie. Teil 108.)

574553A. 1. German language—Grammar. I. Ser.
N. Y. P. L. September 20, 1932

NK 0198955 NN

Knežević, Antun, 1834–1889.
Kratka povjest kralja bosanskih, po izvorima. Za mladež bosansku. U Dubrovniku, D. Pretner, 1884–87.
3 v. 20 cm. (Narodna biblioteka, sv. 17, 21, 24)

1. Bosnia and Herzegovina—Hist. I. Title.

DB245.K69 57–56413

NK 0198956 DLC MH OU

Knežević, Božidar, 1862–1905.
Мисли. [4. изд.] У редакцији Паулине Лебл-Албале, с предговором Ксеније Атанасијевић. Београд [Народна просвета] 1931.
xxxix, 171 p. 19 cm. (Српска књижевна задруга. [Издања] коло 84, бр. 228)

1. Aphorisms and apothegms. *Title transliterated:* Misli.

PG1418.K57M5 1931 41–30348 rev*

NK 0198957 DLC OCl CtY

PG 1618 .N59 L 8 KNEŽEVIĆ, BRANIMIR
Zemlja; novele i nacrti. Zagreb, Vlastita naklada, 1914.
61 p.
Bound with Nikolić, R. Lomnom stazom.

NK 0198958 InU

Knežević, Milan A., joint author.
Osnovi vojne geografije
see under Božić, Ivan A.

Kneževič, Milivoje V., 1899-
Збирка наших псевдонима.
(*In* Библиотекар. Belgrad. 25 cm. г. 2 (1950) p. [26]–54)
——— Photocopy (negative)
Made in 1950 by the Library of Congress.
Z1080.B8K5

1. Anonyms and pseudonyms, Bulgarian.
Title transliterated: Zbirka naših psevdonima.

Z671.B58038 vol. 2 55–25110

NK 0198960 DLC

4TJ 178 Kneževič, Milutin.
Mehanička prerada drveta. Beograd, Naučna knjiga, 1948.
439 p.
At head of title: Univerzitet u Beogradu.

NK 0198961 DLC-P4

Knežević, Milutin.
Механичка прерада дрвета. Београд, Научна књига, 1952–
v. illus. 24 cm.
At head of title: Универзитет у Београду.

1. Woodwork. I. Title.
Title transliterated: Mehanička prerada drveta.

TS843.K6 55–29847 ‡

NK 0198962 DLC

Knežević, Milutin.
Распоред гатерских тестера (шпанунг) при максималном квантитативном искоришћењу. [Београд, Научна књига, 1952]
72 p. illus. 24 cm.
Diss.—Belgrad.

1. Saws. I. Title.
Title transliterated: Raspored gaterskih testera.

TJ1233.K58 59–32316

NK 0198963 DLC

Knežević, Petar, *comp.*
Muka G. N. Isusa Krista i plač Majke Njegove. 31. nepromijenjeno izd. Sarajevo, Franjevački samostan sv. Ante, 1955.
64 p. illus. 15 cm.

1. Jesus Christ—Poetry. 2. Jesus Christ—Passion. I. Title.

PG1618.K54M8 1955 60–31980 ‡

NK 0198964 DLC

Knežević, Petar, tr.
Pisctole, i Evangelja, priko svegga godiscta... Rimu, 1840
see under Bible. N. T. Epistles and Gospels, Liturgical. Serbo-Croatian. 1840. Knezevic.

Knežević, Radoje L., 1901–
Кроз средњу школу. [Београд] Француско-српска књижара А. М. Поповића [1938–
v. 19 cm. (Библиотека "Политика и друштво," 13)

1. Education, Secondary. 2. Education—Yugoslavia. I. Title.
Title romanized: Kroz srednju školu.

LA1005.K6 68–36139

NK 0198966 DLC MH

Knežević, Tone
see Knežić, Antun.

VOLUME 300

LB3205
.W56

Knezevich, Stephen J.

Wisconsin. University. *School of Education. Institute on School Buildings.*
Talking over problems of school plant planning; report of the discussions of the Institute on School Buildings held at the University of Wisconsin, August 15–17, 1950. Reported by Stephen J. Knezevich. Madison, School of Education, University of Wisconsin, 1951.

NK 0198968 [illegible]

Knezevich, Zivan L
General Mihailovich and U. S. S. R., with official memoranda and documents, by Lieut. Colonel Zivan L. Knezevich ... ⌊Washington? 1945⌋
30 p., 1 l. 23cm.

1. Mihailović, Draža, 1893– 2. World war, 1939–1945—Yugoslavia. 3. World war, 1939–1945—Russia.
46–179
Library of Congress DR359.M5K6
⌊2⌋ 949.7

NK 0198969 DLC DS MH KU IaU OrU

Knezevich, Zivan L
Why the allies abandoned the Yugoslav army of General Mihailovich, with official memoranda and documents, by Lt. Colonel Zivan L. Knezevich ... ⌊Washington, 1945⌋
1 v. 35½cm.
Reproduced from type-written copy.

1. World war, 1939– —Yugoslavia. 2. Mihailović, Draža, 1893– 3. Yugoslavia—Pol. & govt. 4. Communism—Yugoslavia. I. Title.
45–5669
Library of Congress D742.Y8K6
⌊4⌋ 940.53497

NK 0198970 DLC CSt-H DS

DB 375
.K68

KNEZOVIĆ, OTON
Hrvatska povijest od majstarijeg doba do godine 1918. ⌊Zagreb, Hrv. književno društvo sv. Jeronima, 1933?⌋
336 p. (Hrvatsko književno društvo sv. Jeronima, knj. 478)

1. Croatia--Hist. I. Title.

NK 0198971 InU

DB 375
K594
1936

Knezović, Oton.
Hrvatska povijest od najstarijeg doba do godine 1918. Zagreb, Jeronimska Knjižnica, 1936-37.
2 v. (336 p.)

1. Croatia - Hist. I. Title.

NK 0198972 CaBVaU

Knézy, Gergely.
Legyészeti tanulmányok. A Dolichopusnem. 1929.

NK 0198973 MiU

Knézy, Lehel
Baja a forradalom és a szerb megszállas allat, 1918-1921; történelmi feljegyzések. [Baja, A szerző kiadasa] Corvin-könyvnyomda [1940?]

214 p.

1. Baja, Hungary - Hist.

NK 0198974 MH

B
K691l1

Kniagevitch, Lydia.
Lights vanished ... illustrations by Woodi Ishmael. New York, N.Y., Snellgrove publications ⌊c1940⌋
229p. incl.illus.

NK 0198975 IU NN CtY

Kniaginichev, Mikhail Ivanovich, 1903–
Биохимия пшеницы; качество зерна пшеницы в зависимости от сорта и условий возделывания. Москва, Гос. изд-во сельхоз. лит-ры, 1951.
415 p. illus. 21 cm.

1. Wheat. I. Title. *Title transliterated:* Biokhimiia pshenitsy.
SB191.W5K73 57–35139 ‡

NK 0198976 DLC

Kniagnitskii, Petr Grigor'evich.
Моя родная шахта. ⌊Литературная запись Г. Корфа и М. Резникова⌋ Москва, Углетехиздат, 1951.
50 p. 20 cm. (Библиотечка стахановца-новатора угольной промышленности)

1. Coal mines and mining—Russia—Moscow Basin. I. Korf, G. II. Reznikov, M. III. Title.
Title transliterated: Moia rodnaia shakhta.
TN808.R92M56 55–30611

NK 0198977 DLC

Kniat, J.
Ein problem aus de analytischen geometrie des raumes. Rössel, 1897.

NK 0198978 NjP

Kniat, Joseph, 1858–
Spinoza's ethik gegenüber der erfahrung ... von Joseph Kniat. Posen, 1888.
3 p. l., ⌊5⌋–47, ⌊2⌋ p. 20cm
Inaug.-diss.—Leipzig.
Lebenslauf.

1. Spinoza, Benedictus de, 1632–1677. Ethica. 2. Ethics.
11–21400
Library of Congress B3999.E8K6

NK 0198979 DLC NjP NIC

Kniat, Marian, 1899–1944.
Dzieje uwłaszczenia włościan w Wielkim Księstwie Poznańskim. Poznań, Skł. gł.: Państwowe Zakłady Wydawn. Szkolnych, 1939–49.
2 v. port. 25 cm.
At head of title: Poznańskie Towarzystwo Przyjaciół Nauk.
L. C. set incomplete: v. 1 wanting.

1. Peasantry—Posen (Province) I. Title.
Full name: Marian Julian Kniat.
HD659.P8K6 53–28451

NK 0198980 DLC NNC MH NN CU OU

Kniaz' Kemskii, *pseud.*
see
Meshcherskii, Vladimir Petrovich, *kniaz'*, 1839–1914.

Князь Олегъ. Петроградъ ⌊Товарищество Р. Голике и А. Вильборгъ⌋ 1915.
1 p. l., iv, 204 p. front., illus., 2 col. mounted pl., ports. 32½cm.
"Любившіе ⌊князя Олега Константиновича⌋ ... рѣшили познакомить русское общество съ исторіей его недолгой жизни."—p. iv.
"Ковылинъ," signed O. K. ⌊*i. e.* Олегъ Константиновичъ⌋: p. ⌊191⌋–204.

1. Romanov, Oleg Konstantinovich, kniaz', 1892–1914. *Title transliterated:* Kniaz' Oleg.
43–43479
Library of Congress DK254.R65K6

NK 0198982 DLC

Князь Сергій Михайловичъ Голицынъ; воспоминанія о пятидесятилѣтней службѣ его въ званіи почетнаго опекуна и предсѣдательствующаго въ Московскомъ опекунскомъ совѣтѣ. Москва, Въ Тип. В. Готье, 1859.
160 p. 24 cm.

1. Golitsyn, Sergii Mikhailovich, kniaz', 1774–1859.
Title romanized: Kniaz' Sergii Mikhailovich Golitsyn.
DK190.6.G6K56 70–267693

NK 0198983 DLC

Князь В-скій и княжна Щ-ва; или, Умереть за отечество славно. Новѣйшее произшествіе во время кампаніи французовъ съ нѣмцами и россіянами 1806 г. Изданное В * З *. Россійское сочиненіе. Москва, Въ Унив. тип., 1807.
2 v. in 1. 15 cm.

I. Z *, V *. *Title transliterated:* Kniaz' V-skii i kniazhna Shch-va.
PG3320.Z3K5 55–46711

NK 0198984 DLC

308t
K683

Kniazeff, Alexis John, 1918-
The influence of pregnancy on the dissemination of Brucella abortus in the rabbit. ⌊Berkeley, 1954⌋
iv,104 *l.* diagrs.,tables.

Thesis (Ph.D. in Bacteriology) - Univ. of California, Sept. 1954.
Bibliography: leaves 92-104.

NK 0198985 CU

Kniazer, Malwina, 1904-
... Ein Fall von Lenta-Form der Meningokokkensepsis ... Charlottenburg, [1931]
Inaug.-Diss. - Berlin.
Lebenslauf.
"Literatur": p. 29.

NK 0198986 CtY

Kniazev, A K
Механизация процессов обработки и сборки изделий из пластических масс. Москва, Гос. науч.-техн. изд-во хим. лит-ры, 1949.
86 p. illus. 21 cm.
At head of title: А. К. Князев и А. Н. Степанов.

1. Plastics. 2. Electric apparatus and appliances. I. Stepanov, A. N., fl. 1949, joint author.
Title transliterated: Mekhanizatsiia protsessov obrabotki i sborki.
TP986.5.E4K6 55–16858
Library of Congress ⌊2⌋

NK 0198987 DLC

VOLUME 300

Kni͡azev, Aleksandr Sergeevich, 1814–1897.
Святые равноапостольные Кvріллъ и Меѳодій, просвѣтители славянъ, и вліяніе ихъ подвиговъ на народное образованіе, как всего славянскаго міра вообще, такъ и Россіи въ частности. Соч. А. С. Князева. Изображенія гравированы Л. Сѣряковымъ по рисункамъ Ѳ. Бронникова. [Изд. Григорія Ширяева]. Санктпетербургъ, Въ Тип. А. Траншеля, 1866.
68, viii p. illus. 32 cm.
On cover: Проповѣдническіе подвиги апостоловъ славянъ святыхъ Кирилла и Меѳодія.

1. Cyrillus, Saint, of Thessalonica, 827 (ca.)–869. 2. Methodius, Saint, Abp. of Moravia, d. 885. I. Title. II. Title: Propovi͡edni-cheskīe podvigi apostolov slavi͡an svi͡atykh Kirilla i Mefodii͡a.
Title romanized: Svi͡atye ravno-apostol'nye Kÿrill i Mefodīĭ.

BX4700.C9K59 72-204017

NK 0198989 DLC

Kni͡azev, Alekseĭ Dmitrievich.
Как работает радиостанция. [Москва, Воен. изд-во, 1954]
214 p. illus. 23 cm.

—— —— Microfilm copy (negative)
Made in 1955 by the Library of Congress.

1. Mobile Radio stations. I. Title.
Title transliterated: Kak rabotaet radiostant͡sii͡a.

TK6550.7.K55 55-32318

NK 0198990 DLC

Kni͡azev, Anisim Titovich, 1716–1790.
Гербовникъ Анисима Титовича Князева 1785 года. Издалъ С. Н. Тройницкій. Санктпетербургъ, 1912.
viii, 4, 190 p. coats of arms, facsims. 39 cm.
"Отпечатано въ количествѣ 400 экземпляровъ."

1. Russia — Geneal. 2. Heraldry — Russia. 3. Russia — Nobility. I. Troĭnit͡skiĭ, Sergeĭ Nikolaevich, 1882– II. Title.
Title transliterated: Gerbovnik Anisima Titovicha Kni͡azeva.

CR2039.K5 1912 66-87719

NK 0198991 DLC MH

Kni͡azev, Evgeniĭ, *pseud.*
Разсказы изъ кавказской жизни. Вильна, Тип. Штаба Виленскаго воен. округа, 1901.
160 p. 21 cm.

I. Title. *Title transliterated:* Rasskazy iz kavkazskoĭ zhizni.

PG3467.K512R3 53-55450

NK 0198992 DLC

Kni͡azev, Gavriil Mikhaĭlovich, ed.
O russkom stikhoslozhenīi
see under Günzburg, David, baron, 1857-1910.

AS262
.A68K6
Kni͡azev, Georgiĭ Alekseevich, 1887–
Краткий очерк истории Академии наук СССР. Москва [etc.] 1945.
92, [3] p. plates, facsims. (1 fold.) 26 cm.
"Печатается по постановлению Президиума Всесоюзного комитета по проведению 220-летия Академии наук СССР."
Bibliography: p. 90–[93]

1. Akademii͡a nauk SSSR Hist. I. Akademii͡a nauk SSSR. Vsesoi͡uznyĭ komitet po provedenii͡u 220-letii͡a Akademii nauk.
Title transliterated: Kratkiĭ ocherk istorii Akademii nauk.

AS262.A68K6 48-21253

NK 0198994 DLC

Kni͡azev, Georgiĭ Alekseevich, 1887– ed.
Rukopisi Lomonosova
see under Modzalevskiĭ, Lev Borisovich, 1902-

Kni͡azev, Georgiĭ Alekseevich, 1887-
Uchet dokumental'nykh materialov
see under Akademii͡a nauk SSSR. Arkhiv.

Kni͡azev, Konstantin Fedorovich, joint author.
Planirovka i blagoustroĭstvo kolkhoznogo sela
see under Martynov, G. M.

Kni͡azev, M S
Оборона стрелкового корпуса. Москва, Воен. изд-во, 1940.
73 p. illus. 20 cm.

1. Attack and defense (Military science) I. Title.
Title transliterated: Oborona strelkovogo korpusa.

U165.K55 56-51137 ‡

NK 0198998 DLC

Kni͡azev, N N
Легендарный барон. Харбин [Издательская часть Глав. бюро по дѣлам россійских эмигрантов] 1942.
211 p. ports., fold. map. 22 cm.

1. Ungern-Sternberg, Roman, 1885–1921. 2. Russia—Hist.—Revolution, 1917–1921. I. Title. *Title transliterated:* Legendarnyĭ baron.

DK254.U5K5 53-49051

NK 0198999 DLC

Kniazev, P. V., joint author.

Bekarevich, Aleksandr Sofronovich.
Изучение налоговых об'ектов и методы обложения. Составили А. С. Бекаревич, П. В. Князев и Н. С. Приклонский. С предисловием ... И. В. Попова. 2 изд. переработанное и расширенное. Москва, Государственное финансовое издательство Союза ССР, 1928.

Kni͡azev, P. V.
Nalogovoe oblozhenie chastnogo sektora
see under Russia (1923- U.S.S.R.)
Laws, statutes, etc.

HJ2802
.K7
Kni͡azev, P V
Роль налогов в политике и экономике Советского Союза. Москва, Гос. фин. изд-во, 1930.
56 p. 20 cm.

1. Taxation—Russia.
Title transliterated: Rol' nalogov v politike i ėkonomike Sovetskogo Soi͡uza.

HJ2802.K7 50-52950

NK 0199002 DLC

TL697
A1K5
Kni͡azev, V N
Оборудование самолетов. Допущено в качестве учеб. пособия для авиационных вузов. Москва, Гос. изд-во обор. промышл., 1952.
463 p. illus. 27 cm.
At head of title: В. Н. Князев и К. Е. Полищук.
Errata slip inserted.
Bibliography: p. [458]

1. Aeroplanes—Apparatus and supplies. I. Polishchuk, K. E., joint author. II. Title. *Title transliterated:* Oborudovanie samoletov.

TL697.A1K5 53-28135

NK 0199003 DLC

TL697
.O8K55
Kni͡azev, V N
Основные вопросы кислородного обеспечения высотных полётов. Москва, Воен. изд-во, 1947.
182 p. diagrs. 18 cm.

1. Aeroplanes—Oxygen equipment. 2. Altitude, Influence of.
Title transliterated: Osnovnye voprosy kislorodnogo obespechenii͡a vysotnykh polëtov.

TL697.O8K55 50-33907

NK 0199004 DLC

Kni͡azev, V P
Полезащитные лесные полосы—верное средство борьбы с засухой и неурожаями. Москва, Изд-во Академии наук СССР, 1951.
154 p. illus., ports. 20 cm. (Академия наук СССР. Научно-популярная серия)
Errata slip inserted.
Bibliography: p. 150–[151]

1. Windbreaks, shelterbelts, etc. 2. Afforestation—Russia. I. Title. (Series: Akademii͡a nauk SSSR. Nauchno-populi͡arnai͡a serii͡a) *Title transliterated:* Polezashchitnye lesnye polosy.

SD409.K57 57-17059

NK 0199005 DLC

Kni͡azev, Vasiliĭ.
Сатирическія пѣсни. С.-Петербургъ, 1910.
47 p. 22 cm.

I. Title. *Title transliterated:* Satiricheskīi͡a pѣsni.

PG3467.K51215S3 61-56774 ‡

NK 0199006 DLC

PG3113
.K58
Kni͡azev, Vasiliĭ.
Современные частушки, 1917–1922 г.г. Москва, Гос. изд-во, 1924.
76 p. 19 cm.

1. Chastushki. I. Title.
Title transliterated: Sovremennye chastushki.

PG3113.K58 53-57201 ‡

NK 0199007 DLC

Kni͡azev, Vasiliĭ Vasil'evich.
...V. Wolodarski. Hamburg: C. Hoym Nachf. L. Cahnbley, 1922. 26 p. ports. 8°. (Beiträge zur Geschichte der Kämpfe des Proletariats in Russland. [Nr.] 4.)
V. Volodarski was the pseudonym used by Moiseĭ Markovich Goldstein.

1. Goldstein, Moiseĭ Markovich, 1890– 1918. 2. Series.
N. Y. P. L. October 9, 1924

NK 0199007-1 NN

Kni͡azhanskiĭ, O. M., joint author.
D. I. Ivanovskiĭ i otkrytie virusov
see under Vaĭndrakh, Grigoriĭ Moiseevich.

VOLUME 300

Kniazhevsko chitalishte
see
Kniazhevsko narodno chitalishte.

Kniazhevsko narodno chitalishte.
Trideset godini Kniazhevsko narodno chitalishte
see under title

TJ1363
.K6

Kniazhitskiĭ, G M
Машинист заливочного, сталеразливочного и миксерного кранов. Свердловск, Металлургиздат [etc.] 1942.
85, [1] p., 1 l. illus., diagrs. 15 cm. (В помощь рабочим массовых профессий)
At head of title: Г. М. Княжицкий, Г. М. Николаевский.

1. Electric cranes. I. Nikolaevskiĭ, G. M., joint author. II. Title.
Title transliterated: Mashinist zalivochnogo, staleraz1ivochnogo i miksernogo kranov.

TJ1363.K6 49-34451

NK 0199012 DLC

Kniazhnin, ÎAkov Borisovich, 1742–1791.
Собраніе сочиненій. [Санктпетербургъ] Въ Тип. Горнаго училища, 1787.
4 v. in 2. 26 cm.

Title transliterated: Sobranie sochineniĭ.

PG3315.K5 1787 54-52031

NK 0199013 DLC

Kniazhnin, ÎAkov Borisovich, 1742–1791.
[Sochineniia]
Сочиненія Якова Княжнина. Изд. 3. Въ Санктпетербургѣ, Въ Тип. И. Глазунова, 1817–18.
5 v. in 3. port. 23 cm.
CONTENTS: т. 1. Дидона; трагедія. Титово милосердіе; трагедія. Росславъ; трагедія.—т. 2. Владисанъ; трагедія. Владиміръ и Ярополкъ; трагедія. Софонисба; трагедія.—т. 3. Хвастунъ; комедія. Чудаки; комедія. Неудачный примиритель; или, Безъ обѣду домой поѣду, комедія. Трауръ; или, Утѣшенная вдова, комедія.—т. 4. Сбитеньщикъ; комическая опера. Несчастіе отъ кареты; комическая опера. Скупой; опера комическая. Притворно сумасшедшая; комическая опера. Мужья—женихи своихъ женъ; комическая опера. Орфей; мело-драма.—т. 5. Мѣлкія сочиненія въ стихахъ и прозѣ.

PG3315.K5 1817 72-226527

NK 0199014 DLC

Kniazhnin, ÎAkov Borisovich, 1742–1791.
Dobrodetel'noĭ volshebnik
see under [Bulant, Jean] fl. 1783-1800.

KNIAZHNIN, Iakov Borisovich, 1742-1791.
The ill-fated coach. Translated from the Russian by Jeannette Eyre. Cambridge, 1940.

Typewritten. 27.5 x 20 cm. ff.(1),17.
At head of title: Yakob Borisovich Knyazhnin.
"This translation is intended for the use of students in Slavic 7 and may not be reproduced.

NK 0199016 MH

Kniazhnin, ÎAkov Borisovich, 1742-1791.
Mel'nik i sbiten'shchik-soperniki
see under Plavil'shchikov, Petr Alekseevich, 1760-1812.

PG3315
.K5R6
1784
Rare Bk.
Coll.

Kniazhnin, ÎAkov Borisovich, 1742–1791.
Росславъ, трагедія въ стихахъ въ пяти дѣйствіяхъ. Въ Санктпетербургѣ, При Имп. Академіи наукъ, 1784.
93 p. 20 cm.

I. Title. *Title transliterated:* Roslav.

PG3315.K5R6 1784 54-49411

NK 0199018 DLC

Kniazhnin, ÎAkov Borisovich, 1742–1791.
Вадимъ Новгородскій; трагедія въ стихахъ въ пяти дѣйствіяхъ. Въ Санктпетербургѣ, При Имп. Академіи наукъ, 1793.
78 p. 21 cm.

1. Vadim Khrabryĭ, 9th cent.—Drama.
Title transliterated: Vadim Novgorodskiĭ.

PG3315.K5V3 54-48981

NK 0199019 DLC

Kniazhnin, ÎAkov Borisovich, 1742-1791, tr.
Zapiski istoriogeograficheskiia o Morei
see under [Coronelli, Vincenzo] 1650-1718.

PG3467
.K513P6

Kniazhnin, P P
По пути къ скользкимъ подмосткамъ сцены. С.-Петербургъ, Тип. А. С. Суворина, 1885.
347 p. 20 cm.

I. Title.
Title transliterated: Po puti k skol'zkim podmostkam sfseny.

PG3467.K513P6 54-49484 ‡

NK 0199021 DLC

Kniazhnin, V. N., *pseud.*
see
Ivoĭlov, Vladimir Nikolaevich.

PG 7157
.R4Z68
K6

Kniaziołucki, Zbigniew, 1851-
Do genezy poematu Mikołaja Reja "Wizerunk żywota poczciwego człowieka". Kraków, Nakł. Akademii Umiejętności, 1908.
118 p.
"Osobne odbicie z tomu 45 Rozpraw Wydziału filologicznego Akademii Umiejętności w Krakowie."

1. Rej, Mikołaj, z Nagłowic, 1505-1569. Zywot człowieka poczciwego.

NK 0199023 ICU MH MiU

Kniaziolucki, Zbigniew, 1851–
Johann I. Albrecht, könig von Polen, in seinen ersten regierungsjahren. Eine historische studie von Zbigniew Kniaziolucki. Leipzig, Druck von C. W. Vollrath, 1875.
62 p., 1 l. 21cm.
Inaug.-dis.—Leipzig.

1. Poland—Hist.—John I Albert, 1492-1501. 2. Jan I Olbracht, king of Poland, 1459-1501.

5-6810

Library of Congress DK427.5.K69

NK 0199024 DLC ICRL

Kniaziuk, K A
Поверхностная обработка дорожных покрытий. Москва, Автотрансиздат, 1954.
71 p. illus. 22 cm.

1. Roads—Maintenance and repair. I. Title.
Title transliterated: Poverkhnostnaia obrabotka dorozhnykh pokrytiĭ.

TE220.K5 56-16100

NK 0199025 DLC

Kniaz'kov, M A
Инженерное черчение для строительных специальностей. Допущено в качестве учеб. пособия для строит. вузов и факультетов. Москва, Гос. изд-во лит-ры по строительству и архитектуре, 1951.
145, [3] p. illus. 29 cm.
At head of title: М. А. Князьков, И. Н. Коковин.
Errata slip inserted.
Bibliography: p. [146]

1. Architectural drawing. I. Kokovin, I. N., joint author. II. Title.
Title transliterated: Inzhenernoe cherchenie.

NA2700.K47 52-36599

NK 0199026 DLC

Kniazkov. P.
... Слънчогледъ (*Helianthus annuus* L.) и неговото подобрение, отъ П. Князковъ ... съ встъпителна статия "Българскиятъ слънчогледъ," отъ проф. Ив. Т. Странски ... Die sonnenblume (*Helianthus annuus* L.) und ihre züchtung, von P. Knjaskoff ... mit einem vorwort ("Die bulgarische sonnenblume") von prof. Iv. T. Stranski ... София, Придворна печатница; Sofia, Hofbuchdruckerei, 1937.
63 p. illus. (incl. tables) diagrs. 23cm.
At head of title: Централенъ земедѣлски изпитателенъ институтъ, София. Zentrales landwirtschaftliches versuchsinstitut, Sofia.
"Zusammenfassung": p. [59]–61.
"Използувана литература": p. [62]–63.
1. Sunflower. I. Stranski, Ivan T., 1886- II. Sofia. TSentralen zemedelski izpitatelen institut. III. Title.
41-37734

Library of Congress SB299.S9K55

NK 0199027 DLC

Kniaz'kov, Sergeĭ Aleksandrovich, ed.

Дѣтская энциклопедія. Подъ редакціей: проф. Ю. Н. Вагнера, С. А. Князькова, проф. И. П. Козловскаго, Н. А. Морозова, проф. С. И. Метальникова, М. В. Новорусскаго. Москва, Типографія т-ва И. Д. Сытина, 1914.

Kniaz'kov, Sergeĭ Aleksandrovich, 1873-1919.
Iz proshlago Russkio zemli
see his Ocherki iz istorii Petra Velikago.

Kniaz'kov, Sergeĭ Aleksandrovich, 1873–1919.
Какъ сложилось и какъ пало крѣпостное право въ Россіи; историческій очеркъ. Подъ ред. А. А. Кизеветтера. Изд. 2., испр. и доп. Москва, Типо-литогр. П. К. Прянишникова, 1904.
155 p. port. 19 cm.
Bibliography: p. 153–155.

1. Serfdom—Russia. 2. Peasantry—Russia. I. Title.
Title transliterated: Kak slozhilos' i kak palo krepostnoe pravo v Rossii.

HT807.K55 1904 56-53504

NK 0199030 DLC

Kniaz'kov, Sergeĭ Aleksandrovich,
... Очеркъ исторіи народнаго образованія въ Россіи до эпохи реформъ Александра II. Составили С. А. Князьковъ и Н. И. Сербовъ. Подъ редакціей проф. С. В. Рождественскаго. Съ рисунками и портретами въ текстѣ. Москва, Книгоиздательство "Польза," В. Антикъ и ко. [1910]
iv, 240 p. illus. (incl. ports., facsim.) 22½cm. (Педагогическая академія въ очеркахъ и монографіяхъ. (Воспитаніе въ семьѣ и школѣ). Подъ общей редакціей проф. Алекс. Петр. Нечаева)
"Источники и пособія" at end of each section.
1. Education—Russia—Hist. I. Serbov, N. I. II. Rozhdestvenskiĭ, Sergeĭ Vasil'evich, ed.
Title transliterated: Ocherk istorii narodnago obrazovaniia v Rossii.

44-31370

Library of Congress LA831.5.K6

NK 0199031 DLC ViU CtY

VOLUME 300

DK131
.K57
Knfaz'kov, Sergeĭ Aleksandrovich, 1873–1919.
... Очерки изъ исторіи Петра Великаго и его времени. С. Князькова. Москва, Типографія т-ва И. Д. Сытина, 1909.
1 p. l., 683, [1] p. illus. (incl. facsims.) plates, ports. 28½cm.
At head of title: Изъ прошлаго Русской земли.

1. Peter I, the Great, emperor of Russia, 1672–1725. 2. Russia—Hist.—Peter I, 1689–1725.
Title transliterated: Ocherki iz istorii Petra Velikago.
44-36620
Library of Congress DK131.K57

NK 0199032 DLC

Kniaźnin, Franciszek Dionizy, 1750–1807.
Dzieła. Wydane przez F. S. Dmochowskiego. Warszawa, Nakł. wydawcy, 1828–29.
7 v. 20 cm. (Biblioteka narodowa)
L. C. set incomplete: v. 1-3, 5 wanting; v. 7 imperfect: all after p. 156 wanting.

PG7157.K58 1828 58-54574

NK 0199033 DLC OU MiU CaBVaU

Kniaźnin, Franciszek Dionizy, 1750-1807
Poezye. Edycya zupełna. W Warszawie, W druk.M. Grölla, 1787-88
3v.

NK 0199034 MH

Kniaźnin, Franciszek Dionizy, 1750–1807.
Wybór poezji. Opracował Wacław Borowy. Wrocław, Wydawn. Zakładu Narodowego im. Ossolińskich [1948]
189 p. 18 cm. (Biblioteka narodowa. Seria 1, nr. 129)

PG7157.K58A17 1948 58-34910 ‡

MB CSt NcU KU CU
NK 0199035 DLC NN NcD ICU CtY MiU PU NNC OU PCamA

Kniaźnin, Franciszek Dionizy, 1750–1807.
Wybór poezyj, 1925
see under Karpiński, Franciszek, 1741–1826.

Knibb, Thomas.
The Psalm singers help, being a collection of tunes, in three parts, that are now us'd in the churches, and dissenting congregations, in London. With a thorough bass for the harpsichord or organ, and an introduction for the use of learners. A new ed. London, Printed for G. Pearch, and J. Gurney [1770?] 172, 4 p. 16cm.
Score: counter tenor, tenor and bass (figured).
Without the words of the Psalms; first lines of most of the hymns given.

The Psalms and hymns referred to are those of Isaac Watts and George Whitefield.—cf. p. 1.
Music of 3 additional hymns in manuscript. [4] p. inserted at end.
With bookplate of T. Beale.

1. Bible. O. T. Psalms, Metrical —Watts, 1770. 2. Hymns. I. Watts, Isaac, 1674–1748. II. Whitefield, George, 1714–1770. III. Title.

NK 0199038 NN PP CtY NcD

Knibb, William, *1803–1845,* and Peter **Borthwick,** *1804–1852.*
Colonial slavery. Defence of the Baptist missionaries from the charge of inciting the late rebellion in Jamaica; in a discussion ... at the Assembly Rooms, Bath ... December 15, 1832. ... 2d edition.
London. Tourist Office. [1832.] (1), 30 pp. 21½ cm., in 4s.

M6267 — Jamaica. Slavery. — Slavery. — Jt. autn.

NK 0199039 MB PHi MiU TxU

Knibb, William, 1803-1845.
Colonial slavery. Defence of the Baptist missionaries from the charge of inciting the late rebellion in Jamaica; in a discussion between the Rev. William Knibb and Mr. P. Borthwick, at the assembly rooms, Bath, on Saturday, December 15, 1832. Taken in short-hand by Mr. T. Oxford, of Clifford's Inn. London, Published at the Tourist office [1833?]
2 p. l., 36 p. 22½cm.
1. Slavery in Jamaica. I. Borthwick, Peter, 1804-1852.

NK 0199040 MiU CtY OO NN TxU

F1881
.F15
Knibb, William, 1803-1845, supposed author.

Facts and documents connected with the late insurrection in Jamaica, and the violations of civil and religious liberty arising out of it. Pub. by especial request. London, Holdsworth and Ball [etc.] 1832.

Knibb, William, 1803-1845.
Jamaica. Speech ... before the Baptist missionary society. London, Dyer [1842]

NK 0199042 MeWC

Slavery
E
441
M46
v.40
no.32
Knibb, William, 1803-1845.
Rev. W. Knibb's speech. [Proceedings of the public meeting held in Exeter-Hall, May 22, 1840 on occasion of the public reception of the Rev. William Knibb, H. Beckford, and E. Barrett] [London, Pub. by G. Wightman, 1840]
24 p. 18cm.
No. 32 in a vol. lettered: May Anti-slavery Pamphlets, v. 40.

1. Slavery in the West Indies.

NK 0199043 NIC NN

UD82
Ep
K74
Knibbe, David, 1639-1701
De brief van Paulus aan die van Ephesen, ... Leyden: Johannes Verbessel, 1694
2 v.

NK 0199044 NjNbS

578.6
K69cg
KNIBBE, David, 1639-1701.
Die Epistel des Apostels Pauli an die Colosser in 108. Predigten schrifftmaessig erklaehret und zum geistlichen Gebrauch zugeeignet...Zu mehrerer Erbauung aber in die Hochteutsche Sprache uebergesetzt von Alrico Plesken. Mit zweyen vollstaendigen Registern versehen. Bremen, Herman Brauer, 1694-95.
2v. in 1. 21.5cm.

NK 0199045 MH-AH NjNbS NjNbT

339.8
K69h
1699
KNIBBE, David, 1639-1701.
De hand Gods uytgestrekt in het oordeelen en bewaren van sijn kerk, aangeweesen in de uytbreyding van I. Eerste Petri Kap. IV: 17, 18.19. II. Jesaias Kap. IV. III. Psalm XLVI. N Nevens eenige mengelstoffen over verscheydene texten van de H. Schriftuer. Hier is ook by gedaan de wederlegging van de dwalingen der Schoristen, of soo genaamde Hebreen. Leyden, Luchtmans, 1699.
208p.,578p.,[44]p. 20.5cm.

NK 0199046 MH-AH NjNbS

824
K69k
1747
KNIBBE, David, 1639-1701.
Katechisatie over het Kort Begrip der Christelijke Gereformeerde religie, getrokken uit den Heidelbergsen Katechismus,...Leiden, Samuel Luchtmans en Zoon, 1747.
4p.l.,221p. 16cm.

Een-en-twintigste druk...

NK 0199047 MH-AH NjNbT

IL62
H46Kn
Knibbe, David, 1639-1701.
Katechisatie over het kort begrijp der Christelijke gereformeerde religie, getrokken uit den Heidelbergsen katechismus ... door David Knibbe ... De vier-en-twintigste druk, vermeerderd en verbetered ... Leiden, Samuel en Johannes Luchtmans, 1771.
4p.l.,221,[3]p. 17cm.

NK 0199048 NNUT

688
Ref.4h
K691h
1751
[KNIBBE, David] 1639-1701.
?Kort onderwijs van de preek-order, om een predikatie ordentelijk te hooren, en te herhaalen;...[Leyden, 1696]
28p. 21cm.

Bound with his: de leere der gereformeerde kerk, volgens de order van de Heydelbergse Katechismus...1751.

NK 0199049 MH-AH

KN86
K74l
1713
Knibbe, David, 1639-1701.
De leere der Gereformeerde Kerk, volgens de order van de Heydelbergse Katechismus verklaard, bevestigt, en tot oeffening der godsaligheyd toegepast. Vermeerderd, verbeterd, en voor yder Sondag met een ontleedende tafel verrijkt. Als meede een kort onderwys, om een predicatie met order to hooren en te herhaalen ... Den 4. druk. Tot Leyden, By S. Luchtmans, 1713.
18 p.l., 825, [37], 28, [2] p. 19½ cm.
Title vignette; initials.
1. Heidelberg Catechism. I. Title. Imprints file (Author and date)

NK 0199050 CtY-D

688
Ref.4h
K691h
1718
KNIBBE, David, 1639-1701.
De leere der gereformeerde kerk, volgens de order van de Heydelbergse Katechismus verklaard, bevestigt, en tot oeffening der godsaligheyd toegepast. Vermeerderd, verbeterd, en voor yder Sondag met een ontleedende tafel verrijkt. Als meede een kort onderwys, om een predikatie met order te hooren en te herhaalen. Leyden, Samuel Luchtmans, 1718.
18p.l., 825,[43],28p. 20cm.

NK 0199051 MH-AH

688
Ref.4h
K691h
1751
KNIBBE, David, 1639-1701.
De leere der gereformeerde kerk, volgens de order van de Heydelbergse Katechismus, verklaard, bevestigt, and tot oeffening der godsaligheyd togepast... Den agste druk. Leyden, Samuel Luchtmans en zoonen, 1751.
17p.l., 825[37]p. 21cm.

With this is bound his: kort onderwijs van de preek-order,...[1696]

NK 0199052 MH-AH NjNbS

Knibbe, David, 1639-1701

Manuductio ad oratoriam sacram...concionibus quibusdam paradigmaticis concinnata et illustrata. Editio secunda. Lugd. Batav., apud Felicem Lopez et Cornelium Boutesteyn, 1679.

472p. 16cm.

—— Same. Pars altera, continens conciones paradigmaticas, in prophetae Jesaiae cap. 26 et 40... Lugd. Batav., apud Jordanum Luchtmans, 1697.

609p. 16cm.

NK 0199053 NjNbS

Knibbe, David, 1639-1701.
Het Ordeel Gods over sijn huis. Leiden, 1682.

NK 0199054 NjNbS

Knibbe, David, 1639-1701, ed.
Socinianismi Confutati Compendium Ipsissimis Cl: Autoris verbis concinnatum. In usum S.S. Theologiae studiosorum
see under Hoornbeek, Johannes, 1617-1666.

VOLUME 300

Knibbe, David, 1639-1701.
Das Urtheil Gottes über sein Hausz. Das ist: eine auss Heil. Schrifft und den Geschichten selbsten hergeholete deutliche Ausslegung der Worte des Apostels 1. Petr. 4:17/18/und 19. worinnen die meisten heimliche Tücke, auch offenbahre Grausamkeiten und Verfolgungen der wahren Kirchen ... entdecket, beschrieben und ... so gezeiget werden, dass die Recht-Glaubigen allemahl errettet ... Eine Verhandlunge ... Anfänglich im Holländischen geschrieben von David Knibben ... und nun in Hoch-Teutsche übersetzet durch J. P. B. Y. Offenbach am Mäyn, druckts Bonav. de Launoy, Franckfurt, zu finden bey Wolffgang Röder, 1696.
4 p.l., 550 p. front. 17.5 cm.
"Approbatio facultatis Theol. Lugd. Batavae" p. 2.
Bound with: Spener, Philipp Jacob, 1635-1705. Christliche Aufmunterung ... [1718]
Calvinist sermons.

NK 0199057 NNUT

BS1505 .K68 KNIBBE, DAVID, 1671-1748.
Histori der propheten. In vier bücher abgetheilt; so da handeln, das I. Von den wahren propheten... II. Von einem jeden derselben propheten... III. Von den falschen propheten. IV. Von den heidnischen wahrsagereyen/denen die Juden nachgefolgt. Durch herrn David Knibbe ... Auss dem holländischen in das teutsche übersetzet/durch Gerold Freytag... Bern, N.E. Haller und compagnie, 1709.
[8], 426, 152, [30] p. 20½x17½cm.
"Das IV.buch" paged separately. Title in red and black.
1. Prophets.

NK 0199058 ICU

Knibbe, David, 1671-1748.
De Republicq der Hebreen, of de Joodsche Oudheden, behelzende al 't voornaemste 't geen hare Kerkelyke, Burgerlyke en Huisselyke gewoonten en Plegtigheden en Levenswyze betreft. Leyden, 1743.
10 books in one volume.
Title page lacking.
Info. obtained from Biographisch Woordenboek (v. 5, p. 59)

NK 0199059 NjNbS

KNIBBE, P. G.
Telefoonverkeer en telefoonbeleid in Nederland, door Mr. Dr. P.G. Knibbe... Leiden: A.W. Sijthoff[, 1931?]. vi, 282 p. tables. 8°.
Bibliography, p. 271-276.

583205A. 1. Telephone— Netherlands.

NK 0199060 NN

Knibbe, P K
Planologie of bodembouwkunde en streekplannen. Leiden [Kamer van Koophandel en Fabrieken voor Rijnland] 1955
62 p. 24cm.

1. Regional planning - Netherlands.

NK 0199061 NNC

KNIBBE, Pieter Gerardus
Doorbraak in onze kerken; om de vrijheid van de Christenmens. Tweede Druk. Leiden, N.V. Grafisch Bedrijf en Uitgeverij de Jong [1951]
49p. 22cm.

NK 0199062 MH-AH

SP87 K74k Knibbe, Pieter Gerardus.
Kerk, zending en communisme. Franeker, T. Wever [1950?]
48 p. 23 cm.

1. Communism and religion. 2. Indonesia - Missions. 3. Verkuyl, Johannes, 1908- I. Title.

NK 0199063 CtY-D NNUT

Knibbe, Rudolf.
Der nährwert der nacktgerste im vergleich zu bespelzten gersten beim schwein.
Landw. vers. stat. bd. 117, p. 131-216. Berlin, 1933.
"Literatur": p. 180.

1. Barley [as feeding stuff] 2. Swine—[Feeding] Agr 34-226

Library, U. S. Dept. of Agriculture 105.8L23 bd. 117
Library of Congress [S7.L293 bd. 117]

NK 0199064 DNAL OU

Knibbe, Willem Arie
De vestiging der monarchie, het conflict Elout—van den Bosch in verband met de wordingsgeschiedenis der regeeringsreglementen van 1830 en 1836. Utrecht, A. Oosthoek, 1935.
128, 209, [1] (i. e. lxi) p. 26 cm. (Utrechtsche bijdragen tot de geschiedenis, het staatsrecht en de economie van Nederlandsch-Indië, 4)
"Errata": slip inserted.
Bibliography: p. 115-117 (1st group)
1. Dutch East Indies—Constitutional history. 2. Elout, Cornelis Pieter Jacob, 1795-1843. 3. Bosch, Johannes, Graaf van den, 1780-1844. I. Title. (Series)

JQ762.K5 54-50529

NK 0199065 DLC ICU ViU CtY MiU HU CU NN OrU IU

Knibbs, Sir George Handley, 1858-1929.
Australia. *Bureau of census and statistics.*
... The Australian commonwealth, its resources and production, 1912. Published under the authority of the minister of external affairs, Hon. Josiah Thomas, M. P. by G. H. Knibbs ... [Melbourne, Bird and co., printers, 1912]

Knibbs, George Handley, 1858-1929
Australia. *Bureau of census and statistics.*
... Australian life tables. Comp. and issued under the authority of the minister of state for home affairs, by G. H. Knibbs ... commonwealth statistician. Melbourne, McCarron, Bird & co., printers [1914]

Knibbs, Sir George Handley, 1858-1929
Census of the Commonwealth of Australia. 3rd April, 1911
see under Australia. Bureau of Census and Statistics.

Knibbs, *Sir* George Handley, 1858-1929.
The classification of disease and causes of death, from the standpoint of the statistician. An address given to the Victorian branch of the British medical association, June 12, 1907. By G. H. Knibbs ... Reprinted from the "Intercolonial medical journal of Australasia", June 20, 1907. Melbourne, Stillwell and co., printers [1907]
cover-title, 24 p. 24½cm.

1. Nosology. 2. Death—Causes. I. Victoria, Australia. Statist's office. II. Title. 9—7747

Library of Congress HB1321.K6

NK 0199069 DLC

Knibbs, George Handley, 1858-1929, ed
British association for the advancement of science. *Federal council in Australia.*
The commonwealth of Australia; federal handbook, prepared in connection with the eighty-fourth meeting of the British association for the advancement of science, held in Australia, August, 1914. Comp. under the authority of the Federal council of the Association, ed. by G. H. Knibbs ... and pub. by the Commonwealth government. Melbourne, A. J. Mullett, government printer [1914]

Knibbs, George Handley, 1858-1929 [1]
Australia. *Bureau of census and statistics.*
The desirability of improved statistics of government railways in Australia. Report by the commonwealth statistician, G. H. Knibbs ... to the Honorable Hugh Mahon ... minister for home affairs. February, 1909. Commonwealth bureau of census and statistics, Melbourne. By authority. Melbourne, J. Kemp, government printer [1909]

Knibbs, G[eorge] H[andley], 1858-1928. SPA
The determination and uses of population norms, representing the constitution of populations according to age and sex, and also according to age only. (In: International Congress on Hygiene and Demography. XV. Washington, 1912. Transactions. Washington, 1913. 8°. v. 6, p. 352-378.)

1. Statistics (Vital). 2. Population. N. Y. P. L.

NK 0199072 NN

Knibbs, George Handley, 1858-1929.
... "The evolution and significance of the census," by G. H. Knibbs ... commonwealth statistician. Reprinted from the Addresses and proceedings, 1910, of the Imperial federation league of Australia. Melbourne, Pub. under the authority of the League, 1910.
cover-title, [16] p. diagr. 22cm. (Australia. Bureau of census and statistics. Professional papers)

1. Census. 2. Australia—Census, 1891. 11-13310

Library of Congress HA29.K72

NK 0199073 DLC

Knibbs, George Handley, 1858-1929.
Australia. *Bureau of census and statistics. Labour and industrial branch.*
... Expenditure on living in the commonwealth, November, 1913. Prepared under instructions from the minister of state for home affairs, by G. H. Knibbs ... commonwealth statistician. August, 1914. Melbourne, By authority: McCarron, Bird & co., printers [1914]

Knibbs, George Handley, 1858-1929.
Australia. *Bureau of census and statistics.*
... Finance. Bulletin no.
Melbourne [1908-

Knibbs, George Handley, 1858-1929
Australia. *Bureau of census and statistics.*
... The first commonwealth census, 3rd April, 1911. Notes by G. H. Knibbs ... commonwealth statistician. Pub. under the authority of the Hon. King O'Malley, M. P., minister of state for home affairs ... Melbourne, J. Kemp, government printer [1911]

HB863 .A.P3 △ no.11 Knibbs, Sir George Handley, 1858-1929.
... The growth of human populations, and the laws of their increase. [Padova, R. Universita-Instituto di statistica, 1925]
16 p. [Pamphlets on Malthusianism ... no. 11]
Caption title.
Reprinted from Metron, vol. v, no. 3, 1925.

NK 0199077 DLC

VOLUME 300

Knibbs, George Handley, 1858-1929.
The history, theory and determination of the viscosity of water by the efflux method. By G. H. Knibbs. (In Journal and Proceedings of the Royal society of New South Wales for 1895 ... vol. 29. Sydney p. 77-146, pl. xi. 22.5 cm.)

NK 0199078 DBS

Knibbs, George Handley, 1858-1929
Australia. *Bureau of census and statistics.*
... Inquiry into the cost of living in Australia, 1910–11. By G. H. Knibbs ... commonwealth statistician ... Melbourne, McCarron, Bird & co., printers, 1911.

Knibbs, Sir George Handley, 1858-1929.
New South Wales. *Commission on primary, secondary, technical, and other branches of education.*
... Interim report of the commissioners on certain parts of primary education. Containing the summarised reports, recommendations, conclusions, and extended report of the commissioners; with illustrations, etc. Sydney, W. A. Gullick, government printer, 1903.

Knibbs, George Handley, 1858-1929.
... 1. The international nosological classification, &c. 2. Secular progress of pulmonary tuberculosis and cancer, &c. 3. The improvement in infantile mortality, &c. 4. Secular and annual fluctuations of deaths from several diseases, &c. G. H. Knibbs ... Sydney, W. A. Gulick, government printer, 1913.
1 p. l., p. [645]–669, [1], 670–679, [1], 680–690. diagrs. 24½cm. (Australia. Bureau of census and statistics. Professional papers)
Paging irregular: 650–654 omitted.
Reprinted from the Journal of the Australian medical congress, Sydney, September, 1911.
1. Nosology. 2. Tuberculosis—Australia. 3. Cancer. 4. Infants—Mortality. 5. Australia—Statistics, Vital.
13-14071
Library of Congress R117.K68

NK 0199081 DLC NN

HB863 no. 12-13
Knibbs, Sir George Handley, 1858-1929.
... The laws of growth of a population ... 2 pt. [Pamphlets on Malthusianism ... no. 12-13]
Reprinted from the Journal of the American statistical association, December, 1926 and March, 1927.

NK 0199082 DLC

Knibbs, George Handley, 1858-1929.
Australia. *Bureau of census and statistics. Labour and industrial branch.*
... Manufacturing industries in the commonwealth, 1912. Prepared under instructions from the minister of state for home affairs, by G. H. Knibbs ... commonwealth statistician. June, 1914. Melbourne, By authority: McCarron, Bird & co., printers [1914]

Knibbs, George Handley, 1858-1929.
... Mathematical analysis of some experiments in climatological physiology, by G. H. Knibbs ... London, Printed by Taylor and Francis, 1912.
cover-title, p. [325]–351. 22cm. (Australia. Bureau of census and statistics. Professional papers)
Reprinted from the Philosophical magazine for September 1912.
1. Climatology, Medical. I. Title.
13-14066
Library of Congress RA795.K6

NK 0199084 DLC NN

Knibbs, Sir George Handley, 1858-1929.
Australia. *Bureau of census and statistics.*
... The mathematical theory of population, of its character and fluctuations, and of the factors which influence them, being an examination of the general scheme of statistical representation, with deductions of necessary formulas; the whole being applied to the data of the Australian census of 1911, and to the elucidation of Australian population statistics generally. By G. H. Knibbs ... commonwealth statistician. Pub. under instructions from the minister of state for home and territories ... Melbourne, McCarron, Bird & co., printers [1917]

Knibbs, George Handley, 1858-1929.
Australia. *Bureau of census and statistics.*
... Monthly summary of Australian statistics. Bulletin. no. 1- January 1912-
Melbourne [1912-

HB863 .A1P3 △ no. 14
Knibbs, Sir George Handley, 1858-1929.
The new Malthusianism in the light of actual world problems of population. [Milano, "Scientia", 1926]
p. [279]-388. [Pamphlets on Malthusianism ... no. 14]
Caption title.
"Extrait de 'Scientia' - décembre 1926."

NK 0199087 DLC

Knibbs, Sir George Handley, 1858-1929
Australia. *Bureau of census and statistics.*
... Official year book of the commonwealth of Australia ...
Melbourne [1908-

Knibbs, George Handley, 1858-1929.
Australia. *Bureau of census and statistics.*
Old-age and invalid pension. Report on extent of the granting of, in Australia, by G. H. Knibbs, commonwealth statistician ... [Melbourne] A. J. Mullett, government printer for the state of Victoria [1913]

Knibbs, G[eorge] H[andley], 1858-1929.
On the establishment of a series of forms of death rates for various diseases. (In: International Congress on Hygiene and Demography, XV. Washington, 1912. Transactions. Washington, 1913. 8°. v. 6, p. 343–351.)
1. Statistics (Vital).
N. Y. P. L. April 19, 1916.

NK 0199090 NN

Knibbs, George Handley, 1858-1929.
... On the influence of infantile mortality on birth rate. By G. H. Knibbs ... commonwealth statistician. Reprinted from the Journal of the Royal society of New South Wales, vol. XLII, pp. 238–250. Sydney, F. W. White, printer, 1908.
cover-title, [1], 238–250 p. incl. tables, diagrs. 21½cm. (Australia. Bureau of census and statistics. Professional papers)
1. Infants—Mortality. 2. Vital statistics.
11-22148
Library of Congress HB1323.I 4K5

NK 0199091 DLC DL

KNIBBS, Sir GEORGE HANDLEY, 1858-1929.
On the influence of infantile mortality on birth-rate. Sydney, F.W. White, printer 1908. p. 238-250. 22cm. (Australia. Census and statistics bureau Professional papers)
Film reproduction. Positive.
Cover title.
"Reprinted from the Journal of the Royal society of New South Wales, vol. XLII. pp. 238-250."
1. Infants--Mortality--Australia. I. Australia. Census and statistics bureau. t. 1908

NK 0199093 NN

Knibbs, George Handley, 1858-1929
... On the influence of infantile mortality on birthrate. By G. H. Knibbs ... commonwealth statistician. Reprinted from the Journal of the Royal society of New South Wales, volume XLIV. Sydney, F. W. White, printer, 1910.
cover-title, 3 p. 22cm. (Australia. Bureau of census and statistics. Professional papers)
1. Infants—Mortality. 2. Vital statistics.
11-13309
Library of Congress HB1323.I 4K6

NK 0199094 DLC DL

Knibbs, George Handley, 1858-1929.
... On the statistical opportunities of the medical profession and tuberculosis duration frequency curves, and the number of existing cases ultimately fatal. By G. H. Knibbs ... Melbourne, J. Kemp, government printer [1908?]
13 p. diagrs. 24cm. (Australia. Bureau of census and statistics. Professional papers)
Reprinted from the Transactions of the 8th session, Australasian medical congress, held at Melbourne, October, 1908, pp. 191–202, vol. II.
1. Medical statistics. 2. Vital statistics. 3. Tuberculosis.
11-14464
Library of Congress RA409.K6

NK 0199095 DLC

KNIBBS, Sir George H[andley], 1858-1929.
Presidential address to the Australasian association for the advancement of Science at the New Zealand meeting January, 1923. Science and its service to man. Wellington, W. A. G. Skinner, 1923.
pp. 46.
Cover serves as title-page.
At head of title: Commonwealth of Australia-Institute of science and industry. Professional papers.

NK 0199096 MH

Knibbs, George Handley, 1858-1929.
Australia. *Bureau of census and statistics.*
... Price-indexes, their nature and limitations, the technique of computing them, and their application in ascertaining the purchasing-power of money. Prepared under instructions from the minister of state for home and territories. By G. H. Knibbs ... commonwealth statistician. December, 1918. Melbourne, McCarron, Bird & co., printers [1918?]

Knibbs, George Handley, 1858-1929.
Australia. *Bureau of census and statistics. Labour and industrial branch.*
... Prices, price indexes & cost of living in Australia, by G. H. Knibbs ... commonwealth statistician. Pub. under the authority of the minister for home affairs. December, 1912. Melbourne, McCarron, Bird & co., printers, 1912.

VOLUME 300

Knibbs, George Handley, 1858-1929.
Prices, purchasing-power of money, wages, trade unions, unemployment, and general industrial conditions ...
see under Australia. Bureau of Census and Statistics. Labour and Industrial Branch.

Knibbs, George Handley, 1858-1929.
Australia. *Bureau of census and statistics.*
... The private wealth of Australia and its growth as ascertained by various methods, together with a report of the war census of 1915. Prepared under instructions from the minister of state for home and territories, by G. H. Knibbs ... commonwealth statistician. Melbourne, McCarron, Bird & co. [1918]

Knibbs, George Handley, 1858-1929.
... The problems of statistics. Address by the president of section G[1], G. H. Knibbs ... Brisbane, A. J. Cumming, government printer, 1910.
cover-title, p. [505]-526. 22cm.
At head of title: Australasian association for the advancement of science.
"Section G[1]": Social and statistical science.
1. Statistics. 2. Vital statistics. I. Australasian association for the advancement of science. II. Title.
14—6475
Library of Congress HA47.K6
NK 0199101 DLC NN

Knibbs, Sir George Handley, 1858-1929.
Australia. *Bureau of census and statistics.*
... Production. Bulletin no. 1-
Summary of Australian production statistics for the years [1901 to 1906—]19
Melbourne [1907-

Knibbs, George Handley, 1858-1929.
New South Wales. *Commission on primary, secondary, technical, and other branches of education.*
... Report of the commissioners, mainly on secondary education, containing the summarised reports, recommendations, and extended reports of the commissioners; with illustrations, etc. ... Sydney, W. A. Gullick, government printer, 1904.

Knibbs, George Handley, 1858-1929.
New South Wales. *Commission on primary, secondary, technical, and other branches of education.*
... Report of the commissioners on agricultural, commercial, industrial, and other forms of technical education, containing the summarised reports, with conclusions and recommendations, etc., and the extended report of the commissioners; with illustrations, etc. ... Sydney, W. A. Gullick, government printer, 1905.

Knibbs, *Sir* George Handley, 1858-1929.
The shadow of the world's future; or, The earth's population possibilities & the consequences of the present rate of increase of the earth's inhabitants, by Sir George Handley Knibbs ... London, E. Benn limited [1928]
131 p. 22cm.
1. Population. 2. Malthusianism. 3. Food supply. I. Title.
29-7182
Library of Congress HB851.K6
NN NjN DL CaBVaU
NK 0199105 DLC DAU CU NcD CtY MiU OU OO ViU WaU ICJ

Knibbs, George Handley, 1858-1929.
Australia. *Bureau of census and statistics.*
... Shipping and oversea migration of the commonwealth of Australia.
Sydney,

Knibbs, George Handley, 1858-1929.
Australia. *Bureau of census and statistics.*
... Social insurance. Report by the commonwealth statistician, G. H. Knibbs ... to the Honorable F. G. Tudor, M. P., minister of state for trade and customs. September, 1910. Melbourne, J. Kemp, government printer [1910]

Knibbs, George Handley, 1858-1929.
Australia. *Bureau of census and statistics.*
... Social statistics. Bulletin no. 1-
Melbourne [1908-

Knibbs, Sir George Handley, 1858-
Conference of government officers engaged in dealing with statistics in the British commonwealth of nations. *1st, London,* 1920.
... Statistical conference (British empire). Report and resolutions accompanied by explanatory memorandum and observations by the commonwealth statistician ... [Melbourne?] Printed and pub. for the government of the commonwealth of Australia by A. J. Mullett, government printer for the state of Victoria [1920]

Knibbs, George Handley, 1858-1929.
... Studies in statistical representation. On the nature of the curve $y=Ax^m e^{nx^p}$, by G. H. Knibbs ... commonwealth statistician ... Sydney, F. W. White, printer, 1911
cover-title, p. 341-367. diagrs. 22cm. (Australia. Bureau of census and statistics. Professional papers)
"Reprinted from the Journal of the Royal society of New South Wales, vol. XLIV., pp. 341-367."
1. Statistics—Graphic methods. I. Title.
18-18283
Library of Congress HA31.K5
NK 0199110 DLC MiU

Knibbs, George Handley, 1858-1929.
... Studies in statistical representation. Statistical application of the Fourier series (illustrated by the analysis of rates of marriage, temperature, suicide, etc.) By G. H. Knibbs ... Sydney, F. W. White, 1911.
cover-title, p. [75]-110. 22cm. (Australia. Bureau of census and statistics. Professional paper)
Reprinted from the Journal of the Royal society of New South Wales. vol. XLV, p. 76-110.
1. Statistics. 2. Vital statistics. 3. Fourier's series. 4. Heat—Conduction.
12-15405
Library of Congress HA33.K6
NK 0199111 DLC

Knibbs, George Handley, 1858-1929.
... Studies in statistical representation, III. Curves, their logarithmic homologues and antilogarithmic generatrices, by G. H. Knibbs ... commonwealth statistician, and F. W. Barford ... commonwealth Bureau of census and statistics ... Sydney, F. W. White, general printer, 1915.
cover-title, p. 473-496. diagrs. 22cm. (Australia. Bureau of census and statistics. Professional papers)
"Reprinted from the Journal of the Royal society of New South Wales, vol. LXVIII., pp. 473-512."
1. Statistics—Graphic methods. I. Barford, F. W., joint author. II. Title.
18-18284
Library of Congress HA31.K6
NK 0199112 DLC NN

Knibbs, George Handley, 1858-1929.
... Suicide in Australia. A statistical analysis of the facts. By G. H. Knibbs ... Sydney, F. W. White, general printer, 1912.
cover-title, 225-246 p. 21½cm. (Australia. Bureau of census and statistics. Professional papers)
Reprinted from the Journal of the Royal society of New South Wales, vol. XLV.
1. Suicide—Stat. 2. Australia—Statistics, Vital.
12-24658
Library of Congress HB1323.S8K6
NK 0199113 DLC NN

Knibbs, George Handley, 1858-1929.
Australia. *Bureau of census and statistics.*
... Superannuation. Report by G. H. Knibbs ... government statistician, to the Honourable King O'Malley, M. P., minister of state for home affairs. October, 1910. Melbourne, J. Kemp, government printer [1910]

Knibbs, George Handley, 1858-1929.
Australia. *Bureau of census and statistics.*
... Trade and customs and excise revenue of the commonwealth of Australia ... 1906-
Sydney [1907-

Knibbs, Sir George Handley, 1858-1929.
Australia. *Bureau of census and statistics.*
... Trade, shipping, oversea migration, and finance of the commonwealth of Australia ... Bulletin no.
Melbourne [1907-

Knibbs, Sir George Handley, 1858-1929.
Australia. *Bureau of census and statistics.*
... Transport and communication. Bulletin no.
Melbourne [1907]

Knibbs, George Handley, 1858-1929.
Australia. *Delegate to International conference on unemployment. 3d, Ghent,* 1913.
Unemployment: Report on the conference of the International association on, held at Ghent, September, 1913— by Mr. Donald Campbell, commonwealth representative; together with note by the commonwealth statistician. [Melbourne, A. J. Mullett, government printer for the state of Victoria, 1913]

PN6101 K55
Knibbs, Sir George Handley, 1858-1929.
Voices of the North, and Echoes of Hellas. Book I-II. London, A. Rivers [1913]
xv, 291 p.
1. Poetry (Collections) 2. English poetry - Translations from foreign literature. I. Title. II. Title: Echoes of Hellas.
NK 0199119 CU TxU WU

Knibbs, Harry Herbert
see
Knibbs, Henry Herbert, 1874-

VOLUME 300

1901 K693f Harris Collection
Knibbs, Henry Herbert, 1874-1945
First poems, by Henry K. Herbert (H. H. Knibbs) [Rochester, N. Y., Genesee Press, 1908]
64 p. 18 cm.
"Three hundred copies ... printed for private circulation." Signed by author.
Copy 1. "No. 164."
Copy 2. "No. 121."

NK 0199121 RPB

Knibbs, Henry Herbert, 1874-1945
Gentlemen, hush! By H. H. Knibbs and Turbesé Lummis. Boston and New York, Houghton Mifflin company, 1933.
3 p. l., 193 p. 19½cm.

I. Lummis, Turbesé, joint author. II. Title.
Library of Congress PZ3.K73Ge 33-28597

NK 0199122 DLC OCl MB PP PPGi

Knibbs, Henry Herbert, 1874-
Jim Waring of Sonora-town; or, Tang of life, by Henry Herbert Knibbs... Illustrations by E. Boyd Smith. New York: Grosset & Dunlap [1918] ix, 393 p. front., plates. 19½cm.

205797B. 1. Fiction, American. I. Title.
N. Y. P. L. January 20, 1943

NK 0199123 NN MH CoU

Knibbs, Henry Herbert, 1874-1945.
Lost Farm camp, by Harry Herbert Knibbs; illustrated by Harold James Cue. Boston and New York, Houghton Mifflin company, 1912.
ix, [1] p., 1 l., 354, [2] p. front., plates. 19cm. $1.25

I. Title.
Library of Congress PZ3.K73L 12-6865

NK 0199124 DLC OClJC MH

Knibbs, Henry Herbert, 1874-1945.
Mladý jezdec od Plamenné Řeky; z angličtiny přeložil Josef Vorel a L. J. Knížek.

The ridin' kid from Powder River.

NK 0199125 OCl

PS 3521 N5 O8
Knibbs, Henry Herbert, 1874-1945.
Overland Red; a romance of the Moonstone Canon trail, with illus. by Anton Fischer. New York, Grosset and Dunlap [1914]
xiv, 348p. illus.

NK 0199126 UU ICN OU OO

[Knibbs, Henry Herbert] 1874-1945.
Overland Red; a romance of the Moonstone Cañon trail; with illustrations by Anton Fischer. Boston and New York, Houghton Mifflin company, 1914.
xiii, [1], 348, [2] p. col. front., illus., col. plates. 19½cm. $1.35
Illustrated t.-p.

I. Title.
Library of Congress PZ3.K73O 14-5042

NK 0199127 DLC OCl OClh NN WaT OU OkU PPL

Knibbs, Henry Herbert, 1874-1945
Partners of chance, by Henry Herbert Knibbs ... Boston and New York, Grosset & Dunlap [c1921]
281 p. 20 cm.

NK 0199128 OU

Knibbs, Henry Herbert, 1874-1945.
Partners of chance, by Henry Herbert Knibbs ... Boston and New York, Houghton Mifflin company, 1921.
3 p. l., 231, [1] p. 19½ cm.

I. Title.
PZ3.K73Pa 21-19388

NK 0199129 DLC OOxM OCl MB MH

Knibbs, Henry Herbert, 1874-1945.

Rhodes, Eugene Manlove, 1869-1934.
The proud sheriff, by Eugene Manlove Rhodes; with a preamble by Henry Herbert Knibbs. Boston and New York, Houghton Mifflin company, 1935.

Knibbs, Henry Herbert, 1874-1945.
Riders of the stars; a book of western verse, by Henry Herbert Knibbs. Boston and New York, Houghton Mifflin company, 1916.
5 p. l., 3-81, [1] p. 20cm. $1.00

I. Title.
Library of Congress PS3521.N5R5 1916 16-20910

NK 0199131 DLC OCl NjP MB NN ViU WaSp PP WaS WaT Or OrP InU MB MoU NcC

Knibbs, Henry Herbert, 1874-1945.
The ridin' kid from Powder River, by Henry Herbert Knibbs ... Boston and New York, Houghton Mifflin company, 1919.
vi p., 1 l., 457, [1] p. col. front., plates. 19½cm. $1.75

I. Title.
Library of Congress PZ3.K73Ri 19-15555

NK 0199132 DLC OCl OU OClh MB NN MtHi PHC PPL PSt

Knibbs, Henry Herbert, 1874-1945.
The ridin' kid from Powder River, by Henry Herbert Knibbs; illustrations by R. M. Brinkerhoff. New York, Grosset & Dunlap [1921]
vi, 457 p. front., plates. 19½cm.

I. Title.
Library of Congress PZ3.K73Ri 3 25-15512

NK 0199133 DLC OO

Knibbs, Henry Herbert, 1874-1945.
Saddle songs and other verse, by Henry Herbert Knibbs ... Boston and New York, Houghton Mifflin company, 1922.
vii, [1], 101 p. 20cm. $1.50

I. Title.
Library of Congress PS3521.N5S3 1922 22-20060

NK 0199134 DLC MB NN OCl OrU IdPI Or WaS OrP WaT UU TxU OrU

Knibbs, Henry Herbert, 1874-1945.
Síla života; přeložil Josef Vorel.

Tang of life.
Bohemian.

NK 0199135 OCl

Knibbs, Henry Herbert, 1874-1945.
Songs of the lost frontier, by Henry Herbert Knibbs. Boston and New York, Houghton Mifflin company, 1930.
ix, [1], 85, [1] p. 20cm.

I. Title.
Library of Congress PS3521.N5S55 1930 30-21435
——— Copy 2.
Copyright A 27003 [2] 811.5

NK 0199136 DLC OClh MB NN MH ViU OCl MiU PPGi PP MtU WaT MtHi WaSp TxU NcD WaS Or

---

Knibbs, Henry Herbert, 1874-1945.
Songs of the outlands; ballads of the hoboes and other verse, by Henry Herbert Knibbs. Boston and New York, Houghton Mifflin company, 1914.
v, [1], 73, [1] p., 1 l. illus. 20cm. $1.25
Reprinted in part from various periodicals.

I. Title.
Library of Congress PS3521.N5S6 1914 14-21450

NK 0199137 DLC ViU MB NN MiU Or OrU WaS WaT NcC NjP TxU PP IEN WU TNJ CoU

Knibbs, Henry Herbert, 1874-1945
Songs of the trail, by Henry Herbert Knibbs, illustrations by Harold Cue. Boston and New York, Houghton Mifflin company, 1920.
ix, [1], 97, [1] p., 1 l. illus. 20cm. $1.50

I. Title.
Library of Congress PS3521.N5S7 1920 20-19670

NK 0199138 DLC MB NN OClh OCl MtBC CaBVaU IdPI Or WaS IdB Wa WaT ICarbS IU

Knibbs, Henry Herbert, 1874-1945.
Stephen March's way, by Harry Herbert Knibbs; illustrated by H. Weston Taylor. Boston and New York, Houghton Mifflin company, 1913.
vii, [1] p., 1 l., 277, [1] p., 1 l. front., plates. 19cm. $1.25

I. Title.
Library of Congress PZ3.K73S 13-4613 Revised

NK 0199139 DLC OClW

Knibbs, Henry Herbert, 1874-1945.
Sundown Slim, by Henry Herbert Knibbs; with illustrations by Anton Fischer. Boston and New York, Houghton, Mifflin company, 1915.
xi, [1], 356, [2] p. col. front., plates. 19½cm. $1.35

I. Title.
Library of Congress PZ3.K73Su 15-11001

NK 0199140 DLC OCl OrCS OrP PPL MH CoU CtY OU PPA PPGi

PS 3521 N5 S8
Knibbs, Henry Herbert, 1874-1945.
Sundown Slim, by Henry Herbert Knibbs; with illustrations by Anton Fischer. New York, Grosset and Dunlap [c1919]
356[1]p. illus.

NK 0199141 UU

VOLUME 300

Knibbs, Henry Herbert, 1874–1945.
The sungazers, by Henry Herbert Knibbs ... Boston and New York, Houghton Mifflin company, 1926.
3 p. l., 248, [1] p. 19½cm.

I. Title.
Library of Congress PZ3.K37Sun 26—5144

NK 0199142 DLC OCl OClh OLak Or WaS PP OU WaT

Knibbs, Henry Herbert, 1874–1945.
Sunny Mateel, by Henry Herbert Knibbs ... Boston and New York, Houghton Mifflin company, 1927.
3 p. l., [3]–278 p. 19½cm.

I. Title.
Library of Congress PZ3.K73Suy 27-3813

NK 0199143 DLC OCl OClh PPL NN MB OU WaS

Knibbs, Henry Herbert, 1874–1945.
Tang of life, by Henry Herbert Knibbs; with illustrations by E. Boyd Smith. Boston and New York, Houghton Mifflin company, 1918.
ix, [1] p., 1 l., 393, [1] p., 1 l. col. front., col. plates. 19½cm. $1.50

I. Title.
Library of Congress PZ3.K73T 18—16487

NK 0199144 DLC CoU CtY OCl OClW PPPH-I MB NN WaS

Knibbs, Henry Herbert, 1874–1945.
Temescal, by Henry Herbert Knibbs ... Boston and New York, Houghton Mifflin company, 1925.
4 p. l., 3-369, [1] p. 19cm.

I. Title.
Library of Congress PZ3.K73Te 25—7941

NK 0199145 DLC OU NcU PPL OCl OO PP PPAmP

Knibbs, Henry Herbert, 1874–1945.
Temescal. New York, Grosset & Dunlap [c.1925]

NK 0199146 MH

Knibbs, Henry Herbert, 1874–1945
The Tonto kid, by Henry Herbert Knibbs. Boston & New York, Houghton Mifflin company, 1936.
4 p. l., 260 p. 19½cm.

I. Title.
Library of Congress PZ3.K73To 36-18758

NK 0199147 DLC OEac

Knibbs, Henry Herbert, 1874–1945.
Wild horses; a novel, by Henry Herbert Knibbs ... Boston and New York, Houghton Mifflin company, 1924.
viii, [1], 271, [1] p. 19½cm.

I. Title.
Library of Congress PZ3.K73Wi 24—4503

NK 0199148 DLC NBuC PPGi OCl OClh PPPH-I NN MB

Knibbs, Norman Victor Sydney, 1894–
The industrial uses of bauxite, with an account of its origin, occurrence, composition and properties, by N. V. S. Knibbs ... London, E. Benn limited, 1928.
viii, [9]–141 p. 22cm.
"References" at end of each chapter.

1. Bauxite. 2. Aluminium.
Library of Congress TN948.B2K6 29-11316

NK 0199149 DLC PPF OCl WaU IU NN ICJ MB OrP

TP886 K55 Engin. Library
Knibbs, Norman Victor Sydney, 1894-
Lime and limestone, by N.V.S. Knibbs and B.J. Gee. Toronto, H.L. Hall Corp.
v.

Cover title.
Includes bibliographies.

Contents.- Pt.1. The origin, occurrence, properties, chemistry, analysis and testing of limestone, dolomite and their products, and the theory of lime-burning and hydration.

NK 0199150 CU IU

666.9 K74li
Knibbs, Norman Victor Sydney, 1894-
Lime and limestone, by N. V. S. Knibbs and B. J. Gee. [Toronto, Salem Engineering, 1952?-
v. diagrs. 29cm.

Includes bibliographies.

NK 0199151 IU

Knibbs, Norman Victor Sydney, 1894–
Lime and magnesia; the chemistry, manufacture and uses of the oxides, hydroxides and carbonates of calcium and magnesium, by N. V. S. Knibbs ... London, E. Benn limited, 1924.
306 p. illus., plates, diagrs. 25cm.
"References" at end of each chapter.

1. Lime. 2. Magnesia.
Library of Congress TP886.K5 24—23266

NK 0199152 DLC OU OClW MiU PPF NN OrP CaBVaU WaTC ICJ NN MB

GN 671 .S6 K69
Knibbs, Stanley George Curthoys, 1886-
The savage Solomons as they were & are; a record of a head-hunting people gradually emerging from a life of savage cruelty & bloody customs, with a description of their manners & ways & of the beauties & potentialities of the islands. London, Seeley, Service & Co., 1929.
282 p. illus. map (fold.) 22cm.

1. Solomon Islands. I. Title. II. Title: Head-hunting.

NK 0199153 DCU CU WaU PU-Mu MH CtY

Knibbs, Stanley George Curthoys, 1886–
The savage Solomons as they were & are, a record of a head-hunting people gradually emerging from a life of savage cruelty & bloody customs, with a description of their manners & ways & of the beauties & potentialities of the islands, by S. G. C. Knibbs ... Philadelphia, J. B. Lippincott company [1929]
2 p. l., 13–282 p. front., plates, ports., fold. map. 22cm.
Printed in Great Britain.

1. Solomon Islands. I. Title. II. Title: Head-hunting.
Library of Congress DU850.K6 1929 29-26485

NK 0199154 DLC PP PPA MiU OCl OCU NN OrU CaBVa MH-P NjN NBuU

Kniberg, Elsa, 1886–1907.
Dagbok, utg. av Karl Gustaf Moselius. Stockholm, Norstedt [1953]
276 p. illus., ports. 20 cm.

I. Moselius, Karl Gustaf, ed.
A 54-2693
Minnesota. Univ. Libr. for Library of Congress [1]

NK 0199155 MnU OCl NN

Knibloe, Walt E.
Schneur's illustrated guide and history of St. Augustine, Fla.
see under title

Knichel, Friedrich: Zur Frage der Halluzinations-Theorien. [Maschinenschrift.] 24 S. 4°. — Auszug: Bonn 1923: Ludwig. 2 Bl. 8°
Bonn, Med. Diss. v. 22. Nov. 1923 [1924] [U 24. 1129

NK 0199157 ICRL

Knichel, Josef, 1908-
Die entwicklungstendenzen in der landwirtschaft im Kreise Simmern seit 1933. ...80 p.
Inaug. Diss. - Bonn, [1938]
Lebenslauf.
Literaturverzeichnis.

NK 0199158 ICRL

Knichen, Andreas, 1560-1621.
Dn. Andreae Knichen in Frecleben. Opera: qvibvs capvt sextvm De ivre territorii, Encyclopaedia iuris Brunouici ciuitatem Brvnowigam concernentis nec non tertia pars De vestiturarum pactionibus accessere. Repexa aucta correcta. Indice rervm ad calcem adiecto. Hanoviae, typis Wechelianis apud haeredes Iohan. Aubrii, M. DC. XIII.
7 p.l., 488, [110] p. 34cm.
Page 465 incorrectly numbered 456.
Publisher's device on t.-p.
Head-pieces; tail-piece; initials.
"De saxonico n[on pr]ovocandi ivre et privilegio comme[nt]atio": p. [145]-294.

NK 0199159 MiU-L

KNICHEN, Andreas von, 1560-1621.
De jure territorii. Editio eruderata & postrema curante Christiano Krembergk. Francofurti, 1658.

16°.

NK 0199160 MH-L

J 436 .467
KNICHEN, ANDREAS VON, 1560-1621.
De Rom. Imperatorum autocratia ad c. I. de jure territorii... Seruestae, Typis Z. Dörfferi, 1621.
113(i.e. 145)p. 20cm.

Page 145 incorrectly numbered 113.

NK 0199161 ICN

KNICHEN, Andreas, 1560-1621.
De saxonico non provocandi jure & privilegio Hanoviae, 1603.

NK 0199162 MH-L

KNICHEN, Andreas, 1560-1621.
De vestiturarum pactionibus, pars prima[-altera]. Hanoviae, 1607.

NK 0199163 MH-L

VOLUME 300

Knichen, Andreas von, 1560-1621.
Dn. Andreae Knichen ... Recentis polituræ pervestigatio de Rom. imperatorum autocratia, ad c. I. de jure territorii. Opera vero caetera trino & uno bene vertente eruderata insequentur. Servestae, Typis Z. Dörfferi, 1621.
[7], 113 (i. e. 145), [1] p. 18 cm.
Caption title: De territorii originatione et definitione.
Bound with Clapmar, Arnold. De arcanis rerumpublicerum libri sex. Francofurti, 1624.

NK 0199164 IaU

Knichen, Rudolph Gottfried von, d. 1682.
Opus politicum in tribus libris, omnes ad doctrinam politicam tàm quo ad pacis quàm belli administrationem, & tranquillum ac turbulentum rerumpublicarum statum, nec non jus publicum Sacri romani imperii nostri spectantes materias exactissimè exhibens. Ex optimis antiqvioribus et recentioribus diversarum nationum politicis, historicis, jurisconsultis ... cvm indicibvs necessariis. Avctore Rudolpho Godofredo Knichen ... Francofurti ad Mœnum, impensis Johann. Davidis Zunneri, typis Balthasaris Christophori Wustii, sen., 1682.
2 v. in 1. 34½cm.
Title vignette; head and tail pieces.
Vol. 2 has only half-title.
1. Political science. 2. International law and relations. 3. Law—Holy Roman empire. I. Title.
Library of Congress JC156.K5 24-16396

NK 0199165 DLC

Knick, Artur, 1883- 617.52 S500 v.6
... Allgemeine Therapie. Von Artur Knick ... Mit 6 Abbildungen ...
(*In* Handbuch der Hals- Nasen- Ohren-Heilkunde. Berlin [etc.] 1926. 25cm. Bd. 6: Die Krankheiten des Gehörorgans, Teil 1, p. 1148-1197. illus.)
"Literatur": p. 1196-1197.

NK 0199166 ICJ

Knick, Artur, 1883-
Ohren-, Nasen-, Rachen- und Kehlkopfkrankheiten. Leipzig, Verb. d. Arzte Deutschlands, 1921.
259 p. (Aerztliche Buecherei für Fortbildung und Praxis. v. 9)

NK 0199167 PPC

M
616.21
K69
Knick, Artur, 1883-
Ohren-, Nasen-, Rachen- u. Kehlkopf-krankheiten. 4. u. 5. Aufl. Leipzig, Verband der Ārzte Deutschlands, 1928.
ix, 294 p. illus. 21 cm. (Ārztliche Bücherei für Fortbildung und Praxis, Bd. 9)
1. Ear. Diseases. 2. Nose. Diseases. 3. Pharnyx. Diseases. 4. Larynx. Diseases. I. Verband der Ārzte Deutschlands. II. Title. (Series)

NK 0199168 N

WV
100
K69o
1931
KNICK, Artur, 1883-
Ohren-, Nasen-, Rachen- u. Kehlkopfkrankheiten. 6. verb. Aufl. Leipzig, Verband der Ārzte Deutschlands, 1931.
ix, 294 p. illus. (Ārztliche Bücherei für Fortbildung und Praxis, Bd. 9)
1. Otorhinolaryngology Series

NK 0199169 DNLM

WV
100
K69o
1935
KNICK, Artur, 1883-
Ohren-, Nasen-, Rachen- u. Kehlkopfkrankheiten. 10. verb. Aufl. Berlin, Verlag der Deutschen Ārzteschaft, 1935.
ix, 295 p. illus. (Ārztliche Bücherei für Fortbildung und Praxis, Bd. 9)
1. Otorhinolaryngology Series

NK 0199170 DNLM

Knick, Artur, 1883-
... Ohren-, nasen-, rachen- u. kehlkopfkrankheiten, von prof. dr. Artur Knick ... 11. u. 12. verb. aufl., mit 172 abbildungen im text und 28 farbigen abbildungen auf 5 tafeln. Berlin, Verlag der Deutschen ärzteschaft, 1936.
ix, 295 p. illus., v col. fold. pl. 21cm. (*Added t.-p.:* Ärztliche bücherei für fortbildung und praxis hrsg. vom Verband der ärzte Deutschlands ... bd. IX)
1. Ear—Diseases. 2. Nose—Diseases. 3. Pharynx—Diseases. 4. Larynx—Diseases. I. Title.
36-29293
Library of Congress RF46.K5 1936
Copyright A—Foreign 33042
[3] [616.21] 617.8

NK 0199171 DLC

WV
100
K69o
1937
KNICK, Artur, 1883-
Ohren-, Nasen-, Rachen- u. Kehlkopfkrankheiten. 15. u. 16. verb. Aufl. Berlin, Verlag der Deutschen Ārzteschaft, 1937.
ix, 295 p. illus. (Ārztliche Bücherei für Fortbildung und Praxis, Bd. 9)
1. Otorhinolaryngology Series

NK 0199172 DNLM

WV
100
K69o
1942
KNICK, Artur, 1883-
Ohren-, Nasen-, Rachen- u. Kehlkopfkrankheiten. 25. u. 26. Aufl. Berlin, Reichsgesundheitsverlag, 1942.
ix, 295 p. illus. (Ārztliche Bücherei für Fortbildung und Praxis, Bd. 9)
1. Otorhinolaryngology
Series

NK 0199173 DNLM

WV
100
K69o
1943
KNICK, Artur, 1883-
Ohren-, Nasen-, Rachen- u. Kehlkopfkrankheiten. 27. u. 28. Aufl. Berlin, Reichsgesundheitsverlag, 1943.
ix, 295 p. illus. (Ārztliche Bücherei für Fortbildung und Praxis, Bd. 9)
1. Otorhinolaryngology Series

NK 0199174 DNLM

WV
100
K69o
1952
KNICK, Artur, 1883-
Ohren-, Nasen-, Rachen- und Kehlkopfkrankheiten. 33. neubearb. Aufl. von Gerhard Eigler. Berlin, Gruyter, 1952.
xii, 230 p. illus.
1. Otorhinolaryngology
I. Eigler, Gerhard

NK 0199175 DNLM

Knick, Artur, 1883- 617.52 S500 v.6
... Serologische Untersuchungsmethoden. Von Artur Knick
(*In* Handbuch der Hals- Nasen- Ohren-Heilkunde. Berlin [etc.] 1926. 25cm. Bd. 6: Die Krankheiten des Gehörorgans, Teil 1, p. 1059-1079)
"Literatur": p. 1079.

NK 0199176 ICJ

Knick, Artur, 1883-
Ueber die histologie der sekundaeren degeneration im rueckenmark.
Inaug. diss. Breslau, 1908. (Leipzig) Bibl.

NK 0199177 ICRL CtY DNLM

WK
880
qK69e
1954
KNICK, Bernhard.
Endokrine und Stoffwechsel-Korrelationen des Insulineffekts in ihrer klinischen und pathophysiologischen Bedeutung. Mainz, 1954.
121 l. illus.
Habilitationsschrift - Mainz.
1. Hypoglycemia 2. Insulin - Effects

NK 0199178 DNLM

Knick, Helmut, 1910-
Beiträge zur konstitution der pflanzlichen herzgifte. ... 1934. 26 p.
Inaug. Diss. - Göttingen, 1934.
Lebenslauf.

NK 0199179 ICRL CtY

Knick, K. D. G.
Homer und seine gedichte. II. n. p., 1855.

NK 0199180 NjP

WG
26583
Knick, Reinhold, 1880-
Ueber die Condensation von p-Nitrobenzaldehyd mit α-Picolin und αγ-Lutidin. Breslau, 1902.
54 p.
Inaug.-Diss. - Breslau.

NK 0199181 CtY ICRL MH NN PU

Knick-knacks to crochet
see under Spool Cotton Co., New York.

Knickenberg, Arthur, 1892-
Ueber die Stroemungsverhältnisse der Zweitluft und die Verbrennungsvorgänge bei Hängelichtbrennern... Von...Arthur Knickenberg... München: R. Oldenbourg, 1918. 84 p. incl. diagrs., tables. 8°.
Dissertation, Karlsruhe, 1917.
Lebenslauf.
1. Gas.—Fixtures, fittings, etc.
N. Y. P. L. May 20, 1924.

NK 0199183 NN ICRL CtY DBS

Knickenberg (Ernst [Adolph]) [1867-].
*Beobachtungen über die Wirkung des salzsauren Orexin. 42 pp., 2 l. 8°. *Bonn, J. Bach Wwe., 1890.*

NK 0199184 DNLM CU

KNICKENBERG, Franz.
De ratione stoica in Persii satiris apparente. Monasterii, sumtibus W. Niemann [typiw Iosephi Krick], 1867.

NK 0199185 MH CU MiU

Knickenberg, Friedrich Adolf, 1863-1932, joint author.
Schmidt, Ferdinand August, 1852-
Das Beethoven-haus in Bonn, von dr. F. A. Schmidt und prof. dr. Fr. Knickenberg. Bonn, Verlag des Beethoven-hauses, 1911.

Knickenberg, Friedrich Adolf, 1863-1932.
Bonn. Beethoven-haus.
Das Beethoven-haus in Bonn und seine sammlungen, von Th. Lohmer. Mit bildtafeln und faksimiles. 3. im anschluss an den Führer von F. A. Schmidt und Fr. Knickenberg bearb. aufl. Bonn, Verlag des Beethoven-hauses, 1936.

Knickenberg, Friedrich Adolf, 1863-1932.
Bonn. Beethoven-haus.
The Beethoven house at Bonn and its collection, by Th. Lohmer, translated into English by K. Krebs ... 4th ed., based on the guide by F. A. Schmidt and Fr. Knickenberg. Bonn, "Beethoven-haus", 1937.

VOLUME 300

870.9 K690 Knickenberg, Friedrich Adolf, 1863-1932.
De deorum invocationibus quas in componendis carminibus poetae Romani frequentant. Marpurgi Cattorum, 1889.
79 p. 22 cm.
Diss. inaug. - Marburg.
Vita.
Bibliographical footnotes.
1. Gods in literature. 2. Latin literature. Hist. and crit. I. Title.

NK 0199189 NcD CU ICRL NjP MH NN

591.51 Q563
Knickenberg, Fritz.
Der Hund und sein "Verstand". Eine Erklärung der Lebensausserungen des Hundes in Hinsicht auf das ihnen zu Grunde liegende "Wollen", "Erkennen" und "Begreifen". Allen Hundefreunden gewidmet, von F. Knickenberg. Cöthen (Anhalt), P. Schettlers Erben, Gesellsch. m.b.H., 1905.
viii, 138 p. 23½cm.

NK 0199190 ICJ

BF660 .K7 Knickenberg, Fritz.
Tier-psychologie. Ist das tier eine maschine oder ein sensitives wesen? ... Graz und Leipzig, U. Moser, 1908.
iv, 190 p.
1. Psychology, Comparative. 2. Animal intelligence.

NK 0199191 ICU MH ICJ

Knickenberg, Rudolf, 1911-
Die voraussetzungen des rücktrittsrechts, der anfechtung und der kündigung im versicherungsvertragsgesetz für den versicherer und ihre wirkungen in bezug auf die bereits erbrachten leistungen ... von Rudolf Knickenberg ... Köln, Orthen, 1936.
49 p., 1 l. 21cm.
Inaug.-diss. - Köln.
"Lebenslauf": 1 l. at end.
"Literaturverzeichnis": p. 7-8.

NK 0199193 MH-L

Knickerbacker, Joseph Foster, 1824-1882.
Centennial day: an oration, delivered at Schaghticoke, N. Y. July the fourth, eighteen hundred and seventy-six, the one hundredth anniversary of American independence, by Joseph Foster Knickerbacker . . . Troy, N.Y., E. Green, printer, 1876.
24 pp. 23cm.
Subject entries: Schaghticoke, N. Y.—Hist.
2-6545
Library of Congress, no. F129.S4K6.

NK 0199194 DLC N

N 973.361 1871 K69 Knickerbacker, Joseph Foster, 1824-1882.
Spirit of the times: an oration, delivered at Schaghticoke, July 4th, 1871 ... Troy, N. Y., A. W. Scribner & co., printers, 1871.
22 p. 22 cm.
1. Fourth of July orations. 2. Title.

NK 0199195 N

Knickerbacker, Joseph Foster, 1824-1882.
A vision of the arch of truth, an allegory; and additional poems, by Joseph Foster Knickerbacker. Troy, N. Y., W. H. Young, 1876.
2 p. l., [7]-144 p. 3 pl. 20½cm.
Plates are mounted photographs.
Verse and prose.
I. Title.
27-25707
Library of Congress PS2196.K6

NK 0199196 DLC NN IU OU

Knickerbocker, *jr., pseud.*
see
Suydam, John Howard, 1832-1908.

Knickerbocker, pseud.
Resumption of specie payment. New York, 1873
see Stevens, John Austin, 1827-1910.

Knickerbocker, Bruce Alexander.
Stovarsol in the peroral treatment of congenital syphilis... [Cincinnait, 1933]
36, 17 l.

NK 0199199 OCU

Knickerbocker, Charles H
The Boy came back. New York, Wyn [1951]
249 p. 21 cm.
I. Title.
PZ4.K69Bo 51-13483 ‡

NK 0199200 DLC NN WaE

Knickerbocker, Diedrich, *pseud.*
see
Irving, Washington, 1783-1859.

Knickerbocker, Edmund, 1815?-
The Knickerbocker genealogical chart; drawn by Edmund Knickerbocker. In...1887. Additions by Homer Staley, 1918. Albany, Weed Parsons & co., 1890 [i. e. 1918] 52 x 44cm. bd.
1. Knickerbocker family. I. Staley, Homer, 1886-
N. Y. P. L. October 4, 1945

NK 0199202 NN

Knickerbocker, Edwin Van Berghen, 1881- ed.
[Clemens, Samuel Langhorne] 1835-1910.
... Life on the Mississippi, by Mark Twain [pseud.] Abridged ed. Edited by Edwin Van B. Knickerbocker ... New York and London, Harper & brothers [c1935]

Knickerbocker, Edwin Van Berghen, 1881- ed.
Shakespeare, William, 1564-1616.
... A midsummer-night's dream, by William Shakespeare; edited with introduction and notes by Edwin Van B. Knickerbocker ... frontispiece by Frank Godwin. Philadelphia, Chicago [etc.] The John C. Winston company [c1925]

Knickerbocker, Edwin Van Berghen, 1881- *ed.*
Notable short stories of today, edited by Edwin Van B. Knickerbocker ... New York and London, Harper & brothers, 1929.
xi, 523, [1] p. 20cm.
Each story preceded by a biographical sketch of the author.
CONTENTS.—pt. 1. The stories.—pt. 2. Studying the stories.—pt. 3. Appendix.
1. Short stories, American. 2. Short stories, English. 3. Short story. I. Title.
29-9874
Library of Congress PZ1.K74No

NK 0199205 DLC TxU MB CaOTP OrAshS OClh Wa WaE Or OrP PPD OCl OEac OU PP PPGi PV

Knickerbocker, Edwin Van Berghen, 1881-
Plays for classroom interpretation, edited by Edwin Van B. Knickerbocker ... drawings by Olindo Ricci. New York, H. Holt and company [c1921]
xviii, 264 p. illus. (incl. music) 19½cm.
CONTENTS.—pt. 1. Classroom work with a play.—pt. 2. The plays: The golden doom, by Lord Dunsany. Two crooks and a lady, by E. Pillot. Will o' the wisp, by Doris F. Halman. Spreading the news, by Lady Gregory. The turtle dove, by Margaret S. Oliver. Allison's lad, by Beulah M. Dix. Ulysses (scene 2, act III) by S. Phillips. Notes on the plays.—pt. 3. Notes to the instructor.
I. Title.
21-11058
Library of Congress PN6120.A4K6

NK 0199206 DLC WaSp CaBVaU Or PPGi PP OCl OEac OClh MB NN PPTU PPPL NcC AAP

Knickerbocker, Edwin Van Berghen, 1881-
Plays for classroom interpretation, edited by Edwin Van B. Knickerbocker ... drawings by Olindo Ricci. New York, H. Holt and company [1923]
xviii, 264 p. front. illus. (incl. music) 19½cm.
"December, 1923."
CONTENTS.—pt. 1. Classroom work with a play.—pt. 2. The plays: The golden doom, by Lord Dunsany. Two crooks and a lady, by E. Pillot. Will o' the wisp, by Doris F. Halman. Spreading the news, by Lady Gregory. The turtle dove, by Margaret S. Oliver. Allison's lad, by Beulah M. Dix. Ulysses (scene 2, act III) by S. Phillips. Notes on the plays.—pt. 3. Notes to the instructor.

NK 0199207 ViU PU MiU MB

Knickerbocker, Edwin Van Berghen, 1881- *ed.*
Present-day essays, ed. by Edwin Van B. Knickerbocker ... New York, H. Holt and company [c1923]
xxvii, 348 p. 19½cm.
CONTENTS.—Fuji-no-Yama, by L. Hearn.—The game, by S. Strunsky.—Woman enthroned, by Agnes Repplier.—Mark Twain, by J. Macy.—Notes from a French village in the war zone, by Dorothy C. Fisher.—From nine to five, by R. C. Benchley.—Hammock nights, by W. Beebe.—The staging of Shakespeare, by T. J. Spencer.—Journeys to Bagdad, by C. S. Brooks.—On a certain blindness in human beings, by W. James.—A key to the labor movement, by W. Lippmann.—Say now shibboleth, by E. M. Rhodes.—Children and play, by Lillian D. Wald.—Movies, by Katharine F. Gerould.—Private school and holidays, by E. F. Benson.
1. American essays. I. Title.
23-2818
Library of Congress PS688.K6

NK 0199208 DLC OrU Or MiU LU ScU WU PU PPGi PPTU OCl OEac PWcS PP WaS WaSpG

Knickerbocker, Edwin Van Berghen, 1881- ed.
Present-day essays. New York, H.Holt and co. [1926, c.1923]

NK 0199209 MH

Knickerbocker, Edwin Van Berghen, 1881- ed.
Present-day essays, ed. by Edwin Van B. Knickerbocker ... New York, H. Holt and company [1928]
xxv, 348 p. 19.5 cm.
"Copyright, 1923 ... [Reprinted] September, 1928."
Contents. - Fuji-no-Yama, by L. Hearn. - The game, by S. Strunsky. - Woman enthroned, by Agnes Repplier. - Mark Twain, by J. Macy. - Notes from a French village in the war zone, by Dorothy C. Fisher. - From nine to five, by R. C. Benchley. - Hammock nights, by W. Beebe. The staging of Shakespeare, by T. J. Spencer. Journeys to Bagdad, by C. S. Brooks. - On a certain blindness in human beings, by W. James. - Individual rights and social justice, by R. L. Finney. - Say now shibboleth, by E. M. Rhodes. - Children and play, by Lillian D. Wald. - Movies, by Katharine F. Gerould. - Private school and holidays, by E. F. Benson. - Suggestions for study, and Notes.
1. American essays. I. Title.

NK 0199211 ViU

VOLUME 300

PS688
K69p Knickerbocker, Edwin van Berghen, 1881-
Present-day essays. New York, Holt [1933, c1923]
348 p. 20cm.

1. American essays. I. Title.

NK 0199212 GU

Knickerbocker, Edwin Van Berghen, 1881-
Short plays, edited by Edwin Van B. Knickerbocker ... New York, H. Holt and company [c1931]
xv, 532 p. plates. 19½cm.
"Music for the plays": p. 509-519.

1. Drama—Collections. 2. College and school drama. I. Title.
31-11085
Library of Congress PN6112.K47
——— Copy 2.
Copyright A 35942 [5] 822.08

OCl
NK 0199213 DLC CaBVa NcD CoU MB TxU WaU NcU PPD

Knickerbocker, Edwin Van Berghen, 1881- *ed.*
Short plays. Rev. New York, H. Holt [1949]
xii, 506 p. illus. 20 cm.

1. Drama—Collections. 2. College and school drama. I. Title.
PN6112.K47 1949 822.082 49-4051*

NK 0199214 DLC OrPR OrU WaT OCl KU MB

Knickerbocker, Edwin Van Berghen, 1881- FOR OTHER EDITIONS SEE MAIN ENTRY
Thinking, speaking and writing English for seventh[-ninth] year ... New York, Newark [etc.] Silver, Burdett and company [c1935]

Knickerbocker, Edwin Van Berghen, 1881- ed.
Shakespeare, William, 1564-1616.
Shakespeare's Twelfth night; or, What you will, edited by Edwin Van B. Knickerbocker ... Chicago, Lyons and Carnahan [c1926]

Knickerbocker, Edwin Van Berghen, 1881- *ed.*
Twelve plays, edited by Edwin Van B. Knickerbocker ... New York, H. Holt and company [c1924]
ix, 336 p. diagr. 19½cm.
"Chapters on studying and acting the plays": p. [277]-336.
CONTENTS.—Where but in America, by O. M. Wolff.—The forfeit, by T. B. Rogers.—Poor Maddalena, by Louise Saunders.—Playing with fire, by P. Wilde.—The stepmother, by A. Bennett.—On vengeance height, by A. Davis.—A marriage proposal, by A. Tchekoff.—A pipe of peace, by Margaret Cameron.—Enter the hero, by Theresa Helburn.—The pot boiler, by Alice Gerstenberg.—Over the hills, by J. Palmer.—The game of chess, by K. S. Goodman.
1. Drama—Collections. 24-5921
Library of Congress PN6112.K5

OCl OCX OU MB WaU NcC CoU
NK 0199217 DLC OrLgE OrP OrU CaBVa OrMonO PPTU PP

Knickerbocker, Edwin Van Berghen, 1881- ed.
Twelve plays, edited by Edwin Van B. Knickerbocker ... New York, H. Holt and company, 1930.
ix, 336 p. diagr. 19.5 cm.

NK 0199218 PPT

Knickerbocker, Edwin Van Berghen, 1881- joint author.
Easterbrook, Mary Herold.
Your English problems; a social approach to problems in oral and written composition, functional grammar, and effective sentence structure, by Mary Herold Easterbrook ... Donald Lemen Clark ... [and] Edwin Van B. Knickerbocker ... New York, Newark [etc.] Silver, Burdett and company [c1935]

Knickerbocker, Evalyn.
From the east side to the west side, by Evalyn A. Knickerbocker. New York, N. Y., The Hobson book press, 1946.
3 p. l., 223 p. 22cm.

I. Title.
PZ3.K735Fr 46-22498

NK 0199220 DLC

Knickerbocker, Evalyn.
Short stories of love and pathos, by Evalyn Knickerbocker ... Red Bank, N. J., The Chat publishing company, inc. [c1931]
188 p. 19cm.
CONTENTS.—The girl who died in prison.—The new minister.—A spot of blood.—His mother's crime.—Giving God thanks.—Over the hill.—Adamant.—Love's redemption.—Thru the years.

I. Title. 31-15688
Library of Congress PZ3.K735Sh

NK 0199221 DLC

Knickerbocker, Frances Wentworth (Cutler)
Free minds: John Morley and his friends, by Frances Wentworth Knickerbocker. Cambridge, Mass., Harvard university press, 1943.
xi, 288 p. 21cm.
Bibliography: p. [275]-279.

1. Morley, John Morley, viscount, 1838-1923. 2. Gt. Brit.—Hist.—Victoria, 1837-1901. I. Title.
A 43-1890
Harvard univ. Library for Library of Congress DA565.M78K6
[15]† 923.242

CaBVaU
OCl OO OU DLC Or MtU OrU OrP WaS NcD MeB KMK OrCS
NK 0199222 MH GU NIC MiU LU PPL PPWe PSt PPA PU

Knickerbocker, Hiram, 1824?-1852, defendant.
Trials of Hiram Knickerbocker & Chauncy Hall, for the murder of Carl Harkner...
see under Buffalo Daily Republican.

Knickerbocker, Hubert Renfro, 1898-1949.
The boiling point; will war come in Europe? By H. R. Knickerbocker; illustrated by Georg Hartmann. New York, Farrar and Rinehart, incorporated [c1934]
xii p., 2 l., 3-267 p. incl. front., illus., ports., maps. 21cm.
Maps on lining-papers.
London edition (John Lane) has title: Will war come in Europe?

1. Europe—Politics—1914- 2. Germany—Pol. & govt.—1933- 3. Europe—Kings and rulers. I. Title.
34-14547
Library of Congress D443.K6S
[a46i1] 940.5

DAU PSC
NK 0199224 DLC WaSp WaS PPM OrP OCl OClh OU NN NIC

Knickerbocker, Hubert Renfro, 1898-1949.
Can Europe recover? By H. R. Knickerbocker. London, John Lane [1932]
viii p., 1 l., 308 p. 18½cm.
"The present volume is the result of a three months' tour of the European capitals undertaken by Mr. Knickerbocker on behalf of his paper, the New York Evening post, in July, August and September of 1932."—Publishers' note.

1. Europe—Econ. condit.—1918- I. Title.
33-23780
Library of Congress HC240.K67
[3] 330.94

NK 0199225 DLC MH OCl MB

KNICKERBOCKER, HUBERT RENFRO, 1898-1949.
...Ci sarà la guerra in Europa? (Will war come to Europe?) Traduzione di Carlo Coardi. Milano: V.Bompiani, 1934. 293 p. 21½cm. (Libri scelti per servire al panorama del nostro tempo. v. 26.)

814621A. 1. Europe—Politics, 1919- . 2. War and peace, 1914- . I. Coardi, Carlo, tr. II. Title. III. Ser.

NK 0199226 NN

Knickerbocker, Hubert Renfro, 1898-
... Да ли не бити рата у Европи? Београд, Издавачко предузеће "Привредник" [1935]
2 p. l., [7]-152 p., 1 l. plates, ports. 21cm.
At head of title: Х. Р. Никербокер.
"По нарочитом овлашћењу са енглеског превео М. Антуновић-Коблишка."

1. Europe—Politics—1914- 2. Germany—Pol. & govt.—1933- 3. Europe—Kings and rulers. I. Antunović-Koblishka, M., tr. II. Title. *Translation of* The boiling point; will war come in Europe?
38-14193
Library of Congress D443.K685

NK 0199227 DLC

Knickerbocker, Hubert Renfro, 1898-1949.
Danger forward...
see under title

Knickerbocker, Hubert Renfro, 1898-1949.
Deutschland so oder so? [Deutsch von Franz Fein] Berlin, Rowohlt, 1932.
x, 231 p. 21 cm.
"Titel der amerikanischen Originalausgabe: German crises [sic.]"

1. Germany — Econ. condit. — 1918-1945. 2. Nationalsozialistische Deutsche Arbeiter-Partei. 3. Germany—Soc. condit. 4. Germany—Pol. & govt.—1918-1933. 5. Hitler, Adolf, 1889-1945. I. Fein, Franz, 1896- tr. II. Title.
DD251.K515 330.943 A F 47-7165*
Harvard Univ. Library for Library of Congress [a65d½]†

CaBVaU
NK 0199229 MH CSt NBC OU GU CU-S NN CtY CU NIC DLC

Knickerbocker, Hubert Renfro, 1898-1949.
...I due volti della Germania; traduzione autorizzata del prof. A. Treves e del dott. C. Coardi. Milano: V. Bompiani, 1932. 308 p. 22cm. (Libri scelti per servire al panorama del nostro tempo. v. 11.)
Translation of his: The German crisis.

676065A. 1. Economic history—Germany, 1918- . 2. Germany—Politics, 1931. I. Treves, Angelo, translator. II. Coardi, Carlo, translator. III. Ser.
N. Y. P. L. November 16, 1933

NK 0199230 NN

Knickerbocker, Hubert Renfro, 1898-1949.
...Economia rossa e benessere bianco. Milano: V. Bompiani, 1936. 187 p. 22cm. (Libri scelti per servire al panorama del nostro tempo. v. 35.)
"Titolo originale: Rote Wirtschaft und weisser Wohistand [sic] Traduzione dal tedesco del prof. Angelo Treves."

858654A. 1. Economic history—Russia, 1917- . 2. Russia—Soc. condit., 1917- . 3. Baltic States—Soc. condit. 4. Poland—Soc. condit. I. Treves, Angelo, tr. II. Ser.
N. Y. P. L. December 22, 1936

NK 0199231 NN

TL723.2.G7
K69en Knickerbocker, Hubert Renfro 1898-1949.
Engeland bereidt zich voor... Vertaling N. van Wezep; met een inleiding van M.A. Cageling. Amsterdam, Nederlandsche Keurboekerij, 1938.
119p. illus., ports. 22cm. (De Periscoop, no.3)

NK 0199232 CoD

VOLUME 300

Knickerbocker, Hubert Renfro, 1898- 1949.
Fighting the red trade menace, by H. R. Knickerbocker ... New York, Dodd, Mead and company, 1931.

v p., 1 l., 295 p. 20 cm.

An examination of the soviet union foreign trade monopoly in Europe's chief industrial cities and of the effects, chiefly on America's export trade.

1. Russia—Economic policy—Five-year plan (1928–1932) 2. Russia—Commercial policy. 3. Russia—Comm.—Europe. 4. Europe—Comm.—Russia. 5. U. S.—Comm. 6. Economic conditions—1918– I. Title.

HC335.K58 31—30491
[330.947] 382.0947

NK 0199233 NN MB MiHM ViU OrP WaS Or OrCS MiU DLC OO OCU OCl OU WaU NcD PPStarr DN

Knickerbocker, Hubert Renfro, 1898- 1949.
The German crisis, by H. R. Knickerbocker; illustrated with photographs by James Abbé. New York, Farrar & Rinehart, incorporated [°1932]

vi p., 2 l., [3]-256 p. front., plates, port. 21cm.

London edition (John Lane) has title: Germany—fascist or soviet?

1. Germany—Econ. condit.—1918– 2. Nationalsozialistische deutsche arbeiter-partei. 3. Germany—Soc. condit. 4. Germany—Pol. & govt.—1918– 5. Hitler, Adolf, 1889– I. Title.

32—7917
Library of Congress DD251.K5
——— Copy 2.
Copyright A 49149 [037n1-] 330.943

NK 0199234 OU MB NN NcU DAU NSyU NIC MeB NcC OrU WaTC DLC WaS WaT OrP DS PJA PU MiU OCl OEac

---

Knickerbocker, Hubert Renfro, 1898- 1949.
Germany—fascist or soviet? By H. R. Knickerbocker. With 16 illustrations. London, John Lane [1932]

vi p., 3 l., 272 p. front., plates, ports. 19cm.

American edition (New York, Farrar & Rinehart) has title: The German crisis.

1. Germany — Econ. condit. — 1918– 2. Nationalsozialistische deutsche arbeiter-partei. 3. Germany—Soc. condit. 4. Germany—Pol. & govt.—1918– 5. Hitler, Adolf, 1889– I. Title.

32-31344
Library of Congress DD251.K5 1932 a
[5] 330.943

NK 0199235 DLC NN OCU

Knickerbocker, Hubert Renfro, 1898- 1949.
... Is tomorrow Hitler's? 200 questions on the battle of mankind. New York, Reynal & Hitchcock [°1941]

xviii, 382 p. $21\frac{1}{2}$cm.

At head of title: H. R. Knickerbocker.
Map on lining-papers.

1. European war, 1939– 2. European war, 1939– —U. S. 3. Europe—Politics—1938– I. Title.

41-51976
Library of Congress D744.K54
[50] 940.53

NK 0199236 IdU DNAL OCU OU WaT MtBC WaSp OrSaW WaS NcC GU FMU TxU MeB DLC Or OrU PP PPL PHC PU PPPL ViU OCl

---

Knickerbocker, Hubert Renfro, 1898–1949.
Kommt Europa wieder hoch? [Deutsch von Franz Fein] Berlin, Rowohlt, 1932.

241 p. 21 cm.

Translation of Can Europe recover?

1. Europe—Econ. condit.—1918–1945. I. Title.

HC240.K673 51-53058

NK 0199237 DLC NN MH CtY MiD

Knickerbocker, Hubert Renfro, 1898–1949.
Kommt Krieg in Europa? [Deutsch von Franz Fein] Berlin, Rowohlt, 1934.

178 p. 21 cm.

"Amerikanischer Titel: The boiling point."

1. Europe—Politics—1918-1945. 2. Germany—Pol. & govt.—1933–1945. 3. Europe—Kings and rulers. I. Title.

D443.K684 940.5 A 51-7282

Harvard Univ. Library
for Library of Congress [1]†

NK 0199238 MH TxU NN OO DLC

Knickerbocker, Hubert Renfro, 1898- 1949.
...La minaccia del commercio rosso. Soviet trade and world depression. Traduzione di Carlo Coardi. Milano: V. Bompiani & c., 1932. 271 p. 22cm. (Libri scelti per servire al panorama del nostro tempo. v. 9.)

Published in the United States under title "Fighting the red trade menace," in Great Britain as "Soviet trade and world depression."

676063A. 1. Commerce—Russia, 1931. 2. Economic hisory—Russia, 1917– . I. Coardi, Carlo, translator. II. Ser.
N. Y. P. L. November 16, 1933

NK 0199239 NN

Knickerbocker, Hubert Renfro, 1898- 1949

The **new** Russia, eight talks broadcast by H. R. Knickerbocker ... [and others] London, Faber and Faber limited [1931]

Knickerbocker, Hubert Renfro, 1898- 1949.
... ¿Pertenece el futuro a Hitler? Prólogo de John Gunther; traducción directa del inglés por Guillermo Díaz Doin. Buenos Aires, A. López [1942]

459 p., 1 l. 20cm.

At head of title: H. R. Knickerbocker.

1. World war, 1939– 2. World war, 1939– —U. S. 3. Europe—Politics—1938– I. Díaz Doin, Guillermo, tr. II. Title. *Translation of* Is tomorrow Hitler's?

43-46270
Library of Congress D744.K544
[3] 940.53

NK 0199241 DLC

Knickerbocker, Hubert Renfro, 1898- 1949.
...Il piano quinquennale sovietico; inchiesta sul fronte industriale russo. IV edizione. Milano: V. Bompiani, 1932. 276 p. plates. 22cm. (Libri scelti per servire al panorama del nostro tempo. v. 6.)

Translation of his: The soviet five-year plan and its effect on world trade.

676061A. 1. Economic history—Russia, 1917– . I. Ser.
N. Y. P. L. November 13, 1933

NK 0199242 NN

Knickerbocker, Hubert Renfro, 1898- 1949.
... Póde a Europa reerguer-se? Porto Alegre, Edição da Livraria do Globo, 1933.

273 p., 1 l. $18\frac{1}{2}$cm.

At head of title: H. R. Knickerbocker.
"Traducção de Marina Guaspari."

1. Europe—Econ. condit.—1918– I. Guaspari, Marina, tr. II. Title.

34-14072
Library of Congress HC240.K675
[2] 330.94

NK 0199243 DLC

Knickerbocker, Hubert Renfro, 1898- 1949.
... Los progresos del plan quinquenal, traducido para la Editorial Ercilla por Raúl Silva Castro. Santiago [de Chile] Ediciones Ercilla, 1933.

148 p., 1 l. 19cm. (*On cover:* Colección Ercilla, no. 19)

At head of title: H. R. Knickerbocker.

1. Russia—Econ. condit.—1918– 2. Russia—Indus. 3. Russia—Economic policy—Five-year plan (1928–1932) 4. Industry and state—Russia. I. Silva Castro, Raúl, 1903– tr. II. Title. *Translation of* The Red trade menace.

45-26465
Library of Congress HC335.K613
[3] 330.947

NK 0199244 DLC

Knickerbocker, Hubert Renfro, 1898- 1949.
...Può l'Europa tornare indietro? (Can Europe come back?) Traduzione di Carlo Coardi. Milano: V. Bompiani, 1932. 279 p. 22cm. (Libri scelti per servire al panorama del nostro tempo. v. 16.)

676070A. 1. Economic history, 1918– I. Coardi, Carlo, translator. II. Ser.
N. Y. P. L. November 8, 1933

NK 0199245 NN

Knickerbocker, Hubert Renfro, 1898- 1949
The red trade menace; progress of the soviet five-year plan, by H. R. Knickerbocker ... New York, Dodd, Mead & company, 1931.

xviii p., 1 l., 277 p. front., plates, port. 19cm.

1. Russia — Econ. condit. — 1918– 2. Russia—Indus. 3. Russia—Economic policy. 4. Industry and state—Russia. I. Title.

31-3203
Library of Congress HC335.K6
——— Copy 2.
Copyright A 33420 [3-2] 330.947

NK 0199246 Or OrU DS PJA PP ICJ MH OCl OCU OO NN MB NjN OrCS DLC KEmT ScU GU OrU OrP WaSp WaT WaS

Knickerbocker, Hubert Renfro, 1898- 1949.
Der rote Handel droht! Der Fortschritt des Fünfjahresplans der Sowjets. [Deutsch von Curt Thesing] Berlin, E. Rowohlt, 1931.

202 p. 21 cm.

Original American ed. (New York, Dodd, Mead) has title: The Red trade menace; progress of the Soviet five-year plan. London ed. (J. Lane) has title: The Soviet five-year plan and its effect on world trade.

1. Russia—Comm. 2. Russia—Economic policy—1928-1932. I. Thesing, Curt Egon, 1879– tr.

HF3626.K553 A F 47-6987*

Columbia Univ. Libraries
for Library of Congress [2]†

NK 0199247 NcD MH DLC NNC OrU MB IaU CU-S TxU WU GU CLU NN

Knickerbocker, Hubert Renfro, 1898- 1949.
Der rote Handel lockt. [Deutsch von Curt Thesing] Berlin, E. Rowohlt, 1931.

235 p. 21 cm.

"Titel der amerikanischen Originalausgabe: Fighting the Red trade menace."

1. Russia—Comm. 2. Russia—Economic policy—1928-1932. I. Thesing, Curt Egon, 1879– tr. II. Title.

HF3626.K543 47-43834*

NK 0199248 DLC NcD NN IaU MH

Knickerbocker, Hubert Renfro, 1898–1949.
Rote Wirtschaft und weisser Wohlstand. Deutsch von Franz Fein. Berlin, Rowohlt, 1935.

123 p. 21 cm.

1. Russia—Econ. condit.—1918-1945. I. Title.

HC335.K6 52-49376

NK 0199249 DLC NN

VOLUME 300

Knickerbocker, Hubert Renfro, 1898–1949.
Die Schwarzhemden in England und Englands wirtschaftlicher Aufstieg. [Deutsch von Franz Fein] Berlin, Rowohlt, 1934.
107 p. 21 cm.

1. Fascism—Gt. Brit. 2. Gt. Brit.—Econ. condit.—1918– 3. Gt. Brit.—Pol. & govt.—1910–1936. I. Fein, Franz, 1896– tr. II. Title.

DA576.K575 942.083 A F 48–173*

Yale Univ. Library for Library of Congress [1]†

NK 0199250 CtY NN DLC MH

Knickerbocker, Hubert Renfro, 1898–1949.
The siege of Alcazar; a warlog of the Spanish revolution, by H. R. Knickerbocker ... Philadelphia, David McKay company, 1936.
5 p. l., 3–199 p. 21cm.
"These warlogs, covering the period from August 22 to October 1, 1936, were sent from the Spanish battlefront."

1. Spain—Hist.—Republic, 1931– I. Title. II. Title: A warlog of the Spanish revolution.
36–35607

Library of Congress DP269.K55
——— Copy 2.
Copyright A 99901 [3] 946.08

NK 0199251 DLC OrPR NIC CaOTP OU NN

DP269 .K55 1937 Knickerbocker, Hubert Renfro, 1898–1949.
The siege of Alcazar; a warlog of the Spanish revolution, by H.R. Knickerbocker. London, Hutchinson [1937]
191p. illus. 22cm.
"These warlogs, covering the period from August 22 to October 1, 1936, were sent from the Spanish battlefront."
Previously published by D. McKay, 1936.

1. Spain - Hist. - Republic, 1931-1939. I. Title. II. Title: A warlog of the Spanish revolution. S

NK 0199252 PSt NNC WU IEN CtY

Knickerbocker, Hubert Renfro, 1898-1949.
Siege of Alcazar: a history of the siege of the Toledo Alcazar. New York, Knopf, c1937. Illus.

NK 0199253 NcC

Knickerbocker, Hubert Renfro, 1898–1949.
The soviet five-year plan and its effect on world trade, by H. R. Knickerbocker, with sixteen illustrations. London, John Lane [1931]
2 p. l., vii–xx, 244, [1] p. front., plates, port. 19 cm.
American edition (New York, Dodd, Mead & company) has title: The red trade menace.

1. Russia—Econ. condit.—1918– 2. Russia—Indus. 3. Russia—Economic policy—1928–1932. 4. Industry and state—Russia. I. Title.

HF3626.K55 1931a 330.947 31–22942

KEmT
NK 0199254 DLC IaU FU MU CSt-H DS MiU ICJ NN MH CtY

Knickerbocker, Hubert Renfro, 1898–1949.
Soviet trade and world depression, by H. R. Knickerbocker. London, John Lane [1931]
xii, [2], 288 p. 19cm.
American edition (New York, Dodd, Mead and company) has title: Fighting the red trade menace.

1. Russia—Economic policy—Five-year plan (1928–1932) 2. Russia—Commercial policy. 3. Russia—Comm.—Europe. 4. Europe—Comm.—Russia. 5. U. S.—Comm. 6. Economic conditions—1918– I. Title.
32–9333

Library of Congress HC335.K58 1931 a
[3] [330.947] 382.0947

NK 0199255 DLC OrU Or IaU MB NN

KNICKERBOCKER, HUBERT RENFRO, 1898-1949.
Soviet trade and world depression, by H.R. Knickerbocker. London, J. Lane [, 1931] xii, 288 p. 12°.

Film reproduction. Positive.
American edition published under title: Fighting the red trade menace.

1. Commerce--Russia, 1917- 2. Economic history--Russia, 1917-

NK 0199256 NN

Knickerbocker, Hubert Renfro, 1898-1949
Soviet war machine. Russia's war machine
Clippings from N.Y.Evening Post, Oct. 1929.
not acc.

NK 0199257 DNW

Knickerbocker, Hubert Renfro, 1898–1949.
Will war come in Europe? By H. R. Knickerbocker; with an introduction by J. W. Wheeler-Bennett. London, John Lane [1934]
xiv p., 1 l., 276 p. 19cm.
American edition (New York, Farrar and Rinehart, incorporated) has title: The boiling point; will war come in Europe?

1. Europe—Politics—1914– 2. Germany—Pol. & govt.—1933– 3. Europe—Kings and rulers. I. Title.
35–2461

Library of Congress D443.K68 1934 a
[5] 940.5

NK 0199258 DLC MB

Knickerbocker, Irving
Union-management cooperation; a psychological analysis, by Irving Knickerbocker and Douglas McGregor. [Cambridge, Mass., 1943] cover-title, 20 p. 23cm. (Massachusetts institute of technology. Dept. of economics and social science. Publications in social science. Series 2, no. 9)

Reprinted from Personnel, v. 19, no. 3, Feb. 1943.

NK 0199259 NNC MH

Knickerbocker, J. Hale.
Biographical sketch of Moses Hale.
(Cut from Medical society of the state of New York. Transactions. [Albany, 1857] P. 73-78)

NK 0199260 MB DLC NN

Knickerbocker, Jacob, *pseud.*
Then and now, by Jacob Knickerbocker, a New Yorker. Boston, B. Humphries, inc. [1939]
474 p. front., plates, ports., diagr. 20½cm.

1. New York (City)—Hist. 2. New York (City) I. Title.
40–4749

Library of Congress F128.37.K55
——— Copy 2. [4] 974.71

NK 0199261 DLC WaWW MH NIC NcU N NcD ViU PPL PP NN

---

*R.9 .482 .2 Knickerbocker, Kenneth Leslie.
An echo from Browning's second courtship. (In Studies in Philology. Chapel Hill, N.C. 25 cm. v. 32, no. 1 (1955) p. 120-124)

1. Browning, Robert, 1812-1889.

NK 0199262 MB

Knickerbocker, Kenneth Leslie, *ed.*
Ideas for writing; readings for college composition. New York, Holt [1951]
xxii, 738 p. 22 cm.

1. College readers. I. Title.

PS507.K56 1951 810.82 51–10347 rev

NK 0199263 DLC IU TU

Knickerbocker, Kenneth Leslie, *ed.*
Interpreting literature [by] K. L. Knickerbocker [and] H. Willard Reninger. New York, Holt [1955]
850 p. 24 cm.

1. English literature (Collections) 2. American literature (Collections) I. Reninger, Harry Willard, 1900– joint ed. II. Title.

PR1109.K47 1955 808.8 55–6033 rev ‡

NK 0199264 DLC OC1W GU NcD FMU NcRS CtY PPD

Knickerbocker, Kenneth Leslie, ed.

Browning, Robert, 1812–1889.
New letters of Robert Browning. Edited with introd. and notes, by William Clyde DeVane and Kenneth Leslie Knickerbocker. London, J. Murray, 1951 [°1950]

Knickerbocker, La Verne Mathew.
The city of Hampton, Va. Also included: the city of Newport News, Va. and the city of Warwick, Va. [Hampton?] 1954.
map 62 x 86 cm.
Scale ca. 1 : 27,000.
Indexed.
Inset: The north extension of the city of Warwick, Va. [ca. 1 : 85,000]

1. Hampton, Va.—Maps. 2. Newport News, Va.—Maps. 3. Warwick, Va.—Maps.

G3884.H2 1954.K5 Map 54–631

NK 0199266 DLC

Knickerbocker, La Verne Mathew.
County of Elizabeth City, Va. [Hampton? Va.] 1949.
map 56 x 56 cm.
Scale ca. 1 : 31,000.

1. Elizabeth City Co., Va.—Maps.

G3883.E4 1949.K5 Map 49–828 rev*

NK 0199267 DLC

Knickerbocker, Nan L.
Minnewaska, "Frozen waters"; the intimate story of the origin and growth of the Lake Minnewaska mountain houses, by Nan L. Knickerbocker. New York, The author, 1937.
87 p. front., plates, ports. 19cm.

1. Lake Minnewaska mountain houses, N. Y. I. Title.
37–12255

Library of Congress F127.M53K6
——— Copy 2.
Copyright A 106643 [2] 974.734

NK 0199268 DLC

Knickerbocker, Ray Gould, 1890–
... The Messina stationary basic copper converter, by R. G. Knickerbocker ... New York, American institute of mining and metallurgical engineers, inc., °1932.
11 p. illus., diagr. 23cm. (American institute of mining and metallurgical engineers. Technical publication no. 458. Class D, Nonferrous metallurgy, no. 37)

1. Copper—Metallurgy. I. Title.
P O 32–20 Revised

Library, U. S. Patent Office TN1.A49
Library of Congress [TN1.A525 no. 458]

NK 0199269 DP

VOLUME 300

F689
.W6K5 Knickerbocker, Vera.
Book of the words. A pageant of Wichita, presented by Wichita high school. Authors: Vera Knickerbocker [and] Miriam Thurman ... Wichita, Kan., The Grit printery [1915?]
[14] p. 25cm.

1. Pageants—Wichita, Kan. 2. Wichita, Kan.—Hist. I. Thurman, Miriam, joint author. II. Title: A pageant of Wichita.

NK 0199270 MB

923.9
G766k Knickerbocker, W H
Riley Grannan's funeral, an eulogy to one of the characters who helped make history in the mining camps during the days of gold strikes in the state of Nevada. Delivered by W.H. Knickerbocker at the bier of Riley Grannan, Rawhide, Nevada, April 3rd, 1908. [Reno, Nev., A. Carlisle & Co., 1929]
17p. 19cm.

NK 0199271 OrU KyU

Knickerbocker, W H
Riley Grannan's funeral; an eulogy to one of the characters who helped make history in the mining camps during the days of gold strikes in the state of Nevada. Delivered by W. H. Knickerbocker at the bier of Riley Grannan, Rawhide, Nevada, April 3rd, 1908. [Reno, Nev., Press of A. Carlisle & co., 1951]
3 p.l.,17 p., 1 l. 19cm.

NK 0199272 CU-B

Knickerbocker, William Edwin, 1885–
Ellipsis in Old French ... New York, 1911.
154 p., 2 l. 18½cm.
Thesis (PH. D.)—Columbia university.
Vita.
"Texts examined": p. [17]–18.
"Principal works consulted": p. [19]–20.
"Periodicals consulted": p. [21]

1. French language—Old French—Ellipsis.

A 11-1071

Columbia univ. Library for Library of Congress PC2871.K6

NK 0199273 NNC MiU DLC CU

Knickerbocker, William Edwin, 1885– joint author.

FOR OTHER EDITIONS SEE MAIN ENTRY

Downer, Charles Alfred, 1866–
A first course in French, by Charles Alfred Downer ... and William Edwin Knickerbocker ... New York, D. Appleton and company [°1922]

Knickerbocker, William Edwin, 1885–
A first course in Spanish, by William E. Knickerbocker ... New York, D. Appleton and company [°1928]
xxx p., 1 l., 303, 56 p. illus., 2 maps (incl. front.) 19½cm.

1. Spanish language—Grammar—1870– I. Title.

28-2699

Library of Congress PC4111.K55

NK 0199275 DLC DN FTaSU PU OCl ViU

Knickerbocker, William Edwin, 1885–
French composition and grammar drill, by William E. Knickerbocker ... New York, D. Appleton and company [°1924]
ix, [1], 164 p. illus. 19½cm.

1. French language—Composition and exercises. 2. French language—Grammar—1870– I. Title.

24-21425

Library of Congress PC2111.K69

NK 0199276 DLC PPTU PU OCl ViU

Knickerbocker, William Edwin, 1885–

U. S. *Immigration and naturalization service.*
... Manual of immigration Spanish, by inspector George Lockwood ... interpreter George N. Vanson ... [and] clerk Josephine Ortiz ... William E. Knickerbocker ... editor ... [Washington?] 1936.

Knickerbocker, William Edwin, 1885– ed.
... Modern Spanish prose readings, 1830–1930. Edited by William E. Knickerbocker ... and Bernard Levy ... New York, London, D. Appleton-Century company, incorporated [°1936]
xl, 439 p. 19½cm. (The Century modern language series; K. McKenzie, editor)
Includes brief biographical sketches of the authors.
"Bibliografía sumaria de interés general": p. 438–439.

1. Spanish prose literature. 2. Spanish language—Chrestomathies and readers. I. Levy, Bernard, 1907– joint ed. II. Title.

36-4940

Library of Congress PQ6248.K6
—— —— Copy 2.
Copyright A 90590 [5] 860.822

NK 0199278 DLC NcD ScU OCl OO OCU PU PRosC

Knickerbocker, William Edwin, 1885–
Spanish composition and grammar drill, by William E. Knickerbocker, PH. D., and Americo U. N. Camera ... New York, D. Appleton and company [°1928]
x, 213 p. illus. 19½cm.

1. Spanish language—Composition and exercises. 2. Spanish language—Grammar—1870– I. Camera, Americo Ulysses Nicholas, joint author.

28-2700

Library of Congress PC4111.K57

NK 0199279 DLC PPT PU OCl DN ViU

---

*AC9
E£464
LSe86
v.1 Knickerbocker, William Skinkle, 1892-
Bellwether, an exercise in dissimulatio. (In The Sewanee review. Sewanee, Tenn., 1932. 25.5cm. v.41,no.1,p.[64]-79)
An essay on T. S. Eliot and Matthew Arnold.

NK 0199280 MH ViU

Knickerbocker, William Skinkle, 1892–
Classics of modern science (Copernicus to Pasteur) Edited by William S. Knickerbocker ... New York, A. A. Knopf, 1927.
xiii p., 1 l., 384 p. 1 illus., diagrs. 22½cm.

1. Science—Collected works. 2. Science—Hist. I. Title.

28-16211

Library of Congress Q111.K5

NK 0199281 DLC FU-HC CU NcRS TxU DNLM MH PSC PPFr MiU OCl OU OO PSt KU ViU ICJ DN

Knickerbocker, William Skinkle, 1892–
Creative Oxford, its influence in Victorian literature, by William S. Knickerbocker ... Syracuse, N. Y., 1925.
ix, 224 p., 1 l. 21½cm.
Thesis (PH. D.)—Columbia university, 1925.
Vita.
Published also without thesis note.
Bibliography: p. 209–219.

1. Oxford. University. 2. English literature—19th cent.—Hist. & crit. 3. Gt. Brit.—Intellectual life. I. Title.

25–24144

Library of Congress PR468.O8K5 1925 a
Columbia Univ. Libr. [s26c2]

NK 0199282 DLC NNC NIC NcU TxU ViU PU

Knickerbocker, William Shinkle, 1892–
Creative Oxford, its influence in Victorian literature, by William S. Knickerbocker ... Syracuse, N. Y., Syracuse university book store [°1925]
ix, 224 p. 22½cm.
Issued also as thesis (PH. D.) Columbia university.
Bibliography: p. 209–219.

1. Oxford. University. 2. English literature—19th cent.—Hist. & crit. 3. Gt. Brit.—Intellectual life. I. Title.

25–20309

Library of Congress PR468.O8K5

NK 0199283 DLC MsSM NcD PU PSC PBm MiU OCU MB WaU TxU

Knickerbocker, William Skinkle, 1892- ed.

Arnold, Matthew, 1822–1888.
Culture and anarchy, by Matthew Arnold, edited by William S. Knickerbocker ... New York, The Macmillan company, 1925.

Knickerbocker, William Skinkle, 1892– ed.
Twentieth century English, edited by William S. Knickerbocker. New York, The Philosophical library [1946]
460 p. illus. 22cm.
Bibliographical references at end of some of the essays.

1. English language—Addresses, essays, lectures. 2. Literature—Addresses, essays, lectures. I. Title.

46-6062

Library of Congress PE25.K5
[12] 420.4

NK 0199285 DLC MiU NBuC PSt MB CU OOxM PWcS PP PU OCl MB MiHM

The Knickerbocker; or, New-York monthly magazine. v. 1–65, v. 66, no. 1–4; Jan. 1833–Oct. 1865. New York, 1833–65.
66 v. plates, ports. 22–24cm.
Title varies: 1833–62, The Knickerbocker: or, New-York monthly magazine (Jan.–June, 1833: The Knickerbocker)
1863–Feb. 1864, The Knickerbocker monthly: a national magazine.
Mar.–Dec. 1864, The American monthly knickerbocker ...
Jan.–June, 1865, The American monthly ...
July–Oct. 1865, Fœderal American monthly. (Caption title: The Fœderal American. Cover-title: Fœderal American monthly)
Editors: 1833, C. F. Hoffman.—Oct. 1833–34, Timothy Flint.—1834–61? L. G. Clark.—Oct. 1862–Feb. 1864, Kinahan Cornwallis.—Mar. 1864–Oct. 1865, J. H. Agnew.
No more published?
I. Hoffman, Charles Fenno, 1806–1884, ed. II. Flint, Timothy, 1780–1840, ed. III. Clark, Lewis Gaylord, 1808–1873, ed. IV. Cornwallis, Kinahan, 1839–1917, ed. V. Agnew, John Holmes, 1804–1865, ed.
Library of Congress AP2.K64 1—2996

NK 0199286 DLC PU PP PPL PHC PPT MiU OU OCl OO NjP NjR MB NN Nh NWM NjR NcD ICN KyU NNC MBU GEU OrP WaS OCH

The Knickerbocker.
The address of the carrier of the Knickerbocker ...
see under title

The Knickerbocker.
An historical notice of Columbia College
see under title

The Knickerbocker.
Sketches here and there. From the Knickerbocker magazine. New York, 1855.
560 + [12] p. 23 cm.

NK 0199289 RPB

VOLUME 300

The Knickerbocker; or, New-York monthly magazine.
Sketches here and there. From the Knickerbocker magazine. By the best American authors. Containing history, biography, poetry, tales, travels, wit, humour, &c. New York, A. Dowling, 1855.
[688, p. 22½cm.
Various paging.
Contains material from The Knickerbocker for March 1849; October, November, and December 1850; January 1851; June and August 1853.
1. American literature (Collections) I. The Knickerbocker, New York, 1849-1853.

NK 0199290 ViU

The **Knickerbocker**; the magazine of the Low Countries. v. 1- Feb. 27, 1941-
[New York, Netherland Pub. Corporation]
v. in illus. 29 cm.
Weekly, Feb. 27, 1941-Mar. 10, 1947; monthly, April 1947-
Supersedes the Knickerbocker; the Netherlands-American digest.
Title varies: Feb. 27, 1941-Mar. 10, 1947, Knickerbocker weekly.
Subtitle varies: Feb. 27, 1941-Mar. 13, 1944, Free Netherlands.—Mar. 20, 1944-Oct. 1947, the Netherlands magazine.
1. Netherlands. 2. World war, 1939-1945—Netherlands. 3. World war, 1939-1945—Period.
DJ1.K52 949.207 43-5620 rev*

OCl OU ICRL MB AxTeS
NK 0199291 DLC FU NN IU NcD ArU ICN MiD NNUN PU PPT

Wason Pamphlet DS Indonesia 56
The Knickerbocker.
Laatste getuigenis, een Amerikaans document. Uitgave in Nederland verzorgd door "De Vrije Amsterdammer" orgaan van de Afd. Amsterdam van de V.V.D. New York, The Knickerbocker, 1949.
32 p. illus. 20 cm.
1. Indonesia--Pol. & govt. I. Title.

NK 0199292 NIC

Wason Pamphlet DS Indonesia 90
The Knickerbocker.
Last testimony; an American document. New York, The Knickerbocker, 1949.
32 p. 19cm.
1. Indonesia--Pol. & govt. I. Title.

NK 0199293 NIC

The **Knickerbocker**; the Netherlands-American digest. v. 1-4, no. 1; Nov. 1938-Jan. 1941. [New York, etc., Netherlands-American digest inc., 1938-41]
4 v. in 2. illus. 29½cm. (v. 1-2, no. 9: 44½cm.) monthly (irregular)
Nov. 1938-Nov. 1939 have title: The Netherlands-American digest.
Edited by Albert Balink.
Nov. 1938-March 1939 were published in Los Angeles.
Superseded by Knickerbocker weekly; "Free Netherlands."
L. C. set incomplete: v. 2, no. 1 wanting.
1. Netherlands. 2. World war, 1939- —Netherlands. 3. World war, 1939- —Period. I. Balink, Albert, ed. II. Title: The Netherlands-American digest.
Library of Congress DJ1.K5 43-35820
[3] 949.207

NK 0199294 DLC

AY256 .N5K6
Knickerbocker almanac. New York, C. Bartlett etc.
v. 21 cm.

CSmH
NK 0199295 DLC PHi PPL NBuG NNC CtY NNC MiD NBuU

Knickerbocker & Hodder, *Aurora, Ill.*
Aurora as it is. First annual gazetteer and directory of the city of Aurora. The history and present growth of Aurora; city ordinances, fines, penalties, and general official record; account of churches; societies; railroad shops; manufactories; city and business directories, &c., &c. Aurora, Ill., Knickerbocker & Hodder, 1868.
148 p. fold. map. 22cm.
1. Aurora, Ill.—Direct. 2. Aurora, Ill.
Library of Congress F549.A9A18 1868 12-26352

NK 0199296 DLC

Knickerbocker and Nevada Silver Mining Company.
The Knickerbocker and Nevada Silver Mining Company... [Statement.] New York: W. C. Bryant & Co., 1865. 20 p. map, pl. 8°.
Cover-title.
1. Silver.—Mines and mining: Companies, U. S.: Nevada.
N. Y. P. L. November 8, 1923.

NK 0199297 NN CtY

Knickerbocker Ball Club.
see Knickerbocker Base Ball Club of New York.

The **Knickerbocker** barque; or, Betsey's voyage from New York around the world. An historical fact. New York, Printed for historical information, 1833.
11 p. 17½cm.
1. Betsey (Ship)
Library of Congress G570.K69 5-38610†

NK 0199299 DLC NN

Knickerbocker Base Ball Club of New York.
By-laws, regulations and rules of the Knickerbocker Base Ball Club of New York. Organized September 23, 1845. New York: F. F. Taylor, 1866. 24 p. 24°.
1. New York City.—Baseball clubs.
N. Y. P. L. October 27, 1921.

NK 0199300 NN

Knickerbocker Base Ball Club of New York.
[Club book.
New York, 18 sq.4°.
v.
Contains list of members, roll calls, record of board of officers, minutes of meetings.
1. New York City.—Baseball clubs.
N. Y. P. L. October 27, 1921.

NK 0199301 NN

Knickerbocker Base Ball Club of New York.
Correspondence. 1846-1876. 2 v. f°.
Manuscript, mounted in scrap books.
1. Baseball.—Assoc. and organiza-
N. Y. P. L. December 23, 1921.

NK 0199302 NN

Knickerbocker Base Ball Club of New York.
Game book.
[Oct. 6, 1845-
New York, 1845- ob. 8°.
v.
Cover-title varies: 1845-55, Knickerbocker Ball Club. Game book: 1856-Knickerbocker Base Ball Club. Game book.
Contains scores of practice games.
Scores are not entered chronologically, nor in consecutive books; some games are duplicated, but scores differ in some instances.
1. New York City.—Baseball clubs.
N. Y. P. L. October 27, 1921.

NK 0199303 NN

The **Knickerbocker** Hoosier.
v. 1-
New York, 1914- 4°.
v. illus. (incl. ports.)
Monthly (except June-Oct.).
v. 2, no. 1 includes supplement.
Published by the Indiana Society of New York.
Ceased publication
1. New York (city)—Societies, National and patriotic—Indiana Society. I. Indiana Society of New York.
N. Y. P. L. July 27, 1931

NK 0199304 NN

Knickerbocker life insurance company, New York.
Wright, Elizur, 1804-1885.
Savings-bank life insurance. Surrender values of every year for a policy of $1000, calculated for the Knickerbocker life insurance company ... By Elizur Wright ... Boston, Wright & Potter, printers, 1872.

Knickerbocker light and heat co., *New York.*
Why, being a brief description of an incandescent gas burner that gives 50% more light per foot of gas than any other. New York, Knickerbocker light and heat co. [1904]
[7] p. incl. front. 42cm.
1. Gas-burners. 2. Incandescent gas-lighting. I. Title.
Library of Congress TH7950.K6 8—21178

NK 0199306 DLC ICJ

Knickerbocker mills company, *New York.*
... A short study of spices, published for its friends on the occasion of its hundredth anniversary by the Knickerbocker mills, New York ... [New York, 1942]
2 p. l., 47, [1] p. col. illus. 25½cm.
Map on lining-papers.
1. Spices. I. Title.
Library of Congress TX406.K5 42-2219
[2] 635.7

NK 0199307 DLC NN OCl

The **Knickerbocker** monthly: a national magazine
see The Knickerbocker; or, New York monthly magazine.

[**Knickerbocker mortgage company**]
The other alternative. [Trenton, N. J., Brandt press, 1899]
37 pp. incl. pl., map. 4°.
Advantages of Bound Brook as a place of residence.
F144.B6K6 1-7808—M 1

NK 0199309 DLC

VOLUME 300

Knickerbocker Mutual Life Insurance Company of New York.
[Prospectus.]
New York. 1868. 12 pp. 16°.

F8953 — Life insurance.

NK 0199310 MB

071 Knickerbocker News, Albany, N. Y.
qA32k1s K-N scrap book, #1-3. [Albany, 1947]
3 no. in 1 v. illus. 28 cm.
Photocopies (positive) of illustrated articles which appeared in the Knickerbocker news June 28-Nov. 14, 1947.
Contents.--no. 1. Social security.--no. 2. Bicycle carnival and Mardi-gras.--no. 3. The New York State freedom exhibit in the State Library.
1. New York (State) History. Sources. 2. Liberty. 3. Insurance, Social. U. S. 3. Cycling. Safety measures. I. Title: K-N scrap book. II. New York State freedom exhibit.

NK 0199311 N

071 Knickerbocker News, Albany, N. Y.
A32k The Knickerbocker News review of 1943. [Junior ed. for the armed forces. Albany, 1943]
8 p. illus., ports. 28 cm.
Running title.
"Holiday greetings to our men and women in service."
1. Albany, N.Y. Social life and customs. 2. World War, 1939-1945. Period. I. Title.

NK 0199312 N

A
974.7 Knickerbocker news, Albany, N.Y.
qK69 The New York state freedom exhibit in the State library... [Albany, 1947]

NK 0199313 N

659.1 Knickerbocker news, Albany
K744s Selling retail advertising, compiled by the Retail advertising dept. of the Knickerbocker news. Albany, N.Y., The Press co., incorporated, c1944.
1v. illus.
1. Advertising. I. Title.

NK 0199314 IU OU

VA65 The Knickerbocker of the U. S. S. New York.
.N6A6 Bremerton, Wash. [etc.] 1920-21.
2 v. in 1. illus. 23 cm. weekly.

NK 0199315 DLC

The Knickerbocker press.
A29.72 [Albany]H.J.Hastings.
60cm. weekly.
Established Sept.4, 1843.
Title varies: Sept.4, 1843-Aug.11, 1877, Albany daily knickerbocker; Aug.13, 1877-Dec.31,1891, Daily press and Albany knickerbocker; 1892-1894, Press and knickerbocker; 1895-Jan.7, 1899, Press and knickerbocker and Albany morning express; Jan.9,1899-1900, Press-knickerbocker and express; 1901-May 20, 1910, Press-knickerbocker-express.
Ceased publication in 1937.
Merged with the Knickerbocker news.

NK 0199317 CtY

Knickerbocker press, Albany.
Carrier's address to the patrons.
[Albany]

NK 0199318 MB RPB PHi CtY CSmH

Knickerbocker press, Albany.
[Knight, Emerson B., inc., *Indianapolis*]
An unbiased study of the family or home units in greater Albany, New York, and Albany trade area ... Manual of market facts for the Knickerbocker press and Albany evening news ... [Albany?] °1931.

Knickerbocker Press, New Rochelle.
The Knickerbocker Press: manufacturers of books. New Rochelle, N. Y., [Knickerbocker Press, 1908]
2 p.l., 21 (1) p. 13 pl. 8°.

NK 0199320 NN MH NNG

The Knickerbocker Press, New Rochelle.
The Knickerbocker Press. Printing and binding... New Rochelle: The Knickerbocker Press[, 1914]. 21 p. col'd front., plates (part col'd). 8°.
1. Publishers and publishing—U. S.—New York. 2. Printing—U. S.—New York.
N. Y. P. L. April 30, 1928

NK 0199321 NN

The Knickerbocker Press, New York.
The Commission of George Washington as commander-in-chief ...
see under title

Knickerbocker Publishing Co.
A craftman's kit of Designs. [n.d.]
[15] l. of illus.

NK 0199323 MiD

Knickerbocker quadrilles. Respectfully dedicated to Washington Irving, Esq. New York, Firth & Hall, c1843.
7 p. 32cm.
Illustrated cover title.
Contents.-1.Peter Stuyvesant.- 2. Wouter van Twiller.- 3.Oloffe, the dreamer.- 4. St. Nicholas.- 5. Ichabod Crane.
1. Piano music- Quadrilles. 2.Quadrilles (Piano)

NK 0199324 CSt

Knickerbocker Ready-Reference Guide, The, to 1000 points around New York, covering all points within 50 miles of New York City. Giving information, alphabetically arranged as to railroads . . . . . . Also the latest official time-tables of all railroads within the territory.
New York. National Publication Co. 18 v. Folded maps. 8°.
In June, 1885, The Knickerbocker Ready-Reference Guide consolidated with Appleton's Railway and Steam Navigation Guide [*4498.5], taking the title: Travelers' Ready Reference Guide [*4498.20].

G7970 — Railroads. Time-tables.

NK 0199325 MB

The Knickerbocker, revised bartender's guide, or, how to mix drinks. [Seattle, Seattle printing & publishing co., inc., °1934]
cover-title, 1 p. l., [5]-104 p. 17½cm. $1.00
1. Liquors.
CA 34-382 Unrev'd
Library of Congress TX951.K5 1934
—— Copy 2.
Copyright AA 144272 663.8

NK 0199326 DLC

Knickerbocker society of Chicago.
Miscellaneous pamphlets, etc.

NK 0199327 ICHi

Knickerbocker syndicate, New York.
The Colorado-Yule Marble Company; reports of engineers and marble experts
see under title

Knickerbocker trust company, New York.
Alabama, Tennessee and northern railroad company.
Alabama, Tennessee and northern railroad company to Knickerbocker trust company, trustee. Deed of trust. Dated October 1st, 1906. New York, Globe lithographing co. [1906]

Knickerbocker trust company, New York.
Chesterfield and Lancaster railroad company.
Chesterfield and Lancaster railroad company to Knickerbocker trust company, trustee. Deed of trust. Dated August 1st, 1905. New York, Evening post job printing office [1905?]

Knickerbocker trust company, New York.
Detroit, Toledo and Ironton railway company.
Detroit, Toledo and Ironton railway company to Knickerbocker trust company. Consolidated mortgage. Dated May 2, 1905. New York, Stillman appellate printing co. [1905]

Knickerbocker Trust Company, New York.
The devolution of real and personal property in the State of New York. New York, Knickerbocker Trust Co., [cop. 1906]
42 p., 1 l. 1 pl. 8°.

NK 0199332 NN

Knickerbocker trust company, New York.
Millen and southwestern railroad company.
Millen and southwestern railroad company to Knickerbocker trust company, trustee. Deed of trust. Dated April 1st, 1905. New York, Evening post job printing office [1905?]

Knickerbocker trust company, New York.
Missouri Pacific railway company.
The Missouri Pacific railway company and Knickerbocker trust company. Agreement of conditional sale. Equipment series 1. Dated April 15, 1907. [n. p., 1907?]

VOLUME 300

Knickerbocker trust company, New York.

Pittsburgh, Binghamton and eastern railroad company.
Pittsburgh, Binghamton and eastern railroad company to the Knickerbocker trust company, trustee. First mortgage. Dated 2nd April 1906. [n. p., 1906?]

Knickerbocker trust company, New York.

Raleigh and Cape Fear railway company.
The Raleigh and Cape Fear railway company to Knickerbocker trust company, trustee. Deed of trust. Dated February 28th, 1903. New York, The Evening post job printing house [1903?]

Knickerbocker trust company, New York.

Raleigh and Southport railway company.
Raleigh and Southport railway company to Knickerbocker trust company, trustee. Mortgage. <Dated June 1st, 1905> New York, Evening post job printing office [1905?]

Knickerbocker trust company, New York.

Tombigbee Valley railroad company.
Tombigbee Valley railroad company to Knickerbocker trust company, trustee. Deed of trust. Dated April 2nd, 1906. New York, Evening post job printing office [1906?]

Knickerbocker Trust Company, New York.
Trust companies and their functions. 1901.
56 p.

NK 0199339 PPProM

---

f655.24 K69b Springer Coll.

Knickerbocker type foundry, Albany, N.Y.
Book of specimens of printing types, cuts, ornaments, &c., cast at the Knickerbocker type foundry of A.S. Gilchrist. Albany, N.Y. [The Company] 1857.
unp. illus. F.
Title within ornamental border.
Printed on one side of leaf only.
Presentation copy to Joel Munsell, esq., autographed with initials A.S.G. [i.e. A.S. Gilchrist]

NK 0199340 IaU

Knickerbocker Villager; the complete newspaper of Knickerbocker Village...
v. 1
New York [1934– 30½ – 36½cm.
v. illus.
Weekly.
Subtitle varies.

1. Habitations for the working class —U. S.—N. Y.—New York.
N. Y. P. L. April 22, 1936

NK 0199341 NN

The Knickerbocker weekly
see Knickerbocker; the magazine of the Low Countries

Knickerbocker Whist Club, New York.
Contract bridge
see under title

Knickerbocker whist club, New York.
Knickerbocker whist club, member of American whist league. Incorporated under the laws of the state of New York. New York [1927] 65 p. 17cm.
Certificate of incorporation, by-laws, house rules, list of members, etc., of the club. "Historical sketch of the Knickerbocker whist club," by August R. Ohman, p. [45]-65.

887946A. 1. Whist—Assoc. and org. —U. S.—N. Y.—New York.
N. Y. P. L. May 19, 1938

NK 0199344 NN ICRL ICJ

Knickerbocker whist club, New York.
The laws of duplicate auction bridge of the Knickerbocker whist club <progressive pairs> effective March 1st, 1926. New York city, Auction bridge bulletin [c1926]
[14] p. 13½cm.

1. Auction bridge. I. Title.
Library of Congress GV1282.K6 26-10018

NK 0199345 DLC

Knickerbocker's almanac
see Knickerbocker almanac.

Knickerbocker Guide Company.
Travelers' ready-reference guide ...
see under title

Knickinik (Joannes Franciscus). * De dysenteria quæ anno 1779, late grassata est. 21 pp. sm. 4°. *Teutoburgi ad Rhenum, F. A. Benthon,* [1780]

NK 0199347 DNLM NNNAM

Knickknackius, Gripholdus, *pseud.*
see **Frey, Janus Caecilius,** *d.* 1631.

Knickknackius *Flochlandus,* **Greisholdus,** *pseud.*
see **Frey, Janus Caecilius,** *d.* 1631.

Knickle, Harry James, 1902–
The first century of Grace Church Parish. Plainfield, N. J., 1952.
205 p. illus. 22 cm.

1. Plainfield, N. J. Grace Church. I. Title.
BX5980.P65G7 283.749 52-65073 ‡

NK 0199350 DLC

57.24 K74

Knickmann, Erich.
Die Phosphatversorgung der Obstbäume. Essen, Tellus, 1955.
80 p.

1. Fertilizers, Phosphatic. 2. Fruit. Fertilization. I. Essen-Bredeney. Landwirtschaftliche Versuchsanstalt der Thomasphosphat-Erzeuger.

NK 0199351 DNAL

S541 .H3 Bd. 1

Knickmann, Erich, ed.

Thun, Richard.
Die Untersuchung von Böden. Neubearb. in 2. Aufl. von Rudolf Herrmann, in 3. Aufl. von Erich Knickmann. 3. Aufl. Radebeul, Neumann, 1955.

Knickmann, Hans.
Die Auswertung der Bodenschätzungsergebnisse für Raumforschung und Landeskunde, dargestellt an einem Beispiel: Die Landwirtschaft im Bezirk Friedberg. Landshut, Verlag des Amtes für Landeskunde, 1951.
30 p. illus., fold. maps. 24 cm. (Forschungen zur deutschen Landeskunde, Bd. 54)

1. Agricultural geography—Friedberg (Bavaria) (Series)
G58.F73 Bd. 54 A 51-8734
Harvard Univ. Library
for Library of Congress [a62b½]†

NK 0199353 MH DNAL DLC MB NN CtY

M/0441 K74ag

Knidson, Vern O.
The absorption of sound in gases. [Menasha, Wis.], 1935.
p. 199-204. tab., diagrs. 27 cm.
[Reprinted from The Journal of the Acoustical society of America, v. 6, no. 4. April, 1935]

NK 0199354 DAS

Knickerbocker Casualty Insurance Company
see **Fidelity and Casualty Company of New York.**

4-Ser.

Knickerbocker Club, New York.
Constitution and rules, officers and members.
v.

NK 0199356 DLC-P4 NN PU PP MB NjP

Knickerbocker club, *New York.*
War records of the Knickerbocker club, 1914–1918. New York, Priv. print. for the Knickerbocker club, 1922.
ix p., 3 l., 3-444 p. front., vi pl. (maps, diagrs.) ports. 24½cm.
The records were collected and edited by Francis R. Appleton, jr. *cf.* Pref.

1. European war, 1914–1918—New York (City) 2. European war, 1914–1918—Registers, lists, etc. I. Appleton, Francis Randall, 1885– ed.
Library of Congress D570.85.N5N66 22-21424

NK 0199357 DLC OKentU PPRCI MB NN

Knickerbocker conservatory, New York.
Menzeli's École de chorographic classic et pantomime, under the accomplished direction of Elizabetta Menzeli. [New York, 1909?] 36 p. illus., ports. 28cm.

1. Menzeli, Elizabetta. 2. Dancing schools—U. S.—N. Y.—New York.

NK 0199358 NN

KNICKERBOCKER CONSERVATORY, New York.
Menzeli's École de chorographie classic et pantomime, under the accomplished direction of Mme. Menzeli. New York [1910?] [16] p. illus., ports. 20cm.

1. Menzeli, Elizabetta. 2. Dancing schools--U.S. --N.Y.--New York. I. Subs for *MG p.v. 343.

NK 0199359 NN

VOLUME 300

Knickerbocker Engine Company, No. 5, San Francisco
see San Francisco. Knickerbocker Engine Company, No. 5.

Knickerbocker exploring company, New York
Constitution of the Knickerbocker exploring company, of the city of New York. [Fort Smith? Ark.,1849]
broadside. 31½x12½cm.
Includes members' names, ages, addresses and occupations.

NK 0199361 CtY

The Knickerbocker Fire Insurance Company of New York.
An act to incorporate the Mutual Assurance Company, of the City of New-York. Passed the 23d day of March, 1798. Together with the bye-laws, rules and regulations, for managing the affairs of said company. New-York: Printed by James Oram. 1798. 24 p. 12°.

Sabin 54410.

1. New York City.—Insurance companies. 2. New York State. Statutes.
N. Y. P. L. September 8, 1915.

NK 0199362 NN NHi

KNICKERBOCKER FIRE INSURANCE Company of New York.
Centennial of the Knickerbocker fire insurance company of New York [originally the mutual assurance company of the city of New York, from 31st Jan.1787, to 31st Jan.1887. Containing the "Deed of settlement", drawn up by Alexander Hamilton, and a history of the company. N.Y., 1887.].

pp.41. Vign. and wdct.

NK 0199363 MH

Knickerbocker fire insurance company of New York.
The deed of settlement of the Mutual assurance company, for insuring houses from loss by fire in New York. New-York: Printed by William Morton. 1787. 16 p. table. 20cm.

Evans 20580. Sabin 51605.
Title-page vignette signed: Maverick, sculpt.
Changes in the table made in ms.

NK 0199364 NN MiU-C CSmH CtY RPJCB

The Knickerbocker Fire Insurance Company of New York.
The Knickerbocker Fire Insurance Company of New York, originally the Mutual Assurance Company of the city of New York, from 31st January, 1787, to the 21st October, 1875. 88 years. [New York: Printed by Francis & Loutrel, 1875.] 50 p. 8°.

Reprint of: Mutual Assurance Company of the City of New York. The deed of settlement of the Mutual Assurance Company, for insuring houses from loss by fire in New-York... New York, 1787, p. 7-23.

1. Insurance (Fire).—Companies, U. S.: New York. 2. Mutual Assurance Company of the city of New York.
N. Y. P. L. August 8, 1919.

NK 0199365 NN MB

The **Knickerbocker** gallery: a testimonial to the editor of the Knickerbocker magazine [*i. e.* Lewis Gaylord Clark] from its contributors. With forty-eight portraits on steel ... engraved expressly for this work. New-York, S. Hueston, 1855.

1 p. l., [ix]-xiv, 15-505 p. 49 port. (incl. front.) 23½cm.

Added t.-p., engr., with vignette.

1. American literature (Collections) 2. Authors, American—Portraits. 3. The Knickerbocker, New York, 1833-65. I. Clark, Lewis Gaylord, 1810-1873.

Library of Congress PS535.K5 20—9536

NK 0199366 DLC InU CU PU NB NBuG CU ICN IaU MH ViU LU PPL PU OCU OO OU NNC MWA WaU NN MB IU MiU

M-film
810.8
Am35
126-12

The Knickerbocker gallery: a testimonial to the editor of the Knickerbocker magazine [i. e. Lewis Gaylord Clark] from its contributors. With forty-eight portraits on steel...engraved expressly for this work. New York, S. Hueston, 1855.
505 p. illus.

Added t.-p., engraved with vignette.
Microfilm (positive) Ann Arbor, Mich., University Microfilms, 1970. 12th title of 12. 35 mm. (American fiction series, reel 126.12)

1. American literature (Collections) 2. Authors, American - Portraits. 3. The Knickerbocker, New York, 1833-65. I. Clark, Lewis Gaylord, 1808-1873.

NK 0199368 KEmT CU

The **Knickerbocker** gallery: a testimonial to the editor of the Knickerbocker magazine [*i. e.* Lewis Gaylord Clark] from its contributors. With forty-eight portraits on steel ... engraved expressly for this work. New York, S. Hueston, 1857.

2 p. l., [ix]-xiv, [15]-505 p. 49 port. (incl. front.) 24cm.

Added t.-p., engraved, with vignette.

1. American literature (Collections) 2. Authors, American—Portraits. 3. The Knickerbocker, New York, 1833-65.

Library of Congress PS535.K5 1857 31—25879
[41b1] 810.8

NK 0199369 DLC CLSU PP TU

Knickerbocker gallery.
The Atlantic souvenir, with twelve elegant portraits on steel, from original pictures. New York, Derby & Jackson, 1859.

The Knickerbocker genealogical chart ...
see under Knickerbocker, Edmund, 1815?-

Knickerbocker Gold Mining Company.
25069 Prospectus of the Knickerbocker Gold Mining Company of Colorado, with statements and reports concerning its property. Organized May 13th, 1864. 35 p. 1 map. Q. New York 1865.

NK 0199372 ICJ

Knickerbocker greys, *New York.*
Drill regulations, Knickerbocker greys, New York. Organized, 1882. Incorporated, 1898. [New York? °1910]

40 p., 1 l., 50-79, [1] p. illus., plates. 14cm. $1.00
4 blank leaves inserted after p. 40.

1. Infantry drill and tactics.

Library of Congress U430.K6 11-571

NK 0199373 DLC

There are no cards for numbers
NK 0199374 to NK 0200000

W 4
D71
1873

KNIE, Adolf
Respirationsgifte. I. Atropin. Blausäure. Dorpat, 1873.
55 p. **W4 D71**
Inaug. - Diss. - Dorpat.

NK 0200001 DNLM

4PZ
Ger. -5000

Knie, Antoinette, 1890-
Der Zirkus ist da; Worte von Antoinette Knie; Bilder von Margrit Roelli. [Zürich, Morgarten Verlag, 1947]

NK 0200002 DLC-P4

Knie, Ferdinand
Geistesblitze. Die geflügelten Worte und Citate des deutschen Volkes für Deutschlands Katholiken zusammengestellt. Paderborn, Bonifacius-Druckerei, 1887.
2v. 21cm.

NK 0200003 InStme OClJC MnCS

4BX
Cath.
1359

Knie, Ferdinand
Geschichtlicher Wahrheitsspiegel; eine Widerlegung der verbreitetsten Entstellungen der Geschichte und des Katholizismus. Nach den besten Quellen bearb. Paderborn, B. Kleine, 1891.
205 p.

NK 0200004 DLC-P4

Knie, Ferd[inand]. **C 3318.94**
Die russisch-schismatische kirche; ihre lehre und ihr cult. Graz, "Styria," 1894.
pp. v, (1), 199.

Raskolniks||AcS 232737

NK 0200005 MH MBtS NcU CLSU NjP IU OO

Knie, Guillermo.
Algebra del spin. Buenos Aires, Tall. Gráf. "Tomás Palumbo," 1943.
54 p. 27 cm. (Monografías físico-matemáticas, no. 1)

1. Nuclear spin.

QC173.K53 64-58797

NK 0200006 DLC

Knie, Guillermo.
Nuevas teorías físicas. Buenos Aires, Tall. Gráf. "T. Palumbo," 1944.
182 p. 27 cm.

1. Mathematical physics. I. Title.

QC20.K58 58-53928 ‡

NK 0200007 DLC CU DPU

QC776
.K6

Knie, Guillermo.
Problemas de mecánica atómica. Buenos Aires, Tall. Gráf. "Tomás Palumbo," 1945.
57 p. 27 cm. (Monografías físico-matemáticas, no. 2)

1. Atomic energy. I. Title. (Series)

A 51-5650

New York. Public Libr.
for Library of Congress [1]

NK 0200008 NN DLC

VOLUME 300

Knie, Johann G.
Alphabetisch-statistisch-topographische Uebersicht der Dörfer, Flecken, Städte und andern Orte der Königl. Preuss. Provinz Schlesien, nebst beigefügter Nachweisung von der Eintheilung des Landes... verfasst von J.G. Knie. 2.verm.und verb.Aufl. Breslau, Grass, Barth, 1845
xxii, 974 p. table
1. Silesia - Gazetteers

NK 0200009 MH CU PPeSchw

HV K69a 1837 KNIE, Johann G.
Anleitung zur zweckmässigen Behandlung blinder Kinder, für deren erste Jugendbildung und Erziehung in ihren Familien, in öffentlichen Volksschulen und durch zu ertheilende Privat-Unterweisung. Breslau, 1837.
67 p. illus. HV K69a

NK 0200010 DNLM

Knie, Johann G.
Geographische beschreibung von Schlesien preussischen antheils, der grafschaft Glatz und der preussischen markgrafschaft Ober-Lausitz. Abth. iii. Breslau, 1830.
Tables.
By Johann P. Knie and J. M. L. Melcher.
Contents: iii. Alphabetische, topographisch-statistische uebersicht aller orte der provinz Schlesien 1830.

NK 0200011 MH PPeSchw

Knie, Johann G.
Guide to the proper management & education of blind children... tr. by Rev. Wm. Taylor, ed. 4. Lond. Simpkin, 1861.
v. p. S.

NK 0200012 OO

Knie, Johann G.
A guide to the proper management and education of blind children during their earlier years (whether in their own family, in public schools, or under private teachers); by J. G. Knie... Translated by the Rev. William Taylor... Who has added an introduction and an appendix... London: S. Low, Marston & Co., 1894.
44 p. New ed. 8°.
Circular (Literature on the blind.) inserted.
At head of title: Re-print, 1894.

1. Blind.—Education. 2. Taylor, William, d. 1869 or 70.
N. Y. P. L. August 8, 1917.

NK 0200013 NN OO CU

Knie, Johann G , tr.
Versuch über den unterricht der blinden ...
see under [Guillié, Sébastien] 1780-1865.

Knie (Julius Andreas). *De aquæ frigidæ viribus, effectu et applicationis externæ modo. 88 pp. 8°. *Dorpat, typ. J. C. Schuenmanni*, 1833.

NK 0200015 DNLM

Knieb, Philipp, 1849–
Geschichte der Katholischen kirche in der freien reichsstadt Mühlhausen in Thüringen von 1525 bis 1629. Nach archivalischen und andern quellen bearb. von Philipp Knieb. Freiburg im Breisgau, St. Louis, Mo. [etc.] Herdersche verlagshandlung, 1907.
xiv, 151 p. 23cm. (*Added t.-p.:* Erläuterungen und ergänzungen zu Janssens Geschichte des deutschen volkes. Hrsg. von L. Pastor. v. bd., 3. hft.)
Double pagination (preliminary matter excepted)
"Verzeichnis der abgekürzt zitierten literatur": p. [ix]-xii.
1. Reformation—Mühlhausen, Ger. (Thuringia)
9-10069
Library of Congress DD176.J26

NK 0200016 DLC MB

Knieb, Philipp, 1849– Ger 1759.2
Geschichte der reformation und gegen-reformation auf dem Eichsfelde; nach archivalischen und anderen quellen bearbeitet. Heiligenstadt, F. W. Cordier, 1900.
pp. xxiv, 364.

Reformation–Eichsfeld |Eichsfeld, Germ.||.

NK 0200017 MH

Kniebe, Helmut, 1906-
Der schutz des rechtsgeschäftlichen verkehrs... Marburg, 1931. 46 p.
Inaug. Diss. -Marburg, 1931.
Lebenslauf.
Bibliography.

NK 0200018 ICRL

Kniebe, Otto Friedrich, 1884 -
Lebbin, Georg, 1865– *ed.*
Nahrungsmittelgesetze mit erläuterungen. 2., stark verm. aufl. in zwei bänden. Von dr. Georg Lebbin ... Berlin und Leipzig, W. de Gruyter & co., 1928, '26.

Kniebe, Otto Friedrich, 1884-
Zur Lehre vom römischen Gewohnheitsrecht in vorjustinianischer Zeit ... von Otto Kniebe ... Freiburg i.B., C. A. Wagner, 1908.
80 p., 1 l. 21½cm.
Inaug.-diss. - Heidelberg.
"Lebenslauf": leaf at end.
"Verzeichnis der benutzten Literatur": p. [43]-9.

NK 0200020 MH ICRL NN NNC MH-L

Kniebe, Rudolf, 1875–
Der schriftenstreit über die reformation des kurfürsten Johann Sigismund von Brandenburg seit 1613. Von dr. R. Kniebe. Halle, M. Niemeyer, 1902.
1 p. l., 161 p. 22½cm. (*On cover:* Hallesche abhandlungen zur neueren geschichte. hft. XLI)
Bibliography: p. 110–161.

1. Johann Sigismund, elector of Brandenburg, 1572–1619. 2. Calvinism in Brandenburg.
3–18135
Library of Congress D6.H2

NK 0200021 DLC PU CU CtY NcD NN

Kniebe, Wolfgang, 1909-
... Bad Wildungen, eine kurortklimatische Studie ... Marburg, 1934.
Inaug.-Diss. - Marburg.
Lebenslauf.
"Schrifttum": p. 32-33.

NK 0200022 CtY

Kniebes, Walter: Ueber das Hypersoma. [In Maschinenschrift.] 50 S. 4°(2°). — Auszug: Bonn 1921: Rhenania-Dr. 16 S. 8°
Bonn, Phil. Diss. v. 15. Okt. 1921, Ref. Beck
[Geb. 16. April 98 Dudweiler; Wohnort: Bonn; Staatsangeh.: Preußen; Vorbildung: OR. Saarbrücken Reife 16; Studium: Frankfurt 1, Heidelberg 2, Bonn 5 S.; Rig. 13. Juli 21.] [U 21. 6094

NK 0200023 ICRL RPB OU

Die Kniebeugung der Protestanten vor dem Sanctissimum der katholischen Kirche ...
see under [Giech, Franz Friedrich Carl Graf von] 1795-1863.

Kniebs, Philipp
... De revocatione codicillorvm, ad L. cvm proponatis 3. C. de codicillis ... svbmittit Philippvs Kniebs ... Argentorati, J. Staedel, 1670.
24 p. 19cm.
Diss. - Strasbourg.

NK 0200025 MH-L

Kniebühler, Martha, 1905-
Das besoldungsrecht der deutschen beamten im Saargebiet ... von Martha Kniebühler ... Frankfurt am Main, Voigt & Gleiber, 1931.
97 p. 20½cm.
Inaug.-diss. - Frankfurt am Main.
"Lebenslauf".
"Literaturverzeichnis": p. 95-96.

NK 0200026 MH-L CtY

Knief, H.
...Schuster Lehmann; oder, Die Glücksstiefel. Schwank in 1 Aufzug, von H. Knief... Mühlhausen i. Thür.: G. Danner [1927]. 24 p. 12°. (G. Danner's Vereinstheater. Nr. 241.)

1. Drama, German. 2. Title. 3. Ser.
N. Y. P. L. September 29, 1928

NK 0200027 NN

Knief, H.
Sie setzt sich den Hut auf. Schwank in einem Akt. Berlin: E. Bloch [1911]. 19 p. 12°. (E. Blochs Theater-Korrespondenz. Nr. 365.)

1. Drama (German). 2. Title.
N. Y. P. L. November 27, 1911.

NK 0200028 NN

Knief, I.
see Knief, Johannes.

Knief, Johannes.
Briefe aus dem Gefängnis. Berlin, A. Seehof, 1920.
96 p. port. 20 cm.

1. Socialism. I. Title.
HX276.K55 A 22–1180 rev*†
Stanford Univ. Librar. for Library of Congress [r47b1]†

NK 0200030 CSt ICJ NN DLC

VOLUME 300

Knief, Karl, 1907-
Der schutz des gutgläubigen dritten beim vertrauen auf eine scheinvollmacht
Inaug. Diss. Marburg, 1929.
Bibl.

NK 0200031 ICRL

Knieger, Bernard Martin,
Samuel Rogers
Thesis - Harvard, 1952

NK 0200032 MH

Kniehase, Gustav, 1899-
Der einfluss der energiewirtschaft auf den standort der industrien. ... Breslau, 1937.
Inaug. Diss. - Techn. Hochschule Breslau, 1937.
Lebenslauf.
Literatur-Verzeichnis.

NK 0200033 ICRL

Knieke, August, 1868-
Die einwanderung in den westfaelischen staedten bis 1400. Muenster, 1893.
Inaug. diss.

NK 0200034 ICRL

Knieke (Heinrich). Die Kassenarztfrage und das öffentliche Gesundheitswesen in Beziehung zu der sozialpolitischen Gesetzgebung. 74 pp. 8°. Berlin-Grunewald, A. Troschel, 1903.

NK 0200035 DNLM

KNIEL, Cornelius, 1860-1940.
Die Benediktiner abtei maria Laach; gedenkblätter aus vergangenheit und gegenwart. Köln, J.P. Bachem, [1893].
Ports. and other illustr.

NK 0200036 MH

Kniel, Cornelius, O.S.B., 1860-
Die Benedictiner Abtei Maria Laach. Gedenkblätter aus Vergangenheit und Gegenwart. 2 Aufl. Mit 32 Abbildungen. Köln, J.P. Bachem, 1894.
6-164 p. illus., ports., 22 cm.
2 copies.

1. Maria Laach (Benedictine Abbey).

NK 0200037 PLatS

Kniel, Cornelius, 1860-1940, ed.
Die Benediktinerabtei Maria Laach; Gedenkblätter aus Vergangenheit und Gegenwart. 3. Aufl. Köln, J. P. Bachem, 1902.
170p. illus. 22cm.

NK 0200038 InStme

Kniel, Cornelius, 1860- ed.
Leben und Regel des heiligen Vaters Benediktus see under Gregorius I, the Great, Saint, Pope, 540 (ca.)-604.

277
058
K74
2ed
Kniel, Cornelius, O.S.B., 1860-
Die St. Benediktsmedaillo; ihre Geschichte, Bedeutung, Weihe, Ablässe und Wirkungen. 2. Aufl. Ravensburg (Württ.) Hermann Kitz, 1895.
xiii, 56p front illus 15cm

NK 0200040 MnCS

Kniel, Heinrich.
Elektrizität?—Ja! Aber fehlerlose anlagen! Die gefahren fehlerhafter elektrischer einrichtungen im bauernbetrieb und ihre beseitigung. Von obering. H. Kniel ... Bonn, Landesbauernschaft Rheinland [1934]
84 p. illus. (incl. plans, facsims.) diagrs. 23½cm.

1. Electricity in agriculture.

Agr 35-540
Library, U. S. Dept. of Agriculture 335K74 [TK4018]

NK 0200041 DNAL

Kniel, Paul, 1920-
Beitrag zur Kenntnis einiger reiner und gemischter halogenierter Kohlenwasserstoffe. Aarau, Buchdr. E. Keller, 1947.
68 p. diagrs. 23 cm.
Promotionsarbeit—Eidgenössische Technische Hochschule, Zürich.
Lebenslauf.
Bibliographical footnotes.

1. Hydrocarbons. I. Title.

QD305.H15K5 57-24221

NK 0200042 DLC

Kniele, Rupert, 1844- 2959a.75
Öffentlicher Vortrag . . . über die Ausbreitung der Weltsprache Volapük, gelegentlich der fünften Generalversammlung des ersten württembergischen Weltsprachevereins in Stuttgart am 1. und 2. Mai 1887. . . .
Konstanz a. B. Schleyer. 1887. 20 pp. 17½ cm.
The title is on the cover.

M9963 — Volapük. — Wuerttemberg ...her Weltspracheverein, Stuttgart. Addresses.

NK 0200043 MB NN

KNIELE, RUPERT, 1844-
Offentlicher Vortrag uber die Ausbreitung der Weltsprache Volapuk, gelegentlich der funften Generalversammlung des ersten wurttembergischen Weltsprachvereins in Stuttgart am 1. und 2. Mai 1887... Konstanz a.B. Schleyer, 1887. 20 p. 18cm.
Film reproduction. Positive.
Cover title.
1. Volapuk.

NK 0200044 NN

3020
.944
.52
Kniele, Rupert, 1844-
The Volapük commercial correspondent, With a vocabulary, explanatory notes, and an appendix by Mr.J.M.Schleyer, containing a nomenclature of the money, weights, and measures of the chief commercial nations in the world. Adapted from R. Kniele's Tedaspod, by G.Krause. London, Sonnenschein, 1889.
6,128 p. 18½ cm.
Added t.-p.in Volapük.

NK 0200045 NjP

Kniele, Rupert, 1844-
Yebalsüp balid volapüka. Das erste Jahrzehnt der Weltsprache Volapük ... Als Jubiläumsgabe ausgearbeitet ... Ueberlingen a. B., A. Schoy, 1889.
3 p.l., (1), 4-125 p. 12°.

NK 0200046 NN

KNIELE, RUPERT.
Yebalsüp balid volapüka. Das erste Jahrzehnt der Weltsprache Volapük. Entstehung und Entwicklung von Volapük in den einzelnen Jahren, nebst Uebersicht über den heutigen Stand der Weltsprache, Weltspracheklubs u.s.w. Als Jubiläumsgabe ausgearbeitet von Rupert Kniese. Ueberlingen a.B., A. Schoy, 1889. 125 p. 19cm.

Film reproduction. Positive.

1. Volapük.

NK 0200048 NN

Knieling, Hans, 1914-
... Untersuchungen über den Streptococcus lacticus. Milchsäurestreptococcen der Mundhöhle in Symbiose mit Darmbakterien ... Leipzig, 1937.
Inaug.-Diss. - Leipzig.
Lebenslauf.

NK 0200049 CtY

Knieling, Moritz Hans
see Knieling, Hans, 1914-

Knieling (Konrad Friedrich) [1878-].
*Beitrag zur Behandlung der Tränennasenkanalerkrankungen mit besonderer Berücksichtigung der Tränensackexstirpation. 25 pp. 8°. Marburg a. L. [F. Reitz, 1910.]

NK 0200051 DNLM ICRL CtY

Knieling, Kurt, 1885-
... Vergleichende untersuchungen über den bau der glandulae bulbo-urethrales einiger männlicher säuger unter spezieller berücksichtigung der durch entfernung der testes entstehenden veränderungen ... Dresden, Buchdr. O. Franke, 1910.
67, [1] p. 9 pl. (5 fold.) 23½cm.
Inaug.-diss.—Leipzig.
Lebenslauf.
"Literatur": p. [65]-67.

1. Cowper's glands. 2. Testicles.

Agr 12-593
Library, U. S. Dept. of Agriculture 444K74

NK 0200052 DNAL ICRL CtY OU

Knieling, Lutz, and A. Boelsche.
...R. I. R. 234; ein Querschnitt durch Deutschlands Schicksalsringen. Zeulenroda-Thür.: B. Sporn[, 1931]. 513 p. illus. (incl. maps, ports.), plates (part col'd). 8°. (Aus Deutschlands grosser Zeit. Bd. 31.)
Some plates printed on both sides.
Bibliography, p. 513.

586101A. 1. European war, 1914- 234th Reserve. 2. Army, German—jt. au. II. Ser. 1918—Regt. hist.—Germany—Inf.—Regt. hist. I. Boelsche, Arnold,
N. Y. P. L. July 1, 1932

NK 0200053 NN

VOLUME 300

281.177 Kniely, Armin.
K74 Mehr Ertrag auf der Alm; Begleitschrift zum Österreichische Almwirtschaftsfilm. [Wien? 1955?]
37 p.
1. Mountain farming. 2. Alps. Dairying. 3. Dairy farm management. I. Austria. Bundesministerium für Land- und Forstwirtschaft.

NK 0200054 DNAL

43
K742 Kniely, Armin.
Rinderzucht des Bergbauern; naturgemässe Haltung. Wien, 1948.
112 p. (Scholle-Bücherei, 92. Bd.)

1. Austria. Cattle. 2. Mountain farming. 3. Cattle. Breeding. I. Scholle-Bücherei. Bd.92.

NK 0200055 DNAL

Kniep, Alwin: Über eine neue Methode der Bestimmung des mechanischen Äquivalentes der Wärme mittelst elektromagnetischer Induktion in körperlichen Leitern. **Berlin:** Trenkel 1910. 44 S. 8° ¶ (Im Buchh. ebd.)
Kiel, Phil. Diss. v. 10. Okt. 1910, Ref. Weber
[Geb. 22. Juni 84 Westerhausen, Harz; Wohnort: Halberstadt; Staatsangeh.: Preußen; Vorbildung: Gymn. Schleiz Reife M. 06; Studium: Halle 1, Leipzig 1, Halle 1, Kiel 4 S.; Rig. 7. Mai 10.] [U 11. 2636

NK 0200056 ICRL PU MH CtY

Kniep, Arthur, 1867-

VK906
.G4 Germany. *Marineleitung.*
... Handbuch der Yangtsefahrt, mit 35 ansichten und 75 kartenskizzen im text ... Berlin, E. S. Mittler & sohn, 1911.

KNIEP, Arthur, 1867-
Der Yang-tzi-kiang als weg zwischen dem westlichen und östlichen China; eine hydrographischverkehrsgeographische studie. Inaug.-diss., Strassburg. Leipzig, 1904.

pp. (4), 34. Maps and ahrt.
"Vita", pp.33, 34.
"Sonderabdruck aus Gerlands Beiträgen zur geophysik, bd.vii, heft.1."

NK 0200058 MH CU PU CtY

Kniep (Christianus Fridericus). *De hæmorrhoidibus suppressis. 46 pp. 4°. *Halæ Magdeb., typ. C. Henckelii.* [1717].

NK 0200059 DNLM PPC

Kniep, Ferdinand, 1830-1920.
Argentaria stipulatio von dr. Ferdinand Kniep ... Jena, G. Fischer, 1911.
2 p. l., [3]-62 p. 23cm.
"Abdruck aus der festschrift für A. Thon."
"Im frühling des jahres 1876 unternahm es eine gesellschaft, alte kupfergruben in der nähe von Aljustrel im südlichen Portugal wieder auszubeuten. Bei dieser gelegenheit kam eine eherne tafel zum vorschein, welche einen teil eines für das vipascensische bergwerksgebiet bestimmten gesetzes enthält ... Im jahre 1906 ist wiederum eine tafel ... aufgefunden ... Mich soll hier die zuerst gefundene tafel näher beschäftigen wegen des ausdruckes argentaria stipulatio, der uns hier zum ersten male entgegentritt."
1. Contracts (Roman law) 2. Auctions (Roman law) 3. Sales (Roman law) 4. Aljustrel, Portugal—Antiquities, Roman. 5. Mines and mineral resources—Portugal. I. Title. II. Title: Vipascense metallum.
33-22603

NK 0200060 DLC

Kniep, Ferdinand, 1830-1920.
Der besitz des Bürgerlichen gesetzbuches gegenübergestellt dem römischen und gemeinen recht, von dr. Ferdinand Kniep ... Jena, G. Fischer, 1900.
xiv, 494 p. 21½cm.

1. Possession (Roman law) 2. Possession (Law)—Germany.
40-20137

NK 0200061 DLC NcD NIC MH-L CtY CU-AL

KNIEP, Ferdinand, 1830-1920.
De cautione et missione legatorum seu fideicommissorum servandorum causa. Diss., Jena. Rostochii, 1872.

6+62+(1) p

NK 0200062 MH-L

Kniep, Ferdinand, 1830-1920.
Einfluss der bedingten novation auf die ursprüngliche obligatio. Eine privatrechtliche abhandlung von dr. Karl Friedrich Ferdinand Kniep ... Wismar und Ludwigslust, Hinstorff, 1860.
viii, 192 p. 21½cm.

1. Novation. I. Title.
33-20506

NK 0200063 DLC CU-AL CtY MH

KNIEP, Ferdinand, 1830-1920
Entgegnung auf des oberlandesgerichtsrates D. Börngen schrift "das statut der stadt Jena vom 22. juni 1881 die einführung des stadtbauplanes u.s.w. betreffend und die dagegen erhobenen rechtlichen bedenken." Jena, Leipzig, 1899.

(4)+82 p.

NK 0200064 MH-L

Kniep, Ferdinand, 1830-1920, ed.

Gaius.
Gai Institutionum commentarius primus; text mit vorwort, erklärung und anhängen von Ferdinand Kniep ... Jena, G. Fischer, 1911.

Kniep, Ferdinand, 1830-1920, ed.

Gaius.
Gai Institutionum commentarius secundus ... Text mit vorwort, erklärung und anhängen, von Ferdinand Kniep ... Jena, G. Fischer, 1912-13.

Kniep, Ferdinand, 1830-1920.
Die mora des Schuldners, nach Römischem und heutigem Recht. Rostock, 1871-72.
2 v.

NK 0200067 MH-L

Kniep, Ferdinand, 1830-1920.
Präscriptio und pactum, von dr. Ferdinand Kniep. Jena, G. Fischer, 1891.
viii, 182 p. 23½cm.
Based on Gaius.

1. Contracts (Roman law) 2. Prescription (Roman law) 3. Gaius. I. Title.
33-19738

NK 0200068 DLC CSt CU-AL NcD CtY NNC MH

Kniep, Ferdinand, 1830-1920.
Der rechtsgelehrte Gajus und die ediktskommentare, von Ferdinand Kniep ... Jena, G. Fischer, 1910.
viii, 347, [1] p. 23cm.

11-12079

NK 0200069 DLC CtY NIC

Kniep, Ferdinand, 1830-1920.
Societas publicanorum, von dr. Ferdinand Kniep ... Erster band. Jena, G. Fischer, 1896.
xvi, 520 p. 22cm.
No more published.
Imperfect: p. 513-520 wanting.

1. Taxes, Farming of—Rome. 2. Partnership (Roman law) 3. Corporation law (Roman law) I. Title.
[Full name: Karl Friedrich Ferdinand Kniep]
40-20897

NK 0200070 DLC NcD NNI CtY ICU NNC IU NjP

KNIEP, Ferdinand, 1830-1920.
Ueber contractsculpa: eine probevorlesung gehalten in der aula der universität. Rostock, 1873.

21+(2) p.

NK 0200071 MH-L

KNIEP, Ferdinand, 1830-1920.
Vacua possessio. Jena, 1886.

v.1.

NK 0200072 MH-L CtY

Kniep, G
Die letzten Dinge des Menschen; ein Betrachtungs- und Gebetbuch, nebst einen Anhange der gewöhnlichen Andachtsübungen. 3., verb. Aufl. Dülmen i.W., A. Laumann; Louisville, Ky., Jos. Stuecker, 1896.
300 p. front.(col. plate) 13 cm.

NK 0200073 PLatS

Kniep, G
Predigten auf die Festtage der allerseligsten Jungfrau Maria. Regensburg, G.J. Manz, 1874.
96p 21cm

Bound with: HOrmann, Aloys, Fastenpredigten.

NK 0200074 MnCS

VOLUME 300

Kniep, Georg
Kurze lebensgeschichte der heiligen Gottes, nebst unterweisungen für einen gottseligen wandel... 608p. Hildesheim, F. Borgmeyer, 1879.

NK 0200075 OCl

Kniep, Hans, 1881-1930.
Beitraege zur keimmungs-physiologie und -biologie von Fucus, Habilitationsschrift ... von Hans Kniep, ... Freiburg, 1907.
Inaug. Diss. (Leipzig)

NK 0200076 ICRL

Kniep, Hans, 1881-1930.
Beiträge zur kenntnis, der Hymenomyceten I. II. Von Hans Kniep. Mit tafel II-V und 1 textfigur.
(*In* Zeitschrift für botanik. Jena, G. Fischer, 1913. 24cm. 5. jahrgang, 8. heft, p. [593]-637. 1 illus., pl. 2-5 (1 double))
Detached copy.
"Zitierte literatur": p. 634-35.
CONTENTS.—I. Die entwicklungsgeschichte von *hypochnus terrestris nov. spec.*—II. Über die herkunft der kernpaare im fruchtkörper von *coprinus nycthemerus fr.*
1. Hymenomycetes.

NK 0200077 MiU MH

Kniep, Hans, 1881-1930, joint ed.
... Festschrift zum 70. geburtstage von Friedrich Oltmanns. Im auftrage seiner freunde und schüler, redigiert von W. Benecke ... L. Jost ... G. Karsten ... H. Kniep ... Jena, G. Fischer. 1930.

4-QH371 K55
Kniep, Hans, 1881-1930.
Fortplanzung und Artentstehung... Berlin, Druck von E. Ebering, 1926.
30 p.
Rede - Berlin (Reichsgründungsfeier) 1926.
Includes "Ansprache des Sprechers der Studentenschaft stud. jur. Grossmann" (p.[25]-28) and "Schlusswort des Rektors" (p.28-30)

NK 0200079 CU

Kniep, Hans, 1881-1930.
—— Geschlechter-verteilung bei den planzen. [Berlin. 1929.] 8°.
"Literatur," at end of each section.
"Tabulae biologicae. Sonderabdruck aus band v. Supplementum 1, 1929."

NK 0200080 MH-A

Kniep, Hans, 1881-1930
Deutsche gesellschaft für pilzkunde.
Die pilze Mitteleuropas, hrsg. von der Deutschen gesellschaft für pilzkunde, der Deutschen botanischen gesellschaft, dem Deutschen lehrerverein für naturkunde, unter redaktion von H. Kniep ... [u. a.] Leipzig, W. Klinkhardt, 1926-

---

Kniep, Hans, 1881-1930.
Die sexualität der niederen pflanzen; differenzierung, verteilung, bestimmung und vererbung des geschlechts bei den thallophyten, von dr. Hans Kniep ... Mit 221 abbildungen im text. Jena, G. Fischer, 1928.
vi, 544 p. illus., diagrs. 25cm.
"Literatur": p. [472]-519.
1. Cryptogams. 2. Plants, Sex of. 3. Plants—Reproduction. 4. Algae. 5. Fungi. I. Title.
28—30513
Library of Congress QK505.K65

NK 0200082 DLC MtU MiU WaU ICU ViU OCU CLU CSt

KNIEP, Hans, 1881-1930
Über die bedeutung des milchsafts der pflanzen. Inaug.-diss., Jena. München, 1904.
"Lebenslauf", after p.81.
"Sonderabdruck aus Flora, oder Allg. bot. zeitung 1905, 94. bd. heft. 1."

NK 0200083 MH ICRL CtY DSI

Kniep, Hans, 1881-1930.
Ueber morphologische und physiologische Geschlechtsdifferenzierung (Untersuchungen an Basidiomyzeten). 18 pp. 8°. Würzburg, H. Stürtz, 1920.
Forms Heft 1, v. 46, n. F. of Verhandl. d. phys.-med. Gesellsch. zu Würzb.

NK 0200084 DNLM

Kniep (Hans). Ueber rhythmische Lebensvorgänge bei den Pflanzen. pp. 107-129. 8°. Würzburg, C. Kabitzsch, 1915.
Forms Heft 2, vol. 44, n. F., of Verhandl. d. phys.-med. Gesellsch. zu Würzb.

NK 0200085 DNLM

Kniep, Hans, 1881-1930.
Vererbungserscheinungen bei pilzen, von H. Kniep.
(*In* Bibliographia genetica. 's-Gravenhage, 1929. 25cm. deel 5, p. [371]-478. illus., tables, diagrs.)
"Literatur": p. 470-475.
1. Heredity. 2. Fungi. I. Title.
A C 33-2613
Title from Grosvenor Library of Congress Libr. QH301.B5 vol. 5 [QH301.B35 vol. 5]

NK 0200086 NBuG CU MiU OO OU

Kniep, Karl.
Durch sturm und sonnenschein in vierzig jahren. Gedichte von Karl Kniep. Newark, N. J., Selbstverlag des verfassers; New York, The International news co., 1906.
204, ii p., 1 l. front. (port.) 17½cm.
I. Title.
29-11968
Library of Congress PT3919.K62D8 1906

NK 0200087 DLC NjR InU PU NN OCU

Kniep, Karl.
Krieg überall. Ein Gedicht, von Karl Kniep. n. p. [1915?]
4 l. 8°.
Cover-title.
1. Poetry (German). 2. Title.
N. Y. P. L. October 12, 1915.

NK 0200088 NN

Kniep, Karl Friedrich Ferdinand
see Kniep, Ferdinand, 1830-1920.

Kniep (Theodor). *Ueber einige pathologisch-anatomische Veränderungen an den serösen Häuten. 23 pp. 8°. *Rostock, Adler's Erben*, 1854.

NK 0200090 DNLM

Kniep, Walter
Ueber Trennungsmethoden des Bariums, Strontiums und Calciums. Berlin, 1889.
WG 33268
32 p.
Inaug.-Diss. - Jena.

NK 0200091 CtY DLC ICRL MH CU PU

Kniepen, Ernst: Uber schwefelhaltige Anthrachinonderivate. Emmendingen: Dölter 1912. 44 S. 8°
Freiburg i. B., Naturw.-math. Diss. v. 1912, Ref. Gattermann
[Geb. 28. Jan. 88 Elberfeld; Wohnort: Freiburg i. B.; Staatsangeh.: Preußen; Vorbildung: Oberrealsch. Baden-Baden Reife Juli 07; Studium: Freiburg i. B. 6 S.; Rig. 2. März 11.] [U 12. 5245

NK 0200092 ICRL MH

---

355 K74r
Kniepen, Hermann.
Das römische kriegswesen bei Cäsar. Für die schule zusammengestellt. Neuss, 1880.
28p.
Programm--Neuss.

NK 0200093 IU MH

Kniepen, Martin: Annettens von Droste-Hülshoff dramatische Tätigkeit. Münster i. W. 1910: Westfäl. Vereinsdr. 104 S. 8°
Münster, Phil. Diss. v. 20. Febr. 1910, Ref. Schwering
[Geb. 27. Dez. 84 Lövenich; Wohnort: Münster i. W.; Staatsangeh.: Preußen; Vorbildung: Gymn. Neuß Reife O. 05; Studium: Freiburg i. B. 1, Marburg 2, Münster 5 S.; Rig. 17. Juli 09.] [U 10. 3781

NK 0200094 ICRL MH IU PU MiU NNU

Knieper (Carl) [1885-]. *Pneumokokken als Krankheitserreger bei osteomyelitischen und arthritischen Prozessen an der Hand eines Falles. 35 pp. 8°. Giessen, O. Kindt, 1917.

NK 0200095 ICRL DNLM

Knieper, Clara, Frau: Ein Fall von doppelseitigem Glioma retinae mit Enucleation des einen und nunmehr fast 11 jähriger Atrophie des andern Auges. Leipzig: W. Engelmann 1911 [hs. verb. 1910]. 21 S. 8° ¶(Aus: v. Graefe's Archiv f. Ophthalmol. Bd 78, H. 2.)
Heidelberg, Med. Diss. v. 24. Jan. 1911, Ref. Leber
[Geb. 24. Juli 81 Belkow; Wohnort: Heidelberg; Staatsangeh.: Preußen; Vorbildung: Luisen-Gymn. Berlin Reife O. 02; Studium: Heidelberg 1, Leipzig 3, Bonn 3, Berlin 1, Greifswald 1, Heidelberg 2 S.; Coll. 26. Juli 10; Approb. 16. Juli 10.] [U 11. 2207

NK 0200096 ICRL MBCo

Knieper, Erich: Der Hypothekenbrief. Plettenberg [1921]: Maercker. 52 S. 8°
Marburg, Jur. Diss. v. 10. Dez. 1919 [1922] [U 22. 7786

NK 0200097 ICRL

940.531IG K695
Knieper, Franz.
Geopolitik für die Unterrichtspraxis. 3. verb. Aufl. Bochum in Westf., F. Kamp, 1934.
149 p. illus., maps. 24 cm.
Includes bibliography.
1. Geopolitics. I. Title.

NK 0200098 N

VOLUME 300

Knieper, Franz.
Geopolitik für die Unterrichtspraxis, mit einem Geleitwort von Karl Haushofer. 4. verb. Aufl. Bochum in Westf., F. Kamp, 1935.
191 p. maps. 24 cm.
"Zur Literatur": p. 186-191.

1. Geopolitics. I. Title.
JC319.K5 1935 50-40190 rev

NK 0200099 DLC N IaU MH WU

Knieper, Franz.
Geopolitik für die unterrichtspraxis, von Franz Knieper; mit einem geleitwort von prof. dr. Karl Haushofer ... 5. verbesserte aufl. Bochum, F. Kamp, 1937.
194, [7] p. illus. (maps). diagr. 24cm.
"Zur literatur": p. 189-192.

NK 0200100 NN CtY CU NNC NcD IaU

Knieper, Werner, 1909-
Treu und glauben im verwaltungsrecht. ... Dortmund-Hörde, 1933. 66 p.
Inaug. Diss. - Heidelberg, 1933.
Lebenslauf.
Bibliography.

NK 0200101 ICRL

Knieper, Wilhelm: Klinische Beiträge zur Suprarenin-Kochsalzinfusion nach Heidenhain. Heidelberg 1911: Hörning. 24 S. 8°
Heidelberg, Med. Diss. v. 29. April 1911, Ref. Menge
[Geb. 26. Aug. 83 Cöln-Nippes; Wohnort: Heidelberg; Staatsangeh.: Preußen; Vorbildung: Städt. Gymn. Cöln Reife O. 02; Studium: Bonn 7, Berlin 1, Greifswald 1, Heidelberg 1 S.; Coll. 2. März 10; Approb. 30. Nov. 08.] [U 11. 2208

NK 0200102 ICRL DNLM MH

Kniepert, Erich.
Die Städtische sparkasse zu Würzburg, in ihrer geschichtlichen entwicklung v. 1822-1922. (Mit einem nachtrag für die jahre 1923/24). Von dr. Erich Kniepert. Leipzig, Erlangen, Deichert, 1925.
xii, 304 p. tables (1 fold.) 23cm. (Added t.-p.: Wirtschafts- und verwaltungsstudien, mit besonderer berücksichtigung Bayerns ... LXIV)
"Verzeichnis der benutzten literatur": p. [vii]-ix.

1. Würzburg. Städtische sparkasse. 2. Savings-banks—Bavaria. I. Title.
Library of Congress HG3060.W84S8 26-21206

NK 0200103 DLC MH NN ICJ

Kniepert, Erni Fellerer-
see Fellerer-Kniepert, Erni.

Kniepert, Friedrich August.
Maria Margarete. Schauspiel in 5 Akten. Berlin, C. Wigand, 1907.
94 p. 12°.

NK 0200105 NN

Kniepf, Albert, 1853-1924.
Das Shakespeare-idol Francis Bacons. Mit neuen faksimiles in autotypie und lichtdruck. Von Albert Kniepf. Hamburg, Hephæstos-verlag, 1914.
256, [2] p. incl. illus., facsims. pl., ports., double facsim. 26cm.
Book-plate of Dr. Ernest Lewis McEwen.

1. Shakespeare, William—Authorship—Baconian theory. 2. Bacon, Francis, viscount St. Albans, 1561-1626. I. Title.
32-32811
Library of Congress PR2945.K6 822.33

NK 0200106 DLC

Kniepf, Albert.
Theorie der geisteswerthe, von Albert Kniepf. Leipzig, C. G. Naumann, 1892.
2 p.l., iv, 158, [2] p. illus. (music) 23 cm
1. Worth.

NK 0200107 CU

Kniepf, Albert, 1853-1924.
Die weissagungen des altfranzösischen sehers Michael Nostradamus und der jetzige weltkrieg, von Albert Kniepf. Hamburg, Hephaestosverlag, 1914.
35 p. 21cm.
Advertising matter: p. 32-35.

1. European war, 1914-1918—Prophecies. 2. Notredame, Michel de, 1503-1566.
24-22736

NK 0200108 DLC

Kniepf, Albert, 1853-1924.
Die weissagungen des altfranzösischen sehers Michael Nostradamus und der weltkrieg, von Albert Kniepf. 3. bedeutend erweiterte aufl. mit anhang: Shakespeare-trug, Bacons lug. Hamburg, Hephæstos-verlag, 1915.
64 p. 22cm.
Pages 56, 62-64, advertising matter.
"Anhang" (p. 57-61) is a prospectus of the author's Das Shakespeare-idol Francis Bacons.
First published 1914.
1. European war, 1914-1918—Prophecies. 2. Notredame, Michel de, 1503-1566. I. Title.
41-40949
Library of Congress D524.K67 1915
[2] [159.9613] 133.3

NK 0200109 DLC CtY

[Kniephof, Henning], 1596-1663.
Consultatio juridica de controversiis ex moneta adulterina noviter exortis secundum adminicula juris ex aeqvo & bono decidendis./ Oder/ Vnvorgreiffliches bedencken/ wie nunmehr nach restituirtem rechtmässigen müntzwesen/ die hierauss angesponnene streitigkeiten mehrentheils/ vermüge der rechte vnd natürlicher billigkeit/ möchten erortert vnd verglichen werden: Worinnen ein jeglicher/ so bey dieser eingeschobener leichter müntz contrahiret vnd gehandelt ... Zu mehrer erforschung der warheit wolmeinend auffgesetzet/ vnd zu pappier gebracht durch Theophilum Gleich rechten JCtum Thryingum. Cum appendice qvaestionis: Ecqvid depositio pecuniae levioris notae pro gravi mutuo qvondam data vim solutionis obtineat? Ed. 2, auctior & correctior, &c. Erffurdt, Gedruckt bey P.Wittel inverlegung J.Birckner, 1623.
2 p.l., 92 [16] p. 19.5 cm. (In Dvtsche mvenz-verfassvng, 1609-1749, no. 3)

NK 0200112 MH-AH NNC

Kniepkamp, Hanns P
Legal dictionary. New York, Oceana Publications, 1954.
216 p.
Added t.-p. in German.
Bibliography: p. 216.
Contents.--pt. 1. English-German.--pt. 2 German-English.

NK 0200113 NNC OU PU-L ViU-L

Kniepkamp, Hanns P
Rechtswörterbuch: Englisch-Deutsch, Deutsch-Englisch. Berlin-Dahlem, Colloquium-Verlag, 1954.
216 p. 22 cm.
Added t. p. in English.

1. Law—Dictionaries—English. 2. Law—Dictionaries—German. 3. German language—Dictionaries—English. 4. English language—Dictionaries—German. I. Title.
54-14790

NK 0200114 TxU IU PPT-L NcD ICU CtY CU-S OO LU DLC CaBVaU WaU-L OCLloyd DS NcU MH-L

Kniepkamp, Heinrich, 1902-
Ueber die anwendbarkeit von entladungsroehren mit edelgasfuellung als photometer. Berlin, 1926.
In. Diss. Bibl.

NK 0200115 ICRL CtY MH

Kniepkamp, Wilhelm: Anatomische Analyse einer Klumphand, und Aufstellung des Skelettes nach Form. [Maschinenschrift.] 44 S. m. Abb. 4°. — Auszug: Berlin (1922): Ebering. 2 Bl. 8°
Berlin, Med. Diss. v. 3. Okt. 1922 [1923] [U 23. 171

NK 0200116 ICRL

Kniepmeyer, Fritz.
... Die wasserversorgung durch die gemeinden; erläuterungen zur mustersatzung des Deutschen gemeindetages über den anschluss an die öffentliche wasserleitung und über die abgabe von wasser nach § 18 der Deutschen gemeindeordnung. Stuttgart und Berlin, W. Kohlhammer, 1939.
iv, [2], 168 p. diagrs. 21cm. (Das Recht der öffentlichen betriebe, herausgeber dr. Herbert Meyer, bd. 2)
At head of title: ... Dr. Fritz Kniepmeyer und Hans Richter ...
"Literaturverzeichnis": p. [163]
1. Municipal ownership—Germany. 2. Water-supply—Germany. 3. Public utilities—Germany. I. Richter, Hans, joint author. II. Deutscher gemeindetag. III. Title.
42-35636
Library of Congress HD4465.G3K6
[2] 352.60943

NK 0200117 DLC

Kniepp, C.
Die Zither; ihr Wesen und ihre Bedeutung in der Musik als Solo-Instrument und ihre Verwendung mit anderen Instrumenten, nebst einem Einblick in die Harmonie- und Kompositionslehre, von C. Kniepp. Paderborn: T. Thiele, 1884. 75 p. 12°.

1. Zither.
N. Y. P. L. November 22, 1927

NK 0200118 NN

Knierer, F. J.
Ueber den einfluss des schonheitsgefuhles auf leben und sprache der griechen. Wurzburg, Thein, 1864.
43 p.

NK 0200119 PU NjP

VOLUME 300

Knierer, Hermann.

Psalm der Liebe, 1. Korinther 13, für gemischten Chor, Sopran-Solo und Orgel (oder Harmonium oder Klavier) Dichtung von Richard Zoozmann. Karlsruhe in Baden, F. Müller [194-?] Pl. no. F. M. 496 S. M.

score (12 p.) 31 cm.

For chorus (SATB), soprano solo, and organ, reed-organ, or piano.

1. Choruses, Sacred (Mixed voices, 4 pts.) with organ. I. Zoozmann, Richard, 1863-1934. Psalm der Liebe. II. Title.

M2072.4.K M 57-250

NK 0200120 DLC IaU NN

W 4 F86 1938 Knierer, Rolf, 1911-
Über die Restabsorption von Serumeiweissfiltraten. Karlsruhe, Wetzel, 1938.
21, [2] p.

Inaug.-Diss. - Freibrug im Breisgau.
Bibliography: p. [22]

NK 0200121 DNLM

4RM-5012 Knierer, Wolfgang, 1899-
Leitfaden der Strahlentherapie der Hautkrankheiten; mit einer Einführung in die allgemeine Strahlenheilkunde (Ultraviolett, Röntgen, radioaktive Substanzen) Stuttgart, Wissenschaftliche Verlagsgesellschaft, 1949.
67 p.

NK 0200122 DLC-P4 DNLM

WR 140 K69p 1951 KNIERER, Wolfgang, 1899-
Propädeutik der Haut- und Geschlechtskrankheiten. München, Urban & Schwarzenberg, 1951.
86 p.
1. Skin - Diseases 2. Venereal diseases

NK 0200123 DNLM

Knierer, Wolfgang, 1899-
Über seltene maligne Tumoren. Stuttgart, Wissenschaftliche Verlagsgesellschaft, 1947.

60, [1] p. illus. 21 cm. (Beihefte zur "Medizinischen Monatsschrift"; Zeitschrift für allgemeine Medizin und Therapie, Heft 1)

"Specielle Literatur": p. 39-41. "Literatur": p. 59-[61]

CONTENTS.—Über eine seltene Form des Hautcarcinoms (Karzinoma basocelluläre keloidiforme).—Über Sarkome auf chronischentzündlichen Veränderungen.

1. Cancer. (Series: Medizinische Monatsschrift. Beihefte, Heft 1)

RC262.K6 49-4007*

NK 0200124 DLC DNLM ICJ MnU NNC IU

Knierer, Wolfgang, 1899-
Über zwei fälle von akuter pityriasis lichenoides ... [n.p., 1932]
Diss. - Munich.

NK 0200125 MiU CtY PPYH

Knieriem, von.

German chemical glossary; comprising some metallurgical expressions relating to propellants. Halstead Exploiting Centre translation. Washington, Hobart Pub. Co. [195-?]

67 l. 28 cm.

Cover title.
"PB-92784."
German and English.

1. Chemistry—Dictionaries—German. 2. German language—Dictionaries—English. I. Title.

QD5.K64 540.3 53-36073

NK 0200126 DLC

GER 916 KNI Knieriem, August von, 1887-
Der Niessbrauch an einer Heerde, von August von Knieriem ... Berlin, Druck der Norddeutschen Buchdruckerei, 1893.

84 p. 21½cm.

Imperfect: p.[1]-8 mutilated.
Bibliographical footnotes.

NK 0200127 MH-L

Knieriem, August von, 1887-
Nürnberg, rechtliche und menschliche Probleme. Vorwort von Eduard Wahl. Stuttgart, E. Klett, 1953.

578 p. 22 cm.

1. War crime trials—Nuremberg, 1946-1949. 2. War crimes.

53-30786 ‡

NK 0200128 DLC NBuC DS CU-AL FU OU NcD PU-L ICU NN MH

Knieriem, August von, 1887-
Wandelungsanspruch unter Miterben nach römischem und heutigem Recht ... von August v. Knieriem ... Borna-Leipzig, R. Noske, 1908.

2 p.l., [vii]-ix, 57 p. 22½cm.

Inaug.-Diss. - Göttingen.
"Literaturverzeichnis": p.[vii]-ix.

NK 0200129 MH-L NN

Knieriem, Friedrich: Die Lage der Siedelungen im Taunus. Mit 3 Kt. Giessen 1911: v. Münchow. 60 S., 3 Kt. 8°
¶(Aus: Geogr. Mitteilungen aus Hessen. H. 7. 1912.)
Gießen, Phil. Diss. v. 17. Nov. 1911, Ref. Sievers
[Geb. 25. April 89 Bad Nauheim; Wohnort: Gießen; Staatsangeh.: Hessen; Vorbildung: Oberrealsch. Gießen Reife O. 07; Studium: Berlin 4, Gießen 4 S.; Rig. 28. Febr. 11.] [U 12. 1439

NK 0200130 ICRL CtY PU MH NN

Knieriem (Joannes Melchior.) *Spicilegium observationum de Arnica montana. 67 pp. 8°. Dorpat, ex off. acad. J. C. Schünmanni, 1823.

NK 0200131 DNLM

HQ 1147 G3 K5 Knieriem, Pauline von
Die deutsche Frau und Fürstin des Mittelalters; historische und literarische Quellen, von P. v. Knieriem. Berlin, F. A. Herbig [1927]
57p. 23cm. (Quellenhefte zum Frauenleben in der Geschichte, Heft 8)

1. Woman - History and condition of women - Middle Ages 2. Women in Germany - Hist. - Sources I. Title

NK 0200132 WU

Knieriem, Walter, 1903-
Das hoebenklima und seine physiologischen wirkungen.
Inaug. diss. Bonn, 1929.
Bibl.

NK 0200133 ICRL CtY

Knieriem, Woldemar von, 1849-
Beiträge zur kenntniss der bildung des harnstoffs im thierischen organismus ... Dorpat, Druck von C. Mattiesen, 1874.

1 p. l., 32 p., 1 l. 23½cm.

Inaug.-diss. (Magister der landwirthschaft)—Dorpat.
Appeared in Zeitschrift für biologie, v. 10, p. 263-294.

1. Urea.

Library of Congress QP801.U7K6 7-22663†

NK 0200134 DLC DNLM

Knieriem, Woldemar von, 1849-
...Meine Lebenserinnerungen. Riga: E. Plates AG., 1931.
32 p. front. (port), illus. 22½cm.

NK 0200135 NN

Knieriem, Woldemar von, 1849-
Der roggen als kraftfuttermittel.
Landw. jahrb. bd. 29, p. 483-523. Berlin, 1900.

1. Rye.

Library, U. S. Dept. of Agriculture Agr 4-1297

NK 0200136 DNAL

Knieriem, Woldemar von, 1849-
Die saatwicken als kraftfuttermittel.
Landw. jahrb. bd. 29, p. 524-540. Berlin, 1900.

1. Vetch.

Library, U. S. Dept. of Agriculture Agr 4-1298

NK 0200137 DNAL

Knieriem, Woldemar von, 1849-
Ueber das verhalten der im säugethierkörper als vorstufen des harnstoffes erkannten verbindungen zum organismus der hühner ... Dorpat, Druck von H. Laakmann's buchdruckerei & lithographie, 1877.

1 p. l., 44 p., 1 l. 23cm.

Inaug.-diss. (Doctor der landwirthschaft)—Dorpat.
Appeared in Zeitschrift für biologie, v. 13, p. 36-79.

1. Urea. 2. Birds—Physiology.

Library of Congress QP801.U7K7 7-22664†

NK 0200138 DLC DNLM ICRL

Knieriem, Woldemar von, 1849-
Ueber die ursache der essiggährung.
Landw. vers. stat. bd. 16, p. 305-329. Chemnitz, 1873.

1. Fermentation. Acetic acid. I. Mayer, Adolf Eduard, 1843- joint author.

U. S. Dept. of agr. Library for Library of Congress [r41b2] Agr 4-2411 Revised

NK 0200139 DNAL

VOLUME 300

L591.13
O401
Knieriem, Woldemar von, 1849-
Über die Verwerthung der Cellulose im thierischen Organismus, von Dr Woldemar von Knieriem ... ⌐Riga, H. Burchardt's Druckerei, 1884⌐
71 p. incl. tables (1 fold.) 30cm.
"Festschrift zur Feier fünfzigjährigen Bestehens der Universität des Heiligen Wladimir zu Kijew glückwünschend dargebracht von der polytechnischen Schule zu Riga."

NK 0200140 ICJ

Knieriem, Woldemar von, 1849-
Untersuchungen betreffend den wert verschiedener kraftfuttermittel.
Landw. jahrb. bd. 27, p. 566-630. Berlin, 1898.

1. Feeding stuffs, Concentrated.

Library, U. S. Dept. of Agriculture Agr 4-1299

NK 0200141 DNAL

Knieriem, Woldemar von, 1849-
Versuche zur wertschätzung des wiesenheues ausgeführt auf der versuchsfarm Peterhof.
Landw. jahrb. bd. 27, p. 521-565. Berlin, 1898.

1. Grasses and forage plants.

Library, U. S. Dept. of Agriculture Agr 4-1300

NK 0200142 DNAL

Knieriem, Woldemar von, 1849-
Das versuchsfeld der lehr- und versuchsfarm Peterhof bei Riga in den jahren 1904 bis 1914.
Landw. jahrb. bd. 62, p. 655-683. Berlin, 1925.

1. Fertilizers ⌐and manures⌐ 2. ⌐Peterhof, Latvia. Lehr- und versuchsfarm⌐

Library, U. S. Dept. of Agriculture 18L23 bd. 62 Agr 26-279

NK 0200143 DNAL

Knierim, Ernst, 1914-
Die bezeichnung, dux in der politischen terminologie von Cicero bis Juvenal. ... Giessen, 1939.
Inaug. Diss. - Giessen, 1939.
Lebenslauf.
Literatur.

NK 0200144 ICRL MH NNC CtY PBm

Knierim, Georg, 1880-
Ueber exstirpation des schulterguertels nach Kuester.
Inaug. diss. Marburg, 1905.
Bibl.

NK 0200145 ICRL CtY DNLM

Knierim (Heinrich Friedrich Walter) [1881-]. *Ueber einen Fall von polypösem Rundzellensarcom des Uterus. [München.] 27 pp., 2 l. 8°. Cassel, 1905.

NK 0200146 DNLM

Knierim (Hermann Philipp). *Ein Fall von Stenose der Aorta in der Gegend der Insertion des Ligamentum arteriosum. 31 pp., 1 l. 8°. *Marburg*, 1880.

NK 0200147 DNLM PPC

Knierim, John Arthur, 1915-
A pollination study of red clover based upon corbicular pollen analysis. c1955.
66 l.
Thesis - Ohio State University.
1. Clover. 2. Fertilization of plants.

NK 0200148 OU

Knierim, John Arthur, 1915-
A pollination study of red clover based upon corbicula pollen analysis. Ann Arbor, University Microfilms ⌐1955⌐
(⌐University Microfilms, Ann Arbor, Mich.⌐ Publication no. 14,470)
Microfilm copy (positive) of typescript.
Collation of the original, as determined from the film: ii, 66 l. illus., diagr., tables.
Thesis—Ohio State University.
Abstracted in Dissertation abstracts, v. 15 (1955) no. 11, p. 2358.
Vita.
Bibliography: leaves 50-51.
1. Red clover. 2. Fertilization of plants. I. Title.
Microfilm AC-1 no. 14,470 Mic 55-1397

NK 0200149 DLC

921
H447km
Knierim, Philippina Henriette Jacomina
Dirc van Herxen (1381-1457) rector van het Zwolsche Fraterhuis. Amsterdam, H. J. Paris, 1926.
174 p.

Proefschrift - Leiden.

1. Herxen, Dirk van, 1381-1457. 2. Zwolle, Netherlands. Sint Agnietenberg (House of Augustinian canons)

NK 0200150 WaU MBCo

Knies, Carl
see Knies, Karl Gustav Adolf, 1821-1898.

W 4
F82
1940
Knies, Gottfried, 1914-
Die Chemotherapie in der Frauenheilkunde. Mainz am Rhein, Schmidt, 1940.
29 p. illus.

Inaug.-Diss. - Frankfurt am Main.
Bibliography: p. 29.

NK 0200152 DNLM

Knies, Hermann, 1913-
Die Vertretung im Steuerrecht und bürgerlichen Recht. Iserlohn i. W., Wichelhoven, 1939.
ix, 55 p.

Thesis - Halle-Wittenberg.
Vita.
Bibliography: p. vii-ix.

NK 0200153 NNC

---

ar W
4685
Knies, Hermann, 1913-
Die Vertretung im Steuerrecht und bürgerlichen Recht. Iserlohn, R. Wichelhoven, 1939.
ix, 55 p. 24cm.

1. Taxation--Law--Germany.

NK 0200154 NIC MH-L

Knies, Karl Gustav Adolf, 1821-1898, ed.
Brieflicher verkehr mit Mirabeau und Du Pont
see under Karl Friedrich, Grand Duke of Baden, 1728-1811.

338.943
K74c
Knies, Karl Gustav Adolf, 1821-1898.
...Commissions-bericht über den entwurf eines gewerbe-gesetzes, erstattet von den abgeorbneten Knies. n.p., [1862]
caption-title, 55p. 26cm.

At head of title: Beil. zum protokoll der 19. offentl. sitzung der II. kammer vom 24. Februar 1862.

1. Industrial laws and legislation. 2. Industry and state. I. Title.

NK 0200156 LU

Knies, Karl Gustav Adolf, 1821-1898.
Der credit, von Carl Knies ... Berlin, Weidmannsche buchhandlung, 1876-79.
2 v. 23cm. (*On cover:* Geld und credit, 2. abth.)
Vol. 2 has added t.-p.: Geld und credit.

1. Credit.

Library of Congress HG3701.K6 6-33757 Revised

NK 0200157 DLC NjNbS PSC

Knies, Karl Gustav Adolf, 1821-1898.
Die dienstleistung des soldaten und die mängel der conscriptionspraxis. Eine volkswirthschaftlich-finanzielle erörterung, von dr. Karl Knies...Freiburg F. Wagner, 1860.
88p.

NK 0200158 MiU

HE1035
K6
Knies, Karl Gustav Adolf, 1821-1898.
Die Eisenbahnen und ihre Wirkungen. Braunschweig, C.A. Schwetschke (M. Bruhn), 1853.
iv, 147 p. 22cm.

1. Railroads. 2. Railroads and state. 3. Railroads - Management. I. Title.

NK 0200159 GU NIC CU MH NN MiU NNU-W

[KNIES, Karl Gustav Adolf] 1821-1898.
Das eisenbahnwesen. n.p., [1855?].

pp.[60].
Without title-page. Caption title.
Die Gegenwart, X, pp.312-370.

NK 0200160 MH

Knies, Karl Gustav Adolf, 1821-1898.
... Festgaben für Karl Knies zur funfundsiebzigsten Wiederkehr seines Geburtstages ...
see Staatswissenschaftliche Arbeiten; Festgaben für Karl Knies ...

Knies, Karl Gustav Adolf, 1821-1898.
Finanzwissenschaft
see under Seitz, G

VOLUME 300

Knies, Karl Gustav Adolf, 1821-1898.
... Finanzpolitische erörterungen ...
see his Rede zum geburtsfeste des höchstseligen grossherzogs Karl Friedrich von Baden und zur akademischen preisvertheilung am 22. November 1871.

Knies, Karl [Gustav Adolf] 1821-1898
Das geld. Darlegung der grundlehren von dem gelde, mit einer vorerörterung über das kapital und die uebertragung der nutzungen, von Carl Knies. Berlin, Weidmannsche buchhandlung, 1873.
xi, 344 p. 22½cm. (*Added t.-p.:* Geld und credit. 1. abth.)

1. Money.

Library of Congress HG221.K6 6-33758†

NK 0200164 DLC OOxM NN NcD PSC NjP

Knies, Karl Gustav Adolf, 1821-1898.
Das geld. Darlegung der grundlehren von dem gelde, insbesondere der wirtschaftlichen und der rechtsgiltigen functionen des geldes, mit einer erörterung über das kapital und die übertragung der nutzungen, von Karl Knies. 2. verb. und verm. aufl. Berlin, Weidmannsche buchhandlung, 1885.
x, 450 p. 23½cm. (*Added t.-p.:* Geld und credit. 1. abt.)

1. Money. 2. Capital.

Library of Congress HG221.K62 10-19270

NK 0200165 DLC NjP MiU NjR

Knies, Karl Gustav Adolf, 1821-1898.
Geld und credit ... von Carl Knies ... Berlin, Weidmann, 1873-79.
2 v. in 3. 23cm.
CONTENTS.—1. abt. Das geld. 2. abt. Der credit.

Library of Congress HG221.K6 2-1089

NK 0200166 DLC TxU KU CtY MtU MH

Knies, Karl [Gustav Adolf]. 1821-95. 332.01 N600
38749 Geld und Credit. Von Karl Knies, ... Berlin, Weidmannsche Buchhandlung, 1876-1885.
3 vol. in 2. 22½cm.
Contents.—1. Abt. Das Geld. ..., Mit einer Erörterung über das Kapital und die Übertragung der Nutzungen. Zweite verbesserte und vermehrte Auflage. x, 450 p. 1885.—2. Abt. Der Credit, von Carl Knies, ... 2 vol. in 1. 1876-1879.
Vol. 2, pt. 1, has no general title-page.

NK 0200167 ICJ CU KU OClW NNU-W

Knies, Karl Gustav Adolf, 1821-1898.
Geld und Credit ... Leipzig, H. Buske, 1931.
3 v. 21.5 cm.
"Neudruck 1931."
Each vol. has also special t.-p.
Contents. 1. Abt. Das Geld; Darlegung der Grundlehren von dem Gelde ... mit einer Erörterung über das Kapital und die Übertragung der Nutzungen. 2. ver. u. verm. Aufl. - 2. Abt. Der Credit. 2 v.

NK 0200168 NcD WaU NN

[KNIES, Karl Gustav Adolf] 1821-1898.
Das heutige credit und bankwesen. n.p.,[18-]

pp.(50).
"Die gegenwart,XI",pp.417-466.

NK 0200169 MH

Knies, Karl Gustav Adolf, 1821-1898.
Historia Praenestis oppidi. Praecedit nominis explicatio et typographiae brevis expositio. Rintelii, 1846.
4°.
Inaug. diss.

NK 0200170 NjP

[KNIES, Karl Gustav Adolf] 1821-1898.
Der patriotismus Machiavelli's. [Heidelberg, 1871.]

pp.35.
"Abdruck aus dem XXVII bande der Preussischen jahrbücher."

NK 0200171 MH

Knies, Karl [Gustav Adolf] 1821-1898.
Die politische oekonomie vom geschichtlichen standpuncte. Von K. Knies. Neue, durch abgesonderte zusätze verm. aufl. der "Politischen oekonomie vom standpuncte der geschichtlichen methode." Braunschweig, C. A. Schwetschke & sohn, 1883.
xii, 533, [1] p. 8°. 1-G-1631

NK 0200172 OO OU ViU MdBP ICJ NjP MH-BA DLC CSt MoU CU NcD CaBVaU CtY PPD PBm

---

Knies, Karl Gustav Adolf, 1821-1898.
Die politische Oekonomie vom geschichtlichen Standpunkte, von Karl Knies. Neue, durch abgesonderte Zusätze vermehrte Auflage der "Politischen Oekonomie vom Standpunkte der geschichtlichen Methode." Leipzig: H. Buske, 1930. xii, 533 p. 8°.

498813A. 1. Economics—Hist.
N. Y. P. L. October 22, 1930

NK 0200173 NN CU MH CSmH

Knies, Karl Gustav Adolf, 1821-1898.
Die politische oekonomie vom standpunkte der geschichtlichen methode, von Karl Knies. Braunschweig, C. S. Schwetschke und sohn, 1853.
xii, 355, [1] p. 21cm.

1. Economics.

Library of Congress HB175.K69 5-17043

NK 0200174 DLC OrPR IdU CtY MiU OCU NjP

KNIES, Karl Gustav Adolf, 1821-1898.
Die punzirung in Oesterreich; eine geschichtliche studie. Wien,Manz,1896.

1.8°. pp.79. Plates.

NK 0200175 MH

Knies, Karl Gustav Adolf, 1821-1898.
Rede zum geburtsfeste des höchstseligen grossherzog Karl Friedrich von Baden und zur akademischen preis vertheilung am 22. november 1871, von Dr. Carl Knies ... Finanzpolitische erörterungen. Heidelberg, Buchdruckerei von G. Mohr, 1871.
50 p. 26½ x 21cm.

1. Finance—Germany.

Library of Congress HJ1117.K7 7-30501†

NK 0200176 DLC NIC ICJ NNU-W

Knies, Karl Gustav Adolf, 1821-1898. 311 L001
Die Statistik als selbstständige Wissenschaft. Zur Lösung des
167408 Wirrsals in der Theorie und Praxis dieser Wissenschaft. Zugleich ein Beitrag zu einer kritischen Geschichte der Statistik seit Achenwall, von Dr. Carl Gustav Adolph Knies ... Kassel, Verlag der J. Luckhardt'schen Buchhandlung, 1850.
vii, [1], 175 p. 21cm.
Bibliographical foot-notes.

NK 0200177 ICJ MiU PU IaU CtY MH-BA NjP CU NIC RPB

[KNIES, Karl] Gustav Adolf] 1821-1898.
Die Statistik auf ihrer jetzigen entwickelungsstufe. n.p.,[1852].

NK 0200178 MH

Knies, Karl Gustav Adolf, 1821-1898.
Der telegraph als verkehrsmittel. Mit erörterungen über den nachrichtenverkehr überhaupt. Von dr. Karl Knies ... Tübingen, H. Laupp, 1857.
viii p., 1 l., 273 p. 21½cm.

1. Telegraph. 2. Communication and traffic.

Library of Congress HE7631.K5 35-22211 384.1

NK 0200179 DLC NcD NIC GU MiU MH NN

Knies, Karl Gustav Adolf, 1821-1898.
Weltgeld und Weltmünzen, von Carl Knies... Berlin: Weidmann, 1874. viii, 60 p. 8°.

1. Money (International).
N. Y. P. L. November 23, 1921.

NK 0200180 NN CU IEN MH ICJ NNU-W

[KNIES, Karl Gustav Adolf] 1821-1898.
Die wissenschaft der nationalökonomie seit Adam Smith bis auf die gegenwart. n.p.,[1852?]

NK 0200181 MH

KNIES, Karl Gustav Adolf, 1821-1898.
Zur lehre vom wirthschaftlichen güterverkehr, vom geld und vom credit. [Progr.]. Freiburg, H.M.Poppen & sohn,1862.

4°. pp.79.

NK 0200182 MH

VOLUME 300

Knies, Ludwig.
Das wuerttembergische Pionier-Bataillon Nr. 13 im Weltkrieg 1914–1918, von Oberstleutnant L. Knies... Stuttgart: C. Belser, A.G., 1927. viii, 250 p. incl. tables. illus. (incl. plans, ports.), maps. 4°. (Die württembergischen Regimenter im Weltkrieg 1914–1918. Bd. 41.)

1 map in pocket on inside back cover.

350736A. 1. European war, 1914– 1918—Regt. hist.—Germany—Württemberg. 2. Army, German—Württemberg. 3. Ser.
N. Y. P. L. March 31, 1928

NK 0200183 NN MiU

Knies, Ludwig.
... Würtembergische Pioniere ... 1932.
see under Deyhle, Willy.

Knies, Max, 1851-1917.
Die Beziehungen des Sehorgans und seiner Erkrankungen zu den übrigen Krankheiten des Körpers und seiner Organe, von Dr. Max Knies ... Zugleich Ergänzungsband für jedes Hand- und Lehrbuch der inneren Medicin und der Augenheilkunde ... Wiesbaden, J. F. Bergmann, 1893.

xi, 484 p. illus. 23cm. (*Added t.-p.*: Grundriss der Augenheilkunde ... von Dr. Max Knies ... 2. Theil)

NK 0200185 ICJ ICRL DNLM PU-Med PPJef PPC MH

617.7 K742g KNIES, Max, 1851-1917.
Grundriss der Augenheilkunde, unter besonderer Berücksichtigung der Bedürfnisse der Studirenden und praktischen Ärzte. Wiesbaden, J. F. Bergmann, 1888-1893.
2 v. illus.

Volume 2 has also special title: Die Beziehungen des Sehorgans und seiner Erkrankungen zu den übrigen Krankheiten des Körpers und seiner Organe.

NK 0200186 WaU CtY PPC DNLM

617.7 K69g2 Knies, Max, 1851-1917.
Grundriss der augenheilkunde, unter besonderer berücksichtigung der bedürfnisse der studirenden und praktischen ärzte ... 2. neu bearb. aufl. Wiesbaden, J. F. Bergmann, 1890.
328p. illus.

NK 0200187 IU-M CtY-M

19th cent RE46 K55 1892 KNIES, Max, 1851-1917.
Grundriss der Augenheilkunde unter besonderer Berücksichtigung der Bedürfnisse der studierenden und practischen Ärzte. 3., neu bearb. Aufl. Wiesbaden, J.F. Bergmann, 1892.
xii, 331p. illus. 23cm.

1. Ophthalmology I. Title

NK 0200188 CtY-M PPJ PPC OClW-H MH IU

Knies, Max, 1851-1917.
Relations of diseases of the eye to general diseases, by Max Knies ... forming a supplementary volume to every manual and text-book of practical medicine and ophthalmology; ed. by Henry D. Noyes ... New York, W. Wood & company, 1895.

x, 467 p. illus. 25cm.

1. Eye—Diseases and defects. I. Noyes, Henry Drury, 1832–1900, ed.
7-14026

Library of Congress RE48.K6

NK 0200189 DLC PU CtY-M OU ICRL PPC MiU ICJ ViU PPJ

Knies, Max, 1851-1917.
The relations of the eye & its diseases to the diseases of the body. Ed. by H. D. Noyes. Wood. N.Y., 1894.
467 pp. 8°. illus.

NK 0200190 OClW-H

Knies, Max, 1851-1917.
. Die verschiedenen Formen von frischen und alten Hornhauttrübungen. 23 pp., 4 pl. 8°. *Breslau, J. U. Kern*, 1894.
Forms 6. Hft. of: Augenärtzl. Unterrichtstaf., Bresl.

NK 0200191 DNLM

Knies, Richard.
Die Herlishöfer und ihr Pfarrer. Berlin, 1919.

NK 0200192 NjP CtY PPG

Knies, Richard.
Die Herlishöfer und ihr pfarrer; ein dorfroman. [3te aufl.] Berlin, E. Fleischel & co., 1920.

NK 0200193 MH

Knies, Richard.
Die Herlishöfer und ihr Pfarrer; ein Dorfroman. Mit Federzeichnungen von Otto Meller. Mainz, Matthias-Grünewald-Verlag [1942]

206 p. illus. 19 cm.

I. Title.

PT2621.N52H4 60-59741

NK 0200194 DLC

WB 26229 **Knies, Richard**
Herzen in Bedrängnis; Erzählungen. Mainz, Matthias-Grünewald-Verlag [195-?].
302p.

NK 0200195 CtY

Knies, Richard.
"Hört, ihr herrn, und lasst euch sagen ..." eine erzählung aus Rheinhessen, von Richard Knies. Berlin, K. W. Mecklenburg, 1911.

149 p., 1 l. 20cm. M. 1

11-31879

NK 0200196 DLC

Knies, Richard.
Servaz Duftigs Frühlingswoche. Berlin, 1920.

NK 0200197 NjP

Knies, Richard.
Sonderlingen von der Gasse. Berlin, 1918.

NK 0200198 NjP

Knies, Richard.
Träume aus verborgenem Leben. Mainz, Matthias-Grünewald-Verlag, 1936.
89 p. 23 cm.

NK 0200199 TU

KNIES, RICHARD.
Träume aus verborgenem Leben. [2. überarbeitete Aufl.] Mainz, Matthias-Grünewald-Verlag [1954]
96 p. 22cm.

1 Poetry, Religious, German. I. Title.

NK 0200200 NN

Kniesch, Joachim.
Grundriss des Gerichtsverfahrensrechts; Wegweiser durch das Wesentliche im Zivil-, Strafprozess-, Verwaltungsstreit- und Verfassungsgerichtsbarkeitsverfahren. Lübeck, Verlag für polizeiliches Fachschrifttum [1954]

179 p. 21 cm.

1. Civil procedure—Germany (Federal Republic, 1949–) 2. Criminal procedure—Germany (Federal Republic, 1949–) 3. Administrative courts—Germany (Federal Republic, 1949–) 4. Germany (Federal Republic, 1949–) Bundesverfassungsgericht. I. Title.

54-37189 ‡

NK 0200201 DLC MH-L

Kniesche, Günther: Aus d. Zool. Inst. d. Univ. zu Halle. Über die Farben der Vogelfedern. 1. Die Grünfärbung auf Grundlage der Blaustruktur. Halle 1914: (Lippert, Naumburg a. d. S.). 30 S., 4 Taf. 8° ¶ Aus: Zool. Jahrbücher. Bd 38. Abt. f. Anat. Als T. 2 gilt die Hallische phil. Diss. v. 1914 v. Walt. Spöttel.
Halle, Phil. Diss. v. 30. Juli 1914, Ref. Häcker
[Geb. 30. April 83 Kottbus; Wohnort: Leipzig; Staatsangeh.: Preußen; Vorbildung: RG. Weimar Reife 05; Studium: Berlin TeH. 3, U. 2, Halle 8 S.; Rig. 1. Aug. 13.] [U 14. 3781

NK 0200202 ICRL PU MH CtY MiU DLC

Kniesche, Herbert.
Der österreichisch-deutsche Wirtschaftszusammenschluss. Der Stand seiner Vorbereitung und die Erfordernisse seiner Vollendung. Mit zwölf vom Verfasser entworfenen Kartenbildern und Diagrammen. Von Dr. Herbert Kniesche... [Stuttgart: Deutsch-Österreichische Arbeitsgemeinschaft für das Reich,] 1930. 89 p. diagrs., illus. (maps.) 8°.

512118A. 1. Germany—Economic rel.—Austria. 2. Austria—Economic rel.—Germany. 3. Economic unions—Austria and Germany. 4. Economic unions—Germany and Austria.
N. Y. P. L. January 30, 1931

NK 0200203 NN CSt-H

HB175 .K72 KNIESCHE, HERBERT.
...Das volk in der wirtschaft; ein versuch vom standpunkt volkstheoretischer wirtschaftsbetrachtung--an beispielen aus dem wirtschaftlichen nationalitätenkampf, von Herbert Kniesche... Jena, G. Fischer, 1937.
xii, 336 p. 24cm. (Schriften des Instituts für grenz- und auslanddeutschtum an der Universität Marburg. hft. 10)
"[Bibliographische] anmerkungen": p. [296]-333.

1. Economics.

NK 0200204 ICU WU InU CSt-H CtY NNC NN

Kniesche, Johannes. Ableitung der constanten der nutation und aberration aus rectascensionen des polarsterns. Inaugural-dissertation, Göttingen. Finsterwalde. 1899. 4°. pp. 30.
"Lebenslauf," p. 30.

NK 0200205 MH NjP CtY

VOLUME 300

Kniesche, Rudolf.
...Betriebswirtschaftliche Probleme der Kohlefabrikate-Industrie, dargestellt am Beispiel eines deutschen Unternehmens, von Dr. phil. Rudolf Kniesche. Leipzig: A. Deichert, 1935. x, 246 p. tables. 22½cm. (Betrieb und Unternehmung. Bd. 15.)
"Zugleich als Dissertation der Universität Leipzig gedruckt."
"Literaturverzeichnis," p. [242]-246.

842275A. 1. Management, Electric industry—Germany. 2. Electric apparatus and appliances—Trade and stat.—Germany. 3. Accounting and bookkeeping for electric industries, Cost—Germany. I. Ser.
N. Y. P. L. October 7, 1936

NK 0200206 NN CtY ICRL

Kmeschek, Iohann
see Knieschek, Jan, 1855-1891.

Knieschek, Ján, 1855-1891, ed.
Der Ackermann aus Böhmen. 1877
see under
Der Ackermann aus Böhmen.

Knieschek, J[án], 1855-1891. 27271.32.5
Der čechische Tristram und Eilhart von Oberge. Wien, C. Gerold's sohn, 1882.
pp. 122.
"Aus dem jahrgange 1882 der *Sitzungs berichte der phil.-hist. classe der K. Akad. der Wiss.* (ci bd., i. hft., s. 319) besonders abgedruckt."

Romances VII§Tristan |Eilhard von Oberg||AcS 232749

NK 0200209 MH OOxM MeB MB

KNIESCHEK, Ján, 1855-1891.
Der streit um die Königinhofer und die Grüneberger handschrift. Prag, A. Haase, 1888.
pp. (1), 58.
(Deutscher verein zur verbreitung gemeinnütziger kenntnisse in Prag. Sammlung gemeinnütziger vorträge, 125-127.)

NK 0200210 MH

Huc55 K81X 1 K742
Knieschek, Ján, 1855-1891.
Der Streit um die Königinhofer und die Grüneberger Handschrift. Prag, 1888.
64 p. 22 cm. (Sammlung gemeinnütziger Vorträge, No. 125, 126, 127)
Cover title.
1. Zelenohorský Manuscript. I. Ser.: Deutscher Verein zur Verbreitung gemeinnütziger Kenntnisse in Prag. Sammlung gemeinnütziger Vorträge, Nr. 125-127.

NK 0200211 CtY

BS 1180 D4.1K6
Knieschke, Wilhelm, 1866-
Bibel und Babel, El und Bel. Eine Replik auf Friedrich Delitzschs Babel und Bibel. Westend-Berlin, W. Faber, 1902.
64 p. 22 cm.
1. Delitzsch, Friedrich, 1850-1922. Babel und Bibel. I. Title

NK 0200212 OCH NN MH

Knieschke, Wilhelm, 1866-
Bibel und Babel, El und Bel. Ed. 2, enl. Lpz., Steuebigs, 1903.
82 p.

NK 0200213 PU

Mlv12 B471 V.11
Knieschke, Wilhelm, 1866-
... Die Erlösungslehre des Qorân. Nach dem Grundtext bearbeitet von W. Knieschke ... Gr.Lichterfelde-Berlin, E. Runge, 1910.
39p. 22cm. (Biblische Zeit- und Streitfragen ... [V.Serie, 11.Hft.])
"Literatur": p.38-39.
1. Atonement. 2. Koran. Ser.added.

NK 0200214 CtY MH NjP

DP40 K742e
Knieschke, Wilhelm, 1866-
Die eschatologie des buches Joel in ihrer historisch-geographischen bestimmtheit. Naumburg a.d.S., Lippert, 1912.
71, [1] p. 22 cm.
Inaug.-diss. - Rostock.
Bibliography: p. [72]
1. Bible. O.T. Joel. 2. Eschatology, Biblical.

NK 0200215 CtY-D DCU-H ICRL

KNIESCHKE, Wilhelm, 1866-
Das heilige land im lichte der neuesten ausgrabungen und funde. Von lic. theol. Knieschke. Berlin, E. Runge, 1913.
32 p. 22 cm. (Biblische zeit- und streitfragen. ix. serie, 5. heft.)

NK 0200216 MH-AH OCH

Mlv12 B471 IX.5
Knieschke, Wilhelm, 1866-
... Das Heilige Land im Lichte der neuesten Ausgrabungen und Funde. Von ... Knieschke ... 3.Tausend. Berlin-Lichterfelde, E. Runge, 1913.
32p. 22cm. (Biblische Zeit- und Streitfragen ... [IX.Serie, 5.Hft.])
"Literatur": p.[2].
1. Bible - Antiq. Ser.added.

NK 0200217 CtY PPLT

Mlv12 B471 XI.2
Knieschke, Wilhelm, 1866-
... Kismet oder Vorsehung? Von Lic. theol. W. Knieschke ... Berlin-Lichterfelde, E. Runge, 1916.
22p. 22cm. (Biblische Zeit- und Streitfragen ... [XI.Reihe, 2.Hft.])
1. Mohammedanism. 2. Christianity and other religions - Mohammedanism. Ser.added.

NK 0200218 CtY NcD PPLT NNUT

Mlv12 B471 XV.9-12
Knieschke, Wilhelm, 1866-
... Kultur- und Geisteswelt des Buches Hiob. Von Lic. Knieschke. Berlin-Lichterfelde, E. Runge, 1925.
110p., 1l. 22cm. (Zeit- und Streitfragen des Glaubens, der Weltanschauung und Bibelforschung ... [XV.Reihe, 9-12.Hft.])
"Literatur": p.[111].
1. Bible. O.T. Job. Ser.added.

NK 0200219 CtY PPiPT CtY-D NN OO MH

.bb81 ·II .929
Kniese, Fritz, 1899-
Psychologische Leistungsprüfungen an mitteldeutschen Volksschülern und Waisenhauskindern ... [Langensalza, 1929]
Pamphlet
Inaug.-Diss. - Jena.
Lebenslauf.
"Diese Arbeit erscheint gleichzeitig in Heft 9 der Jenaer Beiträge zur Jugend- und Erziehungspsychologie. Langensalza 1929."

NK 0200220 CtY PU DLC MH ICRL

Kniese, Hans, 1907-
... Vergleichende histologische Untersuchungen der Keime der bleibenden Zähne eines jungen Schimpansen mit den menschlichen Zahnkeimen ... Hamburg, 1936.
Inaug.-Diss. - Hamburg.
Lebenslauf.
"Literatur-Verzeichnis": p. 12.
Full name: Hans Heinrich Richard Kniese.

NK 0200221 CtY

Kniese, Julie, 1880-
Generalstreik; Frühlingsspiel in einem Aufzug, von Julie Kniese. Kempen, Rh.: Thomas-Druckerei und Buchhandlung G.m.b.H. [1932] 14 p. 19½cm. (Kempener Theater-Bibliothek. Bd. 149.)

757065A. 1. Drama, German. I. Title.
N. Y. P. L. September 16, 1935

NK 0200222 NN

***Kniese, Julie, 1880-**

Kniese, Julius, 1848-1905.
Der kampf zweier welten um das Bayreuther erbe; Julius Knieses tagebuchblätter aus dem jahre 1883. Mit einer einleitung von prof. dr. R. freiherr von Lichtenberg, und 15 bildtafeln. Herausgegeben von Julie Kniese. Leipzig, T. Weicher, 1931.

Kniese, Julie, 1880-
... Kunterbuntes allerlei, herausgegeben unter mitarbeit von hauptlehrer Otto Pfizenmayer. Mit vielen bildern von Karl Mühlmeister. 2. aufl. Stuttgart, Loewes verlag F. Carl [1939]
1 p. l., 80, [2] p. illus. (part col.) 24cm.
At head of title: Julie Kniese u. a.

1. German literature (Selections: Extracts, etc.) I. Pfizenmayer, Otto, ed. II. Title.
[*Full name:* Julie (Kniese) Boess]

PZ31.K54 1939 830.82 46-43568

NK 0200224 DLC

Kniese, Julie, 1880-
Der Wildling vom Kanzenhof. Mit 1 Buntbild und 15 Textillustrationen von Fritz Ahlers. Stuttgart, Loewes Verlag [1934]
96 p. illus. (part col.) 19 cm.

I. Title.
Full name: Julie (Kniese) Boess.

PZ33.K558 52-45334

NK 0200225 DLC NN

Kniese, Julius, 1848-1905.
Der kampf zweier welten um das Bayreuther erbe; Julius Knieses tagebuchblätter aus dem jahre 1883. Mit einer einleitung von prof. dr. R. freiherr von Lichtenberg, und 15 bildtafeln. Herausgegeben von Julie Kniese. Leipzig, T. Weicher, 1931.
1 p. l., 5-135 p. front., plates, ports. 21½cm.

1. Musicians—Correspondence, reminiscences, etc. 2. Wagner, Richard—Performances—Baireuth. I. *Kniese, Julie, 1880- ed. II. Title.

Library of Congress ML410.W2K7 32-12822
Copyright A—Foreign 13187
[2] [927.8] 782.2

NK 0200226 DLC NN TNJ

VOLUME 300

Kniese, Julius, 1848–1905, *comp. and arr.*
Zwölf deutsche Volkslieder für gemischten Chor gesetzt. Partitur. Leipzig, Breitkopf & Härtel [1905]
close score (16 p.) 26 cm. (Edition Breitkopf, Nr. 2060)
For chorus (SATB)

1. Choruses, Secular (Mixed voices, 4 pts.), Unaccompanied. 2. Folk-songs, German.

M1584.K 52-56056

NK 0200227 DLC IaU MB MH NN

Kniese, Louis.
Einführung in das gärtnerische Planzeichnen. Berlin, Verlag des "Gärtnereifachblattes," 1927.
47 p. illus., diagrs., plans. 19 x 25 cm.
CONTENTS.—Planzeichnen.—Perspektivisches Zeichnen.

1. Landscape architecture. 2. Drawing. I. Title.

SB472.K6 29—16070*

NK 0200228 DLC

Kniese, Louis
Planzeichnen und Nivellieren, eine Einführung in das gärtnerische Planzeichnen, in die Konstruktion perspektivischer Schaubilder und in die Höhenmessung durch Nivellieren. 3. neubearbeitete Aufl. Berlin, Gärtnerische Verlagsgesellschaft Dr. W. Lang, 1938.
89 p. illus., diagrs. 23 cm.

NK 0200229 NNC

Knieskern, Peter D 1798-1871.
Catalogue of plants found in the county of Oneida. Compiled and arranged according to John Torrey's report of 1840. [Albany?] 1842. 8°. (Senate. No. 55.)
Cabinet of natural history of the state of New York. Report, 1842, pp. 275–299.

NK 0200230 MH-A

QK130
.K55
Knieskern, Peter D 1798-1871.
A catalogue of plants growing without cultivation in the counties of Monmouth and Ocean, New Jersey, according to the natural system as presented in the 2d ed. of Gray's Manual of botany ... Trenton, Printed at the "True American" Office, 1857.
41 p. 22 cm.

Copy 1: Gray Herbarium purchase August 1970.
1. Botany - New Jersey - Monmouth Co.
2. Botany - New Jersey - Ocean Co. i. t.
a. Harvard University. Gray Herbarium.

NK 0200231 NNBG NjR NjP Nh

Kniess, Georg.
Ueber unendlich kleine schwingungen einer inkompressiblen kugelförmigen flüssigkeitsmasse, deren einzelne teilchen sich nach dem Newton'schen gravitationsgesetze anziehen ... Marburg, C. L. Pfeil'sche universitäts-buchdruckerei, 1888.
2 p. l., 38 p. diagrs. on fold. pl. 22cm.
Inaug.-dis.—Marburg.

1. Hydrodynamics. 2. Oscillations.

Library of Congress QA927.K69 5-18199†

NK 0200232 DLC

PT
2621
K74A9
Kniest, Philipp, 1830-1905.
Aus sturm und not. Neue geschichten von der wasserkante von Philipp Kniest. Berlin. Concordia deutsche verlagsanstalt, 1899.
2 p.l., 190 p. (His Gesammelte schriften. 5. bd.)

Contents:- Gepresst und geworben.- Der alte Hinrichsen.- Der tambourmajor.- Peter Witt's letzte steuermanns-reise.

1. Sea stories. I. Title.

NK 0200233 CLU

Kniest, Philipp, 1830-1905.
Aus Sturm und Not, neue Geschichten von der Wasserkante. 5. Aufl. Berlin, Concordia Deutsche Verlags-Anstalt [19—]
190 p. 20 cm. (*His* Gesammelte Schriften)
CONTENTS.— Gepresst und geworden.— Der alte Hinrichsen.— Der Tambourmajor.—Peter Witt's letzte Steuermannsreise.

I. Title.

PT2621.N54A8 51-37643

NK 0200234 DLC

Kniest, Philipp, 1830–1905.
Von der Wasserkante... Von Ph. Kniest. Bremen: C. W. Roussell, 1884–85. 2 v. 19cm.

CONTENTS.—[Bd. 1] Skizzen aus dem Schifferleben: Die Husheersche. Die alte Brig. Nach dem Eismeer. Der Missionsschuner. Der verrückte Capitän. Abgetakelt und gesloopt. Pedro Garcia.—Bd. 2. Bilder aus dem Schifferleben: Die Nixe. Aus dem alten Hause. Jungfrau Dykstra. Sjoukelina' Jugend. Windstille.

801337–8A. 1. Fiction, German. I. Title. II. Title: Skizzen aus dem Schifferleben. III. Title: Bilder aus dem Schifferleben.
N. Y. P. L. December 4, 1936

NK 0200235 NN FU

Knievel, Hermann Ignatz.
Herr Gott dich loben wir, nach der alten Kirchentonart vierstimmig bearbeitet, mit einer Einleitung und Zwischenspielen ... Lippstadt, [pref. 1826]
2 p.l., 13 p. (music) 22 x 28 cm.

NK 0200236 CtY

BX4705
M543
K55
(LC)
Kniewald, Dragutin
Dr. [i.e. Doktor] Ivan Merz; život i djelovanje. Zagreb, 1932.
272 p. illus., ports. 23 cm.

"Literarna djelatnost dra Ivana Merza": p. 196-199.

1. Merz, Ivan, 1896-1928.

NK 0200237 CtY

Kniewald, Dragutin.
A Pray-kódex tartalma
see under Kniewald, Károly.

KNIEWALD, DRAGUTIN
Proprium de tempore zagrebačke stolne crkve 1094-1788. Zagreb, Tisak Narodne tiskare, 1941.

104 p.
Reprinted from: Katolički List 1940/1941.

NK 0200239 DDO

Kniewald, Dragutin,
Vjerodostojnost latinskih izvora o bosanskim krstjanima. Zagreb, Jugoslavenska akademija znanosti i umjetnosti, 1949.
166 p. illus. 24 cm.
"Poseban otisak iz 270. knjige Rada Jugoslavenske akademije znanosti i umjetnosti. Odjel za filozofiju i društvene nauke. Knjiga I."
Includes bibliography.

1. Catholic Church in Bosnia and Herzegovina. I. Title.

BX1520.B6K6 60-30101 ‡

NK 0200240 DLC NN NNC MH DDO

Z
7838
.L7
K72
Kniewald, Dragutin.
Zagrebački liturgijski kodeksi XI.-XV.stoleca; codices liturgici manuscripti Zagrebienses a saeculo XI.usque ad finem s.XV. Zagreb, Tisak Narodne tiskare, 1940.
128 p.
"Posebni otisak iz 'Croatia Sacra,' br.19, 1940."
Bibliographical footnotes.

NK 0200241 MiU

Kniewald, Karl
see Kniewald, Károly.

4BX
Cath
1815
Kniewald, Károly
A "Hahóti kódex" (zágrábi mr 126. kézirat) jelentősége a magyarországi liturgia szempontjából. Irta és a Szent István Akadémia 1938. febr. 20.-án tartott gyülésén felolvasta Kniewald Károly. Fordította Kühár Flóris. Budapest, Szent István Akadémia, 1938.
19 p.

NK 0200243 DLC-P4 MH

Kniewald, Károly.
A Pray-Kódex Sanctorale-ja. Irta: Kniewald Károly (Zagráb). Forditotta: Kühar, Floris O.S.B.... Budapest, Kir. Magy. Egyetemi Nyomda, 1939.
55 p. 24 cm.

NK 0200244 PLatS MH

BX2037
K56
Kniewald, Károly
A Pray-Kódex tartalma, kora, jelentősége. Fordította Kühár Flóris. Budapest, Kiadja a Magyar Könyvtárosok és Levéltárosok Egyesülete, 1940.
48 p.

"Különlenyomat a'Magyar könyvszemle' 1939. évi IV. számából."

1. Pray - Kodex. 2. Catholic Church. Liturgy and ritual. Sacramentary.

NK 0200245 CU InU NNC WaU DLC-P4 MH

W 4
E69
1939
KNIEWASSER, Hans, 1910-
Zur Kenntnis der Geschwülste der Synovialmembran (Synoviome) Erlangen, Döres, 1939.
26 p. illus.
Inaug.-Diss. - Erlangen.
1. Synovial membranes 2. Synovioma

NK 0200246 DNLM CtY

VOLUME 300

Kniewel, Theodor Friedrich, 1783-1858?
Der christliche hausprediger ueber die Evangelien auf alle Sonn- und festtage des Kirchenjahres. Danzig, Herhard, 1836-37.
2 v.

NK 0200247 PPLT

BX8070 Kniewel, Theodor Friedrich, 1783-1858?
.L7K7 Christliches religionsbuch für mündige Christen und die es werden wollen, auch zum gebrauch in lehrerseminarien und höhern schulanstalten, auf grundlage der Heiligen Schrift und nach ordnung des lutherischen katechismus verfasst von dr. Theodor Friedrich Kniewel ... Danzig, In commission F. S. Gerhard, 1835.
x, 240 p. 17cm.

NK 0200248 ICU

Kniewel, Theodor Friedrich, 1783-1858?
Christliches religionsbuch fuer muendige Christen und die es werden wollen ... auf grundlage der heiligen Schrift und nach ordnung des lutherisches katechismus. 2 ... aufl. Berlin, Gehmigke, 1837.
229 p.

NK 0200249 PPLT

Kniewel, Theodor Friedrich, 1783-1858?
Geistliche wehr und waffe gegen die cholera und ihre traurigen folgen; ansichten und erfahrungen waehren der choleraepidemie in Danzig gesammelt ... Berlin, Author, 1831.
45 p.

NK 0200250 PPLT

371.44 Kniewel, Theodor Friedrich, 1783-1858?
K74k Der kunstgeist im kampf mit dem zeitgeiste, oder, Pestalozzi und seine widersacher. Dargestellt von Theod. Friedr. Kniewel Berlin, Mylius, 1818.
239p. fold.table.

1. Pestalozzi, Johann Heinrich, 1746-1827. 2. Education. I. Title.

NK 0200251 IU

YA 30153 Kniewel, Theodor Friedrich, 1783-1858
"Die wahre evangelisch-apostolische kirche." Predigt am ersten heiligen Pfingsttage den 23. mai 1847 in der St. Marien-oberpfarrkirche zu Danzig ... 2. aufl. Danzig, 1847.
14 p.

NK 0200252 DLC

DB679 .3 .S8 Knieža, Emil F., ed.
Svaz protifašistických bojovníků.
Slovenské národné povstanie vo fotografii. [Spracoval Emil Knieža v spolupráci s redakčnou radou za účastí Ľudovíta Holotíka et al. 1. vyd. Bratislava] V Slovenskom vydavateľstve politickej literatúry [1954]

Kniežata Richarda a kňažny Hesterky, welmi krásna zábawná udalost. Budapesst: Tlačou a nákladom K. Róža a jeho manželky, 1894. 28 p. illus. 16°.
In: * QL p. v. 1, no. 6.

1. Fiction (Slovenish).
N. Y. P. L. August 9, 1911.

NK 0200254 NN

409.4391 K74zHU Kniezsa, István, 1898-
Adalékok a magyar-szlovák nyelvhatár történetéhez. Budapest, Athenaeum, 1941.
60p. col.maps(part fold.) 24cm.
"A mű eredetije 'Zur Geschichte der ungarisch-slowakischen ethnischen Grenze.'"
Bibliographical footnotes.

NK 0200255 IU

Kniezsa, István, 1898-
Cirillbetűs szláv szövegek nemzetközi tudományos átírása. Budapest, Magyar Nemzeti Múzeum Orsz. Széchényi Könyvtára [1939]
14 p. 24 cm. (Az Országos Széchényi Könyvtár kiadványai, 8)
"Különlenyomat a 'Magyar könyvszemle' 1939. ápr.-jún. számából."

1. Cyrillic alphabet. I. Title.
PG92.K6 54-47351 ‡

NK 0200256 DLC NN NNC MiU

PH 2576 .K69 KNIEZSA, ISTVÁN, 1898-
Erdély víznevei, két térképmelléklettel. Kolozsvár, Minerva Irodalmi és Nyomdai Műintézet, 1942.
49 p. maps. (Cluj, Transylvania--Erdélyi Tudományos Intézet [Kiadványai])

1. Hungarian language--Etymology--Names. I. Title.

NK 0200257 InU DLC-P4

Kniezsa, István, 1898-
Helyesírásunk története a könyvnyomtatás koráig. Budapest, Akadémiai Kiadó, 1952.
204 p. 21 cm. (Nyelvészeti tanulmányok, 2)

1. Hungarian language—Orthography and spelling. 2. Hungarian language—Hist. I. Title. (Series)
PH2143.K6 55-19346

NK 0200258 DLC IU ICU NIC NN MH

Kniezsa, István, 1898-
...A magyar helyesírás a tatárjárásig, irta Kniezsa István. Budapest: Magyar nyelvtudományi társaság, 1928. 32 p. 8°. (Magyar nyelvtudományi társaság, Budapest. Kiadványai. Szám 25.)
Cover-title.

1. Hungarian language—Spelling. I. Ser.
N. Y. P. L. April 17, 1931

NK 0200259 NN

Kniezsa, István, 1898-
A magyar helyesirás története. Utánnyomás. Budapest, Tankönyvkiadó, 1953.
29 p. (Egyetemi magyar nyelvészeti füzetek)
Includes bibliographies.

1. Hungarian language - Orthography and spelling. 2. Hungarian language - History.

NK 0200260 NNC DLC-P4

Kniezsa, István, 1898-
A magyar nyelv szláv jövevényszavai. Budapest, Akadémiai kiadó, 1955-
v. 21 cm.
Summaries in Russian and German.
Bibliography: v.1,pt.1,p.25-54.

1. Hungarian language--Foreign words and phrases--Slavic.

NK 0200261 NN CtY DLC-P4 MiU CaBVaU WU IU WaU ICU TxU CU NNC MH

Kniezsa, István, 1898-
Magyarország népei a XI. században. Budapest [Franklin-Társulat] 1938.
cover-title, [365]-472 p. fold. col. map.
Reprinted from v. 2 of Emlékkönyv Szent István király halálának kilencszázadik évfordulóján.
Bibliographical footnotes.

NK 0200262 NNC

PG13 .M3 Kniezsa, István, 1898-
Magyarországi szláv nyelvemlékek. 1- Budapest, Akadémiai Kiadó, 1952-

Kniezsa, István, 1898-
A párhuzamos helynévadás, egy fejezet a településtörténetkutatás módszertanából. Budapest, Magyar Történettudományi Intézet, 1944.
59 p. 25 cm. (Településtörténeti tanulmányok, 2)

1. Names, Geographical—Hungary. 2. Bilingualism. I. Title. (Series)
DB904.K6 49-57068*

NK 0200264 DLC NjP ICU NIC CU InU CSt-H OCl NNC NN

KNIEZSA, ISTVÁN, 1898-
Die Slawenapostel und die Slowaken. Budapest, 1942. 19 p. 25cm. (Etudes sur l'Europe centre-orientale. Ostmitteleuropäische Bibliothek. no.39)
Bibliographical footnotes.

1. Cyrill, Saint, of Thessalonica, 827-869. 2. Methodius, Saint, ca.825-885. I. Ser.

NK 0200265 NN

VOLUME 300

DB 193 .K6 KNIEZSA, ISTVÁN, 1898 ed.
Stredoveké české listiny. ₍Listiny publikovali a historickými poznámkami opatrili: Belo Bottló, Erik Fügedi₎ Budapest, Akadémiai Kiado, 1952.
205 p. facsims. (Slovenské jazykové pamiatky z Mad'arska, 1; Magyarországi szláv nyelvemlékek, 1)

At head of title: Stefan Kniezsa.
Added t.-p. in Hungarian.
Summary in French and Hungarian.

NK 0200266 InU CaBVaU CU NcU DDO TxU WaU CtY NjR

Kniezsa, István, 1898-
A szláv apostolok és a tótok/ Budapest, Athenaeum Irodalmi és Nyomdai RT nyomása, 1942.
18 p. 25 cm.
At head of title: Magyar történettudományi intézet.
"Különlenyomat a Magyar Történettudományi Intézet 1942. évi évkönyvéből."
Bibliographical footnotes.

1. Cyrillus, Saint, of Thessalonica, 827 (ca.)-869. 2. Methodius, Saint, Abp. of Moravia, d. 885. I. Title.

BX4700.C9K6 63-56462

NK 0200267 DLC NN CU

949.7 K742s Kniezsa, István, 1898 -
A Szlávok. Budapest, Magyar Szemle Társaság, 1932.
80 p. (Kincsestár; a Magyar Szemle Társaság, egypengős könyvtára, 26. sz.)

1. Slavs. I. Title.

NK 0200268 WaU CLU NNC DLC-P4

DB 919 K742u Kniezsa, István, 1898-
Ungarns Völkerschaften im XI. Jahrhundert. Budapest, 1938.
171 p. maps. (Etudes sur l'Europe Centre-Orientale. Ostmitteleuropäische Bibliothek, no. 16)

Bibliographical footnotes.

1. Ethnology - Hungary. I. Title. II. Series.

NK 0200269 CLU InU DLC-P4

KNIEZSA, ISTVÁN, 1898 -
Zur Geschichte der ungarisch-slowakischen ethnischen Grenze. Budapest, 1941. 69 p. col.maps. 26cm. (Études sur l'Europe centre-orientale. Ostmitteleuropäische Bibliothek. no. 30/A)

Bibliographical footnotes.

1. Slovaks in Hungary. 2. Hungarians in Slovakia. 3. Ethnology—Hungary—Maps. I. Series.

NK 0200270 NN WU DS

Kniezsa, István, 1898 -
Zur Geschichte der ungarisch-slowakischen ethnischen Grenze. Budapest, 1941.
(Études sur l'Europe centre-orientale. Ostmitteleuropäische Bibliothek. No. 30/A)
Microfilm copy (negative)
Collation of the original: 60 p. maps (part fold.)
"Sonderdruck aus dem Archivum Europae centro-orientalis, vii (1941) Fasc. 1-3."
Bibliographical footnotes.

1. Hungary—Bound.—Slovakia. 2. Slovakia—Bound.—Hungary. 3. Ethnology—Hungary. 4. Ethnology—Slovakia. (Series)

Microfilm 474 DB Mic 60-7112

NK 0200271 DLC

Kniezsa, Stefan
see Kniezsa, István, 1898-

977.8411 C62kn 1898-1905 Knife and Fork Club, Kansas City, Mo.
The book of the Knife and Fork Club of Kansas City; covering the period from December, 1898, to December, 1905; being the time wherein were served in divers places the dinners of the club from the first to the fifty-eighth. ₍Kansas City, Mo.₎ Compiled for the club by F. N. Tufts, J. M. Lee, J. J. Vineyard ₍by₎ F. P. Burnap Stationery and Print. Co., 1906?₎
unpaged illus. 21cm.

NK 0200273 KU IU DPU

The knife and fork for 1849. Laid by the "Alderman." Founded on the culinary principles advocated by A. Soyer, Ude, Savarin, and other celebrated professors. With fourteen choice cuts by Kenny Meadows. London, H. Hurst, 1849.
2 p. l., 96 p. illus. 17cm.
Added t.-p., engr.
"No more published."—Brit. mus. Catalogue.

1. Gastronomy.

Library of Congress TX635.K69 7-26520†

NK 0200274 DLC MU CtY CSmH

The knife-grinder.
see under ₍American Sunday-School Union.

The knife-grinder's budget of pictures & poetry, for boys and girls. London: Printed for T. and J. Allman, 1829. 27 p. incl. front. illus. 9cm.
Frontispiece and p. 27 mounted on inside of original illustrated yellow paper covers.

166094B. 1. Juvenile literature—Picture books. 3. Occupations. Poetry, English. 2. Juvenile literature—Poetry.
N. Y. P. L. July 3, 1942

NK 0200276 NN NNC ICU

Kniffen, Fred Bowerman, 1900-
Achomawi geography, by Fred B. Kniffen ... Berkeley, Calif., University of California press, 1928.
cover-title, 1 p. l., ₍297₎-332 p. illus., pl. 55-59, 2 fold. maps. 28 cm. (University of California publications in America archaeology and ethnology, v. 23, no. 5)

1. Indians of North America—California. 2. Achomawi Indians. 3. Atsugewi Indians. I. Title.

E51.C15 vol. 23, no. 5 A 28—122
——— Copy 2. E99.A15K69

California. Univ. Libr. for Library of Congress ₍a58l₁₎†

NK 0200277 ICJ OCl OCU OU MiU FU FTaSU ViU CLU DAU OrU OrP DLC MU CoU MoU MB PPAmP

G126 .R85 Kniffen, Fred Bowerman, 1900- joint author.

Russell, Richard Joel, 1895-
Culture worlds ₍by₎ Richard Joel Russell ₍and₎ Fred Bowerman Kniffen. New York, Macmillan ₍1951₎

Kniffen, Fred Bowerman, 1900
The delta country of the Colorado, by Fred B. Kniffen ... [Berkeley, 1929]
2 p. l., ii, 202 numb. l. mounted photos., fold. map, diagrs. (part fold.) 29 cm.
Thesis (Ph. D.) - Univ. of California, Dec. 1929.
2nd copy is accompanied by atlas of 7 maps. 58 x 46 cm.
1. Geology - Colorado River. 2. Geology - Mexico - Sonora. 3. Geology - California - Lower. I. Title.

NK 0200279 CU

Kniffen, Fred Bowerman, 1900-
... The Indians of Louisiana, by Fred B. Kniffen ... with illustrations by Mildred Compton. Baton Rouge, La., Bureau of educational materials, statistics and research, College of education, Louisiana State university and agricultural and mechanical college ₍1945₎
108, ₍2₎ p. illus. (incl. maps) 25½cm. (University social studies series; May W. De Blieux, editor)

1. Indians of North America—Louisiana. 2. Mound-builders—Louisiana. I. Title.

45-37197

Library of Congress E78.L8K6
₍4₎ 970.4

NK 0200280 DLC OrCS OCl ICF

Kniffen, Fred Bowerman, 1900-
Lower California studies, III
see his ... The primitive cultural landscape of the Colorado delta.

Kniffen, Fred Bowerman, 1900-
Lower California studies, IV
see his ... The natural landscape of the Colorado delta.

Kniffen, Fred Bowerman, 1900-

Louisiana. *Geological survey.*
... Lower Mississippi River delta: Reports on the geology of Plaquemines and St. Bernard parishes. New Orleans, La., Department of conservation, Louisiana Geological survey, 1936.

Kniffen, Fred Bowerman, 1900-
... The natural landscape of the Colorado delta, by Fred B. Kniffen ... Berkeley, Calif., University of California press, 1932.
cover-title, 2 p. l., iii, ₍149₎-244 p. illus., fold. map, pl. 19-30, diagrs. 28 cm. (University of California publications in geography. v. 5, no. 4)
At head of title: Lower California studies. IV.

1. Colorado river—Delta. 2. Physical geography—California, Lower. I. Title.

G58.C3 vol. 5, no. 4 A 32—265
——— Copy 2. GB126.C2K5

California. Univ. Libr. for Library of Congress ₍a53i1₎†

NK 0200284 TNJ-P MtBuM OrP CaBVaU OrU CLU MU MoU DAU MsSM PU OCl DLC UU FTaSU

Kniffen, Fred Bowerman, 1900-
Pomo geography, by Fred B. Kniffen ... Berkeley, Calif., University of California press, 1939.
cover-title, 2 p. l., p. 353-399 incl. plates. maps (1 fold.) 27cm. (University of California publications in American archaeology and ethnology, v. 36, no. 6)
Bibliographical foot-notes.

1. Pomo Indians. 2. Indians of North America—Culture. 3. Indians of North America—California. I. Title.

A 39-652

California. Univ. Libr. for Library of Congress E51.C15 vol. 36, no. 6
₍12₎ (572.97) 970.3

NK 0200285 OrPS LNHT OCl DLC CU OCU OU FU PU CaBVaU FMU ViU DAU MoU

VOLUME 300

Kniffen, Fred Bowerman, 1900–
... The primitive cultural landscape of the Colorado delta, by Fred B. Kniffen ... Berkeley, Calif., University of California press, 1931.
cover-title, 1 p. l., p. [43]–66. illus. (map) pl. 2–6. 28cm. (University of California publications in geography. v. 5, no. 2)
At head of title: Lower California studies. III.
1. Colorado river—Delta. 2. Physical geography—California, Lower. 3. Indians of Mexico—Culture. I. Title. II. Title: Lower California studies.
A 31-707
California. Univ. Library for Library of Congress [G58.C3 vol. 5, no. 2] [a38i1] (910.82)
NK 0200286 CaBVaU MtBuM OrU ICN PU PPAmP OCl DLC CLU NIC DAU MU TNJ-P FTaSU OrP ICarbS UU

Kniffen, Fred Bowerman, 1900–
Louisiana. *Geological survey.*
... Reports on the geology of Iberville and Ascension parishes, by Henry V. Howe, Richard Joel Russell, Fred B. Kniffen, James H. McGuirt, Stanley M. McDonald. New Orleans, La., Published by Department of conservation, Louisiana Geological survey, 1938.

Kniffen, Fred Bowerman, 1900–
Kroeber, Alfred Louis, 1876– ed.
... Walapai ethnography, by Fred Kniffen, Gordon MacGregor, Robert McKennan, Scudder Mekeel, and Maurice Mook, edited by A. L. Kroeber ... Menasha, Wis., American anthropological association [1935]

Kniffin, Evelyn Gage.
Guide-posts on the foot-path to peace; a book of religious verse, by Evelyn Gage Kniffin ... Brooklyn, N. Y., The author, 1910.
x, 96 p. front. (port.) 16½cm. $1.00
10-29736
NK 0200289 DLC NN

Kniffin, Evelyn Gage.
Rose leaves, by Evelyn Gage Kniffin ... Brooklyn, N. Y., The author, 1910.
vi, 97 p. 16½cm. $1.00
Poems.
10-29734
NK 0200290 DLC

Kniffin, G.C., joint author.
Battle, J H.
Kentucky. A history of the state, embracing a concise account of the origin and development of the Virginia colony; its expansion westward, and the settlement of the frontier beyond the Alleghanies; the erection of Kentucky as an independent state, and its subsequent development. By J. H. Battle, W. H. Perrin, G. C. Kniffin. Louisville, Ky., Chicago, Ill., F. A. Battey publishing company, 1885.

Kniffin, G.C., joint author. FOR OTHER EDITIONS SEE MAIN ENTRY
Perrin, William Henry, d. 1892?
Kentucky. A history of the state, embracing a concise account of the origin and development of the Virginia colony; its expansion westward, and the settlement of the frontier beyond the Alleghanies; the erection of Kentucky as an independent state, and its subsequent development. By W. H. Perrin, J. H. Battle, G. C. Kniffin. Illustrated with numerous engravings. Louisville, Ky., Chicago, Ill., F. A. Battey & company, 1886.

Kniffin, Gilbert Crawford, 1832-1917.
The Army of the Cumberland. By Gilbert C. Kniffin, Lieutenant-Colonel United States Volunteers. [Chattanooga, MacGowan-Cooke, 191-?]
31 p. illus. (port.) 8 vo. In 1/2 dark blue cloth, marbled boards. Original gray front paper bound in.
Author's autograph presentation copy.
Nicholson collection, September 1922.
NK 0200293 CSmH

Kniffin, Gilbert Crawford, 1832–1917.
... Army of the Cumberland and the battle of Stone's River. Prepared by Companion Lieutenant-Colonel Gilbert C. Kniffin ... and read at the stated meeting of April 3, 1907. [Washington, 1907]
24 p. 23cm. (Military order of the loyal legion of the United States. Commandery of the District of Columbia. War papers. 68)
1. Murfreesboro, Battle of, 1862–1863. 2. U. S.—Hist.—Civil war—Regimental histories—Army of the Cumberland.
18-3410
Library of Congress E464.M54 no. 68
NK 0200294 DLC OClWHi

Kniffin, Gilbert Crawford, 1832–1917.
... The Army of the Cumberland at Missionary Ridge. Prepared by Companion Lieutenant-Colonel Gilbert C. Kniffin ... and read at the stated meeting of December 5, 1900. [Washington, 1900]
28 p. 23cm. (Military order of the loyal legion of the United States. Commandery of the District of Columbia. War papers. 37)
1. Missionary Ridge, Battle of, 1863. 2. U. S.—Hist.—Civil war—Regimental histories—Army of the Cumberland.
18-3309
Library of Congress E464.M54 no. 37
NK 0200295 DLC OClWHi

Kniffin, Gilbert Crawford, 1832-1917.
Assault and capture of Lookout Mountain. "The battle above the clouds"...Washington, 1895.
16p. YA14496
NK 0200296 DLC

Kniffin, Gilbert Crawford, 1832–1917.
Assault and capture of Lookout mountain "The battle above the clouds" . . by G. C. Kniffin . . . Published by W. E. Hardison, proprietor, Lookout mountain war relic museum, Lookout Mountain, Tenn. Chattanooga: MacGowan-Cooke [1898?] 31 p. illus. 17cm.
Cover-title.
Also issued under title: The battle above the clouds.
1. United States—Hist.—Civil war—Military, 1863, Nov. 23–25—Chattanooga. I. Lookout Mountain, Tenn. War relic museum. II. Title.
N. Y. P. L. March 15, 1940
NK 0200297 NN CSmH KyHi

Kniffin, Gilbert Crawford, 1832-1917.
... The battle above the clouds. Prepared by Companion Lieutenant-Colonel Gilbert C. Kniffin ... and read at the stated meeting of March 2, 1892. [Washington, 1892]
22 p. 23cm. (Military order of the loyal legion of the United States. Commandery of the District of Columbia. War papers. 10)
1. Lookout Mountain, Battle of, 1863.
13-21580 Revised
Library of Congress E464.M54 no. 10
—— Copy 2. E475.97.K69
NK 0200298 DLC CSmH OClWHi TxU GU

Kniffin, Gilbert Crawford, 1832-1917.
Battle of Stone's river.
20 p. (Johnson, R.U., and Buel, C.C. Battles ... of the Civil war, v. 3, p. 613)
NK 0200299 MdBP

Kniffin, Gilbert Crawford, 1832–1917.
... "The cavalry of the Army of the Cumberland in 1863." Prepared by Companion Lieutenant-Colonel Gilbert C. Kniffin ... and read at the stated meeting of December 2, 1896. [Washington, 1896]
15 p. 23cm. (Military history of the loyal legion of the United States. Commandery of the District of Columbia. War papers. 24)
1. U. S.—Hist.—Civil war—Regimental histories—Army of the Cumberland—Cavalry.
18-3296
Library of Congress E464.M54 no. 24
NK 0200300 DLC OClWHi CSmH

Kniffin, Gilbert Crawford, 1832–1917.
... The East Tennessee campaign, September, 1863. Prepared by Companion Lieutenant-Colonel Gilbert C. Kniffin ... and read at the stated meeting of January 4, 1905. [Washington, 1905]
26 p. 23cm. (Military order of the loyal legion of the United States. Commandery of the District of Columbia. War papers. 57)
1. Tennessee, East—Hist.—Civil war.
18-3323
Library of Congress E464.M54 no. 57
NK 0200301 DLC OClWHi CSmH

Kniffin, Gilbert Crawford, 1832-1917. *"20th".21.34-7
The East Tennessee Campaign, September, 1863.
(*In* Military Historical Society of Massachusetts. Papers. Vol. 7, pp. 409-432. Boston. 1908.)
A discussion of Burnside's failure to reach the vicinity of Chattanooga to reenforce Rosecrans, in September, 1863.
For a different view of the matter, see Burrage, Henry Sweetser. Burnside's East Tennessee campaign.
D7274 — Tennessee. Hist. Civil War, 1861-1865.
NK 0200302 MB

Kniffin, Gilbert Crawford, 1832-1917.
... Estimated effective strength of the Union and Confederate armies, and their respective losses during the war of the rebellion. By Companion Lieutenant-Colonel Gilbert C. Kniffin ... Read at the stated meeting of November 1, 1911 ... [Washington, 1911]
24 p. front. (port.) 23½cm. (Military order of the loyal legion of the United States. Commandery of the District of Columbia. War papers. 84)
1. U. S.—Hist.—Civil war—Stat.
15-1327 Revised
Library of Congress E464.M54 no. 84
—— Copy 2. E491.K69
NK 0200303 DLC OClWHi CSmH

VOLUME 300

Kniffin, Gilbert Crawford, 1832-1917.

Capron, Horace, 1804–1885.
... General Capron's narrative of Stoneman's raid south of Atlanta. Prepared by Companion Lieutenant-Colonel Gilbert C. Kniffin ... and read at the stated meeting of December 7, 1899. [Washington, 1899]

NK 0200305 DLC OC1WHi

Kniffin, Gilbert Crawford, 1832–1917.
... An interview with Abraham Lincoln. Prepared by Companion Lieutenant-Colonel G. C. Kniffin ... and read at the stated meeting of March 6, 1903. [Washington, 1903]
13 p. 23cm. (Military order of the loyal legion of the United States. Commandery of the District of Columbia. War papers. 47)
Includes a short account of the battle of Murfreesboro.
1. Lincoln, Abraham, pres. U. S., 1809–1865. 2. Murfreesboro, Battle of, 1862–1863.
18–3315
Library of Congress E464.M54 no. 47

NK 0200306 DLC ViU MB ICN OC1WHi KF1GS

Kniffin, Gilbert Crawford, 1832-1917.
The life and services of Major General George H. Thomas. A paper read for the District of Columbia commandery of the Military order of the loyal legion of the United States, April 6, 1887. By Companion Gilbert C. Kniffin ... Washington, D. C., Judd & Detweiler, printers, 1887.
21 p. 23½cm.
1. Thomas, George Henry, 1816–1870. I. Military order of the loyal legion of the United States. District of Columbia commandery.
12–21013
Library of Congress E467.1.T4K6

Kniffin, Gilbert Crawford, 1832–1917.
... "The life and services of Major General George H. Thomas." Prepared by Companion Lieutenant Colonel Gilbert C. Kniffin ... and read at the stated meeting of April 6, 1887. [Washington, 1887]
21 p. 23cm. (Military order of the loyal legion of the United States. Commandery of the District of Columbia. War papers. 2)
1. Thomas, George Henry, 1816–1870.
18–3289
Library of Congress E464.M54 no. 2

NK 0200307 DLC OC1WHi CSmH

Kniffin, Gilbert Crawford, 1832–1917.
... Major-General William Starke Rosecrans, U. S. army. Prepared by Companion Lieutenant-Colonel Gilbert C. Kniffin ... and read at the stated meeting of November 4, 1908. [Washington, 1908]
22 p. 23cm. (Military order of the loyal legion of the United States. Commandery of the District of Columbia. War papers. 74)
1. Rosecrans, William Starke, 1819–1898.
18–3416
Library of Congress E464.M54 no. 74

NK 0200308 DLC OC1WHi CSmH

Kniffin, Gilbert Crawford, 1832–1917.
... Raising the siege of Knoxville. Prepared by Companion Lieutenant-Colonel Gilbert C. Kniffin ... and read at the stated meeting of November 7, 1906. [Washington, 1906]
20 p. 23cm. (Military order of the loyal legion of the United States. Commandery of the District of Columbia. War papers. 65)
1. Knoxville—Siege, 1863.
18–3408
Library of Congress E464.M54 no. 65

NK 0200309 DLC CSmH OC1WHi

Kniffin, Gilbert Crawford, 1832-1917.

Furay, W S.
The real Chickamauga. Reprint of articles by W. S Furay, war correspondent, Cincinnati gazette, and Col. G. C. Kniffin, chief commissary, Twenty-first corps, Army of the Cumberland. [n. p., 1888]

Kniffin, Gilbert Crawford, 1832–1917.
... A retrospect. By Companion Gilbert C. Kniffin. Read at the stated meeting of January 1, 1913. [Washington, 1913]
15 p. 23cm. (Military order of the loyal legion of the United States. Commandery of the District of Columbia. War papers. 91)
1. U. S.—Hist.—Civil war—Addresses, sermons, etc. I. Title.
18–3432
Library of Congress E464.M54 no. 91

NK 0200311 DLC OC1WHi

Kniffin, Gilbert Crawford, 1832-1917.
... "A sailor on horseback." Prepared by Companion Lieutenant-Colonel G. C. Kniffin ... and read at the stated meeting of March 7, 1894. [Washington, 1894]
20 p. 23cm. (Military order of the loyal legion of the United States. Commandery of the District of Columbia. War papers. 19)
A narrative of the civil war career of General Samuel P. Carter.
1. Carter, Samuel Powhatan, 1819–1891. I. Title.
13–24526 Revised
Library of Congress E464.M54 no. 19
—— —— Copy 2. E474.7.K69

NK 0200312 DLC TxU KF1GS OC1WHi

Kniffin, Gilbert Crawford, 1832–1917.
... "Streight's raid through Tennessee and northern Georgia in 1863." By Companion Lieutenant Colonel Gilbert C. Kniffin ... read at the stated meeting of November 2, 1910 ... [Washington, 1910]
10 p. 23cm. (Military order of the loyal legion of the United States Commandery of the District of Columbia. War papers. 82)
1. Streight's expedition, 1863.
18–3424
Library of Congress E464.M54 no. 82

NK 0200313 DLC OC1WHi CSmH

Kniffin, Gilbert Crawford, 1832–1917.
... The third day at Stone's River. Prepared by Companion Lieutenant-Colonel Gilbert C. Kniffin ... and read at the stated meeting of May 1, 1907. [Washington, 1907]
22 p. 23cm. (Military order of the loyal legion of the United States. Commandery of the District of Columbia. War papers. 69)
1. Murfreesboro, Battle of, 1862–1863.
18–3411
Library of Congress E464.M54 no. 69

NK 0200314 DLC OC1WHi CSmH

Kniffin, H A.
Mrs. Flynn's lodgers, a play in one act, by H. A. Kniffin ... New York, S. French; [etc., etc.] ©1910.
23 p. 19cm. (*On cover:* French's American acting edition. no. 12)
I. Title.
20–145
Library of Congress PS3521.N533M5 1910

NK 0200315 DLC OrCS Or PU OC1

Kniffin, Harry A.

McKinney, William Kerr.
Commemorative history of the Presbyterian church in Westfield, New Jersey, 1728–1928, by William K. McKinney, PH. D., Chas. A. Philhower, A. M. [and] Harry A. Kniffin. [New York, ©1929]

Kniffin, Herbert Reynolds.
Masks, by Herbert Reynolds Kniffin. Peoria, Ill., The Manual arts press [©1931]
140 p. incl. front., illus. 23cm. (*Half-title:* Books on the arts; ed. by W. G. Whitford)
Bibliography: p. 137.
1. Masks (Sculpture) I. Title. 31–22773
Library of Congress NB1310.K6
—— Copy 2.
Copyright A 42027 [3] 792

NK 0200317 DLC MB NIC OrP WaT WaS NcC GU WaU NcD PP PWcT PU-Mus PPTU OC1 NB OEac OLak PPPL CaBVaU CaBVa Wa Or

Kniffin, Thomas Henderson.
Kentucky of Kentucky; a romance of the blue grass region, by H. Henderson Kniffin. New York, Cochrane publishing co., 1909.
3 p. l., 5–163 p. incl. plates. 19½cm. $1.25
9–26665
Library of Congress PZ3.K74K

NK 0200318 DLC PNt

Kniffin, William Henry, 1873–
American banking practice; a treatise on the practical operation of a bank, intended for students, bank employees and others who would know of the conduct of a bank under recognized American practice, with which is combined the negotiable instruments law, uniform in forty-six states, by William H. Kniffin ... 1st ed. New York [etc.] McGraw-Hill book company, inc., 1921.
xiii, 389 p. illus. (forms) 21cm. $3.50
1. Banks and banking—U. S.
Library of Congress HG1601.K53 21–21283

NK 0200319 DLC ViU PU PPFRB MiU OC1 ODW ICJ NN MB DAU CU NIC OrP IdU

Kniffin, William Henry, 1873–
American banking practice; a treatise on the practical operation of a bank, intended for students, bank employees and others who would know of the conduct of a bank under recognized American practice, with which is combined the negotiable instruments law, uniform in all states, by William H. Kniffin ... 2d ed. New York [etc.] McGraw-Hill book company, inc., 1929.
xiv, 393 p. incl. forms. 21 cm.
1. Banks and banking—U. S.
HG1601.K53 1929 29—12599

NK 0200320 DLC FMU OrP WaS PPT MiU OCU OC1 NN TU

Kniffin, William Henry, 1873- comp.

Illinois. *Laws, statutes, etc.*
The banking laws of Illinois, comp. by W. H. Kniffin, jr. [Chicago] Drovers deposit national bank of Chicago, ©1911.

VOLUME 300

Kniffin, William Henry, 1873- comp.
The banking laws of Missouri, a condensation of the laws as in force in 1911. New York, Bankers publishing co. [c1911]
74 p.

NK 0200322 MH-BA

Kniffin, William Henry, 1873–
Better banking, a treatise on bank management in the light of the depression, by William H. Kniffin ... 1st ed. New York and London, McGraw-Hill book company, inc., 1934.
x, 434 p. 21ᶜᵐ.

1. Banks and banking—U. S. 2. Bankers. I. Title. II. Title: Bank management.
Library of Congress HG1601.K54 34–5510
——— Copy 2.
Copyright A 70576 [5] 332.1

NK 0200323 DLC NIC NN MB WaS Or OrU MtBC IdB OrP TU WaSp PPFRB PPTU PP MiU PU OC1 OU

Kniffin, William Henry, 1873–
The business man and his bank, by William H. Kniffin ... 1st ed. New York [etc.] McGraw-Hill book company, inc., 1920.
xii, 278 p. illus. (forms) 21ᶜᵐ.

1. Banks and banking. I. Title.
Library of Congress HG1601.K55 20–14317

NK 0200324 DLC ViU IdU NIC NcRS CU OrP MtU TU PPTU PP PBm PPFRB MiU OCU OU OC1 NN MB ICJ

Kniffin, William Henry, 1873–
The business man and his bank, by William H. Kniffin ... New York [etc.] McGraw-Hill book company, inc., 1930.
xii, 332 p. illus. (forms) 21ᶜᵐ. $3.00

1. Banks and banking. I. Title.
Library of Congress HG1601.K55 1930 30–6442

NK 0200325 DLC WaS CoU NN MiU OC1 OC1W

Kniffin, William Henry, 1873–
Commercial banking; a treatise covering the practical operation of a commercial bank, the theory of money and banking, and the development of banking in the United States, by William H. Kniffin ... 1st ed. New York [etc.] McGraw-Hill book company, inc., 1923.
2 v. illus. (forms) 21ᶜᵐ. $7.00

1. Banks and banking. 2. Banks and banking—U. S. I. Title.
Library of Congress HG1601.K56 23–18049

NK 0200326 DLC NIC OrU OrCS MtU ICU DNAL CU NN MiU OC1 OU NjP PP PPFRB ICJ MB

Kniffin, William Henry, 1873–
Commercial banking; a treatise covering the practical operation of a commercial bank, the theory of money and banking, and the development of banking in the United States, by William H. Kniffin ... 2d ed. New York [etc.] McGraw-Hill book company, inc. [°1928]
2 v. forms. 21ᶜᵐ. $7.00
Paged continuously.

1. Banks and banking. 2. Banks and banking—U. S. I. Title.
Library of Congress HG1601.K56 1928 28–22197
——— Copy 2.

NK 0200327 DLC CoU NcD PPD ICJ OC1

Kniffin, William Henry, 1873–
Commercial paper, acceptances and the analysis of credit statements; a practical treatise on commercial paper, with particular reference to the processes by which the credit risk is determined where such instruments are purchased as a bank investment, by W. H. Kniffin, jr. ... New York, The Bankers publishing company, 1918.
viii, 162 p. incl. forms. 23½ cm.

1. Negotiable instruments. 2. Credit. 3. Acceptances. 4. Banks and banking. I. Title.
HG3751.K6 332.7 18—4829

NK 0200328 DLC MtU PPT OC1 OU NjP MB NN

HG 3751 K6 1920
Kniffin, William Henry, 1873-
Commercial paper, acceptances and the analysis of credit statements; a practical treatise on commercial paper, with particular reference to the processes by which the credit risk is determined where such instruments are purchased as a bank investment. 2d ed., rev. New York, Bankers Pub. Co. [c1920]
viii, 174 p. illus. 24cm.

NK 0200329 CoU ODW MiD CU PU

Kniffin, William Henry, 1873–
Commercial paper, acceptances and the analysis of credit statements; a practical treatise on commercial paper, with particular reference to the processes by which the credit risk is determined where such instruments are purchased as a bank investment, by W. H. Kniffin New York, The Bankers publishing company, 1924.
ix,208 p. incl. forms. 23½ᶜᵐ. $2.50
* 3d ed., rev. and enl.

NK 0200330 ViU NcRS MiU OC1 NcD

Kniffin, William Henry, 1873–
How to use your bank; a discussion of the relationship of a bank to its customers with practical suggestions as to how advantageously to use banking-services. By William H. Kniffin ... 1st ed. New York and London, McGraw-Hill book company, inc., 1937.
vii, 218 p. 21ᶜᵐ. (*Half-title:* McGraw-Hill practical business manuals)

1. Banks and banking. I. Title. II. Title: The relationship of a bank to its customers.
Library of Congress HG1601.K58 37–28640
——— Copy 2.
Copyright A 111219 [5] 332.1

NK 0200331 DLC WaS OrU NN OC1 MtU IdPI PJB PPTU PP PPGi OC1FRB OU MB

Kniffin, William Henry, 1873–
How to use your bank; a discussion of the relationship of a bank to its customers with practical suggestions on advantageous use of banking services. 2d ed. New York, McGraw-Hill Book Co., 1949.
vii, 229 p. 21 cm.

1. Banks and banking. I. Title.
HG1601.K58 1949 332.1 49–8313*

NK 0200332 DLC CU KyU-A KyLxT OOxM KyU KyU-A IdU OrU OrCS OrPR MtBC CoU ICU TxU OU WaS WaSp WaT OrPS

Kniffin, William Henry, 1873–
Inflation, the gold standard and the banking holiday; a reprint of a series of articles which have been running in the Nassau daily review on subjects of current interest pertaining to money, inflation, the gold standard, and the events leading up to the bank holiday. By William H. Kniffin. Rockville Centre, L. I., The Nassau daily review [1933]
70 p. 30½ᶜᵐ.

1. Banks and banking—U. S. 2. Currency question—U. S. I. Title.
Library of Congress HG538.K6 34–32082
[2] 332.40973

NK 0200333 DLC PPFRB NNQ NNC NN

Kniffin, William Henry, 1873–
New York savings bank cases; a compilation and digest of the leading cases in the New York courts, in which a savings bank has been a party, or in which matters affecting savings bank management have been an issue, arranged and condensed by William H. Kniffin, jr. ... [Brooklyn, N. Y., W. H. Kniffin, jr.] °1910.
5 p. l., 71 numb. l. 29½ᶜᵐ. $5.00
"Loose leaf edition limited to two hundred copies. This book is no. 103."

1. Savings banks — New York (State) 2. Banking law — New York (State)
Library of Congress 10-9810
——— Copy 2. HG1902.N7K6

NK 0200334 DLC

Kniffin, William Henry, 1873–
The practical work of a bank; a treatise on practical banking which aims to show the fundamental principles of money; the practical work of a bank in detail, and particularly, credit in its relation to banking operations, by William H. Kniffin, jr. ... New York, The Bankers publishing company, 1915.
vii, 621 p. illus., fold. tab., forms (1 fold.) 25ᶜᵐ. $5.00

1. Banks and banking. I. Title.
Library of Congress HG1601.K6 15—20406

NK 0200335 DLC OC1 FMU CU ICRL OrPR MiU OCU OC1W NN MB NjP ICJ

Kniffin, William Henry, 1873–
The practical work of a bank; a treatise of practical banking which aims to show the fundamental principles of money; the practical work of a bank in detail, and particularly, credit in its relation to banking operations, by William H. Kniffin, jr. ... 2d ed., rev. New York, The Bankers publishing company, 1916.
xi, 644 p. illus. (incl. plans) fold. tab., forms (1 fold.) 25ᶜᵐ. $5.00

1. Banks and banking. I. Title.
Library of Congress HG1601.K6 1916 16—20128

NK 0200336 DLC WaWW PP PPD MiU OOxM NjP

Kniffin, William Henry, 1873–
The practical work of a bank; a treatise on practical banking which aims to show the fundamental principles of money; the practical work of a bank in detail, and particularly, credit in its relation to banking operations, by William H. Kniffin, jr. ... 4th ed. New York, The Bankers publishing company, 1917. $5.00.
xi, 600 p. illus. (incl. plans) fold. diagr., forms. 25ᶜᵐ.

NK 0200337 Or MB

Kniffin, William Henry, 1873–
The practical work of a bank; a treatise of practical banking which aims to show the fundamental principles of money; the practical work of a bank in detail, and particularly, credit in its relation to banking operations, by William H. Kniffin, jr. ... 4th ed. New York, The Bankers publishing company, 1919.
xi, 600 p. illus. (incl. plans) fold. diagr., forms. 25ᶜᵐ.

NK 0200338 NIC OEac OU

Kniffin, William Henry, 1873–
The practical work of a bank; a treatise of practical banking which aims to show the fundamental principles of money; the practical work of a bank in detail, and particularly, credit in its relation to banking operations, by William H. Kniffin, jr. ... 5th ed. (rev.) New York, The Bankers publishing company, 1919.
xi, 604 p. illus. (incl. plans) fold. diagr., forms. 25ᶜᵐ.

1. Banks and banking. I. Title.
Library of Congress HG1601.K6 1919 19—16057

NK 0200339 DLC Or MiU OC1 CaQML CoU PPFRB NjP ICJ

VOLUME 300

Kniffin, William Henry, 1873-
The practical work of a bank; a treatise on practical banking which aims to show the fundamental principles of money; the practical work of a bank in detail, and particularly, credit in its relation to banking operations. 6th ed. (rev.) New York, Bankers Pub. Co., 1921.
xi, 604 p. illus., forms. 23cm.

1. Banks and banking. I. Title.

NK 0200340 MB TU PPTU IdU IdPI

Kniffin, William Henry, 1873–
The practical work of a bank; a treatise on practical banking which aims to show the fundamental principles of money; the practical work of a bank in detail, and particularly, credit in its relation to banking operations, by William H. Kniffin ... 7th ed. New York, The Bankers publishing company, 1928.
xi, 618 p. incl. illus., forms. 24cm.

1. Banks and banking. I. Title.

Library of Congress HG1601.K6 1928 26-26924

NK 0200341 DLC OrU NBuU CU CaBVa OrU OCl OClh PPFRB PPD ViU

Kniffin, William Henry, 1873–
The practical work of a bank; a treatise on practical banking which aims to show the fundamental principles of money; the practical work of a bank in detail; and, particularly, credit in its relation to banking operations, by William H. Kniffin ... 8th ed. New York, The Bankers publishing company, 1934.
ix, 571 p. incl. illus., forms. 24cm.

1. Banks and banking. I. Title.

Library of Congress HG1601.K6 1934 34-39694
——— Copy 2.
Copyright A 78271 [3] 332.1

NK 0200342 DLC WaSp WaS PPTU MiU OClFRB OCl

Kniffin, William Henry, 1873–
The practical work of a bank; a treatise on practical banking which aims to show the fundamental principles of money, the practical work of a bank in detail and, particularly, credit in its relation to banking operations. 9th ed. Cambridge, Mass., Bankers Pub. Co., 1948.
582 p. illus. 24 cm.

1. Banks and banking. I. Title.

HG1601.K6 1948 332.1 48-10700*

NK 0200343 DLC MB OrCS Wa WaS WaT ViU ICU OU PPFRB

Kniffin, William Henry, 1873–
The savings bank and its practical work; a practical treatise on savings banking, covering the history, management and methods of operation of mutual savings banks, and adapted to savings departments in banks of discount and trust companies, with over 180 illustrations taken from original sources, by Wm. H. Kniffin, jr. ... New York, The Bankers publishing company, 1912.
vi, 551 p. front., illus., plates (1 fold.) 25cm. $5.00

1. Savings-banks. 2. Savings-banks—U. S.

Library of Congress HG1886.K6 13—4442

NK 0200344 DLC WaS OrP CU NIC PU MiU OU OClW NN MB ICJ NjP

Kniffin, William Henry, 1873–
The savings bank and its practical work, a practical treatise on savings banking, covering the history, management and methods of operation of mutual savings banks, and adapted to savings departments in banks of discount and trust companies, with over 180 illustrations taken from original sources, by Wm. H. Kniffin, jr. ... 3d ed. New York, The Bankers publishing company, 1918.
3 p. l., 541 p. front., illus., plates (1 fold.) 25cm.

1. Savings-banks. 2. Savings-banks—U. S.

Library of Congress HG1886.K6 1918 18—18810

NK 0200345 DLC ICRL Or OrU MtU OrP MiU OCl OClFRB OCU PPTU PPFRB

Kniffin, William Henry, 1873–
The savings bank and its practical work; a practical treatise on savings banking, covering the history, management and methods of operation of mutual savings banks, and adapted to savings departments in banks of discount and trust companies, by Wm. H. Kniffin ... 4th ed. New York, The Bankers publishing company, 1928.
xiv, 531 p. incl. illus., forms. plates. 24cm.

1. Savings-banks. 2. Savings-banks—U. S.

Library of Congress HG1886.K6 1928 28-4245

NK 0200346 DLC OrP WaS NcD CU MiU OCl OU PPFRB PU

Kniffler, Carter, 1906–
Die "sozialen" dramen der achtziger u. neunziger jahre des 19. jahrhunderts und der sozialismus ... von Carter Kniffler ... [Wiesbaden] Westdruckerei Wiesbaden g. m. b. h., 1929.
63 p. 21cm.
Inaug.-diss.—Frankfurt am Main.
Lebenslauf.
"Literatur": p. 61-62.

1. German drama—19th cent.—Hist. & crit. 2. Social problems in literature. I. Title.

Library of Congress PT663.K5 42-39065

NK 0200347 DLC

Kniffler, Gustav.
Das jesuiten-gymnasium zu Duesseldorf; ein beitrag zur geschichte des Koeniglichen gymnasiums zu Duesseldorf. Duesseldorf, Jockwer, 1892.
52 p.

NK 0200348 PU

Kniffler, Oscar. *3762.121
Jodoform zur inneren Anwendung.
(In Behring. Gesammelte Abhandlungen zur ätiologischen Therapie von ansteckenden Krankheiten. Theil 1, pp. 14-106. Leipzig. 1893.)
Litteraturnachweis, pp. 105, 106.

F6873 — Iodoform.

NK 0200349 MB PPC DNLM CU

Knific, Franc
Junac s pristave; za slovensko mladino. 172,[2]p. illus., ports. Zagreb, Založili Salezijanci, Tisk. Gašparovic, 1929.

NK 0200350 OCl

Rare Bk Coll **Kniga Bol'shomu chertezhu.**
Древняя россійская идрографія, содержащая описаніе Московского государства рѣкъ, протоковъ, озеръ, кладязей, и какіе по нихъ городы и урочища, и на какомъ оныя разстояніи. Изданная Н. Новиковымъ. Въ Санктпетербургѣ, 1773.
233 p. illus. 20 cm.

1. Russia—Distances, etc. I. Novikov, Nikolaĭ Ivanovich, 1744–1818, ed. *Title transliterated:* Drevnia͡ia rossiĭska͡ia idrografii͡a.

DK17.K59 43-38575 rev 2*

NK 0200351 DLC

K6 1838 Rare Bk Coll **Kniga Bol'shomu chertezhu.**
Книга Большему чертежу; или, Древняя карта Россійскаго Государства, поновленная въ Розрядѣ и списанная въ книгу 1627 года. Изд. 2. Санктпетербургъ, Въ Тип. Имп. Россійской академіи, 1838.
xxxi, 261 p. 26 cm.
Preface signed: Д. Языковъ.
First published in 1773 under title: Древняя россійская идрографія.

1. Russia—Distances, etc. I. I͡Azykov, Dmitriĭ Ivanovich, 1773–1845, ed. *Title transliterated:* Kniga Bol'shemu chertezhu.

DK17.K6 1838 12-11985 rev 2*

NK 0200352 DLC

Kniga Bol'shomu chertezhu.
Книга Большому чертежу. Подготовка к печати и ред. К. Н. Сербиной. Москва, Изд-во Академии наук СССР, 1950.
228 p. facsims. 27 cm.
At head of title: Академия наук СССР. Институт истории. Ленинградское отделение.
Errata slip inserted.
"Таблицы списков Книги Большому чертежу."
Bibliography: p. [190]-201.

1. Russia—Distances, etc. I. Serbina, K. N., ed. *Title transliterated:* Kniga Bol'shomu chertezhu

DK17.K62 1950 51-23492

NK 0200353 DLC OU

K62 1846 Rare Bk Coll **Kniga Bol'shomu chertezhu.**
Книга, глаголемая Большой чертежъ, изданная по порученію Императорскаго общества исторіи и древностей россійскихъ Г. И. Спасскимъ. Москва, Въ Унив. тип., 1846.
xxvii, 327 p. 23 cm.
First published in 1773 under title: Древняя россійская идрографія.

1. Russia — Distances, etc. I. Spasskiĭ, Grigoriĭ Ivanovich, d. 1864, ed. *Title transliterated:* Kniga, glagolema͡ia Bol'shoĭ chertezh.

DK17.K62 1846 12-11986 rev 2*

NK 0200354 DLC

Kniga bytīa nebesi i zemli.
Книга бытіа небеси и земли (Палея историческая), съ приложеніемъ сокращенной Палеи русской редакціи. Трудъ Андрея Попова. Москва, Изд. Имп. Об-ва исторіи и древностей россійскихъ при Московскомъ университетѣ, 1881.
xxxiv, 172, 92, xvi p. 28 cm.
Text in Church Slavic.

1. Bible. O. T. Apocrypha. Church Slavic. I. Popov, Andreĭ Nikolaevich, 1841-1881, ed. II. Moscow. Universitet. Obshchestvo istorii i drevnosteĭ rossiĭskikh.

BS1693.C48K55 72-226451

NK 0200355 DLC

Kniga bytīa nebesi i zemli
see
Kniga bytīa nebesi i zemli.

VOLUME 300

Книга детям; журнал, посвященный вопросам детского и юношеского чтения. ₍г. 1- 1928- Москва, Гос. изд-во.

v. in illus., ports. 23-26 cm.

Monthly, 1928; bimonthly (irregular) 1929-
Ceased publication in 1931? Cf. Union list of serials.
Publication suspended, July 1928-Apr. 1929.
Issued by Nauchno-pedagogicheskaia sektsiia of Gosudarstvennyĭ uchenyĭ sovet RSFSR, 1928.

1. Children's literature, Russian—Bibl.—Period. I. Russia (1917- R. S. F. S. R.) Gosudarstvennyĭ uchenyĭ sovet. Nauchno-pedagogicheskaia sektsiia. *Title transliterated:* Kniga detiam.

Z1037.6.K5 52-21157

NK 0200357 DLC

Kniga ėparkha
see
Byzantine Empire. *Laws, statutes, etc., 886-911 (Leo VI, the Wise)*

Книга героев. ₍Под общей ред. Кави Наджми₎ Казань, Таттосиздат, 1946-

v. ports. (part mounted) 30 cm.

1. World War, 1939-1945—Biog. 2. World War, 1939-1945—Tatar Republic. I. Näjmi Kavi. 1901-1957, ed. *Title transliterated:* Kniga geroev.

D736.K6 52-33215

NK 0200359 DLC

Kniga, glagolemaia Bol'shoĭ chertezh
see **Kniga Bol'shomu chertezhu.**

Kniga glagolemaia Podlinnik
see
Podlinnik ikonopisnyĭ.

Книга и оборона СССР. ₍г. ₎-3₎; 1934. Москва, Гос. воен. изд-во ₍etc.₎

v. illus., ports. 25 cm.
Semimonthly, monthly, 1933-34.
Began publication in 1932.
Supersedes in part Книга строителям социализма.
At head of title, 1933: Критико-библиографический бюллетень.
Title varies: 1933, Военная литература.
Issued by Nauchno-issledovatel'skiĭ kritiko-bibliograficheskiĭ institut (called Kritiko-bibliograficheskiĭ institut) 19 -33; by Politicheskoe upravlenie RKKA, 1934.

1. Military art and science—Bibl.—Period. I. Moscow. Nauchno-issledovatel'skiĭ kritiko-bibliograficheskiĭ institut. II. Russia (1923- U. S. S. R.) Armiia. Glavnoe Politicheskoe upravlenie. *Title transliterated:* Kniga i oborona SSSR.

Z6723.K6 51-54526

NK 0200362 DLC

Книга и профсоюзы.

₍Москва₎ Кн-во ВЦСПС ₍etc.₎

v. 27-35 cm. monthly.

Began publication in 1924. Ceased publication in 1929? Cf. Union list of serials.
Organ of Kul'turnyĭ otdel of Vsesoiuznyĭ TSentral'nyĭ Sovet Professional'nykh Soiuzov, 1928-

1. Russian literature—Bibl.—Period. 2. Library science—Period. 3. Labor and laboring classes—Russia. I. Vsesoiuznyĭ TSentral'nyĭ Sovet Professional'nykh Soiuzov. Kul'turnyĭ otdel. *Title transliterated:* Kniga i profsoiuzy.

Z1035.6.K55 51-52654

NK 0200363 DLC

Книга и пролетарская революция; ежемесячный журнал марксистско-ленинской критики и библиографии.

Москва, Гос. социально-экон. изд-во.

v. in illus., ports. 25 cm.

Began publication in 1932. Cf. Летопись периодических изданий.
Published 19 -Sept. 1935 by Изд-во Правды.

1. Books—Reviews. 2. Communism—Bibl.—Period. *Title transliterated:* Kniga i proletarskaia revoliutsiia.

Z7164.S67K6 51-29077

NK 0200364 DLC

Книга и революция; ежемесячный критико-библиографический журнал. ₍г. ₍1₎-3 (№ 1-28); июнь 1920/21-22/23. Петроград (Петербург) Гос. изд-во.

3 v. in 4. 31 cm.

Publication suspended July-Nov. 1921.

1. Bibliography—Period. 2. Books—Reviews. 3. Russian literature—Hist. & crit.—Period. *Title transliterated:* Kniga i revoliutsiia; ezhemesiachnyĭ kritiko-bibliograficheskiĭ zhurnal.

Z1007.K6 51-52663

NK 0200365 DLC CaBVaU

Книга и революция; журнал политики, культуры, критики и библиографии. ₍г. 1-2₎ № 30; 1929-30. Москва, Гос. изд-во.

2 v. in 4. illus., ports. 26 cm.

Semimonthly, 1929, July-Dec. 1930; every 10 days, Jan.-July 1930.
No more published? Cf. Union list of serials.

1. Books—Reviews. 2. Communism—Bibl.—Period. *Title transliterated:* Kniga i revoliutsiia; zhurnal politiki.

Z7164.S67K63 51-54487

NK 0200366 DLC

Книга именуемая Брюсовской календарь. ₍Москва, 17—₎

35 (i. e. 49) l. illus. 22 x 33 cm.

First ed., published in 1709, compiled by V. A. Kiprianov under the supervision of IA. V. Briūs. Reissued many times with various additions. Cf. V. S. Sopikov. Опытъ россійской библіографіи, 1904, no. 4084; Большая сов. энцикл., 2d ed., v. 6, p. 192.

1. Calendar. I. Kiprianov, Vasiliĭ Anofrievich, d. 1723? II. Briūs, IAkov Villimovich, graf, 1670-1735. III. Title: Briūsovskoĭ kalendar' *Title transliterated:* Kniga imenuemaia Briūsovskoĭ kalendar'.

CE91.K7 56-55812

NK 0200367 DLC

Книга именуемая Брюсовской календарь. ₍Москва, 17—₎

35 (i. e. 51) l. illus. 22 x 33 cm.

First ed., published in 1709, compiled by V. A. Kiprianov under the supervision of IA. V. Briūs. Reissued many times with various additions. Cf. V. S. Sopikov. Опытъ россійской библіографіи, 1904, no. 4084; Большая сов. энцикл., 2d ed., v. 6, p. 192.

1. Calendar. I. Kiprianov, Vasiliĭ Anofrievich, d. 1723? II. Briūs, IAkov Villimovich, graf, 1670-1735. III. Title: Briūsovskoĭ kalendar'. *Title transliterated:* Kniga imenuemaia Briūsovskoĭ kalendar'.

CE91.K7 56-55811

NK 0200368 DLC

Книга юного натуралиста. ₍Составитель И. Халифман₎ Москва, Гос. изд-во детской лит-ры, 1950.

818 p. illus., col. plates, port. 22 cm.
"Для старшего возраста."

1. Plant-breeding. *Title transliterated:* Kniga iūnogo naturalista.

SB123.K6 51-15298

NK 0200369 DLC OCl

HD1491
.R9K54

Книга колхозника по планированию и организации труда. ₍В составлении книги принимали участие: А. Н. Дерябин и др.₎ Москва, Гос. изд-во сельхоз. лит-ры, 1953.

270 p. 21 cm.

1. Collective farms—Russia. I. Deriabin, A. N. *Title transliterated:* Kniga kolkhoznika po planirovaniiu i organizatsii truda.

HD1491.R9K54 53-37220

NK 0200370 DLC

.K56
1781
Rare Bk
Coll

Книга ... кратких поученій ѡ главнѣйших спсительных догматах вѣры, и заповѣдех Бжіих, и ѡ должностах, из разных стых оцъ и оучителей собранна. Въ Москвѣ, 1781.

1 v. (various pagings) 32 cm.

1. Orthodox Eastern Church—Doctrinal and controversial works. *Title romanized:* Kniga ... kratkikh pouchenii ō glavnieĭshikh spasitel'nykh dogmatakh vīery.

BX320.K56 1781 78-203309

NK 0200371 DLC

Книга ... кратких поученій ѡ главнѣйших спсительных догматах вѣры, и заповѣдех Бжіих, и ѡ должностах, из разных стых оцъ и оучителей собранна. Въ Москвѣ, 1795.

₍1₎, 14, 263 l. 33 cm.
Title from verso of prelim. l.

1. Orthodox Eastern Church—Doctrinal and controversial works. *Title romanized:* Kniga ... kratkikh pouchenii ō glavnieĭshikh spasitel'nykh dogmatakh vīery.

BX320.K56 1795 72-203310

NK 0200372 DLC

Книга Марсова или воинскихъ дѣлъ отъ войскъ Царскаго Величества россійскихъ во взятіи преславныхъ фортификацей и на разныхъ мѣстахъ храбрыхъ баталій, учиненныхъ надъ войски Его Королевскаго Величества Свѣйскаго. Съ перваго санктпетербургскаго 1713 г. изд. вторымъ тисненіемъ напечатанная. Въ Санктпетербургѣ, При Морскомъ шляхетномъ кадетскомъ корпусѣ, 1766.

193 p. 23 plans. 25 cm.

1. Military art and science—Early works to 1800. 2. Peter I, the Great, Emperor of Russia, 1672-1725. 3. Attack and defense (Military science) *Title transliterated:* Kniga Marsova.

UG443.K6 54-55819

NK 0200373 DLC

Kniga ... ō dolzhnostiakh presvyterov prikhodskikh.
see under [Georgiĭ, Abp. of Mogilev] 1717-1795.

Книга о духахъ, содержащая начала спиритическаго ученія о безсмертіи души, о натурѣ духовъ и ихъ отношеніи къ людямъ; о нравственныхъ законахъ, о настоящей и грядущей жизни и о будущности человѣчества. По ученію высшихъ духовъ съ помощью многихъ медіумовъ. С.-Петербургъ, Изд. г. П. І. О'Рурkъ, 1889.

lix, 559 p. 22 cm. (Спиритуалистская философія)

1. Spiritualism. I. Series: Spiritualistskaia filosofiia. Title romanized: Kniga o dukhakh, soderzhashchaia nachala spiriticheskago ucheniia o bezsmertii dushi.

BF1266.K59 74-290871

NK 0200375 DLC

VOLUME 300

Книга о книгах; двухнедельный библиографический журнал. № 1–8; апр.–июль 1924. [Москва] Гос. изд-во.

1 v. illus., ports. 25 cm.

L. C. set incomplete: no. 1–3 wanting.

1. Bibliography—Bibl.—Catalogs.
Title transliterated: Kniga o knigakh.

Z1002.K58 52-46452

NK 0200376 DLC

Z
1002
K582
Книга о книге. Le Livre du livre. сборник 1–2; 1927–29. Ленинград.

2 v. 23 cm. irregular.

Issued by Nauchno-issledovatel'skiĭ institut knigovedeniia.
No more published?

1. Bibliography—Bibl. I. Leningrad. Nauchno-issledovatel'skiĭ institut knigovedeniia.
Title transliterated: Kniga o knige.

Z1002.K582 52-50877

NK 0200377 DLC CSt MU

PG3452
Z8 K6
Книга о Леонидѣ Андреевѣ; воспоминанія М. Горькаго, К. Чуковскаго, А. Блока, Георгія Чулкова, Бор. Зайцева, Н. Телешова, Евг. Замятина, Андрея Бѣлаго [*pseud.*] 2. дополненное изд. Берлинъ, Петербургъ [etc.] Издательство З. И. Гржебина, 1922.

191, [1] p., 1 l. front. (port.) 16cm.

St
1. Andreev, Leonid Nikolaevich, 1871–1919. I. Gor'kiĭ, Maksim, 1868–1936.

42-26684

NK 0200378 DLC

PG3452
Z8K6
Книга о Леониде Андрееве; воспоминания М. Горького, К. Чуковского, А. Блока, Георгия Чулкова, Бор. Зайцева, Н. Телешова, Евг. Замятина. Петербург-Берлин, Издательство З. И. Гржебина, 1922.

109 p., 1 l. 21½cm.

1. Andreev, Leonid Nikolaevich, 1871–1919. I. Gor'kiĭ, Maksim, 1868–1936.

42-26683

NK 0200379 DLC NPV

Книга объ избраніи на царство великаго государя, царя и великаго князя Михаила Өедоровича. Москва, Издана Коммиссіею печатанія гос. грамотъ и договоровъ, состоящею при Московскомъ гл. архивѣ Министерства иностранныхъ дѣлъ, 1856.

xi, 119 p. col. illus., col. port. 43 cm.
Possibly compiled by boiarin A. S. Matveev.
Russian and Church Slavic.
1. Michael, Czar of Russia, 1596–1645. I. Matveev, Artamon Sergeevich, 1625–1682, comp. II. Russia. Komissiia pechataniia gosudarstvennykh gramot i dogovorov.
Title romanized: Kniga ob izbranii na tsarstvo velikago gosudariia, tsariia i velikago kniazia Mikhaila Fedorovicha.

DK115.K55 74-290165

NK 0200380 DLC

Kniga peremen
see
I ching.

Kniga Premudrosti Solomona
see
Bible. O.T. Apocrypha. Wisdom of Solomon.

Kniga stepennaia tsarskago rodosloviia.

DK70
.S79
Rare Bk
Coll
Stepennaia kniga.

Книга степенная царскаго родословія, содержащая исторію россійскую съ начала оныя до временъ Государя Царя и Великаго Князя Іоанна Васильевича, сочиненная трудами преосвященныхъ митрополитовъ Купріана и Макарія, а напечатанная подъ смотреніемъ ... Герарда Фридерика Миллера. Въ Москвѣ, При Имп. университетѣ, 1775.

Книга—строителям социализма; бюллетень. г. 1–5, № 7; 1928–32. Москва, Огиз [etc.]

5 v. 18–20 cm.

2 no. a month, 1928–29; 3 no. a month, 1930–32.
Vols. 1–3 called also no. 1–76.
Issued by Bibliograficheskiĭ otdel of Glavnyĭ politiko-prosvetitel'nyĭ komitet of Narkompros RSFSR, 1928–30, no. 16; by Sektor massovoĭ raboty of Narkompros RSFSR, 1930, no. 17–36; by Nauchno-issledovatel'skiĭ kritiko-bibliograficheskiĭ institut (called in 1931, Bibliograficheskiĭ institut, 1931–32.
Title varies: 1928–30, Рекомендательный бюллетень Главполитпросвета.

Since Apr. 1932 divided into 10 independent bulletins of the institute: 1) Биология, медицина, физкультура, 2) Детская литература, 3) Художественная литература, 4) Книга и оборона, 5) Литература национальностей СССР, 6) Обзор искусств, 7) Сельскохозяйственная литература, 8) Техническая литература, 9) Учебно-педагогическая литература, 10) За большевистскую книгу.

1. Russian literature—Bibl.—Period. I. Russia (1917– R. S. F. S. R.) Glavnyĭ politiko-prosvetitel'nyĭ komitet. II. Russia (1917– R. S. F. S. R.) Narodnyĭ komissariat po prosveshcheniiu. Sektor massovoĭ shkol'noĭ i politiko-prosvetitel'noĭ raboty. III. Moscow. Nauchno-issledovatel'skiĭ kritiko-bibliograficheskiĭ institut.
Title transliterated: Kniga—stroiteliam sotsializma.

Z2495.K58 51-46527 rev

NK 0200385 DLC

Kniga Tsviet dobrodieteleĭ i terniĭ porokov
see under Fiore di virtù. Russian.

Kniga tysiachi i odnoĭ nochi
see under Arabian nights. Russian.

Книга в Румынской Народной Республике. Бухарест, 1952.

88 p. (chiefly illus., ports.) 23 cm.

1. Book publishers and publishing—Rumania.
Title transliterated: Kniga v Rumynskoĭ Narodnoĭ Respublike.

Z441.K55 53-29912

NK 0200388 DLC

Книга вожатого. [Москва] Молодая гвардия, 1946.

471 p. illus., col. plates. 25 cm.

"В помощь вожатым пионерских дружин и отрядов."

1. Vsesoiuznaia pionerskaia organizatsiia V.I. Lenina—Handbooks, manuals, etc.
Title transliterated: Kniga vozhatogo.

HS3325.R8K6 51-29958

NK 0200389 DLC

Книга вожатого. [Редколлегия: К. Воронков и др. Москва] Молодая гвардия, 1951.

537 p. illus., col. plates, ports. 26 cm.

1. Vsesoiuznaia pionerskaia organizatsiia V.I. Lenina—Handbooks, manuals, etc.
Title transliterated: Kniga vozhatogo.

HS3325.R8K6 1951 51-34294

NK 0200390 DLC

Книга вожатого. [Состав авторов: Т. Матвеева и др. Редколлегия: З. Туманова и др. Изд. 5., перер. и доп. Москва] Молодая гвардия, 1954.

541 p. illus. 26 cm.

1. Vsesoiuznaia pionerskaia organizatsiia V.I. Lenina—Handbooks, manuals, etc.
Title transliterated: Kniga vozhatogo.

HS3325.R8K6 1954 54-41195 ‡

NK 0200391 DLC

Книга взрослыхъ. Составлена учительницами воскресныхъ школъ при ближайшемъ участіи Х. Д. Алчевской. Москва, Тип. И. Д. Сытина, 1899–1900.

3 v. illus., ports. 24 cm.

1. Russian language—Chrestomathies and readers. I. Alchevskaia, Khristina Danilovna (Zhuravleva) b. 1843.
Title transliterated: Kniga vzroslykh.

PG2117.K55 51-46499

NK 0200392 DLC

Kniĭger, A
Untersuchung über die Balik des Planeten Themis nebst einer neuen Bestimmung der Anziehung des Jupiter.
1 vol. 42pp. Helsingfors: 1866.

NK 0200393 MiU

Kniĭger, Benj. Ephr.,
Vetichab und Danbwart -- die Allemannischen Brüder. 1748.

NK 0200394 MiU

Knigge, freyherr von, pseud.

SEE

Kotzebue, August Friedrich Ferdinand, von, 1761-1819

Knigge, Adolf Franz Friedrich Ludwig, Freiherr von, 1752-1796.
Aus einer alten Kiste. Original briefe. Handschriften und Documente aus dem Nachlasse eines bekamten Mannes.

307p. D. Lpz., 1853.

NK 0200396 OClW

VOLUME 300

PT2383 K35B4 Knigge, Adolf Franz Friedrich Ludwig, Freiherr von, 1752-1796./
Benjamin Noldmann's Geschichte der Aufklärung in Abyssinien, oder Nachricht von seinem und seines Herrn Vetters Aufenthalte an dem Hofe des grossen Negus, oder Priesters Johannes. Frankfurt und Leipzig, 1791.
2 v. in 1.

With this is bound the author's Joseph von Wurmbrand, kaiserlich abyssinischen Ex-Ministers ... politisches Glaubensbekenntniss. 1792.

NK 0200397 CU IEN MH MdBJ NjP CaBVaU

3465 .13 .319 Knigge, Adolf Franz Friedrich Ludwig, Freiherr von, 1752-1796.
Das Betragen des Weisen in den verschiedenen Verhältnissen des Lebens und in dem Umgange mit Menschen. Wien, A.Doll, 1792.
183 p. 18 cm.

NK 0200398 NjP

HS405 K7 [KNIGGE, ADOLPH FRANZ FRIEDRICH LUDWIG, freiherr VON] 1752-1796.
Beytrag zur neuesten geschichte des freimaurerordens, in neun gesprächen mit erlaubniss meiner obern herausgegeben. Berlin, 1786.
[10], 182 p. 16cm.

1. Freemasons.

NK 0200399 ICU NIC

---

833 K742b Knigge, Adolf Franz Friedrich Ludwig, Freiherr von, 1752-1796.
Briefe, auf einer Reise aus Lothringen nach Niedersachsen geschrieben. Hannover, C. Ritscher, 1793.
229, [1] p. 17cm.

1. Germany - Descr. & trav. I. Title.

NK 0200400 TxU CU MH

Knigge, Adolf, Freiherr von, 1752-1796.
Briefe, auf einer reise aus Lothringen nach Niedersachsen geschrieben. 2d ed. Hanover, Ritscher, 1806. 206p. (Schriften von Adolf Freiherrn Knigge. v.12)

NK 0200401 OClW

[Knigge, Adolf Franz Friedrich, freiherr von] 1752-1796.
Des seligen herrn etatsraths Samuel Conrad von Schaafskopf [pseud.] hinterlassene papiere; von seinen erben herausgegeben. 2. auflage. Breslau, 1796.
136 p. 20 cm.
Contents. - I. Bruchstücke aus der lebensbeschreibung des herrn etatsraths von Schaafskopf; von ihm selbst gesammelt. - II. Umständliche nachricht von der verbesserten einrichtung des uralten Pinselordens.
1. Secret societies - Germany.

NK 0200402 CU

PT 2383 K35 D6 1907 Knigge, Adolf Franz Friedrich Ludwig, Freiherr von, 1752-1796.
Doctor Bahrdt mit der eisernen Stirn, oder Die deutsche Union gegen Zimmermann; ein Schauspiel in vier Aufzügen, von Freyherrn von Knigge Leipzig, J. Zeitler, 1907, 1790.
75 p. 18 cm. (Deutsche Litteratur-Pasquille, 1. Stück)

I. Title. II. Title: Die deutsche Union gegen Zimmermann.

NK 0200403 OU NNU-W PHC InU TxU

PT 1265 .N48 v.2 no.12 (Rare) Knigge, Adolph Franz Friedrich Ludwig, Freiherr von, 1752-1796.
Die Gefahren der grossen Welt. Ein Schauspiel in drey Aufzügen. Nach dem Französischen, aus dem ersten Theil des théatre à l'usage des jeunes personnes. Für die deutsche Bühne umgearbeitet. Grätz, 1797.
104 p. (In Neue Sammlung deutscher Schauspiele. Grätz, 17--v.2, no. 12)

NK 0200404 ICU

Beinecke Library Zg18 K742 g793b Knigge, Adolf Franz Friedrich Ludwig, Freiherr von, 1752-1796.
The German Gil Blas; or, The adventures of Peter Claus. Translated from the German of Baron Kuiegge [!] ... Dublin, Printed by N. Kelly, for Messrs. P. Byrne, J. Moore, W. Jones, and J. Rice, 1793.
2 v. 17 cm.
Armorial bookplate of John Slacke; autographs of R. Reynell and Samuel A. Reynell.

NUC. I.Title. 1.Slacke, John - Armorial bookplate. 2.Reynell, R - Autograph 3.Reynell, Samuel A. - Autograph

NK 0200405 CtY ICN OU IU NjP MH

Knigge, Adolf Franz Friedrich Ludwig, Freiherr von, 1752-1796.
The German Gil Blas; or, The adventures of Peter Claus. Translated from the German of Baron Kuiegge [sic] ... London: Printed for C. and G. Kearsley, 1793. 3 v. 17½cm.

958583-5A. 1. Fiction, German. I. Title. II. Title: Claus, Peter, The adventures of. N. Y. P. L. September 20, 1938

NK 0200406 NN CtY NcU CtY PPL ViU MB

Knigge, Adolph Franz Friedrich Ludwig, 1752
Geschichte des Amtraths Gutmann. Hanover, 1794
12°

NK 0200407 NN

PT 2383 K35G4 Knigge, Adolf Franz Friedrich Ludwig, Freiherr von, 1752-1796.
Geschichte des armen Herrn von Mildenburg, in Briefen hrsg. von Adolph Freyherrn Knigge. Hannover, In der Schmidtschen Buchhandlung, 1789-90.
3 v. 17cm.

Vols. 2-3 have imprint: Hannover, C. Ritscher.

NK 0200408 NIC NjP

Knigge, Adolf, Freiherr von, 1752-96
Geschichte des armen Herrn von Mildenburg, in Briefen hrsg. von A. Freyherrn Knigge. Frankfurt, 1792
3 v.

NK 0200409 MH

PT 2383 .K35 G4 Knigge, Adolf Franz Friedrich Ludwig, Freiherr von, 1752-1796
Geschichte des armen Herrn von Mildenburg, in Briefen hrsg. von Adolph Freyherrn Knigge. 2. Aufl. Hannover, Ritscher, 1797-98.
3 v. 18 cm.

NK 0200410 WU

3465 .13 .339 Knigge, Adolf Franz Friedrich Ludwig, Freiherr von, 1752-1796
Geschichte Peter Clausens, von dem Verfasser des Romans meines Lebens. Frankfurt a. M., Im Andreäischen Verlag, 1783.
3 pt. in 1 v. illus. 20 cm.

NK 0200411 NjP

833K74 Oge1784 [Knigge, Adolf Franz Friedrich Ludwig, Freiherr von] 1752-1796.
Geschichte Peter Clausens. Von dem Verfasser des Romans meines Lebens. Riga, 1784.
3v. fronts. 17cm.

Vol.2-3 have imprint: Wien, Im Verlag G. P. Wucherers, und gedruckt mit Weimarschen Schriften.

NK 0200412 IU

Knigge, Adolph Franz Friedrich Ludwig, Freiherr von, 1752-1796.
Geschichte Peter Clausens. Frankfurt am Main, Andreäische Buchhandlung, 1794.
2 v. in 1. 22 cm.

InU NIC NcU
NK 0200413 CU TxU OU NjPT WU NcU CU-W GU NNC CaBVaU

Knigge, Adolf Franz Friedrich Ludwig, freiherr von, 1752-1796.
The history of the Amtsrath Gutman, written by himself. Published by Adolphus Baron Knigge. Translated from the German. London: Printed for Vernor and Hood, 1799.
1 p. l., [v]-xi, [13]-342 p. 18cm.
On spine: Amtsrath Gutman.

I. Title. Translation of Geschichte des Amtsrats Gutmann. II. Title: Amtsrath Gutman.

NK 0200414 ViU

Knigge, Adolf Franz Friedrich Ludwig, Freiherr von, 1752-1796.
Hoe moet ik met vrouwen omgaan?
see under title

940.8 K742j [Knigge, Adolf Franz Friedrich Ludwig, Freiherr von] 1752-1796.
Josephs von Wurmbrand, kaiserlich abyssinischen Ex-Ministers, jezzigen Notarii caesarii publici in der Reichsstadt Bopfingen, politisches Glaubensbekenntniss, mit Hinsicht auf die französische Revolution und deren Folgen. Frankfurt, 1792.
viiip., l.l., 173p. 17cm.
1. Europe - Politics - 18th cent. 2. France - Hist. - Revolution, 1789. I. Title: Josephs von Wurmbrand ... politisches Glaubensbekenntniss. II. Title: Politisches Glaubensbekenntniss.

NK 0200416 TxU CU WaU

VOLUME 300

Knigge, Adolf, freiherr von, 1752-1796.
Knigge redivivus: Über den umgang mit menschen, von Adolf freiherrn Knigge. Neuzeitlich bearbeitet von Curt von Weissenfeld. Oranienburg, Möller [1908]
160 p.

An abridgment adapted to modern life. Cf. p. [5]

1. Social ethics. 2. Conduct of life. I. Title: Über den umgang mit mensche. II. Title: Knigge redivivus. III. Weissenfeld, Curt von, ed.

NK 0200417 NNC

Knigge, Adolf Franz Friedrich Ludwig, Freiherr von, 1752-1796.
Die Kunst mit Menschen umzugehen. Neu dargestellt und bearbeitet. Basel [1950]
71p.

NK 0200418 ICRL ICU

.K754 Hebrai Sect.

[Knigge, Adolf Franz Friedrich Ludwig, *Freiherr* von] 1752-1796.
מהלכים עם אנשים, מאת פייבל שיפער. ווארשא, תרכ"ו.
[Warschau, 1866]
190 p. 21 cm.

Added t. p.: Mehalchim; oder, Umgang mit Menschen.
Abridged translation of the author's Ueber den Umgang mit Menschen.

1. Conduct of life—Early works to 1900. 2. Social ethics. I. Schiffer, Feiwel, tr. II. Title. *Title transliterated:* Mehalkhim 'im anashim.

BJ1563.K754 51-52794

NK 0200419 DLC

BJ 1578 C94 K554 1874

Knigge, Adolf Franz Friedrich Ludwig, 1752-1796.
O obcovaní s lidmi; kniha pro každého. 15.opravené vyd. Praha, Nákl.Mikulaše a Knappa, 1874.
292 p.

1.Conduct of life. I.Title.

NK 0200420 NSyU

Knigge, Adolf Franz Friedrich Ludwig, Freiherr von, 1752-1796.
Объ обращеніи оъ людьми. Сочиненіе барона Книгге. Съ нѣмецкаго перевелъ Яковъ Лангенъ. Новое изд., испр. и доп. С. Петербургъ, Въ Тип. Имп. Воспитательнаго дома, 1820-23.
4 v. in 1. 22 cm.

Vols. 2-4 have imprint: С. Петербургъ, Въ Морской тип.
Translation of Über den Umgang mit Menschen.

1. Conduct of life—Early works to 1900. 2. Social ethics. I. Title.
Title romanized: Ob obrashchenii s lfud'mi.

BJ1563.K7572 77-295510

NK 0200421 DLC

BJ1563 K697 1808

Knigge, Adolf Franz Friedrich Ludwig, Freiherr von, 1752-1796.
Om omgänget med menniskor, af Adolph Friherre Knigge. I tre delar. Efter sjunde förbättrade original upplagan öfversättning af C.E. Rademine. Stockholm, Marquard, 1808-10.
3 v. in 1.

Imprint v. 2-3: Linköping,Groth och Petre, 1810.
Vol.1, 2d ed.

1. Conduct of life. 2. Social ethics.

NK 0200422 CU

833K74 OuDf

Knigge, Adolf Franz Friedrich Ludwig, Freiherr von, 1752-1796.
Over omgang med mennesker. Efter Baron A. Knigges tydske original, af P. D. Fabert. Kiøbenhavn, J. F. Schultz, 1793.
3v. in 1. 18cm.

Translation of Ueber den Umgang mit Menschen.

1. Conduct of life. 2. Social ethics.

NK 0200423 IU

KNIGGE, ADOLF FRANZ FRIEDRICH LUDWIG, FREIHERR, VON, 1752-1796.
Philo's endliche Erklärung und Antwort, auf verschiedene Anforderungen und Fragen, die an ihn ergangen, seine Verbindung mit dem Orden der Illuminaten betreffend. Hannover, In der Schmidtschen Buchhandlung, 1788. 142 p. 17cm.

1. Illuminati.
i. [Title] Endliche.

NK 0200424 NN MH

Knigge, Adolf, freiherr von, 1752-1796.
Practical philosophy of social life, or The art of conversing with men. After the German of Baron Knigge. By P.Will. London, Printed for T.Cadell, jun., and W.Davies, 1799.

2 v.

NK 0200425 MH NN PPL-R

Knigge, Adolf Franz Friedrich Ludwig, *freiherr* von, 1752-1796.
Practical philosophy of social life; or, The art of conversing with men: after the German of Baron Knigge. By P. Will ... 1st American ed. Lansingburgh, Penniman & Bliss, O. Penniman & co., printers, Troy, 1805.
xxxii, 368 p. 21cm.

1. Conduct of life. 2. Social ethics. I. Will, Peter, tr. II. Title.

9-34160

Library of Congress BJ1563.K7

NK 0200426 DLC DGU NcD OU InU CSt NjP MiU NN

PT 2383 K35R2 1805

Knigge, Adolf Franz Friedrich Ludwig, freiherr von, 1752-1796.
Die reise auf die universität, ein seitenstück zu der reise nach Braunschweig, von Adolf freyherrn von Knigge. Neuburg, Im Reichs-commissions und industrie büreau [1805?]
1 p.l., 128 p.

Engraved title-page.

NK 0200427 CLU IU

Knigge, Adolf Franz Friedrich Ludwig, *freiherr* von, 1752-1796.
Die reise nach Braunschweig; ein comischer roman. Von Adolph freyherrn Knigge. Hannover, C. Ritscher, 1792.
5 p. l., [5]-248 p. 16½cm.

1. Voyages, Imaginary. I. Title.

34-30595

Library of Congress PT2383.K35R4 1792 837.6

NK 0200428 DLC MdBJ MH NIC

KNIGGE, Adolf, freiherr von, 1752-1796.
Die reise nach Braunschweig; ein comischer roman. 2. verbesserte aufl. Hannover, C. Ritscher, 1794.

Front.

NK 0200429 MH

Zg18 K741 792rb

Knigge, Adolf Franz Friedrich Ludwig, Freiherr von, 1752-1796
Die Reise nach Braunschweig; ein comischer Roman ... Neue Aufl. mit einem Kupfer. Hannover, in der Ritscherschen Buchhandlung, 1802.
4p.l., 231p. fold.front. 18cm.

NK 0200430 CtY OCU

KNIGGE, Adolf Franz Friedrich Ludwig, freiherr von, 1752-1796.
Die reise nach Braunschweig; ein komischer roman. Von Adolph freiherrn Knigge. Neue auflage mit einem kupfer. Hannover, 1803.
223 p. front.

NK 0200431 WaU

Knigge, Adolf Franz Friedrich Ludwig, *freiherr* von, 1752-1796.
Die reise nach Braunschweig. Komischer roman von Adolph freiherrn Knigge. 7. aufl., hrsg. vom enkel des verfassers. Mit 36 skizzen von G. Osterwald. Hannover, Hahnsch, 1839.
2 p. l., viii, 176 p. front., illus., plates. 20½cm.

Added t.-p., illustrated.
"Vorwort des herausgebers" signed: Freiherr Fr. von Reden, dr.

1. Voyages, Imaginary. I. Reden, Friedrich Wilhelm Otto Ludwig, freiherr von, 1804-1857, ed. II. Title.

34-30596

Library of Congress PT2383.K35R4 1839 837.6

NK 0200432 DLC MH NN

PN6033 .U6 no.14

Knigge, Adolph Franz Friedrich Ludwig, *freiherr* von, 1752-1796.
Die reise nach Braunschweig. Ein komischer roman von Adolph freiherrn Knigge. Leipzig, P. Reclam, jun. [186-?]
130 p. 14cm. [Universal-bibliothek, 14]

NK 0200433 ICU MH OCU NN

KNIGGE, Adolph Franz Friedrich Ludwig, Freiherr von.
Die Reise nach Braunschweig.
(In Humoristischer Hausschatz für's deutsche Volk. Neue Folge, Bd. I, pp. 1-98. Leipzig. [1877?])

NK 0200434 MB

Knigge, Adolf Franz Friedrich Ludwig, freiherr von, 1752-1796. Die reise nach Braunschweig.

Bobertag, Felix, 1841-1907, *ed.*
Erzählende prosa der klassischen periode ... hrsg. von Felix Bobertag. Berlin und Stuttgart, W. Spemann 1886 ...

VOLUME 300

Knigge, Adolf [Friedrich Franz Ludwig] frhr. von, 1752-1796.
Die reise nach Braunschweig, ein komischer roman. Essen, Girardet, 1920.
230p.

NK 0200436 OCU MH

Knigge, Adolph Franz Friedrich Ludwig, *Freiherr* **von,** 1752-1796.
Die Reise nach Braunschweig; ein komischer Roman. Bearb. und hrsg. von Kristian Kraus. Leipzig, H. H. Kreisel [1944]
127 p. 20 cm.

I. Kraus, Kristian, 1880- ed. II. Title.
PT2383.K35R4 1944 837.6 A 48-4544*

Yale Univ. Library for Library of Congress [1]†

NK 0200437 CtY DLC CU

Knigge, Adolf Franz Friedrich Ludwig, freiherr von. 1752-1796
Der roman meines lebens in briefen herausgegeben. 1-2. t. Riga, 1781-
2 v. in 1. illus. T.-p. for v. 1 is wanting.

NK 0200438 OU NjP

Knigge, Adolph Franz Friedrich Ludwig, *freiherr* **von,** 1752-1796.
Der roman meines lebens, in briefen hrsg. von freyherrn von Knigge ... neue aufl. Frankfurt am Main, Andreäische buchhandlung, 1805.
2 v. 18½cm.

1. Title.

18-1079

Library of Congress PT2383.K35R6

NK 0200439 DLC

[Knigge, Adolf, Freiherr von, 1752-96]
Rückblicke auf den, wenn Gott will, für Teutschland nun bald geendigten Krieg. Copenhagen, 1795

NK 0200440 MH

252
K742
ser.3 Knigge, Adolph Franz Friedrich Ludwig, Freiherr von, 1752-1796.
Sechs Predigten über Trost im Leiden, Bezähmung der Leidenschaften, Gute Werke, Verläumdung, Bibelstudium und Schmeicheley; hrsg. von Adolph Freyherrn von K..... Dritte Sammlung. Frankfurt am Main, In der Andreäischen Buchhandlung, 1788.
184p. 16cm.

1. Sermons, German. I. Title.

NK 0200441 TxU

Knigge, Adolf Franz Friedrich Ludwig, Freiherr von, 1752-1796.
Sechs Stimmen über geheimen Gesellschaften
see under title

Knigge (Adolph [Franz Friedrich Ludwig von] *Baron.*
Staatkundige geloofsbelijdenis, met betrekking tot de Fransche revolutie en haare gevolgen ... Uit het Hoogduitsch. *Dordrecht: DeLeeuw & Krap,* 1792. 1 p.l., vi, 132 pp. nar. 8°.

NK 0200443 NN

PT2383
K35A19
1779 Knigge, Adolf Franz Friedrich Ludwig, Freiherr von, 1752-1796.
Theaterstücke. Hanau, G.D. Schulz, 1779-
v.

Contents.- 1.Th. Der Richter, ein Drama in drey Aufzügen aus dem Französischen des Herrn Mercier. Warder, ein Drama in fünf Aufzügen.

NK 0200444 CU

Knigge, Adolf Franz Friedrich Ludwig, *freiherr* **von,** 1752-1796.
Ueber den bücher-nachdruck. An den herrn Johann Gottwerth Müller, doctor der weltweisheit in Itzehoe. Von Adolph freyherrn Knigge. Hamburg, B. G. Hoffmann, 1792.
56 p. 16cm.

1. Copyright—Unauthorized reprints.

34-16021

Library of Congress Z586.A1K7 655.643

NK 0200445 DLC

DJ71
.K69 Knigge, Adolph Franz Friedrich Ludwig, Freiherr von, 1752-1796.
Über den gegenwärtigen Zustand des gesellschaftlichen Lebens in den vereinigten Niederlanden. Als ein Anhang zu dem Werke: Über den Umgang mit Menschen, aus dem Holländischen übersetzt von Adolph Freiherrn Knigge. Hannover, C. Ritscher, 1790.
iv, 147 p.

1. Netherlands--Soc. life & cust. I. Title.

NK 0200446 ICU

*
BJ1563
.K75
1788 Knigge, Adolf Franz Friedrich Ludwig, Freiherr von, 1752-1796.
Ueber den Umgang mit Menschen. Hannover, Schmidtschen Buchhandlung, 1788.
2 v. 16cm.

1. Condudt of life. 2. Social ethics.

NK 0200447 ViU CtY MH PPG MB PU

Knigge, Adolf Franz Friedrich Ludwig, freiherr von, 1752-1796.
Ueber den umgang mit menschen. Von Adolph freyherrn Knigge ... 4. verb. und aufl. Hannover, C. Ritscher, 1792-93.
3 v. in 1. 18 cm.

NK 0200448 CU

BJ 1563
K69
1794 Knigge, Adolf Franz Friedrich Ludwig, Freiherr von, 1752-1796.
Ueber den Umgang mit Menschen. Von Adolph Freyherrn Knigge. 3. verm. und verb. Ausg. Frankfurt, 1794.
3 v. in 1. 18 cm.

1. Conduct of life. 2. Social ethics.

NK 0200449 OU InU

BJ1563
.K75
1796 Knigge, Adolf Franz Friedrich Ludwig, Freiherr von, 1752-1796.
Über den Umgang mit Menschen in drey Theilen, von Adolph Freyherrn Knigge. 6. verm. und verb. Aufl. Wien, F. Haas, 1796-1800 [v.1, 1800]
3 v. in 1 (447 p.) 22 cm.

1. Conduct of life. 2. Social ethics.

NK 0200450 ViU

170
K74u
1797 Knigge, Adolf Franz Friedrich Ludwig, freiherr von, 1752-1796.
Über den Umgang mit Menschen von Adolph Frenherrn Knigge. 5. vermehrte und verbesserte Aufl. Wien, F. Haas, 1797.
447p. 20cm

1. Conduct of life. 2. Social ethics. I. Title. 0 cd.

NK 0200451 KU

170
K69
1799 Knigge, Adolf Franz Friedrich Ludwig, Freiherr von, 1752-1796.
Ueber den Umgang mit Menschen, von A. Freyherrn von Knigge. 6. verb. Aufl. Mit Thurfürstl. Sächs. Privilegio. Hannover, Ritscherschen Buchhandlung, 1799.
3 v. in 1. port. 18 cm.

Vol. 2 and 3 have special t.p. with edition statement: 6. verb. und verm. Aufl.

1. Conduct of life. 2. Social ethics. I. Title.

NK 0200452 N NN

BJ 1563
K69
18-- Knigge, Adolf Franz Friedrich Ludwig, Freiherr von, 1752-1796.
Über den Umgang mit Menschen [hrsg. von Alexander von Gleichen-Russwurm] Berlin, Deutsche Bibliothek [18--]
346 p. 18 cm.

1. Conduct of life. 2. Social ethics. I. Gleichen-Russwurm, Alexander, Freiherr von, 1865-1947, ed. II. Title.

NK 0200453 OU OCl

BJ1560
.K754 Knigge, Adolf Franz Friedrich Ludwig, freiherr von, 1752-1796.
Ueber den umgang mit menschen ... 7. verb. aufl. Mit dem portrait des verfassers ... Hannover, Ritscher, 1801.
3 v. in 1. port.
Imperfect: portrait wanting.

1. Conduct of life. 2. Social ethics.

NK 0200454 ICU

PM 6383
.K35 U4
1804 Knigge, Adolf Franz Friedrich Ludwig, Freiherr von, 1752-1796.
Ueber den Umgang mit Menschen, von Adolph Freiherrn Knigge. In drei Theilen. 8. verb. Aufl. Mit dem Portrait des Verfassers. Hannover, In der Ritscherschen Buchhandlung, 1804.
3 v. in 1. 17 cm.

Portrait wanting.

NK 0200455 MdBJ NN

VOLUME 300

Knigge, Adolf Franz Friedrich Ludwig, freiherr
von, 1752-1796.
K8.K74 Ueber den Umgang mit Menschen. Von Adolf Frei-
ℓ816 herrn Knigge. In drei Theilen. 9.verb. Aufl.
Stuttgart,A.F.Macklot,1816.
iv,103,viii,120,viii,100p. 20cm.

NK 0200456 CtY OOxM PPG

Knigge, Adolph Franz Friedrich Ludwig, Freiherr von, 1752–
1796.
Ueber den Umgang mit Menschen. Von Adolph Freiherrn
Knigge... Neunte Original-Ausgabe. Durchgesehen und vermehrt von F. P. Wilmsen... Hannover: Gebrüder Hahn, 1817–
18. 3 v. in 1. 12°.

Each volume has separate and added title-pages, and separate pagination.

65198A. 1. Conduct of life. 2. Wilmsen, Friedrich Philipp,
1770–1831, editor.
N. Y. P. L. December 9, 1922.

NK 0200457 NN ViU OC1W

---

ar V Knigge, Adolf Franz Friedrich Ludwig,
11770 Freiherr von, 1752-1796.
Ueber den Umgang mit Menschen. 10.
Ausg. Durchgesehen und verm. von F. P.
Wilmsen. Stuttgart, U.F. Macklot, 1822.
ix, 405 p. 19cm.

I. Wilmsen, Friedrich Philipp, 1770-1831,
ed.

NK 0200458 NIC

Knigge, Adolf Franz Friedrich Ludwig,
freiherr von, 1752-1796.
Ueber den Umgang mit Menschen, in drei
Theilen, durchgesehen und vermehrt von F. P.
Wilmsen. Ed. 10. Hannover, Hahn, 1822-24.
4 v.

NK 0200459 PU

BJ 1563
K58 Knigge, Adolf Franz Friedrich Ludwig, Freiherr
1827 von, 1752-1796.
Ueber den Umgang mit Menschen, von
Adolph Freiherrn Knigge. 10. Ausg., durch-
gesehen und verm. von F.P. Wilmsen. Wien,
L. Grund, 1827.
437 p.

1. Conduct of life. 2. Social ethics.
I. Wilmsen, Friedrich Philip, 1770-1831,
ed. II. Title.

NK 0200460 CaBVaU

J1563
K75 Knigge, Adolph Franz Friedrich Ludwig,
Freiherr von, 1752-1796.
Über den Umgang mit Menschen. Nach der
zehnten Original-Ausgabe, durchgesehen und
verm. von F. P. Wilmsen. Wien, A. von Haykul,
1828.
3 v. in 1. 21cm.

1. Conduct of life. 2. Social ethics. I.
Wilmsen, Friedrich Philipp, 1770-1831. II. T.

NK 0200461 MiDW

BJ1563
.K75 Knigge, Adolf Franz Friedrich Ludwig,
1830 Freiherr von, 1752-1796.

Über den Umgang mit Menschen. Mit
Biographie und Portrait. Hildburghausen,
Druck vom Bibliographischen Institut; New
York, H. J. Meyer [183-?]
3 v. in 1. port. 12cm. (Meyer's Groschen-
Bibliothek der Deutschen Classiker für alle Stände.
33.-35. Bdchn.)
1. Conduct of life. 2. Social ethics.

NK 0200462 ViU CaBVaU

Knigge, Adolf Franz Friedrich Ludwig, *freiherr* von,
1752–1796.
Ueber den umgang mit menschen. Von Adolph freiherrn Knigge ... 11. original-ausg. Durchgesehen und
aufs neue stark vermehrt von F. P. Wilmsen. Mit einem
titelkupfer nach Ramberg ... Hannover, Hahn'sche hof-
buchhandlung, 1830.
3 v. front. 18½cm. (*Added t.-p.:* Schriften von Adolph freiherrn
Knigge ... 1.–3. bd.)
"Kurze biographie des freiherrn Adolph Knigge" (with special t.-p.):
v. 1, p. [vii]–xxx.
1. Conduct of life. 2. Social ethics. I. Wilmsen, Friedrich Philipp,
1770–1831, ed.

9—33727

Library of Congress BJ1563.K75

NK 0200463 DLC MH

833K74 Knigge, Adolf Franz Friedrich Ludwig, freiherr
Ou1834 von, 1752-1796.
... Ueber den umgang mit menschen. (Im auszuge.) ... Hildburghausen [etc.] Bibliographisches institut, 1834.
3v. in 1. front.(port.) (Cabinets-bibliothek der deutschen classiker. 67.-69.bdchen.)
At head of title: Adolph v. Knigge.
Half-title: Neue cabinets-bibliothek der deutschen classiker.
With this is bound: Jacobi, J. G. Ausgewählte
gedichte. Hildburghausen, 1834.

NK 0200464 IU MB

Knigge, Adolf Franz Friedrich Ludwig, *freiherr* von, 1752–
1796.
... Ueber den umgang mit menschen. Im auszuge. Mit
biographie und portrait. Hildburghausen und Amsterdam,
Bibliographisches institut, 1844.
254 p., 1 l. front. (port.) 16½cm. (Familien-bibliothek der deutschen
classiker ... 97. bd.)
At head of title: Adolph v. Knigge.

I. Title.

32–3437

Library of Congress PT1101.F3 bd. 97

[2] (830.8) 170

NK 0200465 DLC IEN MB OEac PPG PU OCU

---

ar V Knigge, Adolf Franz Friedrich Ludwig,
12159 freiherr von, 1752-1796.
Ueber den Umgang mit Menschen. 14. Ori-
ginalausg. in einem Bande. Aufs neue durch-
gearbeitet und eingeleitet von Karl Goedeke.
Hannover, Hahn, 1865.
xxiii, 396 p. 19cm.

1. Social ethics. 2. Conduct of life. I.
Goedeke, Karl, 1814-1887, ed.

NK 0200466 NIC MdBJ

Knigge, Adolf Franz Friedrich Ludwig, Freiherr
von, 1752-1796.
Ueber den Umgang mit Menschen. 15. Original
Ausg. Eingeleitet und aufs neue verbessert vc
Karl Goedeke. Hannover, Hahn, 1869.
3v. in 1. 19cm.

1. Conduct of life. 2. Social ethics.
I. Goedeke, Karl, 1814-1887, ed.

NK 0200467 NcU MH

Knigge, Adolph Franz Friedrich, Freiherr
BJ1563 von, 1752-1796.
K75 Ueber den Umgang mit Menschen. [2. Aufl.]
1878 Leipzig, P.Reclam [1878]
374 p. 15cm.(in binder, 18cm.) (Universal-
Bibliothek, 1138-1140)
"Vorwort" signed: W.L.

1.Conduct of life. 2.Social ethics.
I.Title. SC

NK 0200468 CSt RPB MH MiU MdBJ IaU

Knigge, Adolf Franz Friedrich Ludwig,
freiherr von, 1752-1796.
Über den umgang mit menschen..
Nach dem original text hrsg.von V.Berends
Gera, Griesbach, 1891.
xvi,355 p. 18 cm.

I.Berends,V., ed.

NK 0200469 NjP

Knigge, Adolf Franz Friedrich Ludwig, Freiherr von, 1752–1796.
Ueber den Umgang mit Menschen. Von Adolph Freiherrn
Knigge. Nach der neunten Original-Ausgabe. Mit einem Sachregister. Halle: O. Hendel [1894]. vi p., 1 l., 349 p., front.
(port.) 12°.

1. Conduct of life.
N. Y. P. L. August 6, 1917.

NK 0200470 NN

Knigge, Adolf Franz Friedrich Ludwig, Freiherr
von, 1752-1796.
Über den Umgang mit Menschen. [Aufs Neue
hrsg. und mit einer Charakteristik Knigges
versehen von Hans Feigl] München, G. Müller
[1911]
543 p. 19 cm.

NK 0200471 PSt

---

170 Knigge, Adolf Franz Friedrich Ludwig,
K742ul Freiherr von, 1752-1796.
Ueber den Umgang mit Menschen. Ungekürzte
Ausg. Berlin, Globus [19--?]
342 p.

1. Conduct of life. 2. Social ethics.
I. Title.

NK 0200472 WaU ViU

BJ
1563 Knigge, Adolf Franz Friedrich Ludwig,
K69p Freiherr von, 1752-1796.
Über den Umgang mit Menschen; Vorschriften zu einem glücklichen, ruhigen
und nützlichen Leben in der Welt und
unter Menschen. Nach der neunten Original-Ausgabe neu bearb. und mit einem Sachregister versehen von Werner Holl. Berlin, C.Henschel [Vorrede 1912]
448p. 20cm.

NK 0200473 NRU OC1

VOLUME 300

170
K742 **KNIGGE, Adolf Franz Friedrich Ludwig, freiherr von, 1752-1796.**
... Über den umgang mit menschen. Berlin, Deutsche bibliothek [1936]
346, [2] p. 17cm.
"Fur die Deutsche bibliothek hrsg. von Alexander von Gleichen-Russwurm."
1.Gleichen-Russwurm,,Alexander, freihern von, 1865- ed. 2.Conduct of life. 3.Social ethics. I.Title

NK 0200474 MnU

Knigge, Adolf Franz Friedrich Ludwig, freiherr von, 1752-1796
Ueber eigennutz und undank; ein gegenstük zu dem buche: Ueber den umgang mit menschen. Frankfurt, 1796. 295p.

NK 0200475 OClW OU MH

Knigge, Adolf Franz Friedrich Ludwig, *freiherr* **von,** 1752-1796.
Ueber eigennutz und undank; von Adolph freyherrn Knigge; ein gegenstück zu dem buche: Ueber den umgang mit menschen. 2. unveränderte ausg. Leipzig, Jacobäer'sche buchhandlung, 1815.
438 p. 17½cm.

1. Conduct of life. 2. Egoism.

9-34170†

Library of Congress BJ1563.K74

NK 0200476 DLC

WA
11617 Knigge, Adolf Franz Friedrich Ludwig, Freiherr von, 1752-1796.
Ueber Friedrich Wilhelm den Liebreichen und meine Unterredung mit ihm, von J. C. Meywerk [pseud.] Frankfurth, 1788.
39p.

1. Friedrich Wilhelm II, King of Prussia, 1744-1797.

NK 0200477 CtY

[**Knigge, Adolf Franz Friedrich Ludwig,** Freiherr von,] 1752-1796, editor.
Ueber Jesuiten, Freymaurer und deutsche Rosencreutzer. Herausgegeben von Joseph Aloisius Maier [pseud.]... Leipzig, 1781. 129 p. 16cm.

707131A. 1. Jesuits and Jesuitism, Anti. 2. Freemasons. 3. Rosicrucians.
N. Y. P. L. June 12, 1934

NK 0200478 NN MH-AH MH ICU NIC

[KNIGGE,Adolf,freiherr von,1752-1796.]
Über Jesuiten,freymaurer und deutsche Rosencreutzer herausgegeben von J.A.Maier,Leipzig. Eingeleitet und mit nachwort versehen von Alfred Unger. Berlin,A.Unter,[1929].

Added title-page:Neudrucke älterer freimaurerischer literatur,I,5.

NK 0200479 MH

808.9
K74u **Knigge, Adolph Franz Friedrich Ludwig, Freiherr von, 1752-1796.**
Ueber Schriftsteller und Schriftstellerey, von Adolph, Freyherrn Knigge. Hannover, Bey C. Ritscher, 1793.
303p. 17cm.

NK 0200480 IU CU IEN MH

Knigge, Adolf Franz Friedrich Ludwig, Freiherr von, 1752-1796.
Umgang mit menschen, als eine mitgabe fuer die reifere jugend; bearbeitet von Veronika Schweizer. 2e aufl. Leipzig, 1881.

NK 0200481 PPL

BJ1563
K65
1952 KNIGGE, Adolf Franz Friedrich Ludwig, freiherr von, 1752-1796.
Umgang mit Menschen. [Neubearb. Aufl.] Wien, Cerny [1952]
204p. (Schule der Lebenskunst, 1)

1. Social ethics. 2. Etiquette. I. Title.

NK 0200482 CU-Riv

Knigge, Adolph Franz Friedrich Ludwig, Freiherr von, 1752-1796.
Unpartheyische Untersuchung über die Folgen der französischen Revolution auf das übrige Europa, von A. v. K. Thorn, Verlagsgesellschaft, 1794.
104p. 16cm.

1. France - History - Revolution - Foreign public opinion. I. Title.

NK 0200483 TxU

Knigge, Adolf Franz Friedrich Ludwig, freiherr **von, 1752-1796.**
Die verirrungen des philosophen oder Geschichte Ludwigs von Seelberg. Herausgegeben von A. freiherrn von K**** ... Frankfurt am Main, In der Andreäischen buchhandlung, 1787.
2 v. front. 18cm.

I. Title. II. Title: Geschichte Ludwigs von Seelberg.

NK 0200484 ViU TxU MH PPG

Knigge, Adolf Franz Friedrich Ludwig, *freiherr* **von,** 1752-1796.
Le voyage de Brunswick. Roman comique, d'après l'original allemand du baron de Knigge, par J. B. Daulnoy, professeur au Lycée de Dusseldorf. [Dusseldorf?] Chez l'auteur, 1806.
4 p. l., 175, [1] p. 15½cm.

1. Voyages, Imaginary. I. Daulnoy, J. B., tr. II. Title.

34-3992

Library of Congress PT2383.K35R43 837.6

NK 0200485 DLC

PT
2383
.K35
Z38 **Knigge, Adolf Franz Friedrich Ludwig, freiherr von, 1752-1796**
Das Zauberschloss, oder Geschichte des Grafen Junger. Herausgegeben von Adolph Freyherrn Knigge. Hannover, Christian, 1791.
308p. 16cm.

NK 0200486 TNJ

Knigge, Adolf Franz Friedrich Ludwig, freiherr von, 1752-1796
Das zauberschloss, oder Geschichte des grafen Tunger. Neue unveränderte aufl. Hannover, Ritscher, 1804.
nar. 12°. pp. (6), 272.

NK 0200487 MH

Knigge, Erich Herbert, 1911-
... Ueber die posttraumatische Spätapoplexie Bollinger's betrachtet im Lichte der neueren Auffassung des blutigen Hirnschlages ... Speyer a. Rh., 1937.
Inaug.-Diss. - Heidelberg.
Lebenslauf.
"Literatur": p. 16.

NK 0200488 CtY

Knigge, Ernst
Die negative Leistung. Eine Skizze nach dem Bürgerlichen Gesetzbuch ... von Ernst Knigge ... Quedlinburg, Wendehake, Meyer & Stegmann, 1903.
58 p. 21½cm.
Inaug.-diss. - Erlangen.
Bibliography in "Abkürzungen": p.57-58.

NK 0200489 MH-L DLC

---

ar W
13412 **Knigge, Friedrich, 1859-**
Die Sprache des Dichters von Sir Gawain and the Green Knight, der sogenannten Early English alliterative poems und De Erkenwalde. T.1. Marburg [Ger.] 1885.
120 p. 21cm.

Diss.--Marburg.

1. Gawain and the Grene Knight. 2. Erkenwald, Saint. Legend. 3. English language--Middle English (1100-1500)--Phonology.

NK 0200490 NIC NjP NcD MH PBm MiU ICRL TU

Knigge, Friedrich, 1859-
Die sprache des dichters von Sir Gawain and the Green knight, der sogenannten Early English alliterative poems, und de Erkenwalde. Von dr. Friedrich Knigge. Teil I. Lautlehre. Marburg, N. G. Elwert, 1886.
2 p.l., 120 p. 23cm.
No more published?
Published as author's inaugural dissertation, Marburg, 1885.
1. Gawain and the Grene knight. 2. Erkenwald, Saint. Legend. 3.English language--Middle English.(1100-1500)—Phonology.

NK 0200491 ViU NcD MH OCl

Knigge, Fritz, 1900-
Ueber enzephalographie.
Inaug. diss. Wuerzburg, 1925.
Bibl.

NK 0200492 ICRL CtY

KNIGGE,Georg.
Über einige brom- und bromnitroderivate des methyldiphenylketons und déro-benzoylbenzoësäure. Inaug.-diss. Rostock,1906.

NK 0200493 MH-C ICRL

VOLUME 300

PT2639 .T22K3 Knigge, Hans Joachim.

Stammler, Georg, 1872–
... Kampf, arbeit, feier; losungen und werksprüche fürs junge Deutschland. 12.–21. tausend. Braunschweig [etc.] G. Westermann [1939]

Knigge (Helene) [1887–]. *Ueber einen Fall von multiloculärem Echinococcus und Tuberkulose der Leber, unter dem Bilde einer Konglomerattuberkulose der Leber. [Jena.] 13 pp. 8°. Langensalza, Wendt & Klauwell, 1913.

NK 0200495 DNLM CtY

Knigge, Herbert, 1911-
see Knigge, Erich Herbert, 1911-

Knigge, Karl Max, 1926–
The effects of hypophysectomy on the adrenal gland of the hamster (*Mesocricetus auratus*) Ann Arbor, University Microfilms [1954]
([University Microfilms, Ann Arbor, Mich.] Publication 7677)
Microfilm copy of typescript. Positive.
Collation of the original: viii, 67 l. illus.
Thesis—University of Michigan.
Abstracted in Dissertation abstracts, v. 14 (1954) no. 4, p. 579–580.
Bibliography: leaves 44–56.
1. Adrenal glands. 2. Pituitary body. 3. Hamsters.
Microfilm AC-1 no. 7677 Mic A 55-3015
Michigan. Univ. Libr. for Library of Congress [1]†

NK 0200497 MiU DLC

Knigge, Philipp Karl, Freiherr von, 1723-1766
Bp4k 747k De natura et indole castrorum in Germania Gottingae, A. Vandenhoeck, 1747.
4p. l., 200, 15p. 21cm.
Thesis - Gottingen.
Without thesis statement.
Bibliographical footnotes.

NK 0200498 CtY

Knigge, Philippine August Amalie von
see
Reden, Philippine Auguste Amalie (von Knigge) von, 1775-

Knigge, Thomas. De Mentha piperitide, commentatio botanico medica. Erlangae. 1780. 4°. pp. xl. Plate.

NK 0200500 MH-A DNLM

M1503 K59P4 1874 Knigge, Wilhelm, baron.
[Philippine Welser; acc. arr. piano]
La perle d'Augsbourg; grand opéra en 4 actes. Traduction française de G. Lagye. Musique de B. Polak-Daniels [pseud.] Bruxelles, Schott Frères [1874?] Pl. no. S. F. 2633.
280 p.
French words.
Libretto by W. Mannstädt.

NK 0200501 CU MB

M1503 K59P4 Knigge, Wilhelm, baron.
[Philippine Welser, acc. arr. piano]
Philippine Welser; grosse Oper in drei Aufzügen, von W. Mannstädt. Vollständiger Klavierauszug mit Text. Berlin, E. Bote & G. Bock [1872?] Pl. no. 9705.
198 p.
German words.
Also known by title: La perle d'Augsburg.

NK 0200502 CU

M1503 K59P4 1873 Knigge, Wilhelm, baron.
[Philippine Welser; acc. arr. piano]
Philippine Welser; oder, Die Perle von Augsburg. Lyrisch-romantische Oper in vier Aufzügen, componirt von B. Polak-Daniels [pseud.] Vollständiger Clavierauszug bearb. von F. Gleich. Cöln, M. Schloss [1873?] Pl. no. M. S. 675.
261 p.
German words.
Libretto by W. Mannstädt.

NK 0200503 CU

Knigge, Ulrich, tr.
PS3545 .O337 W43
Wolfe, Thomas, 1900–1938.
... Spindelvæv og klippe, roman. Kjøbenhavn, Nyt nordisk forlag, A. Busck, 1940.

Kniggendorf, Walter.
... Friedrich Nietzsche—der Deutsche! Erfurt, Sigrune [1938]
25 p. 20½cm. (*On cover:* Gottgläubiges Deutschland; schriften zum deutschen glaubenskampf, hft. 6)
1. Nietzsche, Friedrich Wilhelm, 1844–1900.
A 41-1496
Harvard univ. Library for Library of Congress [2]

NK 0200505 MH

Kniggendorf, Walter
Das geht zu weit! Eine Antwort an den "Stürmer." Berlin 193-
30

NK 0200506 CtY

Knight, captain.
Brother Bosch
see Knight, Gerald Featherstone, 1894-

Knight, Captain.
Diary of a pedestrian in Cashmere and Thibet
see Knight, William Henry.

Knight, corporal.
See
Knight, Thomas.

Knight, Mr., dramatist
see Knight, Thomas, d. 1820.

Knight, professor.
Andreapolis, being writings in praise of St. Andrews
see Knight, William Angus, 1836-1916.

Knight, A
Bottling and drying of fruit. Melbourne, Albert J. Mullett, Government printer, 1918-21.
[3]-52 p. 25 cm.
Reprinted from the Journal of the Department of Agriculture of Victoria.

NK 0200512 DLC

Knight, A., joint author.
Jull, M A.
... Control of bovine tuberculosis in British Columbia, by M. A. Jull, A. Knight and H. H. S. George. Victoria, Printed by R. Wolfenden, printer to the King's most excellent Majesty, 1911.

Knight, *Mrs.* **A A.**
A primer of botany. By Mrs. A. A. Knight ... Boston, Ginn and company, 1887.
vii, 115 p. illus. 18cm.
1. Botany—Juvenile and popular literature.
Library of Congress QK49.K6 5-25771†

NK 0200514 DLC NcD MBH NNBG PWcS

Knight, A. Charles.
Cordwainer ward in the city of London
see Knight, Athro Charles.

Knight, A. Charles.
Shadows of the old booksellers
see Knight, Charles, 1791-1873.

Knight, A V
Abridged report on an investigation into operating methods in the hardware department of a store. London, Retail Distributors' Association, Inc., 1955.
39 p. illus.

NK 0200517 MH-BA

KNIGHT, Abel F.
Boston independent company of cadets' grand march. [For the pianoforte.]
[Boston. Prentiss. 184-?] 2 pp. F°.

NK 0200518 MB

Knight, Abel F.
Marsh's quick step. Respectfully dedicated to Lieut. L. B. Marsh . . . arranged for the piano forte by A. F. Knight.
— Boston. Prentiss. 1841. 3 pp. Portrait. 33 cm.
D8726 — T.r. — Marches. Pianoforte. — Marsh, Lieut. L. B.

NK 0200519 MB

VOLUME 300

Knight, Abel F
The Maryland cadets' quick step. Respectfully dedicated to Capt. Archer Ropes and the officers and members of the prize banner corps, by the Boston independent company of cadets. Composed and arranged for the piano forte by A.F.Knight. Boston, Henry Prentiss [18--?]
3 l. pl. 33cm.
Title within ornamental border.
Publication date probably between 1839 and 1846.
Vol.VII, no.3: "Music collections".
1. Piano music. 1. Lithographs, Am. I. Title.

NK 0200520 MiU-C

Knight, Abel F.
The umbrella courtship, a comic song arranged for the piano forte by A. F. Knight.
— Boston. Keith's Publishing House. 1845. 3 pp. 32 cm.

D8722 — T.r. — Songs. With music.

NK 0200521 MB

Knight, Abner Richard, 1886-
... The effect of temperature on the registration of single phase induction Watthour meters, by Abner R. Knight ... and Max A. Faucett ... Urbana, University of Illinois [1926]
26 p., 1 l. illus., tab., diagrs. 23cm. (University of Illinois. Engineering experiment station. Bulletin no. 153)
On cover: University of Illinois bulletin. vol. XXIII, no. 21.
Bibliography: p. 24.
1. Watt-hour meter. I. Faucett, Max Albert, joint author. II. Title.
A 26—156
Illinois. Univ. Library for Library of Congress [TK35.K55]
——— Copy 2. [TA410.I 7 no. 153]

NK 0200522 IU MB ICJ PU-Sc OrU IdPI

Knight, Abner Richard, 1885-
Introduction to circuit analysis [by] A. R. Knight ... [and] G. H. Fett ... Champaign, Ill., Stipes publishing co., °1939.
5 p. l., 14, 14a-14b, 15-144 numb. l. incl. illus., tables, diagrs. 27½ x 22½cm.

1. Electric circuits. I. Fett, Gilbert Howard, 1909- joint author. II. Title: Circuit analysis.
39-32239
Library of Congress TK3001.K55
[a44c1] 621.319

NK 0200523 DLC

Knight, Abner Richard, 1885-
Introduction to circuit analysis, by Abner R. Knight ... and Gilbert H. Fett ... New York & London, Harper & brothers [1943]
xx p., 1 l., 447 p. diagrs. 24cm.
"First edition." A preliminary edition was published in 1939.

1. Electric circuits. I. Fett, Gilbert Howard, 1909- joint author. II. Title: Circuit analysis.
43-10622
Library of Congress TK3001.K55 1943
[8] 621.319

PBm PSt PU-El OU ICJ MiHM
NK 0200524 DLC Or WaS OrU NIC ViU TU NcD NcRS PHC PP

Knight, Adam, *pseud.*
see **Lariar, Lawrence,** 1908-

Knight, Addison E., ed.

Youngstown, *O. Ordinances, etc.*
The ordinances of a general nature of the city of Youngstown, Ohio, being the Revised ordinances passed March 27th, 1882, and the General ordinances passed thereafter to July 1st, 1886. Edited, annotated and indexed by A. E. Knight, city solicitor. Published for the city. Youngstown, O., W. H. Woodrow, book and job printer, 1886.

Knight, Adele Ferguson, 1867-
Mademoiselle Celeste; a romance of the French revolution, by Adele Ferguson Knight; frontispiece by Clarence F. Underwood. Philadelphia, G. W. Jacobs & company [1910]
322 p. col. front. 20½cm. $1.50

1. France—Hist.—Revolution—Fiction. I. Title.
10—10698
Library of Congress PZ3.K742M

NK 0200527 DLC WaS NN OU OClW

Knight, Adele Ferguson, 1867-
Mademoiselle Céleste. Bemyndigad översättning från Engelska originalet av Gerda Lindfors. Stockholm, Nordiska förlaget [1912]
189 p. (Världslitteraturens bästa alster, 73)

1. France - History - Revolution - Fiction. I. Title.

NK 0200528 WaU

Knight, Adele Ferguson, 1867-
The right to reign; a romance of the kingdom of Drecq, by Adele Ferguson Knight ... frontispiece by Clarence F. Underwood. Philadelphia, G. W. Jacobs & company [1912]
347 p. col. front. 20cm. $1.25

I. Title.
12-21400
Library of Congress PZ3.K742Ri

NK 0200529 DLC OU MH

QC174 .5 K5 Knight, Alan Campbell, 1922-
Comparison of some numerical approximation methods in quantum mechanical computations. [Berkeley, 1950]
46 l. diagrs., tables.
Thesis (Ph.D.) - Univ. of California, June 1950.

1. Quantum theory 2. Dyes and dyeing - Chemistry 3. Approximate computation 4. Numerical calculations

NK 0200530 CU

Knight, Alan J.
In the land of El Dorado. London, Society for the Propagation of the Gospel in Foreign Parts, 1938.

NK 0200531 MH

Knight, Albert.
A few selections. Providence, 1914.
32 p. port. 14 cm.

NK 0200532 PHi RPB

Knight, Albert.
For friendship's sake. [West Barrington, R.I.?], 1919.
[8] p. port. 16 cm.
Cover title.

NK 0200533 RPB

Knight, Albert Richard, 1881-
Now justice comes to Washington, by Albert R. Knight. [Philadelphia, Business methods publishing co., 1944]
1 p. l., 226 p. 23½cm.
Concerns the efforts of the U. S. government to collect income taxes from the Gulf oil corporation, controlled by the Mellon family and to collect inheritance taxes from Doris Duke. *cf.* p. [1]

1. Gulf oil corporation. 2. Cromwell, Doris (Duke) 1912- 3. Mellon, Andrew William, 1855-1937. I. Title.
44-29641
Library of Congress HD9569.G8K6
[2] 338.476655

NK 0200534 DLC

Knight, Albert Richard, 1881-
Where are our large fellows? By Albert R. Knight. [Philadelphia, Business Methods publishing company [°1931]
98 p. ports. 23½cm.

1. Capitalists and financiers—U. S. I. Title.
32-17797
Library of Congress HF5343.K6
——— Copy 2.
Copyright A 46521 [2] 650.973

NK 0200535 DLC PP

Knight, Albert William, 1887-
Abolish slumps; a diagnosis of the trade cycle, by A. W. Knight. London, P. S. King & son ltd., 1936.
vi, 142 p. diagrs. 19cm.

1. Business cycles. 2. Income. 3. Economics. I. Title.
37-10299
Library of Congress HB3711.K6
[3] 330.1

NK 0200536 DLC ICU OU NN OrP

Knight, Albert William, 1887-
What's wrong with the economic system? By A. W. Knight ... London, New York [etc.] Longmans, Green and co. [1939]
xiii, 179 p. diagrs. 22½cm.
"First published 1939."

1. Economics. I. Title.
40-9600
Library of Congress HB171.K56
[3] 330.1

NK 0200537 DLC CU ScU NcD TU OClW OU MH NN

Knight, Albion W
Lending a hand in Cuba. Hartford, Conn., Church Missions Pub. Co., 1916.
142p. illus. 21cm.

1. Protestant Episcopal Church in the U.S.A. Missions. 2. Cuba. Church history. I. Title.

NK 0200538 IEN PPPD PP

Knight, Alfred, 1874-

Power, *Mrs.* **Bertha (Knight) 1886-1927,** *comp.*
William Henry Knight, California pioneer, by Bertha Knight Power ... [New York] Priv. print., 1932.

VOLUME 300

Knight, Alfred Ernest, 1861-1934.
Amentet; an account of the gods, amulets & scarabs of the ancient Egyptians, by Alfred E. Knight ... with ... 193 illustrations in the text. London, Longmans, Green & co. [etc.] 1915.
ix p., 1 l., 274 p. col. front., illus., IV pl. 22½cm.

1. Egypt—Religion. 2. Animal-worship. 3. Amulets. I. Title.
Library of Congress BL2441.K6 16-9048 Revised

NN OC1 OO
NK 0200540 DLC DNLM OrU NcD MU NjNbS PP PPL CU NNUT

Knight, Alfred Ernest, 1861- ed.
The **Antiquarian** quarterly; incorporating articles on archeology & ancient art. v. 1-2 (no. 1-12); Mar. 1925-Dec. 1927. London, Spink & son limited [1925-27]

Knight, Alfred Ernest, 1861-
A concise history of the church; from the apostolic era to the establishment of the Reformation. London, G. Morrish [n.d.]
xxxi, 544p.

1. Church history. I. Title.

NK 0200542 CSaT

DS 463 .K72 Knight,Alfred Ernest,1861-1934.
India: from the Aryan invasion to the great sepoy mutiny. London, S.W.Partridge,1897.
320 p. front. (The romance of colonization [v.3])

1.India--Hist. 2.British in India. 3.Gt. Brit.--Colonies--India. I.Title.

NK 0200543 MiU ICRL MB

Knight, Alfred Ernest, and Edward **Step.** 1855-
The living plant in leaf, flower, and fruit: a popular book on botany for the general reader.
— London. Hutchinson & Co. [1904.] vii, 420 pp. Illus. Plates. 8°.
Authorities consulted, pp. 409, 410.

F8348 — Botany. — Jt. auth. — T.r.

NK 0200544 MB

Knight, Alfred Ernest, 1861-
The living plant in leaf, flower and fruit. A popular book on botany for the general reader, by Alfred Ernest Knight ..., and Edward Step, ... With 871 illustrations specially drawn for the work by A. E. Knight and 36 plates produced direct from photographs and a coloured plate from an original painting by Sir Harry Johnston, ... London, Hutchinson & Co., 1905.
viii, 420 p. col. front., illus, XXXVI pl. 24½cm.

NK 0200545 ICJ InU

Knight, Alfred Ernest, 1861-
Popular botany; the living plant from seed to fruit, by A. E. Knight and Edward Step ... New York, H. Holt and company [1913]
2 v. col. fronts., illus., col. plates. 25cm.
Printed in Great Britain.

1. Botany. I. Step, Edward, 1855- joint author.
Library of Congress QK50.K5 13-35822 Revised

ICJ NN MB
NK 0200546 DLC WaSp OrP WaS Or PU-B MBH NNC OC1W

Knight, Alfred Ernest, 1861-
The romance of colonization. India: from the Aryan invasion to the great Sepoy mutiny
see his India: from the Aryan invasion to the great Sepoy mutiny.

Knight, Alfred Ernest, 1861-
Victoria, her life and reign; an illustrated biography of the queen, from the year 1819 to the present time. By Alfred E. Knight ... London, S. W. Partridge & co., 1897.
viii, [9]-320 p. incl. front. (port.) illus. 19½cm.

1. Victoria, queen of Great Britain, 1819-1901.
Library of Congress DA556.K69 3-26694 Revised

NK 0200548 DLC OKentU

KNIGHT, Alfred Ernest,1861-
Victoria, her life and reign;an illustrated biography of the queen from the year 1819 to the present time. 3d ed., London, S.W. Partridge & co., 1897.

Ports. and other illustr.

NK 0200549 MH MB

Knight, Alfred Ernest, 1861-
The world war and after; an inquiry and a forecast, by Alfred E. Knight ... London, Morgan & Scott ld., 1915.
2 p. l., vii, 143, [1] p. 19cm.

1. European war, 1914- I. Title.
Library of Congress D523.K5 15-15093

NK 0200550 DLC IEG CtY NN

Knight, Alfred J comp.
The treasury, a carefully compiled collection of recitations for families and schools, from the repertoire of Alfred J. Knight ... New York, M. L. Kellogg, printer [1882]
cover-title, 48 p. 16 x 13cm.
Advertising matter interspersed.

1. Readers and speakers—1870- I. Title.
Library of Congress PN4201.K58 33-9748
Copyright 1882: 5578 808.8

NK 0200551 DLC

UF453 .A69 **Knight, Alfred S., 1892-**
Antiaircraft journal.
Battery duties, Coast artillery corps, a checklist. Washington, Coast artillery journal [1942]

U133 .C62 1942 **Knight, Alfred S., 1892-** FOR OTHER EDITIONS SEE MAIN ENTRY
Company duties, a checklist. War ed. Washington, Infantry journal, incorporated [1942]

Knight, Alice Jones, 1860-
Las Casas, "the apostle of the Indies", by Alice J. Knight ... New York, The Neale publishing company [°1917]
4 p. l., 7-100 p. front. (port.) 19cm.

1. Casas, Bartolomé de las, bp. of Chiapa, 1474-1566.
Library of Congress E125.C4K7 18-288 Revised

NK 0200554 DLC OFH NcD CU DPU MB NN

Knight, Alice M
Caedmon of Streonshalh ... [by] Alice M. Knight ... Whitby [Eng.] Horne and son, ltd., The Abbey press [1944]
40 p. 24cm.
In verse.

1. Caedmon—Poetry. I. Title.
Library of Congress PR6021.N415C3 44-4315
[3] 821.91

NK 0200555 DLC

Knight, Alice M.
The immortals: I. Brigid; II. Persephone, by Alice M. Knight ... London, The C. W. Daniel company ltd. [1941]
55 p. 22cm.
In verse.

1. Brigit (Goddess) 2. Proserpine. I. Title.
Library of Congress PR6021.N415 I 5 42-15077
[2] 821.91

NK 0200556 DLC

Knight, Alice Marie (Neighbour) 1901-
1001 stories for children and children's workers. Grand Rapids, Eerdmans, 1952.
287 p. 24 cm.

1. Christian life—Stories. 2. Homiletical illustrations. I. Title.
BV4571.K6 244 52-10811 rev ‡

NK 0200557 DLC Wa PPEB

Knight, Allan.
Escape from the yellow peril; personal experiences of an evacuee from Burma. [1st ed.] Allahabad, Kitab Mahal [1945]
2p.ℓ.,388p. map. 19cm.

1. World War, 1939-1945 - Personal narratives, English. 2. World War, 1939-1945 - Evacuation of civilians. - I. Title.

NK 0200558 TxU NIC

Knight, Allan R
The new life; six studies on the new life in Christ. A student's manual for a pastor's instruction class, by Allan R. Knight and Gordon H. Schroeder. Philadelphia, The American Baptist Publication Society [1947]
51 p. illus. 22 cm.

NK 0200559 KKcB

VOLUME 300

Knight, Allan R
The new life; six studies on the new life i Christ. A service personnel manual for a chaplain's instruction class, by Allan R. Knight and Gordon H. Schroeder. New York, Distributed by Christian ministry to service personnel, American Baptist Convention, and Chaplains Commission, Southern Baptist Commission, Atlanta [1954]
51 p. illus. 22 cm.

NK 0200560 KKcB

Knight, Allen Thomas, 1913–
Studies in the pot-binding of greenhouse plants, by A. T. Knight ... East Lansing, Mich., 1942 [*i. e.* 1944]
cover-title, 51 p. incl. illus., tables, diagrs. 23cm.
Thesis (PH. D.)—Michigan state college of agriculture and applied science, 1943.
Technical bulletin 191, March 1944, Michigan Agricultural experiment station, Lansing, with addition of cover having thesis note.
"Literature cited": p. 48.

1. Plants, Potted. 2. Growth (Plants) 3. Roots (Botany) I. Title: Pot-binding of greenhouse plants.
A 44-5970
Mich. St. coll. of agr. & applied sc. Library for Library of Congress QK769.K58 635.9652
[2]†

NK 0200561 MiEM DLC

Knight, Almena R
Recollections of a mute. A brief sketch of events & incidents which have transpired within my knowledge. Augusta, Kalamazoo County, Mich., 1857.

On cover: Imprint Cleveland. E. Cowles & co., printers.

NK 0200562 OClWHi PHi

M921
K69
Knight, Almena R
Recollections of a mute; a brief sketch of events and incidents which have transpired within my knowledge, by Miss A.R. Knight, deaf and dumb. Battle Creek, Mich., Review and Herald Steam Press Print, 1864.
16p. illus. 17cm.

1.Deaf-Michigan. I.Title.

NK 0200563 Mi

Knight, Almena R
Recollections of a mute. A brief sketch of events and incidents which have transpired within my knowledge. Ann Arbor, Courier Steam Print. House, 1870.
16 p. 8°.

NK 0200564 NN

PR 10
J3 B4
1830
M6
Knight, Ann.
Mornings in the library [1830]

Item in the Colbeck Collection; enquire at the Information Desk.

I. Barton, Bernard, 1784-1849, contributor

NK 0200565 CaBVaU

Knight, Ann Cuthbert, supposed author.
Home; a poem. Boston, 1806. 144 p.
see under Greenshields, John Blackwood.

PR4889 **Knight, Ann Cuthbert.**
.K26H6 Home: a poem. By Ann Cuthbert Knight. Edinburgh,
1815 A. Constable & co.; [etc., etc.] 1815.
viii, 98, [1] p. 17½cm.

NK 0200567 ICU

KNIGHT, ANN CUTHBERT.
A year in Canada, and other poems. By Ann Cuthbert Knight. Edinburgh: Printed by J. Ballantyne & co. for Doig and Stirling [etc., etc.] 1816. 126 p. 18cm

36873B. 1. Poetry, Scottish. I. Title.

NK 0200568 NN RPB

Knight, Anna.
Mississippi girl, an autobiography. Illus. by Jay Jackson, cover by Clyde N. Provonsha. Nashville, Southern Pub. Association [1952]
224 p. illus. 21 cm.

I. Title.
BX6193.K55A3 922.673 52-64329 ‡

NK 0200569 DLC

Knight, Anna A
The way to peace. Boston, Christopher [1950]
105 p. illus., port., map.. 21 cm.

I. Title.
BF1999.K58 133 51-268

NK 0200570 DLC

Knight, Anne, comp.
Lyriques français: pour la jeunesse. Morceaux choisis par Anne Knight. London: Jarrold and sons, 1864. vii, 104 p. front. 14½cm.

209959B. 1. Poetry, French—Collections.
N. Y. P. L. December 30, 1942

NK 0200571 NN

Knight, Annie (Truluck) 1881–
Truluck and Truluck to 1948. [Tulsa, Okla., 1948]
82 p. ports., col. coat of arms, facsims. 31 cm.
Cover title.

1. Truluck family.
CS71.T8687 1948 50-26009

NK 0200572 DLC

Knight, Antonio.
Miracles of God and the prophets. By Dr. Antonio Knight. Newburyport [Mass.] 1829.
18 p. 18½cm.
In verse.

I. Title.
44-46690
Library of Congress PS2196.K64M5

NK 0200573 DLC MH RPB

Knight, Archibald Patterson, 1859-1935
The effects of polluted water on fish life.
(In Canada. Marine Biological Station. Contributions to Canadian biology. Pp. 9-18. Ottawa, 1901.)

E6703 — Fish and fishing. — Water. Pollution.

NK 0200574 MB

LT
QD45
1895
.K6
Knight, Archibald Patterson, 1859-
High school chemistry, by A.P.Knight... and W.S.Ellis... authorized by the Department of education for Ontario. Toronto, The Copp,Clark co. [°1895]
viii,215p. diagrs.

1.Chemistry - Problems, exercises,etc. I.Ellis, W. S., joint author.

NK 0200575 NNU-W

Knight, Archibald Patterson, 1849–1935.
Hygiene for young people, by A. P. Knight ... New York, C. E. Merrill co. [°1909]
204 p. illus. 19½cm.

1. Hygiene—Juvenile literature.
9-25953
Library of Congress QP37.K76

NK 0200576 DLC

Knight, Archibald Patterson, 1849–1935.
Hygiene for young people; a reader for pupils in form III of the public schools, by A. P. Knight ... Toronto, The Copp, Clark company, limited [1909]
v p., 1 l., 211 p. front. (port.) illus. 19½cm.

1. Hygiene—Juvenile literature.
9-24348
Library of Congress QP37.K75

NK 0200577 DLC

Knight, Archibald Patterson, 1849-1935.
Introductory physiology and hygiene. A series of lessons in four parts designed for use in the first four forms of the public schools. Toronto, The Copp, Clark co., ltd., [°1905]
202p. illus.

NK 0200578 ICRL

Knight, Archibald Patterson, 1849–1935.
SH380
.C3
1918
Canada. *Biological board.*
... Official report on lobster investigations in Canada for 1918, by A. P. Knight ... member of the Biological board of Canada, being the results of investigations carried on under the Biological board of Canada. Ottawa, J. de Taché, printer to the King, 1919.

Knight, Archibald Patterson, 1849–1935.
SH380
.C3
1917 a
Canada. *Biological board.*
Official report on lobster investigations, 1917, and methods of increasing the lobster supply in Canada, by A. P. Knight ... member of the Biological board of Canada, being the results of investigations carried on under the Biological board, 1917. Ottawa, J. de L. Taché, printer to the King, 1918.

VOLUME 300

TX612 .L7C3 Knight, Archibald Patterson, 1849-1935.

Canada. *Biological board.*

Official report on standardization in lobster canning, by A. P. Knight, chairman, Biological board of Canada. Ottawa, F. A. Acland, printed to the King, 1921.

SH380 .C3 1917 Knight, Archibald Patterson, 1849-1935.

Canada. *Biological board.*

... Official report upon lobster conservation in Canada, by A. P. Knight ... member of the Biological board of Canada, being the results of investigations carried on under the Biological board, with the aid of officers instructed by the Department of naval service, during the season of 1916. Ottawa, Printed by J. de L. Taché, printer to the King, 1917

Knight, Archibald Patterson, 1849-1935.

The Ontario public school hygiene ... Tor., Copp, [©1910, repr. 1918]. viii, 248 p. front., illus. 19½ cm.

NK 0200583 CaNSWA

SH380 .C3 1922 Knight, Archibald Patterson, 1849-1935.

Canada. *Biological board.*

Report upon lobster fishing in Northumberland straits from August 1 to September 9, 1922, together with conclusions based upon the facts which were collected during this period, by A. P. Knight, chairman of the Biological board of Canada. Ottawa, F. A. Acland, printer to the King, 1922.

SH335 .C32 1920 Knight, Archibald Patterson, 1849-1935.

Canada. *Biological board.*

Report upon the conditions in and around twenty-three lobster canning factories in Prince Edward island and New Brunswick during the summer of 1920, by A. P. Knight ... chairman of the Biological board of Canada. Ottawa, T. Mulvay, printer to the King, 1921.

Knight, Archibald Patterson, 1849-1935.
A standard pickle for lobster canning. 1923.
(Canada. Biological board. Bulletin. #6)

NK 0200586 OrU

GV1779 K6 **Knight, Arthur**
Dancing in films. ₍New York, Dance index-ballet caravan inc., 1947₎
₍177₎-₍200₎ p. illus., ports. (Dance index, vol.VI, no.8)

1. Dancing in moving-pictures, television, etc. I. Dance index. I. Title.

NK 0200587 CU MiD

---

*PS3511 .A86Z99 .K554L3 1955 Knight, Arthur.
Land of the Pharaohs. New York, 1955.
₍1₎ p. 28cm. ₍Faulkner miscellaneous material₎
Reproduced from The Saturday review, June 25, 1955.

1. Faulkner, William, 1897- . I. Title.

NK 0200588 ViU

---

*EC65 K7433 653s **Knight, Arthur, d.1653.**
The speech of Mr Arthur Knight of Grays-Inne, gentleman; who was executed in the Covent-Garden the second day of March, 1652 [1653].
London, Printed for Tho.Heath at his shop in Russell-street, near the piazza's of Covent-Garden. [1653]
8p. 19cm.
Woodcut illus. on t.-p.
Received by Thomason on Mar. 2, 1653.

NK 0200589 MH ICU

Knight, Arthur C
Preferred stocks as trust investments... Submitted in partial fulfillment of the requirements of the Graduate school of banking... June 1943.
98 mimio. l.
With bibliography.

NK 0200590 OClFRB

Knight, Arthur F
[An account of a two days trip to Mt. Rainier]
[A letter to Mr. Brockman by the author.
front.
t.-p. wanting.
Typewritten letter dated Aug. 29, 1933.

NK 0200591 WaT

KNIGHT, Arthur Francis.
"Well played", or "The major's dilemma" an entirely new and original farce in one act. London, S.French, etc., etc., [1893?]

pp. 17.

On Cover:-French's acting edition 2040.

NK 0200592 MH

973.15 K743c Knight, Arthur George, 1835-1916.
The life of Christopher Columbus, by Arthur George Knight. London, Burns and Oates, 1877.
xxi, 254 p. 19cm.

1. Colombo, Cristoforo. 2. Colombo, Cristoforo--Canonization.

NK 0200593 MoSU CtY MiU-C KAS ViU

Microfilm
Knight, Arthur George, 1835-1916, S. J.
The life of Christopher Columbus, by Arthur George Knight ... London, Burns and Oates, 1877.
Microfilm copy, made in 1959, of the original in St. Louis university library. Negative.
Collation of the original, as determined from the film: xxi, 254 p.
1. Colombo, Cristoforo. I. Jesuits (Works by)

NK 0200594 MoSU

Knight, Arthur George.

The life of Christopher Columbus. By Arthur George Knight ... New York, The Catholic publication society, 1877.

xvi p., 1 l., 231 p. 18cm.

1. Colombo, Cristoforo. 2. Colombo, Cristoforo—Canonization.

17-6918

Library of Congress E111.K692

NK 0200595 DLC OClJC MiU-C WaSpG

Knight, Arthur George.

Life of Christopher Columbus, discoverer of the New world. A biographical sketch. By Rev. A. G. Knight ... New York ₍etc.₎ D. & J. Sadlier & co., 1877.

215 p. 19cm.

1. Colombo, Cristoforo. 2. Colombo, Cristoforo—Canonization.

2-7911

Library of Congress E111.K69

NK 0200596 DLC OCX PPLas MChB

Knight, Arthur Geo.
The life of Christopher Columbus. N.Y., The Catholic publication society, 1896.

NK 0200597 OClJC

DA 153 .K69 Knight, Arthur George, 1835-1916.
The life of King Alfred the Great. London, Burns and Oates, 1880.
xiv, 325 p. 20cm. (Quarterly series, v.32)

1. Alfred the Great, King of England, 849-901. I. Series

NK 0200598 DCU PRosC MB

Knight, Arthur Harold John, joint author.

Reum, Albrecht, 1860–

A dictionary of English style, published with the cooperation of A. H. J. Knight ... by Dr. Albrecht Reum ... Leipzig, J. J. Weber ₍©1928₎–

Knight, Arthur Harold John.

Georg Büchner. Oxford, Blackwell, 1951.

vii, 181 p. 23 cm. (Modern language studies)

Bibliography: p. 177-179.

1. Büchner, Georg, 1813-1837. (Series)

PT1828.B6K5 928.3 52—7820

NK 0200600 OrCS CaBVaU OrPR CaBVa NcU DLC TU RPB MiU IU MB CtY NN NcD MH OrU

Knight, Arthur Harold John.

...Heinrich Julius, duke of Brunswick, by A. H. J. Knight... Oxford, B. Blackwell, 1948. ix, 148 p. port. 22cm. (Modern language studies ₍v. 3₎)

"Select bibliography," p. 144-146.

461878B. 1. Henry Julius, duke of Brunswick-Wolfenbüttel, 1564-1613. I. Ser.
N. Y. P. L. January 8, 1952

NK 0200601 LU IU IaU NcD ICN ICU MiU CoU NjR CtY CU MH CaBVaU NN NNC WU KU NcU NNU-W CoU CSt TxFTC IdU

Knight, Arthur Harold John,
Program notes

see under

International Art Film Festival. 2d, N. Y. city, 1952.

VOLUME 300

Knight, Arthur Harold John.
Some aspects of the life and work of Nietzsche, and particularly of his connection with Greek literature and thought, by A. H. J. Knight ... Cambridge [Eng.] The University press, 1933.
4 p. l., 194 p. 22½cm.
"Select bibliography": p. [191]-192.

1. Nietzsche, Friedrich Wilhelm, 1844-1900. 2. Literature, Comparative—German and Greek. 3. Literature, Comparative—Greek and German. I. Title.

Library of Congress B3317.K64 34-6975
[3] 193.9

NN CaBVaU CaBVa
NK 0200603 DLC NcD PBm CtY MiU OCl OO OCU PU IU ICU

Knight (Arthur L.) Brain tumor. Report o. a case of psammoma of the right frontal lobe. 4 pp. 8°. *Cincinnati*, 1898.
Repr. from: Cincin. Lancet-Clinic, 1898, n. s., xl.

NK 0200604 DNLM

Knight, Arthur Lee.
Assisi, the seraphic city. Florence [G. Cecchi & son] 1908.
71p., 13cm.

1.Assisi.--Descr.

NK 0200605 TU

Knight, Arthur Lee.
The cruise of the "Cormorant"; or, treasure-seekers of the Orient. London. Ward, Lock & Bowden. 1893. Illus. Sm. 8°.

Δ1025 — T.r. — Stories of the sea.

NK 0200606 MB

Knight, Arthur Lee.
Jack Trevor, R.N.
London. Warne & Co. 1890. Sm. 8°.

Δ1025 — T.r. — Stories of the sea.

NK 0200607 MB PPL

Knight, Arthur Lee.
Leaves from a middy's log, by Arthur Lee Knight... London: T. Nelson and Sons, 1896. viii, 10-294 p. front. 12°.
Added t.-p.

471494A. 1. Fiction, French. 2. Sea life—Fiction. I. Title.
N. Y. P. L. August 11, 1930

NK 0200608 NN IU

DG975 .P4K7 (Art)
Knight, Arthur Lee.
Perugia, queen of Umbrian cities. Florence [G. Cecchi, 1910.
105 p. plates.

1. Perugia--Descr. 2. Art--Perugia. 3. Perugia--Churches.

NK 0200609 ICU NIC

Knight, Arthur Lee.
Petals from a Florentine lily, by Arthur Lee Knight... Florence, G. Cecchi e figlio [1908] xi, 162 p. illus. 20cm.

308827B. 1. Florence—Descr. 2. Art, Italian—Florence.
N. Y. P. L. December 17, 1945

NK 0200610 NN N CtY

Knight, Arthur Lee.
Ronald Hallifax; or, he would be a sailor.
London. Warne & Co. [1886.] Illus. Sm. 8°.

Δ1025 — T.r. — Stories of the sea.

NK 0200611 MB

GR 305 .K68
KNIGHT,ARTHUR LEE
Told in the Indian twilight; Mahratta fairy tales. London, G. Allen, 1913.
143 p. illus., port.

1. Folk-lore--India--Mahratta. I. Title.
Folk-lore cds.

NK 0200612 InU OCl MH

Knight, Arthur Lee.
The young rajah. Illustrated by J.B. Greene.
London, E. Nister [1899]
72 p. 8°.

NK 0200613 NN

Knight, Arthur Percival.
The repulsion theory [by] Arthur Percival Knight. Los Angeles, Press of Parker & Stone co., 1907.
2 p. l., [7]-123 p. 23cm.

I. Title.

Library of Congress QC75.K7 7-22920

NK 0200614 DLC ICJ NN

Knight, Arthur Rex
see Knight, Rex.

F127 .A2A2
Knight, Arthur Stanley, ed.

Adirondack guide; vacationland in picture, story and history.
1920-
Lake George, N. Y., Adirondack Resorts Press [etc.]

Knight, Athro Charles.
Cordwainer ward in the city of London, its history and topography, by A. Charles Knight ... London, G. Allen & Unwin ltd. [1917]
111, [1] p. front., plates, ports., maps. 19½cm.
"List of principal authorities": p. 103-105.

1. London—Wards—Cordwainer ward.

Library of Congress DA685.C65K6 18-8681

NK 0200617 DLC ICN NN IU WU CtY

Knight, Augustus C.
The Duke of Volendam. An operetta in two acts. Book by Leon Dadmun. Music by August C. Knight. [Vocal score.]
= Boston. Oliver Ditson Co. [1929.] (7), 130 pp. Illustrated cover. 28 cm.

D2891 — Double main card. — Knight, Augustus C. (M1) — Dadmun, Leon. (M2) — T.r. made. — Operas. (1)

NK 0200618 MB PPT OCl

Knight, Augustus C.
[Pepita. Libretto]
...Pepita, a Mexican operetta in two acts; libretto by Philip A. Hutchins. Ditson [°1923]
44 p., illus.

I. Hutchins, Philip A.

NK 0200619 MiD MB PPT

KNIGHT, AUGUSTUS C
Pepita: a Mexican operetta in two acts, libretto by Philip A. Hutchins, music by Augustus C. Knight. Ditson c1923.
2 v.

NK 0200620 Or

Tapl5 1
Knight, Augustus Smith, 1864-
Addresses delivered by Augustus S.Knight ... and Dr.Louis I.Dublin ... at the annual banquet of the officers and Hygiene reference board of the Life extension institute at the Union league club, New York city, January 31, 1923. [New York,1923]
Pamphlet

NK 0200621 CtY

Knight, Augustus Smith, 1864-
...Life waste in 1922- its warning and its lesson. By Dr. Augustus S. Knight...An address delivered at the sixteenth annual meeting of the Association of life insurance presidents at New York, December 7, 1922. (New York, 1922)
1 p. l., 11 p. 23 cm.
At head of title; Betterment of life insurance service.

NK 0200622 DL MiU DNLM

Knight, Augustus Smith, 1864-
Mortality, morbidity and working capacity of tuberculosis patients
see under Association of Life Insurance Medical Directors of America.

Knight, Augustus Smith, 1864- , and L. I. Dublin.
The relation of cancer to economic condition; the incidence of cancer in the ordinary, intermediate and industrial departments of the Metropolitan Life Insurance Company, compared, by Augustus S. Knight...and Louis I. Dublin... New York: Metropolitan Life Insurance Co., 1917. 1 p.l., 10 p. incl. tables. 8°.

1. Cancer.—Statistics, U. S. 2. Dublin, Louis Israel, 1882- , jt. au.
N. Y. P. L. September 18, 1919.

NK 0200624 NN NIC PPProM PU DL MiU

VOLUME 300

Knight, Austin.
Britain's new order: peace, security and faith, by Austin Knight. London, Chapman & Hall ltd., 1942.
iv, 188 p. fold. diagrs. 19 cm.
Illustrated lining-papers.
"First published 1942."
CONTENTS.—The cause of the world's troubles.—Man and machines.—The meaning of leisure.—The empire also has a part to play.—Democracy and youth.—And what of the women?—What part has the Christian church in this new world we are seeking?—Post-war trading: a financial revolution.—The problem of crime.—Conclusion.—Epilogue.
1. Reconstruction (1939–1951)—Gt. Brit. 2. Gt. Brit.—Economic policy. 3. Gt. Brit.—Soc. condit. I. Title.
D829.G7K55 940.5314442 A 43—961
Harvard Univ. Library for Library of Congress [a65f½]†

NK 0200625 MH DLC DS CtY MB OU DAU

Knight, Austin Melvin, 1854–
Address by Rear Admiral Austin M. Knight, U. S. N., at the annual banquet of the Efficiency club of New York city, Hotel Biltmore, January 25th, 1915. [Newport? 1915]
1 p. l., 30 numb. l. 27cm.
Autographed from type-written copy.
1. U. S.—Navy. 2. U. S.—Defenses. I. Title.
17-29008
Library of Congress VA50.K7

NK 0200626 DLC MB

Knight, Austin Melvin, 1854–
Address by Rear Admiral Austin M. Knight, U. S. N., June 7th, 1916, Worcester polytechnic institute, Worcester, Massachusetts. [Newport? 1916]
1 p. l., 21 numb. l. 27cm.
Autographed from type-written copy.
1. Worcester polytechnic institute, Worcester, Mass. I. Title.
17-29399
Library of Congress T171.W94 1916

NK 0200627 DLC MB

Knight, Austin Melvin, 1854–
Address by Rear Admiral Austin M. Knight, U. S. Navy, president, U. S. Naval war college, at Mohonk conference, May 17, 1916. Are large armaments provocative of war? [Newport? 1916]
1 p. l., 23 numb. l. 27cm.
Autographed from type-written copy.
1. U. S.—Defenses. 2. Armies. 3. Navies. I. Title. II. Title: Are large armaments provocative of war?
17-29009
Library of Congress UA23.K7

NK 0200628 DLC

145
5487 Knight, Austin Melvin, 1854-1927
The estimate of the situation ...
Newport, R. I., Naval war college, 1921.
cover-title, 19 p. 23cm.
"Revised and printed for the use of officers in attendance at the Naval war college."

NK 0200629 MH-L DNW

Knight, Austin Melvin, 1854–
The estimate of the situation. By Rear Admiral Austin M. Knight ...
(*In* Professional memoirs, Corps of engineers, U. S. army, and Engineer department-at-large. Washington, 1915. 23cm. v. 7, p. 629–643)
Copyrighted by the U. S. Naval institute, Annapolis, Md. Reprinted by permission of the Naval institute.
1. Military art and science. 2. Strategy. I. Title.
E S 15-85
Title from U. S. Engineer School Libr. Printed by L. C.

NK 0200630 DES MiU OU

Knight, Austin Melvin, 1854–
Formulation of orders.
U. S. Naval War College, n.d.

NK 0200631 DN

Knight, Austin Melvin, 1854-1927.
History of the U. S. naval war college, by Rear Admiral Austin M. Knight... and Lt. Wm. D. Paleston...Newport, R. I., n.p., 1916.
v.p. 34 cm.
Typewritten pages.

NK 0200632 DNW

VK
541
.K77 Knight, Austin Melvin, 1854-1927.
Manejo marinero, por Austin M. Knight ... Edición traducida al español por oficiales de la Escuela naval del Perú. Para uso exclusivo del personal de la marina del Perú. [La Punta, Talleres tipográficos de la Escuela naval del Perú, 1944.
2 p.l., ii p., 1 l., [3]-795 p. illus., plates (3 col.) diagrs. 25½cm.
Translated from the 10th American edition (New York, D. Van Nostrand, 1937)
"Diccionario de términos navales [English-Spanish]": p. [753]-795.
1. Navigation. I. Lima. Escuela naval.

NK 0200633 MiU

Knight, Austin M[elvin]
Modern seamanship. By Austin M. Knight ... With 136 full page plates. New York, D. Van Nostrand company, 1901.
xii, 428 p. 136 pl. (incl. maps, diagrs.) 24cm.
1. Navigation and seamanship. I. Title.
1-12895/3
Library of Congress
656

NK 0200634 DLC PPRC1 OC1JC DN MB ICJ

VK
541
K73
1902 **Knight, Austin Melvin, 1854-1927.**
Modern seamanship. By Austin M. Knight. With 136 full page plates. 2d ed. rev. New York, D. Van Nostrand company, 1902.
xii, 428 p. 136 pl. (incl. maps, diagrs.) 24cm.
1. Navigation. I. Title.

NK 0200635 DSI DN

623.89
K69MA **Knight, Austin Melvin, 1854–1927.**
Modern seamanship. By Austin M. Knight. 3d ed. rev. New York, D. Van Nostrand, 1903 [c1901]
xii, 428 p. 136 pl. (incl. maps, diagrs.) 24cm.

NK 0200636 NcD NN FMU

Knight, Austin Melvin, 1854-1927.
Modern seamanship. Ed. 4, rev. N.Y., Van Nostrand, 1908.
428 p.

NK 0200637 PPSteph

Knight, Austin Melvin, 1854–1927.
Modern seamanship. By Austin M. Knight ... 5th ed., re-written and enl. 159 full page plates. New York, D. Van Nostrand company, 1910.
xiii, 540 p. 159 pl. (part col.) 24cm.
1. Navigation. I. Title.
10—27608
Library of Congress VK541.K73

NK 0200638 DLC DN ICJ

Knight, Austin Melvin, 1854-
Modern seamanship. 5th ed., re-written & enl. 159 full page plates. N.Y., D. Van Nostrand co., 1912.

NK 0200639 MiU OC1 PPUNA

Knight, Austin Melvin, 1854–
Modern seamanship. By Austin M. Knight ... 6th ed., rewritten and enl. 159 full page plates. New York, D. Van Nostrand company, 1914.
xiii, 540 p. 159 pl. (part col., part fold., incl. diagrs) 24cm. $7.50
1. Navigation. I. Title.
15-3877
Library of Congress VK541.K73 1914

NK 0200640 DLC ViU NN

Knight, Austin Melvin, 1854–
Modern seamanship, by Austin M. Knight ... 7th ed., rev. and enl., 160 full page plates. New York, D. Van Nostrand company, 1917.
xix, 712 p. front., illus., plates (part col.) diagrs. 24cm. $6.50
1. Navigation. I. Title.
17—11225
Library of Congress VK541.K73 1917

NK 0200641 DLC WaSp OrP DSI MiU OC1 OO NN ICJ MB NjP

Knight, Austin Melvin, 1854–1927.
Modern seamanship, by Austin M. Knight... Unabridged reprint of the 7. ed. ... New York: D. Van Nostrand, 1918.
xix, 712 p. illus. (part col'd.) 19cm.
240373B. 1. Seamanship.
N. Y. P. L. August 16, 1943

NK 0200642 NN PU DN-Ob DN MB MH MiEM NcC PPUNA

Knight, Austin Melvin, 1854–1927.
Modern seamanship, by Austin M. Knight ... 8th ed., rev. and enl., 199 full page plates. New York, D. Van Nostrand company, 1921.
xiii, 831 p. front., illus. (part col.) diagrs. 22cm. (*On cover:* Van Nostrand's nautical manuals)
The illustrations are numbered as plates.
1. Navigation. 2. Merchant marine. I. Title.
21—19056
Library of Congress VK541.K73 1921

NK 0200643 DLC MH MiU NN MB NN ICJ OrU

Knight, Austin Melvin, 1854–1927.
Modern seamanship, by Austin M. Knight ... 9th ed., re-written, rev. and enl. by Harry A. Baldridge ... New York, D. Van Nostrand company, inc., 1930.
xv, 936 p. front., illus. (part col.) maps (part fold.) diagrs. 22½cm. (*On cover:* Van Nostrand's nautical manuals)
The illustrations are numbered as plates.
1. Navigation. I. Baldridge, Harry Alexander, 1880– II. Title.
30—10923
Library of Congress VK541.K73 1930
——— Copy 2.
Copyright A 20762 [a37b1-] 656

NK 0200644 DLC PPF MiU OC1 DN WaE OrHi

VOLUME 300

Knight, Austin Melvin, 1854–1927.
Modern seamanship, by Austin M. Knight ... 10th ed., rewritten and rev. by the officers of the Department of seamanship and navigation, United States Naval academy, Annapolis, Maryland. New York, D. Van Nostrand company, inc. [°1937]
1 p. l., v–x, 844, cxxviii p. illus. (part col.) diagrs. 22cm. (On cover: Van Nostrand's nautical manuals)
The illustrations are numbered as plates.
"The rules of the road": cxxviii p. at end.
1. Navigation. I. U. S. Naval academy, Annapolis. Dept. of seamanship and navigation. II. Title.
37–33347
Library of Congress VK541.K73 1937
[a42m2] 656

NK 0200645 DLC NcC PP OCl OClW OU Or WaS OrP WaT WaSp

Knight, Austin Melvin, 1854–1927.
Modern seamanship, by Austin M. Knight ... 10th ed., rewritten and rev. by the officers of the Department of seamanship and navigation, United States Naval academy, Annapolis, Maryland. New York, D. Van Nostrand company, inc., 1941.
2 p. l., vii–x, 845 (i. e. 850) p. illus. (part col.) diagrs. 22cm. (On cover: Van Nostrand's nautical manuals)
The illustrations are numbered as plates.
Includes 5 extra numbered pages.
1. Navigation. I. U. S. Naval academy, Annapolis. Dept. of seamanship and navigation. II. Title.
41–12936
Library of Congress VK541.K73 1941
[3] 656

NK 0200646 DLC MtBuM WaWW OrP Or WaS NcRS DSI OClh ODW OLak

VK541 .K73 1942
Knight, Austin Melvin, 1854-1927.
Modern seamanship. 10th ed., rewritten and rev. by the officers of the Department of Seamanship and Navigation, United States Naval Academy, Annapolis, Maryland. New York, D. Van Nostrand company, inc., [1942]
848 p. illus. 22 cm.
The illustrations are numbered as plates.
1. Navigation. I. U.S. Naval Academy, Annapolis. Dept. of Seamanship and Navigation. II. Title.

NK 0200647 TU InU CtY

Knight, Austin Melvin, 1854-1927.
Modern seamanship. 10th ed., rewritten and revised by the officers of the Department of seamanship and navigation, U.S.Naval academy, Annapolis, Maryland. New York, D.Van Nostrand co., inc. [1943]
x, 847 p. illus., diagrs. 22 cm.
On cover: Van Nostrand's nautical manuals.

NK 0200648 MH NcD PSt

Knight, Austin Melvin, 1854–1927.
Modern seamanship, by Austin M. Knight ... 11th ed., rewritten and revised by Captain Robert A. Hall ... assisted by the officers of the Department of seamanship and navigation, United States Naval academy. Chapters on weather prepared by Professor Frederick L. Caudle ... New York, D. Van Nostrand company, inc., 1945.
xiii, 948 p. illus. (part col., incl. charts) diagrs. 21cm.
1. Navigation. I. Hall, Robert Archibald, 1888– ed. II. U. S. Naval academy, Annapolis. Dept. of seamanship and navigation. III. Caudle, Frederick L. IV. Title.
45–6249
Library of Congress ° VK541.K73 1945
[8] 656

NK 0200649 DLC NIC TxU MsU OCl DI OEac OrU WaS WaT

VK541 .K69 1949
Knight, Austin Melvin, 1854-1927.
Modern seamanship. 11th ed., rewritten and revised by Robert A. Hall, assisted by the officers of the Department of Seamanship and Navigation, United States Naval Academy. Chapters on weather prepared by Frederick L. Caudle. New York, Van Nostrand [1949, c1945]
xiii, 948 p. illus. 22cm.
1. Navigation. I. Hall, Robert Archibald, 1888- ed. II. U. S. Naval Academy, Annapolis. Dept. of Seamanship and Navigation. III. Caudle, Frederick L. IV. Title.

NK 0200650 MB

Knight, Austin Melvin, 1854–1927.
Modern seamanship. Rewritten and rev. by Ralph S. Wentworth, assisted by John V. Noel, Jr., and officers of the U. S. Naval Academy, officers of the U. S. Coast Guard Academy, officers and civilian specialists in the Bureau of Ships and in the Bureau of Naval Personnel, Navy Dept. With chapters on weather prepared by Frederick L. Caudle. 12th ed. New York, Van Nostrand [1953]
xiii, 606 p. illus. (part col.) charts. 24 cm.
1. Navigation. I. Wentworth, Ralph S., 1890– ed. II. Caudle, Frederick L., 1900– III. Title.
VK541.K73 1953 *623.88 656 53–8769

NK 0200651 DLC WaT CaBViP CaBVaU CaBVa Or OrP Wa NcD PPF PP OCl NN MB WaS

Knight, Austin Melvin, 1854–
The Naval War College [Newport, R. I.].
= [Newport, R. I. 1915.] (1), 14 pp. [United States. Naval War College, Newport, R. I. Publications.] 27 cm.
Printed on one side of the leaf only.

L2587 — S.r. — United States. Naval War College, Newport, R. I.

NK 0200652 MB

Knight, Austin Melvin, 1854-
U. S. *Navy dept.*
[Notes on the over-sea towing of destroyers and submarines, May, 1913. Washington, Govt. print. off., 1914]

Knight, Austin Melvin, 1854- FOR OTHER EDITIONS SEE MAIN ENTRY
[Reynolds, Francis Joseph] 1867– *ed.*
The story of the great war ... [Diplomatic ed.] New York, P. F. Collier & sons [°1916–20]

Knight, B Andrews.
Memorial to the Hon. the Senate and the House of Delegates of the state of Maryland.
Baltimore, 1866. YA21275
9p.

NK 0200655 DLC

Knight, B. B. & R., Inc.
Fruit of the loom muslin and other high quality fabrics. Providence, R. I.: B. B. & R. Knight, Inc. [1921.] 28 l. illus. (part col'd). ob. 8°.

22728A. 1. Cotton manufacture, U. S. 2. Title.
N. Y. P. L. November 18, 1921.

NK 0200656 NN

Knight, Benjamin.
History of the Sprague families, of Rhode Island, cotton manufacturers and calico printers from William I. to William IV., with an account of the murder of the late Amasa Sprague, father of Hon. Wm. Sprague, ex-U. S. senator from Rhode Island. By Benjamin Knight, sr. Santa Cruz, H. Coffin, book and job printer, 1881.
2 p. l., [3]–74 p. $23\frac{1}{2}$cm.
1. Sprague family (William Sprague, fl. 1773) 2. Sprague, Amasa, 1798–1843. 3. Sprague, William, 1830–
9–13804
Library of Congress CS71.S766 1881

NK 0200657 DLC MWA

Knight, Benjamin Loyless, 1890–
Poetic sermonettes. Columbia [S. C.] State Commercial Print. Co., 1948.
102 p. 21 cm.
I. Title.
PS3521.N5334P6 811.5 48–27365*

NK 0200658 DLC ViU

Knight, Benjamin Thackston.
... Tack's cartoon tips ... by "Tack" Knight. [Rev. ed.] ... [New York, Chicago, Devoe & Raynolds co., inc., 1944]
cover-title, [28] p. illus. $13\frac{1}{2}$ x 20cm.
1. Caricatures and cartoons. 2. Drawing—Instruction. I. Title.
45–13439
Library of Congress NC1320.K56 1944
[3] 741.5

NK 0200659 DLC

Knight, Bernard Howard.
Builders' materials, by Bernard H. Knight ... and Rena G. Knight ... London, E. Arnold & co. [1939]
viii, 304 p. illus. 28cm.
"First published 1939."
"References": p. 289.
1. Building materials. I. Knight, Rena Gertrude, joint author. II. Title.
42–13549
Library of Congress TA403.K6
[2] 691

NK 0200660 DLC MH NN

Knight, Bernard Howard.
Builders' materials, by Bernard H. Knight and Rena G. Knight. [2d ed.] London, E. Arnold [1948]
viii, 304 p. illus. 22 cm.
"References": p. 292.
1. Building materials. I. Knight, Rena Gertrude, joint author.
TA403.K6 1948 691 49–15890*

NK 0200661 DLC CaBVaU OCl

Knight, Bernard Howard.
Builders' materials, by Bernard H.Knight and Rena G.Knight. [2d ed.] London, E.Arnold [1950]
304 p. illus.
I. Knight, Rena Gertrude, joint author. 691
620.11

NK 0200662 ICJ MB TxU

VOLUME 300

Knight, Bernard Howard.
Builders' materials, by Bernard H. Knight and Rena G. Knight. [3d ed.] London, Arnold [1955]
304 p. illus. 22 cm.

1. Building materials. I. Knight, Rena Gertrude, joint author.
TA403.K6 1955 691 56-20376 ‡

NK 0200663 DLC IU NN MB TxU PP Wa

Knight, Bernard Howard.
Modern road construction, by Bernard H. Knight ... London, C. Lockwood & son ltd. [1938]
viii, 86 p. diagrs. 19cm. (Lockwood's modern handbooks)
"First published 1938."

1. Roads. 2. Road materials. I. Title.
41-7085
Library of Congress TE147.K55 1938
[2] 625.7

NK 0200664 DLC

Knight, Bernard Howard.
Modern road construction, by Bernard H. Knight ... London, C. Lockwood & son ltd [1945]
viii, 84 p. diagrs. 19cm.
"First published 1938. Second edition 1945."

1. Roads. 2. Road materials. I. Title.
A 46-4505
New York. Public library for Library of Congress [TE147.K]

NK 0200665 NN

Knight, Bernard Howard.
... Road aggregates, their uses and testing, by Bernard H. Knight ... London, E. Arnold & co. [1935]
x, 264 p. illus., diagrs. 23½cm. (The roadmakers' library. General editor: Dr. P. E. Spielmann. [v. 3])
"List of references": p. 256-258.

1. Road materials. 2. Petrology. I. Title.
36-9673
Library of Congress TE200.K6
[3] 625.8002

NK 0200666 DLC DNAL NcRS PPF OCl MB TU

Knight, Bernard Howard.
Road aggregates, their uses and testing, by Bernard H. Knight and Rena G. Knight. [2d ed.] London, E. Arnold [1948]
xii, 259 p. illus. 24 cm. (The Roadmakers' library, v. 3)
"List of references": p. 248-251.

1. Road materials. 2. Petrology. I. Knight, Rena Gertrude, joint author. (Series)
TE200.K6 1948 625.8 49-2590*

NK 0200667 DLC CU FMU NcD ICJ NN OrP

Knight, Bernard Howard.
Soil mechanics for civil engineers. London, E. Arnold [1948]
255 p. illus. 23 cm.
"List of references": p. 243-246.

1. Soil mechanics.
TA710.K57 620.19 49-9223*

NK 0200668 DLC CU AU PSt OrP DNAL ViU TU MB TxU

TA 710 .K72 1952
Knight,Bernard Howard.
Soil mechanics for civil engineers. [Reprinted with amendments] London, E.Arnold [1952]
255 p. diagrs.,profiles. 22 cm.
Bibliography: p.243-246.

1.Soil mechanics.

NK 0200669 MiU OU NIC

Knight, Bernard Howard.
Surveying and levelling for students... London, Contractors Record and Municipal Engineering, 1954.
152 p. illus. 22½cm.

NK 0200670 OClW NcD

Knight, Bert Cyril James Gabriel, 1904–
... Bacterial nutrition; material for a comparative physiology of bacteria, by B. C. J. G. Knight. London, H. M. Stationery off., 1936.
182 p. tables. 25 cm. (Medical research council (Gt. Brit.) Special report series, no. 210)
At head of title: ... Privy council. Medical research council.
"References": p. 175-182.

1. Bacteria. I. Title.
QR84.K55 S G 36-82
U. S. National Library of Medicine for Library of Congress [a57g½]†

NK 0200671 DNLM OU MiU PU-D PU-HY MH NcD DLC CaBVaU

Knight, Bert Cyril James Gabriel, 1904-
Bacterial nutrition; material for a comparative physiology of bacteria, by B.C.J.G.Knight. London, HMSO, 1938
182 p. (Medical Research Council. Special report series, 210)
At head of title: Privy Council

1. Bacteria. (Series: Medical Research Council (Gt.Brit.). Special Report, series, 210)

NK 0200672 MH NcRS

Knight, Bert Cyril James Gabriel, 1904- ed.
QR1 .J64
The Journal of general microbiology
Jan. 1947-
London, New York, Cambridge University Press.

Knight, Brigid, *pseud.*
The covenant. New York, Crowell, 1943.
297 p. 21 cm.

I. Title.
PZ3.K7423Co 43-13938 rev*

PNt PP
NK 0200674 DLC CaBVa Or OrP OrU WaS OO OClU OCl PPL

Knight, Brigid, *pseud.*
The covenant. London, Cassell [1944]
308 p. 19 cm.

I. Title.
PZ3.K7423Co 2 44-5988 rev*

NK 0200675 DLC TxU

Knight, Brigid, *pseud.*
I struggle and I rise, a novel. London, Cassell [1947]
431 p. 22 cm.
American ed. (New York, Doubleday) published under title: The valiant lady.
Sequel: Old Amsterdam.

I. Title.
PZ3.K7423 I 48-111 rev*

NK 0200676 DLC

Knight, Brigid, *pseud.*
Not by any single man. [1st ed.] Garden City, N. Y., Doubleday, 1950.
309 p. 22 cm.

I. Title.
PZ3.K7423No 50-7843 rev

KyLx KyBB PP MH OCl WaT
NK 0200677 DLC CaBVa IdB Or WaE WaS OCl WaSp LU KyU

Knight, Brigid, *pseud.*
Old Amsterdam. London, Hutchinson [1955]
315 p. 19 cm.
Sequel to I struggle and I rise.

I. Title.
PZ3.K7423Ol 56-16384 ‡

NK 0200678 DLC NIC

Knight, Brigid, *pseud.*
The piping on the wind. London, Cassell [1940]
349 p. illus. 19 cm.

I. Title.
PZ3.K7423Pi 41-1976 rev 2*

NK 0200679 DLC MH

Knight, Brigid, pseud.
Portrait of a woman. London, Hutchinson [1952]

NK 0200680 CaBVa

Knight, Brigid, *pseud.*
Southern Cross, a novel. [1st ed.] Garden City, N. Y., Doubleday, 1949.
xii, 305 p. 22 cm.

I. Title.
PZ3.K7423So 49-7140 rev*

Or OrP OrU WaE WaS WaSp WaSpG WaT CaBVaU KyLx
KyLx ViU MH OO OEac OClW PPL PP PLF PWcS CaBVa IdB
NK 0200681 DLC KMK FTaSU KMK IaU NNC MsU OrU KyU

823 K743so
Knight, Brigid, pseud.
Southern Cross, a novel. London, Cassell [1949]
312p. 19cm.

NK 0200682 TxU

VOLUME 300

823
K743s Knight, Brigid, pseud.
The sun climbs slowly. London, Cassell [1942]
312p. map. 19cm.

New York ed. (Crowell, 1942) has title: Westward the sun.

NK 0200683 TxU

Knight, Brigid, *pseud.*
The valiant lady, a novel. [1st American ed.] Garden City, N. Y., Doubleday, 1948 [c1947]
xii, 338 p. 22 cm.
London ed. published under title: I struggle and I rise.

1. Netherlands—Hist.—Fiction. I. Title.

PZ3.K7423Val 48-5167 rev*

NK 0200684 DLC CaBVa IdB Or OrP WU MsU PP NcGU OEac OOxM PPT PPPM-I TxU WaE WaT WaSp

---

Knight, Brigid, *pseud.*
Walking the whirlwind. London, Cassell [1940]
343 p. illus. 20 cm.

I. Title.

PZ3.K7423Wal 40-14423 rev 2*

NK 0200685 DLC OrP

Knight, Brigid, *pseud.*
Walking the whirlwind. New York, Crowell, 1941.
543 p. illus. 22 cm.

I. Title.

PZ3.K7423Wal 2 41-3333 rev 2*

NK 0200686 DLC CoU OO Or WaT WaSp WaS WaE

Knight, Brigid, *pseud.*
Westward the sun. New York, Crowell, 1942.
364 p. illus. 22 cm.

1. Transvaal—Hist.—Fiction. I. Title.

PZ3.K7423We 42-36172 rev 2*

NK 0200687 DLC OrP Or IdB WaS Wa WaSp IaU NIC OO OU PP PPL

Knight, Bruce Winton.
Economic principles in practice, by Bruce Winton Knight ... New York, Farrar & Rinehart, inc. [c1939]
xvii, 606 p. diagrs. 23½cm.
"References" at end of most of the chapters.

1. Economics. I. Title.

Library of Congress HB171.K58 39-10077
——— Copy 2.
Copyright A 126909 [3] 330.1

NK 0200688 DLC WaWW OrCS CU NIC NcD TxU ViU PPT OCl OU OCU PHC NN WaS IdPI

Knight, Bruce Winton.
Economic principles in practice, by Bruce Winton Knight ... Rev. ed. New York, Farrar & Rinehart, inc. [1942]
xiv, 659 p. diagrs. 23½cm.
"References" at end of some of the chapters.

1. Economics. I. Title.

42-14928
Library of Congress HB171.K58 1942
[5] 330.1

NK 0200689 DLC MtBC OrStbM WaWW NcD TU ViU PU-W OCl OO OClJC

Knight, Bruce Winton.
Economics, by Bruce Winton Knight ... and Nelson Lee Smith ... New York, The Ronald press company [c1929–
v. diagrs. 22cm. (Industries of America)
"References" at end of most of the chapters.

1. Economics. I. Smith, Nelson Lee, 1899– joint author.
29—18140
Library of Congress HB171.K6

NK 0200690 DLC CoU NcD CU PSC OClND OU PU ViU MB OrSaW OKentU

Knight, Bruce Winton.
Economics; an introductory analysis of the level, composition, and distribution of economic income [by] Bruce Winton Knight and Lawrence Gregory Hines. [1st ed.] New York, Knopf, 1952.
917 p. illus. 25 cm.

1. Economics.

HB171.5.K63 330.1 52-5079 ‡

NK 0200691 DLC MtBC OrCS AAP CU TU NcC NcRS OU PP MU MsU FU Or WaWW

Knight, Bruce Winton.
... How to run a war. New York, London, A. A. Knopf, 1936.
5 p. l., 3-243, iii, [1] p. 19½ cm.
"First edition."

1. War. I. Title.

U21.K5 355 36—30011

NK 0200692 DLC IdPI OrU WaS OrP ViU NN GU OClW NcD PSC NcRS PHC OCl OO OClW MB NIC WaTC

Knight, Burke H. Chapel Hill, 1913.
Distillation of cotton seed oil at very low pressure.

NK 0200693 NcU

Knight, Burton Alfred, 1885–
Analysis of house carpentry with related subjects outlines [!] by B. A. Knight and S. M. Woodruff in collaboration with George K. Wells, state supervisor of industrial education ... Division of vocational education, state Department of public instruction. Indianapolis, Ind., 1929.
folder ([16] p.) 43 x 56cm. folded to 22 x 14cm. (Indiana. Dept. of public instruction. Bulletin no. 103)

1. Carpentry. I. Woodruff, S. M., joint author. II. Wells, George Kimbell, 1887– joint author. III. Indiana. Dept. of public instruction. Division of vocational education. IV. Title.
E 29-258 Revised
Library, U. S. Office of Education TH5607.I 6K7
Library of Congress TH5608.K5
[r35c1] 694

NK 0200694 DHEW DLC MiU OCl

Knight, C F
The peace of Jerusalem: a sermon preached at the opening of St. Mark's church, Boston ...
see Knight, Cyrus Frederick, 1831-1891.

Knight, C.M.
Hints on driving
see Knight, Charles Lewis William Morley.

Knight, C R
Architectual education in the British Empire
see Knight, Cyril Roy.

Knight, C W R
see Knight, Charles William Robert, 1884-

Knight, Caleb. –1854.
A history of the town of Washington.
(In Field, D. D., D.D., editor. 1781-1867. A history of the county of Berkshire, Massachusetts. Pp. 344-349. Pittsfield. 1829.)
Two copies.

G8927 — Washington, Mass. Biog.

NK 0200699 MB

Knight, Cameron
The mechanician, a treatise on the construction and manipulation of tools, for the use and instruction of young engineers and scientific amateurs; comprising the arts of blacksmithing and forging; the construction and manufacture of hand tools ... 2d ed. reprinted from the 1st. New York, London, E. & F. N. Spon, 1879.
3 p. l., 397 p. 28 cm.

NK 0200700 ViU OCl MiEM CU

---

ar X
6737 Knight, Cameron.
The mechanician; a treatise on the construction and manipulation of tools. 3d ed., reprinted from the 1st. London, New York, E. & F. N. Spon, 1881.
397 p. illus. 29cm.

NK 0200701 NIC DN

Knight, Cameron.
The mechanician, a treatise on the construction and manipulation of tools, for the use and instruction of young engineers and scientific amateurs; comprising the arts of blacksmithing and forging; the construction and manufacture of hand tools, and the various methods of using and grinding them; description of hand and machine processes; turning and screw cutting; and the various details of setting out work incidental to the mechanical engineer's and machinist's art ... By Cameron Knight ... 5th ed., reprinted from the 1st. London, E. & F. N. Spon; New York, Spon & Chamberlain, 1897.
3 p. l., 397 p. 96 pl. 28cm.
1. Machine-shop practice. 2. Forging. 3. Tools.
A 10-1184
Title from Leland Stanford Jr. Univ. Printed by L. C.

NK 0200702 CSt PPSteph MiU

Knight, Cameron.
The mechanician and constructor for engineers, comprising forging, planing, lining, slotting, shaping, turning, screw-cutting, &c. Illustrated with ninety-six plates. By Cameron Knight. London, E. and F. N. Spon, 1869.
3 p. l., 397 p. 96 pl. 29cm.

1. Machine-shop practice. 2. Forging. I. Title.

7—14986
Library of Congress TJ1160.K6

NK 0200703 DLC NIC CtY PPF PU ICJ MB

VOLUME 300

Knight, Carlisle P 1880–
Health supervision of school children on a state-wide basis.
(*In* National education association of the United States. Addresses and proceedings, 1921. p. 379-383)

1. School hygiene.

Library, U. S. Bur. of Education E 22-115

NK 0200704 DHEW OO OU

Knight, Carlisle P 1880–
... Progress report on field investigations in child hygiene in the state of Missouri to June 30, 1920, by C. P. Knight, passed assistant surgeon, United States Public health service ... Washington, Govt. print. off., 1921.
24 p. incl. tables, charts, diagrs. 23½cm.
Reprint no. 631 from the Public health reports, v. 35, no. 53, December 31, 1920 (p. 3141-3162)
Running title: Child hygiene in Missouri.

1. Children—Care and hygiene. I. Missouri. Board of health. II. U. S. Public health service. Public health reports. Reprint 631. III. Title. IV. Title: Child hygiene in Missouri.

Library of Congress RA609.K75 21-26144

NK 0200705 DLC

Knight (Charles). Gymnastics in the army. pp. 297-303. 8°. London, 1896.
Cutting from: Strand Mag., Lond., April, 1896.

NK 0200706 DNLM

589.1
F198Z
Knight, Charles , F.L.S.
Contributions to the lichenographia of New Zealand; being an account, with figures, of some new species of Graphideae and allied lichens, by Chas. Knight ... and W. Mitten ... [n.p., 1860?]
p. 101-106. plate. 29½cm. [With Famintsyn, A. S. Zur Entwickelungsgeschichte der Gonidien und Zoosporenbildung der Flechten ... St.-Pétersbourg, 1867]
Caption title.
1. Graphideae. 2. Lichens. New Zealand.

NK 0200707 NcD

589.1
F198Z
Knight, Charles , F.L.S.
On some New Zealand verrucariae ... [n.p., 1860?]
p. 99-100. plate. 29½cm. [With Famintsyn, A. S. Zur Entwickelungsgeschichte der Gonidien und Zoosporenbildung der Flechten ... St.-Pétersbourg, 1867]
Caption title.
1. Verrucaria. 2. Lichens. New Zealand.

NK 0200708 NcD

KNIGHT, Charles, F.L.S.
On the lichenographia of New Zealand. Read before the Wellington philosophical society,13th Feb. 1884. [Wellington, 1884].
1.8°.pp.(9). 3 plates.
Transactions of the New Zealand institute 1884, vol. XVI, pp.400-408.

NK 0200709 MH-G

HD 6331
K5
Knight, Charles, 1791-1873.
An address to the labourers on the subject of destroying machinery. London, 1830.
8 p. 23 cm.
"Published under the authority of the Society for the Diffusion of Useful Knowledge."

NK 0200710 OU NcD ICU

Knight, Charles, 1791-1873. FOR OTHER EDITIONS SEE MAIN ENTRY
Shakespeare, William, 1564-1616.
The American Shakespeare, from the original text: carefully collated and compared with the editions of Halliwell, Knight, and Collier, with historical and critical introductions, and notes to each play, and a life ... by Charles Knight. Illustrated ... New York, H. J. Johnson, °1878.

Knight, Charles, 1791-1873.
Arminius; or, The deliverance of Germany; a tragedy ... Windsor, 1814.

NK 0200712 CSmH

---

*N5303
K6
Knight, Charles, 1791-1873, ed.
The arts and industry of all nations; or Pictorial gallery of arts: illustrating the progress in painting, sculpture, architecture (civil and ecclesiastical), agriculture, raw products, manufactures, trades, etc. from the earliest period to the present time. London, J. G. Sutton & Co. [1860?]
2 vols. illus.,plates. 36cm.

NK 0200713 NBuG InU

Knight, Charles, 1791-1873.
Arts and sciences
see The English cyclopaedia.

PR 10
K1 K5
1867
Knight, Charles, 1791-1873.
Begg'd at court, 1867.

Item in the Colbeck Collection; enquire at the Information Desk.

NK 0200715 CaBVaU

[Knight, Charles] 1791-1873.
... Berkshire: including a full description of Windsor castle ... London, C. Knight & co., 1840.
vii, [1], 147 p. illus., fold. map. 17½cm. (*His* Journey-book of England)
Also issued under title: The journey-book of Berkshire.

Subject entries: Berkshire, Eng.—Descr. & trav.—Guide books.

Library of Congress, no. DA670.B4K7. 2-27343

NK 0200716 DLC

Knight, Charles, 1791-1873.
Best story-tellers (The): a collection of popular fictions of all nations. Edited by C. Knight. With numerous wood-cuts. London: C. Knight. [18] 288 p. 12°. (Knight's Companion Library.)
In two parts. Paging continous.

NK 0200717 NN

22.331
743b
Knight, Charles, 1791-1873.
A biography of William Shakespere ... carefully rev. ... New York, Virtue & Yorston [n.d.]
4 p. l., 188 p. plates. (ports.)

1. Shakespere, William - Biography.

CtY
NK 0200718 WaPS DLC-P4 PP PPDrop PHC OCl NBuG PP ViU

Knight, Charles, 1791-1873.
... Biography; or, Third division of "The English cyclopaedia"
see The English cyclopaedia.

Knight, Charles, 1791-1873.
The bridal of the isles: a mask. 2.ed. The blighted hope: a monody. London, Printed for E.Wilson, etc., 1817.

NK 0200720 MH

Knight, Charles, 1791-1873, ed.
Shakespeare, William, 1564-1616.
Knights cabinet edition of the works of William Shakspere ...
London, W. S. Orr & co., 1851

Knight, Charles, 1791-1873.
Capital and labour; including the results of machinery. By Charles Knight. London, C. Knight & co., 1845.
1 p. l., vii-viii, [9]-250 p. 15½cm.

1. Labor and laboring classes. 2. Machinery in industry. 3. Labor and laboring classes—Gt. Brit.

Library of Congress HD8389.K5 8-9916

OrP MtU CtY NNC PPL PU ICJ NN NjP MtU OrP
NK 0200722 DLC MH-BA CU IEN ICN MH-BA WU CU ICU PU

Knight, Charles, 1791-1873
Capital and labour, including the results of machinery. London, 1853.
12°

NK 0200723 NN

Knight, Charles, 1791-1873.
The case of the authors as regards the paper duty ... London, 1851.
15 p.
No. 8 of a volume of pamphlets.

NK 0200724 NjP

VOLUME 300

Knight, Charles, 1791-1873.
The Charles Knight collection of portraits of booksellers, views of bookshops, etc. [n.p., n.d.]
3 v. Folio. Red morocco; bound by Riviere & Son.
Besides the portraits and views mentioned in the title, these volumes contain many A.L.S.'s miscellaneous printed materials, etc., etc.
In Library, December 24, 1928.

NK 0200725 CSmH

[KNIGHT, Charles, 1791-1873.]
Il compagno dell'operaio. Esibizione dei risultati del meccanismo vale a dire la produzione a basso prezzo e l'incremento del lavoro. Indrizzo agli operai del Regno Unito. Traduzione, dall'inglese di Frederick Sedley. Malta, Tip. Britannica, 1843.
18 cm.

NK 0200726 MH

Knight, Charles, 1791-1873.

Shakespeare, William, 1564-1616.
The complete works of Shakespeare; edited by Clarke & Wright; with his life, an historical summary of the plot and characters and variorum readings to each play, by Charles Knight ... To which are added a concordance of familiar gems ... alphabetical list of all the characters in the plays, glossary, index, etc. Illustrated with fifty-one photogravures ... Philadelphia, G. Barrie & son ⌊1899⌋

Knight, Charles, 1791-1873.
Crown history of England: being our country's history from the earliest records of the kingdom, to our own times, abridged from Charles Knight's Popular history of England, under the superintendence of its author. Lond. Bradbury, 1870.

NK 0200728 MA NN PPL

Knight, Charles, 1791-1873, *ed.*
Knight's cyclopædia of London, 1851. London, C. Knight ⌊1851⌋
4 p. l., ⌊5⌋-860 p. incl. illus. (incl. plans) front. 23cm.
Issued in 36 numbers, each with engraved half-title included in paging.
An abridgment, with additions and corrections, of the editor's "London", 1841-44, 6 v. *cf.* p. ⌊3⌋

1. London. 3-8024

Library of Congress DA683.K71

OC1RC MB NjP ViU OU
NK 0200729 DLC ICU CSt NcU NcD CtY PHi PP PPL MiU

Knight, Charles, 1791-1873.
Knight's cyclopædia of the industry of all nations. 1851. London, C. Knight ⌊1851⌋

Knight, Charles, 1791-1873, pub.
Cyclopædia of the industry of all nations. By Charles Knight. New-York, G. P. Putnam; London, C. Knight, 1851.

⌊**Knight, Charles**⌋ 1791-1873.
... Derbyshire ... London, C. Knight & co., 1841.
v, ⌊1⌋, 150 p. illus., fold. map. 17½cm. (*His* Journey-book of England)

1. Derbyshire—Descr. & trav.—Guide books. 2-27344

Library of Congress DA670.D42K7

NK 0200732 DLC MHi NjP

338.4 [Knight, Charles] 1791-1873.
K743rF1 Des machines et leurs résultats, tr. de l'anglais par M. Lhuillier de l'Etang. Paris, 1833.
277p.

Attributed to Lord Henry Brougham.

NK 0200733 IU

Knight, Charles, 1791-1873.
Description and history of vegetable substances
see under title

Knight, Charles, 1791-1873.
The dairy. London, 1843.
66 p. 15.5 cm.
Part of Knight's "Store of Knowledge."

NK 0200735 CtY

Knight, Charles, 1791-1873, ed.
The diary of Henry Teonge, chaplain on board His Majesty's ships Assistance, Bristol, and Royal Oak
see under Teonge, Henry, 1621-1690.

Ms.L Knight, Charles, 1791-1873
K69h Eight letters. (1) To Leigh Hunt. ⌊London⌋ 19 Nov. ⌊1830?⌋ Concerning his explanations of the cause of any pain Hunt may have received from his correspondence; impossible for him to depart from the strict line of business when dealing with the funds of a public body.
Leigh Hunt Coll.
(2)-(3) Leigh Hunt to Charles Knight. (2) ⌊n.p., 183-?⌋ Concerning his pain caused by a letter to him from the house of Messrs. Whitaker regarding the sum of £25; Hunt's former belief that everybody believed in his honesty and that Knight has run into this hasty error. In Mrs. Hunt's autograph. (3) Chelsea, 2 Apr. 1834. Concerning his thanks for a notice concerning the Indicator in the Printing machine; encloses a copy of the London journal; assures Knight that he had no hand in the attack on him in connection with the Penny magazine.
(4) To Leigh Hunt. ⌊n.p., n.d.⌋ Concerning Hunt's fear of legal perils; Fry to see Hunt and decide what shall be done.
(5) Leigh Hunt to Charles Knight. Chelsea, 25 Oct. ⌊1834⌋ Concerning his

Continued in next column

Continued from preceding column

thanks for Knight's letter; Thornton's and his illnesses; postpones his visit. Address on verso of ℓ.2.
(6) To Leigh Hunt. ⌊London, 1834⌋ Concerning his wishes for the success of Hunt's London journal and his desire to be of any assistance.
(7)-(8) Leigh Hunt to Charles Knight. Kensington. (7) 29 July ⌊1847⌋ Concerning his thanks for Knight's assistance in securing his pension; Knight's well timed notice of Hunt in "Half-hours with the best authors." (8) 11 Aug. ⌊1847?⌋ Concerning Knight's letter, his act of kindness toward Hunt, his notice of Hunt; the receipt of Knight's publications, the Political dictionary and the National cyclopedia; Hunt's desire to move because of his and Mrs. Hunt's health. Mounted and bound. Typed copies follow.
A.L.S. ⌊14⌋ℓ. (2 fold.) Ms.L.⌊1⌋ fold.ℓ. O.

NK 0200742 IaU

QL706 ⌊**Knight, Charles**⌋ 1791-1873.
.K7 The elephant, principally viewed in relation to man. A new ed., rev. by the author. London, C. Knight & co., 1844.
⌊v⌋-viii, ⌊9⌋-292 p. illus. 15cm.
With this are bound: The history of the horse, and The history of the dog, both by W. C. L. Martin.

1. Elephants.

NK 0200743 ICU OrP MH NN OC1W PPL CtY MB

Knight, Charles, 1791-1873, ed.
The English cyclopaedia; a new dictionary of universal knowledge
see under title

Knight, Charles, 1791-1873.
Knight's excursion companion. Excursions from London. 1851. London, C. Knight ⌊1851⌋
2 p. l., ⌊476⌋ p. pl., maps, plans. 21½ cm.
Each number has separate paging.
CONTENTS.—no. 1. Brighton.—no. 2. Hastings.—no. 3. Dover and Canterbury.—no. 4. Isle of Thanet, Sandwich, and Deal.—no. 5. Bath.—no. 6. Bristol.—no. 7. Windsor and Eton.—no. 8. Oxford.—no. 9. Portsmouth and Chichester.—no. 10. Winchester, Southampton, and Salisbury.—no. 11. The Isle of Wight.—no. 12. Dorchester, Weymouth, and the Isle of Portland.—no. 13. Exeter and the south coast of Devon.—no. 14. Plymouth and its environs.—no. 15. Cheltenham and Gloucester.—no. 16. Stratford-upon-Avon and Warwick.—no. 17. Woolwich, etc.—no. 18. Gravesand, and the halls of Kent.—no. 19. Cambridge.—no. 20. Leamington and Coventry.

1. England—Descr. & trav.—Guide-books. 2-29142

Library of Congress DA625.K71

NK 0200745 DLC CtY

Knight, Charles, 1791-1873.
Farmer's library; animal economy. London, n.d.
2 v. il., pl. Q.

NK 0200746 RPB

---

q709
K69f
Knight, Charles, 1791-1873.
Fine arts - architecture, sculpture, and painting. London, New York, London Printing and Pub. Co. ⌊1858?⌋
404p. incl. illus. (His Pictorial gallery of arts, v.2)

1. Art--Hist. I. Title. II. Series.

NK 0200747 ICarbS

VOLUME 300

Knight, Charles, 1791-1873.
... The gallery of portraits, with memoirs. London, Charles Knight, 1833.
7 v. Roy. 8°. Red half lev. mor., t.e.g.
Portraits engraved from noted paintings.
At head of title: Under the superintendence of the Society for the Diffusion of Useful Knowledge.

NK 0200748 CSmH

Knight, Charles, 1791-1873
Geography of the British Empire: a gazetteer of the United Kingdom and its colonies. London [1852]
2 v. illus., maps

NK 0200749 MiD NNUT

PR 10 K1 K5 1881 Knight, Charles, 1791-1873.
Glimpses of the past [1881]

Item in the Colbeck Collection; enquire at the Information Desk.

NK 0200750 CaBVaU MH

942 K7433. Knight, Charles, 1791-1873, comp.
Half hours of English history. From Edward I. to the death of Elizabeth. London, F. Warne [18--]
viii, 565 p. (The "Chandos classics")

1. Gt. Brit. - History. I. Title. II. Chandos classics.

NK 0200751 NNC PP PU NjP NcU WaTC DNW MiEM

DA135 H25 Knight, Charles, 1791-1873, ed.
Half-hours of English history. [n.p., 184-?]

A collection of excerpts covering the period from the Roman conquest to the death of Alfred.

NK 0200752 CU

ar W 8101 Knight, Charles, 1791-1873, comp.
Half hours of English history. Complete ed. London, G. Routledge, 1853.
2 v. in 1. 23cm.

1. Gt. Brit.--Hist.

NK 0200753 NIC MH PU PHatU MB ViU MiU

Knight, Charles, 1791-1873.
Half hours of English history. Complete ed. London, Routledge, Warne and Routledge, 1860.

NK 0200754 MH

Knight, Charles
Half hours of English history. Lond. Rutledge, 1861.
322 p. 8.

NK 0200755 PPG

KNIGHT, Charles, *editor*. 1791-1873.
Half hours of English history [to the death of Elizabeth].

London: F. Warne and co. 1865. 8°.

NK 0200756 MB

Knight, Charles, 1791-1873, *comp.*
Half hours of English history. From the Roman period to the death of Elizabeth. Selected and ed. by Charles Knight. London, F. Warne and co.; New York, Scribner, Welford and co. [1867]
2 p. l., iii-v, 687, [1] p. 22½cm.

1. Gt. Brit.—Hist. I. Title.

Library of Congress DA32.K71 2—16309

NK 0200757 DLC NBuU OClJC

Knight, Charles, 1791 ed
Half-hours of English history
4 v. N.Y. White, 1883.

NK 0200758 OCl

DA30 .K66 **Knight, Charles**, 1791-1873, *comp.*
Half hours of English history ... Selected and ed. by Charles Knight. A new ed. ... London, F. Warne and co. [1884]
4 v. fronts. (ports.) 20½cm.
At head of title: The "Chandos edition." On cover: Cavendish ed.
Vol. 3-4 selected and ed. by Mrs. Valentine.
CONTENTS.—v. 1. From the Roman period to the death of Henry III.—v. 2. From Edward I to the death of Elizabeth.—v. 3. From James the First to William and Mary.—v. 4. From Anne to Queen Victoria.

1. Gt. Brit.—Hist.

NK 0200759 ICU NcU

KNIGHT, Charles, 1791-1873, ed.
Half hours of English history, from the Roman period to the death of Henry III.
Phil. 1887. 4v.

NK 0200760 WaS

Knight, Charles, 1791-1873.
Half-hours with the best authors. Selected and arranged, with short biographical and critical notices, by Charles Knight. Illustrated with portraits ... London, C. Knight [1847-48]
4 v. fronts., ports. 18cm.

1. English literature (Selections: Extracts, etc.) I. Title.

Library of Congress PN6014.K6 11—30778

NK 0200761 DLC OClJC

KNIGHT, CHARLES, 1791-1873.
Half-hours with the best authors. Selected and arranged, with short biographical and critical notices, by Charles Knight. New York: Wiley and Putnam, 1847-49. 4 v. 19cm.

1. Literature—Collections. I. Title.

NK 0200762 NN PPA OCF PPL DNW

PN 6014 K6 1848a Knight, Charles, 1791-1873.
Half-hours with the best authors. With short biographical and critical notices. New York, Argyle Press [1848?]
6 v. fronts., plates, ports.

LITERATURE--COLLECTIONS.
Half-hours with the best authors.

NK 0200763 KMK

Knight, Charles, 1791-1873.
Half-hours with the best authors. With short biographical and critical notices. By Charles Knight ... Philadelphia, Porter & Coates [1848?]
6 v. fronts., plates, ports., 19cm.

1. Literature—Collections. I. Title.

Library of Congress PN6014.K6 1848 12—36083

NK 0200764 DLC WaWW PRosC PHi PP PCC MdBP AU NcD PHC PPSJ NN

[Micro]-film [8]08.8 [K]743h Knight, Charles, 1791-1873, ed.
Half-hours with the best authors. With short biographical and critical notices. Philadelphia, Porter & Coates [1848?]
6 v. in 3. ports.

v. 3, p. 13-16 and v. 5-6 wanting.
Microfilm (negative) Emporia, Kan., William Allen White Library, 1969. 1 reel. 35 mm.

1. Literature - Collections. I. Title.

NK 0200765 KEmT

Knight, Charles, 1791-1873.
Half-hours with the best authors. Selected and arranged, with short biographical and critical notices, by Charles Knight. New York, J. Wiley, 1848-49 [v. 3, '48]
3 v. 19½cm.

1. English literature (Selections: Extracts, etc.) I. Title.

Library of Congress PN6014.K6 1849 26-7383

NK 0200766 DLC NjP MeB MB ViU OO OCl

Knight, Charles, 1791-1873.
Half-hours with the best authors. With biographical and critical notices. 4th ed. London, Routledge, Warnes and Routledge [185-?]

4 v.

NK 0200767 MH

Knight, Charles, 1791-1873.
Half-hours with the best authors ... [London] C. Knight [1850-61]
4 v. in 2. fronts. (ports.) 22cm.
Each volume has separate t.-p. and pagination.
Ornamental t.-p.; headpieces.

1. English literature (Selections: Extracts, etc.) I. Title.

NK 0200768 ViU OOC NcRS MB CtY

VOLUME 300

Knight, Charles, 1791-1873.
Half-hours with the best authors, selected and arranged, with short biographical and critical notices. New York, Wiley, 1853.

NK 0200769 MH NjP PPFr PPGi

There are no cards for numbers NK 0200770 to NK 0200779

Knight, Charles, 1791-1873.
Half-hours with the best authors. With biographical and critical notices, by Charles Knight. The 3d ed. ... London, G. Routledge & co. [1854]
4 v. fronts. (ports.) illus. 19½cm.

1. English literature (Selections: Extracts, etc.) I. Title.
37-12454
Library of Congress PN6014.K6 1854
——— Copy 2. [2] 808.8

NK 0200780 DLC NN IaU

Knight, Charles, 1791-1873
Half-hours with the best authors. Selected and arranged, with short biographical and critical notices, by Charles Knight. N. Y., Wiley and Halsted, 1856.
v.1, 3-4, fronts., ports.

NK 0200781 MiD

Knight, Charles, 1791-1873, ed.
Half-hours with the best authors; with biographical and critical notices, by Charles Knight; with fifty-two illustrations by William Barbey; third edition, two volumes. London, George Routledge & co., 1857.
2 v. front. (por.) D.
Paul H. Hayne's signature on title page.

NK 0200782 NcD

Knight, Charles. 1791-1873.
Half-hours with the best authors... London, New York. 1859.
4 v. in 2. 19cm.

NK 0200783 MdBJ

Knight, Charles, 1791-1873.
Half-hour with the best authors; including biographical and critical notices, by Charles Knight; with fifty-two illustration by William Harvey. A new edition remodelled and revised by the original editor. London Frederick Warne and co. (186-?)
viii, 575p. illus. 19cm.

NK 0200784 KAS CtY

[Knight, Charles,] 1791-1873, editor.
Half hours with the best authors. Quarter [London:] Routledge, Warne, and Routledge [1860?]. v. in . fronts. (port.) 8°.
Illustrated title-pages.

1. English literature.—Collections. 2. Title.
N. Y. P. L. October 2, 1917.

NK 0200785 NN

371
1865
Knight, Charles, 1791-1873, comp.
Half-hours with the best authors. With short biographical and critical notices. By Charles Knight ... New York, J.Bradburn, 1865.
v. 19½cm.

NK 0200786 CtY

Knight, Charles, 1791-1873, editor.
Half-hours with the best authors; including biographical and critical notices, by Charles Knight. With fifty-two illustrations by William Harvey. London: F. Warne and Co. [1866.] 4 v. front., illus. new ed. 12°.

MYER COLLECTION.
1. English literature.—Collections. 2. Harvey, William, illustrator. 3. Title.
N. Y. P. L. May 8, 1915.

NK 0200787 NN MB CtY NIC OCl

820.8
K74h
1867
Knight, Charles, 1791-1873, ed.
Half hours with the best authors. London, F. Warne, 1867.
2v. ports. 23cm.

1. Literature--Collections.

NK 0200788 IU CtY

Knight, Charles, 1791-1873, ed.
Half-hours with the best authors. With short biographical and critical notices ... New York, 1867.
6 v. 21 cm.
1. English literature - Selections, extracts, etc. I. Title.

NK 0200789 CtY ODW

PN6014
.K6
1868
Knight, Charles, 1791-1873.
Half hours with the best authors. A new ed. London, F. Warne, 1868.
2 v. fronts.,plates,ports. 22 cm.

1. English literature (Selections: extracts, etc.) I. Title.

NK 0200790 T

Knight, Charles, 1791-1873, *ed.*
Half-hours with the best authors. With short biographical and critical notices. By Charles Knight ... Philadelphia, Porter & Coates [188-?]
6 v. in 3. fronts. (ports.)

1. Literature—Collections. I. Title.
40-28601
Library of Congress PN6014.K6

NK 0200791 DLC PP OU NNUT NN

PN6014
K612
Knight, Charles, 1791-1873, ed.
Half-hours with the best authors; including biographical and critical notices, by Charles Knight with fifty-two illustrations by William Harvey. A new edition, remodelled and revised by the original editor. London, Frederick Warne & co. c1880?>
4 vols. fronts.(ports.)illus. 20cm.
1. Literature.-Collections. I. Title.

NK 0200792 NBuG

Knight, Charles, 1791-1873.
... Half-hours with the best authors. Including biographical and critical notices, by Charles Knight ... A new ed., remodelled and rev. by the original editor ... London, F. Warne and co. [1884]
4 v. illus. 18½cm. (The "Chandos classics" [61, 62, 63, 64])
Series note also on cover.

1. English literature (Selections: Extracts, etc.) I. Title. II. Ser.

NK 0200793 ViU IU CaBVaU MH OO PU CaQML MdBP CtY

Knight, Charles, 1791-1873.
Half-hours with the best authors. With short biographical & cirtical noteces. N.Y., 1885
v. 1-3, 5.

NK 0200794 ODW

Knight, Charles, 1791-1873
... Half-hours with the best authors. Including biographical & critical notices, with steel portrait & illus. A new ed., with notes & biographies rev. Phila., Lippincott, 1886.
4v.

NK 0200795 OClW

808.8
K69h
1888
Knight, Charles, 1791-1873.
Half-hours with the best authors. Including biographical and critical notices. With fifty-two illustrations by William Harvey. New ed., remodelled and rev. by the original editor. London and New York, F.Warne, 1888.
4v. illus.,ports. 19cm. (The Chandos classics. [no.61-64])
Imprint varies slightly: v.4, London, F.Warne [n.d.]
1.Literature - Collections. I. Title. LC.

NK 0200796 CLSU ICarbS

Knight, Charles, 1791-1873.
Half-hours with the best authors. Including biographical and critical notices, by C. Knight. A new edition. With the notes and biographies revised. London: F. Warne and Co., 1889. 4 v. port. illus. 8°. (Cavendish library.)
v. 4 undated; at head of title: The "Chandos edition."

1. English literature.—Collections.
N. Y. P. L. June 10, 1913.

NK 0200797 NN

PN 6014
.K7
1890
KNIGHT, CHARLES, 1791-1873.
Half hours with the best authors. A new edition. London, F. Warne, 1890.
2 v.

1. English literature--Collections.
I. Title.

NK 0200798 InU

Knight, Charles, 1791-1873.
Half hours with the best authors; with short biographical and critical notes. New York: New York Pub. Co., 1895. 4 v. port. 12°.

CENTRAL RESERVE.
1. Literature.—Collections and selections. 2. Title.
N. Y. P. L. February 23, 1916.

NK 0200799 NN

VOLUME 300

Knight, Charles, 1791–1873, *ed.*
Half-hours with the best letter-writers and autobiographers. Forming a collection of memoirs and anecdotes of eminent persons. By Charles Knight ... London, New York, G. Routledge and sons, 1867–68.
2 v. 20½cm.
"Not ... a mere sequel to the 'Half-hours with the best authors,' although it completes the plan of that popular series, as formed by its editor many years ago."—Pref.
CONTENTS.—ser. 1: I. Howell. II. D'Ewes; Pepys; Lucy Hutchinson; Anne Fanshawe. III. Gray, West and Walpole. IV. Thomas Bewick. V. Mrs. Delany. VI. Mrs. Delany and Miss Burney. VII. Byron and Dallas. VIII. Henry Teonge. IX. Laurence Sterne. X. Horace Walpole and the Miss Berrys. XI. William Shenstone. XII. Richard and Mary Steele. XIII. Sir Thomas Browne, and his son, the sailor. XIV. Fielding and Thackeray—Voyages of two great novelists. XV. Schools and school life. XVI. Lady Mary Wortley Montagu. XVII. Letters of various writers. XVIII. Autobiographic passages of various writers.—ser. 2. I. The Paston letters. II. William Cowper. III. Arthur Wilson. IV. Ballitore. V. Garrard's letters to Sir Thomas Wentworth. VI–VII. Edward Gibbon. VIII. Thomas de Quincy. IX. Junius and Woodfall. X. Hannah More. XI. The Percy correspondence. XII. Unpublished letters of Robert Southey. XIII. Christopher North and John Wilson. XIV. Unpublished letters of George Canning. XV. Detached letters of various writers. XVI. Autobiographical passages from various writers.
1. English letters. 2. Autobiography. I. Title.
15-11411
Library of Congress PR1109.K5

NK 0200801 DLC OClStM OCX PPL OCl NN

[Knight, Charles] 1791–1873.
... Hampshire; including the Isle of Wight ... London, C. Knight & co., 1841.
vi p., 1 l., 192 p. front., illus., fold. maps. 17½cm. (*His* Journey-book of England)
Subject entries: Hampshire, Eng.—Descr. & trav.—Guide books.
2-27345
Library of Congress, no. DA670.H2K7.

NK 0200802 DLC NjP PP

Knight, Charles, 1791–1873.
... The Hindoos. Volume I. London, C. Knight, 1834.
[6], 386 p. front., plates. 17cm. (The library of entertaining knowledge.)
Bibliographical foot-notes.

NK 0200803 ICJ

DA 50 .K6 1789
Knight, Charles, 1791–1873
A history of all the real and threatened invasions of England, from the landing of Julius Caesar, to the present period ... to which is added an appendix, containing a mode of defending the kingdom ... 2d ed. Windsor, Printed and sold by C. Knight, 1789.
3p.ℓ., iv, 208, 48, 12p. 22cm.
1. Gt. Brit. - Defenses. 2. Gt. Brit. - Hist. Invasions. I. Title: Invasions of England.

NK 0200804 MU

[**Knight, Charles**], 1791–1873.
A history of all the real and threatened invasions of England, from the landing of Julius Cæsar, to the present period. Giving a succinct account of the several parties, that either excited, or suppressed the various commotions. Concluding with a view of the present state of affairs. Dedicated to the lord lieutenants of the counties of Great Britain. To which is added, an appendix, containing a mode of defending the kingdom, with an epitome of military horsemanship, and general tactics; taken from Edmonds, Mar. Saxe, Lloyd, Pembroke, Simes and others, the most respectable authors. Windsor, Printed for, and sold by C. Knight, 1794.
4 p. l., iv, 196, 48 p. 21cm.
1. Gt. Brit.—Defenses. 2. Gt. Brit.—Hist.—Invasions. I. Title. II. Title: Invasions of England.
Library of Congress DA50.K6 2-10858 Revised

NK 0200805 DLC NN

[**Knight, Charles**.] 1791–1873.
An history of all the real and threatened invasions of England, from the first landing of the Danes, to the present period; including the descent on the coast of Wales, in 1797, and the late French expedition in Bantry bay in Ireland... To which is added, an appendix, containing difficulties that an invading army must encounter in England... London: Printed for, and sold by the author [, 1797?]. ii, 4–70 p. 8°.
Chapters 1–14 (p. 1–65) are the same as chapters 3–15 in the author's: A history of all the real and threatened invasions of England from the landing of Julius Caesar to the present period. 1794.
553646A. 1. Great Britain—Invasions. I. Title.
N. Y. P. L. November 4, 1931

NK 0200806 NN

Knight, Charles, 1791–1873.
A history of England
see his The popular history of England.

Knight, Charles, 1791–1873.
Martineau, Harriet, 1802–1876.
The history of England during the thirty years' peace: 1816–1846. By Harriet Martineau ... London, C. Knight, 1849–50.

Knight, Charles, 1791–1873. FOR OTHER EDITIONS SEE MAIN ENTRY
Martineau, Harriet, 1802–1876.
The history of England from the commencement of the XIXth century to the Crimean war. By Harriet Martineau ... Philadelphia, Porter & Coates [c1864]

Knight, Charles, 1791–1873. FOR OTHER EDITIONS SEE MAIN ENTRY
Martineau, Harriet, 1802–1876.
History of the peace: being a history of England from 1816 to 1854. With an introduction 1800 to 1815. By Harriet Martineau ... Boston, Walker, Wise, and company, 1864–66.

DA535 .M4
Knight, Charles, 1791–1873.
Martineau, Harriet, 1802–1876.
A history of the thirty years' peace. A. D. 1816–1846. By Harriet Martineau ... London, G. Bell and sons, 1877–78.

Knight, Charles, 1791–1873.
An illustrated history of society and government ...
see his The popular history of England.

Knight, Charles, 1791–1873.
Illustrations to Shakespeare's Tempest.
[London.] Morris. [1825.] 12 plates. 22½ × 22½ cm.
L4420 — Shakespeare, William. Illustrations. Tempest.

NK 0200813 MB

Knight, Charles, 1791–1873,
... The Imperial cyclopaedia
see under title

[Knight, Charles] 1791–1873.
The journey-book of Berkshire: with particular accounts of Windsor and its castle, Eaton and Reading ... London, C. Knight & co. [1840?]
vii, [1], 147 p. incl. front. (fold. map.) illus. 17cm. (*His* Journey-book of England)
Also issued under title: Berkshire: including a full description of Windsor castle.
Subject entries: Berkshire, Eng.—Descr. & trav.—Guide books.
2-27342
Library of Congress, no. DA670.B4K6.

NK 0200815 DLC NjP

Knight, Charles, 1791–1873.
Kapital und arbeit, mit inbegriff der ergebnisse der maschinerie. Von Charles Knight. Aus dem englischen von Theodor Roth. Stuttgart, Expedition der Wochenbände, 1847.
222 p. 16½cm.
1. Labor and laboring classes. 2. Machinery in industry. 3. Labor and laboring classes—Gt. Brit. I. Roth, Theodor, tr. II. Title.
18-10052
Library of Congress HD8389.K55

NK 0200816 DLC OO

[Knight, Charles] 1791–1873.
...[Kent ... London, C. Knight & co., 1842.
vi, 226 p. front. (fold. map) illus. 17½cm. (*His* Journey-book of England)
Subject entries: Kent, Eng.—Descr. & trav.—Guide books.
2-27346
Library of Congress, no. DA670.K3K7.

NK 0200817 DLC NjP NNUT MWA

Knight, Charles, 1791–1873.
Knowledge is power: a view of the productive forces of modern society, and the results of labour, capital, and skill. By Charles Knight ... London, J. Murray, 1855.
x, 486 p. illus. 18cm.
1. Industrial arts. 2. Industry. I. Title.
5—19809
Library of Congress T47.K69
[40g1] NUC

WaU
NK 0200818 DLC CU KMK ICJ NjP OCU PPL PU CtY TxU

T47 .K69 1856
Knight, Charles, 1791–1873.
Knowledge is power: a view of the productive forces of modern society, and the results of labor, capital, and skill. Rev. and edited, with additions, by David A. Wells. Boston, Gould and Lincoln, 1856.
xii, 503 p. illus. 20cm.
1. Industrial arts. 2. Industry. I. Wells, David Ames, 1828-1898. II. Title.

MH MWA PPCC PPL OrU OrP
NK 0200819 ScCleU ICU MeB DLC-P4 OO PU-Penn NcD

Knight, Charles, 1791–1873.
Knowledge is power; a view of the productive forces of modern society and the results of labor, capital and skill...ed. with additions by D.A. Wells. New York, Sheldon, 1856.
503 p.

NK 0200820 PPLT

VOLUME 300

Knight, Charles, 1791-1873.
Knowledge is power: A view of the productive resources of modern society, and the results of labor, capital, and skill. Revised ... by David A. Wells ... Boston, Gould & Lincoln, 1857.
xii, 13-503 p. il. nar. 8°.

NK 0200821 NN ODW PPG NcU

Knight, Charles, 1791-1873.
Knowledge is power: a view of the productive forces of modern society, and the results of labour capital, and skill. By Charles Knight ... 2d ed. London, J. Murray, 1859.
x, 423 p. illus. 18 cm.
1. Industrial arts. 2. Industry.

NK 0200822 CtY CaBVaU

Knight, Charles, 1791-1873.
Knowledge is power. By Charles Knight. ... . A new edition corrected, enlarged, and adapted by the author for elementary instruction. London, Bell and Daldy, 1866.
xvi, 426 p. 18cm.
Contents.—pt. 1. Capital and labour necessary for production.—pt. 2. Capital, labour, and skill working together for production.—pt. 3. Capitalists and labourers: co-operation.

11864S

NK 0200823 ICJ IaAS

Knight, Charles. 1791-1873.
Knowledge is power: a view of the productive forces of modern society and the results of labor, capital and skill. Revised and edited, with additions, by David A. Wells.
Boston. Gould & Lincoln. 1867. 503 pp. 12°.

F6557 — Political economy. — Capital and labor. — Wells, David Ames, ed.

NK 0200824 MB NjP

Knight, Charles, 1791-1873.
Knowledge is power... A new ed., corrected, enlarged; & adapted by the author for elementary instruction. Lond., G. Bell & sons, 1874. xvi, 426 p. D
(Bohn's scientific library)

NK 0200825 OO

H
3
.467

KNIGHT, CHARLES, 1791-1873.
Knowledge is power... London, G.Bell and sons, 1878.
426p. (Bohn's scientific library)

Based upon two books previously written: The results of machinery and Capital and labour.

NK 0200826 ICN INS PPD PP

KNIGHT, Charles, 1791-1873.
The land we live in. A pictorial and literary sketch book of the British empire. [By Charles Knight, Harriet M[ ] & co.,] L. [1847-].

1.8°. Maps, port. of Beau Nash and other illustrs.

Vol. II-IV. have each also a lith. title-page.

NK 0200827 MH MA NN

Knight, Charles, 1791-1873, ed.
The land we live in. A pictorial and literary sketch-book of the British empire. Vol. 2-4. London, Knight [1848?-1850]
3 v. L. 8°.

NK 0200828 MB PHi

Knight, Charles. 1791-1873.
The life of William Shakespeare.
(In Shakespeare, William. Works. The complete works. Vol. 3. pp. vii-lii. New York. [1856.])

K1126 — Shakespeare, William. Biog. and crit.

NK 0200829 MB

Knight, Charles. 1791-1873.
The life of William Shakespeare.
(In Shakespeare, William. Works. The complete works ... Vol. 1, pp. vii-lii. New York. [1861.])

H4123 — Shakespeare, William. Biog. and crit.

NK 0200830 MB

Knight, Charles, 1791-1873, *ed.*
London. Edited by Charles Knight ... [London] C. Knight & co., 1841-44.
6 v. front., illus. (incl. plans) 26cm.

1. London—Hist. 2. London—Descr.

44-32665

Library of Congress DA677.K68

ICJ WaSp CaBVa
OEac ICN NN PU PP CtY IU MH NjP ViU OClRC OU OO PV
NK 0200831 DLC CaOTP NcU IaU PP OkU IaB OClW PPL PPA

Knight, Charles, 1791-1873, *ed.*
London. Ed. by Charles Knight. London, H. G. Bohn, 1851.
6 v. in 3. illus. 25cm.
First published, 1841-1844, in 150 numbers.
Written in greater part by J. C. Platt, J. Saunders, W. Weir, G. L. Craik, and the editor.

1. London—Hist. 2. London—Descr.

3—7547

Library of Congress DA677.K69

PPFr MiU OCl OClU MWA WaU MeB NN MB
NK 0200832 DLC OrP CaBVaU NcD CtY PU-W PU PV PPD

KNIGHT, CHARLES, 1791-1873.
London; rev. and corr. to the present time by E. Walford. London, J.S. Virtue [1875-77]
6 v. in 3. illus. 26cm.

1. London--Hist. 2. London--Descr., 1800-1900. I. Walford, Edward, 1823-1897, ed.

NK 0200833 NN Wa OCU

Knight, Charles, 1791-1873.
The menageries; quadrupeds described and drawn from living subjects
see under title

[Knight, Charles] 1791-1873.
The menageries. The natural history of monkeys, opossums, and lemurs
see under title

Knight, Charles, 1791-1873, ed.

The Lowell offering.
Mind amongst the spindles. A miscellany, wholly composed by the factory girls. Selected from the Lowell offering. With an introduction by the English editor, and a letter from Harriet Martineau. Boston, Jordan, Swift & Wiley, 1845.

Knight, Charles, 1791-1873, ed.
The mineral kingdom. London, 1842.
15.5 cm.

NK 0200837 CtY

[Knight, Charles] 1791-1873, supposed author.
The modern stage. A letter to the Hon. George Lamb, on the decay and degradation of English dramatic literature
see under title

[Knight, Charles] 1791-1873.
The National Cyclopaedia of Useful Knowledge
see under title

Knight, Charles, 1791-1873, attributed author.
Natural history of quadrupeds ... New-York, 1840.
16 cm. (Family library no. 104)

NK 0200840 CtY

[Knight, Charles] 1791-1873.
Natural history. The elephant as he exists in a wild state, and as he has been made subservient in peace and in war, to the purposes of man.
New York, Harper & brothers, 1840.
vi p., 1 l., [9]-300 p. illus. 15.5 cm.
(The Family library. no. 164)
Also issued in London with title The elephant, in 1844, and in 1832 as v. 2 of his Menageries.

NK 0200841 MB CtY

---

v.1430

[Knight, Charles] 1791-1873.
The newspaper stamp, and the duty on paper, viewed in relation to their effects upon the diffusion of knowledge. By the author of The results of machinery. London, C.Knight, 1836.
64p. 22cm.

NK 0200842 CtY NNC MnU PU

Knight, Charles, 1791-1873, ed.
Old England; a pictorial museum of regal, ecclesiastical, baronial, municipal and popular antiquities from the earliest period to the present time. Divisions I-IV. Baltimore, J.Perry [18- ?]

Paper cover serves as title-page.

NK 0200843 MH

VOLUME 300

[Knight, Charles] 1791-1873, *ed.*
Old England: a pictorial museum of regal, ecclesiastical, baronial, municipal, and popular antiquities ... London, C. Knight & co., 1845.
2 v. illus., col. pl. 36½cm.
Added title-pages, illustrated in colors.

1. Gt. Brit.—Antiq. 2. Gt. Brit.—Hist. 3. Gt. Brit.—Descr. & trav. 4. Gt. Brit.—Soc. life & cust. I. Title.

Library of Congress DA90.K69 2—10764
[s22f1]

OC1MA NjP NN MH PP PU UU AU FMU NcD MHi NjR
NK 0200844 DLC OC ICN PP MB OC1W CtY PHi OC1WHi

Knight, Charles, 1791-1873, *ed.*
Old England: a pictorial museum of regal, ecclesiastical, municipal, baronial, and popular antiquities. Ed. by Charles Knight ... London, J. Sangster and co. [185-?]
2 v. col. fronts., illus., 38 col. pl. 34½ cm.
Another edition was published, London, C. Knight & co., 1845.

1. Gt. Brit.—Antiq. 2. Gt. Brit.—Hist. 3. Gt. Brit.—Descr. & trav. 4. Gt. Brit.—Soc. life & cust. I. Title.

DA90.K69 15—3524

NBuU PHi PPD PPT
NK 0200845 DLC CSmH MdBP ViU PU-F OC1 OC1h NcU WU

DA90 f.K7 1854
[Knight, Charles] 1791-1873, ed.
Old England: a pictorial museum of regal, ecclesiastical, municipal, baronial and popular antiquities ... London, Sangster and Fletcher, 1854.
2 v. col. fronts., illus., col. plates. 36cm.

NK 0200846 ICU CtY

---

q913.42 K69o 1860
Knight, Charles, 1791-1873, ed.
Old England: a pictorial museum of regal, ecclesiastical, municipal, baronial, and popular antiquities. New ed. London, Forbes, Sangster [1860?]
2 v. illus., col. pl.

1. Gt. Brit.--Antiq. 2. Gt. Brit.--Hist. 3. Gt. Brit.--Descr. & trav. 4. Gt. Brit.--Soc. life & cust. I. Title.

NK 0200847 ICarbS

Knight, Charles, 1791-1873, ed.
Old England. A pictorial museum of regal, ecclesiastical, municipal, baronial, and popular antiquities. Boston, S. Walker [1872?]
2 v. illus. 36 cm.
1. Gt. Brit. - Antiq. 2. Gt. Brit. - Hist. 3. Gt. Brit. - Descr. & trav. 4. Gt. Brit. - Soc. life & cust. I. Title.

NK 0200848 MdBP

Knight, Charles, 1791-1873.
Old lamps, or new? A plea for the original editions of the text of Shakspere: forming an introductory notice to the Stratford Shakspere, edited by Charles Knight. London, [Woodfall and Kinder, printers] 1853.
lxiii p. 17 cm.
Offprinted from the Intro. to the Stratford Shakspere.

NK 0200849 NcU CtY PU-F

Knight, Charles, 1791-1873.
The old printer and the modern press. By **Charles Knight** ... London, J. Murray, 1854.
3 p. l., [vii]-ix p., 1 l., 314 p. illus. 17cm.
Part I, "The old printer", is a revised edition of the author's "William Caxton", 1844; pt. II, "The modern press", is "a view of the progress of the press to our own day, especially in relation to ... cheap popular literature".

1. Caxton, William, 1422 (ca.)-1491. 2. Press—Gt. Brit. I. Title. 4—4699

Library of Congress Z151.K71

MdBP NN NcWsW
NcU ScU MdBP NcD CtY PPGi PPD PPL PU ViU ICJ MB
NK 0200850 DLC OrP WaSp PPT KyU NcU LU CoU INS OC

Knight, Charles, 1791-1873.
Once upon a time. By Charles Knight ... London, J. Murray, 1854.
2 v. 17cm.
CONTENTS.—v. 1. The Pastons. The discoverer of Madeira. The silent highway. The younger son. Hang out your lights. Evil May-day. Country wayfarers. Philip Sidney and Fulke Greville. Shakespere's first ride to London. May-morning: its poetry and its prose. Amateurs and actors. Ben Jonson's mother. English poets in Scotland. Robert Burton's poetical commonwealth. Milton, the Londoner. Lucy Hutchinson. Astrological almanacs. May fair. John Aubrey, and his Eminent men.—v. 2. The first newspaper stamp. Trivia. Horace Walpole's world of fashion. Horace Walpole's world of letters. Fanny Burney at court. The farmer's kitchen. Windsor, as it was. Crabbe's modern antiques. The leading profession. Dear and cheap. Suburban milestones. An episode of Vathek. The Eton Montem. Items of the obsolete. The first step into the world. Saint John's gate. The tail piece.
1. Gt. Brit.—Hist.—Addresses, essays, lectures. I. Title. 4—8053
[a24e1]
Library of Congress DA27.K69

NK 0200851 DLC NcU ScU PU CtY PPL OC1W MB NjP NN

Knight, Charles, 1791-1873.
Once upon a time. By Charles Knight... Second edition... London: J. Murray, 1859. xii, 531 p. illus. (incl. ports.), plates. 17½cm.
CONTENTS.—The chapel.—The Pastons.—The discoverer of Madeira.—The silent highway.—The younger son.—Hang out your lights.—Evil May-day.—Country wayfarers.—Philip Sidney and Fulke Greville.—Shakespere's first ride to London.—May-morning: its poetry and its prose.—Amateurs and actors.—Ben Jonson's mother.—English poets in Scotland.—Robert Burton's poetical commonwealth.—Milton, the Londoner.—Lucy Hutchinson.—Astrological almanacs.—May-fair.—John Aubrey, and his Eminent men.—The beginnings of popular literature.—The first newspaper stamp.—Trivia.—Horace Walpole's world of fashion.—Horace Walpole's world of letters.—Fanny Burney at court.—The farmer's kitchen.—Windsor, as it was.—Crabbe's modern antiques.—The leading profession.—Dear and cheap.—Suburban milestones.—An episode of Vathek.—The Eton Montem.—Items of the obsolete.—The first step into the world.—Saint John's gate.—The tail-piece.
With autograph of author.

DUYCKINCK COLLECTION.
1. Great Britain—Hist.—Addresses, essays, lectures. I. Title.
N. Y. P. L. *Revised* September 28, 1937

NK 0200853 NN OO OrU CU

Knight, Charles
Once upon a time. New & enl. ed. Lond., Routledge, 1865.
562p.

Contents: The youthful days of Wm. Caxton.- The chapel.-The pastons.-The discoverer of Madeira.-The silent highway.-The younger son.- Hang out your lights.-Evil May-day Country wayfarers.-Philip Sydney & Fulke Greville.- May morning.-Ben Jonson's mother.-Ben Jonson, the Londoner.-Robert

NK 0200854 OC1 OCU OrP

Knight, Charles, 1791-1873.
Passages of a working life during half a century: with a prelude of early reminiscences. By Charles Knight ... London, Bradbury & Evans, 1864-65.
3 v. 19½cm.

1. Publishers and publishing—Gt. Brit. 5—360

Library of Congress Z325.K71K

PPA OC1 OCU OO CSmH ViU NjP IU NN MB MH MdBP CtY
NK 0200855 DLC CaBVaU OrP NcU FTaSU MdBP NcD PPL

B K69k1 1873
Knight, Charles, 1791-1873.
Passages of a working life during half a century: with a prelude of early reminiscences. Reissue with introductory note by James Thorne. London, Knight, 1873.
3v. ports. 20cm.

1. Publishers and publishing--England. I. Title.

NK 0200856 IU CtY PU MeB WU

Knight, Charles, 1791-1873.
Passages from the life of Charles Knight ... New York, G. P. Putnam's sons, 1874.
xiv p., 1 l., [5]-480 p. 19cm.
Abridged edition of the author's "Passages of a working life during half a century ... London, 1864-65." 3 vols.
"Introductory" signed: James Thorne.

1. Publishers and publishing—Gt. Brit. I. Thorne, James, 1815-1881. II. Title.

Library of Congress Z325.K71K1 31-2209
——— Copy 2. 655.50942

OC1W OO PBL NBuG ICU MWA IU MB MiU NjP MdBP
NK 0200857 DLC TU NcU CU MdBP MH OU PU CtY PHC MiU

Knight, Charles, 1791-1873, ed.

[Knight's penny magazine. v. 1-9, Mar. 31, 1832-Dec. 31, 1840; v. 10-14 (new ser. [v. 1-5]) Jan. 2, 1841-Dec. 27, 1845; [v. 15-16 (3d ser.] v. 1-2) 1846. London, C. Knight & co. [1832-46]

Knight, Charles, 1791-1873.
A pictorial and literary sketch book of the British Empire
see his The Land we live in.

Knight, Charles, 1791-1873, ed. FOR OTHER EDITIONS SEE MAIN ENTRY

Shakespeare, William, 1564-1616.
The pictorial edition of the works of Shakspere. Ed. by Charles Knight ... London, C. Knight and co. [1839]-43.

[**Knight, Charles**] 1791-1873.
The pictorial gallery of arts ... London, C. Knight and co. [etc., 1845?]-47.
2 v. col. fronts., illus., pl. 36cm.
Vol. 2 has imprint: London, C. Cox, 1847.
CONTENTS.—[v. 1] Useful arts.—v. 2. Fine arts.

1. Industrial arts. 2. Art. I. Title. 10-3941 Revised

Library of Congress N7521.K6

NK 0200861 DLC OCX NWM MB OC1W OOxM PP NN WaS MH-FA

Knight, Charles, 1791-1873.
Knight's pictorial gallery of arts ...
London, New York, The London printing and publishing company, limited [1858-
v. illus. 34½ x 27cm.
Added t.-p., illus.: The pictorial gallery of arts.

1. Industrial arts. 10—34282

Library of Congress T45.K6

PP NN PV
NK 0200862 DLC ICarbS ViU ICRL CU OFH NcU ICJ KyLoU

VOLUME 300

Knight, Charles, 1791–1873.
Pictorial half-hours of London topography. London, C. Knight [1851] 233 p. illus. 23cm.

569523B. 1. London—Descr., 1800–1900. 2. Architecture—Gt. Br.—Eng.—London. I. Title.
N. Y. P. L. December 18, 1951

NK 0200863 NN

NE1144 .P5
Knight, Charles, 1791-1873, ed.
Pictorial half-hours; or, Miscellanies of art, with illustrative descriptions. London, C. Knight [1850–

Knight, Charles, 1791-1873.
The pictorial history of England.
see under Craik, George Lillie, 1798-1866.

Knight, Charles, 1791-1873
The pictorial museum of animated nature ... London, C. Knight and co. [1844]
2 v. col. fronts., illus. 36cm.
CONTENTS.—v. 1. Mammalia. Birds.—v. 2. Birds. Reptiles. Mollusca. Insects.

1. Zoology—Pictorial works. I. Knight, Charles, 1791–1873, pub.
Library of Congress QL46.P61 11—3678

NK 0200865 DLC

Knight, Charles, 1791–1873.
Charles Knight's Pictorial museum of animated nature; and companion for the zoological gardens. Illustrated with four thousand wood engravings ... London, New York, The London printing and publishing company (limited) [1856–58]
2 v. in 1. illus. 35½cm.
Added t. p., with vignette.
CONTENTS.—I. Mammalia and birds.—II. Reptiles, fishes, molluscs, and insects.

1. Zoology. I. Title.
Library of Congress QL45.K6 35-21093 590

NK 0200866 DLC NjP NcD InU CtY MiU ICJ CaBVaU PP OO OCl

Knight, Charles, 1791-1873, ed.
The Plain Englishman: comprehending original compositions, and selections from the best writers, under the heads of the Christian monitor; the British patriot; the Fireside companion ...
London, Hatchard and son [etc.] 18

[Knight, Charles] 1791-1873.
Political dictionary; forming a work...
see under title

DA30 .K68
Knight, Charles, 1791-1893.
The popular history of England: an illustrated history of society and government from the earliest period to our own times. By Charles Knight... London and New York, F. Warne and co. [18-]
9 v. fronts. (v.1-8) illus., ports., plan, tables. 27cm.

1. Gt. Brit.-Hist.

NK 0200868 ICU NcC

Knight, Charles, 1791-1873.
The popular history of England: an illustrated history of society and government from the earliest period to our own times. By Charles Knight ... London, Bradbury and Evans [1856?–62?]
8 v. fronts., illus. (incl. plans, facsims.) ports., maps (1 double) 23½cm.
Vols. 4–5 have title: A history of England, by Charles Knight ... London, Bradbury, Evans, & co.

1. Gt. Brit.—Hist.
Library of Congress DA30.K7 41-26190

NK 0200869 DLC OrCS WaS CtY ViU-L MB NNC Nh MH PPFr PPWa ICN NN ViU IaU DGU MH MiU OCU RPB CtY OClW CSmH MeB PU ICRL

DA30 K7 1860
Knight, Charles, 1791-1873.
The popular history of England: an illustrated history of society and government from the earliest period to our own times.
London, J. Sangster [1860?]
8 v. illus., ports., maps., facsims. 24cm.
1. Gt. Brit. - Hist.

NK 0200870 CoU

DA30 .K71 1864
Knight, Charles, 1791-1873.
The popular history of England: an illustrated history of society and government from the earliest period to our own times. By Charles Knight ... London, Bradbury and Evans; Boston, Little, Brown, and company, 1864.
8 v. fronts., illus., ports., double map. 23 1/2cm.
From B.C. 56-A.D. 1861.
1. Gt. Brit.—Hist.

NK 0200871 MB PHC PP-W MH T

Knight, Charles, 1791–1873.
Charles Knight's Popular history of England ... London, Bradbury, Evans, & co. [1867–68]
8 v. front., illus., port., map. 22½cm.
From B. C. 55–A. D. 1867.

1. Gt. Brit.—Hist.
Library of Congress DA30.K71 2—8638

NK 0200872 DLC IdB NjNbS PU NjP PPT PPLas OO OU OCl OCU CtY NN WvFT

Knight, Charles, 1791–1873.
The popular history of England; an illustrated history of society and government from the earliest period to our own times. Boston, Estes & Lauriat, 1874.
8 vol. Ports., plan, and other illus.

Gt. Brit.–Hist.

NK 0200873 MH MWelC CtY OrP

Knight, Charles, 1791-1873.
The popular hist. of Eng. 1st Amer. ed. Bost., Lee & Shepard; N.Y., Charles T. Dillingham, 1878. 8v.

NK 0200874 OClW

Knight, Charles, 1791-1873.
The popular history of England. By Charles Knight ... 1st American ed. New York, J. W. Lovell, 1878.
v. 19cm.

1. Gt. Brit.—Hist.
Library of Congress DA30.K715 44-10964

NK 0200875 DLC TxU MB CSmH PP OO

Knight, Charles, 1791-1873.
The popular history of England. Chicago: Belford, Clarke & Co. [188–] 8 v. in 4. pl. 1. Amer. ed. 12°.
v. 1. From the invasion of Cæsar to the end of the reign of Henry IV.
v. 2. From the reign of Henry V. to the reign of Mary.
v. 3. From the reign of Elizabeth to the Commonwealth.
v. 4. From the Commonwealth to the reign of William and Mary.
v. 5. From the reign of William III. to George II.
v. 6. From the defense of the country by foreign troops, 1756, to the assassination of Marat by Charlotte Corday, 1793.
v. 7. From the war of 1793, to the material progress of British India, 1826.
v. 8. From the administration of Lord Goderich, 1827, to the final extinction of the corn-laws, Feb., 1849, with an appendix of annals, 1849-1867, and index.

1. Great Britain.—History.
N. Y. P. L. May 19, 1913.

NK 0200876 NN

DA30 .K717
Knight, Charles
Popular history of England..London, James Sangster & Co., c1880?.
7 v. 25 cm.
Contents:
--3. From the reign of Edward VI to Charles I.--4. From the civil war of the reign of Charles I, 1642, to the commencement of the reign of William and Mary, 1689.--5. From the revolution of 1688 to the accession of George I.--6. From the accession of George I, 1714, to the colse of the American War, 1783.

Contents (cont.):--7. From the close of the American war, 1783 to the restoration of the Bourbons, and the peade of Paris, 1814.--8. From the peace with the United States, 1815, to the final extinction of the corn-laws, Feb., 1849.--9. From the meetingof Parliament, Feb., 1849, to the Fall of Lord Beaconsfield's second ministry, April 1880. Continued by Philip Smith, B. A.
1. Gt. Brit.--Hist. I. Smith, Philip.

NK 0200878 MB NcU

DA30 K715 1880
Knight, Charles, 1791-1873
The popular history of England. 1st American ed. New York, American Book Exchange, 1880.
8 v. in 4. illus. 19 cm.
Bibliographical footnotes.

1. Gt. Brit. - Hist.

NK 0200879 MeB ODW OO NjP MH NBuG OrPR WaWW MA CtY PPeSchw KAS MiU

DA30 .K73 1880
Knight, Charles, 1791-1873.
The popular history of England: of society and government from the earliest period to our own times. By Charles Knight. With tables, appendix and index complete. Letterpress wholly unabridged. New York, I. K. Funk & co., 1880.
8 v. in 2. 28½cm. (Standard series edition)
Bibliographical foot-notes.

1. Gt. Brit.--Hist. I. Ser.

NK 0200880 ViU NcU CoU PPT OClWHi OO

VOLUME 300

942 Knight, Charles, 1791-1873.
K74p The popular history of England ... First American ed. New York, J. W. Lovell, 1880.
8v. fronts., plates, ports.

On cover: Illustrated library edition.

Contents.- v.1. From the invasion of Caesar to the end of the reign of Henry IV.- v.2. From the reign of Henry V. to the reign of Mary.- v.3. From the reign of Elizabeth to the commonwealth.- v.4. From the commonwealth to the reign of William and Mary.-v.5. From the reign of William III to George II.-v.6. From the defence of the country by foreign troops, 1756, to the assassination of Marat by Charlotte Corday, 1793.- v.7. From the war of 1793, to the material progress of British India, 1826.- v.8. From the administration of Lord Goderich, 1827, to the final extinction of the cornlaws, Feb. 1849, with an appendix of annals, 1849-1867, and index.

NK 0200882 IU DN ViU

Knight, Charles, 1791-1873.
The popular history of England. v. 1- New York: J. W. Lovell, 1881. v. 1. Amer. ed. 12°.

1. Great Britain.—History.
N. Y. P. L. June 9, 1914.

NK 0200883 NN MtU MH

Knight, Charles, 1791-1873.
The popular history of England. An illustrated history of society and government from the earliest period to our own times. Volume 9 continued by Philip Smith ,... to the Jubilee year 1887. London, Warne & co. [1883-87]
9 v. illus., portrs., pls. L. 8°.

NK 0200884 MB OrP

Knight, Charles, 1791–1873.
Charles Knight's Popular history of England, abridged, revised, and continued by J. H. Beale, A. M. M. F. Cusack's, S. M. F. C., History of Ireland, condensed, revised, and continued, by J. H. Beale ... New Haven, W. Gay and co. [1883]
4 v in 3. front. (port.) illus., pl., maps, tab. $26\frac{1}{2}$cm. (Gay's series of standard histories. 2d series. The United Kingdom, Great Britain and Ireland, from the earliest periods to 1884)
Vol. 1-3 paged continuously.
Vol. 1 and 4 each have special t.-p.
CONTENTS.—v. 1-3. Knight's History of England. v. 4. Cusack's History of Ireland.
Subject entries: Gt. Brit.— Hist.
2-8609

Library of Congress, no. DA30.K73.

NK 0200885 DLC NN

---

942 Knight, Charles, 1791-1873
K69p The popular history of England...
1883 1st American ed. New York, American publishers corp. [1883?]
9v. fronts.(incl.ports.) tables. D.

Vol.9 by Phillip Smith.
Contents: vol.I. From the invasion of Caesar to the end of the reign of Henry IV.- vol.II. From the reign of Henry V. to the reign of Mary- vol.III. From the reign of Elizabeth to the Commonwealth.- vol.IV. From the Commonwealth to the reign of William and Mary.- vol.V. From the reign of William III to George II.- vol.VI. From

Contents (cont.) the defence of the country by troops, 1756, to the assassination of Marat by Charlotte Corday, 1793.- vol.VII. From the war of 1793, to the material progress of British India, 1826.- vol.VIII. From the administration of Lord Goderich, 1827, to the final extinction of the Corn-laws, Feb., 1849, with an appendix of annals, 1849-1867, and index.- vol.IX. From the meeting of Parliament, February, 1849, to the fall of Lord Beaconsfield's second ministry, April, 1880.

NK 0200887 IaU

Knight, Charles, 1791-1873.
Engl2 ... Postscript to the sixth volume of the
2 pictorial edition of the works of Shakspere;
v.10 detailing the plan for the completion of that publication, and announcing a new library edition, edited by Charles Knight. [London, 1841]
15p. 21cm. [English stage, v.10]

NK 0200888 CtY NN MB

Knight, Charles, 1791-1873.
A present from Windsor. W. F. Taylor's lithographic illustrations of Windsor, Eton, & Virginia Water, with letter-press, and sixteen superior wood engravings
see under Taylor, W.F., firm, booksellers, Windsor, Eng.

Knight, Charles, 1791-1873, ed.
Knight's quarterly magazine. v. 1-3; June 1823–Nov. 1824. London, Printed for C. Knight and co., 1823–24.

[Knight, Charles] 1791-1873.
...The results of machinery, namely, cheap production & increased employment, exhibited; being an address to the workingmen of the United Kingdom. From the Lond. ed. Bost., Stimpson & Clapp, 1831.
230p. (The working-man's companion)
At head of ti.: Under the superindence of the British Society for the diffusion of useful knowledge ...
Attributed to Henry, Lord Brougham, by Halkett & Laing.

NK 0200891 MiU OO

HD [Knight, Charles] 1791-1873.
6331 The results of machinery, namely, cheap
K743r production and increased employment, exhibited:
1831 being an address to the working-men of the United Kingdom. 2d ed. London, C. Knight, 1831.
216 p. (The Working-man's companion)

At head of title: Under the superintendence of the Society for the Diffusion of Useful Knowledge.

NK 0200892 CLU NcD NjP MH

[Knight, Charles] 1791–1873.
... The results of machinery, namely, cheap production and increased employment, exhibited: being an address to the working-men of the United Kingdom. 3d ed. London, C. Knight, 1831.
216 p. $15\frac{1}{2}$cm. (The working-man's companion)
At head of title: Under the superintendence of the Society for the diffusion of useful knowledge ...
Attributed to Henry, lord Brougham, by Halkett and Laing.

1. Machinery in industry. 2. Labor and laboring classes—Gt. Brit. I. Society for the diffusion of useful knowledge, London. II. Title.
7-28419 Revised

Library of Congress HD6331.K6 1831 a

NK 0200893 DLC KMK MiEM NNC

[Knight, Charles] 1791-1873.
The RESULTS of machinery, namely: cheap production and increased employment exhibited, being an address to the working-men of the U.S.Kingdom. 4th ed. London, C.Knight, 1831.

By Charles Knight.
"The working-man's companion."
At head of title: Under the superintendence of the Society for the diffusion of useful knowledge.

NK 0200894 MH

[Knight, Charles] 1791–1873.
... The results of machinery, namely, cheap production and increased employment, exhibited: being an address to the workingmen of the United Kingdom. American ed. Philadelphia, Carey & Hart, 1831.
216 p. $15\frac{1}{2}$cm. (The working-man's companion)
At head of title: Under the superintendence of the Society for the diffusion of useful knowledge ...
Attributed to Henry, lord Brougham, by Halkett and Laing.

1. Machinery in industry. 2. Labor and laboring classes—Gt. Brit. I. Society for the diffusion of useful knowledge, London. II. Title.
7-28422 Revised

Library of Congress HD6331.K6 1831

NK 0200895 DLC TxU FMU CLU InU OClW PU NjR

Knight, Charles, 1791–1873.
... The results of machinery, namely, cheap production and increased employment exhibited. Being an address to the working men of the United Kingdom. Fifth edition. London, C. Knight, 1832.
216 p. 15cm. (The working-man's companion.)
At head of title: Under the superintendence of the Society for the Diffusion of Useful Knowledge.

NK 0200896 ICJ MH-BA

Knight, Charles, 1791-1873.
...The results of machinery, namely, cheap production, and increased employment exhibited. Being an address to the working men of the United Kingdom. 5th American ed. Middletown, N.J., Evans, 1836.
216 p. illus. $15\frac{1}{2}$ cm.

At head of title: Under the superintendence of the Society for the diffusion of useful knowledge.

NK 0200897 NjP ViW

[Knight, Charles] 1791-1873.
... The results of machinery; namely cheap production and increased employment exhibited: being an address to the working men of the United Kingdom. 6th ed. London, C.Knight & co. [etc.,etc.] 1839.
216 p. 16 cm. (The working-man's companion)

At head of title: Under the superintendence of the Society for the diffusion of useful knowledge ...
Attributed to Henry, lord Brougham, by H.S.Foxwell.-cf. Note on lining paper of first edition, 1831.

NK 0200899 MH-BA NcU

[Knight, Charles] 1791-1873.
... The results of machinery, namely, cheap production and increased employment, exhibited: being an address to the working men of the United Kingdom. American edition. New York: Published by Leavitt & Allen [1840?]

1 p. l., [5]-216 p. 17cm.
"Appendix.": p. [207]-216, includes statistical tables.
In [Society for the Diffusion of Useful Knowledge, London] Working-man's companion. New York [1840?]

NK 0200900 MiU-C

[Knight, Charles] 1791–1873.
...The rights of industry: addressed to the working-men of the United Kingdom. By the author of "The results of machinery"... [Section] 1- London: C. Knight, 1831- v. 15cm. (The working-man's companion.)
CONTENTS.—[Section] 1. Capital and labour.

1. Capital and labor. I. Title.
N. Y. P. L. March 24, 1943

NK 0200901 NN ICJ MiU NNC ICarbS CU ICN MH-BA

VOLUME 300

HD8389 K6 1831 Knight, Charles, 1791-1873.
The rights of industry: addressed to the working-men of the United Kingdom. By the author of The results of machinery. I. Capital and labour. 2d ed. London, C. Knight, 1831.
213 p. (The Working-man's companion)

At head of title: Under the superintendence of the Society for the Diffusion of Useful Knowledge.

1. Labor and laboring classes. I. Society for the Diffusion of Useful Knowledge. II. Title.

NK 0200902 CU NNC MiU PU MnU CaBVaU ICarbS ICU

---

331 K69r 1832 Knight, Charles, 1791-1873.
The rights of industry: addressed to the working-men of the United Kingdom, by the author of "The results of machinery." I. Capital and labor. 1st American ed. Philadelphia, Carey & Hart; Boston, Carter, Hendee, & Babcock, 1832.
213p. 15cm. (The working-man's companion)

1. Labor and laboring classes. I. Title. II. Title: Capital and labor.

NK 0200903 ICarbS NNC RPB CtY MiU

[Knight, Charles] 1791-1873.
Rights of industry; being an address to the workingmen of the United kingdom, on capital and labor. 5th American ed. Middletown, 1836.

NK 0200904 Nh

[Knight, Charles] 1791-1873.
The rights of industry: addressed to the working-men of the United Kingdom by the author of "The results of machinery." I. Capital and labor. First American edition. New York: Published by Leavitt & Allen, [1840?]
213 p. 17cm.

Attributed to Knight by the British Museum catalog.
At end: London, November 15, 1831.

In [Society for the Diffusion of Useful Knowledge, London] The working-man's companion. New York [1840?]

1. Capital. 2. Labor and laboring classes. I. t.

NK 0200906 MiU-C

Knight, Charles, 1791-1873.
School history of England. From the earliest period to our own times. Abridged from the Popular history of England, under the superintendence of its author. London, Bradbury & Evans, 1865.
xvi, 912 p. Sm. 8°.

NK 0200907 MB

Knight, Charles, 1791-1873
Shadows of the old book-sellers. London, Bell, 1855.
320 p.

NK 0200908 PP

Knight, Charles, 1791-1873.
Shadows of the old booksellers. By Charles Knight ... London, Bell and Daldy, 1865.
xiv p., 2 l., [3]-320 p. 20cm.

1. Booksellers and bookselling—Gt. Brit. I. Title.

Library of Congress Z325.K71 4—22585

TxU MH I NN MB LU DFo CtY PPL PPA MiU OCU OO OU MdBP MiU-C NjP ICJ
NK 0200909 DLC CtY NcU NcD OU CaBVaU WaSp WaS OrU

Knight, Charles. 1791-1873.
Shadows of the old booksellers.
— London. George Routledge & Sons, Ltd. [1908?] xi, (1), 284 pp. [The new universal library.] Sm. 8°.

G8604 — T.r. — S.r. — Booksellers.

NK 0200910 MB ViU Vi WaU

Knight, Charles, 1791-1873.
Shadows of the old booksellers, by Charles Knight, with a preface by Stanley Unwin. London, P. Davies, ltd., 1927.
xx, 281 p. 19½cm.
First published in 1865.

1. Booksellers and bookselling—Gt. Brit. I. Title.

Library of Congress Z325.K71 1927 29—11550

OCl OCU PSC PPD PU TxU NN TxU CaBViP
NK 0200911 DLC MB MoSW NNC NcU NcD CtY ViU PPT MiU

655.442 K69s 1927 Knight, Charles, 1791-1873.
Shadows of the old booksellers. With a pref. by Stanley Unwin. New York, R. R. Bowker, 1927.
281p.

1. Booksellers and bookselling--Gt. Brit. I. Title.

OClRC FTaSU MtU
NK 0200912 ICarbS CaBVa OrU OrSaW CU NcRS MiEM ICN

Knight, Charles. 1791-1873.
Shakspere and his writings.
[London. 1841?] 17-32 pp. Illus. [Knight's Store of knowledge. No. 2.] 25½ cm.
This is only part of the article, which was begun in No. 1.

K2665 — Shakespeare, William. Biog. and crit.

NK 0200913 MB

Knight, Charles, 1791-1873.

Shakespeare, William, 1564-1616.
Shakespeare's plays: with his life. Illustrated with many hundred wood-cuts, executed by H. W. Hewet, after designs by Kenny Meadows, Harvey, and others. Ed. by Gulian C. Verplanck, LL. D., with critical introductions, notes, etc., original and selected ... New York, Harper & brothers, 1847.

Knight, Charles. 1791-1873.
Sketches of the commercial intercourse of the world with China. Reprinted from Knight's Store of knowledge, with additions by the American editor.
(In Hunt, Freeman. The library of commerce. Pp. 7-120. New York, 1845.)

E5078 — China. For. rel.

NK 0200915 MB MiD OOxM

Knight, Charles, 1791-1873.
Società e governo d'Inghilterra negli ultimi tempi, cioè dalla pace cogli Stati Uniti fino al libero traffico dei grani, con appendice dal 1849 al 1861, per Carlo Knight ... Milano, Corona e Caimi, 1867-68.
3 v. 19cm. (*Half-title:* Collana di storie e memorie contemporanee, diretta da C. Cantù, v. 33-35)
Vol. 3 has title: Società e governo d'Inghilterra ... con appendici fino al 1868.
A translation of the 8th vol. of his Popular history of England.

1. Great Britain—Hist.—19th cent. I. Title.

13-18859

Library of Congress D353.C3 vol. 33-35

NK 0200916 DLC

Knight, Charles, 1791-1873.
Società e governo d'Inghilterra negli ultimi tempi, cioè, dalla pace cogli Stati Uniti fino al libero traffico dei grani, con appendici fino al 1868, per Carlo Knight... Milano: Corona e Caimi, 1870. 3 v. in 1. 12°. (Collana di storie e memorie contemporanee. v. 13-15.)
Bibliographical footnotes.

139054A. 1. Great Britain.—History, 19th century.
N. Y. P. L. October 7, 1924

NK 0200917 NN

[Knight, Charles] 1791-1873.
The standard library cyclopaedia of political, constitutional, statistical and forensic knowledge
see under title

808.8 K74k [Knight, Charles] 1791-1873.
Knight's store of knowledge for all readers: being a collection of treatises, in various departments of knowledge, by several authors. London [1841]
424p.

Imperfect: p.297-377 wanting.
Title page inserted between p.416 and 417.

NK 0200919 IU NN MdBP IU

Knight, Charles, 1791-1873.

Shakespeare, William, 1564-1616.
The Stratford Shakspere, ed. by Charles Knight ... New York, Appleton, 1871.

Knight, Charles. 1791-1873.
Stratford-upon-Avon. Illus. Plates. Map.
(Cut from Knight, Charles, editor. The land we live in. Vol. 1, pp. 225-240. London. [1847.])
The land we live in may be found on shelf-number 2461.48.

K2739 — Stratford-upon-Avon, Warwickshire, England.

NK 0200921 MB

VOLUME 300

Knight, Charles, 1791-1873.
The struggles of a book against excessive taxation. London [Printed by W. Clowes and Sons, 1850]
15 p. 21cm.

1. Book industries and trade - Gt. Brit. 2. Paper - Taxation. I. Title.

NK 0200922 NNC MH-BA CtY IEN

PR2894 .K7 Knight, Charles, 1791-1873.
Studies and illustrations of the writings of Shakspere, and of his life and times. By Charles Knight. In three volumes... London, C. Knight, 1850-51.
2 v. fronts., illus., ports., facsims. 23½cm.
No more published?
Vol. 1: William Shakspere, a biography.
"The present volume, entitled 'Studies of Shakspere', forming the second volume of 'Studies and illustrations', consists of a republication, with additions and corrections, of the critical notices ... scattered through my editions of Shakspere."- Advertisement[2]

NK 0200923 ICU NcU WaU NcD

Knight, Charles, 1791-1873.
Studies of Shakspere. By Charles Knight ... London, New York, G. Routledge and sons, 1868.
1 p. l., ii, [3]-560 p. 23cm.
"A republication, with additions and corrections, of the critical notices that are scattered through my editions of Shakspere, known as 'the Pictorial' and 'the Library'."—Advertisement.

1. Shakespeare, William—Criticism and interpretation.
27-21650
Library of Congress PR2976.K6 1868

NK 0200924 DLC NcU MiU NjP MB OOxM

Knight, Charles, 1791-1873.
Studies of Shakspere: forming a companion volume to every edition of the text. By Charles Knight ... London, C. Knight, 1849.
vii, ii, [3]-560 p. front. (5 port.) 22½cm. [National library of select literature]
"A republication, with additions and corrections, of the critical notices that are scattered through my editions of Shakspere, known as 'the Pictorial' and 'the Library.'"—Advertisement.

1. Shakespeare, William—Criticism and interpretation.
17-29278
Library of Congress PR2976.K6

NK 0200925 DLC OrU TxU NcD GU CtY PU-F MiU OCl NjP OU

Knight, Charles, 1791-1873.
Studies of Shakspere. Forming a companion volume to the national edition of the Pictorial Shakspere. By Charles Knight... London: C. Knight, 1851. iv, 6-560 p. front. (ports.) 22½cm.
"A republication, with additions and corrections, of the critical notices that are scattered through my editions of Shakspere, known as 'the Pictorial' and 'the Library.'" — p. [1]

1. Shakespeare, William—Commentaries and criticism. Revised
N. Y. P. L. September 28, 1937

NK 0200926 NN MdBP ICarbS TU IU OCU ODaU ViU Vi PPL PP-W

914.2 K69K Knight, Charles, 1791-1873.
Knight's tourist's companion through the land we live in. London, Nattali and Bond, 1853.
20 no. in 1 v. illus. 23 cm.
Issued also in 20 separate numbers.
Each no. covers a separate locality and has caption title: Knight's excursion companion.
1. Great Britain. Description and travel. 1801-1900. I. Title. II. Knight's excursion companion.

NK 0200927 NcD

Knight, Charles, 1791-1873.
William Caxton, the first English printer: a biography. By Charles Knight. London, C. Knight and co., 1844.
3 p. l., [vii]-viii, 9-240 p. front. (port.) illus. 14½ cm. [Knight's Weekly volumes]
Revised and reissued as pt. I of Knight's Old printer and the modern press, 1854.
"Postscript. Progress of the press in England": p. 209-240.

1. Caxton, William, 1422 (ca.)-1491.
4—4698
Library of Congress Z232.C38K7

NK 0200928 DLC MH-BA PPT DN TU CSt ViU FMU NN MWA MH OCl OCU OClRC NcD KMK OrP CaBVa MWA PU MB ICJ NN CtY MiD CtY WU MeB OU CtY PP DFo PPL PU

Knight, Charles, 1791-1873.
William Caxton, the first English printer. A biography. By Charles Knight. New ed. London, W. Clowes & sons [etc.] 1877.
ix, 158 p. incl. illus., port. front. 18½cm.
Originally pub. 1844; rev. and reissued as pt. I of the author's The old printer and the modern press, 1854.
"Books printed by Caxton": p. 152-155.
"Authorities": p. 156-158.

1. Caxton, William, ca. 1422-1491.
9—24724
Library of Congress Z232.C38K72

NK 0200929 DLC NjP LU TxU LU OCl MWA NN MB

Knight, Charles, 1791-1873.
"William Shakspeare: A biography." Extra illust. and extended into 4 vols. by the insertion of over 300 portraits and views selected with particular care, including over 40 different portraits of Shakspeare, many unique. Also portraits of the great personages of his time. London, Chas. Knight & Co., 1842.
4 v. Roy. 8°, full cr. pink lev., gilt backs, ornamentations on sides, inside deutelles borders, t.e.g. Bound by Pratt.

NK 0200930 CSmH

Knight, Charles, 1791-1873.
William Shakspere; a biography by Charles Knight. [London, C. Knight and co.] 1843.
6 p. l., 3-544 p. illus. (incl. ports., facsims.) 24½cm. (Shakespeare, William. The pictorial edition of the works ... London [1839]-43. [v. 1])
Illustrated t.-p.
Imperfect: general t.-p. wanting.

1. Shakespeare, William—Biog.
22-379
Library of Congress PR2753.K7 1839

NK 0200931 DLC CaBVa OrP WaS CSmH NIC MH IU CtY MiU MdBP NN

932 K69 wi Knight, Charles, 1791-1873.
William Shakspere, a biography; forming a companion volume to the National edition of the pictorial Shakspere. London, C. Knight, 1851.
x, 329 p. illus., ports., facsims.

1. Shakespeare, William - Biog. I. Shakespeare, William, 1564-1616./ The comedies, histories, tragedies, and poems. Edited by Charles Knight. National ed.

NK 0200932 CU InU NN MH WU PPLT RPB CSmH ICN

PR 2894 K69+ 1860 Knight, Charles, 1791-1873.
William Shakspere: a biography. Rev. and augm. New York, G. Routledge and Sons [1860]
553 p. illus. 26cm.

1. Shakespeare, William, 1564-1616.

NK 0200933 NIC PRosC CaBVaU NjP WaWW WaS PPGi

PR 2894 K5 1865 Knight, Charles, 1791-1873.
William Shakspere: a biography. By Charles Knight. The 3d ed. Rev. and augm. ... London, Virtue [1865]
5 p. l., 553 p. front., illus. (incl. ports., map, facsims.) 25cm.
Uniform with Knight's Pictorial edition of Shakspere, 1867.

NK 0200934 PPT MH

Knight, Charles, 1791-1873.
William Shakspere: a biography. Revised and augmented. New York, G. Routledge and sons [1865]

NK 0200935 MH

Knight, Charles, 1791-1873.
William Shakspere: a biography. By Charles Knight. The 3d ed. Rev. and augm. ... London, New York, G. Routledge and sons, 1867.
5 p. l., 553 p. front., illus. (incl. ports., map, facsims.) 25cm.
Uniform with Knight's Pictorial edition of Shakspere, 1867.

1. Shakespeare, William—Biog.
17-22015 Revised
Library of Congress PR2894.K5

NK 0200936 DLC OCU ViU PU-F

PR 2753 K69 1880+ v.7 Knight, Charles, 1791-1873.
William Shakespere, a biography. Rev. and augm. New York, Collier [1882?]
553 p. illus. 27cm.
Bound with: Shakespeare, Wm. The pictorial ed. of the works of William Shakespere, ed. by Charles Knight, v.8.

1. Shakespeare, William, 1564-1616.

NK 0200937 NIC ICU OKentU

[Knight, Charles] 1791-1873.
The working-men's companion: containing The results of machinery, Cottage evenings, and The rights of industry. Addressed to working-men. New York, Leavitt & Allen [1831?]
3 v. in 1. incl. illus., plan, tables.
"American edition."

NK 0200938 MH-BA

[Knight, Charles, 1791-1873]
The working-man's companion. The results of machinery, namely cheap production and increased employment, exhibited; being an address to the working-men of the United Kingdom. London, C. Knight, 1831.
At head of title: Under the superintendence of the Society for the diffusion of useful knowledge.

NK 0200939 MH

VOLUME 300

HD4841 .K7 [Knight, Charles] 1791-1873.
The working-man's companion. The rights of industry: addressed to the working-men of the United Kingdom. By the author of "The results of machinery." 1st American ed. Philadelphia: Carey & Hart ...; Boston: Carter, Hendee, & Babcock, 1832.
213 p. 15½ cm.

At head of title: Under the superintendence of the Society for the Diffusion of Useful Knowledge.

1. Labor and laboring classes - Hist. I. Society for the Diffusion of Useful Knowledge, London.

NK 0200940 NjR

Knight, Charles, 1791-1873, ed.

FOR OTHER EDITIONS SEE MAIN ENTRY

Shakespeare, William, 1564-1616.
The works of Shakspere. Imperial ed. Edited by Charles Knight; with illustrations on steel from pictures by C. W. Cope, R. A., E. M. Ward, R. A., C. R. Leslie, R. A. ... [and others] New York, Virtue & Yorston [1875-76]

Knight, Charles, 1791-1873.
El zapatero librero y La imprenta en Inglaterra, dos relatos. Traducción y prólogo por M. Cardenal de Iracheta. Valencia, Editorial Castalia, 1947.
79 p. illus., ports. 19 cm. (Gallardo, colección de opúsculos para bibliófilos, 3)
Translation of two selections from The shadows of the old booksellers.
500 copies printed. "Cien ejemplares en papel de hilo superior (1-100) ... [Ejemplar no.] 29."

1. Lackington, James, 1746-1815. 2. Printing—Hist.—Gt. Brit. I. Title. II. Title: La imprenta en Inglaterra. (Series)

Z325.L23K66 655.442 49-24810*

NK 0200942 DLC TxU NN NBuU OU CU-S CU

Knight (Charles) and Co., London, pub.
The cook; plain and practical directions for cooking and housekeeping
see under title

Knight[Charles]and Co., London, pub.
The guide to service. The cook; plain and practical directions for cooking and housekeeping
see The cook; plain and practical directions for cooking and housekeeping.

Knight,(Charles)and Co., London.
The guide to trade. The carver, and gilder
see under title

Knight,(Charles)and Co., London.
The guide to trade. *The printer*
see under title

Knight,(Charles) and co., London.

... The joiner and cabinet-maker. London, C. Knight and co., 1839.

Knight,(Charles) and co., London, pub.

Knight's annotated model bye-laws, comprising the model series issued from the Ministry of health under the Public health acts, with respect to buildings, new streets, removal of house refuse, nuisances, common lodging-houses, baths, wash-houses, bathing places, mortuaries, offensive trades, tents, nursing homes, smoke abatement, parking places, sanitary conveniences, and other matters. With diagrams and approved additional and alternative clauses. 9th ed. Edited and revised by C. Roland Woods ... London, C. Knight & co., ltd. [1938]

Knight (Charles) and co., London, pub.
Knight's guide to the arrangement and construction of workhouse buildings
see under title

Knight (Charles) and co., London, pub.
Knight's handbook for the use of health insurance committees and all other local authorities
see under title

Knight,(Charles) and co., London, pub.
Knight's local government and magisterial reports and statutes, statutory instruments, etc....
see under title

Knight (Charles) and co., London, pub.
Knight's miscellanies
see under title

Knight (Charles) and Co., London, pub.
Knight's penny magazine
see under title

Knight (Charles) and Co., London, pub.
Knight's weekly volume
see under title

---

ar V 18432 Knight *(Charles) and Co, London, pub.*
List of the books & papers authorized by the Local Government Board; with other forms for carrying the orders of the Board into operation... A catalogue of magisterial forms; and a list of legal works and official publications. London [1885]
198 p. 19cm.
I. Gt. Brit. Local Government Board.

NK 0200955 NIC

Knight (Charles) and Co., London, pub.
Pictorial gallery of arts
see under Knight, Charles, 1791-1873.

Knight,(Charles) and co., London, pub.

FOR OTHER EDITIONS SEE MAIN ENTRY

The Public health acts and other statutes and parts of statutes relating to public health and allied subjects, 1875-1939; with a list of the principal statutory rules and orders relating to public health and a complete index. London, C. Knight & co., ltd., 1939.

Knight (Charles) and Co., London, pub.
Quarterly magazine
see Knight's quarterly magazine.

Knight,(Charles) and Co., London, pub.
The suggested new poor law
see under Gt. Brit. Royal commission on poor laws and relief of distress.

Knight,(Charles)and Co), London, pub.
see also Knight, Charles, 1791-1873.

Knight, Charles Brunton.
A history of the city of York, from the foundation of the Roman fortress of Eboracum A. D. 71 to the close of the reign of Queen Victoria A. D. 1901. With brief summaries of the contemporary English history of each successive period. By Charles Brunton Knight. Introduction by Sir John A. R. Marriott ... 2d ed. York and London, Printed by the Herald printing works, 1944.
8 p. l., 774 p. 3 fold. maps. 25cm.
Bibliography: p. [745]

1. York, Eng.—Hist.

A 45-4698

Harvard univ. Library for Library of Congress [2]

NK 0200961 NN MH

Knight, Charles Brunton.
This is York, a personally-conducted tour. Drawings by Alfred Gill. York [Eng.] Herald Print. Works [1951]
244 p. illus. 25 cm.

1. York, Eng.—Descr. 2. York, Eng.—Hist.

DA690.Y6K5 914.274 52-23393 ‡

NK 0200962 DLC NN

Knight, Charles D., *pseud.*
Thump's client. [1880]
see
Gilbert, *Mrs.* R L.

---

ar V 21667 Knight, Charles Frederick.
A study and research on the forms and origin of life, species, and neoplasms. Edinburgh, J. Currie, 1912.
11 p. 17cm.

NK 0200964 NIC

Knight, Charles Huntoon, 1849-1913.
Abscess of the tongue, with report of a case. 8 pp. 8°. [*New York*, 1885.]
Repr. from: Med. Rec., N. Y., 1885, xxviii.

NK 0200965 DNLM

VOLUME 300

Knight, Charles Huntoon, 1849-1913.
[Collected papers on diseases of the nose and throat.]
128892 Reprinted from various medical serials.

NK 0200966 ICJ

Knight, Charles Huntoon, 1849–
Diseases of the nose and throat, by Charles Huntoon Knight ... 147 illustrations. Philadelphia, P. Blakiston's son & co., 1903.
xv, 17-423 p. illus. 23½cm.

1. Nose—Diseases. 2. Throat—Diseases.
3—22119
Library of Congress RF46.K6

NK 0200967 DLC DNLM ICRL PPC PPJ ViU OrU-M OC1W-H

Knight, Charles Huntoon.
Diseases of the nose, throat and ear, by Charles Huntoon Knight ... and W. Sohier Bryant ... 2d ed., rev., with 239 illustrations. Philadelphia, P. Blakiston's son & co., 1909.
xix, 631 p. illus. 24cm. $4.50
First edition has title: Diseases of the nose and throat, by Charles Huntoon Knight.
"Author's bibliography" at end of each chapter on The ear.

1. Nose—Diseases. 2. Throat—Diseases. 3. Ear—Diseases. I. Bryant, William Sohier, 1861–
9-27384
Library of Congress RF46.K62

NK 0200968 DLC DNLM ICRL NIC PPSteph PPJ PPC ICJ ViU OC1W-H

Knight, Charles H.untoon, 1849-
Three cases of laryngeal neoplasm. [Read before the American Laryngological Association, at its sixteenth annual congress. New York, 1894.] 8 p. 12°.
Repr.: New York medical jour. December 1, 1894. Title from cover.

1. Larynx.—Diseases.
N. Y. P. L. February 8, 1913.

NK 0200969 NN

Knight, Charles Huntoon, 1849- *ed.*
... A year-book of surgery for 1883; ed. by Charles H. Knight, M. D. New York [etc.] G. P. Putnam's sons, 1884.
x p., 1 l., 197 p. 24cm. (Year-books of medical progress)

1. Surgery—Year-books.
6—44635
Library of Congress RD9.K7

NK 0200970 DLC DNLM ICJ

Knight, Charles Kelley.
Advanced life insurance, with illustrations of the principles and practices of actuarial science, by Charles K. Knight ... New York, J. Wiley & sons, inc.; London, Chapman & Hall, limited, 1926.
xi, 426 p. incl. tables. 23½cm.

1. Insurance, Life.
26—15038
Library of Congress HG8771.K7

NK 0200971 DLC IdU MtU WU PU PPT MiU NcD ICJ OU NN MB ViU

Knight, Charles Kelley.
... The history of life insurance in the United States to 1870, with an introduction to its development abroad, by Charles Kelley Knight ... Philadelphia, Pa., 1920.
160 p. 24cm.
Thesis (PH. D.)—University of Pennsylvania, 1920.
Bibliographical foot-notes.

1. Insurance, Life—U. S.—Hist.
21—8247
Library of Congress HG8951.K5
Univ. of Pennsylvania Libr.

NK 0200972 DLC IdU MtU OkU NIC FMU CU CoU NcU PBm PHC PU MiU OCU OU ICJ MB

Knight, Charles Langdon, 1867-
Opposing building more battleships, speech... in the House of Representatives, Apr. 16, 1921... Wash., Govt. pr., 1921.
8p. O.

NK 0200973 OO

Knight, Charles Langdon, 1867-
Soldiers' bonus... Speech of Hon. Charles L. Knight of Ohio, in the house of representatives, Mar. 9, 1922. Wash. 1922.
8p. O.

NK 0200974 OO

Knight, Charles Langdon, 1867-
Taxation & state socialism. Speech... in House of Representatives, Thur., Aug. 18, 1921. [Wash., D.C., Gov't. Print. office. 1921.]
2p. Q.

(Congressional record. 67th congress, 1st session.)

NK 0200975 OO

KNIGHT, Charles Lewis William Morley.
Hints on driving. London, etc., G.Bell & sons, 1894.
180 p.
sm. 8°. Front. and other illustr

NK 0200976 MH KMK MB

798.64
K743h
1895
Knight, Charles Lewis William Morley.
Hints on driving, by Captain C. Morley Knight, R.A. Illustrated by G.H.A. White ... London, New York [etc.] G. Bell & sons, 1895.
xivp., 1l., 212p., 1l. incl. front., illus., plates. 19cm.

"Second edition revised."

1. Driving. I. Title.

NK 0200977 TxU CU

Knight, C[harles Lewis William] Morley.
Hints on driving. Illustrated by G. H. A. White. London: G. Bell & Sons, 1902. 3 p.l., (i)x-xiv, 212 p., 1 l., 2 pl. illus. [2. ed.] 12°.

1. Driving. 2. White, Geoffrey Herbert Anthony, illustrator.
N. Y. P. L. October 3, 1912.

NK 0200978 NN

Knight, Charles Lewis William Morley.
Hints on driving; illus. by G. H. A. White. Lond., G. Bell & sons, 1905.
212 p., illus.

NK 0200979 MiD

Knight, Charles Louis, 1900–
... Negro housing in certain Virginia cities, by Charles Louis Knight ... Richmond, Va., The William Byrd press, inc., 1927.
158 p. illus. 22½cm. (Publications of the University of Virginia. Phelps-Stokes fellowship papers. no. 8)

1. Negroes—Virginia. 2. Housing—Virginia. I. Title.
27-5830
Library of Congress E185.93.V8K6

NK 0200980 DLC OrU NcD OC1 OCU OU PPPHA PU ViU-L ICJ DHU ViU

Knight, Charles Louis, 1900–
Secular and cyclical movements in the production and price of copper ... [by] Charles Louis Knight. Philadelphia, 1935.
xiii, 153 p. diagrs. 23cm.
Thesis (PH. D.)—University of Pennsylvania, 1933.
Published also without thesis note.
Studies dealing with various countries since 1860.
"Sources and evaluation of data": p. 7-10. Bibliography: p. 153.

1. Copper industry and trade. 2. Business cycles. I. Title.
35-5241
Library of Congress HD9539.C6K6 1933
Univ. of Pennsylvania Libr.
——— Copy 2. [3] 338.2

NK 0200981 DLC PU CU NcU NIC PSC PU MiU OC1 OCU PBm MB

KNIGHT, CHARLES LOUIS, 1900-
Secular and cyclical movements in the production and price of copper. Philadelphia, University of Pennsylvania press, 1935. xiii,153 p. incl. tables, diagrs.

Film reproduction. Negative.
Issued also as thesis (Ph.D.) University of Pennsylvania.
Studies dealing with various countries since 1860.
"Sources and evaluation of data": p. 7-10; Bibliography: p. 153.
1. Copper--Trade and stat. 2. Prices, Copper.

NK 0200982 NN

Knight, Charles Louis, 1900–
Secular and cyclical movements in the production and price of copper, by Charles Louis Knight. Philadelphia, University of Pennsylvania press; London, H. Milford, Oxford university press, 1935.
xiii, 153 p. incl. tables, diagrs. 23½cm.
Issued also as thesis (PH. D.) University of Pennsylvania.
Studies dealing with various countries since 1860.
"Sources and evaluation of data": p. 7-10; Bibliography: p. 153.

1. Copper industry and trade. 2. Business cycles. I. Title.
35-4658
Library of Congress HD9539.C6K6 1935
——— Copy 2.
Copyright A 80480 [3] 338.2

NK 0200983 DLC OrP WaTC NcD ViU PU-W PU MB

Knight, Charles Morley
see Knight, Charles Lewis William Morley.

Knight, Charles R
Equalizing public assistance payments. The second report to the Legislative Council of Alabama concerning certain aspects of public welfare financing in Alabama. Montgomery, 1949.
cover-title, ii, 14 p. 28cm.

Reproduced from type-written copy.

NK 0200985 ViU-L Vi

VOLUME 300

Knight, Charles R
The financing of elementary and secondary public education in Alabama. A report to the Legislative Council of Alabama showing the growth of expenditures for public education and other developments in the financing of education in Alabama since 1926-27. Montgomery [1949]
2 p. l., ii, 48 p. tables. 28cm.

Cover-title.

NK 0200986 ViU-L

Knight, Charles R
Financing public welfare in Alabama. A report to the Legislative Council of Alabama showing how public welfare is financed in Alabama and pointing out certain weaknesses of the present fiscal system. Montgomery, 1948.
cover-title, iv, 16 p. tables. 28cm.

Reproduced from type-written copy.

NK 0200987 ViU-L N Vi PPULC PU-PSW

Knight, Charles R.

Mayes, Edward, 1846-1917.
Genealogy and history, a branch of the family of Lamar, with it's related families of Urquhart, Reynolds, Bird, Williamson, Gilliam, Garratt, Thompson, Herman, Empson, and others; compiled and written for the private information of his own children by Edward Mays ... [Hattiesburg, Miss., The Southern library service, 1935]

Knight, Charles R
Legislative budget facilities ...
see under Alabama. Legislative Reference Service.

Knight, Charles R
Limitation of election campaign expenditures
see under Alabama. Legislative Reference Service.

Knight, Charles R
The regulation of lobbying. A report to the Legislative council of Alabama showing the extent to which other states regulate lobbying and the arguments pro and con for a state regulation of lobbying act. Montgomery [1949]
2 p. l., 10 l. 28cm.

Cover-title.

NK 0200991 ViU-L

Knight, Charles Raleigh Bruere, 1896-
Historical records of The Buffs, East Kent Regiment (3rd Foot) formerly designated the Holland Regiment and Prince George of Denmark's Regiment ... London, Medici Society, 1935-51.
3 v. illus., ports., maps (part fold.) 23 cm.
Includes bibliographies.
CONTENTS.—pt. 1. 1704-1814.—pt. 2. 1814-1914 and appendices.—[pt. 3] 1919-1948.

1. Gt. Brit. Army. The Buffs (East Kent Regiment)

UA653.5.B8K6 354.42066 36-13839 rev*

NK 0200992 DLC CaBVaU WU NN

Knight, Charles Robert, 1874-1953.
Animal anatomy & psychology for the artist and layman, by Charles R. Knight, with illustrations by the author. New York, London, Whittlesey house, McGraw-Hill book company, inc. [1947]
vii, 149 p. incl. front., illus. 21½ x 27½cm.

Anatomy, Artistic. 2. Animal painting and illustration. I. Title.

NC780.K5 743.6 47-4533

Library of Congress

DNAL NNC TxU MB
NK 0200993 DLC WaS Or CaBVaU OrPS IdPI TU NNC CU NcGU

Knight, Charles Robert, 1874-1953.
Animals of the world for young people, by Charles R. Knight; with an introduction by Tudor Jenks with 40 colour plates. New York, F. A. Stokes company [1908]
xx, [2], xxi-xxxiii p., 1 l., 250 p. illus., 40 col. pl. (incl. front.) 21 cm.
"A brief bibliography": p. [vii]

1. Mammals. 2. Zoology—Pictorial works. I. Title.

QL706.K6 8-31036

NK 0200994 DLC Or WaWW PP OCl OClh OO PPLas NN

Knight, Charles Robert, 1874-
Before the dawn of history, by Charles R. Knight; illustrated by the author. New York and London, Whittlesey house, McGraw-Hill book company, inc. [c1935]
xiii, 119 p. illus. 23½ x 31½cm.
Table and illustrations on lining-papers.
"First edition."

1. Paleontology—Juvenile literature. 2. Man, Prehistoric—Juvenile literature. I. Title.

Library of Congress QE714.K6 35-1358

——— Copy 2.

Copyright A 80092 [5] 560

Or CaBVaU WaS WaSp CaBVa OrMonO OrAshS
ODW MB PPAmP MtBC OrPR MtBuM Or OrCS IdU-SB OrU
OCU WaTC FMU PPT NcD NcRS PP PPD PBm PU OCl OU
NK 0200995 DLC NN NIC IdB WaT CU MU MtU OrP ViU

Knight, Charles Robert, 1874-
Birds of the world for young people, by Charles R. Knight and Ella Hardcastle; with forty-one colour plates and numerous black-and-white illustrations. New York, F. A. Stokes company [1909]
xliv, 260 p. col. front., 42 pl. (40 col.) 21cm. $2.00

1. Birds. I. Hardcastle, Ella, joint author.

Library of Congress QL676.K7 9-29871

NK 0200996 DLC OrP CU OClh OLak

Knight, Charles Robert, 1874- illus.
Cope: master naturalist ...
see under Osborn, Henry Fairfield, 1857-

Knight, Charles Robert, 1874-
Life through the ages, written and illustrated by Charles R. Knight. New York, A. A. Knopf, 1946.
2 p. l., 66, [1] p. illus. 21 x 26cm.
"First edition."

1. Paleontology. I. Title.

Library of Congress * QE763.K5 46-262
[7] 560

ViU PPGi PP OrPS
NK 0200998 DLC Or OrP WaS WaSp OrU GU IU PP MiU PWcS

---

560 Knight, Charles Robert, 1874-
K69p Parade of life through the ages. [Washington, D.C., 1942]
[141]-184 p. illus.(part col.) 26cm.
Detached from The National geographic magazine, v.81, no.2, February, 1942.

1. Paleontology. I. Title.

NK 0200999 CSt

Knight, Charles Robert, 1874-1953.
Prehistoric man, the great adventurer. New York, Appleton-Century-Crofts [1949]
xiv, 331 p. illus. 22 cm.

1. Man, Prehistoric.

GN743.K6 573.3 49-4859*

WaE IdU
NSyU OEac OCl MB OClW PP FMU CaBViP OrP Or WaS OkU
NK 0201000 DLC OkU CU NN ViU TU WaSp PSt PPL PPT

208.2
C71 Knight, Charles S
V.52 The bully of Stony Lonesome and other stories. Chicago, Moody [c1951]
30 p. (Colportage library, no. 208)

Bound with: I saw the Welsh revival. by David Matthews.

I. Title. II. Series. III. Cd., Sem. IV. Cd., UC. V. Cd., NUC.

NK 0201001 CLamB

Knight, Charles S, agriculturist. 910 1002
A corn primer. Manhattan, 1908. 1 p.l., 46 p. illus. 8°. (Kansas. Agricultural College. Agricultural education. v. 1, no. 1.)

1. Corn.
N. Y. P. L. August 1, 1916.

NK 0201002 NN

Knight, Charles S., agriculturist.
...Small grains...by Charles S. Knight... [Fort Wayne:] The Correspondence College of Agriculture, cop. 1910-14. 4 v. diagrs., illus., tables. 8°.
At head of title: The Correspondence College of Agriculture.
Contents: Part 1. Wheat, and how it grows. Part 2. The marketing and grading of wheat. Part 3. Oats and barley. Part 4. The smaller cereals.

1. Grain. 2. Correspondence College of Agriculture, Fort Wayne, Ind.
N. Y. P. L. October 25, 1923.

NK 0201003 NN

Knight, Charles S., agriculturist.
The sugar beet industry in Nevada. Reno: The University of Nevada [1911]. 38 p. 8°. (Nevada. Agricultural experiment station. Bulletin 75.)

1. Beet (Sugar), U. S.: Nevada.
N. Y. P. L. August 4, 1911.

NK 0201004 NN MBH

Knight, Charles Spurgeon.
Both sides of evolution, a debate by Charles Spurgeon Knight ... San Jose, Calif., The Arthur H. Field publishing house, [c]1925.
233 p. 19cm.

1. Evolution. I. Title.

Library of Congress QH367.K6 25-9702

NK 0201005 DLC DSI

VOLUME 300

Knight, Charles Spurgeon.
The mystery and prophecy of the Great pyramid, by Charles S. Knight ... with introduction by Dr. Arthur I. Brown ... San Jose, Calif., Rosicrucian press, AMORC college ₍1933₎
215 p. incl. illus., plan. fold. front. 20cm. (Rosicrucian library, vol. XIV)
"Second edition, August, 1933."
Advertising matter: p. 202-215.
1. Pyramids—Curiosa and miscellany. I. Title.
Library of Congress DT63.5.K55 1933 36-2479
₍2₎ 913.32

NK 0201006 DLC PP OCl

Knight, Charles Spurgeon.
The path to power, by Rev. Charles S. Knight ... Berea, Ky., Berea college press ₍°1913₎
224 p. incl. front. (port.) illus. 18½cm. $0.35
CONTENTS.—I. Growing good Americans.—II. Our national crime.—III. The fetters of habit.—IV. Sanitation and health.—V. The ideal community.—VI. Wages or gift.—VII. Everyday Christianity.
I. Title.
Library of Congress BJ1595.K5 14-248

NK 0201007 DLC

WAA K69s 1880
KNIGHT, Charles W
Sanitary improvements of the village of Cazenovia, N. Y., with reports of Charles W. Knight, on the introduction of water and a system of sewerage. Cazenovia, N. Y., Taylor, 1880.
16 p.

NK 0201008 DNLM

Knight, Charles William Robert, 1884-
The adventures of Mr. Ramshaw, the eagle, by Captain C. W. R. Knight; illustrated from photographs and drawings by the author. New York, Dodd, Mead & company, 1936.
vii p., 1 l., 81 p. incl. front., illus. (incl. ports.) 22cm.
1. Birds—Legends and stories. I. Title.
Library of Congress PZ10.3.K75Ad 36-32328

NK 0201009 DLC NIC PPGi

Knight, Charles William Robert, 1884-
All British eagle. London, Hodder and Stoughton ₍1943₎
178 p. plates, ports. 21 cm.
1. Eagles. I. Title.
QL795.B57K48 598.91 50-51839

NK 0201010 DLC FMU

Knight, Charles William Robert, 1884-
All British eagle. London, Hodder and Stoughton [1944]
177p. plates, ports. 21 cm.
1. Eagle--Gt. Br.

NK 0201011 NN

Knight, Charles William Robert, 1884-
Aristocrats of the air, by Capt. C. W. R. Knight ... and a preface by Viscount Grey of Fallodon, K. G. ... London, Williams and Norgate, ltd., 1925.
xii, 165, ₍1₎ p. col. front., plates. 26½cm.
1. Birds—England. ₍1. England—Ornithology₎ 2. Photography of birds. I. Title.
Library, U. S. Dept. of Agriculture 413K744A Agr 27-93

NK 0201012 DNAL NN CU MH

Knight, Charles William Robert, 1884-
Aristocrats of the air, by Capt. C. W. R. Knight ... and a preface by Viscount Grey of Fallodon, K. G., with frontispiece in colour and 53 other illustrations in black and white. New York, Frederick A. Stokes company ₍1926?₎
xii, 165, ₍1₎ p. col. front., plates. 26cm.
Printed in Great Britain.
1. Birds. 2. Photography of birds. I. Title.
Library of Congress QL676.K73 27-3081

NK 0201013 DLC ICJ

Knight, Charles William Robert, 1884-
Aristocrats of the air; pref. by the late Viscount Grey of Falloden. With front. in colour and 53 other illus. in black and white. ₍2d rev. ed.₎ London, Williams and Norgate ₍1946₎
150 p. illus. (part col.) 26 cm.
1. Birds. 2. Photography of birds. I. Title.
[QL676.K] A 48-3901*
New York. Public Libr. for Library of Congress ₍1₎

NK 0201014 NN MiU LU

Knight, Charles William Robert, 1884-
The book of the golden eagle, by Captain C. W. R. Knight ... ₍London₎ Hodder and Stoughton limited ₍1927₎
xii, 295, ₍1₎ p. col. front., plates. 25½cm.
Illustrated lining-papers.
1. Eagles. 2. Photography of birds.
Library of Congress QL696.A2K5 28-21868

NK 0201015 DLC NN MH IdU

Knight, Charles William Robert, 1884-
Knight in Africa; adventures with a camera in the veldt, by C. W. R. Knight. London, Country life limited, 1937.
130 p. front., plates, ports. 25 x 19cm.
Mainly the story of the filming, capturing and taming of a martial hawk eagle.
1. Eagles. 2. Birds—Cape of Good Hope. 3. Photography of birds. 4. Photography of animals. 5. Zoology—Cape of Good Hope. I. Title.
Library of Congress QH245.K55 1937 38-3931
Copyright A ad int. 23367 ₍5₎

NK 0201016 DLC CtY MH IEN

PZ 10.3 .K75 Mi
Knight, Charles William Robert, 1884-
Mr. Ramshaw, my eagle. London, Arrowsmith. [1933]
128p. illus. 19cm.
1. Birds - Legends and stories. I. Title.

NK 0201017 ScU

Knight, Charles William Robert, 1884-
Wild life in the tree tops, by Capt. C. W. R. Knight ... Fifty-three illustrations from photographs taken by the author. London, T. Butterworth limited ₍1921₎
144 p. front., plates. 25½cm.
1. Birds. 2. Photography of birds. I. Title.
Library of Congress QL676.K65 22-11608

NK 0201018 DLC OClU PHC NcU CaBVaU ICF-A NN WaU

Knight, Charles William Robert, 1884-
Wild life in the tree tops, by Capt. C. W. R. Knight, ... Fifty-three illustrations from photographs taken by the author. New York, G. H. Doran Co.; London, T. Butterworth, [1922].
144 p. front., plates. 26cm.
Printed in Great Britain.

NK 0201019 ICJ CtY CU

HD6483 .C26
Knight, Charlotte, ed.
California. University. *Institute of Industrial Relations.*
The economics of collective bargaining; proceedings of a series of public lectures held during 1948 and 1949 in Berkeley and Los Angeles; edited by Charlotte Knight. Presented by Institute of Industrial Relations in coöperation with the Committee on Drama, Lectures, and Music. ₍Berkeley, 1950₎

Knight, Chester Howard.
The effect of the proposed homestead exemption on assessed value and revenue receipts of various units of the state of Alabama, by C. H. Knight ... University, Ala., Bureau of business research, University of Alabama ₍1936?₎
3 p. l., v-vii, ₍3₎, 41 numb. l. incl. tables. 27½ x 21½cm. (₍Alabama. University. Bureau of business research₎ Mimeographed series. no. 6)
"Indirect, social, economic and fiscal effects of homestead exemptions, by Paul E. Alyea": numb. leaves ₍34₎-41.
1. Homestead law—Alabama. 2. Revenue—Alabama. 3. Taxation—Alabama. I. Alyea, Paul Edgar, 1899- II. Title: Homestead exemption.
Library of Congress HD1337.K6 38-28459
₍3₎ 336.29

NK 0201021 DLC TU OU NN MiU-L

Knight, Chester Howard.
Report on examination of accounts of city of Tuscaloosa, Tuscaloosa, Alabama, September 30, 1942. ₍Tuscaloosa, 1942₎
cover-title, 54 p. 28 cm.
1. Finance—Tuscaloosa, Ala.
HJ9193.T8K5 352.1 47-43138*

NK 0201022 DLC

Knight, Clara M
Greek and Latin adverbs and their value in the reconstruction of the prehistoric declensions. Lond. Camb. univ. press, 1921.

NK 0201023 MA NcD

Knight, Clara M., ed.
Plautus, Titus Maccius.
T. Macci Plavti Menaechmi. Ed. with introduction and notes by Clara M. Knight ... Cambridge, The University press, 1919.

Knight, Clarence A., comp.
Chicago. *Ordinances, etc.*
Supplement to the municipal code of the city of Chicago (from April 18, 1881, to January 1, 1887.) (Published by authority of the City council.) Comp. by Clarence A. Knight ... ₍Chicago, E. B. Myers & company, 1887₎

VOLUME 300

Knight, Clayton, 1891–
The aviator; pictures and story by Clayton Knight. Philadelphia, D. McKay Co. [1947]
[39] p. illus. (part col.) 18 cm.

1. Aeronautics—Juvenile literature. I. Title.
TL547.K63 629.13 47-30559*
Library of Congress

NK 0201026 DLC WaSp

TX769 .C7 Knight, Clayton, 1891– illus.

Cridland, Margery.
The baker; pictures by Clayton Knight. Philadelphia, D. McKay Co. [1947]

Knight, Clayton, 1891–
The big book of real helicopters; text and pictures by Clayton Knight. New York, Grosset & Dunlap, ©1955.
unpaged. illus. 33 cm. (Big treasure books)

1. Helicopters—Juvenile literature. I. Title.
TL716.K53 55-4100 ‡
*629.1335 629.13335

NK 0201028 DLC IU OO OCl PP PWcS Or OrP WaS WaSp

Knight, Clayton, 1891–
The big book of real jet planes. Text and pictures by Clayton Knight. New York, Grosset & Dunlap, ©1952.
unpaged. illus. 34 cm. (Big treasure books)

1. Jet planes—Juvenile literature. I. Title.
TL547.K65 52-12544 ‡
*629.14353 629.13338

NK 0201029 DLC OCl PP IU WaS WaSp Or OrP OrAshS

Knight, Clayton, 1891–
Hitch your wagon; the story of Bernt Balchen, by Clayton Knight and Robert C. Durham. Decorations by Clayton Knight. Drexel Hill, Pa., Bell Pub. Co. [1950]
xi, 332 p. illus., ports., maps (on lining papers) 22 cm.

1. Balchen, Bernt, 1899– I. Durham, Robert C., joint author. II. Title.
TL540.B35K6 926.29 50-5788

NBuU GU OKentU MiU OCl OrU
NK 0201030 DLC WaTC Or WaT OrCS CaBViP WaS OrStbM

PZ7 .S119 Hu Knight, Clayton, 1891– illus.

Sackett, Bert, 1891-1947.
Hurricane treasure, the secret of Injun key, by Bert Sackett, illustrated by Clayton Knight. New York, Random house [1945]

Knight, Clayton, 1891– illus.

Clevenger, Cloyd Peart.
Modern flight, by Cloyd P. Clevenger ... Illustrations by Clayton Knight. New York city, Noble and Noble, inc. [©1941]

Knight, Clayton, 1891–
The non-stop stowaway; the story of a long distance flight. Written & illus. by C. Knight. N.Y., Children's book club, [c1928]
160 p. illus. (port col.) O

NK 0201033 OO ODW PP PJA

Knight, Clayton, 1891–
Pilots' luck, drawings by Clayton Knight; with excerpts from stories by Elliott White Springs, Captain A. Roy Brown, Floyd Gibbons, Norman S. Hall. Philadelphia, David McKay company [©1929]
4 p. l., 11-70, [2] p. illus. (part col.) col. plates. 29cm.

1. European war, 1914-1918—Aerial operations. 2. European war, 1914-1918—Pictorial works. I. Springs, Elliott White, 1896– II. Brown, A. Roy. III. Gibbons, Floyd Phillips, 1886– IV. Hall, Norman Shannon. V. Title.
29-22814
Library of Congress D600.K6

NK 0201034 DLC WaU RPB TxU OrU OCl OrU WaS CaBVa

Knight, Clayton, 1891–
The quest of the golden condor, written and illustrated by Clayton Knight. New York, A. A. Knopf, 1946.
xii, [2], 346 p. illus. (part col.; incl. map) 22cm.
"First edition."

I. Title.
46-2360
Library of Congress PZ7.K736Qe

NK 0201035 DLC MiU PP OrPS OrP WaS Or OrU WaT CaBVa

Knight, Clayton, 1891–
The secret of the buried tomb, written and illus. by Clayton Knight. [1st ed.] New York, A. A. Knopf, 1948.
311 p. illus. 22 cm.

1. World War, 1939-1945—Fiction. I. Title.
PZ7.K736Se 48-5524*

NK 0201036 DLC WaS WaT Or WaSp

Knight, Clayton. 1891–
The secret of the buried tomb...
N.Y. Knopf, 1949, c1948.
311 p. front. illus. O.

NK 0201037 PP

Knight, Clayton, 1891–
Ships aloft; a construction book for future flyers, by Clayton Knight and Harold Platt. New York and London, Harper & brothers, 1936.
[11] p. illus., col. plates. 32½ x 48cm.
Loose-leaf.
"Lithographed."
Illustrated lining-papers; illustrated covers in color.
"First edition."

1. Aeroplanes—Models. 2. Aeroplanes. I. Platt, Harold, joint author. II. Title.
36-25233
Library of Congress TL770.K55
Copyright A 98945 [5] 629.13334

NK 0201038 DLC PPGi

Knight, Clayton, 1891–
Skyroad to mystery, written and illustrated by Clayton Knight. [1st ed.] New York, Knopf, 1949.
243 p. illus. 22 cm.

I. Title.
PZ7.K736Sk 49-11079*

NK 0201039 DLC WaSp WaT Or

PZ7 .S119 Sp Knight, Clayton, 1891– illus.

Sackett, Bert.
Sponger's jinx [by] Bert Sackett, illustrated by Clayton Knight. New York, Random house [1943]

Knight, Clayton, 1891–
The story of flight, written and illustrated by Clayton Knight. New York, Grosset & Dunlap [1954]
150 p. illus. 29 cm. (Illustrated true books)
Includes bibliography.

1. Aeronautics—Hist. I. Title.
TL515.K63 *629.109 629.1309 54-4922 ‡

NK 0201041 DLC Or OrP WaS WaT PPGi MB PPD PP OCl

KNIGHT, Clayton, illustrator, 1891–
War birds; diary of an unknown aviator. Illustrated by Clayton Knight. New York, G.H.Doran Co., [cop. 1926]

Plates and other illustr.
Illustrated end papers.

NK 0201042 MH

PZ3 .M7682 War Knight, Clayton, 1891– illus.

Montgomery, Rutherford George, 1896–
Warhawk patrol, by Rutherford Montgomery; illustrated by Clayton Knight. Philadelphia, David McKay company [1944]

PZ7 .M7685 Yang Knight, Clayton, 1891– illus.

[Montgomery, Rutherford George] 1896–
A Yankee flier on a rescue mission, by Al Avery [*pseud.*] illustrated by Clayton Knight. New York, Grosset & Dunlap [1945]

TS850 .R65 1949 **Knight, Cleve Edward, 1913–**

Rohr, William Henry, 1888–
Machine molder practice; an illustrated manual on molder work, operation and maintenance of the molding machine. Comp. by Cleve E. Knight. Seattle, Quarterman Press [1949]

Knight, Clifford, 1886–
The affair at Palm Springs, by Clifford Knight ... New York, Dodd, Mead & company, 1938.
4 p. l., 303 p. 20½cm.

I. Title.
38-25880
Library of Congress PZ3.K7425Ab

NK 0201046 DLC PPL PBa

Knight, Clifford, 1886–
The affair in Death valley, by Clifford Knight. New York, Dodd, Mead & company, 1940.
4 p. l., 270 p. 20½cm.

I. Title.
40-34071
Library of Congress PZ3.K7425Af

NK 0201047 DLC OEac OOxM OrU

VOLUME 300

Knight, Clifford, 1886–
... The affair of the black sombrero. New York, Dodd, Mead & company, 1939.
4 p. l., 312 p. 20½cm.

I. Title.
39-9211
Library of Congress PZ3.K7425Ac

NK 0201048 DLC WaS OCl OCU OEac PPL

Knight, Clifford, 1886–
The affair of the Circus Queen, by Clifford Knight. New York, Dodd, Mead & company, 1940.
4 p. l., 287 p. 20½cm.

I. Title.
40-7706
Library of Congress PZ3.K7425Ag

NK 0201049 DLC PP OCU WaS

Knight, Clifford, 1886–
... The affair of the corpse escort ... Philadelphia, David McKay company [1946]
4 p. l., 3-217 p. 19½cm.
"An Armchair mystery."

I. Title.
46-18353
Library of Congress PZ3.K7425Acd

NK 0201050 DLC WaE

Knight, Clifford, 1886–
The affair of the crimson gull, by Clifford Knight. New York, Dodd, Mead & company, 1941.
4 p. l., 262 p. 20cm.

I. Title.
41-5437
Library of Congress PZ3.K7425Ace

NK 0201051 DLC PPL PPM PP OLak WaE WaS

Knight, Clifford, 1886-
The affair of the crimson gull. [New York], L.E. Spivak [c1941]
128 p. 20 cm. (Bestseller mystery, B73)

NK 0201052 OrU

Knight, Clifford, 1886–
The affair of the dead stranger, by Clifford Knight. New York, Dodd, Mead & company, 1944.
4 p. l., 197 p. 19½cm.
On cover: Red badge detective.

I. Title.
44-9743
Library of Congress PZ3.K7425Aced

NK 0201053 DLC PPL PP OEac

Knight, Clifford, 1886–
The affair of the fainting butler, by Clifford Knight. New York, Dodd, Mead & company, 1943.
4 p. l., 261 p. 19½cm.
"Red badge detective."

I. Title.
43-15294
Library of Congress PZ3.K7425Acf

NK 0201054 DLC NBuU PPL OCU PP OClh OOxM

Knight, Clifford, 1886–
... The affair of the ginger lei. New York, Dodd, Mead & company, 1938.
4 p. l., 309, [3] p. 20cm.
"Index of clues": [3] p. (sealed) at end.

I. Title.
38-9726
Library of Congress PZ3.K7425Ad

NK 0201055 DLC CLSU PPL OCU OClh

Knight, Clifford, 1886–
... The affair of the golden buzzard. Philadelphia, David McKay company [1946]
3 p. l., 3-236 p. 19½cm.
"An Armchair mystery."

I. Title.
PZ3.K7425Adf 47-599

NK 0201056 DLC

Knight, Clifford, 1886–
... The affair of the heavenly voice. New York, Dodd, Mead & company, 1937.
4 p. l., 295, [3] p. 20½cm.
Index of clues: [3] p. at end, uncut.

I. Title.
37-23345
Library of Congress PZ3.K7425Ae

NK 0201057 DLC CtY PBa OCU OLak WaS

Knight, Clifford, 1886–
The affair of the jade monkey, by Clifford Knight. New York, Detective book club, c1943.
239 p.

Bound with: Halling-A corpse by any other name, and Wylie-Corpses at Indian Stones.

NK 0201058 PBa PPL PP

Knight, Clifford, 1886–
The affair of the jade monkey, by Clifford Knight. New York, Dodd, Mead & company, 1943.
4 p. l., 239 p. 19cm.

I. Title.
43-5354
Library of Congress PZ3.K7425Aed

NK 0201059 DLC OCU WaE WaS

Knight, Clifford, 1886–
The affair of the limping sailor, by Clifford Knight ... New York, Dodd, Mead & company, 1942.
4 p. l., 248 p. 19½cm.

I. Title.
42-10022
Library of Congress PZ3.K7425Aeg

NK 0201060 DLC PPL PP OClh OOxM OrP

Knight, Clifford.
... The affair of the scarlet crab, by Clifford Knight. New York, Dodd, Mead & company, 1937.
3 p. l., 298, [3] p. 20cm.
At head of title: The Red badge $2,000 prize mystery.

I. Title.
37-3294
Library of Congress PZ3.K7425Af

NK 0201061 DLC NcD PPL PPA OCU OEac OClh

Knight, Clifford, 1886–
The affair of the sixth button. Philadelphia, D. McKay Co. [1947]
[2] l., 3-221 p. 20 cm. (An armchair mystery)

I. Title.
PZ3.K7425Ag 47-12474*
Library of Congress

NK 0201062 DLC WaE

Knight, Clifford, 1886–
The affair of the skiing clown, by Clifford Knight. New York, Dodd, Mead & company, 1941.
4 p. l., 256 p. 20cm.

I. Title.
41-18112
Library of Congress PZ3.K7425Ah

NK 0201063 DLC PP PPL OCU

Knight, Clifford, 1886–
The affair of the splintered heart, by Clifford Knight. New York, Dodd, Mead & company, 1942.
4 p. l., 261 p. 19½cm.

I. Title.
42-22618
Library of Congress PZ3.K7425Ak

NK 0201064 DLC PPL OClh OOxM PBa ViU

Knight, Clifford.
The affair on the Painted desert, by Clifford Knight. New York, Dodd, Mead & company, 1939.
3 p. l., 314 p. 20½cm.

I. Title.
39-25961
Library of Congress PZ3.K7425Ap

NK 0201065 DLC PPL OCU WaT WaS WaSp

Knight, Clifford, 1886–
L'affaire du maitre d'hôtel défaillant [tr. par Alphonse Marsan. 1. éd. Montréal?, Éditions Moderne [1944]
219 p. 17 cm. (Collection Petit format, 107)

I. Title.
PS3521.N5335A75 49-39298*

NK 0201066 DLC

Knight, Clifford, 1886–
Dark abyss. [1st ed.] New York, E. P. Dutton, 1949.
222 p. 20 cm. (Guilt edged mystery)

I. Title.
PZ3.K7425Dar 49-7019*

NK 0201067 DLC OrP CaBVa WaE

Knight, Clifford, 1886–
The dark road. [1st ed.] New York, Dutton, 1951.
218 p. 20 cm. (Guilt edged mystery)

I. Title.
PZ3.K7425Dat 51-12231 ‡

NK 0201068 DLC OrCS OrP WaE

VOLUME 300

Knight, Clifford, 1886–
Death and little brother. [1st ed.] New York, Dutton, 1952.
224 p. 20 cm. (Guilt edged mystery)

I. Title.

PZ3.K7425Db 52-6643

NK 0201069 DLC PV OOxM TxU OrP WaT

Knight, Clifford, 1886–
Death of a big shot. [1st ed.] New York, Dutton, 1951.
221 p. 20 cm. (Guilt edged mystery)

I. Title.

PZ3.K7425De 51-9034

NK 0201070 DLC OrP CaBVa

Knight, Clifford, 1886–
Hangman's choice. [1st ed.] New York, E. P. Dutton, 1949.
223 p. 20 cm. (Guilt edged mystery)
"A condensed version ... appeared in Standard magazine, 1948, under the title 'Bells of El Fidel.'"

I. Title.

PZ3.K7425Han 49-9980*

NK 0201071 DLC OCl PP TxU CaBVa

Knight, Clifford, 1886–
The yellow cat. [1st ed.] New York, Dutton, 1950.
222 p. 20 cm. (Guilt edged mystery)

I. Title.

PZ3.K7425Ye 50-5915

NK 0201072 DLC PP TxU WaE WaT CaBVa

Knight, Cornelia, 1757–1837.
Works by this author printed in America before 1801 are available in this library in the Readex Microprint edition of Early American Imprints published by the American Antiquarian Society.
This collection is arranged according to the numbers in Charles Evans' American Bibliography.

NK 0201073 DLC

Knight, Cornelia, 1757–1837.
Autobiography of Miss Cornelia Knight, lady companion to the Princess Charlotte of Wales, with extracts from her journals and anecdote books ... 2d ed. London, W. H. Allen and co., 1861.
2 v. port. 22½cm.

1. Charlotte Augusta, of Wales, consort of Prince Leopold of Saxe-Coburg-Saalfeld, 1796–1817.
[Full name: Ellis Cornelia Knight]
S D 20-6 Revised

U. S. Dept. of state. Library for Library of Congress CT.K744.K7 [r38c2]

NK 0201074 DS TU NN MB WU OCl OU PPL OrP

DA538 .K65A3 1861b Knight, Cornelia, 1757-1837.
Autobiography of Miss Cornelia Knight lady companion to the Princess Charlotte of Wales; with extracts from her journals and anecdote books. 3d ed. London, W. H. Allen, 1861.
2 v. port. 23cm.

1. Charlotte Augusta, of Wales, consort of Prince Leopold of Saxe-Coburg-Saalfeld, 1796-1817.
Full name: Ellis Cornelia Knight.

NK 0201075 MB MeB NcD ViU CtY

---

*K.260 .4. **Knight, Cornelia, 1757-1837.**
Autobiography of Miss Cornelia Knight, lady companion to the Princess Charlotte of Wales; with extracts from her journals and anectdote books. 4th ed. London, W. H. Allen, 1861.
2 v. port. 24 cm.

NK 0201076 MB IU MdBP PP OClW MH

---

*EC8 K7441 800b [Knight, Cornelia, 1757-1837]
The battle of the Nile. A pindarick ode. To His Excellency the Rt. Honble. Sir William Hamilton ...
Vienna, Printed by Widow Alberti. 1800.
4°. 13p. 25cm.
Dedication signed: Ellis Cornelia Knight.

NK 0201077 MH InU

[**Knight, Cornelia**] 1757–1837.
Description of Latium; or, La campagna di Roma ... London, Longman, Hurst, Rees, and Orme, 1805.
xi, 268 p. front. (map) plates. 27 x 21½cm.

1. Latium—Description, geography. 2. Campagna di Roma. 3. Architecture, Domestic—Latium. I. Title.
[Full name: Ellis Cornelia Knight]
4-29469 Revised

Library of Congress DG975.C17K7

NK 0201078 DLC PMA NNC CtY WaU

[**Knight, Cornelia**] 1757–1837.
Dinarbas; a tale: being a continuation of Rasselas, prince of Abissinia ... London, Printed for C. Dilly, 1790.
xii, 336 p. 17½ cm.

I. Johnson, Samuel, 1709–1784. Rasselas. II. Title.

PR4859.K4D5 1790 7—14201

NK 0201079 DLC MH ICU CLU TU ViU FU MiU InU IU MiEM CtY OCU OU CSmH ICN NjP OrU WU OrU

---

*EC8 K7441 790db [Knight, Cornelia, 1757-1837]
Dinarbas; a tale: being a continuation of Rasselas, prince of Abissinia ... The second edition.
London: Printed for C. Dilly, in the Poultry. M.DCC.XCII.
xii, 336p. 17.5cm.
Page 93 misnumbered 39.

NK 0201080 MH

---

*EC75 J6371 759p 1791 [Knight, Cornelia, 1757-1837]
Dinarbas; a tale: being a continuation of Rasselas, prince of Abissinia ...
Philadelphia: Printed by F. Bailey, no. 116, Market-street, and T. Lang, no. 21, Church-alley. M DCC XCII.
1p.l., viii, [9]-200p. 14.5cm.
Bound with Johnson's Prince of Abissinia, 1791.

NK 0201081 MH PPL MHi MWA PSt

[Knight, Cornelia] 1757-1837.
Dinarbas; a tale: being a continuation of Rasselas, Prince of Abissinia. [7 lines, Hor. Lib. IV. Od. 9]. The third edition. London, C. Dilly, 1793.
xii, 336 p. 18cm.
Signatures: A3-P6.
Bookplate: T. R. Francis.
I. Johnson, Samuel, 1709-1784. Rasselas. II. Title.

NK 0201082 FU IU PMA

[Knight, Cornelia,] 1757–1837.
Dinarbas; a tale: being a continuation of Rasselas, prince of Abissinia ... Volume the third. (In: S. Johnson, Rasselas, prince of Abissinia ... Greenfield, 1795. 12°. p. [129]–254.)

1. Fiction (English). 2. Title.
N. Y. P. L. September 15, 1915.

NK 0201083 NN MB

[**Knight, Cornelia**] 1757–1837.
Dinarbas; a tale: being a continuation of Rasselas, prince of Abissinia ... The 4th ed. London, Printed by L. Hansard for T. Cadell, jun. and W. Davies, 1800.
xii, 309 p. 18cm.

1. Johnson, Samuel, 1709–1784. Rasselas. I. Title.
[Full name: Ellis Cornelia Knight]
37-8309

Library of Congress PR4859.K4D5 1800
[2] 823.79

NK 0201084 DLC MB NcU IaU OO

[Knight, Cornelia] 1757–1837.
Dinarbas: a tale ... 1st American ed. Hartford: Printed for and sold by Oliver D. Cooke, 1803. Lincoln & Gleason, printers.
188 p. 14½cm.
A continuation of Rasselas, prince of Abissinia.

I. Johnson, Samuel, 1709–1784. Rasselas. II. Title.
[Full name: Ellis Cornelia Knight]
4-31643 Revised

Library of Congress PZ3.K743D 2

NK 0201085 DLC IEN InU CSt ICU MWA MdBG NBuG NN WU NBu NjP CSmH CtHT-W

An K744 790de [Knight, Cornelia] i.e. Ellis Cornelia, 1757-1837.
Dinarbas; a tale: being a continuation of Rasselas, prince of Abissinia ... The 5th ed.
London: Printed for T. Cadell, and W. Davies, Strand. By J. M'Creery, Blackhorse-Court, Fleet-Street. 1811. xi, 225p. 16cm.
Contents misbound before the Introduction.

NK 0201086 TxU CaBVaU

---

* PR3529 .A1 1813 [**Knight, Cornelia**] 1757–1837.
Dinarbas: a tale. 2d American ed. Brattleborough [Vt.]: Printed by William Fessenden. 1813.
180 p. 15cm. [With Johnson, Samuel. Rasselas, prince of Abyssinia. Brattleborough [Vt.], 1813]
Sequel to Dr. Johnson's Rasselas.

NK 0201087 ViU MBAt Vt MWA InU

[KNIGHT, Cornelia] 1757-1837.
Dinarbas; a tale; being a continuation of Rasselas. (Appended to JOHNSON, Samuel, 1709-1784. Rasselas, etc., 1817-24°. pp.131-266)

NK 0201088 MH

Knight, Cornelia, 1757-1837.
Dinarbas; a tale ... Brattleboro, 1826.

NK 0201089 MB

[KNIGHT, Cornelia] 1757-1837.
Dinarbas, a tale a continuation of Rasselas, prince of Abissinia. 2d ed., London, C. Dilly, 1892.

NK 0201090 MH

VOLUME 300

Pq351
K69L Knight, Cornelia, 1757-1837.
Lines address'd to Victory in consequence of the success of Lord Cornwallis and his army against Tippoo Saïb. Parma, Printed by Bodoni, 1793.
6 l.
English and Italian. Italian translation by Eritisco Pilenejo.
No.495 in Brooks. Edizione Bodoniane; with variation in name of translator.
MS letter written on fly-leaf from Lessing Rosenthal to Wal... or M. Hill, dated Chicag March 8, 1925.

NK 0201091 RP MH

Knight, Cornelia *i. e.* **Ellis Cornelia, 1757-1837.**
Marcus Flaminius; or, A view of the military, political, and social life of the Romans: in a series of letters from a patrician to his friend ... By E. Cornelia Knight ... London, Printed for C. Dilly, 1792.
2 v. 21½cm.

1. Rome—Hist.—Empire, B. C. 30–A. D. 284—Fiction.

Library of Congress PZ3.K743M 7-14288†

NK 0201092 DLC NN IU MoU OU MH PPL CSmH MdBP

Rare book coll. PR4859 .K4 M3 1795 Knight, Cornelia, 1757-1837.
Marcus Flaminius; an historical novel, in a series of letters, supposed to be written in the life-time of Germanicus, by E. Cornelia Knight. London, Printed for C. Dilly, 1795.
2v. 22cm.

1. Rome - Hist. - Empire, 30 B.C.-284 A.D. - Fiction. I. Title.

NK 0201093 NcU PSt ICU WU NjP OO ICN PU

Knight, Cornelia, 1757-1837.
Marcus Flaminius; or, A view of the military, political, and social life of the Romans: in a series of letters from a patrician to his friend; in the year DCC.LXII. From the foundation of Rome, to the year DCC.LXIX. By E. Cornelia Knight... Second edition. London: Printed by J. M'Creery, for T. Cadell, and W. Davies, 1808. 2 v. 18cm.

292142-3A. 1. Rome—Hist.—Empire, B. C. 30 – A. D. 284—Fiction. 2. Fiction, English. I. Title.
N. Y. P. L. *Revised* September 5, 1935

NK 0201094 NN MiU MB

Knight, Cornelia, 1757-1837.
Miscellaneous poems. Windsor, 1812
see under title

Knight, Cornelia, 1757–1837.
... Personal reminiscences by Cornelia Knight and Thomas Raikes. Ed. by Richard Henry Stoddard. New York, Scribner, Armstrong, and company, 1875.
xvi, 339 p. 4 port. (incl. front.) 17½cm. (Bric-a-brac series, no. VII)

I. Raikes, Thomas, 1777-1848. II. Stoddard, Richard Henry, 1825-1903, ed
[*Full name:* Ellis Cornelia Knight]

Library of Congress CT101.B8 no. 7 14-15300 Revised
——— Copy 2. PR452.K5

NK 0201096 DLC PPCCH OrU OrP IdU OrU OKentU FU PPLas PU PHatU PPA MWA OCl OO NN ViU

Knight, Cornelia, 1757-1837.
Personal reminiscences, by Cornelia Knight and Thomas Raikes. Ed. by Richard Henry Stoddard. New York, Scribner, Armstrong, 1876.
xvi, 339 p. 4 port. 18 cm. (Bric-a-brac series, VII)

NK 0201097 OCU

Knight, Cornelia, 1752-1836.
Personal reminiscences of Cornelia Knight and Thomas Raikes, ed. by R.H. Stoddard. New York, Scribner, 1887.
339p. port. 18cm. (Bric-a-brac series)

I. Raikes, Thomas, jt. au. II. Stoddard, Richard Henry, ed.

NK 0201098 TU MeB MiEM

Knight, Cornelia, 1757-1837, comp. and tr.
Prayers and hymns, translated from the German. Windsor, printed by E. Harding, 1812; London, reprinted by W. Nicol, 1832.
xi, 118 p. 18.5 cm.
"Translated from the German by Miss Ellis Cornelia Knight."
Preface signed: Edward Harding.

NK 0201099 NNUT

pTypTS 725 93.492 [Knight, Cornelia, 1757-1837]
Presented to the R.t Hon.ble the Lady Bruce. At her visit to the Bodoni press. Parma. Aug.st 31. 1793.
[Parma, 1793]
broadside. 43.5x29cm.
Brooks 512.
A poem, signed: Uranide Luceio [pseud.].

NK 0201100 MH

Knight, Cornelia, 1757-1837.
Sir Guy de Lusignan; a tale of Italy... London, Saunders and Otley, 1833.
2 v. 20½ cm.
First edition.

NK 0201101 NjP IU

FILM 9135 PR Knight, Cornelia, 1757-1837.
Sir Guy de Lusignan; a tale of Italy. London, Saunders and Ottey, 1833.
2 v.on 1 reel. On film (Negative)
Microfilm. Original in Princeton Univ. Library.

NK 0201102 CU

PR 4859 .K4 S5 KNIGHT, CORNELIA, 1757-1837
Song addressed to Lady Hamilton on her birthday April the 26th, 1800 ... By Miss Knight. [n.p., 1800]
[4] p. 18 cm.
Caption title.
Unbound.

NK 0201103 InU

[**Knight, Cornelia** *i. e.* **Ellis Cornelia**] 1757-1837, *ed.*
Translations from the German in prose and verse ... Frogmore lodge, Windsor, Printed by E. Harding, 1812.
3 p. l., 111 p. pl. 17½cm.
Dedication signed: Ellis Cornelia Knight.
Selections from G. F. Seiler, C. F. Gellert and others.
Only 30 copies printed.

I. Gellert, Christian Fürchtegott, 1715-1769. II. Seiler, Georg Friedrich, 1733-1807. [III. Title.

Library of Congress BV4834.K5 21—12048

NK 0201104 DLC MH

Knight, Cornelia, 1757-1837.
Vie privee, politique et militaire des Romains, sous Auguste et sous Tibers...Paris, 1801.
8°

NK 0201105 NN

HZ 10.6 .K714 KNIGHT, CURTIS HOMER, 1929-
The economics of the Soviet food industry. [Bloomington, Ind.] 1968.
249 p. illus., maps.
Thesis (Ph.D.)--Indiana University.
Vita.

NK 0201106 InU

NA 2185 K69 Knight, Cyril Roy.
Architectural education in the British empire; a report by C. R. Knight. Auckland, 1937.
[2], 59 l. 34cm.
Mimeographed.

1. Architecture—Study and teaching—Gt. Brit. 2. Architecture—Study and teaching—Commonwealth of Nations. I. Title.

NK 0201107 NIC NjP

Knight, Cyril Workman, 1879–
... Abitibi-night hawk gold area, by C. W Knight, A. G. Burrows, P. E. Hopkins and A. L. Parsons; Larder Lake gold area, by P. E. Hopkins, printed by order of the Legislative assembly of Ontario. Toronto, A. T. Wilgress, printer, 1919.
v, [1], 84 p. illus., 2 fold. maps (1 in pocket) diagrs. 24½cm. (Ontario. Bureau of mines. Annual report, 28th, pt. 2, 1919)
Bibliography: p 70.

1. Gold mines and mining—Ontario. I. Burrows, Alfred Granville, 1878– joint author. II. Hopkins, Percy Eugene, 1887– joint author. III. Parsons, Arthur Leonard, 1873– joint author. IV. Title. V. Title: Larder Lake gold area.

——— Copy 2. G S 19-395
Library, U. S. Geological Survey 402(150) On8 vol. 28, pt. 2

NK 0201108 DI-GS MB

Knight, Cyril Workman, 1879-
... Analcite-trachyte tuffs and breccias from south west Alberta, Canada. [N.p.n.pub.]1904.
Illus.O.

NK 0201109 CaBViP

Knight, Cyril Workman, 1879–
... Geology of the mine workings of Cobalt and south Lorrain silver areas, by Cyril W. Knight. Together with a description of milling and metallurgical practice in treatment of silver ores at Cobalt, by Fraser D. Reid, James J. Denny and R. H. Hutchison ... Toronto, C. W. James, printer, 1924.
xiv, 374 p. illus., plates (part fold., incl. col. profiles, tables, diagrs.) 25 cm. *and* atlas of 17 fold. maps and plans in separate portfolio. (Ontario. Dept. of mines. Annual report, 31st, pt. II, 1922)
At head of title: Province of Ontario. Dept. of mines.
Bibliographical references.

1. Silver mines and mining—Ontario. 2. Silver—Metallurgy. I. Reid, Fraser D. II. Denny, James J. III. Hutchinson, R. H. IV. Title.

U. S. Geol. Survey. Libr. for Library of Congress [a57d1] G S 24—296

NK 0201110 DI-GS OClWHi OO NN CU CaBVaU

Sel.30 13 **Knight, Cyril Workman, 1879-**
..., A new occurrence of pseudo-leucite. By C.W.Knight. - The re-formation of soda-leucite. By T.T.Read and C.W.Knight.
[n.p., 1906] cover-title, 286-295pp. illus. 23½cm.
"From the American journal of science, vol. XXI, April 1906"
Stamped on cover-title: Contributions from the Geological department, Columbia university ... vol.XIII, no.118, and on p.294: Contributions ... vol.XIII, no.119.

NK 0201111 CtY

Knight, Cyril Workman, 1879–
... Records of wells drilled for oil and gas in Ontario. Comp. and ed. with an introduction by Cyril W. Knight. Printed by order of the Legislative assembly of Ontario. Toronto, L. K. Cameron, printer, 1915.
[4], 96 p. illus., maps, tables, diagrs. 24½cm. (Ontario. Bureau of mines. Annual report, 24th, pt. 2, 1915)

1. Petroleum—Ontario. 2. Gas, Natural—Ontario. I. Title.
G S 22-277
Library, U. S. Geological Survey 402(150) On8 vol. 24, pt. 2

NK 0201112 DI-GS CaBVaU OClWHi

VOLUME 300

Knight, Cyril Workman, 1879–
... The South Lorrain silver area, by Cyril W. Knight ... Printed by order of the Legislative assembly of Ontario. Toronto, Printed and published by C. W. James, printer, 1923.
55 p. illus., plates (part col., incl. maps, diagrs.) tables, diagrs. 24½cm. (Ontario. Dept. of mines. Bulletin no. 48)
At head of title: Province of Ontario. Dept. of mines.
To accompany Report by Cyril W. Knight on underground workings in cobalt and South Lorrain, in the 31st report of the Ontario Dept. of mines, pt. II.
Folded plate on loose sheet containing maps and diagrams.
1. Silver mines and mining—Ontario. I. Title.
G S 23-283
Library, U. S. Geological Survey 402(150) On82 no. 48
[2]

NK 0201113 DI-GS

Knight, Cyrus Frederick, 1831-1891.
The peace of Jerusalem: a sermon preached at the opening of St. Mark's church, Boston, on the third Sunday in Advent, 1859. By C. F. Knight... Boston, Damrell & Moore, 1859. 15 p. 24cm.

1. Boston—Churches, Episcopal—St. Mark's.
N. Y. P. L. October 30, 1945

NK 0201114 NN RPB

Knight, D.
Morphology of the vertebrata. Dog-fish, cod, pigeon, and rabbit [with development of the dog-fish] By D. Knight ... Edinburgh, Y. J. Pentland, 1883.
48 p. 4 pl. 21½cm.

1. Vertebrates—Anatomy.
A 18-1444
Title from Harvard Univ. Printed by L. C.

NK 0201115 MH

17 Knight, D.C.
Scripture homeopathy. Part first. The deluge and water baptism. Part second. The drunkenness of Noah and the Lord's supper. New York, 1868.
24 p. 8°.

NK 0201116 DLC

HD10000 Knight, Dale Alpheus, 1922-
A study of selected agricultural problematic production situations. 1952.
164 l.

Thesis--Univ. of Chicago.

1. Agriculture--Economic aspects--U.S.

NK 0201117 ICU

PN6071 S2A1 K6985H4
Knight, Damon Francis, 1922-
Hell's pavement [by] Damon Knight.
New York, Lion Books [1955]
192 p. 18cm. (Lion library edition, LL13)
"A Lion science-fantasy novel."
Chapter 1 first appeared in Astounding science fiction. Portions of the rest are based on the author's story Turncoat.

NK 0201118 CSt GU KU

Knight, Damon Francis, 1922- joint author.

Knight, Frederick Stuart, 1884–
The stencil duplicated newspaper, by F. S. Knight and Damon Knight. [Hood River, Or., F. S. Knight and D. Knight, °1941]

Knight, Daniel.
An oration, pronounced at Charlton, (Mass.) on the forty-third anniversary of American independence. By Daniel Knight ... Worcester, Printed by William Manning, 1819.
20 p. 21½cm.

1. Fourth of July orations.
17-9422
Library of Congress E286.C495 1819

NK 0201120 DLC PMA ICN CSt PHi MWA NN MB N

Knight, Daniel K.
Church government of antiquity and the present ... A practical manual for "The evangelical Christian church connection." And Christian workers ... With an introduction by W. R. Gullins. [Atlanta? Ga., 1901]
317, [3] p. 16°.
1-15239—M 3 Aug. 8

NK 0201121 DLC

Knight, Daniel Ridgway, 1845-1924.
Modern paintings, foreign and American schools; comprising all of the remaining works belonging to the late Daniel Ridgway Knight, and selections from the P. H. McMahon, John Dugan and other private collections; exhibition and sale at the American Art Galleries... [New York: Amer. Art Assoc., Inc., 1925.] 59 l. illus., pl. 8°.
Cover-title.
Unrestricted public sale Feb. 4 and 5, 1925.

1. Paintings—Catalogues. 2. Knight, Daniel Ridgway, 1845-1924.
N. Y. P. L. February 21, 1929

NK 0201122 NN

Knight, Donald, J., 1894-

Warner, Pelham Francis, 1873–
Cricket. A new ed. By P. F. Warner; with contributions by the Hon. R. H. Lyttelton, G. L. Jessop, D. J. Knight, J. Shuter, E. R. Wilson; with 52 illustrations. London, New York [etc.] Longmans, Green, and co., 1920.

Knight, Donald J., 1894-
The more compleat cricketer, by Donald J. Knight...with a foreword by Jack Hobbs. London: Country Life, Ltd., 1925. xi, 58 p. plates. 8°.
Plates printed on both sides.

238603A. 1. Cricket—Handbooks, rules, etc.
N. Y. P. L. May 27, 1926

NK 0201124 NN RPB

[**Knight, Doris**]
The bride was late, by Myra Gay [*pseud.*] New York, Arcadia house, inc., 1946.
304 p. 19½cm.

I. Title.
PZ3.K7436Br 46-18419 rev

NK 0201125 DLC WaE

[**Knight, Doris**]
Gardenia angel, by Myra Gay [*pseud.*] New York, Arcadia house, inc., 1947.
272 p. 19½cm.

I. Title.
PZ3.K7436Gar 47-1675

NK 0201126 DLC WaE

Knight, Doris.
Infamous woman, by Doris Knight. New York, W. Godwin, inc., 1934.
269 p. 19cm.

I. Title.
34-9623
Library of Congress PZ3.K7436 In

NK 0201127 DLC

[**Knight, Doris**]
Little jade lady, by Myra Gay [pseud.] New York, Arcadia House, 1948.
255 p. 20 cm.

I. Title.
PZ3.K7436Li 48-3515*

NK 0201128 DLC WaE

819.1 K743v
Knight, Dorothy W. 1881-
Verses. With a preface by [the author's] father. Brockville [Ont.] 1892.
41, 29p. 17cm.

"Other verses, 1893": 29p. at end.

NK 0201129 TxU RPB CaBVaU

Knight, Dorothy W., 1881-
The vision of the seasons, and other verses, by Dorothy W. Knight... Montreal, W. Drysdale co., 1898. 68 p. 20cm.

NK 0201130 NN CaOTP TxU RPB CaBVaU

742 Y17 v.14
Knight, Douglas M., 1921-
Dramatic and descriptive order in the Iliad. (In Yale classical studies. 1955. v.14, p.[107]-122)

NK 0201131 CU

Knight, Douglas M 1921-
Pope and the heroic tradition; a critical study of his Iliad. New Haven, Yale University Press, 1951.
viii, 123 p. 25 cm. (Yale studies in English, v. 117)
"An early version ... was submitted to the Graduate School of Yale University ... for the degree of doctor of philosophy."
Bibliographical footnotes.

1. Homerus. Ilias. 2. Pope, Alexander, 1688-1744. I. Title. (Series)
PA4025.A2P65 1951 883.1 51-14689
——— Copy 2. PR13.Y3 vol. 117

NK 0201132 MB WU CtY MH WaU CoU DAU OrCS IdU OrPR DLC CaBVaU WaS MtU OrU OU NcU ViU TxU NN

378.73 K744
Knight, Douglas M., 1921-
Religious implications in the humanities. [New Haven, Conn., Edward W. Hazen Foundation, 1951]
20p. 24cm. (The Hazen pamphlets. no.27)
"An address before the annual conference of the National Council on Religion in Higher Education, August, 1950."

1. Education, Humanistic. 2. Humanities. I. Title. II. Series.

NK 0201133 OrU

Knight, E.
The veteran; or, The farmer's sons: a comic opera ...
see Knight, Edward, 1774-1826.

VOLUME 300

Knight, E A Lempriere.
Christmas chimes. [1890]
see under title

---

aw
ase)

Knight, E C
A little treatise of baile and maineprize, written by E. C. Knight and now published for a generall good. London, W. Cooke, 1635.
32 p. 18 cm.

1. Bail—Gt. Brit. 2. Suretyship and guaranty—Gt. Brit. I. Title.

66—81734

NK 0201136 DLC

Knight, E F.
The banker's improved day calculator ... Chicago, N. M. Eberhart [°1892]
[14] p. 13½cm.
Copyrighted by E. F. Knight.

1. Banks and banking—Tables, etc.

Library of Congress HG1639.K7 6-29566†

NK 0201137 DLC

Knight, E. Georgina, ed.

TX717 .R412 1942

Red Cross. *Gt. Brit. British Red Cross Society.*
Cookery and catering manual, ed. by E. Georgina Knight. 4th ed. London, Cassell, 1942.

Knight, E P
A chip of the old block; or, The village festival
see Knight, Edward P

Knight, Earl Lawrence, 1906-
Convertible securities ... [Columbus] The O. state univ., 1940.
4p. l., 2-421 numb. l.

Thesis (PH.D.) - Ohio state univ.

NK 0201140 OU

Knight, Edgar Wallace, 1885-1953
The academy movement in the South, by Edgar W. Knight ... [Chapel Hill? N. C., 1919?]
cover-title, 58 p. 19cm.
"Reprinted from the High school journal, volume II, nos. 7 and 8, and volume III, no. 1."
Bibliography: p. 56-58.

1. Education—Southern states. I. Title.

Library of Congress LA222.K6 20-27155

NK 0201141 DLC NN NcRS AAP PU ViU NcU ICJ

Knight, Edgar Wallace, 1885-1953.
Among the Danes, by Edgar Wallace Knignt ... Chapel Hill, The University of North Carolina press; London, H. Milford, Oxford university press, 1927.
2 p. l., [vii]-xii p., 2 l., 236 p. front., plates. 22 cm. (*Half-title:* The University of North Carolina. Social study series)

1. Education—Denmark. 2. Denmark—Soc. condit. I. Title.

LA872.K5 27—12613

WaTC
NK 0201142 DLC OU OC1 PU MiU NcU NcRS ViU WaS Or

Knight, Edgar Wallace, 1885-
Can the South attain to national standards in education?

Reprinted from South Atlantic quarterly, Jan. 1929, v.28, no.1.

NK 0201143 NcU

LB 875 .K 65

Knight, Edgar Wallace, 1885-
[Collected papers, reprints, etc. in education]
6 pam.
[1] The Peabody fund and its early operation in North Carolina. 15 p. (Repr. So. Atl. quar. v. XIV. Apr. 1915) [2] Reconstruction and education in Virginia. 36 p. (Ibid. v. XV. Apr. 1916) [3] Method and method. 8 p. (Repr. No. Car. high school bull. July 1916) [4] Manual labor schools in the South. (Repr. So. Atl. quar. July 1917. p. [209]-221) [5] Reconstruction and education in South Carolina. 28 p. (Ibid. v. XVIII-XIX. 1920) [6] Education in the southern mountains. 13 p. (Repr. Sch. and soc. v. XV. 1922)

NK 0201144 DLC

Knight, Edgar Wallace, 1885-
Consider the deans, how they toil.

Reprinted from School and society, Je.,2, 1928, v.27, no.701.

NK 0201145 NcU

Knight, Edgar Wallace, 1885-
...The consolidation of rural schools, by Edgar W. Knight ... Chapel Hill, N. C., The University, [1920]
26 p. 23cm. (University of North Carolina extension leaflets, vol. III, no. 6. February, 1920)
Bibliography: p. 24-26.

1. Rural schools. 2. Rural schools—North Carolina. I. Title. II. Ser.

NK 0201146 ViU OU NcU MH IU DL

Knight, Edgar Wallace, 1885-
The consolidation of rural schools, 2d ed. Chapel Hill, N. C., the University. [1920]
27 p. 23cm. (University of North Carolina extension leaflets, v. 3, no. 8)
"Selected references on consolidation:" p. 24-27.

1. Schools—Centralization—U. S. 2. Rural schools—U. S. I. Ser.

NK 0201147 ViU DHEW CU

Knight, Edgar Wallace, 1885-1953.
Dr. W.S. Long, teacher.

(In High school journal. Nov. 1922. v.5, no.7.)

NK 0201148 NcU

Knight, Edgar Wallace, 1885-1953, *ed.*
A documentary history of education in the South before 1860. Chapel Hill, University of North Carolina Press [1949-53]
5 v. 25 cm.
CONTENTS.—v. 1. European inheritances.—v. 2. Toward educational independence.—v. 3. The rise of the State university.—v. 4. Private and denominational efforts.—v. 5. Educational theories and practices.

1. Education—Southern States—Hist. I. Title.

LA206.K6 370.975 49-8813 rev*

IdU OrP OrU OrCS OrPR
OCU OO PPLT NN MB ViU MB OrPS OC1W OC1 PSt PPL
NK 0201149 DLC MiU NIC KEmT MU KMK PPPL OU PPT TxU

Knight, Edgar Wallace, 1885- joint author.
[Hamilton, Joseph Grégoire de Roulhac] 1878-
Education for citizenship. January, 1921. Washington, Govt. print. off., 1921.

Knight, Edgar Wallace, 1885-
Education in the South, by Edgar W. Knight ... Chapel Hill, N. C., The University of North Carolina press; London, H. Milford, Oxford university press, 1924.
3 p. l., 31 p. 20½cm.
Appeared as chapter XIV in "Twenty-five years of American education."—Pref.
References: p. 31.

1. Education—Southern states.

U. S. Off. of educ. Library for Library of Congress LA209.K4 [a37d1] E 25-97

NK 0201151 DHEW NcD PPT OOxM IU NcU OC1JC OrPR

Knight, Edgar Wallace, 1885-
Education in the southern mountains.

Reprinted from School and society, July. 29, 1922.

NK 0201152 NcU

Knight, Edgar Wallace, 1885-
Education in the United States, by Edgar W. Knight ... Boston, New York [etc.] Ginn and company [°1929]
xi, 588 p. illus. 21½cm.
"References and readings" at end of each chapter.

1. Education—U. S.—Hist. I. Title.

Library of Congress LA205.K6 29-16334

CaBVaU OrSaW WaTC
PPPL MiU OC1 OCU OO ViU MB MH ICJ Nc WaWW WaSp Or
NK 0201153 DLC MtBC IdU OrPR KEmT MB TU PP PPT PU

Knight, Edgar Wallace, 1885-
Education in the United States. New ed. By Edgar W. Knight ... Boston, New York [etc.] Ginn and company [°1934]
xi, 613, xii p. illus. (incl. ports.) 21½cm.
"References and readings" at end of each chapter.

1. Education—U. S.—Hist. I. Title.

Library of Congress LA205.K6 1934 34-16334
——— Copy 2.
Copyright A 72743 [3] 370.973

PWcS PJB PPT PBm PPPL OCU OC1 ODW NN ViU OrU
NK 0201154 DLC WaTC OrMonO ICRL NBuG LU NcRS MB NcD

VOLUME 300

Knight, Edgar Wallace, 1885–
Education in the United States. 2d rev. ed. By Edgar W. Knight ... Boston, New York [etc.] Ginn and company [°1941]
xvi, 669, xii p. illus. 21½cm.
"A note on readings": p. xi–xvi. "References and readings" at end of each chapter.

1. Education—U. S.—Hist. I. Title.
41-25383
Library of Congress LA205.K6 1941
[8] 370.973

PU-Penn PPT PPPL OCl OCU OU ICJ OrP MtU OrPS OrStbM
NK 0201155 DLC OrU WaT Or OrSaW NBuC NcC MB PPLas

Knight, Edgar Wallace, 1885–
Education in the United States. 3d rev. ed. Boston, Ginn [1951]
xvi, 753, xiv p. illus., ports. 21 cm.
Includes bibliographies.

1. Education—U. S.—Hist. I. Title.
LA205.K6 1951 370.973 51-10341

MiU ViU FTaSU NBuC MB NcU NN TxU OrPS OrStbM
NK 0201156 DLC CaBViP WaS Or OrP OrCS WaT KEmT ICU

Knight, Edgar Wallace, 1885–
Educational practice in colonial North Carolina.
(In N.C. booklet. 1916. v.16, no.1.)

NK 0201157 NcU

Knight, Edgar Wallace, 1885–
The evolution of public education in Virginia. I. Colonial theory and practice, by Edgar W. Knight ... [Sewanee? Tenn., 1916]
20 p. 23cm.
"Reprinted from the Sewanee review for January, 1916."

1. Education—Virginia.
24-9075
Library of Congress LA379.K6

NK 0201158 DLC ViU OU NcU

Knight, Edgar Wallace, 1885–
Fifty years of American education, a historical review and critical appraisal. New York, Ronald Press Co. [1952]
484 p. 24 cm.

1. Education—U. S.—Hist. I. Title.
LA209.K48 370.973 52-6198 ‡

TU Wa IdU OrU OrCS CaBVa MtU OrSaW WaS IdPI MtBC OrPR
ODW PPPD PBa NNC PPCCH PIm TxU NN MB OrP Or CaBVaU
NK 0201159 DLC OrStbM OrPS OrLgE KEmT ViU AU MiU WaSp

Knight, Edgar Wallace, 1885
Fifty years progress in education in North Carolina.
(In N.C. Press association Proceedings of the fiftieth [anniversary] session. 1922.)

NK 0201160 NcU

Knight, Edgar Wallace, 1885–
Gaining public school support.
Reprinted from High school journal, 1928, v.11, nos. 6,7,8.

NK 0201161 NcD

Knight, Edgar Wallace, 1885– *ed.*
The Graduate School research and publications, ed. with a foreword by Edgar W. Knight and Agatha Boyd Adams. Chapel Hill, Univ. of North Carolina Press, 1946.
viii, 461 p. 24cm. (The University of North Carolina sesquicentennial publications)

1. North Carolina. University. Graduate School. I. Adams, Agatha Boyd, joint editor. II. Series: North Carolina. University. The University of North Carolina sesquicentennial publications.
LD3943.K57 378.756 47-32214*
Library of Congress

NcGU OFH ViU ICU MH TxU OrU
NK 0201162 DLC CaBVaU OrCS IdU MtBC OrPR MB NcD NcRS

LC6301 .N43 vol. 26, no. 6
Knight, Edgar Wallace, 1885– ed.
Harrisse, Henry, 1829–1910.
Harrisse's Essay on higher education for South Carolina [by] Edgar W. Knight. Chapel Hill, Univ. of North

Knight, Edgar Wallace, 1885–
"In darkness dwells" by Edgar W.Knight, Kenan professor of Education, University of North Carolina. [1947]
4 p. 26.5cm. (Reprinted from School and society, May 31,1947,vol.65,no.1692,p.385-388)
Double column.

1.Education. 2.William L.Clements library.

NK 0201164 MiU-C

Knight, Edgar Wallace, 1885–
The influence of reconstruction on education in the South, by Edgar Wallace Knight ... New York city, Teachers college, Columbia university, 1913.
100 p., 1 l. 24½cm.
Thesis (PH. D.)—Columbia university, 1913.
Vita.
Published also as Contributions to education, Teachers college, Columbia university, no. 60.

1. Education—Southern states. 3. Reconstruction. I. Title.
14-2088
Library of Congress LA209.K52
Columbia Univ. Libr. 379.75

NK 0201165 NNC DLC NcU MiU OCl ODW NcU

Knight, Edgar Wallace, 1885–
The influence of reconstruction on education in the South, by Edgar Wallace Knight ... New York city, Teachers college, Columbia university, 1913.
100 p. 23½ cm. (Teachers college, Columbia university. Contributions to education, no. 60)
Published also as author's thesis (Ph. D.) Columbia university, 1913.

1. Education—Southern states. 2. Reconstruction. I. Title.
LA209.K5 13—25101
——— Copy 2. L5.C8

NNC
NK 0201166 DLC MtU NcD ViU ScU PU PBm ICJ NN MB KEmT

Knight, Edgar Wallace, 1885–
Influence of the Civil War on education in North Carolina.
(In N.C. Literary and historical association. Minutes. 1917.)

NK 0201167 NcU OO

Knight, Edgar Wallace, 1885– joint author.
Hamilton, Joseph Grégoire de Roulhac, 1878–
The making of citizens, by J. G. de Roulhac Hamilton ... and Edgar W. Knight ... Chicago, A. C. McClurg & co., 1922.

200 [illegible]

Knight, Edgar Wallace, 1885–1953.
Manual labor schools in the South, by Edgar W. Knight. [Durham, N. C., The Seeman printery, 1917]
1 p. l., p. [209]–221. 23 cm.
Reprinted from the South Atlantic quarterly, July, 1917.

1. Education—Southern states. I. Title.
E 17—713
U. S. Office of Education Library
for Library of Congress [a65b]

NK 0201169 DHEW NcU

Knight, Edgar Wallace, 1885–
Method and method [by] Edgar W. Knight ... [Chapel Hill, N. C., 1916]
8 p. 23cm.
Caption title.
Reprinted from the North Carolina high school bulletin for July 1916.

1. Teaching. I. Title.
E 16-1132
Library, U. S. Bur. of Education LB1045.K74

NK 0201170 DHEW NcD NcU

Knight, Edgar Wallace, 1885–
Monkey or mud in North Carolina?
Extract from Independent, May 14,1927.

NK 0201171 NcU

Knight, Edgar Wallace,
North Carolina's taste for the sciences.
Extract from Independent, May 28, 1927.

NK 0201172 NcU

Knight, Edgar Wallace, 1885–
Notes on education, by Edgar W. Knight ... Chapel Hill, 1927.
64 p. 19cm.
Notes on schools and teaching in North Carolina.

1. Education—North Carolina. I. Title.
Library of Congress LA340.K65 28-28201

NK 0201173 DLC NcU

Knight, Edgar Wallace, 1885-1953.
Orange County school news
see under title

VOLUME 300

Knight, Edgar Wallace, 1885- Chic.,[c.1923.]
Our constitutions, national and state;..An elementary text in government and citizenship for use in N.C.

NK 0201175 NcU

Knight, Edgar Wallace, 1885-
Our state government; an elementary text in government and citizenship for use in North Carolina, by Edgar W. Knight ... Chicago, Atlanta [etc.] Scott, Foresman and company [°1926]
152 p. incl. front., illus. 19cm.
"Topic references" at end of each chapter.

1. North Carolina—Pol. & govt. 2. U. S.—Pol. & govt.—Handbooks, manuals, etc. I. Title.
Library of Congress JK4125.1926.K6 26-13776

NK 0201176 DLC NcU

Knight, Edgar Wallace, 1885-
The Peabody fund and its early operation in North Carolina. [By] Edgar W. Knight ... [Durham? N. C., 1915]
15 p. 23cm.
Reprinted from the South Atlantic quarterly for April, 1915, vol. XIV, no. 2.

1. Peabody education fund. 2. Education—North Carolina.
E 15-1058
Library, U. S. Bur. of Education LD4481.P22K7

NK 0201177 DHEW NcU OO

---

301 Knight, Edgar Wallace, 1885-1953.
K69p Progress and educational perspective, by Edgar W. Knight ... New York, The Macmillan company, 1942.
xv p., 2 l., 148 p. 19cm. (On cover: The Kappa delta pi lecture series. [No. 14])

1. Progress. 2. Education—U. S. 3. Education—Aims and objectives. I. Title.
Library of Congress HM101.K65 42-9073
[7] FTaSU * 301

PU-Penn PPL OrU FTaSU
NK 0201178 DLC NcU OrP CU AAP KEmT NcD OCl OCU

Knight, Edgar Wallace, 1885-1953.
Public education in the South, by Edgar W. Knight ... Boston, New York [etc.] Ginn and company [°1922]
xii, 482 p. 20 cm.
Bibliography at end of each chapter.

1. Education—Southern states. I. Title.
LA212.K5 22—10623

NcRS Nc WaTC OrP MtU OrPR WaS OrCS
NK 0201179 DLC MiU OCl OCU PP PWcS PU NN NcU ViU NcD

Knight, Edgar Wallace, 1885-
Public school education in North Carolina, by Edgar W. Knight ... Boston, New York [etc.] Houghton Mifflin company [°1916]
viii p., 1 l., 384 p. 19½cm. $1.50
"References" at end of each chapter.

1. Education—North Carolina. I. Title.
Library of Congress LA340.K7 16—21773

ODW ViU OU ICJ NcU
NK 0201180 DLC MtU LU Nc NcRS NcD AAP PU PPT MiU OCU

Knight, Edgar Wallace, 1885- ed.
Readings in American educational history, by Edgar W. Knight and Clifton L. Hall. New York, Appleton-Century-Crofts [1951]
xxi, 799 p. 25 cm.
Bibliographical footnotes.

1. Education—U. S.—Hist. I. Hall, Clifton L., joint ed. II. Title.
LA201.K6 370.973 51-11499

IdU MtU IdPI OrPS OrPR WaTC OrAshS
MsSM KEmT MB MH TxU TU ViU NcU WaSpG OrCS WaS WaT
NK 0201181 DLC Or WaSp OrSaW Wa OrU DAU KyLx IEN WaU

Knight, Edgar Wallace, 1885- ed.
Readings in educational administration. New York, Holt [1953]
584 p. 24 cm.

1. School management and organization. I. Title.
LB2805.K55 371.2 52-13898 ‡

WaS IdU OrLgE CaBVaU IdPI Or OrU OrSaW
OOxM OO OClW OCU MB TxU OrCS ViU CaBVaU OCl OU PSt
NK 0201182 DLC KEmT MoU WaU NBuC TU PPPL PU PP PRosC

Knight, Edgar Wallace, 1885-
Reconstruction and education in South Carolina, by Edgar W. Knight... (n.p., 1919)
28 p. 23 cm.

Reprinted from The South Atlantic Quarterly vol. XVIII, no.4, October 1919, and vol.XIX no.1, January, 1920.

NK 0201183 DHEW

Knight, Edgar Wallace, 1885-
Reconstruction and education in South Carolina, by Edgar W. Knight... [Durham, N. C., 1920.] 28 p. incl. tables. 8°.
Repr.: South Atlantic quarterly. v. 18, no. 4, v. 19, no. 1. Oct., 1919, Jan., 1920.

1. Education.—History, U. S.: South Carolina.
N. Y. P. L. September 29, 1920.

NK 0201184 NN NcU

Knight, Edgar Wallace, 1885-
Reconstruction and education in Virginia. By Edgar W. Knight ... [Durham, N. C., 1916]
36 p. 23½cm.
Reprinted from the South Atlantic quarterly for January and April, 1916, vol. XV, nos. 1 and 2.
Bibliographical foot-notes.

1. Education—Virginia. I. Title.
E 16-483
Library, U. S. Bur. of Education LA379.K76

NK 0201185 DHEW NcU

Knight, Edgar Wallace, 1885-
The religious training of children of other times.

Extracts from Elementary magazine, Feb. Mar. Apr. May, June, July, 1927.

NK 0201186 NcU

Knight, Edgar Wallace, 1885- ed.
Reports on European education, by John Griscom, Victor Cousin [and] Calvin E. Stowe, edited by Edgar W. Knight ... New York [etc.] McGraw-Hill book company, inc., 1930.
5 p. l., 319 p. front. (port.) 19½cm. (Half-title: McGraw-Hill education classics, E. H. Reisner, general editor) $2.25

Continued in next column

Continued from preceding column

1. Education—Europe. 2. Education—Prussia. I. Griscom, John, 1774-1852. A year in Europe. II. Cousin, Victor, 1792-1867. Rapport sur l'état de l'instruction publique en Prusse. III. Stowe, Calvin Ellis, 1802-1886. Report on elementary public instruction in Europe. IV. Title.
30-19150
Library of Congress LA621.7.K5
Copyright A 26176 [8] 370.94

WaTC NcD NIC PU MiU OCU OCl OU MB ICJ PPPL
NK 0201187 DLC IdU-SB PPCCH OrSaW OrStbM WaS MtU

Knight, Edgar Wallace, 1885-
Soft pedagogy in the colleges.

Extract from Outlook, Jan.16, 1929.

NK 0201188 NcU

Knight, Edgar Wallace, 1885-
Some fallacies concerning the history of public education in the South, by Edgar W. Knight ... [Durham? N. C., 1914]
13 p. 23cm.
Reprinted from the South Atlantic quarterly, October, 1914.

1. Education—Southern states—Hist.
E 14-2259
Library, U. S. Bur. of Education LA215.K74

NK 0201189 DHEW NcD OO NcU

Knight, Edgar Wallace, 1885-
Some principles of teaching as applied to the Sunday-school, by Edgar W. Knight ... with an introduction by Professor Franklin N. Parker ... Boston, New York [etc.] The Pilgrim press [°1915]
x, 157 p. 19½cm. $0.75
Contains bibliographies.

I. Title.
Library of Congress 15—24846

NK 0201190 DLC NcD KEmT NjNbS PCC ICJ NcU

KNIGHT, EDGAR WALLACE, 1885-1953.
The Southern association: retrospect and prospect. [n.p., 1947] 15 p. 26cm.
Cover title.
"Reprinted from the Georgia review, volume 1, number 1, spring, 1947."

1. Southern Association of Colleges and secondary schools.

NK 0201191 NN

Knight, Edgar Wallace, 1885-
State control of education.

Reprinted from South Atlantic quarterly, Jan. 1928, v.27, no.1.

NK 0201192 NcU NcD

Knight, Edgar Wallace, 1885-
The story of teacher training.

Reprinted from the High school journal, 1927, v.10, nos. 6,7,8.

NK 0201193 NcU

Knight, Edgar Wallace, 1885-
A study of Hampton institute ...
see under Hampton Institute, Hampton, Va.

VOLUME 300

Knight, Edgar Wallace, 1885-
A study of higher education for Negroes in Alabama
see under Alabama. Dept. of Education.

NK 0201195

Knight, Edgar Wallace, 1885-
Teachers and teaching.

Reprinted from High school journal, Feb. and Mar. 1928, v.6, nos.2 and 3.

NK 0201196 NcU

Knight, Edgar Wallace, 1885-
Training high-school teachers in Denmark.

Reprinted from School and society, May 14 1927, v.25, no.646.

NK 0201197 NcU

Knight, Edgar Wallace, 1885-
Twenty centuries of education, by Edgar W. Knight ... Boston, New York [etc.] Ginn and company [©1940]
xviii, 622 p. incl. front., illus. (incl. ports., facsims.) diagrs. 24cm.
"Suggested readings" at end of each chapter. "A note on readings": p. xiv-xviii.

1. Education—Hist. 2. Education—Aims and objectives. I. Title.
40-33506
Library of Congress LA13.K5
——— Copy 2.
Copyright [25] 370.9

OrStbM
Or WaWW OrCS MtU WaT OrLgE WaSpG OrPS WaSp CaBVaU NcRS NIC PPT PPD PSC OCl OCU OU ODW ViU PU-Penn WaS
NK 0201198 DLC OrSaW IdU OrPR OrP MtBC KEmT KyLxT

AS36 .P56 1951
Knight, Edgar Wallace, 1885-
Universal salvation and universal education [Chapel Hill, University of North Carolina, 1951]
449-458 p. 26cm. (Phi Beta Kappa address Alpha Chapter, North Carolina, 48th, 1951)
Cover title.
"Reprinted from the Educational forum, May, 1952."

1. Education—Addresses, essays, lectures. I. Title. II. Ser.

NK 0201199 ViU

Knight, Edgar Wallace, 1885- *ed.*
What college presidents say, by Edgar W. Knight ... Chapel Hill, The University of North Carolina press, 1940.
xvi p., 1 l., 377 p. 23½cm.
CONTENTS.—The college presidency.—The purposes of higher education.—The weaknesses of higher education.—Organization and administration.—Faculty relations.—Obligations to society.—What do they say? A summary.

1. Education, Higher. 2. Universities and colleges—U. S.—Administration. I. Title.
40-6812
Library of Congress LB2321.K55
——— Copy 2.
Copyright A 136608 [18] 378.04

OrCS CaBVaU
NcGU NcRS KEmT ScU PSC OCl OO OU PU PPD ViU ICJ OrPR
NK 0201200 DLC OrCS WaTC WaWW OrP OrPS MtBC MtU OrU

Knight, Edith G., and others.
A study of factors concerned in the production of clean milk. Part 1 by Edith G. Knight, Kathleen Freear and R. Stenhouse Williams... London: P. S. King & Son, Ltd., 1920. part. chart, tables. 8°.

1. Dairies and dairying. 2. Milk.—Bacteriology. 3. Freear, Kathleen, jt. au. 4. Williams, R. Stenhouse, jt. au.
N. Y. P. L. January 22, 1921.

NK 0201201 NN DNAL OU

Knight, Edward.
A catalogue of the curious and valuable library of the late Edward Knight. Which will be sold by auction by Evans...May 4, and nine following days (Sundays excepted) [London, Printed by W. Bulmer and W. Nicol] 1821.
68 p. 22cm.

Prices in manuscript in margins.
Bound with Kemble, John Philip. A catalogue of the valuable and extensive miscellaneous library choice prints and theatrical portraits...

[London, 1821; Havley, William. A catalogue of the very valuable and extensive library... [London, 1821; and Banks, John Cleaver. A catalogue of the theological, critical and classical library... [London, 1821]

NK 0201203 WU ICN

3781 S78K
Knight, Edward, engineer.
A surtax on undistributed profits as affecting mining corporations ... [Stanford University, Calif.] 1937.

102, 45 numb. l. diagrs.

Thesis (Engineer) - Stanford University, 1937.
Bibliography: numb.leaves 101-102.

1.Excess profits tax. 2.Mining industry and finance.

NK 0201204 CSt

Knight, Edward, musician.
The false one. A ballad . . . [with accompaniment for pianoforte]. The poetry by Thos. H. Bayley [sic], Esq. Composed . . . by Edwd. Knight.
= New York. Firth & Hall. 1831. 3 pp. 33 cm.

L5199 — Double main card.— Knight, .ward. (M1)— Bayly, Thomas Haynes. (M2) — T.r. (1) — Songs. With music. (1)

NK 0201205 MB

Knight, Edward, musician.
SAVOURNEEN Deelish. An Irish air. Arranged by Edwd. Knight. [Boston, etc.18..]

4°. pp.(2), 3. Port. of Kate Hayes. (Kate Hayes..favorite songs.)

NK 0201206 MH

Knight, Edward, *musician.*
Savourneen Deelish; Irish air. New York, E. S. Mesier [18—]
3 p. 34 cm.
Caption title.
For voice and piano.

1. Songs (Medium voice) with piano. 2. Songs, Irish. I. Title.
M1.A13K M 60-2438

NK 0201207 DLC

Knight, Edward, musician.
Savourneen Deelish. An Irish air. [S. or T.] Arranged by Edwd. Knight. New York, Riley [183-?]
3 p. F°.

NK 0201208 MB

W.C.L. M780.88 C697 no.42
Knight, Edward, musician
When morning like a blushing bride; a national rondo sung with unbounded applause by Mrs Knight. The poetry by Mr F. Hill. Adapted, arr. by Edwd Knight. New York, Published by Dubois & Stodart No. 167 Broadway [ca. 1830]
4 p. 33 cm. (In [Collection of piano and vocal music of the 19th century. No. 42])

Caption title.
For voice and piano.
1. Songs (Medium voice) with piano. I. Hill, F. II. Title.

NK 0201209 NcD

Knight, Edward, 1774-1826.
The veteran; or, The farmer's sons: a comic opera, in three acts, as performed at the Theatre Royal, Drury Lane, with the most distinguished applause. By E. Knight, comedian ... London, Printed by W. Glindon, 1822.
vii, [1], 9-68 p. 21cm.
[Broadhurst, J. Plays. v. 2, no. 1]
Without the music (by T. Cooke and others)

I. Cooke, Thomas Simpson, 1782-1848. II. Title.
21-15044
Library of Congress PR1271.B7 vol. 2

NK 0201210 DLC NN ICU InU CtY MiU CSmH

Knight, Edward, 1774-1826.
The veteran; or, The farmer's sons: a comic opera, in three acts, as performed at the Theatre Royal, Drury Lane, with the most distinguished applause. By E. Knight, comedian ... London, Printed by W. Glindon, 1822; [Louisville, Falls City Microcards, 1965?]
vii, [1], 9-68 p. 21cm. (FCM25342-3)
[Broadhurst, J. Plays. v. 2, no. 1]
Without the music (by T. Cooke and others)
Microcard ed. 1 card. 7 1/2 x 12 1/2 cm.
I. Cooke, Thomas Simpson, 1782-1848. II. Title.

NK 0201211 RPB MsU DLC

Beinecke Library Zc90 +823frx
Knight, Edward, Jr., d. 1833.
Canadian airs, collected by Lieutenant Back, R.N. during the late Arctic expedition under Captain Franklin, with symphonies and accompaniments by Edward Knight Junr The words by George Soane, esqr ... London, J. Power [1823]
4 p. l., 39, 8 p. 34 cm.
Title vignette.
Advertising matter: 8 p. at end.
1. Folk-songs, French-Canadian. I. Back, Sir George, 1796-1878. II. Soane, George, 1790-1860. III. Title (1) NUC

NK 0201212 CtY

6A 498
KNIGHT, EDWARD, jr., d.1833.
The lad that I love and Where is my lover? ...Arranged for the piano forte by Mr Edward Knight. New York, Published by Firth & Hall [182-?]
[2]p. 34cm. (Apollo No.21)
Caption title.
Binder's title: Daniel D. Smith.
On p.[2]: Engrd by T.Birch.
Stamped on p.[1]: Bought of Parker & Ditson..
For voice and piano.
1621 ICN 69 69-1859

NK 0201213 ICN

VOLUME 300

8A
1998 KNIGHT, EDWARD, d.1833.
Where is my lover, sung by Miss Stephens with the most unbounded applause. Words by T. Bailey...arranged for the piano forte by Edwd. Knight, Jr. New York, Published by E.S.Mesier. [18--]
[2]p. 34cm.
Caption title.
Lithographed.
For voice and piano.

NK 0201214 ICN

F127 .A2A2
Knight, Edward Arthur, ed.
Adirondack guide; vacationland in picture, story and **history**. 1920–
Lake George, N. Y., Adirondack Resorts Press [etc.]

[Knight, Edward Arthur] *ed.*
The Adirondacks, guide and history; Arthur S. Knight, editor ... Lake George, N. Y., Press of Lake George printing co., °1924.
176 p. illus. 19cm.
Folded map inserted.
Cover-title: Guide of lake George, lake Champlain and the Adirondacks including Green mt. tour ...
First published in 1920 under the editorship of Edward A. Knight.
1. Adirondack mountains—Guide-books. I. Knight, Arthur S., ed. II. Title.
25-3683 Revised
Library of Congress F127.A2K7 1924

NK 0201216 DLC

917.475 K69
Knight, Edward Arthur, ed.
Tourist guide of Lake George, Lake Champlain and the Adirondacks. Lake George, N.Y., Adirondack Guide Co., °1919.
94 p. illus. (part col.) maps (part col.) 18 cm.
The col. illus. and col. map are on folded plate in pocket.
Includes advertising matter.
1. George, Lake. Descr. & trav. Guide-books. 2. Champlain, Lake. Descr. & trav.

NK 0201217 N

Knight, Edward Collings.
French and English period furniture and decorations, tapestries and Oriental rugs...Artistic property...Edward Collings Knight, jr. and Powell...Sold, Jan 28-31, 1931. N. Y. Amer. art ass'n.
232 p.

NK 0201218 PPPM

Knight, Mrs. Edward Collings
see Knight, Marie Louise LeBel.

F869 S22 .35 K58
[Knight, Edward E]
"San Diego - Go!" [San Diego, Calif., Ralston Realty Co., 1904]
[14] p. fold.map. 16cm.
Cover title: California's Jack in the pulpit preaches today. "'San Diego - Go!,' from the pen of 'Crowquill.'"
1. San Diego, Calif. - Descr. I. Ralston Realty Company, San Diego, Calif. II. Title. III. Title: California's Jack in the pulpit preaches today.

NK 0201220 CU-B

Knight, Edward Frederick, 1852–1925.
Albania: a narrative of recent travel. By E. F. Knight ... London, S. Low, Marston, Searle & Rivington, 1880.
viii, 278 p. front., 7 pl. 19½cm.
1. Albania—Descr. & trav.
5—2505
Library of Congress DR701.S5K6

NK 0201221 DLC OU OCU

Knight, Edward Frederick, 1852–1925.
The awakening of Turkey; a history of the Turkish revolution, by E. F. Knight ... London, J. Milne, 1909.
x p., 1 l., 355, [1] p. 8 ports. (incl. front.) 22½cm.
The portraits are accompanied by guard sheets with letterpress.
1. Turkey—Hist.—1878–1909. 2. Turkey—Pol. & govt.—1878–1909. 3. Eastern question (Balkan) I. Title.
9—35780
Library of Congress DR577.K7

PPL PHC DNW NN DN MiU OCl
NK 0201222 DLC WaS OrP UU OrPS NcD CtY PPDrop PPGi

DR 577 K69
Knight, Edward Frederick, 1852– 1925.
The awakening of Turkey; a history of the Turkish revolution, by E. F. Knight ... **Philadelphia, Lippincott, 1909.**
x p., 1 l., 355, [1] p. 8 ports. (incl. front.) 22½cm.
The portraits are accompanied by guard-sheets with letterpress.

NK 0201223 NIC

G530 K6 1890
Knight, Edward Frederick, 1852-1925.
The cruise of the "Alerte", the narrative of a search for treasure on the desert island of Trinidad. London and New York, Longmans, Green, 1890.
328 p. illus. 20cm.
1. Alerte (Yacht) 2. Voyages and travels. 3. Trinidad, Brazil (Island) 4. Treasure-trove. I. Title.

NK 0201224 CoU RP DN PPL PPFr MB

Knight, Edward Frederick, 1852– 1925.
Cruise of the "Alerte:" the narrative of a search for treasure on the desert island of Trinidad. With two maps and illustrations by Arthur Shephard. 2 ed. London 1891. 12°.
2477

NK 0201225 MdBP

Knight, Edward Frederick, 1852-
Cruise of the "Alerte", the narrative of a search for treasure on the desert island of Trinadad... New ed.
328p., illus. Lond., Longmans, Green & co., 1892.

NK 0201226 OCl

G 131 .466
KNIGHT, EDWARD FREDERICK, 1852-1925.
The cruise of the 'Alerte', the narrative of a search for treasure on the desert island of Trinidad. 3d edition. London, Longmans, Green and Co., 1892.
328p. illus., maps. 19cm.
Bookplate of Edward Eagle Brown.

NK 0201227 ICN NcD

Knight, Edward Frederick, 1852-1925.
The cruise of the "Alerte"; narrative of a search for treasure on the desert island of Trinidad. London, 1904.
328 p.

NK 0201228 WaS DCU-IA

KNIGHT, E[dward] F[rederick], 1852-
The cruise of the 'Alerte'; the narrative of a search for treasure on the desert island of Trinidad. 8th impression. London, etc., Longmans, Green, and Co., 1907.
Plates, and maps.
"Illustrations by Arthur Shephard from the author's sketches".

NK 0201229 MH

Knight, E[dward] F[rederick], 1852 - 1925
The cruise of the "Alerte;" the narrative of a search for treasure on the desert island of Trinidad. London: Longmans, Green, and Co., 1907. 2 p.l., 328 p., 2 maps, 18 pl. illus. 12°. (Silver library.)
1. Trinidad (Brazil). 2. Alerte (ship). 3. Title. N. Y. P. L.
CENTRAL CIRCULATION. February 21, 1912.

NK 0201230 NN

Knight, Edward Frederick, 1852–
The cruise of the "Alerte" in search of treasure, by E. F. Knight. London: P. Allan & Co., Ltd., [1919.] 255 p. incl. front. (map.) 16°. (The Nautilus library. no. 6.)
430366A. 1. Yachting—Cruises. 2. Alerte (ship). 3. Trinidad (island), Brazil. 4. Treasure-hunting. N. Y. P. L.
November 8, 1929

NK 0201231 NN

Knight, Edward Frederick, 1852-1925.
The cruise of the "Alerte" in search of treasure. London, P. Allan [1929]
255 p. illus. 18 cm. (The nautilus library, no. 6)
1. Alerte (Yacht) 2. Voyages and travels. 3. Trinidad, Brazil (Island) 4. Treasure-trove. I. Title.

NK 0201232 CaBVaU PP

Knight, Edward Frederick, 1852–1925.
The cruise of the "Alerte" in search of treasure, by E. F. Knight. New York, W. F. Payson [1931]
255 p. incl. front. (map) 17cm. (*Half-title:* The deep sea library)
Printed in Great Britain.
1. Alerte (Yacht) 2. Voyages and travels. 3. Trinidad, Brazil (Island) 4. Treasure-trove. I. Title.
31-28233
Library of Congress G530.K6
[5] 910.4

NK 0201233 DLC NN OOxM

910.4 K69
Knight, Edward Frederick, 1852-1925.
The cruise of the "Alerte." London, R. Hart-Davis, 1952.
xv, 204 p. port., maps. 20 cm. (The Mariners library)
1. Alerte (Yacht) 2. Voyages and travels. 3. Trinidad, Brazil (Island) 4. Treasure-trove. I. Title.

NK 0201234 N NN MB CaBVa LU Wa INS CaBViP

VOLUME 300

918 Knight, Edward Frederick, 1852-1925.
K744c The cruise of the "Falcon"; a voyage to
188- South America in a 30-ton yacht. London [etc.] T. Nelson [188-]
480p. 19cm.

1. South America. Descr. & trav. 2. Falcon (Yacht) 3. Voyages and travels. I. Title.

NK 0201235 KU OCIMN CaBVaU NjR

Knight, Edward Frederick, 1852-1925.
The cruise of the "Falcon." A voyage to South America in a 30-ton yacht.
London. Low, Marston, Searle & Rivington. 1884. 2 v. Illus. Plates. Maps. Sm. 8°.

G1247—"Falcon," yacht. — I.r. — America, South. Geog.—Voyages and travels.

NK 0201236 MB PP PPFr PPL PHC MH DCU-LA DN

Knight, Edward Frederick, 1852–
The cruise of the "Falcon". A voyage to South America in a 30-ton yacht. By E. F. Knight ... 2d ed. London, S. Low, Marston, Searle & Rivington, 1884.
2 v. fronts., illus., plates, 2 fold. maps. 19½cm.

1. Falcon (Yacht) 2. Voyages and travels. 3. South America—Description and travel. I. Title.

A 22-648

Title from Explorers Club, New York. Printed by L. C.

NK 0201237 NNEC CaBVaU

G KNIGHT, EDWARD FREDERICK, 1852-1925.
98 The cruise of the "Falcon" a voyage to South
.464 America in a 30 ton yacht. 5th edition, revised. London, S. Low, Marston & Co. [1886]
366p. illus., port., fold. maps. 19cm.

Bookplate of Edward Eagle Brown.

NK 0201238 ICN MiD

ar V Knight, Edward Frederick, 1852-1925.
1227 The cruise of the "Falcon". A voyage to South America in a 30-ton yacht. 6th and cheaper ed. London, Sampson Low, Marston & Co. [1886]
vi, 366 p. illus. 19cm.

1. Falcon (Yacht) 2. South America--Description and travel.

NK 0201239 NIC

Knight, Edward Frederick, 1852-1925.
The cruise of the "Falcon"; a voyage to South America in a 30-ton yacht, by E. F. Knight ... 4th ed. rev. London, S. Low, Marston, Searle & Rivington, 1887.
vi p., 1 l., 366 p., 1 l. front., illus., plates, fold. maps. 19½cm.

1. South America—Descr. & trav. 2. Falcon (Yacht) I. Title.

F2223.K7 1887 47-34316

NK 0201240 DLC CoU PBL

Knight, Edward Frederick, 1852-1925.
The cruise of the "Falcon"; a voyage to South America in a 30-ton yacht, by E. F. Knight ... 6th ... ed. London, S. Low, Marston & company [1891]
vi p., 1 l., 366 p., front., illus., plates, fold. maps. 19½cm.

1. South America--Descr. & trav. 2. Falcon (Yacht) I. Title.

NK 0201241 AU CU

Knight, E[dward] F[rederick], 1852-1925.
The cruise of the "Falcon"; a voyage to South America in a 30-ton yacht. London: Longmans, Green & Co., 1906. vi(i), 366 p., 2 maps, 13 pl. 12°.

CENTRAL CIRCULATION.

1. South America.—Travel and description. 2. Voyages. 3. Title.
N. Y. P. L. September 8, 1915.

NK 0201242 NN

980d Knight, Edward Frederick, 1852-1925
K69c The cruise of the "Falcon," a
1914 voyage to South America in a 30-ton yacht. London, Nelson [1914]
480p. front., maps. S.

NK 0201243 IaU

Knight, Edward Frederick, 1852-1925.
The cruise of the "Falcon," a voyage to South America in a 30-ton yacht, by E. F. Knight ... New impression. London, New York [etc.] Longmans, Green and co., 1914.
3 p. l., [v]-vi p., 1 l., 366 p. front., illus., 7 pl., 2 maps. 19cm. (The silver library)
First edition published 1883.

1. South America—Descr. & trav. I. Title. II. Title: "Falcon."

22—4184

Library of Congress F2223.K7

NK 0201244 DLC Or

Knight, Edward Frederick, 1852–
[Description of the Victoria Falls.] Illus. Plates. Maps.
(In Wright, E. H. Smith. Railways in Rhodesia. Pp. 35-47. [London. 190-?])
Reprinted from his South Africa after the war [3056.327].

K9019 — Victoria Falls.

NK 0201245 MB

Knight, Edward Frederick, 1852-1925.
The "Falcon" on the Baltic; a coasting voyage from Hammersmith to Copenhagen in a three-ton yacht. With map and illustrations by Arthur Shephard. London, W.H. Allen & co., 1889.

NK 0201246 MH RP PPL CaBVaU DN

Knight, Edward Frederick, 1852-1925.
The Falcon on the Baltic; a coasting voyage from Hammersmith to Copenhagen in a three-ton yacht. London, W. H. Allen, 1892.
308, [1] p. illus., fold. map. 20cm.

First published 1889. Second edition [i. e. printing] 1892.

1. Denmark--Descr. & trav. 2. Netherlands--Descr. & trav. 3. Falcon II (yacht) I. Title

NK 0201247 AU PP

Knight, Edward Frederick, 1852-1925.
"Falcon" on the Baltic; a coasting voyage from Hammersmith to Copenhagen in a three-ton yacht.
308p. il. map. Lond., Longmans, 1896.

NK 0201248 OCl

D Knight, Edward Frederick, 1852-1925.
965 The Falcon on the Baltic; a coasting
.K57 voyage from Hammersmith to Copenhagen
1902 in a three-ton yacht. London, New York, Longmans, Green, & Co., 1902.
308 p. maps. 19 cm. (The Silver library)

1. Denmark--Descr. & trav.
2. Netherlands--Descr. & trav.
3. Falcon II (Yacht) I. Title

NK 0201249 OKentU

Knight, Edward Frederick, 1852–1925.
The Falcon on the Baltic; a coasting voyage from Hammersmith to Copenhagen in a three-ton yacht. With an introd. by Arthur Ransome. London, R. Hart-Davis, 1951.
300 p. maps. 19 cm. (The Mariners library, 15)

1. Denmark—Descr. & trav. 2. Netherlands—Descr. & trav. 3. Falcon II (Yacht) I. Title. (Series)

D965.K57 1951 914.89 52-1798

NK 0201250 DLC CaBVa CaBViP

Knight, Edward Frederick, 1852-1925.
Bell, Ernest, 1851– ed.
Handbook of athletic sports. Edited by Ernest Bell ... London, G. Bell & sons, 1890–

Knight, Edward Frederick, 1852–
The Harwich naval forces; their part in the great war, by E. F. Knight ... London, New York [etc.] Hodder and Stoughton, 1919.
x, 236 p. 19cm.

1. European war, 1914– —Naval operations. 2. Gt. Brit.—Navy. I. Title.

Library of Congress D581.K75 21-13309

NK 0201252 DLC AU DN NN

Knight, Edward Frederick, 1852–
Letters from the Sudan, by the special correspondent of "The Times" (E. F. Knight) Reprinted from "The Times" of April to October, 1896 ... London, Macmillan and co., limited; New York, The Macmillan company, 1897.
3 p. l., 325, [1] p. front., plates, maps (part fold.) 22cm.

1. Sudan—Descr. & trav. 2. Egypt—Hist.—British occupation, 1882–

1—18697

Library of Congress DT108.5.K7

NcD IEN
NK 0201253 DLC MB CaOTP CU PPL PP PPA DNW MBU WU

Knight, Edward Frederick, 1852–
Madagascar in war time; the 'Times' special correspondent's experiences among the Hovas during the French invasion of 1895, by E. F. Knight ... London, New York, and Bombay, Longmans, Green, and co., 1896.
x p., 1 l., 336 p. front., illus., plates, map. 22½cm.

1. Madagascar. 2. French in Madagascar. I. Title.

4—17774/4

Library of Congress DT469.M34K7
969 [a20g3] F738

OCl DN MH MB
NK 0201254 DLC IEN NSyU CU RPB NcD PP PPL PPA MiU

VOLUME 300

Knight, Edward Frederick, 1852–1925.
Over-sea Britain: a descriptive record of the geography, the historical, ethnological, and political development, and the economic resources of the empire by E. F. Knight ... the nearer empire, the Mediterranean, British Africa, and British America ... London, John Murray, 1907.
ix p., 2 l., [3]–324 p. 9 col. maps (part fold.) 22½cm.

1. Gt. Brit.—Colonies. 2. Africa. 3. British America. I. Title.
War 8–30
Library, U. S. Army War College
Library of Congress JV1027.K6

OClW ICJ
NK 0201255 DNW OrPR NcU MH NN MB CaNSWA CtY OCl

Knight, Edward Frederick, 1852-

Wright, E H Smith
Railways in Rhodesia. A few notes on their construction and on the country through which they pass. By E. H. Smith Wright ... With a description of the Victoria falls, by E. F. Knight. [London, Waterlow & sons ltd., printers, 1904]

Knight, Edward Frederick, 1852–
Reminiscences; the wanderings of a yachtsman and war correspondent, by E. F. Knight ... London, Hutchinson & co., 1923.
320 p. front. (port.) 23cm.

1. Voyages and travels. I. Title.
23–12375
Library of Congress D400.K6A3

NK 0201257 DLC CaBVaU NN

Knight, Edward Frederick, 1852–1925.
Rhodesia of today; a description of the present condition and the prospects of Matabeleland & Mashonaland, by E. F. Knight ... London and New York, Longmans, Green and co., 1895.
vii, [1], 151 p. fold. map. 19½cm.
Half-title: Matabeleland & Mashonaland.

1. Rhodesia. I. Title.
5—18375
Library of Congress DT958.K6

WaSpG PPL
NK 0201258 DLC DI-GS MBU NBuU CU NcD DAU NcU DNW

Knight, Edward Frederick, 1852-1925.
Rhodesia: some personal recollections. Illus. Plate.
(In Creswicke. South Africa and its future. Pp. 55-71. London, 1903.)

NK 0201259 MB

KNIGHT, Edward Frederick, 1852-1925.
Sailing. (3), 156 pp. Illus.
(*In* Handbook of athletic sports. Vol. 2. London, 1890

NK 0201260 MB

Knight, Edward Frederick, 1852-
Sailing... Lond., Geo. Bell & sons, 1909.
156p. illus., diagrs.

NK 0201261 OCl

Knight, Edward Frederick, 1852–1925.
Sailing, by E. F. Knight; revised and brought up to date by J. Scott Hughes. London, G. Bell & sons, ltd., 1938.
xi, 156 p. illus., diagrs. 19cm.

1. Sailing. 2. Yachts and yachting. I. Hughes, John Scott, 1893–
39–30060
Library of Congress GV811.K68 1938
[2] 797.124

NK 0201262 DLC CaBVa AU NN

Knight, Edward Frederick, 1852–1925.
Sailing, by E. F. Knight; revised and brought up to date by J. Scott Hughes. New York, E. P. Dutton & co., inc., 1939.
xi, 156 p. illus., diagrs. 19½cm.
A new edition of the author's Small-boat sailing.
"First edition."

1. Sailing. 2. Yachts and yachting. I. Hughes, John Scott, 1893–
39–10647
Library of Congress GV811.K69 1939
——— Copy 2.
Copyright A 127907 [10] 797.1

NK 0201263 DLC WaT NN NcRS OrP WaS Or OCl OEac OLak

Knight, Edward Frederick, 1852-1925.
Small-boat sailing. An explanation of the management of small yachts, half-decked and open sailing-boats of various rigs; sailing on sea and on river; cruising, etc. With drawings by H. Warington Smyth. xi,297 p. il. 1 pl. O. London: J. Murray, 1901.

NK 0201264 ICJ WaS FMU PPL MB

Knight, Edward Frederick, 1852–
Small-boat sailing; an explanation of the management of small yachts, half-decked and open sailing-boats of various rigs; sailing on sea and on river; cruising, etc. By E. F. Knight ... With drawings by H. Warington Smyth. New York, E. P. Dutton & co., 1902.
xi, 297 p. front., illus., pl. 20½cm.

1. Sailing. I. Title.
4—11767
Library of Congress GV811.K69
797 [a24g1] Vcs

NK 0201265 DLC OCl OCU

Knight, E[dward] F[rederick], 1852-1925.
Small-boat sailing; an explanation of the management of small yachts, half-decked and open sailing-boats of various rigs; sailing on sea and on river; cruising, etc.. with drawings by H. Warington Smyth. London: John Murray, 1905. xi, 297 p., 2 pl. (1 folded). illus. 8°.

CENTRAL CIRCULATION.
1. Sailing. 2. Title.
N. Y. P. L. March 30, 1911.

NK 0201266 NN CaBVa

Knight, E[dward] F[rederick], 1852-1925.
Small-boat sailing; an explanation of the management of small yachts, half-decked and open sailing-boats of various rigs; sailing on sea and on river; cruising, etc.; with drawings by H. Warington Smyth. New York: E. P. Dutton & Co., 1905. 297 p. diagr., illus., fold. pl. 12°.

CENTRAL CIRCULATION.
1. Sailing. 2. Title.
N. Y. P. L. May 25, 1920.

NK 0201267 NN

Knight, Edward Frederick, 1852-1925
Small-boat sailing... N.Y., Dutton, 1920.
305 p.

NK 0201268 PP

Knight, Edward Frederick, 1852–1925.
Small-boat sailing; an explanation of the management of small yachts, half-decked and open sailing-boats of various rigs; sailing on sea and on river; cruising, etc. By E. F. Knight ... with drawings by H. Warington Smyth. New York, E. P. Dutton & company, 1923.
xi, 305 p. front., illus., fold. pl. 19½cm.
Printed in Great Britain.
"First edition, May 1901. Reprinted ... May 1923."

1. Sailing. I. Title.
26—6359
Library of Congress GV811.K69 1923

NK 0201269 DLC OrP PP OLak PPGi AU FMU

Knight, E[dward] F[rederic], 1852-1925.
Small-boat sailing; an explanation of the management of small yachts, half-decked and open sailing-boats of various rigs; sailing on sea and on river; cruising, etc.; with drawings by H. Warington Smyth. London: John Murray[, 1926]. 305 p. diagr. (1 fold.), illus. 12°.

1. Sailing. 2. Title.
N. Y. P. L. April 11, 1927

NK 0201270 NN

Knight, E[dward] F[rederick], 1852-1925.
Small-boat sailing; an explanation of the management of small yachts, half-decked and open sailing-boats of various rigs; sailing on sea and on river; cruising, etc.; with drawings by H. Warington Smyth. New York: E. P. Dutton & Co.[, 1926.] 305 p. diagr., front., illus., fold. pl. 12°.

1. Sailing. 2. Title.
N. Y. P. L. March 15, 1928

NK 0201271 NN CLU NcC MiU

Knight, Edward Frederick, 1852–
South Africa after the war; a narrative of recent travel, by E. F. Knight ... London, New York and Bombay, Longmans, Green, and co., 1903.
xi p., 1 l., 356 p. front., plates, map. 23cm.
"Practically a reproduction of ... articles, which appeared from time to time in the Morning post [London], the alterations being few."—Pref.

1. Africa, South—Descr. & trav. 2. Africa, South—Econ. condit.
4—32186
Library of Congress DT757.K7

NK 0201272 DLC NcD NIC CU IEN DNW PPL PP MB

Knight, Edward Frederick, 1852–
... Turkey; the awakening of Turkey; the Turkish revolution of 1908, by E. F. Knight ... Boston and Tokyo, J. B. Millet company [1910]
x, 324 p. incl. col. front. plates. 25cm. (Oriental series, vol. XXI)
$2.50
Title within colored ornamental border.
Published in 1909, by J. Milne, London, under title: The awakening of Turkey.

1. Turkey — Hist. — 1878–1909. 2. Turkey — Pol. & govt. — 1878–1909. 3. Eastern question (Balkan) I. Title.
11—7749
Library of Congress DR577.K72

NK 0201273 DLC MtHi OrU Or PPT ICJ MB Mi OCU

Knight, Edward Frederick, 1852–1925.
... Turkey; the awakening of Turkey; the Turkish revolution of 1908, by E. F. Knight ... Boston and Tokyo, J. B. Millet company [1920]
x, 324 p. incl. col. front. plates. 25cm. (Oriental series, vol. XXI)
Title within colored ornamental border.
Published in 1909, by J. Milne, London, under title: The awakening of Turkey.
Label pasted on verso of t.-p.: Oriental series, 1920.

NK 0201274 ViU

VOLUME 300

Knight, Edward Frederick, 1852–
The Union-Castle and the war, 1914–1919, by E. F. Knight; illustrated by E. G. Fuller. London: The Union-Castle Mail Steamship Co. Ltd., 1920. 1 p.l., 5-63(1) p., 8 l. facsim., col'd front., illus. 4°.
Reprinted in part from the Morning Post.
1. Shipping, Gt. Br., 1914-19. 2. European war, 1914- —Naval operations. 3. Title.
N. Y. P. L. November 9, 1920.

NK 0201275 NN CtY NNC

Knight, Edward Frederick, 1852–1925.
Where three empires meet; a narrative of recent travel in Kashmir, western Tibet, Gilgit, and the adjoining countries, by E. F. Knight ... With a map and 54 illustrations. London, and New York, Longmans, Green, and co., 1893.
xvi, 495 p. front., illus., plates, fold. map. 22½cm.
1. Kashmir—Descr. & trav. 2. Gilgit. 3. Tibet—Descr. & trav.
I. Title.
DS485.K2K7 1893 47-36119

NK 0201276 DLC OC1 ICN CtY MB GU MiEM OU PPFr PPL DN ICJ

DS 485 .K2K7 Knight, Edward Frederick, 1852-1925.
Where three empires meet. A narrative of recent travel in Kashmir, western Tibet, Gilgit, and the adjoining countries, by E. F. Knight... 2d ed. London [etc.] Longmans, Green and Co., 1893.
xv, 528 p. incl. front., illus., plates. fold. map. 19 cm.

NK 0201277 NBuU CU

Knight, E[dward] F[rederick], 1852 - 1925.
Where three empires meet. A narrative of recent travel in Kashmir, western Tibet, Gilgit, and the adjoining countries. London: Longmans, Green, and Co., 1893. 2 p.l., (i)viii-xv, 528 p., 1 map, 1 pl. illus. 3. ed. 12°.
1. Asia (Central).—Description, 1893.
N. Y. P. L. March 24, 1914.

NK 0201278 NN PP MH

915.4 K744 **Knight, Edward Frederick, 1852-1925.**
Where three empires meet. A narrative of recent travel in Kashmir, western Tibet, Gilgit, and the adjoining countries. New ed. London, Longmans, Green, 1894.
xv,528p. illus.,fold.map. 19cm.
1. Kashmir. Desc. & trav. 2. Gilgit. 3. Tibet. Descr. & trav. I. Title.

NK 0201279 OrU MH MH-A MSaE

Knight, E[dward] F[rederick], 1852 - 1925.
Where three empires meet; a narrative of recent travel in Kashmir, western Tibet, Gilgit, and the adjoining countries. London: Longmans, Green, and Co., 1895. 2 p.l., (i)viii-xv, 528 p., 1 map, 1 pl. illus. New ed. 12°.
1. Kashmir.—Description, etc., 189[5] 2. Tibet.—Description, etc., 1893. 3. Gilgit.—Description, etc., 1893.
N. Y. P. L. April 15, 1914.

NK 0201280 NN CaBVaU MoU CU HU IU

Knight, Edward Frederick, 1852–1925.
Where three empires meet. A narrative of recent travel in Kashmir, western Tibet, Gilgit, and the adjoining countries, by E. F. Knight ... New ed. London [etc.] Longmans, Green and co., 1897.
xv, 528 p. incl. front., illus., plates. fold. map. 19 cm.
1. Kashmir—Descr. & trav. 2. Gilgit. 3. Tibet—Descr. & trav. I. Title.
DS485.K2K7 4—16703

NK 0201281 DLC WaE IdB NcD TNJ DNW MiU NcU WaS

DS 485 K2K7 1900 Knight, Edward Frederick, 1852-1925.
Where three empires meet. A narrative of recent travel in Kashmir, Western Tibet, Gilgit, and the adjoining countries, by E. F. Knight. London, New York, Longmans, Green, 1900.
xv,528p.incl.front.,illus.,plates.fold. map. 19cm.
1.Kashmir - Descr. & trav. 2.Gilgit. 3. Tibet - Descr. & trav. I.Title. //LC

NK 0201282 CLSU

Knight, Edward Frederick, 1852–1925.
With the royal tour; a narrative of the recent tour of the Duke and Duchess of Cornwall and York through Greater Britain, including His Royal Highness's speech delivered at the Guildhall, on December 5, 1901, by E. F. Knight ... With 16 illustrations and a map. London, New York [etc.] Longmans, Green, and co., 1902.
2 p. l., [vii]-xii, 410 p. front., plates, fold. map. 20cm.
Published under the auspices of the Victoria league.
Reprint of letters published in the [London] Morning post.
1. Gt. Brit.—Colonies. 2. George V, king of Great Britain, 1865– 3. Mary, queen consort of George V, 1867– 4. Voyages and travels.
2-21164
Library of Congress DA11.K7

NK 0201283 DLC CaNSWA PPL PP OC1W MB

Knight, Edward Henry, 1824–1883.
Agricultural implements. [By] Edward H. Knight, LL. D.
(*In* U. S. Commission to the Paris exposition, 1878. Reports. Washington, 1880 24½cm. v. 5, p. 1-256)
U. S. 46th Cong., 3d sess. House. Ex. doc. 42, pt. 5.
Library of Congress T802.E1U4
——— ———
(*In* U. S. Commission to the Paris exposition, 1878. Reports. Washington, 1880. 24½cm. v. 5, p. 1-256)
1. Agricultural machinery—Exhibitions. 2. Agricultural tools—Exhibitions.
5-31746-7†
Library of Congress T802.E1U5

NK 0201284 DLC CU MiU OO OCf

620.3 K74al Knight, Edward Henry, 1824-1883.
Knight's American mechanical dictionary: being a description of tools, instruments, machines, processes, and engineering; history of inventions; general technological vocabulary; and digest of mechanical appliances in science and the arts. New York, J. B. Ford & Co. [c1872-c1876]
3 v. illus.

NK 0201285 WaU PP PU PRosC

Knight, Edward Henry, 1824–1883.
Knight's American mechanical dictionary: being a description of tools, instruments, machines, processes, and engineering; history of inventions; general technological vocabulary; and digest of mechanical appliances in science and the arts. By Edward H. Knight ... Illustrated with upwards of five thousand engravings ... New York, J. B. Ford and company, 1874–76.
3 v. fronts., illus., plates, diagrs. 27½cm.
Vol. 3 published by Hurd and Houghton, New York.
Paged continuously.
1. Industrial arts—Dictionaries. 2. Mechanical engineering—Dictionaries. 3. Technology—Dictionaries. 4. Inventions.
4-10577/5
Library of Congress T9.K689
——— Copy 2.
T-5

NK 0201286 DLC PPF NNU DPU NN OC1 ICJ

Knight, Edward Henry, 1824 - 1883.
American mechanical dictionary, a description of tools, instruments, machines processes and engineering...and digest of mechanical appliances in science and the arts. N.Y., Ford, 1874-77, c1872.
3 v.

NK 0201287 PU

Knight, Edward Henry, 1824–1883.
Knight's American mechanical dictionary; being a description of tools, instruments, machines, processes, and engineering; history of inventions; general technological vocabulary; and digest of mechanical appliances in science and the arts.
New York [etc.]. Ford & Co. [etc.]. 1874–84. 3 v. Illus. Plates. Plans. 26 cm.
Contents. — 1. A–En. 2. Ena–Pan. 3. Per–Zym.
M910 — T.r. — Mechanics. Applied. Dict. — Technology. Dict.

NK 0201288 MB

T qK69a 1876 **KNIGHT, Edward Henry, 1824-1883**
American mechanical dictionary. A description of tools, instruments, machines, processes, and engineering; history of inventions; general technological vocabulary. New York, Hurd and Houghton, 1876.
3 v. illus.
1. Industrial arts - Dict. 2. Technology - Dict. Title

NK 0201289 DNLM MWA NjP Nh PPL OC1W PPFr MnHi NN

Knight, Edward Henry, 1824–1883.
Knight's American mechanical dictionary. A description of tools, instruments, machines, processes, and engineering; history of inventions; general technological vocabulary; and digest of mechanical appliances in science and the arts. By Edward H. Knight ... New York, Hurd and Houghton; Cambridge, The Riverside press, 1876–77.
3 v. fronts., illus., plates, diagrs. 23cm.
Paged continuously.
1. Industrial arts — Dictionaries. 2. Machinery. 3. Technology — Dictionaries. 4. Industries.
6–2854
Library of Congress T9.K69 1877

NK 0201290 DLC WaSp WaS MnHi OO

T9 .K692 **Knight, Edward Henry, 1824–1883.**
Knight's American mechanical dictionary. A description of tools, instruments, machines, processes, and engineering; history of inventions; general technological vocabulary; and digest of mechanical appliances in science and the arts. By Edward H. Knight ... Illustrated with upyards of seven thousand engravings ... New York, Hurd and Houghton; Cambridge [Mass.] The Riverside press, 1877.
3 v. fronts. (v. 1, double) illus., plates (part fold.) diagrs. 27cm.
Paged continuously.
Contents.—I. A to Fell.—II. Felt to Per.—III. Per to Z.
1. Industrial arts—Dictionaries. 2. Mechanical engineering—Dictionaries. 3. Technology—Dictionaries. 4. Inventions.
22—25926
Library of Congress
Copyright 1876: 13171-

NK 0201291 DLC MiDW PU OC1 OC OU I MH OCU

*4010C .168 1880 Knight, Edward Henry, 1824-1883.
American mechanical dictionary; a description of tools, instruments, machines, processes, and engineering; history of inventions; general technological vocabulary; and digest of mechanical appliances in science and the arts. Boston, Houghton, Mifflin [188-?]
3 v. illus., plates, diagrs. 27cm.
Paged continuously.
1. Industrial arts—Dictionaries. 2. Mechanical engineering—Dictionaries. 3. Technology—Dictionaries. 4. Inventions.

NK 0201292 MB

VOLUME 300

Knight, Edward Henry, 1824-1883.
Knight's American mechanical dictionary. A description of tools, instruments, machines, processes, and engineering; history of inventions; general technological vocabulary; and digest of mechanical appliances in science and the arts. By Edward H. Knight ... Boston, Houghton, Osgood and co., 1880-81 [1872-76]
3 v. fronts. (1 fold.) illus., plates (part fold.) 27 cm.
Vol. 3 published by Houghton, Mifflin and co., New York.

Paged continuously.
1. Industrial arts—Dictionaries. 2. Mechanical engineering—Dictionaries.

NK 0201294 CU DN IU PU ViU

Knight, Edward Henry, 1824–1883.
Knight's American mechanical dictionary. A description of tools, instruments, machines, processes, and engineering; history of inventions; general technological vocabulary; and digest of mechanical appliances in science and the arts. By Edward H. Knight ... Boston, Houghton, Mifflin and company, 1882.
3 v. fronts. (1 fold.) illus., plates (part fold.) 27cm.
Paged continuously.
1. Industrial arts—Dictionaries. 2. Mechanical engineering—Dictionaries.
Library of Congress T9.K69 1882 14—12010

NK 0201295 DLC OrP GAT MB MWA DN PPA

Knight, Edward Henry
Knight's American mechanical dictionary. A description of tools, instruments, machines, processes, and engineering; history of inventions; general technological vocabulary; and digest of mechanical appliances in science and the arts. By Edward H. Knight... Boston, Houghton Mifflin and company; Cambridge, The Riverside press, 1884.
3v. fronts., illus.,plates, diagrs.
Paged continu ously.

NK 0201296 MiHM KEmT CU ICRL MB PPB MiU OCl OClW

Knight, Edward Henry, 1824–1883.
Clocks and watches. [By] Edward H. Knight, LL. D.
(*In* **U. S. Commission to the Paris exposition, 1878. Reports. Washington, 1880. 24½cm. v. 4, p. 403-415)**
U. S. 46th Cong., 3d sess. House. Ex. doc. 42, pt. 4.
Library of Congress T802.E1U4
——— ———
(*In* **U. S. Commission to the Paris exposition, 1878. Reports. Washington, 1880. 24½cm. v. 4, p. 403-415)**
1. Clocks and watches—Exhibitions.
Library of Congress T802.E1U5 5-31750-1†

NK 0201297 DLC CU MdBP

Knight, Edward Henry. 1824-1883.
The mariners' cautionary signal.
(Excerpt. Harpers' mo., Dec. 1878, p. 95-98.)
41445

NK 0201298 DAS

Knight, Edward Henry, 1824-1883.
Mechanical progress in the U. S.
(First century of the Republic, 1876)

NK 0201299 MnHi

KNIGHT, EDWARD HENRY, 1824-1883.
KNIGHT'S NEW MECHANICAL DICTIONARY: A DESCRIPTION OF TOOLS, INSTRUMENTS, MACHINES, PROCESSES, AND ENGINEERING. WITH INDEXICAL REFERENCES TO TECHNICAL JOURNALS (1876-1880) BOSTON, HOUGHTON MIFFLIN, 1882. 960 P. ILLUS.
1. INDUSTRIAL ARTS--DICTIONARIES.
2. TECHNOLOGY--DICTIONARIES.
3. MACHINERY.
4. INVENTIONS.
TITLE: NEW MECHANICAL DICTIONARY.
TITLE.

NK 0201300 GAT PPULC

---

*4010C
.168
1883
Knight Edward Henry, 1824-1883.
New mechanical dictionary; a description of tools, instruments, machines, processes, and engineering. With indexical references to technical journals (1876-1880.) Boston, Houghton, Mifflin [1883]
viii, 960 p. illus., plates, diagrs. 27cm.
The English ed. has title: The practical dictionary of mechanics.
1. Industrial arts—Dictionaries. 2. Technology—Dictionaries. 3. Machinery. 4. Inventions.

NK 0201301 MB PP

Knight, Edward Henry, 1824–1883.
Knight's new mechanical dictionary. A description of tools, instruments, machines, processes, and engineering. With indexical references to technical journals (1876–1880.) By Edward H. Knight ... Illustrated with more than three thousand engravings ... Boston, New York, Houghton, Mifflin and company, 1884.
viii p., 2 l., 960 p. illus., plates, diagrs. 27½cm.
Issued in four parts, 1882–84.
The English edition has title: The practical dictionary of mechanics.
1. Industrial arts—Dictionaries. 2. Technology—Dictionaries. 3. Machinery. 4. Inventions.
Library of Congress T9.K695 3—23275
603 [a23s27c2] T-5

MH NN NjP Nh DI-GS
NK 0201302 DLC WaSp OrP DNW PU-El PPD PHC PPA MB

K /
v.1-4
Knight, Edward Henry, 1824-1883.
The practical dictionary of mechanics: being a description of tools, instruments, machines, processes and engineering; history of inventions; general technological vocabulary; and digest of mechanical appliances in science and the arts. London, Cassell [n.d.]
4 v. illus., diagrs. 26 cm.
1. Industrial arts - Dictionaries. 2. Technology - Dictionaries. 3. Machinery. 4. Inventions. jk

NK 0201303 CaBVaU ICRL DN

Knight, Edward Henry, 1824-1883.
The practical dictionary of mechanics: being a description of tools, instruments, machines, processes, and engineering; history of inventions; general technological vocabulary; and digest of mechanical appliances in science and the arts. London, Cassell Petter & Galpin; Cambridge [Mass.] H.O. Houghton [187-?]
3 v. (2831 p.) illus.,plates,diagrs. 26 cm

NK 0201304 OkU MiU

Knight, Edward Henry, 1824–1883.
The practical dictionary of mechanics: being a description of tools, instruments, machines, processes and engineering; history of inventions; general technological vocabulary; and digest of mechanical appliances in science and the arts. By Edward H. Knight ... Supplementary volume (With index references to technical journals 1876–1880). Illustrated with upwards of five thousand engravings ... London, Cassell & company, limited; Boston, Houghton, Mifflin & co. [1884]
viii, 960 p. front., illus., plates, diagrs. 26½cm.
The American edition has title: Knight's new mechanical dictionary.
1. Industrial arts—Dictionaries. 2. Technology—Dictionaries. 3. Machinery. 4. Inventions.
Library of Congress T9.K7 3-23276

NK 0201305 DLC MiU

T802
.E1U5
Knight, Edward Henry, 1824-1883.
U. S. *Commission to the Paris exposition,* 1878.
... Reports of the United States commissioners to the Paris universal exposition, 1878. Published under direction of the secretary of state by authority of Congress ... Washington, Govt. print. off., 1880.

Knight, Edward Henry, 1824–1883.
A study of the savage weapons at the Centennial exhibition, Philadelphia, 1876. By Edward H. Knight ...
(*In* **Smithsonian institution. Annual report. 1879. Washington, 1880. 23½cm. p. 213–297. illus.)**
1. Arms and armor.
Library, Smithsonian Institution S 15-489
Library of Congress [Q11.S66 1879]

NK 0201307 DSI MiU OClMN OU OCU

BS
2619
.K56x
Knight, Edward Hooker
A guide in the study of the apostolic age. Hartford, Hartford Seminary Foundation, 1936.
viii, 83 p. 23 cm.
Based on New Testament, revised version.
Bibliography: pp. 3-4.

1. Bible. N. T. Acts and Epistles--Study and teaching. I. Title

NK 0201308 OKentU IaU

---

*
PN6111
.F37
1731-
1916
v.62,
no.5
Knight, Edward P
A chip of the old block; or, The village festival: a musical farce, in two acts: as performed with the greatest applause at the Theatre Royal, Haymarket, August 22d, 1815. The music composed by Whitaker. London: Printed for C. Chapple, 1815.
41 p. 20cm. (Fawcett's collection of 18th and 19th century English drama, v. 62, no. 5)
Without the music (by Whitaker).
I. Whitaker, John. 1776-1847. II. Title.

NK 0201309 ViU MH NN CSmH CtY InU MiU InU ICU

.E3
1943
.K6
Knight, Edward R 1917-
A case-study evaluation of the Oxford method of individualized education... New York, 1943.
2v. (8p.l.,ii-iii,449 typewritten leaves) 29cm.
Thesis (Ph.D.) - New York university, School of education, 1943.
Bibliography: v.2, p.446-449.
Film
T4
- Also have microfilm copy.

NK 0201310 NNU

Knight, Edward R 1917 -
A case-study evaluation of the Oxford method of individualized education [by] Edward R. Knight. [New York] °1943.
Film copy of type-written manuscript. Made in 1943 by University microfilms (Publication no. 609) Positive.
Collation of the original: iii, 449 numb. l.
Thesis (PH. D.)—New York university, 1943.
Abstracted in Microfilm abstracts, v. 5 (1943) no. 2, p. 58.
Bibliography: leaves 446–449.
1. Oxford academy, Pleasantville, N. J. 2. Education—Experimental methods. 3. Children, Abnormal and backward. I. Title: Oxford method of individualized education.
A 44-655
Michigan. Univ. Library for Library of Congress Film AC-1 no. 609
[3]†

NK 0201311 MiU DLC

Knight, Edward W. de
see De Knight, Edward W.

VOLUME 300

Knight, Eleanor (Warner)
see Knight, Elleanor (Warner), 1799-

Knight, Elizabeth Gertude
see
Britton, Mrs. Elizabeth Gertrude (Knight) 1858-

Knight, Elisabeth H.
Album. Newburyport, 1830-
In- A collection of old autograph Albums and scrap-books. Various places and dates 1827-
v. [49]

NK 0201315 RPB

Knight, Ella Bartlett.
A bibliography of geographical literature for elementary grades and junior high school, by Ella B. Knight... Worcester, Dept. of geography, Clark univ., 1926. 48 p. 23cm.

1. Geography—Bibl.
N. Y. P. L. December 28, 1943

NK 0201316 NN Or CU OCl OClh OO

Knight, Ella Bartlett.
A bibliography of geographical literature for elementary grades and junior high school, by Ella B. Knight ... 2d rev. ed. Worcester, Mass., Department of geography, Clark university, 1928.
59 p. 23cm.
Annotated.

1. Geography—Bibl.
35-23862
Library of Congress Z6001.K71 016.91

NK 0201317 DLC PSt IU

Knight, Ella Cornelia,
See:
Knight, Cornelia, 1757-1837.

Knight, Ella D comp.
Directory of Delaware county, Ohio. This list contains the names and addresses of one thousand resident tax payers ... Compiled by Ella D. Knight ... ⌊Delaware? O.⌋ F. B. Volk, printer ⌊°1905⌋
⌊13⌋ p. 20 x 15cm.

1. Delaware co., O.—Direct.
CA 33-740 Unrev'd
Library of Congress F497.D3A18

NK 0201319 DLC

3A
972 KNIGHT, ELLEANOR (Warner), 1799-
A narrative of the Christian experience, life and adventures, trials and labours of Elleanor Knight, written by herself. To which is added a few remarks and verses. Providence, 1839.
iv, ⌊5⌋-126p. 14cm.

NK 0201320 ICN RPB NNU-W

Knight, Ellis Cornelia
see
Knight, Cornelia, 1757-1837.

Knight, Elmer W.,1894- joint author.

Scofield, Carl Schurz, 1875-
... An apparatus for adding gypsum to irrigation water. By C. S. Scofield ... and Elmer W. Knight ... Washington ⌊U. S. Govt. print. off.⌋ 1928.

Knight, Elmer W., 1894- joint author.

Scofield, Carl Schurz, 1875-
... Subsoil waters of Newlands (Nev.) field station. By Carl S. Scofield ... C. Lloyd Moon ... and Elmer W. Knight ... ⌊Washington, U. S. Govt. print. off., 1936⌋

Knight, Elsie.
Tested and tried; or, Cooking made easy. Over two hundred recipes, simple and economical. London: Simpkin, Marshall, Hamilton, Kent & Co., Ltd., 1912. 3 p.l., 101 p. 12°.

1. Cookery.—Receipt books. 2. Cookery (Dietary and invalid).
N. Y. P. L. March 4, 1913.

NK 0201324 NN ICJ

Knight, Elsie V M
The golden nature readers. Junior series, book one, with four coloured plates and other illustrations. London, University of London press, ltd., 1931.

NK 0201325 MH

Knight, Elton Edgecomb.
A study of double grades in New Haven city schools ⌊by⌋ Elton E. Knight ... ⌊Madison, Wis., 1938⌋
p. 11-18. 25½cm.
Abstract of thesis (PH. D.)—Yale university, 1937.
Thesis note on p. 11.
"Reprinted from the September, 1938, issue of the Journal of experimental education."

1. School management and organization—Connecticut—New Haven. 2. Educational psychology. 3. New Haven—Public schools. I. Title: Double grades in New Haven city schools.
39-20571
Library of Congress LB3061.K6 1937
Yale Univ. Libr. ⌊2⌋ 371.25

NK 0201326 CtY DLC

Knight, Elva E
Reading as an integrated course of study in an independent secondary school curriculum.

Thesis - Harvard, 1950.

NK 0201327 MH MH-Ed

NA
6860 Knight,Emerson,1882-
.K7 ... Outdoor theatres and stadiums in the West,by Emerson Knight ...
(In The Architect and engineer. San Francisco, 1924. front.,illus.,plans. 25cm. v.78,no.2,p. ⌊53⌋-91)
Caption title.
Detached copy.

NK 0201328 MiU

Knight, Emerson,1882-

Power, *Mrs.* Bertha (Knight) 1886-1927, *comp.*
William Henry Knight, California pioneer, by Bertha Knight Power ... ⌊New York⌋ Priv. print., 1932.

Knight, Emerson B.

Polk, R. L., & co. *Consumer research division.*
Pittsburgh and the surrounding trade area; a study of families—revealing buying habits and preferences, newspaper and magazine reception, present economic status and potential value as consumers. Presented by R. L. Polk & company, Consumer research division, Emerson B. Knight, director ... Detroit, Mich. ⌊1931⌋

Knight, Emerson B., inc., Indianapolis.
An analysis of the Seattle market, prepared especially for Public library from the 1930 Consumer research ... Seattle, P.I. blue room, 1930.
unp. tab.
"A presentation of facts regarding the habits, preferences and characteristic family units in the metropolitan Seattle market."

NK 0201331 WaS

⌊Knight, Emerson B., inc., *Indianapolis*⌋
An unbiased study of Hartford, Connecticut and small towns ... ⌊Hartford, The Hartford times⌋ °1928.
1 p. l., 42 p. incl. illus., mounted facsim., tables (1 fold.) diagrs. 29½cm.
Survey by Emerson B. Knight, inc.; sponsored by the Hartford times.

1. Hartford—Econ. condit. 2. Cost and standard of living—Hartford. 3. American newspapers—Hartford. 4. Advertising. I. The Hartford times. II. Title.
28-17716
Library of Congress HC108.H4K6

NK 0201332 DLC

⌊Knight, Emerson B., inc., *Indianapolis*⌋
An unbiased study of market habits in Baltimore, Maryland, and the immediate suburbs ... ⌊Baltimore, The Baltimore news⌋ °1929.
1 v. illus. (incl. maps) tables, diagrs., forms. 19½cm.
Loose-leaf.
Lettered on cover: Emerson B. Knight, inc., Indianapolis, Indiana. Market facts.
"Number 62."
"This survey was made ... by Emerson B. Knight, inc."
Contains "Knight systemax linage building index".

1. Baltimore—Econ. condit. 2. Cost and standard of living—Baltimore. 3. American newspapers—Baltimore. 4. Advertising. I. The Baltimore news. II. Title.
29-8344
Library of Congress HC108.B2K4

NK 0201333 DLC OCl

⌊Knight, Emerson B., inc., *Indianapolis*⌋
An unbiased study of market habits in greater Cleveland, Ohio ... ⌊Cleveland, The Cleveland news⌋ °1930.
1 v. illus. (incl. map) tables (1 fold.) diagrs., form. 19½cm.
Loose-leaf.
Lettered on cover: Emerson B. Knight, inc., Indianapolis, Indiana. Market facts.
"Number 52."
"This study was made ... by Emerson B. Knight, inc."—p. 9.

1. Cleveland—Econ. condit. 2. Cost and standard of living—Cleveland. 3. American newspapers—Cleveland. 4. Advertising. I. Cleveland news. II. Title. III. Title: Market habits in greater Cleveland, Ohio.
30-13085
Library of Congress HC108.C7K5
Copyright A 21912 ⌊4⌋ 330.977132

NK 0201334 DLC

VOLUME 300

[Knight, Emerson B., inc., *Indianapolis*]
An unbiased study of market habits in Seattle, Washington, and the Seattle trade area ... [Seattle, Seattle post-intelligencer; ©1930]
1 v. illus. (incl. maps) tables, diagrs. 19½cm.
Loose-leaf.
Lettered on cover: Emerson B. Knight, inc., Indianapolis, Indiana. Market facts.
"Number 64."
"This study was made ... by Emerson B. Knight, inc."—p. 9.
1. Seattle—Econ. condit. 2. Cost and standard of living—Seattle. 3. American newspapers—Seattle. 4. Advertising. I. Seattle post-intelligencer. II. Title.
30-5861
Library of Congress HC108.S77K6

NK 0201335 DLC

[Knight, Emerson B., inc., *Indianapolis*]
An unbiased study of the family or home units in greater Albany, New York, and Albany trade area ... Manual of market facts for the Knickerbocker press and Albany evening news ... [Albany?, ©1931.
1 v. illus. (incl. maps) tables (1 fold.) diagrs., form. 19½cm.
Loose-leaf.
Lettered on cover: Market facts. Certified market studies.
"Number 56."
"This study was made ... by Emerson B. Knight, inc."—p. 9.
1. Market surveys—Albany. 2. American newspapers—Albany. I. Knickerbocker press, Albany. II. Title.
33-13298
Library of Congress HC108.A32K55
[2] [658.80974743] 659.1

NK 0201336 DLC

[Knight, Emerson B., inc., *Indianapolis*]
An unbiased study of the family or home units in greater Charlotte, North Carolina, and Gaston and Lincoln counties ... [Charlotte? The Charlotte news?] ©1931.
1 v. illus. (incl. maps) tables (1 fold.) diagrs., form. 19½cm.
Loose-leaf.
Lettered on cover: Market facts. Certified market studies.
"Number 32."
"This study was made ... by Emerson B. Knight, inc."—p. 9.
1. Market surveys—Charlotte, N. C. 2. American newspapers—Charlotte, N. C. I. The Charlotte news. II. Title.
33-13300
Library of Congress HC108.C33K55
[2] [658.809756] 659.1

NK 0201337 DLC

[Knight, Emerson B., inc., *Indianapolis*]
An unbiased study of the family or home units in greater Houston, Texas, and the Houston trade area ... [Houston, Tex., The Houston chronicle; ©1930.
1 v. illus. (incl. maps) tables (1 fold.) diagrs. 19½cm.
Loose-leaf.
Lettered on cover: Emerson B. Knight, inc., Indianapolis, Indiana. Market facts.
"Number 54."
"This study was made ... by Emerson B. Knight, inc."—p. 9.
Includes an analysis of the Houston market as represented by readers of the Houston chronicle (p. 77-79)
1. Houston, Tex.—Econ. condit. 2. Cost and standard of living—Houston, Tex. 3. American newspapers—Houston, Tex. I. Houston chronicle. II. Title.
30-30046
Library of Congress HC108.H8K6
Copyright A 29439 [3] 330.9764

NK 0201338 DLC

[Knight, Emerson B., inc., *Indianapolis*]
An unbiased study of the family or home units in greater Kansas City, Missouri, and Kansas City trade area ... [Kansas City, Mo., Kansas City journal-post; ©1930.
1 v. illus. (incl. map) tables (1 fold.) diagrs. 19½cm.
Loose-leaf.
Lettered on cover: Emerson B. Knight, inc., Indianapolis, Indiana. Market facts.
"Number 53."
"This study was made ... by Emerson B. Knight, inc."—p. 9.
1. Kansas City, Mo.—Econ. condit. 2. Cost and standard of living—Kansas City, Mo. 3. American newspapers—Kansas City, Mo. I. Kansas City journal-post. II. Title.
30-30672
Library of Congress HC108.K2K6
——— Copy 2.
Copyright A 29795 [3] 330.9778411

NK 0201339 DLC

[Knight, Emerson B., inc., *Indianapolis*]
An unbiased study of the family or home units in greater Monroe, Louisiana, and Monroe trade area ... [Monroe, La., The Monroe news-star-world] ©1931.
1 v. illus. (incl. maps) tables (1 fold.) diagrs., form. 19½cm.
Loose-leaf.
Lettered on cover: Market facts. Certified market studies.
"Number 28."
"This study was made ... by Emerson B. Knight, inc."—p. 9.
1. Monroe, La.—Econ. condit. 2. Cost and standard of living—Monroe, La. 3. American newspapers—Monroe, La. I. The Monroe news-star. II. Title.
31-6763
Library of Congress HC108.M83K6
[2] 330.9763

NK 0201340 DLC

[Knight, Emerson B., inc., *Indianapolis*]
An unbiased study of the family or home units in greater Peoria, Illinois, and the Peoria trade area ... [Peoria, Peoria star company] ©1930.
1 v. illus. (incl. maps) tables (1 fold.) col. diagrs. 19½cm.
Loose-leaf.
Lettered on cover: Emerson B. Knight, inc., Indianapolis, Indiana. Market facts...
"Number 53."
"This study was made ... by Emerson B. Knight, inc."—p. 9.
1. Peoria, Ill.—Econ. condit. 2. Cost and standard of living—Peoria, Ill. 3. American newspapers—Peoria, Ill. 4. Advertising. I. Peoria star. II. Title.
30-32109
Library of Congress HC108.P43K6
[2] 330.977352

NK 0201341 DLC

[Knight, Emerson B., inc., *Indianapolis*]
An unbiased study of the family or home units in greater San Antonio, Texas, and San Antonio trade area ... Manual of market facts for San Antonio express and San Antonio evening news ... [San Antonio?] ©1931.
1 v. illus. (incl. maps) tables (1 fold.) diagrs., form. 19½cm.
Loose-leaf.
Lettered on cover: Market facts. Certified market studies.
"Number 56."
"This study was made ... by Emerson B. Knight, inc."—p. 9.
1. Market surveys—San Antonio. 2. American newspapers—San Antonio. I. San Antonio express. II. Title.
33-13299
Library of Congress HC108.S6K55
[2] [658.809764] 659.1

NK 0201342 DLC

[Knight, Emerson B., inc., *Indianapolis*]
An unbiased study of the family or home units in metropolitan Boston, Massachusetts ... [Boston, The Boston American and Advertiser] ©1929.
1 v. illus. (incl. maps) tables (1 fold.) col. diagrs. 19½cm.
Loose-leaf.
Lettered on cover: Emerson B. Knight, inc., Indianapolis, Indiana. Market facts ...
"Number 80."
"This study was made ... by Emerson B. Knight, inc."—p. 8.
1. Boston—Econ. condit. 2. Cost and standard of living—Boston. 3. American newspapers—Boston. 4. Advertising. I. The Boston American. II. Boston daily advertiser.
30-32122
Library of Congress HC108.B65K6
[3] 330.97446

NK 0201343 DLC

[Knight, Emerson B., inc., *Indianapolis*]
An unbiased study of the family or home units in New Orleans, Louisiana ... [New Orleans, New Orleans item] ©1930.
1 v. illus. (incl. map) tables (1 fold.) diagrs. 19½cm.
Loose-leaf.
Lettered on cover: Emerson B. Knight, inc., Indianapolis, Indiana. Market facts.
"Number 50."
"This study was made ... by Emerson B. Knight, inc."—p. 9.
Includes an analysis of the New Orleans market as represented by readers of the New Orleans item (p. 45-47)
1. New Orleans—Econ. condit. 2. Cost and standard of living—New Orleans. 3. American newspapers—New Orleans. I. The New Orleans item. II. Title.
30-15943
Library of Congress HC108.N4K5 1930 a
Copyright A 24045 [3] 330.9763

NK 0201344 DLC

[Knight, Emerson B., inc., *Indianapolis*]
An unbiased study of the family or home units in New Orleans, Louisiana ... [New Orleans, New Orleans tribune] ©1930.
1 v. illus. (incl. map) tables (1 fold.) diagrs. 19½cm.
Loose-leaf.
Lettered on cover: Emerson B. Knight, inc., Indianapolis, Indiana. Market facts.
"Number 49."
"This study was made ... by Emerson B. Knight, inc."—p. 9.
Includes an analysis of the New Orleans market as represented by readers of the New Orleans tribune (p. 45-47)
1. New Orleans—Econ. condit. 2. Cost and standard of living—New Orleans. 3. American newspapers—New Orleans. I. New Orleans tribune. II. Title.
30-15944
Library of Congress HC108.N4K5 1930
Copyright A 24046 [3] 330.9763

NK 0201345 DLC

[Knight, Emerson B., inc., *Indianapolis*]
An unbiased study of the family or home units in Phoenix, Arizona, and the Phoenix trade area ... [Phoenix, Ariz., The Arizona republican] ©1929.
1 v. illus. (incl. maps) tables, diagrs. 19½cm.
Loose-leaf.
Lettered on cover: Emerson B. Knight, inc., Indianapolis, Indiana. Market facts.
"Number 34."
"This study was made ... by Emerson B. Knight, inc."—p. 8.
1. Phoenix, Ariz.—Econ. condit. 2. Cost and standard of living—Phoenix, Ariz. 3. American newspapers—Phoenix, Ariz. I. Arizona republican, Phoenix, Ariz. II. Title.
30-14598
Library of Congress HC108.P55K5
Copyright A 15848 [3] 330.9791

NK 0201346 DLC

[Knight, Emerson B., inc., *Indianapolis*]
An unbiased study of the family or home units in the city of Buffalo, New York, and the Buffalo suburban trade area ... [Buffalo, The Buffalo times] ©1929.
1 v. illus. (incl. maps) tables (1 fold.) diagrs. 19½cm.
Loose-leaf.
Lettered on cover: Emerson B. Knight, inc., Indianapolis, Indiana. Market facts.
"Number 102."
"This study was made ... by Emerson B. Knight, inc."—p. 8.
1. Buffalo—Econ. condit. 2. Cost and standard of living—Buffalo. 3. American newspapers—Buffalo. 4. Advertising. I. Buffalo times. II. Title.
30-16478
Library of Congress HC108.B8K5
Copyright A 16360 [3] 330.974797

NK 0201347 DLC

Knight, Emery
see Knight, J Emery.

Knight, Enoch, 1834–
The new story of the state of Maine, with an appendix, by Enoch Knight. Portland, Dresser, McLellan & co., 1876.
26 p. 23cm.
At head of text: "Lecture."
Appendix gives list of entries from Maine at the Centennial in Philadelphia.
1. Maine. 2. Philadelphia. Centennial exposition, 1876—Maine.
A 14-2344
Title from Bangor Pub. Libr. Printed by L. C.

NK 0201349 MeBa MWA MeB

Knight, Erastus C., comp.

New York (*State*) *Comptroller's office.*
New York in the revolution as colony and state, supplement; being a compilation by Erastus C. Knight, comptroller, of documents and records ... arranged and classified, 1895–1901, by comptrollers James A. Roberts, William J. Morgan, Theodore P. Gilman, and Erastus C. Knight. Ed. by Frederic G. Mather. Albany, N. Y., O. A. Quayle, 1901.

VOLUME 300

Knight, Eric Mowbray, 1897-1943.
Za ... Boven alles dit eene. Amsterdam,
K744 A.J.G.Strengholt[1947].
Ep947s 456p. 23½cm.
"Nederlandsche bewerking van Freda Sickens".

NK 0201351 CtY

Knight, Eric Mowbray, 1897-1943.
Za ... La cadena invisible, historia novelada
K744 de un gran perro, ilustraciones de Marguerite
Ek944ℓ Kirmse. Buenos Aires,Editorial Claridad
[1944].
220p.,1ℓ. illus. 20½cm. (Biblioteca de grandes novelas, Volumen 6).
"Primera edición, mayo de 1944".
"Traducción directa por Rubén Larra".

NK 0201352 CtY

Knight, Eric Mowbray, 1897–1943.
C'est votre terre qu'ils veulent [by] Eric Knight. [Ottawa, 1942] 11 p. 20cm.
Radio address of March 1, 1942 over Radio-Canada; translated into French by Mrs. Eric Knight, and published by the Canadian information office.

1. World war, 1939– —Canada. I. Canada. Public information, Office of director of.
N. Y. P. L. September 25, 1944

NK 0201353 NN

Knight, Eric Mowbray, 1897-1943.
Za ... Dette fremfor alt, oversatt av
K744 Trygve Width. Oslo,Gyldendal,1945.
Eq945w 543,[1]p. 22cm.

NK 0201354 CtY

Knight, Eric, 1897-1943.
Dette fremfor alt, roman. Oversatt av Trygve Width. Oslo,Gyldendal,1953. 527p.

NK 0201355 CaBVa

Knight, Eric Mowbray, 1897–1943.
... Dir selber treu, roman. Zürich, Humanitas verlag [1943]
618 p. 20½cm.
At head of title: Eric Knight.
"Titel der englischen originalausgabe 'This above all.' Deutsche uebertragung von Elisabeth Rotten."

1. World war, 1939–1945—Fiction. I. Rotten, Elisabeth Friedericke, tr. II. Title.
PR6021.N417T523 47–37512

NK 0201356 DLC OCl

Knight, Eric Mowbray, 1897-1943.
Za The flying Yorkshireman ... Limited
K744 complimentary ed. Toronto,Winnipeg[etc.]
940f C.Bush limited[1940].
47p. 18cm. [Christmas issue]
Originally published in group of stories with title: Sam Small flies again.
Shrotened version.

NK 0201357 CtY CaOTP

Knight, Eric Mowbray, 1897-

The **flying** Yorkshireman, novellas ... with a note by Whit Burnett and Martha Foley. New York and London, Harper & brothers, 1938.

Knight, Eric Mowbray, 1897-1943.
Za ... Fugitivos del amor, novela. Buenos
K744 Aires,Editorial Claridad[1943].
Ek943m 487p. 20½cm. (Biblioteca de grandes novelas, Volumen 2).
"Primera edición, enero de 1943".
"Traducción directa del Inglés por León Mirlas".

NK 0201359 CtY

Knight, Eric Mowbray, 1897–
The happy land, by Eric Knight ... New York and London, Harper & brothers [°1940]
4 p. l., 3-351 p. 21cm.
"First edition."

I. Title. 40-4886
Library of Congress PZ3.K7438Hap

NK 0201360 DLC WaT WaE NBuU PP OCl OEac OClh

Knight, Eric Mowbray, 1897–1943.
Invitation to life, by Eric M. Knight. New York, Greenberg [°1934]
4 p. l., 3-269 p. 19cm.

I. Title.
PZ3.K7438 In 47-34766

NK 0201361 DLC WaSp Mi PP PPL IaU

Knight, Eric Mowbray, 1897–1943.
Invitation to life [by] Eric Knight ... New York, Greenberg [1941]
5 p. l., 3-299 p. 21cm.
"Re-issued September, 1941."

I. Title. A 43-3383
Yale univ. Library for Library of Congress [3]

NK 0201362 CtY MH OU OClh NjP

Knight, Eric Mowbray, 1897–1943.
Invitation to life [by] Eric Knight ... New York, Triangle Books [1942, c1934]
5 p. l., 3-299 p. 21cm. (Triangle books)

NK 0201363 OrU OCl

Knight, Eric Mowbray, 1897-1943.
Za ... Kalifornia, regény. Budapest,Uj idök
K744 irodalmi intézet[ca.1947]
Eu947n 160p. 20cm.
"Jogos kiadás".
"Fordította Nádler Pálma".

NK 0201364 CtY

Knight, Eric Mowbray, 1897–1943.
Lassi på eventyr. Overs. av Håkon Evjenth. Oslo, Gyldendal, 1948.
182 p. 21 cm.
"Originalens titel: Lassie Come-home."

I. Title.
PZ53.K54L3 50-32695

NK 0201365 DLC

Knight, Eric Mowbray, 1897–1943.
Lassie, chien fidèle; traduit par Janine de Villebonne. Illus. de A. Chazelle. [Paris] Hachette [1952]
190 p. illus. 21 cm. [Idéal-bibliothèque]
Translation of Lassie Come-home.

I. Title.
PZ26.3.K55 52-30867 ‡

NK 0201366 DLC

Knight, Eric Mowbray, 1897–
Lassie Come-home, by Eric Knight; illustrated by Marguerite Kirmse. Chicago, Philadelphia [etc.] The John C. Winston company [°1940]
vii, 248 p. col. front., illus. 22½cm.
Map on lining-papers.

1. Dogs—Legends and stories. I. Kirmse, Marguerite, 1885– illus. II. Title.
Library of Congress PZ10.3.K753Las 40-11708

NK 0201367 ODW OEac ViU OrMonO MiU NcD OO OrU OrP Or CaBVa WaS DLC Wa WaT WaSp OrCS OU PP PPT PSt OCl

LIBS-J Knight, Eric Mowbray, 1897-
PZ Lassie Come-home [by] Eric Knight;
10 illustrated by Cyrus Le Roy Baldridge.
.3 New York, Holt, Rinehart & Winston [c1940]
.K758 239 p. illus.
.LAS2

#Dogs--Legends and stories.
Kirmse, Marguerite, 1885-
Lassie Come-home.

NK 0201368 MoU MtU OrPS CaBVaU ViU IdPI

KNIGHT, Eric Mowbray, 1897 - 1943.
Lassie come-home; illus. by Cyrus LeRoy Baldridge.
New York. F. Watts. c1940. 239p.
(A Keith Jennison book)
Large type edition complete and unabridged.

NK 0201369 WaS WaT WaSp

820 **Knight, Eric Mowbray, 1897-1943.**
K69 **Lassie Come-home. Illustrated by Cyrus**
tL **LeRoy Baldridge. Philadelphia, J.C.**
1940 **Winston Co.[c1940]**
239p. illus.,col.plates. 22cm.

I.Baldridge, Cyrus LeRoy, 1889- illus. LC

NK 0201370 CLSU GU PP InU

Knight, Eric Mowbray, 1897-1943.
Za ... Lassie Come-home. Berne,A.Scherz[1945]
K744 240p. 18½cm. (Scherz Phoenix books. Vol.
940ℓc 41)
"First edition".

NK 0201371 CtY

PZ
10.3 Knight,Eric Mowbray,1897-1943.
K713 Lassie Come-Home. New York, Grosset &
195- Dunlap [195-?,c1940]
186 p. (Famous dog stories)

1.Dogs--Legends and stories. I.Title.

NK 0201372 MiU

VOLUME 300

Knight, Eric Mowbray, 1897–1943.
Lassie Come-Home; abridged by Felix Sutton. Illus. by Hans H. Helweg. New York, Grosset & Dunlap, °1954.
unpaged. illus. 34 cm. (Big treasure books)

I. Sutton, Felix. II. Title.
PZ10.3.K753Las 3 54-8555 ‡

NK 0201373 DLC

Knight, Eric Mowbray, 1897-1943.
Za K744 Eu940t ... Lassie Hazatért, regeny. Budapest, Új idők irodalmi intezet[1940?].
168p. 21cm.
"Jogos kiadás."
"Forditotta: Thurzó Gábor".

NK 0201374 CtY OCl

Knight, Eric Mowbray, 1897-1943.
Za K744 Eq946h ... Lassie vender hjem, illustreret af Marguerite Kirmse. København, P.Branner, 1946.
187p. illus. 22½cm.
"Oversat ... af Thora Constantin-Hansen".

NK 0201375 CtY

Knight, Eric Mowbray, 1897–1943.
Lassie vender hjem; med billeder fra filmen. [Overs. af Thora Constantin-Hansen] København, P. Branner, 1947.
192 p. plates. 23 cm.

I. Title.
PZ53.K54L33 50-32686

NK 0201376 DLC

Knight, Eric Mowbray, 1897-1943.
Za K744 Eq946hb ... Lassie vender hjem, mit billeder fra filmen. København, P. Branner, 1947.
192p. plates. 23cm.
"2det oplag"
"Oversat ... af Thora Constantin-Hansen".

NK 0201377 CtY

Knight, Eric Mowbray, 1897-1943.
Légy hu onmagadhoz; forditottak; Kovacs Gyorgy es Tapai-Szabo Gabriella. [Budapest] Anonymus, 1945-1946.
2 v.

Hungarian.

NK 0201378 OCl

Knight, Eric M., 1897-
The Marne. (In Society of arts & sciences, N.Y., O. Henry memorial award. Prize stories of 1936. 1936.
p. [265]-269) "From Story".

NK 0201379 OU OCU

Knight, Eric Mowbray, 1897–1943.
Og livet gaar videre. [Overs. efter Invitation to life ved Hedda Syberg] København, P. Branner, 1947.
277 p. 21 cm.

I. Title.
PR6021.N417 I 63 50-24411

NK 0201380 DLC CtY

Knight, Eric Mowbray, 1897–1943.
Portrait of a flying Yorkshireman; letters from Eric Knight in the United States to Paul Rotha in England, edited by Paul Rotha. London, Chapman & Hall, 1952.
281 p. illus. 23 cm.

I. Title.
PR6021.N417Z52 1952 928.2 52-40040 ‡

NK 0201381 DLC CaBVa IaU NcU CSt NBuU GU MB NN MH

Knight, Eric Mowbray, 1897–1943.
Questo solo conta. [Unica traduzione autorizzata di Curzio Villa. 1. ed. Milano] Mondadori [1945]
577 p. 20 cm. (Collezione "Omnibus")
Translation of This above all.

1. World War, 1939–1945—Fiction. I. Title.
PR6021.N417T524 50-25949

NK 0201382 DLC

Knight, Eric Mowbray, 1897–1943.
Questo sopra tutto. [Traduzione di Andrea Damiano] Milano, A. Martello [1947]
508 p. 22 cm. (I Grandi romanzi Martello)

1. World War, 1939–1945—Fiction. I. Title.
PR6021.N417T5237 50-27143

NK 0201383 DLC OCl CtY

Knight, Eric Mowbray, 1897–1943.
Qui perd gagne. Roman, tr. de l'anglais par Pierre Lambert. Genève, J.-H. Jeheber [1944]
220 p. 19 cm.
Translation of You play the black, and the red comes up.

I. Title.
PR6021.N417Y63 49-41745*

NK 0201384 DLC

Knight, Eric Mowbray, 1897-1943.
Za K744 Eq938s ... Saet ind paa sort - og rødt kommer ud. København, Aschehoug, 1938.
260p. 20cm.
"Autoriseret oversaettelse ... ved G.M. Steffensen".

NK 0201385 CtY

Knight, Eric Mowbray, 1897-1943.
Za K744 En943 ... Sam Small fliegt wieder. Die wunderbaren Erlebnisse des fliegenden Mannes aus Yorkshire. [Berne]A.Scherz[1943].
271p. 20cm.
"Erste Auflage".
"Die Geschichte "Der fliegende Mann aus Yorkshire" wurde nach der Amerikanischen Condensation übersetzt".
"Einzig autorisierte übertragung aus dem Englischen".

NK 0201386 CtY

Knight, Eric Mowbray, 1897–
Sam Small flies again, the amazing adventures of the flying Yorkshireman, by Eric Knight, with drawings by Donald McKay. New York and London, Harper & brothers [1942]
ix p., 2 l., 285, [1] p. illus. (incl. music) 21½cm.
"First edition."

I. Title. 42-5832
Library of Congress PZ3.K7438Sam

NK 0201387 OEac OLak OU WaSpG OrCS OrU ViU LU NcD OCl DLC Or WaS WaSp CaBVa WaE PPL PP PHC

Knight, Eric Mowbray, 1897-1943.
Za K744 942sb Sam Small flies again, the amazing adventures of the flying Yorkshireman, short stories by Eric Knight. London, Toronto[etc.,etc.]Cassell and company ltd.[1943].
254,[1]p. 19½cm.

NK 0201388 CtY

Knight, Eric Mowbray, 1897–1943.
Sam Small prend son vol. Roman, tr. de l'anglais par Pierre Lambert. Genève, J.-H. Jeheber [1944]
207 p. 19 cm.

I. Title.
PR6021.N417S33 49-41737*

NK 0201389 DLC CtY

Knight, Eric Mowbray, 1897–
Song on your bugles [by] Eric Knight ... New York, London, Harper & brothers, 1937.
viii, 404 p. 21cm.
"A Story press book."
"First edition."

I. Title. 37-17035 Revised
Library of Congress PZ3.K7438So

NK 0201390 DLC IU OKentU FU OCl OLak PPL NN

Knight, Eric Mowbray, 1897–
They don't want swamps and jungles [by] Eric Knight. [Ottawa, Director of public information, 1942]
11, [1] p. 19½cm.
"The text of this pamphlet was broadcast by the author ... over the Canadian broadcasting corporation network ... March first, 1942."—p. [2]

1. World war, 1939– —Addresses, sermons, etc. 2. World war, 1939– —Canada. I. Title.
Library of Congress D743.9.K57 42-17505
[2] 940.53

NK 0201391 DLC OrU

Knight, Eric Mowbray, 1897–
PS 3521 N544 T47 This above all, by Eric Knight. New York, Grosset & Dunlap [1941]
5 p. l., 473 p. 21½cm.

NK 0201392 CU-I OrU CaBViP OrSaW

Knight, Eric Mowbray, 1897–1943.
This above all, by Eric Knight. New York and London, Harper & brothers [°1941]
5 p. l., 473 p. 21 cm.
"First edition."

1. World war, 1939–1945—Fiction. I. Title.
41—51668
Library of Congres PZ3.K7438Th

NK 0201393 WaE OrP WaT OU ODW NSyU IdU MtBC CaBVaU OrCS CaBVa WaS WaTC Or DLC MtU OrU IdB PSC PHC PP PPD OCl OC1W

VOLUME 300

Knight, Eric Mowbray, 1897–
This above all, by Eric Knight. New York and London, Harper & brothers [1941]
5 p. l., 473 p. 21½ᶜᵐ.
"Ninth edition."

1. European war, 1939– —Fiction. I. Title.
41-22069
Library of Congress PZ3.K7438Th 9

NK 0201394 DLC IdU WaU CoU NBuU

Knight, Eric Mowbray, 1897-1943.
This above all, by Eric Knight. Toronto, The Musson book company ltd. [c1941]
5 p.l., 473, [1] p.

NK 0201395 CaBVaU CaOTP

Za K744 941f
Knight, Eric Mowbray, 1897-1943.
... This above all. Berne, A.Scherz[1942].
2v. 18½cm. Scherz Phoenix books. Vols. 4-5).
"Third edition".

NK 0201396 CtY OU

Knight, Eric Mowbray, 1897–
This above all, by Eric Knight. New York, Grosset & Dunlap [1942]
5 p. l., 473 p. 21½ᶜᵐ.

1. World war, 1939– —Fiction. I. Title.
42-16506
Library of Congress PZ3.K7438Th 10

NK 0201397 DLC OKentU ViU

4 PZ Fr. 5024
Knight, Eric Mowbray, 1897-1943.
Topsy, chien fidèle; traduit par Janine de Villebonne. Illus. de Roger Barret. Paris, Hachette [1949]
249 p. (Bibliothèque rose illustrée)

NK 0201398 DLC-P4

Knight, Eric Mowbray, 1897–
... A verdade acima de tudo, emocionante e audacioso romance da hora de maior angustia da Inglaterra; tradução de Orlando Rocha. São Paulo, Editora universitária [1941]
vi p., 2 l., 3-475 p., 1 l. 1 illus. 22ᶜᵐ.
At head of title: Eric Knight.

1. World war, 1939– —Fiction. I. Rocha, Orlando, tr. II. Title.
42-20301
Library of Congress PR6021.N417T525
823.91

NK 0201399 DLC

Knight, Eric Mowbray, 1897-1943.

Za K744 En944r
... Wer verliert gewinnt, Roman. [Berne] A.Scherz[c1944].
286p. 20cm.
"Erste Auflage".
"Einzig autorisierte Ubertragung aus dem Englischen von Anna Katharina Rehmann".

NK 0201400 CtY

Knight, Eric Mowbray, 1897-1943.

Za K744 Eu945t
... Yli kaiken ymmärryksen. Helsinki, K. Tammi[1945].
568p. 21½cm.
"Suomentanut Oiva Talvitie."

NK 0201401 CtY

Knight, Eric Mowbray, 1897–
You play the black and the red comes up, by Eric M. Knight ... London [etc.] Cassell and company, ltd. [1938]
261, [1] p. 19½ᶜᵐ.

I. Title.
38-7326 Revised
Library of Congress PZ3.K7438Yo

NK 0201402 DLC

[**Knight, Eric Mowbray**] 1897–
You play the black and the red comes up, by Richard Hallas [*pseud.*] New York, R. M. McBride and company, 1938.
3 p. l., 213 p. 21ᶜᵐ.
"First edition."

I. Title.
38-10443
Library of Congress PZ3.K7438Yo 2

NK 0201403 DLC

Knight, Eric Mowbry, 1897-1943.
You play the black and the red comes up, by Richard Hallas [pseud.] New York, Dell Publishing Co. [c1938]
224p. 16cm. (Dell book, 510)

NK 0201404 OrU

Knight, Errol Lorne, 1893-1923.

G830 .S8 1926
FOR OTHER EDITIONS SEE MAIN ENTRY
Stefánsson, Vilhjálmur, 1879–
The adventure of Wrangel island, written by Vilhjalmur Stefansson, with the collaboration of John Irvine Knight, upon the diary of whose son, Errol Lorne Knight, the narrative is mainly based; with a foreword by the Right Hon. L. S. Amery ... London, J. Cape ltd. [1926]

Knight, Esmond, 1906–
Seeking the bubble, by Esmond Knight, with 9 illustrations. London, New York [etc.] Hutchinson & co., ltd. [1943]
168 p. front., plates, ports. 22ᶜᵐ.
Autobiography.

I. Title.
43-11867
Library of Congress PN2598.K73A3 1943
[3]
927.92

NK 0201406 DLC FMU

Knight, Esmond, 1906–
Seeking the bubble, by Esmond Knight. 2d impression. With 9 illustrations. London, New York [etc.] Hutchinson & co., ltd. [1943]
168 p. front., plates, ports. 22ᶜᵐ.
Autobiography.

I. Title.
44-19510
Library of Congress PN2598.K73A3 1943 a
[2]
927.92

NK 0201407 DLC

Knight, Ethel.
The echo of the black horn, an authentic tale of "the Governor" of "The Free State of Jones." [Soso? Miss., 1951]
328 p. illus. 23 cm.

1. Knight, Newton, 1830– 2. Knight, Thomas Jefferson. 3. Jones Co., Miss.—Hist. I. Title.
F341.K64 976.255 51-37441 ‡

NK 0201408 DLC NcD TxU

Knight, Eugene Vernon, 1876– ed.
Furniere und sperrholz (Veneers and plywood) von E.Vernon Knigth [!] und Meinrad Wulpi. Einzige autorisierte und erweiterte deutsche ausg.hrsg.von direktor L.M.Cohn-Wegner ... Berlin, M.Krayn, technischer verlag g.m.b.h. [1930]-31.
2 v. illus.,plans,diagrs. 24½ᶜᵐ.
Vol.1 has added t.-p.
Text adapted to German requirements and conditions.
CONTENTS.—I.bd. Eigenschaften und herstellung von furnieren und sperrholz.—II.bd. teil A. Furniere und sperrholz in möbeln und panelen vom altertum bis zur gegenwart und ihre holzarten. teil B. Verwendung von sperrholz für andere zwecke als möbel. Technische verwendungsgebiete, prüfung, betriebskontrolle in der fertigung, beurteilung, prüfungszahlen, handelsbräuche.

1.Veneers and veneering. 2.Plywood. I.Wulpi, Meinrad, joint ed. II.Cohn-Wegner, Leo Michael, ed.

NK 0201410 MiU

Knight, Eugene Vernon, 1876– *ed.*
Veneers and plywood, their craftsmanship and artistry, modern production methods and present-day utility, E. Vernon Knight and Meinrad Wulpi, editors. New York, The Ronald press company [c1927]
xxiv, 372 p. front., illus., plates, diagrs. 22ᶜᵐ.
Bibliography: p. 343-355.

1. Veneers and veneering. 2. Plywood. I. Wulpi, Meinrad, joint ed.
27-4100
Library of Congress TS870.K6

NK 0201411 MiU MB ICJ DLC OrP MtU WaT IdU WaS OrCS MiEM NcD

Knight, Eve, *comp.*
When you look back; a collection of letters written to children by illustrious persons, collected by Eve Knight. London, Cobden-Sanderson, 1933.
ix p., 1 l., 178 p. 19½ᶜᵐ.

1. English letters. I. Title. II. Title: Letters to children.
34-1076
Library of Congress PR1349.C5K6
[3]
826.0822

NK 0201412 DLC CaOTP

LC1043 .K7
[Knight, Ewart Broughton] 1896–
...Developing educational opportunities for out-of-school rural young men... Knoxville, Tenn., Department of agricultural education, 1942.
44 p. 23cm. (The University of Tennessee, College of agriculture. Bulletin 9)
Bibliography: p.44.

1.Vocational education--Tennessee.

NK 0201413 ICU MiEM

VOLUME 300

LC1043 .K71 [Knight, Ewart Broughton] 1896-
...Guidance for rural boys... Knoxville, Tenn., Department of agricultural education, 1940.
42 p. 23cm. (The University of Tennessee, College of agriculture. Bulletin 7)
"Selected references": p. 33-36.

1. Agricultural education--Tennessee.

NK 0201414 ICU

Knight, Ewart Broughton, 1896-
... Handbook for students of vocational agriculture; a guide to students desiring to become more familiar with high school procedure in general and with that of vocational agriculture in particular in order that learning may be more readily and pleasantly acquired. Formulated by Ewart B. Knight under the direction of Sherman Dickinson ... Columbia, Mo., 1938.
56 p. 23cm. (The University of Missouri bulletin. v. 39, no. 11. Education series 1938, no. 34)
The University of Missouri bulletin no. changed in manuscript to 11.
"Some more good ideas on agricultural vocations": p. 56.
1. Agricultural education—U. S. 2. Vocational education—U. S. I. Dickinson, Sherman, 1891- II. Title: Vocational agriculture.
40-28289
Library of Congress S533.K5
[4] 630.712

NK 0201415 DLC

Knight, F
Important Official Documents relative to the Disagreements between the Members of the late Army Medical Board
see under Gt. Brit. Army Medical Services.

KNIGHT, F.C.
A volumetric method for the determination of lead. Denver, 1892.

NK 0201417 MH PPAN

KNIGHT, F. E.
Te Deum laudamus. Set to music in the key of D, for the use of churc[h] [c]hoirs, &c. [Organ accompaniment.]
London. Novello, Ewer & co. [188-?] 8 pp. L. 8°.

NK 0201418 MB

Knight, F Hamilton,
See:
Hamilton-Knight, F

Knight, Florence Marian, 1876-
In honey-bird land ... London [n. d.]
75 p. illus. 25 cm.

NK 0201420 CtY

Knight, Florence Marian, 1876-
The shout of a king; a true story of the Zenana Bible and medical mission, by F. M. Knight ... London, Hodder & Stoughton [1938]
viii, 9-256 p. 19cm.
"First printed in 1938."
"The story is a continuation of the earlier book But if not."—Introductory note.

1. Missions—Mohammedans. 2. Missions—India. 3. Missions—Fiction. I. Title.
39-10510
Library of Congress BV2087.K53
[2] [266] 275.4

NK 0201421 DLC CtY-D KyWAT CtY

G161 .T32 **Knight, Francis.**
Récit de sept années d'esclavage chez les Turcs d'Alger, ...
Londres, 1640.

(In Ternaux-Compans, Henri. Archives des voyages. Paris, 1840-41. 8°. v. 2, p. 67-143)

NK 0201422 DLC

Knight, Francis.
A Relation Of Seaven Yeares Slaverie Vnder The Turkes of Argeire, suffered by an English Captive Merchant. Wherein is also conteined all memorable Passages, Fights, and Accidents, which happined in that Citie, and at Sea with their Shippes... during that time. Together with a Description of the sufferings of the . . . Captives . . . Whereunto is added a Second Booke conteining a Discription of Argeire, with its Originall, manner of Government, Increase, and present flourishing Estate... By

Francis Knight. London, Printed by T. Cotes, for Michael Sparke Junior, 1640. 4 p.l., 56 p. incl. front. 1 illus. 18cm. (4°.)

STC 15048. Huntington check-list, 1919, p. 245. Hazlitt, I. 247.

——— ——— [Another issue] London, Printed by T. Cotes, for M. S. Junior, and are to be sold by Tho. Nicholes, 1640.

STC 15048a.
Frontispiece has caption: The manner of Turkish tyrranie over Christian slaves.
Imperfect: a few lower edges cropped.
With supra-libros of H[enri] T[ernaux-Compans]

LENOX COLLECTION.
12928. 1. Captivities—Barbary states. 2. Algiers—Descr. *Card revised* June 5, 1951
N. Y. P. L.

NK 0201425 NN CtY MnU ICN MdBP CU CSmH

FILM **Knight, Francis.**
A relation of seaven yeares slaverie vnder the Turkes of Argeire, suffered by an English captive merchant. Wherein is also conteined all memorable passages, fights, and accidents, which happined in that citie, and at sea with their shippes and gallies during that time. Together with a description of the sufferings of the miserable captives under that mercilesse tyrannie. Whereunto is added a second booke conteining a discription of Argeire, with its originall, manner of government, increase, and present flourishing estate. London, Printed by T. Cotes, for M.S. junior, and are to be sold by T. Nicholes, 1640.
University Microfilms no. 20368 (carton 763)
Short-title catalogue no. 15048a.

1. Algeria--Hist.--1516-1830. 2. Slavery in the Barbary States. I. Title.

NK 0201427 MiU NNC

Knight, Francis.
A relation of seven years slavery under the Turks of Algier ... suffered by an English captive merchant ... By Francis Knight.
(*In* [Osborne, Thomas] comp. A collection of voyages and travels ... London, 1745. 37cm. vol. II, p. [465]-489)
First edition, London, 1640.

I. Title.
CA 7—3576 Unrev'd
Library of Congress G160.O81 vol. 2

NK 0201428 DLC

Knight, Francis.
A relation of seven years slavery under the Turks of Algier, suffered by an English captive merchant . . . whereunto is added . . . . a description of Algier . . . Map.
(In A collection of voyages and travels. Vol. 2, pp. 465-489. London. MDCCXLVII.)

G8879 — Algeria. Geog. — Barbary States. Slav.

NK 0201429 MB

Knight, Francis.
A relation of seven years slavery under the Turks of Algier, suffered by an English captive merchant... whereunto is added a second book, containing a description of Algier...

(In Churchill, Awnsham, comp. A collection of voyages and travels. London, 1752. v.8, p.481-489)

NK 0201430 OCl

Knight, Francis Arnold, 1852- ed.
The **Annual** monitor ... or, Obituary of the members of the Society of Friends in Great Britain and Ireland ... no. [1]-30, 1813-42; new ser., no. 1-66, 1843-1908; no. 96-1909-
York, W. Alexander; [etc., etc.] 1813-19

Knight, Francis Arnold, 1852-
By leafy ways; brief studies from the book of nature.
197p. il. Bost., Roberts, 1889.

NK 0201432 OCl PPL PP PPFr PSt

---

820 K695 tB Knight, Francis Arnold, 1852-
By leafy ways. Brief studies from the book of nature. Illustrated by E. T. Compton. London, E. Stock, 1889.
viii, 197p. front., illus., plates. 23cm.

NK 0201433 CLSU

KNIGHT, Francis Arnold, 1852-
By leafly ways. Brief studies from the book of nature. Ed. 3. London, Elliot Stock, 1889.
8, [1], 197. pp. ills.

NK 0201434 MH-Z

Knight, Francis Arnold, 1852-
By leafy ways. Brief studies from the book of nature. By Francis A. Knight. Illustrated by E. T. Compton. Boston, Roberts brothers, 1890.
vi p., 2 l., 197 p. front., illus., plates. 23cm.

A 24-791
Title from So. Branch, Univ. of Calif. Printed by L. C.

NK 0201435 CU ICJ

Knight, Francis Arnold, 1852-
By leafy ways; brief studies from the book of nature. Ed. 4. Bost., Roberts, 1890.
197 p.

NK 0201436 PU-B

KNIGHT, Francis Arnold, 1852-
By moorland and sea. Illus. by the author.
Lond. Stock. 1893. (9), 215 pp. Illus. Pls. Sm. 8°.

NK 0201437 MB

VOLUME 300

Knight, Francis A[rnold], 1852 –
By moorland and sea. Boston: Roberts Bros., 1894. 4 p.l., 215 p., 9 pl. illus. 12°.
Round the Mull. Loch Duich. Uig, Isle of Skye. Dunvegan. A ride on a railway engine. In the Quantocks. Sounds of the night. The schoolmaster abroad. The midsummer fields. A northern moorland. Camping out. Sedgemoor. An old manor-house. The birds'-nester. An idyll of winter.
1. Scotland.—Travel and description. 2. Title. CENTRAL RESERVE.
N. Y. P. L. May 17, 1912.

NK 0201438 NN CtY PPL MH MB ICJ MiD OCl NcRS

Knight, Francis Arnold, 1852 –
... Devonshire, by Francis A. Knight and Louie M. (Knight) Dutton. With maps, diagrams and illustrations. Cambridge, University press, 1910.
xii, 245, [1] p. incl. illus., map, diagrs. 19cm. (Cambridge county geographies)
Physical and geological maps on end-papers.
1. Devonshire, Eng. I. Dutton, Louie M. (Knight) joint author.
A 11-1145
Title from Enoch Pratt Free Libr. Printed by L. C.

NK 0201439 MdBE OrU PSC PP MiU OO OClW MB

Knight, Francis Arnold, 1852 –
The heart of Mendip; an account of the history, archæology and natural history of the parishes of Winscombe, Shipham, Rowberrow, Churchill, Burrington, Christon, Loxton, Compton Bishop, Axbridge and Cheddar, and of the ancient mining station of Charterhouse-on-Mendip, by Francis A. Knight... London: J. M. Dent & Sons, Ltd., 1915. xvi, 547 p., 1 fold. map. illus. 12°.
1. Mendip Hills, Eng. 2. Somersetshire, Eng.—Description and travel, 1915. 3. Title.
N. Y. P. L. August 30, 1915

NK 0201440 NN CU PPL OClW MH MB NBuG NjP PSC IU

Knight, Francis Arnold, 1852 –
A history of Sidcot school; a hundred years of West country Quaker education 1808–1908, by Francis A. Knight; illustrations and plans by E. T. Compton & others. London, J. M. Dent & co., 1908.
viii, 346 p., 1 l. col. front., illus., plates, ports., maps (partly fold.) plans (partly fold.) 20cm.
1. Sidcot school, Sidcot, Eng.—Hist.
E 9-1146
Library, U. S. Bur. of Education LF795.S56K7

NK 0201441 DHEW PHC ICJ ICU PPF NcD

Knight, Francis Arnold, 1852 –
Idylls of the field... London, 1889.

NK 0201442 PPL

Knight, Francis Arnold, 1852–
Idylls of the field. By Francis A. Knight ... Illustrated by E. T. Compton. Boston, Roberts brothers, 1890.
viii p., 1 l., 182 p. incl. illus., pl. front., 2 pl. 22½cm.
A 24-793
Title from So. Branch. Univ. of Calif. Printed by L. C.

NK 0201443 CU OrP ViU PPFr OCl

KNIGHT, FRANCIS ARNOLD, 1852 –
In the west country, by Francis A. Knight... Bristol: W. C. Hemmons[, etc., etc., 1896]. x, 269 p. front., illus., plates. 20½cm.
"These sketches are, with alterations and additions, reprinted from the 'Daily News' and the 'Speaker'."
720236A. 1. Devonshire, Eng.—Descr. and trav. 2. Somersetshire Eng.—Descr. and trav.

NK 0201444 NN NjP

Knight, Francis Arnold, 1852-
The rambles of a dominie. With illustrations by E.T.Compton. London, W.Gardner, Darton & co. [1891]

NK 0201445 MH PPL PP MB RP MiD

Knight, Francis Arnold, 1852 –
The sea-board of Mendip; an account of the history, archæology, and natural history of the parishes of Weston-super-Mare, Kewstoke, Wick St. Lawrence, Puxton, Worle, Uphill, Brean, Bleadon, Hutton, Locking, Banwell, and of the Steep and Flat Holms; by Francis A. Knight ... With numerous illustrations. London, J. M. Dent & co., 1902.
xiv, 495 p. incl. front., illus., plan, facsim. fold. map. 20cm.
1. Mendip Hills. 2. Somerset, Eng.—Descr. & trav. I. Title.
3—7825
Library of Congress DA670.M5K7

NK 0201446 DLC

Knight, Francis Arnold. 1852-
Sedgemoor. 13 pp. (Contemp. Rev. v. 59, 1891, p. 697.)

NK 0201447 MdBP

Knight, Francis Arnold, 1852 –
... Somerset, by Francis A. Knight assisted by Louie M. (Knight) Dutton. With maps, diagrams and illustrations. Cambridge, University press, 1909.
xi, [1], 192, [1] p. incl. illus., ports., maps, diagrs. 19cm. (Added t.-p.: Cambridge county geographies ...)
At head of title: Cambridge county geographies.
Physical and geological maps on end-papers.
1. Somerset, Eng. I. Dutton, Louie M. (Knight) joint author.
A 15-2085
Title from Wesleyan Univ. Printed by L. C.

NK 0201448 CtW OrU PP MiU OClW OO MB

Knight, Francis Arnold, 1852-
Somerset, by F.A.Knight assisted by Louie M.(Knight) Dutton. Cambridge, University Press, 1915
192 p. illus.

NK 0201449 MH

Knight, Francis Edgar
see
Knight, Frank, 1905-

Knight, Francis Philip, 1902- joint author.
Taylor, George Crosbie.
The propagation of hardy trees and shrubs, by G. C. Taylor ... assisted by F. P. Knight ... London, Dulau & co., ltd., 1927.

Knight, Francis Philip, 1902-
—— The propagation of magnolias. Plate. (In New flora and silva. 1929. i. 193-199.)

NK 0201452 MH-A

Knight, Frank, 1905–
A beginner's guide to the sea. London, Macmillan; New York, St. Martin's Press, 1955.
234 p. illus. 18 cm.
1. Seamanship. I. Title.
VK541.K75 *623.88 656 56–1633 rev ‡

NK 0201453 DLC CaBViP OrP MB NcRS PP PU OCl NN MH

Knight, Frank, 1905–
Clippers to China, a junior novel; illustrated by Patrick Jobson. London, Macmillan; New York, St. Martin's Press, 1955.
268 p. illus. 21 cm.
I. Title.
PZ7.K737Cl 55–12611 rev ‡

NK 0201454 DLC CaBVaU OEac

Knight, Frank, 1905–
The golden monkey; illustrated by J. S. Goodall. London, Macmillan, 1953.
195 p. illus. 21 cm.
I. Title.
PZ7.K737Go 53–11884 rev ‡

NK 0201455 DLC Or OCl OOxM

Knight, Frank, 1905–
Voyage to Bengal, a junior novel. Illustrated by Patrick Jobson. London, Macmillan; New York, St. Martin's Press, 1954.
265 p. illus. 21 cm.
I. Title.
PZ7.K737Vo 54–4895 rev ‡

NK 0201456 DLC NcU OCl NN

HN 17 .K72
Knight, Frank Hyneman, 1885-
The dilemma of liberalism, by Frank P.[i.e. H.] Knight. Ann Arbor, Mich., Photo-lithoprint reproduction of author's manuscript by Edwards Brothers [1933?]
87 p. 22 cm.
The content of three talks to student groups at the University of Chicago, Nov. 1932 and Jan. 1933.
1. Social problems. 2. Liberalism. I. Title.

NK 0201457 MiU

Pamphlet HB 46
Knight, Frank Hyneman, 1885-
Economic freedom and social responsibility; an essay in economics and ethics. [Atlanta, Ga., Emory University, 1952.
24 p. 23cm. (Emory University, Atlanta. School of Business Administration. Studies in business and economics, no. 7)
1. Economics--Addresses, essays, lectures. 2. Social ethics--Addresses, essays, lectures. I. Title. II. Series.

NK 0201458 NIC WaSpG

VOLUME 300

Knight, Frank Hyneman, 1885–
The economic order and religion [by] Frank H. Knight ... and Thornton W. Merriam ... New York and London, Harper & brothers [1945]
viii p., 1 l., 275 p. 22cm.
"Baker Brownell, supervising editor."
"First edition."
CONTENTS.—Liberalism and Christianity, by F. H. Knight.—Economic ideals of liberal Christianity, by T. W. Merriam.—Discussion and critical comments by the authors.
1. Christianity and economics. I. Merriam, Thornton Ward, 1894– II. Brownell, Baker, 1887– ed. III. Title.
44-41896
Library of Congress BR115.E3K6
[10] 261

OrCS WaTC WaS IdPI
OCU ODW OU ViU MiHM NIC MB TU NcC NcGU OrSaW WaSpG
NK 0201459 DLC NcD OrP OrU PSC PP PSt PU PPT OCH

Knight, Frank Hyneman, 1885–
The economic order and religion, by Frank H. Knight and Thornton W. Merriam. [Baker Brownell, supervising editor] London, K. Paul, Trench, Trubner [1948]
viii, 22[?] p. 22 cm. (International library of sociology and social reconstruction. London)
CONTENTS.—Liberalism and Christianity, by F. H. Knight.—Economic ideals of liberal Christianity, by T. W. Merriam.—Discussion and critical comments by the authors.
1. Christianity and economics. I. Merriam, Thornton Ward, 1894– II. Brownell, Baker, 1887– ed. III. Title. (Series)
BR115.E3K6 1948 261 49-14700*

NK 0201460 DLC ScU IU MiU MoSU OrU

HB172
.K73
Knight, Frank Hyneman, 1885-
The economic organization. [Chicago] University of Chicago, c1933.
126 p.

1. Economics.

NK 0201461 ICU WU IU NcU ViU ICarbS FU ICU PSt

Knight, Frank Hyneman, 1885-
The economic organization. [195-?]
cover-title, 126 p.

"Copyright 1933 by the University of Chicago."
"Reprinted with permission of the author."

1. Economics. I. Title.

NK 0201462 NNC

Knight, Frank Hyneman, 1885–
The economic organization. With an article, Notes on cost and utility. New York, A. M. Kelley, 1951.
179 p. 22 cm.

1. Economics. I. Title.

HB171.K615 338 53-2303 ‡

IdPI WaSpG IdU CtY-L ViU CoU MB DAU MnU IaU ScCleU
NN MWelC NIC ScU TU TxU CaBVa CaBVaU MtU WaWW OrCS
NK 0201463 DLC MH OrPR MoU NcU OrPS OClW LU GU MiU

HB73
.K7
Knight, Frank Hyneman, 1885-
Economic theory and nationalism, reprinted with some alterations from the book Ethics of competition and other essays. London, G. Allen & Unwin; New York, Harper, 1935.
83 p.

NK 0201464 ICU

College
D330.4
K744
Knight, Frank Hyneman, 1885-
Economic theory and nationalism. Reprinted with some alterations from the book Ethics of competition and other essays. New York, Harper, 1935.
83 p.

1. Economics - Addresses, essays, lectures.

NK 0201465 NNC

LT
LD914
.S683
Knight, Frank Hyneman, 1885-
Economic theory and nationalism. Chicago [1947]
83 p.
"Reprinted ... from the book Ethics of competition, and other essays."
For use in Social sciences 3, University of Chicago.

NK 0201466 ICU

Knight, Frank Hyneman, 1885–
The ethics of competition, and other essays, by Frank Hyneman Knight ... London, G. Allen & Unwin ltd. [1935]
2 p. l., [7]-363, [1] p. diagrs. 22 cm.
Errata slip inserted.
Essays selected by Milton Friedman, and others. *cf.* Pref.
CONTENTS.—Bibliography (p. [11]-18)—Ethics and the economic interpretation.—The ethics of competition.—Economic psychology and the value problem.—The limitations of scientific method in economics.—Marginal utility economics.—Statics and dynamics.—Cost of production and price over long and short periods.—Fallacies in the interpretation of social cost.—Value and price.—Interest.—Economic theory and nationalism.
1. Economics—Addresses, essays, lectures. 2. Competition. 3. Value. I. Friedman, Milton, 1912– II. Title.
HB171.K62 330.4 36-8504

NN PU PSC PPD ICU
NK 0201467 DLC OU CoU CU NcD NcRS OCU OCl ODW MB

Knight, Frank Hyneman, 1885–
The ethics of competition, and other essays, by Frank Hyneman Knight ... New York and London, Harper & brothers [1935]
2 p. l., [7]-363, [1] p. diagrs. 21½cm.
Errata slip inserted.
Printed in Great Britain.
Essays selected by Milton Friedman and others. *cf.* Pref.
CONTENTS.—Bibliography (p. [11]-18)—Ethics and the economic interpretation.—The ethics of competition.—Economic psychology and the value problem.—The limitations of scientific method in economics.—Marginal utility economics.—Statics and dynamics.—Cost of production and price over long and short periods.—Fallacies in the interpretation of social cost.—Value and price.—Interest.—Economic theory and nationalism.
1. Economics—Addresses, essays, lectures. 2. Competition. 3. Value. I. Friedman, Milton, 1912– II. Title.
Library of Congress HB171.K62 1935 36-9069
[5-5-5] 330.4

OrCS
NK 0201468 DLC OrP WaT IdU OrPR WaWW OrU Or CaBVaU

KNIGHT,Frank Hyneman,1885-
The ethics of competition and other essays. London,G.Allen & Unwin Ltd.,[1936].

22 cm.
"Bibliography",pp.[11]-18.
"2d ed."

NK 0201469 MH

Knight, Frank Hyneman, 1885-
The ethics of competition, and other essays. New York, Harper [1936]
363 p. diagrs. 22 cm.

NK 0201470 TU

Knight, Frank Hyneman, 1885–
The ethics of competition, and other essays, by Frank Hyneman Knight ... New York and London, Harper & brothers [1936]
2 p. l., [7]-363, p. diagrs. 21½cm.
"Second edition 1936."
Printed in Great Britain.
Essays selected by Milton Friedman and others. *cf.* Pref.
CONTENTS.—Bibliography (p. [11]-18)—Ethics and the economic interpretation.—The ethics of competition.—Economic psychology and the value problem.—The limitations of scientific method in economics.—Marginal utility economics.—Statics and dynamics.—Cost of production and price over long and short periods.—Fallacies in the interpretation of social cost.—Value and price.—Interest.—Economic theory and nationalism.

NK 0201471 ViU NNC

HB171
.K62
1951
Knight, Frank Hyneman, 1885-
The ethics of competition, and other essays. London, G. Allen & Unwin [1951]
363 p. diagrs. 22cm.
Essays selected by Milton Friedman, and others. cf. Pref.
CONTENTS.—Bibliography (p. [11]-18)—Ethics and the economic interpretation.—The ethics of competition.—Economic psychology and the value problem.—The limitations of scientific method in economics.—Marginal utility economics.—Statics and dynamics.—Cost of production and price over long and short periods.—Fallacies in the interpretation of social cost — Value and price.—Interest.—Economic theory and nationalism.
1. Economics—Addresses, essays,lectures. 2. Competition. 3. Value. I.Friedman, Milton, 1912– II. Title.

NK 0201472 ViU MtU IdPI NNC MoU MH

Knight, Frank Hyneman, 1885–
Freedom and reform; essays in economics and social philosophy, by Frank H. Knight. New York and London, Harper & brothers [1947]
vii p., 1 l., 409 p. 21½cm.
Essays selected by Hubert Bonner and others. *cf.* Pref.
"In a sense a sequel to ... [the author's] Ethics of competition, published in 1935."—Pref.
CONTENTS.—Freedom as fact and criterion.—Social science and the political trend.—Pragmatism and social action.—Ethics and economic reform.—Socialism: the nature of the problem.—Religion and ethics in modern civilization.—The meaning of democracy: its politico-economic structure and ideals.—Science, philosophy, and social procedure.—Fact and value in social science.—Some notes on the economic interpretation of history.—The rights of man and natural law.—Human nature and world democracy.—Economics, political science, and education.—The planful act: the possibilities and limitations of collective rationality.—The sickness of liberal society.
1. Liberty. 2. Social problems. 3. Economic policy. I. Bonner, Hubert, 1901– II. Title.
HN18.K5 304 47-3030

OrPR IdU CaBVaU WaSpG MtU MtBC OrCS ICU MH ViU MB
OClU TU MiU NcU GU FTaSU OrU OrP IdPI WaTC NSyU
NK 0201474 DLC CaOTP MiHM NcRS CU NcGU MH-BA NcD

HC21
.W46
Knight, Frank Hyneman, 1885- tr.

Weber, Max, 1864–1920.
General economic history, by Max Weber, translated by Frank H. Knight ... New York, Greenberg [1927]

Knight, Frank Hyneman, 1885-
Notes on utility and cost. [n.p., n.d.]
35 l. 28 cm.
"Published as two articles in the Zeitschrift für Nationaloekonomie (Vienna), Band VI, Heft 1, 3 (1935)"
1. Cost. 2. Value. I. Title.

NK 0201476 CaBVaU CU

Knight,Frank Hyneman,1885-
The quantity of capital and the rate of interest [by] Frank H.Knight. Reprinted for private circulation from the Journal of political economy,vol.XLIV,nos.4 and 5,August and October 1936. [Chicago, 1936]
cover-title,433-463,[611]-642 p. diagr. 24cm.

1.Interest and usury. I.Title.

HB521.K7

NK 0201477 MiU CU

VOLUME 300

Knight, Frank Hyneman, 1885-
The Ricardian theory of production and distribution, by Frank H. Knight ... [Toronto, 1935?]
cover-title, [3]-25, 171-196 p. 25½cm.
"Reprinted from the Canadian journal of economics and political science, v.I, no.1 and 2, February and May, 1935."

1. Economics--Addresses, essays, lectures. I. Title. II. Title: Production and distribution. III. Distribution, The Ricardian theory of.
HB161.R492K7

NK 0201478 MiU CU ICU

Knight, Frank Hyneman, 1885-
Risk, uncertainty and profit, by Frank H. Knight ... [Boston and New York, 1921]
4 p. l., vii-xiv, 381, [1] p. diagrs. 20½cm.
Thesis (PH. D.)—Cornell university, 1916.
"Hart, Schaffner & Marx prize essays. XXXI."

1. Risk. 2. Profit. I. Title.
21-18354
Library of Congress HB601.K68
Cornell Univ. Libr. [2]

NK 0201479 NIC ViU DLC

Knight, Frank Hyneman, 1885-
Risk, uncertainty and profit, by Frank H. Knight ... Boston and New York, Houghton Mifflin company, 1921.
xiv, 381, [1] p. diagrs. 21 cm. (*Half-title:* Hart, Schaffner & Marx prize essays, XXXI)
CONTENTS.—pt. 1. Introductory.—pt. 2. Perfect competition.—pt. 3. Imperfect competition through risk and uncertainty.

1. Risk. 2. Profit. I. Title.
HB601.K7 21—12860

MtBC CaBVa CaBVaU
PSC PU PPT NcD CU TxHU NIC MH OU MiU OrP MtU OrPR
NK 0201480 DLC PBm MiU OCl OU OCU ICJ MB NN ViU

Knight, Frank Hyneman, 1885-
Risk, uncertainty and profit, by Frank H. Knight ... Boston and New York, Houghton Mifflin company, 1921. [London, The London school of economics and political science, 1933]
xl, 381 p. diagrs. 21½cm. (*Added t.-p.:* ... Series of reprints of scarce tracts in economic and political science. no. 16)
"With an additional introductory essay hitherto unpublished."
"First published in 1921, as number XXXI in Messrs. Hart, Schaffner and Marx' series of prize essays on economics."—Editorial note.
1. Risk. 2. Profit. I. Title.
35-16561
Library of Congress HB601.K7 1933
——— Copy 2. [3] 330.1

NcD WaWW WaTC OrSaW WaSpG
NK 0201481 DLC IdU OrCS IdPI TU PPD OO OBm OU MB CU

Knight, Frank Hyneman, 1885-
Risk, uncertainty and profit, by Frank H. Knight ... Boston and New York, Houghton Mifflin company, 1921. [London, The London school of economics and political science, 1939]
xl, 381 p. diagrs. 21½cm. (*Added t.-p.:* ... Series of reprints of scarce tracts in economic and political science. no. 16)
"Fourth impression, 1939."
"With an additional introductory essay hitherto unpublished."
"First published in 1921, as number XXXI in Messrs. Hart, Schaffner and Marx' series of prize essays on economics."—Editorial note.
1. Risk. 2. Profit. I. Title.

NK 0201482 ViU

HB601 .K7 1940
Knight, Frank Hyneman, 1885-
Risk, uncertainty and profit ... Boston and New York, Houghton Mifflin, 1921. [London, London school of economics and political science, 1940]
xliv, 381 p. (Added t.-p.: ... Series of reprints of scarce tracts in economic and political science. no.16)
"First published in 1921, as number XXXI in Messrs. Hart, Schaffner and Marx' series of prize essays on economics."--Editorial note.

NK 0201483 ICU

Knight, Frank Hyneman, 1885-
Risk, uncertainty and profit, by Frank H. Knight ... Boston and New York, Houghton Mifflin company, 1921. [London, The London school of economics and political science, 1940]
xliv, 381 p. diagrs. 21½cm. (*Added t.-p.:* ... Series of reprints of scarce tracts in economic and political science. no. 16)
"Fifth impression, 1940."
"With an additional introductory essay hitherto unpublished."
"First published in 1921, as number XXXI in Messrs. Hart, Schaffner and Marx' series of prize essays on economics."—Editorial note.

NK 0201484 ViU

Knight, Frank Hyneman, 1885-
Risk, uncertainty and profit. Boston and New York, Houghton Mifflin co., 1921. [London, The London school of economics and political science, 1948]
lviii, 381 p. diagrs. 22 cm. (Added t.-p: ... Series of reprints of scarce tracts in economic and political science. no. 16)
"With an additional introductory essay hitherto unpublished."
"First published in 1921, as number XXXI in Messrs. Hart, Schaffner and Marx' series of prize essays on economics." -Editorial note.

Knight, Frank Hyneman, 1885-
Risk, uncertainty and profit. Boston and

NK 0201486 PU MiHM

Knight, Frank Hyneman, 1885-
Social economic organization. [194-?]
[125]-250 p.

1. Economics.

NK 0201487 NNC

Knight, Frank Hyneman, 1885-
Unemployment and Mr. Keynes's revolution in economic theory, by F.H. Knight. [Toronto, 1937]
cover title, p. 100-123. 26 cm.
"Reprinted from the Canadian journal of economics and political science, February, 1937."
1. Keynes, John Maynard, 1883- General theory of employment, interest and money.

NK 0201488 CU

Knight, Frank Ozro, 1860-
Book of selected prescriptions, by F. O. Knight; in four departments; medical, veterinary, toilet, miscellaneous, and nearly two hundred choice prescriptions and formulas selected by the author during twenty-five years of practical experience in the drug business ... [Conway? Ark., 1904]
109 p. front. (port.) 23½cm.
Several blank leaves included in paging.
1. Medicine—Formulae, receipts, prescriptions. 7-17686
Library of Congress RS125.K7 Copyright

NK 0201489 DLC DNLM

Knight, Franklin, ed.
Letters on agriculture
see under Washington, George, pres., U.S., 1732-1799.

Knight, Franklin, ed.

Washington, George, *pres. U. S.*, 1732-1799.
Monuments of Washington's patriotism: containing a facsimile of his public accounts, kept during the revolutionary war; and some of the most interesting documents connected with his military command and civil administration. 3d ed., with additions and embellishments. Pub. by the trustees of Washington's manual labour school and male orphan asylum ... Washington, 1841.

Knight, Franklin.
An oration before the Democratic Republicans of Marblehead, delivered at their request, on the Fourth of July, 1834. Boston, Published for the Committee, 1834
23 p.

NK 0201492 MH

Knight, Freda de
see **De Knight, Freda**, 1916-

Knight, Frederic Butterfield, 1891-1948.
Answer book for Standard service arithmetics. Grade VII-VIII. By F.B.Knight, J.W.Studebaker, and G.M.Ruch. Chicago, etc., Scott, Foresman and co. [1926?]
Cover-title.
"Standard mathematical service."

NK 0201494 MH-Ed OrU

Educ T 119.28.491
Knight, Frederic Butterfield, 1891-1948.
Answer book for Standard service arithmetic grade seven. By F.B.Knight, J.W.Studebaker [and] G.M.Ruch. Chicago, etc., Scott, Foresman and co. [1928?]
"Standard mathematical service."
Paper cover serves as title-page."

NK 0201495 MH-Ed

Knight, Frederic Butterfield, 1891-1948.
Arithmetic. 5th-6th grade. Pt. 1-2 Experimental ed. ... By F. B. Knight and G. M. Ruch... Chicago, Atlanta (etc.) Scott, Foresman and company (c1924-
2 v. in 4 illus. 18½cm.

NK 0201496 DHEW ICU

Knight, Frederic Butterfield, 1891-1948.
Arithmetic work-book. Teachers edition. Grade 5-6, by F.B.Knight, G.M.Ruch. J.W.Studebaker. Edited by G.W.Myers. Chicago, etc., Scott, Foresman and co. [c.1925]
2 v. (Standard mathematical service)

NK 0201497 MH CU

Knight, Frederic Butterfield, 1891-
Arithmetic work-book. Grade 3,7. By F.B. Knight, G.M.Ruch, J.W.Studebaker. Edited by G.W.Myers. Chicago, etc., Scott, Foresman and co. [c.1926]
"Standard mathematical service."

NK 0201498 MH-Ed

Knight, Frederic Butterfield, 1891-
Arithmetic work-book. Grade 3,7. By F.B. Knight, G.M.Ruch, J.W.Studebaker. Edited by G.W.Myers. Chicago, etc., Scott, Foresman and co. [c.1926]
"Standard mathematical service."
"Teacher's edition."

NK 0201499 MH-Ed PBm

VOLUME 300

LT QA103 .K684 (Ed) Knight, Frederic Butterfield, 1891-
...Arithmetic work-book, grade 3-8, by F.B. Knight, G.M.Ruch, J.W.Studebaker; edited by G.W. Myers... Chicago [etc.°1925-°27]
6v. illus. 28cm. (Standard mathematical service)

Teacher's edition.

NK 0201500 ICU OCU

Knight, Frederic Butterfield.
Arithmetic work-book. Grade V. by F.B.Knight, G.M.Ruch, J.W.Studebaker. Edited by G.W.Myers. Chicago, etc., Scott, Foresman and co. [c.1925]

"Standard mathematical service."

NK 0201501 MH-Ed OCU

Knight, Frederic Butterfield, 1891- joint author.

Potter, Franklin Hazen, 1869-
Basic drill units in Latin ... for beginning students and comprehensive review for advanced students, by F. H. Potter ... and F. B. Knight ...
New York, Chicago [etc.] Rand, McNally & company [°1930-

Knight, Frederic Butterfield, 1891- joint author.
FOR OTHER EDITIONS SEE MAIN ENTRY

Benz, Harry Edward.
... The efficiency book for high schools, by H. E. Benz ... and F. B. Knight ... New York, Chicago [etc.] Rand, McNally & company [°1929]

LT QA103 1924 .K6 Knight, Frederic Butterfield, 1891-
Fifth grade arithmetic, part one. Experimental edition for use in the university schools, University of Iowa, and in cooperating schools, by F.B. Knight and G.M.Ruch... Chicago, Scott, Foresman and company [1924]
v, [1], 170p. illus. 19cm.

1.Arithmetic - Study and teaching. I.Ruch, Giles Murrel, 1891- joint author.

NK 0201504 NNU-W OU

Knight, Frederic Butterfield, 1891- joint author.

Adams, Maude.
The French work book, by Maude Adams ... and F. B. Knight ... New York, Chicago [etc.] Rand, McNally & company [°1929]

Knight, Frederic Butterfield, 1891-
Happiness, the longer view [by] F. B. Knight.
(*In* National education association of the United States. Addresses and proceedings, 1935. p. 118)

1. Happiness.

E 36-272

Library, U. S. Office of Library of Congress — Education L13.N212 1935 [L13.N4 1935]

NK 0201506 DHEW

Knight, Frederic Butterfield, 1891-
... The learning of the 100 addition combinations and th 100 subtraction combinations, by Frederic B. Knight and Minnie S. Behrens. New York, London [etc.] Longmans, Green and co., 1928.
xiii, 82 p. pl., diagr. $19\frac{1}{2}$cm. (Longmans' monographs in education)

1. Arithmetic—Study and teaching. 2. Educational psychology. I. Behrens, Minnie S., joint author. II. Title.

Library of Congress QA135.K55 28-19928

NK 0201507 DLC MtU PPT MiU OCl OClW OU PPPL PU-Penn WaU KEmT MsU

Knight, Frederic Butterfield, 1891- joint author.
FOR OTHER EDITIONS SEE MAIN ENTRY

Ruch, Giles Murrel, 1892-
Living mathematics [by] G. M. Ruch, F. B. Knight [and] G. E. Hawkins. Chicago, New York [etc.] Scott, Foresman & company [1942]

Knight, Frederic Butterfield, 1891-1948, joint author.

Lane, Ruth O.
... Manual of directions for geometry rapid drill cards [by] Ruth O. Lane ... F. B. Knight ... G. M. Ruch ... Chicago, Atlanta [etc.] Scott, Foresman and company [°1929]

QA43 .R8 1942 Knight, Frederic Butterfield, 1891- joint author.
FOR OTHER EDITIONS SEE MAIN ENTRY

Ruch, Giles Murrel, 1892-
Mathematics and life [by] G. M. Ruch, F. B. Knight [and] J. W. Studebaker. Chicago, Scott, Foresman [1942]

Knight, Frederic Butterfield, 1891-
Mathematics and life, by F. B. Knight, J. W. Studebaker and Gladys Tate. [New ed.] Chicago, Scott, Foresman [1946-
v. illus. (part col.) 21 cm.
Earlier editions by G. M. Ruch and others.

1. Mathematics—Problems, exercises, etc. I. Studebaker, John Ward, 1887- joint author. II. Tate, Gladys, joint author. III. Ruch, Giles Murrel, 1892- Mathematics and life. IV. Title.

QA43.K5 1946 372.7 48-3396*

NK 0201511 DLC

Knight, Frederic Butterfield, 1891-1948.
Mathematics and life, by F. B. Knight, J. W. Studebaker and Gladys Tate. Chicago, Scott, Foresman [1948]
3 v. illus. (part col.) 21 cm.
Vol. 3 by George E. Hawkins and Gladys Tate.

1. Mathematics—Problems, exercises, etc. I. Studebaker, John Ward, 1887- joint author. II. Tate, Gladys, joint author. III. Hawkins, George Edmon, 1901- joint author. IV. Title.

QA43.K5 1948 372.7 48-3325 rev*

NK 0201512 DLC AAP

Knight, Frederic Butterfield, 1891- joint author.

Lapp, Claude Jerome, 1892-
Mathematics for the emergency [by] Lapp, Knight [and] Rietz. [Chicago, Atlanta, etc., Scott, Foresman and company, °1942]

Knight, Frederic Butterfield, 1891- ed.

LB3051 .G68 Greene, Harry Andrew, 1889-
Measurement and evaluation in the elementary school, by Harry A. Greene ... Albert N. Jorgensen ... and J. Raymond Gerberich ... New York, London [etc.] Longmans, Green and co., 1942.

Knight, Frederic Butterfield, 1891-1948 ed.

Greene, Harry Andrew, 1889-
Measurement and evaluation in the secondary school, by Harry A. Greene ... Albert N. Jorgensen ... and J. Raymond Gerberich ... New York, London [etc.] Longmans, Green and co., 1943.

Knight, Frederic Butterfield, 1891- joint author.
FOR OTHER EDITIONS SEE MAIN ENTRY

Studebaker, John Ward, 1887-
... Number stories ... by J. W. Studebaker, W. C. Findley, F. B. Knight and William S. Gray, reading director ... Chicago, New York [etc.] Scott, Foresman and company [°1940-

---

Knight, Frederic Butterfield, 1891- joint author.

Repp, Austin Chauncey.
Objective tests and review units in geography ... by A. C. Repp ... and F. B. Knight ... New York, Chicago [etc.] Rand, McNally & company [°1930]

Knight, Frederic Butterfield, 1891- joint author.

Repp, Austin Chauncey, 1892-
... Objective tests and review units in geography ... with answers for teachers use, by A. C. Repp ... and F. B. Knight ... New York, Chicago [etc.] Rand, McNally & company [°1931-

---

372.7 K69p Exten. Knight, Frederic Butterfield, 1891-
Problems in the teaching of arithmetic; a syllabus for discussions on important aspects of elementary school arithmetic, prepared for use in advanced courses in the teaching of arithmetic, by F.B. Knight, E.M. Luse [and] G.M. Ruch. Iowa City, Ia., Iowa Supply co., c1924.
unp. diagrs. Q.
Blank leaves for "Class notes" at end of each lesson.
Bibliography: p-4.

NK 0201519 IaU OrP OClBE PPPL OCl OU MH IU

LB1589 .K68 (Ed) Knight, Frederic Butterfield, 1891-
Problems in the teaching of arithmetic; a syllabus for discussions on important aspects of elementary school arithmetic ...by F.B.Knight...E.M.Luse ...G.M.Ruch... Iowa City, Iowa, Iowa supply co., c1925.
vi, 162p. diagrs. 27cm.

Includes blank leaves for "Class notes".
Bibliography: p.v.
1.Arithmetic - Study and teaching.

NK 0201520 ICU

Knight, Frederic Butterfield, 1891-
Problems in the teaching of arithmetic; a syllabus for discussions on important aspects of elementary school arithmetic, prepared for use in advanced courses in the teaching of arithmetic, by F. B. Knight...E. M. Luse..[and] G. M. Ruch...Iowa City, Ia., Iowa supply co., c.1935.
vi, 162p. diagrs. 27cm.

NK 0201521 DHEW

VOLUME 300

BF131 .T47 1946 Knight, Frederic Butterfield, 1891– joint author.
FOR OTHER EDITIONS SEE MAIN ENTRY
Tiffin, Joseph, 1905–
The psychology of normal people [by] Joseph Tiffin, Frederic B. Knight and Eston Jackson Asher ... Rev. ed. Boston, D. C. Heath and company [1946]

Knight, Frederic Butterfield, 1891–
Qualities related to success in teaching, by Frederic Butterfield Knight ... New York city, Teachers college, Columbia university, 1922.
x, 67 p., 1 l. diagr. 25cm.
Thesis (PH. D.)—Columbia university, 1920.
Vita.
Published also as Contributions to education, Teachers college, Columbia university, no. 120.
1. Teaching. I. Title.
Library of Congress LB1025.K72 23-4618

NK 0201523 DLC NcU MiU OCIW ODW OO KEmT

Knight, Frederic Butterfield, 1891–
Qualities related to success in teaching, by Frederic Butterfield Knight ... New York city, Teachers college, Columbia university, 1922.
x, 67 p. incl. tables, diagr. 23½cm. (Teachers college, Columbia university. Contributions to education, no. 120)
Issued also as thesis (PH. D.) Columbia university.
1. Teaching. I. Title.
Library of Congress LB1025.K7 22—21000
——— Copy 2. LB5.C8 no. 120

NK 0201524 DLC IdU-SB OrP Or OrCS OrU WaTC NcRS NcD PWcS PU PBm PPPL ICJ MB

Knight, Frederic Butterfield, 1891– joint author.
Lapp, Claude Jerome, 1892–
Review of pre-college mathematics; a work-book for establishing the prerequisites of first courses in mathematics, physics, and chemistry, by C. J. Lapp ... F. B. Knight ... H. L. Rietz ... Chicago, Atlanta [etc.] Scott, Foresman and company, °1934.

Knight, Frederic Butterfield, 1891– joint author.
Ruch, Giles Murrel, 1892–
... Schemata for the analysis of drill in fractions, by G. M. Ruch, F. B. Knight, E. A. Olander, [and] G. E. Russell. Iowa City, The University, 1936.

---

511 K74sp **Knight, Frederic Butterfield, 1891–**
A self-help arithmetic work-book, by F. B. Knight, G. M. Ruch [and] J. W. Studebaker. Chicago, Atlanta [etc.] Scott, Foresman and company [c1939–
v. illus.
1. Arithmetic - Problems, exercises, etc. I. Ruch, Giles Murrell, 1892– jt. auth. II. Studebaker, John Ward, 1887– jt. auth. III. Title.

NK 0201527 KEmT OrCS OrAshS

Knight, Frederic Butterfield, 1891– joint author.
FOR OTHER EDITIONS SEE MAIN ENTRY
Ruch, Giles Murrel, 1892–
... Standard service algebra [by] G. M. Ruch [and] F. B. Knight. Chicago, Atlanta [etc.] Scott, Foresman & company [°1937]

---

512 K69s Educ. Knight, Frederic Butterfield, 1891–
...Standard service algebra work-book, Teacher's ed. By F.B. Knight, G.M.Ruch [and] H.W. McCulloch... Chicago, Scott [c1930]
78p. diagrs., forms. 4. (Standard mathematical service)
Blank pages interspersed for "Teacher's diagnostic record."

NK 0201529 IaU MiU

Knight, Fredric Butterfield, 1891–
Standard service arithmetic work-book, by F.B.Knight, G.M.Ruch [and] J.W.Studebaker. Grades 3-8. Teacher's ed. Chicago, etc., Scott, Foresman and co. [c.1932]
6 v. (Standard mathematical service.)

NK 0201530 MH OrLgE

Knight, Frederic Butterfield, 1891–
... Standard service arithmetics ... by F. B. Knight ... J. W. Studebaker ... G. M. Ruch ...
Chicago, New York [etc.] Scott, Foresman and company [°1926]
v. illus., diagrs. 19½cm. (Standard mathematical service, ed. by G. W. Myers)
1. Arithmetic—1901– I. Studebaker, John Ward, 1887– joint author. II. Ruch, Giles Murrel, 1892– joint author. III. Title.

NK 0201531 ViU

Knight, Frederic Butterfield, 1891–
... Standard service arithmetics ... by F. B. Knight ... J. W. Studebaker ... G. M. Ruch ...
Chicago, New York [etc.] Scott, Foresman and company [°1927]
v. illus., diagrs. 19½cm. (Standard mathematical service, ed. by G. W. Myers)
1. Arithmetic—1901– I. Studebaker, John Ward, 1887– joint author. II. Ruch, Giles Murrel, 1892– joint author. III. Title.
Library of Congress QA103.K7 27—18011

NK 0201532 DLC Wa OrMonO OrLgE OrCS OU OCl OCU PPAp MH CU PPCI PPT

QA106 .K6 Manual Knight, Frederic Butterfield. 1891– joint author.
Studebaker, John Ward, 1887–
... Standard service arithmetics. Course of study and teacher's manual ... by J. W. Studebaker ... F. B. Knight ... W. C. Findley ... Chicago, Atlanta [etc.] Scott, Foresman and company [°1929–

Knight, Frederic Butterfield, 1891–
Standard service arithmetics. Grade IV,VI. By F.B.Knight, J.W.Studebaker, G.M.Ruch. Chicago, etc., Scott, Foresman and co. [1934, c.1927]
"Standard mathematical service."

NK 0201534 MH-Ed OCU ODW

Knight, Frederic Butterfield, 1891–
Standard service arithmetics, grade eight, by F.B.Knight, J.W.Studebaker, G.M.Ruch. Chicago, etc., Scott, Foresman and co. [c.1928]
"Standard mathematical service."
"Temporary printing, chapters I-IV."

NK 0201535 MH-Ed

Knight, Frederic Butterfield, 1891– joint author.
Welte, Herbert David, 1898–
... Standard service geometry work-book. Teacher's ed. By H. D. Welte ... and F. B. Knight ... Chicago, New York [etc.] Scott, Foresman and company [°1929]

Knight, Frederic Butterfield, 1891–1948.
... Study arithmetics ... by F. B. Knight, G. M. Ruch, J. W. Studebaker, W. C. Findley; William S. Gray, reading director. Chicago, Atlanta [etc.] Scott, Foresman and company [°1934–
v. illus. (part col.) diagrs. 19½ cm. (Standard service series)
Revised edition of Standard service arithmetics.
1. Arithmetic—1901– I. Ruch, Giles Murrel, 1892– joint author. II. Studebaker, John Ward, 1887– joint author. III. Findley, William Copley, 1894– joint author. IV. Gray, William Scott, 1885– V. Title.
A 38—352
New York Univ. Wash. Sq. Library QA103 1934.K6
for Library of Congress [QA103.K]

NK 0201537 NNU-W OrLgE CU ODW PPTU PU

QA103 .K73 Knight, Frederic Butterfield, 1891–
... Study arithmetics ... by F. B. Knight, G. M. Ruch, J. W. Studebaker [and] W. C. Findley. Chicago, Atlanta [etc.] Scott, Foresman and company [c1935–
v. illus.(part col.) diagrs. 19½cm. (Standard service series)
1. Arithmetic--1901– I. Ruch, Giles Murrel, 1892– joint author. II. Studebaker, John Ward, 1887– joint author. III. Findley, William C., joint author. IV. Title.

NK 0201538 DLC PPT MH

QA106 .K64 Knight, Frederic Butterfield, 1891–
Study arithmetics ...
by F.B. Knight, G.M. Ruch, J.W. Studebaker [and] W.C. Findley; William S. Gray, reading director. Chicago, Atlanta [etc.] Scott, Foresman and company [c1940–
v. illus. (part col.) diagrs. 19½cm.
1. Arithmetic--1901– I. Ruch, Giles Murrel, 1892– , joint author. II. Studebaker, John Ward, 1887– , joint author. III. Findley, William Copley, 1894– , joint author. IV. Gray, William Scott, 1885– V. Title. -- ---copy 2.

NK 0201539 DLC MH

QA106 .S85 **Knight, Frederic Butterfield, 1891–**
Study arithmetics. Book 3-8, by J. W. Studebaker [and others. New ed.] Chicago, Scott, Foresman and Co. [1943–46]

Knight, Frederic Butterfield, 1891–
Study arithmetics. Grade VI. By F.B.Knight, J.W.Studebaker [and] G.M.Ruch. Chicago, etc., Scott, Foresman and co. [c.1936]
"Standard service series."

NK 0201541 MH-Ed

KNIGHT, F[rederic] B[utterfield],1891–
Syllabus for a first course in educational psychology; thirty lessons designed to introduce students to the applications of psychology to educational practice. By F.B.Knight, G.M.Ruch. Iowa, City, Ia., The Iowa Supply Co., [192-]

NK 0201542 MH-Ed PBm

VOLUME 300

Knight, Frederic Butterfield, 1891-
Syllabus for a first course in educational psychology, thirty lessons designed to introduce students to the applications of psychology to educational practice. 2d rev. ed. Iowa City, Williams, 1928.
n. p. 0.

NK 0201543 NcD OrP

Knight, Frederic Butterfield, 1891-
Syllabus for a first course in educational psychology; thirty lessons designed to introduce students to the applications of psychology to educational practice. 2d revised ed., by F.B.Knight [and] G.M.Ruch. Iowa City, Ia., Williams Iowa Supply, 1929.

Paper cover serves as title-page.

NK 0201544 MH-Ed

LB1051 .K65 Knight, Frederic Butterfield, 1891-
Syllabus for a first course in educational psychology; thirty lessons designed to introduce students to the applications of psychology to educational practice, by F. B. Knight and G. M. Ruch ... Iowa City, Ia. ₍193-?₎
₍69₎ 1.
Interleaved.

1. Educational psychology.

NK 0201545 ICU

370.15 K74s Knight, Frederic Butterfield.
Syllabus for a first course in educational psychology; thirty lessons designed to introduce students to the applications of psychology to educational practice [by] F. B. Knight [and] T. R. McConnell. [Iowa City, Ia., c1931]
[124]p.

NK 0201546 IU

Knight, Frederic Butterfield, 1891-
Syllabus for a first course in educational psychology, 1934-35 edition ₍by₎ F. B. Knight ... ₍and₎ T. R. McConnell ... Iowa City, Williams, c1934.
cover-title, ₍145₎ p. 27½cm.

Contains bibliographies.

1.Educational psychology. I.McConnell, T jt.au.

NK 0201547 NNC OrPR IaAS

+ LT QA103 1932 .K6W3 Knight, Frederic Butterfield, 1891-
... The teacher's arithmetic record book (For use with the Standard service arithmetics) by F.B. Knight... J.W. Studebaker... G.M.Ruch... Chicago, Scott, Foresman and co. ₍1932?₎
vi,175p. 28cm. (At head of title: Standard mathematical service)
1.Arithmetic - Study and teaching. I. Knight,Frederic Butterfield,1891- Standard service arithmetics. II.Studebaker,John Ward,1887- joint auth. III.Ruch,Giles Murrell,1892- joint auth.

NK 0201548 NNU-W

Knight, Frederic Butterfield, 1891- joint author.

Franzen, Raymond Hugh, 1895-
Textbook selection, by R. H. Franzen ... and F. B. Knight ... with an introduction by Ernest Horn. Baltimore, Md., Warwick & York, inc., 1922.

QA135 .S922 Knight, Frederic Butterfield, 1891- joint author.

Studebaker, John Ward, 1887-
Understanding numbers, by J. W. Studebaker, W. C. Findley, F. B. Knight ₍and₎ G. M. Ruch. Teacher's guidebook for the Number stories program. Chicago, New York ₍etc.₎ Scott, Foresman & company ₍1942₎

—— —— Supplement to take the place of pages 139-192. Chicago, New York ₍etc.₎ Scott Foresman & company ₍1944₎

Knight, Frederic Butterfield, 1891- ed.

Greene, Harry Andrew, 1889-
The use and interpretation of high school tests, by Harry A. Greene ... and Albert N. Jorgensen ... New York ₍etc.₎ Longmans, Green and co., 1936.

Knight, Frederic Butterfield, 1891-1948.
The use of scientific measurement as a basis for the improvement of instruction.
(*In* National education association of the United States. Addresses and proceedings, 1921. p. 450-451)

1. Grading and marking ₍(Students)₎

E 22-146

Library, U. S. Bur. of Education

NK 0201553 DHEW OU

Knight, Frederic Butterfield, 1891-1948, joint author.

Albjerg, *Mrs.* Esther Marguerite (Hall) 1895-
We, the guardians of our liberty; an account of the American Bill of rights ₍by₎ Marguerite Hall Albjerg ... Frederic Butterfield Knight ... ₍and₎ E. J. Woodward ... Chicago, Beckley-Cardy company ₍°1940₎

HV245 .K7 Knight, Frederic Winn, 1812-1897.
The parochial system versus centralization: statistics of "close and open parishes:" effects of settlement and removal ... London, Shaw, 1854.
2 pts.

NK 0201555 ICU PPPD NN PU

HV245 .K703 Knight, Frederic Winn, 1812-1897.
... A statistical report to the Poor law board on the subject of close and open parishes ... London, Shaw, 1854.
148 p.
At head of title: Audi alteram partem.

NK 0201556 ICU CSmH CtY

F 0745 468 KNIGHT, FREDERICK.
Knight and Butters' crests of Great Britain & Ireland, Dominion of Canada, India & Australasia. Edited by Joseph MacLaren. London,T.C. Jack₍1885₎
2v. plates.

Vol.2: plates.
Also published under title: Royal book of crests of Great Britain & Ireland, Dominion of Canada, India & Australasia.

NK 0201557 ICN

Knight, Frederick
Knight & Rumley's crests of the nobility & gentry of the United Kingdom of Great Britain & Ireland, designed principally for the use of artists ... London ₍Rumley & Knight, 1827₎
2 p. l., ₍3₎-7, ₍22₎ p. 29 pl. 32cm.
1. Heraldry - Great Britain. I. Title: Crests of the nobility & gentry of the United Kingdom.

NK 0201558 NNC MdBP PP NjP

Knight, Frederick.
Fredk. Knight's crests of the nobility & gentry of the United Kingdom of Great Britain & Ireland. Designed principally for the use of artists ... London, Simpkin & Marshall ₍183-₎
1 p. l., (2), xxvii pl. 28 x 23cm.
Engr. t.-p.

1. Crests. 2. Heraldry—Gt. Brit.

10-1589†

Library of Congress CR57.G7K7

NK 0201559 DLC PPF MB

Knight, Frederick.
Knight's cyclopædia of ornaments, designed for the use of architects, builders, silversmiths, chasers, modellers, jewellers, die sinkers, engravers, founders, carvers and all ornamental manufacturers. ₍London? 183-?₎ 2 v. of mounted pl. 31cm.
No title-pages or letter-press; title in ms.
In portfolios, with title: Knights cyclopedia of ornaments.

311817-18B. 1. Decorative art.
N. Y. P. L. August 8, 1945

NK 0201560 NN

Knight, Frederick.
Knight's cyclopædia of ornaments designed for the use of architects, builders, silversmiths, chasers, modellers, jewellers, die sinkers, engravers, founders, carvers, and all ornamental manufacturers. Edinburgh, T. C. Jack ₍187-₎
1 p. l., 123 pl. 33cm.

1. Decoration and ornament.

12-14929

Library of Congress NK1530.K7

NK 0201561 DLC

Knight, Frederick.
Cyclopædia of ornaments, designed for the use of architects...jewellers... and all ornamental manufacturers. Edin. (1881.) F. 123 pl., no text.
Note.- Plate 50 is missing.

NK 0201562 CU

Knight, Frederick.
Knight's gems; or, Device book. Second edition. London: J. Williams ₍1836₎ 3 p.l., 85 pl. 21cm.
Engraved t.-p., with vignette.
"English and French mottos," 2 p.l.

1. Devices. 2. Mottoes. *Card revised*
N. Y. P. L. December 13, 1940

NK 0201563 NN PPF PP NNC

Jc30 34p Knight, Frederick.
Knight's Gems or device book. 2d ed. ... London,J.Williams[184-?]
1p.l.,3,[4]p. 85pl. 24½cm.
Engraved t.-p. with title vignette.

1.Emblems. 2.Devices. I.Title.

NK 0201564 CtY

VOLUME 300

Knight, Frederick.
Knight's heraldic illustrations, designed for the use of herald painters and engravers. London, T. Griffiths [1843]
20 pl. (incl. t.-p.) 31½cm.

1. Heraldry.

10-2231†

Library of Congress CR125.K7

NK 0201565 DLC NN

*CR51 K6 Knight, Frederick.
Knight & Rumley's Heraldic illustrations, specimen crests & fancy gems. Designed for the use of artists. Edinburgh, Thomas C. Jack [1870?]

XX,XXVII[1]24 plates. 31½cm.

Title vignette.
"This work included the plates in 'Knight's Heraldic illustrations', and in 'Knight & Rumley's crests', etc.; to which several additional plates have been added".-British museum.

NK 0201566 NBuG OClW

Knight, Frederick.
Knight's modern and antique gems. [London] T. Griffiths; [etc., etc.] 1828.
1 p. l., 3, [4] p. 85 pl. 19cm.
Engr. t.-p., with vignette.
"English and French mottos": 4 p. at end.

1. Gems.

12-11896

Library of Congress NK5545.K7

NK 0201567 DLC WU CtY WaSp

Knight, Frederick.
Knight's new book of seven hundred & fifty eight plain, ornamented & reversed cyphers. Engraved by Nathaniel Gill & J. H. Whiteman. London, F. Knight [1830?]
55 pl. (incl. t.-p.) 21½cm.
Engraved throughout.

1. Monograms.

CA 17-1157 Unrev'd

Library of Congress NK3640.K7

NK 0201568 DLC PPF

Knight, Frederick.
Knight's Ornamental alphabets. Improved ed. London, J. Rimell [1832]
cover-title, 5 plates. 21 x 29cm.

1. Alphabets.

NK 0201569 NNC

Knight, Frederick.
Knight's ornamental alphabets. Improved edition. London: J. Rimell [1865?] 5 pl. 22½ x 30cm.
Cover-title.

573501. 1. Alphabet—Specimens. I. Title. *Card revised* December 10, 1940
N. Y. P. L.

NK 0201570 NN

Knight, Frederick
Knight's ornamental designs; a self-explanatory manual, with a treatise on ornamental art, by W. B. Scott. Jack, n. d.
63 p., 120 plates.

NK 0201571 MiD

F 0745 .468a KNIGHT, FREDERICK.
Royal book of crests of Great Britain & Ireland, Dominion of Canada, India & Australasia... London, J. Macveigh [pref. 1883]
2v. plates.

Vol.2: plates.
Also publshed under the title: Knight & Butters' crests of Great Britain & Ireland, Dominion of Canada, India and Australasia.

NK 0201572 ICN

Knight, Frederick.
Knight's scroll ornaments, designed for the use of silversmiths, chasers, die-sinkers, modellers, &c., &c. [London] T. Griffiths; [etc., etc., 1825-30]
7 p. 48 pl. (incl. engr. t.-p.) 31½ x 27cm.

1. Scrolls (Decorative design) 2. Decoration and ornament.

12-14927

Library of Congress NK1580.K7

NK 0201573 DLC PPL NIC MdBP DSI OOC

Knight, Frederick.
Knight's scroll ornaments, designed for the use of silversmiths, chasers, die-sinkers, modellers, &c., &c. ... London: J. Williams [etc., etc., 1833?] 50 pl. 33cm.
Without text.

252184B. 1. Decorative art. November 16, 1943
N. Y. P. L.

NK 0201574 NN PPF

KNIGHT, Frederick.
Knight's Unique fancy ornaments... London: J. Williams [, 1835?] 30 pl. incl. t.-p. 31cm.

672218A. 1. Decorative art.

NK 0201575 NN MdBP PPF PP

Knight, Frederick.
Knight's vases and ornaments. ...
London, 1830.

31
10881

NK 0201576 MdBP

Knight, Frederick.
Vases and ornaments, designed for the use of architects, silversmiths, jewellers, modellers, chasers, die sinkers, founders, carvers, and all ornamental manufacturers. London, 1833.
7 p., 59 plates. 34 cm.

1. Design, Decorative. I. Title.

NK1533.K5 59-57677

NK 0201577 DLC MdBP MH RPB PPF PPL NN

Knight, Frederick, 1791-1849.
Thorn cottage, or The poet's home. A memorial of Frederick Knight, esq., of Rowley, Mass. Boston, Press of Crocker and Brewster, 1855.
108 p. 20cm.
Selections from his manuscripts with a biographical sketch prefixed. Notices of the Cogswell family, by Henry Cogswell Knight: p. [93]-108.

I. Knight, Henry Cogswell, 1788-1835. II. Title. III. Title: The poet's home.

28-1986

Library of Congress PS2196.K65Z8

NK 0201578 DLC MeB ViU OO MWA ICU MB Nh MnHi NN RPB

Lilly Library **KNIGHT, FREDERICK, 1791-1849**
Twilight; a poem ... by A student at law ... New-York, Printed by Collins and Co., 1813.
48 p. 12mo

Shaw, R. R. Am. bibl.: 28889.

NK 0201579 InU PPAmP MWA MHi CtY MBAt PU MH MdBP ViU

Knight, Frederick I[rving], 1841-
The climatic treatment of bronchial asthma. Philadelphia: W. J. Dornan, 1889. 8 p. 8°.
Repr.: American Climatological Association. Transactions. June, 1889.

1. Asthma. July 16, 1912.
N. Y. P. L.

NK 0201580 NN MB

Knight, Frederick I[rving], 1841-
Indications and contra-indications for altitude in the treatment of pulmonary tuberculosis. [Read at the meeting of the American Climatological Association, Washington, September, 1888. Philadelphia,] 1888. 8 p. 16°.
Repr.: Medical news. Philadelphia, November 24, 1888.
Title from cover.

1. Tuberculosis.—Treatment. February 3, 1913.
N. Y. P. L.

NK 0201581 NN MB

Knight, Frederick I[rving], 1841-
"Laryngeal vertigo." n. t.-p. New York, 1886. 12 p. 12°.
Repr.: New York medical jour., 1886. Bibliography, p. 12. Title from cover.

1. Larynx.—Diseases. February 13, 1913.
N. Y. P. L.

NK 0201582 NN MB

KNIGHT, Frederick Irving, 1841-
On the return of cured tubercular patients from high altitudes. N. Y. [1891.] 7 pp. 8°.

NK 0201583 MB

KNIGHT, Frederick Irving, 1841-
Recent progress in the treatment of throat diseases. (Boston Medical & Surgical Journal Vol. 92. (No.14). April 8, 1875. pp.410-414.)

24 1/2 cm.

NK 0201584 MBCo

VOLUME 300

KNIGHT, Frederick Irving, 1841-
A remarkable complication of so-called catarrhal pneumonia. (Boston Medical & Surgical Journal Vol. 92. (No.19). May 13, 1875. pp. 549-553).

24 1/2 cm.

NK 0201585 MBCo

Knight, Frederick I[rving], 1841-
Remarks on sending patients away from home. [Read before the Boston Society for Medical Improvement, October 23, 1893.] Boston: Damrell & Upham, 1893. 6 p. 16°.

Repr.: Boston medical and surgical jour. December 21, 1893. Title from cover.

1. Climate.—Influence on man.
N. Y. P. L. June 9, 1913.

NK 0201586 NN MB

Knight (Frederick Irving) [1841-]. Report on diseases of the throat. 10 pp. 8°. [Boston, 1872.]
Repr. from: Boston M. & S. J., 1872, lxxxvii.

NK 0201587 DNLM

Knight, F[rederick] I[rving], 1841-
Retro-pharyngeal sarcoma; read at the first annual meeting of the American Laryngological Association, held in New York, June 10-12, 1879. St. Louis: G. O. Rumbold & Co., 1879. 16 p., 1 pl. 8°.

Repr.: St. Louis medical and surgical journal. Title from cover.

1. Pharynx.—Diseases.
N. Y. P. L. March 28, 1912.

NK 0201588 NN

Knight, Frederick I[rving], 1841-
Shall anything be done by legal authority to prevent the spread of tuberculosis? Read at the meeting of the American Climatological Association at Washington, May 30, 1894. n. p., 1894. 5 p. 8°.

Repr.: International medical magazine. July, 1894. Title from cover.

1. Tuberculosis.—Prevention.
N. Y. P. L. April 22, 1912

NK 0201589 NN

Knight, Frederick I[rving], 1841-
Singers' nodes. [Read before the American Laryngological Association, at its sixteenth annual congress. New York: D. Appleton and Co., cop. 1894.] 6 p. 12°.

Repr.: New York medical jour. December 1, 1894. Title from cover.

1. Larynx.—Diseases.
N. Y. P. L. February 7, 1913.

NK 0201590 NN

KNIGHT, Frederick Irving, 1841-
The treatment of bronchial asthma.
Boston. Damrell & Upham. 1897. 10 pp. 16°.
Reprinted from the Boston medical and surgical journal, March 25, 1897 [*574 1897].

NK 0201591 MB

Knight, Frederick S., ed.

The Compensation review; reports of all decisions rendered in workmen's compensation cases in the federal courts and in the state supreme courts ... v. 1-
Jan. 1925-
New York, N. Y., The Underwriter printing and publishing company, °1925-

Knight, Frederick S., ed.

The Insurance law journal. Reports of all decisions rendered in insurance cases in the federal courts, and in the state courts of last resort. v. 1-91; Sept. 1871-Dec. 1938. New York [L. A. Mack; etc., etc., 1871]-1938.

Knight, Frederick Stuart, 1884-
The stencil duplicated newspaper, by F. S. Knight and Damon Knight. [Hood River, Or., F. S. Knight and D. Knight, °1941]

126 p. illus. 27½cm.
Reproduced from type-written copy.

1. College and school journalism. I. Knight, Damon Francis, 1922- joint author. II. Title.
41-27601
Library of Congress LB3621.K5
[3] 070.489

NK 0201594 DLC MtU Or Wa KEmT LU OrCS OrU

Knight, Frederick William.
Notes on the family of Ronayne or Ronan of counties Cork and Waterford (as they appeared in the "Journal" of the Cork historical and archæological society for April-June, July-September, October-December, 1916: and April-June, July-September, 1917.) By Frederick W. Knight. To which are appended Notes on the families of Desmond and Ronayne by E. C. R. (Edward Camillus Ronayne), from the April-June, 1916, no. of the same "Journal." Cork, Printed by Guy and co. ltd., 1917.

47, [1] p. front. (coat of arms) 24½cm.
1. Ronayne family. I. Ronayne, Edward Camillus. II. Title.
20-16683
Library of Congress CS499.R7

NK 0201595 DLC CtY

PN 1129
.G3 K5
1887
Knight, G.
The new London echo. Eine sammlung englischer redensarten in zusammenhängenden unterhaltungen, wie sie im geselligen leben vorkommen und die man täglich hören kann, wenn man in London lebt, von G. Knight. Mit einem vollständigen englisch-deutschen wörterbuche über die in dem buche vorkommenden wörter. Mit angabe der aussprache nach Walker und Nuttall. Zum schulgebrach und selbstunterricht. 10. aufl. Leipzig, Dyk'sche buchhandlung [1887]
200 p. 17cm.

NK 0201596 DLC

PE1131
.K69
Knight, G.
The new London echo. Eine sammlung englischer redensarten in zusammenhängenden unterhaltungen ... von G. Knight. Mit einem vollständigen englischdeutschen wörterbuche über die in dem buche vorkommenden wörter. Mit angabe der ausprache nach Walker und Nuttall. Zum schulgebrauch und selbstunterricht. 11. der 10. gleichlautende aufl. Leipzig, Dyk'sche buchhandlung [1888]
200 p. 17cm.

NK 0201597 ICU

KNIGHT, G.A. Frank

See KNIGHT, George Alexander Francis.

Knight, G B

Radiation of UY, by G. B. Knight [and] R. L. Macklin. Oak Ridge, Tenn., Technical Information Division, Oak Ridge Directed Operations [1948]
7 p. diagrs. 27cm.
At head of title: United States Atomic Energy Commission. AECD - 1880.
"Declassified: April 20, 1948."
Bibliography: p. 7.
1. Uranium. 2. Isotopes I. Macklin, R L
II. Title. III. Ser.

NK 0201599 ViU

Knight, G. E.O., 1885- , ed.
German affairs. (Retorts)
see under title

KNIGHT, G E O , 1885-
Germany's demand for security, by G.E.O.Knight. London: The Golden Eagle Pub. Co.[, 1933?] 18 p. 19cm.

732351A. 1. Germany—For. rel., 1918-

NK 0201601 NN

Knight, G E O , 1885- , and G. Moonstone.
...High altitudes, by G. E. O. Knight & Gloria Moonstone. [London] The Golden Eagle Pub. Co., 1935. 30 p. 20½cm. (Problem plays. no. 1.)

1. Drama, English. I. Moonstone, Gloria, jt. au. II. Title. III. Ser.
N. Y. P. L. September 3, 1936

NK 0201602 NN

Bp46d
1
1933k
Knight, G E O 1885-
In defence of Germany ... London[1933]
"Third thousand."

NK 0201603 CtY

KNIGHT, G E O , 1885-
In defence of Germany, by G.E.O.Knight. London: The Golden Eagle Pub. Co. [1934] 39 p. 20½cm.

809537A. 1. Fascism—Germany. I. Title.

NK 0201604 NN

Knight, G. E. O., 1885-
Intimate glimpses of mysterious Tibet and neighbouring countries, [by] G. E. O. Knight... London: The Golden Vista Press, 1930. 72 p. port. 12°.

526399A. 1. Tibet—Descr. and trav., 1910-
N. Y. P. L. June 18, 1931

NK 0201605 NN MH DLC-P4

Knight, G Herbert.
The Christ child, Christmas cantata for chorus of mixed voices with organ accompaniment. By G. H. Knight. Vocal score ... Boston, Boston music company; New York, G. Schirmer, inc., [etc., etc., c1911]
1 p.l., 32 p. 26.5 cm.
At head of title on cover: Boston music co. edition of oratorios & cantatas.

NK 0201606 NNUT

783.4
K74t
Knight, G Herbert.
Lord of our life. Intercessory hymn-anthem for mixed voices. Boston, The Boston music co. c1917.
11p. (Boston music co. series for mixed voice. no.1316)

NK 0201607 IU

Knight, G Herbert.
Trust in God at all times. Cantata for general use, or for times of national peril, for choir and congregation, with organ accompaniment. Music by G. Herbert Knight. Vocal score ... Boston, Boston music company; New York, G. Schirmer, inc., [c1918]
1 p.l., 39 p. 27 cm.

NK 0201608 NNUT

VOLUME 300

Knight, G L.
The royal road to health, and miracles for the nineteenth century. The glove of "Ingersoll, the blatant Goliath", is picked up and the challenge to the church to prove her doctrine by working miracles is accepted. By Rev. G. L. Knight ... Memphis, Tenn., Daily scimitar book and job print., 1886.
195 p. 15½cm.

1. Faith-cure.

Library of Congre RZ401.K6 23-3765

NK 0201609 DLC

KNIGHT, G Wilson

See KNIGHT, George Wilson, 1897-

TK 7855 M33 no.123 Knight, Geoffrey.
Nuclear quadrupole hyperfine structure in slightly asymmetric rotor molecules [by] Geoffrey Knight, Jr. [and] B.T. Feld. [Cambridge] Massachusetts Institute of Technology, Research Laboratory of Electronics, 1949.
23p. (Massachusetts Institute of Technology. Research Laboratory of Electronics. Technical report no.123)
"Based on a thesis."
Bibliography: p.23.

NK 0201611 UU

PR4859 K45 J6 Knight, George.
Joy of living and other verses. Toronto, J.M.Dent [1948]
66p. 19cm.
"First printing, November, 1948."

NK 0201612 RPB CaOTU

Knight, George, of Edinburgh.
The orthoepic New Testament... Edinburgh, 1840
see under Bible. N.T. English. 1840. Authorized.

Knight, George, *of London.*
Dust in the balance. By George Knight. New York, R. F. Fenno & company [1896]
2 p. l., [7]-359, [1] p. 19cm.

Library of Congress PZ3.K744D 7-14179†

NK 0201613- DLC ViU

Knight, George, of London.
Sapphira of the Stage: how Sebastian Goss, being dumb, yet made love to her, and what befell.
= London. Jarrold. 1896. 148, (1) pp. [The daffodil library.] 18½ × 9 cm., in 4s.

NK 0201614 MB MH

Knight, George, *of London.*
A son of austerity; appreciation of the beyond and the flowering of despair. New York, Knickerbocker press; London, Ward, Lock, & co., 1900.
1 p. l., 51 p. 8°.

I. Title.

0—2631

NK 0201615 DLC NN OU

---

823 K7443s **Knight, George, of London.**
A son of austerity. Frontispiece by Harrison Fisher. New York, Hurst [c1912] viii,353p. front. 20cm.

NK 0201616 OrU

309.142 K744o 1829 Knight, George, of the Society of Friends.
Observations on some of the chief difficulties & disadvantages of English society, with suggestions for their remedy. London, Harvey and Darton, 1829.
216p. 22cm.

1. Gt. Brit. Social conditions. 2. Poor. Gt. Brit. 3. Criminal law. Gt. Brit. 4. Gt. Brit. Emigration and immigration. 5. Debts, Public. Gt. Brit. I. Title. 0 cd.

NK 0201617 KU NNC MU CtY

[Knight, George] of the Society of Friends.
Remarks on water baptism...Lond., 1837.

NK 0201618 PHC PPF

Knight, George, 1733-1790.
Catholic registers of Courtfield in the parish of Welsh Bicknor, Monmouthshire, 1773-1832. Contributed by John Hobson Matthews.
(In Catholic Record Society. Miscellanea. Vol. 4, pp. 411-428. London. 1907.)

G6347 — Courtfield, Welsh Bicknor [illegible], Monmouthshire, Eng. — Matthews, John Hobson, ed. — Registers. Parish.

NK 0201619 MB

Knight, George Alexander Francis.
Archæological light on the early Christianizing of Scotland, by G. A. Frank Knight ... with 3 appendices, 5 maps, and 32 illustrations on art paper. London, J. Clarke & company, limited, 1933.
2 v. fronts., plates, illus. (maps) 22½cm.
Bibliography: v. 2, p. 402-419.

1. Scotland—Church history. 2. Christian antiquities—Scotland. I. Title.

Library of Congress BR784.K6 34-22225
[2] 274.1

NK 0201620 DLC ICN MB PPPD

Pam. Coll. 44050 Knight, George Alexander Francis
The new reformation among the Czechs, by G. A. Frank Knight and J. W. Purves. Edinburgh, Publications Offices, United Free Church of Scotland [192-]
48 p. front. 18 cm.

1. Reformation. Czechoslovak Republic. 2. Reformation. Bohemia. I. Purves, J. W., jt. au. II. Title.

NK 0201621 NcD

Knight, George Alexander Francis.
Nile and Jordan, being the archæological and historical inter-relations between Egypt and Canaan from the earliest times to the fall of Jerusalem in A. D. 70, by Rev. G. A. Frank Knight ... London, J. Clarke & co., ltd., 1921.
xi, 13-572 p. v maps (1 fold.) 25½cm.
"The Egyptian origin of the book of Job": p. 379-405.
"Biblical chronology from Abraham to Solomon": p. 515-519.
"Index to the books and journals referred to": p. 520-542.

1. Egypt—Hist. 2. Palestine—Hist. 3. Bible. O. T. Job—Criticism, interpretation, etc. 4. Bible. O. T.—Chronology. 5. Bible—Chronology—O. T. 6. Bible—Criticism, interpretation, etc.—O. T. Job. I. Title.

Library of Congress DT83.K6 21—8728

ODW NjNbS NN NjP PPStC NcU NcD IEG NIC ICMcC CU PPWe
NK 0201622 DLC CtY PU PPDrop PHC PBm OCl OCU OO

Knight, George Alexander Francis.
A sketch of Egyptian history down to the era of Tutankhamen.
(*In* Royal Philosophical Society of Glasgow, Scotland. Proceedings. Vol. 52, pp. 78-96. Glasgow. 1924.)

D4724 — Egypt. Hist. Ancient.

NK 0201623 MB

HV5088 .G7 **Knight, George Alexander Francis.**

Gregory, John Walter, 1864-1932.
Temperance regulations in the Russian & Australian armies; an address by Professor J. W. Gregory ... A plea for prohibition during the war, by Rev. G. A. Frank Knight ... Glasgow ... W. Black & co., 1915.

BT 112 K69 **Knight, George Angus Fulton, 1909-**
A biblical approach to the doctrine of the Trinity. Edinburgh, Oliver and Boyd [1953]
78 p. 22cm. (Scottish journal of theology. Occasional papers, no. 1)

1. Trinity--Biblical teaching. I. Title. II. Series.

ICMcC CtY-D TNJ-P CMenSP KyWAT
NK 0201625 NIC NjPT PPDrop NcD PPPD IaDuU OO IaU

Knight, George Angus Fulton, 1909-
Esther, Song of songs, Lamentations; introduction and commentary. London, SCM Press; [distributed by Macmillan, 1955]
140 p. 20 cm. (Torch Bible commentaries)
Includes bibliographies.

1. Bible. O. T. Five scrolls—Commentaries. I. Title. (Series)

BS1309.K58 223 55—215[illegible]

MH-AH KyWAT NIC
IaU ViU OrStbM NIC PPiPT MU MH-AH IaDL OO CBPac
NK 0201626 DLC ICU NNUT MB PPLT PPD NcU NcD OCH PP

Knight, George Angus Fulton, 1909-
From Moses to Paul; a christological study in the light of our Hebraic heritage. With a foreword by William A. Curtis. London, Lutterworth Press [1949]
194 p. 23 cm.
Bibliography: p. 188-192.

1. Judaism—Relations—Christianity. 2. Bible—Theology. 3. Jesus Christ—Person and offices. 4. Paul, Saint, apostle. I. Title.

BM535.K56 296 A 50-2914 rev
New York. Public Libr. for Library of Congress [r55c1]†

NK 0201627 NN IEG DLC MH-AH ICU PPWe NcD

Knight, George Angus Fulton, 1909-
Ruth and Jonah; introduction and commentary. London, SCM Press [1950]
91 p. 19 cm. (Torch Bible commentaries)
Includes bibliographies.

1. Bible. O. T. Ruth—Commentaries. 2. Bible. O. T. Jonah—Commentaries. (Series)

BS1315.K6 222.3 51-6473 rev

NNU-W NNUT NcD
NK 0201628 DLC OrStbM Or IaDL NIC MH-AH IEG KyWAT

[Knight, George H
Address and memorial in opposition to the bill (S. no. 300 and H. R. no. 1612) "to amend the statutes relating to patents and for other purposes." Read before and adopted by the Cincinnati Board of trade, December 18th, 1878. Cincinnati, Times printing establishment, 1879.
76 p. 23cm.
Caption title: An address on proposed changes in the patent laws, delivered by Geo. H. Knight ...

1. Patent laws and legislation—U. S.

Library of Congress T223.Z1K5 6-2838†

NK 0201629 DLC PPF OFH MH

VOLUME 300

Knight, G[eorge] H.
The patent franchise in the United States. By G. H. Knight ... [New York] 1891.
24 p. front. (port.) 24 x 19cm.

1. Patents—U. S.
Library of Congress T223.Z1K6 5-27346†

NK 0201630 DLC

Knight, George H.
Patent-office manual, including the law and practice of cases in the United States Patent office and the courts holding a revisory relation thereto. Also, an appendix of copyright decisions, etc. By George H. Knight ... Boston, Little, Brown, and company, 1893.
4 p. l., 655 p. 24½cm.

1. Patent laws and legislation—U. S. I. Title.
Library of Congress T223.T2K6 4—10579/3
R3

NK 0201631 DLC ICJ WaU-L

Knight, George H.
Patent-office manual, including the law and practice of cases in the United States Patent office and the courts holding a revisory relation thereto. Also, an appendix of copyright decisions, etc. By George H. Knight ... Boston, Little, Brown, and company, 1894.
iv p., 2 l., 655 p. 24½cm.

1. Patent laws and legislation—U. S. I. Title.
Library of Congress T223.T2K6 1894 41-27921

NK 0201632 DLC PU-L PHi PPB OClW CU GU-L MoS

Knight, George H.
Reasons why action should be delayed on Senate bill 300. Inventors ask to be heard before the patent laws are amended. [Cincinnati? 1879?]
7 p. 23cm.

1. Patent laws and legislation—U. S.
Library of Congress T223.T4 1879 CA 5—2158

NK 0201633 DLC

Knight, George Halley, 1835-1917.
Courageous calm and heroic Christianity. By G. H. Knight ... [London, Hodder & Stoughton [1912]
31, [1] p. 15½cm x 12cm. (The silent hour booklets)

1. Christian life. I. Title.
Library of Congress BV4510.K58 38-4792
[2] 248

NK 0201634 DLC

Knight, George Halley, 1835-1917.
Divine upliftings; the blessed life of peace and victory ... London, Marshall brothers [pref. 1906]
viii, 181 p. 19 cm.

NK 0201635 CtY

Knight, George Halley, 1835-1917.
Divine upliftings; the blessed life of peace and victory, by Rev. G. H. Knight ... Rock Island, Ill., Augustana book concern [1935]
ix, 174 p. 19cm.

1. Christian life. I. Title.
Library of Congress BV4501.K58 36-737
[2] 248

NK 0201636 DLC

Knight, George Halley, 1835-1917.
Full allegiance. By Rev. G. H. Knight ... New York, A. C. Armstrong & son, 1909.
5 p. l., [3]-139p. 19½cm.

1. Christian life. I. Title.
Printed by the Wesleya. University Library, 1936

NK 0201637 CtW NNUT

Knight, George Halley, 1835-1917.
In the cloudy and dark day; God's messages of peace to the weary, the sorrow-laden, the troubled, and the tried, by the Rev. G. H. Knight ... Rock Island, Ill., Augustana book concern [1934]
viii, 190 p. 19cm.

1. Consolation. I. Title.
Library of Congress BV4905.K6 36-110
[3] 242

NK 0201638 DLC PPT

Knight, George Halley, 1835-1917.
In the secret of His presence, helps for the inner life when alone with God...2d ed. Lond., Hodder & Stoughton, 1905.
xi, 230p. D

NK 0201639 OO

Knight, George Halley, 1835-1917.
In the secret of His presence; helps for the inner life when alone with God, by Rev. G. H. Knight ... Rock Island, Ill., Augustana book concern [1934]
xi p., 1 l., 15-201 p. 19cm.
"First U. S. edition, February, 1932 ... Third U. S. edition, June, 1934."

1. Devotion. 2. Devotional literature. I. Title. II. Title: Alone with God.
Library of Congress BV4815.K6 1934 36-108
[3] 242

NK 0201640 DLC

BV4832 KNIGHT, George Halley, 1835-1917.
.K7 The Master's questions to His disciples, by the Rev. G.H.Knight. New York, A.C.Armstrong and son, 1904.
xv, 367 p. 20cm.

1. Devotional exercises.

NK 0201641 ICU PPLT NjNbS

Knight, George Halley, 1835-1917.
The Master's questions to His disciples; thoughts, devotional and practical, for the silent hour. London, Hodder and Stoughton, 1910.

"5th edition."

NK 0201642 MH

Knight, George Halley, 1835-1917.
These three; devotional thoughts for the quiet hour. N.Y. [etc.] Hodder, 1914.
136 p. O.

NK 0201643 PPLT

Knight, George Halley, 1835-1917.
"These three"; devotional thoughts for the quiet hour, by the Rev. G. H. Knight ... Rock Island, Ill., Augustana book concern [1936]
x, 174 p. 19cm.

1. Devotional literature. I. Title.
Library of Congress BV4832.K6 36-31254
[2] 242

NK 0201644 DLC

Knight, George Henry, ed.
Care and training of the feeble-minded
see under International Congress of Charities, Correction and Philantropy, Chicago, 1893. 8th Section.

KNIGHT, George H[enry]
The feeble-minded. Boston, G. H. Ellis, 1895.

pp. 8.
"Read before the National Conference of Charities and Correction at New Haven, May, 1895.

NK 0201646 MH MB MA

KNIGHT, George Henry.
The relation of invention to the conditions of life. [N.Y. 1892].

1. 8°. pp. (12). Port. and wdcts.
Cosmopolitan , Feb. 1892; XII. 441-452.
Life, p.441.

NK 0201647 MH

KNIGHT, George Henry.
The state's duty towards epileptics.
(*In* Kerlin, Isaac N. Provision for idiotic and feeble-minded children. Pp. 11-18. [1886.])

NK 0201648 MB MiU OO DNLM

Knight, George John, 1870-
Knight's interest tables for 4% savings accounts and certificates of deposit, by George J. Knight ... [Pittsburgh, Printed by Shaw bros., °1912]
43 p. 24½ x 28½cm. $5.00

1. Interest and usury—Tables, etc.
Library of Congress HG1630.04.K6 12-27802

NK 0201649 DLC

Knight, George John, 1870-
Knight's interest tables for 3% savings accounts and certificates of deposit, by George J. Knight ... [Pittsburgh, Printed by Shaw bros., °1912]
43 p. 24½ x 28½cm. $5.00

1. Interest and usury—Tables, etc.
Library of Congress HG1630.03.K6 12-27804

NK 0201650 DLC

VOLUME 300

Knight, George John, 1870–
Knight's interest tables for 3½% savings accounts and certificates of deposit, by George J. Knight ... [Pittsburgh, Printed by Shaw bros., °1912]
43 p. 24½ x 28½cm. $5.00

1. Interest and usury—Tables, etc.

Library of Congress HG1630.035.K6 12-27803

NK 0201651 DLC

TL720 .7 .R34
Knight, George Laurence, 1912- joint author.
Rath, Eric, 1911–
Air cargo; the inside story of a new business, by Eric Rath and G. L. Knight, Jr. New York [1947]

Knight, George Litch, comp.
Bourgeois, Louis, *16th cent.*
The four hundredth anniversary of the Genevan Psalter of 1551; a collection of tunes composed and adapted by Louis Bourgeois for the 1551 edition of the Genevan Psalter with hymn texts from fifteen centuries of the church's song. New York, Hymn Society of America [1951]

VK12 H99 pam
Knight, George Litch
... The significance of the Genevan Psalter of 1551, by Reverend George Litch Knight ... The story of the music of the Genevan Psalter, by Reginald L. McAll ... New York, N.Y., Hymn society of America, 1951.

"Addresses given at the inauguration of the American observance of the Geneva Psalter anniversary by the Hymn society of America, Sunday March fourth, 1951, at Saint Michael's episcopal church, New York city."

NK 0201654 NNUT

Knight, George Morgan, 1908-
Ghost skeleton, by George Morgan Knight, jr. [Leonardtown, Md., Knight pub. co., 1947] 21 p. illus. 28cm.

NK 0201655 NN

Knight, George Morgan, 1908–
High school scandals. [On label: Leonardtown, Md., Knight Pub. Co. °1947]
50 p. illus. 28 cm.
First ed. published under title: Petersburg classics.

I. Title.
PS3521.N5336P4 1947 811.5 54-1551 ‡

NK 0201656 DLC RPB

Knight, George Morgan, 1908–
How and where to find immediate potential wealth in the handling of mail order "how to do it" books in your free hours. Leonardtown, Md., Knight Pub. Co., °1949.
11 p. 24 cm.

1. Booksellers and bookselling—Colportage, subscription trade, etc.
HF5456.B8K6 655.57 54-1555 ‡

NK 0201657 DLC

Knight, George Morgan, 1908–
How and where to really put a song over, once you have written and published it and its [sic] been cleared for radio and other performances use. Leonardtown, Md., Knight Pub. Co., °1953.
25 p. illus. 22 cm.

1. Music trade. I. Title.
ML3790.K5 784 53-28549 ‡

NK 0201658 DLC

Knight, George Morgan, 1908–
How to accomplish the phenomenal in ventriloquy as Eddie Burke...does it with "The three Aces" and "Lucy" in their fresh born act today! By George Morgan Knight, jr. ... Leonardtown, Knight pub. co. [1949] 14 p. illus. 30cm.

1. Ventriloquism. 2. Burke, Eddie.
N. Y. P. L. February 5, 1951

NK 0201659 NN

791.1 qB959k
Knight, George Morgan, 1908-
How to accomplish the phenomenal in ventriloquy as Eddie Burke---the world's greatest living ventriloquist does it, with "The three aces" and "Lucy" in their fresh born act today! ... 2d ed. Leonardtown, Md., Knight pub. co., °1949.
25p. illus., music. 29cm.

1. Bourke, Edward G. 2. Ventriloquism. I. Title.

NK 0201660 N NcC

Knight, George Morgan, 1908–
How to accomplish the phenomenal in ventriloquy. [5th ed. Leonardtown, Md., Knight Pub. Co., °1949]
57 p. illus. 29 cm.

1. Ventriloquism.
GV1557.K55 1949 *793.8 791.1 53-29574 ‡

NK 0201661 DLC WaT WaS WaE

Knight, George Morgan, 1908-
How to accomplish the phenomenal in ventriloquy ... [6 ed. Leonardtown, Md., Knight pub. co., [1955] 60 p. illus., port. 29cm.

Cover-title.

1. Ventriloquism. 2. Burke, Eddie, ventriloquist. I. Title.

NK 0201662 NN

Knight, George Morgan, 1908–
How to become a famous personality on the radio, stage, screen, television, and records, locally, nationally, and internationally. [How to crash into show business in its many fields] Leonardtown, Md., Knight Pub. Co. [°1950]
36 p. illus. 29 cm.

1. Acting as a profession. I. Title. II. Title: How to crash into show business.
PN2055.K55 792.069 53-38000 ‡

NK 0201663 DLC

Knight, George Morgan, 1908–
How to become a publisher and other publishing angles. Edited by Leta S. Bender. 4th, rev. ed. [Leonardtown, Md., Knight Pub. Co.] °1946.
65 p. 24 cm.

1. Publishers and publishing.
Z283.K58 1946 655.5 53-30614 ‡

NK 0201664 DLC

Knight, George Morgan, 1908–
How to become a publisher and (other publishing angles)... [Leonardtown, Md., Knight pub. co., 1948] 47 p. illus. 15cm.
New ed.

1. Publishers and publishing.

NK 0201665 NN NNC

Knight, George Morgan, 1908-
How to become a publisher and (other publishing angles) How and where to discover that new cash customer; the best place to advertise; how to circularize your way to success. [Leonardtown, Md., Knight, 1949]
47 p.

"Third autographed edition... New source material added."
Imprint and edition note on labels mounted on p. [2] of cover.

NK 0201666 NNC

Knight, George Morgan, 1908–
How to construct and write song hits of today and tomorrow. 2d ed. Leonardtown, Md., Knight Pub. Co., °1948.
42 p. illus. 22 cm.

1. Music, Popular (Songs, etc.)—Writing and publishing. I. Title.
MT67.K547 1948 784 53-32336 ‡

NK 0201667 DLC NN

Knight, George Morgan, 1908–
How to cut your advertising costs yet get maximum results! [1st ed. Leonardtown, Md., Knight Pub. Co., 1954]
37 p. illus. 24 cm.
Includes bibliography.

1. Advertising. I. Title.
HF5823.K48 659.1 54-9787 ‡

NK 0201668 DLC OrU TxU

Knight, George Morgan, 1908–
How to internationally copyright: your brainchild (including U. S. copr. information), by George Morgan Knight, jr. ... Ed. by Leta S. Bender. [Leonardtown, 1948] 27 p. 15cm. (His: How series.)
"References," p. 25.

1. Copyright, International. I. Bender, Leta S., ed.
N. Y. P. L. July 9, 1948

NK 0201669 NN NBuG IU NjP N NNC

Knight, George Morgan, 1908-
How to internationally copyright your brainchild (including U. S. copyright information) Rev. 2d ed. Leonardtown, Md., Knight, 1948.
27 p.

Title taken from p. [2] of cover.
Imprint on mounted label.
1. Copyright, International. 2. Copyright - U. S.

NK 0201670 NNC

KNIGHT, GEORGE MORGAN, 1908-
How to internationally copyright: your brainchild (including U.S. copr. information) Edited by Leta S. Bender. [3. ed., with pt. 2 added] [Leonardtown, Md., Knight pub. co., c1948] 34, 4 p. 15cm. (HIS: How series)

1. Copyright, International. I. Bender, Leta S., ed.

NK 0201671 NN

VOLUME 300

JX

Knight, George Morgan, 1908-
How to internationally copyright your brainchild (including U.S. copyright information) ... by George Morgan Knight, jr. and Leta S. Bender ... Leonardtown, Md., The Knight publ. co., ©1948.
27, ₍4₎, 8, 13 p. 16cm.
"New 4th revised ed.": typewritten note mounted on fly-leaf.

NK 0201672 MiU-L

Knight, George Morgan, 1908-
How to internationally copyright your brainchild (including U. S. copyright information) by George Morgan Knight, jr. and Leta S. Bender. Leonardtown, Md., Knight pub. co. ₍1949₎
₍55₎ p.

"New 4th edition 1949."--label mounted on p. ₍2₎ of cover.

NK 0201673 NNC MB OO

Knight, George Morgan, 1908–
How to internationally copyright your brainchild, including U. S. copyright information, by George Morgan Knight, Jr. and Leta S. Bender. 6th ed. Leonardtown, Md., Knight Pub. Co. ₍1953, ©1948.
81 p. 17 cm.

1. Copyright. 2. Copyright—U. S. I. Bender, Leta S., joint author. II. Title.
655.63 53–934 ‡

NK 0201674 DLC IdPI MB

D019.2
K744

Knight, George Morgan, 1908-
How to mimeograph your way to fame and fortune. New ed., 1948. rev. Leonardtown, Md., Knight, 1948.
45 p.

Title taken from p. ₍2₎ of cover.
Imprint on mounted label.

1. Mimeograph.

NK 0201675 NNC

Knight, George Morgan, 1908-
How to mimeograph your way to fame and fortune, by George Morgan Knight, jr. [Leonardtown, Md., The Knight pub. co., 1948] 45 p. 15cm.

Imprint from label.
2. rev. ed.

1. Copying machines.

NK 0201676 NN

Knight, George Morgan, 1908–
How to mimeograph your way to fame and fortune. 4th ed., rev. Leonardtown, Md., Knight Pub. Co., ©1949.
56 p. illus. 24 cm.

1. Mimeograph.
Z48.K55 1949 *652.4 53–30613 ‡

NK 0201677 DLC

Knight, George Morgan, 1908–
How to write and publish that song in your heart. ₍3d ed.₎ Leonardtown, Md., Knight Pub. Co. ₍1945₎
43 l. 29 cm.
"New reference data added and also sheet music of hit song Way up in the mountains."

1. Music, Popular (Songs, etc.)—Writing and publishing. I. Title.
MT67.K55 1945 784 47–28177*

NK 0201678 DLC

Knight, George Morgan, 1908–
How to write and publish that song in your heart... By George Morgan Knight jr. ... Leonardtown, Md., The Knight pub. co. ₍1947₎ 43 f. ports. 29cm.

Reproduced from typewritten copy.
"Revised autographed edition."
"Way up in the mountains," song with music by Wanda Daniels, prelim. l. 4–5.
"References," f. 42.

421492B. 1. Songs—Writing and publishing. I. Title. II. Song index (1).
N. Y. P. L. April 12, 1948

NK 0201679 NN

Knight, George Morgan, 1908–
How to write and publish that song in your heart. ₍10th ed.₎ Leonardtown, Md., Knight Pub. Co. ₍1953?₎
₍2₎ v. 30 cm.
Cover title.
Vol. ₍2₎ consists of unacc. melodies (words and music by the author)

1. Music, Popular (Songs, etc.)—Writing and publishing. I. Title.
MT67.K55 1953 784 53–31246 ‡

NK 0201680 DLC

Knight, George Morgan, 1908–
How to write history and make it pay. Leonardtown, Md., Knight Pub. Co. ₍1953₎ ©1952.
46 p. 29 cm.

1. Historiography — Addresses, essays, lectures. 2. Maryland — Hist.—Anecdotes. I. Title.
D13.K56 907 53–5931 ‡

NK 0201681 DLC MB Wa OrLgE

Knight, George Morgan, 1908–
Intimate glimpses of old Saint Mary's, by George Morgan Knight, jr.; illustrated by actual photographs taken by the author, with an introduction by His Excellency Harry W. Nice ... 1st ed. ₍Baltimore, Meyer & Thalheimer, ©1938₎
xviii, 127 p. front., plates, ports. 20cm.

1. St. Marys co., Md.—Hist. 2. St. Marys co., Md.—Historic houses, etc. I. Title.
38–24930
Library of Congress F187.S2K6
——— Copy 2.
Copyright A 120642 ₍3₎ 975.241

NK 0201682 DLC CU ViU

Knight, George Morgan, 1908–
Intimate glimpses of old Saint Mary's, by George Morgan Knight, jr. ... Introduction by the late governor of Maryland, Harry W. Nice; editor's foreword by Richard Harwood-Staderman ... Washington, D. C., The American good government society, 1942.
xviii, 127, ₍3₎ p. plates, ports. 20½cm. (The American good government society. American history series, ed. by Richard Harwood-Staderman, I)
"First edition, 1938. Second edition published March 17, 1942."
1. St. Marys co., Md.—Hist. 2. St. Marys co., Md.—Historic houses, etc. I. Title.
42–12576
Library of Congress F187.S2K6 1942
₍3₎ 975.241

NK 0201683 DLC

Knight, George Morgan, 1908-
The Knight folio of song hits of 1948, by George Morgan Knight, jr. ... Leonardtown, Md., The Knight publishing co. ₍1947₎
v. port. facsims. 30 cm.

An official scrapbook containing biographical notes, and advertisements of the author and his works. Songs included are: I wanta be a cowboy.- You found my heart in Texas !- Way up in the mountains!- I've found romance!- I'm back in circulation!
With music.

1. Knight, George Morgan, 1908- 2. Songs--Bibl.--Catalogs. Publishers'. 3. Music, Popular (Songs, etc.) I. Title.

NK 0201685 RPB

Knight, George Morgan, 1908–
The marvels of Maryland: a new guide to the free state's often neglected places and personalities, of fascinating present-day and historical interest... New York, Washington book co. ₍1951₎
192 p. illus., map. 21cm.
1. ed.

1. Washington, George, 1st pres. U. S. 2. Maryland—Descr. and trav., 1900–
N. Y. P. L. February 28, 1952

NK 0201686 NN

Knight, George Morgan, 1908–
Maryland; a new guide to the Free State's often-neglected places and personalities of fascinating present-day and historical interest. ₍1st ed.₎ New York, Washington Book Co. ₍1951₎
192 p. illus. 21 cm.
Stamped at head of title: The marvels of.

1. Washington, George, Pres. U. S., 1732–1799. I. Title: The marvels of Maryland.
E311.K5 923.173 52–1273 ‡

NK 0201687 DLC

KNIGHT, GEORGE MORGAN, 1908-
Maryland grapevine. Leonardtown, Md., The Knight pub. co. [1946] 11 p. 28cm.

Microfiche (Negative). 1 sheet. 11 x 15cm. (NYPL FSN 720)
At head of title: Studio news.
Imperfect: margins mutilated.

I. Title. II. Title: Studio news.

NK 0201688 NN

Knight, George Morgan, 1908-
Petersburg classics, by George Morgan Knight, jr. [Leonardtown, Md., Knight pub. co., 1947]
50 l. illus. 28cm.

NK 0201689 NN RPB

Knight, George Morgan, 1908–
A strange revenge. Complete in 3 chapters. Friend, Neb., Studio News, 1947.
13 p. 30 cm.

I. Title.
PZ3.K7442St 54–1550 ‡

NK 0201690 DLC

VOLUME 300

Knight, George Morgan, 1908–
Well whatta ya know? ₍How to win money and prizes on radio quiz programs₎ Leonardtown, Md., Knight Pub. Co., °1949.
71 p. 23 cm.
1. Rewards (Prizes, etc.) 2. Radio broadcasting. I. Title. II. Title: How to win money.
PN1991.8.Q5K6 *792.94 791.4 53–29656 ‡
NK 0201691 DLC NN

Knight, George Morgan, 1908–
What you don't know about George Washington, by George Morgan Knight, jr. ... and Richard Harwood-Staderman ... with foreword by U. S. Senator Harry Flood Byrd ... Washington, D. C., The American good government society, 1941.
256 p. incl. illus. (map) plates, ports., facsim. 20½ᶜᵐ. (The American good government society. American history series, ed. by Richard Harwood-Staderman ... II)
"First edition. The first two hundred and fifty copies ... have been designated the de luxe edition ... autographed by the authors. No. 96."
Bibliographical references included in "Footnotes" (p. 193–199) "Annotated bibliography": p. 203–250.
1. Washington, George, pres. U. S., 1732–1799. I. Harwood-Staderman, Richard, 1908– joint author. II. Title.
Library of Congress E312.17.K55 42–2295
₍6₎ 923.173
NK 0201692 DLC WaS OCl OEac MH ViU ViU-L

Knight, George Morgan, 1908–
Who will be elected president in 1952: perhaps no one
see under
Good Government National Committee.

Knight, George Morgan, 1908–
...The Wicomico: the true story of an American river and the fascinating events that occurred in its vicinity. By George Morgan Knight, jr. ... Cincinnati, Harwood & Knight, 1945. 1 v. plates. 17cm.
At head of title: ...No. 96 of the first edition limited to 100 copies...
353842B. 1. Historic houses—U. S. —Maryland. I. Title.
N. Y. P. L. January 20, 1947
NK 0201694 NN MnU MH

Knight, George Morgan, 1908–
The Wicomico: the only collection of fascinating facts ever assembled about the important personalities, who graced the vicinity of this American river, & the far-reaching events that occurred there; including map, many chapters and numerous photographs. 4th ed. Leonardtown, Md., Knight pub co., 1952.
181 p. plates, ports.,facsims. O.
NK 0201695 CaBViP

Knight, George Stephens.
Treatment of foreign corporations in international law, with particular reference to protection of American interests, by George Stephens Knight ... Washington, D. C., 1938.
vii, 110 p. 23ᶜᵐ.
Thesis (S. J. D.)—Georgetown university, 1938.
"Table of cases": p. 105–106.
"Textbooks, law reviews, and other materials": p. 107–110.
1. Corporations, Foreign. 2. Corporations—Nationality.
Library of Congress ₍a45d1₎ 341.57 40–3467
NK 0201696 DLC DS PU-L MH-L NNC ViU-L

Knight, George T₍homson₎
The goodness of God in view of the facts of nature and the supernatural, by George T. Knight ... Boston, The Universalist publishing house, 1904.
ix, 126 p. 17½ᶜᵐ.
4–34573
NK 0201697 DLC MH-AH NN

Knight, George Thomson, 1850–1911.
The praise of hypocrisy; an essay in casuistry, by G. T. Knight ... Chicago, The Open court publishing co.; London, K. Paul, Trench, Trübner & co., ltd., 1906.
85 p. 18ᶜᵐ.
"Reprinted, with additions, from the Open court of September, 1906, and with a preface by Professor D. L. Maulsby."
I. Title. 7–1295
Library of Congress BR125.K5985
NK 0201698 DLC MB PBa ICJ ICRL CoU ViU

Knight, George Wells, 1858–1932.
Asa Smith Bushnell, governor of Ohio. By George Wells Knight ... Reprinted from the "Old Northwest" genealogical quarterly for July, 1904. Columbus, O. ₍Press of Spahr & Glenn₎ 1904.
13 p. 2 port., col. coat of arms. 25ᶜᵐ.
1. Bushnell, Asa Smith, 1834–1904. 2. Bushnell family (Francis Bushnell, d. 1646) 15–7547
Library of Congress F496.B97
NK 0201699 DLC OFH OO OU

Knight, George Wells, 1858–1932, joint author.
Gardner, Henry Brayton, 1863–
... Discussion of the relation of the teaching of economic history to the teaching of political economy, by Profs. Henry B. Gardner, George W. Knight, and Henry R. Seager.
(*In* American historical association. Annual report ... for the year 1897. Washington, 1898. 24½ᶜᵐ. p. 91–98)

Knight, George Wells, 1858–1932 ed.
Guizot, François Pierre Guillaume, 1787–1874.
General history of civilization in Europe, by François Pierre Guillaume Guizot. Ed., with critical and supplementary notes, by George Wells Knight ... New York, D. Appleton and company, 1896.

Knight, George Wells, 1858–
The government of the people of the state of Ohio, by George Wells Knight ... Philadelphia, Eldredge & brother, 1895.
128 p. illus. (incl. ports., map) 19ᶜᵐ.
Cover-title: The civil government of Ohio.
1. Ohio—Pol. & govt. 10–13247†
Library of Congress JK5525.1895.K7
NK 0201702 DLC OFH MiU OCU OU

Knight, George Wells, 1858–
The government of the people of the state of Ohio, by George Wells Knight ... Rev. ed. Philadelphia, Eldridge & brother, 1903.
iv, 5–128 p. illus. (incl. ports., map) 19½ᶜᵐ.
Cover-title: The civil government of Ohio.
1. Ohio—Pol. & govt. 3–28150
Library of Congress JK5525.1903.K7
NK 0201703 DLC OCl OClW OU NN MB

Knight, Geo. Wells, 1858–1932.
Growth of the college idea in O. ...
n.p. 1897?
11p. Caption ti. "Read before the O. college assn. June 29, 1897".
NK 0201704 OU OClWHi

Knight, George Wells, 1858–
... History and management of land grants for education in the Northwest Territory (Ohio, Indiana, Illinois, Michigan, Wisconsin) by George W. Knight, PH. D. New York & London, G. P. Putnam's sons, 1885.
5, v, 7–175 p. 24ᶜᵐ. (Papers of the American historical association. vol. I, no. 3. 5, v, 79–247 p.)
"List of authorities": p. 173–175.
1. School lands—Northwest, Old.
Library of Congress E172.A65 vol. 1 6–28168
——— Copy 2. LB2827.K7
NK 0201705 DLC PPL PHC PSC MiU OCl ODW MdBP PPAmP ICJ WaS Vi NjN WHi

Knight, Geo. Wells 1858–
Hist. of educational progress in O. ...
Columbus, H. Howe & son, 1889.
1p. l., 137–149p.
An introductory article contributed to "His. collections of Ohio. ..." by Henry Howe.
NK 0201706 OClWHi

Knight, George Wells, 1858–1932.
... The history of higher education in Ohio, by George W. Knight ... and John R. Commons ... Washington, Govt. print. off., 1891.
258 p. front., plates. 22½ᶜᵐ. (Contributions to American educational history, ed. by Herbert B. Adams. no. 12)
₍U. S.₎ Bureau of education. Circular of information no. 5, 1891. At head of title: Whole number 175.
1. Universities and colleges—Ohio. 2. Education—Ohio—Hist. Commons, John Rogers, 1862– 6—16474
Library of Congress L111.A5
——— Copy 2. LA346.K7
NK 0201707 DLC NcD TxU MdBP PV PPTU PPPrHi OCl OCU OU OClWHi PBa MH MB NN

F486 [Knight, George Wells] 1858–1932.
0514 The Society and the Quarterly.
v.1
p.79– (In Ohio archaeological and historical
82 publications. Columbus [1888] 23cm. v. 1, p. 79–82)
1. Ohio archaeological and historical quarterly. I. Title.
NK 0201708 NBuG

Knight, George William.
Why Westminster Theological Seminary? [Philadelphia, Westminster Theological Seminary, 1955]
[10]p. paper.
NK 0201709 PPWe

Knight, George Wilson, 1897–
... Atlantic crossing; an autobiographical design. London, J. M. Dent and sons, ltd. ₍1936₎
ix, 337 p., 1 l. front. (port.) 22½ᶜᵐ.
At head of title: G. Wilson Knight.
I. Title. 38–1735
Library of Congress PR6021.N42A9 1936
₍3₎ 928.2
NK 0201710 DLC MtU OCU PSC NN

VOLUME 300

KNIGHT,George Wilson,1897-
Atlantic crossing;an autobiographical design. London,J.M.Dent and Sons Ltd.,[1939].

21 cm. Port.
"First published 1936;reissued at a cheaper price 1939."

NK 0201711 MH

Knight, George Wilson, 1897–
The burning oracle; studies in the poetry of action, by G. Wilson Knight ... London, New York ₍etc.₎ Oxford university press, 1939.

vi p., 1 l., 292 p. 22cm.

CONTENTS.—The Spenserian fluidity.—The Shakespearian integrity.—The frozen labyrinth: an essay on Milton.—Swift and the symbolism of irony.—The vital flame: an essay on Pope.—The two eternities: an essay on Byron.—Conclusion: Christianity and Eros.

1. English poetry—Hist. & crit. 2. Poetry. I. Title.

40–4357
Library of Congress PR502.K55
₍8₎ 821.09

NcD OrP CoU AU ViU AAP MH PPL OCl OU OO ICN PSC PPD
NK 0201712 DLC NcRS WaS TU MiU TxU NIC FMU KU TNJ

Knight, George Wilson, 1897–
Byron's dramatic prose. ₍Nottingham₎ University of Nottingham ₍1953₎

33 p. 22 cm. (Byron Foundation lecture, 1953)

1. Byron, George Gordon Noël Byron, 6th baron, 1788–1824. I. Title. (Series: Nottingham, Eng. University College. Byron Foundation lecture, 1953)

A 55-3696
Cornell Univ. Library
for Library of Congress ₍1₎

OOxM FTaSU
NK 0201713 NIC IU ICU MH NN TU OCl CaBVaU CoU NjR

PR
3588
K5

Knight, George Wilson, 1897–
Chariot of wrath; the message of John Milton to democracy at war, by G. Wilson Knight ... London, Faber and Faber ₍1942₎

194 p. 21 cm.

"First published in Mcmxlii."

1. Milton, John — Political and social views. 2. Milton, John — Religion and ethics. 3. Gt. Brit.—Nationality. I. Title.

PR3588.K5 928.2 42—17809

NcD NcU DFo OU PBm DAU NIC ScCleU OOxM
NK 0201713-1 CU-I WaSpG CaBVaU MtU OrU TNJ ODaU

201.6
K69c

Knight, George Wilson, 1897-
Christ and Nietzsche, an essay in poetic wisdom. London, New York, Staples Press [1948]
244p. 22cm

CONTENTS. - The poetic challenge. - Sword and swastika. - The piercing crucifix. - Eros and Psyche - The golden labyrinth. - King and superman.

1.Psychology, Religious. 2.Religion in literature. I.Title: Christ and Nietzsche.
√LC.

NcWsW OrU
ICN CtY NNUT CU RPB IEN NNU PPT NN NBC ICarbS MoSU-
NK 0201713-2 CLSU MWelC LU TU CtY-D NNC TU ICarbS

Knight, George Wilson, 1897–
The Christian renaissance, with interpretations of Dante, Shakespeare and Goethe, and a note on T. S. Eliot, by G. Wilson Knight ... Toronto, The Macmillan company of Canada limited, 1933.

x, 374 p. 22½ cm.

1. Religion in poetry. 2. Christianity. 3. Bible as literature. 4. Bible. N. T.—Criticism, interpretation, etc. 5. Dante—Criticism and interpretation. 6. Shakespeare, William—Criticism and interpretation. 7. Goethe, Johann Wolfgang von—Criticism and interpretation. I. Title.

PN49.K6 801 33—28567

CaBVaU OrU
DFo ViU CBBD OClJC PBm NcD NN CU NcU MiU OrPR CaBVa
NK 0201713-3 DLC NcD OC OO OCl MiU PU-F PU PPPD NN

Knight, George Wilson, 1897–
The crown of life; essays in interpretation of Shakespeare's final plays. London, New York, Oxford University Press, 1947.

336 p. 22 cm.

CONTENTS.—Myth and miracle.—The writing of Pericles.—Great creating nature: an essay on The winter's tale.—Cymbeline.—The Shakespearian superman; a study of The tempest.—Henry VIII and the poetry of conversion.

1. Shakespeare, William—Criticism and interpretation. I. Title.

PR2976.K618 822.33 47—5849*

MB PU-F WaS
NK 0201713-4 DLC CaBVaU KyLE NIC OrU CaBViP AU ODW

PR
2976
.K618
1948

Knight, George Wilson, 1897-
The crown of life; essays in interpretation of Shakespeare's final plays. ₍2d ed.₎ London, Methuen ₍1948₎
336p. 22cm.

Contents.- Myth and miracle.- The writing of Pericles.- Great creating nature: an essay on The winter's tale.- Cymbeline.- The Shakespearian superman: a study of The tempest.- Henry VIII and the poetry of conversion.
1. Shakespeare, William. Criticism and interpretation. I. Title.

NNC MiD
IdPI OrPR WaTC NcGW NIC OCU IU MiU ICU IaU ViU MH
NK 0201713-5 OrU OO PPL TxU DFo OrMonO OrPS MtU

PR
2976
K58
1952

Knight, George Wilson, 1897-
The crown of life, essays in interpretation of Shakespeare's final plays. London, Methuen ₍1952₎
viii, 336 p. 23 cm.

"Originally published by the Oxford University Press, April 1947; first published by Methuen ... May 1948."
Contents. - Myth and miracle. - The writing of Pericles. - Great creating nature: an essay on The winter's tale. - Cymbeline. - The Shakespearian superman: a study of The tempest. - Henry VIII and the poetry of conversion.

1. Shakespeare, William - Criticism and interpretation. I. Title.

NK 0201713-6 Vi PU-F MH MB CaBVa

Knight, George Wilson, 1897–
The dynasty of Stowe, by G. Wilson Knight. London, The Fortune press ₍1945₎

145 p. incl. front. plates, ports. 22½cm.

"First edition 1945."
"The third part of an autobiographical trilogy."—Pref.

1. Stowe school, Buckingham, Eng. I. Title.

45-10039
Library of Congress * LF795.B87935K5
₍3₎ 373.42

NK 0201713-7 DLC CU FU TxU

373.42
S892K

Knight, George Wilson, 1897–
The dynasty of Stowe, by G. Wilson Knight. London, The Fortune press ₍1946₎

145 p. incl. front. plates, ports. 22½cm.

"Second edition 1946."
"The third part of an autobiographical trilogy."—Pref.

NK 0201713-8 NcD OrU MH CtY

Knight, George Wilson, 1897–
Hiroshima, on prophecy and the sun-bomb, by G. Wilson Knight ... London, A. Dakers limited ₍1946₎

4 p. l., 131 p. 19cm.

"First published May, 1946."

1. English literature—Addresses, essays, lectures. 2. Civilization.

PR99.K54 820.4 47–18847

NK 0201713-9 DLC TxU ICU CtY

Knight, George Wilson, 1897–
The imperial theme; further interpretations of Shakespeare's tragedies including the Roman plays, by G. Wilson Knight ... London, H. Milford, Oxford university press, 1931.

ix p., 1 l., 367, ₍1₎ p. 22½cm.

"The following essays develop further my detailed interpretations of Shakespearian tragedy begun in The wheel of fire, and make clearer, I hope, the necessity of my main contention outlined originally in Myth and miracle." *cf.* Pref.

CONTENTS.—On imaginative interpretation. — The torch of life: an essay on Julius Caesar. — The eroticism of Julius Caesar. — Rose of May: an essay on life-themes in Hamlet.—The milk of concord: an essay on life-themes in Macbeth.—The royal occupation: an essay on Coriolanus.—The transcendental humanism of Antony and Cleopatra.—The diadem of love: an essay on Antony and Cleopatra.—Macbeth and Antony and Cleopatra.—A note on Antony and Cleopatra. — The prophetic soul: a note on Richard II, v, v. 1–66.

1. Shakespeare, William—Tragedies. 2. Shakespeare, William—Criticism and interpretation. I. Title.

32—7024
Library of Congress PR2983.K58
₍a38d1₎ 822.33

PPD PSC PU MiU OCl OCU OU PPA ICJ MB MH NN ViU IdB
NK 0201714 DLC MtU WaS OrU NIC NcU CaBVa OrPR CtY

Knight, George Wilson, 1897–
The imperial theme; further interpretations of Shakespeare's tragedies, including the Roman plays. ₍3d ed.₎ London, Methuen ₍1951₎

xiii, 367 p. 22 cm.

1. Shakespeare, William—Tragedies. 2. Shakespeare, William—Criticism and interpretation. I. Title.

PR2983.K58 1951 822.33 51–13960

IdU NRU MH TU NNC NcC OrMonO OrPS
NK 0201715 DLC DAU KMK MB Or OrU CaBVaU WaSpG IdPI

Knight, George Wilson, 1897–
The imperial theme; further interpretations of Shakespeare's tragedies, including the Roman plays. ₍Reprinted with minor corrections₎ London, Methuen ₍1954₎

367 p. 23 cm.

1. Shakespeare, William—Tragedies. 2. Shakespeare, William—Criticism and interpretation. I. Title.

PR2983.K58 1954 822.33 55–32554 ‡

NK 0201716 DLC OrP IEN NN IaU PSC MiU

Knight, George Wilson, 1897–
The last of the Incas, a play on the conquest of Peru. Leeds ₍Eng.₎ 1954.

82 p. 19 cm.

1. Peru—Hist.—Conquest, 1522–1548—Drama. I. Title.

PR6021.N42L3 822.91 55–25263 ‡

NK 0201717 DLC CU NN PBL

Knight, George Wilson, 1897–
Laureate of Peace; on the genius of Alexander Pope. London, Routledge & Paul ₍1954₎

187 p. 23 cm.

1. Pope, Alexander, 1688–1744. I. Title.

PR3634.K55 821.53 55—831 ‡

MiU OrAshS OKentU OU
ICN RPB NN TxU OO OCl OrU PSt PSC PBm PU IEN NcRS
NK 0201718 DLC CaBVa CaBVaU MtU CU ICU CtY TU OClW

Knight, George Wilson, 1897–
Laureate of Peace; on the genius of Alexander Pope. New York, Oxford University Press, 1955.

187 p. 23 cm.

1. Pope, Alexander, 1688–1744. I. Title.

PR3634.K55 1955 821.53 55–14130 ‡

PPD ViU OOxM IdU OrP
NK 0201719 DLC OrPR AU CU ScU PLF PBL MB OCU PPT

VOLUME 300

Knight, George Wilson, 1897–
Lord Byron; Christian virtues. [London] Routledge and Paul [1952]
xv, 304 p. port. 23 cm.
"First of a trilogy on Byron as man and poet."
Bibliography: p. xiii–xiv.

1. Byron, George Gordon Noël Byron, 6th baron, 1788–1824.
PR4381.K55 1952 821.76 52—4955

PPT PU OO PSt InRenS MsU CaBViP MtU CaBVaU CaBVa OrU
NK 0201720 DLC IEG IU MiU MB NcU TU NN MH TxU NcD

Knight, George Wilson, 1897–
Lord Byron; Christian virtues. New York, Oxford University Press, 1953.
304 p. illus. 22 cm.

1. Byron, George Gordon Noël Byron, 6th baron, 1788–1824.
[PR4381] 821.76 53—2409 ‡
Printed for U. S. Q. B. R. by Library of Congress [59k1]

OOxM OClW ViU Or OrP OrSaW DLC NNC WaT MsSM PWcS
NK 0201721 AU NcGU FTaSU IdPI IdU PRosC PHC PLFM OCl

Knight, George Wilson, 1897–
The mutual flame; on Shakespeare's Sonnets and The phoenix and the turtle. London, Methuen [1955]
233 p. 22 cm.
Includes bibliography.

1. Shakespeare, William. Sonnets. 2. Shakespeare, William. The phœnix and turtle. I. Title.
PR2848.K6 822.33 55—1800 ‡

OrSaW OrLgE NcD FU WaS WaSpG
OrU KMK DAU NN OCl PSC PBL PCM OClW OO MiU LU
PPD PPT PSt TU MB IaU CSt TxU IU ViU ICU WaTC
NK 0201722 DLC CaBVaU CaBVa MoSU NIC OrP OrPR

Knight, George Wilson, 1897-
The mutual flame; on Shakespeare's Sonnets and The phoenix and the turtle. New York, Macmillan, 1955.
xi, 233 p. 22cm.
"Principal works cited": p. 225-226; Bibliographical footnotes.

NK 0201723 OU OOxM MtU KMK CoU OClU

Knight, George Wilson, 1897–
Myth and miracle. An essay on the mystic symbolism of Shakespeare, by G. Wilson Knight. London, Ed. J. Burrow & co., ltd. [1929]
31, [1] p. 19cm.

1. Shakespeare, William—Criticism and interpretation. I. Title.
A 31–842
Peabody inst., Baltimore. Library for Library of Congress [a38c1]

MB MH NN MiU CaBVaU TU KEmT TNJ GAT IEdS
NK 0201724 MdBP OrP NcU CtY PSC PU MiU OCl OClW

Knight, George Wilson, 1897–
The Olive and the sword; a study of England's Shakespeare, by G. Wilson Knight ... London, New York [etc.] Oxford university press, 1914.
4 p. l., 102 p., 1 l. 20½ cm.

1. Shakespeare, William—Criticism and interpretation. 2. Nationalism—Gt. Brit. I. Title.
PR2976.K62 822.33 A 44—6033
Chicago. Univ. Libr. for Library of Congress [a56i½]†

NK 0201725 ICU DLC

PR2976 .K62 1944
Knight, George Wilson, 1897-
The olive and the sword; a study of England's Shakespeare. Folcroft, Pa., The Folcroft Press [1944]
102 p. 22 cm.

1. Shakespeare, William--Criticism and interpretation. 2. Gt. Brit.--Nationality. I. Title.

NK 0201726 TU

Knight, George Wilson, 1897–
The olive and the sword; a study of England's Shakespeare, by G. Wilson Knight ... London, New York [etc.] Oxford university press, 1944.
4 p. l., 102 p., 1 l. 20½ cm.

1. Shakespeare, William — Criticism and interpretation. 2. Gt. Brit.—Nationality. I. Title.
PR2976.K62 822.33 A 44—6033
Chicago. Univ. Libr. for Library of Congress [a60i½]†

MB OrPS OrU CaBVaU
FTaSU InU KEmT ViU PRosC NcD NcGU NcC OOxM MsU NIC
NK 0201727 DLC DFo PP ODW NN OU OCl PPD CoU IaU GU

Knight, George Wilson, 1897–
Principles of Shakespearian production with especial reference to the tragedies, by G. Wilson Knight. London, Faber and Faber, limited [1936]
2 p. l., 7–246 p. 22½cm.

1. Shakespeare, William—Stage history—1800– I. Title.
36–13059
Library of Congress PR3091.K6 1936
Copyright A ad int. 21475 [3] 822.33

OCl PU PPGi PPT NN
NK 0201728 DLC OrU CU-I NcU NIC NcD WaWW CtY MiU OU

Knight, George Wilson, *1897–*
Principles of Shakespearian production, with especial reference to the tragedies. By G. Wilson Knight.
— New York. The Macmillan Co. 1936. 246 pp. 22 cm.

E1956 — T.r. — Tragedy. — Shakespeare, William. Representation of his plays.

NK 0201729 MB IdU PSC OCU MeB ViU NN OOxM OrP

Knight, George Wilson, 1897-
Principles of Shakespearian production with especial reference to the tragedies. New York, Macmillan, 1937.
7-246 p. 23 cm.

NK 0201730 TU

PR 3091 .K72 1949
Knight,George Wilson,1897-
Principles of Shakespearian production,with especial reference to the tragedies. Harmondsworth [Eng.] Penguin Book [1949]
224 p. illus. (Pelican books,A210)
"First published 1936."

1.Shakespeare,William--Stage history--1800-
I.Title.

NRU KMK WaU WaSpG
NK 0201731 MiU OrU CaBVaU OrPR MH CU NNC OCl CoU

Knight, George Wilson, 1897–
This sceptred isle; Shakespeare's message for England at war, by G. Wilson Knight ... Oxford, B. Blackwell, 1940.
2 p. l., 35 p. 18½cm.

1. Shakespeare, William—Quotations. 2. Poetry of places—England. 3. England—Descr. & trav.—Poetry. I. Title.
41–18955
Library of Congress PR3069.E6K6
[4] 822.33

NK 0201732 DLC IaU WU OCl NN OO

Knight, George Wilson, 1897–
... Shakespeare and Tolstoy, by G. Wilson Knight. [London, H. Milford, Oxford university press] 1934.
27 p. 24½cm. (The English association. Pamphlet no. 88)

1. Shakespeare, William—Criticism and interpretation. 2. Tolstoi, Lev Nikolaevich, graf, 1828–1910. I. Title.
34–17963
Library of Congress PR2899.K6
[3] 822.33

NN MB OrCS
NSyU GU KMK ScU MtU ViU OCl OCU OO PU PPT NBuU MtU
NK 0201733 DLC CaBVaU OrPR MsSM CU CSf CoU MiU MU

Knight, George Wilson, 1897–
The Shakespearian tempest, by G. Wilson Knight ... London, H. Milford, Oxford university press, 1932.
viii p., 1 l., 332 p. 22½cm.
A study of the tempest and music themes in Shakespeare.
CONTENTS.—Introduction.—The histories, early tragedies, and poems.—The romantic comedies.—The tragedies.—The final plays.—Conclusion.—Appendixes: A. The Shakespearian aviary. B. The 'Hecate' scenes in Macbeth.

1. Shakespeare, William — Criticism and interpretation. 2. Shakespeare, William—Music. 3. Shakespeare, William—Natural history.
33–8660
Library of Congress PR2976.K63
[3] 822.33

MtU CtY PSC PBm PP MiU OCU OU ODW ViU NN IU PPA PU
NK 0201734 IEdS KMK CaBVaU CaBVa OrPR IdU DLC OrU

Knight, George Wilson, 1897-
The Shakespearian tempest... London, H. Milford, Oxford university press, c1940.
viii, p., 1 l., 332 p. 22 1/2cm.

NK 0201735 PHC NcU

Knight, George Wilson, 1897–
The Shakespearian tempest, with a chart of Shakespeare's dramatic universe. [3d ed.] London, Methuen [1953]
xxiv, 332 p. 23 cm.

1. Shakespeare, William—Criticism and interpretation. 2. Shakespeare, William—Music. 3. Shakespeare, William—Natural history. I. Title.
[PR2976.K] A 55—8672
New York Univ. Wash. Sq. Library for Library of Congress [56f5]

IdPI IaU Or OrCS WaS WaT WaTC DCU OU OOxM TxU PPLas
NcGU NjP CLSU MH NcD NIC IU CU NNC CtY TU ICarbS NcU
NK 0201736 NNU-W OKentU InU CBPac MiD MoSU CaBVaU

Knight, George Wilson, 1897–
The starlit dome; studies in the poetry of vision, by G. Wilson Knight ... London, New York [etc.] Oxford university press, 1941.
4 p. l., 314 p., 1 l. 22 cm.
"Companion study to The burning oracle."—Pref.
CONTENTS.—The Wordsworthian profundity.—Coleridge's Divine comedy.—The naked seraph: an essay on Shelley.—The priest-like task: an essay on Keats.—Symbolic eternities.

1. English poetry—19th cent.—Hist. & crit. I. Title.
A 42—3452
Yale Univ. Library for Library of Congress PR590.K5 [a50k1]† 821.709

WaWW
DLC MB PPT PU PV PSC OCl OO OU ICU MtU CaBVa WaS IdU
NK 0201737 CtY CaBVaU PP OrU NIC MH AU CoU NcD PU-F

Knight, George Wilson, 1897–
The wheel of fire; essays in interpretation of Shakespeare's sombre tragedies, by G. Wilson Knight ... London, H. Milford. Oxford university press, 1930.
xix, 296 p. 22½cm.
These essays continue my interpretation of Shakespeare's plays begun in Myth and miracle. Many represent recastings and expansions of work which has appeared in different journals. cf. Pref.
CONTENTS.—Introduction, by T. S. Eliot.—On the principles of Shakespeare interpretation.—Hamlet's melancholia.—The embassy of death: an essay on Hamlet.—The philosophy of Troilus and Cressida.—Measure for measure and the Gospels.—The Othello music.—Brutus and Macbeth.—Macbeth and the metaphysic of evil.—Lear and the comedy of the grotesque.—The Lear universe.—The pilgrimage of hate: an essay on Timon of Athens.—Shakespeare and Tolstoy.—Symbolic personification.—The Shakespearian metaphysic.
MB 1. Shakespeare, William—Criticism and interpretation. 2. Shakespeare, William—Tragedies. I. Title.
Library of Congress PR2983.K6 31—2952
[a37n1] 822.33

MiU OCU ODW ICU IU MB NN MH ViU
CaBVa IdU OrCS OrU MtU TU CtY PPD PSC PPT PBm PU OU
NK 0201738 DLC MtU NIC TxU CoU NcU KMK PPiU CaBVaU

VOLUME 300

Y
S 3
.A663
KNIGHT, GEORGE WILSON, 1897-
The wheel of fire; essays in interpretation of Shakespeare's sombre tragedies. London, H.Milford,Oxford university press[1937]
xix,296p. 23cm.

"These essays continue my interpretation of Shakespeare's plays begun in Myth and Miracle. Many represent recastings and expansions of work which has appeared … in … journals." cf. Pref.
Bookplate of Morton Dauwen Zabel. Author's autographed presentation copy.

Contents.—Introduction, by T.S.Eliot.—On the principles of Shakespeare interpretation.—Hamlet's melancholia.—The embassy of death: an essay on Hamlet.—The philosophy of Troilus and Cressida.—Measure for measure and the Gospels.—The Othello music.—Brutus and Macbeth.—Macbeth and the metaphysic of evil.—Lear and the comedy of the grotesque. —The Lear universe.—The pilgrimage of hate: an essay on Timon of Athens.—Shakespeare and Tolstoy.—Symbolic personification.—The Shakespearian Metaphysic.

NK 0201741 ICN NcD NcRS CtY MH

822.33
DK74
1941
Knight, George Wilson, 1897-
The wheel of fire; essays in interpretation of Shakespeare's sombre tragedies. London, Oxford University Press [1941]
296p. 22cm. (Oxford bookshelf)

1. Shakespeare, William--Criticism and interpretation. 2. Shakespeare, William--Tragedies. I. Title.

NK 0201742 IU

Knight, George Wilson, 1897–
The wheel of fire; interpretations of Shakespearian tragedy, with three new essays. [4th rev. and enl. ed.] London, Methuen [1949]
xx, 343 p. 22 cm.
CONTENTS.—Introduction, by T. S. Eliot.—On the principles of Shakespeare interpretation.—The embassy of death: an essay on Hamlet.—The philosophy of Troilus and Cressida.—Measure for measure and the Gospels.—The Othello music.—Brutus and Macbeth.—Macbeth and the metaphysic of evil.—King Lear and the comedy of the grotesque.—The Lear universe.—The pilgrimage of hate; an essay on Timon of Athens.—Shakespeare and Tolstoy.—Symbolic personification.—The Shakespearian metaphysic.—Tolstoy's attack on Shakespeare (1934)—Hamlet reconsidered (1947)—Appendix: Two notes on the text of Hamlet (1947)
1. Shakespeare, William—Criticism and interpretation. 2. Shakespeare, William—Tragedies. I. Title.
PR2983.K6 1949 822.33 52-591

NK 0201743 LU TxU OCU CtY TU ICN NcU NNC IdPI MiHM NcU OCl CSt MiU CU MH DFo IaU NRU NN NIC DLC KEmT MB AU AAP NBuU CtY OrSaW IaU WU

Knight, George Wilson, 1897–
The wheel of fire; interpretations of Shakespearian tragedy, with three new essays … New York, Oxford University Press, 1949.
xx, 343 p. 22 cm.
CONTENTS.—Introduction, by T. S. Eliot.—On the principles of Shakespeare interpretation.—The embassy of death: an essay on Hamlet.—The philosophy of Troilus and Cressida.—Measure for measure and the Gospels.—The Othello music.—Brutus and Macbeth.—Macbeth and the metaphysic of evil.—King Lear and the comedy of the grotesque.—The Lear universe.—The pilgrimage of hate: an essay on Timon of Athens.—Shakespeare and Tolstoy.—Symbolic personification.—The Shakespearian metaphysic.—Tolstoy's attack on Shakespeare (1934)—Hamlet reconsidered (1947)—Appendix: Two notes on the text of Hamlet (1947)

1. Shakespeare, William—Tragedies. 2. Shakespeare, William—Criticism and interpretation. I. Title.
[PR2983.K] A 51-8912
New York, State Libr. for Library of Congress [5]

NK 0201745 N NNC WaS OrPS MtBC OrP CaBVaU

Knight, George Wilson, 1897–
The wheel of fire; interpretations of Shakespearian tragedy, with three new essays. [4th rev. and enl. ed., reprinted with minor corrections] London, Methuen [1954]
343 p. 22 cm.

1. Shakespeare, William—Criticism and interpretation. 2. Shakespeare, William—Tragedies. I. Title.
PR2983.K6 1954 822.33 54-2836 ‡

NK 0201746 DLC TxU FTaSU MiU PSC IU NcC CtY

Knight, Gerald Featherstone, 1894–
"Brother Bosch"; an airman's escape from Germany, by Captain Knight… London: W. Heinemann, 1919. 3 p.l., 175 (1) p. 16°.

1. European war, 1914– .—Prisoners and prisons (German). 2. European war, 1914– .—Personal narratives (English). 3. Title.
N. Y. P. L. April 1, 1920.

NK 0201747 NN

Knight, Gerald Hocken, 1908–
[The zeal of thy house. Selections]
… Incidental music to "The zeal of thy house" (Dorothy L. Sayers) arranged by Gerald H. Knight. Canterbury, Kent, Eng. [1938]
10 p. 28cm.
Reproduced from manuscript copy.
Score: solo voice and chorus (SATB in close score)
"Used for the original production of the play during the festival week of the Friends of Canterbury Cathedral, 12–19 June 1937."
1. Music, Incidental—Excerpts—Vocal scores. I. Sayers, Dorothy Leigh, 1893– The zeal of thy house.
45-28136
Library of Congress M1512.K6Z4

NK 0201748 DLC

Knight, Gerald Hocken, 1908–
[The devil to pay. Selections]
… Incidental vocal music to "The devil to pay," play by Dorothy L. Sayers; music by Gerald H. Knight … [Canterbury, Eng., ©1939.
1 p. l., 5 p. 25½cm.
Reproduced from manuscript copy.
"Written for and first performed at the festival week of the Friends of Canterbury cathedral, June 10–17, 1939."
Score: solo voices, and mixed choruses in close score.
1. Music, Incidental—Vocal scores. I. Sayers, Dorothy Leigh, 1893– The devil to pay.
Library of Congress M1512.K6D4 46-29557

NK 0201749 DLC

[Knight, Gertrude C]
The poet's calendar. [Troy, N. Y., Nims & Knight, 1891]
cover-title, 53 l. 13½ x 20½cm.
Text runs parallel with back of cover; text on p. [3] of cover; ornamental borders.

1. Calendars. 2. English poetry (Selections: Extracts, etc.) I. Title.
42-27208
Library of Congress PR1176.K45

NK 0201750 DLC

Knight, Gilbert Howard, 1889–
Charles Knight, the torchbearer of literature, by Gilbert H. Knight. [Cleveland, 1940?]
cover-title, 13 numb. l. 28 x 22cm.
Caption title: The torch bearer of literature—Charles Knight; paper read by Gilbert H. Knight at the Rowfant club, January 13th, 1940.

1. Knight, Charles, 1791–1873.
Z325.K71K6 926.55 44-48989 rev

NK 0201751 DLC

Knight, Gilbert Howard, 1889–
You too can sell insurance, if… by Gilbert Howard Knight. Rochester, N. Y., Mutual underwriter company [1946]
98, [1] p. illus. 21cm.

1. Insurance as a profession. I. Title.
HG8051.K56 368.3069 46-22717

NK 0201752 DLC Wa WaS

Knight, Gilbert Howard, 1889–
You too can sell insurance … if … Rochester, N. Y., Mutual underwriter co., 1948, c1946.
104 p. illus. O.
2nd ed.

NK 0201753 PP

Knight, Gilfred Norman, 1891– joint author.
HC119
.P5
Pick, Fred Lomax, 1898–
The Freemason's pocket reference book, by Fred L. Pick and G. Norman Knight. London, F. Muller [1955]

Knight, Gilfred Norman, 1891– joint author.
HS405
.P55
1953
Pick, Fred Lomax, 1898–
The pocket history of Freemasonry, by Fred L. Pick and G. Norman Knight. London, F. Muller [1953]

Knight, Gladys.
Binney's women, by Gladys Knight. New York, London, The Century co. [©1931]
4 p. l., 3–310 p. 19½cm. $2.00
"First printing."

I. Title.
Library of Congress PZ3.K7445Bi 31-7373

NK 0201756 DLC ViU LU

Knight, Gladys.
Marriage for two, by Gladys Knight. New York, Boni and Liveright [©1924]
vi p., 1 l., 9–256 p. 19cm.

I. Title.
Library of Congress PZ3.K7445Ma 24-15423

NK 0201757 DLC MiU OCl OClh MH

Knight, Gladys (Seale)
A year and a day, a novel. [1st ed.] New York, Pageant Press [1953]
50 p. 21 cm.

I. Title.
PZ4.K7Ye 53-8097 ‡

NK 0201758 DLC

Knight, Glaister, 1894–
The story of my life; or, What I owe to Christ… Brown's Town, St. Ann, Ja., "Evangelical book room" [pref. 1939]
4 p.l., 68 p. 21 cm.
Portrait of the author and his wife on t.-p.

NK 0201759 CtY

VOLUME 300

WB 60982 Knight, Goodwin J 1896-
Good's budget, by Good Knight. San Diego, Calif., Press of Frye and Smith, 1910.
130 p. plate. 19 cm.

NK 0201760 CtY CLU

Knight, Goodwin J 1896 -
see also California. Governor, 1953- (Goodwin J. Knight)

BT75.2 K5 Knight, Gordon F.
Rational theology. Pittsburgh, Duquesne University, 1953.
v.

Contents.--Book One: Book Two: The nature of God.

1. Theology, Doctrinal. 2. Catholic Church--Doctrinal and controversial works--Catholic authors. I. Title. II. Title: The nature of God.

NK 0201762 PPiU

BS509 K6 **KNIGHT, Gordon F**
Theology for laymen: Apologetics. ₑPittsburgh, Pa.ₑ Duquesne University Press, 1948.
177 p. 29 cm.

1. Dogmatic Theology—Textbooks—20th Century. I. Title.

NK 0201763 MBtS

Knight, Gowin, 1713 - 1772.
An attempt to demonstrate, That all the phænomena in nature may be explained by two simple active principles, attraction and repulsion: wherein the attractions of cohesion, gravity, and magnetism, are shewn to be one and the same; and the phænomena of the latter are more particularly explained.
— London, 1748. 95 pp. 8°.

5197 — Forces of nature. — Magnetism. — Attraction.

NK 0201764 MB MiU PPC MdAN NN NNE

Film 1642 Knight, Gowin, 1713-1772.
An attempt to demonstrate? that all the phaenomena in nature may be explained by two simple active principles, attraction and repulsion: wherein the attractions of cohesion, gravity, and magnetism, are shewn to be one and the same; and the phaenomena of the latter are more particularly explained. London, 1748.
95 p.

Microfilm (negative) Ann Arbor, Mich., University of Michigan Library, Photoduplication Service, 1963.
1 reel. 35mm.

NK 0201765 NIC OU

*EC75 K7443 754a Knight, Gowin, 1713-1772.
An attempt to demonstrate, that all the phaenomena in nature may be explained by two simple active principles, attraction and repulsion: wherein the attractions of cohesion, gravity, and magnetism, are shewn to be one and the same; and the phaenomena of the latter are more particularly explained. By Gowin Knight ...
London: Printed for J. Nourse at the Lamb, against Katherine-street in the Strand. 1754.
2p.ℓ., 95p. 26cm.

NK 0201766 MH CSt PPF PPL

Knight, Gowin, 1713 - 1772.
A collection of some papers formerly published in the Philosophical transactions, relating to the use of Dr. Knight's magnetical bars, with some notes and additions. London, 1758.

Diagrs.

Bound with other papers.

NK 0201767 NNE PPC

Knight, Grady.
A guide for judging dairy cattle and dairy products. Fayetteville, University of Arkansas, College of Education, Dept. of Vocational Teacher Education, 1955.
24 l. illus. 27 cm. (University of Arkansas. College of Education. Dept. of Vocational Teacher Education. Monograph 47)

1. Stock-judging. 2. Dairy cattle. 3. Dairy products—Analysis and examination. I. Title.

SF115.K6 636.2074 55-62304 ‡

NK 0201768 DLC

Knight, Grant Cochran, 1893-
American literature and culture, by Grant C. Knight ... New York, R. Long & R. R. Smith, inc., 1932.
ix, 523 p. 20½ cm.
"Selected bibliography" at end of each part.
CONTENTS.—The literature of colonization.—The literature of romanticism.—The literature of realism.

1. American literature—Hist. & crit. I. Title.

PS88.K6 810.9 32—15008

NK 0201769 DLC PPD PBm PPLas OCU OO OCl PU PPT OrSaW OrPR WaSp OrU OrAshS OrCS CaBVaU NcD NN MsU MiU ViU MB ICU UU

Knight, Grant Cochran, 1893-
The critical period in American literature. Chapel Hill, University of North Carolina Press ₍1951₎
xi, 208 p. 21 cm.
Bibliography: p. 177-194.

1. American literature—19th cent.—Hist. & crit. 2. Realism in literature. I. Title.

PS214.K6 810.903 51-13564

NK 0201770 DLC NN MiU MtU Or WaS WaT TxU MB NN MH NcU TU ViU OrSaW CaBVaU OrPS OrCS CaBVa WaSpG IdPI OrPR

Knight, Grant Cochran, 1893-
James Lane Allen and the genteel tradition, by Grant C. Knight ... Chapel Hill, The University of North Carolina press, 1935.
xiii, 313 p. front. (port.) 22½cm.
"Notes on sources": p. 279-287; Bibliography: p. 288-304.

1. Allen, James Lane, 1849-1925. I. Title.

Library of Congress PS1036.K6 35-9575
——— Copy 2.
Copyright A 83942 ₍5-5₎ 928.1

NK 0201771 DLC KMK NjR NcD NcGU IaU KEmT CaBVaU KyLx MsU NIC TU KyHi MtU OrU OrP MiU OCl OCU ODW PU ViU OrSaW WaWW CaBVaU WaSpG WaTC OrCS OrPS

Knight, Grant Cochran, 1893-
The novel in English, by Grant C. Knight ... New York, R. R. Smith, inc., 1931.
viii, 395 p. 20½cm.
"Selected bibliography" at end of each chapter.

1. English fiction—Hist. & crit. 2. American fiction—Hist. & crit. I. Title.

Library of Congress PR821.K6 31-1490
——— Copy 2.
Copyright A 32716 ₍5₎ 823.09

NK 0201772 DLC PU MU ICU MiU KyLxT NcD PP PPD PHC OCl OO ODW OU PPTU MiHM ViU NN MB OrPR WaWW OrCS WaTC CaBVaU

Knight, Grant Cochran, 1893-
The novel in Eng. N.Y., Farrar & Rinehart, 1935, [c1931].
395p.

NK 0201773 OClUr

Knight, Grant Cochran, 1893-1956, *comp.*
Readings from the American mercury. Knight. New York, Knopf, 1926.
x, 328 p. 20 cm.

I. The American mercury. II. Title.

AC5.K55 1926 26-26407 rev 2

NK 0201774 DLC IdU

Knight, Grant Cochran, 1893-
The sealed well ₍by₎ Grant C. Knight. New York, The Fine editions press, 1943.
32 p. 19cm.
Poem.

I. Title.

Library of Congress PS3521.N534S4 43-17750
₍3₎ 811.5

NK 0201775 DLC ViU NBuU OCl

Knight, Grant Cochran, 1893-
The strenuous age in American literature. Chapel Hill, University of North Carolina Press ₍1954₎
xi, 270 p. 21 cm.
Sequel to The critical period in American literature.
Bibliography: p. ₍231₎-253.

1. American literature—20th cent.—Hist. & crit. I. Title.

PS221.K6 810.904 54—13124

NK 0201776 DLC OrCS Wa CaBVa ViU IU MB TU NN TxU PP OC1W NcD OCU MtU Or AAP NBuC NN OrMonO NcGU OOxM PLF MiU KyU OU PBL PHC WaSpG WaS CaBVaU OrPS IdPI OrPR OrP OrSaW OrU WaT

Knight, Grant Cochran, 1893-
Superlatives, by Grant C. Knight ... New York, A. A. Knopf, 1925.
6 p. l., 3-197 p. 19½ cm.
Bibliography: p. 189-190.

1. English fiction—Hist. & crit. 2. American fiction—Hist. & crit. I. Title.

PR99.K55 25—7934

NK 0201777 DLC MsU WaS OrP NN MB PU OC OClh CoU ViU TNJ NcC OCl

Knight, Greta Buedingen.
The staying hand. Philadelphia, Dorrance ₍1955₎
52 p. 20 cm. (Contemporary poets of Dorrance, 478)

I. Title.

PS3521.N5342S7 811.5 55-11264 ‡

NK 0201778 DLC CU IU

Knight, Gvlielmvs.
Mundus alter et Idem ...
see under [Hall, Joseph] bp. of Norwich, 1574-1656.

VOLUME 300

Knight, H., novelist.
The mystery of Stephen Claverton & Co.
London. Routledge. [187-?] Sm. 8°.

Δ1026 — T.r.

NK 0201780 MB

KNIGHT, H., novelist.
The mystery of Stephen Claverton & Co. A novel, by H. Knight. London [etc.] G. Routledge and Sons, Ltd. [1894]
320 p. 18½cm.

With autograph of Geo. A. Routledge.

794509A. 1. Fiction, English. I. Title.

NK 0201781 NN

Knight, H., of Bradford.
Local lyrics. By H. Knight. Bradford [Eng.]: "Yorkshireman" Newspaper Co., Ltd. [1886?] 59 p. 12°.

49599A. 1. Poetry (English).
N. Y. P. L. August 15, 1922.

NK 0201782 NN

178.06
S693k Knight, H B
Anniversary address before the Albany Division, no. 24, S. of T. Prepared by request of the Division, and delivered before them on the occasion of their nineteenth anniversary, March 9th, 1863, at their hall, 586 Broadway. Albany, Weed, Parsons, printers, 1863.
11 p. 20 cm.
Cover title.
1. Sons of Temperance of North America. Grand Division of Eastern New York. Albany Division, no. 24. I. Title.

NK 0201783 N

823
K744c Knight, H B Finlay.
The courage of Sylvia Fulgent. London, R. Bentley, 1893.
3v. 19cm.

NK 0201784 IU

Knight, H. B. Finlay.
A gentleman from the ranks. London, 1899.

NK 0201785 PPL

Knight, H B Finlay.
A girl with a temper; a romance of the Wills act; by H. B. Finlay Knight ... New York, Harper & brothers, 1893.
1 p. l., 300 p. 21½cm. (On cover: Harper's Franklin square library, no. 731)

Library of Congress PZ3.K745G 7-14180†

NK 0201786 DLC

W823
K698i Knight, H.B. Finlay.
In fool's paradise. London, Ward and Downey, 1892.
373 p. 20cm.

NK 0201787 NcU

Knight, H F
An evening meditation. No imprint [c1907]
[14p.] illus. 23½cm.

NK 0201788 NBuG

Knight, Mrs. H L.
Breakfast, dessert, and supper. Two hundred and seventy-five practical recipes. The result of long experience, and thoroughly tested, by Mrs. H. L. Knight ... Auburn, N. Y., The author, 1881.
87 p. 22cm.

1. Cookery. 8-22854†

Library of Congress TX715.K693
(Copyright 1881: 1615)

NK 0201789 DLC

Knight, Mrs. H L
Breakfast, dessert, supper. Four hundred practical receipts ... Auburn, N.Y., J.H. Ivison, 1884.
97 p. 8°.
2nd ed.

NK 0201790 NN

Knight, Harold.
The Hebrew prophetic consciousness. London, Lutterworth Press [1947]
186 p. 22 cm.

1. Bible. O. T. Prophets—Criticism, interpretation, etc. 2. Bible. O. T. Prophets—Theology. I. Title.
BS1505.K57 224 49—495*
——— Copy 2. Label mounted on t. p.: Chicago, A. R. Allenson.

NK 0201791 DLC CSt KyWAT NjP OO MH ICU IU PBm NIC

Knight, Harold, composer.
Do you know?... By Harold Knight, Moe Jaffe and Clay Boland. New York, Mills music inc. [c1930]

First line: I rehearse lovely verse.
Chorus: When I think of lovers.
Portrait of Harold Knight on t.-p.

Printed for the Music Division
1. Knight, Harold—Port. I. Jaffe, Moe, 1901- II. Boland, Clay A., 1903- III. Song index (3).
N. Y. P. L. November 20, 1950

NK 0201792 NN

Knight, Mrs. Harold

see

Knight, Mrs. Laura (Johnson)

Knight, Harold, 1874-

Knight, Mrs. Laura (Johnson)
... The work of Laura & Harold Knight; with a foreword by Ernest G. Halton ... [London] "The Studio" [1921]

Knight, Harold A
Materials buying manual. New York, Book Division Conover-Mast Publications [1951]
x, 340 p. 22 cm.

1. Raw materials. 2. Commercial products. I. Title.

HF1041.K65 338 51—4257

Or UU
NK 0201795 DLC OrCS OrP WaS CaBVa CoU CU CLSU LU NN

Knight, Harold A
Materials buying manual. New York, Book Division, Conover-Mast Publications [1952]
x, 340 p. 22 cm.

1. Raw materials. 2. Commercial products. I. Title.

NK 0201796 ViU PP TxU OU

Knight, Harold Vincent, 1907-
The consumer awakens; the challenge of cooperation [by] Harold V. Knight. Jamestown, N. D., Farmers union cooperative education service [1939]
128 p. diagrs. 23 cm.
"Suggested for further reading": p. 128.

1. Cooperation—U. S. 2. Cooperative societies—U. S. I. Title.
HD3284.K5 334.50973 39-20373 rev
Library of Congress HD3284.K5

NK 0201797 DLC OCl MoU MB CaBVaU OrU Or

Knight, Harold Vincent, 1907-
Farming around the world. Denver, National Farmers Union, °1952.
126 p. illus. 23 cm.

1. Agriculture. 2. Agriculture—Economic aspects. I. Title.

S439.K58 630 52-67109 ‡

NK 0201798 DLC DNAL OrCS AU

Knight, Harold Vincent, 1907-
Grass roots, the story of the North Dakota Farmers Union. Jamestown, North Dakota Farmers Union [1947]
183 p. illus., ports., maps. 23 cm.

1. North Dakota Farmers Union. I. Title.
HD1485.N6K55 334.683 Agr 48-190*
U. S. Dept. of Agr. Libr. 280.29N814
for Library of Congress [3]†

NK 0201799 DNAL WHi MtBC MtU ICU NNC DLC

238
K74 Knight, Harold Vincent, 1907-
Guide for Farmers Union writers. 1st ed. Jamestown, Farmers Union Education Service, 1940.
26 p.

NK 0201800 DNAL

Knight, Harry French.
... Furniture, rugs, Georgian silver, Chinese and Japanese art, brocades, velvets, tapestries, United States and foreign coins: property from the collection formed by the late Harry French Knight ... from the collection of Guy E. Mayer ... estate of the late Allan McCulloh ... with additions. Public sale October 10-13 inclusive. New York, American art association, Anderson galleries, inc., 1934.
3 p. l., 146 p. illus. 24cm.

NK 0201801 NNC PPPM IU KT

VOLUME 300

Knight, Harry Hazelton, 1889 –
The army-worm in New York in 1914, [by] Harry H. Knight. Ithaca: the university, 1916. (1)750–765 p., 4 pl. 8°. (New York State. Cornell Agricultural Experiment Station. Bull. no. 376.)
Cover-title.

1. Army worm, U. S.: N. Y., 1914. 2. Series.
N. Y. P. L. June 1, 1917.

NK 0201802 NN MBH

Knight, Harry Hazelton, 1889–
Bugs of the family *Miridae* of the District of Columbia and vicinity, by H. H. Knight ... and W. L. McAtee ...
(*In* U. S. National museum. Proceedings. Washington, 1929. 23½cm. v. 75, art. 13. 27 p.)
Bibliography: p. 24–27.

1. Miridae. I. McAtee, Waldo Lee, 1883– joint author.
30-12787
Library of Congress Q11.U55 vol. 75

NK 0201803 DLC MiU OCl OU CaBVaU WaS

QL 462 K69 Knight, Harry Hazelton, 1889–
[Collected papers. v.p.]
v. illus. 27 cm.

NK 0201804 NIC

QL 523 .M5 K7 Knight,Harry Hazelton,1889-
Monograph of the North American species of Deraeocoris--Heteroptera,Miridae. University Farm,St.Paul, 1921.
77-210 p. illus. 23 cm. (University of Minnesota Agricultural Experiment Station. Technical bulletin 1)
"Paper no.256 of the Journal series of the Minnesota Agricultural Experiment Station."
"Appeared originally in the Eighteenth repor of the Minnesota State Entomologist,published June 18,1921.
Bibliography p.198-208.
1.Hemiptera-- North America.

NK 0201805 MiU InU OU MH

Knight, Harry Hazelton, 1889–
... The plant bugs, or *Miridae*, of Illinois [by] Harry H. Knight. Printed by authority of the state of Illinois. Urbana, Ill., 1941.
3 p. l., 234 p. illus. (incl. maps) 25cm. (Illinois. Natural history survey. Bulletin, v. 22, article 1)
At head of title: State of Illinois. Dwight H. Green, governor. Department of registration and education. Frank G. Thompson, director. Natural history survey division. Theodore H. Frison, chief.
Bibliography: p. 218–222.

1. Miridae. 2. Hemiptera—Illinois. I. Title.
A 41-4843
Illinois. Univ. Library for Library of Congress QH1.I 25 vol. 22, art. 1
[6]† (574.9773) 595.754

NK 0201806 IU OCU OO OU DLC CaBViP MU MsU NNBG

Knight, Harry Hazelton, 1889–
[Publications ... 1913–1928] No imprint.
2 v.

NK 0201807 MiEM

Knight, Harry Hazelton, 1889 –
A revision of the genus Lygus as it occurs in America north of Mexico, with biological data on the species from New York. [By] Harry H. Knight. Ithaca: the university, 1917. p. 555–645. illus., pl. 8°. (New York State. Cornell Agricultural Experiment Station. Bull. no. 391.)
Bibliography, p. 641–645.

1. Lygus. 2. Series.
N. Y. P. L. December 17, 1919.

NK 0201808 NN PPAmE

Knight, Harry Hazelton, 1889–
Studies on insects affecting the fruit of the apple, with particular reference to the characteristics of the resulting scars ... by Harry Hazelton Knight ... [Ithaca, 1922]
1 p. l., p. 447–498. pl. III–XLII. 22½cm.
Thesis (PH. D.)—Cornell university, 1920.
Descriptive letterpress on versos facing the plates.
"Published as Bulletin 410, Cornell university agricultural experiment station, May 1922."
Bibliography: p. 497–498.

1. Apple—Diseases and pests.
23-9187
Library of Congress SB608.A6K6
Cornell Univ. Libr. [2]

NK 0201809 NIC DNLM MiU OU PP CU DLC

T617.577 K744a Knight, Harry Obadiah, 1880-
Applied anatomy in the treatment of infections of the hand. [n.p., 1929?]
17p. illus. 19cm.
"Read before the Section of Surgery, State Medical Association of Texas, Galveston, May 9, 1968."
"Reprint from Texas State Journal of Medicine, Dec., 1928."

1. Hand - Surgery. I. Title.

NK 0201810 TxU

Knight, Harry Obadiah, 1880- ed.
Keiller, William, 1861–
A laboratory course in applied anatomy, being a supplement to Cunningham's Textbook and Manual of practical anatomy, by William Keiller ... 3d ed., revised by H. O. Knight ... Ann Arbor, Mich., Edwards brothers, inc., °1933.

Knight, Harry S.
One hundred years of uninterrupted banking service. The First national bank of Sunbury, originally Bank of Northumberland. [Sunbury, Pa., The Sunbury daily] 1931.
43, [1] p.incl.illus., ports., facsims.

NK 0201812 MH-BA

Knight, Mrs. Helen Cornelia
see Knight, Mrs. Helen Cross, 1814-1906.

Mu916.66 K743a [KNIGHT, HELEN (CROSS)] 1814-1906.
Africa redeemed: or, The means of her relief, illustrated by the growth and prospects of Liberia. London,J.Nisbet & co., 1851.
xx,300p. front.,plates. 18cm.

The first edition was published in Boston in 1850 under the title: "The new republic".

ICN MH ICU
NK 0201814 PU MWelC PU-Mu MH TNF CtY InU WU CtY-D

[Knight, Helen (Cross)] 1814–1906.
Annie Sherwood; ou, Les jeunes écolières. Traduit de l'anglais. Toulouse: Soc. des livres religieux, 1856. 135 p. illus. 15cm.

NK 0201815 NN

35 Knight, Helen (Cross) 1814-1906.
The beautiful garment, and other stories for girls. Being contributions to the Well-Spring. Boston, Massachusetts sabbath school society, [1853]
72 p. 18°.

NK 0201816 DLC

[Knight, Helen (Cross) 1814 - 1906.
City cousins; a sequel to Annie Sherwood. Written for the American Sunday-School Union, and revised by the committee of publication. Philadelphia: Amer. Sunday-School Union [cop. 1846]. 286 p., front. 16°.
Running-title: Annie Sherwood's winter in the city.

1. Fiction (American). 2. Title.
N. Y. P. L. May 1, 1918.

NK 0201817 NN PU PPULC MH IU MB

Knight, Helen (Cross) 1814 - 1906.
Flowers of spring-time
see under The Child's paper.

Knight, Helen (Cross), 1814 - 1906.
Golden threads, by Mrs. Helen C. Knight and others... New York: Amer. Tract Soc.[, 186–?] 234 p. front., illus. f°.
Title vignette.

160746A. 1. Juvenile literature, American. 2. Title.
N. Y. P. L. January 10, 1925

NK 0201819 NN RPB NNC

Knight, Helen(Cross) 1814 - 1906.
Hannah More; or, life in hall and cottage.
New York. American Tract Society. [1862.] (1), 282 pp. Portrait. Engraved title-page. 12°.
There is another edition on shelf-number 6543.101, with the title: A new memoir of Hannah More; or, life in hall and cottage.

H529 — More, Hannah. 1745-1833.

NK 0201820 MB MnU OO TxU

Knight, *Mrs.* Helen (Cross) 1814 - 1906.
Hannah More; or, Life in hall and cottage. By Mrs. Helen C. Knight. New York, American tract society [1872?]
2 p. l., [3]–282 p. front. (port.) 19½cm.
Added t.-p., engraved, with vignette.
Caption title: A new memoir of Hannah More.
Appeared, 1851, under title, "A new memoir of Hannah More; or, Life in hall and cottage".

1. More, Hannah, 1745–1833. I. Title.
30-32653 Revised
Library of Congress PR3605.M6K6 1872
——— Copy 2. [r40b2] 928.2

NK 0201821 DLC OrU OrPS ScCleU NcD MWA

[KNIGHT, HELEN (CROSS)] 1814 - 1906.
Hugh Fisher: or, Home principles carried out. By the author of "Robert Dawson,"... Philadelphia [etc.] Amer. Sunday-school union [1851] 238 p. front., pl. 15½cm.

988595A. 1. Juvenile literature—Fiction, American.
I. American Sunday-school union. II. Title.

NK 0201822 NN OO NNC ViU

Knight, Helen (Cross) 1814-1906.
Jane Hudson
see under American Sunday-School Union.

[Knight, *Mrs.* Helen (Cross)] 1814 - 1906.
Jane Taylor ... New York, American tract society [°1868]
224 p. front., pl. 17½cm.

1. Taylor, Jane, 1783–1824. I. Title.
14-16800
Library of Congress PR5549.T2Z6

NK 0201824 DLC MWA

VOLUME 300

Knight, Helen (Cross) 1814-1906.
Jane Taylor: her life and letters. By Mrs. H.C. Knight, ... London [etc.] Thomas Nelson and sons, 1880. Pp. 176. 16.4x10.6cm.

NK 0201825 CaOTP MdBP

Knight, Mrs. Helen (Cross) 1814-1906.
BV4571 K6 Jasper and Lucy. By Mrs. Helen C. Knight. New York, Published by the American tract society [c1863]
132 p. illus. 15 1|2 cm. [Life illustrated series] Red cloth.
I. American tract society, New York. II. Title.

NK 0201826 CSmH

35 Knight, Mrs. Helen (Cross) 1814-1906.
Juvenile benevolence. Being contributions to the Well-Spring. Boston, Mass. Sabbath school society, [1853]
90 p. 18°.

NK 0201827 DLC

[Knight, Helen (Cross)] 1814-1906.
Kitty King. New York: The Amer. Tract Soc. [cop. 1861.]
80 p. illus. 16°.
Illustrated t.-p.
1. Juvenile literature.—Fiction (American). 2. Title.
N. Y. P. L. January 21, 1921.

NK 0201828 NN CLSU NNU-W IaU

Knight, *Mrs.* Helen (Cross) 1814-1906.
Lady Huntington and her friends; or, The revival of the work of God in the days of Wesley, Whitefield, Romaine, Venn, and others in the last century. Compiled by Mrs. Helen C. Knight. New York, American tract society [°1853]
292 p. front., ports. 19½cm.
1. Huntingdon, Selina (Shirley) Hastings, countess of, 1707-1791.
Library of Congress DA483.H8K6 11-19849 Revised

NjP MWA TxU CU ScU PJB NjNbS WaTC OrSaW OrU IaU OU KMK NcRS NIC NcD PPRETS
NK 0201829 DLC MeB CaBVaU WaS Wa ODW OEac MiU GU-De

Knight, Helen (Cross) 1814-1906, ed.
Life scenes. Written for the Massachusetts Sabbath school society, and revised by the Committee of publication. Boston, Massachusetts Sabbath school society, 1846.
180 p. illus. 16cm.

NK 0201830 MnU

921 M763k Knight, Mrs. Helen (Cross) 1814-1906.
Life of James Montgomery. Bost. Gould. 1857
416p. front. (port.)

NK 0201831 NcWsW NNUT-Mc

Micro-film PR 215 Knight, Mrs. Helen (Cross) 1814-1906.
Life of James Montgomery. Boston, Gould and Lincoln, 1857.
Negative; Microfilmed by Photoduplication Dept., University of Chicago library.
1. Montgomery, James, 1771-1854.

NK 0201832 ICU

Knight, *Mrs.* Helen (Cross)
Life of James Montgomery. By Mrs. Helen C. Knight ... Boston, Gould and Lincoln: New York, Sheldon, Blakeman & co.; [etc., etc.] 1857.
1 p. l., x, [11]-416 p. front. (port.) 20cm.
Added t.-p., engraved, with vignette.
1. Montgomery, James, 1771-1854.
Library of Congress PR5033.K5 27-4937

OCl ODW ICU MB NN
NK 0201833 DLC IEG PLF OHi InU CtY PHatU PHC PPL PU

[KNIGHT, HELEN (CROSS)] 1814-1906.
Life of John Bunyan. By the author of "Robert Dawson," "Jane Hudson," &c. Philadelphia [etc.] American Sunday-School Union [cop. 1855] 372 p. 2 fronts. (incl. port.), illus., plates. 19½cm.
Added t.-p.: The illustrated life of John Bunyan.
783433A. 1. Bunyan, John. I. Title.

NK 0201834 NN

YA .S175 [Knight, Helen (Cross)] 1814-1906.
The loss of the Atlantic... Boston, 1847. 72p.
(Sunday school books; arr. numerically.)

NK 0201835 DLC OO

Knight, Helen (Cross) 1814-1906.
Memorial of Emma L. Taylor.
n.p., n.d.
8 p. 8°
(Repr't. from the Abbot Courant)

NK 0201836 MWA

Knight, Mrs. Helen (Cross) 1814-1906.
Hallock, William Allen, 1794-1880.
Memorial of Rev. Wm. A. Hallock, D. D., first secretary of the American tract society. By Mrs. H. C. Knight. New York, American tract society [1882]

Knight, Helen (Cross) 1814-1906.
Missionary cabinet. Boston, Massachusetts Sabbath school society, 1847.

NK 0201838 MH

[Knight, Helen (Cross)] 1814-1906.
My early home, and other tales
see under title

[Knight, Helen (Cross)] 1814-1906.
Nancy Fell, the beggar child. By the author of "The important decision," "Anne Allen," etc. Written for the Massachusetts Sabbath school society, and revised by the Committee of publication. Boston, Massachusetts Sabbath school society, 1842.
96 p. front. 61cm.
"Entered according to Act of Congress, in the year 1842, by Christopher C. Dean."
I. Dean, Christopher C

NK 0201840 MnU

PR 3605 .M6K6 1850 Knight, Helen (Cross) 1814-1906.
A new memoir of Hannah More; or, Life in hall and cottage. By Mrs. Helen C. Knight. New York, M. W. Dodd, [1850]
[iii]-viii, [9]-311 p. illus. 19 cm.
1. More, Hannah, 1745-1833.

NK 0201841 OKentU

Knight, *Mrs.* Helen (Cross) 1814-1906.
A new memoir of Hannah More; or, Life in hall and cottage. By Mrs. Helen C. Knight. New York, M. W. Dodd, 1851.
2 p. l., [iii]-viii, [9]-311 p. front. (port.) 19cm.
Added t.-p., illustrated.
1. More, Hannah, 1745-1833.
Library of Congress PR3605.M6K6 12-27297 Revised

NK 0201842 DLC NjR PCC PPL CLSU OO ScU AU

KNIGHT, Mrs. Helen C[ross] 1814-1906.
A new memoir of Hannah More, or Life in hall and cottage. New York, M.W.Dodd, 1853.
Port.
Added engraved title-page.

NK 0201843 MH PU MiU

PR 3605 .M6 Z66 KNIGHT, HELEN (CROSS) 1814-1906.
A new memoir of Hannah More; or Life in hall and cottage. New York, M. W. Dodd, 1856.
311 p. port.
1. More, Hannah, 1745-1833.

NK 0201844 InU MH

Knight, *Mrs.* Helen (Cross) 1814-1906.
A new memoir of Hannah More; or, Life in hall and cottage. By Mrs. Helen C. Knight. New York, American tract society [1862?]
2 p. l., [3]-282 p. front. (port.) 19½cm.
Added t.-p., engr., with vignette.
1. More, Hannah, 1745-1833. I. Title.
Library of Congress PR3605.M6K6 1862 20-9521

NK 0201845 DLC PU CaBVaU OO NjP MB NcWsW KEmT OU

VOLUME 300

[Knight, *Mrs.* Helen (Cross)] 1814-1906.
The new republic. Written for the Massachusetts Sabbath school society, and approved by the Committee of publication. Boston, Massachusetts Sabbath school society, 1850.
252 p. incl. front. 15cm.

1. Liberia—Hist. I. Massachusetts Sabbath school society. ed.
5-15425 Additions
Library of Congress DT631.K6

NK 0201846 DLC MnU NN MiU

[Knight, *Mrs.* Helen (Cross)] 1814-1906.
The new republic. Written for the Massachusetts Sabbath school society, and approved by the Committee of publication. 2d ed. Boston, Massachusetts Sabbath school society, 1851.
252 p. incl. front. 16cm.

1. Liberia—Hist. I. Massachusetts Sabbath school society.
11-8274
Library of Congress DT631.K62

NK 0201847 DLC NjR PU TNF NN InU

CT788 .B877 K6 Knight, Helen (Cross) 1814-1906.
No gains without pains; a true life for the boys. New York, American Tract Society [1856]
120p. illus. 16cm.

Biography of Samuel Budgett based on The successful merchant by W. Arthur.

1. Budgett, Samuel, 1794-1851. I. Title.

NK 0201848 NcU NNU-W IU NjP MH

[Knight, *Mrs.* Helen (Cross)] 1814-1906
Pictorial alphabet. Written for the Massachusetts Sabbath school society, and rev. by the com. of publication. Boston, Massachusetts Sabbath school society, 1845.
36 p. illus. 15½cm.

I. Massachusetts Sabbath school society, ed. II. Title.
16-10114
Library of Congress PZ8.3.K744P

NK 0201849 DLC

B S836k 1873 Knight, Mrs Helen (Cross) 1814-1906.
"Puffing Billy" and the prize "Rocket"; or, The story of the Stephensons and our railways ... London, S. W. Partridge & co. [1873]
152p. front.(port.) illus.
Title vignette.
First published under title: The rocket, 1860; another edition has title: The railway pioneers, 1876.

1. Locomotives--Hist. 2. Stephenson, George, 1781-1848. 3. Stephenson, Robert, 1803-1859. I. Title.

NK 0201850 IU

[KNIGHT, HELEN (CROSS)] 1814-1906.
Reuben Kent at school; or, Influence as it should be. Written for the American Sunday-school union, and revised by the Committee of publication. Philadelphia: Amer. Sunday-school union [c1844] 87 p. front. 15½cm.

884103A .1 Juvenile literature—Fiction, American. I. American Sunday-schoo' union. II. Title.

NK 0201851 NN NIC CtY ICU IU ViU DLC PPAmS

Knight, Helen(Cross) 1814-1906.
Reuben Kent's first winter in the city. By the Author of "Reuben Kent at school."
Philadelphia. American Sunday School Union. [1845.] Illus. 16°.

NK 0201852 MB NjP LU IU NNUT PKsL MH

PZ7 .K738 Re **[Knight, Mrs. Helen (Cross)]** 1814-1906.
Reuben Kent's first winter in the city. By the author of "Reuben Kent at school" ... Philadelphia, American Sunday-school union, 1893.
1 p. l., 7-174 p. incl. plates. front. 17 1/2cm.

NK 0201853 MB PPAmSwM IU

[Knight, Helen (Cross)] 1814-1906.
Richard Harvey, or Taking a stand. By the author of Robert Dawson, Reuben Kent, &c. Worcester, S. A. Howland [c1848]
62 p.incl.front.

NK 0201854 CLU MH

Knight,Helen(Cross)1914-1906.
Robert Dawson:or, The brave spirit
see under American Sunday-School Union.

385.42 K74r [Knight, Mrs. Helen (Cross)] 1814-1906.
The rocket. New York, American tract society [c1860]
118p. illus.

Title vignette.
Preface signed: H. C. K.

NK 0201856 IU

Knight, Helen (Cross)1814-1906.
The rocket. The story of the Stephensons, father and son, by H. C. Knight. With twenty-six engravings. London, T. Nelson & sons, 1890.
vi, [3], 10-128 p. front., illus. 18cm.

1. Locomotives—History. 2. Stephenson, George, 1781-1848. 3. Stephenson, Robert, 1803-1859. I. Title.
A 26-562
Title from Bureau of Railway Economics. Printed by L. C.

NK 0201857 DBRE

B S836k 1892 Knight, Mrs. Helen (Cross) 1914-1906.
The rocket. The story of the Stephensons, father and son ... London [etc.] T. Nelson and sons, 1892.
128p. front., illus.

First published in 1860; other editions have title: "Puffing Billy" and the prize "Rocket", 1873, and The railway pioneers, 1876.

1. Locomotives--Hist. 2. Stephenson, George, 1781-1848. 3. Stephenson, Robert, 1803-1859. I. Title.

NK 0202001 IU

LIBS-J PZ 6 .K59SA **Knight, Mrs. Helen (Cross)** 1914-1906.
Saw up and saw down: or, the fruits of industry and self-reliance, by Mrs. H. C. Knight. New York, American Female Guardian Society [18--?]
2 v. in 1 (64 p.)

Bound with A., Mrs. S. S. What small hands may do. New York [18--?]

NK 0202002 MoU

Knight, Mrs.Helen (Cross) 1814-1906
Saw up and saw down; or, The fruits of industry and self-reliance... New York, American female guardian society, 1852.
32 p. 14½ cm.

With this is bound What small hands may do, by Mrs.S.S.A. [18--?]

I. What small hands may do. [18--?] (set)

NK 0202003 NjP MH

KNIGHT, HELEN (CROSS) 1814-1906.
Saw up and saw down: or, The fruits of industry and self-reliance. By Mrs. H. C. Knight... New York: American female guardian soc. [etc., etc.] 1853. 32 p. 14½cm.

36872B. 1. Juvenile literature—Fiction, American. I. Title.

NK 0202004 NN NNC

Knight, H[elen] (Cross) 1814-1906.
Saw up and saw down; or, The fruits of industry and self-reliance ... and, What small hands may do; or, Filial love rewarded by Mrs. S. S. A. Boston, 1858.
64 p. 15 cm.

NK 0202005 RPB DLC

1853 Juv. coll. Knight, Helen (Cross) 1814-1906.
Summer rambles: lessons by the way. By Mrs. Helen C. Knight. Written for the Massachusetts Sabbath School Society, and approved by the Committee of publication. Boston; Massachusetts Sabbath School Society. Depository. No. 13 Cornhill [c1853]
[5] 6-54 p. 15 cm.

NK 0202006 DLC

813 K738t [Knight, Mrs. Helen (Cross)] 1814-1906.
Taking a stand, by the author of "Hugh Fisher" "Jane Hudson", "Robert Dawson", etc., etc. Boston, H. Hoyt [1860]
94p. front., plates.

NK 0202007 IU

[Knight, Helen (Cross)] 1814-1906.
Taking a stand. By the author of "Hugh Fisher"... Boston: H. Hoyt [1865]. 94 p., 2 pl. (incl. front.) 16°.

1. Temperance.—Fiction. 2. Juvenile literature.—Fiction (American). 3. Title.
BLACK TEMPERANCE COLL.
N. Y. P. L. August 30, 1917.

NK 0202008 NN

YA .S198 Knight,Helen(Cross)1814-1906.
The useful little girl; or, What Fanny did. Boston, 1851.
90p.

(Sunday school books; arr. numerically.)

NK 0202009 DLC

VOLUME 300

Knight, Helen (Cross) 1814-1906, ed.
Whispers and wishes ... written for the Massachusetts Sabbath school society and revised by the Committee of publication. Boston, 1845.
2 p.l.[5]-144 p. front. 16 cm.

NK 0202010 RPB NN

[Knight, Helen M.]
Mother Goose nursery rhymes written for the Bank of Italy. [San Francisco, c1926]
24 p. col. illus. 27 cm.

NK 0202011 RPB

Knight, Henry, of Birmingham.
Multiplication tablets derived from a theorem of S. Slonimski ... Birmingham, 1847.
[34] p. 22 cm.

NK 0202012 RPB

BT130 Knight,Henry, of Chertsey.
.K72 The being and attributes of God demonstrated,in a method intirely new,yet easy to be understood by even the unlearned:or,An essay concerning God... By Henry Knight... London,Printed for J.Noon,etc., 1747.
xxxi,[1],381,[5] p. 20cm.

1.God--Attributes.

NK 0202013 ICU MH NNUT

KNIGHT, Henry, of Chertsey.
The natural and providential effects of national virtue and vice consider'd. Sermon preach'd , the last Fast-day, Nov. 25th, 1741. L. 1742.

pp.34.

NK 0202014 MH

3A
165 KNIGHT, HENRY, of Stamford.
Leaves of autumn from the Vale of the Ems. [poems] Stamford,John Ford,1865.
124p. 17cm.

NK 0202015 ICN

Knight, *Sir* Henry, 1886-
Food administration in India, 1939-47. [Stanford, Stanford University Press [1954]
xii, 323 p. illus., maps. 24 cm. (Food, agriculture, and World War II)
Includes bibliographies.

1. World War, 1939-1945—Food question—India. 2. Food supply—India. I. Title. (Series)
Full name: Sir Henry Foley Knight.

HD9016.I 42K5 338.1 53-9961 rev

PU-SRS PPT OrCS OrP OrU WaS DNAL
OOxM PBL PP TxU DS ViU PPD NIC NN CU TU Or CaBVaU
NK 0202016 DLC OCU NSyU GU CoU KyU OU MB AAP MU KMK

BQ
7085 Knight, Henry Albert.
.L46 A neglected early work of John Henry Newman, the
K7 "Lectures on Justification", a study of their doctrine of grace. Lyon, Unstitut Catholique, 1951.
v, 106 numb. leaves. 26cm.

Thesis(S.T.D.) - Institut Catholique, Lyon.
Bibliographical note: leaf v.

1. Newman, John Henry, cardinal, 1801-1890. Lectures on Justification. 2. Grace (Theology) 3. Justification

NK 0202017 DCU

Beinecke Library
Za
K745
815B
Knight, Henry Cogswell, 1788-1835
The broken harp; poems. By H.C. Knight. Philadelphia, J. Conrad and Co., 1815.
x p., 1l., [9]-176 p. 16 cm.

I. Title (1). Imprint: Pennsylvania. Philadelphia. 1815.

NK 0202018 CtY NIC RPB CtY PPL MWA

FILM
9247
PS
Knight, Henry Cogswell, 1788-1835.
The broken harp; poems. Philadelphia, J. Conrad, 1815.
x,[9]-176 p. On film (Negative)

Microfilm. Original in Brown Univ. Library.

NK 0202019 CU

Knight, Henry Cogwell, 1788-1835.
The Cypriad, in two cantas: with other poems and translations. Boston, J. Belcher, 1809.
68 p. 8°. [Bailey pamphlets, v. 24]

NK 0202020 DLC CtY RPB CSmH InU

KNIGHT, Henry Cogswell. 1788-1835.
Fights of faith. In two parts. [Anon.]
Boston: pr. by Wells and Lilly. 1821. 47 pp. 8°.

NK 0202021 MB

[Knight, Henry Cogswell] 1789-1835.
Fights of faith, in two parts. Boston, Wells and Lilly, 1821.
cover title, 47 p. 24 cm.
A revised version of this poem, entitled The crusade, is to be found in the author's Poems. Boston, 1821. v. 2. p. 1-49.

NK 0202022 RPB MH

252
K745
Knight, Henry Cogswell, 1788-1835.
Lectures and sermons. Boston, Lilly & Wait, 1831.
2v. 20cm.

1. Protestant Episcopal Church in the U.S.A. Sermons. 2. Sermons, American.

NK 0202023 OrU MB RPB PPAN PPL IaU MHi

[Knight, Henry Cogswell] 1788-1835.
Letters from the South and West; by Arthur Singleton, esq. [pseud.] Boston, Richardson & Lord, 1824.
159 pp. 8°.
F210.K69

1. Southern states—Descr. & trav. 2. Philadelphia—Descr. 3. Washington, D. C.—Descr.
1-21522—M 1

MiU-C NIC PHi PPL OCl NN MWA
NK 0202024 DLC NcU IaU KyU ViW ViU OC Vi NcD NcU OO

Micro-card
58-8
ser.B
no.47
[Knight, Henry Cogswell, 1788-1835.
Letters from the South and West: by Arthur Singleton, esq. [pseud.] Boston, Richardson and Lord, 1824. [Louisville, Ky., Lost Cause Press, 1958]
4 cards. (Nineteenth century American literature on microcards. ser.B: The South. no.47)

Microcard edition.
Collation of original: 159 p.

1. Southern states--Desc. & trav. I. Title.

NK 0202025 AU MsU FMU ICRL OOxM FU ViU

Knight, Henry Coggswell, 1789-1835.
Lunar stanzas.
In- Wells, Carolyn. A nonsense anthology. N. Y., 1916. p. 15-16.

NK 0202026 RPB

Knight, Henry Cogswell, 1788-1835. Poems.
4 pp. (Kettell, S., *Specimens of Am. poetry*, v. 2, p. 285.)

NK 0202027 MdBP

Knight, Henry Cogswell, 1788-1835.
Poems ... By Henry C. Knight, A. M. 2d ed. ... Boston, Wells and Lilly, 1821.
2 v. 15cm.

Library of Congress PS2196.K7 15-17425
——— Copy 2.

NK 0202028 DLC CtY PHi PPL MWA MB

Knight, Henry Cogswell, 1788-1835.
The recluse. (In his The broken harp) [by] Henry Coggswell Knight. Philadelphia, 1815.
In Three centuries of drama: American)

Microprint.

I. The broken harp. II. Title.

NK 0202029 MoU

Knight, Henry Cogswell, 1788-1835.
Rustic life. (In his The broken harp [by] Henry Coggswell Knight) Philadelphia, 1815.
(In Three centuries of drama: American)

Microprint.

I. The broken harp. II. Title.

NK 0202030 MoU

VOLUME 300

Knight, Henry Cogswell, 1788-1835.
Sibylline Leaves and Wayward Criticisms. by Arthur Singleton [pseud]
Boston 1825.
24 p. 12°

NK 0202031 MWA

Knight, Henry Cogswell, 1788-1835.

Knight, Frederick, 1791-1849.
Thorn cottage, or The poet's home. A memorial of Frederick Knight, esq., of Rowley, Mass. Boston, Press of Crocker and Brewster, 1855.

Knight, Henry F.
Cape Porpoise, old and new ... Read before the ... society, May 3, 1894.
(In Collections and proceedings of the Maine historical society. Portland, 1895. 23½cm. 2d ser., v. 6, p. 153-175)

1. Kennebunkport, Me.—Hist. 2. Porpoise, Cape, Me.
A 15-1183
Title from Bangor Pub. Libr. Library of Congress F16.M33

NK 0202033 MeBa MiU

Knight, Henry Foley
see Knight, Sir Henry, 1886-

Knight, Henry Gally, 1786-1846.
An architectural tour in Normandy; with some remarks on Norman architecture.
London. Murray. 1836. xi, (1). 258 pp. Plates. 17½ cm., in 12s.

K8876 — Norman architecture. — Church architecture.

NK 0202035 MB PPL

Knight, Henry Gally, 1786-1846.
An architectural tour in Normandy; with some remarks on Norman architecture, by Henry Gally Knight ... 2d ed. London, J. Murray, 1841.
xi, [1], 258 p. 6 pl. 20½cm.

. Church architecture—Normandy. 2. Architecture, Norman. I. Title.
13-15917
Library of Congress NA1049.N7K5

NK 0202036 DLC MiD NcD PPF CtY PU PSC NjP MB

Greenlee
4504
P855
KNIGHT, HENRY GALLY, 1786-1846.
Carta dirigida ao Conde de Aberdeen, secretario d'estado dos negocios estrangeiros... Londres, Impresso por Bingham, 1829.
35p. 22cm.

NK 0202037 ICN DCU-IA

Knight, Henry Gally, 1786-1846.
Eastern sketches in verse. London, Murray, 1819. xlix, 207p. 17cm.

NK 0202038 MWelC CtY

Knight, Henry Gally, 1786-18_.
The ecclesiastical architectvre of Italy. From the time of Constantine to the fifteenth centvry, with an introdvction and text, by Henry Gally Knight ... London, H. Bohn, 1842-44
2 v. illus., 81 pl. (3 col.; incl. plan) 56½cm.
Title within illuminated border.

1. Church architecture—Italy. I. Title.
[Name originally: Henry Gally
8-20536 Revised
Library of Congress NA5613.K7

NK 0202039 DLC MB IU GU NcD MU CoU TxU NIC NjNbS CtY OU NjP OrP WaSp

Knight, Henry Gally, 1786-1846.
The ecclesiastical architectvre of Italy. From the time of Constantine to the fifteenth centvry, with an introdvction and text, by Henry Gally Knight ... London, H. Bohn, 1843.
2 v. illus., 81 pl. (3 col.; incl. plan) 56½cm.
Title within illuminated border.

NK 0202040 ViU PPF PPL PP NN OClStM MH

Knight, Henry Gally, 1786-1846.
Foreign and domestic view of the Catholic question. London, J. Ridgway, 1828.
78 p.
1. Catholic emancipation. I. Title.

NK 0202041 RP

282.42
K69F
Knight, Henry Gally, 1786-1846.
Foreign and domestic view of the Catholic question ... 2d ed. London, James Ridgway, 1828.
78 p. 21 cm.

1. Catholic Church in Great Britain. I. Title.

NK 0202042 NcD

KNIGHT, Henry Gally, 1786-1846.
Foreign and domestic view of the Catholic question. 3d ed. London, J.Ridgway, 1828.
pp.(2). 78.

NK 0202043 MH

4A
7101
KNIGHT, HENRY GALLY, 1786-1846.
Foreign and domestic view of the Catholic question. By Henry Gally Knight ... 4th ed. London, J. Ridgway, 1828.
[1]l., 78p. 20cm.

NK 0202044 ICN

KNIGHT, HENRY GALLY, 1786-1846.
Hannibal in Bithynia. A dramatic poem. By Henry Gally Knight... 3d ed. London, J. Murray, 1839.
1 p. l., iii p., 1 l., 145, [1]p. 18cm.

1. Hannibal. Poetry. I. Title.

Printed by Wesleyan University Library

NK 0202045 CtW InU CtY CSmH MB MH

PR4889
.K3
1817
[Knight, Henry Gally] 1786-1846.
Ilderim: a Syrian tale. In four cantos. London, Printed for J. Murray, 1816.
[5], 74 p. 21½cm. [With his Phrosyne. London, 1817]

NK 0202046 ICU MH NN IU OrU InU CtY TxU CU CSt

[Knight, Henry Gally] 1786-1846.
Ilderim: a Syrian tale. In four cantos. London—Printed: Philadelphia—Reprinted: and published by M. Thomas, no. 52, Chesnut-street. William Fry, Printer. 1816.
2 p. l., [7]-72 p. 15½cm.

I. Title.
[Name originally: Henry Gally]
25-24737
Library of Congress PR4859.K43 I 3 1816

NK 0202047 DLC NN TxU PHi CSmH MB NjP

942.074
K737
Knight, Henry Gally, 1786-1846.
A letter addressed to the Earl of Aberdeen. 2d ed. London, J. Ridgway, 1829.
43 p. 21cm.
To the Earl of Aberdeen, Secretary of state for foreign affairs, on his official policy, etc.
1. Gt. Brit. For. rel. 1820-1830. I. Aberdeen , George Hamilton Gordon, 4th earl of, 1784-1860.

NK 0202048 MnU CtY

Knight (Henry Gally) 1786-1846.
A letter addressed to the Earl of Aberdeen, Secretary of State for foreign affairs [on his official policy etc.] *London: J. Ridgway*, 1830. 43 pp. 3. ed. 8°.
In: *C. p. v. 746.

NK 0202049 NN

Knight, Henry Gally, 1786-1846.
A letter addressed to the Earl of Aberdeen, secretary of state for foreign affairs ... 4th ed., corrected ... London, J. Ridgway, 1830.
43 p. 19 cm. [Binder's title: Great Britain, 19th century]
1. Aberdeen, George Hamilton-Gordon, 4th earl of, 1781-1860.

NK 0202050 CtY

[Knight, Henry Gally] 1786-1846.
Noradin; Or, The Lamps Of Fate. A Dramatic Poem, ... London, 1809.

NK 0202051 CSmH

VOLUME 300

Knight, Henry Gally, 1786-1846.
The Normans in Sicily; being a sequel to "An architectural tour in Normandy." By Henry Gally Knight ... London, J. Murray, 1838.
vii, [1], 355 p. illus. 20cm.
"Introductory historical notice": p. [1]-110.
"Architectural tour": p. [111]-355.
1. Architecture—Sicily. 2. Sicily—Antiquities. 3. Normans in Italy.
[Name originally: Henry Gally]
A 10-1185
Title from Stanford Univ.
Library of Congress NA427.S5K7

MdBP NN
NK 0202052 CSt MiD MdBP DDO CtY PPL PHC PU CU NjP

821
K743p [Knight, Henry Gally] 1786-1846.
Phrosyne: a Grecian tale in two cantos. London, Printed for J. Murray by J. F. Dove, 1814.
50p. 20cm.

NK 0202053 IU

Lilly
PR 4859
.K43 I 3
1816
KNIGHT, HENRY GALLY, 1786-1846
Phrosyne: a Grecian tale. Alashtar: an Arabian tale. By H. Gally Knight, esq. London, J. Murrary, 1817.
2 p. l., 112 p. 21.5 cm.
Bound with his Ilderim. London, 1816.
I. Knight, Henry Gally, 1786-1846--Alashtar: an Arabian tale

NK 0202054 InU CSt NcU MH ICN

Knight, Henry Gally, 1786-1846.
Saracenic and Norman remains, to illustrate the Normans in Sicily, by Henry Gally Knight, esq. London, J. Murray [1840]
2 p. l., xxx (i. e. 29) pl. (3 col.) 57cm.
Engraved t.-p. with vignette, included in list of numbered plates.
1. Architecture, Mohammedan. 2. Architecture, Norman. 3. Architecture—Sicily. 4. Normans in Italy. I. Title.
[Name originally: Henry Galley]
1-4307 Revised
Library of Congress NA427.S5K72

MB MH IU MU LU FU
NK 0202055 DLC OrP CtY PP PPL PBm MiU OCl MH NN NjP

Knight, Henry Gally, 1786-1846.
Substance of Two Speeches delivered at Mansfield & Retford ...; at the General Election in Dec., 1832. London, 1833.
2p.l. 28 cm. 26 cm.

NK 0202056 CtY

1.932
A2Ag8
no.91
also in
1.932
A2K74
Knight, Henry Granger, 1878 - 1942.
...Accomplishments of the Bureau of agricultural chemistry and engineering, U.S. Department of agriculture; remarks of Dr. Henry G. Knight upon receipt of the medal of the American institute of chemists from Vice President Wallace ...in Washington, D.C. ...May 17, 1941. [Washington, 1941]
14 p. 26 1/2cm. (U.S. Bureau of agricultural chemistry and engineering. ACE-91)
Mimeographed.

NK 0202057 DNAL

Knight, Henry Granger, 1878-
Acidity and acidimetry of soils, by Henry Granger Knight ... [Easton? Pa., 1920]
1 p. l., 12, 21, 7, [2] p. diagrs. 23cm.
Thesis (PH. D.)—University of Illinois, 1917.
Vita.
"Reprinted from the Journal of industrial and engineering chemistry, vol. 12, no. 4, p. 340; no. 5, p. 457; no. 6, p. 559. April, May and June 1920."
Bibliographical foot-notes.
1. Soils.
21-27090
Library of Congress S593.K76

NK 0202058 DLC OU MH

1.932
A2Ag8
no.175
Knight, Henry Granger, 1878-1942.
... Cotton's place in the war, remarks... before the third annual Cotton research congress, Dallas, Texas, July 9, 1942. [Washington, 1942]
10 p. 27cm. (U.S. Bureau of agricultural chemistry and engineering. ACE-175)
Processed.
1. Cotton. Research. 2. Cotton, Uses of. 3. War and agriculture (1939-) U.S. I. Title.

NK 0202059 DNAL

Knight, Henry Granger, 1878-1942.
Digestion experiments. II. Native hays, oat straw, pea hay, sweet clover and alfalfa. By H. G. Knight, F. E. Hepner and T. F. McConnell. [Laramie, 1908] 44 p. 8°. (Wyoming. Agricultural experiment station. Bulletin. 78.)
1. Fodder. 2. Cattle.—Feeding. 3. Hepner, Frank E. 4. McConnell, T. F.
N. Y. P. L. February 27, 1911.

NK 0202060 NN

Knight, Henry Granger, 1878-1942.
Meteorology for twenty years. [Laramie, 1913.] 1 p.l., 27-87(1) p., 1 diagr. 8°. (Wyoming. Agricultural Experiment Station. Bull. 100.)
By H.G.Knight and J.C.Fritterer.
——— A second copy.
1. Meteorology, U. S.: Wyo. 2. Fritterer, J. C.
N. Y. P. L. February 6, 1914.

NK 0202061 NN DAS AzU

Knight, Henry Granger, 1878- joint author.
Byers, Horace Greeley, 1872-
Notes on qualitative analysis, by Horace G. Byers ... and Henry G. Knight ... New York, D. Van Nostrand company, 1912.

R
821
.C9K6
Knight, Henry Granger, 1878-1942.
Official diary ... Chief, Bureau of Chemistry and Soils ... from 1929 to 1942. [Washington, 1942]
2 v.
(01) 1. U.S. Bureau of Chemistry and Soils. 2. U.S. Bureau of Agricultural and Industrial Chemistry.

NK 0202063 DNAL

1.932
A2K74
Mar.25,
1942
Knight, Henry Granger, 1878-1942.
... The regional laboratories in national defense, remarks...before the eighth annual Chemurgic conference, Chicago, Illinois... March 25, 1942... [Washington, 1942]
16 p. 27cm.
Processed.
1. Agriculture. Research. 2. Farm chemurgy. 3. U.S. Regional research laboratories. 4. War and agriculture (1939- U.S.

NK 0202064 DNAL

1.932
A2Ag8
no.86
also in
1.932
A2K74
Knight, Henry Granger, 1878 - 1942.
...Regional laboratories progress report; remarks of Dr. Henry G. Knight, chief, Bureau of agricultural chemistry and engineering, United States Department of agriculture, before the seventh Annual chemurgic conference of agriculture, industry, and science...Chicago, Illinois... March 28, 1941. [Washington, 1941]
10 p. 26 1/2cm. ([U.S. Bureau of agricultural chemistry and engineering] ACE-86)

NK 0202065 DNAL

Knight, Henry Granger, 1878 -
... Research on industrial utilization of corn; with special reference to the Northern regional laboratory for research on the utilization of farm products ... [n.p., 1940]
10 p.
At head of title: ACE-38.
Caption title.
Manifold copy.
Address before the Sixth annual chemurgic conference, Chicago, Ill., March 27, 1940.

NK 0202066 MH-BA

1.932
A2Ag8
no.106
also
1.932
A2K74
June 26,
1941
Knight, Henry Granger, 1878-1942.
...Research on present uses of cotton and cottonseed, remarks by Dr. Henry G. Knight, chief, Bureau of agricultural chemistry and engineering, United States Department of agriculture, before the International cotton congress, Waco, Texas, June 26, 1941. [Washington, 1941]
12 p. 26 1/2cm. (U.S. Bureau of agricultural chemistry and engineering. ACE-106)
Processed.

NK 0202067 DNAL

Knight, Henry Granger, 1878-1942.
Soil nitrogen. [Laramie, 1909] 32 p. 8°. (Wyoming. Agricultural experiment station. Bulletin 82.)
By H.G.Knight and F.A.Smith.
1. Soils.—Nitrogenous matter in. 2. Smith, Frank A.
N. Y. P. L. February 24, 1911.

NK 0202068 NN PP

2500
.74
Knight, Henry Granger, 1878-1942.
Speeches, articles, etc.

NK 0202069 DFT

VOLUME 300

Knight, Henry Granger, 1878-1942.
Wyoming forage plants and their chemical composition. Studies No. 3. [By H. G. Knight, F. E. Hepner and A. Nelson] [Laramie, 1908] 119 p. illus. 8°. (Wyoming. Agricultural experiment station. Bulletin. 76.)

1. Fodder, U. S.: Wyoming. 2. Hepner, Frank E. 3. Nelson, Aven.
N. Y. P. L. February 27, 1911.

NK 0202070 NN

Knight, Henry Granger, 1878-1942.
Wyoming forage plants and their chemical composition. Studies no. 4. By H. G. Knight, T. E. Hepner and A. Nelson. [Laramie, 1911] 151 p. illus. 8°. (Wyoming. Agricultural experiment station. Bulletin 87.)

1. Forage plants, U. S.: Wyoming. 2. Hepner, Frank E. 3. Nelson, Aven.
N. Y. P. L. June 22, 1911.

NK 0202071 NN DLC

Knight, Henry Hey, d. 1857.
Specimens of inlaid tiles, heraldic and geometrical, from Neath abbey, Glamorganshire. The descriptive heraldic notices by the Revd. H. H. Knight... The plates from original drawings by Mr. Egbert Moxham... Edinburgh, Committee of the Neath philosophical inst. [1850] 27 p. 7 [i. e. 8] pl. 38 x 56cm.

279970B. 1. Neath abbey. 2. Tiles, British—Wales. 3. Heraldry—Gt. Br.—Wales. I. Moxham, Egbert. II. Neath philosophical institution, Neath, Wales.
N. Y. P. L. January 31, 1945

NK 0202072 NN

---

arZ
735

Knight, Henry Hey, d. 1857.
Specimens of inlaid tiles, heraldic and geometrical, from Neath Abbey, Glamorganshire; the descriptive notices by H. H. Knight, the plates from drawings by E. Moxham. Edinburgh, Published by subscription by the Committee of the Neath Philosophical Institution [187-?]
27 p. 8 plates. 37 x 55cm.

NK 0202073 NIC

Knight, Henry Joseph Corbett, bp. of Gibraltar, 1861-
The church of Asinou, Cyprus, and its frescoes, by the Rt. Rev. the Bishop of Gibraltar, Major Vivian Seymer, W. H. Buckler, and Mrs. W. H. Buckler, communicated to the Society of antiquaries.
Oxford, Printed by John Johnson for the Society of antiquaries of London, 1934.

NK 0202074 MdBJ

Knight, Henry Joseph Corbett, *bp. of Gibraltar*, 1861-
The diocese of Gibraltar; a sketch of its history, work and tasks, by Henry J. C. Knight ... London, Society for promoting Christian knowledge, 1917.
xxvii, 272 p. front., plates, ports., map. 22cm.
"References to authorities": p. xxvii.

1. Gibraltar (Diocese)

18-13654

Library of Congress BX5652.G5K6

NK 0202075 DLC MB FMU IEG ScCleU

Knight, Henry Joseph Corbett, *Bishop of Gibraltar, 1859-1920.*
The temptation of our Lord. Considered as related to the ministry and as a revelation of his person. With . . . an introduction by H. H. Montgomery.
London. Society for Promoting Christian Knowledge. 1922. xxviii, 162 pp. Portrait. [Hulsean Lectures. 1905-06.] 19 cm., in 8s.

M4889 — T.r. — S.r.c. — Christ. Temptation.—Montgomery, Henry Hutchinson, sometime Bishop of Tasmania, pref., 1847–.

NK 0202076 MB NjNbS

Knight, Henry Joseph Corbett, *bp. of Gibraltar*, 1861–1920.
The temptation of Our Lord, considered as related to the ministry and as a revelation of His person, by H. J. C. Knight ... The Hulsean lectures, 1905–6. London, New York, Bombay, and Calcutta, Longmans, Green, and co., 1907.
xiii, 210 p. 20cm.
CONTENTS.—Preface.—The temptation of Our Lord considered in its relation to the ministry.—I. The place of the temptation in the life of Christ, and the nature of it.—II. An interpretation of the three temptations of the forty days.—III. The principles of the ministry, the issue of the temptation.—IV. The person of Christ as seen in the temptations of the forty days.
1. Jesus Christ—Temptation. 2. Jesus Christ—Person and offices. I. Hulsean lectures, 1905–1906. II. Title.

8-5810 rev.

Library of Congress BT355.K5
[r37b2] 235.952

NK 0202077 DLC MB MH NN OO

FS66
K74

Knight, Henry Joseph Corbett, Bp. of Gibraltar, 1861-1920.
The temptation of our Lord; considered as related to the ministry and as a revelation of His person. With portrait and introduction by H. H. Montgomery. London, SPCK, 1922.
xxviii, 162 p. (Hulsean lectures, 1905-06)

1. Jesus Christ - Temptation. 2. Jesus Christ - Person and offices. I. Title. (Series: Hulsean lectures)

NK 0202078 CSaT

Knight, Henry L
A lecture on irresponsibility, moral and natural, including animadversions on the objections of the author of the electrical theory, delivered in the Social Institution, Oldham. Published by A. Heywood. Hulme, Printed for W. Chadwick, 1838.
16 p. 19cm.

NK 0202079 NNC CtY

HD4885
.G7T9

Knight, Henry Newcome.

Twyman, Frank, 1876–
Apprenticeship for a skilled trade. With an appendix: Apprentices and the law, by Henry Newcome Knight ... By F. Twyman ... London, C. Griffin & company, limited, 1944.

Knight, Henry Raleigh.
Historical records of The Buffs, East Kent regiment, 3rd Foot formerly designated the Holland Regiment and Prince George of Denmark's Regiment. Vol. 1.
London. Gale & Polden. 1905. xviii, (1), 564 pp. Maps. Folded charts. 8°.
Contents. — 1. 1572-1704.

G1931 — Great Britain. Army and navy. Army. Regiments. Buffs, formerly 3d Regiment of Foot.

NK 0202081 MB MH NN MiU

KNIGHT, HENRY WILLIAM. Diary of a pedestrian in Cashmere and Thibet. London, 1863. xvi, 385 p. Pl. (part col'd), illus. 8°.

NK 0202082 MSaE PU PBL NN

---

*HG9970.S9
K6

Knight, Herbert M
What is suretyship? By Herbert M. Knight ... Three articles reprinted from Civil engineering for October and November 1935 and for January 1936. New York, N. Y., American society of civil engineers [1936?]

cover-title, 13p. 31cm.

1. Suretyship and guaranty. I. Title.

NK 0202083 NBuG

Knight, Herbert Theodore, 1869-1934.
"Back to Christ!" by the Rev. H. T. Knight ... Oxford, New York [etc.] Milford, 1916.
vii, [1], 104 p. 18½cm. (*Half-title:* The church's message for the coming time, no. 1)
Bibliography: p. 103-104.

1. Church of England — Doctrinal and controversial works. 2. Jesus Christ—Divinity. I. Title.

A 21-686

Title from General Theol. Sem. Printed by L. C.

NK 0202084 NNG

Knight, Herbert Theodore, 1869-1934.
Criticism and the Old Testament; a popular introduction... London, E. Stock, 1906.
xv, 170 p. 20cm.

Bibliography: p. 163-170.

NK 0202085 NjPT NN

Knight, Herbert Theodore, 1869-1934.
Nature and the supernatural, by the Rev. H. T. Knight ... Oxford, New York [etc.] Milford, 1920.
98 p. 18½cm. (*Half-title:* The church's message for the coming time, no. 4)

1. Miracles. I. Title.

A 21-687

Title from General Theol. Sem. Printed by L. C.

NK 0202086 NNG

BX5133
.K7R2
1903

KNIGHT, HERBERT THEODORE, 1869-1934.
Rational religion; some addresses to men, by the Rev. H. Theodore Knight... London, Rivingtons, 1903.
xii, 287 p. 20cm.

1. Sermons, English.

NK 0202087 ICU

Knight, Herbert Theodore, 1869-1934, and F. H. Duffield.
The story of St. Mary's, Shortlands, by Canon H. T. Knight ...and F. H. Duffield... Bromley, Kent: Kentish District Times Co., Ltd., 1926. 81 p. front., plates. 12°.

1. Shortlands, Eng.—Hist. 2. Duffield, F. H., jt. au.
N. Y. P. L. March 9, 1927

NK 0202088 NN

VOLUME 300

KNIGHT, H[erbert] T[heodore], 1861-1934.
The structure of the 1928 liturgy. London, Society for promoting Christian knowledge, [1930]
pp.634. Folded table.

NK 0202089 MH

Knight, Herbert Twombly.
Unstable detonation in the carbon monoxide-oxygen system
Thesis - Harvard, 1952

NK 0202090 MH-C MH

Knight, Hiram.
Biography of Deacon James Allen, by Hiram Knight with genealogical register and testimonials. Worcester, Mass., Printed by C. Hamilton, 1889.
vi, [7]-67 p. front. (port.) 24½cm.

1. Allen, James, 1792-1870. 2. Allen, Samuel, fl. 1632. 3. Allen family 4. Oakham, Mass.—Hist.

Library of Congress F74.O1K7 4-24955

NK 0202091 DLC OClWHi MWA MB

Knight, Holford, 1877-
Advancing woman, by Holford Knight ... foreword by Mrs. Millicent Garrett Fawcett. [London] D. O'Connor, 1921.
3 p. l., 9-95, [1] p. 18½cm.
CONTENTS.—The call to women.—Women jurors.—Women and the legal profession.—Women lawyers.—Women magistrates.—Women clerics.

1. Women as lawyers. 2. Women as ministers. I. Title.
[Full name: Holford George Wilfrid Knight]

Library of Congress HQ1397.K6 22-10175

NK 0202092 DLC CtY ICU NN CU NcGU

Knight, Homer Louis, 1907-
The English game laws with particular reference to reform in the nineteenth century. [Columbia, Mo.] 1945 [c1947]
Microfilm copy of typewritten ms. Made in 1948 by University Microfilms (Publication no. 925) Positive.
Collation of the original: 315 l.
Thesis—Univ. of Missouri.
Abstracted in Microfilm abstracts, v. 8 (1948) no. 1, p. 76.
Vita.
Bibliography: leaves 268-313.
1. Game-laws—Gt. Brit.
Microfilm AC-1 no. 925 Mic A 48-55*

Michigan. Univ. Libr. for Library of Congress [1]†

NK 0202093 MiU DLC

Knight, Howard Lawton, 1881-
Dietary studies in Baltimore. By H. L. Knight, H. A. Pratt, and C. F. Langworthy.
(In Smedley, Emma, and Robert D. Milner. Dietary studies in public institutions in Philadelphia, Pa. Pp. 15-98. Washington. 1910.)

H7898 — Food. — Langworthy, Charles Ford, jt. auth. 1864-. — Baltimore, Md. Char. — Pratt, H. A., jt. auth.

NK 0202094 MB PPAN

Knight, Howard Lawton, 1881-

Smedley, Emma.
... Dietary studies in public institutions in Philadelphia, Pa., by Miss Emma Smedley and R. D. Milner, and Dietary studies in public institutions in Baltimore, Md., by H. L. Knight, H. A. Pratt, and C. F. Langworthy. Washington, Govt. print. off., 1910.

Knight, Howard R.
... Play and recreation in a town of 6000. (A recreation survey of Ipswich, Massachusetts) [By] Howard R. Knight. New York city, Dept. of recreation, Russell Sage foundation [1915]
98 p. illus., diagrs. 23cm. ([Russell Sage foundation, New York. Pamphlet] Rec. 144)

1. Playgrounds—[Ipswich, Mass.] 2. Amusements. [2. Recreation] 3. Social surveys. I. Title.

E 15-2664

Library, U. S. Bur. of Education GV171.K74

NK 0202096 DHEW CLSU NcD DL OrU Or WaS PBm OCl OOxM NN PU

Knight, Howard R. FOR OTHER EDITIONS SEE MAIN ENTRY

Russell Sage foundation, *New York. Dept. of recreation.*
Sources of information on play and recreation (Rev. and enl. ed., 1920) [By] Howard R. Knight [and] Marguerita P. Williams. New York city, Department of recreation. Russell Sage foundation [1920]

Knight, Howard R.

Z7511 .R88 1914

Russell Sage foundation, *New York. Dept. of recreation.*
... Sources of information on recreation [by] Lee F. Hanmer [and] Howard R. Knight. New York city, The Dept. of recreation, Russell Sage foundation [1914]

Knight, Howard Vernon, 1898- *ed.*
Scenic and historic old Virginia and eastern national parks ... compiled and edited by H. V. Knight and R. R. Stripling. Asheville, N. C., and Richmond, Va., Southern parks and playgrounds, c1930.
[96] p. illus. (incl. maps) 26½cm.

1. Virginia—Descr. & trav. 2. National parks and reserves—U. S. I. Stripling, R. R., joint ed. II. Southern parks and playgrounds. III. Title.

Library of Congress F231.K71 31-8396
—— Copy 2.
Copyright A 34255 [3] 917.

NK 0202099 DLC ViU Vi

BF 1325 .H65 no. 7 Houdini Coll.

Knight, Hubert A.
Three weeks' training in clairvoyance. Published by Hubert A. Knight ... [Washington, D. C.? c1902]
30 p. 14.5 cm.
Houdini pamphlets; clairvoyance, no. 7.

NK 0202100 DLC

Knight, Hugh.
The control of citrus insects
see under Quayle, Henry Josef, 1876-

Judaica Bg20y 1

Knight, I F
Zionism vs. history, by I. F. Knight. December 15, 1938. New York City, Issued by the Arab national league [1938]

NK 0202102 CtY

Knight, Isaac.
A narrative of the captivity and sufferings of Isaac Knight, from Indian barbarity. An account of the cruel treatment he received from the savages while afflicted with the small pox. His escape... after enduring the hardships of an Indian prisoner, during two years and six months. Communicated by himself and at his request written by Hiram A. Hunter. Evansville, Printed at the Journal Office, 1829.
34p.

Sabin 33917.

NK 0202103 PPiU ICN CSmH

970.1 K744

Knight, Isaac.
A narrative of the captivity and sufferings of Isaac Knight from Indian barbarity. Giving an account of the cruel treatment he received from the savages ... Communicated by himself, and at his request written by Hiram A. Hunter. Evansville [Ind.] Printed at the Journal Office, 1839.
34 p. 26 cm.

Photocopy (positive)
Errors in paging: p. 12-15 duplicated.

NK 0202104 KyU PPiU CSmH MoKU ICN

Knight, J
Ancient world, a new map of the countries mentioned in the Scriptures. [n.p.,]1839.

NK 0202105 NjP

Z 997 .K 69 1857

Knight, J
A catalogue of the library of J. Knight, jun.; containing seueral rare and curious works in early English poetry; with many volumes illustratiue of that branch of literature; together with Greek, Latin, English, French & Italian classics ... Leeds, 1857.
2 p. l., 368, [1] p. 25½cm.
Manuscript copy.
Bookplate of J. Knight.

NK 0202106 MdBJ

BV 4510 . A1 C6

Knight, J. A.
Andrew Linday; or The experience of a Scotch lad before he attained the fourteenth year of his age. Abridged from the account in the Gospel magazine for 1776. By the late Rev. J. A. Knight. London. Printed by W. Nicholson.
12 p. 18.5 cm.
Cottage Library of Christian Knowledge no. 28

NK 0202107 DLC

Knight, J. A.
Game of Nova Scotia. (In: Canada 1867- dominion. Conservation Commission. Lands, fisheries and game, minerals. Ottawa, 1911. 4°. p. 195-197, 1 pl.)
—— A second copy.

1. Game, Canada: Nova Scotia.
N. Y. P. L. January 15, 1913.

NK 0202108 NN

VOLUME 300

Knight, J. B., and E. W. Horn.
Present state of the dairying industry in Bombay. Bombay: Gov. Central Press, 1914. 2 p.l., 14 p. 8°. (Bombay, presidency. Agriculture Dept. Bull. 56.)

1. Dairies, etc., India: Bombay. 2. Horn, E. W., jt. au.
N. Y. P. L. March 31, 1915

NK 0202109 NN

Knight J. B.
Primary education and the circumstances of the population in Oudh and the northwestern provinces of India [and] The famine and the relief works in Oudh and the northwestern provinces of India in 1877-'78, by S. Mohammad Hossain; [a review]. (In: Journal of the National Indian Association. no. 148, April, 1883. London, 1883. pp. 219-223.)
In: *C. p. v. 389.

NK 0202110 NN

Knight, J. B.
Rice grass-hopper. By J. B. Knight and R. M. Dixon. Bombay, Government Central Press, 1906.
1p. l., 4 p. 8°. (Bombay Land Records and Agriculture Dept. Bull. 27.)

NK 0202111 NN

Knight, J. B.
Substitutes for ráb. Bombay: Gov. Central Press, 1914. 3 p.l., 3-19 p. 8°. (Bombay, presidency. Agriculture Dept. Bull. 63.)

1. Sugar cane, India.
N. Y. P. L. July 31, 1916.

NK 0202112 NN PP

Knight, J. B.
Sugarcane. Bombay, Government Central Press, 1905.
1 p. l., 18 p. 8°. (Bombay Land Records and Agriculture Dept. Bulletin. no. 25.)

NK 0202113 NN

Knight, J. B.
Sugarcane, its cultivation, and gúl manufacture. Bombay: Gov. Central Press, 1914. 3 p.l., 41 p. 8°. (Bombay, presidency. Agriculture Dept. Bull. 61.)

1. Sugar cane, India. 2. Sugar.— Manufacture, India.
N. Y. P. L. July 14, 1916.

NK 0202114 NN

Knight, J. B.
The value of castration of Deccan bullocks. Bombay: Gov. Central Press, 1914. 2 p.l., 6 p., 2 pl. 8°. (Bombay, presidency. Agriculture Dept. Bull. 62.)

1. Cattle, India: Bombay. 2. Castration.
N. Y. P. L. September 15, 1916.

NK 0202115 NN

D
767.6
.K72
Knight, J B H
72 Field Company, K.G.V's.O. Bengal S.& M., R.I.E.; history from January 1942 to April 1946. Cambridge [Eng.] 1947.
55 p. illus.

1. India. Army. King George V's Own Bengal Sappers and Miners. 2. World War, 1939-1945--Regimental histories--India--King George V's Own Bengal Sappers and Miners.

NK 0202116 MiU

Knight, J. Broadus, comp.
U. S. *Laws, statutes, etc.*
... Navy yearbook. Compilation of annual naval appropriation laws ... including provisions for the construction of all vessels of the "new navy", with tables showing present naval strength ...
Washington, Govt. print. off., 1906-

Knight, J Emery.
Liberia's eighteenth president. [Monrovia, 1946]
64 p. ports. 26 cm.

1. Tubman, William V. S., Pres. Liberia, 1895- 2. Liberia.
DT636.T8K5 966.6 50-57432

NK 0202118 DLC CtY

Knight, J. Frank, d. 1889?
... Highly important collection of engraved portraits and views, gathered by the late J. Frank Knight
see under Henkels, firm, auctioneers, of Philadelphia.

Knight, J Frank, d. 1889?
Valuable ... library of the late J. F. Knight, of Philadelphia ... Americana ... and foreign portraits ... sold ... November ... 1891 ... T. Birch's Sons, auctioneers. pt. 1. Philadelphia, T. Birch's Sons, 1891.
1 pt. 8°. (Catalogue, no. 676.)
n. t.-p.

NK 0202120 NN

Knight, J. Martin.
The growth and incidence of municipal expenditure. Tables. (In Co-operative Wholesale Societies Limited. Annual for 1905. Pp. 285-336. Manchester. 1905.)
Refers to Great Britain.

K1714 — Great Britain. Finance. — Municipal finance.

NK 0202121 MB

Knight, J. Martin.
Industrial conditions at home and abroad. Tables. Charts. (In Co-operative Wholesale Societies Limited. Annual for 1906. Pp. 307-345. Manchester. 1906.)

H9257 — Industrial history.

NK 0202122 MB

Knight, J. Martin.
Railway rates and charges. (In Co-operative Wholesale Societies, Limited, England and Scotland. Annual for 1900. Pp. 357-390. Manchester, 1900.)

E6754 — Railroad rates.

NK 0202123 MB

KNIGHT, J. S.
A skit treating of the monetary system of the United States of America and other kindred subjects ... By "Novice" [pseud.].
Mobile. Commercial pr. co. 1895. 65, (1) pp. 24°.

NK 0202124 MB

Knight, J T
Short history of the military forces in N. S. W.
see under title

Knight, J W.
Aid to the concert system of teaching geography; adapted to Pelton's outline maps. By J. W. Knight ... Cincinnati, G. L. Weed [1847]
15 p. 19½cm.

1. Geography—Outlines, syllabi, etc.
Library of Congress G129.K71 5-27310†

NK 0202126 DLC

Knight, Jabez C.
... Jabez C. Knight, vs. Manchester Print Works ... Pawtucket, 1867.
40 p. 24 cm.

NK 0202127 RPB

Knight, Jabez C.
... Manchester print works vs. Jabez C. Knight ...
see under Jenckes, Thomas Allen, 1818-1875.

[Knight, Jabez C.] 1815-1900.
Our golden wedding [by Jabez C. Knight. Providence, September 28, 1892. Providence, 1892]
cover-title, 12 p. 17 cm.
"With our kind regards ... Jabez C. Knight, Catharine A. (Taft) Knight".

NK 0202129 RPB RHi

'76
KN687s
[Knight, Jabez C.] 1815-1900
Some reminiscences, &c. read before the Veteran citizens' historical association, Providence, March 1, 1886, by a member. [Providence, 1886]
11p. 24cm.

A poem.
Caption title.
Has been erroneously ascribed to James N. Arnold.

NK 0202130 RPB

VOLUME 300

Knight, James.
Chemistry, by James Knight ... Ed. by John Adams ... London, Hodder and Stoughton [1919?]
xxiii, [1], 162 p. tables, diagrs. 19cm. (Added t.-p.: The self-educator, ed. by John Adams)

1. Chemistry—[Study and] teaching. I. Adams, John, 1857- ed.
E 20-428
Library, U. S. Bur. of Education QD33.K7

NK 0202131 DHEW

Knight, James.
Food and its functions, a text-book for students of cookery, by James Knight ... London [etc.] Blackie & son, limited, 1895.
vii, [1], [9]-282 p. illus., double col. pl., diagrs. 19cm.
An expansion of a course of lectures on dietetics delivered to the students at the Glasgow schools of cookery. cf. Pref.

1. Food. 2. Cookery. 3. Digestion. 4. Diet.
45-31763
Library of Congress TX353.K57 1895

NK 0202132 DLC NIC PPPL PPD OCl OO OU ICJ MH

Knight, James.
Food and its functions; a text-book for students of cookery, by James Knight ... London, Glasgow and Dublin, Blackie & son, limited [1903]
vii, 8-282 p. illus. 18½cm.
An expansion of a course of lectures on dietetics delivered to the students at the Glasgow schools of cookery. cf. Pref.
First published in 1895.

1. Food. 2. Cookery. 3. Digestion. 4. Diet.
5-5661
Library of Congress TX353.K71

NK 0202133 DLC OrCS NcD CtY OOxM ViU

Knight, James.
The self-educator in chemistry, by James Knight... Edited by John Adams... New York: T. Y. Crowell & Co., 1901. xxiii(i), 162 p. illus. 12°. (Self-educator series.)

1. Chemistry.—Elementary and pop[u]lar works, 1901. 2. Adams, John, 1857- , editor. 3. Series.
N. Y. P. L. March 18, 1916.

NK 0202134 NN ICRL ICJ MB

Knight, James.
Teach yourself chemistry. A practical book of self-instruction in chemistry, based on the work by James Knight ... Completely revised and enlarged by G. B. MacAlpine ... London, English universities press, 1938.
224 p. illus. 18½cm.

1. Chemistry—Study and teaching. I. MacAlpine, George Bruce. II. Title.
A 41-308
Drexel inst. of tech. Sch. of library science for Library of Congress

NK 0202135 PPD Or CaBVa Wa

QD37 .M27
Knight, James.

MacAlpine, George Bruce.
Teach yourself chemistry; a practical book of self-instruction in chemistry, based on the work by James Knight. [3d ed.] completely rev. and enl. by G. Bruce Macalpine. New York, Roy Publishers [1955?]

332.1 K7413
Knight, James, accountant.
The London joint stock banks: their progress, resources and constitution. 3d ed. London, 1853.
38p. tables.

NK 0202137 IU

Knight, James, accountant.
The London joint stock banks: their progress, resources, and constitution ... London, Richardson brothers, 1857.
36 p. xiii tabs.(part fold.) forms.

A renewal of an earlier investigation whose results were shown in a pamphlet published in 1854. cf. Pref.

NK 0202138 MH-BA CtY

Knight, James, accountant.
Private and public guarantee for persons appointed to offices of trust considered. 23 pp. London: E. Wilson, 1847. 8°.
In: TH. p. v. 20.

NK 0202139 NN CtY PU

Knight, James, accountant.
Public guarantee and private suretyship. London, Longman & co., 1849.
iv, (1)6-40, 2p. 8°.

NK 0202140 NN NjP

Knight, James, accountant.
A review of the private and joint stock banks in the metropolis; with remarks upon the constitution of a new chartered joint stock bank, under the provisions of the 7. & 8. Victoria, cap. 113 . . . 2. ed. 39 pp. London: E. Wilson, 1847. 8°.
In: TH. p. v. 15.

NK 0202141 NN

Knight, James, M.D., of New York.
Specifications of A. G. Hull's patents. [An appeal to the public relative to grievances sustained by a suit at law instituted by Dr. Hull, concerning the use of the utero-abdominal supporter.] [New York, 1838.] 36 pp. 8°.

E5285 — Uterus. — Hull, Amos Gerald.

NK 0202142 MB

[Knight, James] 1672 - 1735.
Considerations on Mr. Whiston's Historical preface. Being an answer to his Plain questions, and other most material passages therein contain'd. In a letter to the author of The history of Montanism: and by him recommended. With an appendix: containing an account of the Jewish notion of the Messiah in Our Saviour's time; of the successive modes of subsistence of the divine Logos; of the communication of the supereminent names of God; and of the generation and creation of wisdom. London, Printed by J. L. for R. and J. Bonwicke, 1711.
1 p. l., xliii, [9], 112 p. 19½cm. [With Whiston, William. Athanasius convicted of forgery. London, MDCCXII]
1. Whiston, William, 1667-1752. Historical preface to Primitive Christianity revived. 2. Jesus Christ—Divinity. I. Title.
37-23407
Library of Congress BR1720.A7W5 231

NK 0202143 DLC MH FU CtY IaU

Y942.07 Z2 v.91
KNIGHT, James, 1672 - 1735.
A discourse on the conflagration and renovation of the world. London, Printed for C. Corbett, G. Woodfall; and to be had of Mr. Rhodes [1736?]

31 p. 20cm. [Hanoverian tracts. Ser.2. v.91, no.4]

1. End of the world.

NK 0202144 MnU

Y942.07 Z2 v.50
KNIGHT, James, 1672 - 1735.
A discourse on the conflagration and renovation of the world ... By ... Dr. James Knight, ... To which is added some account of his life. London, Printed for J. Cox, 1736.

v. p.l., 51 p. 20cm. [Hanoverian tracts. Ser.2. v.50, no.6]

NK 0202145 MnU

Knight, James, 1672-1735.

Eight sermons preached at the Cathedral Church of St. Paul, in defence of the divinity of our Lord Jesus Christ, and of the Holy Spirit; at the lecture founded by the Honoured Lady Moyer. [Six lines] London, Printed for R. and J. Bonwicke, 1721.
13 p.l., 300, [12] p. 20cm.

Signatures: A2-X2.

Head and tail pieces. Catchwords.
Textual footnotes.
Bound in calf, stamped boards, raised spine, title in gilt on red.

1. Church of England - Sermons. 2. Sermons, English. 3. Jesus Christ.

NK 0202147 FU NjP MH-AH

Knight, James, 1672 - 1735.
Judgment and justice the solid foundation of human happiness: a sermon preach'd before the Right Honourable the Lord-Mayor and aldermen of the city of London, at the parish-church of St. Lawrence Jewry, on Tuesday, September 29, 1730, before the election of the Lord-Mayor for the year ensuing. Lond. Printed for J. and J. Bonwicke, 1730.

NK 0202148 MA

[KNIGHT, James] 1672-1735.
A letter to the Rev. Dr. Clark. from the author of the true Scripture doctrine, etc., London, 1714.

13 x 20.

NK 0202149 MH-AH

*EC7 K7452 712p
[Knight, James, 1672-1735]
Primitive Christianity vindicated in a second letter to the author of the History of Montanism, against the Arian misrepresentations of it, and Mr. Whiston's bold assertions in his late books. With an appendix, concerning the incommunicable name of God, the pre-existing humanity of Christ, the mercavah of Ezekiel; and several other matters. For the further clearing of some passages in the first letter, against the exceptions of the postscript to

Continued in next column

VOLUME 300

Continued from preceding column

that author's account of the Convocation, &c. By the author of the Considerations on Mr. Whiston's historical preface.
London:Printed for R.and J.Bonwicke,at the Red-Lion in St.Paul's church yard,1712.
1p.ℓ.,vi,112p. 19cm.,in folder 20cm.
Imperfect: p.111-112 wanting.

NK 0202151 MH NcD

BT
112
C5
K6
Cage
⌐Knight, James⌐ 1672-1735.
The Scripture doctrine of the most holy and undivided Trinity, vindicated from the misinterpretations of Dr. Clarke. To which is prefixed a Letter to the Reverend Doctor, by Robert Nelson ... London, Printed for Richard Smith, 1714.
xxvii ⌐5⌐ 139 ⌐13⌐ p. a-b8, B-K8, L4. 8vo.
"Books printed for, and sold by Richard Smith," sig. K6v-L4v.

NK 0202152 DFo NjP RPB CBPac CtY CU-A MH

---

*EC7
K7452
719s
Knight, James, 1672-1735.
A sermon preached at the visitation of the Right Reverend Father in God John 1d. bishop of London, held in the parish-church of St. Sepulchre, Novemb. 10. 1719. By James Knight ...
London:Printed for R.and J.Bonwicke,at the Red Lion,in St.Paul's church-yard.1719. (Price four pence)
8°. 27p. 20.5cm.

NK 0202153 MH

---

x252
K745s
Knight, James, 1672-1735.
A sermon preached to the Societies for Reformation of Manners, at St. Mary-le-Bow, on Monday, January the 15th, 1732. By James Knight, D.D. vicar of St. Sepulchre's. London, Printed for J. Downing, 1733.
40p. 19cm.
"The eight and thirtieth account of the progress made in the cities of London and Westminster, and places adjacent, by the Societies for Promoting a Reformation of manners" p.35-40.

NK 0202154 IU NBuG MB MnU NcD

[KNIGHT, James] 1672-1735.
The true Scripture doctrine of the holy Trinity, the Eucharist, etc., Book, I. London, 1713.
13 x 20.
Continued as "The Scripture doctrine", etc., And.H.

NK 0202155 MH

Knight, James, *d.* 1720?
The founding of Churchill, being the journal of Captain James Knight, governor-in-chief in Hudson bay, from the 14th of July to the 13th of September, 1717; edited, with a historical introduction and notes, by James F. Kenney ... With 5 illustrations. Toronto ⌐etc.⌐ J. M. Dent and sons ltd. ⌐1932⌐
x, 213, ⌐1⌐ p. front. (plan) 1 illus., pl., map, facsim. 19½ cm.
Printed in Great Britain.
"The journal here published forms the latter part of Captain James Knight's York fort journal for the year 1716-17 ... The original ... is preserved among the archives of Hudson's bay house, London ..."—p. 110.

Continued in next column

Continued from preceding column

CONTENTS.—The discovery of Churchill.—The first establishment of the Hudson's bay company at Churchill.—Captain James Knight.—The second founding of Churchill.—The fate of Captain Knight.—The later history of Churchill.—The journal.—Bibliography (p. 191-199)

1. Hudson bay—Hist.—Sources. 2. Hudson's bay company. 3. Churchill, Manitoba. I. Kenney, James Francis, 1884- ed. II. Title.

F1060.7.K67 971.2 32—15510

CaOTP MH TxU OkU MB CU NcD DLC
NK 0202157 WaU CaBVa CaBVaU WaS MtHi MtU WaS ViU OU

Knight, James, fl. 1728.
A defense of the Observations on the assiento trade
see under title

Knight, James, fl. 1728.
Some observations on the assiento trade
see under title

Knight, James, 1793-1863.
Christian courtesy. A sermon, delivered at a monthly assn. of Congregational ministers & churches in connexion with the old college, Homerton, at Dr. Collyer's meeting house. Peckham, Apr. 6, 1815. Lond., Paris, 1815.
32p. O.

NK 0202160 OO

FX35
K69
Knight, James, 1793-1863.
Discourses on the principal miracles of Our Lord. By the Rev. James Knight ... London, R.B.Seeley and W.Burnside,1831.
xxii,500,[4]p. 23cm.

NK 0202161 NNUT

Lmd81
L52
852k
Knight, James, 1793-1863.
Extraordinary facts: as the same were presented in an appeal to the visitor of Lincoln college, Oxford; shortly after the rejection of the appellant from a fellowship in the above-named college on the 20th of November, 1815. To which is subjoined, a brief narrative, which may not be uninteresting to the numerous personal friends of the quondam appellant. By the Rev.James Knight ... [London,T.C.Johns, printer]1852.
34p. 17½cm.

NK 0202162 CtY

Knight, James, 1793-1863.
The practical remembrance of departed pastors. A Sermon, preached ... on occasion of the Death of the Rev. Samuel Redhead. Sheffield, 1845.
24 p. 8°. [In College Pamphlets, v.

NK 0202163 CtY

613
K741i
1875
Knight, James, 1810-1887.
The improvement of the health of children and adults by natural means, including a history of food and a consideration of its substantial qualities. New York, G. P. Putnam's sons, 1875.
406p. illus. 20cm.

1. Hygiene. 2. Children--Care and hygiene. 3. Food.

NK 0202164 IU NN DNLM

Knight, James, 1810-1887.
The improvement of the health of enfeebled children and adults by natural means, including a history of food and a consideration of its substantial qualities. By James Knight ... New York, Sackett & Mackay, 1868.
xv, ⌐1⌐ p., 1 l., ⌐19⌐-406 p. 6 pl. 20½cm.

1. Hygiene. 2. Children—Care and hygiene. 3. Food.

Library of Congress RA776.K69 7—33540

NK 0202165 DLC PU MnU

RD
731
K72
Knight, James, 1810-1887.
Orthopaedia; or, A practical treatise on the aberrations of the human form. By James Knight. New York, J. H. Vail & co., 1874.
364 p. illus. 24 cm.

1. Orthopedia.

NK 0202166 DSI ICJ ViU WU ICRL NN

Knight, James, 1810-1887.
Orthopædia; or, A practical treatise on the aberrations of the human form. A 2d ed., much enl. ... By James Knight ... New York, J. H. Vail & co., 1884.
viii, 388 p. illus., v col. pl. (incl. front.) 24cm.

1. Orthopedia.

Library of Congress RD731.K72 7—5431

NK 0202167 DLC NcD PPC DNLM ICJ

Knight, James, 1810-1887.
A paper read before the Academy of medicine, June 15th, 1882, by James Knight ... New York, E. W. Sackett & Rankin, printers and stationers, 1882.
15 p. 23cm.
Caption-title: Static electricity as a therapeutic agent.

1. Electrotherapeutics. I. Title: Static electricity as a therapeutic agent.

35-36462

Library of Congress RM875.K6

NK 0202168 DLC NN DNLM

Knight, James, 1810-1887.
——. Results of observations in the treatment of 2,072 cases of lateral curvature of the spine during a period of twenty-three years in the Hospital of the New York Society for the Relief of the Ruptured and Crippled. 21. 8°. [*New York, n. d.*]

NK 0202169 DNLM

Knight, James, 1810-1887.
Rules and regulations of the New York surgeon's bandage institute
see under New York Surgeon's Bandage Institute.

LC4015
.T4
Knight, James, 1895- ed.

Texas. University. *Division of Extension. Extension Teaching and Field Service Bureau.*
Handbook for teachers of exceptional children; a workshop project, edited by James Knight, director, Extension Teaching Bureau, Division of Extension. Austin, The University, 1947.

VOLUME 300

Knight, James Albert.
Studies related to olefinic acids. Ann Arbor, University Microfilms, 1950.
(University Microfilms, Ann Arbor, Mich. Publication no. 2260)
Microfilm copy of typescript. Positive.
Collation of the original, as determined from the film: vii, 89 l. diagrs.
Thesis—Pennsylvania State College.
Bibliography: leaves 87-89.
1. Olefines.
Microfilm AC-1 no. 2260 Mic 51-366

NK 0202172 DLC

Knight, James Brookes, 1888-
Collected papers. [Chicago, etc., 1931-34]
9 v. in 1. plates. 25 cm.
Binder's title.
Reprinted from Journal of paleontology and other periodicals.
1. Gasteropoda, Fossil.

NK 0202173 CU

Knight, James Brookes, 1888-
Further new Cambrian bellerophont gastropods. Washington, Smithsonian Institution, 1948.
6 p. 24 cm. (Smithsonian miscellaneous collections, v. 111, no. 3)
Publication 3951.
At head of title: Walcott Fund.
"References": p. 6.
1. Gasteropoda, Fossil. 2. Paleontology—Cambrian. (Series: Smithsonian Institution. Smithsonian miscellaneous collections, v. 111, no. 3)
Q11.S7 vol. 111, no. 3 564.3 49-45596*
——— Copy 2. QE808.K54

TxU OU
NK 0202174 DLC CaBViP CaBVaU ViU NBuU ICJ PP OCU

Knight, James Brookes, 1888-
... The gastropods of the St. Louis, Missouri Pennsylvanian outlier: the Pseudozygopleurinae, by J. Brookes Knight. [Tulsa, Oklahoma, The Society of economic paleontologists and mineralogists] 1930.
cover-title, 88 p. illus., 5 pl., diagrs. 24 cm. (Journal of paleontology. vol. 4, suppl. 1)
1. Gasteropoda, Fossil.

NK 0202175 CU

Knight, James Brookes, 1888 -
The gastropods of the St. Louis, Missouri, Pennsylvania outlier. [Fort Worth, Tex., 1930-31]
3 pts.
Yale university, 1931, Ph.D.
Thesis note on slip mounted p. 177 of pt. 3

NK 0202176 DLC

Sg26rj 706
Knight, James Brookes, 1888-
The gastropods of the St.Louise, Missouri, Pennsylvanian outlier ... [n.p., 1932-34]
5 v. tables, plates. 24cm.
"Reprinted from the Journal of paleontology..."
"References" at end of each volume.

NK 0202177 CtY

Knight, James Brookes, 1888 -
Holopea symmetrica Hall, genotype of Holopea Hall ...
"Reprinted from Journal of the Washington academy of sciences, v.22, Oct. 19, 1932."
"References cited": p.476.

NK 0202178 CtY

Knight, James Brookes, 1888 -
... The location and areal extent of the Saint Louis Pennsylvanian outlier. [By] J. B. Knight ... [New Haven, 1933]
cover-title. p. 25-48, 166-178. illus. (incl. maps) 23½cm. (Contributions from the Paleontological laboratory, Peabody museum, Yale university)
Thesis (PH. D.)—Yale university, 1931.
Without thesis note.
"From American journal of science, vol. xxv, January and February, 1933."
"References": p. 174-175.
1. Geology, Stratigraphic—Carboniferous. 2. Geology—Missouri. 3. Paleontology—Carboniferous. 4. Paleontology—Missouri.
33-15513
Library of Congress QE673.K5 1931
Yale Univ. Libr. [5] 551.750977866

NK 0202179 DLC CtY CaBViP PU

Knight, James Brookes, 1888-
... Paleozoic gastropod genotypes, by J. Brookes Knight. [New York] The Society, 1941.
vi, 510 p. illus., 96 pl. on 48 l. 25cm. (Geological society of America. Special papers, no. 32)
"References": p. 388-405.
1. Gasteropoda, Fossil. I. Title. II. Title: Gastropod genotypes.
41-20026
Library of Congress QE808.K55
[10] 564.3

MtBuM MtBC WaTC CoU MoU MU DSI
NK 0202180 DLC PU PBm OCU OO NNC ViU OU CaBVaU IdPI

Knight, James Brookes, 1888-
Primitive fossil gastropods and their bearing on gastropod classification. Washington, Smithsonian Institution, 1952.
iii, 56 p. illus. 25 cm. (Smithsonian miscellaneous collections, v. 117, no. 13)
Publication 4092.
At head of title: Charles D. and Mary Vaux Walcott Research Fund.
Bibliography: p. 55-56.
1. Gasteropoda, Fossil. 2. Gasteropoda. (Series: Smithsonian Institution. Smithsonian miscellaneous collections, v. 117, no. 13)
Q11.S7 vol. 117, no. 13 564.3 52-63074
——— Copy 2. QE808.K554

WaWW MtBuM
NK 0202181 DLC TxU ViU CU NN PP OCU OO OU NBuU FU

Knight, James Brookes, 1888-
[The St. Louis, Missouri, Pennsylvanian outlier with a detailed study of some of its gastropod fauna] [n. p., 1930-33]
4 pts. illus., plates, diagrs. 24cm.
Title from the Commencement program of Yale university. Each part has cover-title.
Thesis (PH. D.)—Yale university, 1931.
Parts 1-2, 4 without thesis note. Part 3 has thesis note on label, inserted.
"References" at end of parts 2-4.
CONTENTS.—[pt. 1-3] The gastropods of the St. Louis, Missouri, Pennsylvanian outlier: The *Pseudozygopleurinae* (Journal of paleontology, v. 4, suppl. 1, December, 1930) *Aclisina* and *Streptacis* (Reprinted from the Journal of paleontology, v. 5, no. 1, March 1931) The *Subulitidae* (Reprinted from the Journal of paleontology, v. 5, no. 3, Sept. 1931)—[pt. 4] The location and areal extent of the Saint Louis Pennsylvanian outlier (Contributions from the Paleontological laboratory, Peabody museum, Yale university) From American journal of science, v. 25, Jan. and Feb. 1933.
1. Geology, Stratigraphic—Pennsylvanian. 2. Geology—Missouri. 3. Paleontology—Carboniferous. 4. Paleontology—Missouri. 5. Gasteropoda, Fossil.
33-15513 Revised
Library of Congress QE673.K5
[r43f2] 551.7

NK 0202183 DLC NIC

Sg3 415
Knight, James Brookes, 1888 -
... A salt-marsh study ... [New Haven, Conn., 1934]
Pamphlet
(Contributions from the Paleontological laboratory, Peabody museum, Yale university)
"From American journal of science, vol.XXVIII, September, 1934."
"References": p.180.

NK 0202184 CtY

Knight, James Brookes, 1888-
Some new Cambrian bellerophont gastropods. Washington, Smithsonian Institution, 1947.
11 p. illus. 25 cm. (Smithsonian miscellaneous collections, v. 106, no. 17)
Publication 3865.
At head of title: Walcott Fund.
"References": p. 10.
1. Gasteropoda, Fossil. 2. Paleontology—Cambrian. I. Title: Bellerophont gastropods. II. Series: Smithsonian Institution. Smithsonian miscellaneous collections, v. 106, no. 17.
Q11.S7 vol. 106, no. 17 564.3 47-32821*

NK 0202185 DLC OU TxU WaWW CaBViP CaBVaU FU NBuU

Knight, James Lewis
see Knight-Bruce, Sir James Lewis, 1791-1866.

Knight, Jane D
Brief narrative of events touching various reforms. By Jane D.Knight, who was reared in the Society of Friends, and united with the Shakers at Mt.Lebanon, Columbia co., N.Y., in the year 1826, in the twenty-second year of her age. Albany: Weed, Parsons and Company. 1880.
29 p. 15cm.
1.Shakers.2.Friends.Society of. I.t.

NK 0202187 MiU-C CtY PHi ICN MB MH NBuG ICN

Knight, Jean.
... Des états neutres au point de vue de la contrebande de guerre ... Paris, A. Pedone, 1903.
86, (2) p. 25½cm.
Thèse—Univ. de Paris.
"Ouvrages cités": p. [5]-6.
1. Neutrality. 2. Contraband of war.
8-30625
Library of Congress JX5231.K7

NK 0202188 DLC CtY DS

Knight, Jesse William, 1874-
The Jesse Knight family; Jesse Knight, his forebears and family, by Jesse William Knight ... [Salt Lake City] The Deseret news press, 1940.
139 p. front., plates, ports. 20½cm.
1. Knight family. 2. Knight, Jesse, 1845-1921.
41-1646
Library of Congress CS71.K725 1940

NK 0202189 DLC CaBVaU OrU

c922.98 K69
Knight, Jesse William, 1874-
The Jesse Knight family; Jesse Knight, his forebears and family, by Jesse William Knight ... [Salt Lake City] The Desert News Press, 1941.
140 p. front., plates, ports. 20cm.
1. Knight family. 2. Knight, Jesse, 1845-1921.

NK 0202190 C CU-B ICN OClWHi

KNIGHT, Jewell Bennet.
The existing state of Persion agriculture; opportunities for improvement, and suggestions as to how they can be effected.
Manifold copy. 4°. ff.(4). 107.

NK 0202191 MH DNAL

VOLUME 300

Knight, Jewell Bennett.
Informe presentado al ministro de agricultura y trabajo por el Sr. Jewell B. Knight ... Managua, Tipografía alemana de C. Heuberger & co., 1929.
104 p. 23½cm.
"Traducido del inglés por el Sr. ingeniero D. José Andrés Urtecho
1. Agricultural colleges—Nicaragua. 2. Agriculture—Nicaragua. I. Urtecho, José Andrés, tr.
Library of Congress S535.N5K6 30-10858

NK 0202192 DLC CU-B DNAL

QA43 .K69 Rare bk. room **Knight, John.**
[Exercise book on arithmetic and algebra] 1699.
[31],[62] p. 18½cm.
In manuscript.
Unpaged; blank pages between the two groups of paging.

NK 0202193 ICU

Knight, John, commander of the Delfos, defendant.

Washburn, James, jr., plaintiff.
A true and concise narrative of the voyage and sufferings of James Washburn, jr., on board the Delphos of Boston, John Knight, commander. Reduced to writing from the story as told by himself. Together with a report of the trial, Washburn vs. Knight, before the Supreme judicial court, holden at Boston, November term, 1821. Extracted from documents filed in the case. Boston, W. S. Spear, 1822.

Knight, John, D.D.
The samaritan rebels perjured, by a covenant of association: discovered in a sermon preach'd at the assizes holden at Northampton, March 30th. 1682. By John Knight, M.A., late of New-Inn-Hall in Oxford, and now vicar of Banbury. London, Printed for William Thorp, bookseller in Banbury in Oxfordshire, and are to be sold by Randal Taylor near Stationers-Hall, 1682.
1 p. l., vi, 31 p. 20½cm. (A collection of 17th century sermons, 1677-83. no. 6)
Title within double line border.
1. Sermons, Engli ... I. Title. II. Ser.

NK 0202195 ViU MnU NNUT-Mc

Knight, John, D.D.
A sermon at the assizes holden at Northampton, March 30, 1682.

NK 0202196 PPL

Mhc8 1700 K74 Knight, John, D.D.
A sermon preach'd at the funeral of the Right Honourable the Lady Guilford, Nov. 18.1699 ... London, G.Thorp, 1700.
2p.l.,36p. 18½cm.

NK 0202197 CtY

Knight, John, M.B.E.
Early transmission of letters. [Lecture...given to colleagues of the British museum on February 16th and 23rd, 1920] London, Philatelic institute [1920?] 13 p. illus. 19cm. (Philatelic institute papers. no. 6)
1. Postal service—Hist. 2. Postage stamps—Gt Br.

NK 0202198 NN ViU

Knight, John, *pseud.*
The story of my psychoanalysis. New York, McGraw-Hill [1950]
ix, 225 p. 21 cm.
I. Title.
RC608.K6 131.34 50-10447

WaSp OrSaW OrCS NIC GU NN ICJ NcU Or WaE CaBVaU
NK 0202199 DLC DNLM NBuU OkU-M PP PPL PSt TU OrPR

131.34 K745s 1950r **Knight, John, pseud.**
The story of my psychoanalysis. New York, McGraw-Hill [1951, c1950]
ix, 225p. 21cm.
"Second printing, 1951.
1. Psychoanalysis. I. Title.

NK 0202200 TxU OrU TU

---

151 K69s 1952 **Knight, John, pseud.**
The story of my psychoanalysis. New York, Pocket Books [1952]
211 p. 16 cm.

NK 0202201 NcU MH IU PSC

Knight, John, *writer on cabinet making.*
Cabinet making for the amateur, containing many useful and practical designs for making a wide variety of cabinets and other essential pieces of furniture. London, Pearson [1948]
161 p. illus. 19 cm. (Home mechanic series)
1. Cabinet-work. (Series)
TT197.K6 684 50-15611

NK 0202202 DLC CaBVa

Knight, John, d 1606.
Journal of the voyage of John Knight to seek the North-west Passage.
(*In* Markham, Sir Clements Robert, compiler and editor. The voyages of Sir James Lancaster, Kt., to the East Indies. Pp. 279-294. London. 1877.)
The personal journal kept by Captain Knight up to the time of his death.
M1327 — Northwest Passage.

NK 0202203 MB MdBP OCl PU

Bus.Sch. [Knight, Sir John, d.1718]
The following speech being spoke off hand upon the debates in the House of commons, you cannot expect in it the exactness of Roman eloquence; but you have the freedom, and bravery of the old Roman, and true English spirit, zealous for the good of their country, and bold in all its dangers ...
[London,1694]
8p. 18.5cm.
Caption title.

Also published in edition dated 1693[1694?] with title: A speech in the House of commons against the naturalization of foreigners.
In opposition to a bill to naturalize Protestant immigrants, rejected by the House of commons 15 March 1694.
Another copy. 18.5cm.
Imperfect: text slightly mutilated.

NK 0202205 MH-BA

Knight, Sir John, d. 1718.
A speech in the House of Commons, against the naturalizing of foreigners; by Sir John Knight of Bristol, in the year 1693. [London] 1693.
4 p. 4°.
n. t.-p.

NK 0202206 NN

British Tracts 1709 K74 Knight, Sir John, d. 1718.
A speech in the House of Commons, against the naturalizing of foreigners ... in the year 1693. London, Printed and sold by E. Powell [1709?]
19 p. 18 cm.

NK 0202207 CtY

Knight, Sir John, d. 1718.
The speech of Sir John Knight of Bristol, against the bill for a general naturalization in 1693 ... [London? 1694?]
12 p. 17cm. in 21cm.

The speech was delivered in 1694.
Volume of pamphlets.

NK 0202208 NNC NcD

[Knight, Sir John] d.1718.
A speech spoke by Sir J. K--t, in the House of commons, against the bill for naturalizing foreigners. [London,1709?]
8p. 19½cm. 2 copies.
Caption title.
"This speech is not intended upon any score at this time, but to show how improper it was, when spoken in the year 1694, at which time it was then publickly printed." cf. p.8.
Manuscript note at end of Rare Book Room copy: Re-printed in March 1708/9.

NK 0202209 CtY NNC

[Knight, Sir John]d. 1718.
[A speech spoke in the House of Commons against the bill for naturalizing forreigners. 1694.]

DA430 .C65 **(In A collection of scarce and valuable papers. London, Printed for G. Sawbridge, 1712. 19cm. p. 516-522)**

DA300 .S69 **(In Somers tracts. London, Cadell & Davies, 1813 v. 10, p. 591-596)**

NK 0202210 DLC

Knight, John, *fl.* 1818.
The emigrant's best instructor, or, The most recent and important information respecting the United States of America, selected from the works of the latest travellers in that country: particularly Bradbury, Hulme, Brown, Birkbeck, &c. ... The English laws on emigration, and every other information needful to the emigrant. By John Knight. Manchester, Printed by M. Wilson, and may be had of all booksellers, and of J. Knight, 1818.
72 p. 21½cm.
Subject entries: 1. U. S.—Descr. & trav. 2. U. S.—Economic conditions. 3. U. S.—Emig. & immig. 4. Northwest, Old—Descr. & trav.
Library of Congress, no. E165.K71. 8-16075

NK 0202211 DLC NN CtY N IU NNC

Knight, John, fl. 1818.
The emigrant's best instructor, or, The most recent and important information respecting the United States of America, selected from the works of the latest travellers in that country: particularly Bradbury, Hulme, Brown, Birkbeck, &c. Containing ... also, ... The English laws on emigration ... and every other information needful to the emigrant. 2nd ed. London, 1818.
72 p. 21.5 cm.

NK 0202212 CtY

VOLUME 300

Knight, John, fl. 1818-

A full and particular report of the proceedings of the public meeting held in Manchester on Monday the 18th of Jan., 1819, containing an account of the procession to and from the meeting...ₑand theₔ riotous assault upon Messrs. Hunt, Chapman, Whitworth and Johnson at the theatre; Mr. Cross's examination of Mess. Hunt, Whitworth, etc... to-gether with...letters. ₑManchesterₔ Printed for the author by W. Ogden. ₑ1819?ₔ

32,viii p. 23 c.

"Mr. Hunt attended the Magistrates at the Old Bailey, to obtain a warrant against George Torr, who was one of the persons that assaulted Mr. H. on Friday night" (Appendix, p. ii.)

NK 0202214 N MH-BA NIC

Knight, John, fl. 1818.

Important extracts from original and recent letters, written by Englishmen, in the United States of America, to their friends in England. Second series.

Manchester. Reddish [etc.]. 1818. 48 pp. 21½ cm.

About emigration from England to the United States.

M5218 — United States. Emig. — Great Britain. Emig.

NK 0202215 MB MH-BA PPL

Knight, John, fl. 1818, defendant.

Hunt, Henry, 1773-1835, *defendant.*

The trial of Henry Hunt, esq., Jno. Knight, Jos. Johnson ₍and others₎ ... for an alledged conspiracy to overturn the government, &c. Before Mr. Justice Bayley, and a special jury, at the York Lent assizes, 1820 ... London, T. Dolby, 1820.

Knight, John, fl. 1833-1834

Mechanics' magazine, and journal of the Mechanics' institute. v. 1-9; Jan. 1833-May 1837. New-York. D. K. Minor and J. E. Challis ₍etc.₎ 1833-37.

Knight, John, *d.* 1838.

Works by this author printed in America before 1801 are available in this library in the Readex Microprint edition of Early American Imprints published by the American Antiquarian Society.

This collection is arranged according to the numbers in Charles Evans' American Bibliography.

NK 0202218 DLC

Knight, John, d. 1838.

Brackenridge, Hugh Henry, 1748-1816, *ed.*

Indian atrocities. Narratives of the perils and sufferings of Dr. Knight and John Slover, among the Indians during the revolutionary war, with short memoirs of Col. Crawford & John Slover. And a letter from H. Brackinridge, on the rights of the Indians, etc. Cincinnati, U. P. James, 1867.

Knight, John, d. 1838. FOR OTHER EDITIONS SEE MAIN ENTRY

₍**Brackenridge, Hugh Henry**₎ 1748-1816, *ed.*

Narrative of a late expedition against the Indians; with an account of the barbarous execution of Col. Crawford; and the wonderful escape of Dr. Knight & John Slover from captivity in 1782. To which is added, A narrative of the captivity & escape of Mrs. Frances Scott, an inhabitant of Washington county, Virginia. Andover ₍Mass.₎ Printed by Ames & Parker ₍1798?₎

Knight, John, d. 1838.

₍**Brackenridge, Hugh Henry**₎ 1748-1816, *ed.*

The narrative of Dr. Knight ₍and The narrative of Joh Slover₎

(*In* Metcalfe, Samuel L. A collection of some of the most interes ing narratives of Indian warfare in the West. Lexington, Ky., 182 21cm. p. ₍36-71)

Knight, John, d. 1838.

₍**Linn John Blair**₎ 1831-1899, *ed*

The Sandusky expedition.

(*In* Pennsylvania archives. Harrisburg, 1888. 22cm. 2d ser., v. 14, p. ₍690₎-727. facsim.)

KNIGHT, JOHN, 1839-1887.

Civil war letters of John Knight, first lieutenant, 7th Iowa Infantry, July 30, 1861-May 31, 1865. Compiled by his great niece, Lucy E. Brown. Oak Park, Ill. ₑState of Illinois, Daughters of the American Revolutionₔ 1940.

107, ₑ3ₔ ℓ. 29cm.

Type-written (carbon copy)

NK 0202223 ICN

Knight, John, 1871-

New York (*State*) *Commission to recodify the Public service law.*

... Report of commission on revision of the public service commissions law. Transmitted to the Legislature March 3, 1930. Albany, J. B. Lyon company, printers, 1930.

Knight, John, 1871-

New York (*State*) *Commission to recodify the Public service law.*

... Report of Commission on revision of the Public service commissions law including separate reports of commissioners and counsel. Albany, J. B. Lyon company, printers, 1930.

506 p. incl. tables, diagr. 23cm.

At head of title: Legislative document (1930) No. 75. State of New

---

Knight, John, 1871-

New York (*State*) *Commission to recodify the Public servic law.*

... Report of Commission on revision of the Public service commissions law together with separate reports of commis sioners and counsel and public hearings and exhibits ... Albany, J. B. Lyon company, printers, 1930.

Knight, John, 1871- FOR OTHER EDITIONS SEE MAIN ENTRY

New York (*State*) *Crime commission.*

... Report to the commission of the sub-commission on statistics. Albany, J. B. Lyon company, printers, 1928

Knight, John, 1871-

New York (*State*) *Commission to recodify the Public service law.*

... Report₍s₎ of commission ₍1930₎ Brooklyn, N. Y., A. W. Stevens printing co., inc. ₍1930₎

Knight, John, 1871-

New York (*State*) *Crime commission.*

... A statistical analysis of the criminal cases in the courts of the state of New York for the year 1925 by the sub-commission on statistics. Albany, J. B. Lyon company, printers, 1927.

Knight, John, 1900-

Sketchbook of skater, a summary of important skating turns, basic international ice skating figures for self-instruction. Copyright ... by John Knight ... Quincy, Mass., ©1942.

₍50₎ p. illus. 16cm.

Reproduced from type-written copy.

1. Skating.

43-7414

Library of Congress GV849.K57

796.91

NK 0202230 DLC

Knight, John Alden, 1890-

Black bass. New York, G. P. Putnam's Sons ₍1949₎

xix, 200 p. illus. (part col.) 22 cm.

1. Bass fishing. 2. Black bass.

SH681.K5 799.1758 49-8259*

NK 0202231 DLC FU ScU CaBVaU WaS WaE OrP IdU MB TxU

Knight, John Alden, 1890-

Field book of fresh-water angling, by John Alden Knight ... New York, G. P. Putnam's sons ₍1944₎

ix, 207 p. illus., 2 pl. on 1 l., diagrs. 18 x 10½cm. ₍Putnam's nature field books₎

1. Fishing—Implements and appliances. I. Title. II. Title: Fresh-water angling.

44-3578

Library of Congress SH451.K57

₍15₎ 799.1078

NK 0202232 DLC CaBVa Or OrSaW WaSp WaT CaBViP CU TU OCl OEac PP OrCS WaS

Knight, John Alden, 1890-

Fishing for trout and bass. Chicago, Ziff-Davis Pub. Co. ₍1949₎

128 p. illus. 18 cm. (Little sports library, 117)

1. Bass fishing. 2. Trout fishing.

SH687.K59 799.1755 Agr 49-78*

U. S. Dept. of Agr. Libr. for Library of Congress 414K74F ₍3₎†

NK 0202233 DNAL DLC OCl TU OrP

Knight, John Alden, 1890-

Fresh water tackle. Chicago, Ziff-Davis Pub. Co. ₍1949₎

158 p. illus., port. 18 cm. (Little sports library, 118)

1. Fishing—Implements and appliances. I. Title.

SH451.K573 799.1078 Agr 49-72*

U. S. Dept. of Agr. Libr. for Library of Congress 414K74 ₍10₎†

NK 0202234 DNAL CaBViP TU CoU OCl DLC

Knight, John Alden, 1890-

The modern angler, including the solunar theory, by John Alden Knight. New York, C. Scribner's sons; London, C. Scribner's sons, ltd., 1936.

xiv p., 1 l., 260 p. front., plates (2 col.) diagrs. 21cm.

"Some of the material contained in the present volume has previously been used as a basis for articles which were published in Outdoor life, Field & stream, the Sportsman, and Sports afield. It has subsequently been corrected, augmented, and rewritten into its present form."—Acknowledgment.

1. Fishing. I. Title. II. Title: Solunar theory.

36-9031

Library of Congress SH441.K6

——— Copy 2.

Copyright A 92953 ₍5₎ 799.12

NK 0202235 DLC OrU WaS Or WaT CU ViU CoU NIC OrU PPGi OCl OLak OClW PP NN MB

VOLUME 300

Knight, John Alden, 1890–
Modern fly casting, introducing the free wrist grip and the high back cast, by John Alden Knight ... New York, C. Scribner's sons, 1942.
7 p. l., 79 p. illus. 24 x 21ᶜᵐ.

1. Fly-casting. I. Title. 42-12482
Library of Congress SH456.K5 [10] 799.12

NK 0202236 DLC FU CU IU WaT CaBVa CaBViP OrP WaS Or PP OCl PSt

Knight, John Alden, 1890–
Moon up, moon down, by John Alden Knight. New York, C. Scribner's sons, 1942.
x p., 1 l., 163 p. 21ᶜᵐ.

1. Animals, Habits and behavior of. 2. Moon—Influence on man. 3. Hunting. 4. Fishing. I. Title.
42-22349
Library of Congress QH527.K5 [10] 591.5

NK 0202237 DLC CaBVaU WaS PU OKentU

Knight, John Alden, 1890–
Ol' Bill, and other stories [by] John Alden Knight; drawings by Milton C. Weiler. New York, C. Scribner's sons, 1942.
[iii]–vii p., 1 l., 138 p. illus. 24ᶜᵐ.

I. Weiler, Milton C., illus. II. Title.
42-51183
Library of Congress PZ3.K7452Ol

NK 0202238 DLC OrU WaS Or OrU CoU NcD

Knight, John Alden, 1890–
Ruffed grouse; color plates from paintings by Edgar Burke. [1st ed.] New York, A. A. Knopf, 1947.
[4] l., vii–xii, 271, iii p. plates (part col.) map. 27 cm.
"Two hundred and ten copies ... have been printed on Springfair all-rag paper. Each copy is signed by the author ... This is number 210."

1. Grouse. I. Burke, Edgar, 1890– illus. II. Title.
SK325.G7K55 799.24861 Agr 47-24*
U. S. Dept. of agr. Library for Library of Congress 413K742R [10]†

NK 0202239 DNAL PSt CU FU ScU AAP ViW MU TU Or IdU WaE WaTC OrP WaT WaS DLC

Knight, John Alden, 1890–
Solunar tables; forecast of daily feeding times of fresh water fish for the season of 1935–19 Orange, N. J., J. A. Knight, c1935– nos. in v. illus. 16cm.
Title varies.

1. Fishing. 2. Hunting. I. Title.
N. Y. P. L. September 24, 1947

NK 0202240 NN OCl

Knight, John Alden.
The theory and technique of fresh water angling, by John Alden Knight. New York, Harcourt, Brace and company [°1940]
x, 223 p. front., illus., plates (part col.) diagr. 24 x 19ᶜᵐ.
"First edition."

1. Trout fishing. 2. Fly-casting. 3. Flies, Artificial. I. Title.
40-33842
Library of Congress SH441.K62
——— Copy 2.
Copyright [10] 799.12

NK 0202241 DLC FMU ScCleU IdB WaSp WaTC WaS Or OrCS CaBVaU CaBVa PP OCl OEac OLak

Knight, John Alden, 1890–
Woodcock [by] John Alden Knight; color plates from paintings by Dr. Edgar Burke. New York, A. A. Knopf, 1944.
viii p., 2 l., 3–161, ii, [1] p. col. front., plates (part col.) 21½ᶜᵐ.
"First edition."

1. Woodcock. I. Burke, Edgar, 1890– illus. Agr 44-218
U. S. Dept. of agr. Library for Library of Congress SK325.W7K6 [20]† 799.24833

NK 0202242 DNAL OrP CaBViP IdU WaS WaE WaTC GU ScU CU MeB PPA OCl PP PPAN TU ViW NjP NIC DLC

Knight, John Collyer.
Fasting.-An Essay in re-examination of the opinion that Fasting is a Christian Duty. London, 1846.
30 p. 8°. [In v. 1674, College Pamphlets.]

NK 0202243 CtY

Knight, John Collyer.
The incredibilities of Part II. of the Bishop of Natal's work upon the Pentateuch. A lay protest... London, S. Bagster, 1863.
20 p. 22ᶜᵐ.

NK 0202244 NjPT MH

Knight, John Collyer.
"The law, the prophets, and the Psalms:" their divine inspiration asserted upon the authority of our Lord, and vindicated from objections. With animadversions in disproof of the testimony of Josephus in reference to the canon. London: Longman & Co., 1866. 87 p. 16°.

1. Bible.—Old testament. Inspiration.
N. Y. P. L. November 2, 1911.

NK 0202245 NN NjPT MH

Knight, John Collyer.
"The law, the prophets, and the Psalms:" their divine inspiration asserted upon the authority of our Lord, and vindicated from objections. With animadversions in disproof of the testimony of Josephus in reference to the canon. London: Longman & Co., 1866. 87 p. 16°.
Film reproduction. Negative.

1. Bible. O. T. --Inspiration.

NK 0202246 NN

Knight, John Collyer.
The pentateuchal narrative vindicated from the absurdities charged against it by the bishop of Natal. London: S. Bagster and Sons, 1862. 20 p. 8°.

1. Bible.—Old Testament: Pentateuch Apologetics. 2. Colenso, John William, bishop of Natal: Pentateuch, etc.—Criticism of.
N. Y. P. L. February 14, 1912.

NK 0202247 NN MB

Knight, John Collyer.
The Pentateuchal narrative vindicated from the absurdities charged against it by the Bishop of Natal... 2d ed., with large additions. London, S. Bagster, 1863.
22 p. 22ᶜᵐ.

1 Colenso, John William, Bp. of Natal, 1814-1883. The Pentateuch

NK 0202248 NjPT MH-AH

FR K745t Knight, John Collyer.
Two new arguments in vindication of the genuineness and authenticity of the Revelation of St. John. The first, from contemporary but hitherto unnoticed evidence: the second, from certain unheeded and unurged circumstances connected with the early history of the Asiatic churches. London, J.G.F. & J. Rivington, 1842.
44 p. 22 cm.

Bibliographical references included in footnotes.

NK 0202249 CtY-D MB MH CtY

Knight, John E.

Notary's note-book and note-holder's manual, being a brief view of the office and duties of a notary public, and giving some of the principal rules of law touching the liability of parties to, and the rights and duties of, holders of commercial paper, in the matters of its presentment for acceptance or payment, and of the protest and notice of its dishonor. Compiled by an experienced notary. [Little Rock, Ark., Arkansas Democrat co., °1892]

Knight, John George.
The chemical studies of Hermann Boerhaave, 1668–1738. [London] London University Library, 1933.
Microfilm copy of typescript. Made by the Photographic Dept. of the London University Library. Positive.
Collation of the original, as determined from the film: 130 l.
Thesis (M. SC.)—University of London.
In ms. on t. p.: 1934.

1. Boerhaave, Herman, 1668–1738.
Microfilm 4089 QD Mic 55-3065

NK 0202251 DLC

Knight, John George, *d.* 1891, *comp.*
The Australasian colonies at the International exhibition, London, 1862. Extracts from the reports of the jurors and other information taken from official sources. Compiled by J. G. Knight ... Published under the direction of the commissioners for promoting the Intercolonial exhibition of Australasia to be held at Melbourne, 1866. Melbourne, J. Ferres, government printer, 1865.
101 p. 22ᶜᵐ. [*With, as issued:* Melbourne. Intercolonial exhibition of Australasia, 1866–1867. Official record. Melbourne, 1867. Copy 2]
1. London. International exhibition, 1862—Australasia.
45-45284
Library of Congre[ss] T730.1.D65 copy 2

NK 0202252 DLC CSt MH

Knight, J[ohn] G[eorge] *d.* 1891, *comp.*
The Australasian colonies at the International exhibition, London, 1862. Extracts from the reports of the jurors and other information taken from official sources. Compiled by J. G. Knight ... Published under the direction of the Commissioners for promoting the intercolonial exhibition of Australasia to be held at Melbourne, 1866. Melbourne, J. Ferres, 1865.
101 p. 22½ᶜᵐ.
"Second edition."
1. London. International exhibition, 1862—Australasia.

Library of Congress T691.G1A8 5-18024†

NK 0202253 DLC MB

*T730 .1 .D6M5 1867 Knight, John George,d.1891.
Description of the natural and industrial products of Queensland ... compiled ... by J. G. Knight ... [Melbourne, Blundell & co., printers, 1867]
(In Melbourne. Intercolonial exhibition of Australasia, 1866-1867. Official record. Melbourne, 1867. 22 1/2cm. [pt. 2, p. 417]-438)

1. Natural resources—Queensland.

NK 0202254 MB

VOLUME 300

Knight John George, d.1891.
A few particulars relative to the colony of Victoria (Australia). [Issued under the authority of the Victoria Emigrants' Assistance Society. *Liverpool: The Victoria Emigrants' Assistance Soc.*, [1863] 16 pp. 12°.
In: *C. p. v. 745.

NK 0202255 NN

DA559 A2K5
Knight, John George, d.1891.
Narrative of the visit of His Royal Highness the Duke of Edinburgh to the colony of Victoria, Australia. Melbourne, Mason, Firth, 1868.
220 p. port. 29cm.
"The narrative...has been in the main collated from the leading colonial newspapers."

1. Alfred Ernest Albert, Duke of Edinburgh, 1844-1900. 2. Victoria, Australia - Hist

NK 0202256 CSt CtY MH

Knight, John George, d.1891, comp.
Northern territory of South Australia.
Adelaide, 1863.
54 p.

NK 0202257 CSt

KNIGHT, JOHN GEORGE, d. 1891, comp.
The northern territory of South Australia.
Adelaide, E. Spiller, 1880.
(Cited in: Biblio. of Australia)

NK 0202258 MBAt

Knight, John George, d.1891.
Treatise on Australian building stones.
Lond., 1864.
45 p.

NK 0202259 CSt

TC225 .N7A3 1909
Knight, John George David, 1846-1919.
U. S. *Army. Corps of engineers.*
... Jamaica bay, and Rockaway and Dead Horse inlets, New York. Letter from the secretary of war, transmitting, with a letter from the chief of engineers, reports of examination and survey of Jamaica bay, Rockaway inlet, and waters having outlet in Dead Horse inlet, New York ... [Washington, Govt. print. off., 1909]

Knight, John George David, 1846 - 1919.
...Thickness of cover for guns and magazines of fortifications. A study by John G. D. Knight...With a report thereon by the Board of engineers, and a criticism by Henry L. Abbot... Washington, Govt. print. off., 1903.
13 p. fold.pl. 27 cm.

NK 0202261 DNW

813 K74b
Knight, John H
Benshaw of Boston. St. Louis, 1889.
115p. illus. (On cover: Humphrey's popular series. vol.1., no.1)

NK 0202262 IU NcD

Knight, John H., pub.
Memorial of Henry Ward Beacher
see under title

Knight, John Henry.
Catechism of the motor car, containing about 320 questions and answers explaining the construction and working of a modern motor car. Ed. 2, rev.
Lond., Lockwood, 1908.
100 p.

NK 0202264 PPSteph

Knight, John Henry.
A catechism of the motor car, containing about 320 questions and answers explaining the construction and working of a modern motor car, for the use of owners, drivers, and students. 3d ed., rev. and enl. London, C. Lockwood, 1910.
vi, 100 [2] p.

Crosby Lockwood & Son's List of works on civil mechanical, marine and electrical engineering, 32 p. at end.

NK 0202265 MiD

Knight, John Henry.
Electric light for country houses...
Lond. 1895.

NK 0202266 PPL

Knight John Henry.
Electric light for country houses. A practical handbook on the erection and running of small installations, with particulars of the necessary cost of plant and working. *London: C. Lockwood & Son*, 1897. 2 p.l., 76 pp., 1 pl. 12°.

NK 0202267 NN ICJ DNAL

621.31 K74e5
Knight, John Henry.
Electric light for country houses; a practical handbook on the erection and running of small installations, with particulars of the necessary cost of plant and working. 5th ed. London, 1906.
76p. front., illus.

NK 0202268 IU

Knight, John Henry.
Light motor cars and voiturettes.
London. Iliffe & Sons. 1902. 110 pp. Illus. Plates. Plans. 18½ cm., in 8s.

K4325 — Automobiles.

NK 0202269 MB ICJ

Knight, John Henry.
Light motor cars and voiturettes. By John Henry Knight... London, Iliffe & sons, limited 1902.
119p. front., illus., diagrs. 19cm.

1. Automobiles.

NK 0202270 DP MiD DSI

Knight, John Henry.
Motor repairing for amateurs, by John Henry Knight ... London, Iliffe & sons, ltd. [1907]
103, [1] p. illus. 19cm.

1. Automobiles—Repairing.

A 10-2511

Title from Chicago Pub. Libr. Printed by L. C.

NK 0202271 ICU NN ICJ

Knight, John Henry.
Notes on motor carriages, with hints for purchasers and users, by John Henry Knight... London: Hazell, Watson & Viney, Ltd., 1896. 84 p. illus. 12°.

132442A. 1. Automobiles, 1896. August 21, 1924
N. Y. P. L.

NK 0202272 NN CtY PPD OCl MB ICJ DP IEN MiD NIC MiU

Knight, John Hugh.
The history of the Maverick county irrigation project ... by John Hugh Knight ... [Kingsville, Tex., 1939]
v, 142 numb. l. map. 28 x 22½cm.
Thesis (M. S.)—Texas college of arts and industries.
Type-written (carbon copy)
Bibliography: leaves 134-142.

1. Irrigation—Texas—Maverick co. I. Title: Maverick county irrigation project.
43-28774
Library of Congress HD1740.M3K6

NK 0202273 DLC

G830 .S8 1926
Knight, John Irvine, joint author.
FOR OTHER EDITIONS SEE MAIN ENTRY
Stefánsson, Vilhjálmur, 1879-
The adventure of Wrangel island, written by Vilhjalmur Stefansson, with the collaboration of John Irvine Knight, upon the diary of whose son, Errol Lorne Knight, the narrative is mainly based; with a foreword by the Right Hon. L. S. Amery ... London, J. Cape ltd. [1926]

Knight, John James, 1863-
Brisbane; a historical sketch of the capital of Queensland... with a description of Brisbane of the present day... Written by authority by J. J. Knight... Brisbane: Biggs & Morcom, Ltd., 1897. 105 p., 1 fac., 4 pl., 1 port. illus. ob. 24°.
Binder's title: Historical sketch of the capital of Queensland.

1. Brisbane, Queensland.—History. June 10, 1915.
N. Y. P. L.

NK 0202275 NN

994.3 K745i
Knight, John James, 1863 -
In the early days; history and incident of pioneer Queensland, with dictionary of dates in chronological order. Brisbane, Sapsford, 1895.
x, 390 p.

1. Queensland - History. I. Title.

NK 0202276 WaU CaBVaU

VOLUME 300

323.445 Knight, John S
K74p The press is free; the principal and concurring opinions making up the United States Supreme court's unanimous decision absolving the Miami herald of contempt charges and defining the rights of newspapers and of free men under the constitution. [By] John S. Knight ... [Miami? 1946]
cover-title, 39p. illus.

1. Liberty of the press--Florida. 2. Miami herald. I. U.S.--Supreme court. II. Title.

NK 0202277 IU NNC

Knight, John Stearns.
The celebrated Varsovienne. Arranged for the pianoforte by J. S. Knight. Boston, O. Ditson and co., [c1857]
5 p. f°. (Favorite [s] Varsoviennes.)

NK 0202278 NN

KNIGHT, John Stearns.
I'll meet thee in the lane galop. [Boston] etc., etc., 1866].

NK 0202279 MH-Mu

KNIGHT, John Stearns.
La jolie parfumeuse. Pot--pourri. [Boston, etc., cop. 1875].

NK 0202280 MH-Mu

---

*
M1
.S444
v.47,
no.15 Knight, John Stearns.
Knight waltzes. Figure 7 in eight pointed star. Boston, G. D. Russel & Company, 126 Tremont ©1868. Pl. no. 1334.
9 p. 35cm. (Dance music)
[Sheet music collection, v. 47, no. 15]

1. Dance music. 2. Waltzes (Piano). I. Title.

NK 0202281 ViU

Knight, John Stearns, arr.
Mari sage
see under Offenbach, Jacques, 1819-1880.

KNIGHT, John Stearns.
The New Caledonian Quadrilles. Arranged with the Original Figures. B. etc., [1859?]

pp.7.

NK 0202283 MH-Mu

W.C.L. Knight, John Stearns.
M780.88
C699B The original Lancer's quadrilles, arr. by J. S. Knight. Boston, Oliver Ditson, c1857.
no.26 7 p. 34 cm.
For piano with directions for the dance.
[No. 26] in a volume with binder's title: Collection of excerpts from operas, popular dance music ...
1. Quadrilles (Piano) I. Title: Lancer's quadrilles.

NK 0202284 NcD MB NN MH

Knight, John T. How to repel train robbers.
8 pp. (*N. Am. Rev.* v. 160, 1895, p. 254.)

NK 0202285 MdBP

Knight, John T.
U. S. *Bureau of fisheries.*
Letters referring to the presence of shad in the rivers tributary to the Gulf of Mexico. [From John T. Knight, Isaac W. Pollard, George W. Lawrence, Will E. Turner, Holmes A. Pattison]
(*In* Report of the commissioner [of fish and fisheries] for 1872 and 1873. Washington, 1874. 23cm. p. 391-395)

Knight, John Thomas Philip, 1851-1914.
Canadian banking practice
see under title

Knight, John Thomas Philip, 1851–
Incidentally, by John Knight. Montreal: Westmount News Press, 1913. 152 p. 8°.

1. Canada. 2. Banks and banking—Canada. 3. Corporations—Canada. 4. Title.
N. Y. P. L. October 22, 1926

NK 0202288 NN CaBVaU TxU

---

*XH [Knight, John Thomas Philip] 1851-
.C888 A landsman's log-book. By "Vagrant" [pseud.] St.John, N.B. J.& A.McMillan, 98 Prince William
.K74L Street. 1888.

2p.l.,93p. 20cm.
Publisher's monogram device on t.p.
"Prefatory" signed: John T.P. Knight.
Tan wrappers, with illustration, printed in color.

I. Vagrant, pseud. II. Title.

NK 0202289 MB

Knight, Jonas.
Hints on the Yorkshire canary: its breeding, management, and exhibition. By Jonas Knight... London: "The Feathered world" [19—]. 32 p. incl. front. illus. 8°.

Repr.: The Feathered world.

1. Canaries.
N. Y. P. L. June 4, 1919.

NK 0202290 NN NIC

Knight, Jonathan, 1787-1858.
Correspondence between J. Knight...
see under Baltimore and Ohio Rail Road Company.

L091
K69l Knight, Jonathan, 1787-1858.
Letters. [n.p., n.d.]
[50]l. 28cm.

NK 0202292 IEN

Knight, Jonathan, 1787-1858, joint author.
Robinson, Moncure, 1802-1891.
Report of Moncure Robinson ... Jonathan Knight ... and Benjamin Wright ... civil engineers, upon the plan of the New-York and Erie rail road. New-York, Printed by G. P. Scott & co., 1835.

Knight, Jonathan, 1787-1858.
Baltimore and Ohio railroad company.
Report of the chief engineer of the Balt. & Ohio rail road co., on the transportation of passengers and tonnage of that road. 1842. [Baltimore? 1842?]

Knight, Jonathan, 1787-1858.
Baltimore and Ohio railroad company.
Report of the engineers, on the reconnoissance and surveys, made in reference to the Baltimore and Ohio rail road. Baltimore, Printed by W. Woody, 1828.

Knight, Jonathan, 1787-1858.
Report upon the locomotive engines and the police and management of several of the principal rail roads in the northern and middle states, being a sequel to the Report of the 8th of January, 1838 upon railway structures, by J. Knight. Baltimore, Lucas & Deaver, 1838.
36 p., 4 l. 22½cm.

1. Railroads—U. S. I. Latrobe, Benjamin Henry, 1807-1878, joint author.
C 15-45
Library, U. S. Interstate Commerce Commission

MCM MBAt CSmH
NK 0202296 NN DBRE ICJ DIC P NNE NNC NN-P

Knight, Jonathan, 1787-1858.
Report upon the plan of construction of several of the principal rail roads in the northern and middle states, and upon a railway structure for a new track on the Baltimore and Ohio rail road, by J. Knight, chief engineer, and Benj. H. Latrobe ... Baltimore, Printed by Lucas & Deaver, 1838.
79 p. 13 fold. pl., tab. 22 cm.
Sequel: Report upon the locomotive engines, and the police and management of several of the principal rail roads in the northern and middle states.
1. Railroads—U. S. 2. Baltimore and Ohio railroad. I. Latrobe, Benjamin Henry, 1807-1878, joint author.
TF23.K72 6-23497 rev

MdBP NN DBRE NcD DIC DP PHi MCM MBAt MiU-T MWA
NK 0202297 DLC MiU DSI ICJ NN MdBP NNE MnHi PPF

Knight, Jonathan, 1787-1858.
To Philip E. Thomas, president of the B. & O. Railroad Co. n.t.-p. [Baltimore, 1836.] 27 p. 8°.
"A letter from Jonathan Knight, adverse to James Stimpson's Jointed Axle." —*Lee.*
Copies: MiU-T, PPL. 1311

NK 0202298 NN

VOLUME 300

Knight, Jonathan, 1789-1864.
Addresses at the funeral of Timothy Phelps Beers...in the North church, in New Haven, September 24, 1858, by Prof. Jonathan Knight, M. D., and Rev. Samuel W. S. Dutton, D. D. New Haven, W. H. Stanley, 1858. 12 p. 22cm.

1. Beers, Timothy Phelps, 1789-1858. I. Dutton, Samuel William Southmayd, 1814-1866.
N. Y. P. L. September 12, 1945

NK 0202299 NN CtHC CtY-M DNLM CtY MH

CT99
.B415K5 Knight, Jonathan, 1789-1864.
A biographical sketch of Prof. Timothy P. Beers, M.D., by Prof. Jonathan Knight ... [Hartford, Conn., 1859]
p. [85]-89. 23cm.

Detached from Connecticut medical society, Proceedings, 1859.--Surg. gen. catalogue.

1. Beers, Timothy Phelps, 1789-1858.

NK 0202300 DLC MH

Knight, Jonathan, 1789-1864.
An eulogium on Nathan Smith, M. D., late professor of the theory and practice of physic and surgery, in the medical institution of Yale college; pronounced at his funeral. by J. Knight ... New Haven, Printed by H. Howe, 1829.
28 p. 21cm.

1. Smith, Nathan, 1762-1829.

CA 15-944 Unrev'd

Library of Congress R154.S6K5

NIC MH
NK 0202301 DLC MH-AH PHi GEU-M CtY MHi DNLM RPB

Knight, Jonathan, 1789-1864.
A lecture, introductory to the course of instruction in the medical institution of Yale college, delivered Nov. 2, 1838, by Jonathan Knight ... New Haven, Printed by B. L. Hamlen, 1838.
27 p. 21½cm.

1. Medicine—Addresses, essays, lectures.

4—36841

Library of Congress R708.K69

NK 0202302 DLC MB

Knight, Jonathan, 1789-1864.
A lecture, introductory to the course of instruction in the medical institution of Yale College, delivered Nov. 2, 1838. New Haven, Printed by B. L. Hamlen, 1838.
(American culture series, 110: 8)
Microfilm copy (positive) made in 1956 by University Microfilms, Ann Arbor, Mich.
Collation of the original: 27 p.

1. Medicine—Addresses, essays, lectures.
Microfilm 01291 reel 110, no. 8 E Mic 60-7579

NK 0202303 DLC ICRL FTaSU KEmT

KNIGHT, Johathan, 1789-1864.
A lecture, introductory to the course of lectures in the medical institution of Yale College, September 29, 1853. New Haven, printed by W.H.Stanley, 1853.

NK 0202304 MH-Ed DNLM PPC

KNIGHT, Jonathan, 1789-1864.
Observations on the functions of the absorbent system. [n.p., 1824]
[225]-229p. 22cm.
In the New England journal of medicine and surgery, v. 13, no. 3, July 1824.
1. Absorption (Physiology) 2. Lymphatics I. Short title II. Title

NK 0202305 CtY-M

Knight, Jonathan, 1789-1864.
On the propagation of communicable diseases. An introductory lecture to the course of 1849-50, in the medical institution of Yale college. By J. Knight ... New Haven, Printed by B. L. Hamlen, 1849.
20 p. 23cm.

1. Contagion and contagious diseases. 2. Medicine—Addresses, essays, lectures.

24-23951

Library of Congress RC112.K7

NK 0202306 DLC DNLM CtHT-W PPC PU

RC693
848K Knight, Jonathan, 1789-1864.
Popliteal aneurism successfully treated by compression. [Philadelphia, 1848]
p. 255-257. 27cm.
From American journal of the medical sciences, July, 1848.
Caption-title.

1. Aneurism.

NK 0202307 CtY-M

Knight, Joseph. Broom corn. 8°. pp. 14. pl. 8. [Melbourne], 1895. (Victoria. Department of agriculture. Guides to growers, no. 20.)

NK 0202308 MBH

Knight, Joseph.

—— Crystallized or glacéd fruits. 8°. pp. 4. [Melbourne, 1893?]. (Victoria. Department of agriculture. Guides to growers, no. 9.)

NK 0202309 MBH

Knight, Joseph.

—— The peanut. 8°. pp. 8. il. [Melbourne, 1897]. (Victoria. Department of agriculture. Guides to growers, no. 33.)

NK 0202310 MBH

Knight, Joseph, horticulturist.
On the cultivation of the plants belonging to the natural order of *Proteēæ*, with their generic as well as specific characters and places where they grow wild. By Joseph Knight, F. H. S. London, W. Savage, printer, 1809.
xix, 127, [1] p. col. front. 30½cm. (On cover: Horticultural essays. 1)

1. Proteaceae.

Agr 5-655

Library, U. S. Dept. of Agriculture 452.3K74.

NK 0202311 DNAL MBH NN MH-A

Micro-
fiche **Knight, Joseph,** horticulturist.
On the cultivation of the plants belonging to the natural order of *Proteēæ*, with their generic as well as specific characters and places where they grow wild. By Joseph Knight, F. H. S. London, W. Savage, printer, 1809.
xix, 127, [1] p. col. front. 30½cm. (On cover: Horticultural essays. 1)

Microfilm. Zug, Switzerland, Inter Documentation Co. [196-?] 4 sheets. 9 x 12 cm.

NK 0202312 NcD CU-A

Knight, Joseph, of Stafford, Conn.
A Discourse, delivered at Stafford, before Adoniram Chapter & Wolcott Lodge, at the Festival of St. John the Baptist, June 27, 1826. Hartford, 1826.
14 p. 8°. [In v. 569, College Pamphlets.]

NK 0202313 CtY

Knight, Joseph, of Stafford, Conn.
A sermon delivered at the interment of Mrs. Betsey Bartlett, wife of Nathan Bartlett, Esq., who, in a state of insanity, drowned herself on the night of May 5, 1825... Hartford, Ptd. by Goodwin & co., 1825.
18 p.

NK 0202314 MiD-B MH

KNIGHT, Joseph, of Stafford, Conn.
Sermon preached at the funeral of Deacon Cyrus Stowell, Feb. 17, 1859. Pittsfield, 1859.
pp. 16.

NK 0202315 MH RPB

Knight, Joseph, of the Ivy Leaf Society.
A few thought rays, captured while looking towards truth. Be Comforted! London, the author, 1903.
40 p. 16°.

NK 0202316 NN

Knight, Joseph, rector of Kettering.
The Evangelical family Bible... London, 1814
see under Bible. English. 1814. Authorized.

Knight, Joseph, 1781?-1855.
A synopsis of the coniferous plants grown in Great Britain, and sold by Knight and Perry, at the exotic nursery, King's road, Chelsea. London, Longman, Brown, Green, and Longmans [1850]
iv, 64 p. 21½cm.

1. Coniferae. I. Perry, Thomas A., joint author.

Agr 17-659

Library, U. S. Dept. of Agriculture 452.3K74S

NK 0202318 DNAL GU CaBViP PPL MiU MH-A MBH

VOLUME 300

Knight, Joseph. 1829–1907.
Catalogue of a portion of the library of the late Joseph Knight, . . . comprising a valuable collection of books on the drama, private issues of plays, &c., . . . Also French dramatic literature and miscellaneous books of reference, &c. . . . Offered by Francis Edwards, bookseller.
= London. 1907. 23 pp. Facsimile. 21 cm.

K4626 — Edwards, Francis, bookseller — Catalogues. Booksellers'. — Drama. English. Bibl. — Drama. French. Bibl.

NK 0202319 MB

Knight, Joseph, 1829-1907.
Catalogue of the third portion of the valuable & interesting library of Joseph Knight. [Sold at auction by Sotheby, Wilkinson & Hodge, 19 June & 5 following days, 1905.] London [1905]
171p.

NK 0202320 MH

Knight, Joseph, 1829–1907.
David Garrick, by Joseph Knight, F. S. A. With etched portrait by W. Boucher. London, K. Paul, Trench, Trübner & co., ltd., 1894.
vi p., 1 l., 346 p. front. (port.) 23cm.

1. Garrick, David, 1717–1779.
4—17994
Library of Congress PN2598.G3K5
[a40h1] 927.92

MiU OCl OO OU MB NN MiU ViU
NK 0202321 DLC WaU GU NcD WaT OrP CtY PPL PBm PSC

Knight, Joseph, 1829-1907.
David Garrick. With etched portrait by W. Boucher. London, K. Paul, Trench, Trubner & Co., 1894.
346p. illus.
Microcard edition.

NK 0202322 ICRL PPD TU FU PBL AU MoSU LU OCU

Knight, Joseph, 1829-1907, ed.
Sheridan, Richard Brinsley Butler, 1751–1816.
The dramatic works of Richard Brinsley Sheridan, with introduction and notes by Joseph Knight. [London] Oxford university press, H. Milford [1927]

Knight, Joseph, 1829-1907, ed.
AP4 .G3
The Gentleman's magazine. Ed. by Sylvanus Urban, gentleman. v. 1–303, no. [3]; Jan. 1731–Sept. 1907. London.

Knight, Joseph, 1829-1907.
Goethe and Johnson on Dante.
(In Notes and queries. July 13, 1878. 5th series, vol. x, p. 37.)

NK 0202325 NIC

Knight, Joseph, 1829-1907.
A history of the stage during the Victorian era, by Joseph Knight ...
(In Hooper, William Eden, comp. The stage in the year 1900 ... London, 1901. 26½cm. iv p., 1 l., 184 p. at end. 4 plates (ports.) incl. front.)

NK 0202326 PU-F IEN MH

KNIGHT, Joseph, 1829-1907.
Life and writings of D.G.Rossetti. London, etc., Walter Scott publishing Co., ltd., [19-?]
17.5 cm.
Half-title:- Great writers.

NK 0202327 MH MWA PSC

Knight, Joseph, 1829–1907.
Life of Dante Gabriel Rossetti, by Joseph Knight. London, W. Scott, 1887.
186, xix p. 22cm. (*Half-title:* "Great writers." Ed. by Eric S. Robertson)
"Bibliography, and catalogue of pictures, by John P. Anderson": p. [i]–xix.

1. Rossetti, Dante Gabriel, 1828–1882. I. Anderson, John Parker, 1841–
28-88..
Library of Congress PR5246.K5

ODW ViU MdBP NIC TxU NNUT NN ICU MH WaSp WaS WaSpG CaOTP AAP TU CSt NSyU OrP PP PHC PU PBm PSC OCl OCU
NK 0202328 DLC CaBVaU NjP NcD MdBP CU-I NIC FTaSU

Knight, Joseph, 1829-1907, ed.
Notes and queries; a medium of intercommunication for literary men, general readers, etc. ... v. 1–12, Nov. 3, 1849–Dec. 29, 1855; 2d ser., v. 1–12, 1856–61, 3d ser., v. 1–12, 1862–67; 4th ser., v. 1–12, 1868–73; 5th ser., v. 1–12, 1874–79; 6th ser., v. 1–12, 1880–85; 7th ser., v. 1–12, 1886–91; 8th ser., v 1–12, 1892–97; 9th ser., v. 1–12, 1898–1903; 10th ser., v. 1–12 1904–09; 11th ser., v. 1–12, 1910–15; 12th ser., v. 1–1916– London. G. Bell [etc.] 1850–[19

Knight, Joseph, 1829-1907, ed.
Downes, John, *fl.* 1662–1710.
Roscius Anglicanus, or, An historical review of the stage from 1660 to 1706. By John Downes. A fac-simile reprint of the rare original of 1708. With an historical preface by Joseph Knight. London, J. W. Jarvis & son, 1886.

Knight, Joseph, 1829–1907.
Theatrical notes, by Joseph Knight. London, Lawrence and Bullen, 1893.
xvi, 321 p. front. (port.) 23cm.
Running title: Dramatic criticism.

1. Theater—London. I. Title.
15-23437
Library of Congress PN2596.L6K5

GU NcU CtY MiU OCl OCU PU-F PU PPL NRU MB MH
NK 0202331 DLC NNC FTaSU MsU ScU KU WaU OrU CaBVaU

Knight, Joseph, d. 1840.
Winslow, Miron, 1789–1864.
A comprehensive Tamil and English dictionary of high and low Tamil, by the Rev. Miron Winslow ... Assisted by competent native scholars: in part from manuscript materials of the late Rev. Joseph Knight, and others. Madras, P. R. Hunt, 1862.

Knight, Joseph, *d.* 1840.
An English and Tamil dictionary; or, Manual lexicon for schools. Giving in Tamil all important English words, and the use of many in phrases. By the Rev. J. Knight, and the Rev. L. Spaulding ... Revised, in great part, by the Rev. S. Hutchings ... Madras [etc.] American mission press, 1844.
2 p. l., [iii]–xxii, 831 p. 22cm.

1. English language—Dictionaries—Tamil. I. Spaulding, Levi, 1791–1874, joint author. II. Hutchings, Samuel, ed.
35-28624
Library of Congress PL4756.K6
——— Copy 2 494.81132

NK 0202333 DLC ICU CtY OCl OU MH

Knight, Joseph, d. 1840.
English and Tamil dictionary; containing all the more important words in Dr. Webster's dictionary of the English language. 2nd ed., enlarged and revised. Jaffna, American mission press, 1852.
2 p.l., 970 p. 24 cm.
By J. Knight and L. Spaulding.

NK 0202334 CtY MH

494.811 K7453
Knight, Joseph, d. 1840.
English and Tamil dictionary for the use of students and colleges, containing all the important words in Dr. Webster's dictionary of the English language. Originally compiled by Reverends Knight, Spaulding and Hutchings. 3d ed., now enl., improved and romanized. Madras, Higgenbotham, 1888.
vi, 1511 p. 26 cm.

NK 0202335 KyU

Knight, Joseph, d. 1840.
A manual dictionary of the Tamil language. Published by the Jaffna book society. Jaffna, American mission press 1842.

Knight, Joseph, 1845- comp.
Pipe and pouch. The smoker's own book of poetry.
Boston. H. M. Caldwell Co. [1894.] xvi, (1), 182 pp. Plate. Decorated title-page. 16½ cm., in 8s.

K8472 — T.r. — Tobacco.

OCl
NK 0202337 MB PPLas CtY PP ICN OrU DSI IEN CU NcD

Knight, Joseph, 1845- comp.
Pipe and pouch, the smoker's own book of poetry, compiled by Joseph Knight. Boston, L. C. Page and company (incorporated) [c1894]
xvi p., 1 l., 182 p. front. 17 cm. [Golden treasury series]

1. Tobacco - Poetry. I. Title.

NK 0202338 Vi OrU OrP CSt

Knight, Joseph, *b.* 1845, *comp.*
Pipe and pouch, the smoker's own book of poetry, comp. by Joseph Knight. Boston, Joseph Knight company, 1895
xvi p., 1 l., 182 p. front. 17 cm.

1. Tobacco—Poetry. I. Title.
12—34963
Library of Congress GT3020.K6

NcRS MdBP CU NjP MWA CSmH
NK 0202339 DLC WaS MiU OCl OClRC PU PP ViU NN NjP

VOLUME 300

Knight, Joseph, 1845- ,comp.
Pipe and pouch, the smoker's own book of poetry, comp. by Joseph Knight. Boston, L.C. Page and Co., 1897.
xvi p.,1 ℓ.,182p. front. 18cm.

NK 0202340 RPB CU NcU

Knight, Joseph, 1845- comp.
Pipe and pouch. The smoker's own book of poetry.
— Boston. Page & Co. 1900. xvi, (1), 182 pp. Plate. [The C and gown series.] 16°.

NK 0202341 MB RPB

Knight, Joseph, 1845- comp.
A smoker's reveries, a companion book to Pipe and pouch, comp. by Joseph Knight. New York and Boston, H. M. Caldwell co. [c1909]
4 p. l., vii–x p., 1 l., 148 p. front. 17cm. $1.00
Illus. t.-p.

9-25224

NK 0202342 DLC

Knight, Joseph, 1870- joint author.
Carpenter, H Barrett.
An introduction to the history of architecture, by H. Barrett Carpenter ... and Joseph Knight ... London, New York [etc.] Longmans, Green and co., 1929.

285.09769
K745h Knight, Joseph E
History of the Springfield Presbyterian Church in Washington County and city of Springfield, Kentucky from 1792 to 1942. [Springfield, Ky, 1942?]
16p. port. 24cm.

1. Springfield, Ky. Presbyterian Church. Sp.: Littlefield Fund.

NK 0202344 TxU KyHi

Knight, Joseph Hyde.
Launching a corporation: Stockholders' and directors' meetings, by Joseph H. Knight ... Rights of minority stockholders, by Harry S. Gleick ... One of a series of lectures especially prepared for the Blackstone institute. Chicago, Blackstone institute, c1921.
50 p. illus. (ports.) 22cm.

1. Corporations. 2. Corporation law. 3. Promoters. I. Gleick, Harry S., joint author. II. Blackstone institute, Chicago. III. Title.

22-21367 Revised

Library of Congress HD2741.K5

NK 0202345 DLC

Knight, Joseph King.
Memorial Sketch of Hyde Park, Mass.
see under Hyde Park, Mass.

Knight,Joseph Philip,1812-1887.
Arouse ye gay comrades. A song & chorus dedicated to the Tiger boat club. Written by Thomas Power,esq. The music composed by Jos.Philip Knight. Price 37 cts.nett. Boston, Published Parker & Ditson,135 Washington St., 1840.
6 p. illus. 34cm.
Lithograph by "Thayer,successor to Moore,Boston." Vol.VIII,no.25 of "Music Collections."
1.Lithographs,Amer.2.Vocal music. I.Thayer,Benj. W.,lithog.II.t.III. Power,Thomas,1786-1868.

NK 0202347 MiU-C

*
M1
.S444 Knight, Joseph Philip, 1812-1887.
v.119
no. 3 Beautiful bells, varied by J.S. Knight. Figure 6 in a eight pointed sunburst. Boston G. D. Russell & Company, 126 Tremont, Opp. Park St.,St. Louis, Kunkel Bros. ... c1869. Pl. no. 1695-7.
9 p. 34cm. [Sheet music collection, v. 119, no. 3]
To Mrs. A. D. Mulford. Elizabeth, N. J.
1. Songs with piano. I. Title.

NK 0202348 ViU

Knight, Joseph Philip, 1812-1887.
Beautiful Venice! An admired ballad. [Accomp. for pianoforte.]
= Philadelphia. Fiot. [184-?] 3 pp. F°.

G6186 — T.r. — Songs. With music

NK 0202349 MB

Knight, Joseph Philip, 1812-1887.
Beautiful Venice! Ballad . . . [the accomp. arranged for the guitar by R. Culver].
= Philadelphia. Lee & Walker. [184-?] (3) pp. F°.

G3342 — T.r. — Songs. With music. — Culver, R., ed.

NK 0202350 MB

Knight, Joseph Philip, 1812-1887.
Beautiful Venice! Ballad. The poetry written by J.E. Carpenter. The music composed by Joseph Philip Knight. Philadelphia, Lee & Walker, [18--]
7 p. f°.

NK 0202351 NN

*
M1
.A13N Knight, Joseph Philip, 1812-1887.
.K54C6
1839 Come love come! Serenade, as sung with distinguished approbation by Mrs. Watson. Written by Andrew Mc. Makin. Music composed and dedicated to his friend John H. Hewitt Esqr., by Joseph Philip Knight. Pr. 50 cts. Philadelphia, Geo. W. Hewitt & Co. (late Nunns), 70 So Third St., c1839.
5 p. 34cm.
Moland, Sc. (cover); A.F.W., engr. (music)
Stamped on cover: Sold by Peters & Co., Louisville.
1. Songs with piano. I. Title.

NK 0202352 ViU

*
M1
.A13N Knight, Joseph Philip, 1812-1887.
.K54D3
1830 "Day of sacred rest return", a sacred song. The poetry by Rev. T. Grinfield. New York, Atwill, 201 Broadway [183-?]
[3] p. 35cm. (Songs for the Sabbath, no. 2)
Caption title. Cover wanting.

1. Sacred songs with piano. I. Title.

NK 0202353 ViU

KNIGHT, Joseph Philip, 1812-1887.
The Days long Ago Ballad. The Poetry by W.E.Staite;Music by J. P. Knight. B. [18..]

pp. 5.

NK 0202354 MH-Mu

*
M1
.A13N Knight, Joseph Philip, 1812-1887.
.K54D7
1842 The dream. Ballad, sung by Mr. Manvers & Mr. H. Phillips. The poetry by the Honble. Mrs. Norton. Pr. 50 C. New York, James L. Hewitt & Co., 239 Broadway, and by Firth & Hall, 1. Franklin Square [1842?]
6 p. 34cm.
G. W. Quidor, Engvr.
Stamped on cover: Sold by Geo. Willig, 171 Chestnut St., Phila.
1. Songs with piano. I. Title.

NK 0202355 ViU

Knight, Joseph Philip, 1812-1887.
The gipsy's invitation. A cavatina. The poetry by J. B. Phillips, Esqr. The music composed by Joseph Philip Knight. [With accompaniment for pianoforte.]
= Boston. Parker & Ditson. 1840. 5 pp. 33 cm.

L5195 — Double main card. — Knight, Joseph Philip. (M1) — Phillips, Jonas B. (M2) — T.r. Cavatina. (1) — Songs. With music. (1)

NK 0202356 MB

Knight, Joseph Philip, 1812-1887.
Go and forget, that we have met, ballad. The poetry by T. H. Bayly, composed by J. P. Knight. Boston, O. Ditson and co. [186-?]
[2] p. 35 cm.
Caption title.
Engraved.
Pl. no. 395.
For voice and piano.

NK 0202357 ICN

*
M1
.A13N Knight, Joseph Philip, 1812-1887.
.K54G6
1840 Go forget me. The poetry by the Revd. Charles Wolfe. [New York, James L. Hewitt & Co.? 184-?]
6 p. 34cm.
Caption title. Cover wanting.
G. W. Quidor, Engvr.

1. Songs with piano. I. Title.

NK 0202358 ViU

VOLUME 300

*
M1
.A13N Knignt, Joseph Philip, 1812–1887.
.K54G7
1840 The Grecian daughter; a ballad. As sung by Miss Shirreff. Written by T. H. Bayly. ⌈New York, Atwill? 184–?⌉
3 p. 34cm.
Caption title. Cover wanting.
Stamped on p. ⌈1⌉: H. Kleber, 101 3rd St., Pittsburgh.
1. Songs with piano. I. Title.

NK 0202359 ViU

---

*
M1
.S444 Knight, Joseph Philip, 1812–1887.
v.63
no.39 The Grecian daughter. Ballad written by Thos. Haynes Bayly. Music composed by Joseph Philip Knight. Pr. 50 cts. Philadelphia, Geo. W. Hewitt & Co. (late Nunns) 70 So. Third St. ⌈before 1841?⌉
5 p. 34cm. ⌈Sheet music collection, v. 63, no. 39⌉
Moland Sc.
1. Songs with piano. I. Bayly, Thomas Haynes, 1797–1839. II. Title.

NK 0202360 ViU

---

*
M1
.A13N Knight, Joseph Philip, 1812–1887.
.K54H6
1843 How soon, when our path ⌈is o'ershadow'd by sorrow⌉ Song. ⌈Poetry by T. Grinfield⌉ Boston, Wm. H. Oakes & for sale by John Ashton & Co., 197 Washington St., ©1843. Pl. no. 158.
5 p. 34cm. (Sabbath evenings; a collection of original and selected airs, arranged for one, two, three & four voices. 2d series. No. 1)
Stamped on cover: Ben Kassal, Omaha, Nebr.
1. Songs with pia no. I. Title.

NK 0202361 ViU

Knight, Joseph Philip, 1812–1887.
I canna bid him gang, mither; ballad. Written by Andrew McMakin; music by Joseph Philip Knight. Philadelphia, G. W. Hewitt (late Nunns) ©1839.
7 p. 34 cm.
With piano acc.
1. Ballads, Scottish. I. Title.
M1.A13K M 61-643

NK 0202362 DLC

---

*
M1
.S444 Knight, Joseph Philip, 1812–1887.
v.132
no.8 I'm queen of the fairy band. A cavatina written by Albert Surrey. Sung with enthusiastic approbation by Mrs. Morley. Pr. 50 cts. Philadelphia, Geo. H. Hewitt & Co., 70 So. Third St. ⌈after 1839?⌉
7 p. 34cm. ⌈Sheet music collection, v. 132, no. 8⌉
Moland, Sc.
1. Songs with piano. I. Surrey, Albert. I'm queen of the fairy band. II. Title.

NK 0202363 ViU

Knight, Joseph Philip, 1812–1887.
I'm queen of a fairy band. Cavatina [S. Accomp. for pianoforte].
= Boston. Ditson. [184–?] 5 pp. F°.

G417; — T.r. — Songs. With music.

NK 0202364 MB

Knight, Joseph Philip, 1812–1887.
I'm queen of the fairy band; a cavatina. Written by Albert Surrey. The music composed by Joseph Philip Knight. Cincinnati, Peters & Webster ⌈1852?⌉
6 p. 33 cm.
For voice and piano.
⌈No. 15⌉ in an album with binder's title: Music ⌈collected by Emily B. Jones⌉
1. Songs (Medium voice) with piano. I. Surrey, Albert. II. Title.

NK 0202365 NcD

Knight, Joseph Philip, 1812–1887.
The lock of hair; ballad. The poetry by Thomas Haynes Bayly. Pr. 25 cts. nett. New York, Atwill publisher 201 Broadway ⌈184–?⌉
4 p. 33 cm.
For voice and piano.
1. Ballads, American. I. Title.
M1.A13K M 56-22

NK 0202366 DLC

KNIGHT, Joseph Philip, 1812–1887.
The maid of Loire. Ballad [S. or T. Accomp. for pianoforte].
= Phila. Hewitt & co. [183–?] 7 pp. F°.

NK 0202367 MB

Knight, Joseph Philip, 1812–1887.
The miniature. [Song with piano acc.] Written by Geo. P. Morris ... The music by Joseph Philip Knight. New York, Hewitt & Jaques, c1839.
5 p. f°.

NK 0202368 NN

---

*
M1
.A13N Knight, Jospeh Philip, 1812–1887.
.K54M8
1856 Music, sweet music; ballad. ⌈Words by J.E. Carpenter⌉ 25¢ net. Boston, Oliver Ditson, 115 Washington St. ... ⌈1856?⌉
5 p. 34cm.
Caption title: come then sweet music and cheer us to night.
1. Songs with piano. I. Title. II. Title: Come then sweet music and cheer us to night.

NK 0202369 ViU

Knight, Joseph Philip, 1812–1887.
My heart's best treasure; a farewell serenade. Published by John Cole, Baltimore. W. H. Duffy. ⌈18—⌉ Pl. no. 1175.
⌈2⌉ l. 33 cm.
Caption title.
For voice and piano.
1. Songs (High voice) with piano. I. Title.
M1.A13K M 56-32

NK 0202370 DLC

Knight, Joseph Philip, 1812–1887.
The new year's come, song . . . [Accomp. for pianoforte.]
= New York. Horn. [183–?] 6 pp. F°.

NK 0202371 MB

Knight, Joseph Philip, 1812–1887.
O swift we go! Sleighing song ... by J. T. Fields. [Voice & pf.] Boston, 1840. fol. (In "Music Miscel., no. 7)

NK 0202372 CtY

---

*
M1
.S444 Knight, Joseph Philip, 1812–1887.
v.172,
no.8 Of what is the old man thinking. Ballad. Sung with the most enthusiastic success by Mr. Parry, junr. at the London & Provincial concerts. The poetry by Thomas Haynes Bayly. The music composed by J. P. Knight. New York, Firth & Hall, 1 Franklin Square ⌈1832?⌉
5 p. 32cm. ⌈Sheet music collection, v. 172, no.8⌉
Bookstamp of Nash & Woodhouse, Richmond, Va.
1. Songs with piano. I. Bayly, Thomas Haynes, 1797–1839. Of what is the old man thinking. II. Title.

NK 0202373 ViU

Knight, Joseph Philip, *1812–1887*.
Of what is the old man thinking. Words by T. Haynes Bayly. Music by J. P. Knight. [Song with accompaniment for the pianoforte.]
— Boston. Ditson & Co. [186–?] 5 pp. [The boudoir, a collection of favorite songs.] 34 cm.

D3611 — Double main card. — Knigi. .oseph Philip, 1812–1887. (M1) — Bayly, Thomas Haynes, 1797–1839. (M2) — T.r. Song. (1) — Songs. With music. (1)

NK 0202374 MB

Knight, Joseph Philip, 1812–1887.
Of what is the old man thinking. For voice and piano. New York, B. W. Hitchcock, ©1869.
⌈3⌉ p. 27 cm. (Hitchcock's half dime series of music for the million, no. 92)
1. Songs (Medium voice) with piano. I. Title.
M1621.K M 54-85

NK 0202375 DLC

Knight, Joseph Philip, 1812–1887.
Oh! return that happier day. [Song with accompaniment for pianoforte.] The poetry by Rev. J. Greenfield. The music by Joseph Philip Knight.
= Boston. Parker & Ditson. [186–?] 4 pp. 32 cm.

L5201 — Double main card. — Knight, Joseph Philip. (M1) — Greenfield, Rev. J. (M2) — T.r. (1) — Songs. With music. (1)

NK 0202376 MB

Knight, Joseph Philip, 1812–1887.
Old friends & true friends; ballad. The words by T. H. Bayly. Baltimore, G. Willig ⌈18—⌉ Pl. no. 1397.
⌈2⌉ l. 35 cm.
Caption title.
For voice and piano.
1. Songs (Medium voice) with piano. I. Title.
M1.A13K M 60-1552

NK 0202377 DLC NN

VOLUME 300

*
M1
.S444 v.148 no.24
Knight, Joseph Philip, 1812-1887.
Poor Rosalie, ballad, written by T. Haynes Bayly. The music by J. P. Knight. Baltimore, John Cole ₍after 1899?₎ Pl. no. 1192.
₍2₎ p. 33cm. ₍Sheet music collection, v. 148, no. 24₎
Caption title.
W. H. Duffy.
L. W. Webb.
1. Songs with piano. I. Bayly, Thomas Haynes, 1797-1839. Poor Rosalie. I. Title.

NK 0202378 ViU

Knight,Joseph Philip,1812-1887.
The prairie lea. A song. The poetry by Dr. J.K. Mitchell,the music composed & dedicated to Dr. C.H. Stedman,by Joseph Philip Knight. Price 38 cts.nett. Boston,Published by Oakes & Swan, 8½ Tremont Row. 1840.
7 p. illus. 34cm.
"B.Champney,del."
Vol.VIII,no.30 of "Music Collections."
1.Lithographs,American.2.Vocal music. I.t.II. Mitchell,Dr.J.K. III.Champney,Benj..b.1817.lithographer.

NK 0202379 MiU-C

Knight, Joseph Philip, 1812-1887.
Rock'd in the cradle of the deep. ₍New York, C. E. Horn, 1840₎
33-36 p. 33 cm.
Caption title.
Imprint supplied from Dichter & Shapiro, Early American sheet music.
Imperfect: p. 37 wanting.
₍No. 3₎ in a vol. of songs and piano music with binder's title: Music ₍collected by Eva B. Eve₎
1. Songs (Medium voice) with piano.

NK 0202380 NcD

*
M1
.S444 v.83 no. 3
Knight, Joseph Philip, 1812-1887.
Rocked in the cradle of the deep. Words by Mrs. Willard. Music composed and dedicated to Dr. Mitchell. Piano. Figure 3½ in seven pointed star. Boston, Oliver Ditson, 115 Washington St. ... ©1853.
7 p. 33cm. ₍Sheet music collection, v. 83, no. 3₎
1. Songs with piano. I. Title.

NK 0202381 ViU

*
M1
.A13N .K54R6 1855
Knight, Joseph Philip, 1812-1887.
Rocked in the cradle of the deep. Words by Mrs. Willard, of Troy, N. Y. Music composed and dedicated to Dr. Mitchell, by J.P. Knight. 38¢ net. ©1853 by Oliver Ditson, Dist. Court of Mass. Boston, Oliver Ditson, 115 Washington St. ... ₍1855?₎
7 p. 34cm.
Imperfect: last leaf wanting.
1. Songs with piano. I. Title.

NK 0202382 ViU

*
M1
.A13N .K54R6 1857
Knight, Joseph Philip, 1812-1887.
Rocked in the cradle of the deep. Words by Mrs. Willard, of Troy, N. Y. Music composed and dedicated to Dr. Mitchell, by J. P. Knight. Piano, figure 3½; guitar, figure 2½, in 7 pointed stars. ©1853 by Oliver Ditson, Dist. Court of Mass. Boston, Oliver Ditson, 115 Washington St. ... ₍1857?₎
7 p. 34cm.
1. Songs with piano. I. Title.

NK 0202383 ViU

*
M1
.A13N .K54R6 1858
Knight, Joseph Philip, 1812-1887.
Rocked in the cradle of the deep. Words by Mrs. Willard, of Troy, N. Y. Music composed and dedicated to Dr. Mitchell, by J. P. Knight. Piano, figure 3½ in 7 pointed star. ©1853 by O. Ditson & Co., Dist. Court of Mass. Boston, Oliver Ditson, 115 Washington St. ... ₍ca. 1858?₎
7 p. 34cm.
1. Songs with piano. I. Title.

NK 0202384 ViU

Knight, Joseph Philip, 1812-1887.
₍Rocked in the cradle of the deep₎
Rocked in the cradle of the deep. Words by Mrs. Willard Song. Boston: Published by Oliver Ditson & Co., 277 Washington Street ... ₍186-?₎ ©1840.
7 p. 34 cm.
No. 67 in a vol. with binder's title: Songs. ₍v. p., ca. 1835-65₎
1. Songs (Medium voice) with piano. I. Title.
M1.A152 no. 67 M 55-1771

NK 0202385 DLC

Knight, Joseph Philip, 1812-1887.
₍Rocked in the cradle of the deep₎
Rock'd in the cradle of the deep; song. Boston, Koppitz, Prüfer & Co 30 West St. (cor. Mason) N. York, Wm A. Pond & Co Teller & Gipner 147. Spring St New York ₍ca. 1865₎
7 p. 36 cm.
For voice and piano.
1. Songs (Medium voice) with piano. I. Title.
M1621.K 52-50262

NK 0202386 DLC NcD

Knight, Joseph Philip, 1812-1887.
Rocked in the cradle of the deep. [Song, B. Accomp. for piano.] Boston. White & Goullaud. [1871.] 5 pp. [Vocal gems.] F°.

NK 0202387 MB

*
M1
.S444 v.134 no.24
Knight, Joseph Philip, 1812-1887.
Say, what shall my song be tonight. Ballad. Words by W. H. Bellamy. Boston, Oliver Ditson, 115 Washington St. ₍after 1844?₎ Pl. no. 1042.
4 p. 35cm. ₍Sheet music collection, v. 134, no. 24₎
Caption title.
1. Songs with piano. I. Bellamy, W H Say, what shall my song be tonight. II. Title.

NK 0202388 ViU

*
M1
.S444 v.59, no.42
Knight, Joseph Philip, 1812-1887.
Say, what shall my song be to-night. Ballad. ₍Words by W. H. Bellamy₎ 25¢ net. Boston, Oliver Ditson, 115 Washington St., C. C. Clapp & Co. ... N. Orleans, H. D. Hewitt ₍186-?₎ Pl. no. 1042.
₍5₎ p. 35cm. ₍Sheet music collection, v. 59, no. 42₎
1. Songs with piano. I. Title.

NK 0202389 ViU

Knight, Joseph Philip, 1812-1887.
Shall I sing you a song of the past? Ballad [S. or T. Accomp. for pianoforte].
= Boston. Oakes. [184-?] 5 pp. F°.

NK 0202390 MB NcD

Knight, Joseph Philip, 1812-1887.
She wore a wreath of roses; ballad. Written by T. H. Bayly; composed by J. P. Knight. Published by John Cole, Baltimore. ₍18—₎ Pl. no. 1143.
₍2₎ l. 33 cm.
Caption title.
For voice and piano.
1. Ballads, American. I. Title.
M1.A13K M 60-1684

NK 0202391 DLC IaU ViU

*
M1
.S444 v.19 no.30
Knight, Joseph Philip, 1812-1887.
She wore a wreath of roses, a ballad sung by Mrs. Wood, the poetry by Thomas Haynes Bayly. The music dedicated to Miss Norcott. 2d ed. New York, Atwills Music Saloon, 201 Broadway ₍183- or 184-₎
6 p. 35cm. ₍Sheet music collection,v.19,no.30₎
1. Songs with piano. I. Title.

NK 0202392 ViU

*
M1
.A13N .K54S4 1837
Knight, Joseph Philip, 1812-1887.
She wore a wreath of roses. A ballad, sung by Mrs. Wood. The poetry by Thomas Haynes Bayly. The music composed and dedicated to Miss Norcott, by Joseph Philip Knight. Pr 50 cts. New York, Hewitt & Jaques, 239 Broadway ₍ca. 1837?₎
6 p. 32cm.
1. Songs with piano. I. Title.

NK 0202393 ViU PU-FA

Knight, Joseph Philip, 1812-1887.
She wore a wreath of roses. The words by T. H. Bayly. Mr. Knight's improved ed. Boston, C. Bradlee ₍1847?₎
5 p. 36 cm.
Caption title.
With piano acc.
1. Ballads, American. I. Title.
M1.A13K M 60-2186

NK 0202394 DLC

VOLUME 300

M1
.S444 Knight, Joseph Philip, 1812–1887.
v.134
no.23 She wore a wreath of roses. Sung by Madme Dussek O'Conner. The poetry by Thomas Haynes Bayly, Esq. Philadelphia, George Willig, 171 Chesnut ⌊sic⌋ St.; New Orleans, For sale by E. Johns & Co. ⌊before 1853?⌋
⌊2⌋ p. 35cm. ⌊Sheet music collection, v. 134, no. 23⌋
Caption title.
Moland, Sc.
1. Songs with piano. I. Bayly, Thomas Haynes, 1797–1839. She wore a wreath of roses. II. Title.

NK 0202395 ViU NcD

Knight, Joseph Philip, 1812-1887.
There was a time. [Song for voice with piano acc.] The poetry by J. E. Carpenter, the music by J. P. Knight. New York, E. Ferrett and co., [18--]
3 p. f°.

NK 0202396 NN

Knight, Joseph Philip, 1812 – 1887.
There was a time. [Song, S. or T. Accomp. for pianoforte = Boston. Ditson. [185–?] 5 pp. F°.

NK 0202397 MB

Knight, Joseph Philip, 1812–1887.
The tribute of a tear; ballad, written and composed by J. P. Knight. Philadelphia, A.
no.22 Fiot ⌊ca. 1840⌋
3 p. 33 cm.
Caption title.
For voice and piano.
⌊No. 22⌋ in a vol. of vocal music, ca. 1840 ⌊collected by⌋ Caroline B. M'Nairy.
1. Ballads, American. I. Title.

NK 0202398 NcD

Knight, *Mrs.* Josephine Augusta (Clarke)
Symbols of the South, education and early life in Richmond under tutorship of Miss "Jennie" Ellett, by Josephine Augusta Clarke Knight. Richmond, Va., Garrett and Massie, incorporated ⌊°1941⌋
xvi, 113 p. front., illus. (facsims.) plates, ports. 23½cm.

1. Ellett, Virginia Randolph, 1857–1939. I. Title. 41-11552

Library of Congress LA2317.E45K5
⌊2⌋ 923.773

NK 0202399 DLC OrU TxU IU NcD OrU ViU

K⌊night⌋, J⌊udith⌋ B.
Songs in the night, by J. B. K. ⌊Philadelphia, Franklin printing company⌋ 1902.
82 p. 19½cm.

NK 0202400 DLC RPB

Knight, Kate.

Bullock, W H.
The Savior of the world. A lenten cantata for soli, chorus, and organ. The words selected and written by Rev. J. F. Shepherd, M. A., and Mrs. Kate Knight. The music composed by W. H. Bullock. London, J. Curwen & sons, ltd., 1901.

Knight, Kate Brannon.

Connecticut. *Board of lady managers, World's Columbian exposition.*
History of the work of Connecticut women at the World's Columbian exposition, Chicago, 1893. By Kate Brannon Knight, president of the Board of lady managers ... Hartford, Conn. ⌊Hartford press⌋ 1898.

Knight, Kate Brannon

Powers, Martha Elizabeth, 1833–1890.
Poems, by Martha Elizabeth Powers, with an introduction by Kate Brannon Knight ... Cambridge ⌊Mass.⌋ Printed at the Riverside press, 1892.

Knight, Katharine Sturges, illus.

Gates, Arthur Irving, 1890–
All aboard ⌊by⌋ Gates and Bartlett. ⌊New York⌋ The Macmillan company ⌊°1940⌋

Knight, Kathleen Moore.
Acts of black night ⌊by⌋ Kathleen Moore Knight ... Garden City, N. Y., Pub. for the Crime club, inc., by Doubleday, Doran & company, inc., 1938.
5 p. l., 278 p. 20½cm.
"First edition."

I. Title. 38-10849

Library of Congress PZ3.K7453Ac

NK 0202405 DLC CaBVa NN OCl h PPL

Knight, Kathleen Moore.
Acts of black knight. New York, Novel Selections ⌊c1938⌋
128p. 20cm. (Mystery novel classics, 76)

NK 0202406 OrU

Knight, Kathleen Moore.
Acts of black night ⌊by⌋ Kathleen Moore Knight ... New York, The Sun dial press, inc. ⌊1939⌋
5 p. l., 278 p. 20½cm.

I. Title. 39-16859

Library of Congress PZ3.K7453Ac 2

NK 0202407 DLC WaS

Knight, Kathleen Moore.
Akin to murder, a mystery story. ⌊1st ed.⌋ Garden City, N. Y., Published for the Crime Club by Doubleday, 1953.
187 p. 21 cm.

I. Title.

PZ3.K7453Ak 53—5036 ‡

NK 0202408 DLC WaSp WaE OCl OOxM

PS3521
.N5347A38 Knight, Kathleen Moore.
1953
Akin to murder, by Kathleen Moore Knight The iron cobweb, by Ursula Curtiss. Widow's mite, by Elisabeth Sanxay Holding. New York, Detective Book Club by W. J. Black ⌊1953⌋
3 v. in 1. 20cm.
I. Curtiss, Ursula (Reilly) The iron cobweb. II. Holding, Elisabeth (Sanxay) 1889– Widow's mite. III. Title. IV. Title: The iron cobweb. V. Title: Widow's mite.

NK 0202409 ViU NRU PV

Knight, Kathleen Moore.
Bait for murder. ⌊1st ed.⌋ New York, Pub. for the Crime Club ⌊by⌋ Doubleday, 1948.
191 p. 21 cm.

I. Title.

PZ3.K7453Bai 48-8293*

NK 0202410 DLC WaE WaT WaS CaBVa OrP OOxM

Knight, Kathleen Moore.
The Bass Derby murder. ⌊1st ed.⌋ Garden City, N. Y., Pub. for the Crime Club ⌊by⌋ Doubleday, 1949.
224 p. 21 cm.

I. Title.

PZ3.K7453Bas 49-11058*

NK 0202411 DLC ViU WaT WaE OEac OCl

PS3521
.N5347B3 Knight, Kathleen Moore.
1950
The Bass Derby murder, by Kathleen Moore Knight. The corpse with the missing watch, by R. A. J. Walling. The second sickle, by Ursula Curtiss. New York, Pub. for the Detective Book Club by W. J. Black ⌊1950?⌋
3 v. in 1. 20cm.
I. Walling, Robert Alfred John, 1869–1949. The corpse with the missing watch. II. Curtis, Ursula (Reilly). The second sickle. III. Title. IV. Title: The corpse with the missing watch. V. Title: The second sickle.

NK 0202412 ViU WaE Or

Knight, Kathleen Moore.
Bells for the dead, a mystery story by Kathleen Moore Knight. Garden City, N. Y., Published for the Crime club by Doubleday, Doran and co., inc., 1942.
4 p. l., 300 p. 21cm.
On cover: Crime club selection.
"First edition."

I. Title. 42-25579

Library of Congress PZ3.K7453Be
⌊4⌋

NK 0202413 DLC WaS PPL OCU OEac PP

Knight, Kathleen Moore.
Birds of ill omen. Garden City, N. Y., Pub. for the Crime Club ⌊by⌋ Doubleday, 1948.
189 p. 21 cm.

I. Title.

PZ3.K7453Bi 48-6302*

NK 0202414 DLC WaS WaE WaSp TxU OEac

Knight, Kathleen Moore.
The blue horse of Taxco. ⌊1st ed.⌋ Garden City, N. Y., Pub. for the Crime Club by Doubleday, 1947.
221 p. 20cm.
"Appeared in abbreviated form in the Toronto Star weekly."

I. Title.
PZ3.K7453Bl 47-4931*

NK 0202415 DLC WaE OrP CaBVa WaS ViU CoU

VOLUME 300

[Knight, Kathleen Moore]
Borderline murder, by Alan Amos [pseud. 1st ed.] Garden City, N. Y., Pub. for the Crime Club by Doubleday, 1947.
188 p. 21 cm.

I. Title.
PZ3.K7453Bo 48-604*

NK 0202416 DLC PP WaE

Knight, Kathleen Moore.
The clue of the poor man's shilling, by Kathleen Moore Knight. Garden City, N. Y., Pub. for the Crime club, inc., by Doubleday, Doran & company inc., 1936.
4 p. l., vii-viii p., 1 l., 271 p. illus. (map) 20cm.
"First edition."

I. Title.
Library of Congress PZ3.K7453Cl 36-4912

NK 0202417 DLC NN WaT PPL OEac OO OLak

Knight, Kathleen Moore.
The clue of the poor man's shilling, by Kathleen Moore Knight. Garden City, N. Y., The Sun dial press [1936]
4 p. l., vii-viii p., 1 l., 271 p. illus. (map) 19½cm.

I. Title.
Library of Congress PZ3.K7453Cl 2 36-33415

NK 0202418 DLC Or OCU

Knight, Kathleen Moore.
Death blew out the match [by] Kathleen Moore Knight ... Garden City, N. Y., Pub. for the Crime club, inc., by Doubleday, Doran & company, inc., 1935.
7 p. l., 295 p. 19½cm.
Maps on lining-papers.
"First edition."

I. Title.
Library of Congress PZ3.K7453De 35-2489

NK 0202419 DLC CoU ViU OCl OEac PPL

Knight, Kathleen Moore.
... Death came dancing. New York, Pub. for the Crime club by Doubleday, Doran & co., inc., 1940.
5 p. l., 277 p. 20½cm.
"First edition."

I. Title.
Library of Congress PZ3.K7453Ded 40-6299
——— Copy 2

NK 0202420 DLC IU PPL OCl OEac OClh

Knight, Kathleen Moore.
... Death came dancing ... New York, The Sun dial press [1941]
5 p. l., 277 p. 21cm. (Sun dial mysteries)
First published 1940.

I. Title.
Library of Congress PZ3.K7453Ded 2 41-15444

NK 0202421 DLC

Knight, Kathleen Moore.
Death goes to a reunion. [1st ed.] Garden City, N. Y., Published for the Crime Club by Doubleday, 1952.
192 p. 21 cm.

I. Title.
PZ3.K7453Dei 52-5961

NK 0202422 DLC Or OrP WaE GU OC PV

Knight, Kathleen Moore.
... Design in diamonds, a Margot Blair mystery. Garden City, New York, Pub. for the Crime club by Doubleday, Doran & co., inc., 1944.
4 p. l., 199 p. 20½cm.
On cover: Crime club selection.
"First edition."

I. Title.
Library of Congress PZ3.K7453Df 44-668

NK 0202423 DLC OrP PPGi PP PPL OCl OCU OLak

Knight, Kathleen Moore.
Dying echo; adventure and death in the ancient Maya cities of Yucatan. [1st American ed.] Garden City, N. Y., Pub. for the Crime Club by Doubleday, 1949.
185 p. 21 cm
"Appeared in a condensed form in the Toronto star weekly."

I. Title.
PZ3.K7453Dy 49-8387*

NK 0202424 DLC CaBVa OrP ViU OOxM OCl

Knight, Kathleen Moore.
Exit a star, a Margot Blair mystery, by Kathleen Moore Knight. Garden City, N. Y., Pub. for the Crime club by Doubleday, Doran & company, inc., 1941.
4 p. l., 366 p. 20½cm.
"First edition."

I. Title.
Library of Congress PZ3.K7453Ex 41-25824

NK 0202425 DLC CaBVa WaS PPL PP OEac OClh OOxM

Knight, Kathleen Moore.
Footbridge to death, by Kathleen Moore Knight. Garden City, New York, Pub. for the Crime club by Doubleday & company, inc., 1947.
256 p. 20cm.
"First edition."

I. Title.
PZ3.K7453Fo 47-630

NK 0202426 DLC OrU WaE WaS CaBVa OrU PP

Knight, Kathleen Moore.
High rendezvous. [1st ed.] Garden City, N. Y., Published for the Crime Club by Doubleday, 1954.
192 p. 22 cm.

I. Title.
PZ3.K7453Hi 54-6245 ‡

NK 0202427 DLC WaT WaSp PP OOxM PPL

Knight, Kathleen Moore.
Intrigue for empire, an adventure-mystery by Kathleen Moore Knight. Garden City, New York, Pub. for the Crime club by Doubleday, Doran and co., inc., 1944.
4 p. l., 199 p. 20½cm.
"First edition."

I. Title.
Library of Congress PZ3.K7453 In 44-6203

NK 0202428 DLC CaBVa WaSp TxU PP PPL OCl OLak OCU

Knight, Kathleen Moore.
Panic in paradise [by] Alan Amos [pseud. 1st ed.] Garden City, N. Y., Published for the Crime Club by Doubleday, 1951.
189 p. 21 cm.

I. Title.
PZ3.K7453Pan 51-13657 ‡

NK 0202429 DLC WaE

Knight, Kathleen Moore.
Port of seven strangers, by Kathleen Moore Knight. Garden City, New York, Pub. for the Crime club by Doubleday, Doran & co., inc., 1945.
192 p. 19½cm.
"First edition."

I. Title.
Library of Congress PZ3.K7453Po 45-9195

NK 0202430 DLC OrCS WaE KAS NRU OCl OEac PP PPL IdPI WaE WaT Or

[Knight, Kathleen Moore]
Pray for a miracle [by] Alan Amos [pseud. 1st ed.] New York, Duell, Sloan and Pearce [1941]
297 p. 20 cm.

I. Title.
PZ3.K7453Pr 41-4019 rev*
[r48f1]

NK 0202431 DLC ViU OEac PP WaSp

Knight, Kathleen Moore.
... Rendezvous with the past. New York, Pub. for the Crime club by Doubleday, Doran & company, inc., 1940.
5 p. l., 272 p. 20½cm.
"First edition."

I. Title.
Library of Congress PZ3.K7453Re 40-30403
——— Copy 2.

NK 0202432 DLC PPL OEac OClh OOxM

Knight, Kathleen Moore.
The Robineau look. [1st ed.] Garden City, N. Y., Published for the Crime Club by Doubleday, 1955.
187 p. 22 cm.

I. Title.
PZ3.K7453Ro 55-7159 ‡

NK 0202433 DLC WaSp WaE ViU OU OOxM OCl

VOLUME 300

Knight, Kathleen Moore.
... Seven were veiled. Garden City, N. Y., Pub. for the Crime club, inc., by Doubleday, Doran & company, inc., 1937.
4 p. l., 277 p. 20½cm.
"First edition."

I. Title. 37-4078
Library of Congress PZ3.K7453Se

NK 0202434 DLC WaT PP PPL PPA

Knight, Kathleen Moore.
... Seven were veiled. Garden City, N. Y., The Sun dial press, inc. [1938]
4 p. l., 277 p. 21cm.

I. Title. 38-9430
Library of Congress PZ3.K7453Se 3

NK 0202435 DLC OEac OClU

Knight, Kathleen Moore.
The silent partner. [1st ed.] Garden City, N. Y., Published for the Crime Club by Doubleday, 1950.
220 p. 21 cm.

I. Title.
PZ3.K7453Si 50-11090

NK 0202436 DLC WaSp CaBVa WaT

Knight, Kathleen Moore.
... Stream sinister. Garden City, New York, Pub. for the Crime club, by Doubleday, Doran and company, inc., 1945.
191 p. 20cm.
"First edition."

I. Title. 45-2937
Library of Congress PZ3.K7453St

NK 0202437 DLC WaT NRU MeB PPL OCU OEac PP

Knight, Kathleen Moore.
... The tainted token. New York, Pub. for the Crime club, inc., by Doubleday, Doran & co., inc., 1938.
6 p. l., 273 p. 20½cm.
Illustrated t.-p.
"First edition."

I. Title. 38-34800
Library of Congress PZ3.K7453Ta1

NK 0202438 DLC WaS OClh OEac PPL

Knight, Kathleen Moore.
... The tainted token. New York, The Sun dial press, inc. [1939]
5 p. l., 273 p. 20½cm.
Illustrated t.-p.

I. Title. 40-3249
Library of Congress PZ3.K7453Ta1 2

NK 0202439 DLC

Knight, Kathleen Moore.
Terror by twilight, a Margot Blair mystery [by] Kathleen Moore Knight. Garden City, N. Y., Published for the Crime club by Doubleday, Doran and co., inc., 1942.
5 p. l., 294 p. 20½cm.
"First edition."

I. Title. 42-17151
Library of Congress PZ3.K7453Te

NK 0202440 DLC CaBVa WaE WaSp PPL PP OClh OCU OU

Knight, Kathleen Moore.
They're going to kill me. [1st ed.] Garden City, N. Y., Published for the Crime Club by Doubleday, 1955.
186 p. 21 cm.

I. Title.
PZ3.K7453Tg 55-11345 ‡

NK 0202441 DLC WaT WaSp PV OOxM

Knight, Kathleen Moore.
Three of diamonds. [1st ed.] Garden City, N. Y., Published for the Crime Club by Doubleday, 1953.
189 p. 21 cm.

I. Title.
PZ3.K7453Th 53-9346 ‡

NK 0202442 DLC WaT WaSp WaE OU ViU PPL OCl OOxM

Knight, Kathleen Moore.
... Trademark of a traitor. Garden City, New York, Pub. for the Crime club by Doubleday, Doran and co., inc., 1943.
3 p. l., 297 p. 20½cm.
"First edition."

I. Title. 43-10174
Library of Congress PZ3.K7453Tr

NK 0202443 DLC WaS CaBVa NN PP PPL PU OCU OClh OOxM

Knight, Kathleen Moore.
The trouble at Turkey Hill [by] Kathleen Moore Knight. Garden City, New York, Pub. for the Crime club by Doubleday & company, inc., 1946.
4 p. l., [7]-220 p. 19½cm.
"First edition."

I. Title. 46-3160
Library of Congress PZ3.K7453Tu

NK 0202444 DLC WaS Or CaBVa WaE PPL PP ViU NN OCl

Knight, Kathleen Moore.
Valse macabre. [1st ed.] Garden City, N. Y., Published for the Crime Club by Doubleday, 1952.
188 p. 21 cm.

I. Title.
PZ3.K7453Val 52-11008 ‡

NK 0202445 DLC OrP WaT CtY PV OOxM NN

Knight, Kathleen Moore.
... The wheel that turned ... Garden City, N. Y., Pub. for the Crime club, inc., by Doubleday, Doran & company, inc., 1936.
5 p. l., 274 p. 20½cm.
"First edition."

I. Title. 36-23256
Library of Congress PZ3.K7453Wh

NK 0202446 DLC OU NN PPA PP ViU

Knight, Kathleen Moore.
... The wheel that turned ... Garden City, N. Y., The Sun dial press, inc. [1937]
5 p. l., 274 p. 21cm.

I. Title. 37-38313
Library of Congress PZ3.K7453Wh 2

NK 0202447 DLC NN OO

Knight, Kempster W., ed.
The book of the rabbit: history, variations, uses, points, management, selection, mating, breeding, exhibiting, judging, treatment of the diseases, rabbit-farming, and much other information bearing on rabbits and rabbit-keeping ... 2d ed., rev. and enl. by Kempster W. Knight. With a special chapter on "Rabbit-farming," by Major G. F. Morant. London, L. U. Gill, 1889.

Knight, Ken, 1896- *ed.*
The wonders of North Carolina. Photo credits: John Hemmer and others. Winston-Salem, N. C., Collins Co., °1954.
unpaged. illus. 31 cm.

1. North Carolina—Descr. & trav.—Views. I. Title.
Full name: Kenneth Raynor Knight.
F259.K6 917.56 54-4777 ‡

NK 0202449 DLC NcGU NcD

Film 1846 Knight, Kenneth G
Johann Michael Moscherosch: a satirist and moralist of the XVIIth century, by Kenneth G. Knight. [Cambridge, Eng., 1950?]
xii, 378 l.

Thesis - Cambridge University.
Bibliography: leaves 364-378.
Microfilm (negative) of typescript. Cambridge, Eng., University Library, 1967. 1 reel. 35 mm.

NK 0202450 OU

Knight, Kenneth Lee, 1915-
An annotated checklist of the mosquitoes of the subgenus *Finlaya*, genus *Aedes*, by Kenneth L. Knight and Elizabeth N. Marks.
(*In* U. S. National Museum. Proceedings. Washington. 24 cm. v. 101 (1954) p. 513-574)
Bibliography: p. 573-574.

1. Aedes. I. Marks, Elizabeth N., joint author.
Q11.U55 vol. 101 62-2557

NK 0202451 DLC DI MiU

VOLUME 300

Knight, Kenneth Lee, 1915–
... Keys to the mosquitoes of the Australasian region, including a synopsis of their distribution and breeding habits, by Kenneth L. Knight ... Richard M. Bohart ... and George E. Bohart ... Issued by the Office of medical information ... Washington, 1944.
3 p. l., 71 p. 28 x 21½cm.
At head of title: National research council. Division of medical sciences.
Reproduced from type-written copy.
"Additions and corrections to the key": leaf inserted.
"References": p. 70.
1. Mosquitoes—Australasia. I. Bohart, Richard Mitchell, 1913– joint author. II. Bohart, George Edward, joint author. III. National research council. Division of medical sciences. Office of medical information.
Library of Congress QL536.K54 44-41653 Revised
[r46i3] 595.771

PPC DNLM OrCS OrU-M
NK 0202452 DLC MtU TU GU NIC CU NcD PSt DNAL ViU

Knight, Kenneth Lee, 1915–
The morphology and taxonomy of the mature larvae of the family *Geometridae* (*Lepidoptera*) by Kenneth Lee Knight ... Urbana, Ill., 1941.
8 p., 1 l. 23cm.
Abstract of thesis (PH. D.)—University of Illinois, 1941.
Vita.
Bibliography: p. 8.
1. Geometridae. 2. Larvae. A 42-3056
Illinois. Univ. Library for Library of Congress QL561.G6K6

NK 0202453 IU DLC CtY NIC

Knight, Kenneth N.

Los Angeles city school district.
Opportunities for business training in the Metropolitan school of business, graduate department of Metropolitan high school. Teacher's guide for use in orientation, occupations, and senior problems classes. Office of the superintendent, Los Angeles city schools ... [Los Angeles] 1939

Knight, Kenneth Raynor
see
Knight, Ken, 1896–

Knight, Kim.
The bulldogger, by Kim Knight. New York, Dodge publishing company [°1939]
251 p. 20cm.
I. Title. 39-21861
Library of Congress PZ3.K7454Bu

NK 0202456 DLC

Knight, Kim.
Dangerous dust, by Kim Knight. New York, Dodge publishing company [°1941]
255 p. 19½cm.
I. Title. 41-5438
Library of Congress PZ3.K7454Dan

NK 0202457 DLC

Knight, Kim.
Feuders' gold, by Kim Knight. New York, Dodge publishing company [°1940]
256 p. 19½cm.
I. Title. 40-34426
Library of Congress PZ3.K7454Fe

NK 0202458 DLC

Knight, Kim.
Nighthawk's gold, by Kim Knight. New York, Dodge publishing company [°1939]
256 p. 20cm.
I. Title. 39-21860
Library of Congress PZ3.K7454Ni

NK 0202459 DLC

Knight, Kim.
Vengeance trail, by Kim Knight. New York, Dodge publishing company [1942]
250 p. 20cm.
"First edition."
I. Title. 42-12639
Library of Congress PZ3.K7454Ve

NK 0202460 DLC

Knight, Kobold, pseud.
see Giddy, Eric Cawood Gwyddyn, 1895-

Knight (L. A.) Asthma, its cause and cure. Hay fever, rose cold, and catarrh. 30 pp. 12°. [*Cincinnati.* 1882.]

NK 0202462 DNLM

Knight, Landon.
Great women of pioneer times: Charlotte Robertson.

Extract from Delineator, July, 1904.

NK 0202463 NcU

Knight, Landon.
The real Jefferson Davis, by Landon Knight ... Battle Creek, Mich., The Pilgrim magazine company, 1904.
203 p. front., plates, ports. 19cm.
1. Davis, Jefferson, 1808–1889. 4—32330
Library of Congress E467.1.D26K7

CaBVaU
NK 0202464 DLC PPL ICarbS Vi NjP MB ViU OClWHi DNW

Knight, Launce, arr.
Obispah waltzes
see under Atkinson, Robert Whitman, 1868-

[**Knight, Launce.**]
Oyucha San. Composed by Lieutenant F. M. Bostwick, U. S. Navy, and sung to the air of "Rosalie." [Tokyo, Japan: T. Hasegawa, ca. 1900.] 20 f. incl. col'd front., col'd illus., col'd plates. sq. 12°.
English words; music for 1 voice with piano acc. Additional verses follow music.
Music of "Rosalie" was composed by Launce Knight.
Printed on one side only of leaves folded in Japanese fashion.
Caption-title.
382349A. 1. Songs, American. I. Bostwick, Frank M. II. Title.
N. Y. P. L. June 25, 1930

NK 0202466 NN RPB MH ViU

Knight, *Dame* **Laura (Johnson)**
... Laura Knight, D. B. E., A. R. A.; introduction by Malcolm C. Salaman. London, The Studio, ltd.; New York, W. E. Rudge, 1932.
12 p. XII mounted pl. 25 x 32cm. (Modern masters of etching. no. 29)
Each plate accompanied by guard sheet with descriptive letterpress.
I. Salaman, Malcolm Charles, 1855–1940. 32—7145
Library of Congress NE2210.K6A3
[a42k1] 769

OClMA OO MH NBB PPPM NN
NK 0202467 DLC OCU CaBVaU CaBVa WaTC WaS MoU OCl

---

f
ND
497
K5
M3
Knight, Dame Laura (Johnson)
Laura Knight; a book of drawings, with a foreword by Charles Marriott and descriptive notes. London, Lane [1923]
1v. (unpaged) 20 plates (part col.) 32cm.
Edition limited to 500 copies, of which this is No. 430.
I. Marriott, Charles, 1869-1957. II. Title.

NK 0202468 UU PPPM WaSp NN OCl TxU NSyU

Knight, *Dame* **Laura (Johnson)**
Oil paint and grease paint; autobiography of Laura Knight. London, I. Nicholson & Watson, limited, 1936.
x p., 1 l., 397 p. front., plates, ports. 23cm.
I. Title. 36-9489
Library of Congress ND497.K5A25
[3] 927.5

OLak NN OKentU LU TU TNJ WaE CaBVaU
NK 0202469 DLC WaS NcU NIC CtY PPL PPFr PP OCl OClMA

Knight, Laura (Johnson) 8062.04-671
Oil paint and grease paint. By Laura Knight.
— New York. The Macmillan Co. 1936. x, (1), 397 pp. Portraits. Plates. 23 cm., in 8s.
An autobiography.

WaTC Mi GU CoU
NK 0202470 MB NcR MiU OClMA OU NN OCU WaSp OrU OrP

Knight, Dame Laura (Johnson)
Paintings and drawings by Laura Knight
see under Alpine Club, London - - Gallery.

VOLUME 300

Knight, Laura (Johnson).
Twenty-one drawings of the Russian ballet, by Laura Knight, with an introductory note by P. G. Konody. London: Davis & Orioli, 1920. 2 l., 21 pl. (1 col'd.) 41½cm.
Imperfect: 1 pl. wanting.
"Limited to 350 copies."

683490A. 1. Ballet, Russian. 2. Drawings, British.
N. Y. P. L. December 8, 1933

NK 0202472 NN LU WaS PP

Knight, *Mrs.* Laura (Johnson)
... The work of Laura & Harold Knight; with a foreword by Ernest G. Halton ... [London] "The Studio" [1921]
1 p. l., 5, [1] p., 8 l. 8 mounted col. pl. 41cm. (Modern painting. I)
Series called Modern paintings on cover.

I. Knight, Harold, 1874– II. Halton, Ernest G. III. The Studio.
22-8791
Library of Congress ND497.K5A3

NK 0202473 DLC CU MiU OCl OLak MdBP MB NN MiU WaS

Knight, Leona Annie, 1859-
Annie Weldon's secret; or, Doomed to sorrow. A novel embracing scenes of real life in Louisiana. Two pictures visibly sketched of the beautiful Bayou Teche. By (Bay Leaf) Miss Leona A. Knight ... St. Louis, Mo., Alex. Noble, printer [1891]
256 p. port. 17cm.

NK 0202474 NNC

Knight, Leona Annie, 1859–
Book of poems, by Miss Leona A. Knight. [n. p., 1889]
2 p. l., vii, 5-260 p. 17½cm.
Lettered on cover: Gems of thought.

I. Title. II. Title: Gems of thought.
28-1987
Library of Congress PS2196.K8

NK 0202475 DLC

823 Knight, Legh.
K745t Tonic bitters. A novel. London, Chapman and Hall, 1868.
2v. 20cm.

NK 0202476 IU

Knight, Leonard Alfred, 1895–
The creaking tree mystery. London, S. Low, Marston [1931]
248 p. 19 cm.

I. Title.
PZ3.K7455Cr 31-31441 rev*

NK 0202477 DLC

Knight, Leonard Alfred, 1895-
Night express murder. London, S.Low, Marston & co. [1936]
viii, 280 p. 19 cm.

NK 0202478 MH

Knight, Leonard Alfred, 1895–
... The riddle of Nap's hollow. London, S. Low, Marston & co., ltd. [1932]
viii, 312 p. 19 cm.

I. Title.
PZ3.K7455Ri 32-12734 rev

NK 0202479 DLC

Knight, Leonard Alfred, 1895–
Rider in the sky. [1st ed.] London, Gryphon Books [1953]
240 p. 20 cm. (A Gryphon romance)

I. Title.
PZ3.K7455Rg 54-15027 ‡

NK 0202480 DLC

Knight, Leonard Alfred, 1895-
Super-cinema murder. London, S.Low, Marston & co. [193- ?]
viii, 312 p. 19 cm.

NK 0202481 MH

Knight, Lewis Stanley.
Welsh independent grammar schools to 1600. Their charters of foundation, deeds, statutes, customs, &c. By L. Stanley Knight ... Newtown: The Welsh Outlook Press[, pref. 1926]. xii, 139 p. incl. tables. plan. 8°.
Bibliographical footnotes.

303138A. 1. Education—Hist.—Gt. Br.—Wales.
N. Y. P. L. June 9, 1927

NK 0202482 NN CU MH CtY ICN IU

Knight, Lewis Washington, 1816–1904.
The breeding and rearing of jacks, jennets and mules. By L. W. Knight, M. D. Nashville, Tenn., The Cumberland press, 1902.
111 p. front. (port.) plates. 20cm.

1. Asses and mules.
7—8527
Library of Congress SF361.K7

NN
NK 0202483 DLC OrP IdU NcRS IU NIC CU OU TU ICJ MB

NA 5471 Knight, Lionel.
.H26K71 The parish church of Hammoon, Dorset. [Bournemouth, Eng.?] 1946.
20 p. illus., plan.

1. Hammoon, Eng. St. Paul (Church) I. Title.

NK 0202484 ICU

Knight, Lucian Lamar, 1868–1933.
Address of state historian of Georgia, Hon. Lucian Lamar Knight, in the State capitol, November 25th, 1916, on the occasion of the presentation by Mrs. Richard Pleasanton Brooks, regent, through the Piedmont continental chapter of the Daughters of the American revolution of Atlanta, Georgia, of an oil painting representing "Nancy Hart capturing the Tories" in Georgia during the American revolution, 1779. [College Park, Ga., Martin printing co., °1917]
cover-title, [12] p. 1 illus. 22cm.
1. Hart, Mrs. Nancy (Morgan) 2. Georgia—Hist.—Revolution.
17-9246
Library of Congress E263.G3H32

NK 0202485 DLC GU CtY

Knight, Lucian Lamar, 1868–
... Alexander H. Stephens, the sage of Liberty hall, Georgia's great commoner, by Lucian Lamar Knight. [Athens, Ga., The McGregor co., printers, 1930]
v, 169, [1] p. plates, ports. 24cm.
Part I by Lucian Lamar Knight. Parts II and III "Extracts from writings of Mr. Stephens and tributes to his memory compiled by Mrs. Horace M. Holden."

1. Stephens, Alexander Hamilton, 1812-1883. I. Holden, Mary (Corry) "Mrs. H. M. Holden", comp.
37-14792
Library of Congr E467.1.S85K6
[2] 923.273

NK 0202486 DLC NN GU GEU ViU IU NcD

Knight, Lucian Lamar, 1868-

Georgia. *Dept. of archives and history.*
Annual report. 1st-
1919-
[Atlanta? 1920-

Knight, Lucian Lamar, 1868–
The ballad of the broom: a political satire by Lucian Lamar Knight ... [Atlanta? Ga., 1922]
cover-title, [11] p. 25½cm.

I. Title.
22-25269
Library of Congress PS3521.N535B3 1922

NK 0202488 DLC NN

PS 551 Knight, Lucian Lamar, 1868-
.L5 ...Biographical dictionary of authors, comp. by Lucian Lamar Knight.
v.15 [New Orleans, Atlanta, etc. c1910]
xii, 478 p. 24 cm. (Library of southern literature, v.15)

NK 0202489 DLC MH

Knight, Lucian Lamar, 1868–
Centennial oration, the voices of the past, by Lucian Lamar Knight ... delivered in the chapel of the State university at Athens, Ga. ... June 15, 1920, at the centennial exercises of the Phi kappa society, founded by Chief Justice Joseph Henry Lumpkin. [Athens? 1920]
cover-title, 3-26 p. 23cm.

1. Phi kappa. University of Georgia. 2. Georgia. University.
23-852
Library of Congress LD1986.2.P5K6

NK 0202490 DLC

Knight, Lucian Lamar, 1868- ed.

The Colonial records of the state of Georgia, comp. under authority of the legislature by Allen D. Candler ... rev. and pub. by Lucian Lamar Knight ... v. 1- Atlanta, Ga., C. P. Byrd, state printer, 1904-

Knight, Lucian Lamar, 1868– *ed.*
Encyclopedia of Georgia biography, Lucian Lamar Knight ... editor-in-chief ... Atlanta, Ga., A. H. Cawston—managing editor and publisher, 1931–
v. front., ports. 27½cm.

1. Georgia—Biog. I. Cawston, A. H., joint ed. II. Title.
31-13966
Library of Congress F285.K69
——— Copy 2.
Copyright A 37592 [3] 920.0758

NK 0202492 DLC NcD

VOLUME 300

Knight, Lucian Lamar, 1868–
Genealogy of the Knight, Walton, Woodson, Lamar, Daniel, Benning, Cobb, Jackson, Grant and other Georgia families. Including biographies of many distinguished members. By Lucian Lamar Knight ... [n. p., 193–]
3 p. l., 242 numb l. 28cm.
Type-written.

1. Knight family. 2. Walton family. 3. Woodson family. 4. Lamar family. 5. Georgia—Biog. 6. Georgia—Geneal.
37-7888
Library of Congress CS71.K725 193–

NK 0202493 DLC PHi

KNIGHT, LUCIAN LAMAR, 1868–
Genealogy of the Knight, Walton, Woodson, Lamar, Daniel, Benning, Cobb, Jackson, Grant, and other Georgia families, including biographies of many distinguished members, by Lucian Lamar Knight... [Clearwater, Fla., 193–] 260 f. coat of arms. 28cm.

Typewritten.

737716A. 1. Georgia—Geneal. 2. Georgia—Biog. 3. Knight family.

NK 0202494 NN

Knight, Lucian Lamar, 1868- joint comp.

Stewart, Joseph Spencer, 1863- comp.
Georgia oratory, containing selections from Georgians arranged in chronological groupings to illustrate outstanding epochs in Georgia history. Designed for special use of high schools and colleges. By Joseph Spencer Stewart ... and Lucian Lamar Knight ... [Athens, Ga., Printed by The McGregor company, 1933.

Knight, Lucian Lamar, 1868–
Georgia's bi-centennial memoirs and memories; a tale of two centuries, reviewing the state's marvelous story of achievement, since Oglethorpe's landing in 1733. By Lucian Lamar Knight ... [Atlanta] Pub. by the author for private distribution [°1931–
v. front., plates, ports. 27½cm.

1. Georgia—Biog. I. Title.
32-6551
Library of Congress F285.K697
——— Copy 2.
Copyright A 48872 [3] 920.0758

NIC CU
NK 0202496 DLC WaS NcD MB MH DS PHi OCl OU PHC GAU

Knight, Lucian Lamar, 1868-1933.
Georgia's bi-centennial memoirs and memories; a tale of two centuries, reviewing the state's marvelous story of achievement, since Oglethorpe's landing in 1733. By Lucian Lamar Knight ... [Atlanta] Pub. by the author for private distribution [1933-
v. plates, ports. 27½cm.

NK 0202497 ViU NcU ODW MiU

Knight, Lucian Lamar, 1868–1933.
Georgia's landmarks, memorials and legends ... by Lucian Lamar Knight ... Ed. de luxe for private distribution. Atlanta, Ga., Printed for the author by the Byrd printing company, state printers, 1913–14.
2 v. fronts., plates, ports. 23cm.
Contents.—v. 1. Landmarks and memorials. Historical outlines, original settlers, and distinguished residents of the counties of Georgia.—v. 2. Under the code duello. Landmarks and memorials. Historic churchyards and burial-grounds. Myths and legends of the Indians. Tales of the revolutionary camp-fires. Georgia miscellanies. Historic county seats, chief towns, and noted localities.
1. Georgia. 2. Georgia—History, Local. 3. Georgia—Biog. I. Title.
13-11533
Library of Congress F287.K7

MWA ViU MoSU MeB NcGU CU CoU FTaSU NcU NcD ODW PPL
NK 0202498 DLC NjP NN MB PP PU PBm MiU OCl OO GU-De

Knight, Lucian Lamar, 1868- comp.

Georgia. *Dept. of archives and history.*
Georgia's roster of the revolution, containing a list of the state's defenders; officers and men; soldiers and sailors; partisans and regulars; whether enlisted from Georgia or settled in Georgia after the close of hostilities. Comp. under authority of the legislature from various sources, including official documents, both state and federal, certificates of service, land grants, pension rolls, and other records, by Lucian Lamar Knight ... state historian and director of the Department of archives and history. Atlanta, Ga., Index printing co., 1920.

Knight, Lucian Lamar, 1868–
History of Fulton county, Georgia, narrative and biographical, by Lucian Lamar Knight ... Atlanta, Ga., A. H. Cawston, 1930.
2 p. l., [11]–514 p. incl. ports. front., port. 27½cm.

1. Fulton co., Ga.—Hist. 2. Fulton co., Ga.—Biog. 3. Atlanta—Hist. 4. Atlanta—Biog.
31-643
Library of Congress F292.F9K71

NK 0202500 DLC NcD GU GColu GAHi GDS

Ga
F286
K692 Knight, Lucian Lamar, 1868-1933, ed.
In preparation [of] A standard history of Georgia and Georgians. Chicago, Lewis Pub. Co. [1917?]
1 v. illus. 28cm.

An advance notice of A standard history of Georgia and Georgians edited by Lucian Lamar Knight to be published by Lewis publishing company.

NK 0202501 GU

PS551
.L5 Knight, Lucian Lamar, 1868-1933 ed
FOR OTHER EDITIONS SEE MAIN ENTRY

Library of southern literature; compiled under the direct supervision of southern men of letters. Edwin Anderson Alderman, Joel Chandler Harris, editors in chief; Charles William Kent, literary editor ... New Orleans, Atlanta [etc.] The Martin & Hoyt company [°1908–13]

Knight, Lucian Lamar, 1868–1933.
Memorials of Dixie-land; orations, essays, sketches, and poems on topics historical, commemorative, literary and patriotic, by Lucian Lamar Knight ... Atlanta, Ga., Byrd printing company, 1919.
xii, 604 p. front., pl. 23cm.

1. American literature—Southern states. I. Title.
20-1982
Library of Congress PS551.K6

MWA NN NjP ViU TU OU NcGU PAHi FTaSU MoU GColu
NK 0202503 DLC NcRS NcD NcU PHi PPL MiU OClWHi OClW

Knight, Lucian Lamar, 1868–1933.
New England addresses: The Puritan in the South and Intellectual patriotism, delivered by Lucian Lamar Knight at Wallingford, Conn., October 19, 1916. The former at the unveiling of a granite boulder to Dr. Lyman Hall, one of the signers of the Declaration of independence for Georgia, on the site of the old patriot's birthplace; the latter at the corner-stone laying of the Lyman Hall high school ... [Wallingford? 1916]
39 p. 23cm.
1. Hall, Lyman, 1724-1790. I. Title. II. Title: The Puritan in the South. III. Title: Intellectual patriotism.
18-14019
Library of Congress E263.G3H4

NK 0202504 DLC GU

Knight, Lucian Lamar, 1868-

Georgia (*Colony*) *Trustees for establishing the colony of Georgia in America.*
... Original papers. Correspondence, Trustees, General Oglethorpe and others. 1735–17
Atlanta, Ga., C. P. Byrd, state printer, 1910–

Knight, Lucian Lamar, 1868–1933.
Phi beta kappa oration, "Thou art a scholar. Speak to it, Horatio", delivered by Lucian Lamar Knight before the Phi beta kappa society of the University of Georgia in the university chapel, at Athens, during commencement, on Monday, June 19, 1916. [n. p., 1916]
26 p. 23cm.

1. Southern states. 2. Phi beta kappa addresses.
21-20772
Library of Congress F210.K7

NK 0202506 DLC

Knight, Lucian Lamar, 1868–1933.
Reminiscences of famous Georgians, embracing episodes and incidents in the lives of the great men of the state, also an appendix devoted to extracts from speeches and addresses ... 1st ed. By Lucian Lamar Knight ... Atlanta, Ga., Franklin-Turner company, 1907–08.
2 v. fronts., plates, ports. 20cm.

1. Georgia—Biog. 2. American literature—Georgia.
7-20978
Library of Congress F285.K71

NcU NcD GU-De
NK 0202507 DLC NcGU ViU NjP OU MH NcD GMW AU CoU

Knight, Lucian Lamar, 1868-1933, ed.
Reviews of Jefferson Davis, constitutionalist. His letters, papers and speeches
see under Mississippi. Dept. of archives and history.

E
263
G3
R4
v.4 Knight, Lucian Lamar, 1868-1933, comp.
Roster of the Revolution; including continentals, partisans and home defenders who enlisted from Georgia in the struggle for independence, together with veterans from other States who subsequently settled in Georgia on lands granted to them by the State government. Compiled and published under authority of the Legislature. Atlanta, Index Print. Co., 1918.
658 p. 25 cm. (The Revolutionary records of the State of Georgia, v. 4)

Reissued 1920 by Georgia Dept. of Archives and History under title: Georgia's roster of the Revolution.
"Land grants": p. 193-373; "Revolutionary pensioners": p. 436-457; "Revolutionary graves": p. 459-466.
Bibliography: p. 434-435.

1. Georgia - Hist. - Revolution - Registers, lists, etc. 2. Land grants - Georgia I. Title. (Series)

NK 0202510 Vi

Knight, Lucian Lamar, 1868–1933.
Shall our records be lost? Georgia's most vital need: a department of archives. Report of Lucian Lamar Knight, compiler of state records, to the governor, June 30, 1917. Atlanta, Ga., Byrd printing company, 1917.
34 p. 23cm.

1. Archives—Georgia. I. Title.
21-13181
Library of Congress CD3181.K6

NK 0202511 DLC GU NN

VOLUME 300

Knight, Lucian Lamar, 1868-1933.
Souvenir book of the United Conferate Veterans Reunion, 1919
see under United Confederate Veterans.

Knight, Lucian Lamar, 1868-1933.
A standard history of Georgia and Georgians, by Lucian Lamar Knight ... Chicago, New York, The Lewis publishing company, 1917.
6 v. fronts. (v. 1, 3) illus., pl., ports., double geneal. tab. 72½cm.
Paged continuously.
Vols. IV-VI, biographical.

1. Georgia—Hist. 2. Georgia—Biog.
17—1927
Library of Congress F286.K7

NK 0202513 DLC FTaSU FU AAP NcD ViU OCl GMW

Knight, Lucian Lamar, 1868-1933.
Stone mountain; or, The lay of the gray minstrel; an epi poem in twenty-four parts, commemorative of the South's confederate, pre-historic, colonial, revolutionary and world war days, to which are added a number of other poems, patriotic, humorous and occasional, besides a few prose selections. By Lucian Lamar Knight ... Atlanta, Ga., The Johnson-Dallis company, 1923.
xvi p., 1 l., 277 p. front., plates, ports. 20½ cm.

I. Title.
24—4649
Library of Congress PS3521.N535S7 1923

OClWHi ViU OU GOAC
NK 0202514 DLC NcGU NcC NcD NcRS GS NcU MiU OClW

Knight, Lucian Lamar, 1868-1933.
Tracking the sunset; or, The shrines of history around the world, by Lucian Lamar Knight ... Atlanta, Ga., Printed for the author by the Stein printing company, 1925.
xx p., 1 l., 628 p. front., illus. (map) plates. 23cm.

1. Voyages around the world. I. Title.
25—27879
Library of Congress G440.K7

PU PSC OCl OCU OU MB ViU
NK 0202515 DLC NcD GAHi WaSp MtU NcU MsU PPL PPD

Knight, Lucian Lamar, 1868-1933.
Woodrow Wilson, the dreamer and the dream, by Lucian Lamar Knight ... Atlanta, Ga., The Johnson-Dallis co. [°1924]
4 p. l., [7]-135, iv p. front., plates, port. 20½cm.

1. Wilson, Woodrow, pres. U. S., 1856-1924.
24—15276
Library of Congress E767.K68

IdU WaS GOAC NcMHi
ViU NjNbS Or ViU-L TU NcU MsU NIC NcD WaE WaTC MtU
NK 0202516 DLC PBa PHi PV PHC PSC MiU OCU OU ODW MB

Knight, M Forster, 1901-
Mr. Tittlewit's holiday; written and illustrated by M. Forster Knight. Philadelphia, New York [etc.] J. B. Lippincott company [°1940]
153, [2] p. col. front., illus. 22cm.
Illustrated lining-papers.

I. Title.
40-13978
Library of Congress PZ10.3.K755Mi

NK 0202517 DLC ViU OCl WaS

Knight, M Forster, 1901-
The return of Sandypaws, written and illustrated by M. Forster Knight ... Philadelphia, New York [etc.] J. B. Lippincott company [1942]
151 p. col. front., illus. 19cm.

1. Animals, Legends and stories of. I. Title.
42-17224
Library of Congress PZ10.3.K755Re

NK 0202518 DLC OCl PP

Knight, M. J., ed.

Plato.
A selection of passages from Plato for English readers from the translation by B. Jowett ... edited with introductions by M. J. Knight. Oxford, Clarendon press, 1895.

Knight, M R.
Model aeroplanes simply explained; an introduction to the principles of model aviation, with complete instructions for building the successful flying model "Avis", by M. R. Knight; with a foreword by Capt. Geoffrey R. de Haviland ... London, P. Marshall & co., ltd. [1933]
101 p. illus., diagrs. 18½cm.

1. Aeroplanes—Models. I. Title.
34-41393
Library of Congress TL770.K57
629.1307252

NK 0202520 DLC NN

Knight, Marcia.
Milestones; songs from an old house.
London, Constable and Co., Ltd., 1911.
viii, 55 p. front.

NK 0202521 MH

BT921
.K65

Knight, Marcus, 1903-
Spiritualism, reincarnation and immortality.
London, G. Duckworth [1950]
128 p. 18cm. (The Colet library of modern Christian thought and teaching. 6)
"Books for further reading": p. 128.

1. Spiritualism. 2. Reincarnation.
3. Immortality. I. Title.

NK 0202522 MB NRCR NjP CBBD NNUT NjPT NcD N

Knight, Marcus, 1903-
There's an answer somewhere, by Marcus Knight and L. S. Hawkes. With a foreword by the Bishop of Portsmouth. London, New York, Longmans, Green [1953]
134 p. 19 cm.

1. Questions and answers—Theology. I. Hawkes, Leonard Stephen, joint author. II. Title.
BR96.K5 230.076 53-13316 ‡

NK 0202523 DLC MiD OrStbM NcDur

Knight, Margaret, ed.
Beattie and his friends
see under Forbes, Margaret, d. 1903.

BF131
.K65

Knight, Margaret Kennedy, 1903- joint author.

Knight, Rex.
A modern introduction to psychology, by Rex Knight and Margaret Knight. London, University Tutorial Press [1949]

Knight, Margaret Kennedy, 1903-
Morals without religion, and other essays. London, D. Dobson [1955]
124 p. 19 cm.

1. Ethics. I. Title.
BJ1311.K55 170 56-2143 ‡

CaBVa CaBVaU CaBViP
NK 0202526 DLC TU ScU NIC NN CU NcD OO NBC LU NcU

S21h
208
30

Knight, Margery.
... Manx Algae; an algal survey of the south end of the Isle of Man, by Margery Knight .. and Mary W. Parke ... [Liverpool] The University of Liverpool, 1931.
vii, 155p. incl. diagrs., fold. table. II maps, XIXpl. 24cm. (L.M.B.C. memoirs on typical British marine plants and animals ... XXX)
At head of title: Department of oceanography, University of Liverpool ...
The fold. table is numbered as p.148.
Bibliography: p.141-142.

CtY NIC PU-BZ
NK 0202527 CtY NIC ICU PPAmP PPAN PU OClW OU ICJ

Knight, Maria.
See
Candler, Maria (Knight).

Knight, Marian Vera.
... The craniometry of southern New England Indians, by Marian Vera Knight, A. M., with an introduction by Harris Hawthorne Wilder ... New Haven, Conn., Yale university press, 1915.
36 p., 6 l. x pl., 2 fold. tab., diagrs. 30 x 24½cm. (Memoirs of the Connecticut academy of arts and sciences ... vol. IV, July, 1915)

1. Craniometry. 2. Indians of North America — New England. I. Wilder, Harris Hawthorne, 1864-1928.
16—5113
Library of Congress Q11.C85 vol. 4

FTaSU GU NIC ICarbS
NK 0202529 DLC OrU WaU MU MiU OO OU ViU NcD IU MB NN

700
K71f

Knight, Marie Louise LeBel.
Fine American and English furniture, rare Chinese and English porcelains, oil paintings, portraits, library of books, oriental rugs, silver, glass, objects of art. Furnishings of "Stonybrook", the residence of the late Marie Louise LeBel Knight (Mrs. Edward Collings Knight, Jr.), Middletown, R. I. ... Public auction August 16-20, inclusive. Phila., S. T. Freeman [1937]
1 v. (unpaged) illus.

1. Furniture-- Collectors & collecting.
2. Art objects-- Collectors & collecting.

NK 0202530 RP

VOLUME 300

Knight, Marietta.
Dramatic reader for grammar grades, by Marietta Knight. New York, Cincinnati [etc.] American book company [°1910]
267 p. illus. 19cm.

1. Readers and speakers—1870- I. Title.

Library of Congress PE1121.K6 10—13727

NK 0202531 DLC OrP PBa PP PPPL OCl OClh OLak

Knight, Marietta, ed.

Cooper, James Fenimore, 1789-1851.
... The Pathfinder, abridged and edited by Marietta Knight ... Boston, New York [etc.] Allyn and Bacon [°1927]

Knight, Marietta.
Practice work in English, by Marietta Knight ... New York, Chicago, Longmans, Green, and co., 1914.
4 p. l., 206 p. 19cm. $0.60

1. English language—Composition and exercises.

Library of Congress PE1111.K66 14-20385

NK 0202533 DLC PPCCH OO WaS

Knight, Marietta.
Practice work in English. New York, etc., Longmans, Green & co. [1917]

NK 0202534 MH -Ed

Knight, Marietta.
Practice work in English. 4th impression. New York, etc., Longmans, Green and co. [1918]

NK 0202534-1 MH-Ed

Knight, Marietta.
Practice work in English. New impression. New York, etc., Longmans, Green & co. [1928]

NK 0202535 MH-Ed

Knight, Marietta.
A primer of essentials in grammar and rhetoric for secondary schools, by Marietta Knight ... New York, Cincinnati [etc.] American book company [°1905]
64 p. 16½cm.

1. English language—Grammar—1870-

Library of Congress PE1111.K65 5—34643

NK 0202536 DLC NcRS MiU NjP OCl OO

Knight, Marion, *pseud.*
see
Tiedemann, Wilhelmina (Scheda) 1886-

Knight, Marion A., ed.
The book review digest
see under title

Knight, Marion A., ed.

Readers' guide to periodical literature ... Author and subject index to a selected list of periodicals ... v. 1-
Feb. 1901-
Minneapolis, Minn., H. W. Wilson [etc.] 1901-13; White Plains, N. Y., and New York city, The H. W. Wilson company, 1913-

---

Knight, Marjorie.
Alexander's birthday, by Marjorie Knight; illustrated by Howard Simon. New York, E. P. Dutton & company, 1940.
120 p. incl. illus., col. plates. 22½ cm.
Illustrated lining-papers in colors.
"Alexander's birthday song" (words and music) : p. [115]
"First edition."

I. Simon, Howard, 1903- illus. II. Title.

PZ8.9.K64Ag 40-12420 rev

NK 0202540 DLC OCl OEac OO OClh

Knight, Marjorie.
Alexander's Christmas eve, by Marjorie Knight; illustrated by Howard Simon. New York, E. P. Dutton & company, inc., 1938.
92, [1] p. incl. illus., col. plates. col. front. 22½cm.
Illustrated lining-papers in colors.
"Alexander's Christmas carol" (words and music) : p. [70]-[71]
"First edition."

I. Simon, Howard, 1902- illus. II. Title.

Library of Congress PZ7.K739Al 38-19926

NK 0202541 DLC WaSp PP OCl OEac OClh PPI

KNIGHT, MARJORIE.
Alexander's Christmas eve ... illus. by Howard Simon. Hale, E.M. [1940, c1938.

NK 0202542 Or

Knight, Marjorie.
Alexander's vacation, by Marjorie Knight, illustrated by Howard Simon. New York, E. P. Dutton & co., inc., 1943.
105, [1] p. incl. col. front., illus., col. plates. 22cm.
"First edition."

I. Simon, Howard, 1902- illus. II. Title.

Library of Congress PZ8.9.K64Al 43-14781

NK 0202543 DLC PP OCl WaSp

Knight, Marjorie.
The doll house at World's End, by Marjorie Knight; illustrated by Clinton Knight. [New York] E. P. Dutton & co., inc. [°1936]
119 p. incl. front., illus. 23cm.
"First edition."

I. Title.

Library of Congress PZ8.9.K64Do 36-15930

NK 0202544 DLC OCl OClh OEac

Knight, Marjorie.
Humphrey, the pig, by Marjorie Knight; illustrated by Clinton Knight. New York, E. P. Dutton & co., inc. [°1937]
44, [1] p. illus. 21cm.
Illustrated t.-p.
"First edition."

I. Title. 37-16379

Library of Congress PZ7.K739Hu

NK 0202545 DLC OCl OClh

Knight, Marjorie.
The Japanese garden; or, The four white pebbles, by Marjorie Knight; illustrated by Clinton Knight. New York E. P. Dutton & co., inc. [°1934]
171 p. incl. front., illus., plates. 20½cm.
Illustrated lining-papers.
"First edition."

I. Title.

Library of Congress PZ7.K739Jap 34-17243

NK 0202546 DLC OCl

Knight, Marjorie.
The land of lost handkerchiefs; illustrated in color and black and white by Rosalie K. Fry. [1st ed.] New York, Dutton, 1954.
92 p. illus. 23 cm.

I. Title.

PZ7.K739Lan 52-8244 ‡

NK 0202547 DLC

Knight, Mary, 1899-
The fox that wanted nine golden tails, by Kishi Mariko [pseud.] Tokyo, Hokuseido Press [1955]
64 p. 19 cm.

I. Title.

PZ8.K742Fo 55-33525 ‡

NK 0202548 DLC NBC CSt MiU

Knight, Mary, 1899-
On my own, by Mary Knight. New York, The Macmillan company, 1938.
ix, 374 p. 22cm.
Autobiography.
"First printing."

1. Journalists—Correspondence, reminiscences, etc. I. Title.
[Full name: Mary Lamar Knight]

Library of Congress PN4874.K6A3 38-8591
——— Copy 2.
Copyright A 115669 [5-5] 920.

NK 0202549 DLC CaBViP TxU IaU Or PPT OClL OU OLak NN WaE OrP IdU WaS OrCS OrU CaBVa

---

Knight, Mary, 1899-
Red blight. Los Angeles, L. L. Morrison [1951]
208 p. illus., ports. 18 cm.
"Appendix: The Wedemeyer report on China and Korea, submitted to the President of the United States, September 9, 1947, by Albert C. Wedemeyer": p. [151]-187.
Bibliography: p. [189]-191.

1. China—Hist.—1945- 2. Communism—China. I. Wedemeyer, Albert Coady, 1896- Report on China and Korea. II. Title.
Full name: Mary Lamar Knight.

DS777.55.K57 952.03 51-6183

NK 0202550 DLC CSt-H VtU CU ViU DS CaBVaU

VOLUME 300

[Knight, Mary A]
Pageants and plays; four plays which have been awarded prizes by the Imperial order of the Daughters of the Empire. Toronto: T. Nelson and sons, ltd. [c1935] 57 p. 16½cm.

CONTENTS.—The dreams of Glooscap; A day at Mother Nature's court; Christmas Eve in Santa Claus land, by M. A. Knight.—The totem, by Marguerite Letson.

1. Drama, Canadian. 2. Pageants—Canada—Nova Scotia. I. Letson, Marguerite. The totem.
N. Y. P. L. April 12, 1939

NK 0202551 NN

Knight, Mary Alson.
Children's musical reader, by Mary Alson Knight. Boston, Mass., C. W. Homeyer & co., °1916.
23 p. illus. (music) 21½ x 18cm. $0.50

1. Music—Instruction and study. I. Title.

Library of Congress MT925.K74 17-5576

NK 0202552 DLC

Knight, Mary Juliet.
... The Oxford movement, by Mary Juliet Knight ... Hartford, Conn., Church missions publishing company, 1944.
cover-title, 22 p., 1 l. 23cm. (Soldier and servant ... No. 215)

1. Oxford movement.

Library of Congress BX5098.K6 45-17250
[2] 283

NK 0202553 DLC

Knight, Matthew Richey, 1854-
Poems of ten years, 1877-1886. By Matthew Richey Knight. Halifax, N. S., MacGregor & Knight, 1887. 143 p. 19cm.

NK 0202554 NN MH RPB NBuG

PR 6021 .N554 C4 **Knight, Maude C.**
Chance the changeling. London, Greening, 1907.
304p.

NK 0202555 ScU

By28 316 Knight, Mrs. Maude C.
Humphrey, duke of Gloucester, by Mrs. Maude C. Knight. [St.Albans,Printed by Gibbs and Bamforth, ltd.,1905]
p.51-84. illus.(incl.facsim.), 1 plate. 26cm.
Caption title.
From St. Albans and Hertfordshire architectural and archaeological society. Transactions v.II, pt.I, new series, 1903 & 1904.
Author's presentation copy to F.Madan, with her ms. letter tipped in.

NK 0202556 CtY

[Knight, Maude Russell] comp.
For Christmas tide ... Comp. for the Woman's association of the Brighton Congregational church of Boston. Boston, [c1903]
24 p. 18 cm.

NK 0202557 RPB

Knight, Max.
Works by Max Knight in collaboration with Joe Fabry, published under the name Peter Fabrizius, are entered in this catalog under Fabrizius, Peter, pseud.

Knight, Max.
The German executive, 1890-1933. Introd. by Paul Kecskemeti. [Stanford, Calif.] Stanford University Press, 1952.
ix, 52 p. 23 cm. (Hoover Institute studies. Series B: Elites, no. 4)
Bibliographical references included in "Notes" (p. 51-52)

1. Cabinet officers—Germany. I. Title. (Series: Hoover Institution studies)
JN3501.K5 354.43034 52-8307

NK 0202559 DLC IdU WaS MiU TU ViU NN LU TxU CoU PBm DS OU MtBC OrCS NSyU NIC CaOTP MU WaU CaBVa WaWW WaSpG

Knight, Maxwell.
Bird gardening; how to attract birds. Foreword by Viscount Chaplin; illustrated by Jean Armitage. London, Routledge & Paul [1954]
164 p. illus. 23 cm.
Includes bibliography.

1. Birds, Protection of. I. Title.
QL676.5.K5 1954 598.2 54-1780 ‡

NK 0202560 DLC MB CaBViP

Knight, Maxwell.
Crime cargo, by Maxwell Knight. London, P. Allan [1934]
3 p. l., 314 p. 19cm.

I. Title.

Library of Congress PZ3.K7458Cr 34-40294

NK 0202561 DLC

Knight, Maxwell.
A cuckoo in the house. London, Methuen [1955]
79 p. illus. 19 cm.

1. Cuckoos. 2. Birds—Habits and behavior. I. Title.
QL696.C5K6 1955 598.74 55-3211 ‡

NK 0202562 DLC CtY

Knight, Maxwell.
Keeping reptiles and fishes. London, Nicholson and Watson [1952]
207 p. illus. 19 cm. (Country books, no. 8)
Includes bibliography.

1. Reptiles. 2. Batrachia. 3. Fishes. 4. Vivariums. I. Title.
QL78.K58 590.74 52-66472 ‡

NK 0202563 DLC DNAL DI MiD MB CaBVa

Knight, Maxwell.
Letters to a young naturalist. With drawings by Patricia Lambe. London, Collins, 1955.
191 p. illus. 20 cm.

1. Natural history—Outdoor books. I. Title.
QH81.K675 1955 574 55-12795 ‡

NK 0202564 DLC PSt

Knight, Maxwell.
Pets, usual and unusual. London, Routledge and K. Paul [1951]
211 p. illus.

"A few useful books": p. 206.

NK 0202565 MiD CaBVa

Knight, Maxwell.
Some of my animals. Illus. by E. M. Mansell. London, G. Bell [1954]
133 p. illus. 19 cm.

1. Pets. 2. Animals, Habits and behavior of. I. Title.
SF413.K55 1954 636 54-41248 ‡

NK 0202566 DLC CaBVa NN

J 574.02 K71y Knight, Maxwell.
The young field naturalist's guide. London, G. Bell and sons [1952]
144p. illus. 19cm.

1. Natural history--Handbooks, manuals, etc. 2. Natural history--Technique. I. Title.

NK 0202567 TxDaM DNAL

Knight, Mellen Aubrey.
The system, magnesium oxide-boric oxide. Ann Arbor, University Microfilms [1942?]
([University Microfilms, Ann Arbor, Mich.] Publication no. 557)
Microfilm copy of typewritten ms. Positive.
Collation of the original, as determined from the film: 54 l. illus.
Thesis—Pennsylvania State College.
Bibliography: leaves 52-54.

1. Magnesia. 2. Boron compounds.
Microfilm AC-1 no. 557 Mic 50-401

NK 0202568 DLC

Knight, Melvin Moses, 1887-
... Los americanos en Santo Domingo; estudios de imperialismo americano, por Melvin M. Knight ... Ciudad Trujillo, Distrito de Santo Domingo, República dominicana, Imprenta "Listín diario," 1939.
3 p. l., [3]-208 p., 1 l. 24cm.
At head of title: Publicaciones de la Universidad de Santo Domingo.
"Traducción hecha a diligencias de la Universidad de Santo Domingo, con la autorización de la Vanguard press, de New York."

1. Dominican republic—For. rel.—U. S. 2. U. S.—For. rel.—Dominican republic. 3. Dominican republic—Pol. & govt. I. Santo Domingo. Universidad. II. Title.

Library of Congress F1931.K727 41-19135
[8] 325.273097293

NK 0202569 DLC OO OU CtY PU-L PPAmP PPT NN OCU MH NNC DPU NBuU N CoU MoU IU ICRL OCl CU TU ViU

Knight, Melvin Moses, 1887-
... The Americans in Santo Domingo, by Melvin M. Knight. New York, Vanguard press [1928]
xix, 189 p. 19½cm. (*Half-title:* American imperialism ... edited ... by H. E. Barnes)
At head of title: Studies in American imperialism.
"Reference notes": p. 177-189.

1. Dominican republic—For. rel.—U. S. 2. U. S.—For. rel.—Dominican republic. 3. Dominican republic—Pol. & govt. I. Title.

Library of Congress F1931.K72 28-6663

NK 0202570 DLC PSC NcD NcRS CSt-H GU CoU NBuT MsSM NIC MU CU CaOTP NjN MChB DS PP PSC PBm PU PPFr OCl ODW OU OCU ICJ MB MiHM NN WaU ViU WaTC MtU IdB IdU OrPR WaSp IdPI CaBVaU WaS WaWW PSC NcD NcRS CSt-H CoU GU NBuT MsSM MU CU NIC CaOTP

VOLUME 300

Knight, Melvin Moses, 1887–
The conquest of Algeria — a case of historical inertia, by M. M. Knight. (In: Essays in intellectual history. New York, 1929. p. 91–105.)

466556A. 1. Algeria—Hist., 1830– 1847.
N. Y. P. L. May 2, 1930

NK 0202571 NN OCl OU

Knight, Melvin Moses, 1887–
Economic history of Europe, by Melvin M. Knight ... Harry Elmer Barnes ... ⌊and⌋ Felix Flügel ... Boston, New York ⌊etc.⌋ Houghton Mifflin company ⌊©1928⌋
ix p., 3 l., ⌊3⌋–813 p. illus., double maps. 22½cm.
Binder's title: Complete.
Each part also published separately.
"Suggestions for further reading" at end of each chapter.
CONTENTS.—pt. I. To the end of the middle ages.—pt. II. In modern times.
1. Europe—Economic conditions. I. Barnes, Harry Elmer, 1889– joint author. II. Flügel, Felix, 1892– joint author. III. Title.
E 28—602
U. S. Off. of educ. Library for Library of Congress HC240.K7 HC240.K722 ⌊a40b²2⌋

OCX CU PP NcC NcRS WaS OrP OrCS CaBVaU MtU
OU ICJ NN DLC ICU MtBC MtBuM NBuC IdPI MiU CoU ICarbS
NK 0202572 DHEW ViU PU PPFRB PPD PPT PBm MiU OCl OCU

Knight, Melvin Moses, 1887–
Economic history of Europe in modern times, by Melvin M. Knight ... Harry Elmer Barnes ... ⌊and⌋ Felix Flugel ... Boston, New York ⌊etc.⌋ Houghton Mifflin company ⌊©1928⌋
vii p., 2 l., ⌊257⌋–808 p. maps (part double) 22½cm.
"As a compact introduction to the present volume the same publishers brought out in 1926 an Economic history of Europe to the end of the middle ages, by M. M. Knight."—p. ⌊v⌋
"Suggestions for further reading" at end of each chapter.
1. Europe—Econ. condit. I. Barnes, Harry Elmer, 1889– joint author. II. Flügel, Felix, 1892– joint author.
28-3682
Library of Congress HC240.K72

OrPR IdU Or CaBVaU
NK 0202573 DLC IdPI DS NIC PJB NcRS KEmT ViU ICJ

Knight, Melvin Moses, 1887–
Economic history of Europe to the end of the middle ages, by Melvin M. Knight ... Boston, New York ⌊etc.⌋ Houghton Mifflin company ⌊©1926⌋
x p., 2 l., ⌊3⌋–260 p. incl. illus. (maps) plan. 22½cm.
"Suggestions for further reading" at end of each chapter.
1. Europe—Econ. condit. I. Title.
26—14790
Library of Congress HC240.K7

NIC WaS TU PV CaBVaU MtBC WaSpG Or CaBVa
OCU OU OCl ViU ICJ MB NN WU OrStbM OrSaW OrPR NcD
NK 0202574 DLC MtU OrP DDO PWcS PHC PSC PBm PU MiU

Knight, Melvin Moses, 1887–

Sée, Henri Eugène, 1864–
The economic interpretation of history, by Henri Sée ... translation and introduction by Melvin M. Knight. New York, Adelphi company ⌊1929⌋

HC 240 .K713
Knight, Melvin Moses, 1887-
Histoire économique de l'Europe jusqu'à la fin du moyen âge, par Melvin M. Knight. Traduction française par Jean et Elise Picard et Henri Sée. Paris, M. Giard, 1930.
341 p. illus. (Bibliothèque internationale d'économie politique)

NK 0202576 MoU CU

Knight, Melvin Moses, 1887
Introduction to modern economic history, copyright ... ⌊by⌋ Melvin M. Knight. (Economics 10) ⌊San Francisco, Printed by A. Carlisle & co.⌋ ©1940.
cover-title, 192 p. illus. (maps) diagrs. 22cm.
Photoprinted.
"Reading suggestions" at end of each chapter.
1. Economic conditions.
40-34401
Library of Congress HC25.K58
——— Copy 2.
Copyright ⌊2⌋ 330.9

NK 0202577 DLC CU ViU

Knight, Melvin Moses, 1887–
Morocco as a French economic venture, a study of open door imperialism, by Melvin M. Knight ... with a preface by Charles A. Beard. New York, London, D. Appleton-Century company, incorporated ⌊©1937⌋
x p., 1 l., 244 p. front. 21½cm.
1. Morocco—Econ. condit. 2. French in Morocco. 3. Imperialism. I. Title.
37-36881
Library of Congress HC591.M8K55
——— Copy 2.
Copyright A 110996 ⌊5⌋ 330.964

MiHM NN DAU PBm NcD WaS IdU
NK 0202578 DLC OrU MU OU DS PV PP PU OCl OCU OU ODW

Knight, Melvin Moses, 1887–
The new biology and the sex problems in society, by Melvin M. Knight ... ⌊New York, 1921⌋
cover-title, 127 p. 18½cm.
Thesis (PH. D.)—Clark university, 1917.
Reprinted from "Taboo and genetics", by M. M. Knight, I. L. Peters and P. Blanchard, New York, 1920.
Bibliography at end of chapters I–III.
1. Sex (Biology) I. Title.
21-11482
Library of Congress HQ21.K57
Clark Univ. Libr.

NK 0202579 MWC MB DLC PSC

Knight, Melvin Moses, 1887

U. S. *Army. A. E. F., 1917–1920. Air service.*
A practical French-English aeronautic dictionary Dictionnaire pratique d'aéronautique français-anglais .. Information section, Air service, American E. F. ⌊n. p. 1918?⌋

Knight, Melvin Moses, 1887–
Taboo and genetics; a study of the biological, sociological and psychological foundation of the family, by M. M. Knight, PH. D., Iva Lowther Peters, PH. D. ⌊and⌋ Phyllis Blanchard ... New York, Moffat, Yard and company, 1920
xv, 301 p. 19½ cm.
Bibliography at end of each chapter.
1. Taboo. 2. Sex (Biology) 3. Sex (Psychology) 4. Woman. I. Peters, Iva (Lowther) 1876– II. Blanchard, Phyllis Mary, 1895–
20—22080
Library of Congress HQ21.K6

Or OrPR IEM IU OrRP WaTC
NK 0202581 DLC OCl MiU PU PP PPC ODW NN ICJ DNLM NcD

Knight, Melvin Moses, 1887–
Taboo and genetics; a study of the biological, sociological and psychological foundation of the family, by M. M. Knight, PH. D., Iva Lowther Peters, PH. D. ⌊and⌋ Phyllis Blanchard ... New York, Moffat, Yard and company, 1921.
xv, 255 p. 19½ cm.
Bibliography at end of each chapter.

NK 0202582 WaU MiU WaSp FMU TU NIC OO OCl CU

⌊**Knight,** *Mrs.* **Midgie**⌋
Hollywood's famous recipes of the movie stars, in which 100 screen favorites reveal their culinary secrets, with 100 exclusive portraits. Presented by Goodan-Jenkins furniture co. Los Angeles, Calif. ⌊©1932⌋
cover-title, 96 p. illus. (ports.) 24cm.
"The photographs and recipes contained herein are from the private collection of Midgie Knight."—p. ⌊2⌋
1. Cookery, American. 2. Actors. 3. Moving-pictures. I. Goodan-Jenkins furniture co., Los Angeles. II. Title.
32-23867
Library of Congress PN1998.A2K6
Copyright A 55069 ⌊2⌋ 641.5

NK 0202583 DLC

Knight, Mildred.
Poems. Cambridge, 1912.
84 p. 17 cm.
Privately printed.

NK 0202584 RPB

Knight, Mildred J., tr.

Angellier, Auguste, 1847–1911.
To the lost friend; a sonnet-sequence from the French of Auguste Angellier, by Mildred J. Knight and Charles R. Murphy. New York, John Lane company, 1917

Knight, Minnie R Godfrey.
Godfrey-Knight sentences, a text book for advanced practice in lip reading ⌊by⌋ Minnie R. Godfrey Knight. ⌊St. Paul⌋ St. Paul times press, 1931.
111 p. 23cm.
1. Deaf and dumb—Means of communication.
31-32907
Library of Congress HV2487.K53
——— Copy 2.
Copyright AA 80543 ⌊2⌋ 371.912

NK 0202586 DLC MB OCl

Knight, Montagu George, 1844– joint author.

Austen-Leigh, William.
Chawton manor and its owners; a family history, by William Austen Leigh ... and Montagu George Knight ... London, Smith, Elder & co., 1911.

Knight, Montgomery.
Analytical comparison of helicopter and airplane in level flight. ⌊Atlanta, State Engineering Experiment Station, 1938?⌋
431–435 p. diagrs. 28cm. (⌊Georgia. State Engineering Experiment Station. Publications⌋ v.1, no. 7. Reprint 1)
Caption title.
"Reprinted from the Journal of the Aeronautical sciences. v.5, no.11. September, 1938."
"References": p. 435.
1. Aeroplanes. 2. Helicopters. 3. Aeronautics. I. Ser. II. Ser.

NK 0202588 ViU

Knight, Montgomery.
... Experimental determination of jet boundary corrections for airfoil tests in four open wind tunnel jets of different shapes, by Montgomery Knight and Thomas A. Harris. ⌊Washington, U. S. Govt. print. off.⌋ 1930.
cover-title, 27 p. incl. illus., tables, diagrs. 29cm. (⌊U. S.⌋ National advisory committee for aeronautics. Report, no. 361)
1. Aerodynamics. 2. Aeroplanes I. Harris, Thomas Aubrey, 1903– joint author. II. Title.
31-26130
Library of Congress TL521.A33 no. 361
——— Copy 2. TL573.K6
⌊3⌋ (629.13061) 629.13

NK 0202589 DLC MiU OCU OU OCl

VOLUME 300

Knight, Montgomery.
... Pressure distribution over a rectangular monoplane wing model up to 90° angle of attack, by Montgomery Knight and Oscar Loeser, jr. Washington, U. S. Govt. print. off., 1928.
cover-title, 19 p. illus., diagrs. 29cm. ([U. S.] National advisory committee for aeronautics. Report, no. 288)
"References and bibliography": p. 19.
1. Aerodynamics. 2. Aeroplanes. I. Loeser, Oscar Edward, 1898- joint author. II. Title.
Library of Congress TL521.A33 no. 288 28—26391
——— Copy 2. TL574.P7K55

NK 0202590 DLC MiU OCU OCl ICJ OU

Knight, Montgomery, & Clay, William C.
Refrigerated wind tunnel tests on surface coatings for preventing ice formation. Washington. 1930.
21 p. plates. 26½ cm.

NK 0202591 DAS

Knight, Montgomery.
... Rolling moments due to rolling and yaw for four wing models in rotation, by Montgomery Knight and Carl J. Wenzinger. [Washington, U. S. Govt. print. off.] 1931.
cover-title, 27 p. incl. illus., tables, diagrs. 29cm. ([U. S.] National advisory committee for aeronautics. Report. no. 379)
"References": p. 20.
1. Aeroplanes. 2. Aeronautics. I. Wenzinger, Carl Joseph, 1903- joint author. II. Title.
Library of Congress TL521.A33 no. 379 31-26922
——— Copy 2. TL573.K63
[2] (629.13061) 629.13

NK 0202592 DLC MiU OCU OU OCl

Knight, Montgomery.
... Span-load distribution as a factor in stability in roll, by Montgomery Knight and Richard W. Noyes. [Washington, U. S. Govt. print. off.] 1931.
cover-title, 17 p. incl. illus., tables, diagrs. 29cm. ([U. S.] National advisory committee for aeronautics. Report, no. 393)
"References": p. 13.
1. Aerodynamics. I. Noyes, Richard Woodman, 1905- joint author. II. Title.
Library of Congress TL521.A33 no. 393 31-28384
——— Copy 2. TL574.P7K6
[3] (629.13061) 629.13

NK 0202593 DLC MiU OCU OU OCl

Knight, Montgomery.
... Wind tunnel tests on a series of wing models through a large angle of attack range. Pt. I. Force tests, by Montgomery Knight and Carl J. Wenzinger. [Washington, U. S. Govt. print. off., 1929]
cover-title, 49 p. incl. illus., tables, diagrs. 29cm. ([U. S.] National advisory committee for aeronautics. Report. no. 317)
No more published.
Bibliography: p. 10.
1. Aerodynamics. I. Wenzinger, Carl Joseph, 1903- joint author. II. Title.
Library of Congr TL521.A33 no. 317 29-27531
——— Copy 2. TL567.W5K5
[4] (629.13061) 629.13

NK 0202594 DLC OU

Knight, Montgomery.
... Wind tunnel tests on autorotation and the "flat spin", by Montgomery Knight. Washington, U. S. Govt. print. off., 1927.
cover-title, 18 p. incl. illus., tables, diagrs. 29cm. ([U. S.] National advisory committee for aeronautics. Report, no. 273)
"References and bibliography": p. 12.
1. Aeroplanes. 2. Wind tunnels. I. Title.
Library of Congress TL521.A33 no. 273 27—27880
——— Copy 2. TL671.K5

NK 0202595 DLC MiU OCl OCU OU ICJ

Knight, Nehemiah Rice, 1780-1854, **and others.** 4438.211
[Address. To the people of the United States.]
[Providence. 1844.] 15 pp. 18½ cm.
On the suffrage troubles in Rhode Island with reference to Dorr's Rebellion.
There is no title-page.
K8100 — Dorr's Rebellion, 1842.

NK 0202596 MB NN MH

Knight, [Nehemiah Rice], 1780-1854.
Gov. Knight's address to the farmers of Rhode Island [on his own political record, the West India trade, the Indians, etc.]. October, 1832. Providence: Cranston & Hammond [1832]. 15 p. 8°.
1. United States.—Politics, 1832. 2. Indians (N. A.), U. S., 1832.
N. Y. P. L. December 11, 1913.

NK 0202597 NN MBH MH MB MH-BA RPB

Knight, Nehemiah Rice, 1780-1854.
Speech ... on the Resolution to restore the duty on umbrellas and parasols, in Senate United States, March 11, 1840. [Washington, 1840]
9 p. 24 cm.

NK 0202599 RPB NN

Knight, Neil Roy.
Gold horizon; the life story of Manson F. Backus, forty-five years a banker in the Pacific Northwest, by N. R. Knight; with an introduction by Emmanell Backus Braddy. Seattle, F. McCaffrey at the Dogwood press, 1937.
8 p. l., 23-222 p. front., ports. 24½cm.
1. Backus, Manson Franklin, 1853-1935. I. Title.
Library of Congress HG2463.B3K55 37-11681
——— Copy 2.
Copyright A 105901 [3] 923.373

NK 0202600 ICU WaSp WaS MtBuM WaWW CaBVaU CaBVa OrCS Or OrHi DLC WaTC Wa OrP MtU WaT IdB IdU MtBC OrPR

*EC65 K7464 675c
Knight, Nicholas, fl.1675-1677.
A comparison between the trve and false ministers in their calling, lives and doctrine, that all who desire after the Lord may have a right discerning between the true and false, that they may truly know wh[om] to hear, and what church to be gathered into, and wherein to have true communion with Christ, the head of his church. And also a faithfvl warning to the teachers and people of England. By Nicholas Knight ...
[London] Printed in the year 1675.
22p. 18.5cm.
Imperfect: t.-p., p.17-22 mutilated.
Against a paid clergy.

NK 0202602 MH CLU-C PSC-Hi PHC PHi

*EC65 K7464 677s
Knight, Nicholas, fl.1675-1677.
Something concerning the mystery of godliness and something concerniug [!] the mystery of iniquity. By Nicholas Knight.
[London? 1677]
8p. 19cm.
Caption title.
Dated at end: The 19th of the 12th moneth, 1676.

NK 0202603 MH PHC

Knight, Nicholas, fl. 1675-1677.
True and false ministers. Printed, 1675.

NK 0202604 PSC-Hi

Knight, Nicholas, 1861–
A course in quantitative chemical analysis; gravimetric and volumetric, by Nicholas Knight ... New York, A. S. Barnes and company, 1899.
x, 110 p. 18cm.
1. Chemistry, Analytic—Quantitative.
Library of Congress QD101.K71 99—4666

NK 0202605 DLC OCU

Knight, Nicholas, 1861–
A course in quantitative chemical analysis, gravimetric and volumetric, by Nicholas Knight ... Rev. ed. New York and Chicago, The A. S. Barnes company, 1915.
vii, 153 p. 19cm. $1.25
1. Chemistry, Analytic—Quantitative.
Library of Congress QD101.K71 1915 15-15455

NK 0202606 DLC ICJ

Knight, Norma.
Oh Cynthia! By Norma Knight. Indianapolis, The Bobbs-Merrill company [°1932]
317 p. 19½cm.
"First edition."
I. Title.
Library of Congress PZ3.K7460h 32-22559

NK 0202607 DLC Or MB

Knight, Norman, *comp.*
Chess pieces; an anthology in prose and verse, compiled with commentary by Norman Knight, with a foreword by Sir George Thomas, bart. Decorations by Glades Gibberd. London, Low, Marston [1949]
xviii, 315 p. illus. 21 cm.
Corrigenda slip inserted.
1. Chess. I. Title.
GV1447.K53 794.1 50—20158

NK 0202608 DLC UU NN CSt OCl WaS OrU

Knight, Norman L
Crisis in Utopia

see under

Greenberg, Martin, 1918- ed.
The crucible of power.

VOLUME 300

Knight, Norman Victor, ed.

TK6162 .P82 1946

FOR OTHER EDITIONS SEE MAIN ENTRY

Poole, Joseph.
The telephone handbook; being the 8th ed. of the Practical telephone handbook. Completely rev. by N. V. Knight and W. Prickett. London, I. Pitman, 1946.

NK 0202610 ...

Knight, Norton Burtrum, 1911-
The interaction of positive and negative motivation i problem solving: an evaluation of theories of excitatio value, tension reduction and frustration. Ann Arbor, Uni versity Microfilms, 1950.
(University Microfilms, Ann Arbor, Mich. Publication no. 1981)
Microfilm copy of typewritten ms. Positive.
Collation of the original: ii, 58 l. diagrs.
Thesis—University of Michigan.
Abstracted in Microfilm abstracts, v. 10 (1950) no. 4, p. 298-300.
Bibliography: leaves [56]-58.
1. Motivation (Psychology)
Microfilm AC-1 no. 1981 Mic A 50-450
Michigan. Univ. Libr. for Library of Congress [1]†

NK 0202611 MiU DLC

Knight, O M.
Lecture on the antiquity of freemasonry. Delivered by O. M. Knight, before the fraternity in Portsmouth, N. H. ... Boston, A. J. Cummings & co., printers, 1881.
15 p. 23½cm.
1. Freemasons. 2. Mysteries (Religious)
Library of Congress HS491.K7 (Copyright 1881: 19695) 9-27895†

NK 0202612 DLC

Knight, Oliver.
Fort Worth, outpost on the Trinity. [1st ed.] Norman, University of Oklahoma Press [1953]
xiii, 302 p. illus., ports., maps. 22 cm.
Bibliography: p. 279-282.
1. Fort Worth, Tex.—Hist.
F394.F7K5 976.4 53-8817

NK 0202613 TxU ViU MB NN OU AU WaS CaBViP WaT CLSU OKentU DLC Or OrU OOxM OCl OFH PU PPT NcD PP

Knight, Oliver Browning, 1901-
... An economic comparison of developments in the South field oil-producing region of Mexico, by Oliver B. Knight ... New York, American institute of mining and metallurgical engineers, inc., °1930.
7 p. tab. 23cm. (American institute of mining and metallurgical engineers. Technical publication no. 343. Class G, Petroleum and gas, no. 32)
1. Petroleum—Mexico. I. Title.
Library, U. S. Patent Office TN1.A49
Library of Congress [TN1.A525 no. 343] P O 30-164

NK 0202614 DP

Knight, Ora Willis, 1874-1913.
The birds of Maine; with key to and description of the various species known to occur or to have occurred in the state, an account of their distribution and migration, showing their relative abundance in the various counties of the state as well as other regions, and contributions to their life histories, by Ora Willis Knight ... [Subscription ed.] Bangor, Me. [Printed by C. H. Glass & co.] 1908.
xvii, [19]-693 p. front. (map) plates. 24cm.
"The Subscription edition of this book is three hundred copies." This is copy no. 299.
Bibliography: p. [663]-671.
1. Birds—Maine.
Library of Congress QL684.M2K6 8-28289

NK 0202615 MB DLC CU FMU DI ICF-A MeB MiU OO PPAN ICJ

Knight, Ora Willis, 1874-1913.
... A list of the birds of Maine, showing their distribution by counties and their status in each county. Prepared under the auspices of the United ornithologists of Maine by Ora W. Knight ... Augusta, Kennebec journal print, 1897.
184 p. 23cm. (Bulletin no. 3. The University of Maine. Department of natural history)
1. Birds—Maine. I. United ornithologists of Maine.
A 15-405
Title from Bangor Pub. Libr. Printed by L. C.

NK 0202616 MeBa MtU MU CU ICF-A OCl OU MB ICJ

Knight, Oscar Allen, joint author.
Rawdon, Henry S, 1880-
... Comparative properties of wrought iron made by hand puddling and by the Aston process, by Henry S. Rawdon and O. A. Knight ...
(R P 124, *in* U. S. Bureau of standards. Bureau of standards journal of research. Washington, U. S. Govt. print. off., 1929. 23½cm. December, 1929, v. 3, no. 6, p. 953-992 incl. illus., tables, diagrs. plates)

NK 0202617 ...

Knight, Otis Dewey, 1898-
The rose of the figure-ground relation in perceiving & memorizing visual forms ... Columbus The O. state univ., 1936.
392 . numb. l.
Thesis (Ph.D.) - O. state univ.

NK 0202618 OU

DA 990 .E7 K7

Knight, P
Erris in the "Irish Highlands," and the "Atlantic railway." ... Dublin, M.Keene and son; London, Longman, Rees, Orme, Brown, Green, & co., 1836.
vii, 178 p. illus., fold. maps. 19 cm.
1. Erris, Ire. 2. Railroads--Ireland. I. Title: Atlantic railway.

NK 0202619 MiU ICN IU MH-BA NjP

Slavery E 441 M46 v.180 no.7

Knight, P
Human rights, and the way to protect them. A tract for the people, by P. Knight. Cortland, N.Y., Printed by Stedman & Clisbe, 1847.
16 p. 20cm.
May anti-slavery pamphlets, v. 180.

NK 0202620 NIC

Knight, Patrick E.
String-lining of railway curves, by P. E. Knight ... London, The Railway gazette, 1938.
viii, 117 p. incl. 1 illus., tables, diagrs. 22½cm.
Bibliography included in "Author's preface" (p. viii)
1. Railroads—Curves and turnouts. I. Title.
Library of Congress TF216.K55 [2] 39-22318 625.11

NK 0202621 DLC IU

QL 463 .K 67

Knight, Paul, 1899-
The problems of insect study [by] Paul Knight .. Ann Arbor, Mich., Edwards brothers, inc., 1933.
3 p.l., 118 numb. l. illus., plates, 2 maps on 1 l., diagr. 27.5 cm.
Lithoprinted.

NK 0202622 DLC OrCS

Knight, Paul, 1899-
The problems of insect study, by Paul Knight ... 2d ed. Ann Arbor, Michigan, Edwards brothers, inc., 1939.
vii, 132 p. illus., plates, maps, diagrs. 27½cm.
"Lithoprinted."
"The literature of entomology": p. 119-121.
1. Insects, Injurious and beneficial. 2. Agricultural pests. I. Title: Insect study.

NK 0202623 ViU DNAL NIC MiU

Knight, Paul S
The upper room of God's house. Boston, Christopher Pub. House [1951]
213 p. 21 cm.
1. Bible. N. T. Revelation—Criticism, interpretation, etc. I. Title.
BS2825.K67 228 51-9519

NK 0202624 DLC

WM K69o 1829

KNIGHT, Paul Slade.
Beobachtungen über die Ursachen, Symptome und Behandlung des Irrseyns ... Aus dem Englischen übers. von Friedr. Engelken. Köln, Schmitz, 1829.
xvi, 156 p. WM K69o
Translation of Observations on the causes, symptoms, and treatment of derangement of mind.

NK 0202625 DNLM MH IaU ICJ

Knight, Paul Slade.
Observations on the causes, symptoms, and treatment of derangement of the mind, founded on an extensive moral and medical practice in the treatment of lunatics. By Paul Slade Knight ... Together with the particulars of the sensations and ideas of a gentleman during his mental alienation, written by himself during his convalescence. London, Longman, Rees, Orme, Brown, and Green; [etc., etc.] 1827.
viii, 167 p. illus., 2 pl., fold. tab. 22 cm.
1. Psychiatry—Early works to 1900.
RC340.K6 7-34129
——— Copy 2. [Medical pamphlets, v. 3, no. 3] R111.M5 vol. 3, no. 3

NK 0202626 DNLM KyU PPPH DLC

Knight, Pearle Ethel, 1886-
Develop your reading, by Pearle E. Knight ... and Arthur E. Traxler ... Boston, Little, Brown and company, 1941.
vii p., 2 l., [3]-376 p., 1 l. incl. front., illus. 21cm.
"An Atlantic monthly press book."
"Books you will enjoy": p. 42-46.
1. Reading. 2. Readers and speakers—1870- I. Traxler, Arthur Edwin, 1900- joint author. II. Title.
41-4958 Revised
Library of Congress PE1121.K63 [r45g3] 820.822

NK 0202627 DLC WaU Or OrU ViU PU PPPL OU

Knight, Pearle Ethel, 1886- ed.
In America, a literary view of our country, by Pearle Ethel Knight ... and Harry G. Paul ... Drawings by Ernest King. New York, Chicago, Mentzer, Bush & company [1942]
xvi, 1197 p. front., illus. (incl. ports.) diagrs. 23cm.
Illustrated lining-papers.
Includes bibliographies.
1. American literature (Collections) 2. U. S.—Civilization. I. Paul, Harry Gilbert, 1874- joint ed. II. Title.
Library of Congress PS507.K6 [5] 42-3404 810.822

NK 0202628 DLC OrCS

VOLUME 300

Knight, Pearle Ethel, 1886-
Read and comprehend, by Pearle E. Knight ... and Arthur E. Traxler ... Boston, Little, Brown and company, 1937.
ix, 233 p. 24cm.

1. Reading, Psychology of. I. Traxler, Arthur Edwin, 1900- joint author. II. Title.
37-12679 Revised
Library of Congress BF456.R2K6
[r43d5] [159.9464] 158.84

NK 0202629 DLC WaS OrU Wa PU-Penn OCl OLak OCU OClW OEac

Knight, Pearle Ethel, 1886-
Read and comprehend, by Pearle E. Knight and Arthur E. Traxler. Rev. [Boston] D. C. Heath [1949]
xiv, 298 p. illus. 22 cm.

1. Reading, Psychology of. I. Traxler, Arthur Edwin, 1900- joint author. II. Title.
BF456.R2K6 1949 158.84 49-1300*

NK 0202630 DLC MtU OrCS ViU NIC MH PU OU MB ICU OrPR OrP

Knight, Percival.
Detective Keen, a play in one act. [n. p., n. d.] 23 l. 28cm.
Typescript.

1. Drama, American. 2. Drama—Promptbooks and Typescripts, One-act. I. Title.

NK 0202631 NN

Knight, Percival.
... Detective Keen; a play in one act, by Percival Knight ... Washington, Commission on training camp activities, Department of dramatic activities among the soldiers, 1918.
20 p. 17cm.
At head of title: War department service edition, number 14.

I. Title. 19-1739
Library of Congress PS634.U5 no. 14
——— Copy 2. PS3521.N54D4 1918

NK 0202632 DLC ViU OCl OO

Knight, Percival.
"Thin ice," by Percival Knight ... [New York, 1922] 32, 30, 31 f. 29cm.
Prompt-book, typewritten; original cast, light, and property plot, included. First New York production at the Comedy theatre, Oct. 1, 1922.

144653B. 1. Drama, American. 2. Prompt-books. I. Title.
N. Y. P. L. March 31, 1942

NK 0202633 NN

KNIGHT, PERCY HENRY.
Induction curves of commercial American irons... by Percy H. Knight and George W. Bacon. [Ithaca?] 1892. 77 l. tables, 13 fold. charts. 28cm.

Thesis--Sibley college, Cornell university.

1. Iron--Magnetic properties. I. Bacon, George Wood, joint author. t. 1892.

NK 0202634 NN

Knight, Perry G.
A guide for the home-domestick manufacturer, containing some useful observations on the most essential points of manufacturing woollen goods ... Providence, 1821.
12 p. 23 cm.
Cover-title.

NK 0202635 RPB

Knight, Peter.
The 59th division; its war story. Published for the 59th (Staffordshire) infantry division reunion organisation on the 6th June, 1954-the tenth anniversary of "D" day. [London] F. Muller [1954]
110 p. illus., maps. 20cm.

1. World war, 1939-1945--Regt. hist.--Gt. Br.--59th (Staffordshire) infantry division. 2. World war, 1939-1945--Campaigns--France, 1944-1945.

NK 0202636 NN

F336.2
K71s
Knight, Peter Oliphant, 1865-1946.
Statement[s] of Peter O. Knight, of Tampa, Florida, with reference to the so-called taxation situation. [n.p., 193-?]
4 pts. in 1 v. 28cm.

"For immediate release."

1. Taxation - Florida.

NK 0202637 FU

Knight, Peter Oliphant, 1865-1946.
There is one mistake we must not make; an address delivered by Peter O. Knight...at the joint annual convention of the American hardware manufacturers' association and the Southern hardware jobbers' association held in New Orleans, Louisiana, April 8, 1924. Tampa, Fla.: Tribune pub. co. [1924] 34 p. 23cm.

1. United States—For. rel.
N. Y. P. L. August 23, 1940

NK 0202638 NN

Knight, Phillipina (Deane) *lady*, 1726 *or* 7-1799.
Lady Knight's letters from France and Italy, 1776-1795, ed. by Lady Eliott-Drake. London, A. L. Humphreys, 1905.
xii, 229 p. plates, ports., geneal. table. 24 cm.
The letters are addressed to Mrs. Drake.

1. France—Descr. & trav. 2. Italy—Descr. & trav. I. Fuller-Eliott-Drake, Elizabeth (Douglas) lady, ed. II. Drake, Elizabeth (Heathcote) d. 1797.
D917.K6 48-42322*

NK 0202639 DLC CaBVaU PPL MH MB NcD CtY TxU NcD ViU

*265.8
K74b
KNIGHT, Plutarck S
Burial service to be used at the grave after service at the church or home. Salem [Author] n.d.
[4] p.

NK 0202640 Or

SPECIAL COLL.
G
1900
K846
Knight, Plutarck S
The boy who will never come. [Forest Grove, Ore., 1900?]
broadside. 27 x 17 cm.

"Supplement to the Forest Grove Times," at head of title.

NK 0202641 OrU

Knight, Plutark S
The Comforter; Scriptural selections for use at burials. With hints to encourage the bereaved. Arranged and printed for private use by P. S. Knight. Salem, Or., 1889.
79 p. 22cm.

1. Funeral service. I. Title.
43-48876
Library of Congress BV199.F8K55

NK 0202642 DLC OrHi OrU

Ujf31
885k
Knight, R
The "practical" boiler-maker, iron-ship builder and mast maker ... 3d ed. London, Wyman & sons[1885]
vi,151,[4]p. diagrs. 19cm. (Wyman's technical series)

NK 0202643 CtY MiD

Knight, R.
The "practical" boiler-maker, iron-ship builder and mast maker, containing much useful information on the subjects named; also, template making in general, and is specially valuable to all workmen in the iron trade. By R. Knight ... 8th ed. Newcastle-on-Tyne, R. Robinson & co., ltd. [189-]
160 p. incl. tables. diagrs. 18½cm.
Pages 159-160, "Opinions of the press."

1. Ships, Iron and steel. 2. Steam-boilers, Marine. 3. Masts and rigging. I. Title.
41-40792
Library of Congress VM146.K55

NK 0202644 DLC

Knight, R.R.
New year's promise; sermon ...
n.p., [1905]

NK 0202645 NjP

Knight, R.R.
Ultimate authority in moral truth.
n.p., [1912]

NK 0202646 NjP

Knight, R T.
Connection of gales of wind and appearance of the aurora. By R. T. Knight ...
(*In* Smithsonian institution. Annual report. 1871. Washington, 1873. 23½cm. p. 461-462)

1. Auroras.
S 15-330 f
Library of Congress Q11.S66 1871
Library, Smithsonian Institution

NK 0202647 DSI DLC

Knight, Rachel, 1878-1921.
The founder of Quakerism; a psychological study of the mysticism of George Fox, by Rachel Knight, PH. D. London, The Swarthmore press ltd. [1922]
280 p. front., port., diagrs. 22½cm.
"Written as a thesis for the degree of doctor of philosophy at the University of Iowa [1919]"
Bibliography: p. 278-280.
"Introductory note" on the author, by A. Barratt Brown: p. 5-6.

1. Fox, George, 1624-1691.
23-7569
Library of Congress BX7795.F7K5

NK 0202648 DLC WaU NcD DFo CtY PU PHC PSC PPA PPFr OO NjP NN

VOLUME 300

Knight, Rachel, 1878–1921.
The founder of Quakerism; a psychological study of the mysticism of George Fox, by Rachel Knight, PH. D. New York, George H. Doran company, 1923.
280 p. 2 port. (incl. front.) diagrs. 22½cm.
Printed in Great Britain.
"Written as a thesis for the degree of doctor of philosophy at the University of Iowa."
Bibliography: p. 278–280.
1. Fox, George, 1624–1691. I. Title.
Library of Congress BX7795.F7K5 1923 23–8487
NK 0202649 DLC PSC-Hi PPFr PP

ND1265 .B32 Knight, Rachel Theodosia (Gribble) 1869– tr.
Bahr, Hermann, 1863–1934.
Expressionism, by Hermann Bahr; translated by R. T. Gribble. London, F. Henderson [1925]

BL1453 .S35 Knight, Rachel Theodosia (Gribble) 18[illegible]– tr.
Schayer, Stanisław, 1899–
Mahāyāna doctrines of salvation, by Dr. Stanislav Schayer, translated from the German by R. T. Knight. London, Probsthain & co., 1923.

DS793 .M7S7 Knight, Rachel Theodosia (Gribble) 1869– tr.
Strasser, Roland, 1886–
The Mongolian horde, by Roland Strasser; translated from the German by 'R. T. G.' With an introduction by Sir Michael Sadler ... London, Toronto, J. Cape; New York, J. Cape & H. Smith [1930]

PK4474 .A3A6 **Knight, Rachel Theodosia (Gribble) 1869–** tr.
Althaus, Peter Paul, 1892–1965, *tr.*
Mystic lyrics from the Indian middle ages, a free transcription. Rendered into English by R. T. Gribble. London, G. Allen & Unwin [1928]

Knight, Ray.
Where is thy sting? By R. Knight ... London, Authorpartner press, ltd., 1935.
139 p., 1 l. 19cm.
1. Immortality. 2. Philosophy and religion. I. Title.
Library of Congress BL500.K6 1935 36–467
Copyright A ad int. 20[illegible]4 [2] 218
NK 0202654 DLC CtY

[**Knight, Ray Roberts**] 1881–
Knight family; [also] Albertson, Bennett, Gardner, Harding, Schultz, Thorn [and] Wisner [families. Minneapolis 1952?]
1 v. 28 cm.
1. Knight family (Walter Knight, fl. 1625) 2. U. S.—Geneal.
CS71.K725 1952 54–19893 ‡
NK 0202655 DLC NN N

[**Knight, Ray Roberts**] 1881–
Monfort [i. e. Montfort] family; [also] Ray and McChesney families. [Minneapolis, 195–?]
10 l. 28 cm.
1. Montfort family.
CS71.M78 1951 54–19888 ‡
NK 0202656 DLC NN N

[**Knight, Ray Roberts**] 1881–
Morris family; [also] Arnold, Barrett, Clark, Hill, Keaton, Nicholson, Page, Pool, Pritchard, Prather, Shattuck, Symons [and] White [families. Minneapolis, 1952?]
7 l. 28 cm.
1. Morris family (John Morris, fl. 1660) 2. U. S.—Geneal.
CS71.M876 1952 54–19889
NK 0202657 DLC NN

---

q929.2 M876k Sutro Knight, Ray Roberts, 1881–
Morris family [and collateral lines] White, Nicholson, Symons, Pritchard, Hill, Keaton, Page, Shattuck, Arnold, Scott, Clark, Barrett and Prather. [Minneapolis? n. d.]
7 l. illus. 29cm.
Reproduced from typewritten copy.
NK 0202658 C

[**Knight, Ray Roberts**] 1881–
Roberts and Mitchell families. [Minneapolis, 1953]
6, 2 l. 28 cm.
1. Roberts family. 2. Mitchell family. I. Title.
CS71.R64 1953 54–19890 ‡
NK 0202659 DLC NN

Knight, Raymond.
"The critic's circle;" a sketch for the Lambs spring gambol, by Raymond Knight. [New York, 1943] 12 f. 28cm.
1. Drama, American. I. Title.
N. Y. P. L. March 27, 1945
NK 0202660 NN

Knight, Raymond.
Strings; a romantic comedy, by Raymond Knight. (In: Goin' home and other plays of the 1927 contest. New York, 1928. 8°. p. 197–217.)
In one act.
405250A. 1. Drama, American. 2. Title.
N. Y. P. L. August 19, 192[illegible]
NK 0202661 NN OCl OOxM

QA39 .R525 **Knight, Raymond M., joint author.**
Rice, Harold S
Technical mathematics [by] Harold S. Rice and Raymond M. Knight. New York, McGraw-Hill, 1954.

Knight, Reginald Anthony Geoffrey, 1904–
Adhesives for wood. London, Chapman & Hall, 1952.
xi, 242 p. illus., diagrs., tables. (A series of monographs on metallic & other materials published under the authority of the Royal Aeronautical Society, v. 3)
Includes bibliographies.
NK 0202663 NNC MiU NcU ICJ N MB CU NN LU NcRS DNAL CU TxU

Knight, Reginald Anthony Geoffrey, 1904–
Adhesives for wood. New York, Chemical Pub. Co., 1952.
242 p. illus. 23 cm.
1. Adhesives. 2. Wood. 3. Woodworking industries. I. Title.
TP968.K6 668.3 52—13923 ‡
NK 0202664 DLC Wa OClW OCl MiHM PU-Sc PSt OU OrCS IU CaBViP WaE CaBVa CaBVaU WaS IdU WaT MtU OrP

Knight, Reginald Anthony Geoffrey, 1904– 634.9 16 v.14
... The determination of moisture content of timber, by R. A. G. Knight ... London, H. M. Stationery Off., 1932.
iv, 11 p. diagrs. 24½cm. ([Great Britain] Department of Scientific and Industrial Research. Forest Products Research. Bulletin no. 14)
NK 0202665 ICJ

Knight, Reginald Anthony Geoffrey, 1904–
Manual for conducting trials
see under
Princes Risborough, Eng. Forest Products Research Laboratory.

TA420 .K6 1939 Knight, Reginald Anthony Geoffrey, 1904–
Moisture content determination... 2d ed., 1939 (Gt. Brit. Dept. of scientific and industrial research. Forest products research board. Bull. no.14 [a])
NK 0202667 DLC

Knight, Reginald Anthony Geoffrey, 1904– 16 v.20
Requirements and properties of adhesives for wood. London, H. M. Stationery Off., 1946.
vi, 26 p. ([Gt. Brit.] Dept. of Scientific and Industrial Research. Forest Products Research Board. Bulletin, no. 20)
NK 0202668 ICJ MiHM

808.22 K744o **Knight, Reginald Frank Trinder.**
Our Lady's jester; a one-act play. London, I. Pitman [1952]
10 p.
Based on an ancient legend and on the story of the same name by Anatole France.
NK 0202669 MiD

Knight, Reginald Sydney Gilbert. *4028.145.7
The heat balance of a blast-furnace stove. Preliminary report on the heat balance of steel furnaces.
(In Iron and Steel Institute. Carnegie Scholarship Memoirs. Vol. 7, pp. 83–101. Plate. Plans. Charts. London. 1916.)
L1238 — Heat. — Blast-furnace.
NK 0202670 MB

VOLUME 300

Knight, Reginald Sydney Gilbert,

Kingscott, P C R.
Methods of quantitative organic analysis, by P. C. R. Kingscott ... and R. S. G. Knight ... With diagrams. London [etc.] Longmans, Green and co., 1914.

Knight, Rena Gertrude, joint author.

TA403 .K6 1948 **Knight, Bernard Howard.**
Builders' materials, by Bernard H. Knight and Rena G. Knight. [2d ed.] London, E. Arnold [1948]

Knight, Rena Gertrude, joint author.

TE200 .K6 1948 **Knight, Bernard Howard.**
Road aggregates, their uses and testing, by Bernard H. Knight and Rena G. Knight. [2d ed.] London, E. Arnold [1948]

Knight, Rex.
Intelligence and intelligence tests, by Rex Knight ... with two diagrams. London, Methuen & co. ltd. [1933]
ix, 98 p., 1 l. diagrs. 17½cm. (*Half-title:* Methuen's monographs on philosophy and psychology)

1. Intellect. 2. Mental tests. I. Title.
34-24481
Library of Congress BF431.K55
[3] [159.921] 151

NK 0202673 DLC WU-M NcD

Knight, Rex.
A modern introduction to psychology, by Rex Knight and Margaret Knight. London, University Tutorial Press [1949]
242 p. illus. 19 cm.
Includes bibliographies.

1. Psychology. I. Knight, Margaret Kennedy, 1903- joint author.
BF131.K65 150 50-31750

NK 0202674 DLC OKentU IEN IU MB RPB NjR LU

Knight, Rex.
A modern introduction to psychology, by Rex Knight and Margaret Knight. [2d ed.] London, University Tutorial Press [1951]
242 p. illus. 19 cm.

1. Psychology.
BF131.K65 1951 150 51-35583 ‡

NK 0202675 DLC

Knight, Rex.
A modern introduction to psychology, by Rex Knight and Margaret Knight. [4th ed.] London, University Tutorial Press [1954]
242 p. illus.

Includes bibliographies.

1. Psychology. I. Knight, Margaret jt. au. II. Title.

NK 0202676 NNC

Knight, Rex.
Wake up and sleep, by Rex Knight. Los Angeles: Kellaway-Ide co. [1938] [76] p. 18cm.
Various paging.
Issued in spiral binder.

1. New thought. 2. Sleep. I. Title.
N. Y. P. L. December 29, 1939

NK 0202677 NN

Knight, Rex, playwright
see Knight, Reginald Frank Trinder.

Knight, Reynolds.
Tommy of the voices, by Reynolds Knight. Chicago, A. C. McClurg & co., 1918.
5 p. l., 374 p. 20cm. $1.40

I. Title.
Library of Congress PZ3.K747T 18-17607

NK 0202679 DLC OCl

KNIGHT, RICHARD. Address read before the Horton and Cornwallis temperance societies... Hali., Cunnabell, 1846. 22 p. 21 cm.

NK 0202680 CaNSWA

KNIGHT, RICHARD.
A petition to the Congress of the United States for the redress of a grievance occasioned by the corruption of the United States Supreme court (as constituted on March 6, 1944). [New York?] 1945. 12 p. 23cm.

1. Certiorari. 2. United States. Courts: Supreme Court.

NK 0202681 NN

KNIGHT, Richard, of Morecambe.
Laughter in Court; a collection of witticisms of Bench and Bar and of amusing incidents pertaining to the Law & the Lawyers. London, n. d.

184 p.

NK 0202682 MH-L PU-L

Knight, Richard, *of New York.*
The haunted hat; a detective mystery, by Richard Knight. New York city, The Bell publishing company [1898]
cover-title, [3]-253 p. 18cm.
p. [243]-253, advertising matter.

I. Title.
Library of Congress ✱ PZ3 99-710 Revised

NK 0202683

BX6413 .K7 **Knight, Richard, 1771-1863.**
History of the General or Six principle Baptists, in Europe and America: in two parts. Pub. under the patronage of the Rhode-Island yearly meeting. By Richard Knight ... Providence, Smith and Parmenter, printers, 1827.
vii, [8]-367 p. 22cm.
"Errata" slip at end.

1. Baptists—Hist.

NK 0202684 ICU PPL KyLoS MnHi NBuG RPB MWA DLC MB MH IaU RP NcWsW

---

17 1896 K **Knight, Richard, 1771-1863.**
The old Baptist hymn book: By elders R. Knight and J. Tillinhast.
Providence, 1842.
304 p. 15cm.

NK 0202685 DLC RPB

[**Knight, Richard D**]
The better way. Providence, R. I., Westminster company, °1890.
3 p. l., xxiv numb. l. 7½ x 10cm.

I. Title.
Library of Congress PN6161.K57 12-14075

NK 0202686 DLC

Collection BL460 .K6 Knight, Richard Payne, 1750-1824.
An account of the remains of the worship of Priapus, lately existing at Isernia, in the kingdom of Naples: in two letters; one from Sir William Hamilton, K.B. ... to Sir Joseph Banks, bart. ... and the other from a person residing at Isernia: to which is added, a discourse on the worship of Priapus, and its connexion with the mystic theology of the ancients. By R. P. Knight, esq. London, Printed by T. Spilsbury, 1786.

1 p.l., [3]-195 p. illus. 11 plates. 28 cm.

1. Phallicism. 2. Priapus. I. Hamilton, Sir William, 1730-1803. II. Banks, Sir Joseph, 1743-1820.

NK 0202688 NcU MB MHi CtY NNC MH NNNAM

Lilly PR 3539 .K87 A8 KNIGHT, RICHARD PAYNE, 1750-1824.
Alfred; a romance in rhyme, by R. P. Knight ... London, Printed at the Columbian Press by Howlett and Brimmer, 1823.
210 p. 23.5 cm.

Bound in contemporary half calf.

NK 0202689 InU

Y 185 .K 741 KNIGHT, RICHARD PAYNE, 1750-1824.
Alfred; a romance in rhyme. London, Longman, Hurst, Rees, Orme, and Brown, 1823.
xxvii, 360p. 24cm.

NK 0202690 ICN CtY MH WU NjP MBAt

VOLUME 300

Knight, Richard Payne, 1750–1824.
An analytical essay on the Greek alphabet. By Richard Payne Knight ... London, Printed by J. Nichols for P. Elmsly, 1791.
vii, 137 p. xi (*i. e.* ix) pl., fold. tab. 30 x 24½cm.
Plate ix incorrectly numbered xi.

1. Greek language—Alphabet.

10-27401†

Library of Congress PA273.K7

NK 0202691 DLC MdBP NIC TxU CtY MiU PU PPL NN MA

Ex 3815 .97 .312 Knight, Richard Payne, 1750-1824.
An analytical inquiry into the principles of taste... London, Printed for T. Payne and J. White, by C. Mercier and Co., 1805
xxi p.,1 l.,471 p. 21 cm

1. AESTHETICS I. T

NcD DDO
NK 0202692 NjP NcU WaU MoU TxU CtY ViU NNC MH-A PU

N 75 K71 1805 Knight, Richard Payne, 1750-1824.
An analytical inquiry into the principles of taste. 2d ed. London, L. Hansard, 1805.
xxiv, 470 p. 22cm.

1. Aesthetics. I. Title.

NK 0202693 NIC TNJ MH CSmH MB ICN PU MA FU NcD

N 57 .K7 1806 Knight, Richard Payne, 1750-1824.
An analytical inquiry into the principles of taste. 3d ed. London, T. Payne, 1806.
xx,473p. 22cm.

1. Aesthetics. I. Title.

NK 0202694 TNJ NjP NN OO MB PU MdBP MH

Knight, Richard Payne, 1750-1824.
An analytical inquiry into the principles of taste. By Richard Payne Knight. The 4th ed. ... London, T. Payne [etc.] 1808.
xvi, 476 p. 22 cm.

1. Aesthetics. I. Title.

N75.K7 9-12471

TU WU KyLx
NK 0202695 DLC CU PP CtY NjP PPL CSmH I NNUT ViU

Knight, Richard Payne, 1750-1824, ed.
Homerus.
Carmina Homerica, Ilias et Odyssea, a rhapsodorum interpolationibus repurgata, et in pristinam formam, quatenus recuperanda esset, tam e veterum monumentorum fide et auctoritate, quam ex antiqui sermonis indole ac ratione, redacta; cum notis ac prolegomenis, in quibus de eorum origine, auctore, et ætate; itemque de priscæ linguæ progressu, et præcoci maturitate, diligenter inquiritur opera et studio Richardi Payne Knight. Londini, in ædibus Valpianis; [etc., etc.] 1820.

Zeta Myl425 K747 1866 Knight, Richard Payne, 1750-1824.
Le culte de Priape et ses rapports avec la théologie mystique des anciens; suivi d'un essai sur le culte des pouvoirs générateurs durant le moyen age. Traduits de l'anglais par E.W. Luxembourg, Impr. Particulière, 1866.
224 p. 40 plates. 23 cm.
"Du culte des pouvoirs générateurs" (p. [109]-221) has special t.p.

NK 0202697 CtY OCl

R.B.R. Knight, Richard Payne, 1750-1824.
Le culte de Priape et ses rapports avec la théologie mystique des anciens; suivi d'un essai sur le culte des pouvoirs générateurs durant le moyen age [par Thomas Wright] Traduits de l'anglais par E. W. Bruxelles, J. J. Gay, 1883.
xviii, 200 p. 40 plates. 24 cm.
Running titles: Du culte de Priape.-Du culte des pouvoirs générateurs.
Bibliographical footnotes.
1. Phallicism. 2. Priapus. I. Wright, Thomas, 1810-1877. II. Title.

NK 0202698 NcD

BL460 .K7 v.1 Knight, Richard Payne, 1750-1824.
A discourse on the worship of Priapus and its connection with the mystic theology of the ancients, to which is added an account of the remains of the worship of Priapus lately existing at Isernia in the Kingdom of Naples by Sir William Hamilton, K. B. London, Published by the Dilettanti Society, n.d.
217 p. (plates) 24 cm.
"Of this edition 625 copies have been made and numbered, this copy being number 197."

NK 0202699 IEG

HQ61 K74 1865 Knight, Richard Payne, 1750-1824.
A discourse on the worship of Priapus, and its connection with the mystic theology of the ancients. By Richard Payne Knight, esq. (A new edition). To which is added an essay On the worship of the generative powers during the middle ages of western Europe. London, Privately printed [Chiswick press] 1865.
xvi, 254 p. XL plates (1 double, 1 fold.), facsim. 22cm.

Facsim. of original t.-p.: An account of the remains of the worship of Priapus, lately existing at Isernia, in the kingdom of Naples: in two letters ... to which is added, A discourse on the worship of Priapus, and its connexion with the mystic theology of the ancients. By R. P. Knight, esq. London: Printed by T. Spilsbury. Snowhill. M. DCC. LXXXVI.
Half-title reads: Two essays on the worship of Priapus.

1. Phallicism. 2. Priapus. 3. Sex and religion.

MdBP CSt IEdS NcD DNLM WU DCU CoU
NK 0202702 NNC NN MH PPC PPDrop MA NRU RPB MiU CoU

KNIGHT, RICHARD PAYNE, 1750-1824.
A discourse on the worship of Priapus and its connection with the mystic theology of the ancients. A new ed., to which is added an essay On the worship of the generative powers during the Middle Ages of western Europe. London, Privat. print., 1865.
xvi, 254 p. illus. 23cm.
Microfilm.
Bibliographical footnotes.
1. Phallicism. 2. Priapus.

NK 0202703 NN

---

rBL460 K6 1894 Knight, Richard Payne, 1750-1824.
A discourse on the worship of Priapus, and its connection with the mystic theology of the ancients. (A new ed.) To which is added an essay On the worship of the generative powers during the Middle ages of western Europe. London, Privately printed [pref. 1894]
2 p.l., xvi p., 1 l., 254 p. 40 plates (incl. plan)

Half title: Two essays on the worship of Priapus.

A reprint, with added preface and correction of misprints, of the 1865 ed. published by J.C. Hotten.
Includes reproduction of original t.p., 1786: An account of the remains of the worship of Priapus.
The second essay by Thomas Wright.
Limited to 675 numbered copies. No.89.
Bibliographical footnotes.

NK 0202705 CU-A MiD NyU OU NjPT ICU WaU CLU-C NIC N

BL460 K6 1894 in Rare Books Room Knight, Richard Payne, 1750-1824.
A discourse on the worship of Priapus, and its connection with the mystic theology of the ancients. New ed. To which is added an essay On the worship of the generative powers during the Middle Ages of western Europe [by Thomas Wright] London, Privately printed, 1865 [London, C. Skilton, 1952]
facsim.: xvi, 254 p. 40 plates. 21cm.
Photographic reproduction of the 1894 ed., which, with the addition of a preface, was reprinted from the 1865 ed.
With reproduction of original t.p.: An account of the remains of the worship of Priapus ... to which is added, A discourse on the worship of Priapus, and its connexion with the mystic theology of the ancients London, Printed by T. Spilsbury, 1786.
Cover title: Two essays on the worship of Priapus.
1. Phallicism. 2. Priapus. I. Wright, Thomas, 1810-1877. The worship of the generative powers. III. Title.

NK 0202707 CoU NN KU

[Knight, Richard Payne] 1750-1824, supposed author.
Elegies and sonnets
see under Knight, Samuel, 1754?-1829.

Knight, Richard Payne, 1750-1824.
...Inquiry into the symbolical language of ancient art and mythology. London, 1818.

NK 0202709 MdBP CaBVaU PP NNNPsI

Knight, R[ichard] P[ayne], 1750-1824.
An inquiry into the symbolical language of ancient art and mythology. By R. P. Knight, 1818. Reprinted by the Society of Dilettanti. London: Payne and Foss, 1835. 2 p.l., 83(1) p. f°.

Bound with: Society of Dilettanti. Specimens of antient sculpture... London, 1835. f°. v. 2.

1. Art (Ancient). 2. Mythology (Ancient). 3. Symbolism. 4. Society of Dilettanti.
N. Y. P. L. May 31, 1913.

NK 0202710 NN NNC MH

Knight, Richard Payne, 1750–1824.
An inquiry into the symbolical language of ancient art and mythology, by R. P. Knight ... <Privately printed, 1818 ...> Reprinted and pub. by E. H. Barker ... London, Black and Armstrong, 1836.
iv, 78 p. 23cm.

1. Art, Ancient. 2. Mythology. 3. Symbolism. I. Title.

9—18913

Library of Congress N5333.K7

NK 0202711 DLC OCl OU NcD MoSW ViU PPL

VOLUME 300

Knight, Richard Payne, 1750-1824. An inquiry into the symbolical language of ancient art and mythology.
[Barker, Edmund Henry] 1788-1839, *comp.*
A collection of supplements to all editions of Lempriere's Classical dictionary, more especially to the enlarged one by Professor Anthon ... London, Printed by A. J. Valpy, 1837.

Knight, Richard Payne, 1750-1824.
The landscape, a didactic poem. In three books. Addressed to Uvedale Price, esq. by R. P. Knight. London, Printed by W. Bulmer & co. and sold by G. Nicol, 1794.
1 p. l., 77 p. III pl. (2 fold.) 27½ x 23cm.

1. Landscape gardening. I. Title.

12-37048

Library of Congress PR3539.K8A65 1794

NK 0202713 DLC NIC OOxM PU CtY InU PPL MiU DDO IaU NN MdBP M

In K747 806M **Knight, Richard Payne, 1750-1824.**
A monody on the death of the right honourable Charles James Fox. London, T. Payne, 1806-07.
15 p. 21 cm.

1. Fox, Charles James, 1749-1806 - Poetry.

NK 0202714 CtY

Knight, Richard Payne, 1750-1824.
[British museum. *Dept. of coins and medals*]
Nummi veteres, civitatum, regum, gentium, et provinciarum, Londini, in museo Richardi Payne Knight asservati, ab ipso ordine geographico descripti ... Londini, excudebat Gulielmus Nicol, 1830.

L821.6 K71l.2 Knight, Richard Payne, 1750-1824.
The landscape; a didactic poem. Addressed to Uvedale Price, esq. The 2d ed. London, W. Bulmer, 1795.
xv, 104p. 2 fold.pl. 30cm.

With this is bound the author's The progress of civil society. London, 1796.

NK 0202714-1 IEN MdBP ViW CU OrU OCU NN CtY NcD

PR3539 f.K8P9 1796 Knight, Richard Payne, 1750-1824.
The progress of civil society. A didactic poem, in six books. By Richard Payne Knight. London, Printed by W. Bulmer and co. for G. Nicol, 1796.
[1], 155 p. 31cm.

NK 0202715 ICU CtY DFo PPL IU MH NN NjP ICN InU NNC MA OCU RPB MWelC MdBJ NcD OCU IEN

PA4037 .K7 Knight, Richard Payne, 1750-1824.
Prolegomena ad Homerum, sive, De carminum homericorum origine, auctore et aetate, itemque de priscae linguae progressu et praecoci maturitate. Scripsit Richardus Payne Knight... rursus excudi iussit et paucula praefatus est d. Fr. Ern. Ruhkopf. Lipsiae, in libraria Hahnia, 1816.
vi, 194 p. 21cm.
Bibliographical foot-notes.
1. Homerus.

NK 0202716 ICU CtY MA RPB IU MH PU DLC OCU ViW OU NCH NIC

Knight, Richard Payne, 1750-1824.
The symbolical language of ancient art and mythology. An inquiry. By Richard Payne Knight ... A new ed. With introduction, additions, notes, translated into English, and a new and complete index. By Alexander Wilder, M. D. New York, J. W. Bouton, 1876.
xxvii, 240 p. 25cm.
Bibliographical foot-notes.

1. Mythology. 2. Symbolism. 3. Art, Ancient. I. Wilder, Alexander, 1823-1908, ed. II. Title.

A 19-480

St. Paul. Public library for Library of Congress BL313.K6 1876 [a39g1] 291

NK 0202717 MnS WaE OU MiU PPAN PU MiU OCH OCl OCU PPL DLC MB MH MiU NN OrP NBuU WU ICRL IEG ICN InAndC-T

KNIGHT, RICHARD PAYNE, 1750-1824.
The symbolical language of ancient art and mythology. An inquiry. A new edition; with introduction, additions, notes translated into English, and a new and complete index, by A. Wilder. New York, J. W. Bouton, 1876. xxvii, 240 p.

Film reproduction. Negative.
1. Art, Ancient. 2. Mythology. 3. Symbolism. I. Wilder, Alexander, 1823-1908, ed.

NK 0202718 NN

Knight, Richard Payne, 1750-1824.
The symbolical language of ancient art and mythology; an inquiry, by Richard Payne Knight ... New ed., with introduction, additions, notes translated into English and a new and complete index, by Alexander Wilder, M. D. With 348 illustrations by A. L. Rawson. New York, J. W. Bouton, 1892.
xxvii, [1], 452 p. front., illus., plates. 25cm. (*Half-title:* Bouton's archaic library, vol. II)

1. Mythology. 2. Symbolism. 3. Art, Ancient. I. Wilder, Alexander, 1823-1908, ed. II. Title.

31-48

Library of Congress BL313.K6 1892 [a40c1] 291

NK 0202719 DLC OrP TxU NcD ICU MoU PWcS NjP MoSW

Knight, Richmond, *pseud.*
see
Owens, William Thomas, 1903-

Knight, Robert.
A critical commentary on the Epistle of St. Paul, the apostle to the Romans. By Robert Knight ... London, S. Bagster and sons; [etc., etc.] 1854.
xx, 640 p. 23cm.
"Paraphrase on St. Paul's Epistle to the Romans": p. [603]-640.

1. Bible. N. T. Romans—Commentaries. 2. Bible—Commentaries—N. T. Romans. I. Bible. N. T. Romans. English. Paraphrases. 1854. II. Bible. English. Paraphrases. N. T. Romans. 1854.

40-2739

Library of Congress BS2665.K5 [2] 227.1

NK 0202721 DLC NjNbS ODW MH CtW IU

Knight, Robert
Doctrine of Scriptural predestination, briefly stated and considered ... London, 1854.

NK 0202722 NjNbS

Knight, Robert, M. W. S. E.
The location of the Chicago portage route of the seventeenth century; a paper read before the Chicago historical society, May 1, 1923, and later elaborated for publication, by Robert Knight, M. W. S. E. and Lucius H. Zeuch, M. D. Chicago, Ill., Chicago historical society, 1928.
xix, 98 (*i. e.* 99) p., 99-128 numb. l., 130-145 p. incl. front., plates, maps (1 double) facsims., fold. plans. 23½cm. (*Half-title:* Chicago historical society's collection, vol. XII)
Bibliography: p. 130-136.
1. Portages—Illinois—Chicago. 2. Chicago River—Surveys. 3. Chicago—Hist. 4. Physical geography—Illinois—Chicago. I. Zeuch, Lucius Henry P., 1874- joint author. II. Title. III. Title: The Chicago portage route of the seventeenth century.

28-17279

Library of Congress F548.1.C4
——— Copy 2. F548.4.K63

NK 0202723 DLC CU PHi ICHi

Knight, Robert, fl. 1728.
The nature and obligation of relative holiness. A sermon [on Heb.xii.28] preach'd in the cathedral-church of St. Peter in York, on Sunday, November the 17th, 1728 ... York, Printed by T. Gent, for F. Hildyard and sold by J. Osborn [etc.] [1728?]
[8], 40 p. 20cm.

NK 0202724 CLU-C

Knight, Robert, d. 1890.
India: a review of England's financial relations therewith. London, W.J. Johnson, 1868.
58p. 21cm.

"This paper was read... before the East India Association."

NK 0202725 IEN

Knight, Robert, d. 1890.
The Indian national congress; its aims and justification ... By Robert Knight. Calcutta, The "Statesman" office, 1898.
2 p. l., 23 p. 20½cm.
A reprint of certain articles on the subject in the "Statesman and friend of India."

1. Indian national congress. 2. India—Pol. & govt.—1765-

8-13536

Library of Congress JQ215 1898a

NK 0202726 DLC

HC 435 .K72 Knight, Robert, d. 1890
Sir George Couper, and the famine in the North-West Provinces. Calcutta, Statesman's Office, 1878.
64 p. 20 cm.
"Being a revised reprint of certain letters and articles in the Statesman and Friend of India.
Mich.Univ.copy imperfect: many leaves mutilated, none in perfect condition.
With the author's Speech on Indian affairs.
1. Couper, Sir George Ebenezer Wilson, bart., 1824-1908. 2. India--Famines

NK 0202727 MiU

HC 435 .K72 Knight, Robert, d. 1890
Speech on Indian affairs, delivered before the Manchester Chamber of Commerce, on the 24th January, 1866. London, W.J.Johnson, 1866.
63 p. 20 cm.
With this is bound the author's Sir George Couper and the famine in the North-West Provinces.

1. India--Econ.condit.

NK 0202728 MiU

Tzz 976.409 K747s **Knight, Robert Edward Lee.**
Speech delivered before the meeting of Governor William P. Hobby's friends at the Oriental Hotel, Dallas, Texas, January 19th, 1918, held for the purpose of launching his campaign for governor of Texas. [Houston, Tex., 1918]
11p. port. 23cm.

1. Campaign literature, 1918 - Democratic - Texas. 2. Hobby, William Pettus, 1878-

NK 0202729 TxU

VOLUME 300

Div.S. Knight, Robert J
Pam.
Coll. All Saints' Church, Derby. A brief sketch. London, Bemrose and Sons [1879]
1800 15 p. illus. 19 cm.

1. Derby, Eng. All Saints' Church.

NK 0202730 NcD

Z5701
.K5 Knight, Robert L 1907-
Abstract bibliography of cotton breeding and genetics 1900-1950, by R. L. Knight. Cambridge, Eng. [Pref.1954]
256 p. 24 cm. (Technical communication of the Commonwealth Bureau of Plant Breeding and Genetics. 17)

1. Gossypium - Bibl. it. ii.t: Cotton breeding and genetics. iii.s.

NK 0202731 CaBVaU NNBG ICJ NNC MsSM NcD TU KMK ICU LU

Knight, Robert L 1907-
Agricultural science in the Sudan; a bibliography with abstracts, by R. L. Knight and B. M. Boyns. Arbroath, T. Buncle, 1950.
251 p. 22 cm.

1. Agriculture—Sudan—Bibl. 2. Agriculture—Sudan—Abstracts. I. Boyns, B. M., joint author. II. Title.

Z5075.S78K55 016.63 53-18396

NK 0202732 DLC CU NIC MH NN MB IEN TU ICJ DNAL CSt-H

Knight, Robert L 1907-
Dictionary of genetics, including terms used in cytology, animal breeding and evolution. [1st ed.] Waltham, Mass., Chronica Botanica Co., 1948.
183 p. illus., port. 24 cm. (Lotsya, a biological miscellany, v. 2)
Bibliography: p. [179]-183.

1. Genetics—Dictionaries. (Series)

QH13.K5 575.103 48-9468*

NK 0202733 PSt MoU CaBVaU IdU MtU OrCS OrP MtBC OrU WaWW KEmT OClW OOxM Mi PP PPLas DNLM CU OCl MiEM PPT PU DLC MB PPAN ICJ NcU OClU TxU ViU MiD Mil'

Knight, Robert L 1907-
The distribution of wild species of Gossypium in the Sudan. London, 1951.
cover-title, 8 p. diagrs. (Empire cotton growing corporation. Research memoir no. 10)

"Reprinted from 'The Empire cotton growing review', Vol. XXVI., no. 4, 1949."
"References": p. 8.

NK 0202734 NNC

Knight, Robert P., 1902-
Behavior problems and habit disturbances in pre-adolescent children: their meaning and management. [n.p.], 1944.
188-189 p. 28 cm.
"Reprinted from Bulletin of the Menninger clinic, vol. 8, no. 6, November 1944."

NK 0202735 PPT

Knight, Robert P., 1902-
A critique of the present status of the psychotherapies.
(Reprinted from Bulletin of the New York Academy of medicine, February 1949, second series, vol. 25, no. 2, p. 100-114)

NK 0202736 PU-PSW

RC372
.A1A53
1946
Knight, Robert P., 1902-
American Psychopathological Association. *Meeting. 36th, New York, 1946.*
Epilepsy; psychiatric aspects of convulsive disorders. Proceedings. Edited by Paul H. Hoch and Robert P. Knight. New York, Grune & Stratton, 1947.

RC501
.A8
Knight, Robert P., 1902- ed.
Austen Riggs Center for the Study and Treatment of the Neuroses, *Stockbridge, Mass.*
Psychoanalytic psychiatry and psychology; clinical and theoretical papers. v. 1-
New York, International Universities Press [1954-

KNIGHT, Robert T
Bookkeeping.
Seattle. Western institute pr. c1930. v.p.

40 lectures, with questions on each lecture.

NK 0202739 WaS

Knight, Robert T
... The cash journal system of bookkeeping and accounting, by Robert T. Knight ... [Seattle, The Western institute press] 1932 [c1929]
230 p. 23½cm. (Accounting students' series)

NK 0202740 Wa

Knight, Robert Wilson, 1897-
Development of a flight level indicator, by Robert W. Knight and George L. Pigman. Washington, U. S. Dept. of Commerce, Civil Aeronautics Administration, 1945.
10 p. illus. 27 cm. (U. S. Civil Aeronautics Administration. Technical development report no. 46)
Cover title.

1. Aeronautical instruments. I. Pigman, George Leroy, 1912- joint author. II. Title: Flight level indicator. (Series)

TL521.A374 no. 46 53-63364
TL589.2.A6K5

NK 0202741 DLC CU

TL659
.H5K6 Knight, Robert Wilson, 1897-
... The Hindenburg accident...
[Washington] 1938
67p. 27 cm.
(U.S. Bureau of air commerce... Report no.11)

NK 0202742 DLC PP DAS

629.143 Knight, Robert Wilson, 1897-
K741 ... Low visibility airport windrose summaries, by Robert W. Knight ... July 1940. Washington, U.S. Govt. print. off., 1940.
v, 4p. 182 diagrs. (Civil aeronautics authority. Technical development note. no.22)

"This report of wind and climatic conditions during periods of restricted visibility covers the 5-year period from 1934 to 1938, inclusive."- p.v.

1. Meteorology in aeronautics. 2. Winds. 3. Airports--U.S. I. Title.

NK 0202743 IU DAS MH-BA ICU

TL589
.2
.M4K6
Knight, Robert Wilson, 1897-
... The radio telemeter and its importance to aviation.
[Washington] 1938
35p. 27 cm.
(U.S. Civil aeronautics authority... Report no.1)

NK 0202744 DLC PP

Knight, Robert Wilson, 1897-
... The radiotelemeter and its importance to aviation, by R. W. Knight, chief, Air transport section ... September 1938. Washington, U. S. Govt. print. off., 1941.
1v, 16 p. incl. illus., tables. 26½cm. ([U. S.] Civil aeronautics authority. Technical development report no. 16)
Formerly Report no. 1, Planning and development division, Civil aeronautics authority.
"References": p. 16.

1. Meteorology in aeronautics. 2. Meteorological instruments. I. Title.

41-50565
Library of Congress TL521.A374 no. 16
——— Copy 2. TL557.O2K6 1941
[4] (629.1306173) 629.132

NK 0202745 DLC PPD OU

Knight, Rosa.
Bird of happy memory, and other verse, by Rosa Knight. [Wellington] L. T. Watkins [194-?] 10 p. 22cm.

NK 0202746 NN

Knight, *Mrs.* **Rosa Viola (Talbot)** 1873-
Genealogy of the Reid family of North Carolina and Georgia, by Rosa Talbot Knight. [n. p., 1924?]
2 p. l., 57 numb. l. 29cm. [*With her* Genealogy of the Talbot and Wingfield families. [n. p., 1924?]]
Type-written.

1. Read family (Samuel Reid, 1728-1810)

25-24233
Library of Congress CS71.T14 1924

NK 0202747 DLC

Knight, *Mrs.* **Rosa Viola (Talbot)** 1873-
Genealogy of the Talbot and Wingfield families of Virginia and Georgia, by Rosa Talbot Knight. [n. p., 1924?]
2 p. l., 102 numb. l. 29cm.
Type-written.
With this is bound the author's Genealogy of the Reid family of North Carolina and Georgia. [n. p., 1924?]

1. Talbot family. 2. Talbot family (Matthew Talbot, b. 1669) 3. Wingfield family.

25-24232
Library of Congress CS71.T14 1924

NK 0202748 DLC PHi

Knight, Rosa Viola (Talbot) 1873-
Genealogy of the Talbot-Reid and allied families. Safety Harbor, Fla. [194-?]
290 (i. e. 291) l. 30 cm.

1. Talbot family. 2. U. S.—Geneal.

CS71.T14 55-19922 ‡

NK 0202749 DLC

VOLUME 300

Knight, Rosa Viola (Talbot) 1873-
Genealogy of the Talbot, Wingfield and Reid families, by Rosa Talbot Knight. [n. p., 1925?] 147 l. 4°.

Typewritten.

238306A. 1. Talbot family. 2. Wingfield family. 3. Reid family.
N. Y. P. L. July 29, 1926

NK 0202750 NN

Knight, Roy Clement.
Advice to the student of French, by R. C. Knight and F. W. A. George. Oxford, B. Blackwell [1955]
108 p. 19 cm.
Bibliography: p. 105-108.

1. French language. 2. French literature—Hist. & crit. I. George, Frederick William Arthur, joint author. II. Title.
A 57-4825
Wisconsin. Univ. Libr. for Library of Congress [1]

NK 0202751 WU CaBVaU LU OO CU IU

PQ1898 .A2K55
Knight, Roy Clement, ed.
Racine, Jean Baptiste, 1639-1699.
... Phèdre, edited by R. C. Knight. [Manchester] Manchester university press, 1943.

Knight, Roy Clement.
Racine, convention and classicism; inaugural lecture delivered at the College on 17 January 1952. [Swansea] University College of Swansea [1952]
31 p. 23 cm.

1. Racine, Jean Baptiste, 1639-1699.
PQ1905.K57 842.45 57-39309 rev ‡

NK 0202753 DLC FU

Knight, Roy Clement.
Racine et la Grèce. Paris, Boivin [1950]
467 p. facsims. 24 cm. (Études de littérature étrangère et comparée, 23)
Éditions contemporaines.
Appendices (bibliographical): p. [413]-431; Bibliography: p. [432]-451.

1. Racine, Jean Baptiste, 1639-1699. 2. Literature, Comparative—French and Greek. 3. Literature, Comparative—Greek and French.
A 52-284
Yale Univ. Library for Library of Congress

GEU KU InStme OClW CLSU NRU FU WaU P OCU PHC NN NNC ICU NjP OO PU OrU CaBVaU OrCS OrPR CtY NcRS
NK 0202754 CtY MU ViU InU PSC TxU CSt MH MB DLC ScU

Knight, Roy E
Machine shop projects for trade, vocational, and high school shops [by] Roy E. Knight ... Bloomington, Ill., McKnight & McKnight, °1943.
112 p. diagrs. 26cm.
"Lithographed."
Diagrams on versos and operation sheets or blank pages for notes on rectos of p. 10-111.
"References for related topics": p. 9.

1. Machine-shop practice. I. Title.
43-15277
Library of Congress TJ1160.K62
[a44f2] 621.75

NK 0202755 DLC Or NcRS ScCleU KEmT FTaSU

TC 558 .A8E35 K74
Knight, Rupert Grenville
The subsidence of a rockfill dam and the remedial measures employed at Eildon reservoir, Australia. London, Institution [of Civil Engineers] 1938.
109-208, 451-495 p. illus. (part fold.) maps.

"Excerpt Journal of the Institution of Civil Engineers. Session 1937-1938."
Bibliographical footnotes.

NK 0202756 NNC

Knight, Ruth Adams (Yingling) 1898-
... Barry der menschenretter; eine geschichte vom grossen St. Bernhard. Luzern, Rex verlag [1954]
143, [1] p. 21½cm.
"Titel des amerikanischen Originals: Halfway to heaven, the story of the St. Bernard."

NK 0202757 ViW

Knight, Ruth Adams (Yingling) 1898-
Brave companions, by Ruth Adams Knight; frontispiece by Lynd Ward. Garden City, New York, Doubleday, Doran & company, inc., 1945.
4 p. l., 215 p. col. front. 20½cm.
"First edition."

1. Dogs—Legends and stories. I. Ward, Lynd Kendall, 1905- illus. II. Title.
45-35108
Library of Congress * PZ7.K74Br

PPGi
NK 0202758 DLC CaBVa Or OrP OrU Wa WaS PP OCl OO

PZ7 .K74Br 1946
Knight, Ruth Adams (Yingling) 1898-
Brave companions. Frontispiece by Lynd Ward. Garden City, N. Y., Doubleday 1946 [°1945]
215 p. col. front. 21cm.

1. Dogs—Legends and stories. I. Title.

NK 0202759 ViU PBa ViW

Knight, Ruth Adams (Yingling) 1898-
Day after tomorrow. [1st ed.] Garden City, N. Y., Doubleday, 1952.
219 p. 21 cm.

I. Title.
PZ7.K74Day 52-10127 ‡

NK 0202760 DLC WaS Or OEac

Knight, Ruth Adams (Yingling) 1898-
Dr. Christian's office [by] Ruth Adams Knight and Jean Hersholt. New York, Random house [1944]
3 p. l., 3-243 p. 22cm.
"First printing."

I. Hersholt, Jean, 1886- joint author. II. Title.
44-7186 Revised
Library of Congress PZ3.K7475Do

NK 0202761 DLC WaS WaSp ViU WU MsU PP OCl OOxM

813.5 K71D
Knight, Ruth Adams (Yingling) 1898-
Dr. Christian's office [by] Ruth Adams Knight and Jean Hersholt. [Tower books ed.] Cleveland, World Pub. Co. [1946, c1944]
243 p. 21 cm.

NK 0202762 NcD

Knight, Ruth Adams (Yingling) 1898-
Fare by my side, a novel. New York, W. Morrow, 1948.
314 p. 21 cm.
"A condensed version ... has appeared in McCalls magazine."—Dust jacket.

I. Title.
PZ3.K7475Far 47-11885*

NK 0202763 DLC Or

Knight, Ruth Adams (Yingling) 1898-
First the lightning. [1st ed.] Garden City, N. Y., Doubleday, 1955.
224 p. 22 cm.

I. Title.
PZ7.K74Fi 55-10509 ‡

NK 0202764 DLC GU OrMonO OrP Or

Knight, Ruth (Adams) 1898-
A friend in the dark; the story of a "Seeing eye" dog, by Ruth Adams Knight; illustrated by Morgan Dennis. New York, Grosset & Dunlap [°1937]
vii p., 1 l., 64 p., 1 l. incl. illus., plates. plates. 25 cm.

1. Dogs—Legends and stories. 2. Dogs—Training. 3. Shepherd dogs. 4. Seeing eye, incorporated, Morristown, N. J. 5. Blind. I. Title.
HV1598.K55 636.74 37-27193

OU NN
NK 0202765 DLC WaSp Or WaS OrP PWcS PPGi PP OCl

Knight, Ruth Adams (Yingling) 1898-
Halfway to heaven, the story of the St. Bernard; illustrated by Wesley Dennis. New York, Whittlesey House [1952]
184 p. illus. 21 cm.

PZ10.3.K757Hal 52-10848 ‡

OOxM OCl ViW WaSp WaT
NK 0202766 DLC CaBVa ICarbS Or OrP WaE WaS OClND

Knight, Ruth Adams (Yingling) 1898-
... Halvveis til himmelen; oversatt av Jo Tenfjord. Oslo, H. Aschehoug & co. (W. Nygaard) 1955.
126 p. 19cm.
"Oversatt etter Halfway to heaven, the story of the St. Bernard."
"Printed in Norway."

I. Title. II. Tenfjord, Jo, tr.

NK 0202767 ViW

VOLUME 300

Knight, Ruth Adams (Yingling) 1898–
It might be you. [1st ed.] Garden City, N. Y., Doubleday [1949]
206 p. 20 cm.

I. Title.

PZ7.K74 It 49–10567*

NK 0202768 DLC WaT OrAshS WaSp WaE OrU PP Or GU MoU OCl

Knight, Ruth Adams (Yingling) 1898–
The invisible army, by Ruth Adams Knight... [New York, 194–?] 24 f. 27cm. [Writers' war board. War script. no. 15]
Radio script.

1. World war, 1939–1945—Drama. 2. Drama, Radio, American. I. Title. II. Ser.
N. Y. P. L. April 30, 1946

NK 0202769 NN

Knight, Ruth Adams (Yingling) 1898–
The land beyond; a story of the Children's Crusade. Illustrated by Wesley Dennis. New York, Whittlesey House [1954]
218 p. illus. 21 cm.

1. Children's Crusade, 1212. I. Title.

PZ7.K74Lan 54–8814 ‡

NK 0202770 DLC IdB Or OrU WaS WaSp WaT PPT OClW OCl OOxM PP

Knight, Ruth Adams (Yingling) 1898–
Luck of the Irish. [1st ed.] Garden City, N. Y., Doubleday [1951]
242 p. 21 cm.

I. Title.

PZ7.K74Lu 51–12476 ‡

NK 0202771 DLC WaSp WaT WaS Or MiU

Knight, Mrs. Ruth Adams (Yingling) 1898–

Metropolitan opera guild.
Opera cavalcade, the story of the Metropolitan. New York, The Metropolitan opera guild, inc. [°1938]

Knight, Ruth Adams (Yingling) 1898–
Pledge for the future, by Ruth Adams Knight... [New York, 194–?] 16 f. 27cm. [Writers' war board. War script. no. 16]
Radio script.

1. World war, 1939–1945—Drama. 2. Drama, Radio, American. I. Title. II. Ser.
N. Y. P. L. April 30, 1946

NK 0202773 NN

Knight, Ruth Adams (Yingling) 1898–
Stand by for the ladies! The distaff side of radio, by Ruth Adams Knight, illustrated by Eileen Evans, introduction by Lenox R. Lohr ... New York, Coward-McCann, inc. [°1939]
xii, 179 p. illus. 19½cm.

1. Radio broadcasting. 2. Woman—Employment. I. Title.
39–27251 Revised
Library of Congress TK6570.B7K57
[r45x3] 621.384198

NK 0202774 DLC WaSp Or CU WaU WU PP OCl OO OU OLak NN

Knight, Ruth Adams (Yingling) 1898–
Top of the mountain. [1st ed.] Garden City, N. Y., Doubleday [1953]
222 p. 21 cm.

I. Title.

PZ7.K74To 53–9996 ‡

NK 0202775 DLC WaS WaT Or OO PPGi PBa

Knight, Ruth Adams (Yingling) 1898–
Valiant comrades, a story of our dogs of war, by Ruth Adams Knight; jacket design by Morgan Dennis. Garden City, New York, Doubleday, Doran & company, inc. [1943]
ix p., 2 l., 238 p. 20½cm.
Illustrated lining-papers.
"First edition."

1. Dogs, War use of—Juvenile literature. I. Title.
43–16552 Revised
Library of Congress PZ7.K74Val

NK 0202776 DLC Or OrP WaS WaT PPGi PP PBa OCl OO OEac OOxM

Knight, Ruth Adams (Yingling) 1898–
Women must weep, by Ruth Adams Knight. [Boston] Hale, Cushman & Flint [°1941]
256 p. 21cm.
Author's portrait mounted on lining-paper.

I. Title. 41–22358 Revised
Library of Congress PZ3.K7475Wo

NK 0202777 DLC OU PP

Knight, Ruth S.

Public Personnel Association.
Procedures that improve personnel administration [by] Ruth S. Knight [and others. Chicago, 1955]

Pam.
261.7
K74r Knight, Ryland.
Religion a voluntary matter, by R. Knight ... Nashville, S. S. bd., S. B. C., n. d.
11p. 22½cm. (Denominational series)

NK 0202779 LNB

---

*pFB8
N1627
Z805n
Knight, S
Jupiter Bonney granting unto the Dutch frogs a king ...
[London] Publ'd by Walker June 26.1806 nº 7 Cornhill.
plate. 38x28cm.,mounted & bd.to 50x40cm.
George 10581; Broadley A-516.
Engraving, signed.
A satire on the forced Dutch acceptance of Louis Bonaparte as hereditary king.
No.93 in a volume lettered on spine: Napoleonic caricatures.

Another copy. 34.5x24cm.,mounted & bd.to 66x50cm.
Hand-colored.
No.69a in a volume lettered on spine: Caricatures on Napoleon ...

NK 0202781 MH

Knight, S Charles
The truth at last; or, What I know about Pomeroy. New and startling developments. Thrilling disclosures concerning A.H. Horton and S.C. Pomeroy, how Pom. was to be made secretary of the interior. The Kansas Legislature bought and sold. Dr. S. Charles Knight's statement, Kansas City, September, 1874. Kansas City,Mo., Ramsey, Millett & Hudson [1874]
24p. 21.5cm.

NK 0202782 KU

Knight, S. L.
Paragon method for the violin [1886]
see under Phipps, Sireno B.

Knight, Sampson.
Knight's medical adviser. A treatise on domestic medicine ... By Drs. Sampson and Thomas H. Knight ... Ed. by Dr. J. C. Neeley. Nashville, Tenn., S. & T. H. Knight, & S. J. Short, 1854.
x, [11]–736 p. 23cm.

1. Medicine, Popular. I. Knight, Thomas H., joint author. II. Neeley, J. C., ed.

Library of Congress RC81.K82 7–10393†

NK 0202784 DLC

D
93
.69
KNIGHT, SAMUEL, of Huntingdon.
The speech of Samuel Knight, esq. as delivered in the Assembly room at the Town-hall, in Huntingdon, at a meeting held on Tuesday, December 31, 1811, to take into consideration the establishment of an Auxiliary Bible Society for the County of Huntingdon. Cambridge, F. Hodson, 1812.
16p. 22cm.

Binder's title: Tracts. [1797–1820]

NK 0202785 ICN

Knight, (rev. Samuel), Vicar of Halifax.
Forms of prayer, for the use of christian families... 20 th ed. To which is added a second series, by the Rev. James Knight... 4 ed. Halifax Printed for Longman, Rees, Orme, Brown & Green [etc.] 1830.

xii, [13]–175 p.

NK 0202786 NN

Knight, Samuel, Vicar of Halifax.
Forms of prayer, for the use of Christian families. 22d ed. York, Wilson, 1839.

108 p.

NK 0202787 PPPrHi

VOLUME 300

Knight, Samuel, 1675-1746.
The faithful pastor's duty and reward: a sermon [on Luke xvi.10] preached in Lambeth chapel, on Sunday Jan. 23. 1731. At the consecration of ... Thomas Lord Bishop of St. Asaph, and Nicholas Lord Bishop of St. Davids ... London, J. Crownfield, 1731.
[2], 26 p. 20cm.

NK 0202788 CLU-C NjPT InU

BX5133 M2L7 Knight, Samuel, 1675-1746.
The great happiness of a lawful government. A sermon preached before the honourable House of commons, at St. Margaret's Westminster, on Saturday, May 29, 1725. Being the anniversary of the restauration of the royal family. By Samuel Knight ... London, Printed for T. Cox, 1725.
32p. 19½cm. (Bound with: Maddox, Isaac. The love of our country recommended. 1737)
Title vignette.

NK 0202789 NBuG NNG MnU CLU-C

BR350 E7K58 Knight, Samuel, 1675-1746.
Das leben des fürtrefflichen Erasmi von Rotterdam, insonderheit aber derjenige merckwürdigste theil davon, den er in Engeland zugebracht; worinnen eine nachricht von seinen gelehrten freunden, wie auch dem zustand der religion und gelehrsamkeit zur selben zeit, so wohl auf der universität Cambridge als Oxford, ertheilet wird. Nebst einem anhang unterschiedener rarer urkunden. Abgefasset von Samuel Knight ... Ins deutsche übersetzt von Theodoro Arnold ... Leipzig, J.G. Löwe, 1736.
56, 398, 126, [10] p. incl.pl. front., plates (part fold.; incl.ports.) 18cm.

NK 0202790 CU PPC NNF

Knight, Samuel, 1675-1746.
The life of Dr. John Colet, dean of S. Paul's in the reigns of K. Henry VII. and Henry VIII. and founder of S. Paul's school: with an appendix containing some account of the masters and more eminent scholars of that foundation; and several original papers relating to the said life. By Samuel Knight ... London, Printed by J. Downing, 1724.
5 p. l., xiii, [1], 494, [26] p. front., plates, ports. 20cm.
"Catalogus librorum in bibliotheca scholæ Paulinæ": p. 475-494.
1. Colet, John, 1467?-1519. 2. St. Paul's school, London.
BR754.C6K5 1724 46-43652

MiD MdBP IaU MH NIC PPD PU OU ICN NN
NK 0202791 DLC DFo NcD NjNbS NIC MiU CtY-M CtY CSmH

Knight, Samuel, 1675-1746.
The life of Dr. John Colet, dean of St. Paul's in the reigns of K. Henry VII. and K. Henry VIII. and founder of St. Paul's school: with an appendix, containing some account of the masters and more eminent scholars of that foundation, and several original papers relating to the said life. By Samuel Knight ... New ed. Oxford, The Clarendon press, 1823.
xix, [1], 437 p. front., plates, port. 23cm.
"Catalogus librorum in bibliotheca scholæ Paulinæ": p. 409-426.
1. Colet, John, 1467?-1519.
12-34956
Library of Congress BR754.C6K5 1823

PPFr MdBP NNUT UU MsU OrP
NK 0202792 DLC NIC IU TU NcD CtY MoU PPL OU MiU

Knight, Samuel, 1675-1746.
The life of Dr. John Colet, dean of St. Paul's in the reigns of K. Henry VII. and K. Henry VIII. and founder of St. Paul's school: with an appendix, containing some account of the masters and more eminent scholars of that foundation, and several original papers relating to the said life. New ed. Oxford, Eng., The Clarendon Press, 1823.
437p. illus.
Microcard edition.

NK 0202793 ICRL

Knight, Samuel, 1675-1746.
The life of Erasmus, more particularly that part of it, which he spent in England; wherein an account is given of his learned friends, and the state of religion and learning at that time in both our universities. With an appendix containing several original papers. By Samuel Knight ... Cambridge: Printed by Corn. Crownfield, and sold at London, by J. Wyat [etc.] 1726.
4p.l., xxxi, [1], 386, cxliv, [8] p. front., plates, ports. 22.5cm.

MiU NN ICU ICN OCl IU NNC ViU WU CtY MWiW-C NNUnC KU-M NIC CLSU TNJ-R CU InU NcD AkU MoSU ScU MH MB
NK 0202794 NNUT CU-A NjNbS DLC CU-S NjPT CaBVaU IaU

Micro-card EP-63 M980-987 Knight, Samuel, 1675-1746.
The life of Erasmus, more particularly that part of it, which he spent in England; wherein an account is given of his learned friends, and the state of religion and learning at that time in both our universities. With an appendix containing several original papers. By Samuel Knight ... Cambridge: Printed by Corn. Crownfield, and sold at London, by J. Wynt [etc.] 1726.
4 p.ℓ., xxxi, [1], 386, cxliv, [8] p. front., plates, ports. 22.5cm.
Micro-opaque. Lexington, Ky., Published by Microcard Corp. for Erasmus Press, 1963. 8 cards. 8x13cm. (The History of ideas in Europe, series I, EP-63, M980-987)
1. Erasmus, Desiderius, d.1536. 2. Cambridge. University--Hist.--16th cent. 3. Oxford. University--Hist.--16th cent. I. Title.

NK 0202795 CBPac MoU

---

*EC7 G2523 Z731ℓ Knight, Samuel, 1754?-1829.
Elegies and sonnets by Samuel Knight ... London: Printed for T. Cadell, in the Strand. MDCCLXXXV.
4°. 1p.ℓ., v-vi, [7]-70p. 27cm.
Inscribed on t.-p. (partly cropped): from the Author.
No.4 in a volume lettered on spine: Gayana Q. 1.

NK 0202796 MH DFo OCU PPL

QD453 .C79 Knight, Samuel B., joint author.
Crockford, Horace Downs.
Fundamentals of physical chemistry for premedical students [by] H. D. Crockford [and] Samuel B. Knight. New York, Wiley [1950]

Knight, Samuel Bradley.
The decomposition of ammonium-deuterium chloride. Chapel Hill, 1938.
28 + [2] p. illus. Q.
Thesis (Ph.D.) - University of North Carolina, 1938.
Carbon copy of typewritten manuscript.
Bibliography: [2] p. at end.

NK 0202798 NcU

Knight, Samuel Howell, 1892-
The Fountain and the Casper formations of the Laramie basin; a study on genesis of sediments, by S. H. Knight ... Laramie? Wy., 1929.
82 p. illus. (incl. maps) diagrs. 25½cm. (On cover: Contributions from the Department of geology of Columbia university. vol. XL. no. 5)
Thesis (PH. D.)—Columbia university, 1929.
Vita.
Reprinted from the University of Wyoming Publications in geology, vol. I, no. 7.
Bibliography: p. 81-82.
1. Geology—Carboniferous. 2. Geology—Laramie River. 3. Geology—Wyoming. 4. Sedimentation and deposition. I. Title.
30-16508
Library of Congress QE671.K55 1929
Columbia Univ. Libr. [3] [557.87] 551.7509787

NK 0202799 NNC DLC

Knight, Samuel Howell, 1892-
... The Fountain and the Casper formations of the Laramie basin; a study on genesis of sediments, by S. H. Knight. Laramie, Wy., University of Wyoming [1929]
82 p. illus. (incl. maps) diagrs. 25½cm. (University of Wyoming publications in science. Geology v. 1, no. 1 ... July 1, 1929)
Published also as thesis (PH. D.) Columbia university, 1929, forming vol. XL, no. 5 of Contributions from the Department of geology of Columbia university.
Bibliography: p. 81-82.
1. Geology, Stratigraphic—Carboniferous. 2. Geology—Wyoming. 3. Sedimentation and deposition. I. Title. II. Title: Laramie basin.
30-33859
Library of Congress QE671.K55 1929 a
[3] [557.87] 551.7509787

NNC NN ViU CaBViP OrU TxU NIC
NK 0202800 DLC OrU OrCS CU OCU CoU PP PBm OClW OU

Knight, Samuel Howell, 1892-
Physiographic map of Wyoming. [Laramie, Geological Survey of Wyoming] ©1953.
map on sheet 78 x 104 cm.
Scale not given.
Inset: Index map [ca. 1:3,200,000]
1. Wyoming—Maps, Physical. I. Wyoming. Geological Survey.
G4261.C2 1953.K5 Map 53-592

NK 0202801 DLC

Knight, Samuel Howell, 1892-
... The saline lake deposits of Wyoming ... by S. H. Knight. [Laramie] University of Wyoming, 1934-39.
2 v. illus., map, tables. 28-23 cm. (Wyoming. Geological survey. Report of investigations no. 1-2)
Part I mimeographed.
CONTENTS.—I. The Downey lakes, Albany county, Wyoming. 1934.—II. The Rock Creek lakes, Albany County, Wyoming. 1939.
1. Salt mines and mining—Wyoming. I. Title. II. Title: The Downey lakes, Albany co., Wyoming. III. Title: The Rock Creek lakes, Albany co., Wyoming.
[TN903.K] G S 34-158
U. S. Geol. Survey. Libr. for Library of Congress [a50r40f4]

NK 0202802 DI-GS MtBuM NNC NBuU NN GU TxU

Knight, Samuel Kirshbaum, *bp. of Jarrow*, 1868-1932.
Fulfilling the ministry, by the late S. K. Knight, bishop of Jarrow, with an introduction by Herbert Hensley Henson ... Cambridge [Eng.] University press, 1933.
xi, 219 p. 22½ cm. (Cambridge pastoral theology lectures, 1925-1926)
Bibliography at the end of most of the chapters.
1. Church of England—Doctrinal and controversial works. 2. Pastoral theology—Anglican communion. I. Title.
BX5175.K6 253 33-31226

NK 0202803 DLC IEN NcD MH-A

Knight, Samuel Ratcliffe, joint author.
Hall, Henry Sinclair, 1848-
Algebra for beginners. By H. S. Hall and S. R. Knight ... Rev. and adapted to American schools, by Frank L. Sevenoak ... New York and London, Macmillan & co., 1895.

Knight, Samuel Ratcliffe, joint author.
Hall, Henry Sinclair, 1848-
Algebra for colleges and schools, by H. S. Hall, M. A. and S. R. Knight, B. A. Rev. and enl. for the use of American schools, by F. L. Sevenoak ... New York. The Macmillan company, 1919.

QA154 .H1817 Knight, Samuel Ratcliffe, joint author.
Hall, Henry Sinclair, 1848-1934.
Algebra superior, por H. S. Hall y S. R. Knight. Versión castellana por Rafael García Díaz. México, Unión Tip. Editorial Hispano-Americana [1948]

VOLUME 300

Knight, Samuel Ratcliffe. joint author.
FOR OTHER EDITIONS SEE MAIN ENTRY

Hall, Henry Sinclair, 1848–
Elementary algebra, by H. S. Hall, M. A., and S. R. Knight, B. A. [2d ed.] rev. and enl. for the use of American schools by F. L. Sevenoak ... New York, The Macmillan company; London, Macmillan & co., ltd., 1896.

Knight, Samuel Ratcliffe, joint author.

Hall, Henry Sinclair, 1848–
Elementary trigonometry, by H. S. Hall ... and S. R. Knigh ... 4th ed., rev. and enl. London, Macmillan and co., limited 1919.

Knight, Samuel Ratcliffe, joint author.

QA154 .H18 1942 **Hall, Henry Sinclair**, 1848–1934.
Higher algebra, a sequel to Elementary algebra for schools, by H. S. Hall ... and S. R. Knight ... London, Macmillan and co., limited, 1942.

Knight, Samuel Ratcliffe, joint author.
Solutions of the examples in Elementary algebra for schools
see under Hall, H[enry] S[inclair].

Knight, Samuel Ratcliffe, joint author.

Hall, Henry Sinclair, 1848–1934.
Upper school algebra; being an abridged and revised edition of Hall and Knight's Higher algebra, by L. Crosland ... London, Macmillan and co. limited, 1940.

---

752 Knight, Samuel Robinson.

A Thomistic interpretation of Aristotle's theory of universals. [n. p.] 1953.
3, iv, 136 l. 28cm.
Typescript.
Thesis—Univ. of Virginia, 1953.
Includes bibliography.

1. Aristoteles. 2. Thomas Aquinas, Saint, 1225?–1274. I. Title.

NK 0202812 ViU

Knight, Samuel Robinson.
A Thomistic interpretation of Aristotle's theory of universals. Ann Arbor, University Microfilms [1954]
([University Microfilms, Ann Arbor, Mich.] Publication no. 9651)
Microfilm copy of typescript. Positive.
Collation of the original: 3, iv, 136 l.
Thesis—University of Virginia.
Abstracted in Dissertation abstracts, v. 14 (1954) no. 10, p. 1760.
Bibliography: leaf 136.

1. Aristoteles. 2. Thomas Aquinas, Saint, 1225?–1274. 3. Universals (Philosophy) I. Title.

Microfilm AC-1 no. 9651 Mic A 54-2588

Virginia. Univ. Libr. for Library of Congress [1]†

NK 0202813 ViU DLC

Knight, Sarah Ann, 1859–
Knight family records. [A history of the long ago, to the present time, 640–1951. Bellefontaine, Ohio, 1952, °1951]
unpaged. illus. 28 cm.

1. Knight family. I. Title.

CS71.K725 1952 52-24872 ‡

NK 0202814 DLC NN WHi

Knight, Sarah (Jesup) 1798–1828, comp.
[Album] n.p., 1824.

(In- A collection of old autograph Albums and scrap-books. Various places and dates. 1827- v. ill)

NK 0202815 RPB

Knight, Sarah (Jesup) 1798–1828.
Memoir of Sarah Knight... London, 1829.

NK 0202816 PHC

Knight, Sarah (Jesup), 1798–1828.
Memoir of Sarah Knight, wife of Thomas Knight, of Colchester, who died on the 28th of the fifth month, 1828. Philadelphia: T. Kite, 1829. iv, 6–35 p. 24°.

Contains extracts of letters by Sarah Knight, preceded by a memoir.

NK 0202817 NN DLC PHC PSC-Hi MH

Knight, *Mrs.* Sarah (Kemble) 1666–1727.
The journal of Madam Knight, with an introductory note by George Parker Winship. Boston, Small, Maynard & company, 1920.
xiv, 72 p., 1 l. front. (fold. map) 21 x 13cm.
Five hundred and twenty-five copies printed.
Introduction to the edition of 1825. By Theodore Dwight: p. [xi]–xiv.
Half-title: The private journal kept by Madam Knight, on a journey from Boston to New-York, in the year 1704. From the original manuscript.
First published 1825.

1. New England—Descr. & trav.

Library of Congress F7.K723 21-10698

NK 0202818 NRU CLU MnHi OCl NjP ICN MB NN MH DLC MeB CU-A ViU NcU LU MH PP PHC NBuG

Knight, *Mrs.* Sarah (Kemble) 1666–1727.
The journal of Madam Knight; with an introductory note by George Parker Winship. New York, P. Smith, 1935.
xiv, 72 p. front. (fold. map) 21 x 13cm.
"Facsimile reprint of the 1920 edition."
Half-title: The private journal kept by Madam Knight, on a journey from Boston to New-York, in the year 1704. From the original manuscript.
First published 1825.
"Introduction to the edition of 1825. By Theodore Dwight": p. [xi]–xiv.

1. New England—Descr. & trav. I. Title.

Library of Congress F7.K724 35-12871

NK 0202819 WaWW CaBVaU OrCS NNU OCl OO OCU MB RPB WaS MtBC DHEW IEN ICU MnU CSmH ICN ICU OO MWelC ViU NRCR MsU TU ICarbS OrU TxU PMA NcD GU DLC OrPR PU PPT CtY IU KU MH MNS NhD

Knight, Sarah (Kemble) 1666–1727.
The journals of Madam Knight, and Rev. Mr. Buckingham. From the original manuscripts written in 1704 & 1710. New-York, Wilder & Campbell, 1825.
70 p.
Mr. Buckingham's journal not included in this edition.

NK 0202820 NIC MWA

Knight, *Mrs.* Sarah (Kemble) 1666–1727.
The journals of Madam Knight and Rev. Mr. Buckingham. From the original manuscripts, written in 1704 & 1710. New York, Wilder & Campbell, 1825.
129 p. 19cm.
"The private journals kept by Rev. John [i. e. Thomas] Buckingham of the expedition against Canada, in the years 1710 & 1711": p. [71]–129.

1. New England—Descr. & trav. 1—13318

Library of Congress F7.K71

NK 0202821 MB MWA NN RPJCB NjN PPiU DLC MH NcU MiU-C CU OU PPL MiU OClWHi

---

Knight, Sarah (Kemble) 1666–1727.
The private journal kept by Madam Knight, on a journey from Boston to New York, in the year 1704. From the original manuscript. [Edited by W. R. Deane.] n. t.-p. Boston, 1858. 10 l. 4°.
Clippings from Littell's Living age. June 26, 1858. Mounted and bound.

1. United States.—Description and travel, 1704. 2. Deane, William Reed editor.
N. Y. P. L. May 21, 1912.

NK 0202822 NN MB

Knight, *Mrs.* Sarah (Kemble) 1666–1727.
The private journal of a journey from Boston to New York in the year 1704. Kept by Madam Knight. Albany, F. H. Little, 1865.
xii, [13]–92 p. incl. illus., facsim. 21½ x 17cm.
Three hundred copies printed. no. 93.
Edited by William Law Learned. cf. Allibone's Dictionary of authors.
Originally published under title: The journals of Madam Knight and the Rev. Mr. Buckingham, from the original manuscripts written in 1704 and 1710. New York, 1825.

1. New England—Description and travel. I. Learned, William Law, 1821–1904, ed.
A 11-2737 Revised
Title from Univ. of Chicago F7.K71 Printed by L. C

NK 0202823 OCl ViU NN MB RPJCB OCl NBuG PBL NIC IaU NcGU OC MH OCU ICU CU DNW NjN RPB PHi PPL MiU MWA

Knight, Sarah (Kemble) 1666–1727.
The private journal of Sarah Kemble Knight; being the record of a journey from Boston to New York in the year 1704. Norwich, Conn., The Academy press, 1901.
2 p. l., 7–78 p. 22½cm.
"Limited to 210 copies; number 186."
Originally published under title: The journals of Madam Knight and the Rev. Mr. Buckingham, from the original manuscripts written in 1704 and 1710. New York, 1825.
Introduction to the edition of Wilder and Campbell, 1825: p. 21–22.

1. New England—Descr. & trav.
10-3165
Library of Congress F7.K72

NK 0202824 DLC WHi PSC WaU MB

Knight, Seymour.
The history of United States steel in charts, by Seymour Knight. [New York, The Moody magazine and book company, °1915]
cover-title, 1 l., 4 diagr. 28 x 35½cm. $3.00
"Supplementary to the Authentic history of the United States steel corporation, by Arundel Cotter."

1. United States steel corporation. I. Cotter, Arundel.
Library of Congress HD9519.U6K5 16-1089

NK 0202825 DLC

LZ1 .K71 KNIGHT, SHERIFF L ,1910-
An evaluation of State School Board Associations in the Midwest Area. [Typewritten ms. Bloomington, Ind.] 1952.
7+185 p. tables, forms.
Thesis (Ed.D.)—Indiana University.

NK 0202826 InU

VOLUME 300

Knight, Sherwood Sweet, 1876–
Human life, by S. S. Knight. New York, R. F. Fenno & company [°1910]
3 p. l., [9]–199 p. 20cm. $1.00
CONTENTS.—The habitat of man.—The length of time during which man has existed.—The physical limitations of existence.—The purpose of life.—Knowledge and education.—Religion and ethics.—Love.—Problems of the future.
1. Life. 2. Man. 10–27210
Library of Congress BD431.K6
NK 0202827 DLC

Knight, Sherwood Sweet, 1876–
What makes life worth living; or, The moral development of humanity, by S. S. Knight ... New York, R. F. Fenno & company [°1912]
3 p. l., 9–169 p. 20cm. $1.00
CONTENTS.—The great moral epochs of human history.—The development of the ethical ideal.
1. Moral conditions. 2. Ethics. I. Title. 12–21179
Library of Congress BJ71.K5
NK 0202828 DLC ICRL ICJ NN

Knight, Simon Sidney.
Fitness and injury in sport; care, diagnosis, and treatment by physical means. With a foreword by Stanley Rous, and introductory notes by Denis Compton and Bernard Joy. London, New York, Skeffington [1952]
189 p. illus. 22 cm.
1. Sports—Accidents and injuries. I. Title.
[GV344.K A 54–2932
Illinois. Univ. Library for Library of Congress [1]
NK 0202829 IU CaBVaU DNLM PP CU

Knight, Simon Sidney.
Fitness and injury in sport; care, diagnosis, and treatment by physical means. With a foreword by Sir Stanley Rous, and introductory notes by Denis Compton and Bernard Joy. New York, Van Nostrand [1953?]
189 p. illus. 22 cm.
1. Sports—Accidents and injuries. I. Title.
GV344.K6 796 54–804 ‡
NK 0202830 DLC OrMonO OrU OOxM PP PPPL PPT MiD MB OU

Knight, Stephen A
Fundamentals of radar. London, I. Pitman, 1947.
vii, 128 p. diagrs. 19 cm.
1. Radar.
TK6575.K6 621.38 48–19116*
NK 0202831 DLC

Knight, Stephen A
Fundamentals of radar. 2d ed. London, Pitman [1954]
150 p. illus. 19 cm.
1. Radar.
TK6575.K6 1954 *621.381 55–19283 ‡
NK 0202832 DLC WaS OrP Or OU OCl PPD MB TxU NN IaU PP MiU

Knight, Stephen A
Introduction to ultra-high-frequency radio engineering. London, Pitman [1954]
256 p. illus. 19 cm.
1. Radio, Short wave.
TK6553.K595 54—10273
NK 0202833 DLC CaBVa Or OrP NN PPF PPD PP LU MB NcD OCl PU-El PBL OU PSt WaS WaSp

Knight, Stephen H.
The open treatment of fractures... 1912.
NK 0202834 MiU

Knight, Stephenson Y.
Railway brakes, by Stephenson Y. Knight. London, Spottiswoode & co., ltd., 1904.
51 p. illus., fold. pl. 25½cm.
1. Brakes. I. Title. C 15–46
Library, U. S. Interstate Commerce Commission
NK 0202835 DIC NN

Knight, Stuart Walter, 1884–
The Knight method of effective advertising, by Stuart W. Knight. A complete analytical outline and quick-reference classification of the possible selling arguments, purchasing appeals and expository words, phrases and ideas of retail advertising ... Worcester, Mass., S. W. Knight [°1925]
1 p. l., xviii, [188] p. front. (port.) 27cm.
1. Advertising. 25–20280 Revised
Library of Congress HF5823.K6
NK 0202836 DLC MB

[**Knight, Stuart Walter**] 1884–
Know your numbers, by Ali Memmet, ef. [*pseud.*] ... Boston, Mass., Athena publishers [1942]
95 p. 19cm.
Cover-title: Know your numbers; the nature of numbers revealed.
1. Symbolism of numbers. I. Title. 42–25388
Library of Congress BF1623.P9K55
[2] 133.335
NK 0202837 DLC

[Knight, Mrs. Susan G.]
Lottie Wilde's picnic, by Grandmother Hope [pseud.]... New York, Crowell [1867]
174 p. 1 illus. 15½ cm.
Story for children.
NK 0202838 NjP

[**Knight,** *Mrs.* **S G.**]
Man's wrongs; or, Woman's foibles. By Kate Manton [*pseud.*] Boston, Crosby & Damrell, 1870.
272 p. 18½cm.
I. Title. 30–3386
Library of Congress PS2196.K85
NK 0202839 DLC NNC ViU CtY PPL MB

FILM 4274 PR v.2 reel K7 [Knight, Mrs. S G]
Man's wrongs; or, Woman's foibles. By Kate Manton [pseud.] Boston, Crosby & Damrell, 1870.
272 p. (Wright American fiction, v.II, 1851-1875, no.1493, Research Publications Microfilm, Reel K-7)
Also published as: Minnie Maverick.
NK 0202840 CU KEmT

Micro 3 Knight, Mrs. S G
Man's wrongs; or, Woman's foibles. By Kate Manton [pseud.] Boston, Crosby & Damrell, 1870.
272p. 19cm.
Micro-transparency (negative). Louisville, Ky., Lost Cause Press, 1969. 7 cards. 7.5x12.5cm. (L.H. Wright. American fiction, 1851-1875, no.1493)
I. Title. II. Title: Woman's foibles. III. Au./Title of II.
NK 0202841 PSt

* PS646 .F53 .K65M3 1870a Knight, Mrs. Susan G
Minnie Maverick; or, Man's wrongs and woman's foibles. By S. G. K. New-York: Broughton & Wyman, 1870.
272 p. 18cm.
Wright II, 1493n.
NK 0202842 ViU

Knight, Susan G
Ned Harwood's visit to Jerusalem. Illustrated. Boston, D. Lothrop [c1888]
268 p. illus.
NK 0202843 NNC OO MB

[**Knight,** Mrs. Susan G]
Pete, the cunner boy; or, The boy who kept the fifth commandment, by Grandmother Hope [pseud.] Boston: H. Hoyt [1862]
x, 12–186 p. front., plates. 15cm.
937716A. 1. Juvenile literature—Fiction, American. I. Title.
N. Y. P. L. July 25, 1938
NK 0202844 NN MH DLC

Knight, *Mrs.* **S G.**
Tit-bits; or, How to prepare a nice dish at a moderate expense. By Mrs. S. G. Knight. Boston, Crosby and Nichols; New York, O. S. Felt, 1864.
124 p. 19½cm.
1. Cookery, American. I. Title. 8–22856
Library of Congress TX715.K698
NK 0202845 DLC KMK ViU

Knight, *Mrs.* Susan **G**
Tit-bits; or, How to prepare a nice dish at a moderate expense. Boston, Crosby & Ainsworth, 1865.
124 p. 20 cm.
1. Cookery, American. I. Title.
TX715.K698 1865 48–35371†
NK 0202846 DLC

VOLUME 300

Knight, T. D.
The art of short-hand writing, on a new principle of contraction; also, an arrangement of all the characters; exhibiting at one view the entire ground work of stenography in general. London: printed for the author and published by Simpkin & Marshall, 1828. xi, 27 p., 7 pl. 8°.

1. Shorthand.—Systems (English), 1828. 2. Title.
N. Y. P. L. October 7, 1912.

NK 0202847 NN ICN CtY

Knight, T E ed.
Laws and Ordinances, adopted 1901
see under Greensboro, Ala.
Ordinances, etc.

Knight, Tack
see
Knight, Benjamin Thackston.

Knight, Thomas, Corporal.
Adventures in Holland and at Waterloo and expedition to Portugal.
Melb., 1873.
56 p.

NK 0202850 CSt

KNIGHT, THOMAS, corporal.
The British battalion at Oporto, with adventures, anecdotes, and exploits in Holland, at Waterloo, and in the expedition to Portugal, by Corporal Knight. With plan of Oporto, and sketches. London, E. Wilson, 1834. xi, 126 p. illus., map. 23cm.

1. Napoleonic wars, 1803-1815--Personal narratives. 2. Portugal--Hist., 1826-1853.

NK 0202851 NN PPL MH

Knight, Thomas, M.D.
An essay on the transmutation of blood; containing the aetiology; or, an account of the immediate cause of putrid-fevers or agues...Lond., A. Bettesworth, 1725.
52p.

NK 0202852 MiU

18th cent Medical Tracts
KNIGHT, Thomas, M.D.
Reflections upon catholicons; or, Universal medicines. With some remarks on the natural heat that is in animals, and the luminous emanations from human bodies. Also, the sundry experiments and observations made upon human calculus rationally considered; demonstrating that fire is the principal agent in lithontripticks or stone dissolvents. London, Printed for T. Osborne, 1749.
167p. 20cm .
Included in vol. with title on

1. Drugs - Early works to 1800 I. Title II. Title: Universal medicines III. Title: Medical tracts ACK

NK 0202854 CtY-M DNLM PPC

Knight, Thomas, M.D.
...The sundry experiments and observations made upon the human calculus. In(Reflections upon catholicon, ᴇetc.ᴣ London, 1749, 117-167.

NK 0202855 DNLM PPC

Knight, Thomas, M.D. 612.3 F2
110776
A vindication of a late essay on the tranſmutation of blood, containing the true manner of digestion of our aliments, and the ætiology: or, An account of the immediate cauſe of putrid fevers or agues. As alſo obſervations upon the noble ſpecifick Cortex peruvianus. To which is added, (by way of appendix) A dissertation concerning the manner of the operation of chalybeat medicines in human bodies, in oppoſition to the receiv'd opinion of their operating by their pondus, &c. Founded upon experimental obſervations and demonſtrable principles, the ſole original and fundamental of true knowledge, which our ſenſes are witneſs to. . . . By Thomas Knight, M.D. London, Printed for the author and sold by W. Innys, 1731.
xxii, [10], 240 p. 20cm.

NK 0202856 ICJ DNLM PPC MnU

Tat5 G6 D7y
Knight, Thomas, surgeon.
The history of the Dorton Chalybeate, near Brill, Bucks; with a concise treatise on its chemical properties and medicinal uses ... Oxford,Printed by J.Ham for Whittaker and co., London,[etc.,etc.]1833.
21p. front.,map,plan. 23½cm.

1.Mineral waters - Dorton,Eng.(Buckinghamshire)

NK 0202857 CtY

Tat5 G6 D7x
Knight, Thomas, surgeon.
The history of the Dorton Chalybeate, near Brill, Bucks; with a concise treatise on its chemical properties and medicinal uses ... Brill,Printed by J.Ham for Whittaker and co., London[etc.,etc.]1833.
42p. fold.front.,fold.map,fold.plan. 18cm.

1.Mineral waters - Dorton, Eng.(Buckinghamshire)

NK 0202858 CtY

WZ 260 J67G 1792
Knight, Thomas, fl.1809.
An examination of M. La Place's theory, capillary action. London, Printed for J. Deboffe, by T. Bailey, 1809.
[2] l., 36, [1] p. 20 1/2 cm.
"Advertisement" signed: T. K.
Bound with Johnson, J., A guide for gentlemen studying medicine at the University of Edinburgh, London, 1792.

1. Capillarity. I. La Place, Pierre Simon, Marquis de, 1749-1827. Sur l'action capillaire. II. Title.

NK 0202859 WU-M

Knight, Thomas, d. 1820. FOR OTHER EDITIONS SEE MAIN ENTRY
[Howard, Sir Robert] 1626-1698.
... The honest thieves, a farce; by T. Knight. With prefatory remarks ... faithfully marked with the stage business, and stage directions, as it is performed at the Theatres royal. By W. Oxberry, comedian. London, Pub. for the Proprietors, by W. Simpkin and R. Marshall [etc.] 1820.

*EC8 K7478 789j
Knight, Thomas, d.1820.
Jacob's return from London; or, His ramble to Bath; as written, and deliver'd by Mr. Knight, at the Theatre-Royal, Bath.
Bath:Printed for the benefit of the casualty hospital,and sold at the libraries;at W.Gye's printer and stationer,no.14,Market-place,at the box-lobby of the theatre;also to be had in Bristol,of the booksellers,& at the theatre. [1789] <Price six-pence.>
4°. 8p. 26cm.

Advertisement (p.[2]) dated December 1789. In verse.

NK 0202862 MH

KNIGHT, [Thomas], d. 1820.
Jacob's return from London, or His ramble to Bath, as written, and deliver'd by Mr. Knight, at the Theatre Royal. Bath. Bath, printed for the Benefit of the Casualty Hospital [1794?]
pp. 8.

NK 0202863 MH

[Knight, Thomas] d. 1820.
Lovers' quarrels; or, Like master like man
see under Vanbrugh, Sir John, 1664-1726.

Knight, Thomas, d. 1820.
Turnpike gate. London, 1799.
(In Three centuries of drama: English, 1751-1800)

Microprint.

NK 0202865 MoU

Lilly Library PR 4859 .K48 T89
KNIGHT,THOMAS,d. 1820.
The turnpike gate. A farce, in two acts. By T. Knight. ᴇLondon, J. Dicks, n.d.ᴣ
1 p.l., 1205-1214 p. 1 illus 18.5 cm. (Dicks' Standard plays, no. 187)
Copy 1 in cream printed paper wrappers; series advts. to no. 204.
Copy 2 in pink printed paper wrappers; no series advts.

NK 0202866 InU

Knight, Thomas. -1820.
The turnpike gate; a farce, in two acts.
[London. Sherwood & Co. 182-?] 10-16 pp. Illus. [The London stage. Vol. 4.] 21½ cm., in 8s.

NK 0202867 MB

Knight, Thomas, d. 1820.
The turnpike gate
For editions published as a musical work
see under Mazzinghi, Joseph, 1765-1844.

Knight, Thomas Andrew, 1759-1838.
Account of some experiments on the descent of the sap in trees. In a letter to Sir Joseph Banks. ᴇLondon, 1803ᴣ
ᴇ13ᴣ p. (Philosophical transactions of the Royal society of London, 1803. pp. 277-289.)

NK 0202869 MH-A MBH

Knight, Thomas Andrew, 1759-1838.
Destructive effects of the aphis and blights on fruit trees. 1801?

NK 0202870 MBH

VOLUME 300

Knight, Thomas Andrew, 1759-1838.
[Knights Essays.] London, Printed by W. Bulmer and Co.,
110379 1807-1837.
13 vol. in 1. 28½ x 22cm.
Binder's title.
Reprinted from Philosophical transactions.
Contents. — On the economy of bees. 1807. 11 p. — On the formation of the bark of trees. 1807. 13 p. — On the origin and office of the alburnum of trees. 1808. 11 p. — On the inconvertibility of bark into alburnum. 1808. [2], 8 p. — On the origin and formation of roots. 1809. [2], 8 p. — On the parts of trees primarily impaired by age. 1810. 8 p. — On the causes which influence the direction of the growth of roots. 1811. [2], 11 p. — On the motions of the tendrils of plants. 1812. [2], 7 p. — On the action of detached leaves of plants. 1816. 7 p. — Upon the extent of the expansion and contraction of timber in different directions relative to the position of the medulla of the tree. 1817. 8 p. — On the office of the heart wood of trees. 1818. [2], 7 p. — Upon the different qualities of the alburnum of spring and winter-felled oak trees. 1820. [2], 3 p. — On some circumstances relating to the economy of bees. Printed by R. Taylor, 1828. [2] p., p. 319-323. — On the hereditary instinctive propensities of animals. Printed by R. and J. E. Taylor, 1837. [2] p., p. 365-369.

NK 0202872 ICJ

Knight, Thomas Andrew, 1759-1838.
Experiments and observations on the motion of the sap in trees. ‹London, 1804›
Philosophical transactions of the Royal society of London, 1804. pp. 183-190.

NK 0202873 MH-A

SB375 Knight, Thomas Andrew, 1759-1838.
K5 Das Ganze der Ananaszucht ... 2. völlig
1854 umgearb. und reich verm. Aufl. neu hrsg. von Ferdinand, Freiherrn von Biedenfeld ... Weimar, B.F. Voigt, 1854.
vi,188 p. fold.plate.

1. Pineapple.

NK 0202874 CU

Knight, Thomas Andrew, k759-1838.
...On the action of detached leaves of plants; in a letter to Sir Joseph Banks..London, 1816.
7 p. ("From the Philosophical transactions.")

NK 0202875 MBH

Knight, Thomas Andrew, 1759-1838.
...On the causes which influence the direction of the growth of roots; ... London, 1811.
11 p. "From the Philosophical transactions."

NK 0202876 MBH

Knight, Thomas Andrew, 1759-1838.
On the direction of the radicle and germen during the vegetation of seeds, by Thomas Andrew Knight ... London, Printed by W. Bulmer and Co., 1806.
12 p. 25cm.
Reprinted from Royal Society of London. Philosophical transactions. 1806, p. 99-108.

NK 0202877 ICJ

Knight, Thomas Andrew, 1759-1838.
...On the formation of the bark of trees. London, 1807.
13 p. "From the Philosophical transactions."

NK 0202878 MH-A MBH

Knight, Thomas Andrew, 1759-1838.
...On the inverted action of the alburnous vessels of trees. ‹London, 1806›
Philosophicaltransactions of the Royal society of London, 1806, pp. 293-304.

NK 0202879 MH-A

Knight, Thomas Andrew
...On the office of the heart wood of trees. London, 1818.
7 p. ("From the Philosophical transactions.")

NK 0202880 MBH

Knight, Thomas Andrew, 1759-1838.
...On the origin and formation of roots. London, 1809
8 p. "From the Philosophical transactions."

NK 0202881 MBH

Knight, Thomas Andrew , 1759-1838.
...On the parts of trees primarily impaired by age; ... London, 1810.
8 p. "From the Philosophical transactions."

NK 0202882 MBH

Knight, Thomas Andrew, 1759-1838.
Pomona herefordiensis: containing coloured engravings of the old cider and perry fruits of Herefordshire. With such new fruits as have been found to possess superior excellence. Accompanied with a descriptive account of each variety, by Thomas Andrew Knight ... Pub. by the Agricultural society of Herefordshire. London, Printed for the Agricultural society of Herefordshire, 1811.
1 p. l., viii p. 30 col. pl. 32½cm.
Each plate accompanied by one or two pages of descriptive text.
1. Apple. 2. England. Pomology. 3. Pear. I. Herefordshire, Eng. Agricultural society of.
Agr 5-900
Library, U. S. Dept. of Agriculture 93K74.

NK 0202883 DNAL ICJ MH-A OU MBH WU CU LU

Knight, Thomas Andrew, 1759-1838.
...‹Report on the state and prospects of the cotton crop, 1864› n.p.,n.d.
6 p.

NK 0202884 MBH

Knight, Thomas Andrew, 1759-1838.
Sechs pflanzenphysiologische abhandlungen von Thomas Andrew Knight (1803-1812) Uebers. und hrsg. von H. Ambronn. Leipzig, W. Engelmann, 1895.
63, ‹1› p. 19½cm. (*On cover:* Ostwald's Klassiker der exakten wissenschaften, nr. 62)
Published in the Phil. trans., 1803-1812.
Chronological list of the author's papers, with name and date of publication in which they first appeared: p. 59-63.

Contents.—I. Ueber die richtung der jungen wurzel und des jungen stengels bei der keimung. (1806)—II. Ueber die ursachen, die auf richtung und wachsthum der wurzeln einwirken. (1811)—III. Ueber die rankenbewegungen der pflanzen. (1812)—IV. Nachricht von einigen versuchen über das absteigen des saftes in den bäumen. (1803)—V. Ueber die umgekehrte wirkung der splintgefässe der bäume. (1806)—VI. Ueber die neubildung von knospen. (1805)—VIII. Biographische notizen.—VIII. Anmerkungen und aufzählung der Knight'schen schriften.

1. Botany—Physiology. I. Ambronn, Hermann, 1856-1927, ed.
3-12766
Library of Congress QK711.K7

NK 0202886 DLC DNLM CU CU-S PPF OCU OU PU ICJ

Knight, Thomas Andrew, 1759-1838. 581.1 J800
A selection from the physiological and horticultural papers, pub-
113936 lished in the Transactions of the Royal and Horticultural Societies, by the late Thomas Andrew Knight, Esq., ... To which is prefixed, a sketch of his life. London, Longman, Orme, Brown, Green, and Longmans, 1841.
xii, 379 p. incl. front. (port.), 7 pl. 24½cm.
Contents. — Life of Thomas Andrew Knight, Esq. — pt. 1. Papers on vegetable physiology. — pt. 2. Papers on physiological horticulture. — Appendix. Containing papers on animal economy.

MBH DLC OU PPHor InU MiU
NK 0202887 ICJ WU NIC NN CU DNLM MiEM NcD ViLxW

Knight, Thomas Andrew, 1759-1838.

Banks, *Sir* **Joseph,** *bart.*, 1743-1820.
A short account of the cause of the disease in corn, called by farmers the blight, the mildew, and the rust. By Sir Joseph Banks, bart. 3d ed., with additions: and A letter to Sir J. Banks, on the origin of the blight, and on the means of raising late crops of garden pease. By T. A. Knight, esq.
(*In* The Pamphleteer. London, 1815. 22½cm. v. 6, p. ‹401›-419)

Knight, Thomas Andrew, 1759-1838.
...Some doubts relative to the efficacy of Mr. Forsyth's plaister in filling up the holes in trees,... London, 1802.
16 p.

NK 0202889 MH-A PPL

Knight, Thomas Andrew, 1759-1838.
A treatise on the culture of the apple & pear and on the manufacture of cider & perry. Ludlow ‹Eng.› H. Procter, 1797.
162, xxiii p. 17 cm.

1. Apple. 2. Pear. 3. Cider. 4. Perry.
SB356.K7 1797 48-36131*

NK 0202890 DLC MiEM PPL

Knight, Thomas Andrew, 1759-1838.
A treatise on the culture of the apple & pear, and on the manufacture of cider & perry. By T. A. Knight ... 2d ed., enl. Ludlow, Printed by H. Procter, 1802.
181, ‹1› p. 18cm.

1. Apple. 2. Pear. 3. Cider. 4. Perry.
11-26083
Library of Congress SB356.K7

NK 0202891 DLC OrCS WU C MdBP PPL MH MBH

Knight, Thomas Andrew, 1759-1838. 5999-7
A treatise on the culture of the apple and pear, and on the manufacture of cider and perry. 3d edition, enlarged.
Ludlow. Procter. 1809. 156 pp. 16½ cm., in 6s.

L4c63 - Perry. — Cider. — Apple. — Pear.

NK 0202892 MB DNAL MH-BA

Knight, Thomas Andrew, 1759-1838. 634.204 G800
A treatise on the culture of the apple and pear, and on the manu-
103859 facture of cider & perry. With an appendix and postscript. Fourth edition. By T. A. Knight, ... London, printed for B. and R. Crosby and Co., [etc.], 1813.
186, [8] p. 18cm.

NK 0202893 ICJ OU

VOLUME 300

Knight, Thomas Andrew, 1759-1838.
A treatise on the culture of the apple and pear, and on the manufacture of cider & perry, with an appendix. 5th ed. By T. A. Knight ... London, Longman, Hurst, Rees, Orme and Brown, 1818.
177, [8] p. 17½cm.

1. Apple. 2. Cider. 3. Pear. 4. Perry.
Agr 13-1960
Library, U. S. Dept. of Agriculture 93K74A

NK 0202894 DNAL NIC

Knight, Thomas Andrew, 1759-1838.
...Upon the extent of the expansion and contraction of timber in different directions relative to the position of the medulla of the tree... London, 1817.
8 p. "From the Philosophical transactions."

NK 0202895 MBH

Knight, Thomas Arthur, 1876-
The country estates of Cleveland men; views and descriptive matter illustrating the country seats of prominent Cleveland business men ... [Cleveland] 1903.
1 p. l., [5]-142 p., 1 l. illus. 26½ x 36cm.
Copyrighted by Thomas A. Knight.

1. Cleveland—Suburbs. 2. Suburban homes. I. Title.
4-3404
Library of Congress F499.C6K7

NK 0202896 DLC OClJC OClMA OClWHi NN

Knight, Thomas Arthur, 1876-
Country estates of the blue grass, by Thomas A Knight, Nancy Lewis Greene. [Cleveland, O., The Britton printing co.] °1904.
200 p. illus. 26½ x 36cm.

1. Kentucky—Descr. & trav. 2. Country life—Kentucky. I. Greene, Nancy Lewis. II. Title.
5-37596
Library of Congress F451.K71

NK 0202897 DLC TxU KyLx NcRS TU OCl ViU ICJ NN

Knight, Thomas Arthur, 1876-
Picturesque So. Brooklyn village; views & descriptive matter of Cleveland's most charming suburb. unp. il. [1903]

NK 0202898 OCl

Knight, Thomas Arthur, 1876-
The strange disappearance of William Morgan, by Thomas A. Knight; with introduction by J. Hugo Tatsch, P. M. Brecksville, O., The author [°1932]
302 p. incl. front. (port.) illus. (map) plates. 21½cm.
Frontispiece and plates accompanied by guard sheets with descriptive letterpress.
"References consulted by author": p. 274-275; bibliography: p. 291-295.

1. Morgan, William, 1774-ca. 1826. 2. Freemasons. Batavia, N. Y. 3. Antimasonic party. I. Title.
32-33386
Library of Congress HS525.K5
——— Copy 2.
Copyright A 57190 [3] 366.1

NK 0202899 DLC OClW IU OCl OLak

Knight, Thomas Arthur, 1876-
Tippecanoe; being the story of the Tippecanoe and Tyler too! campaign of 1840. A history of the Tippecanoe club of Cleveland, the oldest Whig-Republican club in the United States, by Thomas A. Knight. The genesis of the Republican party—excerpts from speeches of famous Republicans. Introduction by Dr. Nicholas Murray Butler ... Special articles by Colonel Carmi A. Thompson [and] Judge James B. Ruhl. [Cleveland, O., Tippecanoe club, °1940]
2 p. l., 4-138, [10] p. front., illus., plates, ports., facsims. (1 music) 23½cm.

"Some of the Tippecanoe songs", without music: p. 30-36.
Bibliography: p. 138.

1. Tippecanoe club, Cleveland. 2. Republican party. 3. Politics, Practical. 4. Campaign songs, 1840—Whig. I. Thompson, Carmi Alderman, 1870- II. Ruhl, James B., 1864- III. Title.
40-11208
Library of Congress JK2359.C638
——— Copy 2.
Copyright [3] 329.6

NK 0202901 DLC NcD OCl OClh OU PU

Knight, Thomas Cornelius, 1887-
Knights of Columbus; illustrated; a complete ritual and history of the first three degrees, including all secret "work." By a former member of the order ... An historical sketch of the institution, by Thos. C. Knight. Chicago, Ill., E. A. Cook, 1918.
xi, 13-93 p. incl. front. (port.) illus., plans. port. 15cm.

1. Knights of Columbus.
18-14831
Library of Congress HS1538.C73K5

NK 0202902 DLC Wa TxDaM-P OCl

Knight, Thomas Cornelius, 1887-
Knights of Columbus illustrated; a complete ritual and history of the first three degrees, including all secret "work." By a former member of the order. An historical sketch of the institution. Chicago, E. A. Cook [1947]
93 p. illus. 16cm.

1. Knights of Columbus.
HS1538.C73K5 1947 267.242 47-24335*

NK 0202903 DLC

Knight, Thomas F.
Descriptive catalogue of the fishes of Nova Scotia. By Thomas F. Knight ... Pub. by direction of the provincial government. Halifax, Printed by A. Grant, 1866.
54 p. 21½cm.
"Supplementary paper on sea-mammals and shell-fish": p. 37-54.

1. Fishes—Nova Scotia. 2. Mammals—Nova Scotia. 3. Crustacea—Nova Scotia. I. Title.
F 17-63
Library, U. S. Bur. of Fisheries

NK 0202904 DI CaBViP MH ICJ

Knight, Thomas F.
...Nova Scotia and her resources. By Thomas F. Knight ... Halifax, N. S.: A. & W. Mackinlay, 1862. vi, 87 p. 12°.
At head of title: Prize essay.
Published by order of the Nova Scotia commissioners for the International Exhibition.

1. Nova Scotia.
N. Y. P. L. October 11, 1920.

NK 0202905 CaOTU NN MH CaNSWA CaBViP CaBVaU DI-GS

SH224 .N8K6 **Knight, Thomas F.**
Pamphlets on the fishes and fisheries of Nova Scotia.
Halifax, 1866-67
2v.

NK 0202906 DLC CaNSWA

R 72829 .46 KNIGHT, THOMAS F.
Report on the fisheries of Nova Scotia... Halifax, A. Grant, 1867.
33p. (with his Shore and deep sea fisheries. 1867)

NK 0202907 ICN CaNSWA

Knight, Thomas F.
The river fisheries of Nova Scotia. Halifax, N.S., Printed by A. Grant, 1867
80 p. 23.5 cm.
Paper-cover: Pamphlets on the fishes and fisheries of Nova Scotia, 3.

NK 0202908 MH ICN

Knight, Thomas F.
Shore and deep sea fisheries of Nova Scotia. By Thomas F. Knight, author of "Nova Scotia and her resources." (Prize essay) ... Pub. by direction of the Provincial government. Halifax, A. Grant, 1867.
vi (*i. e.* viii), 113 p. 21½cm.
Cover has: Pamphlets on the fishes and fisheries of Nova Scotia. no. II.

1. Fisheries—Nova Scotia.
A 18-1445
Title from Harvard Univ. Printed by L. C.

NK 0202909 MH DLC CaBViP CaOTU

Knight, Thomas H., joint author.

Knight, Sampson.
Knight's medical adviser. A treatise on domestic medicine ... By Drs. Sampson and Thomas H. Knight ... Ed. by Dr. J. C. Neeley. Nashville, Tenn., S. & T. H. Knight, & S. J. Short, 1854.

[**Knight, Thomas Jefferson**]
The life and activities of Captain Newton Knight and his company. [Ellisville, Miss., Printed by the Progress-item, °1934]
cover-title, 90 p. illus. (incl. ports.) 18½cm.
"Thos. J. Knight's story of his father, Newton Knight."—p. 2.

1. Knight, Newton, 1830- 2. Jones co., Miss.—Hist. I. Title.
34-8725
Library of Congress F341.K65
——— Copy 2.
Copyright A 71099 [2] 923.573

NK 0202911 DLC

Div.S. 201 K71A Knight, Titus.
Amyntas and Philetus; or, Christian conversation; illustrated in a friendly visit into the country, in seven dialogues. Leeds [pref. 1770]
xiv, 301 p. 18 cm.

1. Christianity. Philosophy. 2. God. Love. I. Title.

NK 0202912 NcD CU-A

VOLUME 300

Knight, Titus.
An elegy on the death of the late Revd. Mr. George Whitefield ... Exhibiting a brief history of his life, labours, and glorious death. He, having preached the gospel with amazing success for about thirty-five years, finished his work, and fell asleep in the arms of Jesus, on Sunday the 30th of September 1770, at Newberry-Port, near Boston in New England, in the 56th year of his age. By T. Knight... The second edition. Halifax: Printed for the author, 1771. 18 p. 8°.

1. Whitefield, George, 1714–1770. N. Y. P. L. October 18, 1928

NK 0202913 NN

BV 4253 .K72 Knight, Titus.
Sermons on important subjects. With a Treatise on the imputation of sin and of righteousness. Leeds, Printed by G.Wright, 1766.
349,v,101 p.
"Treatise on the imputation of sin and of righteousness" (v,101 p.,2d group) has special t.p.

1.Sermons. 2.Sin. I.Title. II.Title: Treatise on the imputation of sin and of righteousness.

NK 0202914 MiU

---

*pEB65 A100 B675b v.2 Knight, Valentine, fl.1666.
Proposals of a new modell for re-building the city of London, with houses, streets and wharfes, to be forthwith set out by his Majesties and the city surveyors: with the advantages that will accrew by building the same accordingly ...
London,Printed by H.Bruges,for Samuel Speed at the Rainbow in Fleet-street,1666.
broadside. 41x31cm.,mounted & bd.to 66cm.
Signed: Val. Knight.
No. A173 of the Marquess of Bute broadsides.

NK 0202915 MH

Knight, Valentine Catherwood.
Christ our ideal: the satisfaction of the season. A sermon ... Oxford, 1866.
22 p. 8°. [In "College Pamphlets," v. 2010]

NK 0202916 CtY

Knight, Vera.
Air raid precautions for Canada ₍by₎ Vera Knight; illustrations by Margot Bodwell and J. R. Sandham. Toronto, The Macmillan company of Canada limited, 1942.
2 p. l., 76 p. illus. 17cm.

1. Canada—Civilian defense. I. Title. 42-23887

Library of Congress UA929.C2K5 ₍3₎ 355.23

NK 0202917 DLC CaBViP

---

q784.3 So58 v.1 no.51 Knight, Vick, 1908-
Savin' myself for Bill; words and music by Vick Knight ... N[ew] Y[ork] c[ity] Chappell & co. inc.; [etc., etc., c1942]
5p.
[Songs popular during World war II. v.1,no.51]

NK 0202918 IU NN

Knight, Vick, 1908–
We've got a job to do. By Vick Knight. New York, Owens-Kemp music co. ₍c1942₎
First line: Calling all miners.
Chorus: Those fellows up at the front.

~~Printed for the Music Division~~

1. War production board. 2. World war, 1939–1945. I. Song index (3). N. Y. P. L. April 30, 1947

NK 0202919 NN

Z 621.3 K74 Thesis **Knight, W. C.**
A design of a direct -connected generating set.

NK 0202920 WaPS

Knight, W E. , C. F. Armstrong, and J. Gilchrist.
Perth, Western Australia. ₍With vocabularies by W. E. Knight and C. F. Armstrong.₎ (In: E. M. Curr's The Australian race... Melbourne, 1886-87. 8°. v. 1. p. 328-335.)

1. Australian languages: Perth. 2. Jt. au. N. Y. P. L. N. Y. PUBLIC LIBRARY January 13, 1911.

NK 0202921 NN

Knight, W. H.
Diagramettes. Photo-zincograph reductions from large diagrams, with brief descriptive references, for use as students' notes & sketches (for hygiene) Lond., 1896 Chapman, Hall O.

NK 0202922 MiU DNLM

Knight, (W.H.)
Diagrammettes. 3 ed. 1902. Photozincograph reductions from large diagrams, ... London, Chapman & Hall ₍1902₎
62 p.

NK 0202923 DNLM

Knight, W H
Diagrammettes; photozincograph reductions from large diagrams with brief descriptive references for use as notes and sketches. 5th ed. London, Chapman & Hall, c1914.
70 p. illus. 22 x 28 cm.
1. Sanitation. 2. Hygiene. I. Title.

NK 0202924 CaBVaU

Knight, W. H.
Resumé, histroical and practical, with notes and comments on the subject of sewage disposal. London: Sanitary Pub. Co. ₍1903?₎ 38 p. 12°.
Title from cover.

1. Sewage.—Disposal. N. Y. P. L. December 26, 1913.

NK 0202925 NN

G 1850 .K71 W3 folio Knight (W. J.) and F. W. Hart (Firm) Baltimore.
Washington, District of Columbia; compiled from official surveys, private plans and best authorities. Baltimore, Union Engineering & Surveying Co. ₍1909₎
col. map 185 x 157 cm. fold. to 59 x 40 cm.

1. Washington, D. C. - Maps.

NK 0202926 DCU

Knight, W. Kobold, pseud
see
Giddy, Eric Cawood Gwyddyn, 1895-

Knight, W. L. P., *pseud.*
Gold and the future, by W. L. P. Knight. London, Headley brothers ₍°1928₎
3 p. l., ₍5₎-112 p. diagrs. 22cm.

1. Gold. 2. Currency question. 3. Finance. I. Title. 29-5674

Library of Congress HG289.K6

NK 0202928 DLC WaS WaTC CU NcD DS CtY PPFRB MiU NIC DL MB NBuU

Knight, W M.
Business — just as usual; a burlesque in one act. By W. M. Knight. London: A. H. Stockwell Ltd.₍, 1934.₎ 22 p. 18½cm.

1. Drama, English. I. Title. N. Y. P. L. September 28 193

NK 0202929 NN

Knight, *Mrs.* W M.
The very latest on letter writing and etiquette. By Mrs. W. M. Knight. ₍n. p., °1889₎
44, ₍1₎ p. 22½cm.

1. Letter-writing. 2. Etiquette. 11-6165

Library of Congress PE1483.K6

NK 0202930 DLC

Knight, Wade Orel.
A comparative study of laboratories & their equipment for grades 9-12 in rural schools of Clinton County, O.; status & recommended standards... [Cincinnati, 1933]
109 l.

NK 0202931 OCU

Knight, Walter Brown.
Three thousand illustrations for Christian service. Grand Rapids, W. B. Eerdmans Pub. Co., 1947.
745 p. 24 cm.

1. Homiletical illustrations. I. Title.

BV4225.K6 251 47-12162*

NK 0202932 DLC

VOLUME 300

BV 4225 K6 Knight, Walter Brown.
Three thousand illustrations for Christian service. Grand Rapids, W. B. Eerdmans, 1950 [c1947]
745 p. 24 cm.

1. Homiletical illustrations. I. Title.

NK 0202933 CaBVa LU

KNIGHT, Walter David.
Memorial sermon delivered in the Mount Washington Church...Feb.25, 1923.
49p. illus. 23cm.

NK 0202934 MH-AH

BX 8923 K55 Knight, Walter David.
Preparing young people for church membership ... Teacher's book. Philadelphia Board of Christian Education of the Presbyterian church in the U. S. A. [1938]
24p. 28cm.

1. Church membership. I. Title.

NK 0202935 NRCR

Knight, Walter Joseph.
Concerning nature and things, by Walter J. Knight. St. Louis, 1934.
73 p., 1 l. incl. mounted port. 18cm.

1. Title.

Library of Congress PS3521.N547C6 1934 34-15816
Copyright A 71811 [2] 814.5

NK 0202936 DLC

Knight, Walter Joseph.
Pert & pertinent, by Walter J. Knight. St. Louis, 1946.
104 p., 1 l. 20cm.

1. Title.

Library of Congress PS3521.N547P4 46-16080
[2] 814.5

NK 0202937 DLC

Knight, Wilbur Clinton, 1858-1903.
... The birds of Wyoming. By Wilbur C. Knight ... Laramie, 1902.
1 p. l., 174 p. illus., pl. 21½cm. (University of Wyoming. Agricultural college department. Wyoming experiment station, Laramie, Wyoming. Bulletin no. 55)
"A partial list of the publications pertaining to Wyoming birds": p. 3-5.

1. Wyoming. Ornithology.

Library, U. S. Dept. of Agriculture 413K74 Agr 3-290

NK 0202938 NN ICF-A DNAL MtBuM NIC UU CU InU MBH MiU OCl PP

Knight, Wilbur Clinton, 1858-1903.
...The Bonanza, Cottonwood and Douglas oil fields. By W. C. Knight...and E. E. Slosson... [Laramie, Wyo., 1903.] 30 p. diagrs., illus. (maps.) 8°. (Wyoming. University. Mines School. Petroleum series. Bull. no. 6.)

1. Petroleum, U. S.: Wyoming. 2. Slosson, Edwin Emery, 1865- 3. Series.
N. Y. P. L. August 28, 1924

NK 0202939 NN

ar W 54099 no.5 Knight, Wilbur Clinton, 1858-1903.
The Dutton, Rattlesnake, Arago, Oil Mountain and Powder River oil fields, by W. C. Knight and E. E. Slosson. [Laramie, Wyoming, University of Wyoming, 1901]
57 p. illus., map, 23cm. (Wyoming. University. School of Mines. Petroleum series. Bulletin no. 4)

Part of thesis, University of Nebraska.
I. Slosson, Edwin Emory, joint author, 1865-1929.

NK 0202940 NIC PU

KNIGHT, Wilbur Clinton, 1858-1903. *7863.73
The geology and technology of the Salt Creek oil field. Illus. Map.
(In University of Wyoming. School of mines. Petroleum series. Bulletin, no. 1, pp. 5-22. [Laramie, 1896.])

NK 0202941 MB PU

Knight, Wilbur Clinton, 1858-
Geology of Wyoming
see under title

Knight, Wilbur Clinton, 1858-1903
Nebraska Permian. Chic., 1899.

NK 0202943 NjP

Knight, Wilbur Clinton, 1858-1903.
Notes on a set of rocks, from Wyoming, collected, by professor Wilbur C. Knight
see under Hill, Benjamin Felix, 1875-

Knight, Wilbur Clinton, 1858-1903.
...The oil fields of Crook and Uinta counties, Wyoming. By W. C. Knight...and E. E. Slosson... [Laramie, Wyo., 1899.] 31 p. diagrs., illus. (maps.) 8°. (Wyoming. University. Mines School. Petroleum series. Bull. no. 3.)

1. Petroleum, U. S.: Wyoming. 2. Slosson, Edwin Emery, 1865- 3. Series.
N. Y. P. L. August 28, 1924

NK 0202945 NN

Knight, Wilbur Clinton, 1858-1903.
The petroleum of Salt Creek, Wyoming ... Laramie, 1896
47 p. (Wyoming, University. Petroleum series Bulletin, no. 1.)

NK 0202946 RPB

ar W 54099 no.4 Knight, Wilbur Clinton, 1858-1903.
A preliminary report on the artesian basins of Wyoming. [Laramie, Wyoming, University of Wyoming, 1900]
[2], 107-251 p. illus., maps, 23cm. (Wyoming Experiment Station. Bulletin no. 45)

Part of thesis, University of Nebraska.

NK 0202947 NIC DLC RPB PPAN PP DNAL

ar W 54099 no.6 Knight, Wilbur Clinton, 1858-1903.
The Sweetwater mining district, Fremont County, Wyoming. [Laramie, Wyoming, University of Wyoming, 1901]
35 p. map, 23cm. (Wyoming. University. School of Mines. Bulletin of the University Geological Survey of Wyoming)

Part of thesis, University of Nebraska.

NK 0202948 NIC OrCS

Knight, Wilbur Clinton, 1858-1903. *6260a.15.11
The Wyoming fossil fields expedition of July, 1899.
(*In* National Geographic Magazine. Vol. 11, pp. 449-465. Plates. Washington. 1900.)

M1021 — Wyoming. Geol. and paleon.

NK 0202949 MB

Knight, Willard M
Manual, catalogue and history of the Lafayette st. Presbyterian church of Buffalo, N. Y. Prepared and arranged by W. M. Knight. Buffalo, The Courier company, printers, 1876.
3 p. l., [5]-288 p. 23cm.

1. Buffalo. Lafayette avenue Presbyterian church.

BX9211.B9L3 1876 285.174797 35-37080 rev

NK 0202950 DLC NN

Knight, William.
A bill proposed to the Maryland legislature at the session of 1876, and entitled "An act to regulate the catching and to provide for the preservation of fish in the waters of the state and of the Potomac River. By William Knight.
(*In* Bulletin of the United States fish commission for 1882. Washington, 1883. 22½cm. vol. II, p. 265-272)

1. Fishery law and legislation—Maryland.

Library, U. S. Bur. of Fisheries F 18-101

NK 0202951 DI

Knight, William
A letter upon the London and Boston railway, shewing the advantages of a main line in that direction; as also of a direct communication being afforded to Leeds, and the benefits which would thereby accrue to the population and produce of those places; addressed to the directors and provisional committees of the London and Boston railway and Boston Haven improvement company ... London, 1836.
27 p. 20.5 cm.

NK 0202952 MH-BA

Knight, William,
Notes on the mechanics of aviation, by 1st, Lt. Wm. Knight, U. S. A. Air service. n. p. n. d. 1918.
107 p. blue prints 28½ cm. typewritten sheets.

NK 0202953 DNW

VOLUME 300

Knight, William, colonel.
A declaration of the treacherous procedings of the Lord of Inchequin against the Parliament of England, and some officers in their employment in the province of Munster in Ireland. By Collonel William Knight. London, Printed in the yeare 1648.
(1)1-7 p. 22cm. (4°.)

Thomason, v. 1, p. 722. Wing K695.
Published about Feb. 9, 1648/49.
Includes documents of the court martial at which Knight was cashiered from his regiment, p. 3-6.

4I2641. 1. Ireland—Hist., 1641-1660. 2. Inchiquin, Murrough O'Brien, 1st earl of 1614-1674.

NK 0202954 NN ICN MH

Knight, William, esq. F. S. A.
Catalogue of the ... library of the late William Knight, esq., F. S. A., of Canonbury place, Islington, and of Oaklands, near St. Albans, Hertfordshire ... Which ... will be sold by auction, by Messrs. S. Leigh Sotheby & co., auctioneers ... August 2d, 1847, and five following days ... [London] Compton and Ritchie, printers [1847]
115 p. 22½cm.
The 1,373 lots realized £4,502.
Prices and purchasers noted in manuscript.

13—6509

Library of Congress Z997.K71

NK 0202955 DLC MdBP CSmH NjP NN

Knight, William, *of London.*
Oriental outlines; or, A rambler's recollections of a tour in Turkey, Greece, & Tuscany, in 1838. By William Knight ... London, S. Low, 1839.
xi, [3], 342, xiv p. front. (map) 17½cm.

1. Levant—Descr. & trav. 4-21448

Library of Congress D972.K71

NK 0202956 DLC PPL-R MH CtY DGU

Knight, William, prof. of music, comp.
British songs. n.p. [188- ?]

3 v. illus. 31 cm.
Title from label pasted on cover.
A compilation made up of pages taken from Illustrated book of British song and How's Illustrated book of British song, as shown by the running title and pagination.

NK 0202957 MH-Mu

WBA K71p 1884
KNIGHT, William, surgeon.
The patient's vade mecum; or, How to benefit by medical advice and treatment, by William Knight and Edward Knight. London, Chatto and Windus, 1884.
viii, 120 p.
I. Knight, Edward

NK 0202958 DNLM

Knight, William, writer on astrology.
Vox stellarum: or, The voyce of the stars; being a brief and easie introduction, to the knowledge of the number, names and characters of the planets and signs ... Likewise, how to judge of the affairs of the world, by revolutions, eclipses, great conjunctions and blazing-stars. Also, something touching the popish plot, and other remarkable affairs of the year, 1678. By William Knight ... London, Printed by E. T. and R. H. for T. Passinger, 1681.
6 p. l., 156 p. 14½cm.
Pt. II and III have each special t.-p. included in pagination.
1. Astrology. 9-12576†

Library of Congress QB26.K71

NK 0202959 DLC

Knight, William, fl.1612.
A Concordance Axiomaticall: Containing A Svrvey Of Theologicall Propositions: With Their Reasons And vses in holie Scripture. Taken At First By Attent Reading, And after Digested into an Alphabeticall order for the benefit of the Church, especially for such as labour in the Word and Doctrine. Whereunto is annexed (after the Preface) a Practise teaching the vse and application of the whole Worke. By William Knight. Iohn 5.39. [Two lines] 2.Tim.3.16.17. [Three lines. Vignette] At London,Printed for Iohn Bill.1610.

14p.l.,606p. 28½cm.
Signatures: a^{6}b-c^{4}A-Z^{6}Aa-Zz^{6}Aaa-Ddd^{6}Eee^4 (Eee$_4$ blank)
Stained; a few leaves at beginning and end frayed, with damage to text on p.605.

WaPS
NK 0202961 CtY ViU DFo NcD NNC MWA RPB CSmH NNUT-Mc

FILM
Knight,William, fl.1612.
A concordance axiomaticall: containing a svrvey of theologicall propositions: with their reasons and vses in Holie Scripture. Taken at first by attent reading,and after digested into an alphabeticall order for the benefit of the Church,especially for such as labour in the Word and doctrine. Whereunto is annexed (after the preface) a practise teaching the vse and application of the whole worke. London, Printed for I.Bill, 1610.

Caption title: A treasvrie of axioms theologicall: containing a concordance reall,with synonymaes,reasons and vses.
University Microfilms no.20369 (carton 763)
Short-title catalogue no.15049.

1.Bible--Concordances,English. I.Title.

NK 0202963 MiU

K694A.5 Knight, William, fl. 1647-1653.
The case and vindication of William Knight, late minister of Whitbey ... wherein are discovered the design ... of his sequestration, which happened on the 28 of December 1652. at the Committee for plundred ministers ... London, Printed in the year 1653.

[6] 26 p. A-B^4, C^6, D^2. 4to.

NK 0202964 DFo

Knight, William, 1786-1844.
Facts and observations towards forming a new theory of the earth. Edinburgh, Printed for A. Constable, 1818.
xvi,335p. 23cm.

Bibliographical footnotes.
Advertising matter (16p. in front of vol.) not included in paging.

NK 0202965 OkU CtY PPAN IU NjP NWM PPL PPAmP

---

4 v/14
Knight, William, 1786-1844.
Outlines of botany, intended to accompany a series of practical demonstrations in that science, given by William Knight ... Aberdeen, Chalmers, 1813.
32 p. fold. table.

NK 0202966 NNC

Knight, William, 1789 *or* 90-1878.
The arch of Titus and the spoils of the temple, an historical and critical lecture with authentic illustrations, by William Knight ... London, Longmans, Green, Reader, and Dyer, 1867.
4 p. l., 141 p., 1 l. incl. front., plates. 20½cm.

1. Rome (City) Arco di Tito. 2. Jerusalem. Temple. 16—23827

Library of Congress DG69.K6

NK 0202967 DLC NcU NcD DSI CtY MB

DS122 .8 K7
Knight, William, 1789 *or* 90-1878.
... The arch of Titus and the spoils of the temple, by the late William Knight ... with an introduction by the Lord Bishop of Durham ... New York [etc.] F. H. Revell company [18—?]
126, [2] p. incl. front., illus. 18½cm. (By-paths of Bible knowledge)

1. Rome (City) Arch of Titus. 2. Jerusalem—Siege, A. D. 70.

NK 0202968 ICU NNUT NjNbS

DG69 K6 1896
Knight, William, 1789 or 90-1878.
The arch of Titus and the spoils of the temple, an historical and critical lecture with authentic illustrations, by William Knight. London, The Religious Tract Society, 1896.
126p. 18cm. (By-paths of Bible Knowledge, v.22)

1. Rome (City) Arch of Titus. 2. Jerusalem. Temple. I. Title.

NK 0202969 IaU PPDrop MH MiD NNUT

---

ar V 8653
Knight, William, 1789 or 90-1878.
The Arch of Titus and the spoils of the temple. With an introduction by the Lord Bishop of Durham. New York, Revell [introd. 1896]
126 p. illus. 19cm. (By-paths of Bible knowledge, 22)

1. Rome (City) Arch of Titus. 2. Jerusalem. Temple. I. Title.

NK 0202970 NIC NjPT TxU

---

ar U 1576
[Knight, William] 1789 or 90 - 1878.
Psalms and hymns for St. Michael's Church and the Blind Asylum Chapel, Bristol. 3d ed., enl. Bristol, I. E. Chillcott, printe 1862.

Without music.

1. Hymns, English. I. Title.

NK 0202971 NIC

MT70 K748i
Knight, William, 1817-1889.
India's plea for men. The substance of a sermon preached in Trinity church, Cambridge, on Sunday, Nov. 23, 1856. With an appendix. London, Church missionary house, 1857.
61 p. 22 cm.

1. India - Missions. I. Title.

NK 0202972 CtY-D RPB CtY

VOLUME 300

Knight, William, 1817-1889
Memoir of the Rev. H. Venn. The missionary secretariat of Henry Venn... With an introductory biographical chapter and a notice of West African commerce, by his sons... John Venn... and... Henry Venn... London, Longmans, Green, 1880.
x, 551 p. port. 23cm.

1 Venn, Henry, 1796-1873

NK 0202973 NjPT CtY NcD

Knight, William, 1817-1889
Memoir of Henry Venn ... honorary secretary of the Church missionary society ... New ed. ... London, 1882.
vi p., 1 l., 516 p. front. (port.) 19 cm.

NK 0202974 CtY

[Knight, William,] 1817–1889.
Scenes and incidents of missionary labour. London: Seeley, Jackson, and Halliday, 1860. 49 l. front., plates. 4°.

Preface signed: W. Knight.
"The subsequent pages...refer mainly to one missionary organisation—the Church Missionary Society."—Pref.

355697A. 1. Views. 2. Missions, Foreign. 3. Indians—Missions. 4. Church Missionary Society. 5. Title.
N. Y. P. L. July 9, 1928

NK 0202975 NN CtY NIC CaBViPA

PR 4859 .K48 A82
Knight, William, 1825-1866
Auld yule and other poems. With an introductory essay by ...George Gilfillan. And recollections of the author's life. Aberdeen, Lindsay, 1869.
xl,240p. 17cm.
By William Knight, of Portgordon.

NK 0202976 ScU

Knight, William, 1836-1916
see Knight, William Angus, 1836-1916.

Knight, William Abner, 1864-
How to handle a file.
... Files and filing ... New York city, The Industrial press, °1909.

Knight, William Abner, 1864–
... Laps and lapping, by William A. Knight and A. A. Case ... Columbus, O., The University [1915]
cover-title, 45 p. illus., diagrs. 23cm. (Bulletin no. 14, College of engineering)
At head of title: The Ohio state university bulletin, vol. XIX, no. 26. June, 1915.
"Appendix. Bibliography on laps and lapping": p. 43-45.

1. Grinding and polishing. I. Case, Allando A., joint author. II. Title.

Ohio state univ. Library for Library of Congress TJ1296.K6 [a41g1] A 15—1926

NK 0202979 OU OrU NN MB

Knight, William Allen, 1863-1957.
At the crossing with Denis McShane; by William Allen Knight ... drawings by Florence Scovel Shinn. Boston, New York [etc.] The Pilgrim press, 1912.
4 p. l., 3-58 p. col. front., col. plates. 18½cm. $0.60

I. Title.

Library of Congress PZ3.K748At 12-23755

NK 0202980 DLC TNJ IU PPCCH OCl NN

Knight, William Allen, 1863–
A Bedouin lover, by William Allen Knight ... New York, Boston [etc.] The Pilgrim press, 1913.
4 p. l., 3-54 p. col. front., col. pl. 20cm. $0.50
Ornamental borders.

I. Title.

Library of Congress PZ3.K748B 13-23417

NK 0202981 DLC PP OCl OO

Knight, William Allen, 1863–
A Christmas secret, by William Allen Knight. Boston, W. A. Wilde company [1946]
viii p., 1 l., 69 p. illus. 19cm.
First edition published 1910 under title: No room in the inn.

I. Title.
PZ3.K748Ch 46-22593

NK 0202982 DLC WaS OrP

Knight, William Allen, 1863–
A Christmas story and its Easter sequel. Boston, W. A. Wilde Co. [1955]
80 p. 20 cm.

I. Title.
PZ3.K748Ci 55-9055 ‡

NK 0202983 DLC OO WaT

Knight, William Allen, 1863–
A crisis in Morningdale; keeping faith when God seems against us. Boston, W. A. Wilde Co. [1947]
69 p. 20 cm.

I. Title.
PZ3.K748Cr 47-11118*

NK 0202984 DLC ViU MH-AH

Y91 K71f
KNIGHT, William Allen, 1863-1957.
From Brighton meadows. Boston, Pilgrim Press [1916]
47p. illus. (port.) 20cm.

NK 0202985 MH-AH MH

Knight, William Allen, 1863-
From Brighton meadows... Boston, [c1926]
48 p.

NK 0202986 RPB

Knight, William Allen, 1863–
The love-watch, by William Allen Knight ... Boston, New York [etc.] The Pilgrim press [1904]
6 p., 1 l., 7-55 p. 19 cm.

I. Title.

PZ3.K748L 4—9129

NK 0202987 DLC PPT OO MB NN

Knight, William Allen, 1863–
The love-watch, by William Allen Knight ... Boston, New York [etc.] The Pilgrim press [1906]
4 p.l., 7-55 p. 19cm.
"October, 1906".

NK 0202988 ViU

Knight, William Allen, 1863-
The love-watch. New York, etc., Pilgrim press [c.1908]

NK 0202989 MH OCl OO

Knight, William Allen, 1863–
A lovely find, by William Allen Knight ... Boston, W. A. Wilde company [1943]
3 p. l., 41 p. 19cm.

1. Bethlehem. 2. Jesus Christ—Nativity. I. Title.

Library of Congress DS110.B4K47 43-13880
915.69

NK 0202990 DLC WaSp MH-AH ViU OrU

Knight, William Allen, 1863–
No room in the inn, by William Allen Knight ... Boston, New York [etc.] The Pilgrim press [1910]
3 p. l., 58 p. 20cm. $0.50
Colored ornamental borders.

Library of Congress PZ3.K748N 10-19622

NK 0202991 DLC ViU OCl OO OClW

Knight, William Allen, 1863–
On the way to Bethlehem, by William Allen Knight ... New York, Boston [etc.] The Pilgrim press, 1912.
ix, 222 p. front., plates. 19cm. $1.25
Illustrated lining-papers.

1. Palestine—Descr. & trav. I. Title.

Library of Congress D107.3.K6 12-24042

NK 0202992 DLC Wa IEG MH-AH ICRL ViU OCl OO

Knight, William Allen, 1863–
Our Bethlehem guests, by William Allen Knight ... Boston, W. A. Wilde company [1944]
viii, 58 p. 19cm.

I. Title.
Library of Congress PZ3.K748Or 44-47952

NK 0202993 DLC WaS FMU ViU OrP

Knight, William Allen, 1863–
Outside a city wall, by William Allen Knight ... Boston, New York [etc.] The Pilgrim press [1911]
63 p. front. 18½cm. $0.50
Mottoes on end-papers.
CONTENTS.—Gethsemane.—Calvary.—The garden tomb.

Library of Congres 11-6725

NK 0202994 DLC ViU MH-AH PPeSchw OCl OO OCX NN

VOLUME 300

Knight, William Allen, 1863–
Peter in the firelight, by William Allen Knight ... Boston, New York [etc.] The Pilgrim press, 1911.
ix, 102 p., 1 l. front., plates. 18½cm.

1. Peter, Saint, Apostle. I. Title.
11-25687
Library of Congress BS2515.K6

NK 0202995 DLC OU PPL PPFr OO ViU MB CU

Knight, William Allen, 1863–
The pictureland of the heart, by William Allen Knight; illustrated by the photographers of the American colony in Jerusalem. New York, Boston [etc.] The Pilgrim press, 1916.
x, 259 p. front., illus., plates. 19cm. $1.25
Illustrated t.-p. and lining-papers.
Chapters 10–13 pub. in 1914 under title: The well by Bethlehem's gate.

I. Title.
16-19954
Library ot Congress PZ3.K748P

NK 0202996 DLC ViU MH-AH PPM MB OO

Knight, William Allen, 1863–
Saint Abigail of the pines, by William Allen Knight; frontispiece by George A. Williams. Boston, New York [etc.] The Pilgrim press, 1905.
viii p., 1 l., 185 p. front. 20cm.

I. Title.
5-33939
Library of Congress PZ3.K748S

NK 0202997 DLC PBa MH

Knight, William Allen, 1863–
The shepherd of Jebel Nur, by William Allen Knight ... Boston, New York [etc.] The Pilgrim press [1909]
4 p. l., 7–29 p. 18 cm.

I. Title.
PZ3.K748Sh 9-29400

NK 0202998 DLC ICRL MH OCl ViU MH-AH

Knight, William Allen, 1863–
The sign of a child; a story for Christmastide. Boston, W. A. Wilde Co. [1949]
76 p. col. front. 19 cm.

1. Jesus Christ—Biog.—Early life. I. Title.
BT310.K59 232.9 49-48258*

NK 0202999 DLC

Knight, William Allen, 1863–
The signs in the Christmas fire, by William Allen Knight ... Boston, New York [etc.] The Pilgrim press, 1908.
[31] p. front. 20cm.
Ornamental borders in green.

I. Title.
9-103
Library of Congress PZ3.K748Sl

NK 0203000 DLC MH-AH ViU N PP PPT OCl OO OEac

KNIGHT, William Allen, 1863-1957.
Social outlook in Matthew and Luke. [Boston,] [1909].
1 pam. 16 x 23.
Reprints from the Bibliotheca Sacra April, 1909. 193-216.)

NK 0203001 MH

Knight, William Allen, 1863–
The song of our Syrian guest; William Allen Knight. Boston, The Pilgrim press [1904?]
14 p. 16½cm.
Reprinted from the Congregationalist.

I. Title.
5-2880

NK 0203002 DLC IdB WaS WaT RPB LyWAT PPL MH NNUT KyU CSaT

DM 39.5 K748 Knight, William Allen, 1863–
The song of our Syrian guest; William Allen Knight. Boston. The Pilgrim press [1904?]
29 p. 16½cm.
Reprinted from the Congregationalist.

NK 0203003 KyWAT

Knight, William Allen, 1863–
The song of our Syrian guest, by William Allen Knight; illustrations and decorative designs by Charles Copeland. Boston, New York [etc.] The Pilgrim press [c1904]
[44] p. front., 2 plates. 19½cm.
"Shepherd life in Bible lands, [by] Prof. George E. Post": p. [39–41]
"The singing pilgrim, a characterization of the Twenty-third Psalm, [by] Henry Ward Beecher": p. [42–44]

1. Bible. O. T. Psalms XXIII—Criticism, interpretation, etc. I. Copeland, Charles, 1858– illus. II. Title.
4-8304
Library of Congress BS1450.23d.K6

NK 0203004 DLC TU FTaSU CaBVaU ViU MBrZ OU MH-AH NcC OrCS MtBC NcD ViU PPT PBa OCl OEac OU MB PHC NN

Knight, William Allen, 1863–
The song of our Syrian guest, by William Allen Knight. Boston, New York [etc.] The Pilgrim press [c1905]
24 p. 19 cm.
"350th thousand."

1. Bible. O.T. Psalms XXIII – Criticism, interpretation, etc. I. Title.

NK 0203005 Vi OO MH

Knight, William Allen, 1863-1957.
The song of our Syrian guest. Frontispiece and decorations by H. Sichel. Boston: Pilgrim Press, 1906. 15 p., 1 pl. 12°.

1. Bible.—Old Testament: Psalms: 23d Psalm in fiction. 2. Sichel, Harold, illustrator. 3. Title.
N. Y. P. L. March 24, 1913.

NK 0203006 NN

Knight, William Allen, 1863–
The song of our Syrian guest, by William Allen Knight; frontispiece and decorations by Harold Sichel. Boston, New York [etc.] The Pilgrim press, 1906.
[29] p., 1 l. col. front. 20½ cm.
Title within ornamental border.

I. Title.
(✠ BS1450) 6-37616
Library of Congress [a54f1]

NK 0203007 MB OrStbM WaTC OrP

Knight, William Allen, 1863–
The song of our Syrian guest, by William Allen Knight; frontispiece and decorations by Harold Sichel. [200th thousand] Boston, New York [etc.] The Pilgrim press, 1906.
[31] p. col. front. 20½cm.
Title within red ornamental border.

I. Title.
6-34259
Library of Congress

NK 0203008 DLC NjNbS IU MB PSt PHC PPGi OCl OO ViU MB WaSp

Knight, William Allen, 1863-
The song of our Syrian guest. Frontispiece and decorations by Harold Sichel. [550th thousand] Boston, Pilgrim Press [c1906]
[29]p. (unpaged) col. front.
Title within green ornamental border.

1. Bible. O. T. Psalms XXIII - Criticism, interpretation, etc. I. Sichel, Harold, illus. II. Title.

NK 0203009 TNDC

Knight, William Allen, 1863–
The song of our Syrian guest, by William Allen Knight; illustrations and decorative designs by Charles Copeland. Boston, New York [etc.] The Pilgrim press [1908, c1904]
[44] p. front., 2 pl. 19½ cm.
"Shepherd life in Bible lands, [by] Prof. George E. Post": p. [39–41]
"The singing pilgrim, a characterization of the Twenty-third Psalm, [by] Henry Ward Beecher": p. [42–44]

NK 0203010 FU MH PP

KNIGHT, William Allen, 1863-
The song of our Syrian guest. Illustrations and decorative designs by Charles Copeland. Boston, etc., The Pilgrim Press, [cop.1911].

NK 0203011 MH ViU NjP OCl OClW OOxM FMU Mi NIC Or

Knight, William Allen, 1863-
The song of our Syrian guest, by William Allen Knight; decorations by Harold Sichel. Boston, Chicago, The Pilgrim press [1934]
[29] p. 20 cm.
First published 1904.
1. Bible. O.T. Psalms XXIII - Criticism, interpretation, etc. I. Title.

NK 0203012 CU

Knight, William Allen, 1863–
The song of our Syrian guest, by William Allen Knight; frontispiece and decorations by Harold Sichel. Boston, New York [etc.] The Pilgrim press, [c1934]
[29] p., 1 l. col. front. 20 cm.
Title within ornamental border.

NK 0203013 NcGU

BS1450 .23 K6 1945 Knight, William Allen, 1863-
The song of our Syrian guest. Boston, Pilgrim Press [c1945]
[23] p.
First pub. 1904.

1. Bible. O.T. Psalm XXIII - Criticism, interpretation, etc. I. Title.

NK 0203014 CU

VOLUME 300

Knight, William Allen, 1863–
The story of the manger. Boston, W. A. Wilde Co. [1954]
52 p. illus. 20 cm.

1. Jesus Christ—Nativity. I. Title.
BT315.K65 232.921 54-9505 ‡

NK 0203015 DLC WaS NN

Knight, William Allen, 1863–
To little David of Smyrna; an Easter message, by William Allen Knight ... New York: Pilgrim Press, 1913. 31 p. incl. mounted front. 12°.

1. Jesus Christ.—Resurrection. 2. Title.
N. Y. P. L. December 31, 1917.

NK 0203016 NN OO

Knight, William Allen, 1863–
War-time "over here," by William Allen Knight ... Boston, Chicago, The Pilgrim press [1918]
2 p. l., vii-xii, 139 p. 20cm.
"These sketches have been written from day to day throughout the time of America's preparation for the part she is now beginning to play in the drama of world war."

1. European war, 1914– —U. S. I. Title.
Library of Congress D619.K55 18-10292

NK 0203017 DLC NjP OCl OClWHi OO MB

Knight, William Allen, 1863–1967.
The well by Bethlehem's gate, by William Allen Knight ... New York, Boston [etc.] The Pilgrim press, 1914.
55 p. front., plates. 18½ cm.

I. Title.
PZ3.K748W 14—12856

NK 0203018 DLC OO MH-AH

Knight, William Angus, 1836–1916, ed.
Andreapolis, being writings in praise of St. Andrews, chosen and edited by Professor Knight. Edinburgh, D. Douglas, 1903. xxii, 199 p. 18cm.

1. St. Andrews, Scot., in litera- ture.
N. Y. P. L. February 14, 1952

NK 0203019 NN MH MiU

Knight, William Angus, 1836–1916.
Aspects of theism, by William Knight ... London and New York, Macmillan and co., 1893.
x, 220 p. 22½cm.
Lectures, enlarged with addenda, delivered in 1890 at the Theological college, Salisbury, and in 1891 in London.—Pref.

1. Theism. I. Title.
30-28769
Library of Congress BL200.K6 211

CU NNUT NjNbS OU CU NIC
NK 0203020 DLC OrP OrPR NcD ICN PP PPPD PBm MB OClW

Knight, William Angus, 1836-1916, ed.
A book of sacred verse... Lond., [Religious tract of society, 1910.

550 p.

NK 0203021 NNUT CtY WaS PPLT CaBViP

Wordsworth
N
7622
K71
Knight, William Angus, 1836-1916.
A catalogue of portraits of philosophers, poets, and others, presented to the United College of St. Andrews, by Professor Knight, in the year 1902, and hung in the moral philosophy classroom for the use of students. St. Andrews [Scot.] Printed by W. C. Henderson, 1902.
27 p. 16cm.
Nos. 381-407, are portraits of Wordsworth and Lake Country scenes.
Healey 1286.
1. Portraits --Catalogs. 2. St Andrews, Scot. University. I. Title.

NK 0203022 NIC InU

Knight, William Angus, 1836-1916.
The Christian ethic. By William Knight ... London, J. Murray, 1893.
xiv p., 1 l., 178 p. 19½cm.
Bibliography: p. 174-178.

1. Christian ethics. I. Title.
38-4281
Library of Congress BJ1227.K6
[2] 171.1

NK 0203023 DLC CaBVaU PPPD PPL PPPL MB

Knight, William Angus, 1836–
Coleridge and Wordsworth in the West country, their friendship, work, and surroundings, by Professor Knight, illustrated by Edmund H. New. London, E. Mathews, 1913.
xvi, 237, [1] p., 1 l. incl. front., illus., plates. 22½cm.

1. Coleridge, Samuel Taylor, 1772–1834. 2. Wordsworth, William, 1770–1850. I. Title.
A 14-604
Title from Wesleyan Univ. Printed by L. C.

OCU NjP NN MB ICN MU ScU TxU NIC CoU CaBVaU
NK 0203024 CtW WaS OrU NcU CtY PU PHC PPL MiU OClW

Knight, Wm. Angus, 1836-1916.
Coleridge & Wordsworth in the West country, their friendship, work, & surroundings, illus. by Edmund H. New. Lond., E. Mathews, 1914.
242 [2]p.

"2d ed., rev."

NK 0203025 OO PP PSC

PR4483
.K7
Knight, William Angus, 1836–1916.
Coleridge and Wordsworth in the West country, their friendship, work, and surroundings, by Professor Knight, illustrated by Edmund H. New. New York, C. Scribner's, 1914.
xvi, 237, [1] p., 1 l. incl. front., illus., plates. 22½cm.

NK 0203026 ICU MH CaBVa TU NcRS OrP

Knight, Rev. William Angus, 1836–
Colloquia peripatetica. 1873
see under Duncan, John, 1796-1870.

KNIGHT, WILLIAM ANGUS, 1836-1916.
Dove cottage, Grasmere, from 1800 to 1900. Ambleside, George Middleton, 1900.

NK 0203028 InU CtY NRU NjP MH MA PSC NNC NcU

PR
5884
K5
1900
Knight, William Angus, 1836-1916.
Dove cottage, Grasmere; from 1800 to 1900, by Professor Knight. [2nd ed.] Ambleside, G. Middleton, 1900.

1. Wordsworth, William, 1770-1850 - Homes and haunts. I. Title.

NK 0203029 CoU

Knight, William Angus, 1836– ed.
An Easter anthology; collected, arranged, and edited by William Knight ... London, Sidgwick & Jackson, ltd., 1912.
xx, 218, [2] p. 18cm.

I. Title.
W 12-111
Washington, D. C. Public Library

NK 0203030 DWP CaBVa PPLT

Knight, William Angus, 1836-1916.
The English lake district as interpreted in the poems of Wordsworth, by William Knight ... Edinburgh, David Douglas, 1878.
248 p. 17½cm.
1. Wordsworth, William, 1770-1850.
2. Lake district, Eng.
I. Wordsworth, William, 1770-1850.
II. Title.

NK 0203031 NNC MWelC NIC RPB CtY PPFr PSC MiU MdBP

In
W890
Z878kb
Knight, William Angus, 1836-1916.
The English lake district as interpreted in the poems of Wordsworth ... 2d ed., revised and enlarged. Edinburgh, D. Douglas, 1891.
viii, xvi, 270p. incl. front. (port.) 16cm.

1. Wordsworth, William, 1770-1850. 2. Lake district, Eng.

MiU ODW MH
NK 0203032 CtY WaS CaBVaU OrU KMK InU NIC PPL OCl

Knight, William Angus, 1836–1916.
The English lake district as interpreted in the poems of Wordsworth, by William Knight ... 3d ed. Edinburgh, D. Douglas, 1904.
viii, xvi p., 1 l., 270, [2] p. incl. front. (port.) 16cm.

1. Lake district, Eng. I. Wordsworth, William, 1770–1850. II. Title.
10-5838
Library of Congress PR5892.L3K5 1904

NK 0203033 DLC NcU TU CU OrU NcD PV MA DAU

Knight, William Angus, 1836–1916.
Essays in philosophy, old and new, by William Knight ... Boston and New York, Houghton, Mifflin and company, 1890.
2 p. l., [iii]–xx p., 1 l., [23]–367 p. 18½cm.
CONTENTS.—Idealism and experience, in literature, art and life.—The classification of the sciences.—Ethical philosophy and evolution.—Eclecticism.—Pesonality and the infinite.—Immorality.—The doctrine of metempsychosis.

1. Philosophy—Addresses, essays, lectures. 2. Ethics. I. Title.
15—13541
Library of Congress B1646.K73E5

OCl ODW OO IEG CtY
NK 0203034 DLC WU NjNbS DI KMK PSC-Hi PU PPPD MH MB

VOLUME 300

Knight, ⌊William Angus⌋, *1836-1916.*
"Free libraries: their uses and ideals." A lecture given by Professor Knight...at Malvern on the 8th February, 1905. A report of the proceedings...in connection with the laying of the foundation stone of the Malvern Public Library by H. F. Lambert. A retrospect: being the story of the Malvern Public Library by the Chairman of the Committee ⌊i. e. E. A. Heathfield. Malvern: Malvern Urban District Council, 1905⌋ 31 p. 8°.

Repr.: Malvern Gazette, Feb. 10, 1905.

1. Libraries (Public), Gt. Br.: Eng.: Malvern. 2. Lambert, Sir H. F., bart. 3. Heathfield, E. A.
N. Y. P. L. January 25, 1912.

NK 0203035 NN MH MB

101
K74f
Knight, William Angus, *1836-1916.*
The function of philosophy at the present time. n.p. [18--]
16p.

Caption title.

NK 0203036 IU

Knight, William Angus, 1836– *comp.*
The glamour of Oxford; descriptive passages in verse and prose by various writers, chosen and ed. by William Knight ... Oxford, B. H. Blackwell; London, New York ⌊etc.⌋ H. Frowde, 1911.
xxiv, 263, ⌊1⌋ p. 20cm.

1. Oxford. University. 2. Oxford—Descr.

11-11258

Library of Congress LF528.K6

NK 0203037 DLC N IEN CtY PSC MiU OC1W PBa MB

Knight, William Angus, 1836-
Hume. Cheap edition. Philadelphia, Lippincott, n.d.
239p. (Half-title: Philosophical classics for English readers, ed. by William Knight ⌊v.11⌋

NK 0203038 MtBC

192
H88Ykn
KNIGHT, WILLIAM ANGUS, 1836-
Hume, by William Knight ... Edinburgh and London, W. Blackwood and sons, 1886.
x, 239p. front.(port.) 17½cm. (Half-title: Philosophical classics for English readers. [v.11])

1. Hume, David, 1711-1776.

NK 0203039 TxU OrU PPT

Knight, William *Angus, 1836-1916.*
Hume. Philadelphia, Lippincott, 1886.
x, 239 p. port. 18cm. (Philosophical classics for English readers. ⌊v. 11,⌋)

Includes references to Spinoza.

1. Spinoza, Benedictus de, 1632-1677.

NK 0203040 NNC WaS TxDaM NcC MiEM IaU OU MH NjP

Knight, William Angus, 1836–1916.
Hume, by William Knight ... Edinburgh and London, W. Blackwood and sons, 1886, reprint, 1895.
x, 239 p. front. (port.) 17½cm. (*Half-title:* Philosophical classics for English readers. ⌊v. 11⌋)

1. Hume, David, 1711–1776.

Library of Congress B1497.K7 10—32134

PBm MH CMenSP
NK 0203041 DLC WaTC OrU CaBVaU NcD OC1 MiU OO PWcS

Knight, William Angus, 1836-1916.
Hume, by William Knight ... Cheap edition. Edinburgh and London, W. Blackwood and sons, 1901.
1 p.l., [v]-x, 239 p. 17.5 cm. [Philosophical classics for English readers. v. 11]

NK 0203042 CtY

Knight, William *Angus, 1836-1916.*
Hume. Cheap ed. Edinburgh, etc., W.Blackwood and sons, 1902.

NK 0203043 MH

Knight, William Angus, 1836-1916.
Hume, by William Knight. Cheap ed. Edinburgh and London, W. Blackwood and sons, 1905.
1 p.l., [v]-x, 239 p. 18 cm.

NK 0203044 CU MH ViU

B
1497
K7
1910
Knight, William Angus, 1836–1916.
Hume, by William Knight ... Edinburgh and London, W. Blackwood ,1910.
x, 239 p. front. (port.) 17½ cm.

NK 0203045 MU OrPR

Knight, William Angus, 1836-1916, joint author.

Martineau, James, 1805–1900.
Inter amicos; letters between James Martineau and William Knight, 1869–72. London, J. Murray, 1901.

Knight, William Angus, 1836-1916, ed.
FOR OTHER EDITIONS SEE MAIN ENTRY

Wordsworth, Dorothy, 1771–1855.
Journals of Dorothy Wordsworth; ed. by William Knight ... London, Macmillan and co., ltd.; New York, The Macmillan co., 1897.

Knight, William Angus, 1836-1916. ed.

Wordsworth, William, 1770–1850.
Letters of the Wordsworth family from 1787 to 1855, collected and ed. by William Knight ... Boston and London, Ginn and company, 1907.

Knight, William Angus, 1836–1916.
The life of William Wordsworth. By William Knight, LL. D. ... Edinburgh, W. Paterson, 1889.
3 v. front. (port., v. 1) 23 cm.
This copy has lithographed (?) portrait tipped in v. 3.

1. Wordsworth, William, 1770–1850.

A 30—557

Rochester Univ. Libr.
for Library of Congress ⌊a48b1⌋

OrU MB OOxM InU NjP ViU NIC NcU NcD ScU
NK 0203049 NRU OrCS TU PPL PBm PSC OC1JC OO WaU MH

Wordsworth
PR
5884
K71L7
Knight, William Angus, 1836-1916.
A literary shrine: Dove Cottage, the home of Wordsworth and De Quincey. [New York, 1900]
53-[62] p. illus. 23cm.

Extract from Century, v. 60, May 1900.
Healey 1266.

1. Wordsworth, William, 1770-1850--Homes and haunts. 2. De Quincey, Thomas, 1785-1859--Homes and haunts. I. Title. II. Title: Dove Cottage, the home of Wordsworth and De Quincey. III. Century, v. 60, May 1900.

NK 0203051 NIC

Knight, William Angus, 1836-1916, **ed.**

Minto, William, 1845–1893.
The literature of the Georgian era, by William Minto ... ed. with a biographical introduction by William Knight ... New York, Harper & brothers, 1895.

Knight, William Angus, 1836–1916.
Lord Monboddo and some of his contemporaries. London, J. Murray, 1900.
xv p., 1 l., 314 p. incl. front. plates, ports. 22½cm.

1. Monboddo, James Burnett, lord, 1714–1799.

Library of Congress B1520.Z7K5 1-25072

MiU OCU OU OC1W TxU CU ILfC
NK 0203053 DLC CSt NcD PPAmP TU AU NcU CtY PHi PP

Knight, William Angus, 1836-1916.
Lord Monboddo and some of his contemporaries ... New York, 1900.

NK 0203054 MdBJ

Knight, ⌊William Angus⌋ 1836–
Memoir of John Nichol, professor of English literature in the University of Glasgow, by Professor Knight . . . Glasgow, J. MacLehose and sons, 1896.
xxiv, 315, [1] p. front., pl., port. 23½cm.
"List of John Nichol's writings": p. 308–309.
Subject entries: Nichol, John, 1833–1894.

2-7557

MiU OC1 PPFr TxU NIC
NK 0203055 DLC CaBVaU NjP ICU NSyU GU CU CtY PPL

PR
1346
K5
1887
Knight, William Angus, 1836–1916, comp.
Memorials of Coleorton; being letters from Coleridge, Wordsworth and his sister, Southey, and Sir Walter Scott, to Sir George and Lady Beaumont of Coleorton, Leicestershire, 1803 to 1834. Edited with introd. and notes, by William Knight. Boston, Houghton, Mifflin, 1887.
2 v. 20 cm.

Running title: Coleorton letters.

I. Beaumont, Sir George Howland, bart., 1753–1827. II. Beaumont, Margaret (Willes) Lady, d. 1829. III. Coleridge, Samuel Taylor, 1772–1834. IV. Wordsworth, William, 1770–1850. V. Wordsworth,Dorothy, 1771–1855. VI. Southey, Robert, 1774–1843. VII. Scott, Sir Walter, Bart., 1771–1832. VIII. Title. IX. Title: Coleorton letters.

NK 0203056 Vi CtY DLC NNUT MB InU MH NIC

Knight, William Angus, 1836–1916, *ed.*
Memorials of Coleorton, being letters from Coleridge, Wordsworth and his sister, Southey, and Sir Walter Scott to Sir George and Lady Beaumont of Coleorton, Leicestershire, 1803 to 1834. Ed., with introduction and notes, by William Knight ... Edinburgh, D. Douglas, 1887.
2 v. plan. 19½cm.
I. Beaumont, Sir George Howland, bart., 1753–1827. II. Beaumont, Margaret (Willes) lady, d. 1829. III. Coleridge, Samuel Taylor, 1772–1834. IV. Wordsworth, William, 1770–1850. V. Wordsworth, Dorothy, 1771–1855. VI. Southey, Robert. 1774–1843. VII. Scott, Sir Walter, bart., 1771–1832. VIII. Title. IX. Title: Coleorton, Memorials of.

18-20747

Library of Congress PR1346.K5

PPFr MB MA NIC MdBP FTaSU CaBVaU
NK 0203057 DLC OrPR NcU NcD NjP PPL PP PSC OO OU

VOLUME 300

Knight, William Angus, 1836–1916.
Memorials of Thomas Davidson, the wandering scholar; collected and ed. by William Knight. Boston and London, Ginn and company, 1907.
2 p. l., 241 p. front. (port.) 21½cm.
"Bibliography of Thomas Davidson's works": p. 235–241.

1. Davidson, Thomas, 1840–1900. 7—26349
Library of Congress CT275.D25K6

NK 0203058 DLC WaS WaSp NIC NcD MeB PU PPD MiU OCl OO OU MB OrP

Knight, William [Angus], 1836-1916.
Memorials of Thomas Davidson, the wandering scholar; collected and edited by William Knight. London: T. Fisher Unwin, 1907. xi, 241 p., 1 port. 8°.

1. Davidson, Thomas. N. Y. P. L. February 21, 1912.

NK 0203059 NN MH

Knight, William Angus, 1836-1916.
Nineteenth century artists, English and French. Edinburgh: Otto Schulze and Co., 1910. 189 p., 50 pl., 1 port. 8°. (Scammon lectures.)
Some characteristics of the genius of Turner. Modern landscape art in England and France. Ruskin, as art-critic and as moralist, with some personal reminiscences. The Pre-Raphaelites, especially Dante Gabriel Rossetti, with reminiscences. George Frederick Watts, with reminiscences. Edward Burne-Jones, and others.

1. Artists. 2. Five subject anal. 3. Series. N. Y. P. L. April 24, 1913.

NK 0203060 NN TU CU NNCoCi PP NIC CaBVaU

Byc 87w 13 [Knight, William Angus] 1836-1916.
The official catalogue of the contents of Dove Cottage, Grasmere, Wordsworth's home from 1799 to 1808, and afterwards De Quincey's residence. Ambleside, 1902.
Binder's title: Local pamphlets. 13.
"Prefatory note" signed: William Knight

NK 0203061 CtY InU MA

Knight, William Angus, 1836-1916.
Philosophical classics for English readers
see under title

Knight, William Angus, 1836–1916.
The philosophy of the beautiful, being outlines of the history of aesthetics, by William Knight ... London, J. Murray, 1891.
xv, 288 p. 19cm. (*Half-title:* University extension manuals, ed. by Professor Knight. The philosophy of the beautiful, I. Its history)

1. Esthetics—Hist. I. Title. 4—1721
Library of Congress N66.K7 [a37g1] -701

NK 0203063 DLC WaE MtU NcD PHC PPL PBa PPPL OCl MH OClW NN Nh NjP ViU CaOTP CLU CaBVaU

---

701 K748p Knight, William Angus, 1836-1916.
The philosophy of the beautiful ... by William Knight ... New York, C. Scribner's sons, 1891-93.
2v. (Half-title: University extension manuals, edited by Professor Knight)
Vol.2 has imprint: London, J. Murray, 1893.
Contents.- v.1. Outlines of the history of aesthetics.- v.2. A contribution to its theory and to a discussion of the arts.
1. Esthetics. I. Title.

NK 0203064 IU CtY WU NjNbS IaU MB NjP MiU PPFr MH

W 001 .467 v.2 Knight, William Angus, 1836-1916.
The philosophy of the beautiful, being a contribution to its theory, and to a discussion of the arts... London, 1893. (University extension manuals...)
Half-title reads: ...The philosophy of the beautiful: II. Its theory and its relation to the arts.

NK 0203065 ICN MB MH NcD CtY OO OU

Knight, William Angus, 1836–1916.
The philosophy of the beautiful, being a contribution to its theory, and to a discussion of the arts, by William Knight ... New York, C. Scribner's sons, 1898.
xii, 281 p. 18cm. (*Half-title:* University extension manuals, ed. by Professor Knight. The philosophy of the beautiful, II. Its theory and its relation to the arts)
On cover: The university series.

1. Esthetics. I. Title. 4—1721a
Library of Congress N66.K7 [a40g1] -701

NK 0203066 DLC WaTC OrPR WaS FMU Mi TU NjP MWelC NcD ODW IU

Knight, William [Angus], 1836– 157 Q302
The philosophy of the beautiful, ..., by William Knight .... [Part I–II.] London, J. Murray, 1903–1904.
2 vol. 19cm. (*On cover:* University extension manuals.)
Contents.—I. Its history. 1903. xv, 288 p.—II. Its theory and its relation to the arts. 1904. xii, 281 p.
Bibliographical lists at end of chapters VI, VIII–XIII of vol. II.

NK 0203067 ICJ IdU CaBVaU NRU NcD

Knight, William Angus, 1836-1916. 701-K
The philosophy of the beautiful. New York: Charles Scribner's Sons, 1904. 2 v. (University manuals.)
v. 1. Outlines of the history of aesthetics.
v. 2. A contribution to its theory, and to a discussion of the arts.

1. Æsthetics. 2. Art. N. Y. P. L. September 25, 1912.

NK 0203068 NN NNC OCX

N 66 .K7 1906 Knight, William Angus, 1836-1916.
The philosophy of the beautiful, by William Knight, New York, Charles Scribner's sons, 1906-1914.
2v. 19cm. (University manuals)
Contents.- v.1. Its history.- v.2. Its theory and its relation to the arts.
1. Aesthetics - Hist. I. Title.

NK 0203069 TNJ CU

KNIGHT, WILLIAM ANGUS, 1836-
THE PHILOSOPHY OF THE BEAUTIFUL ... LONDON, 1916, 1914.
2 V. 28½CM. (HALF-TITLE: UNIVERSITY MANUALS, ED. BY PROF. KNIGHT)

NK 0203070 MdBJ PPT OClW MdBP

701.17 K748p Knight, William Angus, 1836-1916.
The philosophy of the beautiful... New York, C. Scribner's Sons, 1918.
2 v. 18cm. (University manuals)
Includes bibliographies.
Contents.- pt.1. The philosophy of the beautiful, being outlines of the history of aesthetics.- pt.2. The philosophy of the beautiful, being a contribution to its theory, and to a discussion of the arts.

NK 0203071 MiDW

Knight, William Angus, 1836-1916, ed.
Coleridge, Samuel Taylor, 1772–1834.
The poems and dramatic works of Samuel Taylor Coleridge, edited by William Knight. London, G. Newnes, limited; New York, C. Scribner's sons [1904]

Knight, William Angus, 1836-1916, ed.
Wordsworth, William, 1770–1850.
The poetical works of William Wordsworth; ed. by William Knight ... Edinburgh, W. Paterson, 1882–89.

Knight, William Angus, 1836– *ed.*
The poets on Christmas; selected and edited by William Knight. Published under the direction of the Tract committee. London, Society for promoting Christian knowledge; New York, E. S. Gorham; [etc.] 1907.
xvii, 192 p. 19½cm.

W 8-96
Washington, D. C. Public Library

NK 0203074 DWP AU NNUT IU NN

Knight (William Angus) 1836-1916.
The power of prayer . . . 22 pp. *Dundee: Middleton,* 1873. 8°.
In: **Cl.** p. v. 30.

NK 0203075 NN

Knight, William Angus, 1836–1916.
Prayers, ancient and modern. Chosen, ed., and written by William Angus Knight ... [2d ed.] London, J. M. Dent & sons, ltd., 1912.
270 p., 1 l. 17cm.
"The first edition ... was issued in ... 1905."—Pref. to the 2d ed.
Works on ancient liturgies: p. 20–21.

1. Prayers (Collections) I. Title. A 13—1019
Newberry library for Library of Congress [a41b1]

NK 0203076 ICN NjNbS PPLT MB OCH NRCR

Knight, William Angus, 1836–1916.
Principal Shairp and his friends, by William Knight ... London, J. Murray, 1888.
xix, 457 p. front. (port.) 22cm.

1. Shairp, John Campbell, 1819–1885. 28-21689
Library of Congress PR5349.S8K5

NK 0203077 DLC OrU MU CtY PPGi PHC OClW PPFr PBm MiU OU NNUT MdBP NN IU NjP NIC CaBVaU

Knight, William Angus, 1836– *comp.*
Pro patria et rege, poems on war, its characteristics and results, selected in aid of the Belgian relief fund, from British and American sources, by Professor Knight; with an explanatory preface dedicated to Lord Roberts, F. M. London, J. & J. Bennett ltd. [1915]
xxix, 31–218 p. 19½cm.

1. War poetry. 2. Gt. Brit.—Hist.—Poetry. I. Title. 15-22563
Library of Congress PR1195.H5K5

NK 0203078 DLC MeB CtY NN MB MH

VOLUME 300

Knight, William Angus, 1836– , compiler.
Pro patria et rege; poems on war, its characteristics and results, selected in aid of the Belgian Relief Fund from British and American sources, by Professor Knight; with an explanatory preface, dedicated to Herbert H. Asquith ... Second series. London: J. & J. Bennett, Ltd. [1915.] 2 p.l., vii–xxviii p., 1 l., 31–204 p. 12°.

1. War.—Poetry. 2. Poetry (Patriotic), English.—Collections. 3. Poetry (Patriotic), American.—Collections. 4. Title.
N. Y. P. L. January 26, 1916.

NK 0203079 NN CSt-H

SPECIAL COLLECTIONS
*SCA
.4823F
.1
Knight, William Angus, 1836-1916, **comp.**
Pro patria et regina; being poems from nineteenth century writers in Great Britain and America, issued in aid of Her Majesty Queen Alexandra's fund for soldiers and sailors.
Glasgow, J. MacLehose, 1901.
xxi, 163 p. 18cm.

1. English poetry (Collections) 2. American poetry (Collections). I. Title.

NK 0203080 MB NN NcU MH CSmH MiU CtY IEN PPRCl

Knight, William Angus, 1836–1916.
Reciprocity in trade the empire's safeguard, by Professor Knight. no. 1. Preferential colonial tariffs. London, W. Heinemann, 1903.
58 p. 21½cm.
No more published?

1. Reciprocity. 2. Tariff—Gt. Brit. 3. Imperial federation. I. Title.
5-25826 Revised
Library of Congress HF1733.G7K7

NK 0203081 DLC IEN AU ICJ NN

LF1117
.5
.A3
Knight, William Angus, 1836-1916, ed.
St. Andrews, Scot. University.
Rectorial addresses delivered at the University of St. Andrews; Sir William Stirling-Maxwell, bart., to the Marquess of Bute, 1863–1893; ed. with an introduction by William Knight ... London, A. and C. Black, 1894.

CT782
.K4
1904
Knight, William Angus, 1836-1916.
Retrospects. First series. London, Smith, Elder, 1904.
xiii, 310 p. illus. 21cm.
CONTENTS.—Thomas Carlyle.—Frederick Denison Maurice.—Alfred Tennyson.—Robert Browning.—James Martineau.—Arthur Stanley.—Matthew Arnold.—W. E. Gladstone.—William Davies.—James Smetham.—Whitwell Elwin.—Anna Swanwick.—J. Henry Shorthouse.

1. Gt. Brit.—Biog. 2. Authors, English. I. Title.

NK 0203083 ViU OClW TxU RPB

Knight, William Angus, 1836–1916.
Retrospects, by William Knight ... [1st series] New York, C. Scribner's sons, 1904.
xiii p., 1 l., 310 p. illus. 22cm.
CONTENTS.—Thomas Carlyle.—Frederick Denison Maurice.—Alfred Tennyson.—Robert Browning.—James Martineau.—Arthur Stanley.—Matthew Arnold.—W. E. Gladstone.—William Davies.—James Smetham.—Whitwell Elwin.—Anna Swanwick.—J. Henry Shorthouse.

1. Gt. Brit.—Biog. 2. Authors, English. I. Title.
5—12216
Library of Congress CT782.K4

MiU OO ODW PPA MB
NK 0203084 DLC CaBVaU OrP OKentU CU PPL PP PHC PBm

Knight, William [Angus] 1836-1916, ed.
[Review of: Berendt, Martin, & Friedländer, J.-Spinoza's Erkenntnisslehre in ihrer Beziehung zur modernen Naturwissenschaft und Philosophie. Allgemein verständlich dargestellt. Ber.: Mayer & Müller, 1891.
Edinburgh: T. & T. Clark, 1892. p.296-307.

Extra.: The critical review of theol. & philosophical literature. v.2, no.3.

NK 0203085 OCH

Knight, William Angus, 1836–1916, *ed.*
The Robert Browning centenary celebration at Westminster abbey, May 7th, 1912, ed. with an introduction and appendices by Professor Knight ... Boston and New York, Houghton Mifflin company, 1912.
xiv, 107, [1] p. front. (port.) 17½cm.
Printed in Great Britain.

1. Browning, Robert—Anniversaries, etc., 1912.
12—40588
Library of Congress PR4235.K5 1912

NK 0203086 DLC OrP NIC ICU TxU MB MU NN

Knight, William Angus, 1836– *ed.*
The Robert Browning centenary celebration at Westminster abbey, May 7th, 1912, ed. with an introduction and appendices by Professor Knight ... London, Smith, Elder & co., 1912.
xiv, 107, [1] p. front. (port.) 17½cm.

1. Browning, Robert, 1812–1889.
12-25740
Library of Congress PR4235.K5 1912 a

PPL PWcS ViU MiU
NK 0203087 DLC TU CaBVaU MsSM CU CtY MiU OCl OO ODW

Knight, William Angus, 1836-1916.
Seeking after God: a sermon preached in Portland Street Church, London, May 26, 1872. 2d ed. Glasgow, 1872.
31 p. 8°. [In "College Pamphlets," v. 2009]

NK 0203088 CtY

Knight, William Angus, 1836–1916.
Six lectures on some nineteenth century artists, English and French, delivered at the Art institute of Chicago; being the Scammon lectures for the year 1907, by William Knight ... Chicago, The Art institute of Chicago, 1909.
189 p. front. (port.) 1 pl. 25cm. $2.00
CONTENTS.—Some characteristics of the genius of Turner.—Modern landscape art in England and France.—Ruskin, as art-critic and as moralist, with some personal reminiscences.—The Pre-Raphaelites, especially Dante Gabriel Rosetti, with reminiscences.—George Frederick Watts, with reminiscences.—Edward Burne-Jones and others.
1. Turner, Joseph Mallord William, 1775–1851. 2. Ruskin, John, 1819–1900. 3. Watts, George Frederick, 1817–1904. 4. Burne-Jones, Sir Edward Coley, bart., 1833–1898. 5. Landscape painting. 6. Pre-raphaelitism.
10—3316
Library of Congress ND190.K7

CU FMU PSt NBuT PPPM-I
NK 0203089 DLC CaBVaU OrP WaS Or PWcS MiU OCU OO

Knight, William [Angus] 1836–
Some nineteenth century Scotsmen; being personal recollections by William Knight ... Edinburgh and London, Oliphant, Anderson, & Ferrier, 1903. [1902]
456 p. 23½cm.
"Bibliography of Thomas Davidson's works": p. 448-452.
"Catalogue of mss. left by Thomas Davidson": p. 452-456.

Subject entries: 1. Scotland—Biog. 2. Davidson, Thomas, 1840–1900.
3-3083
Library of Congress, no. DA816.K71.

PPL
NK 0203090 DLC NIC ICU CaBVaU ScU NcD TxU IaU NN PP

PR
10
P6
K5
1908
Knight, William Angus, 1836-1916.
Some nineteenth century Scotsmen; being personal recollections by William Knight. Edinburgh, Oliphant, Anderson & Ferrier, 1908.
456 p. ports. 24 cm.

NK 0203091 CaBVaU

Knight, William Angus, 1836–1916, ed.
Spinoza; four essays, by Land, Kuno Fischer, J. van Vloten, and Ernest Renan. Edited by Professor Knight ... London and Edinburgh, Williams and Norgate, 1882.
xiv. 170 p. 22cm.
CONTENTS.—In memory of Spinoza, by J. Land, translated by Allan Menzies.—The life and character of Baruch Spinoza, by Kuno Fischer, translated by Frida Schmidt.—Spinoza, by J. van Vloten, translated by Allan Menzies.—Spinoza: 1677, and 1877, by Ernest Renan, translated by Mrs. William Smith.
1. Spinoza, Benedictus de, 1632–1677. I. Land, Jan Pieter Nicolaas, 1834–1897. II. Fischer, Kuno, 1824–1907. III. Vloten, Johannes van, 1818–1883. IV. Renan, Ernest, 1823–1892.

ICN
OCU PHC PBm PU OCH OCU OU ODW MnU IU NNUT MdBP NjP
NK 0203092 ViU MiU NcD CU CLSU NNC NIC NBuC CtY

GV967
K6
1894
Knight, William Angus, 1836– **comp.**
Stories of golf, collected by William Knight and T.T.Oliphant. With rhymes on golf by various hands. Also Shakespeare on golf, etc. Enl. ed. London, Heinemann, 1894.
xiii,146p. 19cm.

1. Golf - Anecdotes, facetiae, satire, etc. I. Oliphant, T T jt.comp. II. Title.

NK 0203093 IaU MH

Knight, William Angus, 1836–
Studies in philosophy and literature, by William Knight ... London, C. K. Paul & co., 1879.
xx, 426 p. 19½cm.
Appeared first in various periodicals.

1. Philosophy — Addresses, essays, lectures. 2. Literature — Addresses, essays, lectures.
A 14-2492
Title from Univ. of Chicago B1646.K7S9 1879 Printed by L. C.

InU MH WaS
NK 0203094 ICU NIC NcD InU MdBP CtY MiU OClW PP PU

Knight, William Angus, 1836-1916.

Hunt, Leigh, 1784–1859.
Tales by Leigh Hunt, now first collected; with a prefatory memoir by William Knight ... London, W. Paterson & co., 1891.

Knight, William Angus, 1836–1916.
Through the Wordsworth country. By Harry Goodwin and Professor Knight. London, S. Sonnenschein, Lowrey & co., 1887.
xix, 268 p. front., plates. 30½cm.
On cover: Pictures by Harry Goodwin; text by William Knight.

1. Lake district, Eng. 2. Wordsworth, William, 1770-1850. I. Goodwin, Harry, illus. II. Title.
3—13953
Library of Congress DA670.L1K7

ODW TxU MdBP
NK 0203096 DLC InU ScU NIC PPFr PPL PSC MiU MH

VOLUME 300

914.28 Knight, William Angus, 1836-1916.
K71t Through the Wordsworth country; a companion to the
1890 Lake District. With 56 plates and a front after the statue in Westminster Abbey, by Harry Goodwin 2d ed London, S Sonnenschein, 1890
268p. illus.

On cover: Pictures by Harry Goodwin. Text by William Knight.

1. Lake District, Eng. 2. Wordsworth, William, 1770-1850. Title

NK 0203097 FTaSU NIC PHC

In Knight, William Angus, 1836-1916.
W890 Through the Wordsworth country; a companion
Z887kc to the Lake district, by William Knight ... With 56 plates and a frontispiece after the statue in Westminster Abbey, by Harry Goodwin. 3d ed. London, S. Sonnenschein & co., 1892.
xix, 268p. front., plates. 19½cm.

NK 0203098 CtY MtU CaBVaU GU OCU

PR Knight, William Angus, 1836-1916.
5884 Through the Wordsworth country; a com-
K71 panion to the Lake district. With a frontis-
1906 piece ... and sixteen full page illustrations by Harry Goodwin (specially re-engraved for this edition) London, S. Sonnenschein, 1906.
xix, 268 p. illus. 20cm

"First edition, Dec. 1891...Fifth edition, May, 1906."

On cover: Pictures by Harry Goodwin; text by William Knight.

1. Wordsworth, William, 1770-1850. 2. Lake district, Eng. I. Title.

NK 0203100 NIC IU ScU

Knight, William Angus, 1836- ed.

Wordsworth society.

Transactions of the Wordsworth society. no. 1-8. [Edinburgh, 1882-87]

Knight, Wm. Angus, 1836-1916.
The univ. ext. lecture scheme in Scotland; being, an address, delivered to the University Extension soc. at Perth. Perth, Printed at the Perthshire Constitutional off., 1889.
18 p. D.

NK 0203102 OO

Knight, William Angus, 1836-
The University series
see under title

Knight, William Angus, 1836-

Varia; studies on problems of philosophy and ethics, by William Knight ... London, J. Murray, 1901.

x p., 1 l., 196 p. 23cm.

CONTENTS.—The function of philosophy at the present time.—Nationality as an element in the evolution of philosophy.—Our present philosophical outlook.—Poetry and science, their contrasts and affinities.—The unseen root of ethics.—The correlation of the moral forces.—Corporate responsibility: France, and the Transvaal.—Practical ethics.—Philosophical societies in the universities of Scotland.—The formation of public opinion.—Desiderata in modern philosophy.—The ethics of criticism.

1. Philosophy—Addresses, essays, lectures. 2. Ethics—Addresses, essays, lectures. I. Title.

12-14317

Library of Congress B1589.K53V4

NK 0203104 DLC CaBVaU NNC CtY NjP PPL MB ICJ

Knight, William Angus, 1836- *ed.*

A Victorian anthology; edited by William Knight ... London, G. Newnes, limited; New York, C. Scribner's sons [1907]

xiv, 448 p. front. (port.) 17cm.

Added title-page engraved.
Ornamental end-papers.

1. English poetry.

W 8-40

Washington, D. C. Public Library

NK 0203105 DWP

Knight, Wm. Angus, 1836-1916
Wm. Minto. (in Minto, Wm. The literature of the Georgian era, 1895 p. ix)

NK 0203106 OU

Knight, William Angus, 1836-1916, *ed.*

Wordsworthiana: a selection from papers read to the Wordsworth society; edited by William Knight. London and New York, Macmillan & co., 1889.

xxiv, 352 p. front. (port.) 19½cm.

CONTENTS.—The Platonism of Wordsworth, by J. H. Shorthouse.—Wordsworth's modernisation of Chaucer, by E. Dowden.—The portraits of Wordsworth, by W. Knight.—The earlier and later styles of Wordsworth, by R. H. Hutton.—Reminiscences of Wordsworth amongst the peasantry of Westmorland, by H. D. Rawnsley.—President's address, 1883, by M. Arnold.—Wordsworth's 'Guide to the lakes', by S. Brooke.—The personal character of Wordsworth's poetry, by A. De Vere.—Wordsworth's position as an ethical teacher, by the Dean of Salisbury.—President's address, 1884, by J. R. Lowell.—The poetic interpretation of nature, by R. Noel.—Wordsworth's relations to science, by R. S. Watson.—Wordsworth's treatment of sound, by W. A. Heard.—Wordsworth and Charles Lamb, by A. Ainger.—President's address, 1885, by Lord Houghton.—Wordsworth and Turner, by H. Goodwin.—President's address, 1886, by Lord Selborne.—The theism of Wordsworth, by J. Veitch.—The poets who helped to form Wordsworth's style, by A. Ainger.—Speech by Aubrey De Vere.

Preface contains the constitution of, and historical notes on the Wordsworth society.

1. Wordsworth, William, 1770-1850. 2. Wordsworth, William, 1770-1850—Portraits. I. Wordsworth society. II. Title.

A 38-611

H. E. Huntington library for Library of Congress PR5879.K6 [2]

TU P ICN FMU NIC ICU MA FTaSU NjP TxU NcD WaSpG MtU PPD PBm PPA PBL MiU OClW OO OU InU CSmH

NK 0203108 CSmH NRCR PPT KMK IdU WaS CoU ScU CaBVaU

---

828 Knight, William Angus, 1836-1916, ed.
W930 Wordsworthiana; a selection from papers
K7w read to the Wordsworth society. London,
1889a New York, Macmillan, 1889.
352 p.
Photocopy. Ann Arbor, Mich., University Microfilms, 1967. 352 p. (on double leaves)

1. Wordsworth, William, 1770-1850. 2. Wordsworth, William, 1770-1850--Portraits. I. Wordsworth Society. II. Title.

NK 0203109 MiU NIC KEmT

QV KNIGHT, William Arthur.
K71t A text book of materia medica for
1900 pharmaceutical students. London, Clive, 1900.
312 p. illus.

NK 0203110 DNLM

Bonaparte
Collection KNIGHT, WILLIAM BRUCE, 1786?-1845.
No.7811 A critical review of the Rev. J. Jones's Reply to the Rev. W. B. Knight's Remarks on Welsh orthography... Cardiff, W. Bird, 1831.
133p. 21cm. (with Jones, John. A defence of the reformed system of Welsh orthography... 1829)

NK 0203111 ICN

Knight, William Bruce, 1786?-1845.
A letter on infant baptism. [New York, Protestant Episcopal Tract Society, 18--?]

16 p. 19cm. [American Unitarian Association. Tracts. 39]

Caption title.
At head of title: 125.

1. Infant baptism.

NK 0203112 MnU

Knight, William Bruce, 1786?-1845.
A letter on infant baptism... New ed., London, 1842.
24 p.

NK 0203113 RPB

Bonaparte
Collection KNIGHT, WILLIAM BRUCE, 1786?-1845.
No.7811 Remarks, historical and philological, on the Welsh language, in which the orthography of the received text, as sanctioned by the commission of bishops in 1809, is vindicated, and such objections as have been made to it, are shewn to be without foundation... Cardiff, W. Bird, 1830.
60p. 21cm. (with Jones, John. A defence of the reformed system of Welsh orthography... 1829)

A reply to J. Jones, A defence of the reformed system of Welsh orthography.

NK 0203114 ICN

Knight, William C., ed.
The juvenile harmony, or, a choice collection of psalm tunes, hymns and anthems, ... Second edition, enlarged, enlarged and improved. Cincinnati: Published by Morgan & Sanxay, booksellers, 133 Mainst, 1829.

[144] p.

NK 0203115 InU In

Knight, William C., ed.
The Juvenile Harmony, or, a Choice Collection of Psalm Tunes, Hymns and Anthens, Selected from the Eminent Authors,..... 5th ed. 130 pp. (incomplete?). Cincinnati, Morgan & Sanxay, 1831 (first entered in 1825).

NK 0203116 OCHP OClWHi

Knight, William C. ed.

hMusic
Kn6868j **The juvenile harmony; or, A choice**
1833 **collection of psalm tunes, hymns and anthems, selected from the most eminent**
Harris **authors, and well adapted to all Christian**
Collection **churches, singing schools ... Together with the rules of singing, and an explanation of the rules and principles of the ground work of music. By W.C. Knight. 15th ed., rev. and cor. Cincinnati, Morgan & Sanxay, 1833.**
xii, 13-143, [1]p. 14x23 cm.

NK 0203117 RPB

-VM KNIGHT, WILLIAM C comp.
2121 The juvenile harmony, or, A choice collection
K 71j of psalm tunes, hymns and anthems, selected from
1836 the most eminent authors, and well adapted to all Christian churches, singing schools and private societies. Together with the rules of singing. And an explanation of the rules and principles of the ground work of music... 16th edition, revised and corrected. Cincinnati, Morgan & Sanxay, 1836.
143p.

Character notes.

NK 0203118 ICN

VOLUME 300

Knight, Wm. C., of Virginia, plaintiff.
Contested election in the Senate of Virginia: case of Knight vs. Johnson, session of 1875-6. Printed by order of the Committee of privileges and elections, with consent of Senate. Richmond, R.F. Walker, superintendent public printing, 1875.
386, 11, 10, 11, 8, 10, 39 p.

NK 0203119 ViU-L

Knight, William D 1886–
The prosecutor (outside of Chicago) in felony cases, by William D. Knight. Chapter v of the Illinois crime survey. Chicago, Illinois association for criminal justice [°1929]
2 p. l., 247-279 p. incl. tables. 25cm.
"Published by Illinois association for criminal justice in cooperation with the Chicago crime commission."
1. Public prosecutors—Illinois. 2. Criminal procedure—Illinois. 3. Justice, Administration of—Illinois. I. Illinois association for criminal justice. II. Chicago crime commisson. III. Title. IV. Title: Illinois crime survey.
42-49182

NK 0203120 DLC IU MH-L

Knight, William D 1886–
Tentative draft of report on downstate prosecution, by William D. Knight. [Chicago] Illinois association for criminal justice in co-operation with the Chicago crime commission [1927?]
cover-title, 1 p. l., 51 numb. l. tables. 27½cm.
Mimeographed.
1. Public prosecutors—Illinois. 2. Criminal procedure—Illinois. I. Illinois association for criminal justice. II. Chicago crime commission. III. Title: Downstate prosecution.
36-19671

NK 0203121 DLC

Knight, William David, 1863–
A complete manual of phonography (Pitmanic) by the sentence method; for use in schools and colleges and for self-instruction, by William D. Knight. Kansas City, Mo., Press of Franklin Hudson publishing co., 1905.
186 p. 17cm.
1. Shorthand.
Library of Congress Z56.K71 7—3175

NK 0203122 DLC ICJ

HE8698 .W43
Knight, William Donald, 1916– joint author.
Westing, John Howard, 1911–
The area of effectiveness of a selected VHF television station; a case study based on WBAY-TV, Green Bay, by J. H. Westing, W. D. Knight, and others. Madison, University of Wisconsin, School of Commerce, Bureau of Business Research and Service, 1955.

Knight, William Donald, 1916–
Profit and loss budgeting; a case study of three manufacturing companies. Made in cooperation with Milwaukee Chapter, National Society for Business Budgeting. Madison, University of Wisconsin, School of Commerce, Bureau of Business Research and Service, 1954.
62 p. 28 cm. (Wisconsin commerce reports, v. 3, no. 6)
1. Budget in business. 2. Allis-Chalmers Manufacturing Company. 3. Kimberly-Clark Corporation. 4. Snap-on Tools Corporation. I. Title. (Series: Wisconsin. University. Bureau of Business Research and Service. Wisconsin commerce reports, v. 3, no. 6)
HF5550.K6 658.155 54-4763

NK 0203124 DLC CaBVaU TxU ViU MH-BA OCU OOxM PU-W MiU NsU FTaSU AAP

Knight, William Donald, 1916–
Subsidization of industry in forty selected cities in Wisconsin, 1930-1946. Madison, 1947.
xii, 206 p. map, tables. 23 cm. (Wisconsin. University. Bureau of Business Research and Service. Wisconsin commerce studies, v. 1, no. 2)
Bulletin of the University of Wisconsin. Serial no. 2942. General series no. 2716.
1. Wisconsin—Indus. 2. Cities and towns—Wisconsin. I. Title. II. Series. III. Series: Wisconsin. University. Bulletin. General series no. 2716.
HC107.W6K5 338.91 47-46617*
Limited cataloging

NK 0203125 DLC MsU UU LU NcD FMU OOxM TxU

HD9230 .U52W6
Knight, William Donald, 1916– ed.
Krause, Francis A
The Wisconsin canning industry; ed. by W. D. Knight. Madison, Univ. of Wisconsin, School of Commerce, Bureau of Business Research and Service, 1948.

Knight, Wm. E
Treatise on failure-proof banking. Cleveland, Commercial clearing service, 1924.
16 p.

NK 0203127 OClFRB

Knight, William Edward.
España y el Nuevo Mundo; historia, cuentos y hazañas de los conquistadores y descubridores, by W. E. Knight ... Richmond, Va., Johnson publishing company [°1927]
xi p., 1 l., 185 p. incl. front., illus. 19½cm. [American-Spanish series]
Bibliography: p. 135.
1. Spanish language—Chrestomathies and readers.
Library of Congress PC4117.K65 27-14546

NK 0203128 DLC FTaSU OCl PU FMU

Knight, William Edward.
Norte y sur, geografía, historia y cuento, by W. E. Knight ... Richmond, Va., Johnson publishing company [°1924]
xii, 241 p. col. front., illus. 19½cm. (*Half-title:* American-Spanish series, general editor, C. M. Montgomery)
Maps on lining-papers.
1. Spanish language—Chrestomathies and readers. I. Title.
Library of Congress PC4127.G4K5 24-30792

NK 0203129 DLC ICarbS PU PPCCH OCl OClJC OClW OCX DPU Vi

Knight, William Eliot.
... The Wm. C. P. Breckinridge defence, by Rev. William Eliot Knight ... Colfax, Ia., The Weekly clipper, 1895.
1 p. l., 48, [1] p. front. (port.) 20½cm. (Red-letter sermon series)
1. Breckinridge, William Campbell Preston, 1837-1904. I. Title.
Library of Congress E664.B825K6 24-25480

NK 0203130 DLC

Knight, William Eric, 1920–
Breeding ladino clover for persistence and longevity. Ann Arbor, University Microfilms, 1951.
([University Microfilms, Ann Arbor, Mich.] Publication no. 3221)
Microfilm copy of typescript. Positive.
Collation of the original, as determined from the film: 117 l. illus.
Thesis—Pennsylvania State College.
Vita.
Bibliography: leaves 69-71.
1. Ladino clover.
Microfilm AC-1 no. 3221 Mic 52-603

NK 0203131 DLC

Knight, William F. de
see
De Knight, William F.

Knight, William Francis Jackson, 1895–1964.
Accentual symmetry in Vergil, by W. F. Jackson Knight ... Oxford, B. Blackwell, 1939.
x, 107 p. fold. tab. 19 cm.
1. Vergilius Maro, Publius—Style. 2. Latin language—Metrics and rhythmics. I. Title.
PA6945.K6 873.1 40—3209

NK 0203133 DLC ICU MH OU OClW OCU PBm PSt NIC CaBVaU WaSpG OrU TU NcU NcD CU

Knight, William Francis Jackson, 1895–1964.
Accentual symmetry in Vergil, by W.F. Jackson Knight ... Oxford, B. Blackwell, 1950.
x, 107, [1] p. fold. tab. 19cm.
"First impression 1939. Second impression 1950."
1. Vergilius Maro, Publius - Style. 2. Latin language - Metrics and rhythmics. I. Title.

NK 0203134 TxU MH INS MB CoU GU MoU

Knight, William Francis Jackson, 1895–1964.
Cumaean gates; a reference of the sixth Aeneid to the initiation pattern, by W. F. Jackson Knight ... with drawings by L. J. Lloyd. Oxford, B. Blackwell, 1936.
xv, 190 p. front., illus. (incl. plans) 21½cm.
Bibliographical foot-notes.
1. Vergilius Maro, Publius. Aeneis VI. 2. Dead, The (in religion, folk-lore, etc.) 3. Mythology, Classical. 4. Labyrinths. I. Title. II. Title: Initiation pattern.
Library of Congress PA6825.K57 [3] 873.1 37-18856

NK 0203135 DLC OrPR NcD NcU OCU OU MiU OClW OCX PSC CtY TU MH CU ICU

ML168 .A97
Knight, William Francis Jackson, 1895–
Augustinus, Aurelius, *Saint, Bp. of Hippo.*
De musica, a synopsis, by W. F. Jackson Knight. London, Orthological Institute [1949?]

PA 6826 K71
Knight, William Francis Jackson, 1895– ed.
The great tradition. A course of ten weekly lectures given in the spring of 1945 to the Exmouth branch of the Virgil Society. Exmouth, Raleigh Press, 1945.
16 p. 19cm. (Virgil Society. Exmouth branch. Lectures, 1945)
1. Vergilius Maro, Publius. I. Title.

NK 0203137 NIC OCU CtY

CN76 K5
Knight, William Francis Jackson, 1895–1964.
Maze symbolism and the Trojan game. [Gloucester, Eng.] 1932.
p.445-458, diagr. 25cm.
Bibliographical footnotes.
Cover title.
"Reprinted from Antiquity, December, 1932."
1. Inscriptions. I. Title.

NK 0203138 IaU

VOLUME 300

Knight, William Francis Jackson, 1895–
Poetic inspiration, an approach to Virgil. London, Raleigh Press, 1946.
56 p. front. 19 cm. (Virgilian essays, no. 1)

1. Vergilius Maro, Publius. I. Title. (Series)
A 49-3865*
North Carolina. Univ. Library for Library of Congress [1]

NK 0203139 NcU LU IU OO TxU CU OrU PBm

Knight, William Francis Jackson, 1895–
Roman Vergil, by W. F. Jackson Knight ... London, Faber and Faber limited [1944]
viii, 348 p. 22½cm.
"First published in MCMXLIV."
Bibliographical foot-notes.

1. Vergilius Maro, Publius. I. Title.
44-3670
Library of Congress PA6825.K59 1944
[3] 873.1

PSC PBm CaBVaU WaSpG FTaSU TxU TxFTC
NK 0203140 DLC OrU OrPR NcU FU CtY PPL OCU OC1W OO

870.91 Knight, William Francis Jackson, 1895–
ZV81K7r Roman Vergil. [2d ed.] London, Faber and Faber [1953]
viii, 348 p.

Bibliographical footnotes.

1. VIRGIL I. T.

PSt NIC
NK 0203141 MiD MH CtY ViU RPB PPT IaU MB MiU ScU

Knight, William Francis Jackson, 1895–
Vergil's Troy, essays on the second book of the Aeneid, by W. F. Jackson Knight ... Oxford, B. Blackwell, 1932.
ix, 158 p., 1 l. 19½cm.

1. Vergilius Maro, Publius. Aeneis.
33—21807
Library of Congress PA6825.K6
[a43d1] 873.1

CtW PBL PBm OCU OO OC1W MiU OCX CU TxHR LU
NK 0203142 DLC MtU CaBVaU NcU CtY PSC IaU IU NN ICU

Knight, William Francis Jackson, 1895-1964.
A Virgilian sociology; a paper read to the annual general meeting of the Classical association at St. Alban's, on Wednesday, April 12th, 1944. Cardiff [Wales], Priory press, 1944.
9-17 p. 28 cm.
"Reprinted from 'Comparative literature studies', vols. XIV-XV, 1944."
1. Vergilius Maro, Publius - Addresses, essays, lectures. I. Classical association.

NK 0203143 CU

Knight, William George, 1884–
Practical locomotive running and management. 2d ed., 3d thousand, by W. Geo. Knight. [Bedford, Mass., W. G. Knight, °1920]
3 p. l., [9]–541 p. illus. 19½cm.

1. Locomotives—Handbooks, manuals, etc.
20-18680
Library of Congress TJ607.K65 1920

NK 0203144 DLC MB

Knight, W[illiam] George, 1884–
Practical locomotive running and management; a complete and practical work on the locomotive, treating on combustion and firing — injectors, lubricators, steam gages, safety valves ... New York: The Norman W. Henley Pub. Co., 1921. 541 p. diagr., illus. 2. ed. rev. & enl. 12°.

1. Locomotive.
N. Y. P. L. January 17, 1922.

NK 0203145 NN ICJ

Knight, William George, 1884–
Practical questions on locomotive operating, by W. G. Knight. [Boston, E. L. Grimes company, printers, °1913]
3 p. l., [9]–246 p. 17½cm. $1.75
"The first series of questions are those asked in the examination for engineers on the Boston & Maine system."—Pref.

1. Locomotives—Handbooks, manuals, etc.
Library ot Congress TJ607.K7 13-24491

NK 0203146 DLC ICJ NN

KNIGHT, William H
Strange behavior of Encke's comet, by William H. Knight.
3 p. illus. 23cm. (In the heavens, no. 7, December 1916.)

NK 0203147 DN-Ob

Knight, William Henry.
Diary of a pedestrian in Cashmere and Thibet. By Captain Knight ... London, R. Bentley, 1863.
xvi, 385 p. col. front., illus., col. plates. 22 cm.
Title in red and black, with vignette.

1. Kashmir—Descr. & trav. 2. Tibet—Descr. & trav.
Library of Congress DS485.K2K6 5—7549

NK 0203148 DLC MH PPL MiU OC1 OCU MB NjP NIC CU NcD

Knight, William Henry.
Missions in principle and practice. Nashville, Tenn., Sunday school board of the Southern Baptist convention [1929]
190 p., 19cm.

1. Missions.
A 31-843
Title from Yale Univ. Printed by L. C.

NK 0203149 CtY PCC

Knight, William Henry
Western Australia. Its history, progress, condition, and prospects, and its advantages as a field for emigration, by W. H. Knight. Perth, Western Australia. [Printed by J. Mitchell] 1870.
2 p. l., ii, 163 p. 20cm.

1. Western Australia
8-25331
Library of Congress DU360.K5

NK 0203150 DLC

Knight, William Henry, 1835–1925. *Map 1020.19
Bancroft's Map of the Rocky Mountain States and of the Pacific Coast.
= San Francisco. Bancroft & Co. 1866. Size, 18½ × 16¼ inches. Scale, 75 miles to 1 inch. Folded.

F872 — West, The. Geog. Maps.

NK 0203151 MB

Knight, William Henry, 1835–1925. *Map 1022.5
Bancroft's New map of central California.
San Francisco. Bancroft & Co. 1871. Size, 15⅜ × 19⅛ inches. Scale, 12 miles to 1 inch. Folded.

K6082 — T.r. — California. Geog. Maps.

NK 0203152 MB

F867 Knight, William Henry, 1835-1925.
.5 Bancroft's new map of central California, compiled by Wm.
K5 Henry Knight. San Francisco, A.L. Bancroft & Co., 1871.
1871 39x47cm. fold. in cover 17cm.
x
In case 20cm.
On cover: Revised and enlarged.

NK 0203153 CU-B

Knight, William Henry, 1835-1925, ed.
Hand-book almanac for the Pacific states
see under title

Knight, William J., 1838-1908.

Iowa. *Commissioners to revise the statutes.*
Report of Commissioners to revise the statutes of the state of Iowa, made to the governor of the state, in accordance with chapter seventy-five, acts of 13th General assembly. Wm. H. Seevers ... Wm. J. Knight ... Wm. G. Hammond ... commissioners. Des Moines, G. W. Edwards, state printer, 1871.

Knight, (William Lambdin) [1811-77]
Catalogue of the medical library... To be sold Friday, October 12, 1877. Philadelphia, Selheimer & Moore, [1877]
18 p.

NK 0203156 DNLM

Knight, William Lambdin, 1811-77.
...Catalogue of the medical library of ... Also engravings and paintings of distinguished physicians. [Philadelphia, 1877]
11 p.

NK 0203157 DNLM

R15
.P83K6 Knight, William Lambdin, 1811-1877.
Toner The powers and undeveloped resources of
Coll. the Philadelphia county medical society. An address delivered December 24,1873. By William L. Knight ... Published by the society. Philadelphia, Collins, printer, 1874.
25 p. 23½cm.

1. Philadelphia county medical society

NK 0203158 DLC DAM PU PHi PPC

Knight, William Oscar, 1879-

Sioux Falls, *S. D. Ordinances, etc.*
Revised ordinances of the city of Sioux Falls, South Dakota. 1936. Ordinance in revision no. 1172, effective September 8, 1936. Revised under direction of the Board of commissioners by Hugh Gamble, city attorney [and] W. O. Knight. [Sioux Falls, 1936]

VOLUME 300

[KNIGHT, William P. comp.]
Directory of officers of the 91st infantry division stationed at Camp Lewis, American Lake, Washington ... [Tacoma, Washington, Pioneer bindery & printing co., 1917]
Cover-title. 70 p.

NK 0203160 WaS

Knight, William Stanley Macbean, 1869-
The business encyclopædia and legal adviser, by W. S. M. Knight... With a series of statistical articles and explanatory diagrams by John Holt Schooling... London: Caxton Pub. Co., Ltd., 1912. 7 v. fac., illus., pl., tables. rev. ed. 8°.
v. 6-7 suppl.

1. Commerce.—Dictionaries (English), 1912. 2. Commerce.—Jurisprudence, Gt. Br. 3. Law.—Dictionaries. 4. Schooling, John Holt, 1859- 5. Title.
N. Y. P. L. November 16, 1914.

NK 0203161 NN MnU

Knight, William Stanley Macbean, 1869-
Grotius' earliest years as [a] lawyer. By W. S. M. Knight, esq.
(*In* Grotius society. Problems of the war ... London, 1916-19 22cm. v. 8, 1923, p. 1-19)
Bibliographical foot-notes.

1. Grotius, Hugo, 1583-1645. A 23-1046
——— Copy 2.
Title from Carnegie Endow Int. Peace JX1392.G7 vol. 8
Printed by L. C.

NK 0203162 NNCE MiU DS WaU-L

Knight, William Stanley Macbean, 1869-
Grotius in England: his opposition there to the principles of the Mare liberum. By W. S. M. Knight.
(*In* Grotius society, London. Problems of peace and war ... London, 1920. 22cm. vol. v, p. 1-38)
Bibliographical foot-notes.

1. Grotius, Hugo, 1583-1645. 2. Freedom of the seas.
A 21-1045 Revised
Carnegie endow. int. peace. Library
for Library of Congress JX31.G7 vol. 5

NK 0203163 NNCE MiU DS DLC WaU-L

Knight, William Stanley Macbean, 1869-
A history of Britain during the great war; a study of a democracy at war, by William Stanley Macbean Knight ... London, The Ridd Masson company limited, 1915-
v. plates, ports. 24cm.

1. Gt. Brit.—Hist.—George v, 1910- 2. European war, 1914-
16-6146
Library of Congress DA577.K6

NK 0203164 DLC CtY NN

Knight, William Stanley Macbean, 1869-
The history of the great European war, its causes and effects. By W. Stanley Macbean Knight ... assisted by eminent naval and military experts ... London, Caxton publishing company, limited [1914-
v. col. fronts., illus. (incl. maps) plates (part col.) ports., col. maps (part fold.) 25cm.

1. European war, 1914-
War 15-76
Library, War College Div. General Staff

NK 0203165 DNW CtY DN NN

Knight, William Stanley Macbean, 1869-
Hugo Grotius: his family and ancestry. By W. S. M. Knight.
(*In* Grotius society, London. Problems of peace and war ... London, 1921. 22cm. vol. vi, p. 1-24)
Bibliographical foot-notes.

1. Grotius, Hugo, 1583-1645. 2. Groot (de) family.
A 21-1057
Carnegie endow. int. peace. Library
for Library of Congress JX31.G7 vol. 6

NK 0203166 NNCE DS MiU OC1W DLC WaU-L

JX2093
.E5
1922

Knight, William Stanley Macbean, 1869- tr.
Grotius, Hugo, 1583-1645.
... Hugonis Grotii De jure belli ac pacis libri tres. Selections translated, with an introduction by W. S. M. Knight ... London, Sweet and Maxwell, limited, 1922.

Knight, William Stanley Macbean, 1869-
The infancy and youth of Hugo Grotius. By W. S. M. Knight, esq.
(*In* Grotius society, London. Problems of peace and war ... London, 1922. 22cm. vol. vii, p. 1-32)
Bibliographical foot-notes.

1. Grotius, Hugo, 1583-1645. A 22-682 Revised
Carnegie endow. int. peace. Library
for Library of Congress JX31.G7 vol. 7

NK 0203168 NNCE DS MiU DLC WaU-L

Knight, William Stanley Macbean, 1869-
... The life and works of Hugo Grotius, by W. S. M. Knight ... London, Sweet & Maxwell, limited, 1925.
3 p. l., v-xiv, 304 p. 22cm. (The Grotius society. Publications, no. 4)
"Selection of biographical and critical works on Grotius": p. 294-297.

1. Grotius, Hugo, 1583-1645.
25-18572
Library of Congress JX2099.K6

MH
OO MB NN WaS CaBVaU WaU-L OrCS WU FMU CU CtY-D TxU
NK 0203169 DLC KMK NcD DS PPT MiU OCU FMU OU ViU-L

Knight, William Stanley Macbean, 1869-
A mediæval pacifist—Pierre Du Bois. By W. S. M. Knight ...
(*In* Grotius society, London. Problems of peace and war. London, 1924. 22cm. v. 9, p. 1-16)
Bibliography: p. 16.

1. Dubois, Pierre, fl. 1300. I. Title.
A 24-836
Carnegie endow. int. peace. Library
for Library of Congress JX31.G7 vol. 9

NK 0203170 NNCE WaU-L DS MiU DLC

Knight, William Stanley Macbean, 1869-
Seraphin de Freitas: critic of Mare liberum. By W. S. M. Knight ...
(*In* Grotius society. Problems of peace and war. London, 1926. 22cm. v. 11, p. 1-9)

1. Freitas, Seraphin de, fl. ca. 1571-1640. 2. Grotius, Hugo, 1583-1645. Mare liberum.
A 26-389
——— Copy 2.
Title from Carnegie Endow. Int. Peace JX1392.G7 vol. 11
Printed by L. C.

NK 0203171 NNCE DS WaU-L MiU

Knight, William Thomas.
Algebraic factors: how to find them and how to use them. London, n.d.
80 p.

NK 0203172 RPB

QA43
K71
1886

Knight, Dr. William Thomas.
Mathematical wrinkles for matriculation and other exams...by Dr. W.T.Knight...London: Blackie and Son, Ltd., (1886).
iv, 128 p. 17 cm.

NK 0203173 DAU MH

Knight, William Thomas.
A practical philanthropist and his work.
7 p (Macmillan's Mag. v. 59, 1889, p. 178)

NK 0203174 MdBP

Knight, Willys Raymond, 1917-
Factors affecting farm living levels. [College Park, Md.] 1949.
vi, 102 l. maps (1 col.) diagrs., tables. 28 cm.
Thesis—University of Maryland.
Typewritten (carbon copy)
"Selected bibliography": leaves 89-91.

1. Farm life. 2. Agriculture—Economic aspects—U. S. I. Title: Farm living levels.
HD1761.K6 331.831 A 51-5170
Maryland. Univ. Libr.
for Library of Congress [2]†

NK 0203175 MdU DLC

Knight, Wilmot.
Practical advice to shorthand students: by Wilmot Knight ... London: Hatton & Son[, 18—]. 19 p. 12°.

1. Shorthand.
N. Y. P. L. May 18, 1926

NK 0203176 NN CtY

Knight, Wilson
see
Knight, George Wilson, 1897-

823
K748o

Knight, Wynter Frore.
Our vicar, a novel. London, S. Tinsley, 1879.
3v. 19cm.

NK 0203178 IU

Knight-Anstey, J C
Report on Protestant Telugu Christian literature ... Madras, [etc.] 1917.
91, [1] p. 22 cm.

NK 0203179 CtY

Knight-Anstey, J C
The study and use of the vernacular. A handbook for young missionaries ... London, [1907]
68 p. 18 cm.

NK 0203180 CtY

VOLUME 300

Knight-Bruce, George Wyndham Hamilton, *Bp. of Mashonaland*, 1852–1896.
Gold and the gospel in Mashonaland, 1888, being the journals of: 1. The Mashonaland mission of Bishop Knight-Bruce; 2. The concession journey of Charles Dunell Rudd. Edited respectively by Constance E. Fripp and V. W. Hiller. London, Chatto & Windus, 1949.
ix, 246 p. plates, ports., fold. maps (1 col.) 26 cm. (Oppenheimer series, no. 4)
1. Mashonaland—Descr. & trav. 2. Missions—Mashonaland. 3. Matabeleland—Descr. & trav. I. Rudd, Charles Dunell, 1843 or 4–1916. II. Title. (Series: Rhodesia, Southern. Central African Archives. Oppenheimer series, no. 4)
DT964.M3K5 1949 [266] 276.893 50—1480
CtY
NK 0203181 DLC CaBVaU GU NNC NcD PPF PP CU TxU IEN

Knight-Bruce, George Wyndham Hamilton, *bp. of Mashonaland*, 1852–1896.
Journals of the Mashonaland mission, 1888 to 1892, by G. W. H. Knight-Bruce ... Ed., with an introduction, by L. K. B. ... ⌜London⌝ Society for the propagation of the Gospel in foreign parts, 1892.
viii, 99, ⌜4⌝ p. illus., 3 maps (incl. front., 2 fold.) 22cm.
1. Mashonaland. 2. Missions—Mashonaland. I. Knight-Bruce, Mrs. Louise (Torr)
16-16906
Library of Congress DT964.M3K5
NK 0203182 DLC CtY-D CtY PPL OCl MH

Knight-Bruce, George Wyndham Hamilton, Bp. of Mashonaland, 1852-1896.
Journals of the Mashonaland mission, 1888 to 1892... Edited, with an introduction, by L.K.B.... 2d ed. ⌜London⌝ Society for the propagation of the Gospel in foreign parts, 1893.
viii, 99 p. illus., fold. maps. 22cm.
NK 0203183 NjPT

Knight-Bruce, George Wyndham Hamilton, *bp. of Mashonaland*, 1852–1896.
Memories of Mashonaland, by G. W. H. Knight-Bruce ... London, New York, E. Arnold, 1895.
4 p. l., 242 p. front. 21cm.
1. Mashonaland—Descr. & trav.
1—1505
Library of Congress DT964.M3K6
MB WU CtY-D MiEM WaSpG
NK 0203184 DLC CU NSyU NcD WU PPPD PPL PPA OCl NN

DT795 K5K71
Knight-Bruce, Louise (Torr)
The story of an African chief; being the life of Khama, by Mrs. Wyndham Knight-Bruce. With a pref. by Edna Lyall. London, Kegan Paul, Trench Trübner, 1893.
viii, 71 p. 17cm.
1. Khama, African chief, 1830 (ca.)-1930. 2. Botswana - Hist. I. Title.
NK 0203186 CSt-H MB MH

Knight-Bruce, *Mrs.* **Louise (Torr)**
The story of an African chief, being the life of Khama by Mrs. Wyndham Knight-Bruce, with a preface by Edna Lyall. 2d ed. London, K. Paul, Trench, Trübner, & co., ltd., 1894.
viii, ⌜2⌝, 71, ⌜1⌝ p. 16½cm.
Cover-title: Khama, the African chief.
Revised and reprinted from the author's article "Khamé" in Murray's magazine, Apr. 1889. v. 5, no. 28.
1. Khama, African chief, b. ca. 1830. I. Title.
14-15137
Library of Congress DT795.K5K6
NK 0203187 DLC

DT795 K5 K55 1895
Knight-Bruce, Louise (Torr)
The story of an African chief, being the life of Khama, by Mrs. Wyndham Knight-Bruce, with a preface by Edna Lyall. 5th ed. London, K. Paul, Trench, Trübner, 1895.
viii, 71 p. 17 cm.
1. Khama, African chief, 1830 (ca.)-1923.
NK 0203188 CtY

Knight-Bruce, Mrs. Wyndham
see
Knight-Bruce, Mrs. Louise (Torr)

Q41 L8 v.236 no.634
Knight-Jones, E W
On the nervous system of Saccoglossus cambrensis (Enteropneusta). London, New York, Cambridge University Press [1952].
315-354, [5] p. illus., plates. 30 cm. (Royal Society of London. Philosophical transactions, Ser. B, v. 236, no. 634).
Cover title.
References: p. 353-354.
1. Worms - Anatomy. 2. Nervous system - Worms. 3. Enteropneusta (Series)
NK 0203190 DI

SH255 A27 Ser.2 v. 18 no. 2
Knight-Jones, E W
Reproduction of oysters in the rivers Crouch and Roach, Essex, during 1947, 1948 and 1949. London, H. M. Stationery Off., 1952.
47, [1] p. plate, maps, diagrs., tables. 27 cm. (Gt. Brit. Ministry of Agriculture and Fisheries. Fishery investigations, ser. 2, v. 18, no. 2)
"References": p. 47-[48].
1. Oysters. I. Title. (Series)
NK 0203191 DI

Knight-Patterson, W. M., *pseud.*
see
Kulski, Władysław Wszebór, 1903–

The Knight: the official organ of Gebriel Richard council, no.2463, Knights of Columbus. Detroit, Mich.
v.
NK 0203193 MiD-B

The knight...
see under [Meston, William] 1688?-1745.

Knight among ladies
see under Jameson, Annie Edith (Foster), 1868-1931.

Knight and company, London
see Knight (Charles) and co., firm, London.

Knight and company, New York.
Arbitables. v. 1–
Sept. 1938–
⌜New York, Knight & company, °1939–

F869 S85K5
Knight and Company, Sutter Creek, Calif.
Catalogue of water wheels, hydraulic appliances and mining machinery.
[Sutter Creek, Calif., Amador Record] 18
v. illus. 26cm.
1. Water wheels. 2. Machinery - Catalogs. 3. Sutter Creek, Calif. - Indus.
NK 0203198 CU-B

cTJ 860 T5
Knight and Company, Sutter Creek, Calif.
Catalogue of water wheels and hydraulic appliances. Edward A. Rix and Co., sole agents. San Francisco, 1886.
48 p. diagrs. 27cm.
NK 0203199 C

The knight and friars
see under [Tucker, St. George] 1752-1828.

The knight and his wife.
Halliwell-Phillipps, James Orchard, 1820–1889, *ed.*
The life of St. Katharine: The tale of the knight and his wife: and an account of the magical manuscript of Dr. Caius. Ed. by James Orchard Halliwell ... Brixton Hill, For private circulation only, 1848.

R621.41 K748w
Knight and Kilbourne Patents Company
The world's experience with the Knight motor. Chicago, Barnard & Miller, 1914.
456 p.
1. Automobiles - Motors I. T. II. T.: Knight motor.
NK 0203202 MiD

Rare Book Room In K7l12 801
The knight and mason; or, He who runs may read. A novel ... London:Printed for Crosby and Letterman,Stationer's-Court; by Rowland Hurst,Wakefield.1801.
4v. 17cm.
NK 0203203 CtY

Knight-Bruce, Gordon Kennet, ed.
Zanzibar. *High court.*
... Law reports containing cases determined by the High court for Zanzibar and on appeal therefrom by the Court of appeal for Eastern Africa and by the Privy council. v. 1–
1868/1918– ⌜Zanzibar, Printed by the government printer⌝ 1919–

VOLUME 300

Knight-Bruce, *Sir* **James Lewis,** 1791–1866.
Ecclesiastical duties and revenues bill. Speech delivered in the House of lords, on behalf of the deans and chapters petitioning against the bill, 23 July 1840. By J. L. Knight Bruce ... London, J., L. G. & L. J. Hansard, 1840.
58 p. 21½cm.

1. Church of England—Finance. 2. Ecclesiastical law—Gt. Brit. I. Title.
39-2743

NK 0203205 DLC MH NN MBAt

Knight-Bruce, Sir James Lewis, 1791-1866.

Gt. Brit. *Court of chancery.* FOR OTHER EDITIONS SEE MAIN ENTRY
Reports of cases decided in the High court of chancery, by the Right Hon. Sir J. L. Knight Bruce, vice-chancellor. By Edward Younge ... and John Collyer ... With notes and references to both English and American decisions. By John A. Dunlap ... Michaelmas term, 1841, to [Hilary term, 1844] .. New York, Albany, Banks & brothers, 1864–65.

JS 3115 .K6 Knight-Bruce, Sir James Lewis, 1791-1866.
Speech of Jas. Lewis Knight, Esq., K. C., against the iniquitous Corporation Bill, Friday, 31st July, and Saturday, 1st August, 1835. London, C. F. Cock [1835]
32 p. 17 cm.
U. W. copy imperfect: p. 31-32 wanting. Cf. BM.

1. Municipal corporations - Gt. Brit. 2. Gt. Brit. - Pol. & govt.

NK 0203207 WU NN

Knight-Bruce, John Horace Wyndham.

Lynch, John Gilbert Bohun.
The complete boxer, by J. G. Bohun Lynch, with a preface by the Earl of Lonsdale and with two chapters on army boxing by J. H. W. Knight-Bruce, with seventeen illustrations. New York, F. A. Stokes company [1914]

Knight-Bruce, John Horace Wyndham.
Dartmoor days with the forest hunt, by J. H. W. Knight-Bruce; with illustrations by Lieutenant Picard ... London, J. Murray, 1916.
vii, 329 p. illus. 20cm.

I. Title.
A 17-376
Title from Forbes Libr. Printed by L. C.

NK 0203209 MNF NN

Knight-Bruce, John Horace Wyndham.
Military boxing: its origin and growth. Regimental boxing clubs and military boxing tournaments.
(In Lynch, J. G. Bohun. The complete amateur boxer. Pp. 192–223. Plates. London. [1913.])

NK 0203210 MB

Knight-Bruce, Mrs. Louise (Torr)

Knight-Bruce, George Wyndham Hamilton, *bp. of Mashonaland,* 1852–1896.
Journals of the Mashonaland mission, 1888 to 1892, by G. W. H. Knight-Bruce ... Ed., with an introduction, by L. K. B. ... [London] Society for the propagation of the Gospel in foreign parts, 1892.

Knight & Millet, publ.
Country life in Japan. Ten photographs colored by hand in Japan. Boston [193- ?]

NK 0203212 MH

★ cSF 335 U6 C2 K5 Knight and Parker, inc., Hollywood, Calif.
Public opinion poll., Conducted by Knight and Parker for Western Fairs Association. [n.p.,] 1946.
1 v. (looseleaf) 29cm.

"The survey had as its primary aims the determination of public sentiment in California on ... horse racing and pari-mutuel wagering, and on the utility and value to the State of non-profit fairs."

NK 0203213 C

JK8776 .A2 1949 **Knight and Parker, inc., Hollywood, Calif.**

California. *Legislature. Senate. Interim Committee on Governmental Reorganization.*
Report. Public opinion survey by Knight and Parker, inc. [Sacramento] Senate of the State of California [1949]

... **Knight & Parsons'** business directory, of the city of Cleveland ... [v. 1]–
1853–
Cleveland, E. G. Knight & co. and Parsons & co., 1853–
v. 21cm.

1. Cleveland, O.—Direct.
9-16497
Library of Congress F499.C6A18 1853

NK 0203215 DLC OClW

KNIGHT AND PERRY.
Synopsis of the Coniferous Plants grown in Great Britain. London, [1850].

NK 0203216 MH CU

Knight and Struck Company, New York.
Flower talks
see under title

Knight and Struck Company, New York.
The home of heather. New York: Knight and Struck Co.[, cop. 1915.] 240 p. 8°.
"Heatherhome seed and plant book," second annual edition.

326642A. 1. Plants—Catalogues. 2. Seeds—Catalogues.
N. Y. P. L. January 26, 1928

NK 0203218 NN

---

*pEBB65 **The knight and the begger-wench.** Which doth a wanton prank unfold, in as merry a story as ever was told. To the tune of, The King's delight: or, Turn-coat, &c.
London: Printed by and for W.O. for A.M. and sold by C.Bates in Pye-corner. [1685]
broadside. 1 illus. 22x34cm.
Crawford 598.

NK 0203219 MH

---

*fEC7 A100 731k The knight and the Cardinal. A new ballad. Addressed to the Kings of England and France. Tune of, The King shall enjoy his own again ...
London: Printed by R.Walker, without Temple-bar, and sold by the booksellers of London and Westminster. [1731?] (Price six-pence.)
f°. 8p. 30cm.
Satire on Robert Walpole & Cardinal Fleury.
First line: In time's remembrancers we find.

NK 0203220 MH

The knight & the lady; a domestic legend of the reign of Queen Anne...
see under [Barham, Richard Harris] 1788-1845.

The **knight** and the prelate: a new ballad. To the tune of King John and the Abbot of Canterbury: or, A cobler there was, and he liv'd in a stall, &c. ... [London?] 1734.
8 p. 20cm.
Without the music.
An attack upon Sir Robert Walpole and Gibson, bishop of London.

1. Walpole, Robert, 1st earl of Orford, 1676–1745. 2. Gibson, Edmund, bp. of London, 1669–1748.
21-3029
Library of Congress PR3291.A1K6

NK 0203222 DLC CtY

The knight and the prelate: A new ballad. To the tune of King John and the Abbot of Canterbury ... London, P. Holder, 1734.
8 p. 34cm.
[Poetical pamphlets. v. 8, no. 14]
Attack on Sir Robert Walpole and Gibson, bp. of London. *cf.* Political ballads, ed. by M. Percival, 1916, p. 90.

1. Walpole, Sir Robert, 1st earl of Orford, 1676–1745. 2. Gibson, Edmund, bp. of London, 1669–1748.
25-28143
Library of Congress PR1171.Z5 vol. 8

NK 0203223 DLC OCU NN CLU-C MH

720.975965 K71t
Knight and Wall Company.
Tampa architecture and associated industries. [St. Petersburg] 1946.
1 v. (unpaged) illus., plans. 31cm.

Cover title.

1. Architecture - Tampa. 2. Architecture, Domestic - Tampa. I. Title.

NK 0203224 FU

VOLUME 300

Knight artisans of the world.
Burial, unveiling, memorial and annual celebration ceremonies of the Knight artisans of the world. Author and founder: John Shields ... Dallas, Tex., Texas printing company [1897]
14 p. illus., pl. 21cm.

I. Shields, John.
9-32529†
Library of Congress HS1510.K72 1897 (Copyright 1897: 63493)

NK 0203225 DLC

Knight brothers.
Instructions for obtaining and working foreign patents. Synopsis of the patent laws of various countries. [Washington?] Knight brothers, °1875.
cover-title, 20 p. 14½cm.

1. Patents.
CA 5—1456 Unrev'd
Library of Congress T339.K69

NK 0203226 DLC

The **Knight** company's handy guide to Chicago . . . contains a complete map of the city . . . and a directory to the railroad depots . . . parks . . . prominent buildings, etc. . . . [Chicago, 1890]
1 sheet fold. 16°.
F548.45.K6 1-Rc-2711

NK 0203227 DLC

The knight crusaders' games, being a compilation of interesting games on the chessboard; to which are added, a plan of the knight crusaders' games and other diagrams. London, Houlston and Hughes, 1940.
xii, [13] - 50p. front. (fold.)

NK 0203228 OCl

A Knight errant, pseud.
My pocket book; or, Hints for "a ryghte merrie and conceitede" tour ...
see under [Dubois, Edward] 1774-1850.

... The **Knight** errant, being a magazine of appreciation. v. 1, no. 1-4; Apr. 1892–Jan. 1893. Boston, Printed for the proprietors at the Elzevir press, 1892–93.
3 p. l., 128, [3] p. plates. 32cm.
At head of title: A Quarter-yearly review of the liberal arts called ... No more published.
11-34208
Library of Congress AP2.K66

NhD NNC NB N MnU NjP OCl RPB WU NcU IEN ICN NIC IEN MB MH CSmH CU CtY MBAt MWA MiD
NK 0203230 DLC OCl RPB WU NSyU CU-A OCl CSmH NjP

The **knight** errant; written & composed by Hortencia, Queen of Holland. Translated from the French by Sir Walter Scott. Published by John Cole, Baltimore. [18—] Pl. no. 170.
[2] l. 34 cm.
Caption title.
No. 67 in a vol. with title: [Collection of piano music and songs. v. p., ca. 1826-36]
The music has been variously ascribed to Hortense, consort of Louis, King of Holland, and to L. F. P. Drouet. Cf. Scholes. Oxford companion to music.
For voice and piano.
1. Songs (Medium voice) with piano. I. Hortense, consort of Louis, King of Holland, 1783-1837, supposed composer. II. Drouet, Louis François Philippe, 1792-1873, supposed composer.
M1.A13C no. 67 M 54-2798

NK 0203231 DLC

W.C.L. M780.88 A512CW no.27 The knight errant, written and composed by Hortencia, the late Queen of Holland. Translated from the French by Walter Scott. New York, Published by J. A. & W. Geib, 23 Maiden Lane. Pr. 25 cts. [1818]
[2] l. 32 cm.
Caption title.
For voice and piano.
The music has been variously ascribed to Hortense, consort of Louis, King of Holland and to L. F. P. Drouet. Cf. Scholes, Oxford companion to music.
[No. 27] in a collection of early American music, ca. 1802-30.

NK 0203232 NcD

W.C.L. M780.88 A512CZ no.10 The Knight errant; written and composed by Hortencia, the late Queen of Holland. Translated from the French by Walter Scott. New York, Published by W. Dubois at his Piano forte and Music store No. 126 Broadway [1819]
[2] l. 34 cm.
Caption title.
For voice and piano.
[No. 10] in a collection songs and piano music ca. 1820-35, compiled by Catharine M. Perkins.

NK 0203233 NcD

**M.445.171
The knight errant. Written and composed by Hortencia, the late Queen of Holland. Translated from the French by Walter Scott . . . [Song with accompaniment for the pianoforte.] Boston. Graupner & Co. [182-?] 3 pp. 30 cm.

D5863 — T.r. Song. — Songs. With music. — Scott, Sir Walter, Baronet, tr., 1771-1832.

NK 0203234 MB

The knight errant of the nursery; with illustrations by the knight and his father. New York, F. A. Stokes company [1906]
44, [4] p. illus. (partly col.) 26 x 32cm.

W 6-320
Washington, D. C. Public Library

NK 0203235 DWP

Knight-errantry; or, Don Quixote encountering the wind mill. Being a relation of the siege of Knocke. [n.p., Printed the year 1695]
4 p. 26.5 cm.
Caption title.
In verse.

NK 0203236 CtY

Knight, Frank & Rutley, auctioneers.
Catalogue of the contents of "The Convent," Kingsgate, near Broadstairs. Sold by auction by Knight, Frank & Rutley...September, 1910... [London:] J. Davy & Sons [1910]. 56 p., 9 pl. 8°.

1. Art (Applied).—Collections, Gt. Br.: Eng.: London. 2. Furniture.—Collections, Gt. Br.: Eng.: London.
N. Y. P. L. January 26, 1911.

NK 0203237 NN

Knight, Frank & Rutley, auctioneers.
A catalogue of the Margrave Pallavicini collection
see under Pallavicini, Margraves of.

NA 7625 .H4A3 fol. Knight, Frank & Rutley, auctioneers.
... Illustrated particulars of the freehold, residential, agricultural and sporting estate of "Hemsted" near Cranbrook, in the country of Kent...for sale by auction...the 25th and 26th of June, 1912...by Messrs. Knight, Frank & Rutley... [London, The Press Art Alliance, 1912]
45, [3] p. 37.5 cm.

NK 0203239 DLC

NA 7625 .H4 A3 fol. Knight, Frank & Rutley, auctioneers.
... Illustrated particulars, with plans, of the freehold ... known as Harefield place ... London 1914.
1 pam. f°.
To be offered by auction ... by Messrs. Knight, Frank and Rutley ... the 23rd day of June, 1914 ...

NK 0203240 DLC LU

Knight, Frank & Rutley, auctioneers.
The IZAAK Walton hotel and Dovedale hill and wood. Forming part of the auction particulars of the Ilam Hall estate, dated 26th day of July 1910. Solicitors; Patersons, Snow, Kinder & Lawson. Auctioneers and land agents; Knight, Frank & Rutley. [London, 1910].

Cover-title, 8 p. 4 plates and folded map at end. 1.8°.

NK 0203241 MH

+Z903p Knight, Frank & Rutley, auctioneers.
Plan of Gadshill place near Rochester, Kent. For sale by auction by Messrs. Knight, Frank, & Rutley ... 1923. London, S.W.Rowsell & son [1923]
plan. 31½x21½cm.fold.to 22x13½cm.
"This plan is based upon the Ordnance survey."
In case with Penney & Clark, auctioneers ... Sale of Charles Dickens' birthplace ... [1903]

At head of title: Kent ...
On cover: By direction of the executors of the late F.L.Latham, esq., deceased. Gadshill Place, near Rochester ...
In case with Penney & Clark, auctioneers. ... Sale of Charles Dickens' birthplace ... [1903]

NK 0203243 CtY

+Z903p Knight, Frank & Rutley, auctioneers.
... The singularly interesting freehold residential property known as Gadshill place, the home of Charles Dickens from 1857 to 1870. To be offered for sale by auction by Messrs.Knight,Frank & Rutley ... at ... London ... on Thursday, the 26th day of July, 1923 ... Solicitors: Messrs.Rose,Johnson & Hicks ... London ... [London,S.W.Rowsell & son,printers,1923]
16,[2]p. plate. 24½cm

NK 0203244 CtY

Knight, Harrison, & co.
Canhamo braziliensis perini or Brazilian linen. Prospectus and explanatory notice regarding the cultivation of the above plant ... [By John Knight] Published by the Brazilian Review. Rio de Janeiro, 1905.

NK 0203245 DPU

VOLUME 300

F689 f.W63K7 ₍Knight Investment Co., Wichita, Kan.₎
"The magic city", Wichita, picturesque and descriptive. Neenah, Wis., Art pub. co., 1889.
₍54₎ l. illus. (1 mounted) 34cm.

NK 0203246 MnHi

Knight, Leonard & Co., Chicago.
The Falls of Niagara. Depicted by pen and camera
see under title

Knight, Leonard & co., *Chicago.*
A guide to the Columbian World's fair, Chicago, Illinois. Rev. ed. Chicago, Knight, Leonard & co., 1892.
62 p. illus., fold. plan. 23cm.
Compiled by the publishers.

1. Chicago. World's Columbian exposition, 1893—Guide books.

Library of Congress T500.A2K7 5-28667†

NK 0203248 DLC MB

Knight, Leonard & Co., Chicago.
In the lovely land of sunset
see under [Turner, Henry Lathrop]

Knight Memorial Methodist Episcopal Church, Calais, Me.
see Calais, Me. Knight Memorial Methodist Episcopal Church. (In Supplement)

A knight of Arthur's court or the tale of Sir Gawain and the Green Knight
see under Gawain and the Grene knight.

Knight of Chillon of Switzerland
see
Hawkins, Nehemiah, 1833-

A knight of chivalry.
A friendly letter to the Marquis of Lorn ...
see under title

The knight of curtesy.
... The knight of curtesy and the fair lady of Faguell; a study of the date and dialect of the poem and its folklore origins, by Elizabeth McCausland, M. A. Northampton, Mass., Smith college; ₍etc., etc., 1922₎
4 p. l., vii-xxxii, 32 p. 22½cm. (Smith college studies in modern languages. v. 4, no. 1)
"Presented as a thesis to complete the requirements for the degree of master of arts", Smith college, 1922.
Edited from the edition printed by William Copland.
"Chronique du Châtelain de Coucy et de la dame de Fayel": p. 20-21.
Bibliography: p. xxxi-xxxii.

I. McCausland, Elizabeth. II. Le châtelain de Coucy (Romance)

Library of Congress PC13.S6 vol. 4, no. 1 23-17369

NK 0203254 DLC OrPR DFo PHC PBm PPT OU MiU OCU OClW OO ViU NcD MB

The KNIGHT of Elle; a scarce and favourite Scotch ballad. Glasgow, Printed for the booksellers [1830?] 8 p. 17cm.

Weiss: Chapbooks, 425.
At head of title: No. 33.
Without covers.

NK 0203255 NN MnU

The Knight of Kerry, pseud.
see Fitzgerald, Peter George, 1808-1880.

Knight of labor.
Capitalism on trial
see under title

Knight of Leon
see under [Cobb, Sylvanus] 1823-1887.

Case Y 1565 .K 74 The KNIGHT of Malta: or, The reward of constancy. A novel. To which is added, The unfortunate lovers: or, Virtue in distress. A novel. Both done from the French. London, T. Payne, 1724.
37,72p. 20cm.

NK 0203259 ICN

The knight of Malta, text
see under [Fletcher, John] 1579-1625.

The knight of Mauléon
see under [Dumas, Alexander] 1802-1870.

The Knight of Morar, *pseud.*
see
Fraser, ***Sir*** **William Augustus,** *bart.,* **1826-1898.**

Knight of the burning pestle
see under Beaumont, Francis, 1584-1616.

Knight of the camera.
The gentle art of photography
see under title

The knight of the glen. An Irish romance
see under [Doherty, Ann (Holmes Hunter)] 1789-

Knight of the golden melice
see under [Adams, John Turvill] 1805-1882.

Knights and ladies of honor.
Outgrowth of the degree of protection of the Knights of honor. First annual meeting of Supreme lodge of protection, Knights and ladies of honor was held Sept. 19, 1878. Lodge was incorporated April, 1879.

The Knight of the Grip. New York [1900]
see under [Carey, Thomas Joseph] 1853-

A knight of the grip. Chicago [1918]
see under National Salesman's Training Association.

The knight of the kirk
see under [Meston, William] 1688?-1745.

Knight of the rose
see under Peacock, Lucy, fl. 1786-1815.

The knight of the rum bottle & co.
see under [Rogers, Daniel] 1780-1839.

The knight of the sea
see The heroicall adventvres of the knight of the sea.

Knight of the silver pen, pseud.
How Ben Watson became a Good Templar. By the Knight of the silver pen ... London: Hammond & Co. [18—?] 8 p. 16°.

1. Temperance.—Poetry. 2. Poetry (English). 3. Title.
N. Y. P. L. August 15, 1918.

NK 0203272 NN

Knight of the silver pen, pseud.
Victor and vanquished. "Port or sherry?" By the Knight of the silver pen. London: Hammond & Co. [18—?] 7 p. 16°. (Hammond's new series of Good Templar dialogues. nos. 1 and 2.)

1. Temperance.—Exercises, recitations, etc. 2. Title. 3. Title: "Port or sherry?"
N. Y. P. L. August 15, 1918.

NK 0203273 NN

PZ162 .K71 18-- ... The knight of the silver screw. A fairy tale ... London, Arliss and Huntsman ₍18--₎ ₍1₎, 16 p. col. front. (Entertaining tales)

NK 0203274 ICU

VOLUME 300

Knight of the Swan
see
Chevalier au Cygne.

Knight of the twentieth century
see under [Hensel, Harry C] 1863-

Knight of the white feather
see under Couvreur, Jessie Catherine (Huybers), ca. 1850-1897.

Knight on wheels
see under [Beith, John Hay] 1876-

Knight study club.
[Year book. Detroit]
v.

NK 0203279 MiD-B

Knightage, 1930-1931; a list of the existing recipients of the honour of knighthood,..
see under Bull, Sir William James, 1863-1931.

Knightage of Great Britain and Ireland
see under [Burke, John] 1787-1848.

Knighthood, Independent Order of
see Independent Order of Knighthood.

Y
185
K 747
KNIGHTHOOD, no trifle---- ; or, Lady Wou'd-Be; a tale. 2d ed. Dublin, Printed; London, Reprinted, A. Freeman, 1747.
8p. 39cm.

NK 0203283 ICN OCU

Rare
DA
430
T87++
no.18
Knightley, Alexander, d. 1696, defendant.
The arraignment, confession, and condemnation of Alexander Knightley, for the horrid ... conspiracy to assassinate His Sacred Majesty, K. William, in order to a French invasion of this kingdom; at the Kings Bench bar, Westminster, on the 30th of April and the 20th and 25th of May. London, S. Heyrick and I. Cleave, 1696.
8 p. 32cm.
Publishers' advertisement: p. 8.
No. 18 in vol. lettered: Tryals and confess. &c.

NK 0203284 NIC WaU-L PU CtY MnU NN CLU-C

[Knightley, John]
...Essay toward proving the advantages which may arise from improvements on salt works, and in the fishing trade of Ireland. [n.p., 1733?]
1 p.l., c-vi, 7-32, 4 p.

NK 0203285 MH-BA

[Knightley, John]
Proposals for establishing of a fund of 30,000 L. to be vested in a corporation for the purposes therein mentioned, humbly submitted to the consideration of all true lovers of their country, particularly to the right honourable and honourable the Lords spiritual and temporal and Commons, soon to be assembled in Parliament. Dublin, Printed by S.Powell, 1731.
4 p.l., 5-27 p.incl.tables. 19 cm.
Dedication signed: John Knightley.

NK 0203286 MH-BA NNC CtY

Knightley, Louisa Mary(Bowater) Knightley, baroness, 1842-1913. 4515.183
The journals of Lady Knightley of Fawsley. Edited by Julia Cartwright (Mrs. Ady). 1856–1884.
— London. Murray. 1915. xx, 403, (1) pp. Portraits. Plates. Autograph facsimile. 21½ cm., in 8s.
Much of the book relates to the political history of Great Britain.

K9168 — Diaries. — Great Britain. . hist. — Great Britain. Manners and customs. — Cartwright, Julia Mary, ed.

NK 0203287 MB CtY PPL PU MiU ICN

Knightley, Louisa Mary (Bowater) Knightley, *baroness,* 1842–1913.
The journals of Lady Knightley of Fawsley, ed. by Julia Cartwright (Mrs. Ady) 1856–1884 ... London, J. Murray, 1916.
xx, 403, [1] p. front., plates, ports., plan. 22½cm.
"First edition, December 1915. Reprinted, January 1916."

1. Gt. Brit.—Soc. life & cust. 2. Gt. Brit.—Court and courtiers. I. Ady, Mrs. Julia Mary (Cartwright) ed.

16—13324

Library of Congress DA565.K7A3

NK 0203288 DLC PPA

Knightley, Louisa Mary (Bowater) Knightley, baroness, 1842–1913.
The journals of Lady Knightley of Fawsley; edited by Julia Cartwright (Mrs. Ady) 1856–1884... New York: E. P. Dutton & Co., 1917. xx, 403(1) p., 8 pl., 5 port. (incl. front.) 8°.

1. Gt. Br.—Social life, 1855-85. 2. Court life, Gt. Br., 1855-85. 3. Ady, Julia (Cartwright), editor.
N. Y. P. L. January 28, 1918.

NK 0203289 NN PHC MH

Knightley, Rainald, baron, 1819-1895.

Gardiner, Samuel Rawson, 1829–1902.
Volume belonging to Sir Rainald Knightley, bart.
(*In* Gt. Brit. Historical manuscripts commission. Third report. London, 1872. 32cm. Appendix, p. 254–255)

A Knightly soul
see under Raymond, Gérard, 1912-1932.

The **Knightly** tale of Golagrus and Gawane, and other ancient poems. Printed at Edinburgh by W. Chepman and A. Myllar in the year M.D.VIIJ. [Edinburgh] Reprinted M.DCCC.XXVIJ.
28, [266], xx p. 1 illus. 29 cm.
Margins damaged by a fire which destroyed most of the edition before publication; only 76 copies issued. *cf.* Introd.
David Laing's type-facsimile reprint of 11 tracts published in or about 1508 which were presented to the library of the Faculty of Advocates (now the National Library of Scotland). Cf. Introd., p. 5–7; also The Chepman and Myllar prints (Edinburgh, 1950) p. xxii–xxiii.

CONTENTS.—Introduction.—I. The Knightly tale of Golagrus and Gawane.—II. The golden targe [by Dunbar]—III. The flyting of Dunbar and Kennedy.—IV. The tau marit wemen and the wedo [by Dunbar]—V. The ballad of Lord Barnard Stewart [by Dunbar]—VI. The traitie of Orpheus King [by R. Henryson]—VII. Ane buke of gud counsale [to the King]—VIII. The Maying or disport of Chaucer.—IX. Sir Eglamour of Arteas.—X. A gest of Robyn Hode.—XI. The porteous of noblenes [tr. out of franche in scottis be Maistir Androw Cadiou]—The register and table of errata.

1. English poetry—Middle English (1100–1500) 2. English poetry—Scottish authors. I. Laing, David, 1793–1878. II. Golagros and Gawane.

PR1203.K6 1827 9–26698 rev 2

NK 0203293 DLC MdBP CSmH OCl MiU NjP NIC

Knighton, Dorothea (Hawker) lady, ed.
FOR OTHER EDITIONS SEE MAIN ENTRY
Knighton, *Sir* **William,** *bart.*, 1776–1836.
Memoirs of Sir William Knighton, bart., G. C. H., keeper of the privy purse during the reign of His Majesty King George the Fourth. Including his correspondence with many distinguished personages. By Lady Knighton ... London. R. Bentley, 1838.

PE1109
.K7
Knighton, Frederick, 1812–1888.
The American etymological school grammar, containing copious exercises, and a systematic view of the formation and derivation of words, from the Anglo-Saxon, Latin and Greek ... by Rev. F. Knighton, A. M. **Philadelphia, R. E. Peterson & co., 1852.**
viii, 9–252 p. 18cm. (Robert E. Peterson's cheap educational series)

1. English language—Grammar—1800–1870. 2. English language—Etymology.

NK 0203294 ICU NNC MH

Knighton, Frederick, 1812–1888.
... Primary grammar; or, An introduction to the American school grammar, by the Rev. F. Knighton. Philadelphia, R. E. Peterson & co., 1852.
vi, 7–67 p. 17cm. (R. E. Peterson's cheap educational series)

1. English language—Grammar—1800–1870.

11–5846

Library of Congress PE1111.K68

NK 0203295 DLC

Knighton, Frederick, 1812–1888.
... The young composer; or, Progressive exercises in English composition ... By Rev. F. Knighton ... Philadelphia, R. E. Peterson & co., 1853.
vi, [7]–176 p. 19½cm. (Robert E. Peterson's cheap educational series)

1. English language—Composition and exercises.

10–24550†

Library of Congress PE1109.K73

NK 0203296 DLC PPL

Knighton, Henry, *fl.* 1363.
Chronicon Henrici Knighton; vel, Cnitthon, monachi leycestrensis. Edited by Joseph Rawson Lumby ... Published by the authority of the lords commissioners of Her Majesty's Treasury, under the direction of the master of the rolls. London, Printed for H. M. Stationery off., by Eyre and Spottiswoode, 1889–95.
2 v. 25½cm. (*Half-title:* [Gt. Brit. Public record office] Rerum britannicarum medii ævi scriptores; or, Chronicles and memorials of Great Britain and Ireland during the middle ages. [no. 92])

1. Gt. Brit.—History—Medieval period, 1066–1485. I. Lumby, Joseph Rawson, 1831–1895, ed. II. Title.

A 29–114

Chicago. Univ. Library DA25.B8 vol. 92
for Library of Congress [DA25.B5 no. 92]

NK 0203297 PBm PU PSC MiU OCU OU OClW OCl OO ICU MH MdBP NjP ICU DLC CU NN OrPR CaBVaU CtY PSt PHC

VOLUME 300

card
Ed.

Knighton, Henry, fl. 1363.
Chronicon Henrici Knighton; vel, Cnitthon, monachi leycestrensis. Ed. by Joseph Rawson Lumby... Pub. by the authority of the lords commissioners of Her Majesty's Treasury, under the direction of the master of the rolls. London, Printed for H. M. Stationery off., by Eyre and Spottiswoode, 1889-95.
2v. 26cm. (Half-title: [Gt. Brit. Public record office] Rerum britannicarum medii aevi scriptores. [no.92])
Microcard edition (19 cds.)

NK 0203298 OOxM

Knighton, Henry, fl. 1363.
Henrici Knighton...

(In Twysden, Sir R., bart., ed. Historiae anglicanae scriptores X. Londini, 1652. 37cm. col. 2311-2742)

DA170
.T97

NK 0203299 DLC

Knighton, Joseph Raymond, jr.
... "Voice class in the high school", Music 512 ... [East Lansing, Mich., Michigan state college n.d.]
1 p.l., 23 numb. l., 1 l. 29 cm.
"Research problem in music education."
Typewritten manuscript.
Bibliography: leaf [24]
1. Voice - Study and teaching. 2. Music - Instruction and study. I. Title.

NK 0203300 MiEM

Knighton, Leslie.
Behind the scenes in big football. London, S. Paul [1948]
176 p. front. (port.) plates.

1. Foot-ball.

NK 0203301 NNC NN

Knighton, Marian, joint author.

Hillas, Marjorie.
Athletic dances and simple clogs, by Marjorie Hillas ... and Marian Knighton ... with introduction by Jesse Feiring Williams ... New York, A. S. Barnes and company, 1926.

Knighton, Merrill.
[March miniature]
March miniature; quartet for Bb clarinets. [New York, Boosey & Hawkes, c1951]
score (5 p.) 31cm.
Cover title.

1. Wind quartets (4 clarinets)

NK 0203303 MB

KNIGHTON, SAMUEL.
Feeding New York; radio broadcast (station WOR), by Samuel Knighton... March 7, 1933. [New York, 1933.]
2 l. 23cm.

714935A. 1. New York (City)—Food.

NK 0203304 NN

KNIGHTON, SAMUEL.
Statement of Samuel Knighton, president of the New York Produce Exchange, in respect to exchanges which maintain a market for trading in unlisted securities as affected by S.2693 and H.R.7852, entitled "National securities exchange act of 1934." [New York, 1934] 8 p. 23cm.

821377A. 1. Securities—Transfer and registration—U.S.—N.Y.—New York. 2. Produce exchange—U.S.—N.Y.—New York.

NK 0203305 NN

Knighton, *Sir* William, *bart.*, 1776-1836.
Memoirs of Sir William Knighton, bart., G. C. H., keeper of the privy purse during the reign of His Majesty King George the Fourth. Including his correspondence with many distinguished personages. By Lady Knighton ... London. R. Bentley, 1838.
2 v. front. (port.) fold. facsim. 22cm.

I. Knighton, Dorothea (Hawker) lady. ed.

36-3921

Library of Congress DA538.K7A2 1838 923.242

MH MWA OC1 PBL MdBP NjNbS
NK 0203306 DLC CLU CtY NcU CU NcD InU MiD PU DS ICN

Knighton, *Sir* William, *bart.*, 1776-1836.
Memoirs of Sir William Knighton, bart., G. C. H., keeper of the privy purse during the reign of His Majesty King George the Fourth. Including his correspondence with many distinguished personages. By Lady Knighton. Philadelphia, Carey, Lea & Blanchard, 1838.
viii, [9]-415 p. 24½cm.

I. Knighton, Dorothea (Hawker) lady, ed.

35-36526

Library of Congress DA538.K7A2 1838 a

NK 0203307 DLC PSt GU NcD MU PU NN MWA MB NjR

Knighton, William, *d.* 1900.
Cleon, the demagogue. By William Knighton ...
(*In* Royal society of literature of the United Kingdom, London. Essays by divers hands, being the transactions. London [1888] 22cm. 2d ser., vol. XIV, p. [256]-277)
"Read May 25, 1887."
Bibliographical foot-notes.

1. Cleon, d. B. C. 422.

A C 39-2836

Illinois. Univ. Library for Library of Congress [PN22.R6 ser. 2, vol. 14] [2] (806.242)

NK 0203308 IU DLC

Knighton, William
Conversations with Carlyle. (In Contemporary review. 39 [no. 6] June 1881, p. 904-920.)

NK 0203309 MiU

Knighton, William, *d.* 1900.
Early Roman history. By Dr. Knighton.
(*In* Royal society of literature of the United Kingdom, London. Essays by divers hands, being the transactions. London [1886] 22cm. 2d ser., vol. XIII, p. [265]-290)
"Few notes to Dr. Knighton's paper": p. 286-290.

1. Rome—History—Aboriginal and early period. 2. Rome—History—Kings, B. C. 753-510. 3. Rome—History—Historiography.

A C 39-2825

Illinois. Univ. Library for Library of Congress [PN22.R6 ser. 2, vol. 13] [2] (806.242)

NK 0203310 IU DLC

Knighton, William, d. 1900
Elihu Jan's story; or, The private life of an eastern queen, by William Knighton ... London, Longman, Green, Longman, Roberts, & Green, 1865.
1 p. l., [v]-vi p., 1 l., 210 p. 19cm.
The life of Janáb Aulia, wife of Amjad 'Ali, and mother of Wajid 'Ali, kings of Oudh, as told by one of her attendants.

1. Janáb Aulia, queen consort of Amjad 'Ali, king of Oudh, d. 1858. 2. Oudh—Soc. life & cust. I. Title.

18-10532

Library of Congress DS485.O9K6

NK 0203311 DLC NIC CU OC1 PPL NN

KNIGHTON, William, (d.1900)
European Turkey; its people, its provinces and its history; with an account of the origin of the present war. L. 1854.

Map and wdcts. Ott 3108.54

NK 0203312 MH

Knighton, William, *d.* 1900.
Forest life in Ceylon. By W. Knighton ... London, Hurst and Blackett, 1854.
2 v. 19½cm.

1. Ceylon—Descr. & trav.

5-13889

Library of Congress DS489.K71

NK 0203313 DLC ViU MdBP CU ICU CtY OC1 PPL NjP NN MB

Knighton, William, *d.* 1900.
The history of Ceylon from the earliest period to the present time; with an appendix, containing an account of its present condition. By William Knighton ... London, Longman, Brown, Green & Longmans; [etc., etc.] 1845.
xii, 399 p. 20½cm.

1. Ceylon—Hist.

43-48404

Library of Congress DS489.5.K56

NK 0203314 DLC CU WU CtY ICN PPL PU OC1 OO NN MH

4DS
Ind.
592

Knighton, William, d. 1900.
Ein indischer Königshof; von einem Mitgliede des Hofstaates zu Audh. Nach dem Englischen von Ludwig Thiele. Leipzig, C. B. Lorck, 1856.
158 p.

(Conversations-und Reisebibliothek)

NK 0203315 DLC-P4

Knighton, William, *d.* 1900.
The philosophy of Epicurus and modern agnosticism. By William Knighton ...
(*In* Royal society of literature of the United Kingdom, London. Essays by divers hands, being the transactions. London [1888] 22cm. 2d ser., vol. XIV, p. [41]-67)
"Read June 24, 1885."

1. Epicurus. 2. Agnosticism. I. Title.

A C 39-2830

Illinois. Univ. Library for Library of Congress [PN22.R6 ser. 2, vol. 14] [2] (806.242)

NK 0203316 IU DLC

VOLUME 300

[Knighton, William] d. 1900.
The private life of an eastern king. By a member of the household of His late Majesty, Nussir-u-Deen, king of Oude. 2d ed. London, Hope and co., 1855.
viii, 330 p. 20cm.

NK 0203317 WaU

[Knighton, William] d. 1900.
The private life of an eastern king. By a member of the household of His late Majesty, Nussir-u-Deen, king of Oude. 2d ed. London, Hope and co., 1855.
viii, 330 p. 20cm.

1. Nāsir al-Dīn, king of Oudh, d. 1837. 2. Oudh—Soc. life & cust. I. Title.

Library of Congress DS485.O9K7 9-25104

NK 0203318 DLC NcD CU CtY PSC MB

915.42 [Knighton, William] 1834-1900.
K71 The private life of an Eastern king, by a member of the household of His late Majesty, Nussir-u-Deen, King of Oude. New York, Redfield, 1855.
246 p. 20 cm.

1. Nasir-ud-din Haidar, king of Oudh, d. 1837. 2. Oudh. Social life & customs.

NK 0203319 N NNC CLSU MoKU CU CtY NN MB MH

Knighton, William, LL.D., d. 1900.
The private life of an eastern king. By a member of the household of His late Majesty Nussir-u-Deen, King of Oude.
[New edition. London. Routledge & Co. 1857.] viii, 296 pp. Sm. 8°. 3049.130
The title-page and a few preliminary pages are missing.

G8335 — Nasir-ud-din Haidar, King of Oude. — Oude, India. Manners. — T.r.

NK 0203320 MB PU

Knighton, William, d. 1900.
The private life of an eastern king, together with Elihu Jan's story; or, The private life of an eastern queen, by William Knighton ... ed., with introduction and notes, by S. B. Smith, M. A. London, New York [etc.] H. Milford, Oxford university press, 1921.
xliv, 345 p. front. (port.) 18½cm.
Bibliography: p. xliv.

1. Nāsir al-Dīn, king of Oudh, d. 1837. 2. Janāb Aulia, queen consort of Amjad 'Ali, king of Oudh, d. 1858. 3. Oudh—Soc. life & cust. I. Smith, S. B., ed. II. Title. III. Title: Elihu Jan's story.

Library of Congress DS485.O9K8 22-19724

NK 0203321 DLC WaU CU NcD NN

Knighton, William, d. 1900. Religious fairs in India. 11 pp. (Nineteenth Cent. v. 9, 1881, p. 838.)

NK 0203322 MdBP

Knighton, William, d. 1900.
The sporting literature of ancient Greece and Rome. By William Knighton ...
(In Royal society of literature of the United Kingdom, London. Essays by divers hands, being the transactions. London [1893] 22cm. 2d ser., vol. XVI, p. [1]-20)
"Read May 26th, 1886."

1. Sports—Greece. 2. Sports—Rome. 3. Hunting—Greece. 4. Hunting—Rome. I. Title.

A C 39-2844
Illinois. Univ. Library for Library of Congress [PN22.R6 ser. 2, vol. 16]
[3] (806.242)

NK 0203323 IU DLC

Knighton, William, d. 1900.
Struggles for life. By William Knighton ... London [etc.] Williams and Norgate, 1886.
viii, 312 p. 22½ cm.

1. Civilization. I. Title.

HM101.K66 9—466

NK 0203324 DLC

Knighton, William, 1834-1900. Soc 535.2
Struggles for life. 3d ed., revised. London, Williams and Norgate, etc. etc., 1888.
pp. viii, 289 +.

Labor||AcS 232783

NK 0203325 MH OCl

Knighton, William, d. 1900.
Tropical sketches; or, Reminiscences of an Indian journalist. By William Knighton ... London, Hurst and Blackett, 1855.
2 v. 20cm.

1. India—Descr. & trav. I. Title.

Library of Congress DS412.K71 4—28628

NK 0203326 DLC CtY PV PU

Knighton, Willis Sackett, 1896-
Care of the eyes in middle age. New York [1942?]
7 [1] p. 23cm. (National society for the prevention of blindness. Publication 388)

1. Eye—Care and hygiene. 2. Middle age. I. Title. II. Ser.

NK 0203327 ViU

RE51 Knighton, Willis Sackett, 1896-
K65 Healthy eyes [by] Willis S. Knighton ...
1940 Boston, Life conservation service of the John Hancock mutual life insurance company, [c1940]
20p. illus. 15½cm.

1. Eye.-Care and hygiene.
2. John Hancock mutual life insurance company, Boston.
I. Title.

NK 0203328 NBuG

Knighton, Willis Sackett, 1896-
Outline of refraction with the retinoscope and cycloplegia. [New York, J. H. Twiss, 1929]
44 p.

1. Accommodation and refraction. 617.75
617.707

NK 0203329 ICJ

Knighton, Willis Sackett, 1896-
Vision defects and their correction. New York, National Society for the Prevention of Blindness [1931]
12 p. illus. 24cm. (National Society for the Prevention of Blindness. Publication 86)
"Reprinted from the Sight-saving review, vol I, no. 4, December, 1931."

1. Eye—Care and hygiene. I. Ser.

NK 0203330 ViU MB CU

Knights, Charles C.
Advertisement copy and layouts; a working textbook for all who originate or write advertisements, by Charles C. Knights ... London, C. Lockwood and son, 1927.
189 p. illus., diagrs. 18½cm. (Lettered on cover: Lockwood's manuals)

1. Advertising. 2. Printing, Practical. I. Title.

Library of Congress HF5825.K55 28-12802

NK 0203331 DLC NN

Knights, Charles C.
The business man's guide to printing, by Charles C. Knights ... London: G. Allen & Unwin, Ltd.[, 1927.] 155 p. incl. tables. front. (port.), illus., plates (part col'd). 8°.
Bibliography at end of each chapter.

335597A. 1. Printing.
N. Y. P. L. December 21, 1927

NK 0203332 NN PP OU OCl

Knights, Charles C.
The business man's guide to printing, by Charles C. Knights ... New York, The Macmillan company, 1927.
155, [1] p. incl. front. (port.) illus., plates, tables. col. plates. 21½cm.
Printed in Great Britain.
"Deals with printing solely from the commercial angle."
Bibliography at the end of most chapters.

1. Printing, Practical. I. Title.

Library of Congress HF5825.K6 27-27572

NK 0203333 DLC PPL PU PPGi NN MB Or WaSp OrP

Knights, Charles C.
Colour in advertising and merchandise display; a practical manual embodying an original method of evolving contrasted, balanced and harmonised colour combinations, by Charles C. Knights ... London, C. Lockwood & son, 1926.
x, 122 p. col. front., illus., col. pl., diagrs. 19cm. (Lettered on cover: Lockwood's manuals)

1. Color. 2. Advertising. 3. Show-windows. I. Title.

Library of Congress HF5839.K6 28-21019

NK 0203334 DLC MiU OCl OKentU MB NN

Knights, Charles C.
Commercial art practice, a working text-book for all who produce, buy, sell or use art in commerce, by Charles C. Knights ... and Frank E. Norman ... profusely illustrated by 108 line and half-tone blocks, many of which are in colour. London, C. Lockwood & son, 1927.
xi, 164 p. plates (part col.) 24½cm.

1. Drawing. 2. Posters. 3. Advertising. 4. Photomechanical processes. I. Norman, Frank E., joint author. II. Title.

Library of Congress NC997.K5 28-16062

NK 0203335 DLC OCl PSC NN MB

VOLUME 300

Knights, Charles C., and F. E. Norman.
Commercial art practice; a working text-book for all who produce, buy, sell, or use art in commerce. London: Crosby Lockwood & Son, 1930. 172 p. pl., tables. 2. ed. enl. sq. 8°.

1. Commercial art. 2. Advertising. 3. Norman, Frank E., jt. au.
N. Y. P. L. August 29, 1930

NK 0203336 NN MiEM OCl Vi WaT CaBVa MiD

Knights, Charles C
How to judge character; a guide to the science and art of reading character of the men and women you meet, by Max Crombie... Philadelphia: D. McKay Co.[, 1927.] 92 p. illus. 32°.

Printed in England.

389344A. 1. Character—Analysis. 2. Physiognomy. 3. Title.
N. Y. P. L. December 28, 1928

NK 0203337 NN

Knights, Charles C.
Lay-out and commercial art, by Charles C. Knights ... in collaboration with Edward Swann. London, Toronto [etc.] Butterworth & co , ltd., 1932.
xix, [1], 388, 12 p. front., illus., 193 pl. (1 col.) on 97 l. diagr. 22cm. (*Half-title:* The library of advertising. VII)

1. Advertising, Art in. I. Swann, Edward. II. Title.
33-3919
Library of Congress HF5825.K65
[3] 659.1

NK 0203338 DLC MB

Knights, Charles C.
More sales through the window, by Charles C. Knights ... London, New York [etc.] Sir I. Pitman & sons, ltd., 1931.
xii, 159 p. xiv pl. on 7 l., diagrs. 22cm.

1. Show-windows. I. Title.
33-28424
Library of Congress HF5845.K55
[2] 659.1

NK 0203339 DLC MdBE WaS

Knights, Charles C.
An outline of sales management, by Charles C. Knights ... London, New York [etc.] Sir I. Pitman & sons, ltd., 1926.
ix, [1], 186 p. diagr. 21½cm.

1. Salesmen and salesmanship. I. Title.
28-28198
Library of Congress HF5438.K547

NK 0203340 DLC MiU ICU MH IU

Knights, Charles C., ed.

The Print-user's year book ... v. 1- 1934- London, The editor [1934?-

---

Knights, Charles C.
Printing: reproductive means and materials, by Charles C. Knights ... London [etc.] Butterworth & co. (publishers), ltd., 1932.
xvi, 370, [2], 11 p. illus., plates (part col., 1 fold.) 22cm. (*Half-title:* The library of advertising—VIII)
Bibliography: [2] p.
CONTENTS.—Printing.—Process engraving.—Type and typography.—Paper.

1. Printing, Practical. 2. Photomechanical processes. 3. Type and type-founding. 4. Paper. I. Title.
32-32999
Library of Congress Z244.K71
[5] 655

NK 0203342 DLC NN MB MH-L

Knights, Charles C
Secrets of profitable writing, by Max Crombie... London: G. Allen & Unwin Ltd.[, 1928.] 94 p. 16°. (Practical hand-books.)

392084A. 1. Composition, Literary, English.
N. Y. P. L. January 2, 1929

NK 0203343 NN IU

Knights, Charles C
Secrets of profitable writing, by Max Crombie. London, G. Allen & Unwin [1928] 94 p. 16cm. (Practical hand-books)

Film reproduction. Negative.

1. Authorship.

NK 0203344 NN

Knights, Charles C
Secrets of success in public speaking. 78 p. London, George Allen & Unwin, ltd., [1931]

NK 0203345 OCl

Knights, Charles C.
The technique of salesmanship; a textbook of commercial travelling and speciality selling, by Charles C. Knights ... London, New York [etc.] Sir I. Pitman & sons, ltd., 1927.
ix, 249 p. diagrs. 21½cm.

1. Salesmen and salesmanship. I. Title.
27-17802
Library of Congress HF5438.K55

NK 0203345-1 DLC MiU WaS

Knights, Charles C.
The technique of salesmanship; a textbook of commercial travelling and speciality selling, by Charles C. Knights ... 2d ed. London, Sir I. Pitman & sons, ltd., 1933.
ix, 249 p. diagrs. 22cm.
"Second edition, 1930; reprinted, 1933."

1. Salesmen and salesmanship. I. Title.
35-406
Library of Congress HF5438.K55 1933
[5] 658.846

NK 0203346 DLC

Knights, Charles C.
The technique of salesmanship; a textbook of commercial travelling and specialty selling. 3d ed. Lond., Pitman [1952, 213p.

NK 0203347 CaBVa

Knights, Charles C.
Training for more sales; a textbook of retail salesmanship, by Charles C. Knights ... with a foreword by Frank Henley ... London, New York [etc.] Sir I. Pitman & sons, ltd., 1926.
xvii, 221 p. fold. tab., diagr. 21½cm.

1. Salesmen and salesmanship. 2. Retail trade. I. Title.
29-10142
Library of Congress HF5438.K56

NK 0203348 DLC MiU MH

Knights, Charles C *lieutenant, Home guard.*
What the H. G. needs to know about explosives; their nature, variety and uses as projectile fillings, propellents, mines, demolition charges, etc., etc., by Lieut. Chas. C. Knights ... London, Bernards, ltd. [1943?]
cover-title, 68 p. illus., diagrs. 11½ x 18cm.

1. Explosives, Military.
44-4250
Library of Congress UF860.K5
[3] 623.452

NK 0203349 DLC NN

KNIGHTS, EDWARD S.
Essex folk; tales from village, farm and marsh, by Edward S. Knights, with a foreword by Brig.-General Sir R.B.Colvin ... London: Heath Cranton Ltd., 1935. 185 p. incl. front. 19½cm.

790034A. 1. Essex, Eng.(County). 2. Country life—Gt.Br.—Eng.—Essex. I. Title.

NK 0203350 NN

HD 3488 .R3 K58
Knights, George.
History of the Radcliffe & Pilkington District Co-operative Industrial Society, ltd 1860-1910, by G. Knights [and] A. Farrington. Souvenir to commemorate the Society's jubilee [Manchester, Co-operative Newspaper Society, 1910?]
169 p. illus. 19cm.

1. Radcliffe and Pilkington District Cooperative Industrial Society, lt[d] 2. Cooperative societies - Gt. Brit. I. Farrington, Alfred, joint author.

NK 0203351 WU

537.2 K745c
Knights (James) Company
Crystal handbook; a handbook of crystal theory and application compiled by the Research Division as a service to the electronics field. Sandwich, Ill. [c1953]
36 p. diagrs.

At head of title: JK products.
Bibliography: p. 36.

NK 0203352 MiD

VOLUME 300

Knights, John B. 6268.135
A journal of a voyage in the brig Spy, of Salem (1832–1834), John B. Knights, Master.
(*In* The sea, the ship and the sailor. Pp. 168–207. Plates. Salem. 1925.)
Relates mostly to New Zealand.

N1328 — Spy, brig. — New Zealand. Geog.

NK 0203353 MB DLC OCl

Knights, Lionel Charles, 1906–
Drama & society in the age of Jonson ₍by₎ L. C. Knights. London, Chatto & Windus, 1937.
xii, 346, ₍2₎ p. 23 cm.
Bibliography: p. 333–339.

1. English drama—Early modern and Elizabethan—Hist. & crit. 2. Gt. Brit.—Econ. condit. 3. Gt. Brit.—Soc. condit. 4. Social problems in literature. I. Title.

PR655.K6 822.309 37—19922

KyU MiU CaBVaU OrU
NcD OrCS CaBVa OrPR OrPS WaSpG PV KyLoS Ky-LE ScU
NK 0203354 DLC CtY DFo OO OU OClW PPT PU NcU N ViU

PR655
.K6
1951a Knights, Lionel Charles, 1906-
Drama & society in the age of Jonson.
London, Chatto & Windus, 1951.
xii, 346 p. 23cm.

Bibliography: p. 333-339.

1. English drama--Early modern and Elizabethan--Hist. & crit. 2. Gt. Brit. --Econ. condit. 3. Gt. Brit.--Soc. condit. 4. Social problems in literature. I. Title.

NK 0203355 AAP

Knights, Lionel Charles, 1906–
Drama & society in the age of Jonson. New York, G. W. Stewart ₍1951₎
xii, 346 p. 23 cm.
Bibliography: p. 333–339.

1. English drama—Early modern and Elizabethan—Hist. & crit. 2. Gt. Brit.—Econ. condit. 3. Gt. Brit.—Soc. condit. 4. Social problems in literature. I. Title.
[PR655.K] A 52–9323
Minnesota. Univ. Libr. for Library of Congress ₍5₎

IdPI
NK 0203356 MnU LU NBuG MtU IdU FU MiD MB ViU MH TU

Knights, Lionel Charles, 1906–
Explorations; essays in criticism, mainly on the literature of the seventeenth century, by L. C. Knights. London, Chatto & Windus, 1946.
xii, 198, ₍2₎ p. 21½ cm.
Bibliographical foot-notes.

1. English literature—Early modern (to 1700)—Hist. & crit. 2. English literature—Addresses, essays, lectures. I. Title.

PR433.K5 820.4 46—20227

WaSpG DFo ViU TxU NcD PBm MiU NcU IaU
NK 0203357 DLC CtY WaU MeB FMU NcD CaBVa OrU CaBVaU

Knights, Lionel Charles, 1906–
Explorations; essays in criticism, mainly on the literature of the seventeenth century. New York, G. W. Stewart ₍1947₎
219 p. 22 cm.
Bibliographical footnotes.

1. English literature—Early modern (to 1700)—Hist. & crit. 2. English literature—Addresses, essays, lectures. I. Title.

PR433.K5 1947 820.4 47—5060*

OrPR OrCS
NK 0203358 DLC IdU MtU CoU MB MH NIC PPC MiEM PSt IU

Knights, Lionel Charles, 1906–
How many children had Lady Macbeth? An essay in the theory and practice of Shakespeare criticism, by L. C. Knights. Cambridge ₍Eng.₎ G. Fraser, The Minority press, 1933.
3 p. l., 70 p., 1 l. 20½cm.

1. Shakespeare, William—Criticism and interpretation—Hist. 2. Shakespeare, William. Macbeth. I. Title.

33-34208
Library of Congress PR2965.K6 822.33

MdBJ NCH NN NIC VtU CaBVaU
NK 0203359 DLC WaU KEmT CtY MiU OCl OO OClJC PU PSC

Knights, Lionel Charles, 1906–
Poetry, politics and the English tradition. ₍An inaugural lecture₎ London, Chatto & Windus, 1954.
32 p. 19 cm.

1. Shakespeare, William—Political and social views. 2. Political science in literature. I. Title.

PR3017.K6 822.33 55–1103 ‡

CU MtU CaBVaU KMK CtY PSt PV CSt CoU
NK 0203360 DLC LU OU NcD NN MiU PBm IU TxU NcU NIC

AP4
.S43 Knights, Lionel Charles, 1906- ed.
Scrutiny; a quarterly review ... v. 1– May 1932–
Cambridge ₍Eng.₎ Deighton, Bell & co., inc., 1932–

Knights, Mark.
The highways and byeways of old Norwich. A descriptive ramble through Conisford, the New Burgh, Westwick, Northwic & Tokethorpe. Wymer & the Liberty of the Prior, & down the Wensum ... by Mark Knights. With fifty full-page illustrations drawn by Percy E. Stimpson. Norwich ₍etc.₎ Jarrold and sons, 1887.
xii, ₍13₎–120 p. front., plates. 27½cm.
No. 75 of an ed. of 350 copies, demy quarto.

1. Norwich, Eng.—Hist. I. Title.

1-1885
Library of Congress DA690.N88K7

NK 0203362 DLC CaBViP TxU CtY NN MH

KC 12592
Knights, Mark.
Jarrolds' guide to Norwich, based on the ancient historic divisions of the city. Rev. and enl. 16th ed., with numerous illustrations. Norwich, Jarrold [189?]

NK 0203363 MH

914.25
K74n Knights, Mark.
A new illustrated guide to Norwich, based on the ancient historic divisions of the city ... London ₍etc.₎ Jarrold & sons ₍1894?₎
184p. incl.illus., plates. fold.maps.

Running title: Jarrolds' guide to Norwich.

1. Norwich, Eng.--Descr. I. Title: Jarrolds' guide to Norwich.

NK 0203364 IU MH

Knights, Mark.
Peeps at the past; or, Rambles among Norfolk antiquities. By Mark Knights ... London, Jarrold and sons, 1892.
3 p.l., [v]-x p., 1 l., 184 p. front., plates. 27.5 cm.
"This edition is limited to sixty copies. No. 23."

NK 0203365 CtY CaBVa MB

PR
2807
.K72 Knights, Mark.
Shakespeare's 'Hamlet' interpreted: an exegis of the first edition of the tragedy of 1603, and of actus primus (the prologue) of the first folio edition of 1623. By Mark Knights ... London, Jarrold and sons ₍1893₎
xii,136 p. 19cm.

1. Shakespeare, William. Hamlet.

NK 0203366 MiU ICU MB PU-F OO MB NcU

Knights, R. S., joint author.
Pearce, Thomas Harold, 1919–
Murder by request, a dramatic sketch by T. H. Pearce and R. S. Knights. London, S. French, limited ₍°1941₎

M 366
K 74 Knights and daughters of Tabor.
Why you should become A Knight and Daughter of Tabor. n.p., n.p., n.d.
11 p. 23 cm.

NK 0203368 DHU

Knights and ladies of honor.
Constitution and laws of the Knights and ladies of honor, governing the Supreme, Grand and subordinate lodges, as amended at the fifth regular session, September, 1885, and compiled by the Committee on laws. St. Louis, Mo., C. Niehouse, printer, 1885.
80 p. 14½cm.

44-48950
Library of Congress HS1510.H78A5 1885

NK 0203370 DLC

Pam
HS1510
.H78A5
1879 Knights and Ladies of Honor.
Constitution governing the Supreme Lodge of Protection and subordinate lodges of Knights and Ladies of Honor. St. Louis, Mo., Printed by the supreme Lodge of Protection, K. & L. of H., 1879.
cover-title, 47 p. 14 cm.

NK 0203371 T

Knights and ladies of honor: Grand lodge of Penn.
Proceedings of the organization and of the annual session. Towanda, 1879.
v.1

NK 0203372 Nh

VOLUME 300

Knights and Ladies of Honor. Lessing Lodge no. 1018.
By-laws of Lessing Lodge No. 1018. Knights and Ladies of Honor. Organized March 16th, 1885. New York: T. Gaus' Sons, printers, 1904. 12 p. 15½cm.

779488A. 1. New York (City)— Societies, Mutual aid.
N. Y. P. L. October 22, 1935

NK 0203373 NN

Knights and ladies of honor. Pearl Lodge no. 123, Worcester, Mass.
Cook book and business directory, 1887. Worcester, Mass., 1887.
46 p.
1. Cookery, American. I. Title.

NK 0203374 KMK

Knights and ladies of honor. Supreme lodge.
Proceedings of the annual session. St.L., 1878-87.
v.1-6.

NK 0203375 Nh

Knights and ladies of honor of the world.
Ritual of the Knights and ladies of honor of the world. Adopted by the Supreme lodge in 1895. Printed by order of Supreme lodge K. & L. of H. of the world. [n. p., 1897]
47 p. diagrs. 17cm.

9-34100†

Library of Congress HS1510.H782 1895

NK 0203376 DLC

Knights and ladies of security. v. 1-
Apr. 1895-
Topeka, Kan.
v. ports. 40 cm. monthly.
Official organ of the Knights and Ladies of Security.

I. Knights and Ladies of Security.

HS1510.K65 48-40110*.

NK 0203377 DLC

RH A51

Knights and Ladies of Security. National Council.
Constitution and laws, in force September 1, 1912. [n.p., 1912]
147p. 15cm.

NK 0203378 KU

RH B555

Knights and Ladies of Security.
Ritual of the order of Knights and Ladies of S..urity. Comprising the rite of in..tiation, from opening and closing councils, order of business, and ceremony of installation. Topeka, E.G. Miner & Co., 1893.
32p. 19cm.

NK 0203379 KU

Knights and ladies of the golden rule.
... Funeral ceremony, adopted by the Supreme commandery, August 10th, 1881. Cincinnati, O., T. J. Smith & co., printers, 1881.
11 p. 15cm.

9-32537†

Library of Congress HS1510.G682 1881

NK 0203380 DLC

HS 1510 .G683A5 1881

Knights and ladies of the golden rule.
In excelsis. Knights of the golden rule. A popular beneficial order, organized in 1879 ... Cincinnati, O., T.J. Smith & co., printers, 1881.
8 p. 22 cm.

NK 0203381 DLC

K 941 .46

Knights and ladies of the golden rule.
...Proceedings of the Supreme commandery K.G.R....
1st (1880)
3d (1882)
6th (1886)
v.p.,1880- v.

Title varies.
The 6th sess. contains only "Reports of the supreme officers, K.G.R."

NK 0203382 ICN

Knights and ladies of the golden rule.
... Ritual of the Knights and ladies of the golden rule, also installation and institution ceremonies. Cincinnati, O., T. J. Smith & co., printers, 1882.
41 p. diagrs. 19½cm.

9-32536†

Library of Congress HS1510.G682 1882

NK 0203383 DLC KyHi

Knights and ladies of the golden rule.
Ritual of the Knights of the golden rule. Together with initiation and installation ceremonies. Cincinnati, T. J. Smith & co., printers, 1879.
32 p. diagrs. 20½cm.

9-32538†

Library of Congress HS1510.G682 1879
(Copyright 1879: 12885)

NK 0203384 DLC

Knight's Annotated model bye-laws of the Local Government Board, relating to: I. Cleansing of privies, etc.; II. Nuisances; III. New streets and buildings. v pp., 1 l., 155 pp., 7 pl. 8°. *London, Knight & Co.*, 1883.

NK 0203385 DNLM

Knight's annotated model bye-laws comprising the model series of the local government board, under the public health acts, ... London, 1905.

NK 0203386 PPB MH

Knight's annotated model bye-laws, comprising the model series issued from the Ministry of health under the Public health acts, with respect to buildings, new streets, removal of house refuse, nuisances, common lodging-houses, baths, wash-houses, bathing places, mortuaries, offensive trades, tents, nursing homes, smoke abatement, parking places, sanitary conveniences, and other matters. With diagrams and approved additional and alternative clauses. 9th ed. Edited and revised by C. Roland Woods ... London, C. Knight & co., ltd. [1938]
xi, 410 p. diagrs. (part fold.) 25cm.
1. Gt. Brit.—Sanit. affairs. 2. Hygiene. Public—Gt. Brit. 3. Building laws—Gt. Brit. I. Woods, Charlie Roland, 1885- ed. II. Knight, Charles, and co., London, pub. III. Gt. Brit. Ministry of health.

39-24932

NK 0203387 DLC

Knight's annotated model byelaws, comprising the Model series [4] issued in November 1952, from the Ministry of Housing and Local Government, under the Public health acts. With diagrs. and additional sections giving details of relevant British standards and British standard codes of practice. 10th ed. London, C. Knight [1953-
v. diagrs. 26 cm.
CONTENTS.—v. 1. Buildings, by C. R. Woods.

1. Public health laws—Gt. Brit. 2. Building laws—Gt. Brit. I. Woods, Charlie Roland, 1885- ed. II. Gt. Brit. Ministry of Housing and Local Government. Model byelaws.

56-47499

NK 0203388 DLC

Knight's annotated model byelaws. 11th ed. London, C. Knight [1953]-57.
2 v. diagrs. 26 cm.
Vol. 1 edited by C. R. Woods; v. 2 by A. N. C. Shelley.

1. Public health laws—Gt. Brit. 2. Building laws—Gt. Brit. I. Woods, Charlie Roland, 1885- ed. II. Shelley, Adrian Noel Christian, ed. III. Gt. Brit. Ministry of Housing and Local Government. Model byelaws.

56-47295 rev

NK 0203389 DLC CaBVaU

Ib55 td1

The knight's companion: or, Windsor miscellany ... London, S. Longbottom, 1733.
1p.l.,14p. 25cm.
Poems.
Pamphlet.

I.c.w.t.: Windsor miscellany.

NK 0203390 CtY

Knight's cyclopaedia of London, 1851
see under Knight, Charles, 1791-1873, ed.

Knight's cyclopædia of the industry of all nations. 1851. London, C. Knight [1851]
1 p. l., xxiv, 1806 col., 1807-1810 p. front., 36 pl. 22cm.
Ed. by George Dodd.
American edition published 1851 with title: Cyclopædia of the industry of all nations. By Charles Knight.

1. Industrial arts—Dictionaries. I. Dodd, George, 1808-1881, ed. II. Knight, Charles, 1791-1873, pub.

5-34936

Library of Congress T9.K68

ICU CaBViP
NK 0203392 DLC CU NcRS ICU CtY OClJC ViU MWA PPF PP

VOLUME 300

*7569a.173
Knights' Day, The. Published by members of Webster Groves Council No. 2119, Knights of Columbus. Vol. 2 (no. 8). July 1, 1922. Webster Groves, Mo. 1922. v. Portrait. 22½ cm.

Beginning with the July, 1922, issue, a series of 24 poems about the big cities of this country is included in the publication.

M4746 — Knights of Columbus. Webster Groves Council, Mo. Periodicals. — Periodicals. English.

NK 0203393 MB

Knight's excursion companion
see under Knight, Charles, 1791-1873.

AC-L Knight's gems; or Device book. 2d ed. ...
W357L London, Published by J. Williams and C. Tilt.
K748 Sold by Simkin & Marshall [18--]
85 plates. 25cm.

Inscribed to W.F.S. from John Merrifield, 16 July 1850.
Armorial bookplate of Evelyn Waugh.

I. Title: Device book.

NK 0203395 TxU

Knights Grand Commanders of the Sun of the U.S. of America
see Freemasons. U.S. Scottish Rite.

Knight's guide to the arrangement and construction of workhouse buildings, with notes and diagrams of the requirements and recommendations of the local government board, in regard to the erection of poor law institutions. London, Knight & co., 1889.
vi, 115 p. plans. 25cm.

1. Almshouses and workhouses.

NK 0203397 ICU

Knight's handbook for the use of health insurance committees and all other local authorities, approved societies, and medical practitioners affected by the National Insurance Act, 1911. London: C. Knight & Co., Ltd., 1913. xii, 377(1) p., 1 fold. table. 8°.

1. Insurance (Sickness), Gt. Br., 1911. 2. Insurance (Workmen's), Gt. Br., 1911.
N. Y. P. L. January 8, 1915.

NK 0203398 NN

Knights Hospitalers
see **Knights of Malta.**

Knights Hospitalers of St. John of Jerusalem
see **Knights of Malta.**

Knight's Landing ridge committee.

Haviland & Tibbetts, *San Francisco.*
Report on Knight's Landing cut project to the Knight's Landing ridge committee. San Francisco, Oakland [etc.] Haviland & Tibbetts, 1912.

Knight's local government and magisterial reports and statutes, statutory instruments, etc... v.1- 1903-
London, Charles Knight & Co. Ltd.
v.
Title varies slightly.
Issued in several parts beginning with vol.32, 1934.

NK 0203403 NcD-L

Knight's miscellanies.
London, 1840- [C. Knight & co.]

NK 0203404 DLC PU

Knight's Monthly volumes, 1846-49
see
Knight's Weekly volume

[Knights must fall ...
see under [Clapp, Roger Tillinghast]
1897?- (Class of 1919)

Knight's new mechanical dictionary
see under Knight, Edward Henry, 1824-1883.

Knights of Albion
see Ancient Heraldic and Chivalric Order of Albion.

Knights of Alcántara
see Orden de Alcántara.

Knights of alpha and ladies of omega of the world.
Ritual, subordinate assembly of the order of Knights of alpha and ladies of omega of the world, a fraternal benevolent association, detail of officers and order of business, adopted by the Supreme assembly, August 30, 1910. [St. Paul, Minn., The Volkszeitung company] ©1911.
3 p. l., [9]-92 p. illus. (port.) 19½cm. $1.00

Library of Congress HS1510.K82 1911 11-14191

NK 0203410 DLC

Knights of America Protestantism.
The K. A. P. magazine
see under title

Knights of Cerberus.
Ritual and detail of officers of the order of the Knights of Cerberus. Port Townsend, Wash., Printed by the Call job office [1895]
1 p. l., 14 p. 17½cm.

9-32551†

Library of Congress HS1510.C472 1895

NK 0203412 DLC

Knights, The, of Charlemagne. New York: H. M. Caldwell [191-?]. 128 p. 12°. (Stories old and new.)

1. Juvenile literature (Scottish). 2. Charlemagne romances, etc.
N. Y. P. L. April 28, 1913.

NK 0203413 NN

PZ8
.1 The knights of Charlemagne. London,
.C382K Blackie [1911]
1911 128 p. col. illus. 18cm. (Stories old and new)

CONTENTS.—The charcoal burner.—How Oliver fought for France and the faith.—The keeping of the passes.—Ogier the Dane.

1. Charlemagne (Romances, etc.)

NK 0203414 ViU

Knights of Columbus.
Addresses by Knights of Columbus. Twenty-eighth International Eucharistic Congress, Chicago, U.S.A., 1926. New Haven, Conn., Knights of Columbus, [1926]

48p. front., (ports.) 23cm.

1. Eucharist--Addresses, sermons.

NK 0203415 PLatS

Knights of Columbus.

... **Army** and navy athletic training, comp. for the use of K. of C. athletic directors. New York, Chicago [etc.] A. G. Spalding & bros., ©1919.

Knights of Columbus.
Charter, constitution and laws of the Knights of Columbus, governing the supreme, state and subordinate councils, with amendments to and including the year 1955. New Haven, Conn. [1955?]
204 p. 19 cm.
1. Knights of Columbus. I. Title.

NK 0203417 KAS

Knights of Columbus.

Harris, William Richard, 1847-1923.
The Catholic church in Utah, including an exposition of Catholic faith by Bishop Scanlan. A review of Spanish and missionary explorations. Tribal divisions, names and regional habitats of the pre-European tribes. The journal of the Franciscan explorers and discoverers of Utah lake. The trailing of the priests from Santa Fe, N. M., with map of route, illustrations and delimitations of the Great basin. By Very Reverend W. R. Harris ... Salt Lake City, Utah, Intermountain Catholic press [©1909]

VOLUME 300

Knights of Columbus.
Charter of Knights of Columbus, constitution of National council, and laws, rules of national, state and subordinate councils. Revised to October 15th, 1895, inclusive. Bridgeport, Conn., 1895.

NK 0203419 CtY

Knights of Columbus.

Columbia. v. 1- Aug. 1921-
New Haven [etc.] Knights of Columbus [1921-

208
P191
v.9
no.10
Knights of Columbus.
Criminal libels against the Knights of Columbus exposed. New Haven, Conn. [c1928?]
38p. 24cm. (In Pamphlets on religion. v.9,no.10)

NK 0203421 OrU

Knights of Columbus.
Criminal libels against the Knights of Columbus exposed. New Haven, Conn., Issued by Knights of Columbus [1931]
69 p., 1 l. facsim. 25cm.

I. Title.

A 33-1729

Title from Evansville. Ind., Pub. Libr. Printed by L. C.

ViU NN
NK 0203422 InE OrStbM OrP Or WaT CU OClWHi OCl MB

F203.4
G43K5
W
Knights of Columbus.
Dedication of memorial statue, James Cardinal Gibbons, August 14, 15, 16, 17, 1932, Washington, D. C. [New York, The Trades Unionist publ. co. 1932]
[20] p. illus. 31 cm.
At head of title: Golden jubilee convention.

1. Gibbons, James, cardinal, 1834-1921. 2. Washington, D. C. Gibbons statue.

NK 0203423 DI

Knights of Columbus.
The Guide; a monthly magazine ...
see under title

Knights of Columbus.
Knights of Columbus vs. criminal libel and malicious bigotry; issued by Supreme board of directors, Knights of Columbus, November, 1914. [Boston, Washington press, 1914]
1 p. l., 29, [1] p. incl. facsim. 21cm.
Caption title: Criminal libel and malicious bigotry ... the truth and its proof regarding the spurious K. of C. oath or Fourth degree oath.

I. Title: Criminal libel and malicious bigotry.

17-22557

Library of Congress HS1538.C74A4

NK 0203425 DLC NN

HS
1538
.C74
A41
Knights of Columbus.
Knights of Columbus vs. criminal libel and malicious bigotry, issued by Supreme Board of directors. [New Haven, 1920?]
47 p. 19 cm.

Cover title.
Caption title: Criminal libel and malicious bigotry as committed and practised to injure the Catholic Church and its members, particularly the Knights of Columbus.
I. Title: Criminal libel and malicious bigotry.

NK 0203426 DCU Or OrU

F203.4
G43K4
W
Knights of Columbus.
The late James Cardinal Gibbons, Archbishop of Baltimore, his memorial statue. Proposed as a gift of the Knights of Columbus... Washington, D. C., Cardinal Gibbons Memorial Statue Provisional Committee [1929?]
[24] p. illus. 31cm.
1. Gibbons, James, cardinal, 1834-1921. 2. Washington, D. C. Gibbons statue. I. Cardinal Gibbons Memorial Statue Provisional Committee.

3079

NK 0203427 DI

Knights of Columbus.
Statement of Knights of Columbus war work, prepared for use in connection with United war work campaign for $170,5000,000, November 11-18, 1918. New Haven, 1918.
12 p. 23.5 cm. [Hospitals, charities, etc. in the war]

NK 0203428 CtY

Knights of Columbus. California Council.
The Californian, "880"
see under title

KNIGHTS OF COLUMBUS. Canadian army huts.
War services of Canadian knights of Columbus, 1939-1947; a history of the work of the Knights of Columbus, Canadian army huts. [Montreal, 1948] 257 p. illus., plates. 24cm.

1. World war, 1939-1945--War work--Knights of Columbus.

NK 0203430 NN

N.J.-Y
HS1538
.K7405
1949
Knights of Columbus. Carroll Council, No. 1378, Union City, N.J.
Fortieth anniversary ... History and program of Carroll Council No. 1378, Knights of Columbus, Union City, N.J. ... Saturday, May 28th, 1949. [Union City, N.J., 1949]
[23]p. illus. (incl. ports.) 23½cm.
"The Columbian Club, 'the home of Carroll Council'; 35th anniversary, 1914-1949": p.[11-13]
1. Catholics in Union City, N.J. 2. Columbian Club, Union City, N.J.

NK 0203431 NjP

Knights of Columbus. Catholic truth committee.

The Catholic encyclopedia; an international work of reference on the constitution, doctrine, discipline, and history of the Catholic church; edited by Charles G. Herbermann ... Edward A. Pace ... Condé B. Pallen ... Thomas J. Shahan, D. D., John J. Wynne, S. J., assisted by numerous collaborators ... Special ed., under the auspices of the Knights of Columbus Catholic truth committee. New York, The Encyclopedia press, inc. [c1913]

Knights of Columbus. Chicago chapter.

Chicago. Public library.
Catholic reading list; a catalogue of books (in English) by Catholic authors in the Chicago public library. Comp. by a committee of the Catholic writers guild. [Chicago] Chicago chapter of the Knights of Columbus, 1908.

K
940
.C 43
Knights of Columbus—Chicago council, no.182, Chicago.
History Chicago council no.182, Knights of Columbus, pioneer council of the West, instituted July 7, 1896... By R.J.Murphy. Silver jubilee souvenir edition, 1896-1921. Chic. c1921. S.

"Obituary sketches": p.90-112.

NK 0203434 ICN ICU

Knights of Columbus. Columbus Council, no. 126.
Columbus
see under title (Supplement)

Knights of Columbus. Committee on Education.
Bulletin
see under Knights of Columbus. Educational Bureau.

Knights of Columbus. *Committee on war activities.*
... Scholarships for demobilized service men, awarded by the Knights of Columbus, Committee on war activities. New Haven, Knights of Columbus, Educational bureau, 1919.
cover-title, 38 p. illus. (ports.) 19½cm. ([Knights of Columbus. Educational bureau] Bulletin no. 3)

1. Scholarships—U. S.

Library of Congress LB2338.K6 20-9888

NK 0203437 DLC

Knights of Columbus. Delaware.
A plea for justice... Protest against Appleton's cyclopaedia and atlas by the Knights of Columbus of Delaware. [Wilmington, Del.] 1902. 16 p. 13cm.

1. Education, Sectarian, Roman Catholic. 2. Appleton's New cyclopaedia and atlas.
N. Y. P. L. April 30, 1945

NK 0203438 NN MB

Knights of Columbus. Detroit Council no. 305.
Official directory. [Detroit]

NK 0203439 MiD

Knights of Columbus. Detroit Council no. 305.
Pocket directory. 1903. [Detroit, 1903?]
122 p.

Contains a list of members of Detroit Council no. 305, national supreme officers, district officers, etc.

NK 0203440 MiD-B

VOLUME 300

Knights of Columbus. *Educational bureau.*
Accounting, first year ... arranged for correspondence instruction, by W. D. Jordan ... New Haven, Conn., Knights of Columbus, Educational bureau, Home study division [°1923]–
pt. 23cm.
First year, part 1, "based on Kester—Accounting, theory and practice, volume 1".
1. Accounting. I. Jordan, William Donald, 1899–
Library of Congress HF5635.K75 CA 23-487 Unrev'd

NK 0203441 DLC

Knights of Columbus. Educational Bureau.
Bulletin.
no. 1-6
New Haven, 1919-1925 12°.
nos. illus.
Cover-title.
no. 6 issued by its Committee on education.
no. 1. The educational program...its origin, scope and purpose. 1919.
no. 2. Evening schools for demobilized service men. 1919.
no. 3. Scholarships for demobilized service men. 1919.
no. 4. Addresses and proceedings of the educational convention, held at Chicago, Ill., July, 1920. 1920.
no. 5. Knights of Columbus council schools. 1920.

NK 0203443 NN ICJ DLC

Knights of Columbus. Educational bureau.
... Course of study in automobile maintenance and repair. New Haven, Knights of Columbus Educational bureau, 1921.
77 p. illus. 19½ cm.
At head of title: Knights of Columbus evening schools.

NK 0203444 DHEW

Knights of Columbus. *Educational bureau.*
Lectures in advertising ... arranged for correspondence instruction, by George B. Hotchkiss ... New Haven, Conn., Knights of Columbus, Educational bureau, Home study division [°1923]
4 pt. 23cm.
1. Advertising. I. Hotchkiss, George Burton. II. Title.
Library of Congress HF5823.K5 CA 23-488 Unrev'd

NK 0203445 DLC

Knights of Columbus. *Educational bureau.*
Show card writing, course I ... arranged for correspondence study. New Haven, Conn., Knights of Columbus, Educational bureau, Home study division [°1923]–
pt. illus. 23cm.
1. Advertising cards. 2. Lettering. I. Title.
Library of Congress HF5851.K6 CA 23-489 Unrev'd

NK 0203446 DLC

Knights of Columbus. Forest Glen council, no. 2169.
... Souvenir program, golden jubilee of the ordination of Rev. Charles Oscar Rosensteel, pastor, St. John's church, Forest Glen, Md., Sunday, November 4, 1934. Sponsored by Knights of Columbus, Forest Glen council, no. 2169. [n. p., 1934]
cover-title, 20 p. illus. (incl. ports.) 24cm.
At head of title: 1884. 1934.
"Jubilee sermon, by Rev. Dr. Peter Guilday": p. 11-16.
1. Rosensteel, Charles Oscar, 1855– 2. Forest Glen, Md. St. John's church. I. Guilday, Peter Keenan, 1884– II. Title.
35-14134
Library of Congress BX4705.R725K6
——— Copy 2. 922.273

NK 0203447 DLC

Knights of Columbus. Gabriel Richard Council, no. 2463.
The Knight ...
see under title

Knights of Columbus. General James Shields council, no. 967.
Grosscup, Peter Stenger, 1852–
... Celebration of Abraham Lincoln's birthday and second anniversary of institution of General James Shields council no. 967, Knights of Columbus ... Tuesday, February 12, 1907 ... Address of the Hon. Peter S. Grosscup ... on "Abraham Lincoln". [Chicago, 1907]

A976.3 (267.242) K71
Knights of Columbus. Hammond council no. 2063, Hammond, La.
Convention number, K. of C ... Hammond, Louisiana, May 22, 23, 1921. [Morgan City, La., King-Hahhaford co. inc., Printers, 1921]
cover-title, 26,2p. illus. ports. 45cm.
1. Louisiana - Parishes (Tangipahoa).
2. La. - Knights of Columbus.

NK 0203450 LNHT

Knights of Columbus. *Historical commission.*
... Boletín ... Comisión histórica de los Caballeros de Colón ... no.
Boston, Mass. [192
v. 23cm.
Library of Congress E172.K73 CA 28-720 Unrev'd

NK 0203451 DLC

Knights of Columbus. *Historical commission.*
... Bulletin, no. 1 Boston, Mass., Knights of Columbus historical commission [1921–
v. 23cm.
1. U. S.—Hist.—Societies.
Library of Congress E172.K7 22-17159

NK 0203452 DLC ICJ NN OO Or

Knights of Columbus. Historical commission.
Schreiner, George Abel, 1875–
Cables and wireless and their rôle in the foreign relations of the United States, by George Abel Schreiner ... Introduction by Edward F. McSweeney ... Boston, Mass., The Stratford co., 1924.

Knights of Columbus. Historical commission.
Mahony, Thomas Harrison, 1885–
The Monroe doctrine, the vital necessity of its continued maintenance, published by the Knights of Columbus Historical commission, by Thomas H. Mahony ... with a foreword by Rear-Admiral W. S. Benson ... [Boston?] 1921.

Knights of Columbus. Historical Commission. *2320a.88.3
Non-competitive historical programme. Supplementary to the prize competition in American history.
= [Boston. 1921.] 11 pp. [Bulletin, no. 3.] 23 cm.
M3760 — United States. Hist.

NK 0203455 MB OrU OClWHi DHEW

Knights of Columbus. Historical Commission. *2320a.88.2
Prizes for original studies in American history.
= [Boston. 1921.] 10 pp. [Bulletin no. 2.] 23 cm.
M3757 — T.r. — United States. Hist. — S.r.c.

NK 0203456 MB DHEW OO OClWHi

Knights of Columbus. Historical commission.
McSweeney, Edward Francis, 1864–
The racial contribution to the United States ... Introduction to series [by] Edward F. McSweeney ... [New Haven, Conn., Knights of Columbus historical commission, 1923?]

Knights of Columbus. *Historical commission.*
Studies in history, ed. by Edward F. McSweeney, chairman, Knights of Columbus Historical commission, Committee of judges for awarding of prizes ... [New Haven, Conn., Knights of Columbus, °1922]
vii, 151 p. 23½cm.
Includes bibliographical references.
CONTENTS.—Origins of the propaganda movement to pervert American history, by C. E. Russell.—Charters of liberty, by F. J. Kinsman.—The Monroe doctrine, by T. H. Mahony.
1. U. S.—Hist.—Addresses, essays, lectures. I. McSweeney, Edward Francis, 1864– ed. II. Title.
22-18524
Library of Congress E178.6.K69

NK 0203458 DLC MB IdU

Historical Library HS 1538 C7 I4
Knights of Columbus. Illinois State Council.
Knights of Columbus in Illinois; first 25 years. [n.p. 192-?]
916 p. illus. 22½ cm.
Title page missing.
1.Catholic church-Societies, etc. 2.Knights of Columbus-Illinois. I.Title.

NK 0203459 WHi

Knights of Columbus. Iowa.
A protest and a plea. [Sioux City, Iowa, 1914]
32 p. port. 24cm.

NK 0203460 MnU

Knights of Columbus. *Manila Council, No. 1000.*
Directory.
[Manila]
v. 23 cm.
HS1538.C74M3 267.242 52-64596 ‡

NK 0203461 DLC

VOLUME 300

Knights of Columbus. *Manila Council. No. 1000.*
Golden jubilee book, 1905–1955. Manila, 1955.
unpaged. illus. 31 cm.

1. Knights of Columbus. Philippine Islands.

HS1538.C74A54 56-57878 ‡

NK 0203462 DLC

Knights of Columbus. Marquette council, no. 606, St. Louis.
St. Louis. Public library.
Catalogue of books by Catholic writers in the St. Louis public library, including works in English and in foreign languages. Comp. and pub. under the auspices of Marquette council no. 606, Knights of Columbus. St. Louis, Mo. [Marquette council no. 606, Knights of Columbus] 1911.

Knights of Columbus. Massachusetts State Council. *7567.70
Report of the annual convention of the Massachusetts State Council, Knights of Columbus, held . . . 1900–02.
Boston. 1900–02. v. 21½ cm.
The issues for 1900, 01 are entitled Proceedings.
The issue for 1900 includes Proceedings of the quarterly meeting held June 17, 1900.

L1237 — Societies. Proc., trans., etc.

NK 0203463 MB

Knights of Columbus. Milwaukee council, no. 524.
Milwaukee. Public library.
Catalogue of Catholic books in Milwaukee public library, including 1. Finding list of Catholic authors, 2. Classification by subject. Prepared under the auspices of Milwaukee council no. 524, Knights of Columbus. 1904. [Milwaukee, Cannon printing co.] 1904.

Knights of Columbus. *Missouri state council.*
Report of the proceedings of the ... annual convention.
St. Louis, Mo.
v. 22cm.

CA 16-504 Unrev'd

Library of Congress HS1538.C7M82

NK 0203465 DLC

Knights of Columbus. National Council. *7567.72
Proceedings . . . with reports of State Councils. [Held at New Haven, March 6th, 1900.]
= [New Haven. 1900.] 54, (1) pp. 8°.

G6460 — Societies. Proceedings, transactions, etc.

NK 0203466 MB

Knights of Columbus. New York state council. Historical committee.
The Knights of Columbus in the state of New York, 1891–1945; David P. Henry, ed. [New York] New York state council, Knights of Columbus, Historical committee, 1945. 431 p. 22cm.

390407B. 1. No subject. I. Henry, David P., ed.
N. Y. P. L. June 26, 1947

NK 0203467 NN

Knights of Columbus - Ohio state council.
Knights of Columbus, 50th anniversary, 1882-1932. Golden jubilee souvenir history. Cleveland, O., [1932]
18 p. ports.

NK 0203468 OCl

KNIGHTS OF COLUMBUS. OREGON.
History of Knights of Columbus in Oregon. [Author?] [1926?]
72 p. illus.

NK 0203469 Or

Knights of Columbus. Religious Information Bureau.
The Bible is a Catholic book. St. Louis, Religious Information Bureau, Knights of Columbus [n.d.]
24 p. illus. 19 cm. (Its [Pamphlet series], no. 3)
Published ca. 1950.

NK 0203470 PLatS

Knights of Columbus. Religious Information Bureau.
The Bible is not our sole guide. St. Louis, Religious Information Bureau, Knights of Columbus [n.d.]
44 p. illus. 19 cm. (Its [Pamphlet series], no. 32)
Published ca. 1950.

NK 0203471 PLatS

Knights of Columbus. Religious Information Bureau.
But can it be found in the Bible? St. Louis, Religious Information Bureau, Knights of Columbus [n.d.]
48 p. illus. 19 cm. (Its [Pamphlet series], no. 13)
Published ca. 1950.

NK 0203472 PLatS

Knights of Columbus. Religious Information Bureau.
But do you really understand the Bible? St. Louis, Religious Information Bureau, Knights of Columbus [n.d.]
40 p. illus. 19 cm. (Its [Pamphlet series], no. 22)
Published ca. 1950.

NK 0203473 PLatS

Knights of Columbus. Religious Information Bureau.
But how can educated people be Catholics? St. Louis, Religious Information Bureau, Knights of Columbus [n.d.]
48 p. illus. 19 cm. (Its [Pamphlet series], no. 17)
Published ca. 1950.

NK 0203474 PLatS

Knights of Columbus. Religious Information Bureau.
But why don't YOU pray to the saints? St. Louis, Religious Information Bureau, Knights of Columbus [n.d.]
44 p. illus. 19 cm. (Its [Pamphlet series], no. 47)
Published ca. 1950.

NK 0203475 PLatS

Knights of Columbus. Religious Information Bureau.
"But why the candles, holy water and beads?" St. Louis, Religious Information Bureau, Knights of Columbus [n.d.]
48 p. illus. 19 cm. (Its [Pamphlet series], no. 38)
Published ca. 1950.

NK 0203476 PLatS

Knights of Columbus. Religious Information Bureau.
But would Christ call you a Christian? St. Louis, Religious Information Bureau, Knights of Columbus [n.d.]
28 p. illus. 19 cm. (Its [Pamphlet series], no. 29)
Published ca. 1950.

NK 0203477 PLatS

Knights of Columbus. Religious Information Bureau.
Christ's seven sacraments. St. Louis, Religious Information Bureau, Knights of Columbus [n.d.]
40 p. illus. 19 cm. (Its [Pamphlet series], no. 5)
Published ca. 1950.

NK 0203478 PLatS

Knights of Columbus. Religious Information Bureau.
Do you understand what God told us? St. Louis, Religious Information Bureau, Knights of Columbus [n.d.]
40 p. illus. 19 cm. (Its [Pamphlet series], no. 30)
Published ca. 1950.

NK 0203479 PLatS

Knights of Columbus. Religious Information Bureau.
Does science prove the Bible wrong? St. Louis, Religious Information Bureau, Knights of Columbus [n.d.]
48 p. illus. 19 cm. (Its [Pamphlet series], no. 48)
Published ca. 1950.

NK 0203480 PLatS

Knights of Columbus. Religious Information Bureau.
Does the Bible contradict itself? St. Louis, Religious Information Bureau, Knights of Columbus [n.d.]
44 p. illus. 19 cm. (Its [Pamphlet series], no. 42)
Published ca. 1950.

NK 0203481 PLatS

Knights of Columbus. Religious Information Bureau.
The early years of the Catholic Church. St. Louis, Religious Information Bureau, Knights of Columbus [n.d.]
40 p. illus. 19 cm. (Its [Pamphlet series], no. 45)
Published ca. 1950.

NK 0203482 PLatS

Knights of Columbus. Religious Information Bureau.
Fatima -- Mary's peace plan from heaven. St. Louis, Religious Information Bureau, Knights of Columbus [n.d.]
36 p. illus. 19 cm. (Its [Pamphlet series], no. 41)
Published ca. 1950.

NK 0203483 PLatS

VOLUME 300

Knights of Columbus. Religious Information Bureau.
The Holy Sacrifice: the Catholic Mass. St. Louis, Religious Information Bureau, Knights of Columbus [n.d.]
32 p. illus. 19 cm. (Its [Pamphlet series], no. 6)
Published ca. 1950.

NK 0203484 PLatS

Knights of Columbus. Religious Information Bureau.
"I am a Catholic priest." St. Louis, Religious Information Bureau, Knights of Columbus [n.d.]
32 p. illus. 19 cm. (Its [Pamphlet series], no. 37)
Published ca. 1950.

NK 0203485 PLatS

Knights of Columbus. Religious Information Bureau.
"I was warned about the Catholic Church." St. Louis, Religious Information Bureau, Knights of Columbus [n.d.]
48 p. illus. 19 cm. (Its [Pamphlet series], no. 43)
Published ca. 1950.

NK 0203486 PLatS

Knights of Columbus. Religious Information Bureau.
"I'll tell you why I am a Catholic." St. Louis, Religious Information Bureau, Knights of Columbus [n.d.]
52 p. illus. 19 cm. (Its [Pamphlet series], no. 26)
Published ca. 1950.

NK 0203487 PLatS

Knights of Columbus. Religious Information Bureau.
Is the Catholic Church a menace to democracy? St. Louis, Religious Information Bureau, Knights of Columbus [n.d.]
32 p. illus. 19 cm. (Its [Pamphlet series], no. 21)
Published ca. 1950.

NK 0203488 PLatS

Knights of Columbus. Religious Information Bureau.
Is the Catholic Church out of place here? St. Louis, Religious Information Bureau, Knights of Columbus [n.d.]
24 p. illus. 19 cm. (Its [Pamphlet series], no. 49)
Published ca. 1950.

NK 0203489 PLatS

Knights of Columbus. Religious Information Bureau.
Let us judge Catholics by the Bible. St. Louis, Religious Information Bureau, Knights of Columbus [n.d.]
40 p. illus. 19 cm. (Its [Pamphlet series], no. 28)
Published ca. 1950.

NK 0203490 PLatS

Knights of Columbus. Religious Information Bureau.
Let's stick to Moses! St. Louis, Religious Information Bureau, Knights of Columbus, [n.d.]
40 p. illus. 19 cm. (Its [Pamphlet series], no. 12)
Published ca. 1950.

NK 0203491 PLatS

Knights of Columbus. Religious Information Bureau.
Let's test Catholic loyalty. St. Louis, Religious Information Bureau, Knights of Columbus [n.d.]
44 p. illus. 19 cm. (Its [Pamphlet series], no. 35)
Published ca. 1950.

NK 0203492 PLatS

Knights of Columbus. Religious Information Bureau.
A letter to our non-Catholic neighbors. St. Louis, Religious Information Bureau, Knights of Columbus [n.d.]
24 p. illus. 19 cm. (Its [Pamphlet series], no. 23)
Published ca. 1950.

NK 0203493 PLatS

Knights of Columbus. Religious Information Bureau.
No --- belief in God is not enough. St. Louis, Religious Information Bureau, Knights of Columbus [n.d.]
40 p. illus. 19 cm. (Its [Pamphlet series], no. 18)
Published ca. 1950.

NK 0203494 PLatS

Knights of Columbus. Religious Information Bureau.
[Pamphlet series]

NK 0203495 PLatS MoSU

Knights of Columbus. Religious Information Bureau.
The real secret of successful marriage. St. Louis, Religious Information Bureau, Knights of Columbus [n.d.]
40 p. illus. 19 cm. (Its [Pamphlet series], no. 19)
Published ca. 1950.

NK 0203496 PLatS

Knights of Columbus. Religious Information Bureau.
The "Reformation," was it reform or revolt? St. Louis, Religious Information Bureau, Knights of Columbus [n.d.]
36 p. illus., chart. 19 cm. (Its [Pamphlet series], no. 39)
Published ca. 1950.
"Reference reading list": p. 36.

NK 0203497 PLatS

Knights of Columbus. Religious Information Bureau.
Remember the Sabbath -- keep it holy! St. Louis, Religious Information Bureau, Knights of Columbus [n.d.]
36 p. illus. 19 cm. (Its [Pamphlet series], no. 36)
Published ca. 1950.

NK 0203498 PLatS

Knights of Columbus. Religious Information Bureau.
Should children learn about God in school? St. Louis, Religious Information Bureau, Knights of Columbus [n.d.]
32 p. illus. 19 cm. (Its [Pamphlet series], no. 31)
Published ca. 1950.

NK 0203499 PLatS

Knights of Columbus. Religious Information Bureau.
These are our 7 deadly enemies. St. Louis, Religious Information Bureau, Knights of Columbus [n.d.]
40 p. illus. 19 cm. (Its [Pamphlet series], no. 34)
Published ca. 1950.

NK 0203500 PLatS

Knights of Columbus. Religious Information Bureau.
These 920,000 men they call "Knights." St. Louis, Religious Information Bureau, Knights of Columbus [n.d.]
36 p. illus. 19 cm. (Its [Pamphlet series], no. 9)
Published ca. 1950.

NK 0203501 PLatS

Knights of Columbus. Religious Information Bureau.
This is the Catholic Church. St. Louis, Religious Information Bureau, Knights of Columbus [n.d.]
40 p. illus. 19 cm. (Its [Pamphlet series], no. 50)
Published ca. 1950.

NK 0203502 PLatS

Knights of Columbus. Religious Information Bureau.
This was the faith of our fathers. St. Louis, Religious Information Bureau, Knights of Columbus [n.d.]
28 p. illus. 19 cm. (Its [Pamphlet series], no. 33)
Published ca. 1950.

NK 0203503 PLatS

Knights of Columbus. Religious Information Bureau.
What do you mean -- only one true Church? St. Louis, Religious Information Bureau, Knights of Columbus [n.d.]
40 p. illus. 19 cm. (Its [Pamphlet series], no. 16)
Published ca. 1950.

NK 0203504 PLatS

Knights of Columbus. Religious Information Bureau.
What happens after death? St. Louis, Religious Information Bureau, Knights of Columbus [n.d.]
40 p. illus. 19 cm. (Its [Pamphlet series], no. 14)
Published ca. 1950.

NK 0203505 PLatS

Knights of Columbus. Religious Information Bureau.
What makes a woman choose such a life? St. Louis, Religious Information Bureau, Knights of Columbus [n.d.]
32 p. illus. 19 cm. (Its [Pamphlet series], no. 25)
Published ca. 1950.

NK 0203506 PLatS

VOLUME 300

Knights of Columbus. Religious Information Bureau.
Why a woman needs the Catholic faith. St. Louis, Religious Information Bureau, Knights of Columbus [n.d.]
24 p. illus. 19 cm. (Its [Pamphlet series], no. 44)
Published ca. 1950.

NK 0203507 PLatS

Knights of Columbus. Religious Information Bureau.
Why Catholics "keep running to church." St. Louis, Religious Information Bureau, Knights of Columbus [n.d.]
32 p. illus., chart. 19 cm. (Its [Pamphlet series], no. 2)
Published ca. 1950.

NK 0203508 PLatS

Knights of Columbus. Religious Information Bureau.
"Why I had to embrace the Catholic faith." St. Louis, Religious Information Bureau, Knights of Columbus [n.d.]
40 p. illus. 19 cm. (Its [Pamphlet series], no. 40)
Published ca. 1950.

NK 0203509 PLatS

Knights of Columbus. Religious Information Bureau.
Why millions call him "Holy Father." St. Louis, Religious Information Bureau, Knights of Columbus [n.d.].
32 p. illus. 19 cm. (Its [Pamphlet series], no. 4)
Published ca. 1950.

NK 0203510 PLatS

Knights of Columbus. Religious Information Bureau.
Why so many decide to become Catholics. St. Louis, Religious Information Bureau, Knights of Columbus [n.d.]
44 p. illus. 19 cm. (Its [Pamphlet series], no. 27)
Published ca. 1950.

NK 0203511 PLatS

Knights of Columbus. Religious Information Bureau.
Why the Catholic Church says "Investigate." St. Louis, Religious Information Bureau, Knights of Columbus [n.d.]
40 p. illus. 19 cm. (Its [Pamphlet series], no. 7)
Published ca. 1950.

NK 0203512 PLatS

Knights of Columbus. Religious Information Bureau.
Yes, a priest can forgive your sins! St. Louis, Religious Information Bureau, Knights of Columbus [n.d.]
32 p. illus. 19 cm. (Its [Pamphlet series], no. 46)
Published ca. 1950.

NK 0203513 PLatS

Knights of Columbus. Religious Information Bureau.
"Yes --- I condemned the Catholic Church." St. Louis, Religious Information Bureau, Knights of Columbus [n.d.]
48 p. illus. 19 cm. (Its [Pamphlet series], no. 15)
Published ca. 1950.

NK 0203514 PLatS

Knights of Columbus. Religious Information Bureau.
Yes, the Mother of God will help you. St. Louis, Religious Information Bureau, Knights of Columbus [n.d.]
48 p. illus. 19 cm. (Its [Pamphlet series], no. 24)
Published ca. 1950.

NK 0203515 PLatS

Knights of Columbus. Religious Information Bureau.
You hear strange things about Catholics. St. Louis, Religious Information Bureau, Knights of Columbus [n.d.]
32 p. illus. 19 cm. (Its [Pamphlet series], no. 1)
Published ca. 1950.

NK 0203516 PLatS

Knights of Columbus. Sandusky council, no. 546.
A remembrance of the Knights of Columbus. Commemorating the 25th year of its organization and published on the occasion of the annual outing at Cedar Point: Sandusky, Ohio, July 9th to 11th, 1906. Detroit, Mich. Pub. under the auspices of the General committee of Sandusky council, no. 546, 1906.
v.

NK 0203517 OClWHi

R366.6 KNIGHTS of Columbus. Seattle council, no.676.
K7481D Directory.
Author.

NK 0203518 WaS

Knights of Columbus. Seattle council, no. 676.

Seattle. Public library.
Subject list of Catholic books in the Seattle public library. Pub. under the auspices of the Knight [!] of Columbus, Seattle council no. 676. Seattle, Wash., 1909.

Knights of Columbus. Supreme council.
Acitivities of the Knights of Columbus; Goldan anniversary, 1882-1932. New Haven, Supreme council [1932] 23 p. illus. 19cm.

NK 0203520 NN Or

Knights of Columbus. Supreme council.
Handbook for discussion groups, the what, the why, the how, the wherefore. New Haven, Division of social education, Knights of Columbus, Supreme council, c1947.
32 p. 21 cm.

NK 0203521 Mi

Knights of Columbus. *Supreme council.*
Mexico? New Haven, Conn., Knights of Columbus, Supreme council, 1926.
31, [1] p. 15½cm.
"First edition—one million copies."
Articles by various authors on the regime of President Calles.

1. Mexico—Pol. & govt.—1910– 2. Church and state in Mexico. I. Title.
27-5369
Library of Congress F1234.K67

NK 0203522 DLC CU-B

Knights of Columbus. *Supreme council.*
Mexico, bolshevism the menace. Knights of Columbus, Supreme council. New Haven, Conn. [Boston, Washington press] 1926.
31, [1] p. 15½ x 8½cm.
"First edition—one million copies."
Composed chiefly of selections from magazine and newspaper articles.

1. Bolshevism—Mexico. 2. Catholic church in Mexico. 3. Church and state in Mexico. I. Title.
27-14527
Library of Congress F1234.K672

NK 0203523 DLC CU-B DW NN

Knights of Columbus. Supreme council.
Pastoral letter of the Catholic Episcopate of the United States ...
see under Catholic church in the U.S. Bishops.

940.93144 Knights of Columbus. Supreme Council.
F191 Peace program proposed by the Knights of
v.4 Columbus, adopted by Supreme Council, August
no.25 19, 1943. [New Haven, Conn., 1943]
7p. 20cm. (In Pamphlets on post-war planning. v.4, no.25)

Cover title.

1. World war, 1939-1945. Peace. I. Title.

NK 0203525 OrU MH

Knights of Columbus. Supreme council.
...Proceedings. Annual meeting [no.]

[New Haven, 1 v. 23cm.

NK 0203526 NN

F1206 Knights of Columbus. Supreme Council.
K57 Red Mexico: the facts. [1st ed.] New Haven, Conn., 1926.
30 p. 15x19cm.

"The information in this booklet is compiled almost entirely from non-Catholic sources."

NK 0203527 CU-B

Knights of Columbus. *Supreme council.*
Red Mexico; the facts. New Haven, Conn., Knights of Columbus, Supreme council, 1926.
30, [2] p. 15 x 8½cm.
Second edition.
"The information in this booklet is compiled almost entirely from non-Catholic sources."

1. Mexico—Hist.—Revolution, 1910– 2. Church and state in Mexico. 3. Catholic church in Mexico. I. Title.
27-4708
Library of Congres F1234.K68

NK 0203528 DLC DNW OrU MB

VOLUME 300

F1206
K575 Knights of Columbus. Supreme Council.
Resolution on Mexican situation adopted unanimously by Supreme Council, Knights of Columbus, assembled at Philadelphia, Pa., August 3-5, 1926. [New Haven, Conn., 1926?]
5,[1] p. 19cm.

NK 0203529 CU-B

F1235
K58 Knights of Columbus. Supreme Council.
The United States Constitution and its Mexican travesty. New Haven, 1926.
10 p. 23cm.

Cover title.

1. Mexico - Pol. & govt. - 1910-1946. 2. Mexico - Constitution, 1917. 3. Mexico - Church and state. 4. Church history - Mexico - Catholic Church. I. Title.

NK 0203530 CU-B

HS1538
C7A2 Knights of Columbus. Supreme council. Commission on religious prejudices.
Report [s] 1915-17.
[Chicago?, 1915-17]
3v in 1.

NN
NK 0203531 DLC ICRL DCU DPU IMunS Or PPDrop OCl OCX

Knights of Columbus. Syracuse Council, no.191.
Dedication of Jesuit well and reproduction of French chapel and fort of Ste. Marie of Ganentaa (Onondaga Lake) August 16, 1933. Edited by William E.McClusky. Syracuse [1933?]
31p. illus.,ports.,map. 23cm.

1. Onondaga Co., N.Y. - Hist. 2. Le Moine, Simon, 1604-1665. I. McClusky, William E ed. II. Title.

NK 0203532 NRU

381
K56 Knights of Columbus. Texas state council. Historical commission.
Minutes of the ... regular meeting (of the Texas Knights of Columbus historical commission)
Austin?
v.

NK 0203533 DLC ICN AzU CSmH OCU OO NN CU-B

Knights of Columbus. *Texas State Council. Historical Commission.*
Our Catholic heritage in Texas, 1519–1936, prepared under the auspices of the Knights of Columbus of Texas, Paul J. Foik, editor. By Carlos E. Castañeda. Austin, Von Boeckmann-Jones Co., 1936–58.
7 v. plates, ports., maps (part fold.) facsims. 27 cm.
Vols. 5–6 edited by J. P. Gibbons; v. 7 by J. P. Gibbons and W. H. Oberste.
Includes bibliographies.
CONTENTS.—v. 1. The mission era: the finding of Texas, 1519–1693.—v. 2. The mission era: the winning of Texas, 1693–1731.—v. 3. The mission era: the missions at work, 1731–1761.—v. 4. The mission era: the passing of the missions, 1762–1782.—v. 5. The mission era: the end of the Spanish regime, 1780–1810.—v. 6. Transition period: the fight for freedom, 1810–1836.—v. 7. The church in Texas since independence, 1836–1950. Supplement, 1936–1950.

1. Texas—Hist. 2. Catholics in Texas. 3. Indians of North America—Missions. I. Castañeda, Carlos Eduardo, 1896–1958. II. Foik, Paul Joseph, 1880–1941, ed. III. Title.

F386.K66 976.4 36–18384 rev 2*
—— —— Copy 2. BX1415.T4K6

NjP NBuG OU MoSU IaU DCU PU MdBJ InNd CaOTU ICN MnU NcU ViU MH MsU NbU TxU NN RPB CU NhD CtY IU
NK 0203535 DLC WHi OU MnHi MiU NcD CoU DCU MnU NNC

Knights of Columbus. Texas state council. Historical commission.
Texas Catholic historical society.
Preliminary studies of the Texas Catholic historical society ... distributed under the auspices of the Texas Knights of Columbus historical commission ... [Austin, Tex., °19

Knights of Columbus. Texas state council. Historical commission.
... Report of the proceedings
see its Minutes of the ... regular meeting.

Knights of Columbus. *Washington Council, no. 224.*
Golden anniversary, 1897–1947. Washington [1947]
138 p. illus., ports. 25 cm.
Cover title.

HS1538.C74A55 267.242 48–14408*

NK 0203538 DLC MB

Knights of Columbus. Webster Groves Council, no. 2119.
The Knights' day
see under title

K
940
.W 97 KNIGHTS OF COLUMBUS. Wisconsin State Council.
The history of the Knights of Columbus in Wisconsin from their beginnings in the year 1900. Golden anniversary of the Wisconsin State Council in 1952. [Oshkosh, Castle-Pierce Printing Co., 1952]
xlvii, 734p. illus., ports., facsims. 28cm.

NK 0203540 ICN

027.67
K71k Knights of Columbus Foundation for the Preservation of Historic Documents at the Vatican Library, St. Louis.
The Knights of Columbus Foundation for the preservation of historic documents at the Vatican Library. [St. Louis, 1951?]
11p. illus. 29cm.

Cover title.

1. Vatican. Biblioteca vaticana.

NK 0203541 CLSU PLF NN

Z810
.R76
qK6
pam Knights of Columbus Foundation for the Preservation of Historic Documents at the Vatican Library.
[Report. New Haven, Conn., 1952?]
11 p. illus. 28½cm.

1. Vatican. Biblioteca Vaticana.

NK 0203542 OrCS

Knights of Columbus Foundation for the Preservation of the Historic Documents at the Vatican Library, St. Louis.
Manuscripta. v. 1, no. 1-2; Apr.-Oct. 1954. St. Louis.

Knights of Columbus historical series.
New York, 1923-

NK 0203544 DLC OO

Knights of Columbus hymnal
see under Fischer, George H

Knights of Columbus racial contribution series
Boston, Mass. [c1924-

NK 0203546 DLC DPU

Knights of Damon of Virginia. Grand lodge.
Constitution, by-laws, rules of order and general laws for the government of the Grand lodge, Knights of Damon and the order in general under the control and government of Knights of Damon of Virginia. Compiled by Sir J. C. Randolph, R. W. G. C. Richmond, Va., Reformer print, 1904.
32 p. 22.5 cm.
Text on p. [3] of cover.
1. Knights of Damon of Virginia. Grand lodge. 2. Negroes - Societies. I. Randolph, John C., comp.
HS2259.D16.V8 3-42

NK 0203547 Vi

The Knights of Dee, by D. A. S. Oxford, University Press, 1923.
51 p. 20cm.

Poems.

I. S., D. A.

NK 0203548 NNC

Knights of fidelity.
Ritual of the Knights of fidelity; incorporated May 16th, 1901. Chicago, Allied print. trades council [1901]
23 p. 16°.

1-12896

Library of Congress (Copyright 1901 A 10894)

NK 0203549 DLC

Pam.
Coll.
44355 Knights of Harmony.
Charter, constitution and laws of the Knights of Harmony, governing the supreme, grand, and subordinate lodges. New Bern, W. T. Hill, printer, 1894.
92 p. 14 cm.

NK 0203549-1 NcD

Knights of honor.
Drill tactics for Knights of honor. Sword and bugle signals ... Pub. by authority of the Supreme lodge, Knights of honor. By H. B. Grant ... Cincinnati, The Pettibone m'f'g co., 1888.
224 p. illus., diagrs. 16cm.

I. Grant, Henry B.

9-32532†

Library of Congress HS1510.H753G8
(Copyright 1888: 15479)

NK 0203550 DLC

VOLUME 300

366.9202
K748rg **Knights of Honor.**
Ritual of the Grand Lodge, Knights of Honor. Prepared by a special committee. St. Louis, Nixon-Jones Print. Co., 1888.
25p. 20cm.

NK 0203551 TxU

Knights of Honor. Alabama. Grand lodge.
Proceedings of the organization and of the annual meeting. Montgomery, 1877-88.
v. 1-8.

NK 0203552 Nh NcD

Knights of Honor. Alabama. Grand lodge.
Reports of the Grand lodge officers and supreme representatives. Montgomery, 1887.
(Bound with its proceedings. 1877-88. v. 1-8)

NK 0203553 Nh

Knights of Honor. Alpha Lodge no. 245, Manchester, N.H.
By-laws. Manchester, 1876.

NK 0203554 Nh

Knights of Honor. Alpha Lodge no. 245, Manchester, N.H.
Constitution and by-laws. Concord, 1876.

NK 0203555 Nh

Knights of Honor. Alpha Lodge no. 245, Manchester, N.H.
Constitution and by-laws. Manchester, 1880.

NK 0203556 Nh

Knights of Honor. Alpine Lodge no. 2886, N.H.
By-laws. Manchester, 1883.

NK 0203557 Nh

Knights of Honor. Arkansas. Grand lodge.
Journal of proceedings of the Grand lodge, 1878-1900. Little Rock, 1879-1900.

NK 0203558 Nh

Knights of Honor. California. Grand lodge.
Proceedings at the organization and annual session of the Grand lodge. San Francisco, 1880-99.
v. 1-18.

NK 0203559 Nh

Knights of Honor. Connecticut. Grand lodge.
Proceedings of the annual session. Hartf., and N.H., 1878-99.
v. 1-22.

NK 0203560 Nh

Knights of honor. District of Columbia. Grand lodge.
Constitution of the grand lodge....
Washington, Polkinhorn, 1882.
10 p. 24 °

NK 0203561 DLC

Knights of honor. District of Columbia. Grand lodge.
Proceedings of the first, second and third annual sessions... Washington, D.C., R.O. Polkinborn, 1882.

NK 0203562 DLC Nh

Knights of honor. District of Columbia. Grand lodge.
Proceedings of the grand lodge, Knights of honor of the district of Columbia, fourth annual session, and of special meetings held since the third annual session. Washington, D.C., R.O. Polkinborn, 1885.
36 p. 1 pt.

NK 0203563 DLC

Knights of Honor. District of Columbia. Grand Lodge.
Report of the supreme representative, of the grand lodge of the District of Columbia [at the meeting held at Minneapolis, Minn., May 10-17, 1881. Washington, D.C., R.O. Polkinborn, 1881.
20 p.

NK 0203564 DLC Nh

Knights of honor. District of Columbia. Grand lodge.
Report to the grand lodge. ...held at Baltimore, Md. May 9-18, 1882. [Washington, 1882]
xix p.

NK 0203565 DLC

Z
366.9201
K748b **Knights of Honor.** Eureka Lodge no. 2524, New Orleans.
By-laws of Eureka Lodge No.2524, Knights of Honor, New Orleans, La. [New Orleans, 1893]
13p. 16cm.
Cover title.

NK 0203566 TxU

Knights of Honor. Excelsior Lodge no. 633, Providence, R.I.
By-laws ... Providence, 1888.
[7] p. 14 cm.
Incorrectly paged.

NK 0203567 RPB

Knights of Honor. Excelsior Lodge no. 633, Providence, R.I.
Constitution and by-laws... Providence, 1880.
5 p.

NK 0203568 RPB

Knights of Honor. Florida. Grand lodge.
Organization and proceedings of the annual meeting. v.p.1882-8.
v.

NK 0203569 Nh

Knights of Honor. Franklin Lodge no. 709, Franklin Falls, N.H.
Constitution, by-laws and rules of order; also the general laws of the Supreme lodge. Concord, 1878.

NK 0203570 Nh

Ga
HS1510
H774G42 Knights of Honor. Gate City Lodge no. 346, Atlanta.
By-laws of Gate City Lodge, no. 346, Knights of Honor. Atlanta, Ga., October 21st, 1881. Atlanta, Ticknor, Dunlop, 1881.
7 p. 15cm.

NK 0203571 GU

Knights of Honor. Georgia. Grand lodge.
Proceedings. Augusta,1878-92.
v

NK 0203572 Nh

Knights of Honor. Golden Rule Lodge no. 2445.
Constitution and by-laws. Boston, 1882.

NK 0203573 Nh

Knights of Honor. Holliston Lodge no. 647, Holliston, Mass.
General laws, constitution, by-laws and rules of order. Holliston lodge, no. 647, Knights of honor. Holliston, Mass. Boston, J. A. Cummings & co., 1878. 40 p. 15cm.

NK 0203574 NN

Knights of Honor. Illinois. Grand lodge.
Journal of the proceedings of the annual session. v.p. 1878-98.
v

NK 0203575 Nh

Knights of Honor. Illinois. Grand lodge.
Organization and proceedings. Peoria, 1877.

NK 0203576 Nh

VOLUME 300

Knights of H-nor. Indiana. Grand lodge.
Proceedings of the onstitution and annual meeting. Indianapolis, 1877-1900.
v

NK 0203577 Nh

Knights of Honor. Iowa. Grand lodge.
Proceedings of the organizing session and annual session. Luons,1879-91.
v.1-9.

NK 0203578 Nh

Knights of honor. Kansas. Grand lodge.
Proceedings of the organization and annual session. v.p. 1878-99.
v. 1-18.

NK 0203579 Nh

Knights of honor. Kentucky. Grand lodge.
Organization and proceedings. Louisville, 1876-91.
vl-11.

NK 0203580 Nh

HS1510 K55S25 Knights of Honor. Keystone Lodge no. 2107, San Francisco.
By-laws, rules of order and order of business of Keystone Lodge, no. 2107, Knights of Honor. San Francisco, J. Winterburn & Co., Book and Job Printers, 1880.
12 p. 15cm. in cover 20cm.

NK 0203581 CU-B

Knights of honor. Louisiana. Grand lodge.
Proceedings of the annual session. New Orleans, 1882-9.
v.

NK 0203582 Nh

Knights of honor. Louisiana. Grand lodge.
Proceedings of the first session. N.O., 1881.

NK 0203583 Nh

Knights of honor. Maine. Grand lodge.
Journal of proceedings at the organization and the annual session.
Lewiston, 1878-1900.
v.1-23.

NK 0203584 Nh

Knights of honor. Maryland. Grand lodge.
Annual session. Balt.,1879-89.
v.1-10

NK 0203585 Nh

Knights of honor. Massachusetts. Grand lodge.
Journal of proceedings of the organization and of the annual session. Bost.,1877-92.
v.1-17.

NK 0203586 Nh

Knights of honor. Michigan. Grand lodge.
Proceedings of the...Grand Lodge, Knights of honor of Michigan...
1 v.

10th -17th are 1st-8th biennial.
Subtitle varies.
1878 includes the Proceedings of the special and annual sessions.

Bound with these are Constitution...1884, 1890.
Reports of the Grand reporter, Grand treasurer, State medical examiner, etc. 1885, 1891, 1893.

NK 0203588 MiD Nh

Knights of honor - Michigan - Grand lodge.
...Reports... Allegan, Mich.
v.

NK 0203589 MiD-B

Knights of honor. Minnesota. Grand lodge.
Proceedings at the organization of the lodge. Minneapolis, 1878.

NK 0203590 Nh

Knights of honor. Minnesota. Grand lodge.
Proceedings of the organization and of the annual session. v.p. 1880-1900.
v.1-12

NK 0203591 Nh

Knights of honor. Mississippi. Grand lodge.
Proceedings of the annual session. Jackson, 1878-88.
v.1-11.

NK 0203592 Nh

Knights of honor. Missouri. Grand lodge.
Proceedings of the annual session.
St. L.,1878-92.
v.4-14.

NK 0203593 Nh

Knights of Honor. Mount Coit Lodge no. 286.
Constitution, by-laws, and rules of order. Concord, 1878.

NK 0203594 Nh

Knights of honor. Nebraska. Grand lodge.
Proceedings of the organization and annual session. Omaha,1879-84.
v.1-6.

NK 0203595 Nh

Knights of honor. New Hampshire. Grand lodge.
Annual report of the committee on correspondence. Manch.,1889.
v.7.

NK 0203596 Nh

Knights of honor. New Hampshire. Grand lodge.
Constitution governing subordinate lodges; also the general laws of the Supreme lodge. Concord, 1878.

NK 0203597 Nh

Knights of honor. New Hampshire. Grand lodge.
Journal of proceedings of organization and of the annual session. v. p. 1878-98.
v. 1-17.

NK 0203598 Nh NhDo

Knights of honor. New Jersey. Grand lodge.
Proceedings of the annual meeting. v.p.1878-99.
v

NK 0203599 Nh

Knights of honor. New York. Grand lodge.
Journal of proceedings of the organizatic and of the annual session. v.p.1877-92.
v.1-2

NK 0203600 Nh

Knights of Honor.New York.Grand lodge.
Constitution of the Grand and subordinate lodges... Buffalo, Haas, Nauert & Klein., 1879.
46p.

NK 0203601 OClWHi

Knights of honor. New York. Grand lodge.
Reports.
Binghamton, N.Y.? 1900

HS1510 .H75A4

NK 0203602 DLC MB

Knights of honor. North Carolina. Grand lodge.
Proceedings. 1875?-
v. 22 cm.

NK 0203603 NcD

Knights of honor. North Carolina. Grand lodge.
Journal of the proceedings of the organization and of the annual session. Charlotte, 1878-99.
v

NK 0203604 Nh

VOLUME 300

Knights of honor. Ohio. Grand lodge.
Proceedings of the organization and annual meeting. v. p. 1876-88.
v. 1-11.

NK 0203605 Nh

HS1510 K55S27 Knights of Honor. Oriental Lodge no. 2163, San Francisco.
By-laws and rules of order of Oriental Lodge, no. 2163, Knights of Honor. San Francisco, Taylor & Nevin, Steam Printers, 1880.
11 p. 15cm. in cover 20cm.

NK 0203606 CU-B

Knights of honor. Pennsylvania. Grand lodge.
Proceedings of the organization and annual session. Corry, 1876-99.
v.

NK 0203607 Nh

Knights of Honor. Rhode Island.
[By-laws. Sick benefit association, Knights of Honor and Knights and Ladies of Honor, Rhode Island] Providence, 1884.
11 p.

NK 0203608 RPB

Knights of honor--Rhode Island--Grand lodge.
Proceedings, ... 1878, '85, '90. Providence, 1878-90.
3 v.

NK 0203609 RPB Nh

Knights of Honor. South Carolina. Grand lodge.
Journal of proceedings of the organization and of the annual session. Columbia, 1878-94.
v.

NK 0203610 Nh

Knights of Honor. South Carolina. Supreme Council.
Proceedings... Charleston

NK 0203611 MiD-B

Knights of honor. Supreme lodge.
Constitution and general laws of the knights of honor for the government of the supreme and subordinate lodges. Louisville, C.H. Bradburn & co. 1875.
40p.

NK 0203612 OClWHi PPL

Knights of Honor. Supreme lodge.
Constitution and general laws governing the supreme, grand and subordinate lodges as adopted June, 1898. n.p. 1898.

NK 0203613 Nh

Knights of honor. Supreme lodge.
Constitution and genera laws governing the supreme, grand and subordinate lodges as adopted June, **1899. n.p. 1899.**

NK 0203614 Nh

HS1510 K55A3 1902 Knights of Honor. Supreme Lodge.
Constitution and general laws governing the Supreme, Grand and subordinate lodges, as revised and adopted at the Twenty-ninth Annual Session of the Supreme Lodge, held in Cleveland, Ohio, June 10 to 17, 1902. [n. p.] Published by the Supreme Lodge, 1902.
157 p. 14cm.

NK 0203615 CU-B OCl

Knights of honor. *Supreme lodge.*
Digest of the constitutions, laws and decisions of the Supreme lodge, Knights of honor, with explanatory notes: together with an appendix, containing the official forms used in the order, act of incorporation, etc. Comp. by Alfred Mathias. Pub. by authority of the Supreme lodge. Boston, J. A. Cummings & co., 1880.
129 p. $23\frac{1}{2}^{cm}$.

I. Mathias, Alfred. 9-32522†

Library of Congress HS1510.H752A5 1880 (Copyright 1880: 5060)

NK 0203616 DLC AU

Knights of honor. *Supreme lodge.*
Digest of the official decisions of the Knights of honor. Comp. by A. R. Savage ... Boston, J. A. Cummings printing co., 1890.
135 p. $22\frac{1}{2}^{cm}$.

I. Savage, A. R. 9-32521†

Library of Congress HS1510.H752A5 1890 (Copyright 1890: 28816)

NK 0203617 DLC

Knights of honour. Supreme lodge.
[Manual of procedure] n. p., n. p., n. d.
38 p.
No title page.

NK 0203618 NcD

Knights of honor. Supreme lodge.
Proceedings of the annual session of the Supreme lodge. v.p. 1874-99.
v.1-26.

NK 0203619 Nh Mi TxU MiD-B

Knights of Honor. Supreme Lodge.
Report of the committee of physicians, Supreme Lodge, Knights of Honor. Tenth annual session, held in Galveston, Texas, May 8, 1883. Louisville, Ky. 1883.
23 p.

NK 0203620 DNLM

Knights of Honor. Temple Lodge no. 2065.
By-laws. Manchester, 1891.

NK 0203621 Nh

Knights of Honor. Temple Lodge no. 2065.
Constitution and by-laws. Manchester, 1880.

NK 0203622 Nh

Knights of Honor. Temple Lodge no. 2065.
Constitution and by-laws. Boston, 1882.

NK 0203623 Nh

Pam HS1510 .H755A5 1877 Knights of Honor. Tennessee.
Constitution and general laws of the Knights of Honor, governing Grand and subordinate lodges in Tennessee. Rev. ed. Nashville, Tavel, Eastman & Howell, 1877.
79 p. 15 cm.

NK 0203624 T

KNIGHTS OF HONOR. *Tennessee.* **78**
Epidemic of 1876. Report of the central relief committee. Memphis, 1879. 60 pp. 8°.

B 5197

NK 0203625 MB

Knights of honor. Tennessee. Grand lodge.
Proceedings of the organization and of the annual session. Nashville, 1876-91.
v.1-14.

NK 0203626 Nh

Knights of honor. Texas. Grand lodge.
Proceedings of the annual meeting. Hempstead and Houston, 1878-99.
v. 1-15.

NK 0203627 Nh

Knights of honor. Texas. Grand lodge.
Proceedings of the first session. Tyler, 1878.
(Bound with its Proceedings of the annual meeting. 1878-84. v.1-7)

NK 0203628 Nh

Knights of Honor. Union Lodge no. 281, Boston, Mass.
By-laws, list of members, officers, committees, etc. Boston, 1890.

NK 0203629 Nh

Knights of honor. Vermont. Grand lodge.
Organization and proceedings of the annual session. v.p. 1879-99.
v

NK 0203630 Nh

VOLUME 300

HS
1510 Knights of Honor. Virginia. Grand Lodge.
H752 Constitution. [n. p., 188-?]
V82 8 p. 23 cm.

NK 0203631 Vi

HS
1510 Knights of Honor. Virginia. Grand Lodge.
H752 Proceedings. 1st- 1878?-
V8 Danville, Va., Daily Press, Print.
v. 22 cm.

Caption title: 18 - : Journal of proceedings.

NK 0203632 Vi Nh

Knights of Honor. West Virginia. Grand lodge.
Proceedings of the session.
v.p. 1882-98.
v.1-16.

NK 0203633 Nh

Knights of Honor. Wisconsin. Grand lodge.
Proceedings of the organization and of the annual session. Milwaukee, 1878-99.
v.

NK 0203634 Nh

"Knights of honor reporter" directory and digest. A complete list of all lodges, Knights of honor. Giving name, number, location, night and place of meeting and address of reporter ... and a Knights and ladies of honor directory ... 1879-80. Boston, J. A. Cummings & co., 1879.

2 p. l., [3]-127 p. 15cm.

Advertising matter included in paging.

1. Knights of honor—Direct. 2. Knights and ladies of honor—Direct.

Library of Congress HS1510.H75Z6 1879 9-32533†
(Copyright 1879: 12564)

NK 0203635 DLC

HFA58 Knights of Industry.
MIS Preamble to the Declaration of Principles. [n.p., n.d.]
1 l 30 x 20cm. fold to 20 x 15cm.

Broadside.

1. Labor & laboring classes - U.S. - Societies.

NK 0203636 WHi

Knights of Jericho. *Georgia. Grand lodge.*
... The English revised ritual of the Knights of Jericho. Prepared by a committee appointed by and acting under authority of the Grand lodge of Georgia: containing a synopsis of the ceremonial rites, etc. (encampment excepted) of the order ... Atlanta, Ga., J. J. Toon's Franklin printing house, 1872.

72 p. diagr. 21cm.

10-4531†

Library of Congress HV5287.J4G4 1872

NK 0203637 DLC

Knights of Jericho. *Georgia. Grand lodge.*
... The English revised ritual of the Knights of Jericho. Prepared by a committee appointed by and acting under authority of the Grand lodge of Georgia, containing a synopsis of the ceremonial rights [!] of the order. Rev. by the Grand chief ... Atlanta, Ga., Southern publishing co., printers, 1874.

42 p. diagr. 22½cm.

10-3870†

Library of Congress HV5287.J4G4 1874

NK 0203638 DLC

Knights of Jerusalem, Ancient order of
see Ancient order of Knights of Jerusalem.

Knights of Jerusalem, Female department of the
see Ancient order of daughters of Jerusalem

Knights of Jesus Christ, Order of
see Order of the Knights of Jesus Christ.

Knights of Jethero, Richmond, Va.
Constitution and by-laws ... Richmond, 1874.
16 mo. Violet paper covers.
Brock Collection, October 1922.

NK 0203641 CSmH

Knights of Khorassan.
An El Wakodis offering. Pub. by the Committee on education and publicity of El Wakodis temple, no. 165, D. O. K. K. ... [Milwaukee, 1918]

30 p., 1 l. 18½cm.

"A dramatic ceremony used by El Wakodis temple, no. 165, Oasis, Milwaukee, D. O. K. K., in addition to and in connection with the ritual for the opening ceremony, scene five (Saruk) and the eighth scene or order of business ... written, arranged and compiled by J. Elmer Lehr."

I. Lehr, J. Elmer. II. Title.

Library of Congress HS1350.K4 1918 19-1785

NK 0203642 DLC

F444
q.C4K5 Knights of Khorassan.
Chattanooga, the dynamo of Dixie. Scenic center of the South Civil War historic vicinity. Greetings from El Kedan Temple, No. 120, D. O. K. K. to Providence Convention of The Imperial Palace: D. O. K. K. August 11 to 14, 1925. Chattanooga, Published by El Kedan Temple Number 120 [1925]
cover-title, 1 p. l. [84] p. illus.(1 double; incl.ports.,map) 35x18 cm.

Running title: Chattanooga-"The dynamo of Dixie" The home of El Kedan Temple-No. 120.
"This work planned and produced by Andrews Printery. Acknowledgment is made to Walter Cline for the photographs used in its production".-Preliminary leaf.
Includes advertising.

1. Chattanooga--Descr. I. Title.

NK 0203644 T

Knights of Khorassan.
Ritual of the Dramatic order Knights of Khorassan. John B. Powell, author and supreme prince ... [Milwaukee, Wis., Swain & Tate co., printers, 1895]

32 p. plan. 23½cm.

I. Powell, John B., of Milwaukee.

CA 10-3255 Unrev'd

Library of Congress HS1350.K4 1895

NK 0203645 DLC

Knights of King Arthur.
King Arthur's herald ...
see under title

Knights of labor [authorship phrase]
The object and duty of civil government.
Phila., 1886

see

Brindle, William

HFA6 Knights of Labor.
.A Adelphon kruptos. [n.p., n.d.]
26 p. 15cm.

Secret ritual for assembly meetings.

HFA6 --- ---- Another issue. [n.p., n.d.]
.A 57 p. 15cm.
2

HFA6 --- ---- Another issue. [n.p., n.d.]
.A 36 p. 16cm.
3

HFA6 --- ---- French translation. [n.p., n.d.]
.A 56 p. 15cm.
.F

HFA6 --- ---- German translation. [n.p., n.d.]
.A 56 p. 15cm.
.G

1. Knights of Labor - Rituals.

NK 0203649 WHi

Knights of Labor.
Adelphon Kruptos. [Toledo? 1879?] 26 p. 24°.

1. Labor—Assoc. and org.—U. S.
N. Y. P. L. July 18, 1930

NK 0203650 NN

R331.882 Knights of Labor
K748aa Adelphon Kruptos. [Chicago? 1881?]
33 p.

Earlier ed. pub. in German under title: Adelphon Kryptos.

1. KNIGHTS OF LABOR - Rituals I. Title

NK 0203651 MiD

VOLUME 300

Knights of Labor.
Adelphon Kruptos. [Toledo? 189–?] 57 p. incl. plan. 24°.

1. Labor—Assoc. and org.—U. S.
N. Y. P. L. July 18, 1930

NK 0203652 NN

Knights of Labor.
Adelphon Kruptos. Toledo, Ohio, 1891. 58 p. incl. plan. 24°.

1. Labor—Assoc. and org.—U. S.
N. Y. P. L. July 18, 1930

NK 0203653 NN MH-BA

Knights of Labor.
Adelphon Kruptos
see also its Knights of labor illustrated. Adelphon Kruptos.

[Knights of Labor.] 331.06146 26
80047 Adelphon kryptos.
36, [2] p. diagr. 15cm.
Text in German; translated from the English by Theo. F. Cuno, 1881.

NK 0203655 ICJ MiD

Knights of Labor L331.06146 24
48489 [Circulars.]
5 broadsides.
Contents.—Preamble and declaration of principles of the Knights of Labor of North America. [1881.] 25 x 20cm.—*Another issue; on verso of this:* The requirements of knighthood. 28½ x 15cm.—Shall our grand officers be autocrats? [The celebrated "yellow circular", 1881.] 25½ x 19cm.—Changes in the A. K. and F. and I. [1881.] 25½ x 19½cm.—Instructions to organizers. 27 x 21½cm.

NK 0203656 ICJ

Knights of Labor.
Constitution of the general assembly, and for national, trade, district and local assemblies ...
18

Washington, D. C., [etc.,] 18 24°.
nos.

Annual.
Sub-title varies slightly.
1883 in SIE p.v.67 no.4.
1887 in TDR p.v.19 no. 11.
1890 in TDR p.v.18, no. 9.

1. Labor—Assoc. and org.—U. S.
N. Y. P. L. April 8, 1929

PHi
NK 0203657 NN WHi DL MoU InU CU TxU N MH Or MiD-B ICJ

Knights of labor.
Constitution of the General assembly, district assemblies, and local assemblies, of the order of the Knights of labor of North America. Adopted at Reading, Pa., Jan. 1–4, 1878. Revised at St. Louis, Mo., Jan. 14–17, 1879; at Chicago, Ill., Sept. 2–6, 1879; at Pittsburg, Pa., Sept. 7–11, 1880, and at Detroit, Mich., Sept. 6–10, 1881 ... [n. p., 1881?]
180 p. 11½cm.

L. C. copy imperfect: 2 prelim. leaves wanting.

43–44858

Library of Congress HD8055.K7A42
[2]

NK 0203658 DLC

[Knights of Labor.]
Decisions of the general master workman, revised and codified. Published by the General Assembly.
[18

Philadelphia[, 18 24°.
nos.

1. Labor—Assoc. and org.
N. Y. P. L. August 20, 1929

NK 0203659 NN MH MoU WHi

Knights of labor.
Forms with notes and instructions, for Knights of labor courts, by L. C. Baker, member of L. A. no. 1410. [Independence? W. Va.] 1887.
cover-title, [3]–8 p. 23cm.

I. Baker, L. C.

CA 9-4434 Unrev'd

Library of Congress HD8055.K7B2
(Copyright 1887: 22668)

NK 0203660 DLC

[Knights of Labor.] 331.06146 28
80049 Founding ceremony.
18 p. 14½cm.
Caption title.
With this: Cypher, and Key to Cypher.

NK 0203661 ICJ

Knights of Labor 331.06146 22
39747 Founding ceremony. [188–?]
23, [1] p. front. (diagr.) 16cm.
Caption title.

NK 0203662 ICJ

[Knights of Labor.] 331.06146 27
80048 Gründungs-Ceremonie.
22, [2] p. front. 15cm.
Caption title.
Translated by Theo. F. Cuno.

NK 0203663 ICJ

Knights of Labor.
HFA6
MIS
An Historical paper showing the aims and objects of the Order of Knights of Labor, as promulgated by the founder in 1869. Its growth and success caused by appealing to reason and not to passion. [n.p., 189–?]
[4] ℓ. 23cm.

Caption title.

1. Knights of Labor.

NK 0203664 WHi

Knights of labor.

Journal of the Knights of labor.

Washington, D. C.,

KNIGHTS OF LABOR.
Knigh-s of labor illustrated. "Adelphon kruptos." The full, illustrated ritual including the "unwritten work" and an historical sketch of the order. Chicago, Ill.: E.A. Cook, 1886. 56 p. incl. plan. illus. 19cm.

NK 0203666 NN NNC IU NcD MnHi

KNIGHTS OF LABOR.
Knights of labor illustrated. "Adelphon kruptos." The full, illustrated ritual including the "unwritten work" and an historical sketch of the order. Chicago, E. A. Cook, 1886. 56 p. incl. plan. illus. 19cm.

Microfiche (neg.) 2 sheets. 11 x 15cm. (NYPL FSN 11,141)

NK 0203667 NN

Knights of labor.
Official handbook....
1899 1 v

NK 0203668 DL

Z
q331.8806
K748pr KNIGHTS OF LABOR.
Preamble and declaration of principles of the Knights of labor. [Philadelphia? 1881?]
[2]p. 29 x 15cm.

On verso: The requirements of knighthood.

NK 0203669 TxU

KNIGHTS OF LABOR *7560.40
Proceedings of regular session, held at Minneapolis, October to 19, 1887.
= Minneapolis, 1887. v. 8°.

NK 0203670 MB

KNIGHTS OF LABOR.
Proceedings of the general assembly. 1st-30th; 1878-1913. Washington [etc.] 30 v. illus. 8°.

Film reproduction on 2 reels made by the State historical society of Wisconsin. Positive.
No. 10, 1886, also called v. 4.
Title from cover (1878-1900, title on t.p.: Record of

proceedings of the general assembly.
Includes also proceedings of special sessions held June 1878, May/June 1886, June 1900.

1. Trade unions--U.S. I. Knights of labor. Record of proceedings of the general assembly.

NK 0203672 NN MB MoSW CU ICU

Knights of Labor.
Proceedings of the general assembly ...
see also its Record of the proceedings of the General Assembly.

Knights of labor.
Proposition for membership. (n.p., n. d.)
1 sheet. 25 x 21½ cm.

NK 0203674 DL

Knights of Labor.
Record of the proceedings of the General Assembly.

[n. p.]
v. 23 cm.
Includes proceedings of special session held May 25–June 3, 1886.

HD8055.K7A17 50-41093 ‡

NK 0203675 DLC ICJ NNC WHi NcD

VOLUME 300

Knights of Labor.
Record of the proceedings of the General Assembly
see also its Proceedings of the general assembly...

Knights of labor.
Revised forms for Knights of labor courts, with notes and instructions agreeably to the constitution and G. W. M. decisions as amended, revised and codified in the year 1887. By L. C. Baker, member of L. A. no. 1410. Independence, W. Va., 1887.
cover-title, 15, [1] p. 20½cm.

I. Baker, L. C.
CA 9-4435 Unrev'd
Library of Congress HD8055.K7B22 (Copyright 1887: 34163)

NK 0203677 DLC

HFA6 .MIS Knights of Labor.
Ritual and regulations. [n.p., n.d.]
31 ℓ. 20cm.

1. Knights of Labor - Ritual.

NK 0203678 WHi

331.88 A7sec Knights of labor.
Secret circular. Noble order of the Knights of labor of America. Philadelphia, Pa., 1886.
3p.

Caption title.
Signed: T. V. Powderly, general master workman.

1. Strikes and lockouts. 2. Labor and laboring classes--U.S.. I. Powderly, Terence Vincent, 1849-1924.

NK 0203679 IU

Knights of Labor. *District Assembly No. 3.* 331.06146 93
Constitution adopted by the General Assembly, of the Knights of Labor, of North America, for the government of district assemblies; and by-laws of District Assembly No. 3. Pittsburgh, Beymer & Gazzam, printers, 1882.
vi, 7-30 p. 17cm.

NK 0203680 ICJ

HFA6Z .P854L W652 Knights of Labor. District Assembly no. 16, District Statistician
Report...July 30-31 and August 1-2, 1888. Philadelphia, Printed at office of Journal of United Labor, 1888.
12 p. 22cm.

Cover title.

1. Coal-miners - Pennsylvania.

NK 0203681 WHi

HFA6Z .P884L SA24 Knights of Labor. District Assembly no. 17,
Constitution and by-laws, together with the rules of order. St. Louis, J.H. McLean print., [n.d.]
16 p. 13½cm.

NK 0203682 WHi

HFA6Z .P844L B657 MIS Knights of Labor. District Assembly no. 30.
Charter. Boston, 1896.
Broadside, fold. to 25cm.

NK 0203683 WHi

HFA6Z .P844L B657 MIS Knights of Labor. District Assembly no. 30,
Directory of the Knights of Labor assemblies of district no. 30. Boston, Co-operative print. & pub. co., 1886.
13 p. 21½cm.

NK 0203684 WHi

HFA6Z +P844L B657 L 1893 Knights of Labor. District Assembly no. 30,
Official journal, Labor Day, September 4, 1893. [Boston, 1893]
1 v. (unpaged) ports. 28cm.

Seventh edition.
Contains short historical sketches of the member local assemblies of District 30.

1. Labor day.

NK 0203685 WHi

Knights of Labor. *District Assembly No. 30.*
Quarterly report.
Boston.
v. 23 cm.

HD8055.K7A255 52-17627 ‡

NK 0203686 DLC MiD WHi ICJ

HFA6Z +P844L B657 MIS Knights of Labor. District Assembly no. 30,
Second annual picnic and reunion of District 30, K. of L. ... September 7, 1891, Labor day. Boston, 1891.
1 v. (unpaged) ports. 28cm.

1. Labor day.

NK 0203687 WHi

331.8809771 K71t
Knights of Labor. District Assembly no. 47.
Twenty year history of District Assembly 47, Knights of Labor, organized May 30, 1882. [Cleveland?] 1902.
104 p. ports. 24cm.

NK 0203688 FU

R331.882 K7483c Knights of Labor. District Assembly, no. 49
Convention of the New York Protective Associations affiliated with D. A. 49, on Labor Day. [New York]

NK 0203689 MiD ICJ WHi

HFA6Z .P851L N489 Knights of Labor. District Assembly no. 64,
By-laws. New York, Co-operative print., 1887.
8 p. 13cm.

NK 0203690 WHi

Knights of labor. District Assembly no. 66.
... Memorial of District assembly no. 66, Knights of labor, and the Federation of labor unions praying for the passage of House bill no. 8537 limiting the hours of labor on public work to eight per day. (Washington, 1892)
5 p. 28½ cm.

NK 0203691 DL

HFA6Z .P851L B791 Knights of Labor. District Assembly no. 75.
By-laws of the Empire Protective Association, D.A. no. 75, K. of L. New York, Concord Co-operative print., 1888.
16 p. 15cm.

NK 0203692 WHi

HFZ6Z .P844L L993 Knights of Labor. District Assembly no. 77,
Proceedings. 1886-
Lynn, Mass.
v. 22cm.

NK 0203693 WHi

HFA6Z .P846 Knights of Labor. District Assembly no. 95.
Annual convention and reunion of the Connecticut Protective Associations under the Auspices of District Assembly 95. 1894-
[Hartford, Conn.?]
v. ports. 29cm.

1894 contains articles on labor problems.

NK 0203694 WHi

HFA6Z .P846L H253 Knights of Labor. District Assembly no. 95,
Proceedings. 1887-
Hartford, Conn.
1 v. 22½cm.

NK 0203695 WHi

HFA6Z .P851L N489 Knights of Labor. District Assembly no. 97,
By-laws of the Enterprise Association, K. of L. New York, Concord co-operative print., 1889.
7 p. 12½cm.

NK 0203696 WHi

HFA6Z .P931L B981 Knights of Labor. District Assembly no. 98,
Proceedings of the semi-annual session. 18 - . Philadelphia, Journal of the Knights of Labor print.
v. 22½cm.

NK 0203697 WHi

VOLUME 300

HFA6Z "P845 Knights of Labor. District Assembly no. 99,
Official souvenir. 18 -
[n.p.]
v. ports. 30cm.

Title varies: Official handbook; Official reunion journal and labor day gazette.

NK 0203698 WHi

Knights of Labor. *District Assembly 99.* 331.06146 60
Quarterly report of District Assembly 99, K. of L. .... Boston, Co-operative Printing and Publishing Co., 1886.
July 1886. 24cm.

NK 0203699 ICJ

HFA6Z .P884L SE27 Knights of Labor. District Assembly no. 101,
By-laws. Sedalia, Mo., Labor Union print., 1886.
5 p. 12½cm.

NK 0203700 WHi

KNIGHTS OF LABOR. District Assembly no. 126.
Report of the executive board of District assembly 126, K. of L. n.p., n. d.

NK 0203701 MH

HFA6Z .P854L T541 Knights of Labor. District Assembly no. 169,
Secret directory of D.A. no. 169 and L.A.'s within this district. [n.p., 1888?]
8 p. 14cm.

Caption title.
"For D.A. officers."

NK 0203702 WHi

HFA6Z .P853L J487 Knights of Labor. District Assembly no. 197,
Official reunion journal and Labor Day gazette. 18 - . [n.p.]
v. ports. 27cm.

Contains biographical sketches.

NK 0203703 WHi

HFA6Z .P851L N489 T981 P Knights of Labor. District Assembly no. 250.
Proceedings of the...annual convention of D.A. 250, K. of L. (Journeymen Typefounders of North America)
v. 14½cm.

Library has:

2d, 1889, has imprint: New York, Concord Co-operative print., 1890.
1. Typefounders - U.S. - Societies, etc.

NK 0203704 WHi

HFA6 .MIS Knights of Labor. General co-operative board.
Skeleton form of articles of incorporation and by-laws for co-operative societies, in United States and Canada. Minneapolis, T.A. Clark, 1887.
26 p. 14cm.

--- ---- Another edition, 1888. (22 p., 14½cm)

1. Cooperation - U.S.

NK 0203705 WHi

HFA6 .MIS Knights of Labor. General Executive Board.
The order and the cigar makers. Circular and statement by the general executive board, together with the testimony recently taken concerning the trouble growing out of the lock-out declared on February 18, 1886, by the United Cigar Manufacturers' Association of New York. Philadelphia, 1886.
48 p. 21 cm.

Caption title.

1. Cigar Makers' International Union of America.

NK 0203706 WHi

HFA6Z .P912 Knights of Labor. Iowa.
Proceedings.
[various places] 18 -
v. 17½-21cm.

NK 0203707 WHi

HFA6Z .P912 Knights of Labor. Iowa. State statistician.
Report...1888. Mapleton, Iowa, Home Advocate print., [1888?]
12 p. 19½cm.

NK 0203708 WHi

HFA6 .MIS Knights of Labor. Legislative committee.
Report. [n.p.] 1886?
17 p. 23cm.

Caption title.

1. U.S. 49th Cong., 1st sess., 1885-1886.
2. U.S. 49th Cong., 2d sess., 1886-1887.

NK 0203709 WHi

HFA6Z .P851L N489 Knights of Labor. Local Assembly no. -----, New York (city)
By-laws and rules of order of the United Blank Book Workers of New York and vicinity. New York, Concord print., [18--?]
16 p. 14½ cm.
Article 1 of by-laws: "Section 1. This L.A. shall be known as the United Job Blank Book Workers."

1. Bookbinders - New York (city)

NK 0203710 WHi

HFA6Z .P892L C599 Knights of Labor. Local assembly no. 451, Cleveland, Ohio
Price list and by-laws of the Cleveland Musical Union of Cleveland, Ohio, Local assembly 451, K. of L. Organized March 21, 94. Cleveland, West Side print., 1895.
16 p. 12cm.

1. Musicians - Cleveland.

NK 0203711 WHi

HFA6Z .P902L M648 Knights of Labor. Local Assembly no. 757, Milwaukee, Wisc
By-laws. Milwaukee, [n.d.]
4 p. 14½cm.

NK 0203712 WHi

HFA6Z .P925L W726 Knights of Labor. Local Assembly no. 780. [Winfield, Kan.?]
By-laws...to govern Almoner's fund. Weir City, Kan., Hayden & Kirk print., 1888.
8 p. 14cm.

NK 0203713 WHi

HFA6Z .P925L W726 Knights of Labor. Local Assembly no. 780, [Winfield, Kan.?]
By-laws of Hopeful Assembly 780 of the Knights of Labor. Winfield, Kan., H. & L. Vincent print., 1891.
8 p. 14½cm.

NK 0203714 WHi

HFA6Z .P851L C66 Knights of Labor. Local assembly no. 1482, Cohoes, N.Y.
Constitution and by-laws of the Liberty Association of Rib Knitters, L.A. 1482, K. of L. [Cohoes, N.Y., n.d.]
9 p. 13cm.

1. Textile workers - Cohoes, N.Y.

NK 0203715 WHi

HFA6Z .P851L N489 Knights of Labor. Local Assembly no. 1553, New York (city)
By-laws and rules of the Shoe Cutters' and Stitchers' Protective and Mutual Aid Association, local assembly 1553, Knights of Labor. Organized Jan. 6, 1901. [New York? 1901]
32 p. 14 cm.

p. 28-32 are blank, for Amendments and Memoranda.

1. Shoemakers - New York (city)

NK 0203716 WHi

HFA6Z .P851L R586 Knights of Labor. Local Assembly no. 1727, Rochester, N.Y.
By-laws of the Clothing Cutters' and Trimmers' local assembly, 1727, K. of L., of Rochester, N.Y. Rochester, N.Y., St. John & Spinning print., 1890.
16 p. 14 cm.

1. Clothing workers - Rochester, N.Y.

NK 0203717 WHi

Knights of Labor. *Local Assembly no. 1755, Chicago, Ill.*
By-laws of Foundrymen's Assembly No. 1755, Knights of Labor. Chicago, W. C. Hollister & Bro., printers, 1887.
6 p. 17cm.

NK 0203718 ICJ

HFA6Z .P896L C432 Knights of Labor. Local Assembly no. 2154, Chicago, Ill.
By-laws of the Chicago Bedding Finishers' Union, Local Assembly no. 2154, Knights of Labor. Chicago, J.B. Lenau print., [1900?]
8 p. 14 cm.

1. Beds and bedsteads - Employees.

NK 0203719 WHi

HFA6Z .P826L T624 Knights of Labor. Local Assembly no. 2211, Toronto.
By-laws of Pioneer Assembly no. 2211... founded September, 1882. [Toronto?] Mail job print., [1887?]
13 p. 15cm.

NK 0203720 WHi

VOLUME 300

HFA6Z .P851L N489 Knights of Labor. Local Assembly no. 2291, New York (city)
By laws of L.A. 2291 of N.T.A. 252, K. of L. New York, Concord Co-operative print., 1892.
31 p. 14½cm.

Cover title.

1. Knights of Labor. National Trade Assembly no. 252.

NK 0203721 WHi

HFA6Z .P851L R586 Knights of Labor. Local Assembly no. 2372, Rochester, N.Y.
Bill of wages adopted...for 1888. Rochester, Democrat & Chronicle print., [1888?]
8 p. 14½cm.

NK 0203722 WHi

HFA6Z .P851L N489 Knights of Labor. Local Assembly no. 2383, [New York (city)?]
By-laws. New York, Solidarity press, [n.d.]
14 p. 14½cm.

NK 0203723 WHi

HFA6Z .P851L SY81 Knights of Labor. Local Assembly no. 2762, Syracuse, N.Y.
By-laws of Shoemakers' Assembly, 2762, K. of L., city of Syracuse, N.Y., 1886. [Syracuse, N.Y.] F.L.Dillaye print., [1886?]
9 p. 14 cm.

1. Shoemakers - Syracuse, N.Y.

NK 0203724 WHi

HFA6Z .P851L N489 Knights of Labor. Local Assembly no. 3038, New York.
By-laws of the Gotham Association (Knife Cutters) of New York and Vicinity. New York, Concord Co-operative print., 1887.
7 p. 12½ cm.

Cover title.

1. Clothing workers - New York (city)

NK 0203725 WHi

HFA6Z .P851L N489 Knights of Labor. Local Assembly no. 3420. New York (city).
By-laws...adopted July 23, 1887. New York, Concord co-operative print., 1887.
16 p. 12cm.

NK 0203726 WHi

Knights of Labor. Local Assembly no. 3540, Chicago, Ill. 331.06146 50
By-laws of the Barrel Makers Local Assembly No. 3540, Knights of Labor, of Chicago, Illinois. Chicago, W. C. Hollister & Bro., printers, 1887.
10, [2] p. 17cm.

NK 0203727 ICJ

Knights of Labor. Local Assembly no. 3570 [Chicago, Ill.] 331.06146 75
By-laws of the Mattress Tick Sewers' L. A. 3570, Knights of Labor. Chicago, W. C. Hollister & Bro., [189-?].
4 p. 17cm.

NK 0203728 ICJ

HFA6Z .P844L L993 Knights of Labor. Local Assembly no. 3662, Lynn, Mass.
Official manual and reference book of the Boot and Shoe Cutters, L.A. 3662, K. of L. Lynn, Mass., 1905.
64 p. ports., illus. 20 cm.

p. 39-48: History of the shoe industry in Lynn, Mass.
p. 49-62: Brief history of the Assembly.

1. Shoemakers - Lynn, Mass. 2. Lynn, Mass. - History.

NK 0203729 WHi

HFA6Z .P892L C599 Knights of Labor. Local Assembly no. 5406, Cleveland, Ohio.
By-laws of the Cleveland Rulers' Union no. 5406 of Cleveland, Ohio; organized April 26, 1891. [Cleveland] Forest City Printing House [1891?]
12 p. 14½ cm.
Cover title.

1. Paper ruling - Cleveland - Societies, etc.

NK 0203730 WHi

HFA6Z .P851L N489 Knights of Labor. Local Assembly no. 5732, New York (city).
By-laws. New York, Concord Co-operative print., 1887.
14 p. 13½cm.

NK 0203731 WHi

Knights of labor. Local Assembly no. 5848, Cincinnati.
Bill of wages adopted by Hannah Powderly assembly...1886. Cincinnati, 1886.
22 p. 20 cm.

---By-Laws... 1886.

NK 0203732 DL

HFA6Z .P892L C49 Knights of Labor. Local Assembly no. 5848, Cincinnati.
By-laws of Hannah Powderly Assembly 5848, K. of L. Cincinnati, G.E. Bryan print., 1887.
14 p. 13cm.

Title page mutilated.

NK 0203733 WHi

Knights of Labor. Local assembly no. 6392, Chicago, Ill.
By-laws of the Paper Hangers' Local Assembly of Chicago, Illinois. Chicago, W. C. Hollister & Bro., printers, 1887.
cover-title, 4 p. 17cm.

NK 0203734 ICJ

Knights of Labor. Local Assembly no. 6578, Chicago, Ill. 331.06146 125
. . . By-laws of the Boot and Shoe Lasters' Assembly No. 6578, K. of L. of Chicago, Illinois. Chicago, W. C. Hollister & Bro., printers, 1888.
8 p. 17cm.

NK 0203735 ICJ

Knights of Labor. Local Assembly no. 6768, Chicago, Ill. 331.06146 130
By-laws and rules of order of Lakeside Assembly No. 6768, K. of L. of Chicago, Illinois. Chicago, W. C. Hollister & Bro., printers, 1887.
12 p. 17cm.

NK 0203736 ICJ

HFA6Z .P844L B783 Knights of Labor. Local Assembly no. 6927, Brockton, Mass.
By-laws of the Hand Sewers' Assembly, no. 6927, K. of L. ... 1887. [n.p., 1887?]
[4] p. 12½ cm.

Cover title.

1. Shoemakers - Brockton, Mass.

NK 0203737 WHi

Knights of Labor. *Local Assembly No. 6962.* Chicago, Ill. 331.06146 70
By-laws of Labor Assembly No. 6962, Knights of Labor. Chicago, W. C. Hollister & Bro., [189-?].
7 p. 17cm.

NK 0203738 ICJ

Knights of Labor. Local Assembly no. 7173, Chicago, Ill. 331.06146 45
By-laws and rules of order of the Brushmakers' Local Assembly No. 7173, Knights of Labor, of Chicago, Illinois. Chicago, W. C. Hollister & Bro., printers, 1887.
12 p. 17cm.
P. 3-4, 9-10 duplicated; p. 5-8 wanting.

NK 0203739 ICJ

F869 S3P18 v.1:21 x Knights of Labor. Local Assembly No. 7338.
An appeal for justice. Why the requests of car drivers on the Sutter and Geary St. lines are just ... San Francisco, 1886.
broadside 30x14cm. [Pamphlets on San Francisco. v. 1, no. 21]

Dated: San Francisco, December, 1886.

1. Sutter and Geary Street Railway Company Carmen's Strike, 1886-1887. 2. San Francisco - Carmen's Strike, 1886-1887. I. Title. [Series]

NK 0203740 CU-B

F869 S3P18 v.1:19 x Knights of Labor. Local Assembly No. 7338.
The Carmen's line. To the travelling public of San Francisco. Locked-out Carmen have started a bus line on Post Street ... [San Francisco, 1886?]
broadside 21x14cm. [Pamphlets on San Francisco. v. 1, no. 19]

Signed: Locked-out Carmen of Sutter and Geary St. Roads.

1. Sutter and Geary Street Railway Company Carmen's Strike, 1886-1887. 2. San Francisco - Carmen's Strike, 1886-1887. 3. Motor bus lines - San Francisco. I. Title. [Series]

NK 0203741 CU-B

VOLUME 300

F869
S3P18
v.1:22
x
Knights of Labor. Local Assembly No. 7338.
Read and consider! To the public in general and to the street car travelers in particular. [San Francisco] "Weekly Star" Print [1887]
broadside 21x14cm. [Pamphlets on San Francisco. v.1, no. 22]

1. Sutter and Geary Street Railway Company Carmen's Strike, 1886-1887. 2. San Francisco - Carmen's Strike, 1886-1887. I. Title. [Series]

NK 0203742 CU-B

F869
S3P18
v.1:20
x
Knights of Labor. Local Assembly No. 7338.
That dynamite plot! The real facts ... [San Francisco? 1887?]
broadside 21x14cm. [Pamphlets on San Francisco. v.1, no. 20]

1. Sutter and Geary Street Railway Company Carmen's Strike, 1886-1887. 2. San Francisco - Carmen's Strike, 1886-1887. I. Title. [Series]

NK 0203743 CU-B

F869
S3P18
v.1:23
x
Knights of Labor. Local Assembly No. 7338.
The truth! McCord's reply to the citizens ... [San Francisco? 1887]
broadside 21x14cm. [Pamphlets on San Francisco. v.1, no. 23]

1. Sutter and Geary Street Railway Company Carmen's Strike, 1886-1887. 2. San Francisco - Carmen's Strike, 1886-1887. 3. McCord, James. I. Title. [Series]

NK 0203744 CU-B

Knights of Labor. Local Assembly no. 7527, Chicago, Ill. 331.06146 90
By-laws for the government of Phoenix Local Assembly No. 7527, K. of L. of Chicago, Illinois. Adopted February 6th, 1888. Chicago, W. C. Hollister & Bro., printers, 1888.
cover-title, 16 p. 17cm.

NK 0203745 ICJ

Knights of Labor. Local Assembly no. 7744, Chicago, Ill.
By-laws of the Trunk Factory Employes Assembly, No. 7744 of the Noble Order of the Knights of Labor of America. Chicago, Illinois. Chicago, W. C. Hollister & Bro., 1887.
10 p. 17cm.

NK 0203746 ICJ

Knights of Labor. Local Assembly no 8650, Chicago, Ill. 331.06146 55
By-laws of the Fort Dearborn Carriage Makers' Assembly No. 8650, Knights of Labor, of Chicago, Illinois. Chicago, W. C. Hollister & Bro., 1887.
8 p. 17cm.

NK 0203747 ICJ

Knights of Labor. Local Assembly no. 9083, Chicago, Ill.
By-laws of the Upholsterers' Assembly No. 9083. Founded October 22, 1877. Chicago, W. C. Hollister & Bro., [189-?].
8 p. 17cm.

NK 0203748 ICJ

HFA6Z
.P851L
N489
Knights of Labor. Local Assembly no. 8742, [New York (city)?]
By-laws of the Magnolia Association, L.A. 8742, K. of L. New York, Concord Co-operative print., 1888.
8 p. 13cm.

NK 0203749 WHi

HFA6Z
.P851L
R586
Knights of Labor. Local Assembly no. 9722, [Rochester, N.Y.?]
By-laws of the Lasters' Protective Assembly no. 9722, K. of L. Rochester, N.Y., E. Saxton print., 1887.

Cover title.

1. Shoemakers - Rochester, N.Y.

NK 0203750 WHi

Knights of Labor. Local Assembly, no. 9880. 1.06146 110
By-laws of the Iron Belt Local Assembly, No. 9880, K. of L. of Roseland, Illinois. Chicago, W. C. Hollister & Bro., printers, 1887.
10 p. 17cm.

NK 0203751 ICJ

HFA6Z
.P851L
B791
Knights of Labor. Local Assembly no. 9887, Brooklyn, N.Y.
By-laws of the Brighton Association, Knights of Labor...1888. New York, Concord Co-operative print., 1888.
12 p. 13½cm.

NK 0203752 WHi

Knights of Labor. Local Assembly no. 10,108, Chicago, Ill.
By-laws of the Ship Carpenters and Caulkers' L. A. 10,108, K. of L. of Chicago. Chicago, W. C. Hollister & Bro., printers, 1888.
8 p. 17cm.

NK 0203753 ICJ

HFA6Z
.P851L
N489
Knights of Labor. Local Assembly no. 10558, New York (city)
Constitution and by-laws of Progressive Pavers' Union no. 1 of New York. Rev. and amended. New York, Solidarity press, [n.d.]
14 p. 14½cm.

1. Pavers - New York (city)

NK 0203754 WHi

Knights of Labor. Local Assembly no. 10984, Chicago, Ill. 331.06146 120
By-laws and order of business of Bolt Workers' Assembly No. 10984, K. of L. of Chicago, Illinois. Chicago, W. C. Hollister & Bro., printers, 1888.
12 p. 17cm.

NK 0203755 ICJ

Knights of labor. Massachusetts. State assembly.

Eastman, Hiram W K.
The science of government. A true assay of the crude ore of political economy, by H. W. K. Eastman. Printed by order of the Massachusetts state assembly of the Knights of labor ... Lawrence, Mass., H. W. K. Eastman, °1888.

Knights of Labor. National Assembly of Boot and Shoe Cutters.
Proceedings...
[no.] 1
Washington, 1907- 8°.
nos.

1. Trades unions, Boot and shoe workers—U. S.
N. Y. P. L. April 8, 1929

NK 0203757 NN

HFA62
.G463
P
Knights of Labor. National trade assembly no. 8 (Glass Workers)
Proceedings of Window Glass Snappers National District Assembly no. 8 held at Muncie, Indiana, April 21, 22, 23, 1902.
30 p. 19 cm.

Part of a series?

1. Glass workers - U.S. - Societies, etc.

NK 0203758 WHi

HFA62
.C227
R
Knights of Labor. National trade assembly no. 126 (Carpet workers)
Report of the...regular convention. [New York] 1886.
16 p. 20cm.

Cover title.

1. Textile workers - U S.

NK 0203759 WHi

HFA62
.M184
C
Knights of Labor. National trade assembly no. 198 (Machinists)
Constitution of National Trade Assembly 198, Knights of Labor (Machinery Constructors' Association of North America)...adopted at Pittsburg, Pa., June 6-10, 1887. New York, Concord Co-operative print., 1887.
32 p. 14½ cm.

1. Machinists - U.S. - Societies, etc.

NK 0203760 WHi DL

HFA62
.B65
C
Knights of Labor. National Trade Assembly no. 230 (Bookbinders)
Constitution. 18
New York [etc.]
v. 14 cm.

1. Bookbinders - U.S. - Societies, etc.

NK 0203761 WHi

HFA62
.M564
C
Knights of Labor. National trade assembly no. 252 (Metal-workers)
Constitution. New York, 18
v. 15cm.

NK 0203762 WHi

HFA62
.G463
C
Knights of Labor. National trade assembly no. 300 (Glass workers)
By-laws of Window Glass Workers' Assembly, no. 300, K. of L. Pittsburgh, R.V. Barker print., 1886.
32 p. 15 cm.

1. Glass workers - U.S. - Societies, etc.

NK 0203763 WHi

VOLUME 300

Film Reproduction
KNIGHTS OF LABOR. National trade assembly no 300 (Glass workers)
By-laws; revised in seventh National convention, Pittsburgh, Pa., July 8 to 20, 1895. Pittsburgh, Herald print co., 1895. 38 p. 15cm.

Film reproduction. Negative.

1. Trade unions, Glass workers'--U.S.

NK 0203764 NN

HFA6Z .P851L N489 Knights of Labor. New York (city)
By-laws of the Vulcan protective association. New York, Concord co-operative print., 1887.
8 p. 12½cm.

NK 0203765 WHi

HFA6Z +P851 Knights of Labor. New York (state).
Address of the Congress of the Knights of Labor of the State of New York to the sovereign electors. [n.p., 1896]
[10] p. 29cm.

Cover title.
Refers to railway management in New York.

1. Railroads - New York (state)

NK 0203766 WHi

HFA6Z +P851 P Knights of Labor. New York (state).
Proceedings. [New York?] 18 -19
v. 29cm.

NK 0203767 WHi

HFA6Z +P851 Knights of Labor. New York (state). Legislative committee.
Report...1899. [n.p., 1899?]
[15] p. 28cm.

Caption title.

NK 0203768 WHi

HFA6Z .P902 Knights of Labor. Wisconsin.
Record of the proceedings of the... annual session. [n.p.] 1886-
v. 22cm.

NK 0203769 WHi

Knights of labor and protective association. R.I. district assembly, 99
see Independent Knights of Labor. District Assembly, no. 99, Rhode Island.

Knights of Labor Building Association, *Minneapolis.* 331.06146 105
Articles of incorporation and by-laws of the K. of L. Building Association, Minneapolis, Minn. Organized July 1st, 1886. .... Minneapolis, T. A. Clark & Co., 1886.
cover-title, 15 p. 17cm.

NK 0203771 ICJ WHi

HFA6Z .P911L M665 Knights of Labor Building Association, Minneapolis
The Labor Temple now in course of erection ...Minneapolis, Minn., the first structure of its kind in the history of the world. History and description of the building, articles of incorporation, by-laws, etc., of the Association. 1st. ed. Minneapolis, T.A. Clark, 1887.
52 p. illus. 22cm.

Includes advertising.

1. Minneapolis - Buildings.

NK 0203772 WHi

Knights of labor-co-operative boot and shoe association. Worcester, Mass.
By-laws... Worcester, 1887.
cover-title, 8 p. 19½ cm.

NK 0203773 DL

Knights of Labor Co-operative Manufacturing Tailoring Company, Chicago.
By-laws of the Knights of Labor Co-operative Manufacturing Tailoring Co. .... Chicago, W. C. Hollister & Bro., printers, 1887.
10, [2] p. 17cm.
2 blank pages for "Memoranda".

NK 0203774 ICJ

HFA6Z .P892L C49 Knights of Labor Hall Company, Cincinnati.
Articles of incorporation and constitution. Cincinnati, G.E. Bryan print., 1887.
15 p. 13cm.

I. Knights of Labor. Cincinnati.

NK 0203775 WHi

Knights of Labor illustrated
see under [Cook, Ezra Asher] 1841-1911, comp.

Knights of Labor, Independent Order
see Independent Order of Knights of Labor.

Knights of Labor Joint-stock Co-operative Cigar Co., Chicago. 331.06146 100
By-laws of the Knights of Labor Joint-stock Co-operative Cigar Co. of Chicago, Illinois. Adopted November 24, 1882. Revised January 2, 1888. Chicago, W. C. Hollister & Bro., printers, 1888.
5 p. 17cm.

NK 0203778 ICJ

Knights of Labor of America
see
Knights of Labor.

Knights of Labor of North America
see Knights of Labor.

Knights of liberty
see also
International order of twelve of knights and daughters of Tabor.

The "Knights of Liberty" mob and the I. W. W. prisoners at Tulsa, Okla.
see under American Civil Liberties Union.

Knights of Malta.
Aggiunte e varianti al ruolo generale, 1932 al 20 ottobre 1934. Roma, 1934.
42 p.

NK 0203783 DCU

CR 4715 .A61 Knights of Malta.
Annales de l'Ordre Souverain Militaire de Malte. Année 1.-
1937-1952; 1958-
Rome.
v. illus. 31 cm. quarterly.

NK 0203784 DCU NN

Knights of Malta.
Arrestz notables rendvs par les covrs sovveraines de France. En favevr de l'ordre s. Iean de Hiervsalem svr differentes matieres. Recueillis par le sieur chcuallier Desclozeaux, agent du l'ordre en France... Paris, Chez Remy Sovbret, 1649.
CR 4717 .A 3 1649 C 2 v. in 1. 22½cm. [With its Privilleges des papes, emperevrs, roys et princes de la crestienté en favevr de l ordre sr. Iean de Hiervsalem. 2. ed. Paris, 1649]

Engraved t.-p. initials; head and tail pieces.

NK 0203785 MdBJ

Knights of Malta.
The begynnynge and foundacyon of the holy hospytall of the ordre of the knyghtes hospytallers...
see under title

Knights of Malta.
[Zondadari, Marco Antonio] 1658-1722.
Breve e particolare istruzione del sacro ordine militare degli Ospitalari, detto oggidì volgarmente di Malta, e della diversa qualità di persone, e di gradi che lo compongono. Stesa da un cavalier professo della medesima religione. Edizione seconda, arricchita della parafrasi al Salmo XLI., composta dallo stesso autore. Padova, Nella stamperia di Giuseppe Comino. Per Giovanni Baldano, CIƆIƆCCXXIV.

Knights of Malta.
Cartulaire général de l'Ordre des hospitaliers de S. Jean de Jérusalem (1100-1310) [Édité] par J. Delaville Le Roulx. Paris, E. Leroux, 1894-1906.
4 v. 45 cm.

CONTENTS.—t. 1. 1100-1200.—t. 2. 1201-1260.—t. 3. 1261-1300.—t. 4. 1301-1310. Supplément. Additions, notes et corrections. Table générale.

I. Delaville Le Roulx, Joseph Marie Antoine, 1855-1911, ed.

CR4715.A3 52-57158

MiU OCU DDO MoU NN MH IU PU
NK 0203788 DLC CLU MB NNU-W OCU ICN NcD ICU CtY PU

VOLUME 300

Knights of Malta. Cartulaire général.

DC801
.C685 O 8

Ourliac, Paul.
Les sauvetés du Comminges; étude et documents sur les villages fondés par les hospitaliers dans la région des côteaux commingeois. Toulouse, Impr. F. Boisseau, 1947.

Knights of Malta. Charters.

Templaria. Papers relative to the history, privileges and possessions of the Scotish Knights templar, and their successors the Knights of Saint John of Jerusalem. ⌈Edinburgh, Stevenson⌉ 1828–⌈29⌉

CR
4717 Knights of Malta.
.A4 Codice del Sacro militare ordine gerosolimitano, riordinato per comandamento del Sacro generale capitolo celebrato nell'anno MDCCLXXVI.
1782 Sotto gli auspici di Sua Altezza Eminentissima il gran maestro fra Emanuele de Rohan. In Malta, Nella Stamperia del Palazzo di S.A.E., per fra G.Mallia, 1782.
xxiv,505,⌈1⌉,128 p. port. 35 cm.
"Privilegi della Sagra religione di san Giovanni gerosolimitano, con un indice volgare" (128 p.at end) has special t.p., dated 1777.
Inscribed presentation copy to George Hastings 7th Earl of Granard, from John Cashel Hoev.

--Compendio delle materie contenute nel Codice del Sacro militare ordine gerosolimitano. In Malta, Nella Stamperia del Palazzo di S.A.E., per fra G.Mallia, 1783.
ix,162 p. 37 cm.
Compiled by Gaetano Bruno. cf.Hellwald, F.de, Bibliographie méthodique de l'Ordre souv.de St.Jean de Jérusalem, p.219-220.

I.Bruno, Gaetano.

NK 0203792 MiU DCU MH PU ICN

Knights of Malta.
Codice diplomatico del Sacro militare ordine gerosolimitano oggi di Malta, ...
see under Pauli, Sebastiano, 1689-1751.

Greenlee
6A Knights of Malta.
19 Collecção geral dos antigos, e modernos privilegios concedidos successivamente a Sagrada, e Militar Ordem de S. João do Hospital de Jerusalem, e confirmados pelos Senhores Reis de Portugal athe el-Rei Nosso Senhor D. Miguel I.º por alvará de 12 de Novembre de 1830. Lisboa, Na Regia Typografia Silviana, 1832.
⌈1⌉ℓ.,30,40p. 31cm.

In 2 pts., separately paged, each with special t.-p.: ⌈1⌉ Privilegios, concedidos, e confirmados por el-Rei D. João V. á Ordem, e Milicia da Sagrada Religião de S. João do Hospital de Jerusalem de Malta em 3 de Dezembro de 1728 ... Lisboa ... 1814. ⌈2⌉ Sanctissimi in Christi Patris et Domini Nostri Domini Benedicti ... Papae XIV. litterae

apostolicae super confirmatione, & innovatione privilegiorum, gratiarum, & jurium militarium, & Hospitalis Ordinis Sancti Joannis Jerosolymitani ...

NK 0203796 ICN

Knights of Malta.
Compendio alfabetico de Statvti della sacra religione Gerosolimitana per facilità alla ricognitione de medemi
see under Garavita.

Wing
fZP Knights of Malta.
7275 Compendio delle materie contenute nel Codice
.M 254 del Sacro militare ordine Gerosolimitano. Malta, Nella Stamperia del palazzo S.A.E. per G. Mallia, 1783.
ix 162p. 35cm. (with its Codice ... 1782)

35 ms. pages added at end, containing the beginning of the first part of some "Ordinazioni" (1688-1759)

NK 0203799 CtY-L ICN

KNIGHTS OF MALTA.
...Deux lettres escrites aux Estats Generaux des provinces-vnies des Païs-Bas, par le Grand Maistre de Malthe sur la restitution que cet ordre leur demande, des biens qui lui appartiennent dans lesdites provinces. [Lyon, Chez Iacqves Ollier, ce 4 fevrier 1661] p. 85-96. 23cm.(4°.) (IN: Gazette. Lyon. 1661. N. 12)

Caption title and colophon.

At head of title: Extraordinaire dv XXVII. ianvier M.DC.LXI.
Letters signed: Le Grand Maistre, Lascaris.
Second letter dated: De Malthe, le 15 septembre 1660.

Ford Collection

1. Netherlands (United Provinces, 1581-1795). Staten generaal.

NK 0203801 NN

CR
4715 Knights of Malta.
.I69 The early statutes of the Knights Hospi-
n.5 tallers; being a translation into English, together with an introduction and notes, by Colonel E. J. King. [London] Printed for private circulation, 1932.
25p. 25 cm. (Library Committee, Order of St. John of Jerusalem. Historical pamphlets, n. 5)

Contents.—Statutes of Fr. Jobert, 1172-1177.—Statutes of Fr. Roger des Moulins, 1177-1187.— Statutes of Fr. Alfonso of

Portugal, 1203-1206.—From the "Judgments and customs of the Hospital."

I. King, Edwin James, 1877- ed. & tr.

NK 0203803 DCU

Knights of Malta.
L'église militante et triomphante en l'Ordre de Malte
see under title

Knights of Malta.
[El exceso en lutos, entierros, exequios funerales, y toques de campanas. Lima, 1795].

f°.pp.12.
Ordered by Francisco Gil de Taboada y Lemos y Villamarin. SA 20.3 (vol. 7)

NK 0203805 MH

Knights of Malta.
Exordium Hospitalariorum.
(In Recueil des historiens des Croisades. Historiens occidentaux. T. 5, partie 2, pp. (1), 399-435. Paris, 1895.)

NK 0203806 MB

Knights of Malta.
Inc [Begins, c3r:] Le fondement du saint hospital
8316.5 & de lordre de la cheualerie des hospitaliers de saint iehan baptiste de iherusalē.
[Paris, Pierre Le Dru?, ca.1495]

f°. [250]p. 28cm.
Reichling 1437=Copinger 1438; Pellechet 3221; Proctor 8819 (France, unknown places); BMC VIII.193; Goff C-115.
Signatures: a-p^8,q^6 (q6 blank).
Leaf a1r begins "Exordium in volumen

stabilimēto[rum] Rhodiorū militū sacri ordinis hospitalis sācti iohānis iherosolimitani", a letter of Pierre d'Aubusson regarding the French translation by Guillaume Caoursin; this is followed (a1v-c2v) by a bull of Innocent VIII, a letter of Aubusson in French, and a table of the chapters.

Ornamental capitals (from an alphabet used by Jean Tréperel); leaf a1r has ornamental borders and, at foot, a cut of Aubusson's arms.
"Proctor ... thought that this book might be assignable to Provins, the type being very like that used there by Tavernier. But all the material is Parisian and such a text is much more likely to have been printed in the capital.

The letters P L at end may well stand for Pierre Ledru, but this cannot be considered certain."--BMC.
Full 18th-century French calf; unidentified English arms stamped on covers, probably in the 19th century; autographed in lower margin of leaf a1r: Stephanus Baluzius Tutelensis.
Blank leaf q6 not present.

NK 0203810 MH

Knights of Malta.

Xavier Monteiro, Antonio José, *d.* 1820, *comp.*
Formulario de oraçoens, e ceremonias para se armarem cavalleiros, e se lançarem os habitos das ordens, e milicias de Nosso Senhor Jesus Christo, S. Tiago da Espada, S. Bento de Aviz, S. Joaõ de Malta. Dado a' luz por Antonio Joze Xavier Monteiro ... Porto, Na Officina de J. Agathon, 1798.

Knights of Malta.

Rossi, Ettore.
Historical resume of the Order of Malta made under the direction of Ettore Rossi. Translated from the Italian by James J. Walsh ... Rome, Official publication of the grand master, 1932.

Knights of Malta.
Insignes et uniformes de l'Ordre Souverain des Hospitaliers de Saint-Jean de Jerusalem... Paris, 1927
see under Pierredon, Marie Henri Thierry Michel de, comte.

CR
4727 Knights of Malta.
.K72 Istituto per lo studio e la cura della lebbra nell'Africa orientale italiana. Roma, Palazzo magistrale del S.M.O. di Malta, 1937.
35 p. illus., 2 fold. plans 35 cm.

1. Leprosy- Italian East Africa. 2. Knights of Malta - Hospitals, charities, etc.

NK 0203814 DCU

VOLUME 300

Knights of Malta.
Istruzioni sopra gli obblighi piu' principali de' Cavalieri d Malta; opera d'uno di essi [Gio. Battista Alessandri] della veneranda lingua di Francia tradotta in lingua italiana. Malta, N. Capaci, 1758.
sm. 4°. pp. (12), jx, (3), 149 +. Front. and vigns.

NK 0203815 MH

Knights of Malta.
Lezioni su gli statuti del Sagr' Ordine Gerosolimitano nell' Università degli studj di Malta per l'anno 1792
see under Valetta, Malta. Royal University.

CR4731 P8A6 **Knights of Malta.**
Livro dos forais, escripturas, doações, privilegios e inquirições. Prefacio de José Mendes da Cunha Saraiva. Lisboa, Arquivo Histórico do Ministério das Finanças, 1946- v. (Subsidios para a historia da Ordem de Malta. 2-

NK 0203817 CU

Knights of Malta.
Memoria dirigida às altas potencias alliadas pelos plenipotenciarios da Ordem de S. João de Jerusalem no Congresso Geral de Vienna d'Austria. Lisboa, A. Rodrigues Galhardo, 1815.
19 p. 21 cm.
Text in French, with title: Mémoire présenté par les ministres plénipotentiaires de l'Ordre souverain de St. Jean de Jérusalem au Congrès général à Vienne.
I. Title. II. Title: Mémoire présenté par les ministres plénipotentiaires de l'Ordre souverain de St. Jean de Jérusalem.
CR4725.A5 1815 50-40963

NK 0203818 DLC ICN

Knights of Malta.
Ordinationi del capitolo generale celebrato nell' anno 1631 dal frà Antonio de Paola. Borgo Nuovo, Rocca Forte, il Stampator camer°. 1674.
f°. pp. (2), 180 +. Port. of Nicholaus Cotoner.
The title is within engraved border.

NK 0203819 MH

Knights of Malta.
L'origine della Sacra et Eminentissima Religione Gerosolimitana, con la serie de' suoi gran maestri e di Rodi, e di Malta, e delle imprese più segnalate de' suoi cavalieri
see under Fontana, Aldigherio.

CR 4717.2 .A2 1496 Knights of Malta.
Privilegia Ordinis Domus Hospitalis Hierosolymitani S. Johannis. [Ulm? 1496?]
41 leaves 29 cm.
No title page, no colophon.
Hellwald, p. 225: "Mr. Delaville Le Roulx suppose que ce recueil est sorti vers 1496 des presses de Jean Reger de Kemnat a Ulm."
An inserted dealer's note gives imprint: Strassburg or Cologne? after 1495.

NK 0203821 DCU

Knights of Malta.
Privilegi della sacra religione di san Giovanni Gerosolimitano, con un indice volgare. In Malta, nella Stamperia del Palazzo di S.A. S. presso Fra Giovanni Mallia suo Stampatore, 1777.
128 p. 35 cm.

I. Catholic Church. Pope. II. Title.

NK 0203822 DLC ICN PU

Knights of Malta.
Li privilegii della sacra religione di S. Gio. Gierosolimitano. Con vn'indice volgare copiosissimo, aggiunto da Iacomo Bosio per maggior commodità de i caualieri... In Roma, appresso Giacomo Tornieri, 1589.
96, [24] p. 21 1/2 cm.
Signatures: A-P4
Title vignette (ecclesiastical arms); initials.
Page 41 partly supplied in manuscript.
In Latin and Italian.

NK 0203823 CtY-L

Knights of Malta.
Privilegii della Sacra Religione di San Gio. Gerosolimitano. Borgo Nuovo, Rocca Forte, il Stampatore camerale, 1674.
f°. pp. (2), 100 +.
Colophon: "1675."
The title is within engraved border.

NK 0203824 MH

4504 P855 Greenlee Knights of Malta.
Privilegios concedidos e confirmados por elrey d. João V...á Ordem a Milicia da Sagrada Religiam de S. João do Hospital de Jerusalem de Malta em 3. de dezembro de 1728... Lisboa Occidental, T. Antunes Lima, 1737.
[20], 31p. 20cm.

NK 0203825 ICN

4552 M26 M26 1764 Greenlee Knights of Malta.
Privilegios concedidos, e confirmados por elrei D. João o V...a'Ordem, e Milicia da Sagrada Religião de S. João do Hospital de Jerusalem de Malta em 3. de dezembro de 1728... Lisboa, M. Manescal da Costa, 1764.
[8], 48p. 21cm.
Two leaves bound in at back contain further confirmation of the privileges; dated 1778, and signed: Rainha [Maria I]

NK 0203826 ICN CtY

Knights of Malta.
Privilegios concedidos e confirmados por el Rei D. João o V... a' Ordem e Milicia da Sagrada Religião de S. João do Hospital de Jerusalem de Malta em 3 de Dezembro de 1728. Lisboa, na regia typog. Silviana, 1814.

NK 0203827 MH

CR 4717 .A 3 1649 C Knights of Malta.
Privilleges des papes, emperevrs, roys et princes de la crestienté en favevr de l'ordre s. Iean de Hiervsalem. Recueillis par le s^r. cheuallier des Clozeaulx, agent dudict ordre en France. 2. ed. Paris, Chez Remy Sovbret, 1649.
4 p.l., 245 p., 2 l. 22½cm.
Engraved t.-p.; initials; head and tail pieces.
With this is bound as issued its Arrestz notables rendvs par les covrs sovverainos de France ... Paris, 1649.

NK 0203828 MdBJ

Knights of Malta.

Hume, Edgar Erskine, 1889-
A proposed treaty of alliance between the Sovereign order of Malta and the United States of America, 1794, by Edgar Erskine Hume ... [Williamsburg? Va., 1936]

Knights of Malta.
RAGGUAGLIO dell'impresa fatta dalle galere, e galeoni della Sacra Religione Ierosolimitana. Per ordine dell'illustriss. gran maestro delle due fortezze di Lepanto nella Morea, alli 20 d'aprile 1603. Pavia, 1603.
ff(8).

NK 0203830 MH

DC 141 F87+ v.499 **Knights of Malta.**
Réclamation de l'Ordre de S.-Jean de Jérusalem à l'effet d'obtenir la restitution de ses biens qui n'ont pas été vendus, adressée à la Chambre des députés des départemens. Paris, Egron, 1816.
29 p. 22cm.
Signed: Bailli de Lasteyrie du Saillant [et al.]

NK 0203831 NIC

DC 141 F87+ v.499 **Knights of Malta.**
Réclamation de l'Ordre souverain de S. Jean de Jerusalem adressée au roi de France et aux deux chambres dans l'intérêt général de l'ordre. Paris, Le Normant, 1815.
15 p. 22cm.
Signed: Prince Camille de Rohan [et al.]

NK 0203832 NIC

Knights of Malta. Crus 720.11
Réclamation de l'Ordre Souverain de St.-Jean-de-Jérusalem. Adressée au roi de France et aux deux chambres dans l'intérêt général de l'ordre et dans l'intérêt particulier des trois langues françaises. n.p., 1817.
pp. (4), 29. Large paper.

NK 0203833 MH

Knights of Malta. Crus 728.11
Réclamation de l'Ordre Souverain de Saint Jean de Jérusalem au congrès d'Aix-la-Chapelle. [Paris], A. Égron, 1818.
pp. 12.

NK 0203834 MH

Knights of Malta.
[Regla de los Cavalleros Ospitaleros del Horden de San Juan Batista del Hospital de Jerusalem.] 151 pp., 8l. *n.p.n.d.* f°.
The above is a manuscript and the title is written in pencil on the front leave.

NK 0203835 NN

Knights of Malta.
Regolamento dell' Ospedale del Sovrano Militare Ordine di Malta, per fanciulli. Milano, L. F. Cogliati, 1886.

NK 0203836 DNLM

VOLUME 300

Knights of Malta

16th Cent. The regulation of the old hospital of the Knights of St. John at Valetta, from a copy printed at Rome, and preserved in the archives of Malta. With a translation, introduction, and notes explanatory of the hospital work of the order, by the Rev. W. K. R. Bedford ... Edinburgh and London, William Blackwood and sons, 1882.
xiip., 1l., 59p. front., plans, fold. tables. 26cm.
A reprinting of the order's Notizia della sacra Infermeria, e della Carica delli commissari delle povere inferme, Rome, R. Bernabo, 1725, with special t.-p. in facsimile.
Italian and English on opposite pages.
Includes a chapter on the order in England.

1. Malta, Knights of, in England. I. Bedford, William Kirkpatrick Riland, 1826-1905, ed. & tr. II. Title.

NK 0203838 CtY-M MnU

CR 4727 .K71 Knights of Malta.
[Religi. Hioros.]

[150] l. 20 cm.
Binder's title.
Incipit p. [2]: Dignità dollo gran priori o priorati doll'otto linguo dolla Roligion Hyerosollimitana.
Manuscript, early 17th cent., written in Italian, containing information on dignities, finances, arms and navy of the Knights of Malta.

NK 0203839 DCU

Knights of Malta.
The rule statutes and customs of the Hospitallers, 1099–1310; with introductory chapters and notes by Colonel E. J. King ... London, Methuen & co., ltd. [1934]
3 p. l., [ix]–xv, 224 p. front. (facsim.) plates, maps, plans. 23 cm.
"The original Latin and old French versions ... were first published in 1894 in Delaville Le Roulx's Cartulaire-général des Hospitaliers."—p. ix.

1. Knights of Malta. I. King, Edwin James, 1877– ed. and tr. II. Title.
CR4717.A3 929.711 34–32701 rev
[r53d⅔]

NK 0203840 DLC CtY OClW ICN ICU NN DDO DNLM TxU

CR 4719 .A2 1938 Knights of Malta.
Ruolo generale. Roma, Pubblicazione ufficiale del Gran Magistero, 1938.
200 p. front. (port.) 35 cm.
At head of title: Il Sovrano Militare Gerosolimitano di Malta.
"Supplemento al No 4 della Rivista mensile illustrata del Sovrano Militare Ordine di Malta.

I. Rivista illustrata del Sovrano Militare Ordine di Malta.

NK 0203841 DCU

Knights of Malta.
Ruolo generale ufficiale del gran magistero, 1949. Milano, Ciarrocca [1949]
383 p. illus. (part col.) ports. (part col.) maps. 25 cm.

Published also in English.

CR4719.K5 50–55401

NK 0203842 DLC NN

Knights of Malta **G.404.6
[Seal]
(In Rainaudo, Teofilo. Erotemata de malis ac bonis libris. Title-page. Lvgdvni, 1653.)

NK 0203843 MB

Knights of Malta.
Il Sovrano militare ordine gerosolimitano di Malta; la storia, l'organizzazione, le opere umanitarie, il ruolo generale dei cavalieri. Roma: Pubblicazione ufficiale del gran magistero, 1932 [i. e. 1933]. 588 p. maps, port. 24½cm.

NK 0203844 NN NNC MiD DCU CLU

N 929.711 qK71 Knights of Malta.
Statvta hospitalis Hiervsalem. [Rome, 1586-88]
203, [17] p. illus., plates, ports., maps. 33 cm.

Edited by J. B. Rondinellus. Index by Ptolemaeus Veltronius has special t.p., dated 1588.
Bound in vellum, gold tooled.
I. Rondinellus, Joannes Baptista, ed. II. Title.

NK 0203845 N MiU NN MH CtY CtY-M ICN DFo

Knights of Malta. Crus 680.1F
Statuta Ordinis Domus Hospitalis Hierusalem. [Didacus Rodriguez summa diligentia edi curavit. [*Colophon*: Romæ, apud A. Bladum, 1556.]
f°. ff. (3), 72. Wdct. and vigns.
The title is within wood-cut border. MS. marginal notes.

NK 0203846 MH

Knights of Malta. Crus 680.2
Statuta Ordinis Domus Hospitalis Hierusalem. [*Colophon*: Romæ, apud A. Bladum, 1556.]
24°. ff. (8), 205, (1). Vigns.

Print. spec.||AcS 26339

NK 0203847 MH NN DCU

Knights of Malta. Crus 680.4.5
Statuti della Religione de Cavalieri Gierosolimitani. Tradotti di latino in lingua toscana dal R. F. Paolo del Rosso cavalier' di detto ordine. Con la descrizione dell' Isola di Malta nuovamente stampati. Fiorenza, per li Ciunti, 1567.
pp. (16), 414 +.

Print. spec.||Rosso|AcS 26338

NK 0203848 MH IU

CR 4717 1570 Cage Knights of Malta.
Statuti della religione de' Caualieri Gierosolimitani. Tradotti di latino in lingua toscana dal R.F. Paolo del Rosso... Nuouamente ristampati. In Firenze, Nella Stamperia di Filippo Giunti, e fratelli, 1570.
Colophon.

[16] 486 [2] p. $*^8$, A-2G^8, 2H^4. 8vo.

NK 0203849 DFo

Knights of Malta.
Gli Statvti Della Sacra Religione Di S. Giovanni Gierosolimitano. Tradotti Di Latino In Volgare da Iacomo Bosio... Aggiuntoui li Priuilegij dell' istessa Religione... Il modo, e le cerimonie, che s'vsano nel creare i Caualieri... Roma: Appresso Giacomo Tornieri, 1589. 10 p.l., 280 p., 34 l., 96 p., 12 l. 23cm. (4°.)

Leaves 4 and 34 following p. 280 blank.
"La Confermatione De Gli Statvti. Sisto Papa Qvinto," l. 7, dated March 20, 1586.

"Li Privilegii Della Sacra Religione Di S. Gio. Gierosolimitano," 96 p., 12 l., has special t.-p., and colophon: In Roma, Appresso Iacomo Ruffinello, 1589.
With autograph of Gio: Batt[ist]a Baldovinj.
With portrait of Giovanni de' Valletta (signed: D[ome]n[ic]o. Zenoi) inserted.

630103. 1. No subject. I. Bosio, Giacomo, tr. II. Knights of Malta. Li Privilegii.
N. Y. P. L. *Card revised* April 16, 1943

NK 0203851 NN

Knights of Malta. Crus 680.9
Statuti della Sac. Religione di S. Gio. Gerosolimitano con le ordinationi dell' ultimo capitolo generale celebrato nell' anno 1631 dal fra Antonio de Paula. Aggiontivi li privilegij, il modo di dar la croce e di fare li miglioramenti alle commende. Di nuovo ristampati. Borgo Nuovo, Roccaforte, 1674.
f°. pp. (20), 244, (64), 10, 10. Port. of Nicolaus Cotoner.
Dedication dated "1675" is signed Frà Paolo Rafaele Spinola.
The title is within engraved border.
Each part has separate title-page and pagination.

NK 0203852 MH

CR4723 .B6 1643 Knights of Malta.
Les statvts de l'Ordre de Sainct Iean de Hiervsalem [et les ordonnances dv Chapitre Général, tenue en l'année M.DC.III par l'illustrissime & reuerendissime Grand-Maîstre Frère Alof de Vignacovrt. MDCXXIX. Paris, Iacques d'Allin] 1643.
331 p. port. 44 cm.

Half-titles.

Translated by I. Baudoin (or rather, by Pierre de Boissat the younger)--cf. Brit. Mus. Catalogue.
Imperfect: p. 75-76, 81-82 wanting; p. 77-80 duplicated. Errors in paging.
In Bosio, Giacomo, d. ca. 1629. Histoire des Chevaliers de l'Ordre de S. Iean de Hiervsalem. Dernière éd. Paris, 1643. [pt.2]

NK 0203854 RPB

Knights of Malta.
Summarium. Romae, 1810-12.
9 pts. in 1. Q.
Includes 36 mss. p.

NK 0203855 RPB

929.711D M295.4.EK Knights of Malta.
...The thirteenth-century statutes of the Knights Hospitallers. Being a translation into English, together with an introduction and notes. By Colonel E.J.King... St.John's Gate, London, Printed for private circulation, 1933.
40p. 25cm. (Order of St.John of Jerusalem. Library committee. Historical pamphlets: no.6)

Contents. -Introduction. -Statutes of Fr. Hugh Revel, 1258-1277. -Statutes of Fr.Nicholas Le Lorgne, 1277-1285. -Statutes of Fr.John de Villiers, 1285-1294. -Statutes of Fr.Odo des Pins, 1294-1296. -Appendix: On the priories of 1294.

NK 0203857 PU DCU

VOLUME 300

DG 403 C76 v.79 Knights of Malta.
Volvme che contiene gli statvti della sacra religione gerosolimitana; le ordinazioni dell'vltimo capitolo generale, che sono le sole, che sussistono; il nvovo cerimoniale prescritto dalla santità di n. sig. Papa Vrbano VIII. sopra l'elezione de' gran maestri; il modo, o sia instrvzione di far i processi de' miglioramenti delle commende, che serue ancora per i priorati, e baliaggi, e come deuono farsene li cabrei; l'ordine, che si tiene nel dar l'abito, a chi professa nella religione; e per ultimo i privilegi concessi da' sommi pontefici alla religione, e suoi dependenti. Borgo Novo, A. Scionico, 1719.
4 v. in 1. [Consilia/statuti collection, v. 79]

NK 0203859 CLU MH CtY-L DCU N

CD1707 .A7A5 Knights of Malta. Arnhem, Netherlands.
Netherlands (*Kingdom, 1815-*) *Rijksarchief in Gelderland, Arnhem.*
Het archief der Commanderij van St. Jan te Arnhem, door J. Loeff. 's-Gravenhage, Ministerie van Onderwijs, Kunsten en Wetenschappen, 1950.

Knights of Malta. Association francaise
see Knights of Malta. France.

Knights of Malta. Association of Master Knights of the Sovereign Military Order of Malta in the United States of America.
The Association of Master Knights of the Sovereign Military Order of Malta in the United States of America. [New York, 1933.] 44 p. 22cm.
CONTENTS.—Historical sketch of the Knights of Malta, by Doctor James J. Walsh.—Constitution and by-laws of the Association...promulgated as of November 7, 1932.

NK 0203862 NN DCU

CR 4731 .U5 A8 D5 Knights of Malta. Association of Master Knights of the Sovereign Military Order of Malta in the United States of America.
Dinner of the Association of Master Knights of the Sovereign Military Order of Malta in the United States of America ... The Waldorf-Astoria, New York City.
Library had 1933, 1934, 1936-55.

NK 0203863 DCU

CR 4729 .P53 A8 Knights of Malta. Association of Master Knights of the Sovereign Military Order of Malta in the United States of America.
In memoriam, James J. Phelan, K.M., Grand Cross member. [Minutes adopted at a meeting of the founder members of the Association of Master Knights of the Sovereign Military Order of Malta in the United States of America, May 29, 1935. [New York, 1935]
[8] p. 24 cm.
1. Phelan, James Joseph, 1871-1934.

NK 0203864 DCU

Knights of Malta. Associazione dei cavalieri italiani
see Knights of Malta. Italy.

Knights of Malta. Associazione italiana
see
Knights of Malta. Italy.

CR 4727 .A84 A2 1934 Knights of Malta. Associazione missionaria.
[Statuto della] Associazione missionaria del sovrano militare ordine di Malta. [Roma, 1934]
21 p. 22 cm.
1. Knights of Malta - Missions.

NK 0203867 DCU

Knights of Malta. Ballei Brandenburg
see also Ritterlicher Orden Sankt Johannis vom Spital zu Jerusalem, Brandenburg.

Knights of Malta. Belgium.
Dansaert, Georges, 1876-
Histoire de l'Ordre souverain et militaire de Saint-Jean de Jérusalem, dit de Rhodes ou de Malte, en Belgique, par G. Dansaert ... Préface de S. A. le prince Albert de Ligne ... Bruxelles et Paris, Librairie nationale d'art et d'histoire, 1932.

Knights of Malta. *England.*
The book of deliberations of the Venerable Tongue of England, 1523-1567. Ed. with an historical introd., index of names, glossary and notes, and 4 full-pages of the text reproduced in facsimile from the original ms. by Hannibal P. Scicluna. Malta, "Empire Press," 1949.
xxix, 98, [4] p. facsims. 26 cm.
"Errata-corrige": slips inserted.
Bibliography: 4 p. at end.
I. Scicluna, Hannibal Publius, 1880- ed. II. Title.
CR4731.G7A42 929.711 49-27733 rev*

NK 0203870 DLC DCU

KNIGHTS OF MALTA. England.
Historical pamphlets. no. [1]-2, 4-7
London, 1925-35. no. 25cm.

NK 0203871 NN

Knights of Malta. *England.*
... A Kentish cartulary of the Order of St. John of Jerusalem, by Charles Cotton ... [Canterbury] Kent archæological society [1930]
xxx, 188 p. plates, facsim. 22 cm. (*Added t.-p.:* Kent archæological society. Records branch. [Kent records] vol. XI)
Series note in part at head of title.
I. Cotton, Charles, 1856-1939, ed. II. Title.
CS435.K6 vol. 11 31-4228 rev
(929.094223) [333.3094223] 929.7110942

NK 0203872 DLC CSt IEG MiU PHC NIC WU

Knights of Malta. England.
The Knights Hospitallers in England
see under Philippus, de Thame, fl. 1338-

Knights of Malta. *England*
see also
Grand Priory in the British Realm of the Most Venerable Order of the Hospital of St. John of Jerusalem.
Joint Council of the Order of St. John and the British Red Cross Society.

Knights of Malta. Eterpigny (Commandery)
Le cartulaire de la Commanderie d'Eterpigny, analysé avec extraits textuels... Amiens, 1911
see under Menche de Loisne, Auguste Charles Henri, comte, 1853-

---

CR 4731 .F8 A8 A3 Knights of Malta. France.
Compte rendu de l'Assemblée générale de l'Association française des chevaliers de l'Ordre de Malte ... Poitiers, Imprimerie du Poitu.
v. 22 cm.

NK 0203876 DCU

CR 4731 .F8 A8 A2 1930 Knights of Malta. France.
Statuts de l'Association française des membres de l'Ordre souverain de Malte. Poitiers, Imprimerie Moderne, Nicolas, Renault & cie, 1930.
4 p. 22 cm.

NK 0203877 DCU

Knights of Malta. France. Velay
see Knights of Malta. Velay, France.

CR 4720 1934 F7 Knights of Malta. General Convention, Rome, 1934.
[Fotografie del Convegno dei Cavalieri del S. M. Ordine di Malta a Roma, marzo, 1934]
9 photos, 18 x 24 cm.
In folder.

NK 0203879 DCU

CR 4720 1934 A2 Knights of Malta. General convention, Rome, 1934.
Il Sovrano Militare Ordine Gerosolimitano di Malta: Il S.M. Ordine di Malta e Roma; Convegno dei cavalieri in Roma 14-20 marzo 1934; Associazione missionaria dell'Ordine. Roma, Collegio Araldico, 1934.
34 p. front. (port.) 25 cm.
Half title: Convegno dei Cavalieri di Malta.
Estratto dalla "Rivista araldica", marzo 1934.
1. Knights of Malta - Rome. 2. Knights of Malta. Associazione missionaria.

NK 0203880 DCU

230.2 B766c Knights of Malta. Gran Priorato de Castilla y León. Gran prior, 17 -17 (Gabriel Antonio)
Carta pastoral, dirigida a todos los subditos, y religiosas del sagrado, y militar orden de San Juan de Jerusalen. Barcelona, T.Piferrer, 1767.
32p. 29cm.
1.Catholic Church - Doctrinal and controversial works - Catholic authors. I.Title.

NK 0203881 CLSU

VOLUME 300

Knights of Malta. Gran Priorato de Castilla y León. Gran prior, 17 -17 (Gabriel Antonio)
Carta pastoral, dirigida a todos los subditos, y religiosas del sagrado, y militar Orden de San Juan de Jerusalén, por el serenisimo Señor D. Gabriél Antonio de Borbon, infante de España, y gran prior de Castilla; y en su real nombre el venerando baylio Fr. D. Luis Arias Davila, baron de Relleu, lugar-teniente de Su Alteza Real. Madrid: Por J. Ibarra, 1767. 1 p.l., lxvii p. 28½cm.

At head of title: arms of the Knights of Malta.
Dated: Madrid, y diciembre 9. de 1767 (the "9." supplied in ms.).
With paper seal "Gabriel. Hisp. Inf. Mag. Pr. Ord. Hierosol. in Reg. Cast. et Leg." affixed at end.

FORD COLLECTION.
1. Knights of Malta. I. Arias Dávila, Luis.
December 26, 1940

NK 0203883 NN

Knights of Malta. Gran Priorato de Lombardia. Gran prior, -17 (Garavita)
see Garavita.

CR 4715 B93 F8 folio
Knights of Malta. Grand Magistery.
Bulletin officiel du Grand Magistère de l'Ordre S. M. H. Malte. 1.- année. 19 - Rome.
v. illus. 32 cm. 6 nos. a year.

1. Knights of Malta - Period.

NK 0203885 DCU

CR 4715 .B93 E5 folio
Knights of Malta. Grand Magistery.
Official bulletin of the Grand Magistry of the S. M. Order of Malta. v. 1- 19 - Rome.
v. illus. 32 cm. quarterly.

1. Knights of Malta - Period.

NK 0203886 DCU

Knights of Malta. Grand Magistery.
The official general roll of the Grand Magistery, 1949. Milan, Ciarrocca edition [1949]
383 p. illus. 25 cm.
Historic summary of the Sovereign Military Order of St. John of Jerusalem and Malta by Giacomo Carlo Bascapè: p. [15]-71.

NK 0203887 OCl

Special Collection CR 4718 .A2 1912
Knights of Malta. Grand Master.
Arteggio dei gran maestri con i duchi d'Urbino (1558-1623) Pisa, F. Mariotti, 1912.
xxvi, 142 p. 30 cm. (Studie e ricerche sulla storia del Sovrano Ordine di Malta)
At head of title: Prof. Fedeli.
"Edizione di 200 esemplari fuori commerci". This is n. 18.
"Bibliografia": p. [xxv]-xxvi.
1. Knights of Malta - History - 1523-1798. 2. Montefeltro family I. Fedeli, Carlo, 1851-

NK 0203888 DCU

Incun. 1480 .S19
Knights of Malta. Grand Master, 1476-1489 (Pierre d'Aubusson)
[De obsidione urbis Rhodiae ad Fridericum imperatorem]. Serenissimo ... domino friderico Romanorum Imperatori ... Petrus Daubussen magister hospitalis Hierosolomitani. [Strassburg, 1480?]
[6] l. 21 cm.
Leaf 6 blank.

Goff A 1181.
GW 2775. Hain 5922. Stillwell A1046.
Bound with Samuel Marochitanus. Incipit Epistola qvam misit Rabi Samvel. 1480.

1. Rhodes - Siege, 1480.

NK 0203890 DCU

CR 4718.2 1663-1680 .A2
Knights of Malta. Grand Master, 1663-1680 (Nicolas Cotoner)
[Authentication of a notorial document by Nicholas Cotoner, grand master of the Sov. Mil. Order of Malta; with paper seal, 6 April 1674]
[23] p. 31 cm.

Manuscript.

NK 0203891 DCU

CR 4718.2 1741 .M4
Knights of Malta. Grand Master, 1741-1773. (Emmanuele Pinto)
Medaglie rappresentanti i piu gloriosi avvenimenti del magistero di S.A.E. fra D. Emmauele Pinto.
22 l. illus. 30 cm.

1. Knights of Malta - History - 1523-1798. 2. Medals.

NK 0203892 DCU

Special Collection CR 4718.2 1775-1797 .A4
Knights of Malta. Grand Master, 1775-1797 (Emmanuel Marie de Rohan)
[Two letters in French (manuscript) dated 16 janvier 1776 and 13 avril 1777; each letter with seal]

NK 0203893 DCU

Special Collection CR 4718.2 1931 .A4
Knights of Malta. Grand Master, 1931- (Ludovico Chigi)
Voyage officiel en France de Son Altesse Eminentissime le prince Ludovic Chigi-Albani della Rovere, LXXVIe grand-maistre de l'Ordre souverain de Malte (12-19 juillet 1932) Par le baillie comte Michel de Pierredon. Paris, Oeuvres hospitalières françaises de l'Ordre souverain de Malte, 1933.
41 p. plates, port. 25 cm.
1. Knights of Malta- France. I. Pierredon, Mario Hon ri Thiomy Michel de. II. Title.

NK 0203894 DCU C

Knights of Malta. Ireland. Kilmainhaim
see Knights of Malta. Kilmainham, Ire.

CR 4731 .I81 R76 P7
Knights of Malta. Italy.
Poliambulanza del Sovrano Ordino Militare di Malta. Roma, Danesi, 1928.
12 p. plates 34 cm.

1. Knights of Malta - Hospitals, charities, etc. I. Title.

NK 0203896 DCU

Knights of Malta. Italy.
Rapporto del servizio sanitario prestato in Gattinara dall' associazione dei cavalieri italiani del sovrano ordine Gerosolimitano, presso il 1° corpo d' armata durante le grandi manovre. Alessandro Ceccarelli. Roma, tip. Romana, 1881.
26 p. fol.

NK 0203897 DNLM

Knights of Malta. Italy.
Regolamento pel tempo di guerra. Roma, 1896.
153 p. 8°

NK 0203898 DNLM

CR 4731 .I8 A84 R3
Knights of Malta. Italy.
Relazione sul servizio sanitario svolto durante la Campagna nazionale 1915-18. Roma, Tipografia del Senato, 1919.
58 p. illus. 34 cm.
1. European War, 1914-1918.- Hospitals, charities, etc. 2. Knights of Malta - Hospitals, charities, etc.

NK 0203899 DCU DNLM

Knights of Malta. Italy.
Ruolo dei cavalieri, cappellani conventuali, serventi d'armi e donati ricevuti nella veneranda Lingua d'Italia del Sovrano ordine Gerosolimitano. Compilat dal commendatore Felice Patroni Griffi. Roma, Tipogr. della Rev. Cam. Apostolica, 1861.
pp. 93. Crus 735.11

NK 0203900 MH

Knights of Malta. Italy.
Ruolo delli cavalieri, cappellani conventuali e serventi d'armi ricevuti nella veneranda Lingua d'Italia della Sagra Religione Gerosolimitana e distinti nelli respettivi priorati. Malta, Stamperia del Palazzo di S. A. E. per Fra Giovanni Mallia, 1789.
pp. 116, (1) 4°. Crus 735.5

NK 0203901 MH

Knights of Malta. Italy.
Ruolo generale de' Cavalieri Gerosolimitani della veneranda Lingua d'Italia, raccolto dal comre fr. Bartolomeo del Pozzo, per sin' all'anno 1689; continuato dal comre fr. Roberto Solaro di Govone per tutto l'anno 1713. Torino, G. F. Mairesse e. G. Radix, 1714.
pp. (4), 295+. f°. Crus 735.3

NK 0203902 MH

4K 10248
Knights of Malta. Italy.
Ruolo generale del Sov. Mil. Ordine di S. Giovanni di Gerusalemme ovvero di Malta. Roma, Tip. Poliglotta, 1900.
319 p.

NK 0203903 DLC-P4

VOLUME 300

Knights of Malta. Italy.
Statuto dell' associazione dei cavalieri italiani del sovrano ordine di Malta, pel servigio sanitario militare in guerra. Roma, tipog. della S. C. di propagande fide, 1884.
20 p. 12°.

NK 0203904 DNLM

Knights of Malta. *Kilmainham, Ire.*
... Registrum de Kilmainham. Register of chapter acts of the Hospital of Saint John of Jerusalem in Ireland, 1326–1339, under the grand prior, Sir Roger Outlawe, with additions for the times of his successors, Sir John Mareschall, Sir John Larcher and Sir John Fitzrichard, grand priors of Ireland. Edited from the Bodleian ms. Rawl. B. 501, by Charles McNeill. Dublin, Stationery office [1932]
1 p. l., xvi, 172 p. 25 cm.
At head of title: Coimisiún láimhscríbhinní na hÉireann. Irish manuscripts commission.
"The text of this edition has been prepared for the press by Mr. Newport B. White, by whom also the index was compiled."—p. xvi.
I. Irish free state. Manuscripts commission. II. McNeill, Charles, ed. III. Title.
CR4731.I 7K5 929.71109415 32–25918 rev

NK 0203905 DLC CtY PHC CU MiU MBtS NcD MB NIC

Knights of Malta. Lingua d'Italia
see
Knights of Malta. Italy.

Knights of Malta. Liturgy and ritual
see under Catholic Church. Liturgy and ritual. Knights of Malta.

CR 4725 .N32 A2 1704 folio
Knights of Malta. Navy.
[Flag signal book and regulations for the Navy of the Knights of Malta. Malta, ca.1704]
116 l. 21 water color drawings 40 cm.
Manuscript on paper, bound in contemporary vellum. Prince Liechtenstein copy.
Text in Italian.
Comprises chapters 21-36, 38, 40-42 of a larger body of statutes. This work is, however, complete in itself, with its own tables of contents and index.
1. Manuscripts, Italian. I. Catholic University of America. Library. Mss.

NK 0203908 DCU

Knights of Malta. *New Zealand*
see also **Joint Council of the Order of St. John and the New Zealand Red Cross Society.**

CR 4731 .F81 P14 A2 folio
Knights of Malta. Pailhès (Commandery)
[Visite de la Commanderie de Pailhès près Nîmes: 1657, 1662, 1670]
3 manuscripts in portfolio.

NK 0203910 DCU

Knights of Malta. Portugal.
Index histórico e diplomatico do cartorio de Leca
see under Leça do Balio, Portugal (Monastery)

Knights of Malta. Portugal.
Lista dos cavalleiros, freires capellães conventuaes, e serventes d'armas do venerado priorado de Portugal
see under Knights of Malta. Priorado de Crato.

Knights of Malta. *Priorado de Crato.*
Lista dos cavalleiros, freires capellães conventuaes, e serventes d'armas do venerado priorado de Portugal. Lisboa, Off. de A. Rodrigues Galhardo, impressor, 1800.
59 p. port. 22 cm.
CR4731.P9C7 52-56140

NK 0203913 DLC

Knights of Malta. Priory of Canada.
see Grand Priory in the British Realm of the Most Venerable Order of the Hospital of St. John of Jerusalem. Priory of Canada. [supplement]

CR4731 R9A5 Law Libr.
Knights of Malta. *Russia.*
Actes du chapitre du Grand-Prieuré de Russia. St. Petersbourg, Impr. impériale, 1798.
[14] p. 32 cm.
CR4731.R9A5 55-45977
Library of Congress [3]

NK 0203915 DLC

CR 4729 .A33 G4
Knights of Malta. Saint-Gilles (Grand prieurate)
[Preuves de noblesse pour Malte de Michel d'Albertas. 1658]
[54] p. 32 cm.
Manuscript.
The testimonials are signed by François de Foresta-Collongue and Michel de Verdolin, of the Grand Priory of St. Gilles.
1. Albertas, Michel d'. I. Title.

NK 0203916 DCU

Knights of Malta. Saint-Paul-lès-Romans (Commandery)
Cartulaires des Hospitaliers et des Templiers en Dauphiné... Vienne, 1875
see under Chevalier, Cyr Ulysse Joseph, 1841-1923, ed. [also in Supplement]

Knights of Malta. Tongue of England.
see Knights of Malta. England.

Knights of Malta. *Velay, France.*
Cartulaire des hospitaliers (Ordre de Saint-Jean de Jérusalem) du Velay. Publié par Augustin Chassaing. Paris, A. Picard, 1888.
lxvii, 270 p. 25 cm.
I. Chassaing, Augustin, 1830–1892. ed.
CR4731.F8V5 12–31726 rev*

NK 0203919 DLC MdBWA CtY CU

Knights of Malta (Incorporated 1911 in Pa.)
History of the ancient and illustrious order, Knights of Malta, also declaration of principles, scriptural quotations and allusions, showing the interrelation of Malta and the Holy Word, and the scriptural source of Malta philosophy. Phila[delphia] Pa., A. J. Holman co., °1929.
24 p. 18½ cm.
1. Knights of Malta. I. Title.
CR4723.K58 929.711 30–19858 rev
Library of Congress [r54c1]

NK 0203920 DLC

Knights of Malta (Incorporated 1911 in Pa.)
Official circular. Phil.,1896-8.
no.

NK 0203921 Nh

Knights of Malta (Incorporated 1911 in Pa.)
Official circular. No. 46. April, 1912.
— [Philadelphia. 1912.] v. Portraits. 23 cm.
The Protestant order of Knights of Malta.

NK 0203922 MB

CR473 .U64 1896
Knights of Malta (Incorporated 1911 in Pa.)
Ritual of the Knight of Malta degree of the ancient and illustrious order Knights of Malta, issued by the Supreme grand commandery, continent of America. Philadelphia, Pa., 1896.
40 p. 18cm.

NK 0203923 MnHi

Knights of Malta (Incorporated 1911 in Pa.)
see also, for publications issued after the society changed its name in 1953:
Sovereign Order of St. John of Jerusalem (Incorporated 1911 in Pa.)

The Knights of Malta; an account of their history and aims, 1050–1932. New York, 1932. 34 p. front., plates, ports. 27½cm.
Appendices, reprinted from The Commonweal, and The Catholic register and Canadian extension, p. 25–34.
735344A. 1. Knights of Malta—Hist.
N. Y. P. L. November 2, 1934

NK 0203925 NN NNF DCU

Knights of Modern Maccabees.
...The complete illustrated ritual of the order, including the unwritten work. New York, 1897.
44p.

YA 11408

NK 0203926 DLC

Knights of modern Maccabees.
The Modern Maccabee.
Port Huron, Mich. [Riverside printing co.] 18

VOLUME 300

Knights of Momus.
A history of the Knights of Momus, published on the occasion of the annual banquet, 18th March, 1922. [New Orleans, 1922.] 15 p. nar. 8°.

1. Mardi Gras, U. S.: La.: New Orleans. 2. New Orleans.
N. Y. P. L. January 26, 1923.

NK 0203928 NN LNHT IU

KNIGHTS OF MONTESA.
See ORDER OF MONTESA.

Knights of Pythias.
A brief history of the rise and progress of the order of Knights of Pythias...
see under Dawleas, F W

Knights of Pythias.
F C B Knights of Pythias. Savannah, Georgia, May 20th to 22d, 1908. [Savannah, 1908]
30 unnumbered leaves. Illustrations. Oblong folio.
Pasted slip of correction on leaf 14.
Cover title.
Imprint on back cover: The Morning News, printers and book binders, Savannah, Ga.
With covers.

NK 0204002 GU-De

Knights of Pythias.
Odes and marches of the order of Knights of Pythias. Nashville, n.d.
23 p. ob. 16°

NK 0204003 MWA

Knights of Pythias.
Revised ritual for subordinate lodges ...
see Knights of Pythias. Supreme lodge.

Knights of Pythias.
The secret work; or, Knights of Pythias ritual. In cipher ... Chicago, W. S. Smith & co., 1883.
70 p. illus. 16cm.

1. Knights of Pythias—Rituals.

Library of Congress HS1233.A3 1883 9-18088†
(Copyright 1883: 3094)

NK 0204005 DLC

Knights of Pythias
see also Princes of Syracuse.

Knights of Pythias. Akron, Ohio. Aetolia lodge, no. 24.
By-laws, rules of order ... Akron, Beacon pub. co., 1878.
47, [1] p.

NK 0204007 OClWHi

366.2
K748g
1909

Knights of Pythias. Alabama. Grand lodge.
Grand constitution and grand statutes of the order of Knights of Pythias as adopted by the Grand lodge of Alabama at the convention of 1909, held at Florence, Ala., May 18-19, 1909. Pub. by order of the Grand lodge. Montgomery, Ala., Brown Printing Co. [1909?]
183 p. 24cm.

NK 0204008 AU

Knights of Pythias. Alexander City, Ala. Jonathan lodge, no. 92.
By-laws of Jonathan lodge No. 92 K. of P., Alexander City, Ala. Columbus, Ga., Thos. Gilbert, 1891.

NK 0204009 NcD

Knights of Pythias. Ambler, Pa. Fort Washington Lodge, No. 148.
Constitution, by-laws and rules of order of Fort Washington Lodge, No. 148, K. of P., of the state of Penns. Norristown, Pa.: R. C. Fries, printer, 1870. 58 p. 13cm.

Imperfect: t.-p. mutilated.

NK 0204010 NN PNortHi

HS1254
B6M6

Knights of Pythias. Bodie, Calif. Mono Lodge, no. 59.
By-laws, order of business, and rules of order of Mono Lodge, no. 59, Knights of Pythias, located at Bodie, Cal. San Francisco, C. W. Nevin & Co., Printers, Publishers and Engravers, 1891.
13 p. 15cm. in cover 20cm.

NK 0204011 CU-B

Knights of Pythias. Buffalo, N.Y. William McKinley lodge, no. 399.
Address of Edward T. Durand ... and reports of master of finance and master of exchequer for Supplemented by address of Senator Henry M. Hill ... Buffalo, N.Y., The White-Evans Penfold co., n.d.
38p.

—— 1st report.

NK 0204012 OClWHi

Knights of Pythias. Buffalo, N. Y. *William McKinley lodge, no. 399.*
Report.
Buffalo, 1905–
v. 20cm.
Lodge instituted, June 24, 1903.

Library of Congress CA 5-1724 Unrev'd

NK 0204013 DLC

Knights of Pythias. Carson City, Nev. Damon lodge, no.2.
Constitution and by-laws of Damon lodge, no.2, Knights of Pythias, Carson City, Nevada ... Carson City, Nev., Carson appeal steam print. [1873]
29, [1]p. 11x15cm.
Original wrappers.

NK 0204014 CtY

Knights of Pythias. Claremont, N.H. Claremont lodge, no. 15.
By-laws as revised and amended December, 1892. Clare., n.d.

NK 0204015 Nh

Knights of Pythias. Claremont, N.H. Claremont lodge, no. 15.
Roster. n.p., 1897.

NK 0204016 Nh

Knights of Pythias. Cleveland, Ohio
History of the order of Knights of Pythias for the jurisdiction of Cleveland, Ohio. Cleveland, O. Williams, 1892.
384p.

NK 0204017 OCl

Knights of Pythias. Cleveland, Ohio.
Speakers list. [Cleveland, 1922?]
6p.

Pages multigraphed on one side only.

NK 0204018 OCl

Knights of Pythias. Cleveland, Ohio. Cleveland Pythian pilgrimage club
SEE
Cleveland Pythian pilgrimage club

Knights of Pythias. Cleveland, Ohio. Standard lodge no. 46.
By-laws and directory.

NK 0204020 OCl

Knights of Pythias. Cleveland, Ohio. Standard lodge, no. 46.
Fiftieth anniversary, souvenir pamphlet of Standard lodge no. 46 ...
see under Beman, Lamar Taney, 1877-

C366.2

Knights of Pythias. Colorado. Grand lodge
Official record of the proceedings of the Grand lodge of Colorado, Knights of Pythias, annual convention.
Denver. Smith-Brooks. 187?- v. ports. 23cm.

Cover titles: Proceedings of the Grand lodge of Colorado.

NK 0204022 CoD

Knights of Pythias. Columbia, S.C. Myrtle Lodge, No. 3.
Knights of Pythias
see Condensed history of Myrtle Lodge, no. 3.

366.201
C723b

Knights of Pythias. Columbus, Ga. Columbus Company No.9.
By-laws of Columbus Company No.9 of Georgia, U.R.K.P. Columbus, Ga., T. Gilbert, printer, 1903.
3p. 13cm.

Cover title.

NK 0204024 TxU

VOLUME 300

Knights of Pythias. Concord, N.H. Concord lodge, no. 8.
Constitution and by-laws. Conc., 1871.

NK 0204025 Nh

Knights of Pythias: Concord, N.H. Concord lodge, no. 8
Constitution and by-laws. Manch., 1874.

NK 0204026 Nh

Knights of Pythias. Cornelius, Ore. Simonides Lodge, no. 37.
Constitution and by-laws. Instituted January 1, 1891. Hillsboro, Ore., Independent Book and Job Off., 1891.
39 p. 15 cm.

NK 0204027 OrU

Knights of Pythias. Cuyhoga county, Ohio.
... Official review, Knights of Pythias; Pythian association of Cuyhoga county, Pythian sisters, 192 [Cleveland]
No more published

NK 0204028 OCl

Knights of Pythias. Cuyahoga county, Ohio.
Silver jubilee, Cuyahoga county association... Public auditorium, Oct. 20th, 1924. 1899-1924. Historical review of Pythianism in Cuyahoga county. [Cleveland, Cleveland printing co., 1924]
64p.

NK 0204029 OCl

Knights of Pythias. Dakota Territory. Grand Lodge.
Journal of proceedings of the first session of the Grand Lodge, Knights of Pythias of Dakota. Held at the city of Huron, Dakota, April 30th and May 1st and 2d, 1885. P. P., XXII. Printed by order of the Grand Lodge, 1885. Huron, Dakota: Dakota Huronite Printing House. 1885.
37 p. 19.5 cm.

NK 0204030 SdHi

Knights of Pythias. Dakota Territory. Grand Lodge.
Journal of proceedings of the second session of Grand Lodge of Dakota, Knights of Pythias, held at Rapid City, Dakota, June 15 to 17, 1886. P.P. XXIII. Rapid City Daily Journal Print. [1886.]
64 p. 19.5 cm.

NK 0204031 SdHi

Knights of Pythias. Dakota Territory. Grand Lodge.
Journal of proceedings of the third session of the Grand Lodge of Dakota, Knights of Pythias, held at Watertown, Dakota, June 21 to 23, 1887. P.P. XXIV. Herald Print, Grand Forks, Dakota. 1887.
52 p. 19.5 cm.

NK 0204032 SdHi

Knights of Pythias. Dakota Territory. Grand Lodge.
Journal of proceedings of the fourth session of the Grand Lodge of Dakota, Knights of Pythias. Held at Wahpeton, Dakota, August 21 to 24, 1888. P.P. XXV. Sioux Falls: Argus-Leader Print. 1888.
99 p. 19.5 cm.

NK 0204033 SdHi

Knights of Pythias. Dakota Territory. Grand Lodge.
Journal of proceedings of the fifth annual session of the Grand Lodge of Dakota, Knights of Pythias, held at Sioux Falls, Dakota, July 16, 17 and 18, 1889. P.P. XXVI. Sioux Falls, S. Dak. Press of Sutton & Beach. 1889.
120 p. 20 cm.

NK 0204034 SdHi

Knights of Pythias. Dakota Territory. Grand Lodge.
Knights of Pythias. Programme of entertainment. Fifth annual session of the Grand Lodge of Dakota, Knights of Pythias, Sioux Falls, commencing July 15, 1889. Pythian Period XXVI. Sutton & Beach, society printers, Sioux Falls. [1889.]
[8]p. 15 x 15 cm.

NK 0204035 SdHi

HS1254 .D3I76 Knights of Pythias. Dayton, Ohio. Iola lodge, no. 83.
... Souvenir ... [Dayton, O., 1909?]
31, [17] p. incl. port. (group of ports.) illus. col. fold. pl. 23 x 31 cm.

NK 0204036 DLC

Knights of Pythias. Derry Depot, N.H. Rockingham lodge, no. 29.
By-laws. Manchester, 1887.

NK 0204037 Nh

Knights of Pythias. *District of Columbia. Calanthe Lodge No. 11.*
Constitution and by-laws. Rev. Jan. 1878. Washington, R. O. Polkinhorn, printer, 1878.
37 p. 13 cm.

HS1254.W32C3 1878 58-53564

NK 0204038 DLC

Knights of Pythias. *District of Columbia. Grand Lodge.*
Journal: proceedings
see its
Official record of the proceedings.

Knights of Pythias. *District of Columbia. Grand Lodge.*
Official record of the proceedings.
Washington.
v. ports. 23 cm.
Irregular -1876/79; semiannual, 1879-1886/87; annual, 1888-
Title varies: -1891, Proceedings.—1892- Journal: proceedings.

HS1254.W32G7 58-51325

NK 0204040 DLC

Knights of Pythias. *District of Columbia. Grand Lodge.*
Proceedings
see its
Official record of the proceedings.

Knights of Pythias. *District of Columbia. Mount Vernon Lodge No. 5.*
Constitution and by-laws. Rev. Jan. 1878. Washington, R. O. Polkinhorn, printer, 1878.
39 p. 13 cm.

HS1254.W32M6 1878 58-53563

NK 0204042 DLC

1885 Knights of Pythias. District of Columbia, Syracusians lodge, no. 10.
Constitution and by-laws of Syracusians lodge, no. 10, K. of P. Revised January, 1878. Washington, D.C., R.O. Polkinborn, 1878.
1 p.l., 39 p. 24°.

NK 0204043 DLC

Knights of Pythias. Endowment rank.
Report of the board of control, 1888-90. Chic., 1890.
v.1

NK 0204044 Nh

Ga HS1253 G4A3 GU Knights of Pythias. Georgia. Grand Lodge.
Constitution and statutes of the Grand Lodge, Knights of Pythias, domain of Georgia. Savannah, Commercial Lithograph & Printing Co., 1907.
158 p. illus. 22cm.
Cover title: t.p. missing.

NK 0204045 GU

Knights of Pythias. Georgia. Grand Lodge.
Official proceedings of the twelfth annual session of ... the Grand Lodge K. of P., N. A., S. A., E., A., and A., jurisdiction of Georgia, held at Bainbridge, Georgia, July 9th and 10th, 1901. [Darien? Ga., 1901?]
66 p. illus., ports. 22 cm.

1. Knights of Pythias. Georgia. Grand Lodge.
HS1253.G4A35 73-153435 MARC

NK 0204046 DLC

Knights of Pythias. Georgia. Grand Lodge.
Official record of the proceedings. [1st]-7th-sess.
1871-76- Savannah, Ga. [etc.] Braid & Hutton [etc.]
v. 7 & 8.
Title varies: 1871-95, Proceedings (1871-76, 1892-95, have title page, Journal of Proceedings) 1896, Official record.
Vols. for 1896- have running title: Proceedings.
Vols. paged continuously from 1871-76.
With proceedings for 1877 is bound: its Report of contributions received for the relief of Knights of Pythias, of Savannah, Georgia, during the Yellow Fever epidemic of 1876. Macon, Ga., 1877.

NK 0204048 NcD

VOLUME 300

Knights of Pythias. Georgia. Grand Lodge.
366.2 K710 1st-13th 1871-1882
Report of contributions received for the relief of Knights of Pythias, of Savannah, Georgia, during the Yellow Fever epidemic of 1876. Macon, Ga., G. F. Wing, 1877.
17 p. 20 cm. [With its Official report of the proceedings, 1877. [n.p., n.d.]]

1. Yellow fever. Savannah, Ga., 1876.

NK 0204049 NcD

Knights of Pythias. Georgia. Grand Lodge.
Synopsis of the proceedings. 18 -
[v.p.]

NK 0204050 GU

Knights of Pythias. Hartford, Conn. Lincoln lodge no. 55
[... His name we bear.] (Officers for 1909 and program for January, 1909. n.p., n.d.
[4]p.

NK 0204051 OClWHi

Knights of Pythias. Hillsdale, Mich. Hillsdale Lodge, no.45.
Knights of Pythias carnival and June festiv Souvenir, Hillsdale and vicinity. June 6 to 11 1904. Hillsdale, 1904.
1v. illus.,ports. 25cm.

On cover: The city of Hillsdale and vicinity.

1. Hillsdale, Mich.-Descr. & tr.

NK 0204052 Mi

Knights of Pythias. Indiana. Grand lodge.
Constitution ... and general laws for the government of subordinate lodges under the jurisdiction of the Grand lodge of Indiana. [Indianapolis] n.p., 1890.

NK 0204053 InU

Knights of Pythias. Indiana. Grand lodge.
Proceedings of the Grand Lodge of Indiana, 1869-70. Indianapolis, 1870.
8°

NK 0204054 MnHi

Knights of Lythias. Iowa. Grand lodge. Fraternal correspondent's report.
Knights of Pythias. *Iowa. Grand lodge.*
Journal of proceedings. 1st- annual convention. Des Moines, Ia. [etc., 1872-

---

Knights of Pythias. *Iowa. Grand lodge.*
Grand constitution and grand statutes of the order of Knights of Pythias as adopted by the Grand lodge of Iowa at the convention of 1895. Pub. by order of the Grand lodge. Des Moines, Conaway & Shaw, printers, 1895.
137 p. illus. 21½cm.

17-11181

Library of Congress HS1225.I 8A3 1895
——— Copy 2. HS1253.I 8A2 1895
[With its Journal of proceedings, 1895-96]

NK 0204056 DLC

Knights of Pythias. *Iowa. Grand lodge.*
Grand constitution and grand statutes of the Grand lodge, Knights of Pythias, domain of Iowa, adopted at Council Bluffs, August 13, 1903. [Cedar Rapids, Ia., Press of the Republican, 1903]
155, xlvii p. 23cm.

17-6281

Library of Congress HS1225.I 8A3 1903

NK 0204057 DLC

Knights of Pythias. *Iowa. Grand lodge.*
Grand constitution and grand statutes of the Grand lodge, Knights of Pythias, domain of Iowa. Revised grand statutes adopted at Sioux City, August 13, 1909. [Oskaloosa, Ia., Presses of the Globe, 1909]
189 p. 22½cm.

17-6282

Library of Congress HS1225.I 8A3 1909

NK 0204058 DLC

Knights of Pythias. *Iowa. Grand lodge.*
Journal of proceedings. 1st- annual convention. Des Moines, Ia. [etc., 1872-
v. fronts., illus., plates, ports. 20-22cm.

Title varies: 1870/71-1877, 1879, Proceedings ...
1878, ... Annual convention ...
1880-83, ... Annual communication ...
1884, Journal of proceedings ...
1885-95, Minutes ...
1896- Journal of proceedings.

Continuously paged 1870-95; 1896-1900; 1901-02; 1903-04 (paging irregular)
1st-2d, 1870-71, are in one pamphlet, reprinted 1909.
19th- conventions, 1888- have vol. nos. "v. 3, no. 2-
The Fraternal correspondent's report (Fraternal review) published annually since 1901 in advance of the sessions of the Grand lodge, is bound with the Journal of proceedings for 1901- (except 1913-14)

I. Knights of Pythias. Iowa. Grand lodge. Fraternal correspondent's report. II. Fraternal review.

17-11180

Library of Congress HS1253.I 8A2

NK 0204060 DLC

Knights of Pythias. Kansas. Grand Lodge.
Proceedings of the Grand Lodge Knights of Pythias of Kansas, at its First Session, held in the city of Lawrence, Sept. 4 & 5, 1872. Leavenworth, John C. Ketcheson - (Times Steam Book & Job Printing Establishment) 1872.
40 p. 12.5 x 20 cm. Printed blue paper wrappers.

NK 0204061 KHi

Knights of Pythias. Kansas. Grand Lodge.
Proceedings of the Grand Lodge Knights of Pythias, of Kansas, had at the Semi-annual Session of 1873, the Annual Session of 1874, at Leavenworth, and the Annual Session of 1875, at Olathe. Wyandott, Kansas, Herald Steam Printing House, 1875.
136 p. 12.5 x 20 cm. Printed blue paper wrappers.

NK 0204062 KHi

Knights of Pythias. Kansas. Grand Lodge.
Knights of Pythias. Proceedings of the Grand Lodge of Kansas at its Annual Session held at Leavenworth, April 11, 12 & 13, 1876. [Cut of emblem] Leavenworth, Ketcheson & Durfee, Steam Book and Job Printers, 1876.
51, [1] p. 12.5 x 20 cm. Printed gray paper wrappers.

NK 0204063 KHi

976.3 (366.2) K72z
Knights of Pythias. Louisiana.
Publications of, and relating to, individual lodges in Louisiana.

v. cm.

1. Louisiana - Knights of Pythias.

NK 0204064 LNHT

La 366.2 L93c
Knights of Pythias. Louisiana. Grand lodge.
Constitution and laws of the Grand lodge, and constitution of the subordinate lodges, Knights of Pythias, of Louisiana. Compiled by Harvey Skolfield, Dr. J.M. Watkins, C.K. Browning, Committee on law and supervion. By authority of the Grand lodge K. of P. of Louisiana... New Orleans, Mystic tie printing office, 1890.
150p. 15cm.

1. Secret societies--Louisiana.

NK 0204065 LU

R 366.2 K71g
Knights of Pythias. Louisiana. Grand lodge.
Grand constitution and grand statutes of the grand domain of Louisiana ... as adopted ... at the convention of 1895. [New Orleans, Mystic Tie Printing off., 1895]
150 p. illus.

1. Knights of Pythias. I. Title.
11.2.72

NK 0204066 LN

La 366.2 L93
Knights of Pythias. Louisiana. Grand lodge.
Official journal of the 1st- annual convention... 18 -19
[New Orleans, 18 -19
cover-title, v. illus., ports. 23cm.

1. Secret societies--Louisiana.

NK 0204067 LU

Knights of Pythias. Manchester, N.H. Golden Rule lodge, no. 45.
By-laws, approved Nov. 29, 1892.
Manch., 1893.

NK 0204068 Nh

Knights of Pythias. Massachusetts. Grand lodge.
Proceedings,1870. Bost.,1870.

NK 0204069 Nh

Knights of Pythias. Michigan. Grand lodge
Constitution and rules of order, for the government of subordinate lodges in the jurisdiction of Michigan. As revised by the Grand lodge at the annual session held Feb. 3rd and 4th, 1880, P. P. XVI. Detroit, Pub. by the Grand lodge, 1880.
32 p.

NK 0204070 MiD-B

VOLUME 300

Knights of Pythias. - Michigan. Grand lodge.
Constitution and rules of order for the government of subordinate lodges, in the jurisdiction of Michigan, as revised by the Grand lodge at the annual session, held Feb. 3 and 4, 1880, P. P. XVI. Amended October 7th, 1884, P. P XXI. Bay City, Pub. by the Grand lodge [1884]
41 p.

NK 0204071 MiD-B

Knights of Pythias. Michigan. Grand lodge.
Proceedings... 1st- , 1873- Grand Rapids, Mich., 1873-

NK 0204072 MiD-B

F902 .8KN Knights of Pythias. Milwaukee, Wisc. Schiller Loge No.3.
Constitution und Nebengesetze.
Milwaukee, 1879-1880
2 v. 14 cm.

NK 0204073 WHi

Knights of Pythias. Michigan. Uniform rank
see Knights of Pythias. Uniform rank. Michigan.

*HS1225 .M65 1903 **Knights of Pythias. Minnesota. Grand lodge.**
Grand constitution and grand statutes of the Grand lodge Knights of Pythias, domain of Minnesota, adopted September 25, 1895, P.P. XXXII. Revised 1903. Including the legislation of the annual conventions of 1896 to 1903 inclusive. Published by order of the Grand lodge, 1903. [Minneapolis, Minn., Printed by the Pythian advocate, 1903]
128 p. 24cm.

NK 0204075 MnHi

*HS1225 .M65 1917 Knights of Pythias. Minnesota. Grand lodge.
Grand constitution and grand statutes of the Grand lodge Knights of Pythias, domain of Minnesota, in effect October 9, 1917. [Minneapolis, 1917]
61 p. 23cm.

"Published by order of the Grand lodge."

NK 0204076 MnHi

Knights of Pythias. Montana. Grand lodge.
Constitution and statutes of the grand lodge Knights of Pythias, domain of Montana ... Jacob Loeb, comp., 1904.
201 p.

NK 0204077 MtHi

Knights of Pythias. Montana. Grand lodge.
Montana lodge record.
monthly.

NK 0204078 MtHi

Knights of Pythias. New Hampshire. Grand Lodge
Constitution for subordinate lodges. Manch., 1890.

NK 0204079 Nh

Knights of Pythias. New Hampshire. Grand Lodge.
Constitution instituted Oct. 20,1870. Manch, 1874.

NK 0204080 Nh

HS1253 .N4A2 Knights of Pythias. New Hampshire. Grand lodge.
Official record of the proceedings of the annual convention of the Grand lodge, Knights of Pythias of New Hampshire, 1870-
Manchester, N.H., 1873-
v. plates, ports. 22 cm.
Title varies: 1870-1914, Proceedings ...; 1915- Official record of the proceedings.

NK 0204081 DLC NhDo Nh

Knights of Pythias. New Hampshire. Grand Lodge
Report of supreme representatives,1894,1900. Dover,1894-1900.

NK 0204082 Nh

Knights of Pythias. New Hampshire. Grand Lodge
Report of the Grand keeper of records and seal,1892. Lancaster,1892.

NK 0204083 Nh

Knights of Pythias. New Hampshire. Grand Lodge.
Roster, 1894- n.p. 1894-7.

NK 0204084 Nh

Knights of Pythias: New Hampshire brigade.
By-laws. Indianapolis,1897.

NK 0204085 Nh

366.201 L93 1894 Knights of Pythias. New Orleans, La. Paragon Lodge No.16.
By-laws of Paragon Lodge No.16, Knights of Pythias. Located at New Orleans, La. Instituted May 14, 1880. Incorporated December 23, 1891. New Orleans, Malus & Hofeline, 1894.
23p. 15cm.

NK 0204086 TxU

Knights of Pythias. New York (State) Grand Lodge
.... Proceedings of Grand Lodge of the Knights of Pythias of the State of New York at its ... annual session .... Albany, J. B. Lyon, printer, 1894.
No. 26, 1894. 24cm.

NK 0204087 ICJ

Knights of Pythias. *New York (State)* *Grand lodge.*
... Proceedings ... annual convention ...
[New York, 1921-
v. 23cm.
On cover: Journal of the proceedings.

22-22082

Library of Congress HS1253.N7A2

NK 0204088 DLC

Knights of Pythias. *Newport, N. H. Newport lodge, no. 43.*
Constitution and by-laws of Newport lodge, no. 43, Knights of Pythias, Newport, N. H. Instituted May 24, 1892. Newport, N. H., Hitchcock & Wright, printers, 1892.
1 p. l., 58 p. 14cm.

Library of Congress 5-25846†

NK 0204089 DLC Nh

Knights of Pythias. North Attleboro, Mass. Sumner lodge, no. 2.
Constitution, by-laws and rules of order. Attleboro, 1875.
43 p. 14 cm.

NK 0204090 RPB

C366.6 K71c **Knights of Pythias. North Carolina. Grand Lodge.**
Constitution and grand statutes of the grand domain of North Carolina, adopted at the annual convention of 1907. Goldsboro, N.C., Nash Brothers [1907]
54, vii p. 24cm.

NK 0204091 NcU

HS1254 O2B7 Knights of Pythias. Oakland, Calif. Brooklyn Lodge, no. 32.
Constitution and by-laws of Brooklyn Lodge, no. 32, Knights of Pythias, located at East Oakland, Cal. San Francisco, C.W. Nevin & Co., Printers and engravers, 1883.
74 p. 15cm. in cover 20cm.

NK 0204092 CU-B

Knights of Pythias. Oberlin, Ohio. Oberlin lodge, no. 662
[Miscellaneous pamphlets] Oberlin, Ohio, 18—

In envelope.

NK 0204093 OO

HS1253 .O3A3 Knights of Pythias. Ohio. Grand lodge.
Annual convention, Grand lodge Knights of Pythias, ...
[Springifeld, Ohio, 19-

NK 0204094 DLC OCl

36o.2 K748g **Knights of Pythias. Ohio. Grand lodge.**
Gesetze der Pythias-ritter des staates Ohio. Enthaltend die constitution der gross-loge und die allgemeinen gesetze für die regierung der unter-logen. Angenommen in der mai-sitzung von 1884. Genehmigt durch den supreme-kanzler am 5. juni 1884. Cincinnati, O., 1884.
cover-title, 40p.

NK 0204095 IU

Knights of Pythias. Ohio. Grand lodge
Laws of the Knights of Pythias the state of Ohio... Columbus, G. & Heide, 1872.
36p.

NK 0204096 OClWHi

VOLUME 300

Knights of Pythias. Ohio. Grand Lodge.
Proceedings of the Grand Lodge of Ohio, 1870-71.
Columbus, 1871.
8°

NK 0204097 MnHi OClWHi

Knights of Pythias. Oregon. Grand lodge.
Journal of proceedings of the annual convention. 1st-21st, 23d, 1881-1903 Oh 2062

NK 0204098 OrHi Or

Knights of Pythias. *Pennsylvania. Grand lodge.*
A digest of the laws of the order of Knights of Pythias in the state of Pennsylvania. Comp. and pub. by authority of the Grand lodge of Pennsylvania, by William Blancbois, P. G. C. Philadelphia, Knights of Pythias journal print, 1872.
iv p., 2 l., 13-190 p. illus. 16cm.

I. Blancbois, William.

Library of Congress HS1225.P4A3 1872 9-18097†
(Copyright 1872: 10015)

NK 0204099 DLC PPL

Knights of Pythias. Pennsylvania. Grand Lodge.
Proceedings of preliminary meetings held previous to and for the purpose of forming the Grand lodge of Pennsylvania. Phil.,1870.

NK 0204100 Nh

Knights of Pythias, Pennsylvania. Grand Lodge.
Proceedings of the...annual session...
18
Philadelphia, 18 8°.
v.
18 called

NK 0204101 NN

366.2 K748b **Knights of Pythias. Portland, Ore. Ivanhoe Lodge No.10.**
By-laws. ⌜Compiled by Thad L. Graves. Portland, Ore., 1929⌝
22p. 16cm.

NK 0204102 OrU

Knights of Pythias, Portland, Ore. Mystic Lodge no. 2.
Constitution and by-laws. Portland, Himes, 1873.
32 p.

NK 0204103 OrHi

Knights of Pythias. Providence. R.I., Elmwood lodge, no. 16.
Constitution and by-laws. Providence, 1888.
34 p. 15 cm.

NK 0204104 RPB

Knights of Pythias. Providence, R.I., Oriental lodge, no. 9.
Constitution, by-laws, order of business and list of officers and members. Providence, 1872.
31 p. 15 cm.

NK 0204105 RPB

Knights of Pythias. Providence, R.I., St. George lodge, no. 14.
Constitution and by-laws. Providence, 1879.
24 p. 16 cm.

NK 0204106 RPB

Knights of Pythias. Providence, R.I., St. John's lodge, no. 6.
By-laws, adopted May 4, 1871. Providence, 1871.
28 p. 13 cm.

NK 0204107 RPB

Knights of Pythias. Providence, R.I., Union lodge, no. 2.
Constitution, by-laws and rules of order. Providence, 1873.
28 p. 14 cm.
Instituted April 26, 1870.

NK 0204108 RPB

HS1261 .Q4A2 vol. 1 **Knights of Pythias.** Quebec (Province) Grand lodge.
Constitution and statutes of the Grand lodge,... [Montreal, 1917]

NK 0204109 DLC

HS1261 .Q4A2 Knight of Pythias. Quebec (Province) Grand lodge.
Official record of proceedings ...
Montreal, [1905?-

NK 0204110 DLC

Knights of Pythias, Riverpoint, R.I., Narragansett lodge, no. 8.
Constitution, by-laws and rules of order Phoenix, 1871.
[29] p. 14 cm.
Instituted June 28, 1871.

NK 0204111 RPB

Knights of Pythias. Riverside, R.I. Riverside lodge, no. 21.
Constitution, by-laws and rules of order. Providence, 1889.
[44] p. 13 cm.
Instituted, Jan. 16, 1889.

NK 0204112 RPB

*
HS1254 .R608 1910 Knights of Pythias. Roanoke, Va. Osceola Lodge No. 47.

Constitution, by-laws and rules of order. Adopted June 2, 1910; approved and in effect, July 1, 1910, and amended to date. ⌜Roanoke, Va., Stone Printing and Manufacturing Co.? 1910?⌝
57 p. 12cm.

NK 0204113 ViU

Knights of Pythias. South Dakota. Grand Lodge.
Journal of proceedings of the Grand Lodge, K. P. of Dakota, and the first annual session of the Grand Lodge of South Dakota Knights of Pythias. June 17th to 19th, 1890. Yankton: Press of L. E. Cavalier Printing House. 1890.
207 p. 20.5 cm.

NK 0204114 SdHi

HS1253 .S8A35 **Knights of Pythias. South Dakota. Grand lodge.**
Reports of officers, fraternal correspondent and supreme representatives of the Grand lodge,... [Aberdeen? -

NK 0204115 DLC

HS 1253 C2A2 Knights of Pythias. Supreme Lodge.
Constitution and by-laws. Adopted at the session held at Pittsburgh, Pa., session of 1874. Pythian period XI. [n.p.] 1874.
22 p.

Bound with Knights of Pythias. California. Grand Lodge. Proceedings, 1st-5th. San Francisco, 1869-73.

NK 0204116 CLU

Knights of Pythias.Supreme lodge.
Constitution and by-laws and rules of order . Columbus, 1880.

NK 0204117 Nh

Knights of Pythias. Supreme lodge.
Courts martial and courts of inquiry of the uniform rank Knights of Pythias. By authority of the Supreme lodge. Prepared by James R. Carnahan... Approved and adopted by the Special committee of the Supreme lodge, Knights of Pythias of the world. Indianapolis ⌜Ind.⌝ Baker and Randolph, 1890.
125p.

NK 0204118 OClW

Knights of Pythias. *Supreme lodge.*
Drill regulations, uniform rank, Knights of Pythias ... Prepared under authority of the Supreme lodge K. of P. of the world. By Major-Gen. James R. Carnahan ... Cincinnati, O., The Pettibone mfg. co., 1894.
iv, 537, xxx p. illus., diagrs. 12½cm.

1. Knights of Pythias—Rituals. I. Carnahan, James Richards, 1840-1905.

Library of Congress HS1285.A3 1894 9-17860†
(Copyright 1894: 11596)

NK 0204119 DLC

Knights of Pythias. Supreme lodge.
Drill regulations, uniform rank, Knights of Pythias. By Major-Gen. James R. Carnahan. Cincinnati, O., Pettibone Bros. Mfg. Co., 1899.
537p. illus.

NK 0204120 ICRL

VOLUME 300

Knights of Pythias. *Supreme lodge.*
First digest of the laws of the Supreme lodge of the world, Knights of Pythias. Chicago, Knight & Leonard, 1877.
160 p. 16cm.

1. Knights of Pythias—Law.

Library of Congress HS1223.A3 1877 (Copyright 1877: 2327) 9-18085†

NK 0204121 DLC

Knights of Pythias. *Supreme lodge.*
Form of installation for subordinate lodges, adopted by the Supreme lodge, Knights of Pythias, at its ninth annual session, held at Cleveland, Ohio, August 17, 1877. Also, form of funeral service. Columbus, O., Supreme lodge, Knights of Pythias, 1877.
1 p. l., [5]-22 p. 20cm.

1. Knights of Pythias—Rituals.

Library of Congress HS1231.A2 1877 (Copyright 1877: 12801) 9-18095†

NK 0204122 DLC

HS1274 .A4 1877 Toner Coll.
Knights of Pythias. Supreme lodge.
General laws and constitution for the government of sections of the Endowment rank, adopted by the Supreme lodge, Knights of Pythias. August, 1877. Indianapolis, Baker & Randolph, book and job printers, 1878.
cover-title, 23 p. 13½cm.

1. Knights of Pythias--Laws, decisions, etc.

NK 0204123 DLC

Knights of Pythias. Supreme Lodge.
Journal of proceedings. v. 1- 1868- Columbus, Ohio
see its Official record of proceedings of the convention.

HS1231 .A5 1925
Knights of Pythias. Supreme lodge.
Latest ritual of the Knights of Pythias of the universe,...
[Shreveport, La., c1925]

NK 0204125 DLC

Pam. Coll. 21034
Knights of Pythias. Supreme Lodge
Laws governing the Insurance Department of the Supre Lodge, Knights of Pythias. 5th ed. [Nashville, Tenn.] 1908.
98 p. 15 cm.

1. Insurance, Fraternal.

NK 0204126 NcD

Knights of Pythias. *Supreme lodge.*
Official digest and compilation of the laws, decisions and enactments of the Supreme lodge, Knights of Pythias, from its organization, August 11, 1868, to and including ... 1876 ... Prepared by authority by F. P. Dann ... Columbus, O., Pub. by order of the Supreme lodge, Knights of Pythias, 1877.
xii, 188 p. illus., pl. 23cm.

I. Dann, Frederick P., d. 1884.

Library of Congress HS1223.A3 1876 (Copyright 1877: 8838) 9-18086†

NK 0204127 DLC ScU

Knights of Pythias. *Supreme lodge.*
Official digest of the Supreme lodge, Knights of Pythias of the world. 1890. Issued by order of the Supreme lodge. [Chicago, Stromberg, Allen & co., printers] 1891.
300 p. 24cm.
Compiled by William D. Kennedy.

1. Knights of Pythias—Laws, decisions, etc. I. Kennedy, William Dames, 1844-

Library of Congress HS1223.A3 1890 (Copyright 1891: 5206) 9-17857†

NK 0204128 DLC

Knights of Pythias. *Supreme lodge.*
Official jewels of the order of Knights of Pythias. [Minneapolis, The Murphy-Travis printing co., ©1914]
cover-title, 2 p. l., [12] p., 1 l. 5 mounted pl. 35½cm.

1. Knights of Pythias—Costumes, supplies, etc. I. Title.

Library of Congress HS1235.A4 14-4987

NK 0204129 DLC

Knights of Pythias. *Supreme lodge.*
Official manual of drill and tactics of the Knights of Pythias, comp. by G. S. Dana; and General laws and constitution of the uniform rank, as adopted by the Supreme lodge, August 30, 1878. P. P. XV. Columbus, O., Supreme lodge, 1878.
2 v. in 1. 14½cm.
"General laws" has special t.-p.

1. Knights of Pythias—Rituals I. Dana, G. S.

Library of Congress HS1285.A18 (Copyright 1878: 14657) 9-17858†

NK 0204130 DLC

Knights of Pythias. *Supreme lodge.*
Official record of proceedings of the ... convention of the Supreme lodge Knights of Pythias ... also annual reports of the officers ...
Columbus, O.,
v. illus., port., tables. 23½cm.
Title varies: Journal of proceedings ... Official record of proceedings ...

CA 11-2157 Unrev'd

Library of Congress HS1251.A2

NK 0204131 DLC ICRL Nh WHi

Knights of Pythias. *Supreme lodge.*
Ritual for subordinate lodges of Knights of Pythias; adopted by the Supreme lodge, August 16, 1930, P. P. LXVII. [Minneapolis, 1930]
3 p. l., 5-116 p. 1 illus., diagrs. 19½cm.
"Copyright 1931."
"Manual for subordinate lodges of Knights of Pythias": p. [93]-116.

1. Knights of Pythias—Rituals.

Library of Congress HS1233.A4 1930 42-45115

NK 0204132 DLC

Knights of Pythias. *Supreme lodge.*
Ritual for subordinate lodges of Knights of Pythias. Adopted by the Supreme lodge, Aug. 29, 1892, P. P. XXIX. Edited by Douglas Roberts. New-York, Dick & Fitzgerald, 1894.
94 p. diagrs. 17cm.

1. Knights of Pythias—Rituals. I. Roberts, Douglas, ed.

Library of Congress HS1233.A4 1894 9-18090 Revised

NK 0204133 DLC

Knights of Pythias. *Supreme lodge.*
Rules of the Supreme tribunal, Knights of Pythias. 1894. [Cincinnati, O., 1895]
64 p. 13cm.

1. Knights of Pythias—Law, decisions, etc.

Library of Congress HS1223.A5 1894 (Copyright 1895: 3269) 9-18098†

NK 0204134 DLC

Knights of Pythias. *Supreme lodge.*
Supreme constitution and supreme statutes of the order of Knights of Pythias, adopted by the Supreme lodge, at the convention of 1894. Pub. by order of the Supreme lodge. Nashville, Tenn., Brandon printing company, 1894.
141 p. illus. 22½cm.

1. Knights of Pythias—Law, decisions, etc.

Library of Congress HS1223.A4 1894 (Copyright 1894: 45742) 9-18100†

NK 0204135 DLC

Knights of Pythias. *Supreme lodge.*
Supreme constitution and supreme statutes of the order of Knights of Pythias, as adopted by the Supreme lodge, at the convention of 1894, revised so as to include the legislation of the conventions of 1896, 1898, 1900, 1901 and 1902. Published by order of the Supreme lodge. Nashville, Tenn., Brandon printing company, 1903.
191 p. 21½cm.

3-6852

NK 0204136 DLC

Knights of Pythias. *Supreme lodge.*
Supreme constitution and supreme statutes of the order of Knights of Pythias, adopted by the Supreme lodge at the convention of 1906. Nashville, Tenn., Brandon printing company, 1906.
173 p. 23½ cm.

1. Knights of Pythias—Laws, decisions, etc.

Library of Congress HS1223.A4 1906 7—3904

NK 0204137 DLC

Knights of Pythias. *Supreme lodge.*
Supreme constitution and supreme statutes of the order of Knights of Pythias adopted by the Supreme lodge at the convention of 1906, revised so as to include all amendments up to and including August, 1922. Minneapolis, Minn., Murphy-Travis company, 1922.
200 p. 24cm.

Library of Congress HS1223.A4 1922 23-3310

NK 0204138 DLC

Knights of Pythias. *Supreme lodge.*
Supreme constitution and supreme statutes of the order of Knights of Pythias adopted by the Supreme lodge at the convention of 1906, revised so as to include all amendments up to and including August, 1924. Minneapolis, Minn., Murphy-Travis company, 1924.
199 p. illus. 22cm.

Library of Congress HS1223.A4 1924 25-1389

NK 0204139 DLC

VOLUME 300

Knights of Pythias. *Supreme lodge.*
Supreme constitution and supreme statutes of the order of Knights of Pythias, adopted by the Supreme lodge at the convention of 1906, revised so as to include all amendments up to and including August, 1926. Minneapolis, Minn., Murphy-Travis company, 1926.
224 p. illus. 22cm.

27-5510
Library of Congress HS1223.A4 1926

NK 0204140 DLC OCl

Knights of Pythias. *Supreme lodge.*
Supreme constitution and supreme statutes of the order of Knights of Pythias adopted by the Supreme lodge at the convention of 1906, revised so as to include all amendments up to and including August, 1928. Minneapolis, Minn., Murphy-Travis company, 1928.
229 p. illus. 22cm.

1. Knights of Pythias—Laws, decisions, etc.

28-28651
Library of Congress HS1223.A4 1928

NK 0204141 DLC

Knights of Pythias. *Supreme lodge.*
Supreme constitution and supreme statutes of the order of Knights of Pythias adopted by the Supreme lodge at the convention of 1906, revised so as to include all amendments up to and including August, 1930. Minneapolis, Minn., Murphy-Travis company, 1930.
233 p. 22cm.

1. Knights of Pythias—Laws, decisions, etc.

30-33392
Library of Congress HS1223.A4 1930
[2] 366.2

NK 0204142 DLC

Knights of Pythias. *Supreme lodge.*
Supreme constitution and supreme statutes of the order of Knights of Pythias adopted by the Supreme lodge at the convention of 1906; revised so as to include all amendments up to and including August, 1938. Minneapolis, Minn., Murphy-Travis company, 1938.
182, [2] p. 22cm.

1. Knights of Pythias—Laws, decisions, etc.

39-2052
Library of Congress HS1223.A4 1938
[3] 366.2

NK 0204143 DLC

Knights of Pythias. *Supreme lodge.*
Supreme constitution and supreme statutes of the order of Knights of Pythias, adopted by the Supreme lodge at the convention of 1906, with amendments adopted at the conventions of 1908, 1910, 1912 and 1914. Minneapolis, Minn., Murphy-Travis company, 1914.
188 p. 23½cm.

16-3840
Library of Congress HS1223.A4 1914

NK 0204144 DLC

Knights of Pythias. *Supreme lodge.*
Tactics and manual for the uniform rank, Knights of Pythias ... Prepared under authority of the Supreme lodge K. of P. of the world, by Brig.-Gen. James R. Carnahan ... and Wm. R. Hamilton ... Cincinnati, The Pettibone m'f'g co., 1883.
xix, 244 p. illus., diagrs. 13½ x 10½cm.

1. Knights of Pythias—Rituals. I. Carnahan, James Richards, 1840-1905. II. Hamilton, William Reeve, 1855- joint author.

9-18220†
Library of Congress HS1285.A3 1883
(Copyright 1883: 7644)

NK 0204145 DLC

Knights of Pythias. *Supreme lodge.*
Tactics and manual for the uniform rank Knights of Pythias ... Prepared under authority of the Supreme lodge K. of P. of the world, by Major-Gen. James R. Carnahan ... and Wm. R. Hamilton ... 2d ed. Rev. by Maj.-Gen. James R. Carnahan. Cincinnati, The Pettibone m'f'g co., 1884.
xx, 278 p. illus., diagrs. 14½cm.

1. Knights of Pythias—Rituals. I. Carnahan, James Richards, 1840-1905. II. Hamilton, William Reeve, 1855- joint author.

9-19624†
Library of Congress HS1285.A3 1884
(Copyright 1884: 21588)

NK 0204146 DLC OCl

Knights of Pythias. *Supreme lodge.*
Tactics and manual for the uniform rank Knights of Pythias ... Prepared under authority of the Supreme lodge K. of P. of the world. By Major-Gen. James R. Carnahan ... and Wm. R. Hamilton ... 3d ed. Rev. by Maj.-Gen. James R. Carnahan. Cincinnati, The Pettibone m'f'g co., 1886.
xx, 289 p. illus., diagrs. 14½cm.

1. Knights of Pythias—Rituals. I. Carnahan, James Richards, 1840-1905. II. Hamilton, William Reeve, 1855- joint author.

9-19623†
Library of Congress HS1285.A3 1886
(Copyright 1886: 24619)

NK 0204147 DLC

Knights of Pythias. *Supreme lodge.*
Tactics and manual for the uniform rank Knights of Pythias ... Prepared under authority of the Supreme lodge K. of P. of the world. By Major-Gen. James R. Carnahan ... 4th ed. Rev. and enl. Cincinnati, The Pettibone mfg. co., 1889.
xv, 16-383 p. illus., diagrs. 12cm.

1. Knights of Pythias—Rituals. I. Carnahan, James Richards, 1840-1905.

9-17859†
Library of Congress HS1285.A3 1889
(Copyright 1889: 1753)

NK 0204148 DLC

HS1255 .T2A2 1901
Knights of Pythias. Tennessee. Grand Lodge.
Constitution of the Grand Lodge Knights of Pythias of the State of Tennessee, in effect May 8, 1901; and general laws for subordinate lodges, in effect July 1, 1901. Nashville, Published by order of the Grand Lodge, 1901.
56 p. 15 cm.

NK 0204149 T

Knights of Pythias. *Tennessee. Grand lodge.*
Official digest of the Grand lodge Knights of Pythias of the state of Tennessee. By R. L. C. White ... Printed by order of the Grand lodge. [Lebanon, Tenn., Herald printery] 1885.
88 p. 16cm.

I. White, Robert Looney Caruthers, 1844-

9-18096†
Library of Congress HS1225.T2A3 1885
(Copyright 1885: 19488)

NK 0204150 DLC

Knights of Pythias. Tennessee. Grand lodge.
Official proceedings of the 25th annual session of the grand lodge Knights of Pythias, N.A.S.A., E., A., A and A. Jurisdiction of Tennessee, held in the Pythian temple, Nashville, Tennessee, July 24, 25, 26, 27, 1923.
89 p.

NK 0204151 TNF

Knights of Pythias. Uniform rank. California brigade. 3d regiment.
Souvenir of Third regiment, Southern California, August 11th, 1902. [Los Angeles, 1902] 127 p. illus. 14 x 23cm.

1. Los Angeles—Descr.
N. Y. P. L. December 10, 1943

NK 0204152 NN

Knights of Pythias. Uniform rank. Michigan.
Journal of proceedings...of the Grand division of Michigan... 1st- 1883- Lansing, Mich., 1883-

NK 0204153 MiD-B

Knights of Pythias. *Uniform rank. Supreme assembly.*
Drill regulations, Uniform rank, Knights of Pythias. Rev. 1911. By authority of the Supreme assembly. [Minneapolis, Murphy-Travis co., °1911]
224 p. illus. 15cm. $0.75
Contains music.

1. Knights of Pythias—Rituals.

11-23524
Library of Congress HS1285.A3 1911

NK 0204154 DLC

Knights of Pythias. Uniform Rank. Supreme Assembly.
Rules and regulations of the Uniform Rank, Knights of Pythias, 1916, as amended by Supreme Assembly, 1912-1914. [Grand Rapids, Mich., 1916.] 95 p. 23cm.
"Price list...September 20, 1920," mounted on p. 45; "General orders," issued 1912-1920, inserted at end.

NK 0204155 NN

Knights of Pythias. Victoria, B.C., Far West lodge, no. 1.
By-laws. Victoria [1926]
15 p. 14 cm.
Cover title.
Accompanied by 4 p. supplement of amendments, dated 1927.

NK 0204156 CaBViPA

HS 1253 V8 A3
Knights of Pythias. Virginia. Grand Lodge.
Proceedings. [1st]- sess. 1868/69-
Petersburg, Va. [etc.]
v. in ports. 22-24 cm. annual.
1868/69-1870/71 not numbered.
Title varies: -19 , Journal of proceedings.

NK 0204157 Vi

Knights of Pythias. Washington (State) Grand lodge.
Constitution and grand statutes as adopted May 1896 session, revised to July 1909, with amendments adopted 1910, 1911 and 1912. Colfax, Wash., Bramwell Brothers 1909 [-1912]
1 v. illus.

NK 0204158 Wa

VOLUME 300

Knights of Pythias. Washington (State) Grand Lodge.
Constitution of the Knights of Pythias for subordinate lodges, Grand Jurisdiction, State of Washington. Adopted at ninth annual session of Grand Lodge at Tacoma, May 17, 18 and 19, 1892. Seattle, Koch & Oakley Printing Co., 1892.
96 p.

NK 0204159 WaU

Knights of Pythias. Washington (State) Grand Lodge.
Reports ... to the convention ... 19
[Spokane?]
v.

NK 0204160 Wa

Knights of Pythias. Washingtonville, Ohio. Welcom Lodge, no. 247.
By-laws ... Salem, O. Harris & co., 1898.
15p.

NK 0204161 OClWHi

Knights of Pythias. *West Virginia. Grand lodge.*
Proceedings ... regular convention.
[Parkersburg,
v. ports. 23cm.

CA 18-422 Unrev'd

Library of Congress HS1253.W4A2

NK 0204162 DLC

Knights of Pythias. *West Virginia. Grand lodge.*
Pythian booklet. Copyright ... by W. Frank Stout. [Clarksburg] Clarksburg publishing company, °1944.
[12] p. 23cm.
Cover-title: Diamond jubilee, commemorating seventy-fifth anniversary, Knights of Pythias, grand domain, West Virginia, Berkeley Springs, Aug. 23, 24, 25, 1944.

I. Stout, W. Frank, 1867– comp. II. Title.

44-9140

Library of Congress HS1253.W4A7
[2] 366.2

NK 0204163 DLC

---

*
HS1254
.W5W56
1896
Knights of Pythias. Winchester, Va. Winchester Lodge No. 65.
By-laws and rules of order of Winchester Lodge, No. 65; instituted Thursday, Dec. 1, 1887. New Market, Va., Henkel & Co., 1896.
20 p. 16cm.

NK 0204164 ViU

Knights of Pythias. *Wisconsin. Grand lodge.*
First digest of laws of the Grand lodge of Wisconsin, Knights of Pythias. Issued by authority of the Grand lodge. 1885. By L. W. Coe ... Milwaukee, Burdick & Armitage, printers, 1885.
73, [1], xlii p. 15½cm.

I. Coe, Ledyard W.

9-18094†

Library of Congress HS1225.W6A3 1885
(Copyright 1885: 1958)

NK 0204165 DLC

Knights of Pythias. *Wisconsin. Grand Lodge.*
Grand constitution and grand statutes, adopted at the 47th Annual Convention, Sheboygan, Wisconsin, June 18 and 19, 1918. [Milwaukee?] 1918.
95 p. 24 cm.

HS1253.W6A32 51-49594

NK 0204166 DLC

Knights of Pythias. Wyoming. Grand Lodge.
Grand Lodge of Wyoming, Knights of Pythias; Proceedings of the meeting of organization and First Annual Session at Cheyenne, Wyoming Territory. August 23-5, 1884. ... Cheyenne, Wyo., Bristol & Knabe, 1884.
64, 88, 39, cxiv p. 22 cm.

NK 0204167 Wy

Knights of Pythias beneficial association of Massachusetts.
Laws and regulations. Malden, 1877.

NK 0204168 Nh

Knights of Pythias illustrated
see under [Cook, Ezra Asher] 1841-1911.

Knights of Pythias library association, *San Francisco.*
Annual report.
San Francisco, 18
v. 22cm.

8-24409†

Library of Congress Z733.S192

NK 0204170 DLC

Knights of Pythias (Negro)
see Knights of Pythias of North and South America, Europe, Asia, Africa and Australia.

HS
2259
P94
V8
Knights of Pythias of North and South America, Europe, Asia, and Africa. Virginia. Grand Lodge.
Proceedings of the session. 1st–
1886?–
Richmond, Planet Electric Power Print.
v. ports. 23 cm. annual.

NK 0204172 Vi

Knights of Pythias of North and South America, Europe, Asia, Africa and Australia. New Jersey. Grand lodge.
History of Knights of Pythias, supreme jurisdiction North America, South America, Europe, Asia, Africa and Australia, state of New Jersey, by Joseph H. Morgan, grand historian, giving a brief account of the origin and growth of the Grand and subordinate lodges, Uniform Rank, Court of Calanthe, and D.O.K.K. ... [Nashville, Tenn., A.M.E. Sunday School Union, 1912?]
182, [1] p. front. (port.) illus. (incl. ports. 23.5 cm.
1. Negroes - New Jersey. 2. Morgan, Joseph H 1843-

NK 0204173 NjR

Knights of Pythias of North and South America, Europe, Asia, Africa and Australia. Supreme lodge.
Revised Ritual for subordinate lodges of Knights of Pythias of No. Am., So. Am., E., A., A., and Australia, edited by Douglas Roberts. New York, Fitzgerald publishing corporation, °1922.
104 p. diagrs. 17cm.

1. Knights of Pythias—Rituals. I. Roberts, Douglas, ed.

22-20902 Revised

Library of Congress HS1233.A4 1922
[r42c2]

NK 0204174 DLC

Knights of Pythias of North and South America, Europe, Asia, Africa and Australia. Supreme lodge.
Revised ritual for subordinate lodges of Knights of Pythias of No. Am., So. Am., E., A., A., and Australia; edited by Harold Sander. Danbury, Conn.: Behrens Pub. Co., 1932. 107 p. 17cm.

On cover: Sander's Ritual of Knights of Pythias.

780987A. 1. No subject. I. Sander, Harold, ed.

NK 0204175 NN

HS
2259
P95
V8
Knights of Pythias of the Eastern and Western Hemispheres. Virginia. Grand Lodge.
Proceedings of the session. 1st–
1892?–
Richmond.
v. 23 cm. annual.

NK 0204176 Vi

Knights of Red Cross of Constantine
see Freemasons. Red Cross of Constantine.

Knights of Rhodes
see Knights of Malta.

HFB87
.K748
C
Knights of St. Crispin.
Constitution. [n.p.] 1869-1872.
5 v. 13-15½ cm.

Library has: 1869 (Boston ed.); 1869 (Haverhill ed.), 1870, 1871, 1872

1869 (Haverhill, ed.) also contains Local no. 213, Danville, N.H. constitution.

I. Knights of St. Crispin. Local no. 213, Danville, N.H.

NK 0204179 WHi

Knights of St. Crispin.
Constitution of state and subordinate lodges, 1871. Albany, 1871.
16°

NK 0204180 MnHi

VOLUME 300

Knights of St. Crispin.
Constitution of the International grand lodge of the order K.O.S.C. Also the constitution of the subordinate lodges of the above order, adopted at Worcester, April 23, 1869. Boston, Printed at "Weekly American workman" office, 1869.

Paper cover: Constitution and by-laws of Friendship lodge, no. 219, Knights of St. Crispin of Philadelphia, Pa.

NK 0204181 MH

Knights of St. Crispin.
K.O.S.C. monthly journal
see under title

HFBB7 .K748 MIS
Knights of St. Crispin.
A list of lodges, numbers and post office addresses of the Order...December 1st, 1870. [n.p., 1870?]
[4] p. 35 x 22 cm. fold. to 22 x 18 cm.
Caption title.

NK 0204183 WHi

HFBB7 K748 MIS
Knights of St. Crispin.
[Miscellaneous ephemeral materials not fully catalogued.]

NK 0204184 WHi

HFBB7 .K748 P
Knights of St. Crispin.
Proceedings. v. 2-5, 1869-1872.
[n.p.]
3 v. 21½-23 cm.
Lack vol. 4

1. Shoemakers - U.S. - Societies, etc.

NK 0204185 WHi

HFBB7 .K748 MIS
Knights of St. Crispin.
Ritual of the degree of * * * in the Order...Temple of * * * . Boston, Printed at Weekly American workman office, 1870.
9 p. 18 cm.

NK 0204186 WHi

Knights of St. Crispin.
Ritual of the order of the Knights of St. Crispin. Boston, Printed at "Weekly American workman" office, 1869.
24 p. 18½cm.

19-2129

Library of Congress HD6515.B6K6

NK 0204187 DLC

HFBB7 .K748 R
Knights of St. Crispin.
Ritual of the order. Milwaukee, Riverside printing house, 1870.
17, 16, 18 p. 19 cm.

In English, German and French. Each in its own separately paginated part, having its own title page.

NK 0204188 WHi NcD

366.6 K748rG
Knights of St. Crispin.
Ritual des Ordens der Ritter des Hl. Crispinus. Milwaukee, Uebersetzt und gedruckt im Riverside Printing House, 1870.
16p. 19cm.

NK 0204189 IU

HFA6Z .P88L SA24
Knights of St. Crispin. Assembly no. 495, St. Louis, Mo.
Consitution and by-laws of Knights of St. Crispin assembly no. 495, K. of L., adopted January 1st, 1883. St. Louis, J.H. Crole print., 1887.
16 p. 15 cm.

Cover title.

1. Shoemakers - St. Louis.
I. Knights of Labor, St. Louis St. Crispin Assembly no. 495, Knights of Labor, St. Louis

NK 0204189-1 WHi

Knights of St. Crispin. City of the straits lodge no. 26, Detroit, Mich.
By-laws of City of the straits lodge No. 26, Detroit, Michigan. [Also Constitution of International grand lodge and subordinate lodges. Boston, pr. of Rockwell & Churchill, 1877.
24 p. 24°.

NK 0204189-2 MB

HFBB7 .K748 MIS
Knights of St. Crispin. Eureka lodge, no. 34, Marlboro, Mass.
Constitution and by-laws. Boston, Printed at Weekly American workman office, 1869.
[3]-10, [3]-16 p. 15 cm.
Cover title.
In three parts, each with separate title-page: [1] Constitution of the International Grand Lodge of the Order.-[2] Constitution of subordinate lodges.-[3] By-laws of Eureka Lodge, no. 34, Marlboro, Mass.

NK 0204189-3 WHi

Knights of St. Crispin. Hanson lodge, no. 135, Boston, Mass.
Constitution and by-laws of Hanson lodge, Knights of St. Crispin, no. 135. Boston, Off. of "American workman," 1869. 14 p. 15cm.

NK 0204190 NN

Knights of St. Crispin. International Grand Lodge, Boston, Mass.
Constitution of the International grand lodge of the order K.O.S.C. Also the constitution of the subordinate lodges ...
see under Knights of St. Crispin.

---

*7567.77

Knights of St. Crispin. International Grand Lodge, Boston, Mass., 1878.
Synopsis of proceedings . . . June 11-14, 1878.
[Boston. 1878.] 17 pp. 23 cm.
There is no title-page.

NK 0204192 MB

Knights of St. Crispin. Lodge no. 37, Spencer, Mass.
Constitution and by-laws of Knights of St. Crispin, No. 37, of Spencer, Mass. Boston, "American workman," 1869. 13 p. 14cm.

1. Trade unions, Shoemakers'—U. S.—Mass.—Spencer.
N. Y. P. L. May 24, 1943

NK 0204193 NN

HFBB7 .K748 MIS
Knights of St. Crispin. New York (state)
Proceedings. , 1870-
[n.p.]
1 v. 22 cm.

Library has: vol. 2, 1870.

NK 0204194 WHi

HFBB7 .K748 MIS
Knights of St. Crispin. Special committee on co-operation.
Report...adopted April 26th, 1871. Lowell, Mass., Stone & Huse...print., 1871.
10 p. 24 cm.

Cover title.

1. Cooperation - U.S.

NK 0204195 WHi

Knights of St. George. (f. 1880) Commandery no. 115, Dayton, Ohio.
Constitution und Neben-Gesetze des Deutschen Römisch-Katholischen St. George Ritter-Vereins von der Emmanuel's Kirche zu Dayton, Ohio... Dayton: "Daytoner Volkszeitung," 1901. 20, 20, 21, 12 p. 16°.

Includes: The English translation of Constitution and Neben-Gesetze, Constitution and by-laws of the St. George Commandery No. 115, and of the St. Johns Beneficial Branch, each with separate pagination.

1. Societies, Mutual aid—U. S.—O.—Dayton. 2. Germans in the U. S.—O.—Dayton.
N. Y. P. L. February 28, 1929

NK 0204196 NN

Knights of St. James of Compostella, Order of
see
Orden Militar de Santiago.

Knights of St. John of Jerusalem
see **Knights of Malta.**

---

27 5605
Knights of St. John and Malta.
Regulations for the uniform of the kts. of St. John. Compiled under resolutions passed at the 18th annual convention held at Dayton, Ohio, June 24, 1896, by the military committee. Rochester, N.Y., the John P. Smith printing house, 1897.
12 p. 4°.

NK 0204199 DLC

Knights of St. John. and Malta.
Souvenir program. International convention.
Peoria, Ill.,
v. ports. 15 x 23cm.
Cover-title.

CA 5-1725 Unrev'd

Library of Congress

NK 0204200 DLC

VOLUME 300

Knights of St. John and Malta. Detroit.
...Installation of officers, presentation of charter... Detroit, Michigan, April 15, 1939. n. imp.
[12] p., ports.
[Reported as the functions of "Canadian Legion, United States, Knights of Malta, Post 129, Detroit." Identification above is tentative]

NK 0204201 MiD-B

Knights of St. John and Malta. Michigan.- First regiment
...Annual military day and competitive prize drill... [Detroit]

NK 0204202 MiD-B

The Knights of St. John: with the Battle of Lepanto and Siege of Vienna
see under [Drane, Augusta Theodosia] 1823-1894.

Knights of St. Patrick, *St. Louis.*
Thirty-seventh annual banquet, Knights of St. Patrick, Southern hotel, St. Louis, Tuesday, March seventeenth nineteen hundred and three. [St. Louis, The W. F. Burke printing co., 1903]
58, [6] p. illus., ports. 22cm.

CA 7-6159 Unrev'd

NK 0204204 DLC

Knights of St. Patrick, San Francisco.
43rd annual banquet of the Knights of St. Patrick, San Francisco, Hotel St. Francis, Saturday evening, March 16, 1918. Report of C. B. Flanagan. San Francisco, 1918.
12 p. illus. 23 cm.

I. Flanagan, C B

NK 0204205 CSf

Knights of St. Stqhen
see
Ordine de cavalieri di Santo Stefano

Knights of '76.
Constitution, Knights of '76, for the government of the illustrious Grand lodge, the state grand lodges, and subordinate forts, as adopted by the illustrious Grand lodge. Ottawa, Ill., W. K. Lecky, I. G. lodge, printer, 1875.
28 p. 15cm.
"Corrections," mounted on second and third pages of cover.

19-4685

Library of Congress HS1510.K86A5 1875

NK 0204207 DLC

Knights of '76.
Constitution of the Knights of '76, as adopted by the illustrious Grand lodge. 1776-1876. Chicago, Jameson & Morse, printers, 1876.
20 p. 16½cm.

19-4664

Library of Congress HS1510.K86A5 1876

NK 0204208 DLC

27.4
5605
Knights of '76.
Constitution with notes, references, and forms of procedure. By Geo. S. Williams. Chicago, Jameson & Morse, 1880.
48, 3-23 p. 12°.

NK 0204209 DLC

Knights of Solomon of America, Grand United Order of
see Grand United Order of Knights of Solomon. [Supplement]

Knights of Tabor.
A manual of the Knights of Tabor, and Daughters of the tabernacle, including the ceremonies of the order, constitutions, installations, dedications, and funerals, with forms, and the Taborian drill and tactics. By Moses Dickson ... St. Louis, Mo. [Press of G. I. Jones and company] 1879.
255 p. incl. plates, port., plans, diagrs. front. 21cm.
L. C. copy imperfect: p. 55-58 (including portrait) wanting.

I. Dickson, Moses. II. Daughters of Tabor.

45-52410

Library of Congress HS2259.T33K5
[2]

NK 0204211 DLC

Knights of Tabor
see also
International order of twelve of knights and daughters of Tabor.

Knights of temperance.
Ritual of the Knights of temperance. [New Castle, Pa., The News co., printers, °1891]
13 p. incl. plan. 19½cm.

CA 10-2970 Unrev'd

Library of Congress HV5287.K62 1891

NK 0204213 DLC

Knights of temperance. *Georgia.*
Ritual for the use of subordinate councils Knights of temperance, under the jurisdiction of the Grand council of Georgia ... By authority of the Grand council ... Atlanta, Ga., Judson, Dunlop & co., 1882.
48, ii p. incl. plan. 17½cm.

CA 10-2971 Unrev'd

Library of Congress HV5287.K62 1882

NK 0204214 DLC

366.o
K74r
Knights of the American brotherhood.
Ritual of the Knights of American brotherhood. n.p., 1880.
20p.

NK 0204215 IU

Knights of the Ancient Essenic Order.
Knights' review
see under title

---

*BROAD-
SIDE
1897
.K65
Knights of the Ancient Essenic Order. Danville Senate.
[Membership brochure. Danville? Va?, 1897?]
broadside ([4] p.) 10 x 12cm.

NK 0204217 ViU

Knights of the Bath
see Order of the Bath.

Knights of the cross. 1884
see under [Ramon, Ellen Margaret (Cox)] b. 1830-

Knights of the Cross; or, the Hermits Prophecy
see under [Beazley, Samuel] 1786-1851.

The knights of the frozen sea. A narrative of Arctic discovery and adventure. By the author of "Harry Lawton's adventures." With a map, and forty-four illustrations. New York, D. Appleton & co., 1867.
viii, 360 p. incl. front., illus., plates. fold. map. 19cm.

1. Arctic regions.

5-39952†

Library of Congress G620K69

NK 0204221 DLC CaBViPA WaS MnU OClW PPL CaOTP PPUNH

919.8
K748
1868
The knights of the frozen sea. A narrative of Arctic discovery and adventure. By the author of "Harry Lawton's adventures." With a map, and forty-four illustrations. 2d ed. London, Seeley, Jackson, & Halliday, 1868.
viii, 360p. incl. front.,illus.,plates. fold. map. 19cm.

1. Arctic regions.

NK 0204222 TxU PPFr

Knights of the globe.
Ritual for subordinate garrisons of the order of the Knights of the globe ... [Freeport, Ill., 1894]
48 p. diagrs. 21½cm.

9-32539†

Library of Congress HS1510.G582 1894
(Copyright 1894: 22006)

NK 0204223 DLC OkU

VOLUME 300

Knights of the Golden Circle.
Authentic exposition of the "K. G. C." ...
see under title

Knights of the golden circle
K.G.C.Haga V. bien a los pobres, tenga compasion de los infortunados, y dios cuidar de lo demas. n.p., 1860.
29p.

NK 0204225 PP

Knights of Golden Circle.
Rules, regulations & principles. N.Y., 1859.

NK 0204226 NjP

Tz 363.973 K748c.b Knights of the Golden Circle. Castroville, Tex. Castroville Castle.
By-laws of the Castroville Castle, "K.G.C." Approved August 16, 1861. [Castroville, Tex., 1861]
[7]ℓ. 28cm.
Caption title.
Typewritten copy of original in the possession of Sam Lanham, Waco, Tex.

NK 0204227 TxU

Tz 363.973 K748c.f Photo-copy Knights of the Golden Circle. Castroville, Tex. Castroville Castle.
First, or military degree. [Castroville, Tex., 1861]
13p. 16cm.
Caption title.
Photocopy (positive) from original in the possession of Sam Lanham, Waco, Tex.

NK 0204228 TxU

Knights of the Golden Eagle.
Brief history of the order. n.p.n.d.

NK 0204229 Nh

Knights of the Golden Eagle.
Proceedings of the Supreme castle. Phil., 1895-8.
v.

NK 0204230 Nh

Knights of the golden eagle. Connecticut. Grand castle.
Constitution and laws ... governing the Grand and subordinate castles of the state of Connecticut. [1896] Bridgeport, Conn, 1896-
1 v. 14.5 cm. in envelope 22.5 cm.

NK 0204231 CtY

Knights of the Golden Eagle. *Pennsylvania. Grand Castle.*
Proceedings of the annual session.
Philadelphia.
v. illus. 24 cm.

HS1510.K9P4 51-38866 ‡

NK 0204232 DLC

Knights of the golden horse shoe. Supreme lodge.
Constitution and laws of the Supreme lodge of the Knights of the golden horse shoe, governing the supreme, grand and subordinate lodges ... Adopted by the Supreme lodge, Richmond, Va., 1900. [Richmond, Va.] F. L. Aikman, c1900.
84 p. 16 cm.

NK 0204233 Vi

The Knights of the golden Horse-shoe; a traditional tale ...
see under [Caruthers, William Alexander] ca. 1800-1846.

Knights of the Golden Horseshoe, The Shenandoah - Daughter of the stars
see under [Davidson, Arthur] of Virginia.

Reference card

Knights of the golden rule
see
Knights and ladies of the golden rule.

Knights of the Grail
see under [Underdown, Emily]

Knights of the grand legion. Providence, R.I. Spartan lodge, no. 1.
Constitution and by-laws. Providence, 1873.
19 p. 16 cm.

NK 0204238 RPB

Knights of the holy cross.
Ritual of the Knights of the holy cross. Cheboygan, Mich., Cheboygan castle [1919]
cover-title, 20, [1] p. 21½cm.

Library of Congress BX8203.K7A5 1919 19-6764
Copyright A 511823 [2]

NK 0204239 DLC

Knights of the Holy Sepulchre
see Order of the Holy Sepulchre.

The knights of the horse-shoe...
see under [Caruthers, William Alexander] ca. 1800-1846.

Knights of the Klan versus Knights of Columbus
see under [Thomas, Charles G]

Knights of the Ku Klux Klan
see
Ku Klux Klan (1915-)

Knights of the Ku Klux Klan is the official name, Ku Klux Klan the form in general use. To distinguish the Klan from that of the reconstruction period (1866-1869) the date (1915-) is added to the name when used as a heading on the catalogue cards.

PR 3991 A1K47 **The Knights of the lion, a romance of the thirteenth century. With a pref. by the Marquess of Lorne. London, Chatto & Windus, 1889.**
ix,397 p.

I. Argyll, John George Edward Henry Douglas Sutherland Campbell, 9th duke of, 1845-1914.

NK 0204244 CLU NcU

HS2330 .K5A13 Knights of the long table.
The **Archives**: record of the Knights of the long table.
[Brooklyn? 18

Knights of the loyal guard.
Constitution and laws of the Knights of the loyal guard, governing the supreme division, grand council, grand divisions and subordinate divisions ... Flint, Mich., Wolverine citizen print, 1897.
55 p. 23cm.

9-32528†

Library of Congress HS1510.L88A5 1897 (Copyright 1897: 57515)

NK 0204246 DLC

Knights of the loyal guard.
Laws of the Loyal guard. [Flint? Mich.] 1906.
77 p. fold. tab. 18cm.

15-339

Library of Congress HS1510.L88A5 1906

NK 0204247 DLC

Knights of the loyal guard.
Ritual of the Loyal guard. Complete ed., including opening, closing, initiation, together with installation, memorial and burial services, to be used by all subordinate, auxiliary and union divisions. Approved and adopted, 1905. [Flint? Mich., 1905?]
72 p. incl. plan. 20cm.

15-338

Library of Congress HS1510.L882 1905

NK 0204248 DLC

VOLUME 300

Knights of the Maccabees
see
Maccabees, Knights of

Knights of the Maccabees of the State of Michigan
see
Knights of Modern Maccabees

Knights of the Most Illustrious Order of St. Patrick.
Statutes. Dublin, printed by George Grierson, 1809.
112 p. 20 cm.

NK 0204251 IEdS

Knights of the mystic chain. *New York (State) Select castle.*
Proceedings of the 1st- annual session of the Select castle, Ancient order knights of the mystic chain, of the state of New York ...
Binghamton, N. Y., 1890-
v. 22cm.

9-31821†
Library of Congress HS1510.M94N7

NK 0204252 DLC

Knights of the mystic chain. *Pennsylvania. Select castle.*
Proceedings of the ... annual session of the Select castle, Ancient order, Knights of the mystic chain of the state of Pennsylvania ...
Pittsburgh, 18
v. ports. 22cm.

9-26189
Library of Congress HS1510.M94P4

NK 0204253 DLC

Knights of the mystic chain. *Supreme castle.*
Formation and proceedings of the Supreme castle of the world, Ancient order knights of the mystic chain ... Kutztown, Pa., "Kutztown journal" printing office, 1872.
34 p. illus. 23cm.

9-32523†
Library of Congress HS1510.M94A5 1872

NK 0204254 DLC

Knights of the mystic chain. *Supreme castle.*
Proceedings of the annual session of the Supreme castle, Ancient order, knights of the mystic chain ...
Pittsburgh, 18
v. 22cm.

9-31808†
Library of Congress HS1510.M94A2

NK 0204255 DLC

Knights of the mystic chain. *Supreme lodge.*
Constitution and laws ... together with by-laws prescribed for the government of subordinate lodges. Adopted July, 1900. Lynchburg, Va., 1900.
66 p., 1 l. nar. 12°.

Nov. 1, 1900-155
Library of Congress (Copyright 1900 A 18420)

NK 0204256 DLC

Knights of the mystic chain. *Supreme lodge.*
Ritual ... containing the opening and closing ceremonies, degrees of knighthood, mystery and chivalry, and installation. Adopted by the Supreme lodge, July 1900. Lynchburg, Va. [1900]
63 p. 12°.

Nov. 1, 1900-154
Library of Congress (Copyright 1900 A 18419)

NK 0204257 DLC

HS155 .K6 1875 Knights of the Orient, their rites and ceremonies, No., 15 ... Arranged in accordance with the standard formula. New York, Redding & Co., 1875.
67 p. 15 cm.
Copyright by M.W. Redding.

NK 0204258 DLC

HS155 .K6 1876 Knights of the Orient, their rites and ceremonies, No., 15....
New York, 1876.
1v. 16°

NK 0204259 DLC

Knights of the orient; their rites and ceremonies. 17 W.B. Arranged in accordance with the standard formula. N.Y., Redding & co., 1887.
67 p. T.

NK 0204260 PP

Knights of the Red Cross of Rome and Constantine
see
Freemasons. *Red Cross of Constantine.*

CR 4869 K5 Knights of the Round Table Club.
The manual of the Knights of the Round Table Club (A.D. 1720) (Confirmed in General Council, 12 December, 1927) [n. p.] 1927.
140 p. illus., ports. 25 cm.
Title within ornamental border.
"Limited to 500 copies."

NK 0204262 OU

Knights of the Round table of King Arthur, Tintagel, Eng.
see
Order of the fellowship of the knights of the Round table of King Arthur.

Knights of the royal arch.
Ritual ... by the ... founder Dr. C. S. Rogers. Hot Springs, Ark., 1900.
31 p. incl. plan. 17cm.

Nov. 1, 1900-156
Library of Congress (Copyright 1900 A 4075)

NK 0204264 DLC

Knights of the sacred goat, a side degree for ... fraternal orders that need a "tonic."
Omaha, n.d.
15 p. 19 cm.
Cover title.
Copyright by Sam E. Smith.

NK 0204265 RPB

The knights of the seal; or, The mysteries of the three cities
see under [Duganne, Augustine Joseph Hickey] 1823-1884.

Reference card
Knights of the Sherwood forest
see
Foresters of America. *Knights of the Sherwood forest.*

Knights of the Sun of the United States of America
see Freemasons. U.S. Scottish Rite.

KNIGHTS OF THE SWORD OF LIVONIA.
Founded 1201 and in 1237 merged with the Teutonic Kngiths.
See TEUTONIC KNIGHTS.

Knights of the white camelia.
Constitution adopted at a general convention held in the city of New Orleans, on the 4th of June, 1868. New Orleans, L. R. Simmons & co., print, 1868. 20 p. 20cm.

532707B. 1. United States—Hist.—Reconstruction period, 1865-1877. I. Title.
N. Y. P. L. September 5, 1950

NK 0204270 NN MH

Knights of the white camelia.
... The constitution and the ritual of the Knights of the white camelia. Morgantown, W. Va., 1904.
32 p. 19cm. (West Virginia university. Documents relating to reconstruction. Ed. by Walter L. Fleming ... no. 1)
Advertising matter: p. 32.

1. Reconstruction.
4-16328
Library of Congress E668.F59

NK 0204271 DLC TxU ViU OO MiU OU OClWHi PU ICJ MB

Knights of Toussaint L'Ouverture of the world.
Ritual of the Knights of Toussaint L'Ouverture of the world, inc. ... Washington, D. C., Murray bros. printing co., inc., 1913.
32 p. 14½cm.

15-187
Library of Congress HS2259.T682 1913

NK 0204272 DLC

VOLUME 300

Knights of Uncle Sam.
The Knights of Uncle Sam. A call to action. Foundation, faith and objects. The nine demands of liberalism, revised. Knights of Uncle Sam calendar. The new ten commandments. Litany... Sterling, Colo.: J. G. Schwalm, 1920. 16 p. 16°.

Cover-title.

1. Freethinking.—Assoc. and organizations.
N. Y. P. L. April 25, 1921.

NK 0204273 NN

Knights of valor.
Constitution and by-laws of the Knights of valor and the parent order of the Knights of valor for the public schools of America, by Ernest Joseph Robinson ... [Aspinwall? Pa., 1914?]

32 p. 17½cm.

Cover-title: The Knights of valor; a boys organization for the public schools of America.

I. Robinson, Ernest Joseph.

E 14-1965

Library, U. S. Bur. of Education HS3319.K74

NK 0204274 DHEW

Knights of Vartan, Inc.
Yeghisheh
see under Eghishe, Saint, d. 480.

27.4 **Knights of Venus of the United States.**
5605 Ritual. [Lexington, Ky., 1895]
58 p., 1 l. incl. front. 16°.

NK 0204276 DLC

Knight's ornamental alphabets. Improved edition. London: J. Rimell [18—]. 5 pl. ob. 8°.

Title from cover.

1. Handwriting.—Specimens. 2. Alphabets.
N. Y. P. L. September 27, 1911.

NK 0204277 NN

Knight's penny magazine. v. 1–9, Mar. 31, 1832–Dec. 31, 1840; v. 10–14 (new ser. [v. 1–5]) Jan. 2, 1841–Dec. 27, 1845; [v. 15–16 (3d ser., v. 1–2) 1846. London, C. Knight & co. [1832–46]

16 v. in 15. illus. 19½–29 cm. weekly.

Title varies: 1832–45, The Penny magazine of the Society for the diffusion of useful knowledge.
1846, Knight's penny magazine.
C. Knight, editor.
No more published.

I. Knight, Charles, 1791–1873, ed. II. Society for the diffusion of useful knowledge, London. III. The Penny magazine of the Society for the diffusion of useful knowledge.

AP4.K7 1—26474

PPAmP AAP CtNIC CSt AzU VtMiM CaBVaU
NK 0204278 DLC MNS NN MB PPT PV NcD NcU PHC TNJ-P

Knight's pictorial gallery of arts ...
see under Knight, Charles, 1791-1873.

Knight's quarterly magazine. v. 1–3; June 1823–Nov. 1824. London, Printed for C. Knight and co., 1823–24.

3 v. 22cm.

Charles Knight, editor.
Continued as the Quarterly magazine (new ser., no. 1, 1825) *cf.* Brit. mus. Catalogue.

I. Knight, Charles, 1791–1873, ed.

7–19882†

Library of Congress AP4.K68

NK 0204280 DLC OrU MiU OO NcD NN

Micro Film F117
Knight's quarterly magazine. v.1-3; June 1823-Nov. 1824. London.
1 reel. 35mm. (English literary periodicals, 87E)
Editor: Charles Knight.
Superseded by Quarterly magazine.
Microfilm (positive). Ann Arbor, Mich., University Microfilms, 1961.
Filmed with Hunt's London journal.

I. Knight, Charles, 1791-1873, ed.

NK 0204281 PSt ViU NBuU

Knight's quarterly magazine.

Macaulay, Thomas Babington Macaulay, *1st baron*, 1800–1859.
... The works of Lord Macaulay complete. Ed. by his sister, Lady Trevelyan ... New York, London and Bombay, Longmans, Green, and co., 1897.

HS 1510 .K53
Knights' review. v.1, no.1-6.
Louisville, Ky., Knights of the Ancient Essenic Order, 1896.
1v. illus.,ports. 22cm.

Vol.1 issued 1892 and 1895 but not actually published until 1896. cf. Union List of Serials.

I. Knights of the Ancient Essenic Order.

NK 0204283 OrU

Knight's store of knowledge for all readers
see under [Knight, Charles] 1791-1873.

Knights Templar Council Officers' Association of the Metropolitan District of New York.
Commandery comment
see under title

Knights Templars (Masonic)
see Freemasons. Knights Templars.

Knights Templars (*Monastic and military order*)
see
Templars.

Knights templars and Masonic mutual aid association, Cincinnati, O.
Annual report... Cincinnati,
v. 12 1/2cm

NK 0204288 OClWHi

Knights templars and Masons life indemnity company, *Chicago.*
The Knights templars and Masons life indemnity company. Constitution ... [Chicago?] °1885.

[4] p. 30½cm.

Caption title.

CA 9-5595 Unrev'd

Library of Congress HG9243.K56
(Copyright 1885: 11745)

NK 0204289 DLC

Knights templars' manual... 1879
see under Coney, H. M.

[Knight's tour manuscript. 37p. n.d.]

NK 0204291 OCl

Knight's tourist's companion through the land we live in
see under Knight, Charles, 1791-1873.

Knight's weekly volume. London, C. Knight & co., 1844-
v. 15 cm.
Title varies: 1846- Knight's monthly volumes.

NK 0204293 DLC PU OU

Knightsbridge, Eng. Chapel of the Holy Trinity.
Register of the Chapel of the Holy Trinity, Knightsbridge, 1658–1681. Transcribed by J. Harvey Bloom, M. A. London, Mitchell, Hughes and Clarke [1925]

1 p. l., 140 p. 26cm.

1. Registers of births, etc.—Knightsbridge, Eng. I. Bloom, James Harvey, 1860–

40-37678

Library of Congress CS436.K65
[2] 929.3094213

NK 0204294 DLC NN OClWHi NcD ViU OKentU

Knightstown, Ind. Board of trustees.
Report 1888/89 90/91 92/93 95/96; 97/98 and announcement 1887/88 91/92 93/94 96/97 98/99
Knightstown, Ind., 1887-93)
5 v.

NK 0204295 DHEW

Knightstown, Ind. Indiana soldiers' and sailors' children's home
see
Indiana. Soldiers' and sailors' children's home, *Knightstown.*

Knightwick, *Eng.* (*Parish*)
see
Knightwick with Doddenham and Broadwas, *Eng.* (*Worcestershire*) *Parish.*

Knightwick with Doddenham and Broadwas, *Eng.* (*Worcestershire*) *Parish.*
The parish registers of Knightwick and Doddenham in the diocese and county of Worcester from A. D. 1538 to A. D. 1812, edited by Joseph Bowstead Wilson ... London, Printed at the Chiswick press, 1891.

vi p., 1 l., 206 p., 1 l. 29½cm.

"Only 52 copies ... no. 48 [signed] J. Bowstead Wilson."

1. Registers of births, etc.—Knightwick with Doddenham and Broadwas, Eng. (Worcestershire) I. Wilson, Joseph Bowstead, ed.

44-11106

Library of Congress DA690.K66A3

NK 0204298 DLC PHi MdBP

VOLUME 300

Книги для детских и школьных библиотек; рекомендательный указатель литературы.
Москва.

v. in 23 cm. 4 no. a year.

Began in 1952.
Issued by Gosudarstvennaiа biblioteka SSSR imeni V. I. Lenina.

1. Children's literature, Russian—Bibl.—Period. I. Moscow. Publichnaiа biblioteka.
Title romanized: Knigi dliа detskikh i shkol'nykh bibliotek.

Z1037.6.K52 67-123629

NK 0204299 DLC

JN6500 A2 855 [Knigi razriadnyia]
Книги разрядныя, по оффиціальнымъ оныхъ спискамъ, изданныя съ высочайшаго соизволенія II-мъ отдѣленіемъ Собственной Его Императорскаго Величества канцеляріи ... Санктпетербургъ [Тип. II отдѣленія Собственной Е. И. В. канцеляріи] 1853–55.

2 v. 28cm.

Vol. 2, p. viii–ix, contains a list of the original documents, with the numbers under which they may be found at the various Moscow archives.

1. Russia—Hist.—1613–1689—Sources. 2. Russia—Pol. & govt.—1613–1689. I. Russia. Sobstvennaiа Ego Imperatorskago Velichestva kantseliаriiа.

CA 14—229 Unrev'd

NK 0204300 DLC

Knigoizdatel'skoe tovarishchestvo "Prosveshchenie," *Leningrad*
see **Tovarishchestvo "Prosveshchenie,"** *Leningrad.*

Knigoizdatel'stvo D. I. Tikhomirova, *Moscow*
see **Tikhomirov, D. I.,** *firm, Moscow.*

Knigoizdatelstvo i uchebni pomagla Khristo G. Danov, *Sofia*
see **Danov, Kh. G.,** *firm, Sofia.*

Knigoizdatelstvo Khr. G. Danov, *Sofia*
see **Danov, Kh. G.,** *firm, Sofia.*

Knigoizdatel'stvo Khristianskogo soiuza molodykh liudeĭ, *Paris*
see
Young Men's Christian Associations. *Paris.*

Knigoizdatel'stvo "Pchela," *Leningrad*
see **Pchela, Knigoizdatel'stvo,** *Leningrad.*

Knigoizdatel'stvo "Vozrozhdenie"
see
Vozrozhdenie, Izdatel'stvo, *Moscow.*

Z1007 .K63
Книгоноша. г. [1]–4, № 47 (№ 1–168); 16 апр. 1923–26. Москва, Гос. изд-во [etc.]

4 v. ports. 27–48 cm. weekly.

Issued by TSentral'noe biuro partiĭnykh, sovetskikh, professional'nykh i kooperativnykh izdatel'stv VKP(b) (under its earlier name, Biuro partiĭnykh izdatel'stv SSSR, Apr. 1923–May 1924)
L. C. set incomplete: v. 1, no. 8–9; v. 2, no. 38–50; v. 4, no. 14, 19, 28, wanting.

1. Bibliography—Period. I. Vsesoiuznaiа Kommunisticheskaiа partiiа (bol'shevikov) TSentral'noe biuro partiĭnykh, sovetskikh, professional'nykh i kooperativnykh izdatel'stv.
Title transliterated: Knigonosha.

Z1007.K63 51–34534

Library of Congress [2]

NK 0204308 DLC

Knigosbyt ONTI
see
Russia (*1923– U. S. S. R.*) *Ob"edinennoe nauchno-tekhnicheskoe izdatel'stvo. Sbytovoe upravlenie.*

Knigotorgovaiа baza Mogiza, *Moscow*
see **Knigotorgovoe ob"edinenie gosudarstvennykh izdatel'stv.** *Moskovskoe oblastnoe otdelenie.*

Knigotorgovoe ob"edinenie gosudarstvennykh izdatel'stv.
Каталог почтовых марок СССР. [Составлен А. С. Чумаковым; редактор И. С. Петрухин. Москва] Филателическая контора Когиза, 1948.

133 p. 22 cm.

1. Postage-stamps—Russia. 2. ~~Postage-stamps—Catalogs.~~ I. Chumakov, A. S.
Title transliterated: Katalog pochtovykh marok SSSR.

HE6185.R9K6 49–29291*

NK 0204311 DLC

Knigotorgovoe ob"edinenie gosudarstvennykh izdatel'stv.
Книги по металлургии; каталог. Москва, 1948.

30 p. 17 cm.
Cover title.

1. Metallurgy—Bibl.—Catalogs.
Title transliterated: Knigi po metallurgii.

Z6678.K6 50–28398

NK 0204312 DLC

Z372 .S6
Knigotorgovoe ob"edinenie gosudarstvennykh izdatel'stv.
Советская книжная торговля. авг. 1948–
[Москва, Искусство, etc.]

Z2495 .S68
Knigotorgovoe ob"edinenie gosudarstvennykh izdatel'stv.
Советский книжник. г. 8–[19]; 1929–40. Москва.

Knigotorgovoe ob"edinenie gosudarstvennykh izdatel'stv. *Leningradskoe oblastnoe otdelenie.*
Авиация; каталог книг, имеющихся на складе Ленокогиз'а. [Ленинград] 1935.

16, [8] p. 21 cm.

1. Aeronautics—Bibl.—Catalogs. *Title transliterated:* Aviatsiiа.

Z5066.K55 50–42398

Library of Congress

NK 0204315 DLC

Knigotorgovoe ob"edinenie gosudarstvennykh izdatel'stv. *Moskovskoe oblastnoe otdelenie.*
М. В. Фрунзе, 1885–1925. [Составил А. Тимофеев. Москва, 1939]

4 p. port. 18 cm. (В помощь библиотекарю)

1. Frunze, Mikhail Vasil'evich, 1885–1925. I. Timofeev, Aleksandr Semenovich.
Title transliterated: M. V. Frunze.

Z8317.82.K6 52–47254

NK 0204316 DLC

Knigotorgovoe ob"edinenie gosudarstvennykh izdatel'stv. *Moskovskoe oblastnoe otdelenie.*
Учебники и учебные пособия для высших учебных заведений; каталог книг. Москва, 1941.

7 p. 15 x 41 cm. fold. to 15 x 8 cm.

1. Text-books—Russia—Bibl.—Catalogs.
Title transliterated: Uchebniki i uchebnye posobiiа dliа vysshikh uchebnykh zavedeniĭ.

Z5817.K55 53–53135

NK 0204317 DLC

Knigotorgovoe ob"edinenie gosudarstvennykh izdatel'stv. *Nauchno-tekhnicheskiĭ sektor.*
Труды научно-исследовательских институтов и лабораторий промышленности (бывш. НТУ ВСНХ СССР) Каталог книг. [Составила П. П. Штеренталь] Москва, Советская книготорговля, 1933.

31 p. 20 cm.

Microfilm LC copy replaced by microfilm

1. Russia—Indus.—Bibl. I. Shterental', P. P. II. Title.
Title transliterated: Trudy nauchno-issledovatel'skikh institutov.

Z7915.R9K6 52–52044

NK 0204318 DLC

Knigotorgovoe ob"edinenie gosudarstvennykh izdatel'stv. *Sektor partiĭnoĭ i komsomol'skoĭ literatury.*
Книговедение; каталог книг. Москва, Когиз, 1934.

27 p. 18 cm.

1. Bibliography—Bibl.—Catalogs. I. Title.
Title transliterated: Knigovedenie; katalog knig.

Z1002.K6 52–46457

NK 0204319 DLC

Knigotorgovoe ob"edinenie gosudarstvennykh izdatel'stv. *Sektor partiĭnoĭ i komsomol'skoĭ literatury.*
Социально-экономическая литература; каталог. Москва, Когиз, 1935.

309 p. 21 cm.

1. Socialism—Bibl. 2. Economics—Bibl. I. Title.
Title transliterated: Sotsial'no-ekonomicheskaiа literatura.

Z7164.S67K65 53–53318

NK 0204320 DLC

(Knigovēdēnie)
Книговѣдѣніе; ежемѣсячный библіографическій журналъ (съ иллюстраціями) Органъ Московскаго библіографическаго кружка. г. 1.–3.; 1894–96. Москва, 1894–97.

3 v. illus., ports. 25½–26½cm.

Monthly (irregular): v. 1, no. 7/8, 9/10, 11/12; v. 2, no. 4/5, 6/8, 9/12; v. 3, no. 3/12 issued as 1 no. each.
Edited by A. D. Toropov.
The following monographs each have special t.-p. and separate paging:
"В. Н. Сторожевъ. Новое изданіе 'Наказа' императрицы Екатерины II": г. 1 (1894) no. 3. 16 p.
"В. Н. Сторожевъ. Родоначальникъ русской вѣтви Лермонтовыхъ": г. 1 (1894) no. 5, 6, 7/8. 34 p.

"Комиссія по организаціи домашняго чтенія, состоящая при Учебномъ отдѣлѣ Общества распространенія техническихъ знаній. Программы домашняго чтенія на 1894–95 годъ": г. 1 (1894) no. 9/10, 11/12. 118 p.
"Томачинскій, Василій. Начало библіотековѣдѣнія. Извлеченіе изъ соч. dr. Arnim Gräsel—Grundzüge der bibliothekslehre": г. 2 (1895) no. 1. 18 p.
"А. А. Сидоровъ. Историческій очеркъ русской печати въ Привислянскомъ краѣ": г. 3 (1896) no. 1, 2, 3/12. 69 p.
"А. Н. Лебедевъ. Надписи на старинныхъ книгахъ": г. 3 (1896) no. 1, 2. 34 p.
"Указатель къ журналу 'Юридическій вѣстникъ'. 1867–1892": г. 2 (1895) no. 1, 3, 6/8. 88 p.

No more published.

1. Russian literature—Bibl.—Period. 2. Bibliography—Period. 3. Russian periodicals—Bibl. 4. Russian periodicals—Indexes. 5. Libraries—Russia. 6. Siberia—Hist.—Bibl. 7. Publishers and publishing—Russia. 8. Press law—Russia. I. Toropov, Andreĭ Dmitrievich, 1851–1927, ed. II. Moskovskiĭ bibliograficheskiĭ kruzhok. III. Storozhev, Vasiliĭ Nikolaevich, 1866– IV. Catharine II, empress of Russia, 1729–1796. V. Obshchestvo rasprostraneniiа tekhnicheskikh znaniĭ, Moscow. Uchebnyĭ otdel. Komissiiа po organizatsii domashniago chteniiа. VI. Tomachinskiĭ, Vasiliĭ. VII. Sidorov, A. A. VIII. Lebedev, A. N. IX. Юридическій вѣстникъ (Indexes)

18–7192 Revised

Library of Congress Z2495.K6

NK 0204323 DLC

VOLUME 300

Kniha.
Ročník 1 (23 rijna, 1919–20 září, 1920)

Praha, 1919–20. 1 v.

Irregular.
Editor: L. J. Živný.
Superseded by Bibliografický katalog časopisectva Republiky Československé...

1. Library science.—Per. and soc. publ. 2. Bibliography.—Per. and soc. publ. 3. Živny, Ladislav J., editor.
N. Y. P. L. October 20, 1922.

NK 0204324 NN

Kniha, *Prague.*
Antonín Zápotocký. ⌜K sedmdesátinám presidenta republiky. V Praze⌝ 1954.
46 p. illus. 21 cm.

1. Zápotocký, Antonín, Pres. Czechoslovak Republic, 1884–1957.

DB217.Z3K6 58–33877 ‡

NK 0204325 DLC

Kniha, *Prague.*
František Kubka. ⌜Praha⌝ 1954.
15 p. illus. 21 cm.

1. Kubka, František, 1894–

PG5038.K86Z7 57–48295 ‡

NK 0204326 DLC

Kniha, *Prague.*
Josef Vissarionovič Stalin, 1879–1953. ⌜Ve spolupráci se Státním nakl. politické literatury a Národní knihovnou v Praze. V Praze⌝ 1954.
39 p. 21 cm.

1. Stalin, Iosif, 1879–1953—Bibl.

Z8833.5.K6 57–43131

NK 0204327 DLC

Kniha, *Prague.*
Julius Fučík, 23. II. 1903–8. IX. 1943. ⌜Bibliografie. Praha⌝ 1954.
23 p. illus. 21 cm.

1. Fučík, Julius, 1903–1943—Bibl.

Z8317.84.K6 56–29180

NK 0204328 DLC

Kniha, *Prague.*
Klement Gottwald, 1896–1953. ⌜Ve spolupráci se Státním nakl. politické literatury, Národní knihovnou v Praze a Ústavem dějin KSČ. Praha⌝ 1954.
22 p. 21 cm.

1. Gottwald, Klement, Pres. Czechoslovak Republic, 1896–1953.

DB217.G6K53 56–23165

NK 0204329 DLC

Kniha, *Prague.*
Konstantin Biebl, 1898–1951. ⌜Připravilo Tiskové oddělení nakl. Československý spisovatel. Praha, 1955⌝
16 p. illus. 21 cm.

1. Biebl, Konstantin.

PG5038.B5Z68 57–22828 ‡

NK 0204330 DLC

Kniha, *Prague.*
Národní umělkyně Marie Majerová. ⌜Bibliografii připravila ve spolupráci s Propagačním odborem SNKLHU a vydala Kniha. Praha⌝ 1955.
30 p. illus., ports. 21 cm.

1. Majerová, Marie, 1882– —Bibl.

Z8543.82.K55 60–39009

NK 0204331 DLC

Kniha, Prague.

Z2124
.S5S53

Slovenská kniha, *Prague.*
Sláva vám ... Seznam knih k 10. výročí slovenského národního povstání, 1944–1954. Slovenská kniha, Kniha. ⌜Praha, 1954⌝

Kniha, *Prague.*
Studujeme dějiny KSSS a KSČ. ⌜V Praze, 1954⌝
29 p. 21 cm.

1. Kommunisticheskaia partiia Sovetskogo Soiuza—Bibl. 2. Komunistická strana Československa—Bibl. I. Title.

Z7164.S67K66 58–42128 ‡

NK 0204333 DLC

Kniha, *Prague.*
V. I. Lenin. ⌜K 30. výročí úmrtí V. I. Lenina připravil kolektiv pracovníků propagace národního podniku Kniha v red. Zdeňka Eise. Praha⌝ 1954.
24 p. 20 cm.

1. Lenin, Vladimir Il'ich, 1870–1924—Bibl. I. Eise, Zdeněk, ed.

Z8500.8.K6 57–43130

NK 0204334 DLC

Kniha, *Prague.*
Včera a dnes; seznam knih ke květnovým volbám 1954. ⌜Brno, 1954⌝
54 p. illus. 21 cm.

1. Czechoslovak Republic—Imprints. 2. Communism—Czechoslovak Republic—Bibl. I. Title.

Z2138.A5K55 65–80387

NK 0204335 DLC

Kniha, *Prague.*
Zdeněk Nejedlý. ⌜Praha⌝ 1955.
39 p. illus. 21 cm.

1. Nejedlý, Zdeněk, 1878–

DB217.N55K55 57–15205

NK 0204336 DLC

B 7097.15F

Kniha a narod, 1879-1939. Zvláštní číslo časopisu Knihkupec a nakladatel... K šedesátiletému trvání Svazu českých knihkupců a nakladatelů... [V Praze] Vydané redakcí V.Mikoty, 1939.

222 p. ports., illus.

NK 0204337 MH

CZE
905.01
KNI/B

Kniha Drnovská; kritickými i věcnými poznámkami opatřenou vydal V. Brandl. (Podporou slav. výboru Mar. Mor.) Brno, Nákl. vlastním, tiskem nár. kněhtiskárny J. Šnaidra, 1868.

2 p.l., lxxxvi, 141, ⌜1⌝ p. 25cm.

"Kniha Ctibora Drnovského z Drnovic".
Also known as Codex Dirnovicianus, containing Moravian law of XVI. century.
Errata printed on p.⌜142⌝

NK 0204338 MH-L

Kniha Josefova
see under [Zieger, **Franz A**

Kniha Komenského; k 250. výročí smrti J. A. Komenského. Uspořádal Frant. Pražák. Brno, Nákl. Ústředního spolku učitelského na Moravě a ve Slezsku, 1920.

47 p. port. 22 cm.

"Ceske spisy J. A. Komenského": p. 46–47.

CONTENTS.—Hviezdoslav. Prolog k slávnostem J. A. Komenského.—Masaryk, T. G. J. A. Komenský.—Denis, A. Jan Amos Komenský.—Herben, J. J. A. Komenského návrat do vlasti.—Machar, J. S. Komenský.—"Ukolébavka" z Komenského "Informatoria."

1. Comenius, Johann Amos, 1592–1670. I. Comenius, Johann Amos, 1592–1670. II. Prazak, Frantisek, ed.

LB475.C6K58 72–241436

NK 0204340 DLC

Kniha o Praze. (Pražský almanach.)
⌜Svazek⌝

Praha: Nakladatelství Melantrich a.s., 1932. 20½cm.
v. plans, plates.

Editor : ⌜Svazek⌝ , A. Rektorys.

1. Prague—Per. and soc. publ. I. Rektorys, Artuš, 1877– editor.
N. Y. P. L. August 28, 1933

NK 0204341 NN IU InU NNC ICU

Kniha památni na sedmisetleté založeni českých křižovníků s č. hv. (1233-1933)
see under **Křižovnici s červenou hvězdou.**

Kniha Rožmberská
see under **Brandl, Vincenc, 1834-1901, e(**

Kniha svědomí města Nového Bydžova z 1. 1311-1470, s výsadami a akty o výkupu svobody
see under **Kapras, Jan, 1880- ed.**

VOLUME 300

PG5038 .A1 K5 Kniha veršů o pivě čili Piviáda... V Praze, Jos. R. Vilímka, 1875.
126p.

1. Czech poetry - Collections.

NK 0204345 NcU

891.86 V44 DS94 Kniha vzpomínek na Petra Bezruče [pseud.] a jeho dílo. [Napsali: Jaroslav Šulc, et al. V Praze, Vilém Šmidt] 1937.
68p. illus. 22cm.
"Kresby a typografie: K. Svolinský. -- vydal Vilém Šmidt v Praze jako IV. soukromý tisk. Typy Baskerville vytisklo Družstvo knihtiskárny v Hranicích ve 100 číslovaných výtiscích na Van Gelderu a 300 na dílovém papíře."
1. Vašek, Vladimír, 1867-1958.

NK 0204346 IU ICU

Kniha wsseobecných zákonů mestských pro wssecky německé dědičné země mocnárstwi rakauského ...
see under Bohemia. Laws, statutes, etc.

KNÍHA zázrakow; swate ustné pozostalosti a prostonárodnie rozprawky, etc., Budapest, nakladom K. Razsó a jeho manželky 1896.
Illustr. Slav 8067.11

NK 0204348 MH

Kniha žilinská
see under Chaloupecký, Václav, 1882- ed.

KNIHA života; práce a osobnost F.F. Plamínkové, 1875-1935. [Praha, Ženské ústředí Čsl. strany národně socialistické, 1935?] 1 v.(499-776 p.) ports. 20cm.
Část 2.
"F.F. Plamínkové k šedesátým narozeninám."
1. Plamínková, F.

NK 0204350 NN

LIBRARY SERVICE D655.4437 K74 Knihkupec a nakladatel.
roč. 1-
6. led. 1939-
V Praze, 1939-
v. illus., ports., tables. 30cm.
weekly.
Issued by Svaz knihkupců a nakladatelů ČSR.
Supersedes Československý knihkupec?

NK 0204351 NNC

Knihkupec a nakladatel.
Kniha a národ, 1879-1939
see under title

Knihomil
see Knihomol.

[Knihomilova maturita z Bezruče. [V Praze, Soukromý tisk, 1935]
3p.l., [4] p., 2 l., [3] p. 12mo
77 copies printed.
Half bound in green calf, marbled boards; spine lettered in gilt; paper wrappers bound in.
Signed F.F.

NK 0204354 InU

Z 990 .K71 Knihomol; list pro knižní kulturu, bibliofilství a sběratelství.
1917-
Král.Vinohrady, Ludvík Bradáč.
v. illus.
Subtitle and frequency vary.
Issues for 1917-19 published under title Knihomil.
With the 1927 v.are bound issues of "Knihomolův diář" which was published separately, and miscellaneous exhibit and auction catalogs.

NK 0204355 MiU InU

Z2131 .C85 Knihopis československých tisků od doby nejstarší až do konce XVIII. století.
see under
Czechoslovak Republic. *Komise pro knihopisný soupis československých a slovenských tisků až do konce XVIII. století.*
Topiče, 1925-

Knihovna. roč. 1- 1945-
[Ve Praze, Státní pedagogické nakl.]
v. in illus., ports. 23 x 29 cm.
Frequency varies.
Issued, 1945- by the Svaz českých knihovníků; 19 the Ministerstvo školství.
Editor: 1945- J. Drtina.

1. Libraries—Period. 2. Library science—Period. I. Drtina, Jaroslav, ed. II. Czechoslovak Republic. Ministerstvo školství. III. Svaz českých knihovníků, Prague.

Z671.K53 65-30659

NK 0204357 DLC IU InU

Knihovna Akademického spolku Kapper. V Praze

sv.47, etc. - Kalendar ceskožidovský. V Praze

NK 0204358 MH

Knihovna Aktualit a kuriosit. V Praze, V.Boučková

6 (1923) - [Bouček, Antonín]
Padesát historek ze života Jaroslava Haška

NK 0204359 MH

Knihovna aktualit Světových rozhledů.
Praha, Svoboda,
v. illus. 22 cm.

1. World politics—1945- —Addresses, essays, lectures. 2. History, Modern—20th cent—Addresses, essays, lectures.

D414.K55 53-27603

NK 0204360 DLC OO

Knihovna Bedřicha Smetany, Prague
see Prague. Městská lidová knihovna. Knihovna Bedřicha Smetany.

58.8 K74 Knihovna ČSSS-STS.
Praha,

1. Traction-engines in agriculture. I. Jednota svaz českých Zemědělců.

NK 0204362 DNAL

Z 201 .466 KNIHOVNA čes. těsnopisu. Praha-Dejvice, 1920-[194-?]
6v.in 1. 21cm.
Prepared and edited by F.Slabý.
Contents.--Obchodní korespondence. 1920.--Čtení a úkoly pro začátečníky. 1.č.: Tvoření slov.--Mezi námi děvčaty.--Těsnopisná obchodní korespondence. 5.vyd.--Těsnopisná obchodní korespondence. 6.vyd., upravil J.Matoušek.--Deník malého dareby. [Řídí J.Matoušek]

NK 0204363 ICN

Knihovna České matice technické.
Praha.
v. illus. 21 cm.
Summaries in German and Russian.

1. Technology—Societies, etc. I. Česká matice technická, Prague.

T4.C43 55-41231

NK 0204364 DLC

Knihovna českého lidu. V Táboře, Kraus

3 (1903) - Janda, Bohumil, 1831-75
Boček

NK 0204365 MH

Knihovna česko-americkych autorů. Bohemian-American authors' library. Omaha, Nebr., nakladatel Otakar Charvat, 190
v.

NK 0204366 NbHi

Knihovna Československé matice lesnické.
Písek, 19
v. illus. 22 cm.

1. Forests and forestry—Period. 2. Forests and forestry—Czechoslovak Republic.

SD1.K5 51-36404

NK 0204367 DLC

Knihovna Československého denníka. V Irkutski, Nákl. Informačně-osvětového odboru Ministerstva vojenství

5(1919) - Medek, Rudolf
Lví srdce

NK 0204368 MH

VOLUME 300

Knihovna českých loutkařů.
Svazek

Praha: J. R. Vilímek, 19 19½cm.
nos.

Editor : Svazek J. Veselý.

1. Drama, Bohemian—Collections. I. Veselý, Jindřich, 1885- , editor.
N. Y. P. L. November 21, 1934

NK 0204369 NN

Knihovna Divadlo-lidu.
Praha, Svoboda
v. 18 cm.

1. Russian drama—20th cent. 2. Russian drama—Translations into Czech language. 3. Czech language—Translations from Russian.
PG3250.C9K5 52-28691

NK 0204370 DLC

KNIHOVNA dokumentů.
[Praha]

Published by Kruh čtenářů Světa sovětů.

I. Kruh čtenářů Světa sovětů.

NK 0204371 NN DLC

Knihovna Dramatického svazu. Praha, V.Tomsa

1 (1943) - Tetauer, Frank, 1903-
Drama i jeho svět

NK 0204372 MH

Knihovna funkcionáře.
Praha.
no. 23 cm. 15 no. a year (irregular)
Issued by Ústřední výbor KSČ.

1. Kommunisticheskaia partiia Sovetskogo Soiuza. I. Komunistická strana Československa. Ústřední výbor.
JN6598.K4K5 59-35078

NK 0204373 DLC

Knihovna hlav. města Prahy, *Prague*
see
Prague. Městská knihovna.

Knihovna Hosta. V Přerově, Nákl. Obzoru

1 (1923) - Blatný, Lev, 1894-1930
Vítr v ohradě

NK 0204375 MH

280.28
K74
Knihovna JZD.
Praha, Jednotného svazu českých zemědělců,

1. Agriculture, Cooperative. Czechoslovak Republic. I. Jednota svaz českých zemědělců. II. Jednota zemědělska druzstva.

NK 0204376 DNAL DLC

Knihovna Kruhu pro pěstování dějin umění. Praha

1 (1927) - Friedl, Antonín, 1880-
Hildebert a Everwin

NK 0204377 MH

Knihovna Kulturního odboru Vlajky". [Praha, Nákl. Kulturního odboru Vlajky"]

sv.5(1935) - Mareš, František, 1857-1942
Poslední vzdory pravdě o Rukopisech

NK 0204378 MH

Knihovna kuriosit. V Praze, Šolc

5 (1913) - Kuriosní historický kalendár M.Jana Husi

NK 0204379 MH

W 1
KN595
KNIHOVNA lékařských rozhledů. sv. 1-
1914-
Praha, Spolek českých lékařů.
v. illus.
1914- issued as supplements to the Časopis lékařů českých.
1. Medicine - Collected works
I. Časopis lékařů českých. Supplement
II. Spolek českých lékařů v Praze

NK 0204380 DNLM DLC

Knihovna "Literární kroužku." Sv. I. 4879a.189
Chicago. 1910. v. 19 cm.

I.6029 — Bohemia. Lang. Works in Bohemian.

NK 0204381 MB

Knihovna Měsíc. V Brně, B.Kilian

1(1932) - Nezval, Vítězslav
Pět prstu

NK 0204382 MH

Knihovna Metropolitní kapitoly, *Prague*
see
Prague. Chrám sv. Víta. *Kapitola. Knihovna.*

Knihovna národních výborů... [sv.] 2-3. Brno, Zář, 1946.
2 v. map. 22cm.

CONTENTS.—2. Šulc, Stanislav. Národní výbory.—3. Šulc, Stanislav. Obnovení národních výborů.

1. Government, Local—Czechoslovakia. I. Šulc, Stanislav.

NK 0204384 NN

Knihovna Nové ženy. V Praze, Obrodné hnutí československých mladých žen

1 (1927) - Záhoř, Zdeněk
Božena Němcova

NK 0204385 MH

Knihovna Numismatického časopisu ceskoslovenského. V Praze

2 (1935) - Katz, Viktor
O chronologii denáru Boleslava I a Boleslava II

NK 0204386 MH DDO

W 1
KN598
KNIHOVNA Odboru pro studium a přípravu reformy zdravotní péče při Ministerstvu veřejného zdravotnictví a tělesné výchovy. čís. 1-
1923-
V Praze.
v. illus.
1. Public health - Collected works

NK 0204387 DNLM

Knihovna Památkového sboru hlav. města Prahy. Praha

1 (1928) - Vojtíšek, Václav, 1882-
O pečetech a erbech měst pražských a jiných českých

NK 0204388 MH

Knihovna Památníku Odboje. Praha

29 (1923) - Beneš, Vojta, 1878-
Vojáci zapomenuté fronty

NK 0204389 MH

Knihovna Památníku Petra Bezruče v Opavě.
[V Ostravě, Krajské nakl., 19
v. facsims., ports. 21 cm.
Title varies Knihovna Památníku Petra Bezruče.

1. Vašek, Vladimír, 1867-1958. I. Opava, Czechoslovak Republic. Památník Petra Bezruče.
PG5038.V35Z716 67-36918

NK 0204390 DLC

Knihovna pod záštitou pražského sdružení přátel baroka
Praha, Jitro

4 (1940) - Bitnar, Vilém, 1874-
Zrození barokového básnika

NK 0204391 MH

VOLUME 300

Knihovna Pokroku. Praha, Pokroku

158 (1940)- Polanský, Václav
O Josefu Holečkovi

NK 0204392 MH

W 1 KN605 KNIHOVNA praktického lékaře.
Praha ⌈194-?⌉-
v. illus.
1. Medicine - Period.

NK 0204393 DNLM

Knihovna pražských loží, *Prague*
see **Prague. Knihovna pražských loží.**

Knihovna rolníka. Libochovice, Novák

1 (1930) - Janda, Antonín
Dějiny stavu rolnického v Čechách

NK 0204395 MH

Knihovna Rozprav. Praha, Edice Rozprav

sv.4(1946) - Mařan, Ctibor,comp.
Kniha o Alfredu Fuchsovi

NK 0204396 MH

Knihovna rozprav lidových. V Praze, Nákl. Ústředního nakl.učitelstva československého

3,6 (1921) - Chýna, Jan
Předchůdci Husovi

NK 0204397 MH

Knihovna sborníku věd právních a státních... Nová řada. B. Obor státovědecký. čís.

Praha, 21cm.
Published with the assistance of the Ministerstvo školství a osvěty of Czecho-Slovakia.

CONTENTS.

*QT
čís. 24. EHLER, ZDENĚK. Vypovědění války. 1946.

NK 0204399 NN

Knihovna Sněmů Českých
see under Czechoslovak Republic. Archiv bývalé země české.

Knihovna Socialistické akademie. Praha, Osvěta

41 (1952) - Buriánek, František, 1917-
Proti buržoasni literární "vědě" Arne Nováka

NK 0204401 MH

W 1 KN608 KNIHOVNA sociálně-lékařského sboru.
V Praze, Nákl. Mladé generace lékařu při Ustřední jednotě čsl. lékařu ⌈19--?⌉-
v.
1. Public health - Period. 2. Social medicine - Period. I. Ustřední jednota československých lékařu. Mladá generace lékařů

NK 0204402 DNLM

Knihovna "Spolku péče o blaho venkova" ...
svazek 1-
V Brne [etc.] 1928-
no. in v. illus. 29 cm.
According to checklist in no. 17, no. 3 is wrongly numbered no. 2; no. 6, no. 5; no. 15, no. 14.
Articles in Bohemian, French, English or Russian.
1. Sociology, Rural - Societies, etc. 2. Country life - Societies, etc. 3. Country life - Czechoslovak Republic.

NK 0204403 CU

Knihovna Statistického obzoru.
see under Czechoslovak Republic. Státní Úřad Statistický.

Knihovna statistického věstníku.
see under Czechoslovak Rep. Státní úřad statistický.

Z 201 .4661 KNIHOVNA Státního ústavu těsnopisného. Praha ⌈1946⌉
4v.in 1. 24cm.

Contents.--První poselství presidenta dra Edvarda Beneše k lidu osvobozené československé republiky. ⌈1946⌉--Klančík-Matoušek. Těsnopisná obchodní korespondence s diktáty. ⌈1947⌉ --Havelka, Ludevít. Učebnice anglického těsnopisu. ⌈1948⌉--Čáp, Jindřich. Těsnopisná literatúra česká a slovenská v r. 1938-48. 1949.

NK 0204406 ICN

Knihovna Stožár. Praha [Hyperion]

6 (1926) - Macháček, Simeon Karel, 1799-1846
Ženichové

NK 0204407 MH

Knihovna tělesné výchovy mládeže.

Praha, Komenium,
v. 21 cm.
Principally unacc. melodies.
Supplements accompany some numbers.

1. Folk-songs, Czech. 2. Dancing—Czechoslovak Republic.

M1704.K55 52-33156

NK 0204408 DLC

Z 201 .4662 KNIHOVNA těsnopisných listů. Praha, První pražský spolek stenografů, 1937-⌈49⌉
20v.in 1. 23cm.

Contents.--sv.3. Slovníček samoznaku Mikulíkovy-Heroutovy těsnopisné soustavy, zpracovali Miroslav Unger a Vladimír Šmolík. 8.vyd. 1938.--sv.3. Slovníček samoznaků, zpracovali Miroslav Unger a Vladimír Šmolík. 13.vyd. 1940. --sv.9,24. Dějiny slovanských stenografií. Část československá. I:Stručné dějiny československého těsnopisu II: Bibliografie československého těsnopisu. Napsal Alois Kratochvil. 1937-39.--sv.12. Slovník komorních zkratek, sestavil Miroslav Unger. 1939.--sv21. Zábavná těsnopisná čítanka, sestavil Václav Freml. 1939.--sv.23. Těsnopisné kresby. Nakreslil Vladimír Šmolík. 1939.--sv.27. Moderní těsnopisná obchodní korespondence, Napsal Miroslav Kamínek. 2.vyd. 1941.--sv.28. Původní soustava Krondlova v poslední své podobě. Napsal Alois Ždímal. 1939.--sv.31. Anglická stenografie, převod soustavy Mikulíkovy-Heroutovy. Sestavili Karel Petro a Václav Freml. 1939.--sv.32. Obchodní těsnopisná čítanka. Napsal Miroslav Kamínek. 1940.--sv.38. Ruský těsnopis, převod soustavy Mikulíkovy-Heroutovy Zpracovali Vladimír Kalačevskij a Heřman Prokop. 1941.--sv.39. Německa těsnopisná obchodní korespondence podle soustavy Mikulíkovy-Heroutovy. 1941.--sv.40. Těsnopisu bez učitele. 1.díl: Písmo korespondenční. Sestavili Miroslav Kamínek a Vladimír Šmolík. 2.vyd. 1944.--sv.41. Hradecký, František. Z naší květnové revoluce. --sv.42. Mikulík, M. Slovník samoznaků. ⌈1947⌉ --sv.43. Smích za scénou. Vybral Milan Kutílek. ⌈1947⌉--sv.44. Uvedení v těsnopisnou theorii. Napsal Alois Kratochvil. ⌈194-?⌉--sv.46. S parlamentní tribuny. Sestavili Jiři Bělohubý a Prokop Machaň. ⌈1948⌉--sv.47. Chodska čítanka. Uspořadal Jan Hofmann. ⌈1949⌉

NK 0204412 ICN

Knihovna Ústřední sociální pojišťovny, *Prague*
see
Ústřední sociální pojišťovna. *Knihovna.*

Knihovna venkova; spisy všeobecně vzdělávací. Praha

sv.1 (1915) - Vratislav, Frant
Mistr Jan Hus

NK 0204414 MH

Knihovna Vinice. Praha

2 (1922) - Rossetti, Dante Gabriel, 1828-82
Ruka a duše

NK 0204415 MH

Knihovna Vlny. V Praze, Nákl. Časopisu pokrokového studentstva

1 (1909) - Mach, Josef S ,1883-
Robinson Krusoe
Various

NK 0204416 MH

Knihovna Volné myšlenky. Větše vyd. Král.Vinohrady

19 (1911) - Franta, Karel
O vzniku a vývoji poddanství českého lidu

NK 0204417 MH DLC

VOLUME 300

Knihovna volné myšlenky mužovo Česko reformace. Svazek 1 -

Prague, Volne Myslenky, 19- v. D

NK 0204418 OO

Knihovna vysokých škol technických, *Prague*
see **Prague. Knihovna vysokých škol technických.**

Knihovna Vzdělání lidu; sbírka spisů populárně vzdělavacích. V Moravanech

5 (1907) - Jíl, A
Bílá Hora

NK 0204420 MH

Knihovna zabraniční politiky; sbírka prací věnovaných studiu mezinárodních otázek politických, právních, národohospodářských a sociálních...
Č.

Praha: Vydává "Orbis," 192 8°.
v.

NK 0204421 NN

Knihovna zemědělské mládeže...
Svazek

Praha, 19 20cm.
no.

Editor : sv. , Josef Horák.

NK 0204422 NN

Knihovna Zemědělské rady pro Království české, *Prague*
see **Bohemia.** *Landeskulturrat. Bibliothek.*

19.5
K742 **Knihovna zemědělských aktualit.**

Praha, Jednotného svazu českých zemědělců

1. Czechoslovak Republic. Agriculture. I. Jednota svaz českých zemědělců.

NK 0204424 DNAL

Knihovnička dnešní Lužice. Praha, Společnost přátel Lužice

NK 0204425 MH

Nx55
A96
C99d Knihovnička "Duch národa". č.1-
Praha[Československá Strana Národně Socialistická[1945-
14-15cm.

NK 0204426 CtY

Knihovnička úderníků. Praha, Práce-Vyd-vo ROH

63 (1954) - Kéňa, Vašek, pseud., 1905-
Byl jsem při tom

NK 0204427 MH

19.5
K743 **Knihovnička zemědělce.**
Praha,

1. Czechoslovak Republic. Agriculture.

NK 0204428 DNAL

Knihovny v Československu. Libraries in Czechoslovakia. ₍Napsali: Jiří Riess et al. V Praze, Svaz českých knihovníků₎ 1945.

61 p. illus. 21 cm.

Cover title.

1. Libraries—Czechoslovak Republic.

Z795.K55 027.0437 53-18391 ‡

NK 0204429 DLC CtY IU

Knihtiskař zákazníkovi
see under [Dyrynk, Karel] 1876-

Knihy Hollara.
Svazek 1

V Praze: Sdružení českých umělců grafiků Hollar, 1932
no. illus. 28cm.

Editor : Svazek 1 A. Novák.

1. No subject. I. Novák, Arthur, editor. II. Sdružení českých umělců grafiků "Hollar," Prague.
N. Y. P. L. May 14, 1934

NK 0204431 NN

943.7
K748 **Knihy městských počtů z doby předhusitské, vydává Československý Státní Ústav Historický. 1-**

V Brně, 1935-
v. illus.

At head of title, v.1- : Libri rationum civitatum bohemoslovenicarum ante belli hussitici tempora confecti.
Each volume has also special title-page. Latin and Czech text.

NK 0204432 WaU

Knihy o knihách.
Svazek 1

V Praze, 1925 18cm.
no.

Contents:
Svazek I. Collin, E. Utahovák. 1925

NK 0204433 NN DLC

Knihy osudů.
sv.

Praha, J. R. Vilímek, 1946- v. illus.
22-25cm.

NK 0204434 NN DLC

Knihy osudů a práce.
sv.

Praha, Orbis, 19 v. illus. 21cm.

NK 0204435 NN DLC

Knihy počtů města Brna z let 1343-1365
see under Brünn.

W 1
KN613 **KNIHY praktického lékaře.**

V Praze ₍19C-?₎-
v. illus.
1. Medicine - Collected works

NK 0204437 DNLM

Knihy pre Verejne Knižnice. Bratislava, 1, 1949//?

issued with the journal Kniznica.

NK 0204438 CaOTU

Knihy pro každého; sbírka spisů poučných.
Ročník ₍1₎

v Praze, 1923-28. 16°.
v.

Ročník 4, sv. 1, R. 5, sv. 1, R6, sv. 1 also called sv. 16, 21, 26.
Editor : 1923- K. Veleminský.

Contents:
Ročník 1, sv. 1. Masaryk, T. G. Politické myšlenky. Vybral V. K. Škrach. ed. 2. 1923.

NK 0204439 NN DLC

Knihy Života. Praha

1 (1928) - Doležal, Josef
Politická cesta českého katolicismu, 1918-1928

NK 0204440 MH

Knihy Zvonu. V Praze, Nákl. České grafické unie

31 (1921) - Haškovec, Prokop Miroslav, 1876-1935
Proudy

NK 0204441 MH

Knijff, G H van
... Ad locum codicis civilis de regimine dotali ... offert G.H. van Knijff ... Groningae, I.I. Homkes ₍1817₎

2 p.l., 96, ₍12₎ p. 19cm.

Diss.- Groningen.
Bibliographical footnotes.

NK 0204442 MH-L

VOLUME 300

Knijpinga, Focko
... Ad orationem Divi Marci de transactione alimentorum ... submittit Focko Knijpinga ... Groningae, N. Veenkamp et filius, 1807.
2 p.l., 75, [7] p. 19½cm.
Diss.- Groningen.

NK 0204443 MH-L

Kniker, Hedwig Thusnelda.
... Comanchean and Cretaceous *Pectinidae* of Texas, by Hedwig T. Kniker. Austin, Tex., The University [1918]
56 p. x pl. 23cm. (University of Texas bulletin, no. 1817: March 20, 1918)
Bibliography: p. [55]-56.

1. Pectinidae, Fossil.
Library of Congress QE812.P4K7 19—27014
——— Copy 2. AS36.T4 no. 1817

NK 0204444 DLC OrU MtBC PP OCU MiU OCl OU ICJ NN MB KMK MsU

Kniker, Hedwig Thusnelda, joint author.

Beede, Joshua William, 1871-
... Species of the genus *Schwagerina* and their stratigraphic significance, by J. W. Beede and Hedwig T. Kniker. Austin, Tex., The University [1924]

Knilis (Pierre-Marie). *Sur la grippe épidémique. 36 pp. 4°. *Paris,* 1838, No. 108, v. 329.

NK 0204446 DNLM PPC

Knill, John, 1827-1831.
Memoir of John Knill
see under [Knill, Richard] 1787-1857.

Knill, Sir John, 1856-

Knill, *Sir* **Stuart,** 1824-1898.
A potpourri of London antiquities. By Sir Stuart Knill ... portreeve ... of the Sette ... Delivered after dinner, at Limmer's hotel, on the evening of Friday, 7th June, 1895. London, Imprynted for his son, Sir John Knill, at the Bedford press, 1900.

Knill, Lucy (Willis) *lady,* 1887-
The Mansion house, by Lady Knill, with 17 illustrations. London, S. Paul & co. [1937]
288 p. front. (port.) plates. 22cm.

1. London. Mansion house.
Library of Congress DA687.M25K6 44-27935
[2] 942.12

NK 0204449 DLC CtY NcD CU FMU

KNILL, R.
Y bwystfil anghristaidd wedi ei euogfarnu; neu, Gynnadledd rhwng offeiriad pabaidd a'r Parch. R. Knill. Abertawy, E. Griffiths, 1841.
pp. 24.
Celt 5160.45.30

NK 0204450 MH

YARC K69 **Knill, Richard,** 1787-1857.
The false hope...
[n.p.,n.d.]
4 p.

NK 0204451 DLC

YAR 311 Knill, Richard, 1787-1857.
The farmer and his family. New ed. New York, [n.d.]
80 p.

NK 0204452 DLC NN

Knill, Richard, 1787-1857.
The life of the Rev. Richard Knill, of St. Petersburg: being selections from his reminiscences, journals, and correspondence. By the Rev. Charles M. Birrell ... With a Review of his character, by the late Rev. John Angell James. New York, Printed by the American tract society [1859]
x, 11-358 p. front. (port.) 16cm.

I. Birrell, Charles Morton, ed. II. James, John Angell, 1785-1859. III. American tract society.
Library of Congress BX7260.K6A3 38-37395

NK 0204453 DLC MiD NjPT CtY OO OC MiU NIC WU NN NNUT CCC MWA

Knill, Richard, 1787-1857.
Life of the Rev. Richard Knill, being selections from his reminscences, etc. with a review of his character by Rev. J. A. James. London, 1860.
268 p.

NK 0204454 MWA ViLxW

Knill, Richard, 1787-1857.
The life of the Rev. Richard Knill of St. Petersburgh; being selections from his reminiscences, journals, and correspondence, with a review of his character, by the late Rev. John Angell James. Ed. 3. London, James Nisbet & co., 1860.
viii, [3], 4-268 p.

NK 0204455 OCl

Knill, Richard, 1787-1857.
The life of the Rev. Richard Knill, of St. Petersburgh: being selections from his reminiscences, journals and correspondence, with a review of his character, by the late Rev. John Angell James. By Charles M. Birrell. 4th ed. London, James Nisbet and co., 1860.
viii, 268 p. front. (port.) 18½cm.

NK 0204456 NcD

BX 7260 K6 A3 1860 Knill, Richard, 1787-1857
The life of the Rev. Richard Knill, of St. Petersburg: being selections from his reminiscenes, journals, and correspondence. by the Rev. Charles M. Birrell....With a Review of his character, by the late Rev. John Angell James. New York, R. Carter, 1860.
358 p.

NK 0204457 KMK CtY NcD NN MWA NjR

Knill, Richard, 1787-1857.
The life of the Rev. Richard Knill... N.Y., 1862.

NK 0204458 NjNbS

BX7260 .K6A3 1878 Knill, Richard, 1787-1857.
The life of the Rev. Richard Knill, of St. Petersburg, by the Rev. C.M. Birrell. With a review of his character by the late Rev. John Angell James. Special ed. [London] Printed by the Religious Tract Society [1878]
xiv, 272 p. illus., front. (port.) 19cm.
I. Birrell, Charles Morton, ed.
II. James, John Angell, 1985-1859.

NK 0204459 ViU NIC MWA WaU

[**Knill, Richard**] 1787-1857.
Memoir of John Knill; a little boy who died of the cholera, in St. Petersburg, July 1, 1831. Boston, Peirce and Parker; New York, H. C. Sleight, 1832.
x, [11]-36 p. 15cm.
Letter (p. [v]-vi) signed: Richard and Sarah Knill.

1. Knill, John, 1827-1831. I. Knill, Mrs. Sarah (Notman) II. Title.
37-20269
Library of Congress BR1715.K6K6
[2] 922

NK 0204460 DLC

Knill, Richard, 1787-1857.
Memoir of the life and character of Walter Venning, Esq... By Richard Knill, with a preface by Robert Winter... London: J. & A. Arch, 1822. 102 p. front. (port.), plate. 8°.

1. Venning, Walter, 1781-1821. 2. Prisons, Russia.
N. Y. P. L. March 5, 1921.

NK 0204461 NN MiU

KNILL, RICHARD, 1787-1857.
Memoir of the life and character of Walter Venning, Esq... By Richard Knill, with a preface by Robert Winter... London, J. & A. Arch, 1822. 102 p. front. (port.), plate. 8°.

NK 0204462 NN

285.173 P928 no.22 **Knill, Richard, 1787-1857.**
The missionary's wife; or, a brief account of Mrs. Loveless, of Madras, the first American missionary to foreign lands. Philadelphia, Presbyterian Board of Publication [1839]
24 p. 19 cm. ([Presbyterian tracts] no.22)

NK 0204463 NcD CU

PL6515 A1T3 no. 32 x [Knill, Richard] 1787-1857.
E parau, no, te haapao raa a te hoe tamaiti John Knili te ioa. I pohe oia i te mai rahi buai i parauhia e colera. Aore oia i tae i te maha o tona matahiti i te pohe raa ra. I papaihia e tonaiho Medua tane. [Tahiti, Printed at the Windward Mission Press, 1834]
12 p. (incl. cover) 19cm. [Tahitian imprints, no. 32]
Caption title.
Harding, The Tahitian imprints of the London Missionary Society, no. 73.
Provenance: Alphonse Pinart; Thomas W. Streeter.
1. Knill, John, 1827-1831. 2. Linguistics - Tahitian - Texts. 3. Early printing - Tahiti. I. London Missionary Society. II. Title. (Series)

NK 0204464 CU-B MiU

Knill, Richard, 1787-1857.
The poor blacksmith made rich; or, Godliness profitable. Phila., Pres. Pub., Com. n.d.

NK 0204465 PPPrHi

VOLUME 300

Knill, Richard, 1787–1857.
A village preacher. Petersburg, Va., G. LeRoi [1863?]
broadside (4 p.) 17 x 22cm. fold. to 17 x 11cm. (Evangelical Tract Society, No. 152)

NK 0204466 ViU

Knilling, Rudolf, 1852-1923. 510.7 P700
Die naturgemässe Methode des Rechen-Unterrichts in der deutschen Volksschule. Ein neues theoretisch-praktisches Handbuch. 2 vol. il. O. München: R. Oldenbourg, 1897–1899.
Contents: Vol. 1. Die psychologischen Grundlagen der naturgemässen Rechenmethode. xii,372 p. il. 1897. Vol. 2. Der Aufbau der naturgemässen Rechenmethode. xvi,266 p. il. 1899.
Bibliography, vol. 1, p. 16–27.

NK 0204467 ICJ OU OOxM PU CU NNU-W

PT2383 Knilling, Rudolf, 1852–1923.
.K36T2 Ein Tannhäuserlied aus dem Chiemgau, der geburts- und
1916 heimatstätte unseres Minnesängers. Von Rudolf Knilling. 1. t. Auf schloss Marquartstein ... Dresden, E. Pierson [1916]
[1], viii, 350 p. pl. 19cm.
No more published.

1. Tannhäuser.

NK 0204468 ICU

Knill, Mrs. Sarah (Notman)

[Knill, Richard] 1787–1857.
Memoir of John Knill; a little boy who died of the cholera, in St. Petersburg, July 1, 1831. Boston, Peirce and Parker; New York, H. C. Sleight, 1832.

Knill, Sir Stuart, 1824–1898.
A potpourri of London antiquities. By Sir Stuart Knill ... portreeve ... of the Sette ... Delivered after dinner, at Limmer's hotel, on the evening of Friday, 7th June, 1895. London, Imprynted for his son, Sir John Knill, at the Bedford press, 1900.
53, [3] p. front. (port.) 14½ x 12cm. (Half-title: Privately printed opuscula issued to members of the Sette of odd volumes. no. XL)
"This edition is limited to 199 copies, and is imprynted for private circulation only. no. 53."
"Dedicated to the Sette of odd volumes in affectionate remembrance of his father, by Alderman Sir John Knill."
Lists of club's members and publications: [36]–53, [3] p.
1. London—Antiq. I. Knill, Sir John, 1856– II. Title.

17-17594

Library of Congress AC1.S5 no. 40

NK 0204470 DLC MH MB MiU

Knill, William.
Television and the high school student. An interim report, based on data gathered in the Saskatoon High School Study, submitted to the Canadian Education Association. [n.p.]
87 l. illus. 28 cm.
Spiral binding.

NK 0204471 CaBVaU

N Knille, Otto, 1832-
70 Grübeleien eines Malers über seine Kunst.
K5 Berlin, Gebrüder Paetel, 1887.
1887 143 p.
Bibliographical footnotes.

1. Art--Philosophy. 2. Painting--Germany--Addresses, essays, lectures. 3. Painters. I. Title.

NK 0204472 NSyU

Kniller, Andreas
see
Kneller, Andreas, 1649–1724.

Kniller, Gottfried
see
Kneller, Sir Godfrey, bart., 1646-1732

KNILLING, von.
Speech of the Bavarian premier von Knilling delivered in the Bavarian diet June 27, 1923. München, the German Society for truth, right and honour, [1923].

Pamphlet.
Cover serves as title-page.

NK 0204475 MH

PT162 [Knilling, Herbert]
.K7 Eine gallerie von zeitgenossen (1853) [Berlin, 1930]
[3], 16, [4] p. illus., ports.
"Steingravuren von Gustav Reisacher ... steindruck, buchdruck und buchbinderarbeiten von E. Heckendorff ... Einmalige auflage von 450 exemplaren auf büttenpapier. Den mitgliedern und freuden des Berliner bibliophilen-abends aus anlass der feier des fünfundzwanzigjährigen bestehens am 15. märz 1930 gewidmet von E. Heckendorff und Gustav Reisacher."

"Unter dem genannten Herbert K. verbirgt sich aller wahrscheinlichkeit nach Herbert Knilling ... Von wem diese ... reime stammen, wird nich verraten."--Postscript.
Edited by Paul Alfred Merbach.

1. Authors, German--Caricatures, cartoons, etc.

NK 0204477 ICU ViU MoU NN

Knillmann, Walter, joint author.
Wort und Satz

see under

Gressmann, Ludwig.

Knin, Dalmatia. Muzej hrvatskih spomenika
see
Split, Yugoslavia. Muzej hrvatskih starina.

Kninski, Ivan Bojničić
see
Bojničić, Ivan, 1858–1925.

Knip, Pauline (de Courcelles) 1781-1851

Les pigeons, par Madame Knip, née Pauline de Courcelles ... le texte par C.J. Themminck [sic] ... A Paris, Chez Mme. Knip, auteur et
SSyl5 éditeur, Rue de Sorbonne, Musée des artistes;
C6 Garnery libraire, Rue de Seine, Hôtel Mirabeau,
811K no. 6; De l'imprimerie de Mame, MDCCCXI.
2p.l., iii, 1-[14], [23]-41, 128, 30p. 87col. plates. 53cm.
"A noted work, stolen from Temminck, the original author, by Madame Knip ..." For

details of theft see Bull. U.S. Geol. Geog. Surv. Terr. 5. (1). p. 794-6. 1878.
Description accompanying plate no. 47 incorrectly numbered.

NK 0204482 CtY MH NN MdBP ICF-A

QL Knip, Pauline (de Courcelles) 1781-1851.
696 Les pigeons. Le texte par C. J. Themminck
C6 [et Florent Prévost] Paris, Bellizard, Du-
K69++ four [1838]
1838 2 v. col. plates. 56cm.

Vol. 1 : 2. éd.

1. Pigeons. 2. Birds--Pictorial works. I. Temminck, Coenraad Jacob, 1778-1858. II. Prévost, Florent.

NK 0204483 NIC CtY

Knipe, Alden Arthur, 1870- joint author.

Knipe, Mrs. Emilie (Benson) 1870–
Beatrice of Denewood; a sequel to "The lucky sixpence", by Emilie Benson Knipe and Alden Arthur Knipe; illustrated by C. M. Relyea. New York, The Century co., 1913.

Knipe, Alden Arthur, 1870–
Bunny plays the game, by Alden Arthur Knipe ... New York and London, Harper & brothers, 1925.
4 p. l., 295 p. front., plates. 19½cm.

I. Title.

Library of Congress PZ7.K743Bu 25—17625

NK 0204485 DLC

Knipe, Alden Arthur, 1870–
Captain of the eleven, by Alden Arthur Knipe ... New York and London, Harper & brothers, 1910.
4 p. l., 269, [1] p. front., 3 pl. 19½cm. $1.25

I. Title.

Library of Congress PZ7.K743C 10—21026

NK 0204486 DLC PP PU OEac OLak OClh OCl NN

Knipe, Alden Arthur, 1870- joint author.

Knipe, Mrs. Emilie (Benson) 1870–
A cavalier maid, by Emilie Benson Knipe and Alden Arthur Knipe ... illustrated by Emilie Benson Knipe. New York, The Macmillan company, 1919.

Knipe, Alden Arthur, 1870- joint author.

Knipe, Mrs. Emilie Benson, 1870–
A continental dollar, by Emilie Benson Knipe, and Alden Arthur Knipe ... Illustrated by Emilie Benson Knipe. New York and London, The Century co., 1923.

[Knipe, Alden Arthur] 1870–
The cowboy and the duchess, by Timothy Shea [pseud.] ... New York, Dodd, Mead and company, 1932.
3 p. l., 310 p. 19½cm.

I. Title.

Library of Congress PZ3.K7486Co 32-15763

NK 0204489 DLC CoU

VOLUME 300

Knipe, Alden Arthur, 1870- joint author.

Knipe, *Mrs.* **Emilie (Benson)** 1870–
Diantha's quest; a tale of the Argonauts of '49, by Emilie Benson Knipe and Alden Arthur Knipe. New York, The Macmillan company, 1921.

Knipe, Alden Arthur, 1870–
Everybody's Washington, by Alden Arthur Knipe, illustrated by Mead Schaeffer. New York, Dodd, Mead and company [c1931]
viii p., 2 l., 282 p. col. front., col. plates. 24cm.
Illustrated lining-papers.

1. Washington, George, pres. U. S., 1732–1799. I. Schaeffer, Mead, 1898– illus. II. Title.
31-31822
Library of Congress E312.K72
——— Copy 2.
Copyright A 43874 [7] 923.173

NK 0204491 DLC Or WaS PP PHC PU OCl OClh OEac MB NN ViU

Knipe, Alden Arthur, 1870- joint author.

Knipe, *Mrs.* **Emilie (Benson)** 1870–
The flower of fortune, by Emilie Benson Knipe and Alden Arthur Knipe ... illustrated by Emilie Benson Knipe. New York, The Century co., 1922.

Knipe, Alden Arthur, 1870- joint author.

Knipe, *Mrs.* **Emilie (Benson)** 1870–
Girls of '64, by Emilie Benson Knipe and Alden Arthur Knipe ... illustrated by Emilie Benson Knipe. New York, The Macmillan company, 1918.

Knipe, Alden Arthur, 1870–
The last lap, by Alden Arthur Knipe ... New York and London, Harper & brothers, 1911.
4 p. l., 340 p., 1 l. front., plates. 19½cm. $1.25

I. Title.
11—24115
Library of Congress PZ7.K743La

NK 0204494 DLC MB NN

Knipe, Alden Arthur, 1870- joint author.
Knipe, *Mrs.* **Emilie (Benson)** 1870–
Little Miss Fales, by Emilie Benson Knipe and Alden Arthur Knipe; frontispiece by Frances Rogers. New York and London, Harper & brothers, 1910.

Knipe, Alden Arthur, 1870- joint author.

Knipe, *Mrs.* **Emilie (Benson)** 1870–
Lost—a brother, by Emilie Benson Knipe and Alden Arthur Knipe, illustrated by Henry Pitz. New York, The Macmillan company, 1928.

Knipe, Alden Arthur, 1870- joint author.

Knipe, *Mrs.* **Emilie (Benson)** 1870–
The lost little lady, by Emilie Benson Knipe and Arthur Alden Knipe ... illustrated by Emilie Benson Knipe. New York, The Century co., 1917.

Knipe, Alden Arthur, 1870- joint author.

Knipe, *Mrs.* **Emilie (Benson)** 1870–
The luck of Denewood, by Emilie Benson Knipe and Alden Arthur Knipe ... illustrated by Emilie Benson Knipe. New York, The Century co., 1921.

Knipe, Alden Arthur, 1870- joint author.
Knipe, *Mrs.* **Emilie (Benson)** 1870–
The lucky sixpence, by Emilie Benson Knipe and Alden Arthur Knipe; illustrated by Arthur E. Becher. New York, The Century co., 1912.

Knipe, Alden Arthur, 1870- joint author.
Knipe, *Mrs.* **Emilie (Benson)** 1870–
A maid of old Manhattan, by Emilie Benson Knipe and Alden Arthur Knipe ... illustrated by Emilie Benson Knipe. New York, The Macmillan company, 1917.

Knipe, Alden Arthur, 1870- joint author.

Knipe, *Mrs.* **Emilie (Benson)** 1870–
A maid of '76, by Emilie Benson Knipe and Alden Arthur Knipe; illustrated by Emilie Benson Knipe. New York, The Macmillan company, 1915.

Knipe, Alden Arthur, 1870- joint author.

Knipe, *Mrs.* **Emilie (Benson)** 1870–
A Mayflower maid, by Emilie Benson Knipe and Alden Arthur Knipe; illustrated by Emilie Benson Knipe. New York, The Century co., 1920.

Knipe, Alden Arthur,
Knipe, *Mrs.* **Emilie (Benson)** 1870–
The missing pearls; little Miss Fales goes West, by Emilie Benson Knipe and Alden Arthur Knipe ... New York and London, Harper & brothers, 1911.

Knipe, Alden Arthur, 1870- joint author.
Knipe, *Mrs.* **Emilie (Benson)** 1870–
Now and then, by Emilie Benson Knipe and Alden Arthur Knipe ... illustrated by Emilie Benson Knipe. New York & London, The Century co. [c1925]

Knipe, Alden Arthur, 1870- joint author.

Knipe, *Mrs.* Emilie (Benson) 1870–
A patriot maid, and other stories, by Emilie Benson Knipe and Alden Arthur Knipe; illustrated by W. M. Berger. New York & London, The Century co. [1928]

Knipe, Alden Arthur, 1870- joint author.
Knipe, *Mrs.* **Emilie** (Benson) 1870–
Peg o' the ring, a maid of Denewood, by Emilie Benson Knipe and Alden Arthur Knipe ... illustrations by C. M. Relyea. New York, The Century co., 1915.

Knipe, Alden Arthur, 1870- joint author.

Knipe, *Mrs.* **Emilie (Benson)** 1870–
The pirate's ward, by Emilie Benson Knipe and Alden Arthur Knipe, illustrated by Marguerite de Angeli. New York, The Macmillan company, 1929.

Knipe, Alden Arthur, 1870- joint author.
Knipe, *Mrs.* **Emilie (Benson)** 1870–
Polly Trotter, patriot, by Emilie Benson Knipe and Alden Arthur Knipe ... illustrated by Emilie Benson Knipe. New York, The Macmillan company, 1916.

Knipe, Alden Arthur, 1870- joint author.

Knipe, *Mrs.* **Emilie** (Benson) 1870–
Powder, patches and Patty, by Emilie Benson Knipe and Alden Arthur Knipe ... illustrated by Emilie Benson Knipe. New York and London, The Century co. [c1924]

Knipe, Alden Arthur, 1870–
The red magic book, by Emilie Benson Knipe, verses by Alden Arthur Knipe. New York, Doubleday, Page & co., 1910.
[51] p. col. illus. 22½ x 18cm.
Sheet of transparent red celluloid attached to back of cover, which, placed over illustration, changes drawing.
Illustrated end-papers.

10-30442
Library of Congress

NK 0204510

Knipe, Alden Arthur, 1870–
Remember rhymes, by Arthur Alden Knipe, illustrated by Emilie Benson Knipe. [New York] Hearst's international library co. [c1914]
80 p. illus., col. plates. 26cm.

I. Knipe, Mrs. Emilie (Benson) 1870– illus. II. Title.
15—2294
Library of Congress PZ8.3.K748R

NK 0204511 DLC OrCS MB

PZ
8
.3
.K748R2
Knipe, Alden Arthur, 1870-
Remember rhymes, by Arthur Alden Knipe, illustrated by Emilie Benson Knipe. [New York] Penn publishing co. [c1914]
80 p. illus. 26 cm.

NK 0204512 OKentU

[**Knipe, Alden Arthur**] 1870–
Sarah and son, by Timothy Shea [*pseud.*] New York, Dodd, Mead & company, 1929.
viii, 296 p. 19½cm.

I. Title.
29-15478 Revised
Library of Congress PZ3.K7486Sar

NK 0204513 DLC MH

VOLUME 300

Knipe, Alden Arthur, 1870- joint author.

Knipe, *Mrs.* **Emilie (Benson)** 1870–
The shadow captain; an account of the activities of one Christopher Rousby in the town of New Yorke during several months of the year of Our Lord 1703 ... by Emilie Benson Knipe and Alden Arthur Knipe. New York, Dodd, Mead and company, 1925.

NK 0204521 NN CaBVaU PU-Mu ICN CSmH CtY WaU

Knipe, Alden Arthur, 1870- joint author.

Knipe, *Mrs.* **Emilie (Benson)** 1870–
Silver dice, by Emilie Benson Knipe and Alden Arthur Knipe. New York, Dodd, Mead and company, 1928.

Knipe, Alden Arthur, 1870- joint author.

Knipe, *Mrs.* **Emilie (Benson)** 1870–
The story of Old Ironsides, the cradle of the United States navy, by Emilie Benson Knipe and Alden Arthur Knipe; illustrated by Mead Schaeffer; with an introduction by Rear-Admiral William Sims. New York, Dodd, Mead & company, 1928.

Knipe, Alden Arthur, 1870- joint author

Knipe, *Mrs.* **Emilie (Benson)** 1870–
The treasure house, by Emilie Benson Knipe and Alden Arthur Knipe ... illustrated by Margaret Ayer. New York, London, The Century co. [°1930]

Knipe, Alden Arthur, 1870- joint author.

Knipe, *Mrs.* **Emilie (Benson)** 1870–
Treasure-trove, by Emilie Benson Knipe and Alden Arthur Knipe; illustrated by Louis Schroeder. New York & London, The Century co. [°1927]

Knipe, Alden Arthur, 1870- joint author.

Knipe, *Mrs.* **Emilie (Benson)** 1870–
Vive la France; a narrative founded on the diary of Jeannette de Martigny, by Emilie Benson Knipe and Alden Arthur Knipe. Illustrated by Emilie Benson Knipe. New York, The Century co., 1919.

Knipe, Bazett N. C.

St. Helena. *Colonial secretary's office.*
Census of the island of St. Helena, in 1881. St. Helena, E. Watson, government printer, 1881.

[**Knipe,** Rev. **C.**]
Some account of the Tahkaht language, as spoken by several tribes on the western coast of Vancouver island. London: Hatchard and Co., 1868. 2 p.l., 80 p. 12°.

1. American languages: Tahkaht. 2. Title.
N. Y. P. L. May 16, 1912.

NK 0204521 NN CaBVaU PU-Mu ICN CSmH CtY WaU

Knipe, Charles, *fl.* 1715.
A city ramble: or, The humours of the compter. As it is acted at the theatre in Lincoln's-Inn-Fields. By Mr. Charles Knipe ... London, E. Curll [etc.] 1715.
3 p. l., 57 p. front. 16½cm.
[Longe, F. Collection of plays. v. 201, no. 5]

I. Title.
25-27820
Library of Congress PR1241.L6 vol. 201

NK 0204522 DLC ICU CtY OCl IU CSmH ICN

Knipe, Charles, fl. 1715.
City ramble [or, The humours of the compter] London, 1715.
(In Three centuries of drama: English, 1701-1750)

Microprint.

NK 0204523 MoU

Knipe, Charles, *fl.* 1715.
A city ramble: or, The humours of the compter. As it is acted at the theatre in Lincoln's-Inn-Fields. By Mr. Charles Knipe ... London, Printed for W.Feales, 1736.
3 p. l., 57 p. front. 16½cm.

NK 0204524 MiU CtY NIC MH

[Knipe, Delia]
The picture alphabet, by Cousin Daisy [pseud.] Philadelphia, J. B. Lippincott, c1879.
[56] p. illus.

NK 0204525 NNC ViU

[**Knipe, Delia**] *comp.*
Uncle Herbert's speaker and autograph-album verses. A choice collection carefully selected and arranged by Uncle Herbert [*pseud.*] ... Philadelphia and Chicago, J. A. Ruth & co., 1886.
xii, 13-416 p. 20½cm.

1. Readers and speakers—1870- I. Title.
12-4601
Library of Congress PN4201.K6

NK 0204526 DLC RPB OCl

[Knipe, Delia]
The youngster, by Cousin Daisy [pseud.] With illustrations by Kate Greenaway and others. Philadelphia, J. B. Lippincott [c1880]
96 p. illus.

I. Greenaway, Kate, 1846-1901, illus.

NK 0204527 NNC

Knipe, Elizabeth
see
Cobbold, *Mrs.* **Elizabeth (Knipe)** 1767-1824.

Knipe, Emilie Benson, 1870-1958
For works published under her pseudonym Therese Benson see: Benson, Therese, pseud.

Knipe, *Mrs.* **Emilie (Benson)** 1870- 1958.
Beatrice of Denewood; a sequel to "The lucky sixpence", by Emilie Benson Knipe and Alden Arthur Knipe; illustrated by C. M. Relyea. New York, The Century co., 1913.
6 p. l., 3-437 p. incl. front., illus., plates. 19½cm. $1.25

I. Knipe, Alden Arthur, 1870- joint author. II. Title.
13-21024
Library of Congress PZ7.K745B

NK 0204530 DLC Or WaS OEac OCl OClh OO OLak NN PBa OU

Knipe, Emilie Benson, and Alden Arthur Knipe. Z.F.7k5
Beatrice of Denewood. A sequel to "The lucky sixpence" [Z.F.7k2].
— New York. The Century Co. 1916. Plates. 19 cm.
A story of the closing years of the Revolutionary War, in which Washington, Cornwallis and Sir Joshua Reynolds appear as characters.

NK 0204531 MB PU

Knipe, *Mrs.* Emilie Benson, 1870–
Beatrice of Denewood; a sequel to "The lucky sixpence", by Emilie Benson Knipe and Alden Arthur Knipe; illustrated by C. M. Relyea. New York, The Century, 1920 [c1913]
4 p. l., 3-437 p. incl. front., illus., plates. 19½cm. $1.25

NK 0204532 OU

Knipe, Mrs. Emilie (Benson) 1870-
Beatrice of Denewood...
N.Y. Appleton-Century, 1939, c1913.
407p. front. illus. D.
By Emilie Benson Knipe and Alden Arthur Knipe.

NK 0204533 PP

Knipe, Mrs. Emilie (Benson) 1870- illus.

Haines, Alice Calhoun.
Boys; with full-page colour plates after drawings by Emilie Benson Knipe, and with new stories and verses by Alice Calhoun Haines. New York, F. A. Stokes company [1905]

Knipe, *Mrs.* **Emilie (Benson)** 1870–
A cavalier maid, by Emilie Benson Knipe and Alden Arthur Knipe ... illustrated by Emilie Benson Knipe. New York, The Macmillan company, 1919.
4 p. l., 255 p. front., plates. 20cm.

I. Knipe, Alden Arthur, 1870- joint author. II. Title.
19-15572
Library of Congress PZ3.K749Ca

NK 0204535 DLC WaS OEac OLak OClh OCl MB

Knipe, Emilie Benson, 1870 -
Cavalier maid, by E. B. Knipe & Arthur Alden. 1928.

NK 0204536 PJA

Knipe, *Mrs.* **Emilie Benson,** 1870–
A continental dollar, by Emilie Benson Knipe, and Alden Arthur Knipe ... Illustrated by Emilie Benson Knipe. New York and London, The Century co., 1923.
5 p. l., 3-372 p. front., plates. 20½cm. $1.75

I. Knipe, Alden Arthur, 1870- joint author. II. Title.
23-12966
Library of Congress PZ7.K745Co

NK 0204537 DLC Or WaS OrP PPGi OCl OClh OLak

VOLUME 300

Knipe, *Mrs.* Emilie (Benson) 1870–
Diantha's quest; a tale of the Argonauts of '49, by Emilie Benson Knipe and Alden Arthur Knipe. New York, The Macmillan company, 1921.
4 p. l., 295 p. front., plates. 19½cm.

I. Knipe, Alden Arthur, 1870– joint author. II. Title.
21—18585
Library of Congress PZ7.K745Di

NK 0204538 DLC WaS PWcS PP OClh OEac MB NN

Knipe, Mrs. Emilie (Benson), 1870–
Dr. Franklin's party, by Emilie Benson Knipe and Alden Arthur Knipe.
455 +1
From Child life, v.3, p.588-591, 616,666-669, 702,782-785,800-801, v.4, p.28-31,44, Oct.,1924-Jan.,1925.

NK 0204539 CtY

Knipe, Emilie (Benson) 1870–
The flower of fortune, by Emilie Benson Knipe and Alden Arthur Knipe ... illustrated by Emilie Benson Knipe. New York, The Century co., 1922.
5 p. l., 3-354 p. front., plates. 19½ cm.

I. Knipe, Alden Arthur, 1870– joint author. II. Title.
22—17942
Library of Congress PZ3.K749Fl

NK 0204540 DLC Or NN PBa OU

Knipe, Emilie Benson, 1870–
Gallant adventures ...
see Benson, Therese, pseud.

Knipe, Mrs. Emilie (Benson) 1870– illus.

Haines, Alice Calhoun.
Girls; with full-page colour plates after drawings by Emilie Benson Knipe, and with new stories and verses by Alice Calhoun Haines. New York, F. A. Stokes company [1905]

Knipe, Emilie Benson, 1870–

Haines, Alice Calhoun.
Girls and boys; with full-page colour plates after drawings by Emilie Benson Knipe, and with new stories and verses by Alice Calhoun Haines. New York, F. A. Stokes company [1905]

Knipe, *Mrs.* Emilie (Benson) 1870–
Girls of '64, by Emilie Benson Knipe and Alden Arthur Knipe ... illustrated by Emilie Benson Knipe. New York, The Macmillan company, 1918.
4 p. l., 262 p. front., plates. 20cm.

I. Knipe, Alden Arthur, 1870– joint author. II. Title.
18—20475
Library of Congress PZ3.K749G

NK 0204544 DLC Or WaS OEac OClh OLak OO PWcS MB NN

Knipe, *Mrs.* Emilie (Benson) 1870–
Little Miss Fales, by Emilie Benson Knipe and Alden Arthur Knipe; frontispiece by Frances Rogers. New York and London, Harper & brothers, 1910.
3 p. l., 225, [1] p. col. front. 19½cm.

I. Knipe, Alden Arthur, 1870– joint author. II. Title.
10—9256
Library of Congress PZ7.K745L

NK 0204545 DLC PU

Knipe, *Mrs.* Emilie (Benson) 1870–
Lost—a brother, by Emilie Benson Knipe and Alden Arthur Knipe, illustrated by Henry Pitz. New York, The Macmillan company, 1928.
5 p. l., 239 p. incl. plates. col. front. 19½cm.

1. U. S.—Hist.—War of 1812—Fiction. I. Knipe, Alden Arthur, 1870– joint author. II. Title.
28—22313
Library of Congress PZ7.K745Ll

NK 0204546 DLC OO OClh PHatU PP

Knipe, Emilie(Benson), 1870–
Lost little lady, by E.B. Knipe and A.A. Knipe. Century, 1912.

Knipe, *Mrs.* Emilie (Benson) 1870–
The lost little lady, by Emilie Benson Knipe and Arthur Alden Knipe ... illustrated by Emilie Benson Knipe. New York, The Century co., 1917.
6 p. l., 3-410 p. incl. front., plates. 19½cm.

I. Knipe, Alden Arthur, 1870– joint author. II. Title.
17—25247
Library of Congress PZ7.K745Lo

NK 0204548 DLC PU OO OLak PPFr NN

Knipe, Emilie (Benson), 1870–
The lost little lady, by Emilie Benson Knipe and Alden Arthur Knipe ... Illustrated by Emilie Benson Knipe. New York: The Century co., 1918. 410 p. incl. plates. front. 19½cm.

203101B. 1. Juvenile literature—Fiction, American. I. Knipe, Alden Arthur, 1870– , jt. au. II. Title.
N. Y. P. L. December 3, 1942

NK 0204549 NN

Knipe, *Mrs.* Emilie (Benson) 1870–
The luck of Denewood, by Emilie Benson Knipe and Alden Arthur Knipe ... illustrated by Emilie Benson Knipe. New York, The Century co., 1921.
5 p. l., 3-359 p. front., plates. 19½cm. $1.90

I. Knipe, Alden Arthur, 1870– joint author. II. Title.
21—16535
Library of Congress PZ7.K745Lr

NK 0204550 DLC OEac OO OClh PBa NN MB

Knipe, *Mrs.* Emilie (Benson) 1870–
The luck of Denewood, by Emilie Benson Knipe and Alden Arthur Knipe ... illustrated by Emilie Benson Knipe. New York, The Century co. , 1923 [c1921]
5 p. l., 3-359 p. front., plates. 19½cm. $1.90

NK 0204551 OU

Knipe, Emilie (Benson) 1870–
The lucky sixpence, by Emilie Benson Knipe and Alden Arthur Knipe; illustrated by Arthur E. Becher. New York, The Century co., 1912.
5 p. l., 3-408 p. incl. plates. front. 20cm.

I. Knipe, Alden Arthur, 1870– joint author. II. Title.
12—22556
Library of Congress PZ7.K745Lu

NK 0204552 DLC OrP CoU PP PU OCl OEac OLak OClh MB OO NN PPFr Or WaS

Knipe, *Mrs.* Emilie (Benson) 1870–
A maid of old Manhattan, by Emilie Benson Knipe and Alden Arthur Knipe ... illustrated by Emilie Benson Knipe. New York, The Macmillan company, 1917.
4 p. l., 292 p. front., plates. 20cm.

I. Knipe, Alden Arthur, 1870– joint author. II. Title.
17—24856
Library of Congress PZ7.K745Ma

NK 0204553 DLC OKentU Or WaS OrP PNt PPFr PU OEac OClh OLak OCl NN MB

Knipe, *Mrs.* Emilie (Benson) 1870–
A maid of '76, by Emilie Benson Knipe and Alden Arthur Knipe; illustrated by Emilie Benson Knipe. New York, The Macmillan company, 1915.
4 p. l., 276 p. front., plates. 20cm. $1.25

I. Knipe, Alden Arthur, 1870– joint author. II. Title.
15—19078
Library of Congress PZ3.K749Ma

NK 0204554 DLC WaS OrP OEac OClh OLak OCl PHatU MB NN

Knipe, Mrs. Emilie (Benson), & Knipe, A.A.
A maid of '76.
N.Y. Macmillan, 1940,c1915.
276p. pl. D.

NK 0204555 PP

Knipe, *Mrs.* Emilie (Benson), 1870–
A Mayflower maid, by Emilie Benson Knipe and Alden Arthur Knipe; illustrated by Emilie Benson Knipe. New York, The Century co., 1920.
5 p. l., 3-287 p. front., plates. 19½cm. $1.90

I. Knipe, Alden Arthur, 1870– joint author. II. Title.
20—16501
Library of Congress PZ3.K749May

NK 0204556 DLC WaS OrP PBa PHatU PU OEac MiU OO OClh OLak MB

Knipe, *Mrs.* Emilie (Benson) 1870–
The missing pearls; little Miss Fales goes West, by Emilie Benson Knipe and Alden Arthur Knipe ... New York and London, Harper & brothers, 1911.
4 p. l., 286, [1] p. front., plates. 19½cm. $1.25

I. Knipe, Alden Arthur, 1870– joint author. II. Title.
11—26612
Library of Congress PZ7.K745Mi

NK 0204557 DLC PU

VOLUME 300

Knipe, *Mrs.* Emilie (Benson) 1870–
Now and then, by Emilie Benson Knipe and Alden Arthur Knipe ... illustrated by Emilie Benson Knipe. New York & London, The Century co. [°1925]
5 p. l., 3-150 p. incl. front., illus. 19½cm. $1.50
CONTENTS.—Now and then.—Dr. Franklin's party.

I. Knipe, Alden Arthur, 1870– joint author. II. Title.
Library of Congress PZ7.K745No 25—17935

NK 0204558 DLC

Knipe, *Mrs.* Emilie (Benson) 1870–
A patriot maid, and other stories, by Emilie Benson Knipe and Alden Arthur Knipe; illustrated by W. M. Berger. New York & London, The Century co. [1928]
5 p. l., 3-220 p. incl. front., illus. 19½cm. $1.75
CONTENTS.—A patriot maid.—The flight of the brown bird.—For peace and Concord.—General George Washington's birthday present.—A thousand pounds.—Courage.—A Tory torch.—Christmas 1783.

1. U. S.—Hist.—Revolution—Fiction. I. Knipe, Alden Arthur, 1870– joint author. II. Title.
Library of Congress PZ7.K745Pa 28-21826

NK 0204559 DLC PP

Knipe, *Mrs.* Emilie (Benson) 1870–
Peg o' the ring, a maid of Denewood, by Emilie Benson Knipe and Alden Arthur Knipe ... illustrations by C. M. Relyea. New York, The Century co., 1915.
5 p. l., 3-375 p. front., plates. 20cm. $1.25

I. Knipe, Alden Arthur, 1870– joint author. II. Title.
Library of Congress PZ3.K749Pe 15—19077

NK 0204560 DLC Or PP PPFr OEac OClh OO MB NN

Knipe, Mrs. Emilie (Benson), 1870 –
Peg o' the ring; a maid of Denewood, by Mrs. E. B. Knipe & A. A. Knipe. N.Y., Century, 1917, [c1914-15].
375p.

NK 0204561 PU

Knipe, *Mrs.* Emilie Benson, 1870–
Peg o' the ring, a maid of Denewood, by Emilie Benson Knipe and Alden Arthur Knipe ... illustrations by C. M. Relyea. New York, The Century co., 1920 [c1915]
5 p. l., 3-375 p. front., plates. 20cm. $1.25

NK 0204562 OU

Knipe, *Mrs.* Emilie (Benson) 1870–
The pirate's ward, by Emilie Benson Knipe and Alden Arthur Knipe, illustrated by Marguerite de Angeli. New York, The Macmillan company, 1929.
6 p. l., 267 p. incl. plates. front. 19½cm.

I. Knipe, Alden Arthur, 1870– joint author. II. Title.
Library of Congress PZ7.K745Pi 29-22805

NK 0204563 DLC PPA PHatU PP OO OClh NN

Knipe, *Mrs.* Emilie (Benson) 1870–
Polly Trotter, patriot, by Emilie Benson Knipe and Alden Arthur Knipe ... illustrated by Emilie Benson Knipe. New York, The Macmillan company, 1916.
4 p. l., 3 p. front., plates. 19½cm.

I. Knipe, Alden Arthur, 1870– joint author. II. Title.
Library of Congress PZ7.K745Po 16—22754

NK 0204564 DLC WaS PPFr MB NN

Knipe, *Mrs.* Emilie Benson, 1870–
Polly Trotter, patriot, by Emilie Benson Knipe and Alden Arthur Knipe ... illustrated by Emilie Benson Knipe. New York, Macmillan, 1920 [c1916]
4 p. l., 303 p. front., plates. 19½cm. $1.25

NK 0204565 OU

Knipe, Mrs. Emilie (Benson), 1870-
Polly Trotter, patriot, by Emilie Benson Knipe and Alden Arthur Knipe ... illus. by Emilie Benson Knipe. N.Y., Macmillan [c1916] 1927.

NK 0204566 OO OClh OLak

Knipe, *Mrs.* Emilie (Benson) 1870–
Powder, patches and Patty, by Emilie Benson Knipe and Alden Arthur Knipe ... illustrated by Emilie Benson Knipe. New York and London, The Century co. [°1924]
4 p. l., 3-305 p. front., plates. 20cm.

1. U. S.—Hist.—Revolution—Fiction. I. Knipe, Alden Arthur, 1870– joint author. II. Title.
Library of Congress PZ3.K749Po 24—21809

NK 0204567 DLC PHi

Knipe, Mrs. Emilie (Benson) 1870– illus.
Knipe, Alden Arthur, 1870–
Remember rhymes, by Arthur Alden Knipe, illustrated by Emilie Benson Knipe. [New York] Hearst's international library co. [°1914]

Knipe, *Mrs.* Emilie (Benson) 1870–
The shadow captain; an account of the activities of one Christopher Rousby in the town of New Yorke during several months of the year of Our Lord 1703 ... by Emilie Benson Knipe and Alden Arthur Knipe. New York, Dodd, Mead and company, 1925.
3 p. l., 347 p. mounted col. front. 19½cm. $2.00

I. Knipe, Alden Arthur, 1870– joint author. II. Title.
Library of Congress PZ3.K749Sh 25—6389

NK 0204569 DLC WaE OU OEac OClh OLak OCl MB NN PPM PPL

Knipe, Emilie (Benson) 1870-
Silver dice, by Emilie Benson Knipe and Alden Arthur Knipe. New York, Grosset & Dunlap [c.1927]
19.5 cm.

NK 0204570 MH PPL

Knipe, *Mrs.* Emilie (Benson) 1870–
Silver dice, by Emilie Benson Knipe and Alden Arthur Knipe. New York, Dodd, Mead and company, 1928.
4 p. l., 3-415 p. 19½cm.
Published 1927.

I. Knipe, Alden Arthur, 1870– joint author. II. Title.
Library of Congress PZ3.K74981 27-23605

NK 0204571 DLC OU PPM PP MB

Knipe, *Mrs.* Emilie (Benson) 1870–
The story of Old Ironsides, the cradle of the United States navy, by Emilie Benson Knipe and Alden Arthur Knipe; illustrated by Mead Schaeffer; with an introduction by Rear-Admiral William Sims. New York, Dodd, Mead & company, 1928.
vii p., 1 l., 321 p. col. front., col. plates. 23cm.
Illustrated colored lining-papers.

1. Constitution (Frigate) I. Knipe, Alden Arthur, 1870– joint author. II. Schaeffer, Mead, 1898– illus.
Library of Congress E182.K72 28-29393

NK 0204572 DLC OKentU NcC ViU PPL PP OCl OClh MB DN

Knipe, Mrs. Emilie (Benson) 1870-
973.525 The story of Old Ironsides, the cradle of
K718 the United States Navy, by Emilie Benson Knipe and Alden Arthur Knipe; illustrated by Mead Schaeffer; with an introd. by Rear-Admiral William S. Sims. New York, Dodd, Mead & Co., 1929 [c1928]
vii, 321 p. col. plates. 23 cm.
Illustrated colored lining-papers.
1. Constitution (Frigate) I. Knipe, Alden Arthur, 1870- jt. au. II. Schaeffer, Mead, 1898- illus. III. Title.

NK 0204573 NcD WaE

Knipe, Emilie (Benson) and A. A. Knipe. J359.09-K
The story of Old Ironsides; the cradle of the United States Navy; illustrated by Mead Schaeffer; with an introduction by William S. Sims. New York: Tudor Pub. Co., 1935 [cop. 1928] 321 p. col'd front., col'd pls. 8°.

1. (J.) United States—Navy. Hist. 3. Title. 4. Constitution (ship). 2. (A.) United States—Navy— 5. Knipe, Alden Arthur, jt. au.
N. Y. P. L. March 11, 1936

NK 0204574 NN OO OU

Knipe, Emilie Benson, 1870-
Strictly private ...
see Benson, Therese, pseud.

Knipe, *Mrs.* Emilie (Benson) 1870–
The treasure house, by Emilie Benson Knipe and Alden Arthur Knipe ... illustrated by Margaret Ayer. New York, London, The Century co. [°1930]
vii, 300 p. front., plates. 19½cm. $2.00
"First printing."

1. New Orleans—Hist.—Fiction. I. Knipe, Alden Arthur, 1870– joint author. II. Title.
Library of Congress PZ7.K745To 30-22901

NK 0204576 DLC WaS PPL PBa NN

Knipe, Emilie (Benson) 1870–
Treasure-trove, by Emilie Benson Knipe and Alden Arthur Knipe; illustrated by Louis Schroeder. New York & London, The Century co. [°1927]
v, 330 p. front., plates. 19½ cm.

I. Knipe, Alden Arthur, 1870– joint author. II. Title.
PZ7.K745Tr 27—19640

NK 0204577 DLC OO

Knipe, Emilie Benson, 1870-
The unknown daughter ...
see Benson, Therese, pseud.

VOLUME 300

Knipe, *Mrs.* Emilie (Benson) 1870–
Vive la France; a narrative founded on the diary of Jeannette de Martigny, by Emilie Benson Knipe and Alden Arthur Knipe. Illustrated by Emilie Benson Knipe. New York, The Century co., 1919.
6 p. l., 3-364 p. front., plates. 19½cm. $1.50

1. European war, 1914-1918—Fiction. I. Knipe, Alden Arthur, 1870– joint author. II. Title.
19—14014
Library of Congress PZ3.K749Vi

NK 0204579 DLC WaWW Or OrU ViU OO OCLh OLak NN MB PU

Knipe, George Linley
Relation of the municipality to the state, New York state.
80LL
Univ. of Penna., Ph. D. thesis.

NK 0204580 PU

[Knipe, H M M]
A modern pilgrimage. By H. M. M. K. London, Printed for private circulation only [Caxton press, 1871]
vi, [3], 14-152 p. front., plates. 22cm.
A tour in Egypt, Palestine, Greece, etc.

1. Palestine—Descr. & trav. 2. Levant—Descr. & trav. I. Title.
20-14252 Revised
Library of Congress DS48.K7
[r32c2] 915.69

NK 0204581 DLC

Knipe, Helen Alden, illus.
Hawthorne, Nathaniel, 1804-1864.
A wonder-book, and Tanglewood tales, by Nathaniel Hawthorne; illustrated by Elenore Plaisted Abbott and Helen Alden Knipe ... Philadelphia, G. W. Jacobs and company [1911]

Knipe, Henry Robert.
Evolution in the past, by Henry R. Knipe ... with illustrations by Alice B. Woodward and Ernest Bucknall. London, Herbert and Daniel, 1912.
xv, 242 p. incl. front., illus. plates. 26cm.

1. Paleontology. 2. Evolution.
12—29966
Library of Congress QE711.K5

MiU OO OClW OCl PWcS ICJ WaU OrPR
NK 0204583 DLC MU KMK CU NIC WaU ViU NcD PP PBa PU-BZ

Knipe, Henry Robert. 575-K
Evolution in the past; with illustrations by Alice B. Woodhouse & Ernest Bucknall. Philadelphia: J. B. Lippincott Co. [1912?] iii-xv, 242 p., 56 pl. 4°.
Authorities consulted, p. 217-226.

NK 0204584 NN WaSp MB

Knipe, Henry Robert.
Nebula to man, by Henry R. Knipe ... London, J. M. Dent & co., 1905.
xvi, 251, [1] p. front., plates (part col.) 30 x 23½cm.
Poem.
"List of principal books consulted": p. 243-244.

1. Evolution. 2. Paleontology. I. Title.

NK 0204585 MiU MH OCl OU CtY PU IU

Knipe, Henry Robert, editor.
Tunbridge Wells and neighbourhood. A chronicle of the town from 1608 to 1915; and papers by various writers relating to the geology, plant and animal life, archaeology, and other matters of the district. Edited by Henry R. Knipe... Tunbridge Wells: Pelton, 1916. 207 p., 4 pl. 8°.
Tunbridge Wells authors of the last 50 years, p. 193-200.

1. Tunbridge Wells. September 29, 1916.
N. Y. P. L.

NK 0204586 NN ViU

Knipe, Irvin Poley, 1866-1929.
Norristown, Pa. *Ordinances, etc.*
A digest of the laws and ordinances of and applicable to the borough of Norristown, Pennsylvania, with such resolutions of council as are of a permanent nature; including an index-digest of proceedings of town council from the incorporation of the borough, March 31, 1812, and a list of monuments, bench marks and other important data. By Irvin P. Knipe ... Rev. to July 4, 1904, and pub. by authority of town council. [Norristown] Printed by Norristown herald, 1904.

CS71
.K727
1930
Knipe, Irvin Poley, 1866-1929
Lineage of Johannes Kneip (now Knipe,)...
[Philadelphia] c1930

NK 0204588 DLC

Knipe, Irvin Poley, 1866-1929.
The Pennsylvania-German in the civil war, by Irvin P. Knipe ... Address delivered at the annual meeting of the society, held at Norristown, Pa., November 2, 1916. Lancaster, Pa. [Press of the New era printing company] 1917.
12 p. 25½cm. (*In* Pennsylvania-German society. Proceedings and addresses ... Nov. 2, 1916. 1920. v. 27)

1. Pennsylvania—Hist.—Civil war. 2. Germans in Pennsylvania. I. Title.
24-23947
Library of Congress F146.P23 vol. 27

NK 0204589 DLC MoU InU OCU OCl ViU PU

Knipe, J M
"Stymied;" a comedy in one act... Belfast, 1950. 21 p. 19cm. (Carter plays series)

1. Drama, Irish.

NK 0204590 NN MH

Knipe, James A
Geological & mineralogical map of England and Wales, with parts of Scotland, Ireland & France, showing also the inland navigation by means of rivers & canals, with their elevation in feet above the sea. Together with the railroads & principal roads. 3d ed. with additions from the 11th meeting of the British Association and corr. down to Jany. 1842. London, Published by J.A. Knipe, 1842.
col. map. 93 x 81 cm.

Scale ca. 1:760, 320.
Engraved by J. Dower.
Shows several sections.
"Places where the members of the British Association have assembled" 1831-1842 listed.

I. British Association for the Advancement of Science. II. Title.

NK 0204592 OkU

Knipe, James A
Geological map of Scotland; lochs, mountains, islands, rivers and canals, the railways and the principal roads, and sites of the minerals. London, E. Stanford, 1859 [i.e. 9th Sept.1858]
col.map 95x110cm. fold to 23x13cm.

Scale not given.
Colored by J. Cox.

NK 0204594 OkU CtY

Knipe, James A. 554.2 Loo1
Geological map of the British Isles and part of France, showing also the inland navigation by means of rivers and canals, the railways and principal roads, and sites of the minerals. 1 map in 4 parts. 79.5x67 cm. nar.O. London; Saunders, 1850.

NK 0204595 ICJ

Knipe, James A.
Geological map of the British Isles and part of France, showing also the inland navigation by means of rivers and canals, the railways and principal roads, and sites of the minerals ... I. A. Knipe. 2d ed. London, Stanford; [etc., etc.] 1862.
162 x 132 cm. fold. to 28 x 23 cm.
Scale: 10.5 cm. - 50 mi.
1. Geology - Gt. Brit. - Maps. 2. Geology - France - Maps.

NK 0204596 CU

HC101
.N352
no. 63
Knipe, James Launcelot, 1904– , joint author.
Calder, Alexander, 1886–
The guaranteed annual wage, an individual report by Alexander Calder and James L. Knipe. [Washington] National Planning Assn. [1948]

Knipe, James Lloyd, 1894–
Early Knipe families of Pennsylvania (including the male line of descent to the present generation) Lancaster, Pa., 1949.
Microfilm copy (positive) of typescript.
Collation of the original, as determined from the film: 593 l.

1. Knipe family.
Microfilm 4341 CS Mic 58-6230

NK 0204598 DLC WHi NN

Knipe, James Lloyd, 1894–
The families of Louis Hartman and Peter Rodenhauser of Columbia, Lancaster County, Pennsylvania. [Lancaster, Pa., 1952]
Microfilm copy (positive) of typescript.
Collation of the original, as determined from the film: 55 l.

1. Hartman family. 2. Rodenhauser family.
Microfilm 4340 CS Mic 58-6234

NK 0204599 DLC WHi NN

Knipe, James Lloyd, 1894–
The Heindel (Heindle-Haindel-Hindel-Heindell) family of Windsor Township, York County, Pennsylvania, Lancaster, Pa., 1953.
Microfilm copy (positive) of typescript.
Collation of the original, as determined from the film: 571 l. facsims.

1. Heindel family.
Microfilm 4338 CS Mic 58-6229

NK 0204600 DLC Mi WHi NN

VOLUME 300

Knipe, James Lloyd, 1894–
The Jacobs family of Windsor Township, York County, Pennsylvania. Lancaster, Pa., 1955.
Microfilm copy (positive) of typescript.
Collation of the original, as determined from the film: 192 l. illus.

1. Jacobs family.

Microfilm 4339 CS Mic 58–6228

NK 0204601 DLC WHi NN

FILM E.F 0516 K71 Knipe, James Lloyd, 1894
The Olp family of Shrewsbury township, York county, Pennsylvania. Lancaster, Pa., 1952.
Microfilm copy of typewritten original in the Lancaster county historical society. Positive.
Collation of the original as determined from the film: 71 l.

NK 0204602 WHi NN

Knipe, John, pseud.
see Richings, Mildred Gladys.

Knipe, John, Rev.
Substance of a charge delivered ... to the Rev. Mr. John Heslup at his ordination ... by the Rev. Mr. John Knipe, together with an exhortation to the people by the Rev. Mr. James Brownfield. New Castle, pr. by Saint, 1777.
32 p.

NK 0204604 PPPrHi

Knipe, Joseph William.
The development of literary criticism in England. By J. W. Knipe ...
(*In* Royal society of literature of the United Kingdom, London. Essays by divers hands, being the transactions. London, 1898. 22cm. 2d ser., vol. XIX, p. [223]–254)
"Read June 8th, 1898."

1. Criticism—Hist. 2. English literature—Hist. & crit.

A 44–5592

Illinois. Univ. Library for Library of Congress PN22.R6 2d ser., vol. 19

NK 0204605 IU DLC

Knipe, Rest.
A course of lectures: containing remarks upon the government and education of children, thoughts upon the present plan of education, and an essay upon elocution. As read lately in many parts of England and Scotland. To which is added a sermon. By the Rev. Rest Knipe. Edinburgh, Printed for the author, 1783.
338 p. 22cm.

1. Education. 2. Elocution. 3. Education—Gt. Brit.

E 10–1896

Library, U. S. Bur. of Education LB575.K74

NK 0204606 DHEW PU

Knipe, Rest.
A course of lectures: containing remarks upon the government and education of children, thoughts upon the present plan of education, and an essay upon elocution. To which is added, a sermon. By the Rev. Rest Knipe. Aberdeen: The author, 1786. 304 p. 21cm.

255441B. 1. Education, 18th cent. 2. Elocution.
N. Y. P. L. January 25, 1944

NK 0204607 NN

Knipe, Robert.
And there were voices, a play in three acts, concerning the first years in Springfield, Illinois, in the life of Abraham Lincoln. By Robert Knipe. Boston, Mass., and Los Angeles, Calif., Baker's plays [1943]
125 p. 1 illus., diagr. 19½cm.
On cover: Acting ed.

1. Lincoln, Abraham, pres. U. S.—Drama. I. Title.

43–5689

Library of Congress PS3521.N58A8
[3] 812.5

NK 0204608 DLC

Knipe, Robert.
Heritage of Wimpole street; a play in one act by Robert Knipe. Boston, Mass., and Los Angeles, Calif., Baker's plays [c1941]
41 p. pl. 18½cm. (*On cover:* Baker's royalty plays)

I. Title.

41–11860

Library of Congress PS3521.N58H4 1941
[2] 812.5

NK 0204609 DLC

Knipe, Robert.
One who came to Gettysburg, a play in one act, by Robert Knipe ... Boston, Mass., and Los Angeles, Cal., Baker's plays [c1942]
41 p. diagr. 19cm. (*On cover:* Baker's royalty plays)

1. Lincoln, Abraham, pres. U. S.—Drama. I. Title.

42–3412

Library of Congress PS3521.N58O5 1942

NK 0204610 DLC

Knipe, Theodore.
Arizona hunt information
see under Arizona. Wildlife Restoration Division.

Knipe, Theodore.
The status of the antelope herds of northern Arizona [by] Theodore Knipe. Pittman-Robertson project, Arizona 9–R. [Phoenix] Arizona Game and fish commission, Federal aid division, 1944.
40 p. incl. illus. (incl. maps (1 double)) tables. 23cm.

1. Antelopes. I. Pittman-Robertson project. Arizona. II. Arizona. Game and fish commission.

44–42641

Library of Congress SK305.A6K6
[3] 799.2773584

NK 0204612 DLC OrCS Or NcD PP OCl

Knipe, William.

Criminal chronology of York castle; with a register of criminals capitally convicted and executed at the County assizes, commencing March 1st, 1379, to the present time ... Carefully comp. from prison documents, ancient papers, and other authentic sources, materially assisted by William Knipe ... York [Eng.] C. L. Burdekin; [etc., etc.] 1867.

Kniper, Taco
Philodemus over den dood. Amst., Paris, 1925.
165p.
Amsterdam univ. Ph. D. diss. 1925.

NK 0204614 PU

---

ar W 54560 no.2 Knipfer, Friedrich.
Die Streikversicherung in Deutschland; ihre Entwicklung und heutiger Stand. Nürnberg, Buch- und Kunstdr. B. Hilz, 1928.
59 p. 22cm.

Inaug.-Diss.--Erlangen.

NK 0204615 NIC

Knipfer (Henricus Guilelmus) [1805–]. Observatio de magna glandularum vasorumque lymphaticorum, post castrationem in abdomine orta, degeneratione. 24 pp. 8°. *Berolini, typ. Brandesianis et Kleuertianis*, [1829].

NK 0204616 DNLM

---

ar V 12194 Knipfer, Julius, 1833-1905.
Die Dichter der Befreiungskriege und die Lieder des deutsch-französischen Krieges. Für die reifere Jugend bearb. 2. erweiterte Aufl. Altenburg, O. Bonde, 1897.
195 p. illus. 20cm.

1. German poetry--19th cent.--Hist. & crit. 2. War poetry.

NK 0204617 NIC PU NjP OCl

Knipfer, Julius, 1833-1905.
Das kirchliche Volkslied in seiner geschichtlichen Entwicklung. Bielefeld, Velhagen & Klasing, 1875. v,285p. 19cm.

Bibliographical footnotes.

1. Hymns, German. History and criticism.

NK 0204618 MWelC MH-AH

ML3129 K5 Knipfer, Julius, 1833-1905
Das Kirchliche Volkslied in seiner geistlichen Entwicklung. Bielefeld und Leipzig, Belhagen & Klasing, 1895.
285p. 19cm.

1. Folk-songs, German. Hist. & crit. 2. Church music. Germany. 3. Church music. Hist. & crit.

NK 0204619 IaU PU OCl NjP IU NN

VM20 G315 Xk74 Knipfer, Julius, 1833-1905.
Paul Gerhardt. Gesammelte aufsätze. Leipzig, A. Deichert, 1906.
vii, 56 p. 21 cm.

1. Gerhardt, Paulus, 1607-1676.

NK 0204620 CtY-D MH-AH

Knipfer, Kurt, 1892 -

Darsow, Hubert.
Kommentar zum Luftschutzgesetz und den durchführungsbestimmungen nebst den einschlägigen erlassen, dienstvorschriften und polizeilichen bestimmungen von dr. Hubert Darsow, dr. Berthold Müller ... [und] dipl.-ing. Friedrich Nicolaus ... mit einem geleitwort von dr.-ing. e. h. Kurt Knipfer ... 4. bis 6. tausend. München und Berlin, Beck, 1938.

VOLUME 300

Knipfer, Kurt, 1892–
Luftschutz in bildern; eine gemeinverständliche darstellung des gesamten luftschutzes für jeden volksgenossen, von ministerialrat dr. ing. e. h. Kurt Knipfer ... und kapitänleutnant a. d. Werner Burkhardt ... Berlin-Schöneberg, Landsmann-verlag g. m. b. h. [1935]
80 p. illus., diagr. 23cm.

1. Air defenses. 2. Germany—Air defenses. I. Burkhardt, Werner, joint author. II. Title.
39-24139
Library of Congress UG635.G3K55
[2] 623.3

NK 0204622 DLC OO MH NN CtY

Knipfer, Kurt, 1892– *ed.*
Der zivile luftschutz; ein sammelwerk über alle fragen des luftschutzes, herausgegeben von dr. ing. Knipfer ... [und] Erich Hampe ... Berlin, O. Stollberg g. m. b. h. [c1934]
346 p., 1 l., 52 p. incl. illus., plates, diagrs. 29½cm.
"Bilderteil": 1 l., 52 p.
CONTENTS.—Allgemeines.—Der luftangriff.—Die luftabwehr.—Der deutsche zivile luftschutz.—Behördliche aufgaben.—Der werkluftschutz.—Der selbstschutz.—Einzelgebiete.
1. Air defenses. 2. Aeronautics, Military. 3. Germany—Defenses. I. Hampe, Erich, joint ed. II. Title.
35-25708
Library of Congress UF625.K5
[3] 623.74

NK 0204623 DLC NcD ICU CU CtY NN

Knipfer, Kurt, 1892– *ed.*
Der zivile Luftschutz, ein Sammelwerk über alle Fragen des Luftschutzes, hrsg. von Dr. Ing. E. h. Knipfer [und] Erich Hampe. 2. völlig neu bearb. Aufl. Berlin, O. Stollberg [1937]
391 p. illus. 30 cm.
CONTENTS. — Allgemeines über Luftkrieg und Luftschutz.—Die Luftwaffe.—Der deutsche zivile Luftschutz: Allgemeines. Der Sicherheits- und Hilfsdienst. Der Werkluftschutz. Einzelgebiete des Werkluftschutzes. Der Selbstschutz. Einzelgebiete.—Die Technik im Luftschutz.
1. Air defenses. 2. Air warfare. 3. Civilian defense. I. Hampe, Erich, 1889– joint ed. II. Title.
UG630.K6 1937 623.74 A F 48-72*
New York. Public Libr.
for Library of Congress [2]†

NK 0204624 NN DLC

Knipfing, John R
... The date of the Acts of Phileas and Philoromus... [N.Y., Macmillan, 1923]
p. 198-203.

"Reprinted from the Harvard theological review, Vo. XVI, no. 2, April, 1923".

NK 0204625 OU

Knipfing, John R
Religious tolerance during the early part of the reign of Constantine the Great (306-313). [Washington, 1925.]
20p.

Caption title.

Article signed: John R. Knipfing.

NK 0204626 OU

Kniphausen, Ferdinand Folef von Innhausen
see Innhausen und Kniphausen, Ferdinand Folef von.

Kniphausen, George Willem, graaf van
see Kniphuysen Nienvort, George William, count of.

Kniphausen (*Freie herrschaft*) *Laws, statutes, etc.*
Sammlung der landesherrlichen verordnungen und rescripte, so wie der bekanntmachungen der landesbehörden von allgemeinem und bleibenden interesse für die freie herrschaft Kniphausen ... Varel, Gedruckt bei W. Wesche, 1839–
v. 20cm.
Half-title: Gesetzsammlung für die freie herrschaft Kniphausen ...

1. Administrative law—Kniphausen. I. Title. II. Title: Gesetzsammlung für die freie herrschaft Kniphausen.
35-38005
Library of Congress [2]

NK 0204629 DLC

Kniphof (Joh. Gottfried). *De pilorum usu. 32 pp. 4°. *Erfordiæ, stanno Heringiano,* [1755].

NK 0204630 DNLM

Kniphof (Joh. Melchior). *De requisitis veri medici. 63 pp. 4°. *Erfordiæ, typ. Kindlebi,* [1692].

NK 0204631 DNLM

Kniphof (Joh. Melchior). *Disp. qua ægrum artuum tremore correptum ... exhibet. 16 pp., 6 l. 4°. *Erfurti, lit. Kindlebianis,* [1694]. [P., v. 1913.]

NK 0204632 DNLM

Kniphof, Johann Hieronymus, 1704-1763.
Antiquissimum fruendae carnis usum planum facit atque comprobat
see under Fischer, Johann Andreas, 1667-1729.

Kniphof, Johann Hieronymus, 1704–1763.
Johannis Hieronymi Kniphofs ... Botanica in originali, das ist: Lebendig kräüter-bůch, in welchen so wohl diejenigen blumen- baum- und kůchen-gewåchse, welche in denen gårten Teutschlandes ůberall bekannt sind ... Samtdem oeconomischen oder physicalischen nutzen ... zum gebrauch aller liebhaber derer garten-gewåchse und natůrlicher wissenschafften / beygebracht und hinlånglich beschrieben. Von C. R. Effurt, In verlag Joh. Mich. Funckens / buchhåndl. und universitåtsbuchdrucker, 1734.
2 p. l., 124 p. illus., 200 (*i. e.* 224) col. pl. 32cm.
2. hundert has half-title: Joh. Hieron. Kniphofs ... Lebendig kräuterbůch ... Von Christian Reicharden ...
1. Herbs. [1. Herbals] 2. Botany, Medical. [2. Medical botany] I. Reichard, Christian.
Agr 30-1417
Library, U. S. Dept. of Agriculture 452.2K74B

NK 0204634 DNAL

Kniphof, Johann Hieronymus, 1704–1763.
Johannis Heironymi Kniphofs ... Botanica in originali pharmacevtica, das ist: Lebendig-officinal kräüter-bůch, in welchen alle in denen apothecken gebräuchliche kräüter / so zubekommen ... mit erzehlung des nutzens dem die officinalkräuter in fast unzehlichen kranckheiten der menschen und des viehes haben ... Erffurt, In verlag Joh. Mich. Funckens, buchhåndl. und universitåts-buchdrucker, 1733.
1 p. l., 182 (*i. e.* 192) p. 200 col. pl. 32cm.
Page 189–192 erroneously numbered 179–182.
1. Herbs. [1. Herbals] 2. Botany, Medical. [2. Medical botany]
Agr 30-1418
Library, U. S. Dept. of Agriculture 452.2K74

NK 0204635 DNAL

Kniphof, Johann Hieronymus, 1704–1763.
D. Io. Hieron. Kniphofii ... Botanica in originali, sev Herbarivm vivvm, in qvo plantarvm tam indigenarvm qvam exoticarvm pecvliari qvadam operosaqve enchiresi atramento impressorio obdvctarvm nominibvsqve svis ad methodvm illvstrivm nostri aevi botanicorvm Linnaei et Lvdwigii insignitarvm elegantissima ectypa exhibentvr, opera et stvdio Ioannis Godofredi Trampe, typographi halensis. Centvr. I–XII. Halae Magdebvrgicae, 1758–64.
4 v. col. plates. 34½cm.

Continued in next column

Continued from preceding column

Title within floral border; head and tail pieces, initials.
Each "Centvr." has special t.-p. (not consecutively dated)
"Vorbericht" (v. 1) signed: D. Johann Hieronymus Kniphof; "Vorrede" (v. 2 and 3): Friedrich Wilhelm von Leyser (who furnished the descriptions of part of the plates)
"Index vniversalis in omnes XII. centvrias Botanicae in originali ... Halae Magdebvrgicae, apvd Ioanne Godofredo Trampe, 1767", with special t.-p.: 1 l., 14 p. at end of v. 4.

1. Botany—Pictorial works. I. Leysser, Friedrich Wilhelm von, 1731–1815. II. Title: Botanica in originali.
25-13130
Library of Congress QK98.K5

NK 0204637 DLC MBH NNBG ICJ MH-A CU

Kniphof, Johann Hieronymus, 1704-1763.
——. De manuscriptis præcipue medicis nonnulla commentatus. 31 pp. 4°. *Erfordiæ, typ. J. C. Heringii,* [1745].

NK 0204638 DNLM

Kniphof, Johann Hieronymus, 1704–1763, *praeses.*
... De pedicvlis ingvinalibvs insectis et vermibvs homini molestis. Von spul-wurm, hertz-wurm, St. Veit-wurm, maden, band-wurm, kürbiskern-wurm, nestel-wurm, floh, indianisch kleinen floh, jungen hunden, blutigeln, mücken, mit-esser, reitliesen, wantzen, kopf- kleider- und filtz-läusen ... Erfurti, stanno Heringiano, acad. typogr., 1759.
1 p. l., 51, [3] p. illus., III pl. 23cm.
Diss.—Erfurt (C. W. E. Reichard, respondent)
1. Worms. [1. Vermes] 2. Lice. I. Reichard, Christoph Wilhelm Emanuel, respondent.
Agr 28-1446
Library, U. S. Dept. of Agriculture 436K74

NK 0204639 DNAL

Kniphof (Johann Hieronymus) [1704–63]. *Disp. med. exhibens, lepram Arabum, sive elephantiasin observatam et curatam. 30 pp., 1 pl. 4°. *Erfordiæ, typ. Groschianis,* [1727]. [P., v. 1865: 1921.]

NK 0204640 DNLM PPC

Kniphof, Johann Hieronym 1704-1763.
Facultatis medicae ... Decanus Jo. Hieronymus Kniphof ... et de trito dicto quemque suus vellicat vermis ... paucula commentatus ad dissertationem inauguralem de hydrope a vermibus causato ... invitat. Erfordiae [1748]
Helm. T. v. 5

NK 0204641 PPAN

Kniphof, Johann Hieronymus, 1704-1763.
—— —— Index universalis in omnes xii. centurias Botanicae in originali. Halae Magdeburgicae. 1767. f°. pp. 14. (*Appended to* cent. xii.)

NK 0204642 MH-A

Kniphof (Johann Hieronymus) [1704–63]. *Lepra Arabum sive elephantiasis observata et curata. 30 pp., 1 l., 1 pl. 4°. *Erfordiæ, typ. Groschianis,* [1727].

NK 0204643 DNLM

 Kniphof, Johann Hieronymus, 1704-1763.
Physicalische Untersuchung des Petzes welchen die Natur durch Fäulniss auf einigen Wiesen hervorgebracht 1752. Erfurt, J. A. Görling, 1753.
24 p. 21 cm.

4751 Pritzel.

NK 0204644 NNBG DNLM

VOLUME 300

Kniphorst, Lambertus
... De mutuo, secundum principia juris hodierni ... submittit Lambertus Kniphorst ... Trajecti ad Rhenum, N. van der Monde [1837]
2 p l., 36 p. 21cm.
Diss.- Utrecht.
Bibliographical footnotes.

NK 0204645 MH-L

QD305 **Kniphorst, Lambertus Casper Everhard.**
.N8K7 Nitratie van symmetrische aryl-alkyl-urea ... Leiden, Drukkerij L. H. Becherer, 1923.
xii, 111, [4] p. 23½cm.
Proefschrift—Leiden.

1. Nitro-compounds.

NK 0204646 ICU ICRL PU

Kniphorst, Nicolaas
... Continens casus quosdam, ubi sponsi sponsaeque eodem, ac conjuges, aut diverso jure utuntur ... submittit Nicolaus Kniphorst ... Groningae, H. Spandaw, 1758.
2 p.l., 30 p., 1 l. 23cm.
Diss. - Groningen.

NK 0204647 MH-L

Kniphuisen, Jan Carel Ferdinand van in-en.
... De peculiari permutationis indole quantum in primis ad traditionem adtinet ... submittit Jan Carel Ferdinand van In- en Kniphuisen ... Groningae, F. Vos [1793]
2 p.l., 40, [19] p. 24cm.
Diss.- Groningen.

NK 0204648 MH-L

BV
245
K53 Kniphuysen Nienvort, George William, Count of.
Prayers and meditations, composed in the French language in the year 1693, tr. by an American ...New York, T. & J. Swords, 1813.
105 p. 15 cm.

1. Prayers. 2. Meditations. I. Title.

NK 0204649 NRCR MWA NcD

Knipling, Edward Fred, 1909 -
Insect control investigations of the Orlando, Fla., laboratory during World War II.
(*In* Smithsonian Institution. Annual report, 1948. Washington [1949] 24 cm. p. 331–348. 6 plates)

1. Insects—Florida—Orlando

Q11.S66 1948 51–1436

NK 0204650 DLC TxU

Knipling, Edward Fred, 1909-
A key for blowfly larvae concerned in wound and cutaneous myiasis. [n.p., 1939]
p. [376-383].

"Reprinted from Annals of the Entomoligical society of America, vol. XXXII, no. 2, June, 1939."

NK 0204651 OU

1.98
R31
no.83 [Knipling, Edward Fred, 1909-
Residual-type DDT sprays control houseflies [Washington?] 1947.
[2] p. (U.S. Agricultural Research Administration. Research achievement sheet. 83)

Issued Sept.1947.

NK 0204652 DNAL

HD1992
.K6 **Knipovich, Boris Nikolaevich,** 1890–1924.
... Главные черты сел.-хоз. эволюции европейской России в 1916–1921 гг. Москва, Издательство Наркомзема "Новая деревня," 1923.
iv, [5]–113, [1] p., 2 l., [2] p. 24 maps on 12 l. 27 cm. (*On verso of t.-p.:* Управление сельско-хозяйственной экономии и плановых работ. Труды. т. II, no. 1. Народный комиссариат земледелия. Материалы к плану ... на 1923 г. вып. I)

1. Agriculture—Russia—Stat. [1. Russia—Agriculture—Stat.]
Title transliterated: Glavnye cherty sel.-khoz. ėvoliûtsiĭ evropeĭskoĭ Rossii.

HD1992.K6 Agr 25–425 rev
U. S. Dept. of Agr. Libr. 267N16M no. 1
for Library of Congress [r50c½]†

NK 0204653 DNAL DLC

Knipovich, Boris Nikolaevich, 1890–1924.
... Главные черты сел.-хоз. эволюции европейской России в 1916–1921 гг. Москва, Издательство Наркомзема "Новая деревня," 1923.
iv, [5]–113, [1] p., 2 l., [2] p. 24 maps on 12 l. 27 cm. (*On verso of t.-p.:* Управление сельско-хозяйственной экономии и плановых работ. Труды. т. II, no. 1. Народный комиссариат земледелия. Материалы к плану ... на 1923 г. вып. I)
Photocopy. Cleveland, Micro Photo Division, Bell & Howell Co. [1967?]

NK 0204654 NIC

Knipovich, Boris Nikolaevich, 1890–1924.
... Сельско-хозяйственное районирование; с приложением биографии автора и некролога. Москва, "Новая деревня", 1925.
2 p. l., viii, 192 p. illus., port., maps (part fold.) diagrs. 27cm. (Р.С.Ф.С.Р. Народный комиссариат земледелия. Труды Земплана, под общей редакцией И. А. Теодоровича. вып. III. ч. 1)
At head of title: ... Б. Н. Книпович.

1. Agricultural administration—Russia. 2. Agriculture—Russia. 3. Agriculture—Economic aspects. I. Title.

Library of Congress S241.A485 вып. 3, ч. 1 40–20389

NK 0204655 DLC MH

Knipovich, Evgeniĭ F.

Chukovskiĭ, Korneĭ Ivanovich, 1882–
... Книга об Александре Блоке, с приложением хронологического списка стихотворений А. Блока составленного Е. Ф. Книпович ... Петербург, "Эпоха," 1922.

SH211
E5
no.172 **Knipovich, K M**
The work of the Azov Expedition in 1922-1924. Works of the Azov Black Sea Scientific Commercial Expedition. Kerch, R.S.F.S. National Commissariat of Agriculture, 1926.
1 p. l., 40 l. tables. 36 cm. (English translations of fishery literature, no. 172).
Translated by F. M. Davis.

1. Azov Expedition, 1922-24. 2. Fisheries - Black Sea. 3. Fisheries - Sea of Azov. I. Davis, F. M., tr.

NK 0204657 DI

Knipovich, M F
Словарь медицинской терминологии: латинско-украинско-русский. Составлен при участии И. Ф. Ерофеева [и др.] 20 000 слов. Киев, Гос. мед. изд-во УССР, 1948.
442 p. 21 cm.
Added t. p. in Ukrainian.

1. Medicine—Dictionaries. 2. Dictionaries, Polyglot. 3. Latin language—Dictionaries—Polyglot.
Title transliterated: Slovar′ medifsinskoĭ terminologii.

R121.K55 50–22169

NK 0204658 DLC

Knipovich, Nikolaĭ Mikhaĭlovich, 1862-1939.
Expedition für wissenschaftlich-praktische Untersuchungen an der Murman-Küste [Bericht über die Tätigkeit]
see under Murmanskaia nauchno-promyslovaia ėkspeditsiia, 1898-1908.

Knipovich, Nikolaĭ Mikhaĭlovich, 1862–1939.
Гидрология морей и солоноватых вод в применении к промысловому делу. Москва [Пищепромиздат] 1938.
513 p. illus., maps (part fold.) 27 cm.
At head of title: Всесоюзный научно-исследовательский институт морского рыбного хозяйства и океанографии.
Added t. p. in English.
Errata slip inserted.
"Список литературы": p. [476]–492.

1. Marine biology. 2. Sea-water. 3. Fisheries. I. Title.
Title transliterated: Gidrologiia moreĭ.

QH91.K6 49–41248*

NK 0204660 DLC CtY

Knipovich, Nikolaĭ Mikhaĭlovich, 1862–1939.
Положеніе морскихъ рыбныхъ и звѣриныхъ промысловъ Архангельской губерніи (изъ отчетовъ Министерству земледѣлія и государственныхъ имуществъ по командировкамъ 1893 и 1894 гг.). С.-Петербургъ, Тип. В. Киршбаума, 1895.
104, 17 p. 24 cm.
At head of title: М. з. и г. и. Департментъ земледѣлія.
1. Fisheries—Russia—Archangel (Province) I. Title.
Title romanized: Polozhenīe morskikh rybnykh i zvfěrinykh promyslov Arkhangel′skoĭ gubernīi.

SH284.R92A74 72–215799

NK 0204661 DLC

Knipovich, Nikolai Mikhailovich, 1862-1939.
... Reports of the Caspian expedition in the years 1914-1915 ... [By] Professor N. M. Knipovich. Hydrological investigations in the Caspian Sea in the years 1914-1915 ... [St. Petersburg, Govt. edition] 1912-
1 v. 2 fold. maps, 3 fold. diagrs. 27 cm.
Text in Russian; title in English and Russian.
1. Scientific expeditions. 2. Caspian Sea.

NK 0204662 CU

Knipovich, Tatiana Nikolaevna, 1895 -
Танаис; историко-археологическое исследование. Москва, Изд-во Академии наук СССР, 1949.
176 p. illus., map. 27 cm.
At head of title: Академия наук СССР. Институт истории материальной культуры имени Н. Я. Марра.
Errata slip inserted.
Bibliographical footnotes.

1. Tanais (Greek colony) *Title transliterated:* Tanais.

DK651.T32K55 50–27970

NK 0204663 DLC OrU ICU

VOLUME 300

Knipovich, Tat'iana Nikolaevna 1895–
...Untersuchungen zur Keramik römischer Zeit aus den Griechenstädten an der Nordküste des Schwarzen Meeres...von T. Knipowitsch. ₍Bd.₎ 1– Frankfurt a. M.: J. Baer & Co., 1929– v. illus., plates. f°. (Archaeologisches Institut des deutschen Reichs. Römisch-Germanisch Kommission. ₍no.₎ 4.)
Bibliographical footnotes.
Contents: 1. Die Keramik römischer Zeit aus Olbia in der Sammlung der Eremitage.

1. Pottery, Roman—Collections—Russia—Leningrad. 2. Ser.
N. Y. P. L. July 1, 1929

NK 0204664 NN NjP MH IaU ViU OCU NIC OC1W CtY

Knipovych, M F
see **Knipovich, M F**

Knipowitsch, N. M.
see
Knipovich, Nikolaĭ Mikhaĭlovich, 1862–1939.

W 4 M31 1938
KNIPP, Alfred, 1909-
Zur Frage der primären Wundnaht nach Antrotomien. Marburg, Hamel, 1938.
15 p.
Cover title.
Inaug.-Diss. - Marburg.
1. Maxillary sinus 2. Sutures

NK 0204667 DNLM

Knipp, Anna (Heubeck)
The history of Goucher college, by Anna Heubeck Knipp ... and Thaddeus P. Thomas ... Baltimore, Md., Goucher college, 1938.
x p., 1 l., 659 p. front., plates, ports. 23½ cm.
"Notes and references": p. 583–637.

1. Goucher college, Baltimore—Hist. I. Thomas, Thaddeus Peter, 1867–1936, joint author.
LD7251.B32K6 376.87526 39—25273

NK 0204668 DLC PU PSC PPTU OrPR OrU PBm OU OC1W OC1 OCU OO ViU CSmH DAU GU NIC CU

Knipp, Anna Heubeck.
...Solving the money problem, by Anna Heubeck Knipp... Baltimore, Md., 1919. 19 p. incl. tables. 8°. (Goucher College. Bull. Aug., 1919.)

1. Colleges and universities.—Student earnings, U. S. 2. Goucher College, Baltimore.
N. Y. P. L. August 25, 1921.

NK 0204669 NN MH

KNIPP, Arthur Russell.
[Calculation and measurement of the detection coefficient of a triode for large signal strengths.] Thesis, Harvard University. 1926.

Typewritten. 4°. ff.(2),a-e,116. Diagrs.
Official copy of a thesis presented for the doctor's degree at Harvard University.

NK 0204670 MH

Knipp, Charles Tobias, 1869- joint author.

Brown, Hugh Alexander, 1889–
... Alkali-vapor detector tubes, by Hugh A. Brown ... and Chas. T. Knipp ... Urbana, University of Illinois ₍1923₎

---

530 K74p
Knipp, Charles Tobias, 1869
Physics at the University of Illinois. [Lancaster, Pa., 1922] p.180-191.

"Reprinted from the Proceedings of the Society for the promotion of engineering education. Vol.XXX".

NK 0204672 IU OO

Knipp, Charles Tobias, 1869-

FOR OTHER EDITIONS SEE MAIN ENTRY

Duff, Alexander Wilmer, 1864– *ed.*
Physics for students of science & engineering: Mechanics and sound ₍by₎ A. Wilmer Duff (editor) Wave motion and light ₍by₎ E. Percival Lewis. Heat ₍by₎ Charles E. Mendenhall. Electricity and magnetism ₍by₎ Albert P. Carman and C. T. Knipp. 6th rev. ed., 630 illustrations. Philadelphia, P. Blakiston's son & co. ₍©1926₎

Knipp, Charles Tobias, 1869–
The surface tension of water above 100° C. ... ₍New York, 1900₎
cover-title, 129–154 p. illus., tables. 24½cm.
Thesis (PH. D.)—Cornell university, 1900.
"Reprinted from the Physical review, vol. XI, no. 3, September, 1900."

1. Capillarity.
5—1934
Library of Congress QC183.K71

NK 0204674 DLC MiU

Knipp, Elizabeth Merrick.
Color and how to teach it. By Elizabeth Merrick Knipp ... Buffalo, N. Y., W. H. Smith ₍©1897₎
₍18₎ p. 20cm.

1. Color—Study and teaching. I. Title.
Library of Congress ND1283.K7 CA 17-661 Unrev'd

NK 0204675 DLC

Knipp, Erwin, 1900–
Fehlererscheinungen an Gussstücken; Ursachen und Vermeidung. Düsseldorf, Giesserei-Verlag, 1953.
275 p. illus. 24 cm.
Bibliography: p. ₍262₎–268.

1. Founding. I. Title.
A 54–132
Illinois. Univ. Library for Library of Congress ₍1₎

NK 0204676 IU OU ICJ NN

Knipp, Erwin, 1900–
Korrosionsbeständige überzüge auf stahlgusstücken
Inaug. Diss. Braunschweig, 1931.

NK 0204677 ICRL

Knipp, Ewald.
... Deheim on dusse. Siegen, Vorländer, 1943.
68 p., 1 l. illus. 21 cm.
Poems.

I. Title.
PT4849.K6D4 47–41837

NK 0204678 DLC

Knipp, Franz.
Die sinnwelt der schmerzen, ein psychologisch-philosophischer grundriss, von Franz Knipp. Frankfurt am Main, V. Klostermann ₍1937₎
4 p. l., 137 p., 1 l. 23 cm.

1. Pain. I. Title.
BF515.K6 49–58628

NK 0204679 DLC CSt DNLM

Knipp, Helen Bachmann.
Basic vocabulary, phrases, and sentences for early reading instruction. Meadville, Pa., Keystone View Co. ₍1952₎
56 p. 23 cm.

1. English language—Glossaries, vocabularies, etc. 2. English language—Terms and phrases. I. Title.
PE1691.K55 372.4 53–16724 ‡

NK 0204680 DLC OrAshS OrU WU MoU

TK7872 .V3H28
Knipp, Julian Knause, 1910- joint author.

Hamilton, Donald Ross, 1914–
Klystrons and microwave triodes, by Donald R. Hamilton, Julian K. Knipp ₍and₎ J. B. Horner Kuper. Editorial staff: George B. Collins, Albert G. Hill ₍and₎ Winifred McCulloch. ₍Prepared under the supervision of the₎ Office of Scientific Research and Development, National Defense Research Committee. 1st ed. New York, McGraw-Hill Book Co., 1948.

Knipp, Julian Knause, 1910–
On the capture of electrons by fast ions. Oak Ridge, Tenn., Technical Information Branch, Tennessee AEC, 1949.
24 p. diagrs. 27 cm.
At head of title: United States Atomic Energy Commission. AECD-2430.
1. Electrons. 2. Ions. I. Title. II. Ser.

NK 0204682 ViU

Knipp, Minnie Bruning, 1896–
An investigation of experimental studies which compare methods of teaching arithmetic. Baltimore, 1948.
v, 46 p. tables. 23 cm.
Thesis—Johns Hopkins Univ.
Vita.
Bibliography: p. 41–46.

1. Arithmetic—Study and teaching.
QA135.K57 372.7 A 49–8171*
Johns Hopkins Univ. Library for Library of Congress ₍2₎†

NK 0204683 MdBJ PU CU CtY DLC

Knipp, Robert, 1902–
Beitrag zur Kenntnis der Tetraphenylaethanfarbstoffe ... Köln, [1931]
Inaug.-Diss. - Bonn.
Lebenslauf.

NK 0204684 CtY

VOLUME 300

Knipp, Victor, Referendar: Der Garantievertrag. Bonn: Georgi 1912. IX, 97 S. 8°
Marburg, Jur. Diss. v. 2. Aug. 1912, Ref. André
[Geb. 6. Dez. 86 Limburg a. L.; Wohnort: Bonn; Staatsangeh.: Preußen; Vorbildung: Gymn. Limburg Reife O. 06; Studium: Bonn 4, Berlin 2 S.; Rig. 20. Mai 12.] [U 12. 3451

NK 0204685 ICRL

Knippel, Charles F.
Two year olds in training; foals of 1891. Comp. by C. F. Knippel ... San Francisco, Pacific printing co. [°1893]
63 p. 14½cm.

1. Horse-racing. I. Title.
12—16544
Library of Congress SF325.K7

NK 0204686 DLC

Knippel, Dolores, *comp.*
Poems for the very young child, compiled by Dolores Knippel; illustrated by Mary Ellsworth. Racine, Wis., Whitman publishing co. [°1932]
2 p. l., 9-123, [2] p. front., illus. 19cm.
Illustrated lining-papers.

1. Children's poetry. I. Title.
A 33-2369
Toledo. Public library for Library of Congress PN6110.C4K6
[a38b1] 808.81

NK 0204687 OT OrMonO Or CoU DLC

Knippel, Karl.
Leitfaden zur Pflege der Kakteen ... 5. verb. Aufl. ... Frankfurt/Oder [n. d.]
Pamphlet.

NK 0204688 CtY

Knippel, Karl.

SB438 Leitfaden zur pflege der kakteen, von Karl
K56 Knippel. Sechste verbesserte auflage, mit sechs abbildungen. Frankfurt / Oder und Berlin, Trowitzsch & sohn, g.m.b.h. [1930]
23 p. illus. 22 1/2 cm.

1. Cactaceae.

NK 0204689 CSmH

Knippel, Karl H.
Taschenbuch des obstbaus; fachbuch für gartenbesitzer ur erwerbsobstbauer; zugleich wegweiser für anfänger, fortg schrittene, schüler und lehrer, von K. H. Knippel ... 160 seite text mit 46 meist ganzseitigen federzeichnungen vom verfasser. Die 50 fruchtbilder auf den 24 farbigen tafeln sind von Fr. Kotzian. Esslingen a. N. und München, J. F. Schreiber, 1940.
viii, 152 p. illus., 24 col. pl. 17cm.

1. Fruit-culture. I. Kotzian, Franz, illus. II. Title.
40-35039
Library of Congress SB357.K56
Copyright A—Foreign 46532
[2] 634

NK 0204690 DLC DNAL IU

Knippel, Richard.
Schillers verhältnis zur idylle, von dr. Richard Knippel. Leipzig, Quelle & Meyer, 1909.
3 p. l., 86 p. 24cm. (*Added t.-p.:* Breslauer beiträge zur literaturgeschichte ... neue folge, hft. 8, der ganzen folge 18. hft.)
"Nachweis der benutzten literatur": p. [83]-86.

1. Schiller, Johann Christoph Friedrich von—Criticism and interpretation. 2. Pastoral poetry, German. 3. German poetry—Hist. & crit. 4. Poetics. I. Title.
25-14697
Library of Congress PT2492.K5

ICRL NjP
NK 0204691 DLC NN ICarbS CU CtY PU PBm MiU OU OCU

Knippel, Robert.
Hundert Werst jede Nacht! Fluchtabenteuer im Osten. Görlitz, F. Bokämper, 1936.
303 p. ports., fold. maps. 20 cm.

1. Russia—Hist.—Revolution, 1917-1921—Personal narratives. I. Title.
DK265.K52 52-58982

NK 0204692 DLC

Knippen, Joseph
Ueber einen fall von doppelseitigem angeborenen schulterblatthochistand (Sprengel'sche deformität kombiniert mit rhachischisis und hydrocephalus.
Inaugural dissertation, 1926. Köln,

NK 0204693 PPWI

Knippen (Maria) [1886-]. *Ueber Anaemia splenica infantum und ihre Stellung unter den Blutkrankheiten. 36 pp. 8°. Bonn, H. Trapp. 1914.

NK 0204694 DNLM ICRL MBCo MH

Knippen, Rudolf.

Zur methodik der lektüre; fünf beiträge von ... K. Eckermann ... W. Bohn ... R. Knippen ... K. Schümmer ... [und] ... W.[!] Lauschus ... Frankfurt am Main, M. Diesterweg; [etc., etc.] 1932.

Knippen-Breitenberg, Rudolf.
...Symphonie eines Lebens; der Weg des Michael Franzen. Roman vom Niederrhein. Köln, A. Kemmerich, 1948. 294 p. 21cm.

502130B. I. Title.
N. Y. P. L. November 25, 1949

NK 0204696 NN

Knippenberg ([Didericus Ferdinandus Ludovicus] Hermannus) [1820-]. *De prolapsus uteri medela. Accedit morbi historia tabula lithographica illustrata. 18 pp., 1 l., 1 pl. 4°. *Berolini, typ. Schnitzerianis.* [1843]

NK 0204697 DNLM

Knippenberg, Henry, 1843-1924.
History of the Society of the framers of the constitution of the state of Montana. July 4, 1889. August 17, 1889. Written and arranged by Henry Knippenberg ... [Indianapolis, Press of Baker-Randolph lithograph and engraving co., 1890]
154 p. 23½cm.
Includes biographical sketches of members.
"First reunion, Helena, Montana ... November 8th, 1890": p. [129]-154.

1. Society of the framers of the constitution of the state of Montana. 2. Montana—Biog.
3—9742
Library of Congress F726.S75

NK 0204698 DLC Nh CaBViP WaSp MtU WaS

Knippenberg, Henry, 1843-1924.
Reunion of the Society of the framers of the constitution of the state of Montana, 1891.
v.2 n.p.n.d.

NK 0204699 Nh

Knippenberg, Hermann, 1904-
Der eigentumsvorbehalt beim kauf unter besonderer berücksichtigung seiner wirksamkeit im konkurse... Marburg, 1931. 93 p.
Inaug. Diss. -Marburg, 1931.
Lebenslauf.
Bibliography.

NK 0204700 ICRL

Knippenberg, Hermannus, 1820-
see Knippenberg, [Didericus Ferdinandus Ludovicus] Hermannus, 1820-

---

Knippenberg, Hermanus Hubertus, 1879-
Dr Hendrik W. E. Moller; levenschets. In opdracht van de R. K. Schoolvereniging "Ons middelbaar onderwijs in Noord-Brabant" te Tilburg. Tilburg, Drukkerij van het R. K. Jongensweeshuis, 1952. 144 p. illus., ports. 20cm. (Opvoedkundige Brochurenreeks, 157)

1. Moller, Hendrik Willem Evert, 1869-1940.

NK 0204702 NN

Knippenberg, Hermanus Hubertus, 1879-
Kultuur tusschen puin in Noord-Brabant en Limburg. Eindhoven, Uitg. "Het Hooghuis," 1945.
31 p. 21 cm.

1. World War, 1939-1945—Netherlands—Brabant, North (Province) 2. World War, 1939-1945—Netherlands—Limburg (Province) 3. Brabant, North (Province)—Hist. 4. Limburg, Netherlands (Province)—Hist. I. Title.
D763.N42N6 A F 49-1151*
New York. Public Libr. for Library of Congress [2]†

NK 0204703 NN DLC MiU

Knippenberg, Hermanus Hubertus, 1879-
Memoriaal; herinneringsbeelden met enige portretten en naamregister. Helmond, Uitgeverij "Helmond" [1949?]
106 p. ports. 20 cm.

1. Netherlands—Biog. 2. Dutch literature—Bio-bibl. 3. Catholics in the Netherlands.
DJ283.A2K55 920.0492 50-21636

NK 0204704 DLC

VOLUME 300

PT5602 .Z8K7 KNIPPENBERG, HERMANUS HUBERTUS, 1879 -
Reyer Anslo; zijn leven en letterkundig werk... Amsterdam, E. van der Vecht, 1913.
[7], 348, [4]p. front.(port.) 23cm.
Proefschrift--Amsterdam.
"Tijdrekenkundige lijst van R. Anslo's gedichten": p.[342]-344.

1. Anslo, Reyer, 1626-1669.

NK 0204705 ICU MH

Knippenberg, Hermanus Hubertus, 1879–
Van Moerdijk tot Peelland. Zoeklicht over Brabant. [Helmond, Boekdrukkerij "Helmond," 1945]
79 p. 20 cm.

1. Brabant, North (Province)—Descr. & trav.—Gazetteers. 2. Churches—Brabant, North (Province) I. Title. II. Title: Zoeklicht over Brabant.

DJ401.B73K55 A F 48-2927*

New York. Public Libr. for Library of Congress [1]†

NK 0204706 NN MiU MnU DLC

GR 181 K749v Knippenberg, Hermanus Hubertus, 1879–
Verhalen, van Dr. H. H. Knippenberg. Groningen, J. B. Wolters, 1919–
v.

Contents.-
2. Demonen-verhallen.

1. Tales, Dutch.

NK 0204707 CLU

Knippenberg, Hermanus Hubertus, 1879–
Zon over het leven, litterair-culturele verkenning. Helmond, Uitgeverij "Helmond" [1948]
80 p. 21 cm.

1. Dutch wit and humor. I. Title.

PT5346.K6 49-25315*

NK 0204708 DLC

Knippenberg, Joan
SEE
Knippenbergh, Joannes, 1662-1742

Knippenberg, Wilhelm, 1898-
Der deutsche laendliche realkredit waehrend der inflation and nach der waehrungsstabilisterung. Auszug. Inaug. diss. Kiel, 1927

NK 0204710 ICRL

Knippenbergh, Joannes, 1662-1742.
Continuatio historiae ecclesiasticae ducatus Geldriae
see under Goyers, Jacques, 1719-1809.

BR 907 .G32 K72 Knippenbergh, Joannes, 1662-1742.
Historia ecclesiastica ducatus Geldriae, in qua Catholicae fidei origo in eodem ducatu, ejusque propagatio ... recensentur, insertis etiam, quae in regimine politico memoratu digna acciderunt à Christo nato usque ad annum MDCC. Authore Joanne Knippenbergh ... Bruxellis, typis F. Foppens, 1719.
8 p.ℓ., 296, [24] p. 26^{cm}.
Title vignette (printer's device); head and tail pieces; initials.
With this are bound Goyers, Jacques. Continuatio historiae ecclesiasticae ducatus Geldriae. 1806; Notitia necrologica ... d. Joannis Baptistae Roberti, baronis van Velde de Melroy et Sart-Bomal [1824]
1. Gelderland-- Church hist.

NK 0204712 MiU CU-L

Knipper, Christoph, 1877-
Der Berliner Effektenhandel unter dem Einflusse des Börsengesetzes ... von Christoph Knipper ... Halle a.S., 1901
47, [1] p. 21cm.
Inaug.-diss. - Halle-Wittenberg.
Published also in fuller form as 20. Bd. 1. Hft. of Staats- und socialwissenschaftliche Forschungen.
"Vita": p.[48]
Bibliographical footnotes.

NK 0204713 MH-L CtY PU MH ICRL CU

Knipper, Christoph.
Der Berliner effektenhandel unter dem einflusse des reichsbörsengesetzes vom 22. juni 1896. Von dr. Chr. Knipper. Leipzig, Duncker & Humblot, 1902.
4 p. l., 102 p. $22\frac{1}{2}^{cm}$. (*Added t.-p.:* Staats- und socialwissenschaftliche forschungen, hrsg. von G. Schmoller. 20. bd., 1. hft.)
"Litteratur": p. [101]-102.
Published originally as the author's inaugural dissertation, Halle.

1. Berlin. Fondsbörse. I. Title. 5—3102

Library of Congress HB41.S7

NK 0204714 DLC PU MB

Knipper, Christoph, joint author.

Friedländer, Heinrich, 1885– *ed.*
Die metallhandelsgesetze (gesetz über den verkehr mit unedlen metallen und gesetz über den verkehr mit edelmetallen, edelsteinen und perlen vom 11. juni 1923) für die praxis erläutert von dr. Heinrich Friedländer ... und dr. Christoph Knipper ... Berlin, Spaeth & Linde [1923]

---

ar W 723 Knipper, Helmut, 1914-
Systematische, anatomische, ökologische und tiergeographische Studien an südosteuropäischen Heliciden (Moll. Pulm.) Leipzig, Akademische Verlagsgesellschaft, 1939.
[327]-517 p. illus. 23cm.
Diss.--Berlin.

1. Snails. 2. Mollusks--Europe.

NK 0204716 NIC

Knipper, Leo, 1898-
see Knipper, Lev Konstantinovich, 1898-

KNIPPER, LEV KONSTANTINOVICH, 1898-
[CANDIDE. SELECTIONS. ARR. FOR PIANO]
Aus der Musik der Bühnenvorstellung Candide [von] Lew Knipper, op. 16. Für Klavier übertragen von W. Wassiljew. Moskau, Musiksektion des Staatsverlages, 1928. 4 nos. in 1 v. 36cm.

Title also in Russian.
Originally for orchestra.

Based on Voltaire.
CONTENTS.--Marsch Buenos-Ayres.--Bulgaren-Marsch.--Portugiesischer Tanz.--Menuett.

1. Suites (Piano) 2. Incidental music. I. Voltaire, François Marie Arouet de, 1694-1778. Candide. II. Title: Candide.

NK 0204719 NN

KNIPPER, LEV KONSTANTINOVICH, 1898-
Cavalry of the Steppe. English text: M. L. Korr. Music: L. Knipper. New York, The New singers, 1936. [2] p. 28cm.

Caption title.
For 3 voices (tenors?)
First line: Meadowland, meadowland, meadows green and fields in blossom.
Inserted are a typescript (carbon copy) of the translation by M. L. Korr and a mimeographed setting for piano with interlinear words (first line: Heroes are threading thru meadow lands)

1. War songs, Russian, 1917- . 2. War songs, Russian.

NK 0204721 NN

Knipper, Lev Konstantinovich, 1898–
[Children's miniatures]
Четыре детских миниатюры. [Соч. 27] Москва, Гос. музыкальное изд-во, 1935.
score (17 p.) 31 cm.
The 1st piece for flute, viola, and tuba; the 2d, for clarinet, trumpet, and violoncello; the 3d, for violin, English horn, and trombone; and the 4th, for flute, English horn, clarinet, trumpet, trombone, tuba, violin, viola, and violoncello.
CONTENTS.—Kolybel'naîa.—Marsh.—Pesnîa.—Final.
1. Chamber music. I. Title.
Title transliterated: Chetyre detskikh miniatîury.

M1415.K M 56-1489

NK 0204722 DLC

Knipper, Lev Konstantinovich, 1898–
[Improvisations, string orchestra]
Четыре импровизации на темы албанских народных песен. Для смычкового оркестра и арфы. Партитура. Москва, Музыкальный фонд СССР, 1955.
score (44 p.) 30 cm.
With harp.

1. String-orchestra music—Scores. I. Title.
Title transliterated: Chetyre improvizatsii na temy albanskikh narodnykh pesen.

M1145.K74 I 5 M 58-37

NK 0204723 DLC

KNIPPER, LEV KONSTANTINOVICH, 1898-
[CONCERTO, VIOLIN]
Concerto for violin and orchestra [1943] Moscow, State music publishers, 1946. 125 p. 29cm.

Score, violin and orchestra. Violin part edited by A. Yampolsky. Title also in Russian.

Drexel Musical Fund.
1. Concertos (Violin). I. Yampol'ski, A. I., ed.

NK 0204724 NN ICN

VOLUME 300

Knipper, Lev Konstantinovich, 1898–
[Kandid. Selections; arr.]

Из музыки к театральному представлению "Кандид. Op. 16. Переложение для фортепиано В. Васильева. Москва, Музсектор Госиздата, 1928.

4 items. 35 cm. (Universal Edition, No. 9073-9076)

L. C. set incomplete: no. 1 and 3 wanting.
For piano; originally orchestral pieces in the opera-ballet.

1. Ballets—Excerpts—Piano scores. I. Title: Kandid.
Title transliterated: Iz muzyki k teatral'nomu predstavleni͡iu "Kandid."

M 56-1429

NK 0204725 DLC

Knipper, Lev Konstantinovich, 1898–

...Kleine lyrische Suite...für kleines Orchester... Op. 18. Wien [etc.] Universal-Edition A. G.; Moskau: Musiksektion d. Staatsverlages, 1930. Publ. pl. no. U.E. 9299; M. 10117 Г. 21 p. 36cm.

Full score.
Title-page in Russian and German.

CARNEGIE CORP. OF NEW YORK.

1. Suites—Orchestra—1800– I. Title.
N. Y. P. L. January 17, 1940

NK 0204726 NN ICN

Knipper, Lev Konstantinovich, 1898–
[Maku]

Маку; сюита на иранские темы, для симфонического оркестра. Москва, Союз советских композиторов, 1946.

score (100 p.) 30 cm.

Caption title: Makou, suite iranienne.

1. Suites (Orchestra)—Scores.
M1003.K7M3 1946 49-25019*

NK 0204727 DLC

Knipper, Lev Konstantinovich, 1898–

Maku, suite [on Iranien themes] for orchestra. Moscow, VOKS, 1944.

score (100 p.) 30 cm.

1. Suites (Orchestra)—Scores. I. Title.

M1003.K7M3 47-27708*

NK 0204728 DLC

Knipper, Lev Konstantinovich, 1898–
[Lyric suite, orchestra, op. 18]

Маленькая лирическая сюита, для малого оркестра. Op. 18. Партитура. Москва, Музсектор Госиздата, 1930.

score (21 p.) 36 cm. (Universal Edition, No. 9299)

Duration: 8 min., 25 sec.

1. Suites (Chamber orchestra)—Scores. I. Title.
Title transliterated: Malen'kai͡a liricheskai͡a si͡uita.

M1003.K68 op. 18 M 56-1431

NK 0204729 DLC

Knipper, Lev Konstantinovich, 1898–

Meadowland (Cavalry of the steppes) band arrangement by Philip J. Lang; music by Lev Knipper ... New York, N. Y., Am-Rus music corporation [1943]

[5] p. and 17 pts. 27cm.

Reproduced from manuscript copy.
Condensed score and parts (2 on each leaf)

1. Band music, Arranged—Scores (reduced) and parts. I. Lang, Philip J., arr.

Library of Congress M1258.K6M4 46-13787

NK 0204730 DLC

Knipper, Lev Konstantinovich, 1898–

Meadowland; cavalry of the steppes. English version by Harold J. Rome, transcribed by Albert Sirmay. [Arrangement by Paul Weirick] New York, Am-Rus Music Corp. [1943]

piano-conductor score (4 p.) and parts. 28 cm.

For dance orchestra; originally for orchestra.

1. Dance-orchestra music—Scores (reduced) and parts. I. Title.

M1350.K M 54-570

NK 0204731 DLC

M1757
.K55M4 Knipper, Lev Kostantinovich, 1898-

Meadowland (Cavalry of the steppes) Russian lyrics by Victor Gussev. English lyrics by Harold J. Rome. Transcribed by Albert Sirmay. Am-Rus ed. New York, Leeds Music Corp. [c1943]
5 p. 31cm.
Cover title.
Words in English, Russian and Russian transliterated.

"Part of the first movement of Knipper's Fourth Symphony."

1. Songs, Russian. 2. Songs with piano. I. Title. II. Title: Cavalry of the steppes.

NK 0204733 MB

Knipper, Lev Konstantinovich, 1898–

Meadowlands. Cavalry of the steppes. For four part chorus of mixed voices with optional piano acc. English version by Alice Mattullath from the Russian text of V. A. Gusev. Arr. by John Verrall. [Boston] Boston Music Co., °1947.

score (7 p.) 27 cm. (Secular choral music by Russian composers)

1. Choruses, Secular (Mixed voices, 6 pts.), Unaccompanied. I. Verrall, John, arr. II. Mattullath, Alice, tr.

M1586.K 48-14332*

NK 0204734 DLC

COLLECTION
*M1145
.K7M6 Knipper, Lev Konstantinovich, 1898-

Mountain serenade, for string orchestra. [Am-Rus ed.] Moscow, State Music Publishers, 1947.
score (43 p.) 30cm.
Title page also in Russian.
Publisher's pl. no.: M. 18703 l.
CONTENTS.—Sonatina.—Night piece.—Dance.—Romance.—Ballad.
1. String orchestra music—Scores.

NK 0204735 MB

Knipper, Lev Konstantinovich, 1898–
[Preli͡udii͡a-shutka, orchestra, op. 12b, no. 1]

Прелюдия-шутка, для оркестра. Op. 12b, № 1. Партитура. Москва, Музсектор Госиздата, 1928.

score (19 p.) 35 cm. (Universal Edition, No. 9080)

1. Orchestral music—Scores. I. Title.
Title transliterated: Preli͡udii͡a-shutka.

M1045.K7 op. 12b, no. 1 M 56-1432

NK 0204736 DLC ICN NN

Knipper, Lev Konstantinovich, 1898–
[Symphony, no. 3, op. 32]

Симфония № 3, для большого симфонического оркестра, солистов, самодеятельного хора, баянов и военного оркестра. Текст Виктора Гусева. Москва, Музгиз, 1935.

score (114 p.) 30 cm.

At head of title: Лев Книппер.
For 2 tenors, baritone, men's chorus, 2 accordions, band, and orchestra.

1. Choruses, Secular (Men's voices) with orchestra—Scores. 2. Symphonies—Scores.
Title romanized: Simfonii͡a nomer tri.

M1538.K63 op. 32 78-231856

NK 0204737 DLC

Knipper, Lev Konstantinovich, 1898–
[Symphony no. 4]
...Symphony no. 4 for chorus and orchestra... Op. 41. New York, Leeds music corp., 1946. 145 p. port. 22cm. (Leeds Am-Rus orchestra scores.)

Miniature score: double chorus (SATB and TB), solo tenor and bass, and orchestra.
Russian words.
"Edited with special annotations by Harold Sheldon."

404430B. 1. Choral symphonies—Score. 2. Symphonies—Score.
I. Sheldon, Harold, ed.
N. Y. P. L. October 28, 1947

NK 0204738 NN NBuG MH ICN MB NBC IEdS ICU IaU

Knipper, Lev Konstantinovich, 1898–

Три казачьих песни; для запевалы и смешанного хора без сопровождения. Слова А. Машистова. Москва, Гос. музыкальное изд-во, 1948.

score (11 p.) 29 cm.

For chorus (SSATTBB) the 1st and 3d pieces with baritone solo.

CONTENTS.—Akh, ty, step' kubanskai͡a.—Gasnut vdali zarnit͡sy.—Ne reki v buri͡u.

1. Choruses, Secular (Mixed voices, 7 pts.), Unaccompanied. I. Title.
Title transliterated: Tri kazach'ikh pesni.

M1586.K M 56-1414

NK 0204739 DLC

Knipper, Lew, 1898-
see Knipper, Lev Konstantinovich, 1898-

Knipper, Ol'ga Leonardovna
see Chekova, Ol'ga Leonardovna (Knipper) 1870-

Knipper (Theodor Eduard Joseph) [1892–]. *Ueber das Myom der Portio vaginalis anknüpfend an zwei Fälle von Portiomyomen aus der Universitäts-Frauenklinik Göttingen. [Göttingen.] 29 pp. 8°. Bonn, E. Eisele, 1920.

NK 0204742 DNLM CtY

Knipper, Werner, 1908-
Das eisenbahn-frachtbriefduplikat. ... Göttingen, 1933. 50 p.
Inaug. Diss. - Göttingen, 1933.
Lebenslauf.
Bibliography.

NK 0204743 ICRL

Knipper-Chekhova, Ol'ga Leonardovna
see Chekhova, Ol'ga Leonardovna (Knipper) 1870–

VOLUME 300

Knippers, Ottis J 1913–
Who's who among southern singers and composers, by Ottis J. Knippers ... Hot Springs National Park, Ark., Knippers brothers [1937]
2 p. l., 7–168 p. illus. (ports.) 20cm.

1. Musicians—Southern states. 2. Musicians—Dictionaries. I. Title.
Library of Congress ML106.U3K71 37—29045
——— Copy 2.
Copyright AA 242853 [39d2] 927.8

NK 0204745 DLC FU WaSp WaS OCl

Knippers, Ottis J , 1913–
Who's who among Southern singers and composers, by Ottis J. Knippers... Lawrenceburg, Tenn.: J. D. Vaughan [c1937] 168 p. illus. (ports.) 20cm.

1. Musicians—U. S.—Southern states. 2. Musicians—Dictionaries. I. Title.
CARNEGIE CORP. OF NEW YORK.
N. Y. P. L. August 23, 1938

NK 0204746 NN

Knipping (August) [1867–]. *Beiträge zur Lehre der Hernia obturatoria nebst Beschreibung eines operirten Falles. 32 pp. 8°. Leipzig, Gebr. Gerhardt, 1896.

NK 0204747 DNLM

Knipping, Bonfilius, *father*
see
Knipping, John Baptist, 1899–

Knipping, Enno, 1900–
Zur symptomatologie der partiellen Stirnhirn-Atrophie (Pick'sche Atrophie) Rostock, 1927.
Inaug. diss. Rostock
Bibl.

NK 0204749 ICRL

Knipping, Erwin Rudolf Theobald, 1844–1922.
Achtzehn Reisen von Kapt. R. Hilgendorf zwischen Hamburg und Südamerika. Von E. Knipping. [Berlin, 1899?] 14 p., 1 fold. map. Tables. 4°.
Caption-title.
Repr.: Annalen der Hydrographie und maritimen Meteorologie. Dezember, 1898.

1. Voyages and travels. 2. Meteorology, Atlantic Ocean. 3. Hilgendorf, R.
N. Y. P. L. November 5, 1917.

NK 0204750 NN

Knipping, Erwin Rudolf Theobald, 1844–1922.
Einige Beobachtungen über Luftdruckschwankungen an Bord. [Berlin, 1899.] p. 65–68. 4°.
Caption-title.
Repr.: Annalen der Hydrographie und maritimen Meteorologie. Februar, 1899.

1. Pressure (Atmospheric).
N. Y. P. L. October 30, 1917.

NK 0204751 NN

Knipping, Erwin Rudolf, Theobald, 1844–1922.
Der Fohn bei Kanazawa. Yokohama. 1890.
p. 149-155. 30 cm.
P.5292

NK 0204752 DAS

Knipping, Erwin Rudolf, Theobald, 1844–1922.
Ein Führer durch die meteorologischen Schiffstagebücher der Seewarten oder die Veröffentlichung von Auszügen daraus... Hamburg: Hammerich & Lesser in Altona, 1896. 1 p.l., 44 p., 1 chart. 4°. (Germany. Seewarte, Direktion der. Aus dem Archiv der deutschen Seewarte. Jahrg. 19, 1896, Heft 1.)
p. 24-44 printed on one side only.

1. Meteorology (Marine), Germany.
N. Y. P. L. March 15, 1912.

NK 0204753 NN

KNIPPING, Erwin Rudolf, Theobald, 1844–1922. *7405.50.61
Die jährliche Periode der mittleren Richtung der Winde, unteren und oberen Luftströmungen, in Japan.
(In Academia Cæsarea naturæ curiosorum. Nova acta. T. 61, pp. 217–288. Halle, 1894.)

NK 0204754 MB MdBP DAS MH

Knipping, Erwin Rudolf Theobald, 1844–1922.
Japanische Wetterregeln. 1886.
p. 223-229. 4.
P.2803 By E. Knipping and K. Kawashima.

NK 0204755 DAS

G1060 .P38 1922 Map Div.

Knipping, Erwin Rudolf Theobald, 1844–1922.
FOR OTHER EDITIONS SEE MAIN ENTRY
Perthes, Justus, *firm, publishers, Gotha.*
Justus Perthes' See-atlas. Eine ergänzung zu Justus Perthes' Taschen-atlas, entworfen und bearbeitet von Hermann Habenicht. 24 kolorierte karten in kupferstich mit 127 hafenplänen. Mit nautischen notizen und tabellen von Erwin Knipping, neu bearbeitet von kapitän L. Schubart ... 11. aufl. Gotha, Justus Perthes, 1922.

Knipping, Erwin Rudolf Theobald, 1844–1922. Library map of Japan. London, n. d. 8°. 1453

NK 0204757 MdBP

Knipping, Erwin Rudolf Theobald, 1844–1922.
Rein, Johann Justus, 1835–
Der Nakasendô in Japan. Nach eigenen beobachtungen und studien im anschluss an die itinerar-aufnahme von E. Knipping und mit benutzung von dessen notizen dargestellt von professor dr. J. J. Rein. Mit drei karten ... Gotha, J. Perthes, 1880.

Knipping, Erwin Rudolf Theobald, 1844–1922. 2289a.69
Nautische Notizen und Tabellen.
(In Habenicht, H. Justus Perthes' See-Atlas. Pp. 9–48. Gotha. 1901.)

H2156 — Navigation.

NK 0204759 MB

Knipping, Erwin Rudolf Theobald, 1844–1922.
...Report of an expedition to Mount Fuji. E. Knipping. 1887. Tokio: Meteorological Central Observatory [1887]. 7 p. plans, tables. 4°.
Cover-title.
At head of title: Geographical Bureau, Home Department. Tokio, Japan.

1. Meteorology, Japan: Fujiyama. 2. Japan, Geographical Bureau.
N. Y. P. L. September 18, 1922.

NK 0204760 NN DAS CtY

Knipping, Erwin Rudolf Theobald, 1844–1922.
Die Samoa-Orkane im Februar und März 1889... Vortrag gehalten vor der Versammlung der Deutschen meteorologischen Gesellschaft in Braunschweig am 8. Juni 1892. Von E. Knipping ... [Berlin, 1892.] p. [267–]275, 1 fold. pl. 4°.
Caption-title.
Repr.: Annalen der Hydrographie und maritimen Meteorologie. August, 1892.

1. Cyclones, Samoa, 1889.
N. Y. P. L. October 30, 1917.

NK 0204761 NN

Knipping, Erwin Rudolf Theobald, 1844–1922
Der Schneesturm vom 30. Januar bis 2. Februar 1886.
p. 188-192. 4.
P. 3914

NK 0204762 DAS

Knipping, Erwin. Rudolf Theobald, 1844–1922.
Seeschiffahrt für Jedermann. Hamburg: G. W. Niemeyer Nachfolger, 1898. viii, 199(1) p., 1 diagr. 8°.

1. Navigation, 1898.
N. Y. P. L. January 6, 1914.

NK 0204763 NN

Knipping, Erwin Rudolf Theobald, 1844–1922.
Sprunge in der Temperatur des Meerwassers. Nach den Tabellarischen Reiseberichten der deutschen Seewarte, Band 1. Von E. Knipping. [Berlin, 1906.] p. [18–]23, 1 fold. chart. 4°.
Caption-title.
Repr.: Annalen der Hydrographie und maritimen Meteorologie. Januar, 1906.

1. Ocean.—Temperature.
N. Y. P. L. October 30, 1917.

NK 0204764 NN

Knipping, Erwin Rudolf Theobald, 1844–1922.
Die tropischen Orkane der Südsee zwischen Australien und den Paumotu-Inseln. Hamburg: Hammerich & Lesser in Altona, 1893. 1 p.l., 28 p., 2 charts. 4°. (Germany. Seewarte, Direktion der. Aus dem Archiv der deutschen Seewarte. Jahrg. 16, 1893, Heft 1.)

1. Storms, Pacific ocean (South).
N. Y. P. L. March 15, 1912.

NK 0204765 NN

Knipping, Erwin Rudolf Theobald, 1844–1922.
Ueber die Häufigkeit, Bewegung und Tiefe der barometrischen Minima in Japan. Von E. Knipping. [Berlin, 1892.] p. 281–287, 1 fold. diagr. 4°.
Caption-title.
Repr.: Meteorologische Zeitschrift. August, 1892.

1. Pressure (Atmospheric), Japan.
N. Y. P. L. October 30, 1917.

NK 0204766 NN

VOLUME 300

Knipping, Erwin Rudolf Theobald, 1844–1922.
Das Wetter auf dem Nordatlantischen Ozean vom 5. bis 19. Dezember 1902. Von E. Knipping. [Berlin, 1903.] p. [89]–100, 1 fold. diagr. 4°.
Caption-title.
Repr.: Annalen der Hydrographie und maritimen Meteorologie. März, 1903.

1. Meteorology, Atlantic ocean (North), 1902.
N. Y. P. L. October 30, 1917.

NK 0204767 NN

Knipping, Erwin Rudolf Theobald, 1844-1922
Wetter-Beobachtungen. Aufgezeichnet zu Tokio...1872-77.
(Incomplete.)
30271

NK 0204768 DAS

Knipping Erwin Rudolf Theobald, 1844-1922.
Die Wettertelegraphie in Japan. Yokohama. 1884.
19 p. 21½ cm.
P.3295 10/20/1884

NK 0204769 DAS

Knipping, Erwin Rudolf Theobald, 1844–1922.
Der Wolkenbruch auf der Kii-Halbinsel, Japan, am 19. August 1889. Von E. Knipping... [Wien, 1890.] p. 281–296, 2 fold. diagr. 4°.
Caption-title.
Excerpt: Meteorologische Zeitschrift. Aug. 1890.
Contains also his: Veränderlichkeit der Tagestemperatur in Japan, p. 291–296.

1. Rainfall, Japan, 1889: Aug. 19. 2. Temperature (Atmospheric).—Diurnal variation, Japan.
N. Y. P. L. November 12, 1917.

NK 0204770 NN

Knipping, Erwin Rudolf Theobald, 1844–1922.
Zum Klima von Nauru. [Berlin, 1899.] p. [369–]377. Tables. 4°.
Caption-title.
Signed: E. Knipping.
Repr.: Annalen der Hydrographie und maritimen Meteorologie. Juli. 1899.

1. Meteorology, Pleasant Island.
N. Y. P. L. October 30, 1917.

NK 0204771 NN

Knipping, Erwin Rudolf Theobald, 1844–1922.
Zur Entwickelungsgeschichte der Cyklonen in subtropischen Breiten. Nach Beobachtungen in Naha auf den Liukiu-Inseln. Vortrag, gehalten auf der Lübecker Naturforscher-Versammlung, September 1895, von E. Knipping. [Berlin, 1895?] 6 p. diagr., tables. 4°.
Caption-title.
Repr.: Annalen der Hydrographie und maritimen Meteorologie. September, 1895.

1. Cyclones.
N. Y. P. L. October 30, 1917.

NK 0204772 NN

Knipping, Erwin Rudolf Theobald, 1844–1922.
Zur Form der Cyklonen... Von E. Knipping... [Berlin: E. S. Mittler & Sohn, 1890.] 4 p., 1 fold. chart. 4°.
Caption-title.
Repr.: Annalen der Hydrographie und maritimen Meteorologie. Heft 3, März, 1890.

1. Cyclones.
N. Y. P. L. October 30, 1917.

NK 0204773 NN

Knipping, Franz, 1875–
... Konstruktion und ausführung, bearbeitet von prof. Knipping ... Halle (Saale), W. Knapp, 1930.
viii, 166 p. illus., diagrs. 24cm. (Added t.-p.: Die neuzeitliche strassenbau, hrsg. von dr.-ing. e. h. Hentrich ... t. 2)
Series title also at head of t.-p.

1. Roads. 2. Streets.
Agr 31-937
Library, U. S. Dept. of Agriculture 288K74

NK 0204774 DNAL

Knipping, Franz, 1875–
Die Siedlungsfrage in den Grosstädten und Industriebezirken, von Professor Knipping... Münster (Westf.): Wirtschafts- und Sozialwissenschaftlicher Verlag e. V., 1934. 39 p. 22cm. (Münster, Germany. Universität. Forschungsstelle für Siedlung und Wohnungswesen. Materialien-Sammlung. Bd. 12.)

1. Land settlement—Germany. 2. Cities—Growth—Germany. I. Ser.
N. Y. P. L. August 10, 1936

NK 0204775 NN

Knipping, Franz, 1875–
... Steinstrassen, bearbeitet von prof. Knipping ... Mit 72 abbildungen. Halle (Saale) W. Knapp, 1928.
viii, 108 p. illus., diagrs. 24cm. (Added t.-p.: Der neuzeitliche strassenbau, hrsg. von dr.-ing. e. h. Hentrich ... t. III)
Series title also at head of t.-p.

1. Stone, Crushed. 2. Roads.
P O 28-443
Library, U. S. Patent Office TE235.K71

NK 0204776 DP

Knipping, Franz, 1875–
Der strassenbau der Vereinigten Staaten von Amerika unter berücksichtigung der nutzanwendung für Deutschland. Von F. Knipping ... K. Gölz ... H. Mittmeyer ... Berlin, J. Springer, 1934.
vii, [1], 278 p. illus., maps (part fold.) diagrs. 24cm.
"Literatur-verzeichnis": p. [255]–271.

1. U. S.—Roads. 2. U. S.—Streets. I. Gölz, K., joint author. II. Mittmeyer, Hans, 1901– joint author.
Agr 34-611
Library, U. S. Dept. of Agriculture 288K74V [TE23]

NK 0204777 DNAL

Knipping, Heinrich: Münchener Grabmalplastik. Von 1500—1800. [Ausz.: Die archit. Entw. d. Münch. Grabdenkmäler u. Epitaphien in d. Zeit v. 1630—1770.] [Maschinenschrift.] 125 S. 4° [Lag nicht vor.] — Auszug: (Köln 1921: Kerschgens). 4 Bl. 8°
Darmstadt TeH., Diss. v. 18. März 1925 [U 25. 8914

NK 0204778 ICRL

Knipping, Hugo Wilhelm, 1895- joint author.
Kestner, Otto, 1873–
FOR OTHER EDITIONS SEE MAIN ENTRY
... Die ernährung des menschen; nahrungsbedarf, erfordernisse der nahrung, nahrungsmittel, kostberechnung, von professor dr. Otto Kestner ... und dr. H. W Knipping ... in gemeinschaft mit dem Reichsgesundheitsamt, Berlin. Mit zahlreichen nahrungsmitteltabellen und 6 abbildungen. Berlin, J. Springer, 1924.

Knipping, Hugo Wilhelm, 1895–
Klinische gasstoffwechseltechnik, von dr. H. W. Knipping ... und dr. H. L. Kowitz ... Mit 72 abbildungen im text und auf 2 tafeln. Berlin, J. Springer, 1928.
vi, 193, [1] p. incl. illus., tables. 2 fold. diagr. 21cm.
"Literaturverzeichnis": p. 185.

1. Metabolism. 2. Respiration. 3. Gases. I. Kowitz, Hans Ludwig, 1889– joint author. II. Title: Gasstoffwechseltechnik.
28-23988
Library of Congress QP171.K6

NK 0204780 DLC ICJ PPC

Knipping, Hugo Wilhelm, 1895- joint author.
Rona, Peter, 1871–
Praktikum der physiologischen chemie, von Peter Rona ... Berlin, J. Springer, 1926–29 [v. 3, '28]

Knipping, Hugo Wilhelm, 1895-
Sondersitzung am 10. März 1954 in Düsseldorf

see under

Arbeitsgemeinschaft für Forschung des Landes Nordrhein-Westfalen.

WG 200 K71u 1955
KNIPPING, Hugo Wilhelm, 1895-
Untersuchung und Beurteilung des Herzkranken; praktische Routineuntersuchung, präoperative Herzdiagnostik; Funktionsanalyse für die Herzprophylaxe und Sporttherapie; Cor pulmonale, von H. W. Knipping [et al.] Stuttgart, Enke, 1955.
xx, 461 p. illus.
1. Heart - Diseases - Diagnosis

NK 0204783 DNLM PP OCIW-H NNC MnU

Knipping, John Baptist, 1899– , comp.
Harp van Erin, twaalf Ierse sprookjes, verzameld en ingeleid door Dr John B. Knipping... Amsterdam [etc.] Elsevier, 1947.
287 p. illus. 25cm.

436951B. 1. Fairy tales, Irish. I. Title.
N. Y. P. L. June 28, 1948

NK 0204784 NN MH CtY OU

Knipping, John Baptist, 1899–
Hooglied in steen, de kathedraal. Arnhem, Van Loghum Slaterus, 1949.
67 p. plates. 22 cm. (Gastmaal der eeuwen; taferelen uit de cultuurgeschiedenis van Europa)
Bibliography: p. 65–67.

1. Cathedrals. I. Title.
Name in religion: Bonfilius, *Father.*
NA4830.K58 56-39182

NK 0204785 DLC

Knipping, John Baptist, 1899-
Hugo van der Goes. Amsterdam, Becht [19--]
60p. illus. 26cm. (Palet Serie; ein Reeks Monografieën over Hollandsche en Vlaamsche Schilders. 15.en 16.eeuw)

1. Goes, Hugo van der, ca.1440-1482. Series.

NK 0204786 MWelC

Knipping, John Baptist, 1899-
Hugo van der Goes ... Amsterdam, Becht [1940.]
60 p. illus. 27 cm. (Palet serie, een reeks monografieën over hollandsche en vlaamsche schilders)
Bibliography: p.60.

1. Goes, Hugo van der, 1435?-1482.

NK 0204787 NjP MH

VOLUME 300

Knipping, John Baptist, 1899–
De iconografie van de contra-reformatie in de Nederlanden. Hilversum, P. Brand, 1939–40.
2 v. illus. 30 cm.
Vol. 1 issued also as thesis, Nijmegen.
Includes bibliographies.

1. Art—Netherlands. 2. Christian art and symbolism. 3. Counter-Reformation. I. Title.
Name in religion: Father Bonfilius.
N6946.K5 61-56176

NK 0204788 DLC OU NjP DCU CLU NNC NN CU OO CtY MH

Knipping, John Baptist, 1899–
Inleiding tot de Engelse kunst. Amsterdam, H. J. W. Becht [1947]
202 p. plates, map. 25 cm. (Hoogtepunten der Engelse cultuur, 1)
"Literatuur": p. [193]-197.

1. Art—England. (Series)
Name in religion: Bonfilius, *Father.*
A 51-1372
Harvard Univ. Library
for Library of Congress [1]

NK 0204789 MH CtY OU

Knipping, John Baptist, 1899–
Jan Toorop. Amsterdam, H. J. W. Becht [1947]
59, [1] p. illus. 27 cm. (Palet serie; een reeks monografieën over Hollandsche en Vlaamsche schilders. Negentiende en twintigste eeuw)
Bibliography: p. [60]

1. Toorop, Jan Theodoor, 1858–1928. (Series)
Name in religion: Bonfilius, *Father.*
ND653.T6K55 56-41532

NK 0204790 DLC MH NN

FA 4098.28
Knipping, John Baptist, 1899-
Het kind in Neerlands beeldende kunst. 1. Wageningen, N.v.gebr.Zomer en Keuning's uitgeversmaatschappij [1942?]

colored plates, illus. 20.5 cm.
At head of title: John B.Knipping en M.Gerrits.

NK 0204791 MH

Knipping, John Baptist, 1899–
Het kind in Neerlands beeldende kunst [door] John B. Knipping en M. Gerrits. Wageningen, Gebr. Zomer en Keuning [1944–
v. illus. (part col.) 27 cm.
CONTENTS.—1. Tot aan het einde van de 18e eeuw.

1. Children in art. 2. Art, Dutch. 3. Art, Belgian. I. Gerrits, Maria, joint author.
Name in religion: Bonfilius, *Father.*
N6931.K6 A F 47-6978*
New York. Public Library
for Library of Congress [2]†

NK 0204792 NN MB OU MiU NcD CU CtY DLC

Knipping, John Baptist, 1899–
De laatste communie van Sint Franciscus van Assisië [van] Rubens. Leiden, L. Stafleu [1949]
40 p. plates (part col.) 24 cm. (Paneel en doek, ser. 1, nr. 3)
Bibliographical footnotes.

1. Rubens, Sir Peter Paul, 1577–1640. (Series)
Name in religion: Bonfilius, *Father*
A 50-2296
Harvard Univ. Librar.
for Library of Congress [1]

NK 0204793 MH DLC CaBVaU

ND673 B7K6
Knipping, John Baptist, 1899-
Pieter Bruegel de oude. 2. druk. Amsterdam, H. J. W. Becht [1945]
60 p. illus. (Palet serie; een reeks monografieën over Hollandse en Vlaamse schilders. Vijftiende en zestiende eeuw.)
Bibliography: p. 59-60.

1. Brueghel, Peeter, the elder, d. 1569.

NK 0204794 CU NjP MH

Knipping, John Baptist, 1899–
Symbool en allegorie in de beeldende kunst. Nijmegen, Dekker & Van de Vegt, 1941.
22 p. 24 cm.
"Aantekeningen" (bibliographical): p. 21–22.

1. Symbolism in art. 2. Christian art and symbolism. 3. Emblems. I. Title.
Name in religion: Bonfilius, *Father.*
N7740.K57 A F 48-491*
Harvard Univ. Library
for Library of Congress [2]†

NK 0204795 MH DLC ICA

ND673 .B73K5
Knipping, John Baptist, 1899–
De val der opstandige engelen [van] Pieter Bruegel de Oude. Leiden, L. Stafleu [1949]
40 p. plates (part col.) 24 cm. (Paneel en doek, ser. 1, nr. 4)
Bibliographical footnotes.

1. Brueghel, Peeter, the elder, d. 1569. (Series)
Name in religion: Bonfilius, *Father.*
A 50-2652
Harvard Univ. Library
for Library of Congress [1]

NK 0204796 MH DLC CaBVaU

BX4638 .N4A6
Knipping, John Baptist, 1899- joint author.

Heel, Dalmatius van, *father,* 1874–
Van schuilkerk tot zuilkerk, geschiedenis van de Mozes en Aäronkerk te Amsterdam, door p. Dalmatius van Heel, O. F. M. en p. Bonfilius Knipping, O. F. M. Met een woord vooraf door den hoogeerw. p. Regalatus Hazebroek, O. F. M. Amsterdam, Urbi et orbi, 1941.

Knipping, John Baptist, 1899–
De Vlaamse schilders. Amsterdam, V/h Van Ditmar [1950]
24 p. mounted col. illus. 32 cm. (Meesterwerken der schilderkunst)

1. Paintings, Flemish. I. Title.
Name in religion: Bonfilius, *Father.*
ND665.K58 54-24572 ‡

NK 0204798 DLC

Knipping, Paul.
Betriebsführung und lohnkosten im deutschen schiffbau, erläutert an einem beispiel ... [Berlin, Druck von F. Weber, 1914]
70 p. 29cm.
Inaug.-diss.—K. Tech. hochschule, Berlin.

1. Ship-building—Germany. 2. Ship-building—Costs. 3. Cost—Accounting.
17-3994
Library of Congress VM73.K6

NK 0204799 DLC ICRL PU

Knipping, Paul, 1883-
Ueber den einfluss der vorgeschichte auf verschiedene eigenschaften des fleies ... Borna-Leipzig, Buchdruckerei, R. Noske, 1913.
3 p.l., 65 p., 1 l. 23 cm.
Inaug. diss. Muenchen.
Lebenslauf.

NK 0204800 DBS CtY PU MH

Knipping, Paul A 1920–
Notes on the distribution of Wisconsin ticks [by] Paul A. Knipping, Banner Bill Morgan and Robert J. Dicke.
(*In* Wisconsin Academy of Sciences, Arts and Letters. Transactions. Madison. 23 cm. v. 40, pt. 1 (1950) p. 185–197. maps)
P. A. Knipping's thesis (M. SC.)—University of Wisconsin.
"References": p. 196–197.

1. Ticks.
AS36.W7 vol. 40 A 51-2963
Wisconsin. Univ. Libr.
for Library of Congress [2]†

NK 0204801 WU DLC

Knipping, Paul A 1920–
Preliminary list of some fleas from Wisconsin [by] Paul A. Knipping, Banner Bill Morgan and Robert J. Dicke.
(*In* Wisconsin Academy of Sciences, Arts and Letters. Transactions. Madison. 23 cm. v. 40, pt. 1 (1950) p. 199–206)
"References": p. 206.

1. Fleas.
AS36.W7 vol. 40 A 51-2962
Wisconsin. Univ. Libr.
for Library of Congress [2]†

NK 0204802 WU DLC

Knipping, Richard, 1865-
Beiträge zur diplomatik der Kölner erzbischöfe des 12. jahrhunderts. ... Bonn, C. Georgi, 1889.
41, [1] p. 25 cm. [Bonn. Universität. Dissertationen. v. 11, no. 23]
Inaug.-diss. - Bonn.
Lebenslauf.
1. Cologne (Archbishopric) - Pol. & govt.
2. Cologne (Archbishopric) - Hist.

NK 0204803 ICRL CU

Knipping, Richard, 1865–
Die Kölner stadtrechnungen des mittelalters mit einer darstellung der finanzverwaltung. Bearb. von dr. Richard Knipping ... Bonn, H. Behrendt, 1897–98.
2 v. 31½cm. (*Added t.-p.:* Publikationen der Gesellschaft für rheinische geschichtskunde. xv)
CONTENTS.—1. bd. Die einnahmen und die entwicklung der staatsschuld.—2. bd. Die ausgaben.

1. Finance—Cologne. I. Cologne.
11-21237
Library of Congress HJ1106.C7K6

NK 0204804 DLC IaU PU

Knipping, Richard, 1865–
Die neuen dienstgebäude der Staatsarchive zu Coblenz und Düsseldorf, von dr. Richard Knipping ... und dr. Theodor Ilgen ... Leipzig, S. Hirzel, 1907.
5 p. l., 62 p. illus., fold. diagr. 25cm. (*Added t.-p.:* Mitteilungen der K. Preussischen Archivverwaltung. hft. 9)

1. Library architecture. 2. Archives—Prussia. I. Ilgen, Theodor, 1854?–1924, joint author.
7—33575
Library of Congress CD1250.P7

NK 0204805 DLC MH NN

VOLUME 300

Knipping, Richard, 1865–
Niederrheinische archivalien in der Nationalbibliothek und dem Nationalarchiv zu Paris. Zusammengestellt von dr. Richard Knipping ... Leipzig, S. Hirzel, 1904.
viii, 126 p. 25cm. (*Added t.-p.:* Mittellungen der K. Preussischen archivverwaltung, hft. 8)

1. Rhine province—Hist.—Sources—Bibl. I. Paris. Bibliothèque nationale. II. France. Archives nationales.
4-36904 Revised
Library of Congress CD1250.P7 hft. 8

NK 0204806 DLC NcD CLU MH NN

Knipping, Richard, 1865– ed.
Die Regesten der Erzbischöfe von Köln im Mittelalter
see under Cologne (Archdiocese)

WC 15218
Knipping, Wilhelm
Das chimärische Problem gewisser Glaubenstheorien; als solches dargestellt durch Glossen zu einigen Partien aus dem Werke des Herrn Dr. Schmid: "Wissenschaftliche Richtungen auf dem Gebiete des Katholicismus." Münster, F. Regensberg, 1864.
xvi, 216 p.

1. Apologetics - 19th cent. I. Schmid, A. Wissenschaftliche Richtungen ...

NK 0204808 CtY

Knipple, Walter Robert. No. 4 in *Cab.23.38 8
The East Haven estate. [Report on] the suitability of this estate for the purposes described in the company's charter . . .
Broadside. Boston. 1881. Size, 14 × 8½ inches.

NK 0204809 MB

Knipprath, George Frank, 1883–
Qualifications for teaching commercial subjects in secondary schools.
(*In* National education association of the United States. Addresses and proceedings, 1921. p. 373-375)

1. Business education.
E 22-112
Library, U. S. Bur. of Education

NK 0204810 DHEW OO OU

Knips, Franz Lorenz: Entwicklung und Tätigkeit der Bank für Handel und Industrie. Leipzig 1912: Hoffmann. 206 S., 2 Tab. 8°
Heidelberg, Phil. Diss. v. 17. Juli 1912, Ref. Gothein
[Geb. 21. Juli 84 Fulda; Wohnort: Heidelberg; Staatsangeh.: Preußen; Vorbildung: Oberrealsch. Fulda Reife O. 04; Studium: München 4, Berlin 2, Halle 3, Heidelberg 2 S.; Rig. 24. Okt. 11.] [U 12. 2331

NK 0204811 ICRL PU MH CtY

KNIPS, Hubert, 1906–
De orationibus κατα Θεομνηστου quae decima et undecima inter Lysiacas feruntur. Borna-Leipzig, R. Noske, 1931.

Commentatio philologa - [Münster i.W.]
"Vita", at end.

NK 0204812 MH CU NcD

KNIPS-HASSE, A.
...Das Automaten-Kabinett. Von A.Knips-Hasse. Berlin: E.Bloch [1893] 25 p. 19cm. (Fastnachts-Buhne. Heft 41.)

883423A. 1. Tableaux. I. Title.

NK 0204813 NN

Knips-Hasse (Victor) [1864–]. *Das Angioma arteriale racemosum, speciell der oberen Extremität. 29 pp., 1 pl. 8°. *Erlangen, Brückner & Niemann.* 1888.

NK 0204814 DNLM

Knips-Macoppe, Alessandro, 1662-1744.
——. Aphorismi medico-politici centum. Edidit nunc primum et præfatus est Florianus Caldanius. lxii pp. 8°. *Venetiis,* 1795.

NK 0204815 DNLM NNNAM

WZ 290 K71a 1822
KNIPS-MACOPPE, Alessandro, 1662-1744
Aforismi medico-politici. Volgarizzati col testo a fronte da Giuseppe Antonio del Chiappa. Pavia, Fusi, 1822.
xix, 115 p. WZ290 K71a
I. Chiappa, Giuseppe Antonio del, ed.

NK 0204816 DNLM

Knips-Macoppe, Alessandro, 1662-1744
Aforismos médico-politicos; texto del siglo XVIII. Publicado por el librero anticuario Antonio Palau y Dulcet. Barcelona, Imp. Rafols, 1928

43 p.

NK 0204817 MH

WZ 290 K71a 1813
KNIPS-MACOPPE, Alessandro, 1662-1744
Cento aforismi medico politici.
Tr. e comentati da Giovanni Luigi Zaccarelli, ... Pavia, Capelli, 1813.
84 p. WZ290 K71a
Translation of Aphorismi medico-politici centum.
I. Zaccarelli, Giovanni Luigi, ed.

NK 0204818 DNLM

WZ 250 K71ba 1693
KNIPS-MACOPPE, Alessandro, 1662-1744
De aortae polypo epistola medica ... Carolo Patino ... qua ejusdem abditissimum morbum a polypo arteriam magnam insidente dependere demonstratur, ac de ejus natura, dignotione, & curatione disseritur. Cum ejusdem cadaveris historia anatomica eventum comprobante ... Lugduni, Sumptibus Cadorini, 1693.
[8], 31, [1] p. plate. 22 cm.

1. Patin, Charles, 1633-1693

NK 0204819 DNLM

RB351. Knips-Macoppe, Alessandro. 1662-1744.
De aortae polypo epistola medica... Carolo Patino...
Brixiae: sumpt. C. Gromi, [1731].

NK 0204820 NNNAM

Knips-Macoppe, Alessandro, 1662-1744. 611.04 A337
Pro empirica secta adversus theoriam medicam prælectio habita in Archilyceo Patavino ab Alexandro Knips Macoppe. Dum à lectura simplicium ad medicinam theoriam adduceretur XXVIII. novembris MDCCXVI. Patavii, Typis J. B. Conzatti, 1717.
86, [1] p. 22½cm.
Bound with: Albinus, B. S. Oratio qua in veram viam, quae ad fabricae humani corporis cognitionem ducat, inquiritur. 1721.

NK 0204821 ICJ

Knipschaar, Karl.
Kurfürst Philipp Christoph von Trier und seine beziehungen zu Frankreich. Von Karl Knipschaar. Marburg, N. G. Elwert, 1895.
66 p. 23½cm.
Appeared also as author's inaug.-diss., Marburg, 1895.

1. Philipp Christoph von Sötern, abp. of Treves, elector, 1567-1652. 2. Germany—For. rel.—France. 3. France—For. rel.—Germany.
8-11494
Library of Congress DD116.K5

NK 0204822 DLC MH PU ICRL

Knipschaar, Liselotte, 1906–
... Kritisch-statistische übersicht über die leichenbefunde an den im Gerichtlich-medizinischen institut in München wegen kindsmord u. kindsmordverdacht sezierten neugeborenen ... Köln am Rhein, 1932.
Munich diss. 1932

NK 0204823 MiU CtY PPWI

Knipschaar, Otto
Die aufwertung insbesondere von hypotheken, industrieobligationen, staats- und gemeindeanleihen, sparkassen-guthaben und lebensversicherungen gemäss der dritten steuernotverordnung vom 14. Februar 1924. Allgemeinverständliche kurze darstellung und kritik der bestimmungen der dritten steuernotverordnung über die aufwertung und die neuen steuern (geldentwertungsausgleich) sowie der die aufwertung betreffende wortlaut der verordnung nebst erläuterungen von dr. Otto Knipschaar ... [Wiesbaden, L. Schellenberg, 1924]
37 p. 19cm.
Includes legislation.

NK 0204825 MH-L

Knipschaar, Otto, Referendar: Der Sühnevertrag in seiner regelmäßigen Gestalt. Ein Versuch, das Wesen, d. strafprozessuale Bedeutung u. d. zivilrechtl. Wirkung d. wichtigsten z. Abwendung d. Strafe geschloss. Verträge darzustellen. Cöln 1913: Greven & Bechtold. IX, 80 S. 8°
Marburg, Jur. Diss. v. 17. März 1913, Ref. Traeger
[Geb. 14. Jan. 86 Cöln; Wohnort: Cöln; Staatsangeh.: Preußen; Vorbildung: Apostel-G. Cöln Reife 05; Studium: Heidelberg 1, Marburg 2, Heidelberg 1, Bonn 2 S.; Rig. 2. Aug. 12.] [U 13. 1116

NK 0204826 ICRL MH-L

Knipscheer, Frederik Samuel, 1871–
Demonen... 51p. il. Baarn, Hollandia-drukkerij [1908] (His Bijgeloof uit alle tijden, 4)

NK 0204827 OCl

Knipscheer, Frederik Samuel, 1871–
De duivel... 52p. il. Baarn, Hollandia-drukkerij [1908] (His Bijgeloof uit alle tijde[n,] 1)

NK 0204828 OCl

VOLUME 300

Knipscheer, Frederik Samuel, 1871-
Heksenij... 51p. il. Baarn, Hollandia-drukkerij [1908] (His Bijgeloof uit alle tijden, 3)

NK 0204829 OCl

LL54 B639 Xk74h Knipscheer, Frederik Samuel, 1871-1955.
Hendrik van Bommel (1490?-1570) kerkhervormer in Nederland en de Rijnlanden, door F.S. Knipscheer. [n.p.] 1955.
142 p. illus., facsims. 20 cm.
"Afkortingen" (bibliographical): p. 139-142.
Bibliographical footnotes.
1. Bomelius, Henricus, 1500?-1570. 2. Reformation - Netherlands. 3. Brothers of the common life.

NK 0204830 CtY-D ViHarEM

Knipscheer, Frederick Samuel, 1871-
Henricus Leo; een remonstrantsch-gereformeerd predikant (1575-1648)
Huis ter Heide, N. V. Uitgeversammatschappij "de Tijdstroom," 1929.
188p. 25cm.
Includes bibliography.
1. Leo, Henricus, 1575-1648.

NK 0204831 MoSCS CtY-D NcD CtY-D NjPT MH-AH MH

Knipscheer, Frederik Samuel, 1871-
De invoering en de waardeering der Gereformeerde belijdenisschriften in Nederland vóór 1618, door F. S. Knipscheer... Leiden: A. H. Adriani, 1907. 2 p.l., 208 p. 8°.
1. Church history, Netherlands.
N. Y. P. L. October 28, 1919.

NK 0204832 NN MH-AH

Knipscheer, Frederik Samuel, 1871-
Satansdienst... 52p. il. Baarn, Hollandia-drukkerij [1908] (His Bijgeloof uit alle tijden, 2)

NK 0204833 OCl

Knipscheer, Frederik Samuel, 1871-
Verhalen uit "De betoverde weereld"... 50p. il. Baarn, Hollandia-drukkerij [1908] (His Bijgeloof uit alle tijden, 5)

NK 0204834 OCl

943 Ref.346 K71v KNIPSCHEER, Frederik Samuel, 1871-
De vestiging der Gereformeerde Kerk in Noord-Holland, 1572-1608. Overgedrukt uit het:
NEDERLANDSCH Archief voor Kerkgeschiedenis, Dl. IV, V en VI. ('s-Gravenhage, Martinus Nijhoff, 1908), 172p.

NK 0204835 MH-AH

Knipscheer, Hermanus Marius.
Intramoleculaire atoomverschuiving bij azoxybenzolen. Amsterdam: Coöperatieve drukkerij-vereeniging "Plantijn," 1902. 5 p.l., 75 p., 2 l. 8°.
Dissertation, Amsterdam.
1. Azoxybenzols.
N. Y. P. L. June 3, 1913.

NK 0204836 NN

Knipscheer, James M W
The Aleutian blue mink, by James M. Fox [pseud. 1st ed.] Boston, Little, Brown, 1951.
215 p. 20 cm.
I. Title.
PZ3.K752Al 51-3968

NK 0204837 DLC WaE NN

Knipscheer, James M W
Bright serpent, a John and Suzy Marshall mystery, by James M. Fox [pseud. 1st ed.] Boston, Little, Brown [1953]
212 p. 20 cm.
I. Title.
PZ3.K752Br 53-5254 ‡

NK 0204838 DLC WaE WaT

[Knipscheer, James M W
Cheese from a mousetrap, by James M. Fox [pseud.] London, P. Davies [1944]
3 p. l., 190 p. 19 cm.
"First published June 1944; reprinted October 1944."
I. Title.
PZ3.K752Ch 45-4224 rev

NK 0204839 DLC

Knipscheer, James M W
Code Three, by James M. Fox [pseud. 1st ed.] Boston Little, Brown [1953]
213 p. 20 cm.
I. Title.
PZ3.K752Co 53-7328 ‡

NK 0204840 DLC WaE Or OEac

Knipscheer, James M W
Dark crusade, a novel by James M. Fox [pseud. 1st ed.] Boston, Little, Brown [1953]
240 p. 20 cm.
I. Title.
PZ3.K752Dar 54-5105 ‡
Library of Congress [5]

NK 0204841 DLC Or OrU WaT TxU CoU

[Knipscheer, James M W
Death commits bigamy, by James M. Fox [pseud.] New York, Coward-McCann [1948, °1947]
214 p. 20 cm. (A Gargoyle mystery)
I. Title.
PZ3.K752De 48-603 rev*

NK 0204842 DLC WaE OOxM TxU

[Knipscheer, James M W
Geen grapjes, alsjeblieft! Een verhaal over de vijfde kolonne. [Door] James M. Fox [pseud.] Utrecht, A. W. Bruna [1948]
215 p. 20 cm. (Het Boek van de maand)
I. Title. (Series)
PT5850.K54G4 48-3865*

NK 0204843 DLC

Knipscheer, James M W
The gentle hangman, by James M. Fox [pseud. 1st ed.] Boston, Little, Brown, 1950.
216 p. 20 cm.
I. Title.
PZ3.K752Ge 50-8348

NK 0204844 DLC WaE CaBVa OCl TxU

[Knipscheer, James M W
The inconvenient bride, by James M. Fox [pseud.] New York, Coward-McCann [1948]
186 p. 20 cm. (A Gargoyle mystery)
I. Title.
PZ3.K752 In 48-8787*

NK 0204845 DLC WaT CaBVa OOxM

Knipscheer, James M W
The iron virgin, by James M. Fox [pseud. 1st ed.] Boston, Little, Brown, 1951.
200 p. 20 cm.
I. Title.
PZ3.K752 Ir 51-14224 ‡

NK 0204846 DLC WaT WaE NN

[Knipscheer, James M W
... The lady regrets. New York, Coward-McCann, inc. [1947]
4 p. l., 181 p. 21cm.
Author's pseud., James M. Fox, at head of title.
"A Gargoyle mystery."
I. Title.
PZ3.K752Lad 47-24203

NK 0204847 DLC

Knipscheer, James M W
The scarlet slippers, by James M. Fox [pseud. 1st ed.] Boston, Little, Brown [1952]
214 p. 19 cm.
I. Title.
PZ3.K752Sc 52-5522 ‡

NK 0204848 DLC WaE

Knipscheer, James M W
A shroud for Mr. Bundy, by James M. Fox [pseud. 1st ed.] Boston, Little, Brown [1952]
218 p. 20 cm.
I. Title.
PZ3.K752Sh 52-9068 ‡

NK 0204849 DLC WaE TxU

Knipscheer, James M W
The wheel is fixed, by James M. Fox [pseud. 1st ed.] Boston, Little, Brown, 1951.
216 p. 20 cm.
I. Title.
PZ3.K752Wh 51-9027

NK 0204850 DLC WaE WaSp

VOLUME 300

Knipscheer, L[eendert] D[ionys] G[eerten] 1903-
Verhalen uit de Doopsgezinde geschiedenis naverteld door L.D.G. Knipscheer. Amsterdam, Algemene Doopsgezinde Sociëteit [n.d.]

31p. 24 1/2cm.

NK 0204851 ViHarEM

Knipscheer, L[eendert] D[ionys] G[eerten], 1903-
Wie zijn wij? door L. D. G. Knipscheer en H. Bremer. Groningen, Verenigde Doopsgezinde Gemeente te Groningen, 1947.

79 [1]p. 24 cm.

NK 0204852 ViHarEM

DD 67 .K5 Knipschild, Heinz
1870-1970 [i. e. Achtzehnhundertsiebzig bis neunzehnhundertsiebzig] Das deutsche Jahrhundert; ein Bekenntnis. Leipzig, Wolkenwanderer-Verlag, 1926.
252 p. 22 cm.

1. Germany - Civilization. 2. National characteristics, German. I. Title.

NK 0204853 WU NN

Knipschildt, Hans Erik Ove, 1913–
Undersøgelser over Coligruppens Serologi med særligt Henblik paa Kapselformerne. With an English summary. Kjøbenhavn, Nyt nordisk Forlag, 1945.

[5] l., 9–178 p. 24 cm.

Thesis—Copenhagen.
"Litteraturfortegnelse": p. 173–177.

1. Bacillus coli communis. 2. Antigens and antibodies.

QR82.B23K55 Med 47–3024*

NK 0204854 DLC OrU-M CU CtY DLC

KNIPSCHILDT, Philipp, 1595-1657.
De fideicommissis familiarum nobilium, sive de bonis quae pro familiarum nobilium conservatione constituuntur: von stammgutern tractatus. Ulmae, 1654.

Also an engraved title-page.

NK 0204855 MH-L

Knipschildt, Philipp, 1595-1657
De fideicommissis familiarum nobilium, sive, De bonis, quae pro familiarum nobilium conservatione constituuntur. Von stammgütern tractatus, authore Philippo Knipschildt ... Ulmae, typis & sumptibus Balthasari Kühnen, 1661.

6 p.l., 862, [119] p. front. (port.) 20cm.

Added engraved t.-p.

NK 0204856 MH-L WU

4K 10033 Knipschildt, Philipp, 1595-1657.
Informatio de obligatione domini & vasalli; oder, Kurtzer Bericht, was ein Leheherr seinem Lehenman zu thun schuldig? Auch, ob und auss was Ursachen das Eigenthum verlohren werde etc. Wie auch, was ein Lehenmann für Gerechtigkeiten auf dem Lehen habe? Was er derentwegen dem Lehenherrn zu thun schuldig? und auss was Ursachen er selbiges verliere etc. [ ] G. W. Kühnen, 1687.
p.

NK 0204857 DLC-P4

Knipschildt, Philipp, 1595-1657
... Tractatus de fideicommissis familiarum nobilium, von stam-güteren: sive de bonis quae pro familiarum nobilium conservatione constituuntur ... Coloniae, sumptibus Sebastiani Ketteler, 1696.

5 p.l., 696, [94] p. 20½cm.

NK 0204858 MH-L

Knipschildt Philipp, 1595–1657.
Philippi Knipschildt ... Tractatus de fideicommissis familiarum nobilium, von stamm-gütern. Sive De bonis quæ pro familiarum nobilium conservatione constituuntur ... Editio nova & emendata ... Augustæ-Vindelicorum, typis & sumptibus Joannis Jacobi Lotteri hæredum, 1750.

7 p. l., 704, [103] p. 21cm.
Head and tail pieces.

1. Entail—Germany. 2. Germany—Nobility. I. Title: Tractatus de fideicommissis.

25–22837

NK 0204859 DLC

Rare Books Dept. Knipschildt, Philipp, 1595- 1657.
Tractatus politico-historico-juridicus de juribus et privilegiis civitatum imperialium, tam generalibus, quàm specialibus, & de earundem magistratuum officio: in sex libros divisus ... Ulmae Suevorum, Typis & Impensis Balthasari Kühnen, 1657.
9 p.ℓ., 1180, [74] p. 34cm.

Added illus. t.p., engr.
Printer's device on t.p.

1. Holy Roman empire - Pol. & govt. 2. Holy Roman empire - Constitutional law. *I. Holy Roman empire. Laws, statutes, etc.

NK 0204860 CU ICN MH-L

Beinecke Library Nta30 +657Kb Knipschildt, Philipp, 1595-1657.
Tractatus politico-historico-juridicus, de juribus et privilegiis civitatum imperialium, tam generalibus, quàm specialibus, & de earundem magistratuum officio: in sex libros divisus ... Authore Philippo Knipschildt ... Editio secunda, priore correctior ... Ulmae Suevorum, sumptibus Georgii Wilhelmi Kühnen, typis haered. Christiani Balthasaris Kühnen, reipubl. typogr., 1687.
7 p.ℓ., 570 (i.e.578)p., 625-918 (i.e.916), 1001-1164, [75] p. 34 cm.

Added engr. t.-p.
Signatures: $a^6A\text{-}Bbb^6Ccc^1AA\text{-}ZZ^6AAA\text{-}BBB^4$ $a\text{-}n^6o^4(a)\text{-}(i)^4(k)^2$.

1. Cities and towns - Hist.

NK 0204862 CtY MiU-L MH-L

FL6 K71tra 1693 Knipschildt, Philipp, 1595-1657.
Tractatus politico-historico-juridicus, de juribus et privilegiis nobilitatis et ordinis equestris S.R.I., liberi et immediati, in libros tres, divisus, quibus plenissimè tractatur in genere, De nobilitate sagata et togata: antiqua et nova ... in specie, De nobilibus ordinis equestris S.R.I. liberi et immediati in Svevia, Franconia, ad Tractvm Rheni, et Alsatia, eorumdemque iuribus et privilegiis ... Opera et studio domini Philippi Knipschiltii ... Opus posthumum ... Cum indice triplici ... Campoduni, 1693.
3 v. in 1. 32cm.
With this is bound Baumann, Johann Friedrich von. Voluntarium Imperii consortium inter Fridericum Austriacum et Ludovicum Bavarum. Francofurti et Lipsiae, 1735.
1. Nobility - Germany. 2. Nobility.

NK 0204864 MiU-L PU

fJ 447 .4652 KNIPSCHILDT, PHILIPP, 1595-1657.
Tractatus politico-historico-juridicus, de juribus et privilegiis nobilitatis et ordinis equestris S.R.I. liberi et immediati, in libros tres, divisus, quibus plenissimè tractatur in genere, de nobilitate sagata et togata...in specie de nobilibus ordinis equestris S.R.I. liberi et immediati in Sueuia, Franconia, ad tractum Rheni, et Alsatia, eorumdemq; iuribus et privilegiis... Opus posthumum...editum a Johanne Rudolpho libero barone ab Ow; Campoduni, 1693.
5 pt.in 1v. 32cm.
Armorial book-plate: Revisionsrath von Chlingensperg.

NK 0204865 ICN WU MH-L

KNIPSCHILDT, Philipp, 1595-1657.
Tractatus politico-juridicus de juribus et privilegiis civitatum imperialium tam generalibus, quam specialibus et de earundem magistratum officio in sex libros divisus. Ed.3a, prioribus multo auctior. Accedunt in hac editione J.J.Schmaussii notae insignes nec non J.Sturm de Sturneck extractus omnium eorum quae in comitiis imp.ab.a.1427 usque ad a1517 celebratis fuere tractata, ex editione & cum notis luculentis J.Wenckeri. Argentorati, sumptibus J.Beckii, 1740

f°. pp.(14),616,520,(76),51.
The Anhang is separately paged.

NK 0204867 MH CLL

Knipschildt, Philipp, 1595-1657
Vnfürgreiffliches bedencken, vber etliche fragen der freyen reichs-ritterschafft in Schwaben, Francken vnd am Rheinstrom. Standt vnnd session betreffendt. Authore Hippolito von Treisspach. [Regenspurg] Philiberti Brunnij, 1644.

[32], 276, [2] p. 20cm.

NK 0204868 MH-L

Knipser, Friedrich.
Die Streikversicherung in Deutschland; ihre Entwicklung und heutiger Stand...von Friedrich Knipser... Nürnberg, 1928. 59 p. 8°.

Dissertation, Erlangen.
Bibliography, p. [6.]

471274A. 1. Insurance, Strike—Germany.
N. Y. P. L. April 24, 1930

NK 0204869 NN PU CtY

KNIRCK, Erich, 1920-
Briefe an die Kirche; die sieben Sendschreiben der Offenbarung des Johannes, ausgelegt von Erich Knirck. [Bad Cannstatt, Veroeffentlicht unter der Zulassung ... der Nachrichtenkontrolle der Militaerregierung, 1947]
29p. 20.8cm.

NK 0204870 MH-AH CtY-D

KNIRIM, Ewald, 1903-
Die verschiebungen der volksdichte im engeren westfälischen Ruhrgebiet von 1818 bis 1925 und ihre geographischen grundlagen. Inaug. Diss. Münster i.Westf., C.J.Fahle g.m.b.h., [1928].

pp.(2),79. Maps.
"Lebenslauf", p.79.
"Literatur-verzeichnis", pp.73-78.
Econ 6135.01.3

NK 0204871 MH

VOLUME 300

751 Knirim, Friedrich
K 749 E Die endlich entdeckte wahre Maler-Technik des klassischen Alterhums und des Mittelalters, sowie die neuerfundene Balsamwachsmalerei ... Nebst einer vollständigen Lösung des Problems der alten Enkaustik und der angeblich alten Freskomalerei. Leipzig, Friedrich Fleischer, 1845.
xii, 420 p. 22cm.

NK 0204872 OO

ND2480 **Knirim, Friedrich.**
.K7 Die harzmalerei der alten. Ein versuch zur einführung einer, weit mehr vortheile als oel-, wachs-, fresco- und temperawasser-malerei gewährenden und sowohl zu wand- als zu staffelei-gemälden von allen grössen brauchbaren malerei, nach dem beispiele der alten, sowie zur verbesserung der fundamente, und zur ausbildung der farbengebung nach Göthe's Farbenlehre ec. Von Friedrich Knirim. Leipzig, F. Fleischer, 1839.
xii, 232 p. front. (port.) 20½cm.
Bibliographical foot-notes.
1. Encaustic painting.

NK 0204873 ICU NjP MH

Knirps; erzählung für jung und alt
see under Oertzen, Margarete von (von Plüskow) 1854-1934.

Knirsch, Ernst.
Deutsche Literaturgeschichte im Uberlick; mit einem Literaturverzeichnis von Ernst Knirsch und Klaus Weiss. Bamberg, Reiter [c.1949]
80 p. 21 cm. (Vermächtnis und Aufgabe ... Reihe A., Bd. 2)

NK 0204875 NcD

Knirsch, Hans, 1877-1933.
Hans Knirsch, ein sudetendeutscher Edelmensch, von Rudolf Zeidler. Schwerin i. M., Verlag Niederdeutscher Beobachter, 1938.
307 p. plate, port. 20 cm.
"Briefe [von Hans Knirsch] von 1906 bis 1933": p. 71-287.
1. Knirsch, Hans, 1877-1933. I. Zeidler, Rudolf.
DB215.K56 48-42328*

NK 0204876 DLC CU

BTE p.v.192, no.1
Knirsch, Hans, 1877-1933.
Die Stellung der Deutschen zum tschechischen Staat. Referat, erstattet am 1. Gesamtparteitag der deutschen nationalsozialistischen Arbeiterpartei zu Dux am 16. November 1819, von Hans Knirsch. Dux: Buchdruckerei "Gutenberg"[, 1919?]. 15 p. 8°.
Repr.: "Tag," Folge 190.
1. Germans in Czecho-Slovakia.
N. Y. P. L. April 25, 1928

NK 0204877 NN

L595.76 R001 v.79
Knisch, Alfred.
... *Hydrophilidae.* Berlin, W. Junk, 1924.
[2], 306 p. 26cm. (Coleopterorum catalogus ... pars 79)
At head of title: ... A. Knisch.

NK 0204878 ICJ

Knischewski, Franz.
Einführung in die anatomie und physiologie unter besonderer berücksichtigung der zahnprothetik, nebst einem anhang, Elementare einführung in die lateinische terminologie, von Franz Knischewski. Berlin, Verlag der Deutschen arbeitsfront [1941]
227 p. illus., diagrs. 23cm.
"2., erweiterte und verbesserte auflage. 4. und 5. tausend."
1. Mouth. 2. Teeth. 3. Dentistry.
44-26095
Library of Congress RK280.K57 1941
[2] 617.6

NK 0204879 DLC DNLM NNU-D

WU 101 K71e 1942
KNISCHEWSKI, Franz
Einführung in die Anatomie und Physiologie, unter besonderer Berücksichtigung der Zahnprothetik. Nebst einen Anhang: Elementare Einführung in die lateinische Terminologie. [3. verb. Aufl.] Berlin, Deutsche Arbeitsfront [c1942]
227 p. illus.
1. Head - Anatomy 2. Teeth - Anatomy

NK 0204880 DNLM

WU 190 K71m 1943
KNISCHEWSKI, Franz
Materialienkunde der Zahntechnik. [3. verb. Aufl.] Berlin, Verlag der Deutschen Arbeitsfront [etc., c1943]-50.
2 v. illus.
Contents. - T. 1. Nichtmetallische Werkstoffe. - T. 2. Metallkunde.
1. Dental chemistry 2. Dental materials 3. Dentistry - Metallurgy (v. 2)

NK 0204881 DNLM

WU 190 K71m
KNISCHEWSKI, Franz
Materialienkunde der Zahntechnik. 4. verb. Aufl. München, Pflaum, 1951-
v. illus.
Contents.— T. 1. Nichtmetallische Werkstoffe.
1. Dental chemistry 2. Dental materials

NK 0204882 DNLM IEN-D

Knischewsky, Olga.
Beitrag zur morphologie von thuja occidentalis. Zuerich, 1905.
In. Diss. Bibl.

NK 0204883 ICRL

Knischewsky, Olga.
Tagesringe bei *Penicillium luteum.* illus.
Landw. jahrb. bd. 38, suppl. 5, p. 341-343. Berlin, 1909.
1. Penicillium luteum.
Library, U. S. Dept. of Agriculture Agr 9-1958

NK 0204884 DNAL NN

KNISCHEWSKY, Paul.
Das preussische gesamtministerium; eine staatsrechtliche studie. Bartenstein, 1901.
(2)+66 p.
Inaug.-diss. --- Erlangen.

NK 0204885 MH-L ICRL

Knischewsky, Paul.
Das preussische gesamtministerium. Eine staatsrechtliche studie. Von dr. jur. Paul Knischewsky. Berlin, Struppe & Winckler, 1902.
66 p., 1 l. 22½cm.
1. Prussia—Pol. & govt. 2. Prussia—Constitutional law. I. Title.
Library of Congress JN4508.K6 2-25740 Revised

NK 0204886 DLC ICJ NN

Knisel (Johann Samuel). *Diss. anat. de vasorum lymphaticorum administratione, observatis ac observandis n. et p. n. eorumque causis. 18 pp. sm. 4°. *Tubingæ, vidua J. H. Reisl,* 1687.

NK 0204887 DNLM

Knisel, Nicolaus, respondent.
... De receptatoribus ...
see under Gravius, Johann, praeses.

Knisel, Nicolaus, respondent.
Remedium legis ultimae, Cod. de fideicommissis ...
see under Harpprecht, Ferdinand Christoph, 1650-1714, praeses.

Kniseley, Bob
... Target pistol shooting and the services. Norman, Okla., University of Oklahoma, [1933]
15p. illus. (The Univ. of Oklahoma bulletin, New series no. 586, Aug. 1, 1933)

NK 0204890 OU

BX8076 P6K59
Kniseley, John B
A memorial history of the Port Royal Lutheran Charge, Port Royal and St. Paul's churches, including a history of the pictures and records of the soldiers of the charges. Compiled and edited by Rev. John B. Kniseley. Port Royal, Pa., 1919.
68 p. ports. 24cm.
1. Port Royal, Pa. Lutheran Church - Hist. I. Title.

NK 0204891 GU

Kniseley, John M
The necessity for leadership and financial support in a state program for adult education.
(*In* National education association of the United States. Addresses and proceedings, 1927. p. 302-306)
1. Education of adults. 2. Education—U. S. [1, 2. Adult education—U. S.]
E 28—248
U. S. Office of Education. Library for Library of Congress [a48c½]

NK 0204892 DHEW OU OO

Film 1322
Kniseley, Wade Allen.
An investigation of the phenomenon of stage fright in certain prominent speakers. [Los Angeles] 1950.
Microfilm copy (positive) of typescript.
Collation of the original as determined from the film: 157 l.
Thesis- University of Southern California.
Bibliography: leaves [149]-155.
1. Stage fright.

NK 0204893 OU

VOLUME 300

Knisely, Abraham Lincoln, 1865–
... Acid soils ... By A. L. Knisely ... Corvallis, Ore., Oregon agricultural college press, 1906.
23, [1] p. col. illus., tables. 21cm. (Oregon. Agricultural experiment station, Corvallis. Bulletin no. 90)

1. Soils—Oregon. I. Title.

A 15-2614

Title from Oregon Agr. College. Printed by L. C.

NK 0204894 OrU MB

Knisely, Abraham Lincoln, 1865–
... Comments upon the state fertilizer law. By A. L. Knisely ... Corvallis, Ore., Oregon agricultural college press, 1908.
11, [1] p. tables. 21cm. (Oregon. Agricultural experiment station, Corvallis. Bulletin no. 97)

1. Fertilizers and manures. I. Title: State fertilizer law.

A 15-2621

Title from Oregon Agr. College. Printed by L. C.

NK 0204895 OrU OrPR OrCS MB

Knisely, Abraham Lincoln, 1865- joint author.

Withycombe, James, 1854–
... Digestibility of vetch hay and corn silage. By James Withycombe and A. L. Knisely ... Corvallis, Ore., Oregon agricultural college press, 1905.

Knisely, Abraham Lincoln, 1865–
... Plant-food and use of fertilizers. By A. L. Knisely ... [Corvallis, Ore.] Agricultural college printing office, 1904.
40 p. tables. 21cm. (Oregon. Agricultural experiment station, Corvallis. Bulletin no. 79)

1. Fertilizers and manures. I. Title.

A 15-2604

Title from Oregon Agr. College. Printed by L. C.

NK 0204897 OrU OrCS OrPR PP

Knisely, Abraham Lincoln, 1865- joint author

Withycombe, James, 1854–
... Preliminary report on steamed silage. [By] Jas. Withycombe [and] A. L. Knisely ... [Corvallis] Oregon agricultural college printing office, 1902.

Knisely, Abraham Lincoln, 1865 -
Report on potash.
(In U. S. Dept. of agriculture. Bureau of chemistry. Bulletin 105. p. 190-196. 23cm. Washington, 1907)

1. Potash.

Agr 7-2073 Revised

Library, U. S. Dept. of Agriculture

NK 0204899 DNAL OCU OCl OO

Knisely, Clyde J.
Gravel road construction, with specifications, by Clyde J. Knisely ... Columbus, O., The F. J. Heer printing co., 1917.
29 p. 23cm.

1. Roads, Gravel. I. Title.

17-21693

Library of Congress TE233.K6

NK 0204900 DLC

Knisely, Clyde J.
Macadam road construction, with specifications, by Clyde J. Knisely. Columbus, O., The F. J. Heer printing co., 1917.
56 p. 23cm. $0.50
"Considerable of the subject matter has been presented to the public by the author in the form of papers and discussions during the past ten years."—Pref.

1. Roads, Macadamized.

17-4983

Library of Congress TE243.K5

NK 0204901 DLC

Knisely, Clyde J.

Ohio. *Bureau of inspection and supervision of public offices.*
... Report on economic highway survey of Ohio, by C. J. Knisely ... Columbus, O., The F. J. Heer printing co., 1920.

PS635 .Z9K7 Knisely, Elsie.
"False witness"...
Minneapolis, c1933.
1 pam. 12°

NK 0204903 RPB DLC

Knisely, J[ames] C.
Historical record of the Knisely Wolf and Norris-McCoy families.
n.p., 1923.
81 p. 8°

NK 0204904 MWA OClWHi

Knisely, Levi Myron.
The great creamery secret process. A guide for farmers and dairymen, containing recipes, processes, calculations, and other valuable information pertaining to milk, butter and cheese; diseases of cattle and their cure. By L. M. Knisely. Cleveland, O., C. R. Clarke & co., printers, 1883.
32 p. 17½cm.

1. Dairying. 2. Creameries.

12-15041

Library of Congress SF239.K7

NK 0204905 DLC

Knisely, Melvin Henry, 1904–
Selective phagocytosis ... by Melvin H. Knisely, Edward H. Bloch, and Louise Warner. København, I kommission hos E. Munksgaard, 1948–
v. diagrs. 27 cm. (Det Kgl. Danske videnskabernes selskab. Biologiske skrifter, bd. 4, nr. 7)
CONTENTS.—1. Microscopic observations concerning the regulation of the blood flow through the liver and other organs and the mechanism and rate of phagocytic removal of particles from the blood.
1. Phagocytosis. I. Bloch, Edward H., joint author. II. Warner, Louise, joint author. III. Title. (Series: Danske videnskabernes selskab, Copenhagen. Biologiske skrifter, bd. 4, nr. 7)
[QH7.D4 bd. 4, nr. 7] A 49-2349*

Columbia Univ. Libraries for Library of Congress [3]

NK 0204906 NNC ViU OrU-M OClW UU PU MU DNLM OClW-H OU

Knisely, Melvin Henry, 1904–
... Spleen studies. 1. Microscopic observations of the circulatory system of living unstimulated mammalian spleens ... by Melvin Henry Knisely ... [Philadelphia, 1936]
1 p. l., p. 23-50. illus. 25½cm.
Thesis (PH. D.)—University of Chicago, 1935.
"Private edition, distributed by the University of Chicago libraries, Chicago, Illinois."
"Reprinted from the Anatomical record, vol. 65, no. 1, April 1936."
"Literature cited": p. 50.

1. Spleen. 2. Vascular system—Mammals.

36-24112

Library of Congress QL868.K6 1935
Univ. of Chicago Libr.
——— Copy 2. [2] 591.44

NK 0204907 DLC OCU NcD

QA103 K69 1870 **Knisely, Rev. U. Jesse**
Arithmetical Questions for the recreation of the teacher and the discipline of the pupil. ...Philadelphia, Cowperthwait and Co. 1870.
69, 3(catalogue) p. 19 cm.

NK 0204908 DAU OO

---

*Knisely, Mrs. Verona (Butzer) 1904- joint author.

Brewington, Ann.
The social concept of money; a bibliography, by Ann Brewington ... and Verona B. Knisely ... Chicago, Ill., The University of Chicago press [1935]

Knisely, Von E
The new freedom, an Armistice Day pageant ... by Von E. Knisely... East Dearborn, Mich., c1932.
16 p. 23 cm.

NK 0204910 RPB

Knisely & Miller, *Chicago.*
... Galvanized iron cornices, window caps ... etc. ... Fire proof floors, iron lath, slate, tin and iron roofing, and the Hayes patent ventilating ... skylights ... Copper and iron lightning rods, manufactured by Knisely & Miller ... [Chicago, Hack & Anderson, printers, °1884]
112 p. front., illus., plates. 26½cm.

1. Cornice work—Catalogs. 2. Architectural metal-work—Catalogs.

CA 9-3634 Unrev'd

Library of Congress TH2481.K7 (Copyright 1884: 16669)

NK 0204911 DLC

Knish, Annie, *pseud.*
see
Ficke, Arthur Davison, 1883–

Kniskern, Philip Wheeler, 1889 -
Practical suggestions for the appraisal of residential properties for real estate loans [by] Philip W. Kniskern ... New York city, N. Y., National reserve corporation [°1928]
1 p. l., 45, [1] p. illus. (incl. plans) 20cm.
"This address, with lantern slide illustrations, was presented before the general session of the National association of real estate boards at the Seattle convention, August 12, 1927."—p. [2] of cover.

1. Real property—Valuation. I. Title.

29-18524

Library of Congress HD1387.K45

NK 0204913 DLC

VOLUME 300

Kniskern, Philip Wheeler, 1889–
Real estate appraisal and valuation, by Philip W. Kniskern ... New York, The Ronald press company [c1933]
xvi, 532 p. illus., diagrs. 22cm.

1. Real property—Valuation. I. Title.
Library of Congress HD1387.K46 33-3300
Copyright A 59217 [2] 333.3

NK 0204914 DLC MiU NBuU NNC WaS OrCS PP PU PU-W PPT MiU OCl MB ICJ ViU TU

Kniskern, Philip Wheeler, 1889–
Real estate appraisal and valuation, by Philip W. Kniskern ... New York, The Ronald press company [c1933]
xvi, 532 p. illus., diagrs. 22cm.

Film reproduction. Negative.

1. Land values--U.S.

NK 0204915 NN

Kniskern, Philip Wheeler, 1889–
Valuation report on 225 Wedgewood Street, Oakdale, New York ... 1930.

NK 0204916 MiU

Kniskern, Verne Burton, 1921–
The life cycle and biology of *Rhipidocotyle septpapillata* Krull, 1934 (Trematoda), and a review of the family Bucephalidae. Ann Arbor, University Microfilms, 1950.
([University Microfilms, Ann Arbor, Mich.] Publication no. 1982)
Microfilm copy of typewritten ms. Positive.
Collation of the original: v, 114 l. Plates, map, photos, diagr., tables.
Thesis—University of Michigan.
Abstracted in Microfilm abstracts, v. 10 (1950) no. 4, p. 357-358.
"Literature cited": leaves 99-105.
1. Rhipidocotyle septpapillata. 2. Bucephalidae.
Microfilm AC-1 no. 1982 Mic A 50-451
Michigan. Univ. Libr. for Library of Congress

NK 0204917 MiU DLC

DKLA .3K71 Knisley, Alvin, 1873–
Biographical dictionary of the Latter-day Saints ministry from the rise of the Church to 1948. About 375 names. Independence, Mo., 1948.
1 v. (unpaged) 23cm.

Loose-leaf.
Includes adherants of all branches of the Mormon faith.

1. Mormons & Mormonism - Biography.

NK 0204918 WHi

Knisley, Alvin.
Dictionary of all proper names in the Book of Mormon. Independence, Mo., Ensign Pub. House [1909]
118 p. 19 cm.

1. Book of Mormon - Dictionaries. 2. Book of Mormon - Names. I. T.

NK 0204919 NjP

Knisley, Alvin.
Dictionary of the Book of Mormon. Revised with some enlargement. By Alvin Knisley ... Total vocabulary over 650 ... Independence, Mo. [Printed by L. Moon] 1945.
2 p. l., 7-155, [2] p. 19½cm.
"First printed and published 1909."

1. Book of Mormon—Dictionaries.
45-19785
Library of Congress BX8627.A1K6 1945
289.3

NK 0204920 DLC CU-B

Knisley, Alvin, comp.
Doctrinal references; texts from the three standard books arranged under subject heading. 4. ed. Comp. by Alvin Knisley. Independence, Mo., Ensign Pub. House, 1914.
71 p. 16 cm.

1. Book of Mormon - Corcordances. 2. Smith, Joseph, 1805-1844./Book of doctrine and covenants. 3. Reorganized Church of Jesus Christ of Latter Day Saints - Doctrinal and controversial works.

NK 0204921 NjP

F835 K87 Knisley, Alvin comp.
Infallible proofs ... Independence, Mo., Printed by Herald Publishing House, 1930.
204 p. 20cm.

NK 0204922 CU-B

Knisley, Alvin, 1873– comp.
Revelations in our times; a collection of tongue prophecies, visions, dreams and other spiritual communications, received by saints...Comp. and pub. by Alvin Knisley. Independence, Mo., 1913.
208 p. 20 cm.

1. Mormons and Mormonism - Doctrinal and controversial works. 2. Prophecies. I. T.

NK 0204923 NjP

Knispel, Charles P.
Charter and revised ordinances of the City of Belleville
see under Belleville, Ill. Ordinances, etc.

429 K74a **Knispel, Eva, 1900–**
..., Der altenglische instrumental bei verben und adjektiven und sein ersatz im verlaufe der englischen sprachgeschichte ... Breslau, 1932.
82p.

Inaug.-diss.--Breslau.
Lebenslauf.
"Quellen": p.VII-VIII; "Sprachwissenschaftliche literatur": p.VIII-X.

NK 0204925 IU ICRL PU CtY

Knispel, Fritz, 1910–
... Das Ergebnis der häuslichen Geburtshilfe in Mecklenburg-Schwerin vom Jahre 1931 ... Rostock, 1935.
Inaug.-Diss. - Rostock.
Lebenslauf.
"Literatur-Verzeichnis": p. 24.

NK 0204926 CtY

PN 2641 .K65 1901 Knispel, Hermann, 1855-1919
Bunte Bilder aus dem Kunst- und Theaterleben. 2. Aufl. Darmstadt, J. C. Herbert, 1901.
vi, 308p. 22cm.

1. Theater - Germany. I. Title.

NK 0204927 TNJ MB

Knispel, Hermann, 1855–1919.
Das Grossherzogliche hoftheater zu Darmstadt von 1810–1890. Mit einem geschichtlichen rückblick auf die dramatische kunst zu Darmstadt von 1567–1810. Im auftrage der grossh. hoftheater-direction nach urkunden bearbeitet von Hermann Knispel ... Mit dem bildniss Sr. Kgl. Hoheit des grossherzogs Ludwig IV. von Hessen und bei Rhein und einem titelkupfer. Darmstadt und Leipzig, E. Bernin, 1891.
2 p. l., 288 p. front. (port.) 26cm.
L. C. copy imperfect: portrait wanting.
1. Darmstadt. Grossherzogliches hoftheater. 2. Theater—Darmstadt.
45-32644
Library of Congress PN2656.D42G7

NK 0204928 DLC PU IU

Knispel, Hermann, 1855–1919.
Das Grossherzogliche hoftheater zu Darmstadt von 1810–1910. Mit einem geschichtlichen rückblick auf die dramatische kunst zu Darmstadt von 1567–1810. Zur hundertjahr-feier des hoftheaters. Nach amtlichen quellen bearbeitet von Hermann Knispel ... Darmstadt, Verlag der J. C. Herbert'schen hofbuchdruckerei nachf. dr. A. Koch, 1910.
vi p., 1 l., 247 p. plates, ports. 26cm.
On cover: ... Hundert jahre Darmstädter hoftheater.
Includes a summary (p. 1–70) of the earlier work of the same title (1891)
1. Darmstadt. Grossherzogliches hoftheater. 2. Theater—Darmstadt.
13–14284
Library of Congress PN2656.D42G72

NK 0204929 DLC NN

Knispel, [Oskar]
Anleitung für einrichtung und verwaltung von züchtervereinigungen. Im auftrage des direktoriums der Deutschen landwirtschafts-gesellschaft nach beratungen in der tierzuchtabteilung zusammengestellt von Bureau-vorsteher Knispel, mit einem vorwort von Landesökonomierat Wölbling ... Berlin, 1902.
93 p. 18cm. (Deutsche landwirtschafts-gesellschaft. Anleitungen für den praktischen landwirt. nr. 12)

Subject entries: Stock breeders' associations.
Agr 2-165
Library, U. S. Dept. of Agriculture, no. 40K74.

NK 0204930 DNAL ICJ

Knispel, Oskar.
Anleitung für züchtervereinigungen zur ordnungsmässigen führung der zuchtregister. Von bureauvorsteher Oscar Knispel. Berlin, 1914.
2 p. l., 99 p. 18cm. (*Added t.-p.:* Anleitungen für den praktischen landwirt. Hrsg. vom vorstand der Deutschen landwirtschafts-gesellschaft. Der sammlung nr. 17)

1. [Cattle]—Herd-books.
Agr 26-113
Library, U. S. Dept. of Agriculture 40K74A

NK 0204931 DNAL ICJ NN

Knispel, Oskar.
Die massnahmen zur förderung der nutzgeflügelzucht in Deutschland nach dem stande vom jahre 1907. Im auftrage der Deutschen landwirtschafts-gesellschaft, Tierzucht-abteilung zusammengestellt von bureau-vorsteher Oskar Knispel, Berlin. Berlin, Deutsche landwirtschaftsgesellschaft, 1908.
xxvi, 346 p. incl. illus., tables. fold. map. 24cm. (*Added t.-p.:* Arbeiten der Deutschen landwirtschafts-gesellschaft ... hft. 145)

1. Poultry. I. Deutsche landwirtschafts-gesellschaft—Tierzucht-abteilung.
Agr 8-764
Library, U. S. Dept. of Agriculture 18D48 hft. 145

NK 0204932 DNAL ICJ

VOLUME 300

Knispel, Oskar.
Die öffentlichen massnahmen zur förderung der rinderzucht nach dem stande vom jahre 1904. Im auftrage der Deutschen landwirtschafts-gesellschaft, Tierzucht-abteilung, zusammengestellt von bureau-vorsteher Oskar Knispel. Berlin, Deutsche landwirtschafts-gesellschaft, 1905.
xx, 502 p. 24cm. (*Added t.-p.:* Arbeiten der Deutschen landwirtschafts-gesellschaft ... hft. 108 ...)

1. Germany. Cattle. Agr 7-1551

Library, U. S. Dept. of Agriculture 18D48, no. 108

NK 0204933 DNAL ICJ

Knispel, Oskar.
Die oeffentlichen Massnahmen zur Förderung der Rinderzucht nach dem Stande vom Jahre 1904. Im Auftrage der Deutschen Landwirtschafts-Gesellschaft, Tierzucht-Abteilung, zusammengestellt von Bureau-Vorsteher Oskar Knispel. Berlin: P. Parey, 1905. xx, 502 p. incl. tables. 4°. (Deutsche Landwirtschafts-Gesellschaft, Berlin. Arbeiten. Heft 108.)

1. Cattle—Breeding and raising—Germany. 2. Ser.
N. Y. P. L. July 7, 1926

NK 0204934 NN

Knispel, Oskar.
Die öffentlichen massnahmen zur förderung der schweinezucht nach dem stande vom jahre 1902. Im auftrage der Deutschen landwirtschafts-gesellschaft, tierzucht-abteilung, zusammengestellt von bureau-vorsteher Oskar Knispel. Berlin, Deutsche landwirtschafts-gesellschaft, 1903.
xvi, 135 p. 23½cm. ([Arbeiten der Deutschen landwirtschafts-gesellschaft. hft. 77])

Subject entries: 1. Germany. Domestic animals. 2. Swine.
Agr 3-285

Library, U. S. Dept. of Agriculture, no. 18D48.

NK 0204935 DNAL ICJ

Knispel, Oskar.
Die oeffentlichen Massnahmen zur Förderung der Schweinezucht nach dem Stande vom Jahre 1902. Im Auftrage der Deutschen Landwirtschafts-Gesellschaft, Tierzucht-Abteilung, zusammengestellt von... Oskar Knispel. Berlin: P. Parey, 1903. xvi, 135 p. incl. tables. 4°. (Deutsche Landwirtschafts-Gesellschaft, Berlin. Arbeiten. Heft 77.)

1. Hog—Breeding and management—Germany. 2. Ser.
N. Y. P. L. April 14, 1926

NK 0204936 NN

Knispel, Oskar.
Die verbreitung der pferdeschläge in Deutschland nach dem stande vom jahre 1898 nebst darstellung der öffentlichen zuchtbestrebungen. Im auftrage der Deutschen landwirtschafts-gesellschaft, Tierzucht-abteilung, bearb. von Oskar Knispel ... mit einer einleitung von Berthold Wölbling ... Berlin, Druck von Gebr. Unger, 1900.
xvii, 405, [1] p. fold. map. 24cm. (*Added t.-p.:* Arbeiten der Deutschen landwirtschafts-gesellschaft ... hft. 49)

1. Germany. Horse. I. Wölbling, Berthold.
Agr 11-937

Library, U. S. Dept. of Agriculture 18D48 no. 49

NK 0204937 DNAL NN MoU

Knispel, Oskar.
Die verbreitung der pferdeschläge in Deutschland nach dem stande von jahre 1911 nebst darstellung der öffentlichen zuchtbestrebungen. Im auftrage der Deutschen landwirtschafts-gesellschaft, Tierzucht-abteilung, bearb. von büro-vorsteher Oskar Knispel. 2. aufl. von heft 49. Berlin, Druck von W. Greve, 1915.
xiv, 693 p. incl. illus., fold. tab. fold. map in pocket. 24cm. (*Added t.-p.:* Arbeiten der Deutschen landwirtschafts-gesellschaft ... hft. 274)

1. [Germany]—Horse. 2. Horse breeding. [2. Horse—Breeds] I. Deutsche landwirtschafts-gesellschaft, Berlin. Tierzucht-abteilung.
Agr 16-542

Library, U. S. Dept. of Agriculture 18D48 no. 274

NK 0204938 DNAL MoU

Knispel, Oskar.
Die verbreitung der pferdeschläge in Deutschland nach dem stande von jahre 1911 nebst darstellung der öffentlichen zuchtbestrebungen. Im auftrage der Deutschen landwirtschafts-gesellschaft, Tierzucht-abteilung, bearb. von büro-vorsteher Oskar Knispel. 2. aufl. von heft 49. Berlin, P. Parey, 1915.
xiv, 693 p. incl. illus., fold. tab. fold. map in pocket. 24cm. (*Added t.-p.:* Arbeiten der Deutschen landwirtschafts-gesellschaft ... hft. 274)

NK 0204939 ICJ NN

Knispel, Oskar.
Die verbreitung der rinderschläge in Deutschland nebst darstellung der öffentlichen zuchtbestrebungen, im auftrage der Deutschen landwirtschaft-gesellschaft, Tierzucht-abteilung, bearb. von Oskar Knispel ... mit einer anleitung von Berthold Wölbling ... Berlin, Druck von A. Klarbaum, 1897.
xiii, 144 p. incl. tables. fold. map, III fold. tab. 24cm. (*Added t.-p.:* Arbeiten der Deutschen landwirtschafts-gesellschaft ... hft. 23 ...)

—— Die verbreitung der rinderschläge in Deutschland nebst darstellung der öffentlichen zuchtbestrebungen. 2. aufl. Im auftrage der Deutschen landwirtschafts-gesellschaft, Tierzucht-abteilung, bearb. nach dem stande von 1906 von bureauvorsteher Oskar Knispel ... Berlin, Deutsche landwirtschafts-gesellschaft, 1907.
3 p. l., [iii]-xvi, 287 p. incl. tables. II fold. maps in pocket. 24cm. (*Added t.-p.:* Arbeiten der Deutschen landwirtschafts-gesellschaft ... hft. 23 ...)

1. Cattle. Statistics. 2. Germany. Cattle. Agr 7-1552-3

Library, U. S. Dept. of Agriculture 18D48 no. 23

NK 0204941 DNAL

Knispel, Oskar.
Die züchter-vereinigungen im Deutschen Reiche nach dem stande vom 1. januar 1901. Im auftrage der Deutschen landwirtschafts-gesellschaft, Tierzucht-abteilung, bearb. von bureau-vorsteher Oskar Knispel. Berlin [Druck von W. Greve] 1901.
2 p. l., xliv, 257 p. 24cm. (*Added t.-p.:* Arbeiten der Deutschen landwirtschafts-gesellschaft ... hft. 66)

1. Stock breeders' societies.
Agr 11-938

Library, U. S. Dept. of Agriculture 18D48 no. 66

NK 0204942 DNAL NN

Knispel, Rudolf, 1887-
Lokale transitorische polycythaemie bei vasomotorisch trophischer neurose.
Inaug. diss. Berlin, 1916.
Bibl.

NK 0204943 ICRL DNLM CtY

Kniss, Erwin, 1913-
Über die thermische zersetzung sauerstoffreier enamine. ... Würzburg, n.d.
Inaug. Diss. - Berlin, [1939]
Lebenslauf.

NK 0204944 ICRL CtY MH

Kniss, Francis Roscoe, 1898–
The construction of an achievement test in tenth grade world history, by F. Roscoe Kniss ... State College, Pa. [1937]
cover-title, [4] p. 23cm.
Abstract of thesis (ED. D.)—Pennsylvania state college, 1937.
Vita.

1. History, Universal—Study and teaching. I. Title: Achievement test in tenth grade world history.
39-25070

Library of Congress D21.K65 1937
Pennsylvania State College Libr.
[2] 907.61

NK 0204945 PSt DLC MtU

Knister, Raymond, 1900-1932, ed.
Canadian short stories, edited by Raymond Knister. Toronto, The Macmillan company of Canada limited, 1928.
xix, 340 p. 20 cm.
List of Canadian short stories in books and magazines: p. 329-340.

1. Short stories, Canadian. I. Title.

PZ1.K749Can 29—8655

NK 0204946 DLC WaT CaBVaU OrCS MoSW TxU OO MiU PU NN

Knister, Raymond, 1900-1932.
Collected poems. Edited, and with a memoir by Dorothy Livesay. Toronto, Ryerson Press [1949]
xli, 45 p. group port. 22 cm. (Ryerson library of Canadian poets)
"Raymond Knister: a bibliography of his works by Margaret Ray": p. 39-45.

A 50-7908

New York. Public Libr.
for Library of Congress [2]

NK 0204947 NN RPB PSt TxU MH CaOTU CtY CaBVaU CaBVa ICU

Knister, Raymond, 1900-1932.
My star predominant. Toronto, Ryerson Press [1934]
319 p.

NK 0204948 CaOTU TxU CaBVa CaBVaU

Knister, Raymond, 1900-1932.
White narcissus, a novel, by Raymond Knister ... New York, Harcourt, Brace and company [°1929]
250 p. 19½cm.

I. Title.
Library of Congress PZ3.K753Wh 2 29-15565

NK 0204949 DLC WaSp CaBVaU OrU ViU

Knister, Raymond, 1900-1932.
White narcissus, a novel by Raymond Knister. Toronto The Macmillan company of Canada limited, 1929.
3 p. l., 9-254 p. 19½cm.

I. Title.

Library of Congress PZ3.K753Wh 29-8390

NK 0204950 DLC TxU

Knister, Raymond, 1900-1932.
Youth goes west; a play in one act, by Raymond Knister.
(*In* Poet lore. Boston, 1928. 25½cm. vol. XXXIX [no. 4] p. 582-595)

I. Title.
C D 30-44

Library of Congress (Card Division) PN2.P7 vol. 39

NK 0204951 DLC MB MH

Knit goods. Published for the advancement of the industry.
Textiles; a monthly technical journal. v. 1–
May 1910–
New York city, McCready publishing company, 1910–
Boston, Mass., The Textiles company, 19

VOLUME 300

Knit goods buyer. New York.

Issued in conjunction with Underwear and hosiery review, and Sweater news.

[Mr 1919-D1921]

NK 0204953 MdBE

Knit goods manufacturers of America
see
Associated knit underwear manufacturors of America

Knit goods publishing corporation.
Knitted fabrics & apparel
see under title

Knit-goods review, devoted to American hosiery and knit-goods industry & trade.
New York [F. E. Fitch]
illus. 35cm. monthly.
Title varies -Sept. 1907, The American knit-goods review. Oct. 1907- Knit-goods review.

1. Knit goods—Period. 2. Hosiery—Period.
CA 8-1892 Unrev'd
Library of Congress TT679.K6

NK 0204956 DLC MH

Knit goods weekly
see
Knitting industry weekly.

Knit goods weekly trade record
see Knitting industry weekly.

Knit goods
see also Knitgoods.

Knit-knacks. no. 1- winter 1949- ed.
[New York, World Editions]
no. in v. illus. 28 cm. 4 no. a year.

1. Knitting—Period. 2. Crocheting—Period.
TT820.K694 646.2605 52-34899 ‡

NK 0204960 DLC

Knit one for the crib kids ...
see under Chestnut Hill, Pa. St. Paul's Church. Woman's Auxiliary.

Knitel, F
see
Knittel, F

Knitel, Walter O.
See
Knittel, Walter O.

Knitgoods workers progressive group.
Progressive unionism; program of the Knitgoods workers progressive group, December 1935. n.p. [1935]
15 p. 21.5 cm.

NK 0204964 MH-PA

Knitgoods workers voice.
Brooklyn.

NK 0204965 NN

Knitgoods
see also Knit goods.

Knitl, Alois,
Ueber das umbelliferen-opopanax. Bern,1899.
In. Diss.

NK 0204967 ICRL DNLM

Knitl, Elisabeth, 1910-
Die sprache der ionischen kykladen nach den inschriftlichen quellen. ... 1938. 120 p.
Inaug. Diss. - München, 1938.
Lebenslauf.
Quellen und literaturverzeichnis.

NK 0204968 ICRL CU CtY OCl PBm

Knitl, Kaspar, 1644-1702.
Conciones dominicales academicae, per omnes anni dominicas distributae. Pragae, typis Universitatis Carolo-Ferdinandeae, 1687.
v 22cm
Library has Pars hyemalis.
Bound in pigskin.

NK 0204969 MnCS

Knitl, Kaspar, 1644–1702, *praeses.*
Cosmo-graphia elementaris, propositionibus physico-mathematicis proposita ... Pragæ, typis Universitatis Carolo-Ferdinandeæ, in Collegio Soc: Jesu [1673]
[56] p. illus. 33½cm.
Diss.—Prague (Balthasar Tobias Türchner, respondent and author)
Signatures: 2 leaves, unsigned, A-N².
CONTENTS.—Prodromus astronomicus.—Geographia.—Hydrographia.—Aero-graphia.—Pyro-graphia.
1. Geography—17th-18th cent. 2. Meteorology—Early works to 1800. 3. Science—Early works to 1800. I. Türchner, Balthasar Tobias, respondent. II. Title.
Library of Congress G114.K55 41-32097

NK 0204970 DLC

Knitl, Kaspar, 1644-1702.
Via regia ad omnes scientias et artes. Hoc est: Ars universalis scientiarum omnium artiumque arcana faciliùs penetrandi, et de quocunque proposito themate expeditiùs differendi... Conscripta à R. P. Casparo Knittel... Et cum adjunctis thesibus philosophicis curiosis propugnata in universitate Carolo-Ferdinandea Pragensi, à perillvstri D. Ioanne Francisco Morak... Pragæ. Typis Vniv. Carolo-Ferd., 1682. 20 p.l., 506 p., 30 l. plate, tables. 8°.

184185A. 1. Reasoning. 2. Aristotle. 3. Kabbala. 4. Morak, Joannes Franciscus, fl. 1682.
N. Y. P. L. December 17, 1925.

NK 0204971 NN

501
K74v
1691
Knitl, Kaspar, 1644-1702.
Via regia ad omnes scientias et artes. Hoc est: Ars universalis scientiarum omnium artiumqve arcana faciliùs penetrandi, et de quocunq proposito themate expeditiùs disserendi: practice, clare, succincte, curioso ac studioso lectori conscripta à r.p. Casparo Knittel, è Societate Jesu: et cum adjunctis Thesibus philosophicis curiosis propugnata in Universitate Carolo-Ferdinandea pragensi, à perillustri d. Joan. Francisco Morak, equite de Mörensfeldt præside auctore. Primùm prodiit Pragæ: nunc verò denuo prostat Norimbergæ, consensu r.p. autoris, sumtibus Johannis Ziegeri, 1691.
18 p.l., 286, [47]p. front., 2 fold.tab. 13½cm.
Added t.-p., engr.
The Theses philosophicae have half-title: Mantissa thesium curiosarum philosophicarum.

1. Science--Methodology. 2. Logic. 3. Philosophy. I. Morak, Joannes Francisco, respondent. II. Title.

NK 0204973 IU

Knitl, Max.
Scheyerns stellung in der kulturgeschichte ... Freising, Druck von F. P. Datterer, 1880.
1 p. l., 39 p. 22cm.
Inaug.-diss.—Jena.

1. Scheyern, Ger. (Benedictine monastery) I. Title.
20-13210
Library of Congress DD901.S16K6

NK 0204974 DLC MH

Knitschke, Marie.
Fräulein Doktor. Schwank in einem Akt, von Marie Knitschke. Dritte Auflage. Berlin: E. Bloch [1912] 24 p. 18½cm. (Ludwig Blochs Damen-Bühne. Nr. 4.)

883423A. 1. Drama, German I. Title.
N. Y. P. L. June 7, 1937

NK 0204975 NN PPT

832.9
K71s
Knitschke, Marie.
Die Schwesterkirchen, von Marie und Benno Knitschke. [n.p.] 1911.
45p. 23cm.

NK 0204976 IEN

Knitschky, Wilhelm Ernst, 1848-
De praescriptionibus juris canonici ... scripsit Guilhelmus Knitschky ... Jenae, F. Maukius, 1873.
60 p., 1 l. 21cm.
Diss. - Jena.
Bibliographical footnotes.

NK 0204977 MH-L MH

VOLUME 300

4K Ger 1341 Knitschky, Wilhelm Ernst, 1848-
Das Rechtsverhältniss zwischen Eltern und Kindern nach dem Bürgerlichen Gesetzbuch. Berlin, D. Häring, 1899.
274 p.

NK 0204978 DLC-P4 CtY MH

Knitschky, Wilhelm Ernst, 1848– *ed.*
... Die seegesetzgebung des Deutschen reiches. Text-ausg. mit anmerkungen und sachregister von dr. jur. W. E. Knitschky ... Berlin und Leipzig, J. Guttentag, 1883.
iv, 392 p. 15½cm. (Deutsche reichsgesetzgebung. [nr. 19])

1. Maritime law—Germany. I. Germany. Laws, statutes, etc. II. Title.
34-28508

NK 0204979 DLC

KNITSCHKY, Wilhelm Ernst, 1848-
Die seegesetzgebung des Deutschen Reichs, nebst den entscheidungen des reichsoberhandelsgerichts, des reichsgerichts und der seeämter. 2te auf. Berlin, 1894.

24°.
"Guttentag'sche sammlung deutscher reichgesetze. Nr.19."

NK 0204980 MH-L ICU

Knitschky, Wilhelm Ernst, 1848–
... Die seegesetzgebung des Deutschen Reiches. Unter berücksichtigung der entscheidungen des Reichsoberhandels- und des Reichsgerichts, des Hanseatischen oberlandesgerichts und der seeämter. Textausg. mit anmerkungen und sachregister von weil. dr. jur. W. E. Knitschky. 5. verm. und verb. aufl. bearb. von Otto Rudorff ... Berlin, J. Guttentag, 1913.
1 p. l., v-xxiv, 1024 p. 15½cm. (Guttentag'sche sammlung deutscher reichsgesetze. nr. 19)

I. Rudorff, Otto, ed. II. Germany. Laws, statutes, etc.
15-22387

NK 0204981 DLC MH-L

Knitschky, Wilhelm Ernst, 1848-
Staat und kirche, von ... W.E. Knitschky. Rostock, W. Werther, 1886.
1 p.l., 94 p. 23cm.
Book review by Adolph Frantz inserted.

NK 0204982 MH-L

Knitschky, Wilhelm Ernst, 1848–
...Stato e chiesa. (Biblioteca di scienze politiche e amministrative. Torino, 1892. 8°. [ser. 1.] v. 8, p. 515–581.)

1. Church and state.
N. Y. P. L. February 20, 1929

NK 0204983 NN

Knitschky, Wilhelm Ernst, 1848–
Das Verbrechen des Hochverraths. Jena, Mauke, 1874.
170 p. 22 cm.
Includes bibliographical references.

1. Treason—Germany. I. Title.
68-40052

NK 0204984 DLC CtY MH-L

Knitted fabrics & apparel. [A monthly trade journal for the producers and buyers of knitted fabrics and apparel] v. 1, v. 2, no. 1–6; Apr. 1922–June 1923. [New York, The Knit goods publishing corporation, 1922–23]
2 v. in 1. illus. 30cm.

1. Knit goods—Period.
27-21826
Library of Congress TT679.K7

NK 0204985 DLC

Knitted lace edgings
see under [Burrell, Mrs. J]

Knitted outerwear association, National
see National knitted outerwear association.

Knitted outerwear times ...
New York [National knitted outerwear association] 19
v. illus. 30cm. weekly.
Caption title.
Title varies: Knitting times

1. Knit goods—Period. I. National knitted outerwear association.
42-48416
Library of Congress TT679.K75
[2] 677.66

NK 0204988 DLC IU PSt AAP NN

Knitted outerwear times.
Yearbook.
New York, National Knitted Outerwear Association.
v. illus. 30 cm.

1. Knit goods—Yearbooks. I. National Knitted Outerwear Association.
TT679.K752 54-37315 ‡

NK 0204989 DLC NN LU

HD9969 .K7U64 **Knitted Textile Association.**
Knitting times. Yearbook.
[New York] National Knitted Outerwear Association.

---

334 K749
Knittel, Albert
Beiträge zur Geschichte des deutschen Genossenschaftswesens. Freiburg, Akademische Verlagsbuchhandlung von J. C. B. Mohr, 1895.
vi, 124 p. tables.

1. Cooperation - Germany. 2. Cooperative societies - Germany

NK 0204991 NNC IU NN MH

274.94 K749r Knittel, Alfred L
Die Reformation im Thurgau zum vierhundertjährigen Jubilaum, herausgegeben vom Evangelischen Kirchenrat des Kantons Thurgau. Frauenfeld, Huber [1929]
360 p. illus., plates, facsims. (1 fold.)

1. Switzerland - Church history. I. Title.

NK 0204992 WaU MH-AH CtY

Knittel, Alfred L
Werden und Wachsen der Evangelischen Kirche im Thurgau von der Reformation bis zum Landfrieden von 1712. Bearb. im Auftrage des Evangelischen Kirchenrates des Kantons Thurgau. Frauenfeld, Kommissionsverlag von Huber [1946]
436 p. illus. 23 cm.
Includes bibliography.

1. Evangelische Kirche des Kantons Thurgau—Hist. I. Title.
BX9436.T5K6 59-35657 ‡

NK 0204993 DLC MH-AH MoSCS MH

ND538 .K58P3
Knittel, Anna, 1841–1915.
Anna Stainer-Knittel; aus dem Leben einer Tiroler Malerin. Hrsg. von Karl Paulin. Innsbruck, Wagner [1951]
112 p. plates (part col., incl. ports.) geneal. table. 21 cm.

I. Paulin, Karl, 1888– ed.
A 52-2663
Harvard Univ. Library for Library of Congress [2]

NK 0204994 MH NN DLC

Knittel, Anna Rosa Stainer-
see **Knittel, Anna**, 1841–1915.

Mic 1136 **Knittel, Bernard J**
John Evans; speaker and empire builder. 1950.
xvii, 495 l.
Thesis--University of Denver.
Microfilm of typescript. Denver, Colo., State Historical Society, Div. of State Archives, Microfilm Department, 1950. 1 reel. 35 mm.

1. Evans, John, 1814-1897. I. Title.

NK 0204996 OCH

Knittel, Caspar
see Knitl, Kaspar, 1644-1702.

Knittel, Charles.
D'r Unkel Théophile; Lustspiel in 3 Akten. Mulhouse, Editions Salvator, 1955. 29 p. 21cm. (Salvator-Theater. no. 841)

1. Drama, German. 2. German

NK 0204998 NN

KNITTEL, CHARLES.
Ehre Vater un Muetter; Volksstück in 4 Akten. Mulhouse, Editions Salvator, 1953. 40 p. 21cm. (Salvator-Theater. Nr.723)

1. DRAMA, GERMAN 2. GERMAN LANGUAGE--DIALECTS--ALSACE

NK 0204999 NN

VOLUME 300

Knittel, Eberhard, 1899–
Carlyles stellung zu staat und gesellschaft seiner zeit ... Giessen, 1926.
2 p. l., 88 p., 1 l. 23cm.
Inaug.-diss.—Giessen.
Lebenslauf.
"Literatur-verzeichnis": p. [87]–88.

1. Carlyle, Thomas, 1795–1881.
27–17989
Library of Congress PR4433.K6

NK 0205000 DLC CtY ICRL ICU

Knittel, Eberhard, 1899–
Carlyles stellung zu staat und gesellschaft seiner zeit... Giessen, 1926.
Cover-title, 1 l., 88p. 1 l.

NK 0205001 MiU PU

Knittel, Eduard.
Die vindikation der inhaber- und orderpapiere nach dem geltenden deutschen recht ... Strassburg, J. H. E. Heitz (Heitz & Mündel) 1890.
82 p. 23 cm. [Strassburg. Universität. Dissertationen. v. 3, no. 4]
Inaug.-diss. - Strassburg.

NK 0205002 CU ICRL

KNITTEL, Emil.
Die nachnahme im speditions- und frachtgeschäft. Inaugural-dissertation. Strassb., 1886.

NK 0205003 MH-L

Nc 1939 K749
Knittel, Ernst, 1904–
Die agrarpolitische Problematik in der Marktorientierung der landwirtschaftlichen Produktion Niederländisch-Indiens ; eine wirtschaftskritische Betrachtung auf historischer Grundlage. [n.p.]1939.
148p.
Inaug.-Diss. - Berlin.

NK 0205004 CtY NIC

Knittel', F
Что такое КИМ. [Москва] Молодая гвардия, 1939.
69 p. 15 cm.

1. Young Communist International. I. Title.
Title transliterated: Chto takoe KIM.
HX11.Y6K5 54–46019 ‡

NK 0205005 DLC

HX11 .K5 Hebraic Sect.
Knittel', F
... וואס איז אזוינס קאמוניסטישער יוגנט אינטערנאציאנאל. קיעוו, מעלוכע פארלאג פאר די נאציאנאלע מינדערהייטן אין אוססר, [Київ] 1940
75, [1] p. 14cm.

1. Communist International of youth.
Title transliterated: Wos iz azoins Komunistisher yugnt-internazional.
46–37123
Library of Congress HX11.K5

NK 0205006 DLC

T113 Z8 1940
Knittel, Franz, 1911–
... Das Knochenmark bei experimenteller Hyperthyreose ... Zürich, 1940.
Inaug.-Diss. - Zürich.
Curriculum vitae.

NK 0205007 CtY

FR K71
Knittel, Franz Anton, 1721-1792.
Beyträge zur Kritik über Johannes Offenbarung. Ein Synodalschreiben von Franz Anton Knittel ... Braunschweig und Hildesheim, Schröder, 1773.
92p. 22.5cm.

NK 0205008 NNUT

Knittel, Franz Anton, 1721-1792.
Fragmenta versionis Ulphilanae...
Upsaliae, 1763
see under Bible. N.T. Romans. Gothic. 1763.

KNITTEL, Franz Anton, 1721-1792.
Neue Gedanken von den allgemeinen Schreibfehlern in den Handschriften des Neuen Testaments. Ihr System ist durch [ ] neue Auslegungsmuthmassungen über die beyden berühmten Stellen Johan XIX.14. und Luc. III, 35.36. erläutert. Nebst einem Versuche einer hermeneutischen Muthmassungssittenlehre der ersten Kirche. Braunschweig, 1755.

4°. ff.(4), pp.92. 2 tables.

NK 0205010 MH

Knittel, Franz Anton, 1721-1792.
... Neue Kritiken über das weltberühmte Zeugniss des alten Juden Flavius Josephus von unserm Herrn und Heiland Jesu Christo. Ein synodalische Vorlesung ... Braunschweig und Hildesheim, 1779.
71 p. 21.5 x 17 cm.

NK 0205011 CtY

KNITTEL, Franz Anton.
Neue kritiken über den berühmten spruch: Drey sind, die da zeugen im himmel, etc. Braunschweig, 1785.

13 x 20.

NK 0205012 MH-AH

BS2805 .K71
Knittel, Franz Anton, 1721-1792.
New criticisms on the celebrated text, 1 John V. 7. "for there are three that bear record in heaven, the Father, the Word, and the Holy Ghost; and these three are one." A synodical lecture, by Francis Anthony Knittell. Published at Brunswick in 1785. Translated from the original German by William Alleyn Evanson. London, C. and J. Rivington, J. Hatchard, 1829.
li, 263p. 24cm.
1. Bible. N.T. Epistles of John. 1 John V, 7.

NK 0205013 IEG CU

Knittel, Franz Anton, 1721-1792, ed.
Ulphilae versionem Gothicam nonnullorum capitum Epistolae Pauli ad Romanos... eruit... [Brunovici, 1762]
see under Bible. N.T. Romans. Gothic. 1762.

Knittel, Georg, 1893–
Die tiefen-antisepsis in der zahnmedizin,... Inaug. diss. Leipzig, 1926 (Strasbourg)
Bibl.

NK 0205015 ICRL CtY

Knittel, Gottlob, 1898–
Veränderungen an leber und gallenblase als folgen toxischen eiweisszerfalls. 1929.
Inaug.-Diss.- Universitat zu Berlin.

NK 0205016 OU CtY

Knittel, Jean.
... L'Allemagne au carrefour. [Strasbourg] Éditions des Dernières nouvelles de Strasbourg, 1930.
3 p. l., [5]–216 p., 2 l. 19½cm.

1. Germany—Econ. condit.—1918– 2. Germany—Hist.—Revolution, 1918– I. Title.
32–34418
Library of Congress DD237.K6
[2] 943.085

NK 0205017 DLC NN MH

Knittel, John, 1891–
Aaron West, by John Knittel; with preface by Robert Hichens. New York, George H. Doran company [c1921]
ix p., 2 l., 15–361 p. 19½cm. $2.00

I. Title.
Library of Congress PZ3.K755Aa 22–6516

NK 0205018 DLC MH

---

828 K716m.G 1931
Knittel, John, 1891–
...Abd-el-Kader; roman aus dem marokkanischen Atlas. Berlin, Krüger [1931]
382p. D.

NK 0205019 IaU MH

Knittel, John, 1891–
... Abd-el-Kader; roman aus dem marokkanischen Atlas. Zürich und Leipzig, Orell Füssli [c1931]
446 p. 19cm.
"1.–6. tausend."

I. Title. *Translation of* Midnight people.
[*Full name:* John Herman Emanuel Knittel]
32–5898
Library of Congress PR6021.N45M53
Copyright A—Foreign 15111
[2] 823.91

NK 0205020 DLC NN

Knittel, John, 1891–
... Abd-el-Kader; roman aus dem marokkanischen Atlas. Zürich-Leipzig, Orell Füssli [c1933]
446 p. 19 cm.
"14.-17. tausend."

NK 0205021 CtY PPG

Knittel, John, 1891–
Abd-el-Kader; roman aus dem marokkanischen Atlas. Berlin, Büchergilde Gutenberg, 1934.
299 p. 24 cm.
Translation of Midnight people.
Full name: John Herman Emanuel Knittel.

NK 0205022 PU

VOLUME 300

*PR6021 .N45A53 Knittel, John, 1891-
Abd-el-Kader; Roman aus dem marokkanischen Atlas. Berlin, W. Krüger [1941]
382 p. 20cm.

1. Cooperative acquisitions project (Library of Congress)—German texts, 1938-1945. I. Title.
Translation of Midnight people.
Full name: John Herman Emanuel Knittel

NK 0205023 MB TxDaM NN ViU NNC CU

Knittel, John, 1891-
Abd-el-Kader; roman aus den marokkanischen atlas. [5. überarbeitete aufl.] Zürich, Füssli [c1941]
362 p.
I. Title.

NK 0205024 NNC

Knittel, John, 1891-
Abd-el-Kader, Roman aus dem marokkanischen atlas. Hamburg, Krüger [1952, °31] 398p.

NK 0205025 CaBVa

Knittel, John, 1891-
... Amadeus, roman. Berlin, W. Krüger [1939?]
577, [1] p. 19½cm.
"32.-51. tausend."

I. Title.
[Full name: John Herman Emanuel Knittel]
46-41870
Library of Congress PT2621.N6A7
[2] [833.91] 823.91

NK 0205026 DLC ICRL IaU MB MH TxDaM CU CtY PPG

Hum PT 2621 N6 A7 Knittel, John, 1891-
Amadeus; Roman. Berlin, Büchergilde Gutenberg, 1940.
2v.

NK 0205027 FTaSU WaU

Knittel, John, 1891-
Amadeus, door John Knittel. Antwerpen, Van Ditmar; [etc., etc., 1943]
485 p., 1 l. 18½cm.
"Geautoriseerde vertaling."

I. Title.
[Full name: John Herman Emanuel Knittel]
PT2621.N6A73 [833.91] 823.91 47-37990

NK 0205028 DLC UU

Knittel, John, 1891-
Amadeus, Roman. Zürich, Orell Füssli [1947]
505 p.

NK 0205029 OCl

---

833 K749am G Knittel, John, 1891-
Amadeus; Roman. Frankfurt Am Main, Büchergilde Gutenberg, 1953.
491p.

NK 0205030 P

PT 2621 N6A7 1953 Knittel, John, 1891-
Amadeus, roman. [Hamburg] Bertelsmann, 1953.
416 p. 19 cm.

NK 0205031 NBuU

PT 2621 .N6 A73 1953 Knittel, John, 1891-
Amadeus; Roman. [Hamburg, W. Krüger] 1953.
415p. 19cm.

NK 0205032 TNJ WaS

4PR-5066 Knittel, John, 1891-
Amédée, roman. Traduit de l'anglais par G. Sellier-Leclercq. Paris, A. Michel [1950]
525 p.

NK 0205033 DLC-P4

Knittel, John, 1891-
The asp and other stories. London, Hutchinson [194-?]
288 p.

Contents.-The asp.-Two pair of silk stockings.-Ferry Tony.-Father Neptune's influence.-Devil medicine.-St. Louis of Carthage.-The perroquet.-A little bit of justice.-Moccouss.-Little Ali and his dog.-Two blues.

NK 0205034 ICarbS

Knittel, John, 1891-
Die Aspis-Schlange, und andere Erzählungen. Zürich, Orell Füssli [1942]
327, [1] p. 20 cm.

I. Title.
Full name: John Herman Emanuel Knittel.
PT2621.N6A9 [833.91] 823.91 47-39741*

NK 0205035 DLC PPG NN NNC

Knittel, John, 1891-
... Der blaue basalt, roman. Zürich und Leipzig, Orell Füssli [°1930]
309, [1] p. 19½cm.

I. Title. Translation of Nile gold.
[Full name: John Herman Emanuel Knittel]
31-5873
Library of Congress PR6021.N45N53
Copyright A—Foreign 10294
[2] 823.91

NK 0205036 DLC NN PPG

Knittel, John, 1891-
Der blaue basalt, romen. [5. aufl.] Zürich, Füssli [1944]
319 p.
I. Title.

NK 0205037 NNC

Knittel, John, 1891-
... Der commandant, roman. Zürich und Leipzig, Orell Füssli [°1933]
192 p. 19½cm.
"1.-6. tausend."

I. Title.
[Full name: John Herman Emanuel Knittel]
33-11277
Library of Congress PT2621.N6C6 1933
Copyright A—Foreign 19910
[2] 833.91

NK 0205038 DLC NN PPG

Knittel, John, 1891-
... Der commandant, roman. Zürich-Leipzig, Orell Füssli [c1933]
194, [1] p. 19.5 cm.
"3. Aufl., 9.-13. Tausend."

NK 0205039 CtY

Knittel, John, 1891-
Le commandant, roman; tr. de l'anglais par la princesse Sixte de Bourbon. Paris, A. Michel [1949]
287 p. 19 cm.

I. Title.
Full name: John Herman Emanuel Knittel.
PT2621.N6C63 [833.91] 823.91 49-24309*

NK 0205040 DLC

PR6021 .N82C7 1950 Knittel, John, 1891-
Der Commandant, Roman. [8. Aufl.] Zürich, O. Füssli [1950, c1933]
191 p.

NK 0205041 ICU

Knittel, John, 1891-
Cyprus wine from my cellar, by John Knittel ... London, J. Long, limited [1933]
288 p. front., illus. 22cm.

1. Cyprus—Descr. & trav. I. Title.
[Full name: John Herman Emanuel Knittel]
34-1452
Library of Congress DS54.K6 1933
Copyright A ad int. 18518 [3] 915.64

NK 0205042 DLC NN

Knittel, John, 1891-
Ὁ διοικητής [Μετάφραση Χρ. Καβαφάκη. Ἀθῆναι] Οἱ Φίλοι του βιβλίου [1944]
207 p.

Title transliterated: Ho dioikētēs.

I. Title. II. Kabaphakēs, Chr tr.

NK 0205043 NNC

Knittel, John, 1891-
Dr. Ibrahim; a biographical novel, by John Knittel ... New York, Frederick A. Stokes company, 1935.
xiii, 386 p. 21½cm.

I. Title.
[Full name: John Herman Emanuel Knittel]
35-23922
Library of Congress PZ3.K755Dr

OClW ViU MB NNC-M WaE OrP WaS Or OrCS
NK 0205044 DLC PPJ WU PPL PP OClW OO OClW-H MiU OCl

PZ3 .K755 Do 3 Knittel, John, 1891-
Doctor Ibrahim el Hakim, by John Knittel. Leipzig, B. Tauchnitz [°1937]
358, [2] p. 18cm. (Half-title: Tauchnitz edition of British and American authors, v. 5275)

I. Title.
[Full name: John Herman Emanuel Knittel]
46-31649
Library of Congress PZ3.K755Do 3
[2]

NK 0205045 DLC

VOLUME 300

Knittel, John, 1891-
Fata morgana, roman uit het hedendaagse Marokko. Amsterdam,"De Gulden ster"‹n.d.› 400p.

NK 0205046 CaBVa

Knittel, John, 1891-
El Hakim, Doctor Ibrahim, by John Knittel. Leipzig, B. Tauchnitz [1939]
358, [2] p. 18cm. (Half-title: Tauchnitz edition of British and American authors, v. 5275)
"Second impression."
First published in London, 1935, under title: Doctor Ibrahim.
I. Title.
[Full name: John Herman Emanuel Knittel]
46-4274
Library of Congress PZ3.K755Hak

NK 0205047 DLC

Knittel, John, 1891-
... El hakim, roman aus dem heutigen Ägypten. Berlin, W. Krüger [1936]
2 p. l., 7-442 p. 19½cm.
I. Title. Translation of Dr. Ibrahim.
[Full name: John Herman Emanuel Knittel]
44-28392
Library of Congress PT2621.N6D6
[2] [833.91] 823.91

NK 0205048 DLC WaS IaU NNC ICU MB

Knittel, John, 1891-
... El hakim, roman aus dem heutigen Agypten. Berlin, W. Krüger [1943, c1936]
2 p.l., 7-44, [1] p. 19.5 cm.

NK 0205049 CtY

Knittel, John.
El Hakim; Roman aus dem neuzeitlichen Ägypten. Zürich: Orell Füssli [19—?] 442 p. 12°.

NK 0205050 NN ViU

Knittel, John, 1891-
El hakim; roman aus dem neuzeitlichen Agypten. Zürich, Füssli ‹1943?›
447 p.

NK 0205051 NNC

Knittel, John, 1891-
El hakim, roman, tr. de l'anglais par Marguerite Gay. Paris, A. Michel [1947]
452 p. 21 cm.
Translation of Doctor Ibrahim.
I. Title.
Full name: John Herman Emanuel Knittel.
PT2621.N6D613 48-25496*‡

NK 0205052 DLC

Knittel, John, 1891-
El Hakim; egy orvos regenye. 2v. in 1. Budapest, Hungaria koenyvkiado, n.d.
Forditotta Gaal Andor.
Hungarian.

NK 0205053 OCl PPG

Knittel, John, 1891-
... El hakim, egy orvos regénye ... 5. kiadás. Budapest, Hungária könyvkiadó [1941]
2 v. in 1. 19cm.
"Fordíttotta Gaál Andor."
I. Gaál, Andor, 1895- tr. II. Title. Translation of Dr. Ibrahim.
[Full name: John Herman Emanuel Knittel]
46-30532
Library of Congress PT2621.N6D62 1941

NK 0205054 DLC

Knittel, John, 1891-
... In de schaduw van het geluk. Geautoriseerde vertaling van Cor Tepe. Amsterdam-C., Uitgeverij "De Gulden ster" [1943]
413 p. 23½cm.
I. Tepe, Cor, tr. II. Title. Translation of Aaron West.
[Full name: John Herman Emanuel Knittel]
PR6021.N45A63 A F 47-2131
Yale univ. Library for Library of Congress [2]†

NK 0205055 CtY DLC

Knittel, John, 1891-
In de schaduw van het geluk. Geautoriseerde vertaling van Cor Tepe. Antwerpen, Van Ditmar [1943]
443 p. 18 cm.
A novel.
Translation of Aaron West.
I. Tepe, Cor, tr. II. Title.
Full name: John Herman Emanuel Knittel.
PR6021.N45A63 1943 A F 48-2938*
California. Univ. Libr. for Library of Congress [1]†

NK 0205056 CU NN DLC

Knittel, John.
Into the abyss, by John Knittel ... London, W. Heinemann, ltd. [1927]
3 p. l., 524 p. 19½cm.
I. Title.
28-2378
Library of Congress PZ3.K755 In

NK 0205057 DLC

Knittel, John.
Into the abyss, by John Knittel ... Garden City, N. Y., Doubleday, Doran & company, inc., 1928.
3 p. l., 446 p. 19½cm.
I. Title.
28-15789
Library of Congress PZ3.K755 In 2

NK 0205058 DLC OU LU OCl PHC PU ViU

Knittel, John, 1891-
Into the abyss, by John Knittel ... New York, Frederick A. Stokes company, 1936.
3 p. l., 446 p. 21½cm.
I. Title.
[Full name: John Herman Emanuel Knittel]
36-29012
Library of Congress PZ3.K755 In 7

NK 0205059 DLC NcU OCU

PT2621
.N6J4
1953
Knittel, John, 1891-
Jean Michel, Roman. Hamburg, W. Krüger ‹1953›
299 p. 21cm.

NK 0205060 MB CtY PPG OCl

961
K71
jeaG
1953
Knittel, John, 1891-
Jean Michel, Roman. Hamburg, W. Krüger [1954, c1953]
299 p.

NK 0205061 CU

Knittel, John, 1891-
Jean-Michel. London, R. Hale [1954]
222 p. 19 cm.
I. Title.
Full name: John Herman Emanuel Knittel.
PZ3.K755Je 54-20005 ‡

NK 0205062 DLC NN PU ViU CaBVa

961
K71
JeaFs
Knittel, John, 1891-
Jean-Michel, roman. Traduit de l'anglais par G. Sellier-Leclercq. Paris, A. Michel [1954]
284 p.

NK 0205063 CU

Knittel, John, 1891-
Kapitän West; Roman. [3.Aufl. 10.-13.Taus.] Zürich,O.Füssli[1939,c1928]
358p. 19cm.

NK 0205064 CtY

Knittel, John, 1891-
Kapitän West; roman. Zürich Füssli ‹1942›
358 p.

NK 0205065 NNC

Knittel, John, 1891-
Kapitän West, Roman. [7. Aufl.] Zürich, Orell Füssli [1944]
358 p. 19 cm.
Translation of Aaron West.
I. Title.
Full name: John Herman Emanuel Knittel.
PR6021.N45A65 1944 A F 48-2937*
California. Univ. Libr. for Library of Congress [1]†

NK 0205066 CU CtY DLC

Knittel, John, 1891-
... Midnight people. Garden City, N. Y., Doubleday, Doran & company, inc., 1931.
4 p. l., 377 p. 20cm.
"First edition."
I. Title.
[Full name: John Herman Emanuel Knittel]
31-29489
Library of Congre PZ3.K755Mi
[5]

NK 0205067 DLC PP

VOLUME 300

KNITTEL, JOHN, 1891-
...Moccouss; roman, av John Knittel. Stockholm: Iduns redaktion, 1932. 32 p. 18cm. (Iduns romanbibliothek. "Supplement to Idun." [v.] 48.)

761121A. 1. Fiction, English. I. Title. II. Ser.

NK 0205068 NN

Knittel, John.
Nile gold, a legend of modern Egypt, by John Knittel. Garden City, N. Y., Doubleday, Doran and company, inc., 1929.
4 p. l., 3-322 p. 19½cm.
"First edition."

I. Title.
Library of Congress PZ3.K755Ni 2 29-18943

NK 0205069 DLC MB PP

Knittel, John.
Nile gold, a legend of modern Egypt, by John Knittel ... London, W. Heinemann limited [1929]
3 p. l., 3-295 p. 19½cm.

I. Title.
Library of Congress PZ3.K755Ni 29-12407

NK 0205070 DLC

Knittel, John, 1891-
Power for sale; a novel by John Knittel. New York, Frederick A. Stokes company, 1939.
vi, 436 p. 21cm.

I. Title. [Full name: John Herman Emanuel Knittel]
Library of Congress PZ3.K755Po 39-25877

NK 0205071 DLC WaS WaT PP OEac OLak OCl OClW PPD

Knittel, John, 1891-
Protektorat; ein volkstümliches drama unseres zeitalters in elf bildern, von John Knittel. Zürich-Leipzig, Orell Füssli [c1935]
93 p. 20cm.

I. Title. [Full name: John Herman Emanuel Knittel] 37-4826
Library of Congress PT2621.N6P7 1935
Copyright D pub. 47706 [2] 832.91

NK 0205072 DLC OCl NN

KNITTEL, John.
Die reisen des Aaron West; roman. Zürich, etc Orell Füssli, [1925].

Verso of title-page: Die Neue Schweiz; sammlung bester zeitgenössischer literatur.
Translated by Nanny Collin.

NK 0205073 MH

Knittel, John, 1891-
... Die reisen des Aaron West, roman. Zürich and Leipzig, O. Füssli, [1928]
[3. umgearb. auf. [1928]

NK 0205074 OCl PPG

Knittel, John, 1891-
Sokrates, Drama...der antiken Chronik nachgebildet von John Knittel. Zürich [etc.] Orell Füssli [1941] 80 p. 20cm.

1. Socrates—Drama. 2. Drama, German—English authors.
N. Y. P. L. November 17, 1949

NK 0205075 NN MH

Knittel, John, 1891-
Terra magna, ein Roman aus Nordafrika. Zürich, Orell Füssli [1948]
2 v. 20 cm.

I. Title. Full name: John Herman Emanuel Knittel.

PT2621.N6T4 [833.91] 823.91 49-20137*

NK 0205076 DLC PPG OCl CtY

3465 Knittel, John, 1891-
.132 Terra magna, Roman aus Nordafrika.
.369 Hamburg, Krüger [1950,c1948]
847 p. 21 cm.

NK 0205077 NjP

Knittel, John, 1891-
Terra magna, roman aus Nordafrika. Hamburg, Kruger [1951, c48] 847p.

NK 0205078 CaBVa

4PR-5124 Knittel, John, 1891-
Terra magna, roman. Traduit de l'anglais par Marguerite Gay. Paris, Michel [1951]
2 v.
Contents. - [1] La maison des Pèlerins. [2] L'Orphelin.

NK 0205079 DLC-P4

Knittel, John, 1891-
833.914 Terra magna, Roman aus Nordafrika. Wien,
K71T Büchergilde Gutenberg, 1954 [c1936]
759 p. 21 cm.

NK 0205080 NcD

Knittel, John, 1891-
Terra magna, roman uit het hedendaagse Egypte. Amsterdam, "De Gulden Ster" [1949?] 400p.

NK 0205081 CaBVa

Knittel, John, 1891-
... Therese Etienne, roman. Berlin, W. Krüger [c1928]
2 p. l., 7-446 p. 20cm.
"9. bis 13. tausend."

I. Title. [Full name: John Herman Emanuel Knittel] 43-28068
Library of Congress PT2621.N6T5
[2]

NK 0205082 DLC CoFS NN CtY WU OrP WaS

Knittel, John.
Therese Etienne, Roman. 271 S.8. Berlin, Büchergilde Gutenberg, 1932.

NK 0205083 PPG

Knittel, John, 1891-
Thérèse Etienne; roman. Traduit par Marie Mirande. Bruxelles, Librairie de Belgique [c.1942]

NK 0205084 MH

Knittel, John, 1891-
... Thérèse Étienne, roman, traduit de l'allemand par Marie Mirande. Paris, A. Michel [1942]
2 p. l., [7]-444 p., 1 l. 20cm.

I. Mirande, Marie, tr. II. Title. [Full name: John Herman Emanuel Knittel] 46-41869
Library of Congress PT2621.N6T53
[2] [833.91] 823.91

NK 0205085 DLC NN IU CU

Knittel, John, 1891-
Therese Etienne, roman. [6. aufl.] Zürich, Füssli [1945]
460 p.

NK 0205086 NNC

Knittel, John, 1891-
... Therese, regény. Budapest, Bárd Ferenc és fia [1941]
523 p. 21cm. (Half-title: A szép írások. 9. köt.)
"Bálint György fordítása."

I. Bálint, György, tr. II. Title. Translation of Therese Etienne. [Full name: John Herman Emanuel Knittel] 46-32253
Library of Congress PT2621.N6T54

NK 0205087 DLC

Knittel, John.
A traveller in the night, by John Knittel ... London, T. F. Unwin, ltd. [1924]
512 p. 19½cm.

I. Title.
Library of Congress PZ3.K755Tr 24-31792

NK 0205088 DLC

Knittel, John, 1891-
... Via Mala, roman. Berlin, Buchmeister-verlag [c1934]
3 p. l., 9-817, [1] p. 19½cm.
Published also in English.

I. Title. [Full name: John Herman Emanuel Knittel] 35-6229
Library of Congress PT2621.N6V5 1934
Copyright A—Foreign 27233
[2] 833.91

NK 0205089 DLC PPG

Knittel, John, 1891-
... Via Mala. London, Hutchinson & co., ltd. [1934]
576 p. 19½cm.
At head of title: By John Knittel.

I. Title. [Full name: John Herman Emanuel Knittel] 34-23467
Library of Congress PZ3.K755Vi

NK 0205090 DLC

VOLUME 300

Knittel, John, 1891-
... Via Mala. Roman. Zürich, Orell Füssli [c1934]
816 p. 19 cm.
"101.-106. Tausend."

NK 0205091 CtY

Knittel, John, 1891-
Via Mala, a novel, by John Knittel. New York, Frederick A. Stokes company, 1935.
5 p. l., 667 p. 21½cm.

I. Title.
[Full name: John Herman Emanuel Knittel]
Library of Congress PZ3.K755Vi 2 34-39937

OO OCIh OLak OCl MB
NK 0205092 DLC OU LU WaSp WaE NcU WU OClW OU OEac

Knittel, John, 1891-
Via mala. 1938.
Translated by L.J. Wirski.
Polish.

NK 0205093 OCl

Knittel, John, 1891-
Via Mala, roman. Zürich, Füssli [1944]
686 p.
I. Title.

NK 0205094 NNC

PT2621 .N6V5 Knittel, John, 1891-
Via Mala, roman. Hamburg, W. Krüger [1949]
693 p. 21cm.

NK 0205095 OCU

Knittel, John, 1891-
Via Mala, Roman. Hamburg, W. Krüger [c1951]
693 p. 21 cm.

NK 0205096 OOxM

833G K749V KNITTEL, John.
Via Mala; Roman.
Hamburg. W. Krüger. 1952. 693p.

NK 0205097 WaS

Knittel, John, 1891-
Via Mala; volkstümliches Drama aus dem Bündnerland, in vier Akten, von John Knittel. Zürich [etc.] Orell Füssli [1937]
93 p. 20cm.

1. Drama, English. I. Title.
N. Y. P. L. April 23, 1940

NK 0205098 NN

Knittel, John.
Der Weg durch die Nacht[; übertragen von Paul Baudisch].
Zürich: Orell Füssli[, cop. 1927]. 537 p. 12°.

NK 0205099 NN

Knittel, John.
... Der weg durch die nacht, roman. Zürich [etc.] Orell Füssli [1927]
566 p. 19½cm.
"Übertragen von Paul Baudisch. Die englische originalausgabe dieses romans ist unter dem titel 'A traveller in the night' erschienen."

I. Baudisch, Paul, 1899- tr. II. Title.
Library of Congress PR6021.N45T75 1927 27-20486

NK 0205100 DLC OCl

Knittel, John, 1891-
... Der weg durch die nacht, roman. Zürich-Leipzig, Orell Füssli [1937]
544, [1] p. 19½ cm.
"Die englische ausgabe dieses romans erschien unter dem titel 'A traveller in the night' im verlag T. Fisher Unwin ltd., London. Übertragen von Paul Baudisch."
"Vierte auflage (9.-13. tausend)"

I. Baudisch, Paul, 1899- tr. II. Title.
[Full name: John Herman Emanuel Knittel]
PR6021.N45T75 1940 A F 47-6256
Yale univ. Library for Library of Congress [1]†

NK 0205101 CtY DLC

Knittel, John, 1891-
Der weg durch die nacht, roman [übertragen von Paul Baudisch. 6. aufl.] Zürich, Füssli [1946]
544 p.
I. Baudisch, Paul, 1889- tr. II. Title.

NK 0205102 NNC

Knittel, John Herman Emanuel
SEE
Knittel, John, 1891-

Knittel, Karl.
Ueber das Gedächtsnis ostafrikanischer Neger. Von Karl Knittel... Langensalza: H. Beyer & Söhne, 1924. 30 p. 8°. (Paedagogisches Magazin. Heft 962.)
Bibliography, p. 30.

1. African tribes, Africa (East). 2. Psychology of peoples, African tribes. 3. Memory. 4. Series.
N. Y. P. L. October 14, 1924

NK 0205104 NN

KNITTEL, Michel.
Ueber sporadische psychische ansteckung.
Strassburg, 1884.

NK 0205105 MBCo DNLM ICRL

Knittel, Otto
Wie arbeitet eine Kollektivwirtschaft in der Sowjetunion? Vortrag gehalten am 1.April 1953 im Haus der Kultur der Sowjetunion Berlin. Berlin, Verlag Kultur und Fortschritt, 1953
28 p. (Vorträge im Haus der Kultur der Sowjetunion Berlin, 5)

NK 0205106 MH

Knittel, Richard, 1902-
Untersuchungen über den verschleiss von hochwertigem grauguss und legiertem grauguss unter berücksichtigung der an kolben und zylinder von verbrennungsmotoren gestellten anforderungen ... Düsseldorf, 1933.
Stuttgart diss. 1933

NK 0205107 MiU

914.3 K749a Knittel, Walter O
Allemagne: heure zéro. Paris, Nouvelles Presses Mondiales [c1955]
222 p. plates (part fold.) map. (Collection "Documents du monde.")

1. Germany - Social life and customs. 2. Germany - Politics and government, 1945- I. Title.

NK 0205108 WaU NN

Knittelfeld (Austria). Gemeinderat.
Bericht des Gemeinderates der Stadt Knittelfeld über dessen Tätigkeit.

[Knittelfeld, 8°.

1. Municipal government—Austria—Knittelfeld.
N. Y. P. L. January 12, 1926

NK 0205109 NN

Knittelmair, Lambert, 1769-1845.
[Variations. (Aline, Marche)]
Variations pour le piano-forte à quatre mains sur la marche favorite de l'opéra Aline, composées... par Lampert Knittelmair. Munic, Falter et fils [1817?] 19 p. 23 x 33cm.
For piano, 4 hands.

274262B. 1. Piano, 4 hands.
N. Y. P. L. January 31, 1946

NK 0205110 NN

Knitter, Bernhard, 1870-
Casuistische beitraege zur lehre von der extrautern-schwangerschaft.
Inaug. diss. Wuerzburg, 1902
Bibl.

NK 0205111 ICRL DNLM

Knitter, Ernst: Beziehungen zwischen den klimatischen Faktoren und dem Pflanzenbau in Schlesien. [Maschinenschrift.] 94 S. m. Tab. 4°. — Auszug: Breslau (1925): Hochschulverl. 3 Bl. 8°
Breslau, Phil. Diss. v. 25. Juli 1925 [U 25. 1105

NK 0205112 ICRL

Knitter, Kurt, 1890- Studienassessor: Zur Differentialgeometrie der Fläche-Strahlen-Verbindungen. [In Maschinenschrift.] x, 51 S. 4°(2°). — Auszug in: Inaug.-Dissertationen d. phil. Fak. Königsberg i. P. 1920. o. O. S. 64—67. 8°
Königsberg, Phil. Diss. v. 6. Dez. 1920 [1921], Ref. Meyer
[Geb. 10. Dez. 90 Schubin; Wohnort: Marggrabowa; Staatsangeh.: Preußen; Vorbildung: G. Bromberg Reife 10; Studium: Königsberg 8 S.; Rig. 27. Juli 20.]
[U 21. 7151

NK 0205113 ICRL

TT679 .K6x The KNITTER.
v. 1- 1937-
Charlotte, N. C., Clark Publishing Co.
v. illus. monthly.

NK 0205114 GAT AAP NN

Knittermeyer, Hinrich, 1891-1958.
Bremen; Lebenskreis einer Hansestadt herausgegeben von H.Knittermeyer und D.Steilen. Bremen, A.Geist, 1940.
397 p. illus. 25 cm.

NK 0205115 MH

VOLUME 300

943.52 Knittermeyer, Hinrich, 1891- ed.
K74b Bremen. Lebenskreis einer Hansestadt. Hrsg.
1941 von H. Knittermeyer und D. Steilen. 2. Aufl.
Bremen, A. Geist, 1941.
397p. illus., 124 plates., ports., maps. 25cm.

"Schrifttum": at the end of each chapter.

1. Bremen--Hist. 2. Bremen--Descr. I. Steilen, Diedrich, joint ed.

NK 0205116 IU OU

Knittermeyer, Hinrich, 1891- *ed.*
Bremen, Lebenskreis einer Hansestadt, hrsg. von H. Knittermeyer und D. Steilen. 3., durchgesehene Aufl. Bremen, NS. Gauverlag Weser-Ems, 1942.
397 p. illus., plates, maps. 25 cm.

1. Bremen. I. Steilen, Diedrich, joint ed.
DD901.B74K6 1942 943.525 52-57612

NK 0205117 DLC ICU

Nn29 Knittermeyer, Hinrich, 1891-1958.
1 Erweckung der Universität, von H. Knittermeyer. Berlin, H. Schüller im Auftrage der
1919K Freien Hochschulgemeinde [1919]
11 p. 22 cm. (Der Aufbau; Flugblätter an Jugend, 6)

NK 0205118 CtY

B2855 Knittermeyer, Hinrich, 1891- ed.
.K6
Schelling, Friedrich Wilhelm Joseph von, 1775-1854.
Gedanken von Schelling. Berlin-Zürich, Atlantis verlag [1942]

Knittermeyer, Hinrich, 1891-
Grenzen des Staates. Berlin, E. Runge, 1932.
64 p. 20 cm. (Gegenwart; deutsche Zeit- und Streitschriften, 3)

1. Church and state in Germany. I. Title. (Series)
BR853.K58 51-52211

NK 0205120 DLC

Knittermeyer, Hinrich, 1891-
... Immanuel Kant; vorlesungen zur einführung in die kritische philosophie, von Hinrich Knittermeyer. Bremen, A. Geist, 1939.
160 p. 23½cm. (Abhandlungen und vorträge, hrsg. von der Bremer wissenschaftlichen gesellschaft, bd. 12, hft. 4)
On p. [2] of cover: Schriften der Bremer wissenschaftlichen gesellschaft. Reihe D: Abhandlungen und vorträge.

1. Kant, Immanuel, 1724-1804.
A 42-3751
New York. Public library for Library of Congress [AS182.B75 bd. 12] [2] (082)

NK 0205121 NN MH TxU CU

Knittermeyer, Hinrich, 1891-
Jacob Burckhardt; Deutung und Berufung des abendländischen Menschen. Stuttgart, S. Hirzel, 1949.
292 p. 21 cm. (Welt und Genius)

1. Burckhardt, Jakob Christoph, 1818-1897.
D15.B8K6 1949a 928.3 51-31342 rev

NK 0205122 DLC NcD CLSU NcU NIC

Knittermeyer, Hinrich, 1891-
Jacob Burckhardt; Deutung und Berufung des abendländischen Menschen. Zürich, S. Hirzel, 1949.
292 p. 21 cm.

1. Burckhardt, Jakob Christoph, 1818-1897.
D15.B8K6 928.3 50-27703

NK 0205123 DLC OCU CU NNC InU NN IU MH NSyU NBuU N

Knittermeyer, Hinrich, 1891-
Metaphysik und wissenschaft, von dr. Hinrich Knittermeyer ... Vortrag, gehalten bei der gründungssitzung der Bremer wissenschaftlichen gesellschaft am 14. 2. 1925.
(*In* Bremer wissenschaftliche gesellschaft. Schriften. Reihe D: Abhandlungen und vorträge. Bremen, 1926. 25cm. jahrg. 1, hft. 1, p. [9]-26)

1. Metaphysics. 2. Philosophy—History.
A C 30-2213
Columbia univ. Librar. for Library of Congress [AS182.B75 jahrg. 1, hft. 1] [2] (082)

NK 0205124 NNC DLC

B819
.K58
Knittermeyer, Hinrich, 1891-
Die Philosophie der Existenz von der Renaissance bis zur Gegenwart. Wien, Humboldt Verlag [°1952]
504 p. 18 cm. (Sammlung Die Universität, Bd. 29)
Includes bibliographies.

1. Existentialism.
A 54-4082
Harvard Univ. Library for Library of Congress [3]

PSt ICMcC
NK 0205125 MH NjPT NBC IU NjP NN NIC VtMiM DLC NcD

KNITTERMEYER, HINRICH, 1891-
Philosophie der Lebensalter. Oldenburg, G. Stalling, 1944. 96 p. 21cm. (Bremen. Wittheit. Abhandlungen und Vorträge. Reihe D. Sonderheft)

1. Aged--Philosophical and inspirational works. I. Bremen. Wittheit. Abhandlungen und Vorträge. Reihe D. Sonderheft.

NK 0205126 NN MH

Knittermeyer, Hinrich, 1891-
... Die philosophie und das Christentum; acht vorlesungen zur einleitung in die philosophie. 1. und 2. tausend. Jena, E. Diederichs, 1927.
1 p. l., 141, [1] p. 22cm.
CONTENTS.—Die philosophie und das Christentum.—Griechischer und christlicher logos.—Die totalität und der geist des idealismus.—Kant und die kritik.—Spruch und widerspruch.—Die kritik des systems und der wissenschaft.—Von der kritik zur reflexion.—Von der reflexion zur antwort.

1. Philosophy and religion. 2. Christianity. 28-22587
Library of Congress BL51.K6

NK 0205127 DLC MH-AH

Knittermeyer, Hinrich, 1891-
Schelling und die romantische schule, von Hinrich Knittermeyer ... mit einem bildnis Schellings. München, E. Reinhardt, 1929.
481, [1] p. front. (port.) 20cm. (Geschichte der philosophie in einzeldarstellungen. abt. VII. Die philosophie der neueren zeit I. bd. 30/31)
"Bibliographischer wegweiser": p. 459-462.

1. Schelling, Friedrich Wilhelm Joseph von, 1775-1854. 2. Philosophy, German. 3. Romanticism—Germany.
33-6748
Library of Congress B2899.R6K6 [193.4] 921.3

ODW NBC OrU PPT FU ICRL NIC CLSU
NK 0205128 DLC NN CU MH NcD PBm PU OC1W OC1 OCU

Knittermeyer, Hinrich: [1891-] Der Terminus transszendental in seiner historischen Entwickelung bis zu Kant. Marburg 1920: Hamel. 213 S. 8°
Marburg, Phil. Diss. v. 3. Dez. 1918 [1920], Ref. Natorp
[Geb. 20. Febr. 91 Hamburg; Wohnort: Hamburg; Staatsangeh.: Preußen; Vorbildung: RG. d. Johanneums Hamburg Reife 09; Studium: Jena 2, Heidelberg 1, Marburg 8 S.; Rig. 5. Okt. 14.] [U 20. 3784

NK 0205129 ICRL PU MH CtY

Knittermeyer, Hinrich, 1891- ed.

Färber, Johann Michael, 1778-1844.
... Unbekannte briefe und urkunden aus dem Goethekreis. Aus dem nachlass Johann Michael Färbers, herausgegeben von Hinrich Knittermeyer. [Bremen] Arthur Geist verlag (vormals G. Winters buchhandlung, Fr. Quelle nachf.) [1935]

DD61 Knittermeyer, Hinrich, 1891-
.3
.W55 **Wittig, Hans,** 1910-
Volkstum und Technik [von] Hans Wittig. Tecknik und Wissenschaft [von] Hinrich Knittermeyer. Bremen, NS-Gauverlag Weser-Ems, 1942.

Knittermeyer, Hinrich, 1891-
Von Wesen und Wirklichkeit des Krieges. Bremen, NS.-Gauverlag Weser-Ems, 1942.
64 p. 24 cm. ([Bremen] Wittheit zu Bremen. [Einzelschriften] Heft 1)

1. War. (Series)
U21.K54 355 A F 47-4039 rev*
Minnesota. Univ. Libr. for Library of Congress [r50d1]†

NK 0205132 MnU CtY NN DLC

Knittermeyer, Hinrich, 1891-
Von Wesen und Wirklichkeit des Krieges. 2. durchgesehene Aufl. Bremen, NS. Gauverlag Weser-Ems, 1943.
66 p. 24 cm. ([Bremen] Wittheit zu Bremen [Einzelschriften] Heft 1)

1. War. I. Title.
U21.K54 1943 55-45689 ‡

NK 0205133 DLC

The knitter's note book
see under
Corbould, Elvina M.

Knitterscheid, A.
Ein neues supplement zum Problem des Apollonius. n.p., 1863.

NK 0205135 NjP

Knitterscheid, A
Sagen aus dem Schwarzwalde. Saarbrücken, Druck von Gebrüder Hofer, 1881.
53p.

In verse.

NK 0205136 OC1

Knitterscheid, Erich: Die Voraussetzungen für die Haftung der Eisenbahn nach dem (sog.) Reichshaftpflichtgesetz. [Maschinenschrift.] IV, 105 S. 4°. — Auszug: Kirchhain 1922: Schröder. 8 S. 8° Marburg, Jur. Diss. v. 27. Febr. 1922 [U 22. 7756

NK 0205137 ICRL

VOLUME 300

TT820
.K695 Knitting ... [New York city, Lab publishing company, c1935-
v. illus. 26cm.

Cover-title.

1. Knitting.

NK 0205138 DLC

Knitting and crochet. With hints for beginners. London: Aldine Pub. Co., Ltd. [1915.] 2 p.l., (1)8–96 p. illus. 12°. (Aldine handy series. no. 1.)

Contains advertisements.

1. Knitting and crocheting. 2. Series.
N. Y. P. L. August 30, 1915.

NK 0205139 NN

Knitting for the army
see under Gt. Brit. Directorate of Voluntary organizations.

Knitting for young America
see under Institute for Hand Knitting.

Knitting industry
see Knitting industry weekly.

TT679
.K65
Knitting industry weekly.

New York [Howes Pub. Co.]
Apply for vol. desired
v. in illus., ports. 31 cm.

Issued daily during the Knitting Arts Exhibition in Apr. or May each year, 19 -41.

Began publication with Apr. 28, 1923 issue. Cf. Union list of serials.

Title varies: -Aug. 30, 1948, Knit goods weekly.—Sept. 6, 1948- Hosiery industry weekly.

Vols. 41-56, no. 4 include section: Hosiery merchandising, later published separately.

1. Knit goods—Period. 2. Hosiery—Period.

TT679.K65 687.305 55-16754 rev

NK 0205143 DLC NcU NN DFT NcRS

Knitting Machine Pattern Service.
[How to knit by machine. [Seattle, Wash., n. d.]
32 p. illus.

NK 0205144 Wa

TT679 **Knitting mill news.**
K84 v.1- 1923-
Tex. Philadelphia, Knitting Mill News and Knitting
Lib. Trades Service Bureau, Inc., 1923-
v. illus. 28cm.

1. Knit goods - Periodicals

NK 0205145 NcRS NN

Knitting Mill News and Knitting Trades Service Bureau.
Knitting mill news
see under title

Knitting mill supply directory.
New York, Howes Pub. Co.
v. illus. 29 cm. annual.

1. Knit goods industry—Direct.

TT695.K55 63-59146

NK 0205147 DLC

Knitting, netting, and crotchet work. A winter gift for ladies ... Containing the newest and most fashionable patterns. From the latest London ed. Rev. and enl. by an American lady. New York, Burgess and Stringer, 1844.

1 p. l., [v]-x, [11]-65 p. 16½cm.

1. Knitting. 2. Netting. 3. Crocheting.

8-28129†

Library of Congress TT820.K69

NK 0205148 DLC

Knitting, netting and crotchet work. A winter gift for ladies ... containing the newest and most fashionable patterns. From the latest London ed. Rev. and enl. by an American lady. Philadelphia, G. B. Zieber & co., 1847.

1 p. l., [v]-x, [11]-65 p. 15cm.

1. Knitting. 2. Netting. 3. Crocheting.

22-5267

Library of Congress TT820.K7 1847

NK 0205149 DLC

Knitting, netting, and crotchet work. A winter gift for ladies ...containing the newest and most fashionable patterns. From the latest London ed. Rev. and enl. by an American lady. Philadelphia, G. B. Zieber & co., 1848. x, 11–65 p. 15cm.

1. Knitting and crocheting. I. An American lady.
N. Y. P. L. August 11, 1949

NK 0205150 NN

Knitting times
see Knitted outerwear times.

Knitting times buyers' guide directory.
[New York]
v. 22 cm. annual.

Continues Knitted outerwear times buyers' guide directory.
Official publication of the National Knitted Outerwear Association.

1. Knit goods industry—United States—Directories. I. National Knitted Outerwear Association.

TT695.K53 338.4'7'67702824 72-627060

NK 0205152 DLC

The KNITTING trade directory.
19

Manchester: J. Heywood Ltd. [19 16cm.
v.

19 directory issued.

1. Knit goods—Directories—Gt.Br.

NK 0205153 NN

Knittl, Vladimír.
...Zdeněk Fibich. Populární životopisný a kriticky nastin. V Praze, F. A. Urbánek [191-] 64 p. illus. 17cm. (Knihovna "Smetany". c. 12.)

"Chronologický přehled veškerých prací Fibichových," p. 52–64.

1. Fibich, Zdeněk, 1850–1900.
N. Y. P. L. June 30, 1944

NK 0205154 NN

Knittle, Jessie Mahn.
The circus train, verses; illus. by Dorcas. Racine, Wis., Whitman Pub. Co., °1948.

[32] p. col. illus. 17 cm. (Tell-a-tale books, 890)

I. Title.

PZ8.3.K75Ci 49-4086 rev

NK 0205155 DLC OO

Knittle, Jessie Mahn.

PZ7
.G1795
Tr
Garfield, Robert, *pseud.*
Train stories, by Robert Garfield [pseud.] and Jessie Knittle. Pictures by Tibor Gergely. New York, Simon and Schuster [1949]

Knittle, Jessie Mahn.
The truck that stopped at Village Small, verses. Illus. by Dorcas. Racine, Wis., Whitman Pub. Co., °1951.

[32] p. col. illus. 17 cm. (Tell-a-tale books, 813)

I. Title.

PZ8.3.K75Tr 51-25621

NK 0205157 DLC

R748
K71
Knittle, Rhea (Mansfield) 1883-

Early American glass. Garden City Pub. Co. [c1927]
496 p. plates.

1.Glassware. 2.Glass manufacture. I.Title.

NK 0205158 OrP

Knittle, Rhea (Mansfield) 1883–
Early American glass, by Rhea Mansfield Knittle. New York, London, The Century co. [°1927]

xxiii, 496 p. front., illus. (facsims.) plates. 21½cm. (*On cover:* Century library of American antiques)

Bibliography: p. 449–453.

1. Glassware—U. S. 2. Glass manufacture—U. S. I. Title.

27—24362

Library of Congress NK5112.K6

Wa NCorniC KEmT NcC NIC FMU OO
NN MWA PU-Mus PP PPFr PPD WaS Or IdB WaSp OrP OrPR
NK 0205159 DLC WaE NcD OCl OOxM MiU OClW OLak ICJ MB

Knittle, Rhea Mansfield.
Early American glass, by Rhea Mansfield Knittle. New York, London, The Century co. [1929]

xxiii, 496 p. front., plates. 21cm. (Century library of American antiques)

"First printing November, 1927; second printing, August, 1929."
Bibliography: p. 449–453.

1. Glassware—U. S. 2. Glass manufacture—U. S. I. Title.

33—18310

Library of Congress NK5112.K6 1929
[40d1] 748

NK 0205160 DLC

VOLUME 300

Knittle, Rhea Mansfield.
Early American glass, by Rhea Mansfield Knittle, New York, Century, 1934.
496 p.

NK 0205161 NcRS

8173
.04-108 Knittle, Rhea (Mansfield) 1883-
Early American glass. New York, Appleton-Century, 1937 c1927
xxiii, 496 p. illus., plates. 22 cm.
(Century library of American antiques)

1. Glassware—U. S. 2. Glass manufacture—U. S. I. Title.

NK 0205162 MB OU

Knittle, Rhea Mansfield.
Early American glass, by Rhea Mansfield Knittle. New York, Appleton-Century, 1939 [c27]
xxiii, 496 p. front., illus. (facsims.) plates. 21.5 cm. (On cover: Century library of American antiques)
Bibliography: p. 449-453.

NK 0205163 CaBVaU CaBVa

Knittle, Rhea (Mansfield) 1883–
Early American glass. Garden City, N. Y., Garden City Pub. Co. [1948, °1927]
xxii, 496 p. plates. 23 cm.

1. Glassware—U. S. 2. Glass manufacture—U. S. I. Title.

NK5112.K6 1948 748 48-10807*

NK 0205164 DLC MB ICN ViU

Knittle, Rhea (Mansfield) 1883–
Early Ohio silversmiths and pewterers, 1787–1847 [by] Rhea Mansfield Knittle ... [Cleveland, Printed by the Calvert-Hatch co., 1943]
1 p. l., 5–63 p. illus. 23cm. (The Ohio frontier series, 1787–1847)
"A check-list of early Ohio silversmiths": p. 24–40. "A check-list of early Ohio pewterers and makers of britannia ware": p. 57–62.
Bibliography: p. 63.

1. Silversmithing—Ohio. 2. Pewter.

43-10754

Library of Congress NK7112.K6
[3] 739.23

PPHi PPPM
NK 0205165 DLC WaS OrP MB OOxM OCl OClWHi OU PP PPD

Knittle, Rhea (Mansfield) 1883–
Early Ohio taverns; tavern-sign, barge, banner, chair and settee painters [by] Rhea Mansfield Knittle ... [Ashland, O., Priv. print., °1937]
39, [1] p. 22½cm. (On cover: The Ohio frontier series ... no. 1)
"Errata" slip inserted.
"Suggested supplementary reading": p. [40]

1. Hotels, taverns, etc.—Ohio. 2. Art industries and trade—Ohio. 3. Ohio—Biog. I. Title.

38-11591

Library of Congress F495.K65
[a46f1] 917.71

OClMA OCl OOxM OClWHi OU
NK 0205166 DLC ODW MH NNC OO WaS OFH PP CtY OClW

Knittle, Rhea(Mansfield) 1883 -
The Ohio frontier series, 1767-1847. no. 1-
[Portland, Me., Southworth-Anthoenses press, 1937-

Privately printed and limited to 2000 numbered copies each.

NK 0205167 OCl OO

Knittle, Walter Allen, 1905–
The early eighteenth century Palatine emigration; a British government redemptioner project to manufacture naval stores ... [by] Walter Allen Knittle. Philadelphia, 1936.
xix, [1] p., 1 l., 320 p. front., illus. (incl. ports., maps, facsims.) 23cm.
Thesis (PH. D.)—University of Pennsylvania, 1931.
Published also without thesis note.
Bibliography: p. [229]–241.

1. Palatines. 2. Palatines in New York (State) 3. New York (State)—Hist.—Colonial period. 4. Gt. Brit.—Colonies—Emig. & immig. 5. Naval stores. I. Title.

37-16677

Library of Congress F130.P2K59
Univ. of Pennsylvania Libr.
——— Copy 2. [3] 325.24309747

OO MiU MB OOxM ViU
NK 0205168 PU PHC PSC DLC WaTC CU Vi NcU PBm OU OCl

Knittle, Walter Allen, 1905–
Early eighteenth century Palatine emigration; a British government redemptioner project to manufacture naval stores, by Walter Allen Knittle ... with a foreword by Dixon Ryan Fox. Philadelphia, Dorrance & company [°1937]
xix, [1] p., 1 l., 320 p. front. (port.) illus. 23½cm.
Issued also as thesis (PH. D.) University of Pennsylvania.
Bibliography: p. [229]–241; bibliographical foot-notes.

1. Palatines. 2. Palatines in New York (State) 3. New York (State)—Hist.—Colonial period. 4. Gt. Brit.—Colonies—Emig. & immig. 5. Naval stores. I. Title.

37—522

Library of Congress F130.P2K6
——— Copy 2.
Copyright A 102167 [a40w3] 325.2430974

PCC OU OClW ViU MB
NK 0205169 DLC IdU OrU WaWW OrPR WaS MtU NcD PHi PPT

Kniva, A
see
Knyva, A

Knivet, Anthony, *fl.* 1591.
Aanmerklyke reys ... van Antoni Knivet, uyt Engelland na de Zuyd-Zee, met Thomas Candish, gedaan anno 1591 en in de volgende jaren. Nu aldereerst uyt het Engelsch vertaald ... Leyden, P. vander Aa, 1706.
(*In* Aa, Pieter van der. De aanmerkenswaardigste en alomberoemde zee- en landreizen. Leyden [1727?] 37cm. [v. 5, no. 10] 1 p. l., 42 col., [1] p. illus.)
Title vignette.

1. Pacific Ocean. I. Cavendish, Thomas, 1555?–1592.

CA 8–1744 Unrev'd

Library of Congress G160.A14 vol. 5

NK 0205171 DLC CU-B TU PU

Knivet, Anthony, *fl. 1591.*
Admirable adventures and strange fortunes...
(In Purchas, Samuel. Pilgrimes. London, 1625 34 1/2 cm. v. 4, p. 1201-1242)

G159
.P98

NK 0205172 DLC OCl

Knivet, Anthony, *fl.* 1591.
Anthony Knivet in Kongo and Angola: being extracts from The admirable adventures and strange fortunes of Master Antonie Knivet, which went with Master Thomas Candish in his second voyage to the South Sea, 1591, published in Purchas his pilgrimes, part IV, lib. VI, c. 7. London, 1625. (*In* Ravenstein, E[rnest] G., ed. The strange adventures of Andrew Battell. London, 1901. 23cm. p. [89]–101)

2-7588

NK 0205173 DLC MB

G918.1
So85d KNIVET, ANTHONY, fl. 1591.
Narração da viagem que, nos annos de 1591 e seguintes, fez Antonio Knivet da Inglaterra ao Mar do Sul, em companhia de Thomaz Candish; traducção do hollandez pelo dr. José Hygino Duarte Pereira ... Rio de Janeiro, Typographia e lithographia de Pinheiro & c., 1879.
2p.ℓ.,90p. 21½cm. [With Sousa, Pedro Lopes de. Diario da navegacão da armada. Lisboa, 1839]
"Extrahida do 2.º trimestre do tomo XLI da Revista do Instituto historico geographico e etnographico do Brasil."

1. Brazil - Descr. & trav. 2. Cavendish, Thomas, 1555?-1592. I. Duarte Pereira, José Hygino, 1847- tr.

NK 0205175 TxU

Knivet, Anthony, fl. 1591.

Battel, Andrew, *fl.* 1589.
The strange adventures of Andrew Battell of Leigh, in Angola and the adjoining regions. Reprinted from "Purchas his Pilgrimes". Ed., with note and a concise History of Kongo and Angola, by E. G. Ravenstein. London, Printed for the Hakluyt society, 1901.

fG160
H27
v.1
x Knivet, Anthorny, fl. 1591.
The strange Adventures of Anthony Knivet, (who went out with Admiral Candish in his last Expedition) amongst the Portuguese and Indians; together with his Travels thro' those parts, and the account of the People, their Customs, and the Products of their Countries.
(In Harris, John. Navigantium atque Itinerantium Bibliotheca ...London, 1705. 40cm. v.1, p. 698-710)

1. West Indies - Description and travel.

NK 0205177 CU-B

Knivet, Anthony, *fl.* 1591.
Vária fortuna e estranhos fados de Anthony Knivet, que foi com Tomás Cavendish, em sua segunda viagem, para o Mar do Sul, no ano de 1591. Versão do original inglês por Guiomar de Carvalho Franco. Com anotações e referências de Francisco de Assis Carvalho Franco. São Paulo, Editora Brasiliense, 1947.
187 p. 22 cm. (Coleção "A Conquista da terra," v. 5)
Translation of The admirable adventures and strange fortunes of Master Antonie Knivet, which went with Master Thomas Candish in his second voyage to the South Sea, 1591; an extract from the 1625 London edition of Hakluytus posthumus, or Purchas his pilgrimes ... by Samuel Purchas (v. 4, p. 1201-1242)
1. Voyages and travels. I. Title. (Series)

G460.K55 1947 52-15235

NK 0205178 DLC LNHT NIC TxU

Knivett, Thomas
see Knyvett, Thomas, 1596–1658.

8A
392 KNÍŽE, FRANTIŠEK MAX, 1784-1840.
[Missa pastoralis, D; Pastoral-Messe in D...Nachgelassenes Werk... Prag, J. Hoffmann, [18--]
16 parts. 35cm.

Pl.no. 496.
Parts for SATB, 2 violins, viola, violoncello, double-bass, organ, flute, 2 horns, 2 trumpets, and timpani.

NK 0205180 ICN

Gft66
y4
K74 Kníže, Rudolf
... Posouzeni slohu Thukydidova ... Smíchov, 1908.
Pamphlet
Programm - Reálný a vyšší gymnasium, Smíchov.

NK 0205181 CtY

VOLUME 300

Knížek, B
Sociologie družstevního hnutí. Předml. opatřil Fr. Modráček. V Praze, Orbis, 1929.
70 p. 20 cm. (Politická knihovna. Řada I, kn. 18)

1. Cooperation. I. Title.

HD2961.K56 59-58872 ‡

NK 0205182 DLC

[**Knizek's Kunstverlag.**]
Wien. [Dresden: Jacobi & Zobel, 187-?] folder of 24 pl. obl. 48°.
Cover-title: Wien.

1. Vienna—Views. 2. Title.
N. Y. P. L. June 13, 1928

NK 0205183 NN

Kniżetstvi Opavské
see **Opava** (*Duchy*)

Kniževnik
see Knjizevnik.

PQ4675
.K6
Rare Bk. Coll.

Книжка, содержащая въ себѣ разныя любовныя повѣсти. Переведена съ италіанскаго языка. Въ Санктпетербургѣ, Напечатана при Морскомъ шляхетномъ кадетскомъ корпусѣ, 1774.
161 p. 17 cm.
Bound with Любовь Палиріа и Дирфіи. Въ Санктпетербургѣ, 1774.

Title transliterated: Knizhka, soderzhashchaiã v sebiê raznyiã liũbovnyiã poviêsti.

PQ4675.K6 55-49181

NK 0205186 DLC

AP50
.K6
Книжки Недѣли.
С.-Петербургъ.
v. in 21-24 cm. monthly.
Published 1878-1901? Cf. Union list of serials.
Title varies: 1878-1884, Журналъ романовъ и повѣстей.

I. Nedfelîâ. Supplement. *Title transliterated:* Knizhki Nedfelî.

AP50.K6 51-28292

NK 0205187 DLC MH PNsT

Z3413
.K3K6
Книжная летопись; орган государственной библиографии Казахской ССР.
Алма-Ата, Казахское гос. изд-во.
v. 22 cm.
Began publication in 1937. Cf. Летопись периодических изданий СССР, 1950-1954, № 2090.
Issued by Knizhnaiâ palata Kazakhskoĭ SSR.
Kazakh and Russian; title in Kazakh precedes title in Russian.

1. Kazakh literature—Bibl.—Period. 3. Kazakh literature—Translations from Russian. 3. Russian literature — Translations into Kazakh. I. Knizhnaiâ palata Kazakhskoĭ SSR.
Title transliterated: Knizhnaiâ letopis'.

Z3413.K3K6 59-36468

NK 0205188 DLC

Книжная летопись; орган государственной библиографии СССР. г. 1- 14 июля 1907-
Москва.
v. in 22-27 cm.
Frequency varies.
Supersedes Списокъ книгъ, вышедшихъ въ Россіи.
Organ of Glavnoe upravlenie po delam pechati, 1907-17, no. 26 (Osobaiâ komissiiâ po likvidatšii Glavnogo upravleniiâ po delam pechati, 1917, no. 9-26); of Rossiĭskaiâ knizhnaiâ palata (called in 1917, no. 27-1919, no. 17, Knizhnaiâ palata) 1917, no. 27-1920, no. 32; of Gosudarstvennaiâ tšentral'naiâ knizhnaiâ palata RSFSR (called in 1920, no. 33-1925, no. 18, Rossiĭskaiâ tšentral'naiâ knizhnaiâ palata; 1925, no. 19-1927, no. 14, Gosudarstvennaiâ tšentral'naiâ knizhnaiâ palata) 1920, no. 33-1935; of Vsesoiûznaiâ knizhnaiâ palata, 1936-
Issued 1907-17, no. 8, as Книжная лѣтопись. Subtitle added since 1929.
Published in Leningrad (Petrograd-S. Peterburg), 1907-20, no. 32.
~~Vol. 5, no. 50; v. 7, no. 11-12, 45-49; v. 33, no. 29-34, 40-52; v. 39, no. 40-52 are photostatic copies; v. 36, no. 1-12, 19, 20-21, 23-24; v. 39, no. 16, 34-35, 38; v. 40, no. 30-32; v. 41, no. 1-22, microfilm copies.~~
Some volumes are accompanied by separately numbered supplements.
Indexes for 1917, 1927-30, 1933, 1939 and 1940, each bound separately.
Vols. for 1907- reprinted 1964- by Kraus Reprint Ltd., Vaduz.

——— Microfilm copies of v. 35, no. 1-27, 29-50; v. 36, no. 1-12, 18, 20-21, 23-24 (positive); v. 37, no. 6-9 (negative), 15-24; v. 38, no. 31-34, 40-52; v. 39, no. 1-12 (positive), 3-4, 9 (negative), 14-15 (positive), 16, 24-27, 29, 34-35, 38, 40-52; v. 40, no. 1-25, 27-32; v. 41, no. 1-22 (negative).
Microfilm Z27

1. Russian literature—Bibl. I. Russia. Glavnoe upravlenie po delam pechati. II. Rossiĭskaiâ knizhnaiâ palata, Leningrad. III. Gosudarstvennaiâ tšentral'naiâ knizhnaiâ palata RSFSR. IV. Vsesoiûznaiâ knizhnaiâ palata. *Title transliterated:* Knizhnaiâ letopis'.

Z2491.K5 51-30521

CU-Riv NcD FU FTaSU MoSW MH MiU CtY
NK 0205191 DLC MBCo AzU CoBBS OrU CU OU ScU CaOTU

Knizhnaiâ palata, *Leningrad*
see **Rossiĭskaiâ knizhnaiâ palata,** *Leningrad.*

Z2514
.A85E9
Knizhnaiâ palata Azerbaĭdzhanskoĭ SSR.
Ежегодник книги Азербайджана.
Баку.

Z2514
.A85L4
Knizhnaiâ palata Azerbaĭdzhanskoĭ SSR.
Летопись печати Азербайджана.
Баку.

Z2514
.W5L4
Knizhnaiâ palata BSSR.
Летапіс друку БССР. Летопись печати БССР. 1925-
Мінск.

Z6956
.W4P4
Knizhnaia palata BSSR.
Перыядычны друк БССР; сістэматычны паказнік часопісаў і газет. 1933/34-
Менск.

Knizhnaiâ palata Ėstonskoĭ SSR
see
Tallinn. Friedrich Reinhold Kreutzwaldi nimeline Eesti NSV Riiklik Raamatukogu. *Raamatupalat.*

Knizhnaiâ palata Gruzinskoĭ SSR
see **Gosudarstvennaiâ knizhnaiâ palata Gruzinskoĭ SSR.**

Z3413
.K3K6
Knizhnaiâ palata Kazakhskoĭ SSR.
Книжная летопись; орган государственной библиографии Казахской ССР.
Алма-Ата, Казахское гос. изд-во.

Knizhnaiâ palata Litovskoĭ SSR
see
Lietuvos TSR Knygų rūmai.

Knizhnaia palata RSFSR
see Gosudarstvennaia tsentral'naia knizhnaia palata. RSFSR.

Z3413
.T3L4
Knizhnaiâ palata Tadzhikskoĭ SSR.
Летопись печати Таджикской ССР.
Душанбе.

Knizhnaiâ palata Ukrainskoĭ SSR
see
Knyzhkova palata Ukraïns'koï SSR.

Z278
.K53
Книжная торговля; пособие для работников книжного дела. Под ред. М. В. Муратова и Н. Н. Накорякова. Москва, Гос. изд-во, 1925.
479 p. 26 cm.

1. Booksellers and bookselling. I. Muratov, Mikhail Vasil'evich, 1892-1957, ed. II. Nakoriâkov, Nikolaĭ Nikandrovich, 1881- ed.
Title romanized: Knizhnaiâ torgovliâ.

Z278K53 77-244100

NK 0205204 DLC

Knizhnik, Grigoriĭ, *pseud.*
see **Gennadi, Grigoriĭ Nikolaevich,** 1826-1880.

~~.R9K58~~
Knizhnik, Ivan Sergeevich, 1878-
Новая Россія и евреи; книжка религіозно-историческая для солдатъ, рабочихъ и крестьянъ и для духовенства всѣхъ религій. Петроградъ, Кн-во "Народъ и Богъ," 1917.
46 p. 19 cm.
At head of title: Андрей Кратовъ (И. С. Книжникъ)

1. Jews in Russia. I. Title.
Title transliterated: Novaiâ Rossiiâ i evrei.

DS135.R9K58 53-50330

NK 0205206 DLC

Knizhnik, Ivan Sergieevich, 1878-
... Систематический указатель литературы по общественным наукам. Коммунистическая и марксистская литература 1917-1922 г. г. ... Петроград, Рабочее кооперативное издательство "Прибой", 1923.
206 p. 20cm.
At head of title: Ив. Книжник.
Cover-title: Что читать по общественным наукам.

1. Social sciences—Bibl. 2. Russia—Hist.—Revolution, 1917- —Bibl. 3. Russia—Econ. condit.—1918- —Bibl. I. Title: Что читать по общественным наукам.

30-5986
Library of Congress Z7161.K72

NK 0205207 DLC

VOLUME 300

Knizhnik, Izrail' Samoĭlovich
see **Knizhnik, Ivan Sergeevich,** 1878–

Knizhnik-Vetrov, Ivan Sergeevich, *pseud.*
see
Knizhnik, Ivan Sergeevich, 1878–

Книжное дѣло. Съ нѣмецкаго переработано АКС. С.-Петербургъ, Изд. Н. О. Строчилова, 1904–
v. 24 cm.
Contents.—т. 1. Книжный торговецъ; теорія, практика, отчетность.

1. Booksellers and bookselling—Handbooks, manuals, etc. I. A. K. S. II. S., A. K.
Title romanized: Knizhnoe dfelo.

Z283.K6 70–267118

NK 0205210 DLC

Knizhnye magaziny M. O. Vol'f, *Leningrad and Moscow*
see **Tovarishchestvo M. O. Vol'f,** *Leningrad.*

Книжные знаки русских художников. ₍Под редакцией Д. И. Митрохина, П. И. Нерадовского и А. К. Соколовского₎ Петербург ₍Издательство₎ "Петрополис", 1922.
238, ₍1₎ p. incl. front., plates (part col.) 27ᶜᵐ.
"Настоящее издание отпечатано в количестве пятисот экземпляров нумерованных I–L и 1–450... Экземпляр nº 303.".
"Обложка, фронтиспис и книжные украшения работы Д. И. Митрохина."
Contents.—Нерадовский, П. И. Книжные знаки русских художников.—Соколовский, А. Материалы для словаря русских художников работавших над книжными знаками.
1. Book-plates, Russian. I. Mitrokhin, Dmitriĭ Isidorovich, 1883– ed. II. Neradovskiĭ, Petr Ivanovich, 1875– joint ed. III. Sokolovskiĭ, A. K., joint ed.
28–22353
Library of Congress Z994.R8K7

NK 0205212 DLC

Knizhnyĭ magazin B. Posta. Biblioteka dli͡a chtenii͡a.
Catalogue français de la Librairie B. Post à Moscou. Moscou, Impr. Barnett & Piggott, 1880.
95 p. 21 cm.
Bound with its Каталогъ русскихъ книгъ. Москва, 1881.
At head of title: Bibliothéque française, russe, allemande et anglaise.

I. Title.
Z939.K66A6 16–23313
rev ₍r71b2₎

NK 0205213 DLC

Knizhnyĭ magazin B. Posta. Biblioteka dli͡a chtenii͡a.
Kata g der Deutschen Leihbibliothek der Buchhandlung von B. Post in Moskau. Moskau, Buchdr. von E. Liessner, 1886.
100 p. 21 cm.
Bound with its Каталогъ русскихъ книгъ. Москва, 1881.
At head of title: Leihbibliothek in deutscher, russischer, französischer und englischer Sprache.

I. Title.
Z939.K66A6 16–23312
rev ₍r71b2₎

NK 0205214 DLC

Knizhnyĭ magazin B. Posta. Biblioteka dli͡a chtenii͡a.
Каталогъ русскихъ книгъ Библіотеки для чтенія Книжнаго магазина Б. Поста. Москва, Тип. А. Клейнъ, 1881.
278 p. 21 cm.
At head of title: Библіотека русская, нѣмецкая, французская и англійская.
Bound with its Catalogue français. Moscou, 1880, and its Katalog der Deutschen Leihbibliothek. Moskau, 1886.

I. Title.
Title romanized: Katalog russkikh knig.
Z939.K66A6 16–23304

NK 0205215 DLC

Knizhnyĭ magazin M. M. Lederle
see **Lederle, M. M.,** *firm, Leningrad.*

Knizhnyĭ magazin Nikolai͡a I͡Akovlevicha Ogloblina, *Kiev*
see **Ogloblin, N. I͡A.,** *firm, Kiev.*

Knizhnyĭ magazin "Novago vremeni" A. S. Suvorina, *Leningrad*
see **Suvorin, A. S.,** *firm, Leningrad.*

Knizhnyĭ magazin S. Skirmunta "Trud"
see
Trud, Knizhnyĭ magazin.

Knizhnyĭ magazin Sokrata Isakova.

Z939
.C452

Cherkesov, *firm, Leningrad.*
Каталогъ Библіотеки Черкесова и Книжнаго магазина Сократа Исакова. С.-Петербургъ, 1884.

Knizhnyĭ magazin Torgovago doma "M. P'i͡ankov s brat'i͡ami," *Khabarovsk*
see
P'i͡ankov (M.) s brat'i͡ami, *Khabarovsk.*

Knižka, Jan, *z Tulechova*
see
Kodycyllus, Jan, *z Tulechova,* 1557–1585.

Knižka, Petr, *z Tulechova*
see
Kodycyllus, Petr, *z Tulechova,* 1533–1589.

PG
5038
.S7
Z52

Knížka o Šrámkovi. K básnikovým padesátinám uspořadalo Sdružení studujicich sobotec kých ₍za spolupráce Josefa Knapa₎ Praha, Nakl. Fr. Borový, 1927.
162 p. 20cm.

1. Šramek, Fraňa, 1877-1952. I. Sdružení studujicich sobotec kých.

NK 0205224 NNC

Knižka rytmovní; w kterej jest vyložene klesnuti a padnuti duchovniho Babylona skrz obnoveni cirkve, ze skušenosti a z Pisma svateho gruntovne vynaleznuta, všem vericim krestanum naboženstvi evangelickeho se pridržejicim uprimne predložena. Básnická skladba neznámeho autora v odpise z r. 1751. Z rukopisu pre vydanie upravil... Jan Mišianik. Zredigovala redakčná rada: Karol Rosenbaum et al.] Bratislava, Nakl. Slovenskej akadémie vied a umeni, 1952. 113 p.

facsims. 21cm. (Pamiatky starsej literatúry slovenskej. sv. 1)

"...uložená v rukopisnom oddelení univerzitnej knižnice v Budapešti pod sign. A 134."

1. Poetry, Slovak. I. Misianik, Ján, ed. II. Budapest. Tudomány-egyetem. Könyvtár. Mss. (A 134). III. Series.

NK 0205226 NN CtY

Knižní novinky, 1935-1947
see under Prague. Městská knihovna.

Knižní velkoobchod, Prague.

B301
.E3

Ediční plán českých nakladatelství.
₍Praha₎

097.05
KN

Knižní značka. 1- 1937-
Praha.
v. illus., plates. 22cm.

Suspended publication Apr. 1942-1945.
Issued by Spolek sběratelů a přátel exlibris v Praze.

NK 0205229 IU

Knižnica; časopis pre knižnú kultúru. roč. 1–
1949–
V Martine, Matica slovenská ₍etc.₎
v. in illus. 24 cm. irregular.
Vols. 1–2 called also v. 5–6, continuing the vol. numbering of Slovenská národná knižnica, which it supersedes.
Tables of contents also in English and Russian.
Subtitle varies slightly.

1. Library science—Period. 2. Libraries—Slovakia. I. Matica slovenská, Turčiansky sv. Martin.
Z671.K58 59–31822

NK 0205230 DLC CaOTU MiU CLU NNC MiU NN IU

Knižnica marxizmu-leninizmu. 1–
Bratislava, Pravda, 1949–
no. in v. illus. 20 cm. irregular.

1. Communism—Collections.
HX15.K6 59–28269

NK 0205231 DLC

Knižnica "Prúdov."
Sväzok 1

Bratislave, 1925– 8°.
nos.

Contents:
Sväzok 1. Osusky, S. George D. Herron... 1925.

NK 0205232 NN MH

Knižnica Slováka. Bratislava, Slovák

NK 0205233 MH

Knižnica Slovenskej Univerzity, *Bratislava*
see **Bratislava. Univerzita.** *Knižnica.*

TA145
K59

Knižnica stavebného priemyslu.
Bratislava, Vydavateľstvo ROH.
v. illus. 21 cm.

1. Civil engineering — Collected works. 2. Building — Collected works.
TA145.K59 61–40902

NK 0205235 DLC

VOLUME 300

T4
.K6
Knižnice časopisu SIA. sv. 1–
Praha, 1948–
v. 30 cm.

1. Engineering—Period.
T4.K6 51-22144

NK 0205236 DLC

Knižnice Československá. Plaček

NK 0205237 MH

Knižnice československych amatérů vysilačů
see under Českoslovenští amatéři
vysilači, Prague.

AC60
.K55
Knižnice československých listů.
Moskva, Vydavatelství cizojazyčné lit-ry
v. illus. 17 cm.

AC60.K55 52-28692

NK 0205239 DLC

HE5601
.K55
Knižnice dopravní bezpečnosti.
[Praha, Naše vojsko]
no. col. illus. 18 cm.

1. Traffic safety—Periodicals.
HE5601.K55 72-622211

NK 0205240 DLC

TS843
.K62
Knižnice dřevařského průmyslu.
Praha, Průmyslové vydavatelství,
v. illus. 21 cm.

1. Woodworking industries.
TS843.K62 56-34695

NK 0205241 DLC

HD2951
.K5
Knižnice Družstevní zeměpis.
Praha [Svépomoc]
no. 22 cm.
No. Issued by Ústřední rada družstev.

1. Cooperation—Periodicals. I. Ústřední rada družstev, Prague.
II. Title: Družstevní zeměpis.
HD2951.K5 72-622215

NK 0205242 DLC

ML160
K7
Knižnice Hudebních rozhledů. roč. 1-
Praha, 1955-
v. in illus., ports., music. 21 cm.
Issued by Svaz československých skladatelů.

I. Svaz československých skladatelů.
ML160.K7 58-28659

NK 0205243 DLC

Knižnice Lyra. V Praze, B.Stýblo

NK 0205244 MH

Knižnice Ministerstva průmyslu. Příručky pro průmysl a řemeslo. Praha, Čin

NK 0205245 MH

KNIŽNICE národních umělců československých.
Praha.

Some volumes are numbered.
Issued by the Ministerstvo informací (later by the Státní nakladatelství krásné literatury, hudby a umění).
Editor: František Rachlík.
x Rachlík, František, ed. x Czechoslovakia. Ministerstvo informací.
x Czechoslovakia. Státní nakladatelství krásné literatury, hudby a umeni.

NK 0205246 NN

Knižnice posluchače rozhlasu. Praha, Nákl. Českého rozhlasu

NK 0205247 MH

W 1
KN626
KNIŽNICE pracovního lékařství.
V Praze, Československá společnost pracovního lékařství [1946?]-
v. illus.
1. Industrial medicine - Collected works
I. Československá společnost pracovního lékařství v Praze

NK 0205248 DNLM

Knižnice pracujícího člověka. Praha, Československá sociální demokracie

NK 0205249 MH

19.5
K744
Knižnice pro DŠP a ZŠP: zemědělské aktuality.
Praha, Ministerstvo zemědělství a lesního hospodářství,

1. Czechoslovak Republic. Agriculture
I. Czechoslovak Republic. Ministerstvo zemědělství a lesního hospodářství.

NK 0205250 DNAL

Knižnice pro mládež Sad. V Praze, Státní nakl.

NK 0205251 MH

HA37
C92K5
Knižnice SÚS: Směrnice a pokyny.
V Praze, Státní úřad statistický.
v. in 21 cm.
"Pro úřední potřebu."

1. Czechoslovak Republic—Stat. I. Czechoslovak Republic. Státní úřad Statistický. II. Title: Směrnice a pokyny.
HA37.C92K5 64-51036

NK 0205252 DLC

HV13
K55
Kniznice sociální revue. sv. 1-
Praha, 1946-
no. in v. illus.

Issued by Ministerstvo sociální péče.

NK 0205253 CU

Knižnice Sokolských besed. Praha

NK 0205254 MH

TH4
K6
Knižnice stavebního průmyslu.
Praha, Průmyslove vydavatelství, 19
no. illus. 20 cm.

1. Building—Period. 2. Architecture—Period.
TH4.K6 64-46475

NK 0205255 DLC

Knižnice Um. Brno

NK 0205256 MH

DB785
.U7K5
Knižnice Ústecka.
[V Ústí, Krajské nakl.]
v. illus., ports. 30 cm.
Editor: 19 J. Malý.

1. Ústí nad Labem, Czechoslovak Republic (Region) I. Malý, Jaroslav.
DB785.U7K5 60-43128
Library of Congress [8]

NK 0205257 DLC

891.8
K74
Knižnice z dávných věků.
1-
Brno, 1947-
v. illus., plates, maps (part fold.)
25cm.

Issued by Ústav pro prehistorii a protohistorii při Masarykově universitě v Brně and Moravský archeologický klub v Brně.
Summaries in Russian and English.
Editor: 1- Emanuel Šimek.

NK 0205258 NNC

Knižnice zahraničního obchoru. Praha

NK 0205259 MH

VOLUME 300

KNIŽNIČNÝ sborník.
Martin, Matica slovenská. v. illus., tables.
25cm.

1. Libraries--Per. and soc. publ. I. Matica slovenská, Turčiansky Sv. Martin.

NK 0205260 NN

Knjasew, W.
See
Knyazev, Vasiliĭ Vasil'yevich.

Knjiga; glasilo slovenskih založb.
[V Ljubljani, Cankarjeva založba, etc.]
v. illus., ports. 20 cm. monthly.
Began publication in 1953.

1. Slovenian literature—Bibl.—Period.

Z2957.S6K6 59-52153

NK 0205262 DLC InU MiU OU

Knjiga o Titu
see under [Bevk, France] 1890-

TX145
K65
Knjiga za svaku ženu; uzorna domaćica. [Urednik Drago Chloupek] Zagreb, Seljačka sloga, 1952.
479 p. illus. (part col.)

1. Home economics - Yugoslavia. I. Chloupek, Drago, ed.

NK 0205264 CU

CROATIAN
640
C45k
Knjiga za svaku ženu; uzorna domaćica.
4. prošireno izdanje. Zagreb, Seljačka sloga, 1955.
511 [1] p. illus.

NK 0205265 MiD OCl

657.05
KNJ
Knjigovoda. god. 1- 1955-
Zagreb, Savez knjigovoda Hrvatske.
v. 29cm.

"Casopis za računovodstveno-financijske kadrove."

NK 0205266 IU

Knjižarnica Rajkovića i Čukovića, *Belgrad*
see **Rajković i Čukovic,** *firm, publishers, Belgrad.*

Z443
A1K6
Knjižarski priručnik. 1953-
Zagreb, Tehnička knjiga.
v. 20 cm. annual.

1. Book industries and trade—Yugoslavia—Direct. 2. Yugoslav literature—Bibl.—Catalogs.

Z443.A1K6 57-36313

NK 0205268 DLC

Književna republika . . .
God 1-
Zagreb, 1923- 8°.
v. illus., plates.

Monthly.
Dec., 1923 incorrectly called Nov., 1923.
God 2 repeated in numbering.
Editor : Nov., 1923- Miroslav Krleža.

AP95 . C8 K8

1. Periodicals—Croatian.
N. Y. P. L. January 19, 1926

NK 0205269 NN MH NNC IU PNsT DLC

AP56
K614
Књижевне новине. г. 1- 14 јан. 1954-
Београд.
v. illus., ports. 47 cm. weekly.
Issued by Udruženje književnika Srbije.
In Serbian.

I. Udruženje književnika Srbije.
Title transliterated: Književne novine.

AP56.K614 60-35112

NK 0205270 DLC MiU IU

Književne novine; list za književnost, umetnosti i društvena pitanja. g. 1- 17 febr. 1948-
Beograd [Kultura]
v. in illus., ports. 52-64 cm.
Frequency varies.
Vols. 6- called Nova serija.
Subtitle varies.
Organ of Savez književnika Jugoslavije.
Publication suspended Oct. 1953-Feb. 7, 1955.
In Croatian.
Vol. 2, no. 48-49 incorrectly numbered 47-48; v. 3-5 called also no. 1-66; v. 6- new series, no. 1-
I. Savez književnika Jugoslavije.

AP56.K615 60-34756 rev

NK 0205271 DLC TxU CSt MB PSt

Hag10
K749
Književni horizonti; zagrebačka književna revija. God. 1- velj. 1934-
Zagreb.
v. illus., ports. 24 cm. monthly.

Cover title.

1. Croatian literature - Periodicals, etc.

NK 0205272 CtY MH

PG 1400
K6
KNJIZEVNI jug. knj. 1-4, 1918-19.
Zagreb.
v. illus. 27 cm. monthly.

1. Croatian literature - Period.

NK 0205273 CaBVaU CtY MiU NN ICU

Književni vjesnik; bibliografski list.
Tecaj
Zagreb, 19 8°.
v.

Monthly (irregular).
Editor : 19 Vlad. Prestini.

1. Bibliography—Per. and soc. publ.
N. Y. P. L. October 15, 1924

NK 0205274 NN MH

AP56
K54
Književnik; časopis za jezik i poviest hrvatsku i srbsku, i prirodne znanosti. Uredjuju i izdaju (podporom Matice ilirske) Fr. Rački, V. Jagić, J. Torbar. U Zagrebu, 1864-66.
3 v. illus.

No more published.

NK 0205275 CU IU CaBVaU CU NN ICU

Književnik; hrvatski književni mjesečnik.
Zagreb.
v. illus., ports., maps. 23 cm.
Began publication in 1928.
Editor: 19 M. Durman.

I. Durman, Milan, ed.

AP56.K623 58-50026

NK 0205276 DLC CSt MiU PNsT InU CaBVaU

AP
56
K63
Књижевност.
g.
Београд.
v. in illus., ports. 24 cm. monthly.
Began publication in 1946.
Vol. 1- called also book 1-
Title varies: 19 -June 1947, Наша књижевност.

Title transliterated: Književnost.

AP56.K63 52-21488

NK 0205277 DLC CaBVaU CSt ICU MH CU NNC InU KU NjP

Knjižnica Naša gruda. [Zagreb, Naša gruda]

NK 0205278 MH

Knjižnica Osvit, *Madrid*
see
Osvit, Knjižnica, *Madrid.*

Knjižnica za Klasičnu starinu . . .
see under Matice hrvatska, Zagreb.

Knjižnica za vzgojo kadrov v gozdarstvu in lesni industriji.
zv. 1-
Ljubljana, Založba lista "Les," 1950-
no. illus. 24 cm.
Issued by Ministerstvo za lesno industrijo LRS.

1. Woodworking industries—Collected works. I. Slovenia (Federated Republic, 1945-). Ministerstvo za lesno industrijo.

TS800.K57 72-622209

NK 0205281 DLC

Књижничар. г. 1- (бр. 1-) јан./март 1952-
Нови Сад.
v. in illus., ports. 24 cm. irregular.
Issued by the Bibliotečki centar NR Srbije and other institutes.

1. Library science—Period. 2. Libraries—Serbia—Period. I. Belgrad. Bibliotečki centar NR Srbije. *Title transliterated:* Knjižničar.

Z671.K593 61-48562

NK 0205282 DLC

Knob, John Joseph, 1898-
Summary of the law of evidence. By John J. Knob ... [Long Beach, N. Y., 1936]
2 p. l., 2-57 numb. l. 30cm.
Loose-leaf; mimeographed.

1. Evidence (Law)—New York (State) I. Title.
CA 36-320 Unrev'd
Library of Congress

NK 0205283 DLC

VOLUME 300

Knob, John Joseph, 1898–
Summary of the New York law of pleading and practice. By John J. Knob ... [Long Beach, N. Y., 1936]
2 p. l., 2–81 numb. l. 30cm.
Loose-leaf; mimeographed.

1. Pleading—New York (State) I. Title.
CA 36-319 Unrev'd
Library of Congress

NK 0205284 DLC

Lilly PR 3991 .K6
Knob-stick; or, The assassin actor: an entirely new-novel, theatric-al, physic-al, catholic-al, curr-ical, salter-ical, vandoff-ical and serior-ical, tragedy, in one act ... Manchester, Printed by T. Wilkinson, 1822.
23 p. 19.5 cm.

First edition.
Bound in quarter red morocco.

NK 0205285 InU

---

ar X 1456
Knobbe, Albert, 1874-
Die Faust-idee in Lord Byrons Dichtungen. Stralsund, 1906.
19 p. 26cm.

Separate from "Programm No. 192" (Ostern) --Realgymnasium, Stralsund.

1. Byron, George Gordon Noël Byron, 6th baron, 1788- 1824. 2. Faust.

NK 0205286 NIC CU MH NcD NjP

Knobbe, Albert, 1874–
Über die mittelenglische dichtung Le bone Florence of Rome ... von Albert Knobbe ... Marburg i. H., 1899.
3 p. l., 59, [1] p. 21½cm.
Inaug.-diss.—Marburg.
Lebenslauf.

1. Le bone Florence of Rome.
[Full name: Wilhelm Albert Knobbe]
G-2405 Revised
Library of Congress PR2065.B6K5

NK 0205287 DLC NjP MiU CtY PBm OCl MH PU

Knobbe, Albert, 1874-
Untersuchung des Denkmals
see Florence de Rome.
Le bone Florence of Rome. [pt. 2]

Knobbe, Berthold.
... Ueber die einwirkung menschlicher und rindertuberkelbazillen auf das euter der ziege, ein beitrag zur frage der beziehungen zwischen der tuberkulose des menschen und der tiere ... Lehrte, Druck von O. Hoffmann, 1909.
44 p. 22cm.
Inaug.-diss.—Bern.
"Literatur": p. 43-44.

1. Goats. Diseases. 2. Tubercul-is. 3. Udder. Diseases.
Agr 10-581
Library, U. S. Dept. of Agriculture 41K

NK 0205289 DNAL DNLM PU ICJ

Knobbe (Joachimus Henricus). *De circulatione sanguinis in fœtu maturo, novis observationibus anatomicis exaratæ. 3 p. l., 111 pp., 4 pl. 4°. *Bonnæ, typ. C. Georgii,* [1834].

NK 0205290 DNLM

Knobbe, Robert. Ueber die knospen unserer holzgewächse. [Königsberg. 1846.] 8°.
Königsberger naturwissenschaftliche unterhaltungen. 1846, i, 229–243.

NK 0205291 MH-A

Knobbe, Robert.
... Das Weizenkorn und seine Keimung ... Königsberg, Universitäts-Buch- und Steindruckerei von E. J. Dalkowski, 1871.
p. 1-17. 25cm. bound 29cm.
At head of title: ... Abhandlung des G.-L. Dr. Knobbe.
Programm — Kneiphöfisches Stadt-Gymnasium zu Königsberg i. Pr.

NK 0205292 ICJ

Knobbe, Wilhelm Albert
SEE
Knobbe, Albert, 1874-

... **Knobcone** pine. *Pinus attenuata.* [Washington, Govt. print. off.] 1908.
2 p. 23cm. (U. S. Dept. of agriculture. Forest service. Silvical leaflet 36)

1. Knobcone pine.
Agr 9-823
Library, U. S. Dept. of Agriculture

NK 0205294 DNAL

Knobe, Damaris.
The ancestry of Grafton Johnson, with its four branches: the Johnson, the Holman, the Keen, the Morris; the history and genealogy of paternal progenitors, as confined to the United States, of the second Grafton Johnson of Greenwood, Indiana, great-great-grandson of the first Isaac Johnson, who reverts to the middle of the eighteenth century in Virginia, by Damaris Knobe ... [Indianapolis, Hollenbeck press, °1924]
xx p., 1 l., 384 p. front., plates, ports., facsims. 25cm.
1. Johnson family (Isaac Johnson, fl. 1748) 2. Holman family (Isaac Holeman, d. 1808) 3. Keen family (Dudley Keen, fl. 1787) 4. Morris family (John Morris, fl. 1753) 5. Johnson, Grafton, 1864- I. Title.
25-18792
Library of Congress CS71.J7 1924

NK 0205295 DLC MWA OClWHi

Knobel, August Wilhelm, 1807-1863.
Die bücher Exodus und Leviticus. Erklärt von August Knobel ... Leipzig, S. Hirzel, 1857.
xxiv p., 1 l., 591, [1] p. 21½cm. [Added t.-p.: Kurzgefasstes exegetisches handbuch zum Alten Testament. 12. lfg.]
Added t.-p. wanting.

1. Bible. O.T. Exodus—Commentaries. 2. Bible. O.T. Leviticus—Commentaries. 3. Bible—Commentaries—O.T. Exodus. 4. Bible—Commentaries—O.T. Leviticus. I. Ser.

NK 0205296 ViU NcD MH NNUT CtY PU PPLT OCH NN CU DCU

Knobel, August Wilhelm, 1807-1863.
Die bücher Exodus und Leviticus
see also under Dillman, August, 1823-1894.

Knobel, August Wilhelm, 1807–1863.
Die Bücher Numeri, Deuteronomium und Josua; erklärt von Dr. August Knobel ... Nebst einer Kritik des Pentateuch und Josua. Leipzig: S. Hirzel, 1861. xvi, 606 p. 22cm. (Added t.-p.: Kurzgefasstes exegetisches Handbuch zum Alten Testament. Lief. 13.)

997849A. 1. Bible. O. T. Numbers—Commentaries. 2. Bible. O. T. Deuteronomy—Commentaries. 3. Bible. O. T. Joshua—Commentaries.
N. Y. P. L.
Card revised June 15, 1942

NK 0205298 NN CU NNUT NcD OCH OO OClW CtY OU PU PPLT MH-AH IU NcD NjPT IEG DCU

Knobel, August Wilhelm, 1807-1863.
Die Bücher Numeri, Deuteronomium, und Josua
see also under Dillman, August, 1823-1894.

KNOBEL, August Wilhelm.
Commentar über das Buch Koheleth.
Leipzig. Barth. 1836. viii, (4), 372 pp. 8°.

NK 0205300 MB NjPT CtY OCH PU PPLT NjNbS NNUT MB IEN

Knobel, August Wilhelm, 1807-1863.
De carminis Jobi argumento et fine. Vratislaviae, 1825.

NK 0205301 IEN

BS3585 .K7
Knobel, August Wilhelm, 1807–1863.
De Evangelii Marci ... origine dissertatio ... Vratislaviae, typis Kupferianis [1831]
[3], 58 p. 19½cm.
Inaug.-diss.—Breslau.

1. Bible. N. T. Mark—Criticism, interpretation, etc.

NK 0205302 ICU IEN MH

BS 1154 .K96 v.1
Knobel, August, d. 1863.
Die Genesis, erklärt. Leipzig, Weidmann'sche Buchhandlung, 1852.
xxii, 349 p. 23 cm. (Kurzgefasstes exegetisches Handbuch zum Alten Testament, 11. Lfg.)

Bibliographical references interspersed.

1. Bible. O.T. Genesis - Commentaries.

NK 0205303 DCU OCH NNUT MH-AH CtY MoSCS

BS 1235 K6 1860
Knobel, August Wilhelm, 1807-1863.
Die Genesis. Erklärt von August Knobel. 2. verb. Aufl. Leipzig, S. Hirzel, 1860.
xxvi, 382 p. 22 cm. (Kurzgefasstes exegetisches Handbuch zum Alten Testament, 11. Lfg.)

Bound with the author's Die Bücher Exodus und Leviticus, Leipzig, 1857.

1. Bible. O. T. Genesis - Commentaries.

NK 0205304 OU CU CtY OCH ODW NNUT NNC PPEB PPT

BS1154 .K83 lfg. 11 c
Knobel, August Wilhelm, 1807-1863.
Dillmann, August, 1823–1894.
Die Genesis. Erklärt von dr. August Dillmann ... 4. aufl. Leipzig, S. Hirzel, 1882.

Knobel, August Wilhelm, 1807-1863.
Jeremias chaldaizans. Vratislaviae, 1831.

NK 0205306 IEN

Knobel, August Wilhelm, 1807–1863.
Der Prophet Jesaia. Erklärt von August Knobel ... Leipzig: Weidmann'sche Buchhandlung, 1843. xxxii, 444 p. 22cm. (Added t.-p.: Kurzgefasstes exegetisches Handbuch zum Alten Testament. Lief. 5.)

1. Bible. O. T. Isaiah—Commentaries.
N. Y. P. L.
Card revised June 12, 1942

NK 0205307 NN CtY PU CU MH-AH TxDaM-P NjPT

VOLUME 300

Knobel, August Wilhelm, 1807-1863.
Der prophet Jesaia. Erklärt von August Knobel ... 2. verb. aufl. Leipzig, S. Hirzel, 1854.
xxiv, 467, [1] p. 21½cm. (Added t.-p.: Kurzgefasstes exegetisches handbuch zum Alten Testament...5. lfg.)
With Hitzig, Ferdinand. Das Hohe Lied ... Leipzig, 1855.

1. Bible. O.T. Isaiah—Commentaries. 2. Bible—Commentaries—O.T. Isaiah I. Ser.

NK 0205308 ViU DCU MH-AH PPLT PU RPB OCH

BS 1515 K56 1861
Knobel, August
Der Prophet Jesaia. Erklärt von August Knobel. 3. verb. Aufl. Leipzig, S. Hirzel, 1861.
xxiv, 471p. 23cm. (His Kurzgefasstes exegetisches Handbuch zum Alten Testament, Lfg. 5)

1. Bible. O.T. Isaiah--Commentaries. I. Title.

NK 0205309 UU OCH DLC-P4

BS 1515 .K72 1872
Knobel, August, Wilhelm, 1807-
Der Prophet Jesaia erklärt. 4. Aufl. hrsg. von Ludwig Diestel. Leipzig, S. Herzel, 1872.
xxviii, 519 p. 23 cm. (Kurzgefasstes exegetisches Handbuch zum Alten Testament, 5.Lfg.)

Bibliography: p. ix.

1. Bible. O.T. Isaias - Commentaries. I. Diestel, Ludwign, 1825-1879, ed.

NK 0205310 DCU ODW PU OClW OO NcD PPGratz

Knobel, August Wilhelm, 1807-1863.

Dillmann, August, 1823-1894.
Der prophet Jesaia; für die fünfte auflage erklärt von dr. August Dillmann ... Leipzig, S. Hirzel, 1890.

Knobel, August Wilhelm, 1807-1863.
Der Prophetismus der Hebräer vollständig dargestellt, von August Knobel ... Breslau: J. Max und Komp, 1837. 2 v. in 1. 21½cm.

341695. 1. Prophecy, Biblical. 2. Bible. O. T.—Prophets.
N. Y. P. L. Card revised October 23, 1942

CU CtY ICN TxDaM
NK 0205312 NN NcD PPDrop PPGratz PPLT OCH NjPT

BS661 .K72
KNOBEL, AUGUST WILHELM, 1807-1863.
Die völkertafel der Genesis. Ethnographische untersuchungen von August Knobel... Giessen, J. Ricker, 1850.
xii, 359, [1]p. 22cm.
Bibliographical foot-notes.

1. Bible--Ethnology.

NjPT
NK 0205313 ICU TxDaM NIC PPAN OCH PU PPPD MdBP IEG

Knobel, August [Wilhelm] 1807-1863.
Zur geschichte der Semaritaner. n. p., n. p., 1846.
p. 129-172. 8°.
Bound with Cowley, A[rthur Ernest] 1861-
Samaritan doctrine of the Messiah. 1895.

NK 0205314 PU

Knobel, Betty.
Dänische Reisebriefe. Illustrationen von Werner Lauper. Zürich, Schweizer Spiegel Verlag [1952]
56 p. illus. 19 cm.

1. Denmark—Description and travel. I. Title.
DL118.W4 52-36462 ‡

NK 0205315 DLC MnU

4DA 250
Knobel, Bruno
Das grosse Abenteuer, Lord Baden-Powells; sein Leben und Werk. Zürich, Polygraphischer Verlag [c1954]
244 p.

NK 0205316 DLC-P4 NN

WA 10226
Knobel, Bruno.
Horoskopiere dich glücklich! Die zwölf Bilder des Tierkreises und ihr unleugbarer Einfluss auf die Menschen. Zürich, Diogenes Verlag[1955]
45p. illus.

NK 0205317 CtY

Knobel, Bruno.
Wie ein Film entsteht. Bern, Hallwag [1955]
95 p. illus. 15 cm. (Hallwag-Taschenbücher, 46)

1. Moving-pictures. 2. Moving-pictures—Production and direction. I. Title.
A 56-2790
Southern Calif., Univ. of. Library
for Library of Congress [$\frac{1}{2}$]

NK 0205318 CLSU

Knobel, Edmund Wilhelm, 1889-
Soil survey, Akron area, Colorado, by E. W. Knobel [and others. Washington, 1947]
80 p. plates, maps (1 fold. in pocket) tables (1 fold. in pocket) 24 cm. (U. S. Bureau of Plant Industry, Soils, and Agricultural Engineering. [Soil survey report] ser. 1938, no. 14)
Cover title.
"In cooperation with the Colorado Agricultural Experiment Station."
"Literature cited": p. 80.
1. Soil-surveys—Colorado. I. Colorado. Agricultural Experiment Station, Fort Collins. (Series)
[S591.A22 1938, no. 14] (631.470973) Agr 48-95*

U. S. Dept. of Agr. Libr. 1So32F 1938, no. 14
for Library of Congress [5*]

NK 0205319 DNAL

Knobel, Edmund Wilhelm, 1889- joint author.

Phillips, Samuel William, 1894-1933.
... Soil survey, Dooly county, Georgia, by S. W. Phillips ... and E. W. Knobel, G. L. Fuller, and J. W. Moon ... Washington, U. S. Govt. print. off., 1928.

Knobel, Edmund Wilhelm, 1889-
Soil survey, Grand Junction area, Colorado [by E. W. Knobel, R. K. Dansdill and M. L. Richardson. Washington, U. S. Govt. Print. Off.] 1955.
118 p. illus., maps (4 fold. col. in portfolio) 25 cm. (U. S. Soil Conservation Service. Soil survey, ser. 1940, no. 19)
Cover title.
"Literature cited": p. 118.

1. Soil-surveys—Colorado. (Series)
[S591.A22 1940, no. 19] Agr 55-349

U. S. Dept. of Agr. Libr. 1So32F 1940 no. 19
for Library of Congress [3*]

NK 0205321 DNAL

Knobel, Edmund Wilhelm, 1889- joint author.

Taylor, Arthur Elijah, 1877-
... Soil survey, Lake county, Florida, by Arthur E. Taylor ... E. W. Knobel, S. W. Phillips, E. H. Bailey, H. M. Smith ... and Emory J. Close ... Washington, U. S. Govt. print. off., 1928.

Knobel, Edmund Wilhelm, 1889-
... Soil survey of Cass county, North Dakota, by E. W. Knobel ... and M. F. Peightal and J. E. Chapman ... Pt. 2. The chemical composition of the soils of Cass county, by T. H. Hopper and H. L. Walster ... Washington [U. S. Govt. print. off., 1929]
cover-title, 80 p. 4 pl. on 2 l., 3 maps (2 fold.) diagr. 23½cm. (U. S. Bureau of chemistry and soils. Soil survey report, series 1924, no. 29)
At head of title: United States Department of agriculture. Bureau of chemistry and soils. In cooperation with the North Dakota Agricultural experiment station.
1. Soil-surveys. 2. Soils—North Dakota. I. Chapman, James Everett, 1887- joint author. II. Hopper, Turner Harcourt, 1894- III. Peightal, M. F., joint author. IV. Walster, Harlow Leslie, 1883- joint author.
Agr 29-1731 Revised
U. S. Dept. of agr. Library 1So32F 1924, no. 29
for Library of Congress [S591.A22 1924, no. 29]
[r38d2]

NK 0205323 DNAL DLC WaWW

Knobel, Edmund Wilhelm, 1889-
... Soil survey of Chattahoochee county, Georgia, by E. W. Knobel ... J. W. Moon, S. W. Phillips, and A. T. Sweet. Washington, U. S. Govt. print. off., 1928.
iii, 97-124 p. 2 maps (1 fold.) 23½cm. (U. S. Bureau of chemistry and soils. Soil survey report, series 1924, no. 4)

At head of title: United States Department of agriculture. Bureau of chemistry and soils. In cooperation with the Georgia State college of agriculture.

1. Soil-surveys. 2. Soils—Georgia. I. Moon, Joseph Worley, 1891- joint author. II. Phillips, Samuel William, 1894-1933, joint author. III. Sweet, Arthur T., 1869- joint author.
Agr 29-673 Revised

U. S. Dept. of agr. Library 1So32F 1924, no. 4
for Library of Congress [r38d2]

NK 0205324 DNAL WaWW NBuU OO PP DLC

Knobel, Edmund Wilhelm, 1889- joint author.
Layton, Marvon Harold, 1898-
... Soil survey of Crawford county, Kansas. By M. H. Layton ... J. A. Kerr, and E. W. Knobel ... and H. W. Higbee and R. W. O'Hara ... Washington [U. S. Govt. print. off., 1931]

Knobel, Edmund Wilhelm, 1889-
... Soil survey of Doniphan county, Kansas. By E. W. Knobel ... and R. H. Davis and H. W. Higbee ... Washington [U. S. Govt. print. off., 1931]
cover-title, 34 p. 3 pl. on 2 l., 2 maps (1 fold.) 23½cm. (U. S. Dept. of agriculture. Bureau of chemistry and soils. [Soil survey report] Series 1927, no. 25)
In cooperation with the Kansas Agricultural experiment station.

1. Soil-surveys. 2. Soils—Kansas. I. Davis, Raymond Howard, 1906- joint author. II. Higbee, Howard William, joint author.
Agr 32-14
Library, U. S. Dept. of Agriculture 1So32F 1927, no. 25
Library of Congress [S591.A22 1927, no. 25]
[5*]

NK 0205326 DNAL WaWW DLC

Knobel, Edmund Wilhelm, 1889-
... Soil survey of Johnson county, Kansas. By E. W. Knobel ... and R. H. Davis ... Washington [U. S. Govt. print. off., 1932]
cover-title, 32 p. 2 pl. on 1 l., 2 maps (1 fold.) 23½cm. (U. S. Department of agriculture. Bureau of chemistry and soils. [Soil survey report] Series 1928, no. 17)
In cooperation with the Kansas Agricultural experiment station.

1. Soil-surveys. 2. Soils—Kansas. I. Davis, Raymond Howard, 1906- joint author.
Agr 32-580
Library, U. S. Dept. of Agriculture 18o32F 1928, no. 17
Library of Congress [S591.A22 1928, no. 17]
[4*]

NK 0205327 DNAL WaWW DLC

Knobel, Edmund Wilhelm, 1889-
... Soil survey of Kingman county, Kansas. By E. W. Knobel ... and R. O. Lewis and C. E. Dornberger ... Washington [U. S. Govt. print. off., 1938]
cover-title, 35 p. 3 pl. on 2 l., 2 maps (1 fold.) 23½cm. (U. S. Bureau of chemistry and soils. [Soil survey report] Series 1932, no. 24)
At head of title: ... United States Department of agriculture.
In cooperation with the Kansas Agricultural experiment station.

1. Soil-surveys. 2. Soils—Kansas. I. Dornberger, Calvin Elmer, 1909- joint author. II. Lewis, Ralph Oscar, 1905- joint author.
Agr 38-283
U. S. Dept. of agr. Library 1So32F Series 1932 no. 24
for Library of Congress [S591.A22 1932, no. 24]
[6*]

NK 0205328 DNAL WaWW DLC

VOLUME 300

Knobel, Edmund Wilhelm, 1889–
... Soil survey of Labette county, Kansas. By E. W. Knobel ... and R. L. von Trebra and H. W. Higbee ... Washington [U. S. Govt. print. off., 1931]
cover-title, 23 p. 2 pl. on 1 l., 2 maps (1 fold.) 23½cm. (U. S. Bureau of chemistry and soils. Soil survey report, series 1926, no. 30)
At head of title: United States Department of agriculture. Bureau of chemistry and soils. In cooperation with the Kansas agricultural experiment station.
1. Soil-surveys. 2. Soils—Kansas. I. Higbee, Howard William, joint author. II. Von Trebra, Richard Louis, joint author.
Agr 31-121 Revised
U. S. Dept. of agr. Library for Library of Congress 1So32F 1926, no. 30 [S591.A22 1926, no. 30] [r38c3]
NK 0205329 DNAL WaWW DLC

Knobel, Edmund Wilhelm, 1889–
... Soil survey of Le Flore county, Oklahoma. By E. W. Knobel ... and C. B. Boatright and W. C. Boatright ... Washington [U. S. Govt. print. off., 1936]
cover-title, 38 p. 2 pl., 2 maps (1 fold.) 23cm. (U. S. Bureau of chemistry and soils. [Soil survey report] Series 1931, no. 15)
At head of title: United States Department of agriculture. In cooperation with the Oklahoma Agricultural experiment station.
1. Soil-surveys. 2. Soils—Oklahoma. I. Boatright, Charles B., 1895– joint author. II. Boatright, William Carl, 1902– joint author.
Agr 36-98
Library, U. S. Dept. of Agriculture 1So32F 1931, no. 15 Library of Congress [S591.A22 1931, no. 15]
NK 0205330 DNAL WaWW DLC

Knobel, Edmund Wilhelm, 1889–
... Soil survey of McIntosh county, Oklahoma. By E. W. Knobel ... and O. H. Brensing ... Washington [U. S. Govt. print. off., 1938]
cover-title, 45 p. 2 pl. on 1 l., 2 maps (1 fold.) 23½cm. (U. S. Bureau of chemistry and soils. [Soil survey report. Series 1933, no. 11)
At head of title: ... United States Department of agriculture. In cooperation with the Oklahoma Agricultural experiment station.
1. Soil-surveys. 2. Soils—Oklahoma. I. Brensing, Oliver Henry, 1906– joint author.
Agr 38-148
U. S. Dept. of agr. Library for Library of Congress 1So32F 1933, no. 11 [S591.A22 1933, no. 11] [5*] (631.470973)
NK 0205331 DNAL WaWW DLC

Knobel, Edmund Wilhelm, 1889–
... Soil survey of Marion county, Kansas. By E. W. Knobel ... and R. O. Lewis ... Washington [U. S. Govt. print. off., 1935]
cover-title, 35 p. 2 pl. on 1 l., 2 maps (1 fold.) 23cm. (U. S. Bureau of chemistry and soils. [Soil survey report] Series 1930, no. 35)
At head of title: United States Department of agriculture. In cooperation with the Kansas Agricultural experiment station.
1. Soil-surveys. 2. Soils—Kansas. I. Lewis, Ralph Oscar, 1905– joint author.
Agr 35-568
Library, U. S. Dept. of Agriculture 1So32F 1930, no. 35 Library of Congress [S591.A22 1930, no. 35]
NK 0205332 DNAL WaWW DLC

Knobel, Edmund Wilhelm, 1839– joint author.
Fowler, Earl Donald, 1890–
... Soil survey of Polk county, Florida. By Earl D. Fowler ... Arthur E. Taylor, E. W. Knobel, S. W. Phillips, F. R. Lesh, A. L. Gray, A. T. Sweet, M. J. Edwards, H. M. Smith, R. E. Devereux, A. H. Hasty, and Robert Wildermuth ... Washington [U. S. Govt. print. off., 1932]

Knobel, E. W., joint author.
Phillips, Samuel William, 1894–
... Soil survey, Randolph County, Georgia, by S. W. Phillips ... Earl D. Fowler, E. W. Knobel, and J. W. Moon ... and G. L. Fuller ... Washington. U. S. Govt. print. off., 1928.

Knobel, Edmund Wilhelm, 1889– joint author.
Wildermuth, Robert.
... Soil survey of Rankin county, Mississippi. By Robert Wildermuth ... E. W. Knobel, A. L. Gray and Grove B. Jones ... Washington [U. S. Govt. print. off., 1931]

Knobel, Edmund Wilhelm, 1889–
... Soil survey, Tulsa county, Oklahoma, by E. W. Knobel ... and O. H. Brensing ... Washington [U. S. Govt. print. off., 1942]
cover-title, 68 p. illus., maps. 23cm. (U. S. Bureau of plant industry. [Soil survey report] Series 1935, no. 22)
"In cooperation with the Oklahoma Agricultural experiment station."
1. Soil-surveys—Oklahoma. I. Brensing, Oliver Henry, 1906– joint author.
Agr 42-437 Brief cataloging
U. S. Dept. of agr. Library for Library of Congress 1So32F 1935, no. 22 [S591.A22 1935, no. 22] [4*] (631.470973)
NK 0205336 DNAL DLC

Knobel, Edward, 1839–
Beetles of New England and their kind; a guide to know them readily, by Edward Knobel. Boston, B. Whidden [c1895]
45 p. illus. 14½ x 21cm.
1. Beetles—New England.
Library of Congress QL583.K7 6—22073
IU MB
NK 0205337 DLC WaTC ICJ MeB PPAmE PHC OO OCU MH

Knobel, Edward, 1839–
The day butterflies and duskflyers of New England, how to find and know them. By Edward Knobel. Boston, B. Whidden, 1895.
40 p. illus. 15½ x 21½cm.
1. Butterflies—New England. 2. Moths—New England.
6-21636
Library of Congress QL549.K718
NK 0205338 DLC WaTC MeB OO IU PPAmE MH

Knobel, Edward, 1839–
Ferns and evergreens of New England. A simple guide for their determination. By Edward Knobel. Boston, B. Whidden, 1895.
[26] p. XI pl. 15½ x 21½cm.
1. Ferns—New England.
4—30240
Library of Congress QK525.K72
NK 0205339 DLC WaTC ICJ MBH OCl

Knobel, Edward, 1839–
Field key to the land birds ... by Edward Knobel. Boston, B. Whidden, 1899.
3 p. l., 55 p. illus., IX col. pl. 19cm.
1. Birds—U. S.
Library of Congress QL681.K72 99-2668 Revised
NK 0205340 DLC ICF-A NIC PP ICJ MB

Knobel, Edward, 1839–
The fresh water fishes of New England and those ascending the streams from the sea, by Edward Knobel. Boston, B. Whidden [c1896]
40 p. illus. 15½ x 21½cm.
1. Fishes—New England.
6—12115
Library of Congress QL627.K72
NK 0205341 DLC CaBVaU WaTC OO ICJ MB

Knobel, Edward, 1839–
The grasses, sedges and rushes of the northern United States, illustrated; an easy method of identification, by Edward Knobel. Boston, B. Whidden, 1899.
78 p. illus., pl. 21½cm.
1. Grasses—U. S. 2. Cyperaceae. 3. Juncaceae. I. Title.
99—2276
Library of Congress QK118.K72 [a42r30f1] -584
NK 0205342 DLC PP PWcS PU OCl ICJ MB ViU

[**Knobel, Edward**] 1839–
A guide to find the names of all wild-growing trees and shrubs of New England by their leaves. [Boston, L. Barta & co., 1894]
48 p. illus. 15½ x 21½cm.
1. Trees—New England. 2. Shrubs—New England.
4-30241
QK482.K72
NK 0205343 DLC WaTC ICJ

Knobel, Edward, 1839–
A guide to find the names of all wild-growing trees and shrubs of New England, by their leaves, by Edward Knobel. Boston: B. Whidden, cop. 1894. 48 p. illus. obl. 24°.
O'KEEFE COLLECTION.
1. Trees—U. S.—New England. 2. Shrubs—U. S.—New England.
N. Y. P. L. April 19, 1926
NK 0205344 NN ICJ MH-A MBH Nh MWA CtY PU OU

Knobel, Edward.
A guide to find the names of all wild-growing trees and shrubs of New England by their leaves.
Boston. Whidden. [190-?] 48 pp. Illus. Plates. 14 cm. × 20 cm.
H8710 — Trees. — New England. Botany.
NK 0205345 MB

Knobel, Edward, 1839–
Mosquitoes, gnats, craneflies, midges and flies of the northern states, by Edward Knobel. Boston, B. Whidden [c1897]
64 p. illus. 15 x 22½cm.
1. Diptera—U. S. I. Title.
6-32526
Library of Congress QL535.1.K72
NK 0205346 DLC WaTC PPAmE PHC OCU OO ICJ MB

Knobel, Edward, 1839–
The night moths of New England, how to determine them readily. By Edward Knobel. Boston, B. Whidden, 1895.
63 p. illus. 15½ x 22cm.
1. Moths—New England.
6-21635†
Library of Congress QL549.K72
NK 0205347 DLC WaTC ICJ IU OO MeB PPAmE

Knobel, Edward, 1839–
The spiders of the northern states, by Edward Knobel. Boston, Knight and Millet [c1901]
54 p. illus. 14½ x 21½cm.
1. Spiders—U. S.
5—32412
Library of Congress QL457.1.K72
NK 0205348 DLC WaTC CU OO ICJ

VOLUME 300

Knobel, Edward, 1839-
The turtles, snakes, frogs and other reptiles and amphibians of New England and the north by Edward Knobel. Boston, B. Whidden [°1896]
47 p. illus. 15½ x 21½cm.

1. Reptiles—New England. 2. Batrachia—New England.
6-15575
Library of Congress QL653.K7

NK 0205349 DLC WaTC OO OCl PPAN ICJ

Knobel, Edward, 1839-
The wild animals of North America, by Edward Knobel ... with all illustrations drawn by the author ... New York, The Authors and newspapers association [°1908]
9 pt. illus. 28 x 34½cm.

1. Mammals—North America. 2. Zoology—Pictorial works.
13-13592
Library of Congress QL715.K68

NK 0205350 DLC ICarbS MiU NN

Knobel, Edward, 1839-
The wild animals of North America. By Edward Knobel, ... [In nine sections.] New York, The Authors and Newspapers Association, [1910].
9 pts. in 1 vol. illus. 28 x 34cm.

NK 0205351 ICJ

Knobel, Edward Ball, 1841- 1930.
Address delivered by the president Mr. E. B. Knobel, on presenting the gold medal to Prof. H. C. Vogel. February 10, 1893 ... London [Spottiswoode & co., printers] 1893.
16 p. 21cm.
"Reprinted from the Monthly notices of the Royal astronomical society vol. LIII., no. 4."

1. Vogel, Herman Carl, 1842-1907. 2. Stars—Spectra.
26-11108
Library of Congress QB36.V65K6

NK 0205352 DLC

Knobel, Edward Ball, 1841-
Address... On presenting the gold medal to Profl. E. C Pickering...
London, 1901

QB36
.P5K6

NK 0205353 DLC NN

Knobel, Edward Ball, 1841-
Petrie, *Sir* William Matthew Flinders, 1853-
... Athribis, by W. M. Flinders Petrie ... with chapters by Dr. J. H. Walker and E. B. Knobel. London, School of archaeology in Egypt [etc.] 1908.

Knobel, Edward Ball, 1841-
The chronology of star catalogues, by E. B. Knobel... London. Spottiswoode & co., 1877.
cover-title. 74 p. 26½ cm.
Bibliographical foot-notes.
"Reprinted from the Memoirs of the Royal astronomical society."

NK 0205355 DN-Ob CtY ViU

Knobel, Edward Ball, 1841-
The dating of the horoscopes.
(In Petrie, William M. F. Athribis. Pp. 23, 24. London. 1908.)

L4439 — Astrology. — Egypt. Astrology.

NK 0205356 MB PU OCl

Knobel, Edward Ball, 1841-1930.
The heliacal rising of Sirius. (In: Historical studies by E. B. Knobel... London, 1911. f°. p. 6-7.)
British School of Archaeology in Egypt. Studies. v. 2.

1. Calendar, Egypt.
N. Y. P. L. October 14, 1911.

NK 0205357 NN

Knobel, Edward Ball, 1841-
Note on the comparative brightness of the nebula of Orion.
London, 1881
(4) p. 22 cm.
Astron. Soc. Month. Not., 41, 1880-81, p. 311-314.

NK 0205358 DN-Ob

Knobel, Edward Ball, 1841-
Note on the regnal years in the Aramaic papyri from Assuan.
(Edinburgh, 1906.)
(5) p. 22cm.

Astron. Soc. Month. Not., 69, 1908-09, p. 8-11.

NK 0205359 DN-Ob

Knobel, Edward Ball, 1841-
Notes on a Persian ms. of Ulugh Beigh's Catalogue of stars belonging to the Royal Astronomical Society.
London, 1879
(29) p. 22cm.

Astron. Soc. Month. Not., 39, 1878-79, p. 337-363.

NK 0205360 DN-Ob

Knobel, Edward Ball, 1841-
Notes on Mr. Burnham's paper entitled "An examination of the double-star measures of the Bedford catalogue." [1880]
532-557 p. 22cm. in 24cm.

"Reprinted from the Monthly notices of the Royal Astronomical Society, vol. XL, no. 8."
Volume of pamphlets.

NK 0205361 NNC

Knobel, Edward Ball, 1841-
Notes on sketches of comet b, 1881.
London, 1881
1 pl. (4) p.

Astron. Soc. Month. Not., 42, 1881-82, p. 75-76.

NK 0205362 DN-Ob

Knobel, Edward Ball, 1841-
Obituary notice of the late Edward Singleton Holden. By E. B. Knobel...
Edinburgh, Printed by Neill & Co., ltd....1915.
(6) p. 22cm.

Astron. Soc. Month. Not., 75, 1914-15, 264-268.

NK 0205363 DN-Ob

CT99
.B187K6 Knobel, Edward Ball, 1841-
Obituary notice of the late Robert Stawell Ball. By E. B. Knobel ... Edinburgh, Printed by Neill & co., ltd., 1915.
1 p.l., p. 231-235. 22cm.

"Extract from the Annual report of the Council [of the Royal astronomical society] February 12, 1915."

1. Ball, Robert Stawell, 1840-1913.

NK 0205364 DLC DN-Ob

Knobel, Edward Ball
Obituary notice of the late Robert Stawell Ball. By E. B. Knobel...
Edinburgh, Printed by Neill & Co...Ltd...1918.
(7) p. 22cm.

Astron. Soc. Month. Not., 75, 1914-15, 230-236.

NK 0205365 DN-Ob

Knobel, Edward Ball, 1841-
Observations of Mars at the opposition of 1884.
London, 1885
3 pl. (8) p. 28cm.
Astron. Soc. Mem., 48, 1884, p. 275-282.

NK 0205366 DN-Ob

Knobel, Edward Ball, 1841-
On a Chinese planisphere.
(Edinburgh, 1909.)
2 pl., 1 f. 11 p. 22cm.

Astron. Soc. Month. Not., 69, 1908-09, p. 434-445.

NK 0205367 DN-Ob

Knobel, Edward Ball, 1841-
On the astronomical observations recorded in the Nihongi, the ancient chronicle of Japan.
London, 1905.
(8) p. 22 cm.

Astron. Soc. Month. Not., 66, 1905-06 p. 67-74.

NK 0205368 DN-Ob

Knobel, Edward Ball, 1841- ed.

Ptolemaeus, Claudius.
Ptolemy's catalogue of stars; a revision of the Almagest by Christian Heinrich Friedrich Peters ... and Edward Ball Knobel ... [Washington, D. C.] The Carnegie institution of Washington, 1915.

Knobel, Edward Ball, 1841-
Reference catalogue of astronomical papers and researches.
(London,) 1876.
28 p. 22cm.

Astron. Soc. Month. Not., 36, 1875-76, p. 365-392.

NK 0205370 DN-Ob

Knobel, Edward Ball, 1841-
Suggested explanation of the ancient Jewish calendar dates in the Aramaic papyri translated by Professor A. H. Sayce and Mr. A. E. Cowley.
London, 1905.
(13) p. 22cm.

Astron. Soc. Month. Not., 68, 1907-08, p. 334-345.

NK 0205371 DN-Ob

VOLUME 300

Knobel, Edward Ball, 1841-1930, ed.

Ulugh Beg, 1394-1449.
Ulugh Beg's catalogue of stars, rev. from all Persian manuscripts existing in Great Britain, with a vocabulary of Persian and Arabic words, by Edward Ball Knobel ... Washington, The Carnegie institution of Washington, 1917.

[Knobel, Elizabeth]
Our Miss Patterson and her Class C,...
[Chicago, c1923]

NK 0205373 DLC

Knobel, Elizabeth.
When little thoughts go rhyming, by Elizabeth Knobel; illustrated by Maginel Wright Enright. Chicago, Rand, McNally & company [1916]
96 p. incl. col. front., illus. (part col.) 20½cm.

I. Enright, Maginel Wright, illus. II. Title.

W 16-42

Washington, D. C. Public Library

NK 0205374 DWP MB NN

KNOBEL, FRIDOLIN MARINUS, 1857- Dagvlinders. [Diary of travels in Russia and the Far East.] Peking, 1901. 3 p.l., 481, [2] p. 8°.
"Niet in den handel."

NK 0205375 MSaE NN

Knobel, F[ridolin] M[arinus] 1857-
Dwars door het land van Roosevelt, door F. M. Knobel. Amsterdam, H. J. W. Becht, 1906.
5 p. l., [3]-269 p. 21½cm.

1. U. S.—Descr. & trav.

7-5369

Library of Congress E168.K7

NK 0205376 DLC MiU CU CtY MsU MoU NN

Knobel, Fridolin Marinus, 1857-
Dwars door het land van Roosevelt, door F. M. Knobel. Amsterdam, H. J. W. Becht, 1906.
Microcard edition (7 cards) (Travels in the New South II, 432) microprinted by LCP, Louisville, 1965.

1. U. S.—Descr. & trav. I. Title. II. Ser.

NK 0205377 ViU TxU

Knobel, Fridolin Marinus, 1857-
...Geschichte des Kantonallehrervereins nebst Beiträgen zur neueren glarnerischen Schulgeschichte, bearbeitet von Frid. Knobel. Glarus: Druck und Verlag R. Tschudy, 1932. 124 p. incl. tables. 22cm. (Glarner Beiträge zur Geschichte, Rechtswissenschaft, Sozialpolitik und Wirtschaftskunde. Heft 18.)
"Literatur-Verzeichnis," 1 p. at end.

1. Teachers—Assoc. and org.—Switzerland—Glarus. 2. Teachers—Salaries—Switzerland—Glarus. 3. Education—Switzerland—Glarus. I. Ser.
N. Y. P. L. February 20, 1934

NK 0205378 NN MH

Knobel, Fridolin Marinus, 1857-
Oostersche verpoozingen. Amsterdam, J. H. de Bussy, 1902.
vi, 434 p. maps.
1. East (Far East) - Descr. & trav. 2. China - Descr. & trav. I. Title.

NK 0205379 CU MH

Knobel, Fridolin Marinus, 1857-
Oostersche verpoozingen, door F. M. Knobel... Amsterdam: H. J. W. Becht, 1908. vi, 434 p. incl. plans, tables. 8°.

191820A. 1. China—Descr. and trav., 1875-1900.
N. Y. P. L. November 21, 1925

NK 0205380 NN

Knobel, Fridolin Marinus, 1857-
Perzische schetsen, door F. M. Knobel. Amsterdam, J. H. de Bussy, 1903.
2 p. l., iii, 272 p. fold. map. 24cm.

1. Persia—Descr. & trav. I. Title.

21-7685

Library of Congress DS258.K7

NK 0205381 DLC

Knobel, Fridolin Marinus, 1857-
Sprokkelingen uit Azië. [Leipzig, 1924]
viii, 80 p. 21cm.

Cover title.

1. Indonesia--Descr. & trav.--1800-1945. 2. Asia--Descr. & trav. I. Title.

NK 0205382 NIC

Knobel, Fridolin Marinus, 1857-
Thuisvaart. [Chemnitz i. Sa., G. Lamprecht, 1923]
82 p. 23cm.

"Niet in den handel."

1. East--Description and travel. I. Title.

NK 0205383 NIC CtY

Knobel, Fridolin Marinus, 1857-
Uit zonnenland. Amsterdam, H.J.W. Becht, 1909.
viii,182p. 22cm.

NK 0205384 IEN NN

Knobel, Fridolin Marinus, 1857-
...Van Bachtiaar naar Arabier, door F. M. Knobel. Potchefstroom: "Het Westen"-drukkerij, 1909. p. 53-180. 21cm.
Paged continuously with the author's Van Teheran naar Ispahan.

1. Asia Minor—Descr. and trav.
N. Y. P. L. January 20, 1944

NK 0205385 NN

Knobel, Fridolin Marinus, 1857-
...Van Teheran naar Ispahan, door F. M. Knobel. Pretoria: "Volkstem" drukkerij, 1909. 52, v p. 22cm.
The pagination of this work is continued in his: Van Bachtiaar naar Arabier.

1. Persia—Descr. and trav., 1900-1910.
N. Y. P. L. January 20, 1944

NK 0205386 NN MH

Knobel, Fritz, 1903-
Die grundzuege des oesterreichischen und des reichsdeutschen immobiliarzwangsversteigerungsrechts. ...
Inaug. diss. Jena, 1930.
Bibl.

NK 0205387 ICRL MH-L

Knobel, Joachim.
Illustrierter reisebegleiter für die Alpenstrasse des Klausen und ihre zufahrtslinien. Glarus, J. Spälti, 1900.
113 p. illus. 19cm.
1.Alps. Description and travel.

NK 0205388 MnU

Knobel, Johannes.
... Der mensch in der verkehrswirtschaft, von dr. Johannes Knobel ... Jena, G. Fischer, 1944.
vii, 188 p. 23½cm. (Verkehrswissenschaftliche und volkswirtschaftliche arbeiten, hrsg. von dr. Karl Bräuer ... Hft. 2)
"Literaturverzeichnis": p. 170-177.

1. Transportation. I. Title.

46-19801

Library of Congress HE151.K6
[2] 385

NK 0205389 DLC CU MH NjP

Knobel, John Esher, ed.

Heidner, John Edward, 1871-
The business counselor, a complete commercial instructor and adviser, by J. Edward Heidner, assisted by F. W. Heidner ... rev. and cor. to date by John Esher Knobel ... 12th ed. ... Chicago, The Heidner publishing company, 1902.

Knobel, Max, 1898-
...The activities of the ions of potassium hydroxide in aqueous solution, by M. Knobel. [Boston, 1923.] p. [70-]76. 8°. (Massachusetts Institute of Technology. Research laboratory of physical chemistry. Contributions. no. 150.)
Cover-title.

1. Electrolysis of solutions. 2. Ions.—Velocity. 3. Potassium hydroxide. 4. Series.
N. Y. P. L. June 5, 1923.

NK 0205391 DLC OU NN

Knobel, Max, 1898-
Bibliography of electro-organic chemistry, by Max Knobel, C. J. Brockman and Research information service, National research council. Washington, D. C., National research council, 1926.
4 p. l., 2-70, 30 numb. l. 26½ x 20½cm.
Autographed from type-written copy.

1. Electrochemistry—Bibl. 2. Chemistry, Organic—Bibl. 3. Reduction, Electrolytic—Bibl. I. Brockman, Charles Joseph, 1897- joint author. II. National research council. Research information service. III. Title.

30-8042

Library of Congress Z5524.E36K7

NK 0205392 DLC ICJ MiU OOxM OCU

Knobel, Max, 1898-
...Commutator measurements on polarized electrodes, by Max Knobel. [Boston,] 1925. 2614-2621 p. diagrs. 8°. (Mass. Institute of Technology. Rogers Laboratory of Physics. Contributions. ser. 2, no. 23.)
Cover-title.
Repr.: Amer. Chemical Soc. Jour. v. 46, no. 12. 1924.

1. Electricity—Potential. 2. Ser.
N. Y. P. L. August 26, 1925

NK 0205393 NN OU

VOLUME 300

Knobel, Max, 1898-
...The effect of current density on overvoltage, by M. Knobel, P. Caplan, and M. Eiseman. [Boston, 1923.] 20 p. incl. diagrs., tables. 8°. (Mass. Institute of Technology. Rogers Laboratory of Physics. Contributions. Series 2, no. 15.)

Cover-title.
"A paper presented at the forty-third general meeting of the American Electrochemical Society, held in New York City, May 3, 4, and 5, 1923."

1. Electrolysis. 2. Caplan, P., jt. au. 3. Eiseman, Martha, jt. au. 4. Series.
N. Y. P. L. October 10, 1923.

NK 0205394 NN OU DLC

Knobel, Max, 1898-
...Effect of pressure on overvoltage, by Max Knobel. [Boston,] 1925. 2752–2753. 8°. (Massachusetts. Institute of Technology. Rogers Laboratory of Physics. Contributions. ser. 2, no. 22.)

Cover-title.
Repr.: Amer. Chemical Soc. Jour. v. 46. Dec., 1924.

1. Electricity—Potential. 2. Ser.
N. Y. P. L. July 14, 1925

NK 0205395 NN

Knobel, Max, 1898-
...Effect of surface condition on overvoltage, by Max Knobel. [Boston,] 1925. 131–136 p. 8°. (Mass. Institute of Technology. Rogers Laboratory of Physics. Contribution. ser. 2, no. 30.)

Cover-title.
"Paper presented at the forty-seventh general meeting of the American Electrochemical Society... April 25, 1925."

1. Electrodes. 2. Ser.
N. Y. P. L. May 29, 1926

NK 0205396 NN OU

Knobel, Max, 1898-
...The effect of temperature on overvoltage, by M. Knobel and D. B. Joy. [Boston, 1923.] p. 27–34. diagrs. 8°. (Mass. Institute of Technology. Rogers Laboratory of Physics. Contributions. Series 2, no. 16.)

Cover-title.
Advance copy.

1. Electrolysis. 2. Joy, David Bartlett, jt. au. 3. Series.
N. Y. P. L. October 9, 1923.

NK 0205397 NN OU DLC

Knobel, Max, and R. B. Norton.
...The penetration of electrolytic hydrogen through iron, by Max Knobel and Ralph B. Norton. [Boston, Mass.,] 1926. 76–83 p. incl. diagr., tables. 8°. (Massachusetts Institute of Technology. Rogers Laboratory of Physics. Contributions. Ser. 2, no. 34.)

Cover-title.
Repr.: Jour. of mathematics and physics. v. 5, no. 2. Feb., 1926.

1. Metals—Corrosion—Iron and steel. 2. Norton, Ralph B., jt. au. 3. Ser.
N. Y. P. L. October 6, 1926

NK 0205398 NN OU

Knobel, Max, 1898-
...A porous electrode for oxidations or reductions, by Max Knobel. [Boston,] 1925. 2 p. 8°. (Mass. Institute of Technology. Rogers Laboratory of Physics. Contribution. ser. 2, no. 31.)

Cover-title.
Repr.: Industrial and engineering chemistry. v. 17, no. 8. Aug., 1925.

1. Electrodes. 2. Ser.
N. Y. P. L. May 29, 1926

NK 0205399 NN OU

Knobel, Max, 1898-
...The reactions of the lead storage battery, by M. Knobel. [Boston,] 1923. p. 29–34. 8°. (Massachusetts Institute of Technology. Rogers Laboratory of Physics. Contribution. Series 2, no. 13.)

Cover-title.
"A paper to be presented at the forty-third general meeting of the American Electrochemical Society to be held in New York City, May 3, 4, and 5, 1923." — *p. 29.*

1. Electricity.—Batteries (Storage), 1923. 2. Series.
N. Y. P. L. May 15, 1923.

NK 0205400 NN OU DLC

Knobel, Max, 1898-
...The theory of overvoltage, by Max Knobel. [Boston,] 1926. [65–]74 p. 8°. (Massachusetts Institute of Technology. Rogers Laboratory of Physics. Contributions. ser. 2, no. 33.)

Cover-title.
Repr.: Jour. of mathematics and physics. v. 5, no. 2. Feb., 1926.

1. Electricity, Potential. 2. Ser.
N. Y. P. L. October 21, 1926

NK 0205401 NN OU

Knobel, Max, 1898-
...The transference numbers of potassium hydroxide in aqueous solution, by M. Knobel, D. K. Worcester and F. B. Briggs. [Boston, 1923.] p. [77–]79. 8°. (Massachusetts Institute of Technology. — Rogers Laboratory of Physics. Contributions. Series 2, no. 14.)

Cover-title.

1. Electrolysis of solutions. 2. Potassium hydroxide. 3. Worcester, D. K., jt. au. 4. Briggs, F. B., jt. au. 5. Series.
N. Y. P. L. June 6, 1923.

NK 0205402 NN OO

Knobeloch, Elsie Louise.
Afterglow, a brief book of verse, by Elsie Louise Knobeloch... Boston, The author [1943] 33 p. 17cm.

NK 0205403 NN

Knobeloch (Georgius Gottlieb). *De atrophia. 32 pp. sm. 4°. *Francof. ad Viadr., typ. C. Zeitleri,* [1684].

NK 0205404 DNLM

Knobeloch (Georgius Gottlieb.) *De nexu principiorum physicorum in homine. unp. 21 l. 4°. *Francof. a. O., typ. hæredum J. Ernesti,* [1679].

NK 0205405 DNLM

Knobeloch, Samuel, respondent.
...De sanctitate ecclesiarvm
see under Böhmer, Just Henning, 1674-1749, praeses.

*GC5 Knobelsdorf, Eustathius von, 1520-1571.
K7507 De bello tvrcico elegia Evstathii a Knobelsdorf.
539d Vitebergae.M.D.XXXIX.
8°. [18]p. 16cm.
Signature: A10 (A10 blank).
Colophon: Excvsvm Vitebergae per Iosephvm Clvg. Anno. M.D.XXXIX.

NK 0205407 MH

KNOBELSDORF, Eustathius von.
Jeanne d'Arc, ou La vierge de Lorraine. Fragment d'un poème traduit en français avec introduction par l'abbé Valentin Dufour. Lat. and French. Orléans, H. Herluison, 1879.

pp. 41+. Port.
"Tiré à 60 exemplaires, n° 17."

NK 0205408 MH

Knobelsdorf, Eustathius von, 1519-1571.
Lutetiae Parisiorvm descriptio, avthore
Gr8 Evstathio à Knobelsdorf Pruteno. Parisiis.
229 Apud Christianum Wechelum sub Scuto Basiliensi, in uico Iacobaeo: & sub Pegaso in uico Bellouacensi. An. 1543.
f1, [1]p., 1l. 16cm.
Signatures: A-D8.
In verse.

NK 0205409 CtY NjP

Knobelsdorf, Hans-Friedrich
see Knobelsdorff, Hans Friedrich.

Knobelsdorff, Constance Katharine, 1907-
... Marcel Proust as a painter of contemporary society, by Constance Knobelsdorff ... [Pittsburgh, 1933]
7 p. 23cm.
Caption title.
Abstract of thesis (PH. D.)—University of Pittsburgh, 1932.
Vita.
"Reprinted from University of Pittsburgh bulletin, vol. 29, no. 3, January, 1933."

1. Proust, Marcel, 1871-1922.

34-357
Library of Congress PQ2631.R63Z65 1932
Univ. of Pittsburgh Libr. [2] 843.91

NK 0205411 PPiU DLC

ar W Knobelsdorff, Frederic Wilhelm Adrian van
30740 Disputatio historica juris publici continens Ordinum generalium totius Belgii historiam ab obitu requesentii usque ad expugnatam Antverpiam, 1576-1584. Lugduni Batavorum, J. C. Emeis, 1835.
114 p. 23cm.

Thesis--Leyden.

1. Belgium--Constitutional history.

NK 0205412 NIC

4D-525 Knobelsdorff, Fritz von.
Geschichte der Befreiungskriege. Nach den besten Quellen und zeitgenössischen Berichten. Berlin, Meidinger's Jugendschriften Verlag [
322 p.

NK 0205413 DLC-P4 NcD

KNOBELSDORFF, Karl von.
Vorschläge zur erreichung mittlerer feststehender getreidepreise. Berlin, 1824.

NK 0205414 MH

Knobelsdorff, Manfred, von.
R. Walther Darré. Berlin, Reichsnährstand Verlags -G. [1935]

99 p. (Die Ahnen deutscher Bauernführer, 1)

NK 0205415 MH

Bon.
Coll. KNOBELSDORFF, OTTO VON.
No.11171 Die keltischen Bestandtheile in der englischen Sprache, eine Skizze. Berlin, W. Weber, 1870.
73p. 20cm.

NK 0205416 ICN OCl PU MH

VOLUME 300

Knobelsdorff, Viktor von, 1885-
Unter Zuchthäuslern und Kavalieren; Russische Gestalten und Erkenntnisse. Stuttgart: Robert Lutz [19—?]. 335 p. 12°.

1. Knobelsdorff, Viktor von. 2. European war—Prisoners and prisons. 3. Title.
N. Y. P. L. November 10, 1925

NK 0205417 NN PPG

Knobelsdorff, Viktor von, 1885-
Unter Zuchthäuslern und Kavalieren. Russische Gestalten und Erkenntnisse. 4. Auflage.
= Stuttgart. Lutz. [192-?] 334, (1) pp. [Lutz' Memoiren Bibliothek. Reihe 6, Band 11.] 19½ cm., in 8s.

N2148 — T.r. — S.r. — European War, 19 4-1919. Prisons. Russian.

NK 0205418 MB

Knobelsdorff, Viktor von, 1885–
Unter zuchthäuslern und kavalieren; russische gestalten und erkenntnisse, von Viktor v. Knobelsdorff. 1. aufl. Stuttgart, R. Lutz [1925]
334, [1] p. 20½cm. (Added t.-p.: Lutz' Memoiren bibliothek. 6. reihe, 11. bd.)

1. European war, 1914-1918—Prisoners and prisons, Russian. 2. European war, 1914-1918—Personal narratives, German. I. Title.
Library of Congress D627.R8K6 33-32448
[2] 940.47247

NK 0205419 DLC ICN

Knobelsdorff, Viktor von.
Unter Zuchthäuslern und Kavalieren; russische Gestalten und Erkenntnisse, von Viktor v. Knobelsdorff... Stuttgart: R. Lutz Verlag, G.m.b.H., [1925.] 334 p. 3. ed. 12°. (Lutz' Memoiren Bibliothek. Reihe 6. Bd. 11.)

203981A. 1. European war, 1914–1918—Personal narratives, German. 2. European war, 1914-1918—Prisoners and prisons, Russian.
N. Y. P. L. October 27, 1925

NK 0205420 NN

Knobelsdorff-Brenkenhoff, Nataly Auguste Amalie Hermine (v. Eschstruth) von.
see
Eschstruth, Nataly von, 1860-

Knoben, Horst, 1916–
Der Grundgedanke des Betrugstatbestandes. Jena, 1940.
68 p. 21 cm.
Inaug.-Diss.—Jena.
Vita.
"Schrifttum": p. [66]-68.

1. Fraud—Germany.
50-41249

NK 0205422 DLC

Knobil, Ernest Richard, 1926-
The relation of some steroid hormones to the B-glucuronidase activity in the accessory organs of reproduction. [Ithaca, N. Y.] 1951.
68 l. 27cm.

Thesis (Ph.D.)—Cornell Univ., June 1951.

NK 0205423 NIC

Knobl, Shevah
see
Knöbil, Schewach.

Knoblach, Franz, 1890- Rechtsprakt.: Die juristische Natur der eherechtlichen Dispensatio in radice. Würzburg 1914: Staudenraus. 72 S. 8°
Würzburg, Rechts- u. staatswiss. Diss. v. 30. Aug. 1914, Ref. Meurer
[Geb. 14. Jan. 90 Heidenheim; Wohnort: Würzburg; Staatsangeh.: Bayern; Vorbildung: Neues G. Würzburg Reife 09; Studium: Würzburg 8 S.; Rig. 1. Juli 14.] [U 14. 1225

NK 0205425 ICRL MH-L

---

ar W 53897 no.11
Knoblach, Gottfried, 1868-
Über einen Fall von Tuberkulose des Pharynx. Erlangen, Buchdr. von Junge & Sohn, 1906.
16 p. 23cm.

Inaug.-Diss.--Erlangen.

NK 0205426 NIC NN DNLM

220.53
R137
Knoblach, Johann Heinrich, d. 1699, praeses.
DISSERTATIO PHILOLOGICA POSTERIOR,/ QUA/ OBSERVATIONES/ BIBLICAS/ Mense JANUARIO nuper emissas,/ modeste sub examen vocant,/ & D. Lutheri versionem tuentur,/ PRAESES,/ M. JOHANN-HENRICUS/ Knoblach,/ WITTEBERGA-SAXO,/ &/ RESPONDENS/ BALTH. BENJAMIN Werther,/ Rachitha-Saxo/ Anno M DC XCV. d.V.Junii./H.L.Q.C./ VITTEBERGAE,/Typis CHRISTIANI SCHRÖDTERI, Acad. Typ./
[16] p. 21 x 16 cm.

Bound with Raith, Balthasar, 1616-1683. Vindiciae versionis S.Bibliorum Germanicae.
Provenance: Bp. Whittingham, Maryland Diocesan Library.

1. Bible. Versions, German. Luther. I. Werther, Balthasar Benjamin, respondent. II. Title.

NK 0205428 NNG

220.53
R137
Knoblach, Johann Heinrich, d. 1699, praeses.
DISSERTATIO PHILOLOGICA PRIOR,/ QUA/ OBSERVATIONES/ BIBLICAS/ Mense JANUARIO nuper emissas,/ Modeste sub examen vocant,/ & D. Lutheri versionem tuentur,/PRAESES/ M. JOHANN-HENRICUS/ Knoblach,/ WITTEBERGA-SAXO,/ &/ RESPONDENS/ JOH. HENRICUS Hertel,/ Zittavia-Lusatus,/ Anno M DC XCV.d.X.Aprilis./H.L.Q.C./WITTEBERGAE,/ Typis CHRISTIANI SCHRÖDTERI,Acad.Typ./
[16] p. 21 x 16 cm.
Provenance: Bp. Whittingham, Maryland Diocesan Library.

Bound with Raith, Balthasar,1616-1683.Vindiciae versionis S.Bibliorum Germanicae.

1. Bible. Versions, German. Luther. I. Hertel, Joannes Henricus, respondent. II. Title.

NK 0205430 NNG

220.53
R137
Knoblach,Johann Heinrich, d 1699, praeses.
DISSERTATIONEM PHILOLOGICAM,/ in qva/ OBSERVATIO-/ NES BIBLICAE,/ Mense FEBRUARIO emissae, modeste,/ sub examen vocantur,/ Et D. LUTHERI Versio defenditur,/ PRO LOCO,/ In Amplissima Facultate Philosophica/ benevole sibi concesso,/ solenni eruditorum lisqvisitioni subiicit/ PRAESES/ M.JO. HENRICUS Knoblach,/ WITTEBERGA-SAXO,/ RESPONDENTE/ M.JO. CHRISTIANO Bundermann,/ BUDISS.LUSAT./ D.XXI.Novembr. Anno M DC XCV./ In Auditorio Majori./ WITTEBERGAE,/ Typis CHRISTIANI KREUSIGII,Acad.Typ./

Continued in next column

Continued from preceding column

[24] p. 21 x 16 cm.
Provenance: Bp. Whittingham, Maryland Diocesan Library.
Bound with Raith, Balthasar,1616-1683. Vindiciae versionis S.Bibliorum Germanicae.
1. Bible. Versions, German. Luther. I. Gundermann, Johann Christian, respondent. II. Title.

NK 0205432 NNG

220.53
R137
Knoblach, Johann Heinrich, d. 1699.
M. Johann Heinrich Knoblachs,/ Fac. Phil. Adjunct./ Grundlicher/ Beweiss,/ Dass ihn bissher von Seiten/ Dn. M. August Herrmann/ Franckens,/ Graec. & Orient. Lingg. Prof. Ordin./ & PAST. GLAUCH./ auffseine Disputationes nichts gründliches geant-/ wortet, sondern eitel nichtige und vergebliche/ Aussflüchte gesuchet worden./ Wittenberg,/ Gedruckt bey Johann Wilcken, Univ. Buchdr./ Im Jahr Christi 1696./
[32] p. 21 x 16 cm.

Provenance: Bp. Whittingham, Maryland Diocesan Library.
Bound with Raith, Balthasar,1616-1683. Vindiciae versionis S. Bibliorum Germanicae.

I. Francke, August Hermann, 1663-1727. II. Title.

NK 0205434 NNG

220.53
R137
Knoblach, Johann Heinrich,d. 1699.
M.Johann Heinrich Knoblachs,/ Kurtze Erinnerung/ An/ Herrn M. August/ Hermann Francken,/ Graec. & Orient. Lingg. Prof. Ordin./ & PAST. GLAUCH./ Dass derselbe sich besser verantworten, und so/ wohl mit dem seel/ LUTHERO, als andern/ rechtsch affenen THEOLOGIS,/ bescheidener verfahren möge./ Wittenberg,/ Gedruckt bey Johann Wilcken, Univ. Buchdr./ Im Jahr Christi 1695./
[16] p. 21 x 16
Provenance: Bp [illegible]tinghan, Maryland Diocesan Library.

Bound with Raith, Balthasar, 1616-1683. Vindiciae versionis S.Bibliorum Germanicae.

I. Francke, August Hermann, 1663-1727. II. Title.

NK 0205436 NNG

Knoblauch, Adolf, 1882–
Dada, von Adolf Knoblauch. Leipzig, K. Wolff [1919]
75, [1] p., 1 l. incl. front. 21½cm. [Bücherei "Der Jüngste tag," bd. 73/74]

I. Title.
Library of Congress PT2621.N62D3 45-42031
[2]

NK 0205437 DLC CaBVaU NBuG MU CtY IaU PU MH IEN

834K751 K1908
Knoblauch, Adolf, 1882-
Gedichte ... Berlin, Oesterheld & co.[1908]
43p.

NK 0205438 IU

Knoblauch, Adolf, 1882-
Impressionismus und Mystik. [Berlin, Schneider, n.d.]
p. 325-464. 26 cm.
"Sonderdruck aus dem Deutsche Bande der Weltliteratur der Gegenwart."

NK 0205439 PPT

VOLUME 300

Ger
Kn
Knoblauch, Adolf, 1882-
Die schwarze Fahne; eine Dichtung. Berlin, Der Sturm, 1915.
88p. 24cm.

NK 0205440 IEN PPT

Knoblauch, Adolf, 1882-
Sendung und Werk weiblicher Prosadichtung. München, Jos. Köselsche Buchhandlung, 1929-30.
[19 p.]

NK 0205441 OC1W

ND497
B5
K58
Knoblauch, Adolf, 1882-
William Blake; ein Umriss seines Lebens und seiner Gesichte, von Adolf Knoblauch Berlin, Furche-Kunstverlag [1925]
32 p. incl. col. mounted front., 2 illus., 23 plates. 25cm. (Schöpfung; Beiträge zu einer Weltgeschichte religiöser Kunst, Bd.7)
"Literatur- und Quellenverzeichnis": p. 31-32.

NK 0205442 MWiW-C MH

Knoblauch, Adolf, 1885-
Versuche über die Giftigkeit der Dämpfe von Perchloraethylen, Tetrachloraethan und Pentachloraethan. Würzburg 1911: Staudenraus. 22 S. 8°
Würzburg, Med. Diss. v. 10. Dez. 1911, Ref. Lehmann
[Geb. 13. Nov. 85 Würzburg; Wohnort: Würzburg; Staatsangeh.: Bayern; Vorbildung: Realgymn. Würzburg Reife Juli 05; Studium: Würzburg 10 S.; Coll. 14. Dez. 10; Approb. 9. Febr. 12.] [U 12. 4662

NK 0205443 ICRL DNLM CtY

Knoblauch, Alfred, 1870-
Die Nötigung zur Arbeitseinstellung (§ 153 der Reichsgewerbeordnung vom 21. Juni 1869) ... [von] Alfred Knoblauch ... Opponenten: ... Heinrich von Helldorff-Baumersroda ... Hans Schlieckmann ... Halle a.S., C. A. Kaemmerer & Co., 1894.
52 p., 2 l. 22cm.
Inaug.-diss. - Halle-Wittenberg.
"Lebenslauf": 1st leaf at end.
Bibliographical footnotes.

NK 0205444 MH-L ICRL

Knoblauch, Alois, ed.
Reiterland Ostpreussen; 100 Jahre Renn- und Turniersport, Insterburg-Trakehnen. Im Auftrage des Turnier- und Rennvereins Insterburg verfasst. Tilsit, Holzner [1939]
49 p. illus., maps. 22 cm.
1. Turnier- und Rennverein, Insterburg. I. Title.
GV204.G4K6 49-39259*

NK 0205445 DLC

KNOBLAUCH, Arthur Lewis.
The public-relations service of a selected group of American city school systems.
Typewritten. 28 x 20 cm.
Thesis, Ed.D.- Harvard University, 1942.

NK 0205446 MH

Knoblauch, August, 1836-1919.
Krause, Fedor, 1857- ed.
Die allgemeine chirurgie der gehirnkrankheiten, bearbeitet von dr. A. Knoblauch, prof. dr. K. Brodmann und priv.-doz. dr. A. Hauptmann. Redigiert von prof. dr. F. Krause ... Stuttgart, F. Enke, 1914.

Knoblauch, August, 1836-1919
Anatomie und Topographie des Gehirns und seiner Häute.
8°, pp. 3-80.
Neue Deutsche Chirurgie, Band 11, 2 Teil. Ferdinand Enke, Stuttgart, 1914.

NK 0205448 OC1W-H

616.8
K72k
Knoblauch, August, 1836-1919.
Klinik und atlas der chronischen krankheiten des zentralnervensystems ... Berlin, J. Springer, 1909.
608p. illus.(part col.) diagrs.
"Verzeichnis des autoren, aus deren werken und arbeiten abbildungen entnommen bezw. nachgebildet sind": p.[598]-600.
1. Nervous system--Diseases.

NK 0205449 IU-M OrU-M DNLM PPC MiU ICJ NNC

Knoblauch, August, 1836-1919.
Über Störungen der musikalischen Leistungsfähigkeit infolge von Gehirnläsionen ... Leipzig, Druck von J. B. Hirschfeld, 1888.
24 p. incl. diagrs. 24 cm. [Heidelberg. Universität. Dissertationen. v. 2, no. 14]
Inaug.-diss. -Heidelberg.

NK 0205450 CU DNLM PPC

Knoblauch, Carl Hermann, 1820-1895.
Ule, Willi i. e. Wilhelm, 1861-
Geschichte der Kaiserlichen Leopoldinisch-Carolinischen deutschen akademie der naturforscher während der jahre 1852-1887 mit einem rückblick auf die frühere zeit ihres bestehens im auftrage des präsidenten herrn geheimen rathes professors dr. Hermann Knoblauch verfasst von dr. phil. Willi Ule ... Halle, Druck von E. Blochmann und sohn in Dresden, 1889.

Knoblauch, Carl Hermann, 1820-1895, ed.
Leopoldina. Amtliches organ der Kaiserlichen Leopoldinisch-Carolinischen deutschen akademie der naturforscher. 1.-58. hft.; junius 1859-juli 1922/aug. 1923. Jena [etc.] 1859-1923.

**NA5585
K6
Knoblauch, Carl Heinrich Eduard, 1801-1865.
Die Neue Synagoge in Berlin, entworfen und ausgeführt von Eduard Knoblauch, vollendet von August Stüler; herausgegeben von G. Knoblauch und F. Hollin. Neuer abdruck. Berlin, Ernst & Korn, 1878.
2p.l.,7 plates. 65cm.
1. Berlin.-Synagogues.
1. Stülor, August.
II. Title.

NK 0205453 NBuG MB OCH

QC
71
P57+
v.33
Knoblauch, Carl Hermann, 1820-1895.
[Papers on heat. v. p., 1848-1877]
15 nos in 1 v. illus. 21cm.
1. Heat--Collected works.

NK 0205454 NIC

Knoblauch, Carl Hermann, 1820-1895.
Scientific memoirs, selected from the transactions of foreign academies of science, and from foreign journals. Natural philosophy. Ed. by John Tyndall ... and William Francis ... [v. 1] London, Taylor and Francis, 1853.

Knoblauch, Carl Hermann, 1820-1895.
Ueber das verhalten der metalle gegen die strahlende Warme. Dresden, 1877.
4°

NK 0205456 NN

Knoblauch, Carl Hermann, 1820-1895.
Ueber den Durchgang der Wärme-und Lichtstrahlen durch geneigte diathermane und durchsichtige Platten. Berlin, A.W. Schade, 1866.
8 p. 22 cm.
Reprinted from Poggendorff's Annalen der Physik und Chemie, Bd.CXXVIII, no.5, 1866, p.161-166.

NK 0205457 OkU

Knoblauch, Carl Hermann, 1820-1895.
Ueber den Durchgang der Wärmestrahlen durch geneigte diathermane Platten. Berlin, A.W. Schade, 1872.
55 p. 21 cm.
Reprinted from Poggendorff's Annalen der Physik und Chemie, Bd.CXLVI, no.7., 1872, p. 321-375.

NK 0205458 OkU

Knoblauch, Carl Hermann, 1820-
Ueber die elliptische solarisation der waermestrahlen bei der reflexion von metallen. Lpz., Engelmann, 1887.
(Halle-Kaiser liche Leopoldinisch-Carolinische deutsche akademie der naturforscher Novaacta v. 50, no. 6)

NK 0205459 PU-P MH

Knoblauch, Carl Hermann, 1820-1895.
Ueber die enterferenzfarben der strahlenden Wärme. Berlin, A.W. Schade, 1867.
33 p. fold. tables. 22 cm.
Reprinted from Poggendorff's Annalen der Physik und Chemie, Bd.CXXXI, no.5, 1867, p.1-33.

NK 0205460 OkU

Knoblauch, Carl Hermann, 1820-1895.
12489 .... Ueber die Polarisation der strahlenden Wärme durch totale Reflexion. Von Dr. Hermann Knoblauch, ... Mit 6 Tafeln Nr. V-X und 6 in den Text eingedruckten Zinkographieen. .... Halle, In Commission bei W. Engelmann in Leipzig, 1890.
[2, 283]-304 p. v-x fold. diagr. 33cm. (Nova acta der Ksl. Leop.-Carol. Deutschen Akademie der Naturforscher. Bd. LV. Nr. 4.)

NK 0205461 ICJ

Knoblauch, Carl Wilhelm Hermann Oscar
see
Knoblauch, Oscar, 1862-

VOLUME 300

Knoblauch, Cornelius.
... Über die veränderung der weissen blutzellen des rindes und des hundes unter dem einfluss verschiedener infektions- und invasions- krankheiten. (Berlin, 1924).
(4) p. 23 cm.
Inaug.-diss. - Tierärzt. hoohechule, Berlin, Auszug.

NK 0205463 DNAL

Knoblauch, Dorothea, 1903–
Die Methodologie François Simiands...von Dorothea Knoblauch... Wuppertal-Elberfeld: Wuppertaler Druckerei A.-G., 1935. 143 p. 22½cm.

Inaugural-Dissertation — Köln, 1935.
Lebenslauf.
"Literaturverzeichnis," p. 9–12.

873386A. 1. Simiand, François, 1873–1935. 2. Economics—Methodology.
N. Y. P. L. March 17, 1937

NK 0205464 NN CtY NNC

Knoblauch, Eduard
see Knoblauch, Carl Heinrich Eduard, 1801-1865.

Knoblauch, Edward
see
Knoblock, Edward, 1874–1945.

Knoblauch, Elisabeth.
... Zur psychologie der studierenden frau; eine untersuchung über die einstellung zum studium und zur späteren berufstätigkeit bei studentinnen, von Elisabeth Knoblauch. Leipzig, J. A. Barth. 1930.

88 p. 23cm. (Schriften zur psychologie der berufseignung und des wirtschaftslebens ... hft. 38)

1. Psychology, Applied. 2. Education of women.

A C 38-235

New York univ. Library for Library of Congress BF431.S3 hft. 38 [2]

NK 0205467 NNU

Knoblauch, Emil
Beitrag zur kenntnis der splitzenentladung aus einem teslapole.
Inaug. Diss. Rostock, 1901 (Leipzig)

NK 0205468 ICRL CtY

Knoblauch, Emil.
Oleaceae, von E. Knoblauch. Mit 48 einzelbildern in 9 fig.

(*In* Die natürlichen pflanzenfamilien, begr. von A. Engler und K. Prantl. Leipzig, 1887- 25cm. IV. teil, 2. abt. (1895) p. 1-16)

"Gedruckt im märz 1892."
Supplement, by A. Engler, in Nachträge z. II.-IV. t. (1897) p. 281, and in Ergänzungsheft I (1900) p. 54.
Classed under [haupt]abt. IV, *Embryophyta siphonogama.*

1. Oleaceae. I. *Engler, Adolf, 1844–

3—30320

Library of Congress QK97.E6

NK 0205469 DLC OU PPT

Knoblauch, Emil.
Salvadoraceae, von E. Knoblauch. Mit 12 einzelbildern in 1 fig.

(*In* Die natürlichen pflanzenfamilien, begr. von A. Engler und K. Prantl. Leipzig, 1887- 25cm. IV. teil, 2. abt. (1895) p. 17-19)

"Gedruckt im juni 1892."
Supplement by H. Harms, in Nachträge z. II.-IV. t. (1897) p. 281-282.
Classed under [haupt]abt. IV, *Embryophyta siphonogama.*

1. Salvadoraceae. I. Harms, Hermann, 1870-

3—30321

Library of Congress QK97.E6

NK 0205470 DLC OU PPT

Knoblauch, Emil [Friedrich] 1864–
Anatomie des holzes der laurineen ... Regensburg, F. H. Neubauer, 1888.

66, [2] p. fold. tables. 22½cm.
Inaug.-diss.—Königsberg.

1. Laurineae. 2. Wood.

1-G-2412

Library of Congress QK687.K72

NK 0205471 DLC MH-A ICRL CU DNLM

Knoblauch, Emil Friedrich, 1864-

Warming, Eugenius, 1841-1924.
A handbook of systematic botany, by Dr. E. Warming ... with a revision of the *Fungi* by Dr. E. Knoblauch ... tr. and ed. by M. C. Potter ... London, S. Sonnenschein & co.; New York, Macmillan & co., 1895.

Knoblauch, Emil Friedrich, 1864- tr.

Warming, Eugenius, 1841-1924.
Handbuch der systematischen botanik. Von dr. Eug. Warming ... Deutsche ausg., von dr. Emil Knoblauch ... Mit einer einleitung in die morphologie und biologie von blüte und frucht. Vom verfasser durchgesehene und ergänzte ausg. Berlin, Gebrüder Borntraeger (E. Eggers) 1890.

Knoblauch, Emil [Friedrich] 1864-
Ökologische anatomie der holzpflanzen der südafrikanischen immergrünen buschregion ... Tübingen, Druck von H. Laupp, jr., 1896.

2 p. l., 44 p., 1 l. 23cm.
Inaug.-diss.—Giessen.

1. Botany—Oecology. 2. Botany—Anatomy. 3. Trees—Africa, South.

1-G-2406

Library of Congress QK903.K72

NK 0205474 DLC NN

NA1088 Knoblauch, Ernst
K58C7 Ernst Knoblauch, von Paul Joseph Cremers. Berlin, F. E.
Arch. Hübsch [1929]
Library viii p., 44 plates, plans. (Neue Werkkunst)

I. Cremers, Paul Joseph, 1897-

NK 0205475 CU NNC MH

Knoblauch, Ferdinand.
Bettel und landstreicherei im königreich Bayern von 1893–1899. Eine kriminalstatistische studie nach amtlichem material bearbeitet, von dr. Ferdinand Knoblauch. München, E. Reinhardt, 1910.

70 p. double map. 25cm. (Statistische und nationalekonomische abhandlungen ... hft. VI)

1. Begging—Bavaria. 2. Tramps—Bavaria. 3. Criminal statistics—Bavaria. I. Title.

39-20346

Library of Congress HV4560.B3K55 [2]

NK 0205476 DLC MH-L NN

4TT Knoblauch, Ferdinand
110 Wissenschaftliche Ergebnisse der Ausstellung München 1927 "Das bayerische Handwerk". [Im Auftrage des Bayerischen Handwerkskammertages hrsg. von Ferd. Knoblauch unter Mitwirkung von Ludw. Pfeuffer. München, Selbstverlag der Handwerkskammer von Oberbayern, 1927]
160 p.

NK 0205477 DLC-P4

---

ha
TX Knoblauch, G
721 Kochbuch oder meine vieljährigen Erfahrungen.
K72 2. Aufl. Berlin, Stuhr, 1829.
296p.

1. Cookery, German. 2. Cookery-Early works, 1800-1850. I. Title.

NK 0205478 NIC

Knoblauch, Georg, 1912-
see Knoblauch, Hans Georg, 1912-

Knoblauch, Gustav
Die neue Synagoge in Berlin
see under Knoblauch, Carl Heinrich Eduard, 1801-1865.

Knoblauch, Gustav, 1865-
Über myomoperationen. Beitrag zur transperitonealen enucleation ... Halle a.S., C.A. Kaemmerer & co., 1890.
52, [2] p. 23 cm. [Halle. Universität. Dissertationen. v. 13, no. 4]
Inaug.-diss. - Halle.
Lebenslauf.

NK 0205481 CU DNLM PPC

Knoblauch, Hans, 1894-
Die organisation der deutschen brauindustrie. 1920.
Dissertation.

NK 0205482 PU CtY

AC Knoblauch, Hans Georg, 1912-
831 Chemische reaktionen mit aktivem stickstoff. ... Jena, 1935.
Inaug. Diss. - Berlin, 1935.
Lebenslauf.
Literaturverzeichnis.

NK 0205483 ICRL CtY

Knoblauch, Heinz, 1903-
Die Rechtsstellung des Verkäufers bei Verschulden seines Lieferanten ... [von] Heinz Knoblauch. Berlin, 1927.

vii, 46, [2] p. 22cm.

Inaug.-Diss. - Freiburg i. B.
"Lebenslauf": p. [48]
"Literatur": p. v-vii.

NK 0205484 MH-L ICRL

VOLUME 300

Knoblauch, Helmut.
Versuche über den Wärmeaustausch zwischen Bremstrommel und Felge bei Lastkraftwagen und Omnibussen... von Diplom-Ingenieur Helmut Knoblauch... [München: J. B. Lindl,] 1932. 44 p. incl. diagrs., tables. illus. 30cm. (Reichsverband der Automobilindustrie. Versuchsbericht. Nr. 5.)
Dissertation — München, 1932.
1. Brakes, Automobile. I. Ser. N. Y. P. L. June 12, 1934
NK 0205485 NN

Knoblauch, Henning, 1904-
Entwicklung von hochspannungsionenröhren hoher leistungsfähigkeit, insbesondere für kathodenstrahloszillographen. ... 30 p.
Inaug. Diss. -Techn. Hochsch. Berlin, 1932.
Lebenslauf.
Bibliography.
NK 0205486 ICRL

Knoblauch, Henning, 1904 -

Ardenne, Manfred, *baron* von, 1907–
Die kathodenstrahlröhre und ihre anwendung in der schwachstromtechnik, von Manfred von Ardenne, unter mitarbeit von dr.-ing. Henning Knoblauch. Mit 432 textabbildungen. Berlin, J. Springer, 1933.

Knoblauch, Hermann
see
Knoblauch, Carl Hermann, 1820-1895

914.364 Knoblauch, Hugo.
K751m2 Meran; ein führer für kurgäste und touristen ... 2.aufl. Meran, S. Pötzelberger, 1870.
175p. fold.map.
1. Meran, Austria--Descr.--Guide-books.
NK 0205489 IU

Knoblauch, Hugo.
Meran, führer für kurgäste und touristen. Mit medicinischer einleitung von Dr. Joseph Pircher... 5. aufl. verichtigt und ergänzt von F. W. Ellmenreich...Meran, Pötzelberger, 1891.
182 p. S.
NK 0205490 NRU

Knoblauch, Hugo
Meran. Führer für Kurgäste und Touristen von Hugo Knoblauch. Mit medicinischer Einleitung vom Kais. Rath Dr. Josef Pircher von Pirchof... 6. Auflage. Berichtigt und ergänzt von F.W. Ellmenreich. Mit Karte von Meran und Umgebung Meran, F.W. Ellmenreich, 1884.
240p. [6]p.
NK 0205491 MiU

Knoblauch, Hugo.
Meran. Führer für Kurgäste und Touristen von Hugo Knoblauch. Mit medicinischer Einleitung vom Kais. Rath Dr. Josef Pircher von Pirchof. Neunte Auflage. Berichtigt und ergänzt von F. W. Ellmenreich. Mit Karte von Meran und Umgegend. Meran, F. W. Ellmenreich, 1892.
xxiii, 259, [6] p. incl. tables. 1 fold. map in pocket. 17cm.
"Memorandum zum Meraner Führer," p. [2-3].
Map wanting.
NK 0205492 ICJ

Knoblauch, Hugo.
Meran und umgebung
see under Ellmenreich, F W

Knoblauch, Hugo, b. 1829. ed.
JN3835 Die deutschen Reichstagswahlen der I. II. III.
K72 IV. legislaturperiode 1871, 1874, 1877 und 1878. Gesammelt und graphisch dargestellt von Hugo
Hoover Library Knoblauch ... Berlin, C. Heymann, 1878.
cover title, 1 p.l.,3-8 p. fold.map. 25½cm.
1. Germany. Reichstag - Elections. I.Title.
NK 0205494 CSt-H PU

Knoblauch, Hugo, b. 1829.
Deutschlands tabaks-bau und ernte. Nach amtlichen, von den steuerbehörden direct erhaltenen quellen berechnet und graphisch dargestellt, von Hugo Knoblauch ... Berlin, Verlag des Patent- und technischen bureaus von H. Knoblauch & co., 1878.
[8] p. incl. tables (2 fold.) fold. map. 20 cm.
1. Tobacco - Statistics - Germany.
NK 0205495 CU

Knoblauch, Hugo, *b.* 1829, *ed.*
Das Patentgesetz für das Deutsche reich. Vom 25. mai 1877. Durch die bisher ergangenen instructionen, verfügungen, entscheidungen etc. etc. erläutert von Hugo Knoblauch ... Berlin, E. Grosser, 1880.
2 p. l., 368 p. 18cm.
1. Patent laws and legislation—Germany. I. Germany. Laws, statutes, etc. II. Title.
42-40906
NK 0205496 DLC

Knoblauch, Johann Georg, 1697-1753.
Dissertatio juridica inauguralis de zittaviensi communione bonorum inter conjuges, ejusque praecipuis effectibus in foro. Lipsiae, n.d.
32 p. 16°
Diss. --- Leipzig, 1731.
NK 0205497 MH-L

B [Knoblauch, Johann Georg] 1697-1753.
M9583k Herrn Gottfried Polycarp Müllers, Direct. Gymn. Zittav. und Bischoffs der Mährischen Brüder in Herrnhut; Leben und Schriften, wie solches mit grosser Mühe gesammlet worden. Franckfurth, 1750.
120p. 17cm.
1. Müller, Gottfried Polycarp, 1685-1747. I. Title: Herrn Gottfried Polycarp Müllers - Leben und Schriften.
NK 0205498 IU

[Knoblauch, Johann Georg] 1697-1753.
Zg17 Unpartheyische Nachricht von der Gemeine zu
Z67 Herrn-Hut in Ober-Lausitz. Schlesswig, 1737.
735b 45p. 17½cm. [Binder's title: Zinzendorf. Herrnhut. Sieben Schriften]
NK 0205499 CtY MH

FILM [Knoblauch, Johann Georg] 1697-1753.
4333 Unpartheyische Nachricht von der Gemeine zu
PT Herrn-Hut in Ober-Lausitz. Schlesswig, 1737.
Reel 45p. 18cm. [Binder's title: Zinzendorf.
481 Herrnhut. Sieben Schriften]
(German Baroque Literature, No.1485, reel No. 481, Research Publications, Inc.)
Microfilm.
NK 0205500 CU

Knoblauch, Johannes: Über das Carcinom der Nase und der Nasennebenhöhlen, im Anschluß an zwei in d. hiesigen Universitätsklinik f. Ohren-, Nasen- u. Kehlkopfkrankheiten beobachtete Fälle. [Maschinenschrift.] 53 S. 4°. — Auszug: Halle a. S. 1922. 2 Bl. 8°
Halle, Med. Diss. v. 15. Febr. 1922 [U 22. 4185
NK 0205501 ICRL

Knoblauch, Johannes, 1855-1915.
Einleitung in die allgemeine theorie der krummen flächen, von dr. Johannes Knoblauch ... Leipzig, B. G. Teubner, 1888.
viii, 267 p. 25½cm.
"Literatur": p. [264]
1. Surfaces.
NK 0205502 PU-Math ICJ TxFTC ViU NBuU MiEM CU NcU CtY NjP MiU OU OO

Knoblauch, Johannes, 1855–1915.
Grundlagen der differentialgeometrie. Von Johannes Knoblauch. Leipzig und Berlin, B. G. Teubner, 1913.
x, 634 p. illus. 23½cm. mk. 20
"Literatur": p. [607]-614.
1. Geometry, Differential.
Library of Congress QA641.K7 14—2042
NK 0205503 ICJ NN NcD NjP CaBVaU DLC MtU IaU CU OU OC1W MiU PU-Math NcU

---

q512 Knoblauch, Johannes, 1855-
K75a Der innere zusammenhang der flächentheoretischen grundformeln. [Berlin, 1904]
p.[113]-143.
No.4. in a volume lettered: Knoblauch. Abhandlungen.
"Sonderabdruck aus hft.2 bd.130 des Journals für die reine und angewandte mathematik."
NK 0205504 IU

Knoblauch, Johannes, 1855-1915, ed.

Weierstrass, Karl Theodor Wilhelm, 1815-1897.
Mathematische werke von Karl Weierstrass. Herausgegeben unter mitwirkung einer von der Königlich preussischen akademie der wissenschaften eingesetzten commission ... Berlin, Mayer & Müller. 1894-1927.

---

q512 Knoblauch, Johannes, 1855-
K75a ... Ueber biegungscovarianten. [Berlin, 1892]
p.[277]-289.
No.1 in a volume lettered: Knoblauch: Abhandlungen.
"Sonderabdruck aus hft. 4 bd. 111 des Journals für die reine und angewandte mathematik."
NK 0205506 IU

VOLUME 300

Knoblauch, Johannes, 1855-1915.
Über die allgemaine wellenfläche ...
Berlin, G. Schade (O. Francke) [1882]
1 p.l., 40 p., 1 l. 27 cm. (German mathematical dissertations. Berlin, v. 7)
Inaug.-diss. - Berlin.
Vita.

NK 0205507 RPB

q512 K75a Knoblauch, Johannes, 1855-
Über die geometrische bedeutung der flächentheoretischen fundamentalgleichungen. [Berlin, 1889]
p.249-257.
No.5 in a volume lettered: Knoblauch. Abhandlungen.
"Abdruck aus Acta mathematica, Bd.15."

NK 0205508 IU

q512 K75a Knoblauch, Johannes, 1855-
Zur simultanen transformation quadratischer differentialformen. [Berlin, 1894]
p.[185]-200.
No.3 in a volume lettered: Knoblauch. Abhandlungen.
"Sonderabdruck aus hft.3 bd.115 des Journals für die reine und angewandte mathematik."

NK 0205509 IU

q512 K75a Knoblauch, Johannes, 1855-1915.
Zur theorie der differentialparameter. [Berlin, 1892]
p.[329]-343.
No.2. in a volume lettered: Knoblauch. Abhandlungen.
"Sonderabdruck aus hft.4 bd.111 des Journals für die reine und angewandte mathematik."

NK 0205510 IU

WM K71e 1815 KNOBLAUCH, Joseph Wilhelm
Epidemion; oder, Annalen der Epidemieen, Endemieen, Contagien, Constitutionen und des Genius der Krankheiten. 1. Heft. Leipzig, Mittler, 1815.
xvi, 190 p.
No more published?

NK 0205511 DNLM

WA K72v 1810 KNOBLAUCH, Joseph Wilhelm
Von den Mitteln und Wegen, die mannichfaltigen Verfälschungen sämmtlicher Lebensmittel ausserhalb der gesetzlichen Untersuchung zu erkennen, zu verhüten, wo möglich wieder aufzuheben Leipzig, Mittler, 1810.
3 pts. in 2 v.
"Eine durch die königl. böhm. Gesellschaft der Wissenschaften zu Prag genehmigte Preisschrift."

NK 0205512 DNLM

Knoblauch, Karl, 1875-
Das verhältnis der "Croniques admirables" zu den "Croniques inestimables" und zu Rabelais ... Von Karl Knoblauch ... Jena, A. Kämpfe, 1904.
76 p., 1 l. 22 cm.
Inaug.-diss. - Würzburg.
Lebenslauf.
"Literatur": p. [75]-76.
1. Girault, François, fl. 1534. Les croniques admirables du puissant roy Gargantua. 2. Les grandes chroniques de Gargantua. 3. Rabelais, François, 1490(ca.)-1553?

NK 0205513 MiU NjP ICRL MH

B 3999 M6 K72 [Knoblauch, Karl von] 1756-1794.
Anti-Taumaturgie; oder, Die Bezweiflung der Wunder. Loretto, 1790.
190 p. 16cm.
"Ueber Wunder. Ein Versuch nach Spinogens Grundsäzen": p. [7]-46.
1. Miracles--Early works to 1800. 2. Spinoza, Benedictus de, 1632-1677. I. Title.

NK 0205514 NIC

[Knoblauch, Karl von, 1756-1794.]
Über den Pan, und sein verhältnis zum Sylvanus; eine antiquarisch-philosophische abhandlung. Biel, 1794.
pp. 71.

Pan (God)|Silvanus (God)|Title|

NK 0205515 MH

Knoblauch, Kurt von.
Das kleine wörterbuch in sechs sprachen mit bildern, von Kurt v. Knoblauch. Berlin, F. Winckler & co., 1939.
72 p. illus. 16½cm.
"Neben den bildern ist die bezeichnung in sechs sprachen angegeben ... links: deutsch, englisch, französisch; rechts: italienisch, portugiesisch und spanisch."—Vorwort.
1. Dictionaries, Polyglot. I. Title. 42-30271
Library of Congress PB331.K6
[2] 413

NK 0205516 DLC

Knoblauch, Leonhard Paul
see Knoblauch, Paul, 1887-

Knoblauch (Leop. Bernh.) *De rigiditate orificii uteri. 15 pp. 8°. Jenæ, typ. Schreiberi et fil., 1857. [P., v. 401.]

NK 0205518 DNLM

F547 .D9F4 1951 Knoblauch, Marion, 1909- ed.
FOR OTHER EDITIONS SEE MAIN ENTRY
Federal Writers' Project. *Illinois.*
Du Page County, a descriptive and historical guide. Edited by Marion Knoblauch. Special [rev.] ed. published in commemoration of its twenty-fifth anniversary, 1925-1950. Wheaton, Ill., Du Page Title Co. [1951]

QD95 .K72 Knoblauch, Oscar, 1862-
Absorptions-spectralanalyse sehr verduennter loesungen.
Leipzig, 1891
Habilitationsschrift - Erlangen

NK 0205520 DLC DNLM CU

Knoblauch, Oscar, 1862-
Anleitung zu genauen technischen temperaturmessungen mit flüssigkeits- und elektrischen thermometern, von dr. Osc. Knoblauch ... [und] dr.-ing. K. Hencky ... mit 65 textabbildungen. München und Berlin, R. Oldenbourg, 1919.
xiii, 128 p. illus., diagrs. 21½cm. (Added t.-p.: Oldenbourgs technische handbibliothek, bd. XXII)
1. Thermometers and thermometry. I. Hencky, Karl, 1889- joint author.
[Full name: Carl Wilhelm Hermann Oscar Knoblauch]
Library of Congress QC271.K6 21-2646

NK 0205521 DLC CU ICJ

4QC 665 Knoblauch, Oscar, 1862-
Anleitung zu genauen technischen Temperaturmessungen, von Osc. Knoblauch [und] K. Hencky. 2., völlig neu bearb. und erweiterte Aufl. München, R. Oldenbourg, 1926.
174 p.

NK 0205522 DLC-P4 NNC OO DAS ICJ

Knoblauch, Oscar, 1862- joint author.
Wartenberg, Hans von, 1880-
Hohe und tiefe temperaturen, von H. von Wartenberg ... Gasverflüssigung und ihre thermodynamischen grundlagen, von H. Lenz ... Wärmeleitung, von Osc. Knoblauch ... und H. Reiher ... Wärmestrahlung, von W. Wien und C. Müller ... Leipzig. Akademische verlagsgesellschaft m. b. h., 1929.

Knoblauch, Oscar, 1862-
...Merkblatt fuer temperaturmessungen mit fluessigkeits-und elektrischen thermometern...Bearb. auf. veranlassung und unter mitwirkung der Hauptstelle [fuer waerme wirtschaft] [Berlin, 1923]
7 p. 32 cm.

NK 0205524 DBS

Knoblauch, Oscar, 1862-
Die spezifische wärme *cp* des überhitzten wasserdampfes für drucke von 2 bis 8 kg/qcm und temperaturen von 350 bis 550° C. (Mitteilung aus dem Laboratorium für technische physik der Kgl. technischen hochschule München) Von Osc. Knoblauch und Hilde Mollier.
(*In* Mitteilungen über forschungsarbeiten auf dem gebiete des ingenieurwesens ... Berlin, 1911. 26½cm. hft. 108 und 109, p. [79]-106 incl. illus., tables, diagrs.)
Bibliographical foot-notes.
1. Specific heat. 2. Steam, Superheated. I. Mollier, Hilde, joint author.
[Full name: Karl Wilhelm Hermann Oscar Knoblauch]
Library, U. S. Patent Office TA3.F732 P O 28-249

NK 0205525 DP

Knoblauch, Oscar, 1862-
... Die spezifische wärme *cp* des überhitzten wasserdampfes für drücke von 8 bis 20 at und von sättigungstemperatur bis 380° C, von Oscar Knoblauch und Alexander Winkhaus.
(*In* Forschungsarbeiten auf dem gebiete des ingenieurwesens ... Berlin, 1917. 26½cm. hft. 195, p. [3]-30 incl. illus., tables, diagrs.)
Bibliographical foot-notes.
1. Specific heat. 2. Steam, Superheated. I. Winkhaus, Alexander, joint author.
[Full name: Carl Wilhelm Hermann Oscar Knoblauch]
Library, U. S. Patent Office TA3.F732 P O 28-330

NK 0205526 DP NN

Knoblauch, Oscar, 1862-
... Die spezifische waerme des ueberhitzten wasserdampfes für drucke von 20 bis 30 at und von saettigungs. temperatur bis 350° C ... (Mitt a.d. Lab. t. tech. physik, T.H. Muenchen) [Berlin, 1922]
6 p. 32 cm.
By Oscar Knoblauch and Erwin Raish.

NK 0205527 DBS

QC 71 P57+ v.11 no. 6 Knoblauch, Oscar, 1862-
Strahlende Wärme [n. p., 18--]
42 p. 22cm.
A review of 20 works on the subject of radiant heat.
1. Radiant heating--Bibl.

NK 0205528 NIC

VOLUME 300

Knoblauch, Oscar, 1862–
Tabellen und diagramme für wasserdampf, berechnet aus der spezifischen wärme, von dr. phil. dr.-ing. e. h. Osc. Knoblauch ... dipl.-ing. E. Raisch ... dipl.-ing. H. Hausen ... mit 4 abbildungen im text und 3 diagrammtafeln als beilage. München und Berlin, R. Oldenbourg, 1923.
32 p. tables, diagrs. (3 fold.; in pocket) 27cm.
1. Steam—Tables, calculations, etc. I. Raisch, E., joint author. II. Hausen, H., joint author.
[Full name: Carl Wilhelm Hermann Oscar Knoblauch]
24-103
Library of Congress TJ270.K4

NK 0205529 DLC NN

TJ 270 K72+ 1932
Knoblauch, Oscar, 1862-
Tabellen und Diagramme für Wasserdampf, berechnet aus der spezifischen Wärme, bearb. von Osc. Knoblauch [et al.] 2. neubearb. und erweiterte Aufl. der "Tabellen und Diagramme für Wasserdampf" von Knoblauch, Raisch, Hausen. München, R. Oldenbourg, 1932.
vi,40 p. 2 fold. diagrs. (in pocket) 27cm.
R-1/26/65 C-3/3/65 L.C.
1. Steam--Tables, calculations, etc. I. Title.

NK 0205530 NIC NN

Knoblauch, Oscar, 1862–
Technisch-physikalisches praktikum; ausgewählte untersuchungsmethoden der technischen physik, von dr. phil. dr.-ing. eh. Osc. Knoblauch ... und dr.-ing. We. Koch ... mit 104 textabbildungen. Berlin, J. Springer, 1934.
iv p., 1 l., 167, [1] p. incl. illus., tables, diagrs. 24cm.
1. Physical measurements. 2. Physics—Laboratory manuals. I. Koch, Werner, joint author. II. Title.
[Full name: Carl Wilhelm Hermann Oscar Knoblauch]
35-8967
Library of Congress QC41.K6
Copyright A—Foreign 26991
[2] 530.72

NK 0205531 DLC OrCS NcU

Knoblauch, Oscar, 1862–
Die thermischen eigenschaften des gesättigten und des überhitzten wasserdampfes zwischen 100° und 180° C. I. teil. Bericht über die bestimmung der dichte des gesättigten und des überhitzten wasserdampfes zwischen 100° und 180° C. Von Osc. Knoblauch, R. Linde und H. Klebe.
(*In* Mitteilungen über forschungsarbeiten auf dem gebiete des ingenieurwesens ... Berlin, 1905. 26½cm. hft. 21, p. [33]–55. tables, diagrs. (1 fold.))
"Mitteilung aus dem Laboratorium für technische physik der Kgl. technischen hochschule, München."
Bibliographical foot-notes.
1. Steam, Superheated. I. Linde, Richard, 1880– joint author. II. Klebe, Heinrich, 1877– joint author.
[Full name: Carl Wilhelm Hermann Oscar Knoblauch]
P O 28-115
Library, U. S. Patent Office TA3.F732

NK 0205532 DP

Knoblauch, Oscar, 1862–
Ueber die abhängigkeit der spezifischen wärme c_p des wasserdampfes von druck und temperatur. (Mitteilung aus dem Laboratorium für technische physik der Kgl. technischen hochschule, München) Von Osc. Knoblauch und Max Jakob.
(*In* Mitteilungen über forschungsarbeiten auf dem gebiete des ingenieurwesens ... Berlin, 1906. 26½ cm. hft. 35 und 36, p. [109]–152. illus., tables, diagrs. (1 fold.))
Bibliographical foot-notes.
1. Specific heat. 2. Steam. I. Jakob, Max, 1879– joint author.
[Full name: Carl Wilhelm Hermann Oscar Knoblauch]
P O 28—154
U. S. Patent Office. Libr. for Library of Congress TA3.F732 [a48b½]

NK 0205533 DP DLC

Knoblauch, Oscar, and Hilde **Mollier,** 1862–
Über die spezifische Wärme c_p des überhitzten Wasserdampfes für Drucke bis 8 Atmosphären und Temperaturen von 450°C. bis 550°C.
(*In* Koeniglich-bayerische Akademie der Wissenschaften. Munich. Mathematisch-physikalische Klasse. Sitzungsberichte. Jahrgang 1910, Abhandlung I. 6 pp. Chart. München. 1910.)

M262 — Steam. Superheated. — Specific heat. — Jt. auth.

NK 0205534 MB MdBJ

Knoblauch, Oscar & Hencky, K., 1862-
...Ueber die temperatur der von der sonne bestrahlten eisenbahnschienen und die bestimmung der temperatur derselben beim verlegen... (Mitt a.d.Lab.f.tech.physik,T.H.Muenchen). [Muenchen,1918].
cover-title,4 p. 32 cm.

NK 0205535 DBS

Knoblauch, Oscar, 1862–
Untersuchungen über die bewegung eines flüssigen, homogenen ellipsoides, in welchem die elementaranziehung der entfernung direct proportional ist ... von Oscar Knoblauch ... Bonn, Universitäts-buchdruckerei von C. Georgi, 1887.
2 p. l., 62 p., 1 l. 21½cm.
Inaug.-diss.—Bonn.
Lebenslauf.
1. Hydrodynamics.
[Full name: Carl Wilhelm Hermann Oscar Knoblauch]
5-18202 Revised
Library of Congress QA913.K72

NK 0205536 DLC MiU

QC274 .V4 1940
Knoblauch, Oscar, 1862–
Verein deutscher ingenieure. *Ausschuss für temperaturmessregeln.*
VDI-temperaturmessregeln. 2. auflage des teiles I der Regeln für messverfahren bei abnahmeversuchen und in der betriebsüberwachung, herausgegeben vom Verein deutscher ingenieure im NS-bund deutscher technik. Berlin, VDI-verlag g. m. b. h., 1940.

Knoblauch, Oscar, 1862-
Wärmeleitung, von Osc. Knoblauch ... und H. Reiher ...
(In Handbuch der experimentalphysik ... hrsg. von W. Wien ... und R. Harms ... Leipzig, 1929. 25 cm. bd. 9, t. 1, p. [187]-344. illus., tables. diagrs.)

NK 0205538 RPB

---

761 K75b
Knoblauch, Paul, 1887-
Die bildinitialen der Augsburger Zainerbibel und der Sensenschmidbibel. Greifswald, 1916.
116p.
Inaug.-diss.--Greifswald.
Lebenslauf.
"Literatur": p.[3]-4.

NK 0205539 IU CtY

---

738 K75s
Knoblauch, Peter
Studien zur archaisch-griechischen tonbildnerei in Kreta, Rhodos, Athen und Böotien ... Halle (S), 1937.
230p. incl.plates.
Inaug.-diss.--Halle.
Lebenslauf.
"Literaturverzeichnis": p.209-217.
1. Terra-cotta statuettes. 2. Greece--Antiq.

NK 0205540 IU MH PBm ICRL CtY NNC CU

Knoblauch, Peter.
Studien zur archaisch-griechischen tonbildnerei in Kreta, Rhodos, Athen und Böotien, von Peter Knoblauch. Bleicherode am Harz, C. Nieft, 1937.
219 p. plates. 21cm.
"Diese arbeit hat im februar 1937 der Philosophischen fakultät der Martin-Luther-universität Halle-Wittenberg als doktor-dissertation vorgelegen."
"Literaturverzeichnis": p. 209–217.
1. Terra-cottas, Greek. I. Title: Tonbildnerei in Kreta, Rhodos, Athen und Böotien.
40-1620
Library of Congress NB155.K5
[2] 738

NK 0205541 DLC NIC NcD OCU

Knoblauch, Richard.
Vom Mälzen und Brauen; eine Wanderung durch den neuzeitlichen Braubetrieb, von Richard Knoblauch. Mit 16 Aquarellen von Franz Peffer. Berlin: Im Verlage der Landsbergschen Buchhandlung [1929] 17 l. mounted col'd illus. 29 x 23cm.
Printed on double leaves folded in Chinese style.
914973A. 1. Brewing.
N. Y. P. L. December 17, 1937

NK 0205542 NN

KNOBLAUCH, Rudolf, 1861-
Die rechtsverhältnisse und das kreditwesen der lüneburgschen ritterschaft. Inaug.-diss. Berlin, 1902.
"Lebenslauf," after p.35.

NK 0205543 MH ICRL CtY PU

---

von Knoblauch (Rudolph) [1864–].
* Ein Beitrag zur Behandlung der acuten Osteomyelitis. 30 pp., 1 l. 8°. *Marburg, R. Friedrich*, 1892.

NK 0205544 DNLM

Knoblauch, W von
see Knoblauch zu Hatzbach, Wilhelm Philipp von, 1860-

Knoblauch, Walter, 1880-
Nichtigkeit und Anfechtbarkeit einer Ehe ... von Walter Knoblauch ... Berlin, G. Schade, 1910.
108 p. 21½cm.
Inaug.-diss. - Heidelberg.
"Lebenslauf": p. 108.
"Literatur-Verzeichnis": p.[7]-8.

NK 0205546 MH-L ICRL

Knoblauch, Wilhelm von
see Knoblauch zu Hatzbach, Wilhelm Philipp von, 1860-

WA 14304
Knoblauch zu Hatzbach, Wilhelm Philipp von, 1860-
A dictionary of Argot (French-English) London, G. Routledge, New York, E. P. Dutton [n.d.]
110 p.
1. French language - Slang - Dictionaries.

NK 0205548 CtY OrP CU MiEM

Knoblauch zu Hatzbach, Wilhelm Philipp von, 1860- ed.
The early life of Goethe
see under Goethe, Johann Wolfgang von 1749-1832.
Aus meninem Leben. Selections. English.

Knoblauch zu Hatzbach, Wilhelm Philipp von, 1860-
Der englische Dolmetscher mit englischer Aussprache (methode Thimm),... Neubearbeitete und erweiterte Aufl....2.Aufl.,durchgesehen von Heinrich Dorgeel. Philadelphia, D.McKay [1905]
At head of title: Marlborough's English self-taught for Germans.

NK 0205550 MH-Ed MiD WaS

VOLUME 300

Knoblauch zu Hatzbach, Wilhelm Philipp von, 1860-
... Der englische dolmetscher mit englischer aussprache ... zweite auflage ... Lond.Marlborough,1919.
Front.D. (Marlborough's self-taught series)

NK 0205551 CaBViP

Knoblauch zu Hatzbach, Wilhelm Philipp von, 1860-
English self-taught for the Germans. Der englische dolmetscher mit englischer aussprache (méthode Thimm) ... neubearb. und erweiterte aufl., von W. von Knoblauch. 2. aufl., durchgesehen von Heinrich Dorgeel. Philadelphia, D. McKay [19—?]
120 p. 14 x 7cm.
"39 valuable books": p. 2.
Blank lines for "notes" at the bottom of every page.

1. English language—Conversation and phrase-books—German. I. Title.

A 12-274

Title from City Library, Springfield, Mass. Printed by L. C.

NK 0205552 MS

Knoblauch zu Hatzbach, Wilhelm Philipp von.

Thimm, Carl Albert.
... German technical words & phrases. An English-German and German-English dictionary of technical and business terms and phrases used in commerce, arts, sciences, professions and trades ... by C. A. Thimm and W. von Knoblauch. 2d ed. rev. and enl. London, E. Marlborough & co., 1913.

T10 .M35 1932
Knoblauch zu Hatzbach, Wilhelm Philipp von, 1860-
Marlborough's German technical words & phrases, in Roman characters, ideal for quick reference; English-German and German-English dictionary. 3d ed. enl. and rev. by E. M. Rolffs ... London, E. Marlborough & co. ltd. [1932]

Knoblauch zu Hatzbach, Wilhelm Philipp von, 1860-
Die moderne Leihbibliothek, von Wilhelm von Knoblauch. Leipzig, H. Beyer, [1909].
[4], 52 p. 22cm.

NK 0205555 ICJ

Knoblaugh, Armand Franklin
The "wolf" tone of the pianoforte... Cin., 1929. [1], 23. pl. diagrs. Thesis, Univ. of Cincinnati, PH.D., 1929.

NK 0205556 OCU

Knoblaugh, H Edward, 1904-
Correspondent in Spain, by H. Edward Knoblaugh. London & New York, Sheed & Ward, 1937.
xii p., 1 l., 233 p. ports. 21½cm.
"First printing, October, 1937."

1. Spain—Hist.—Civil war, 1936-1939. I. Title.

38-867

Library of Congress DP269.K56 [a43k1] 946.08

NK 0205557 DLC OrP WaS PP PV MB OCl OOxM OClND OEac OU OClJC OrU OrStbM DNW NN CoU CLSU IEdS

Knoblaugh, H Edward.
Correspondent in Spain, by H. Edward Knoblaugh. London & New York, Sheed & Ward, 1937 [i. e. 1938]
xii p., 1 l., 251 p. ports. 21½cm.
An appendix (p. 234-251), designed to bring the work up to date, has been added to the text of the 1937 edition.

1. Spain—Hist.—Civil war, 1936- I. Title.

38-37973

Library of Congress DP269.K56 1938
——— Copy 2.
Copyright A 123827 [5] 946.08

NK 0205558 DLC CaBVaU NcD GU

Knoblaugh, H Edward.
Correspondent in Spain, by H. Edward Knoblaugh. London & New York, Sheed & Ward, 1939.
xii p., 1 l., 233 p. ports. 22½cm.
"First printing, October, 1937; cheap edition, September, 1939."

1. Spain—Hist.—Civil war, 1936-1939. I. Title.

40-6571

Library of Congress DP269.K56 1939 [2] 946.08

NK 0205559 DLC

Knoblaugh, W C
The firing of rotary kilns with powdered coal.
(In Mining technology. York, Pa., 1937-48. 23 cm. v. 10, no. 5, Sept. 1946. 2 p. diagr.)
American Institute of Mining and Metallurgical Engineers. Technical publication no. 2042 (Class H, Industrial minerals division, no. 149)

1. Kilns, Rotary. 2. Coal, Pulverized. I. Title.
[TN1.A5256 vol. 10, no. 5] P O 51-84

U. S. Patent Office. Library for Library of Congress [1]

NK 0205560 DP

Knoble, Cliff, 1892 -
Automobile selling sense; a book on the merchandising of motor cars, prepared in the good interest of distributor, dealer, and salesman, with the ambition to aid in more effective sales-making, by Cliff Knoble. New York, Prentice-Hall, inc., 1923.
xii, 225 p. 19½cm.

1. Salesmen and salesmanship. 2. Automobiles. I. Title.

23-9477

Library of Congress HF5439.A8K6

NK 0205561 DLC ICRL WaS MiU OU OCl CU ICJ

Knoble, Cliff.
Automobile selling sense. A book on the merchandising of motor cars . . . [2d printing.]
— New York. Prentice-Hall, Inc. 1925. xii, 225 pp. Illus. Plate. Tables. Business forms. 19 cm.

N7015 — T.r. — Salesmen. — Automobiles.

NK 0205562 MB

Knoble, Cliff, 1892-
His own people, by Cliff Knoble. Chicago, Reilly & Lee [c1940]
283 p. 21cm.

I. Title.

40-35540

Library of Congress PZ3.K7555Hi

NK 0205563 DLC PP

Knoblich, A[ugustin].
Herzogin Anna von Schlesien, 1204-1265; erinnerungsblätter zu ihrem sechshundertjährigen todestage gesammelt. Breslau, G. P. Aderholz, 1865.
4°. pp. (1), vi, (1), 136, (2), 38. Front.

Anna, herzogin von Schlesien

NK 0205564 MH

BX4700 .H4K7
Knoblich, Augustin.
Lebensgeschichte der heiligen Hedwig, herzogin und landespatronin von Schlesien. 1174-1243: Festtag den fünfzehnten october. Nach den besten ältesten und neuesten quellenschriften zum ersten male ausführlich, nebst kurzen lebensumrissen der übrigen glaubenshelden der diöcese Breslau, chronologisch bearb. von Augustin Knoblich ... Breslau, Schletter (H. Skutsch) 1860.
xxx, [1], 272 p. front., pl. 21½cm.

1. Hedwig, Saint, ca. 1174-1243.

NK 0205565 ICU

Knoblich, Augustin.
Lebensgeschichte der Heiligen Hedwig, Herzogin und Landespatronin von Schlesien, 1174-1243 ... 2 Ausgabe. Breslau, Schletter, 1864.

xxx, 4-272 p. front., illus., plates, 22 cm.

Literatur: p. xvii-xxvi.

1. Hedwig, Saint, 1174-1243.

NK 0205566 PLatS

Knoblich, Gerhard, 1926-
Eine Vektormultiplikation über Gruppen. Mainz, 1955.
30 p. 21 cm.
Diss. (gekürzt)—Mainz.
Vita.
Bibliography: p. 29.

1. Groups, Theory of. 2. Vector analysis. I. Title.

QA171.K56 65-39600

NK 0205567 DLC FTaSU

Knoblich, Max, 1901-
Alkohol und zurechnungsfaehigkeit.
Inaug. diss. Breslau, 1928.
Bibl.

NK 0205568 ICRL

Knoblich, Otto, 1904 -
Die beeinträchtigung des grundeigentums durch den luftverkehr.
Inaug. Diss. Breslau, 1929
Bibl.

NK 0205569 ICRL

Knoblich, Paul, 1900-
Der einfluss verstaerkter eiweitzfuetterung auf das wachstum der wolle.
Inaug. diss. Breslau, 1926.
Bibl.

NK 0205570 ICRL MH CtY

Knoblich, Paul, joint author.

S517 .G3F3 1936
Fahl, Robert.
Die Schule als Mitkämpferin in der Erzeugungsschlacht. Von R. Fahl u. P. Knoblich. 2. Aufl. Breslau, H. Handel, 1936.

Knobling, Alois, 1904-
Die Waage. Hamburg, H. Ellermann, 1949.
41 p. (Das Gedicht; Blätter für die Dichtung)

NK 0205572 CU

VOLUME 300

Knobling, Lorenz, *ed.*
Strafrecht der zoll-, finanz-, post- und gemeindebehörden bei zuwiderhandlungen gegen die vorschriften über die erhebung öffentlicher abgaben und gefälle im königreiche Bayern. Nach amtlichen quellen und unter berücksichtigung der rechtsprechung und praxis dargestellt von L. Knobling ... Miltenberg a. M., F. Halbig, 1896.
x, 414 p. 20cm.
1. Tax evasion and avoidance—Bavaria. 2. Criminal law—Bavaria. I. Bavaria. Laws, statutes, etc.
43-35926

NK 0205573 DLC

Knobloch, Ada von
see Gersdorff, Ada von, 1854-

Knobloch (Adolphus Franciscus) [1820-].
* De pneumonia. 27 pp., 2 l. 8°. *Berolini, typ. Nietackianis,* [1844].

NK 0205575 DNLM

Knobloch, Arthur Frederick.
A digest of the reported decisions in criminal cases, contained in the reports of the Supreme court of the state of Louisiana, from first Martin to thirty-ninth Louisiana annual, with notes, and references to approved text books. By Arthur F. Knobloch. New Orleans, F. F. Hansell & bro., 1887.
2 p. l., 462 p. 23½cm.
"List of works cited and abbreviations used": verso of 2d prelim. leaf.
1. Criminal law—Louisiana. 2. Law reports, digests, etc.—Louisiana. I. Louisiana. Supreme court.
Library of Congress 32-738

NK 0205576 DLC MH-L PP-L

Knobloch, Arthur Frederick.
The Louisiana civil and criminal justice, containing numerous forms for justices of the peace, constables, young men just entering upon the practice of the law, and business men in general. By Arthur F. Knobloch ... with an appendix, containing The parish officer's guide, by Judge Edward R. Olcott and Judge Henry M. Spofford. Rev., cor. and enl. New Orleans, F. F. Hansell, 1883.
2 p. l., 263, xxxii p. 23cm.
Appendix: p. [195]-263.
1. Justices of the peace — Louisiana. 2. Constables—Louisiana. 3. Forms (Law)—Louisiana. I. Olcott, Edward Rufus. II. Spofford, Henry Martyn, 1821-1880 III. Title. IV. Title: The parish officer's guide.
Library of Congress 32-4578

NK 0205577 DLC NcD MH-L

Knobloch, Arthur Frederick.
The Louisiana justice's manual and parish officer's guide, by A. F. Knobloch. New Orleans, F. F. Hansell & bro., 1893.
iv, 434 p. 24cm.
1. Justices of the peace—Louisiana. 2. Sheriffs—Louisiana. 3. Constables—Louisiana. 4. Coroners—Louisiana. I. Title.
Library of Congress 12-34865

NK 0205578 DLC LN MH-L

Knobloch, Arthur Frederick.
The Louisiana justice's manual and parish officer's guide, by A. F. Knobloch. 2d ed., rev. and annotated, by Theodore Roehl ... New Orleans, F. F. Hansell & bros., ltd., 1924.
vi, 455 p. 24cm.
1. Justices of the peace—Louisiana. 2. Sheriffs—Louisiana. 3. Constables—Louisiana. 4. Coroners. I. Roehl, Theodore Julius, 1880- ed. II. Title.
Library of Congress 25-2293

NK 0205579 DLC

Knobloch, C., joint author.
Kunze, Karl.
Lehrbuch für anfänger auf der raschelmaschine. Von Karl Kunze und dr.-ing. C. Knobloch ... 1. aufl. Hrsg. von der Deutschen wirker-zeitung, Apolda. [Apolda] R. Birkner, 1925.

Knobloch, C L E von.
Staatswirthschaftliche vorschläge zur förderung des gemein-wohls der völker, von C. L. E. von Knobloch ... [1 heft.] Berlin [C. F. Plahn] 1833.
1 p. l., xxvi p., 1 l., 190 p., 1 l. 21cm.
No more published?
CONTENTS.—1. heft. Die benutzung des geld-stempels betreffend.
1. Money.

NK 0205581 MiU CtY

Knobloch, Carl
Zur kenntniss des orthocymol's und seiner derivate.
Freiburg I. B., 1887
Inaug. diss. Freiburg I. B.

QD341
.H9K74

NK 0205582 DLC

Knobloch, Christoph, respondent.
... De invito ... Rostochii, formis academicis Wepplingianis [1689]
see under Klein, Johann, 1659-1732, praeses.

1890-
Knobloch, Conrad, Referendar, Nimptsch: Anstiftung zum Beamtendelikt mit besonderer Rücksicht auf die Beamtenbestechung. Breslau 1912: Gutsmann. VIII, 37 S. 8°
Breslau, Jur. Diss. v. 24. Juli 1912, Ref. Gretener, O. Fischer
[Geb. 6. April 90 Breslau; Wohnort: Breslau; Staatsangeh.: Preußen; Vorbildung: Elisabeth-Gymn. Breslau Reife M. 08; Studium: Breslau 1, Lausanne 1, Breslau 4 S.; Rig. 21. Juni 12.] [U 12. 591

NK 0205584 ICRL MH-L

Knobloch, Cyril.
De conditionibus matrimonio appositis ...
see under Janke, Robert, b. 1822.

Knobloch, Cyril.
De Vratislaviae arce Caesarea. Breslau, 1870.

NK 0205586 NjP

Knobloch, Cyril.
Gregorii Bar-Hebraei scholia in Psalmum LXVIII. e codicibus mss. Vratislaviae, 1852
see under Bar Hebraeus, 1226-1286.

W 700 K72s 1953
KNOBLOCH, Edvard.
Soudní lékařství a lékařská kriminalistika. [1. vyd.] Praha, Státní pedagogické nakl., 1953.
240 p. (Učební texty vysokých škol)
1. Medical jurisprudence - Czechoslovak Republic

NK 0205588 DNLM

W 700 qK72so 1955
KNOBLOCH, Edvard.
Soudní lékařství pro studující stomatologie [napsali] Edvard Knobloch [a] Stanislav Hájek. [1. vyd.] Praha, Státní pedagogické nakl., 1955.
181 p. illus. (Učební texty vysokých škol)
1. Medical jurisprudence - Czechoslovak Republic I. Hájek, Stanislav

NK 0205589 DNLM

W 4 M96 1955
KNOBLOCH, Erich, 1928-
Untersuchungen über Veränderungen der Pregnandiolausscheidung nach Injektion von Steroid- und gonadotropen Hormonen. [München] 1955.
47, 4 *l.* illus.
Inaug.-Diss. - Munich.
1. Corpus luteum - Hormones 2. Gonadotropins 3. Hormones - Steroid

NK 0205590 DNLM

Knobloch, Erich Julius: Die Rügepflicht bei der Falschlieferung. [Maschinenschrift.] 75 S. 4°. — Auszug: (Naumburg a. d. S.) 1922: (Pätz). 2 Bl. 8°
Halle, R.- u. staatswiss. Diss. v. 23. Mai 1922 [U 22. 4065

NK 0205591 ICRL

Knobloch, Eugen, 1903-
Bericht über die zweite Hälfte des XXVII. Tausend der Geburten an der Universitäts-Frauen-Klinik zu Würzburg ... Würzburg, 1928.
Inaug.-Diss. - Würzburg.
Lebenslauf.

NK 0205592 CtY

W 1 TH865 no. 252 1948
KNOBLOCH, Ferdinand
O biologii schizofrenie. V Praze, Nákl. Spolku českých lékařů, 1948.
33 p. illus. (Thomayerova sbírka přednášek a rozprav z oboru lékařského, 252)
Cover title.
Supplement to Časopis lékařů českých, čís. 16, 1948.
1. Schizophrenia - Etiology & pathogenesis Series

NK 0205593 DNLM

Knobloch, Ferdinand.
Repetitorium soudní psychiatrie. Ferd. Knobloch, Jiřina Knoblochová. [Vyd. 1.] Praha, Státní pedagogické nakl., 1954 [i. e. 1955]
117 p. 29 cm. (Učební texty vysokých škol)
At head of title: Karlova universita v Praze. Fakulta právnická.
1. Forensic psychiatry. I. Knoblochová, Jiřina, joint author. II. Title.
RA1151.K69 57-58300 ‡

NK 0205594 DLC DNLM

Knobloch, Frederick S.
Manhattan college, *New York.*
The Bishop Bonaventure F. Broderick collection of ancient coins, catalogued by Frederick S. Knobloch ... New York city, Manhattan college [pref. 1942]

Knobloch, Fritz.
Deutschlands Kali-Industrie [Karte] herausgegeben von der Mitteldeutschen Privat-Bank, Aktiengesellschaft, Magdeburg.
— [Magdeburg. 1912.] Title-page. 12 folded maps. Scale: Übersichtskarte, 1:500000 (or, 7.9 miles to 1 inch). Blatt 1–10, 1:100000 (or, 1.6 miles to 1 inch). Blatt 11, 1:50000 (or, 4166⅔ feet to 1 inch. In portfolio, 52 × 42 cm.
H9388 — Germany. Mines. — Potash. – Mitteldeutsche Privat-Bank, Aktiengesellschaft. Pubs.

NK 0205596 MB NNC

VOLUME 300

Knobloch, Georg von, 1881-
Ueber familiaeres vorkommen von lichen ruber planus.
Inaug. Diss. Rostock, 1907.
Bibl.

NK 0205597 ICRL MBCo DNLM

W 4 F86 1939 Knobloch, Gerhard, 1915-
Ueber den Na/Cl Quotienten bei Leberkranken und Kranken mit pathologischen Wasseransammlungen. [Freiburg im Breisgau? 1939?]
24 p.
Inaug.-Diss. - Freiburg
Bibliography: p. 20-22.

NK 0205598 DNLM

Knobloch, Günter, 1910-
Die rechtliche Stellung des Werberats der deutschen Wirtschaft von Günter Knobloch. Coburg: Gedruckt im Tageblatt-Haus, 1938. 75 p. 22½cm.
Dissertation — Breslau, 1937.
Lebenslauf.
"Literaturverzeichnis," p. 5-6.

1. Publicity—Jurisp.—Germany. 2. Germany. Wirtschaft, Werberat der.
N. Y. P. L. February 27, 1940

NK 0205599 NN CtY

AC 831 Knobloch, Günther
Die vom staate garantierten anleihen öffentlicher körperschaften im falle der gebietsveränderung ...
59 p.
Inaug. Diss. -Würzburg, n.d.
Bibliography.

NK 0205600 ICRL

Knobloch, Hans, pseud.
See
Knobloch, Hilda, 1890-

Knobloch, Hans.
... Die ballistik in der luftwaffe, vom bombenwerfen, schiessen und vom treffen, von dr.-ing. Hans Knobloch; mit 72 abbildungen. Berlin, Dr. M. Matthiesen & co., 1942.
78 p. incl. plates, diagrs. 21cm. (Luftfahrt-lehrbücherei, bd. 12)
Bibliography: p. 69-70.

1. Ballistics. 2. Air warfare. I. Title.
44-989
Library of Congress UF820.K6
[3] 623.54

NK 0205602 DLC WaS MCM

Knobloch, Hans.
Die Ballistik in der Luftwaffe, vom Bombenwerfen, Schiessen und vom Treffen. 2., verb. Aufl. Mit 76 Abbildungen. Berlin, W. de Gruyter, 1945.
76 p. illus. 21 cm. (Luftfahrt-Lehrbücherei, Bd. 12)
Bibliography: p. 66-67.

1. Ballistics. 2. Air warfare. (Series)
UF820.K6 1945 623.54 A 51-3584
New York. Public Libr. for Library of Congress [1]†

NK 0205603 NN DLC

Knobloch, Hans.
Der Tonband-Amateur. [1. Aufl.] München, Franzis-Verlag [1955]
84 p. illus. 20 cm.

1. Magnetic recorders and recording. I. Title.
A 55-2932
Mass. Inst. of Tech. for Library of Congress Library [1]

NK 0205604 MCM

Knobloch, Hans, *graphologist.*
Die Lebensgestalt der Handschrift; Abriss der graphologischen Deutungstechnik. Saarbrücken, West-Ost Verlag [1950]
208 p. illus. 27 cm.
Bibliography: p. 201-206.

1. Graphology. I. Title.
BF893.K65 137.72 51-17505

NK 0205605 DLC OAU

Knobloch, Hans, 1910-
Witzgegenstände und Witzformen in der erzählenden Prosa Voltaires
see under Knobloch, Hilda, 1890-

Knobloch, Hans, 1911-
... Atrophie und Arthritis deformans des Kiefergelenkes ... Osnabrück, 1935.
Inaug.-Diss. - Kiel.
Lebenslauf.
"Literaturverzeichnis": p. [4]

NK 0205607 CtY

Knobloch, Hans Max, 1912-
Über die konservative Behandlung der Thyreotoxikosen und des Morbus Basedow. Ein Vergleich zwischen interner und Röntgenstrahlenbehandlung ... Erlangen-Bruck, 1938.
Inaug.-Diss. - Heidelberg.
Lebenslauf.
"Schrifttum": p. [41]-42.

NK 0205608 CtY

Knobloch, Hans Werner, 1909-
Schmerzbeseitigung unter besonderer Berücksichtigung von Optalidon ... Heidelberg, 1933.
Inaug.-Diss. - Heidelberg.
Lebenslauf.
"Benutzte Literatur": p. [19]-21.

NK 0205609 CtY

840.9 K75s Knobloch, Heinrich, 1862-
Die streitgedichte im provenzalischen und altfranzösischen.... Breslau, Druck von Wilh. Gottl. Korn, 1886.
[2] l., 79p., [1] l. 22cm. (Jahresverzeichnis der an den deutschen universitäten und hochschulen erschienenen schriften, v.1, 1885-86, Breslau 68)
Inaug.-diss.-Breslau.
Vita.

NK 0205610 LU MH CtY CU NIC

QP801 V5V62 Knobloch, Heinrich, 1915- ed.
Vogel, Hans, Feb. 5, 1900-
Chemie und Technik der Vitamine. 3. Aufl. bearb. von Heinrich Knobloch. Stuttgart, F. Enke, 1950-55.

Knobloch, Heinz.
Der bakteriologische Krieg. [1. Aufl.] Berlin, Dietz, 1955.
336 p. illus. 21 cm.

1. Bacterial warfare. I. Title.
UG447.8.K6 56-29770
[2]

NK 0205612 DLC NjR ICU CtY-M NN DS DNLM

Knobloch, Hellmuth.
TAN in der Spinnerei und Weberei; eine Einführung. Leipzig, Fachbuchverlag, 1955.
107 p. illus. 24 cm.

1. Textile industry and trade. 2. Time study. I. Title.
TS1449.K57 55-39282 ‡

NK 0205613 DLC NN

Knobloch, Hertha von.
Wodurch imponieren wir in der Welt am meisten? Verhandlungsbericht von der grossen internationalen Hundeversammlung; eine Gesellschaftssatire, von Hertha von Knobloch. Mit 10 Bildern von Käthe Olshausen-Schönberger. Wolfenbüttel: J. Zwissler, 1915. 42 p. illus. 4°.

1. Satire (German). 2. Olshausen-Schönberger, Käthe, illustrator.
N. Y. P. L. November 16, 1916.

NK 0205614 NN

4PT Ger-5401 Knobloch, Hilda, 1890-
Aji, Roman. Wien, Kremayr & Scheriau [1951]
438 p.

NK 0205615 DLC-P4 CtY

Knobloch, Hilda, 1890-
Die allwissenden Augen, der Roman Hans Holbeins. Berlin, K. H. Bischoff, 1944.
303 p. 20 cm.

1. Holbein, Hans, the Younger, 1497-1543—Fiction. I. Title.
PT2621.N625A7 A F 48-472*
Yale Univ. Library for Library of Congress [1]†

NK 0205616 CtY OrU DLC CU

Knobloch, Hilda, 1890-
Die allwissenden Augen; der Roman Hans Holbeins. Mit 8 Bildbeigaben nach Werken von Hans Holbein. Wien, P. Zsolnay, 1952.
303 p. illus. 20 cm.

1. Holbein, Hans, the younger, 1497-1543—Fiction. I. Title.
PT2621.N625A7 1952 833.91 52-68681 ‡

NK 0205617 DLC PPG NN

Knobloch, Hilde, 1890-
...Der Dom; Roman des Wiener Stephansdomes. Graz [etc.] A. Pustet [1947] 355 p. illus. 21cm.

441498B. I. Title. II. Title: Der Stephansdom.
N. Y. P. L. April 21, 1948

NK 0205618 NN DLC-P4

VOLUME 300

Knobloch, Hilda, 1890–
Farben und Frauen; ein Makartroman. Wien, P. Zsolnay, 1953.
278 p. illus. 21 cm.

1. Makart, Hans, 1840–1884—Fiction. I. Title.
PT2621.N625F3 833.91 53–39270 ‡

NK 0205619 DLC PPG NN CtY

Knobloch, Hilda, 1890–
Der Feuergeist; das Leben Friedrich Ludwig Schröders; Roman. Graz, Steirische Verlagsanstalt, 1943 [°1941]
357 p. ports., facsim. 22 cm.

1. Schröder, Friedrich Ludwig, 1744–1816—Fiction. I. Title.
PT2621.N625F4 1943 833.91 A F 48–5032*

Yale Univ. Library for Library of Congress [1]†

NK 0205620 CtY CU DLC

Knobloch, Hilda, 1890–
Der Feuergeist; das Leben Friedrich Ludwig Schröders; Roman. [3. Aufl.] Graz, A. Pustet [1949, °1941]
356 p. 21 cm.

1. Schröder, Friedrich Ludwig, 1744–1816—Fiction. I. Title.
PT2621.N625F4 1949 833.91 50–37047

NK 0205621 DLC

Knobloch, Hilda, 1890–
...Die grosse Verwandlung; Alchimisten-Roman. Wien, Bellaria-Verlag [1948] 399 p. 20cm.

NK 0205622 NN

Knobloch, Hilda, 1890–
...Ein Kaiser will Frieden; der Roman Karls I. von Österreich. Graz [etc.] A. Pustet [1951] 363 p. 20cm.
1. Aufl.

1. Charles I., emperor of Austria and king of Hungary, 1887–1922—Fiction. I. Title.
N. Y. P. L. January 29, 1952

NK 0205623 NN DLC-P4

PT2621
K72K2 Knobloch, Hilda, 1890-
Ein Kaiser will Frieden; der Roman Karls I. von Österreich. [2. Aufl.] Graz, A. Pustet [1951]
363 p. 20cm.

I. Title.
Full name: Hilda Ruth Knobloch.

NK 0205624 GU

Knobloch, Hilda, 1890-
WB 15695 Der Kuss der Fürstin; Postillion Waldmeisters Liebersroman. Graz, O. Karinger [1954]
1. Aufl.

NK 0205625 CtY NN

Knobloch, Hilda, 1890–
...Der letzte Monarch; Lebensroman Kaiser Franz Josephs. Graz [etc.] A. Pustet [1949] 483 p. 20cm.

518169B. 1. Francis Joseph I, emperor of Austria, 1830–1916—Fiction. I. Title.
N. Y. P. L. February 24, 1950

NK 0205626 NN

Knobloch, Hilda, 1890–
Maria Theresia; Roman ihres Lebens. [1. Aufl.] Graz, A. Pustet [1946]
408 p. 22 cm.

1. Maria Theresia, Empress, of Austria, 1717–1780—Fiction.
PT2621.N625M3 47–27391 rev*

NK 0205627 DLC PPG

4PT
Ger5237 Knobloch, Hilda, 1890-
Der Robinson unseres Waldes, Roman mit 22 illus. von Otto Huter. Wien, P. Zsolnay, 1949.
474 p.

NK 0205628 DLC-P4 NN

Knobloch, Hilda, 1890-
Tanz der Kronen; Roman um den Wiener Kongress. Klagenfurt, Verlag Carinthia des St.-Josef—Vereines [1954] 278 p. 20cm.

Vienna. Congress, 1814-1815—Fiction. I. Title.

NK 0205629 NN CtY

Knobloch, Hilda, 1890-
Unter der Teufelsfichte; Roman. Donauwörth, L. Auer [1954?] 179 p. 20cm.

NK 0205630 NN

Knobloch, Hilda, 1890-
Witzgegenstände und witzformen in der erzählenden prosa Voltaires, von dr. Hans Knobloch [pseud.] Würzburg, Triltsch, 1937.
vii, 59 p. 21 cm.
"Bibliographie": p. iii.

1. Voltaire, François Marie Arouet de, 1694-1778.

NK 0205631 NjP TxU NN NNC CtY

Knobloch, Horst O H
Anschriften-Verzeichnis für Deutschland von Behörden, Körperschaften und Verbänden des politischen, wirtschaftlichen und kulturellen Lebens. Loseblattausg. [2. wesentlich erweiterte und verb. Aufl.] Frankfurt am Main, A. Lutzeyer [1950–
1 v. (loose-leaf) 32 cm.

1. Germany (Federal Republic, 1949–)—Direct. I. Title.
DD15.5.K56 51–24195

NK 0205632 DLC

Knobloch, Horst O H
Anschriften-Verzeichnis von Behörden und Verbänden der gewerblichen Wirtschaft des Vereinigten Wirtschaftsgebietes. Minden i. W., A. Lutzeyer [1948?]
204 p. (p. [201]–204 advertisements) 21 cm.

1. Trade and professional associations — Germany. 2. Germany (Federal Republic, 1949–)—Registers. I. Title.
HD2429.G3K6 331.880943 50–29175

NK 0205633 DLC

Knobloch, Irving William, 1907–
... Development and structure of *Bromus inermis* Leyss ... By Irving William Knobloch ... [n. p., 1944]
cover-title, 67–98 p. incl. v pl. 25½ᶜᵐ.
Portion of thesis (PH. D.)—Iowa state college of agriculture and mechanic arts, 1942. Doctoral thesis no. 697[a]
"Iowa Agricultural experiment station, Ames, Iowa, Project 580. Journal paper no. J-1215."
"Reprinted from Iowa state college journal of science, vol. 19, no. 1, October, 1944."
"Pertinent literature": p. 94–98.

1. Brome-grass. A 45–3491

Iowa. State coll. Library for Library of Congress QK495.G74K73 [2]†

NK 0205634 IaAS DLC

Knobloch, Irving William, 1907– *ed.*
Readings in biological science. New York, Appleton-Century-Crofts [1948]
xiii, 449 p. 25 cm.
"Good browsing": p. 446–449.

1. Biology—Collected works. I. Title.
QH302.K58 574.082 48–3032*

NK 0205635 CU TxU WaT IdU MtU WaWW WaSpG OrStbM Or OrPS MiEM NNBG PWcS CtY-M PPT DLC CaBVaU WaTC TU OU MB ViU ICU OCl IEN

QK177
K6 Knobloch, Irving William, 1907-
... Some recent observations on and additions to the flora of western New York [by] Irving William Knobloch... [No imprint, 1935?]
7-10p. 23cm. in 25½cm.
"Separately printed without change of paging from Torreya 35: 7-10, February, 1935"

1. Botany. New York (State)
I. Title

NK 0205636 NBuG

Knobloch, Isabelle S
Lithographs and drawings by Stow Wegenroth
see under Boston. Public Library. Isabelle S. Knobloch Collection.

WS 270 qK72c 1953 KNOBLOCH, Jan, ed.
Chirurgie pohybového ústrojí v dětském veku [napsali] Otakar Hněvkovský [et al.] [1. vyd.] Praha, Státní pedagogické nakl., 1953.
406 p. illus. (Učební texty vysokých škol)
1. Orthopedics 2. Surgery - Children I. Hněvkovský, Otokar

NK 0205638 DNLM

W 1 TH865 čís. 225 1945 KNOBLOCH, Jan
O léčbě konečníkových a kolemkonečníkových píštělí. V Praze, Nákl. Spolku českých lékařů, 1945.
35 p. (Thomayerova sbírka přednášek a rozprav z oboru lékařského, 225)
Cover title.
Supplement to Časopis lékařů českých, čís. 29, 1945.
1. Anus - Diseases 2. Fistula 3. Rectum - Diseases Series

NK 0205639 DNLM

VOLUME 300

WO 100 K72o 1950
KNOBLOCH, Jan
Obecná chirurgia. V Praze, Zdravotnické nakl., 1950.
444 p. illus.
1. Surgery

NK 0205640 DNLM

W 1 UC331 sv. 5 1945
KNOBLOCH, Jan
První pomoc. [Vyd. 1.] V Praze, Nákl. Spolku českých lékařů [1945]
71 p. illus. (Učebnice pro ošetřovatelské školy a ústavy pro vzdělání ošetřovatelek v pomoc. oborech, sv. 5)
1. First aid Series

NK 0205641 DNLM

Knobloch, Jan.
První pomoc. [Vyd. 2.] V Praze, Vydal Československý Červený kříž; nákl. Zdravotnického nakl., 1950.
129 p. illus. 21 cm.

1. First aid in illness and injury. I. Title.

RC87.K58 1950 57-30973 ‡

NK 0205642 DLC

W 1 TH865 no. 233 1946
KNOBLOCH, Jan
Úkoly chirurgie v sociálním pojištění. V Praze, Nákl. Spolku českých lékařů, 1946.
14 p. (Thomayerova sbírka přednášek a rozprav z oboru lékařského, 233)
Cover title.
Supplement to Časopis lékařů českých, čís. 36, 1946.
Lecture in honor of Dr. Otakar Kukula.
1. Medical care 2. Surgery Series

NK 0205643 DNLM

PN4701 D4
Knobloch, Jaroslav, ed.
The Democratic journalist. v. [1]– Nov. 1953– [Prague]

Knobloch, Johann, *comp. and tr.*
Sammlung der vorzüglichsten schriften aus der thierarzney ... Von Johann Knobloch ... Prag, Gedruckt bey J. E. Diesbach, 1785
v. front., fold. pl. $18\frac{1}{2}^{cm}$.
Title vignette.

1. Veterinary medicine.

CA 17-2624 Unrev'd

Library of Congress SF743.K72

NK 0205645 DLC

Knobloch (Johannes). Disputatio institutionum anatomicarum xii. De collo. 8 l. sm. 4°. *Witebergæ*, 1607.
In: KNOBLOCH (T.) Disp. anat. [etc.]. sm. 4°. *Witebergæ*, 1608, 8 l.

NK 0205646 DNLM

W 4 F83 1593 K.1
KNOBLOCH, Johann, 1529-1599, praeses
Themata de pestis essentia et natura. Conscripta & ad disputandum in Academia Francofordiana proposita a Johanne Cnoblochio ... Francofordiae ad Oderam, Andreas Eichorn, 1593.
[8] p. 20 cm.
Thesis — Frankfurt an der Oder (J. Fersius and M. Dētharding, respondents)
I. Dētharding, Michael, fl. 1587-1614, respondent II. Fersius, Johannes, d. 1611, respondent

NK 0205647 DNLM

16th cent
KNOBLOCH, Johannes, 1529-1599.
Von der jtzundt einschleichende Haupt-Kranckheit; ein Rathschlag der Herrn Doctorn Medicae facultatis zu Franckfurdt an der Oder ... Franckfurdt an der Oder, Gedruckt durch Johan Eichorn, 1572.
[26]p. 20cm.
Signatures: A2-D.
acc. no. ACK cat. LC NLM (16th cent. print.)

1. Plague - Early works to 1800

... 1572 (Card 2)
I. Title ACK

NK 0205649 CtY-M

P26 .A7
Knobloch, Johann, 1919- *ed.*
Ammann-Festgabe. Innsbruck, Selbstverlag des Sprachwissenschaftlichen Seminars der Universität, 1953–54.
2 v. illus., port., facsim., music. 25 cm. (Innsbrucker Beiträge zur Kulturwissenschaft, Bd. 1–2)
Also published separately in 10 parts.
Errata and addenda slip inserted.
Includes bibliographies.

1. Ammann, Hermann, 1885– 2. Philology—Collections.

P26.A7 55-32152

MiU CU OU NIC MH ICU
NK 0205650 DLC CSt MU CoU TxU OrU IEN LU NcU MB IaU

PK2890 .K75
Knobloch, Johann, 1919-
Romani-Texte aus dem Burgenland; Berichte, Erzählungen und Märchen der burgenländischen Zigeuner, aufgezeichnet, übers. und mit sprachlichen Bemerkungen versehen. Eisenstadt [Buchdruckerei M. Rötzer] 1953.
97 p. (Burgenländische Forschungen, Heft 24)
Gipsy texts and German translations on opposite pages.
Contents.--Literaturverzeichnis.--Der Louwära-Dialekt.--Der burgenländische Romani-Dialekt.--Der Liebinger Dialekt (šuow-Dialekt)--Der kroatische Dialekt von Langental.
1. Gipsies--Burgenland.

NK 0205651 ICU NN MH

P 29 .K6
Knobloch, Johann, 1919- ed.
Sprachwissenschaftliches Wörterbuch. Hrsg. von Johann Knobloch in Verbindung mit Eugenio Coseriu [et al.] Heidelberg, C. Winter, 19
v. 25cm. (Indogermanische Bibliothek. II. Reihe. Wörterbücher)

1. Language and languages. Dictionaries. I. Title. II. Series.

NK 0205652 OrU

Knobloch, Johann Cyril Karl.
See
Knobloch, Cyril.

Knobloch, Joseph
Der deutsche scharfrichter und die schelmensippe; ein kulturbild von Joseph Knobloch. Naumburg a.d.S., C.A. Tancré, 1921.
93 p. $20\frac{1}{2}$ cm.

1. Executions (Criminal law) - Germany. I. Title Scharfrichter.

NK 0205654 NNC

Knobloch, Karl.
63277 Augenblicksbilder zur Feldgeschützfrage. Von Karl Knobloch. .... Wien, L. W. Seidel & Sohn, 1903.
[2], 47 p. 22 illus., 14 pl. $23\frac{1}{2}^{cm}$.

NK 0205655 ICJ DNW

DD 901 .W71 W93 v.10
Knobloch, Ludwig.
Agrar- und Verfassungsgeschichte des Wormsgaues im Mittelalter. [Worms] Verlag der Stadtbibliothek Worms, 1951.
181 p. map. (Der Wormsgau. Beiheft 10)
Includes bibliography.

1. Worms, Ger.--Econ. condit. 2. Worms, Ger.--Constitutional history. I. Title.

NK 0205656 MiU PU CtY NN MH CU

KNOBLOCH, Ludwig, 1883-
Das territorium der stadt Strassburg bis zur mitte des 16. jahrhunderts. Inaugural-dissertation, Strassburg. Leipzig-Reudnitz, druck von August Hoffmann, 1908.

Map.
"Lebenslauf," after p.152.

NK 0205657 MH NN CtY ICRL PU

Knobloch, M
Der galvanismus in seiner technischen anwendung seit dem jahre 1840; oder, Galvanoplastik, mit besonderer berücksichtigung der kunst, auf galvanischem wege typen und metallplatten zum abdrucke darzustellen, erzeugung galvanischer kupferstiche, aetzung vermittelst galvanismus, und vergoldung, versilberung, verplatinung &c. auf nassem und galvanischem wege, für natur- und kunstfreunde, wie auch zum technischen gebrauche, dargestellt von dr. M. Knobloch. Erlangen, F. Enke, 1842.
xii, 116 p. diagrs., fold. plate. 21^{cm}

NK 0205658 NNC PPF ICJ

Knobloch, Max, 1912-
see Knobloch, Hans Max, 1912-

Knobloch (Michael. Ludovicus). * De cancro mammæ sinistræ observato et curato. 22 pp., 1 l. 4°. *Erfordiæ, prelo Heringiano*, [1740].

NK 0205660 DNLM

Knobloch, Pavel.
Železo-ocel-pětiletka; uvedení do hutnictví a přehled výroby, zpracování a použití technického železa. 51 obrázků. V Praze, Práce; vydavatelstvo ROH, 1950.
151 p. illus., diagrs. 21 cm. (Technické příručky Práce, sv. 51)
Bibliography: p. 149-150.

1. Iron industry and trade—Czechoslovak Republic. 2. Steel industry and trade—Czechoslovak Republic. I. Title.

TN704.C9K6 54-19613

NK 0205661 DLC

TN704 .C95K7
KNOBLOCH, PAVEL
Železo-ocel pětiletka. Uvedení do hutnictví a přehled výroby, zpracování a použiti technického železa. 2.vyd. Praha, Práce, 1951.
153 p. illus. (Technické příručky práce, sv.51)

Iron-steel five year plan ...

1. Iron industry and trade--Czechoslovak Rep. I. Title.

NK 0205662 InU

VOLUME 300

Knobloch, Philip George, 1893–
Good practice in construction, by Philip G. Knobloch, with a preface by Thomas Hastings ... New York, The Pencil points press, inc., 1923.
vii, [1] p., 52 pl. 30½cm. (The Pencil points library; E. Clute, editor. [v. 2])

1. Building—Details—Drawings. I. Title.
Library of Congress TH2031.K6 23—5461

MB OrCS WaS Wa ViU
NK 0205663 DLC CU CSt TxU CtY MiU OC1W OCU OU PPD

Knobloch, Philip George, 1893-
Good practice in construction. New York, Pencil Point Press, Inc., 1923-25.
2v. illus. (Pencil Points Library)

WaS MtBC
NK 0205664 ICRL NBuU ViU NcRS CoU PU-FA OC1 MiU OO

TH2031 K6 1925 Knobloch, Philip George, 1893-
Good practice in construction. Preface by Thomas Hastings. New York, Pencil Points Press, 1925-27.
2 v. illus. 21cm. (The Pencil points library)

1. Building - Details - Drawings. I. Title.

NK 0205665 CoU PP

Knobloch, Philip George, 1893–
Good practice in construction, by Philip G. Knobloch, A. I. A., preface by Thomas Hastings ... New York, The Pencil points press, inc., 1927–
v. plates. 30½cm. (The Pencil points library)
"Third edition, revised."

1. Building—Details—Drawings. I. Title.
Library of Congress TH2031.K6 1927 27-12042

NK 0205666 DLC OrU OrP FMU OC1W OOxM PPPM-I ViU ICJ

Knobloch, Philip George, 1893–
Good practice in construction, by Philip George Knobloch. A. I. A. New York, The Pencil points press, inc., 1931.
6 l. 114 pl. 30½cm.
Lettered on cover: Parts I and II, combined and revised.

1. Building—Details—Drawings. I. Title.
Library of Congress TH2031.K6 1931 31-9652
——— Copy 2.
Copyright A 36432 [3] 692.2

OU MB WaSp CaBVaU IdU
NK 0205667 DLC MtBC OrCS MH NcD CU NcRS PP OC1 OCU

---

ar X 2967 no.8 **Knobloch, Reinhold.**
Das römische Lehrgedicht bis zum Ende der Republik. Halle, Buchdr. des Waisenhauses, 1881.
24 p. 26cm.

"Wissenschaftliche Beilage zum Programm der Klosterschule Rossleben."
No. 8 in a vol. lettered: Programmes: Latin literature. I.

1. Didactic poetry, Latin--Hist. & crit.

NK 0205668 NIC

KNOBLOCH, Richard von.
Klinische beobachtungen bei künstlichem pneumothorax. Inaug.-diss. Rostock, Adler, 1913.

"Lebenslauf," at end.

NK 0205669 MBCo DNLM ICRL

W 1 TH865 no. 235 1946 KNOBLOCH, Rudolf
O operačním odchlípení sítnice. V Praze, Nákl. Spolku čes. lékařů, 1946.
11 p. (Thomayerova sbírka přednášek a rozprav z oboru lékařského, 235)
Cover title.
Supplement to Časopis lékařů českých, čís. 48, 1946.
Habilitační přednáška - Universita Karlova, Praha
1. Retina - Detachment Series

NK 0205670 DNLM

Knobloch, Rudolf, 1887-
Kondensation des dihydrokollidindikarbonsaeureesters mit aldehyden.
Inaug. diss. Berlin, tech. hoch., 1914.

NK 0205671 ICRL

Knobloch, Sigismund.
Handbuch der gebräuchlichsten Fremdwörter welche in der deutschen Kunst- und Umgangssprache, sowie in Zeitungen, im Amts- und bürgerlichen Geschäftsleben u. s. w. vorkommen. Ein Hülfsbuch für Kaufleute, Fabrikanten, Beamte und jeden Gebildeten. Von Dr. Sigismund Knobloch. Bockenheim bei Frankfurt a. M.: J. B. Levy, 1836. 516 p. 8°.
Binder's title: Fremdwörterbuch.

251436A. 1. German language—Dictionaries. Foreign words and phrases—
N. Y. P. L. November 26, 1926

NK 0205672 NN

Knobloch, Tobias, fl. 1601-1607.
De lue venerea, von Frantzosen kurtzer Bericht. Hampelius, Giessen, 1620.
191 p. 12°.

NK 0205673 OC1W-H

Knobloch, Tobias, fl. 1601-1607, praeses
Disputatio institutionum anatomicarum primae, de hominis praestantia hvivsqve corporis partibvs in genere. Quam sub praesidio Dn. Tobiae Knoblochii ... Witebergae, typis Mullerianis, 1607.
24 v. in 1. illus. 19 cm.
Part 24 missing.

NK 0205674 CtY-M

WZ 250 K71d 1608 KNOBLOCH, Tobias, fl. 1601-1607, praeses
Disputationes anatomicae explicantes mirificam corporis humani fabricam & usum ... Witebergae, Typis Cratonianis, per Johannem Gorman, impensis Pauli Helwigii, 1608.
[457] p. Illus. 20 cm.
Contains 24 Wittenberg theses, each with special title page dated 1607. (Respondents: J. Wilkofer, no. 1; J. Janike, no. 2 & 22; G. Hezmanseder, no. 3; J. Frick, no. 4; C. Bilitzer, no. 5; G. Eberlin, no. 6; L. Baudiss, no. 7 & 21; S. Hase, no. 8 & 11; T. Bohemus, no. 9 & 16; F. Eckart, no. 10; J. Knobloch, no. 12; S. Stangius, no. 13 & 14; A. Bogner, no. 15; J. Widholtz, no. 17; J. Stotmeister, no. 18; N. Olschlegel, no. 19; J. Jentsch, no. 20)

I. Baudiss, Leonhart, fl. 1607-1608 II. Bilitzer, Christopher, fl. 1607-1609 III. Bogner, Abraham, fl. 1607 IV. Bohemus, Tobias, fl. 1607-1614 V. Eberlin, Georg, 1585-1628 VI. Eckart, Friedrich, fl. 1607-1611 VII. Frick, Johann, fl. 1607 VIII. Hase, Simon, fl. 1607-1614 IX. Hezmanseder, Georg, fl. 1607 X. Janike, Joachim, fl. 1607 XI. Jentsch, Johann, fl. 1607 XII. Knobloch, Johann, fl. 1607 XIII. Olschlegel, Nicolaus, fl. 1607 XIV. Stangius, Samuel, fl. 1607 XV. Stotmeister, Joachim, fl. 1607 XVI. Widholtz, Jeremias, fl. 1607 XVII. Wilkofer, Johann, fl. 1607

NK 0205677 DNLM CtY-M MiU

Knobloch, Tobias, fl. 1601-1607.
Institutiones anatomicae et psychologicae recens ed., & plurimis in locis locupletatae ... additis humani corporis affectibus praecipuis ... Autore Tobia Knoblochio ... Wittebergae, Sumptibus J. W. Fincelij, 1661.
8 p.l., 713, [30] p. illus. 16 cm.

NK 0205678 CtY-M

WZ 250 K72k 1606 KNOBLOCH, Tobias, fl. 1601-1607
Kurtzer Bericht von dem Podagra, und andern Gliedsüchten ... Wittemberg, Gedruckt bey Wolffgang Meissnern, in Vorlegung Paul Helwigens, 1606.
[8], 110 p. 16 cm.

NK 0205679 DNLM

Knobloch, Walstan Emile, 1862–
The methods of levee location. By Mr. W. E. Knobloch ...
(*In* Professional memoirs, Corps of engineers, U. S. army, and Engineer department-at-large. Washington, 1917. 25cm. v. 9, no. 44, p. 170-183, incl. illus., maps)
Comments by Maj. W. G. Caples: p. 172-182.
Comments by Col. C. McD. Townsend: p. 182-183.

1. Levees. 2. Mississippi River. I. Caples, William Goff, 1878– II. Townsend, Curtis McDonald, 1856–
E S 17-34
Title from U. S. Engineer School Libr. Printed by L. C.

NK 0205680 DES OU MiU

Knobloch, Wenzel.
Blitzableiter und Blitzschutzeinrichtungen, von W. Knobloch
160740 ... Mit 172 Abbildungen. Leipzig, O. Leiner, 1926.
vi, 135 p. illus., diagrs. 22½cm.

NK 0205681 ICJ

Knobloch, Wenzel.
Elektrische Schwachstromtechnik. Eine Darstellung der
160729 gebräuchlichsten Fernmeldeapparate und Anlagen und anderen Schwachstromapparaten nebst einer Einleitung, von W. Knobloch ... Mit vielen Abbildungen. I.–[II.] Band. Leipzig, O. Leiner, 1922–1924.
2 vol. in 1. illus., diagrs. 25½cm.
Contents.—1. Bd. Einleitung. 1. Tl. Haustelegraphen-, Signal-, Alarm-, Sicherheits-, Kontroll-, Feuermeldeanlagen. 2. Tl. Telegraphenapparate und Anlagen. [4], 1–263 p.—2. Bd. 3. Tl. Telephonapparate und Anlagen. 4. Tl. Leitungen und Leitungsbau. 5. Tl. Blitzableiter, Blitz- und Starkstromschutzeinrichtungen, Sicherungen. 6. Tl. Drahtlose Telegraphie und Telephonie. 7. Tl. Verschiedene Schwachstromapparate. 8. Tl. Anhang, Tabellen. viii, [265]–634 p.

NK 0205682 ICJ

Knobloch, Wenzel.
95735 ... . Messapparate und Messmethoden für den praktischen Installateur und Monteur elektrischer Stark- und Schwachstromanlagen, zusammengestellt von W. Knobloch, ... Dritte Auflage — mit 251 Figuren. Leipzig, O. Leiner, 1913.
vii, [1], 263 p. incl. illus., tables, diagrs. 19cm. (Leiners technische Bibliothek. Band 2.)

NK 0205683 ICJ

Knobloch, Wenzel
Messapparate und messmethoden für den praktischen installateur und monteur elektrischer stark- und schwachstromanlagen, zusammengestellt von W. Knobloch ... 6. aufl. Mit 241 figuren. Leipzig, Leiner, 1921.
vii, 258 p. illus., diagrs. 20 cm.

NK 0205684 NNCoCi

VGK
Knobloch, Wenzel.
Messapparate und Messmethoden für den praktischen Installateur und Monteur elektrischer Stark- und Schwachstromanlagen, zusammengestellt von W. Knobloch... Leipzig: O. Leiner, 1924. vii, 221 p. incl. diagrs., tables. illus. 10. ed. 8°.

172241A. 1. Electricity—Measurements—Instruments and apparatus, 1924.
N. Y. P. L. March 11, 1925

NK 0205685 NN

VOLUME 300

Knobloch, Wilhelm.
Die Kanoniere von Lissa; zur Erinnerung an die heldenmüthige Vertheidigung der Insel Lissa durch die österreichische Artillerie am 18., 19. und 20. Juli 1866. Pola, 1896.
84 p. map. 23cm
Includes bibliography.

1.Lissa, Battle of, 1866. I.Title. SC

NK 0205686 CSt

Knobloch, Wilehlm.
Munition der k. u. k. festungeartillerie als orientisrungsbehelf zusammengestellt von Hauptmann Wilhelm Knobloch. Budapest, L. W. Seidel und sohn, 1907.
8 l. fold. in 1. 18.5 cm.

NK 0205687 DNW

Knobloch, Wilhelm
Praktische winke für die artilleristische zielaufklärung; beiträge zur rationellen technik und systematik des aufklärungsdienstes, von Wilhelm Knobloch... Budapest 1910. Wien, L.W.Seidel und sohn 1910.
26 p. 24 cm.

NK 0205688 DNW

Knobloch, Wilhelm.
Sammlung artilleristischer Schiessaufgaben nebst Lösungen. Mit Berücksichtigung der das Schiesswesen der Festungsartillerie betreffenden Vorschriften applikatorisch bearbeitet von Hauptmann Wilhelm Knobloch .... Dritte, neu bearbeitete Auflage. Mit 17 Beilagen. .... Wien, im Selbstverlage des Verfassers, 1903.
50 p. 17 fold. pl. (plan, tables, diagrs.) 23cm.

NK 0205689 ICJ DNW

Knobloch, Wilhelm.
Zur Technik des Schiessens der Artillerie gegen Ziele in Bewegung auf Grund der Schiessregeln. Von Hauptmann Wilhelm Knobloch, ... Mit einer Figurentafel. Wien, L. W. Seidel & Sohn, 1902.
36 p. 1 fold. diagr. 22cm.

NK 0205690 ICJ

Knobloch, William
Over land and sea,...
[n.p., 1912]

NK 0205691 DLC

Knobloch, Winfried.
Moderne AM-FM-Reparaturpraxis. Berlin-Borsigwalde, Verlag für Radio-Foto-Kinotechnik [1955]
67 p. illus. 21 cm. (His Prüfen, Messen, Abgleichen) (Funk-Technik-Bücher, Bd. 4)

1. Radio—Repairing. I. Title. II. Series: Funk-Technik-Bücher, Bd. 4.

A 55-5500

Mass. Inst of Tech. Library rev

NK 0205692 MCM

Knobloch, Winfried.
Prüfen, Messen, Abgleichen; moderne AM-FM-Reparaturpraxis. Berlin-Borsigwalde, Verlag für Radio-Foto-Kinotechnik [1955]
67 p. illus. 21 cm. (Funk-Technik-Bücher, Bd. 4)

1. Radio—Repairing. I. Title. (Series)

A 55-5500

Mass. Inst. of Tech. for Library of Congress Library [2]

NK 0205693 MCM

Knoblochová, Jiřina, joint author.

Knobloch, Ferdinand.
Repetitorium soudní psychiatrie. Ferd. Knobloch, Jiřina Knoblochová. [Vyd. 1.] Praha, Státní pedagogické nakl., 1954 [i. e. 1955]

Knoblock, Byron William.
Banner-stones of the North American Indian, by Byron W. Knoblock. A specialized illustrated volume prepared for the primary purpose of putting forth conclusions regarding distribution, possible uses, methods of manufacture, evolution of types, adoption of special materials for particular types, and to establish a system for classifying the diversity of shapes of banner-stones by their lines and planes. With articles by Prof. Charles E. Brown, Dr. Fay-Cooper Cole ... [and others] La Grange, Ill., The author, 1939.
596 p., 1 l. incl. front., illus., plates, maps. 28cm.

Illustrated lining-papers.
At foot of t.-p.: First edition.
Bibliography: p. 577-579.

1. Indians of North America—Antiq. 2. Indians of North America—Art. I. Brown, Charles Edward, 1872- II. Title.

40-903

Library of Congress E98.I 4K66
——— Copy 2.
Copyright A 135836 [4] 970.657124

NK 0205696 DLC

Knoblock, Byron William.
Banner-stones of the North American Indian, by Byron W. Knoblock. A specialized illustrated volume prepared for the primary purpose of putting forth conclusions regarding distribution, possible uses, methods of manufacture, evolution of types, adoption of special materials for particular types, and to establish a system for classifying the diversity of shapes of banner-stones by their lines and planes. With articles by Prof. Charles E. Brown, Dr. Fay-Cooper Cole ... [and others] La Grange, Ill., The author, 1939.
596 p., 1 l. incl. front., illus., plates, maps. 28cm.

Illustrated lining-papers.
At foot of t.-p.: Popular edition.
Bibliography: p. 577-579.

NK 0205698 WaU FTaSU OKentU PU

Knoblock, Curt George, 1895-
Above below; text and illus. by C. G. Knoblock. [Detour? Mich., 1952]
238 p. illus. 22 cm.

I. Title.

PZ4.K72Ab 52-20984 ‡

NK 0205699 DLC CaBVa IU

Knoblock, Curt George, 1895-
Above below; text and illus. by C.G. Knoblock. [Norwood, Mass., Plimpton press, 1952]
238 p. illus. 22 cm.

NK 0205700 OClW

Knoblock, Edward, 1874- 1945.
The ant heap, a novel, by Edward Knoblock. London, Chapman and Hall, ld. [1929]
3 p. l., 327 p. 19½cm.

I. Title.

Library of Congress PZ3.K756An 29-28790

NK 0205701 DLC

Knoblock, Edward, 1874-
The ant heap, a novel, by Edward Knoblock. New York, Minton, Balch & company, 1930.
4 p. l., 3-326 p. 19½cm.

I. Title.

Library of Congress PZ3.K756An 2 30-12147

NK 0205702 DLC OU PPL

Knoblock, Edward, 1874-
Behind the mask. A play...by Edward Knoblock. London [19—] 43, 40, 28 f. 29cm.
Typescript, with ground plans.

1. Drama, English. I. Title.
N. Y. P. L. May 8, 1944

NK 0205703 NN

Knoblock, Edward, 1874-
A charity committee; a comedy for nine women, by Edward Knoblock. London, S. French, limited [c1939]
20 p. diagr. 18½cm. (*On cover:* French's acting edition. no. 1536)

I. Title.

39-11181

Library of Congress PR6021.N47C5 1939
Copyright D pub. 62587 [2] 822.91

NK 0205704 DLC CaBVaU

Knoblock, Edward, 1874-
"The clock," a musical play, by Edward Knoblock & George Grossmith. London, E. Knoblock [19—] 103 f. 29cm.
Typescript.

1. Drama, English. I. Grossmith, George, 1874-1935, jt. au. II. Title.
N. Y. P. L. May 8, 1944

NK 0205705 NN

Knoblock, Edward, 1874-
Conchita; a romantic play in three acts, by Edward Knoblock ... [London? 19—?] 41, 37, 32 f. 28cm.
Typescript.

1. Drama, English. I. Title.
N. Y. P. L.

NK 0205706 NN

Knoblock, Edward, 1874-
"Courage;" a play...by Edward Knoblock... London [19—] 1 v. 39cm.
Typescript.

1. Drama, English. I. Title.
N. Y. P. L. May 8, 1944

NK 0205707 NN

VOLUME 300

Knoblock, Edward, 1874–
The equinox; a play...by Edward Knoblock... London [19--] 28, 42, 23 f. illus. 28cm.
Typescript, with ground plan.
1. Drama, English. I. Title.
N. Y. P. L. May 8, 1944

NK 0205708 NN

Knoblock, Edward, 1874–
Evensong, a play in three acts, adapted from the novel of Beverley Nichols, by Edward Knoblock and Beverley Nichols ... London, S. French, ltd.; New York, S. French, inc., ©1932.
90 p. plates. 21½cm. (On cover: French's acting edition. no. 1357)
I. Nichols, Beverley, 1899– joint author. II. Title.
CA 33-514 Unrev'd
Library of Congress PS3521.N63E8 1932
Copyright D pub. 21950 [2] 812.5

NK 0205709 DLC

Knoblock, Edward
(A) faun ... angolbol forditotta Sebestyen Karoly. Budapest, Franklin, 1913.
140 p.

NK 0205710 OCl

Knoblock, Edward, 1874-
The faun; or, Thereby hangs a tale, by Edward Knoblock [with Synopsis and scenario entitled: Marriage maker, by Clara Beranger] [1923]
[284] leaves. 34cm.
Various paging.
Reproduced from type-written copy.
Original title of screen play: Spring magic.
Paramount pictures, 1923.

NK 0205711 CLSU

Knoblock, Edward, 1874- joint author.
Priestley, John Boynton, 1894–
The good companions; a play in two acts, by J. B. Priestley and Edward Knoblock (from the novel by J. B. Priestley) ... London [etc.] S. French, ltd.; New York, Los Angeles, Cal., S. French, inc.; [etc., etc.] ©1935.

KNOBLOCK, EDWARD, 1874-1945.
Hatter's castle; adapted from A. J. Cronin's novel. London, R. Golding Bright [1932?] 39, 43, 39 l. 28cm.
Typescript; includes floor plans.
Produced at the Lyceum theatre, Edinburgh 20 June, 1932.
1. Drama, English. 2. Drama—Promptbooks and typescripts. 3. Drama—Adaptations—Cronin, Archibald Joseph, 1896- . I. Cronin, Archibald Joseph, 1896- . Hatter's castle. II. Title.

NK 0205713 NN

Knoblock, Edward, 1874- joint author.
Coleby, Wilfred T.
The headmaster; a domestic comedy in four acts, by Wilfred T. Coleby and Edward Knoblauch ... New York, S. French; [etc., etc.] ©1913.

Knoblock, Edward, 1874–
Home on leave; a play in three acts, by Edward Knoblock. London [1916] 35, 34, 35 f. 29cm.
Typewritten.
"First produced at the Royalty theatre, London ... the 18th of October 1916."
1. Drama, English. I. Title.
N. Y. P. L. November 16, 1943

NK 0205715 NN

Knoblock, Edward, 1874–
Immortal madness; a play...by Edward Knoblock. New York: Amer. play co. [19—] 42, 30, 30 f. illus. 29cm.
Typescript, with ground plan.
1. Drama, English. I. Title.
N. Y. P. L. May 8, 1944

NK 0205716 NN

Knoblock, Edward, 1874–
Kismet; an "Arabian night" in three acts, by Edward Knoblauch. New York, G. H. Doran company [©1911]
128 p. 20cm.
I. Title.
13—4645
Library of Congress PR6021.N4785 1911

NK 0205717 DLC Or WaS WaT PP PU PHC OO OCl OCU NN MB NcD

Knoblock, Edward, 1874-
Kismet; an "Arabian night" [in three acts] by Edward Knoblauch. [Toronto], Canada, 1911.
Various paging. 16 cm.

NK 0205718 RPB

Knoblock, Edward, 1874–1945.
Kismet, an "Arabian night" in three acts. By Edward Knoblauch. London, Methuen & co ltd. [1912]
128 p. 17½ cm.
I. Title.
[PR6021.N47K] A 13—822
Newberry Library for Library of Congress [a66r22e½]

NK 0205719 ICN CaBVaU MH PPL

Knoblock, Edward, 1874–
... Kismet, groteskes traumspiel aus "Tausend und eine nacht". Englisches original von Eduard Knoblauch. Nach der uebersetzung von Carl Lindau für das Künstlertheater neu bearbeitet in 8 bildern. Musik von Josef Gustav Mraczek. München, Drei masken-verlag, g. m. b. h., ©1912.
121 (i. e. 122) p. 16½cm.
At head of title: Als manuskript gedruckt.
Extra page numbered: 16*.
Without the music.
I. Lindau, Carl, 1853– tr. II. Mraczek, Josef Gustav, 1878– III. Title.
33-34228
Library of Congress PR6021.N47K64 1912 822.91

NK 0205720 DLC

Knoblock, Edward, 1874–
Kismet; conte arabe d'Edward Knoblauch; texte français de Jules Lemaître ... Paris [L'Illustration] ©1913.
28 p. illus. 29cm. (On cover: L'Illustration théâtrale ... no. 232, 1er février 1913)
Title vignette (portrait of author)
"Kismet a été représenté pour la première fois en France sur la scène du théâtre Sarah-Bernhardt ... le 18 décembre 1912."
I. *Lemaître, Jules, 1853–1914, tr. II. Title.
A C 34-3007
Title from New York Univ. PQ1223.I 6 1913
Library of Congress [PQ1223.I 6 no. 232]
[2]

NK 0205721 NN ViU MH MB WaS OCU OClW PBm

Knoblock, Edward, 1874–
Kismet, an "Arabian night" in three acts. By Edward Knoblauch. [London, Methuen & co., ltd. [1919] 4th ed.
128 p. 17½cm.
"Fourth edition 1919."

NK 0205722 ViU

Knoblock, Edward.
Kismet, an "Arabian Knight" in three acts. Boston, W. H. Baker Co., 1922.
161 p. 19cm. (Baker's standard plays)

NK 0205723 ViU NcRS MiEM NIC ICN PPT MH

Knoblock, Edward, 1874–
The ladies of Cranford; a play in two scenes, dramatized from Mrs. Gaskell's "Cranford," by Edward Knoblock. London, S. French, limited [©1938]
42 p., 1 l. 18½cm. (On cover: French's acting edition. no. 1702)
I. Gaskell, Mrs. Elizabeth Cleghorn (Stevenson) 1810-1865. Cranford. II. Title.
38-34504
Library of Congress PR4710.C72K6
Copyright D pub. 59030 [3] 822.91

NK 0205724 DLC OrU

Knoblock, Edward, 1874- joint author.
FOR OTHER EDITIONS SEE MAIN ENTRY
Bennett, Arnold, 1867–1931.
London life; a play in three acts and nine scenes, by Arnold Bennett and Edward Knoblock. New York, George H. Doran company [©1924.

Knoblock, Edward, 1874–
The love lady, by Edward Knoblock. London, Chapman and Hall, ltd. [1933]
vii, 309, [1] p. 19½cm.
I. Title.
Library of Congress PZ3.K756Lo 34-1052

NK 0205726 DLC

Knoblock, Edward, 1874–
Lullaby. A warning in three acts to the women that men have forgotten. By Edward Knoblock... [n. p., n. d.] 1 v. illus. 26cm.
Typescript; with cast of characters, and property, light, and dress plots. Program inserted.
"Produced at the Globe theatre... Nov. 6th 1925."
260082B. 1. Drama, English. I. Title.
N. Y. P. L. January 25, 1944

NK 0205727 NN

Knoblock, Edward, 1874–
The lullaby, and other plays by Edward Knoblock, with an introduction by Geo. P. Baker ... New York & London, G. P. Putnam's sons, 1924.
ix, [1], 323 p. 20½cm. $2.50
Music on lining-papers.
CONTENTS.—The lullaby.—Marie-Odile.—Tiger! tiger!
I. Title. II. Title: Marie-Odile. III. Title: Tiger! tiger!
24—14154
Library of Congress PS3521.N63L8 1924

NK 0205728 DLC NcRS CaOTP NcD OU WaU NIC OrP WaSpG PU OCl PPT NN MB

Knoblock, Edward, 1874–
"Makeshifts," a play in three acts, by Edward Knoblock. [New York, 19—] 28, 29, 36 f. 29cm.
Typescript.
1. Drama, English. I. Title.
N. Y. P. L. May 8, 1944

NK 0205729 NN

VOLUME 300

Knoblock, Edward, 1874–
... The man with the two mirrors. London, Chapman and Hall, ltd., 1931.
5 p. l., 3-376 p. 19½cm.
At head of title: By Edward Knoblock.

I. Title.

Library of Congress PZ3.K756Man 31-31447

NK 0205730 DLC PPL PU

Knoblock, Edward.
The man with the two mirrors. [Authorized edition.]
— New York. Holt & Co. [1932.] 19 cm.
The scene is laid in London and Paris.
376 p.

D600 — T.r.

NK 0205731 MB ViU OU

Knoblock, Edward, 1874–
"Marie Odile," a play...by Edward Knoblock. [n. p., 19—] 40, 43, 18 p. 29cm.
Typescript.

1. Drama, English. I. Title.
N. Y. P. L. May 8, 1944

NK 0205732 NN

Knoblock, Edward, 1874–
"Marie-Odile"; a play in three acts. By Edward Knoblauch ... [New York, Printed by Tower bros. stationery co., °1915]
77 p. 19½cm.

I. Title.

Library of Congress PS3521.N63M3 1915 15-2633 Revised

NK 0205733 DLC TNJ NN

Knoblock, Edward, 1874- joint author.

FOR OTHER EDITIONS SEE MAIN ENTRY

Bennett, Arnold, 1867-1931.
Milestones; a play in three acts, by Arnold Bennett and Edward Knoblauch. London, Methuen & co., ltd. [1912]

Knoblock, Edward, 1874- joint author.

Bennett, Arnold, 1867–
Mr. Prohack; a comedy in three acts, by Arnold Bennett and Edward Knoblock. London, Chatto & Windus, 1927.

Knoblock, Edward, 1874–
The mulberry bush; a comedy...by Edward Knoblock. New York [19—] 43, 32, 31 f. 28cm.
Typescript.

1. Drama, English. I. Title.
N. Y. P. L. May 8, 1944

NK 0205736 NN

Knoblock, Edward, 1874–
Mumsee, by Edward Knoblock. [New York, 19—] 1 v. 29cm.
Typescript.

1. Drama, English. I. Title.
N. Y. P. L. May 8, 1944

NK 0205737 NN

Knoblock, Edward, 1874-
My lady's dress; a play in three acts by Edward Knoblock, with an introduction by Frank Chouteau Brown. Garden City, New York, Samuel French c1911.
165p. (The drama league series of plays. vol. xi)

NK 0205738 PPT

Knoblock, Edward, 1874–
My lady's dress; a play in three acts, by Edward Knoblauch. [n. p., °1914]
cover-title, 86 p. 20cm.

I. Title.

Library of Congress PS3521.N63M8 1914 14-21746 Revised

NK 0205739 DLC NN

Knoblock, Edward, 1874–
My lady's dress; a play in three acts, by Edward Knoblauch, with an introduction by Frank Chouteau Brown. Garden City, New York, Doubleday, Page & company, 1916.
xxvi, [2], 165, [1] p., 1 l. 18cm. (Half-title: The Drama league series of plays. vol. xi) $0.75

I. Title.

Library of Congress PS3521.N63M8 1916 16-2241 Revised

NcD CaOTU WaU FMU MiU TxU CoU NcRS
NK 0205740 DLC PU PP PSC OLak OCU OOxM OCl NN MB KyU

810 Knoblock, Edward, 1874-
K72 My lady's dress; a play in three acts.
tM.3 With an introduction by Frank Chouteau Brown. New York, S.French, c1916.
165p. 19cm. (On cover: French's standard library edition)

NK 0205741 CLSU ViU NcC OCl NN OCIh NNC

PS 3521 KNOBLOCK, EDWARD, 1874-1945
.N63 M9 My lady's dress; a play in three acts.
1927 With an introd. by Frank Chouteau Brown. New York, S. French [1927]
165 p. (French's standard library edition)

NK 0205742 InU

Knoblock, Edward, 1874–
My lady's lace, a play in one act by Edward Knoblock. New York, c1927.
18 p. 19 cm.
On cover: French's international copyrighted ... ed. of the works of the best authors. No. 584.

NK 0205743 RPB OrCS

Knoblock, Edward, 1874–
Noblesse oblige; a play...by Edward Knoblock... [New York, 19—] 41, 37, 34 p. illus. 29cm.
Typescript, with ground plans.

1. Drama, English. I. Title.
N. Y. P. L. May 8, 1944

NK 0205744 NN

Knoblock, Edward, 1874–
One; a play in three acts, by Edward Knoblock. [New York, 19—] 41, 35, 29 f. 29cm.
Typescript.

1. Drama, English. I. Title.
N. Y. P. L. May 8, 1944

NK 0205745 NN

Knoblock, Edward, 1874–
"Paganini"; a play in three acts, by Edward Knoblauch. [New York, Printed by Tower bros. stationery co., °1915]
3 p. l., 3-230 p. 19cm. $0.50

I. Title.

Library of Congress PS3521.N63P3 1915 15-24215 Revised

NK 0205746 DLC MH

Knoblock, Edward, 1874–
The paying guest; a comedy...by Edward Knoblock. [London, 19—?] 48, 43, 38 f. 29cm.
Typescript; with floor plan.

1. Drama, English. I. Title.
N. Y. P. L. May 8, 1944

NK 0205747 NN

Knoblock, Edward, 1874–
Round the room [by] Edward Knoblock; an autobiography; with eight illustrations. London, Chapman and Hall ltd. [1939]
356 p. front., pl., ports. 22cm.

I. Title.

Library of Congress PR6021.N47Z5 1939 40-11378
[3] 928.2

NK 0205748 DLC WaU GU CtY ICU

Knoblock, Edward, 1874-

Fairbanks, Douglas, 1883–
The three musketeers, as interpreted for the screen from Alexander Dumas' immortal novel, by Douglas Fairbanks and Edward Knoblock. [New York, Prospect press, °1921]

Knoblock, Edward, 1874–
"Tiger! Tiger!" A play...by Edward Knoblock. [New York, 1918] 1 v. 29cm.
Typescript, with cast of characters as originally produced at the Belasco theatre, New York, Nov. 12, 1918.

1. Drama, English. I. Title.
N. Y. P. L. May 8, 1944

NK 0205750 NN

Knoblock, Edward, 1874–
"Tornado;" a play in three acts by Edward Knoblock and Anthony Blake. New York: Amer. play co. [etc., etc., 1916] 36, 40, 23 f. 28cm.
Typewritten.

1. Drama, English. I. Blake, Anthony, jt. au. II. Title.
N. Y. P. L. November 17, 1943

NK 0205751 NN

VOLUME 300

Knoblock, Edward, 1874–
A war committee, by Edward Knoblauch. New York, S. French; ₍etc., etc.₎ ᶜ1915.
32 p. 18½ᶜᵐ. (*On cover:* French's acting edition, no. 2533)
"The little silver ring": p. 27–32.

I. Title. II. Title: The little silver ring. 16-1049 Revised
Library of Congress PS3521.N63W3 1915

NK 0205752 DLC

Knoblock, Edward, 1874–
Who's who; a farce in three acts, by Edward Knoblock. London ₍19—₎ 41, 41, 32 f. illus. 29cm.
Typescript; with ground plans, showing the location of properties and the lines of the set.

1. Drama, English. I. Title.
N. Y. P. L. November 16, 1943

NK 0205753 NN

Knoblock, Frederick Delbridge.
Investigations on the application of the hot wire anemometer for turbulence measurements. Pasadena, 1939.
Microfilm copy of typewritten ms. Made by the Recordak Corp., New York. Positive.
Collation of the original, as determined from the film: viii, 185 l. illus.
Thesis—California Institute of Technology.
Bibliography: leaf vii.

1. Anemometer. 2. Turbulence.

Microfilm TA-1 Mic 51-458

NK 0205754 DLC

Knoblock, Kenneth Thomas, 1898–
Murder in the mind, by K. T. Knoblock ... New York and London, Harper & brothers, 1932.
4 p. l., 233 p. 19½ᶜᵐ.
A Harper sealed mystery story (p. 157–233 sealed)
"First edition."

I. Title. 32-4640
Library of Congress PZ3.K7563Mu

NK 0205755 DLC MH NcD

Knoblock, Kenneth Thomas, 1898–
Take up the bodies, by K. T. Knoblock. New York and London, Harper & brothers, 1933.
4 p. l., 261 p. 19ᶜᵐ.
A Harper sealed mystery story (p. 183–261 sealed)
"First edition."

I. Title. 33-12237
Library of Congress PZ3.K7563Tak

NK 0205756 DLC

Knoblock, Kenneth Thomas, 1898–
"There's been murder done", a novel of crime, police work, and punishment, by K. T. Knoblock. New York and London, Harper & brothers, 1931.
xv p., 1 l., 337 p. 19½ᶜᵐ.
A Harper sealed mystery story (p. 329–337 sealed)
"First edition."

I. Title. 31-3839
Library of Congress PZ3.K7563Th

NK 0205757 DLC PBa PPL

Knoblock, Kenneth Thomas, 1898–
A winter in Mallorca, by K. T. Knoblock. New York and London, Harper & brothers, 1934.
4 p. l., 327 p. 19½ᶜᵐ.
"First edition."

I. Title. 34-24140
Library of Congress PZ3.K7563W1

NK 0205758 DLC IU PPL PBa

Knoblock, Otto M.
Early navigation on the St. Joseph River, by Otto M. Knoblock ... Indianapolis, Printed for the Society, 1925.
1 p. l., p. 185–200. illus. (map) 24ᶜᵐ. (Indiana historical society. Publications, v. 8, no. 4)

1. St. Joseph River. I. Title. 26-15611
Library of Congress F521.I41 vol. 8

NK 0205759 DLC MWA MB NcD Vi OCl OFH ODW OClWHi

Knoblock, Richard von, 1882-
Klinische beobachtungen bei kunstlichem pneumothorax. Rostock, 1913.
Inaug. diss.
Bibl.

NK 0205760 ICRL

Knoblock, William.
The lead storage battery, by William Knoblock, S. B. E., assisted by Morris E. Booten, S. B. E. Gardena, Calif., William Knoblock electrical laboratories ₍ᶜ1929₎
3 p. l., 186, ₍4₎ p. illus., plates, diagrs. 20½ᶜᵐ.

1. Storage batteries. I. Booten, Morris E., joint author. II. Title. 29-29421
Library of Congress QC605.K65

NK 0205761 DLC MB WaS PPESB

Knoblokh, ÎA
see
Knobloch, Jaroslav.

BS1965 1926

Knoch, Adolf E., comp.
Bible. *N. T. Greek. 1926.*
Concordant version, the Sacred Scriptures, designed to put the English reader in possession of all the vital facts of divine revelation without a former knowledge of Greek, by means of a restored Greek text, with various readings, conforming, as far as possible, to the inspired autographs, a consistent sublinear based upon a standard English equivalent for each Greek element, and an idiomatic, emphasized English version with notes, which are linked together and correlated for the English reader by means of an English concordance and lexicon and a complementary list of the Greek elements. Los Angeles, Calif., The Concordant publishing concern ₍1926₎

BS1965 1931a

Knoch, Adolf E.
Bible. *N. T. Greek. 1931.*
Concordant version, the Sacred Scriptures, designed to put the English reader in possession of all the vital facts of divine revelation without a former knowledge of Greek, by means of a restored Greek text, with various readings, conforming, as far as possible, to the inspired autographs, a uniform sublinear based upon an exclusive English equivalent for each Greek element, and a consistent, emphasized English version with notes, which are linked together and correlated for the English reader by means of an English concordance and lexicon and a complementary list of the Greek elements. Completely rev., 1930. Los Angeles, Calif., The Concordant publishing concern ₍1931₎

Knoch, Adolf E.
The divine mysteries. The mystery of the Gospel ...
see under title

Knoch, Adolf E.
The divine mysteries; the unveiling of Jesus Christ, commonly called the Revelation of St. John, with a revised Concordant version, including the Mystery of the seven stars... Los Angeles, Cal. Concordant pub. concern, 1935.
591 p.

NK 0205768 PP

Knoch, Albrecht, 1864-
see Knoch, Wilhelm Arnold Albrecht, 1864-

Knoch, Armin, 1911-
Die stellung des begünstigten dritten im lebensversicherungsvertrag auf den todesfall des versicherungsnehmers. ... 1934. 74 p.
Inaug. Diss. - Heidelberg, 1934.
Lebenslauf.
Bibliography.

NK 0205770 ICRL

Knoch, August, 1892-
Der **grammatische** unterricht in den neueren sprachen; vier aufsätze von A. Knoch ... J. Gerhards ... A. Poch ... ₍und₎ J. Plaut ... Frankfurt am Main, M. Diesterweg; ₍etc., etc.₎ 1931.

Knoch, August, 1892-
... Hamm, Westf.
see under Hamm, Germany. Stadtbauamt.

Knoch, August, 1892-
Planmässiger aufbau der lektüre auf der oberstufe; drei aufsätze von dr. W. Göcking ... O. Grüters ... ₍und₎ A. Knoch ... Frankfurt am Main, M. Diesterweg; ₍etc., etc.₎ 1930.

Knoch, August, 1892–
Die schottische Liviusübersetzung des John Bellenden (1533) ... Königsberg i. Pr., Hartungsche buchdr., 1915.
3 p. l., 136 p. 22ᶜᵐ.
Inaug.-diss.—Königsberg.
Lebenslauf.
"Literaturnachweis": p. 129–134.

1. Bellenden, John, ca. 1495–1550. 2. Livius, Titus—Translations. 3. English language—Dialects—Scotch.
24-9515
Library of Congress PR2211.B5K6

NK 0205774 DLC CtY PU ICRL IU MiU OU MH

Knoch, August, 1892-
Sprachwissenschaftliche grundlegung von studienrat dr. Knoch... (In Der grammatische unterricht in den neuren sprachen. 1931, p. ₍3₎ - 60)

NK 0205775 OU

Knoch, August, 1892-
Studies in early Irish law, by R. Thurneysen, Nancy Power, Myles Dillon, Kathleen Mulchrone, D. A. Binchy, August Knoch, John Ryan, S. J. Published by the Royal Irish academy. Dublin, Hodges, Figgis & co.; London, Williams & Norgate, 1936.

VOLUME 300

95.78 Knoch, August Wilhelm, 1742-1818.
751b Beiträge zur insektengeschichte ... Leipzig, Schwickert, 1781-83.
3v. in 1. col.plates.

Title vignette, engraved, in vol.1.
Mainly descriptions of Lepidoptera.

1. Lepidoptera.

NK 0205777 IU NcRS IaU PPAN PPULC HU OU MH PPAmE

595.76 Knoch, August Wilhelm, 1742-1818.
K751n Neue beyträge zur insectenkunde ... 1. theil. Leipzig, Schwickert, 1801.
209p. col.plates.

No more published.

1. Beetles.

NK 0205778 IU PPAN MH OU IaU NcRS NIC PPAmE

Knoch, Augustin.
De libertate in societate civili ad norman encycl. Leonis pp. XIII "Libertas" ... Lovanii, J. Vanlinthout [1895]
xii, 413 p. 23cm.
Diss.—Louvain.

1. Liberty. 2. Leo XIII, pope, 1810-1903. Libertas pretiossimum.

JC585.K6 Cal. 14—55

NK 0205779 DLC DCU MoSCS

Knoch, Carl, 1864-
Handbuch der neuzeitlichen milchverwertung für molkereipraktiker, milchwirte und die gesamte milchindustrie, bearb. von dr. C. Knoch ... Berlin, P. Parey, 1926.
xii, 564 p. illus., plans (1 fold.) 22cm.

1. Dairying. [1. Dairy]

Agr 26-1542

Library, U. S. Dept. of Agriculture 44K75H

NK 0205780 DNAL

Knoch, Carl, 1864-
Handbuch der neuzeitlichen milchverwertung für molkereipraktiker, milchwirte und die gesamte milchindustrie, bearb. von dr. C. Knoch ... 2. umgearb. und verm. aufl. ... Berlin, P. Parey, 1927.
xi, 668 p. illus., plans (2 fold.) 23½cm.

1. Dairying. [1. Dairy]

Agr 28-1447

Library, U. S. Dept. of Agriculture 44K75H

NK 0205781 DNAL CU CtY

Knoch, Carl, 1864-
Handbuch der neuzeitlichen milchverwertung für molkereipraktiker, milchwirte und die gesamte milchindustrie, bearbeitet von dr. C. Knoch ... dritte, neubearbeitete und vermehrte aufl. Berlin, P. Parey, 1930.
xii, 719 p. illus., fold. plan, diagrs. (part fold.) 23½cm.

1. Dairying. [1. Dairy]

Agr 31-75

Library, U. S. Dept. of Agriculture 44K75H

NK 0205782 DNAL

SF251
.K6

Knoch, Carl, 1864-
Использованіе снятаго молока въ молочныхъ. Сводъ различныхъ способовъ использованія на основаніи данныхъ періодической печати и о привиллегіяхъ и патентахъ, а также по частнымъ сообщеніямъ изобрѣтателей. Составилъ д-ръ Кнохъ ... Переводъ со второго нѣмецкаго, заново переработаннаго изданія, О. М. Коржинской, подъ редакціей П. М. Дубровскаго. С.-Петербургъ [Типографія "Сельскаго вѣстника"] 1913.
280 p. illus. 23½cm.

Supplement to "Сельское хозяйство и лѣсоводство," v. 241-242.

1. Milk. 2. Dairying. I. Dubrovskiĭ, Pavel Mikhaĭlovich. II. Korzhinskaia, Ol'ga Mikhaĭlovna, tr. III. Сельское хозяйство и лѣсоводство (*transliterated:* Sel'skoe khoziaĭstvo i lѣsovodstvo) Supplement. *Translation of* Die magermilch-verwertung in den molkereien. *Title transliterated:* Ispol'zovanie sniatago moloka.

19-4394 Revised

Library of Congress SF251.K6

NK 0205784 DLC

Knoch, Carl, 1864-
Die magermilch-verwertung in den molkereien. Eine zusammenstellung der verschiedenen verwertungsmethoden auf grund der periodischen und der patentliteratur, sowie nach privaten mitteilungen der erfinder. Von Dr. C. Knoch ... Leipzig, M. Heinsius nachfolger, 1903.
viii, 222 p. illus. 23cm.

1. Skim milk.

Agr 4-444

Library, U. S. Dept. of Agriculture. no. 44K75.

NK 0205785 DNAL ICJ PU-V

Knoch, Carl, 1864-
Die magermilch-verwertung in den molkereien. Eine zusammenstellung der verschiedenen verwertungsmethoden auf grund der periodischen und der patentliteratur, sowie nach privaten mitteilungen der erfinder. Von dr. C. Knoch ... 2., neubearb. und verm. aufl. Leipzig, M. Heinsius nachfolger, 1912.
ix, 249 p. illus. 23cm.

1. Skim milk.

Agr 12-661 Revised

U. S. Dept. of agr. Library for Library of Congress 44K75 [r41b2]

NK 0205786 DNAL CtY

Knoch, Carl, 1864-
Neuere Milchpulver, ihre Herstellungsmethoden und ihre Bewertung. Von Dr. C. Knoch. Leipzig, M. Heinsius Nachfolger, 1904.
24 p. illus. 24cm.

NK 0205787 ICJ

Knoch, Carl, 1864-
Die städtische milchzentrale. Vorschläge für anlage und betrieb von einrichtungen zur vorsorgung grosser städte mit hygienisch einwandfreier konsummilch. Von dr. C. Knoch ... Leipzig, M. Heinsius nachfolger, 1906.
vii, 175 p. illus., fold. plan. 23cm.

1. Milk supply.

Agr 6-1649 Revised

Library, U. S. Dept. of Agriculture 44K758

NK 0205788 DNAL ICJ ICRL

Knoch, Carl, 1864-
Topographie des excretions-apparates und nervensystems von distomum lanceolatum ... Würzburg, Köhl & Hecker, 1894.
18 p. plate. 23 cm. [Würzburg. Universität. Dissertationen. v. 2, no. 3]
Inaug.-diss. - Würzburg.
"Litteratur": on verso of plate.

NK 0205789 CU ICRL

Knoch, Carl, 1864-
Das trocknen kolloidaler flüssigkeiten insbesondere der milch und anderer fett- und eiweisshaltigen stoffe. Eine übersicht der in der welt- und patentliteratur bekannt gewordenen methoden und apparate, von dr. C. Knoch ... Berlin, P. Parey, 1927.
viii, 226 p. illus., diagrs. 23½cm.

1. Drying apparatus. [1. Drying milk apparatus] 2. Milk, Condensed. [2. Milk, Desiccated]

Agr 28-1448

Library, U. S. Dept. of Agriculture 309K75

NK 0205790 DNAL IU NN

Knoch, Charlotte, A., tr.

Kittel, Rudolf, 1853-1929.
Great men and movements in Israel, by Rudolf Kittel ... authorized translation by Charlotte A. Knoch and C. D. Wright. New York, The Macmillan company, 1929.

Knoch, Christianus Fridericus, 1840-
De diabete mellito,
Inaug. Diss. Berlin, 1865

NK 0205792 ICRL

Knoch, Clemens: 1878- Aus d. chir. Abt. d. Diakonissenh. zu Leipzig-Lindenau ⟨Chefarzt Sick⟩. Über Intussusception des Darmes. Borsdorf-L. 1910: Hoppe. 31 S. 8°
Leipzig, Med. Diss. v. 9. Juli 1910, Ref. Trendelenburg
[Geb. 27. März 78 Weckersdorf; Wohnort: Leipzig; Staatsangeh.: Reuß j. L.; Vorbildung: Gymn. Schleiz Reife O. 98; Studium: Leipzig 4, Freiburg i. B. 1, Leipzig 18 S.; Coll. 20. Juli 10.] [U 10. 3007

NK 0205793 ICRL DNLM

Knoch, Eduard [Ludwig Franz] 1867-
Untersuchungen über die morphologie, biologie und physiologie der blüte von *Victoria regia* ... Marburg, 1897.
3 p. l., 56 p., 2 l. 30 x 23½cm.
Inaug.-diss.—Marburg.
Lebenslauf.
"Litteraturverzeichnis": p. 55-56.

1. Flowers—Morphology. 2. Victoria regia.

5-35070†

Library of Congress QK653.K53

NK 0205794 DLC CtY PU-B

Knoch, Eduard Ludwig Franz, 1867-
Untersuchungen ueber die Morphologie, biologie und physiologie der Bluete von Victoria regia. Stuttgart, 1898.

(Bibl. Botan. H.47)

NK 0205795 PPAN

Knoch, Eduard Ludwig Franz, 1867-
Untersuchungen über die morphologie, biologie und physiologie der blüte von *Victoria regia*. Von dr. Eduard Knoch. Mit 6 tafeln. Stuttgart, E. Nägele, 1899.
3 p. l., 60 p. vi pl., fold. diagr. 31cm. (*Added t.-p.:* Bibliotheca botanica ... hft. 47)
Also issued as the author's inaugural dissertation, Marburg, 1897.
"Litteraturverzeichnis": p. 55-56.

1. Flowers—Morphology. 2. Victoria regia.

6-46021

Library of Congress QK653.K72

NK 0205796 DLC OU MiU PU-B ICJ

Knoch (Fridericus Ferdinandus). * Diss. sistens meletemata quædam ad physiologiam nervi sympathetici spectantia. 32 pp. 4°. *Giessæ*, [1824].

NK 0205797 DNLM

VOLUME 300

Knoch, Friedrich Richard Alfons
see Knoch, Richard, 1875-

Z7771
.G3W6
Rare bk.
Coll.

Knoch, Georg Ludolph Otto, d. 1783, comp.

Wolfenbüttel. Herzog-August-bibliothek.
Bibliotheca biblica; das ist, Verzeichnis der Bibelsammlvng welche die dvrchlavchtigste fvrstinn vnd frav frav Elisabeth Sophia Maria erst verwittwete herzogin zv Bravnschweig vnd Lvnebvrg gebohrne herzogin zv Schleswich-Holstein etc. zum beweise der avsbreitvng vnd verherrlichvng des nahmens Gottes in mancherley sprachen, absonderlich der tevtschen dvrch d. Mart. Lvthern, gesammlet vnd in dero bvcher-schatz avf dem graven hofe, der christlichen kirche zvm besten avfgestellet hat. Bravnschweig, 1752.

Knoch, Georg Ludolph Otto, d. 1783, comp.
Historisch-critischer nachrichten von der braunschweigischen Bibelsammlung erster band ...
see under Wolfenbüttel. Herzogliche bibliothek.

WQ
100
qK72v

KNOCH, H
Verloskunde. [Amsterdam, Kolff, 1938-
v. (loose-leaf) illus.
In filing carton.
Contents. —

[v. ?] Therapie.
1. Obstetrics - Outlines

NK 0205801 DNLM

Knoch, Hans.
Weerzien der schaakmeesters; de wedstrijd te Hastings, 1945–1946, door H. Kmoch en Lod. Prins. Amsterdam, Uitg. Vrij Nederland [1946]
95 p. ports., diagrs. 20 cm.

1. Chess—Tournaments, 1945. I. Prins, Lodewijk, joint author. II. Title.

GV1455.K57 794.1 52–68242

NK 0205802 DLC

Knoch, Hans Harald, b. 1902
Beitrag zur lymphogranulomatose.
Inaug. Diss. Koenigsberg, 1928
Bibl.

NK 0205803 ICRL CtY

Knoch, Harvey W.

Milwaukee. Boys' technical high school.
Plumbing instruction book. Milwaukee, Wis., Boys' technical high school [°1934]

---

ar W
53884
no.13

Knoch, Heinrich, 1855-
Vier Fälle von Resektion des karzinomatösen Pylorus. Erlangen, Buchdr. von Junge & Sohn [188-?]
30 p. tables. 23cm.

Inaug.-Diss.--Erlangen.

NK 0205805 NIC NN DNLM DLC

Knoch, Irene.
Kindergarten und volksschule organisch verbunden, von Irene Knoch, Sonjamaria Mentz und Gertrud Stricker, mit einer einführung von Peter Petersen ... Weimar, H. Böhlaus nachfolger, 1940.
xiv, 283 p. illus., diagrs. 22½cm. (Neue forschungen zur erziehungswissenschaft, hrsg. von prof. dr. dr. h. c. Peter Petersen. 2. bd., hft. 1–4)
Four parts, preceded by an introduction; each part has special t.-p. and was also published separately, the last part as Irene Knoch's dissertation, Jena.
Bibliography at end of each part.
CONTENTS.—Einführung: Von der Fröbelschen "vermittlungsschule" zur deutschen Fröbelschule, von Peter Petersen-Jena.—Kindergartenkinder unter volksschülern während des schultages, von Sonjamaria Mentz. Anhang: Kindergartenkinder und volksschüler, von Lotte Vollbarth.—Die pädagogischen aufgaben des kindergartens am schulpflichtigen, aber schulunreifen einkinde, von Irene Knoch.—Kindergartenkinder als schulanfänger, von Gertrud Stricker.—Faule kinder im kindergarten, von Irene Knoch.

1. Kindergarten. 2. Education—Germany. I. Mentz, Sonjamaria 1913- II. Stricker, Gertrud. III. Petersen, Peter, 1884- IV. Title.

LB1342.K58 372.2 47–38607

NK 0205807 DLC TxU CtY

Knoch, Irene.
Die pädagogischen Aufgaben des Kindergartens am schulpflichtigen aber schulunreifen Einkinde. Weimar, H. Böhlaus Nachfolger, 1940.
139 p. 23 cm. (Neue Forschungen zur Erziehungswissenschaft, Bd. 2, Heft 2)

1. Only child. 2. Kindergarten. I. Title.

LB1167.K55 55–55729 ‡

NK 0205808 DLC IaU CtY IU

Knoch (Julius) 1828-1893. De nervi sympathetici vi ad corporis temperiem, adjectis de aliis actionibus nec non de origine observationibus. 64 pp. 8°. *Dorpat, typ. vid. J. C. Schünmanni et C. Mattieseni,* 1855.

NK 0205809 DNLM

A42
+Ak136M
5

Knoch, Julius, 1828-1893.
Die Naturgeschichte des breiten Bandwurms (Bothriocephalus latus auctt.) mit besonderer Berücksichtigung seiner Entwickelungsgeschichte. St.Petersburg, Eggers, 1862.
134 p. 2 plates. 32cm. (Mémoires de l'Académie Impériale des Sciences de St.Pétersbourg, VIIe série. T.5, no.5)

NK 0205810 CtY DNLM

Knoch (J[ulius]) [1828–93]. Vorläufige Mittheilungen über den Bothriocephalus latus, die Entwickelung desselben, die Wanderung und endliche Uebertragung seines Embryo's in den Menschen. 9 pp. 8°. [*Berlin, G. Reimer,* 1862.] [P., v. 1495.]
Repr. from: Arch. f. path. Anat. [etc.], Berl., 1862, xxiv.

NK 0205811 DNLM

Knoch, Karl, 1864-
see Knoch, Carl, 1864-

614.424 R687w

Knoch, Karl, 1883-
Average annual precipitation in Europe.

(In World atlas of epidemic diseases, p. I/110 and Map 34, C1/III)

NK 0205813 DAS

Knoch, Karl, 1883-
Ein Beitrag zur Kenntnis der Temperatur- und Feuchtigkeitsverhältnisse in verschiedener Höhe über dem Erdboden. Berlin: Behrend & Co., 1909. 29 p. f°. (Prussia. Meteorologisches Institut. Veröffentlichungen 214. Abhandlungen. Band 3, no. 2.)

1. Meteorology. 2. Hygrometry. 3. Air.—Temperature.
N. Y. P. L. May 29, 1916.

NK 0205814 NN

Knoch, Karl, 1883-

Bericht über die Arbeiten aus dem Gebiete der geographischen Meteorolgie 1926-28.

p. 37-144. 21½ cm.

NK 0205815 DAS

Knoch, Karl, 1883-
Betrachtungen über das geographische Moment in der Mikroklimatologie.
unp. 24½ cm.

NK 0205816 DAS

614.424 R687w

Knoch, Karl, 1883-
Distribution of the actual average temperature in Europe.

(In World-atlas of epidemic diseases, ed. by Ernst Rodenwaldt, p. I/112, and Maps 35-38, C2/III-C5/III)

NK 0205817 DAS

Knoch, Karl, 1883-
Der Einfluss geringer Geländeverschiedenheiten auf die meteorologischen Elemente im norddeutschen Flachlande. Berlin: Behrend & Co., 1911. 51 p. f°. (Prussia. Meteorologisches Institut. Veröffentlichungen 237. Abhandlungen. Bd. 4, no. 3.)

1. Meteorology.—Observations. Germany (North).
N. Y. P. L. June 18, 1915.

NK 0205818 NN

Knoch, Karl, 1883-

Die Eintrittszeiten der Spät- und Frühfroste in Norddeutschland. Berlin. 1927.
24 p. figs. plates. 33 1/2 cm.

NK 0205819 DAS

Knoch, Karl, 1883-
...Ergebnisse von Hoehenwindmessungen auf dem Nordatlantischen Ozean und dem Karibischen Meer im April und Mai 1927, von Prof. Dr. K. Knoch und Dr. A. Lohr... Hamburg, 1928. 44 p. incl. tables. charts, illus. 4°. (Germany. Seewarte, Direktion der. Aus dem Archiv der deutschen Seewarte. Bd. 46, Nr. 2.)

1. Winds—Atlantic ocean, North. 2. Winds—Caribbean sea. 3. Lohr, Alfred, 1887- , jt. au. 4. Ser.
N. Y. P. L. October 7, 1929

NK 0205820 NN

Knoch, Karl, 1883- ed.

Hann, Julius von, 1839-1921.
Handbuch der klimatologie, von Julius von Hann. 4., umgearb. und verm. aufl., von Karl Knoch ... Stuttgart, J. Engelhorns nachf., 1932-

---

Knoch, Karl, 1883-
...Die Haupttypen des jaehrlichen Ganges der Bewölkung über Europa, von K. Knoch. Berlin: J. Springer, 1926. 44 p. incl. tables. illus. (charts.) f°. (Prussia. Meteorologisches Institut. Veröffentlichungen. Nr. 333. Abhandl. Bd. 8, Nr. 3.)

1. Clouds—Europe. 2. Ser.
N. Y. P. L. January 28, 1927

NK 0205822 NN

VOLUME 300

Knoch, Karl, 1883- ed.

G1928 .B3G47 1953 Map Div. **Germany** (*Federal Republic, 1949-*) *Wetterdienst.*
Klima-Atlas von Baden-Württemberg. ⌈Planung und Leitung: K. Knoch⌉ 75 Karten, 9 Diagramme und Erläuterungen. Bad Kissingen, 1953.

Knoch, Karl, 1883- ed.

G1928 .B4D4 1952 Map Div. **Deutscher Wetterdienst in der US Zone.**
Klima-Atlas von Bayern, bearb. von der Klima-Abt. des Zentralamtes des Deutschen Wetterdienstes in der US-Zone unter Leitung von Karl Knoch. 79 Karten, 8 Diagramme und Erläuterungen. Bad Kissingen, 1952.

Knoch, Karl, 1883- ed.

G1923 .H4G4 1950 **Germany** (*Territory under Allied occupation, 1945- U. S. Zone*) *German Meteorological Service.*
Klima-Atlas von Hessen, bearb. von der Klima-Abteilung des Zentralamtes des Deutschen Wetterdienstes in der US-Zone unter Leitung von Karl Knoch. 75 Karten, 9 Diagramme und Erläuterungen. Bad Kissingen, 1950 ⌈cover 1949-50⌉

Knoch, Karl, 1883-
... Klima und klimaschwankungen, von dr. Karl Knoch ... Leipzig, Quelle & Meyer, 1930.
150, ⌈1⌉ p. diagrs. 18½cm. (Wissenschaft und bildung, einzeldarstellungen aus allen gebieten des wissens. 269)
"Literaturverzeichnis": p. ⌈151⌉
1. Climatology. I. Title.
A 32-1243
Title from Univ. of Mich. QC981.K72 Printed by L. C.

NK 0205826 MiU MH CU DAS DNAL MiU

Knoch, Karl, 1883-
...Klimakunde von Südamerika, von Prof. Dr. K. Knoch... Berlin: Gebrüder Borntraeger, 1930. viii, 349 p. incl. tables. diagrs., illus. (charts.) 4°. (Handbuch der Klimatologie. Bd. 2, Teil G.)
Bibliography, p. ⌈330-⌉349.
1. Meteorology—South America. 2. Climate—South America. I. Ser.
N. Y. P. L. December 16, 1931

NK 0205827 NN RPB OU PSt

Knoch, Karl, 1883-
Luftverhältnisse in Hüttenanlagen und billige Beschaffungsmöglichkeit trockener Luft.
p. 1747-1750. 27½ cm.
Stahl und Eisen. 23. Nov., 1922.

NK 0205828 DAS

Knoch, Karl, 1883-

Linke, Franz, 1878- *ed.*
Meteorologisches taschenbuch. 3. ausg. Unter mitarbeit von T. Bergeron, C. Kassner, K. Keil und K. Knoch herausgegeben von F. Linke ... Leipzig, Akademische verlagsgesellschaft m. b. h., 1939.

Knoch, Karl, 1883-
Methoden der Klimaklassifikation, von K. Knoch und A. Schulze. Gotha, J. Perthes, 1952.
vii, 78 p. 10 fold. col. maps (in pocket) tables. 28 cm. (Ergänzungsheft Nr. 249 zu "Petermanns geographischen Mitteilungen")
Bibliography: p. ⌈69⌉-78.
1. Climatology. 2. Climatology—Charts, diagrams, etc. I. Schulze, Alfred, climatologist, joint author. II. Title. (Series: Petermanns geographische Mitteilungen. Ergänzungsheft Nr. 249)
G1.P44 Nr. 249 56-1684

NK 0205830 DLC DAS KU MH-GM MoU NIC MB NN TxU ViU OU

Knoch, Karl, 1883-
Die niederschlagsverhältnisse der atlaslaender.
Inaug. diss. Marburg, 1906.

NK 0205831 ICRL MH CtY DAS PU

Knoch, Karl, 1883-
...Die Verteilung der Bewölkung über Europa, von K. Knoch ... Berlin: Behrend & Co., 1923. 8 p. maps. sq. f°. (Prussia. Meteorologisches Institut. Veröffentlichungen. Nr. 319.)
1. Clouds.—Observations, Europe. 2. Series.
N. Y. P. L. March 31, 1924.

NK 0205832 NN DNW

Knoch, Karl, 1883-
... Verteilung und jährlicher gang der niederschläge in den Alpen, von K. Knoch und E. Reichel. Berlin, J. Springer, 1930.
84p. (Veroffentlichungen des Preussischen meteorologischen instituts... nr. 375. Abhandlungen bd. ix, nr. 6) Maps in pocket.

NK 0205833 OU

Knoch, Karl, 1883-
Die Wintersonne des Hohen Harzes. 1932.
p. 539-546. fig. 23 1/2 cm.

NK 0205834 DAS

Knoch, Karl, 1883-
Zur Methodik klimatologischer Forschung. Berlin. 1925.
p. 49-59. 25 cm.
44891

NK 0205835 DAS

KNOCH, Marcel, 1902-
De la castration de la truie par un procédé nouveau. [Thèse, Paris.] Meaux, Ch. Descaves, 1927

At head of title: École nationale vétérinaire d'Alfort.

NK 0205836 MH DNLM CtY

Knoch, Mrs. Margaretha (Dreier)

In memory of the one hundredth anniversary of the birth of Dorothea Adelheid Dreier, born in Lehe in the free state of Bremen, Germany, November 5th, 1840-1940. Her living children: Margaret Dreier Robins, Mary Elisabeth, Henry Edward ⌈and⌉ Katherine S. Dreier present this translation of the stories of her life, realistically and poetically transcribed and composed by her sister, Meta Dreier Knoch, and assisted by her mother, her husband, her children, and their cousin Hans Dreier for the celebration of the silver wedding at Marienbad, Austria, July 12, 1889 ... ⌈Springfield, Mass., Priv. print. by the Pond-Ekberg company, °1941⌉

Knoch, Max.
...Der Schiffsrumpfbau nach dem Schichtsystem; ein Lehrbuch für die sachgemässe Fertigung von Modell-Schiffsrümpfen, von Max Knoch...Robert Loef...⌈und⌉ August Reng... Ergänzt durch: Gewerbeoberlehrer Ing. O. M. Friedemann... Zweite Auflage. Burg b.Mgb.: E. Loef, 1938. 40 p. incl. diagrs. 21cm. (Der praktische Modell-Schiffbau. Bd. 1.)
1. Ships—Models. I. Loef, Robert, jt. au. II. Reng, August, jt. au. III. Friedemann, Otto Martin, ed. IV. Title. V. Ser.
N. Y. P. L. June 5, 1940

NK 0205839 NN

QD543 .K6 **Knoch, Max, 1878-**
Ueber loeslichkeiten in loesungsmittelgemengen.
Breslau, 1905.
38p.
Inaug. diss. Breslau.

NK 0205840 DLC MH ICRL CtY

Knoch, Nancy Jane.
Our Missouri; a pageant in two acts for schools, churches, P. T. A. or other community organizations ... Kansas City, Mo., Burton Pub. Co. ⌈1949⌉
50 p. illus. 25 cm.
1. Missouri—Hist.—Drama. 2. Pageants—Missouri. I. Title.
F467.K6 977.80088 50-17730

NK 0205841 DLC

Knoch (Otto). *Lipoidbestimmungen in Organen und einigen fettreichen Nahrungsmitteln. 19 pp. 8°. Zürich, Buchd. Winthur, 1924.

NK 0205842 DNLM

Knoch, Reinhold.
... Landwirtschaftliche baukunde ... Von regierungsbaumeister R. Knoch ... Hannover, M. Jänecke, 1908-
v. illus. 17½cm. (Bibliothek der gesamten landwirtschaft. Hrsg. von dr. Karl Steinbrück ... 43- bd.)
At head of cover-title on t. II: Jäneckes bibliotheken, reihe B.
CONTENTS.—t. I. Landwirtschaftliche bautechnik.—t. II. Scheunen und ställe.
1. Architecture, Rural.
Agr 9-2089
Library, U. S. Dept. of Agriculture 296K75

NK 0205843 DNAL OU ICJ

Knoch, Richard, 1875-
*Ein Beitrag zur Kenntnis der cerebrospinalen Lues. 30 pp., 1 l. 8°. Jena, G. Neuenhahn, 1904.

NK 0205844 DNLM MBCo ICRL

TX7 .U6 no. 38 **Knoch, Ruth E**
Buying your home sewing machine ⌈prepared by a committee composed of Ruth Knoch and others. Washington, U. S. Govt. Print. Off.⌉ 1954.
13 p. illus. 23 m. (U. S. Dept. of Agriculture. Home and garden bulletin 38)
1. Sewing-machines. (Series)
[TX7.U6 no. 38] Agr 54-128
U. S. Dept. of Agr. Libr. for Library of Congress 1Ag84Hg no. 38 ⌈3°⌉†

NK 0205845 DNAL DLC

VOLUME 300

Knoch, Sigmund, 1881-
Die allgemeinen grundsätze des bayerischen forst-strafrechtes ... von Sigmund Knoch ... Nürnberg, U. E. Sebald, Kgl. bayer. hofbuchdruckerei, 1908.
viii, 224 p. 22cm.
Inaug.-diss.—Würzburg.
"Verzeichnis benützter werke": p. vi-vii.

1. Forestry law and legislation—Bavaria. 2. Criminal law—Bavaria. I. Title.

39-25852

NK 0205846 DLC ICRL MH-A MH

Knoch, Vasilii Ivanovich.
Knoch's album
see under title

WA 29831
Knoch, Vasilii Ivanovich.
Short history of Austria and the Habsburgs, beauties of Vienna. With illustrations and description of the Hofburg, Schönbrunn and the Spanish Riding School [Knoch's informator ed.] Vienna, Wassili J. Knoch [19--]
127 p. illus. 19 cm.

1. Austria - Hist. 2. Hapsburg, House of 3. Vienna - Descr. - 1900- I. Title: The Spanish riding school(1)

NK 0205848 CtY

Koch, Vasilii Ivanovich
see also Knoch, W J firm, publishers, Vienna.

Knoch, W. J., firm, Vienna.
Knoch's album; Schubert and Vienna
see under title

MT95 K48
Knoch, W J firm, publishers, Vienna
Knoch's opera guide: contains over two hundred and fifty descriptions of celebrated operas with short biographies of their composers. Vienna, W.J.Knoch ⌊192-?⌋
556p. 18cm. (Knoch's Informator edition)

Added t.-p.: Tales from the operas, retold by Addie Funk. 1st ser.

NK 0205851 IaU

HD7096 .G3K5
Knoch, Walter.
Reich und Länder in der Organisation der Sozialversicherung. Leipzig, R. Noske, 1932.
ix, 51 p. 21cm.

Bibliography: p. v-ix.

1. Insurance, Social—Germany. I. Title.

NK 0205852 ViU ICRL

Knoch, Wassili J G
see Koch, Vasilii Ivanovich.

Hie 9 K75
Knoch, Werner, 1907-
Ernst von Kirchberg; seine Herkunft und seine Auseinandersetzung mit der Sprache in der Mecklenburgischen Reimchronik. Schwerin(Meckl.)1941.
100p.
Inaug.-Diss. - Berlin.

1. Kirchberg, Ernst von, 14th cent. cdu.

NK 0205854 CtY NcU MH

Knoch (Wilhelm Arnold Albrecht) [1864-]. *Ueber die Berechtigung der seitlichen Incisionen der Cervix bei unvollkommen eröffnetem Muttermunde. 30 pp., 1 l. 8°. *Berlin, G. Schade,* [1888].

NK 0205855 DNLM PPC

KNOCHE, Alfred, 1901-
Der genossenschaftsverband der reichs-landbundes e.V: ein beitrag zur organisation der deutschen landwirtschaft und ihrer genossenschaften. Diss., Giessen. Magdeburg, A. Sorgler, [1928].

pp.(8), 58.
Cover serves as title-page.
"Lebenslauf", at end.

NK 0205856 MH ICRL PBm PU

Knoche, Armin
see Knoche, Hermann, 1851-

Knoche (Augustus Godofr.) *De lacte mulierum. 28 pp., 2 l. 8°. *Halis, typ. Semmlerianis,* [1845].

NK 0205858 DNLM

Knoche, Bernhard Franz Maria, 1908-
... Über den Grundstoffwechsel bei Säuglingen mit Rachitis und Tetanie ... Düsseldorf, 1935.
Inaug.-Diss. - Münster.
Lebenslauf.

NK 0205859 CtY

Knoche, Elsbeth, comp.
Briefe [von Goethe]
see under Goethe, Johann Wolfgang von, 1749-1832.
Correspondence.

WA 11592
Knoche, Elsbeth ed.
George, Morgenstern, Carossa; eine Auswahl aus ihren Gedichten für den Schulgebrauch. Berlin, B.Schulz, 1950.
72p. illus. (Kristall-Bücher, No.6)

I. Carossa, Hans, 1878- . II. Morgenstern, Christian, 1871-1914. III. George, Stefan Anton, 1868-1933.

NK 0205861 CtY

---

*GC9 R4574 948k2
Knoche, Elsbeth.
Rainer Maria Rilke, mit einer Auswahl aus seinen Werken für den Schulgebrauch von Elsbeth Knoche. Genehmigt für den Gebrauch in Schulen durch Control Commission for Germany (B. E.) 1948, Pädagogischer Verlag Berthold Schulz, Berlin W 50.

80p. 17cm. (On verso of t.-p.: Kristall-Bücher, 3)
Ritzer A14.
"Schriften über Rilke": p.80.
Original tan and gray boards.

NK 0205862 MH

Hkg8 403
Knoche, Elsbeth
Wege zu Goethes "Faust". Berlin, Pädagogischer Verlag B.Schulz, 1948.
96p. 17cm. (Kristall-Bücher, Nr.4)

1. Goethe. Faust.
x.ser.

NK 0205863 CtY

Knoche, Erich, 1884-
... Die behandlung der sogenannten prognathie, von dr. Erich Knoche ... Berlin, Meusser, 1923.
66 p. illus. 24cm. (Sammlung Meusser; abhandlung aus dem gebiete der klinischen zahnheilkunde, hft. 15)

"Verzeichnis der wichtigsten benutzten literatur": p. 66.

1. Prognathism. 2. Jaws - Abnormities and deformities. I. Sammlung Meusser; abhandlung aus dem gebiete der klinischen zahnheilkunde.

NK 0205864 NNC DNLM PU-D PP DC

Knoche, Erich, 1884-
Praktische Beiträge zur prothetischen Keramik. 43p. 8° Lpz., 1931.
Forms H. 80, Deut. Zahnh.

NK 0205865 DNLM

Knoche, Ernst, 1867-
Beiträge zur generationsfrage der borkenkäfer ... Halle a. S., 1904.
44, [2] p. illus. 23cm.
Inaug.-diss.—Halle.
Lebenslauf.
"Abgebrochen am schluss des zweiten teiles ... Der schluss befindet sich im Forstwissenschaftlichen-centralblatt. Berlin, Verlag von Paul Parey. Jahrgang 1904."

1. Hylesinus.

Library of Congress QL596.B5K7 7-6297

NK 0205866 DLC DNAL NIC MiU MH-A CtY PU

Knoche, Ernst, 1895-
Beitrag zur degeneration und regeneration der volarnerven des pferdes nach der neurektomie.
Inaug. diss. Giessen, 1926.
Bibl.

NK 0205867 ICRL MH

RD662 K75
Knoche, Franz, 1864-
... Ueber lipome der mundhöhle ... Siegburg, Reckinger, 1888.
38, ⌊2⌋ p.

Inaug.-diss., Bonn, 1888.
Vita.

1. Mouth - Tumors.

NK 0205868 NNC DNLM CU

Knoche, Franz Friedrich Hermann
see
Knoche, Hermann, 1851-

Knoche, Friederich Franz, 1864-
see Knoche, Franz, 1864-

VOLUME 300

ar W 54459 no.1 Knoche, Fritz.
Der Eidesnotstand des Zeugen. Berlin, Alliance Buchdr., 1914.
iv, 10-48 p. 22cm.

Inaug.-Diss.--Erlangen.

NK 0205871 NIC ICRL

Knoche, Georg [Adolf Wilhelm] 1863-
Über die aus der komplexen multiplikation der elliptischen funktionen entspringenden algebraischen gleichungen ... Marburg, 1892.
3 p. l., 38, [2] p. 23½cm.
Inaug.-dis.—Marburg.
Lebenslauf.

1. Functions, Modular.

4-26012†

Library of Congress QA343.K72

NK 0205872 DLC NjP

---

212 K75 Knocho, Grace Frances.
... The mystery-schools, by Grace Frances Knoche. Point Loma, Calif., Theosophical university press, 1940.
3 p. l., 124 p. 15cm. (Theosophical manual no. XIV)
1. Theosophy.
I. Title.

NK 0205873 NNC

Knoche, Grace Frances.
... The mystery-schools, by Grace Frances Knoche. Covina, Calif., Theosophical university press, 1943.
3 p. l., 124, [3] p. 15cm. (Theosophical manual no. XIV)
"Second printing, 1943."
"Books for further study": p. [125]

1. Mysteries, Religious. 2. Theosophy. I. Title.

44-46070

Library of Congress BL610.K6
[2] 291.3

NK 0205874 DLC UU

Knoche, Grace Frances, comp.

Tingley, *Mrs.* Katherine A (Westcott) 1852-
Theosophy, the path of the mystic; links for your own forging from the lectures and writings of Katherine Tingley ... comp. by Grace Knoche ... Point Loma, Calif., The Woman's international theosophical league [°1922]

AC 831 Knoche, Hedwig, 1899-
Über die gegenseitige beeinflussung von chromihydroxyd und ferrihydroxyd, sowie von einigen anderen metallhydroxyden, in ihrem verhalten gegen alkalilauge. ... Würzburg, 1933.
46 p.
Inaug. Diss. - Leipzig, 1933.
Lebenslauf.

NK 0205876 ICRL CtY

Knoche, Heinrich.
Theoretisch-praktische Anleitung zur Erteilung des Rechen- und Raumlehrunterrichtes für Lehrerbildungsanstalten und Volksschullehrer, von H. Knoche. Ein neuer Versuch zur Lösung der Frage: "Wie wirkt der Rechenunterricht sittliche Bildung?" Arnsberg, J. Stahl, 1908.
xvi, 172 p. incl. tables. 22cm.

NK 0205877 ICJ

Knoche, Heinrich, 1897-
Über technik und erfolge der tubenimplantation ... Bonn, 1931. 50 p.
Inaug. Diss. -Bonn, 1931.
Lebenslauf.
Bibliography.

NK 0205878 DNLM CtY

Knoche (Henricus). *De crisi. 2 p. l., 51 pp., 1 l. 8°. Lugd. Bat., L. Herdingh, 1802.

NK 0205879 DNLM

Knoche, Herman.
... Étude phytogéographique sur les îles Baléares ... Montpellier [France] Imprimerie Roumégous et Déhan, 1923.
4 p. l., 170 p., 2 l. front., illus., 10 pl., maps (1 fold.) 3 fold. tab. 25½cm.
Thèse—Univ. de Montpellier.
"Bibliographie": p. 159-170.

1. Botany—Balearic Islands. 2. Geology—Balearic Islands. I. Title.

Library of Congress QK329.K55 23—18703

NK 0205880 DLC CU NNBG OU CtY MH-A

Knoche, Herman.
Étude phytogéographique sur les îles Baléares. With "Liste alphabétique des localités citées des Baléares." Montpellier, 1923.
[8], 170, [22] p. Plates, maps and tables. l. 8°. (Université de Montpellier. Faculté des sciences)

NK 0205881 MH-A

Knoche, Herman.
Flora balearica, étude phytogéographique sur les îles Baléares, par Herman Knoche ... [Montpellier, France, Imp. Roumégous et Déhan] 1921-23.
4 v. front. (v. 4) illus., plates, maps (2 fold.) fold. tables. 25½cm.
CONTENTS.—I-II. Catalogue raisonné de toutes les plantes connues. 2 v.—III. Partie générale.—IV. Planches.

1. Botany—Balearic Islands.

Library of Congress QK329.K6 23-1689 Revised

PPAN TxDaM
NK 0205882 DLC DNAL IU KU CU PU-B MiU OU MH-A ViU

QK329 .K72 Knoche, Herman.
... Die Kanarische Inseln 1923. Strasbourg [etc.] Librairie Istra [1924]
304 p. front., illus. (incl. charts) xxiv pl. (Vagandi mos. Reiseskizzen eines botanikers, von dr. Hermann Knoche. 1)
"Bibliographie": p. 40-41.

1. Botany—Canary Islands.

NK 0205883 ICU CU CtY

Knoche, Herman.
Vagandi mos. Reiseskizzen eines botanikers, von dr. Herman Knoche ... Strasbourg [etc.] Librairie istra, 1923-
v. illus., plates, maps. 25½cm.

1. Botany—Canary islands. [1. Canary islands—Botany] I. Title.

Agr 26—114

U. S. Dept. of agr. Library for Library of Congress 460.52K75 [a40c1]

CoU MtU TxDaM WaU
NK 0205884 DNAL CaBVaU TU OU NcD TxU OCU OC1W PU-B

Knoche, Hermann.
Moderne Verkehrsregelung; die Behebung der Verkehrsnot. Lübeck, Verlag für Polizeiliches Fachschrifttum [1955]
116 p. illus. 25 cm.

1. Traffic regulations. I. Title.

HE369.K56 56-24518 ‡

NK 0205885 DLC

Knoche, Hermann.
Schriftverkehr im Dienst des Polizeibeamten. Duisburg, C. Lange [1952]
48 p. forms. 21 cm. (Die Blauen Polizeifachbücher)

1. Police—Germany—Records and correspondence. I. Title.

A 53-6077

Illinois. Univ. Library for Library of Congress [1]

NK 0205886 IU

Knoche, Hermann, 1851-
Vergilius quae graeca exempla secutus sit in Georgicis ... Lipsiae, typis Metzgerii & Wittigii, 1877.
1 p. l., 58 p., 1 l. 21½cm.
Inaug.-diss.—Leipzig.
Vita.

1. Vergilius Maro, Publius. Georgica. 2. Literature, Comparative—Latin and Greek. 3. Literature, Comparative—Greek and Latin.

[*Full name:* Franz Friedrich Hermann Knoche]

30-18122

Library of Congress PA6804.G4K6

NK 0205887 DLC CU PU OC1W MiU

Knoche, Joachim Heinrich.
Commentationes de Babrio poeta caput I. n.p., 1835.

NK 0205888 NjP

KNOCHE, Joachim Heinrich.
Untersuchungen über des Proklus Diadochus commentar zu Euklids Elementen. [Progr.] Herford, E. Heidemann, 1862.

4°. pp.(2),22.

NK 0205889 MH NjP PBm

Knoche, Paul.
Anleitung zur röntgenphotographie, von dr. Paul Knoche. Mit 35 abbildungen im text und auf tafeln, sowie einem einbanddeckenbild von Karl Hansen, Berlin. Berlin, Union deutsche verlagsgesellschaft [°1925]
111 p. incl. illus., plates, diagrs. 20cm. (*On cover:* Photographische bibliothek ... (bd.) 35)
Plates printed on both sides; illustration mounted on front cover.

1. Radiography.

Library of Congress TR750.K6 25-24465

NK 0205890 DLC ICJ

Knoche, Paul Ludwig, 1887-
Über das verhalten des bromsilbers in eiweiss. [Berlin, Alliance, 1914]
48 p. illus. 23cm.

Thesis, Berlin.
Bibliographical footnotes.

NK 0205891 NNC CtY

Knoche, Richard.
Erbarmet euch der theire! ... dritte auflage. Hannover, Schmorl & von Seefeld, 1880.
8p.

AC931 .H3 v.177 [Hartford-Bauer pamphlets, v. 177, no. 5]

NK 0205892 ICRL

VOLUME 300

Knoche (Richard). Het wetenschappelijk dierenmarteln. Eene reeks van feiten uit verschillende anthenthieke bronnen bijeengebracht. 20 pp. 8°. [*Amsterdam*, 1891. *vel subseq.*]

NK 0205893 DNLM

KNOCHE, Rudolf, 1895-
Studien an cyclobutanderivaten. Inaug.-diss. Munster i.W. Borna-Leipzig, R. Norske, 1925.

pp. 31. +.
"Lebenslauf," at end.

NK 0205894 MH-C

Knoche, Traute, 1912–
"Johann Jacob Michael Küechel", 1703–1769; ein Beitrag zum deutschen Rokoko... von Traute Knoche... Marburg: Hessischer Verlag K. Euker, 1937. 95 p. 21½cm.

Inaugural-Dissertation — Marburg, 1936.
Lebenslauf.
"Literaturverzeichnis," p. 92.

1. Küchel, Michael, 1703–1769. 2. Rococo.
N. Y. P. L. September 28, 1939

NK 0205895 NIC NN NNC MH CtY PU

Knoche, Ulrich, 1902–
Handschriftliche grundlagen des Juvenaltextes, von Ulrich Knoche. Leipzig, Dieterich'sche verlagsbuchhandlung, 1940.

xi, 394 p. tables. 24cm. (Philologus. Supplementband XXXIII, hft. 1)
Bibliographical foot-notes.

1. Juvenalis, Decimus Junius. I. Title.
A 45–2838

Western Res. univ. Libr. for Library of Congress [PA3.P55 bd. 32, hft. 1]
[4]

NK 0205896 OClW InU PU OCU IEN CU

Knoche, Ulrich, 1902–
Magnitudo animi, untersuchungen zur entstehung und entwicklung eines römischen wertgedankens, von Ulrich Knoche ... Leipzig, Dieterich'sche verlagsbuchhandlung, 1935.

4 p. l., 93 p. 23½cm. (Philologus, Supplementband XXVII, hft. 3)
Bibliographical foot-notes.

1. Philosophy, Ancient. 2. Character. 3. Worth. I. Title.
A C 35–633

Title from Illinois Univ. Library of Congress [PA3.P55 xxvii, hft. 3]
[2]

NK 0205897 IU CU PPT PBm PU MiU OCU OCl ViU

Knoche, Ulrich, 1902–
Der philosoph Seneca, von Ulrich Knoche. Frankfurt am Main, V. Klostermann, 1933.

32 p. 24½cm.
"Dieser vortrag wurde am 16. 1. 1933 als antrittsvorlesung in Köln gehalten."—Anmerkungen.

1. Seneca, Lucius Annaeus.
A C 34–3731

Title from Princeton Univ. Printed by L. C.

NK 0205898 NjP NcD

Knoche, Ulrich, 1902–
Die römische Satire. Berlin, Wissenschaftliche Editionsgesellschaft, 1949.

110 p. 24 cm. (Handbuch der griechischen und lateinischen Philologie. 1. Vorklassische und klassische Zeit. 1. Dichtung)

1. Satire, Latin—Hist. & crit. I. Title. (Series)

PA6056.K6 51–24177

IaU OU
NK 0205899 DLC NcU NN CU DDO MH NIC NNC CaBVaU CtY

Knoche, Ulrich, 1902– ed.
Saturae, mit kritischem Apparat
see Juvenalis, Decimus Junius.
Satirae. 1950.

AS182
.G83
v.3
no.3
1938

Knoche, Ulrich, 1902–
Über einige Szenen des Eunuchus (2.T.)
Göttingen, Vandenhoeck & Ruprecht, 1938.
87 p. 25cm. (Gesellschaft der Wissenschaften zu Göttingen. Philologisch-Historische Klasse. Nachrichten. Fachgruppe 1. Altertumswissenschaft. N.F., Bd. 3, Nr. 3)
Cover title.
Bibliographical footnotes.
1. Terentius Afer, Publius. Eunuchus—Criticism, Textual. I. Ser.

NK 0205901 ViU

Knoche, Ulrich, 1902 -
Die überlieferung Juvenals, von dr. Ulrich Knoche. Berlin, E. Ebering, 1926.

4 p. l., 74 p., 1 l. 24cm. (*Added t.-p.*: Klassisch-philogische studien ... hft. 6)
"Verzeichnis der handschriften": 4th prelim. leaf.

1. Juvenalis, Decimus Junius—Criticism, Textual. 2. Juvenalis, Decimus Junius—Manuscripts. I. Title.
26–24640

Library of Congress PA6448.K6

NK 0205902 DLC MH IU

B34W12
DK75

Knoche, Viola Emma.
The early influence of Richard Wagner in America. [Urbana] c1915.
51p.

Reprinted from Deutsch-amerikanische geschichtsblaetter, Jahrbuch der Deutsch-amerikanischen historischen gesellschaft von Illinois--jahrgang 1914 (vol.XIV)

NK 0205903 IU

Knoche, Walter.
Das Gewerbe-Betriebshaus. Ein Beitrag zur Mittelstandsfrage. Von W. Knoche. Lübeck, C. Coleman, 1906.
[8], 104 p. 22cm.

NK 0205904 ICJ

A/614.722
K72

Knoche, Walter, Alfred, 1881-1945
Algunas apuntes sobre le producción del anhidrido carbónico antropógeno. Buenos Aires. 1938.
p.41-46. 28cm.

(De los "Anales de la Sociedad científica Argentina". Julio de 1938. E. I, T. CXXVI.)

NK 0205905 DAS

Knoche, Walter, Alfred, 1881-1945.
Algunas indicaciones sobre los Uti-krag del río Doce (Espíritu Santo) por Walter Knoche ... Santiago de Chile, Imprenta universitaria, 1913.

13 p. 4 pl. 24½cm.
"Trabajo publicado en la 'Revista de historia y geografía', año III, t. V."

1. Botocudo Indians. I. Title.
20—17482

Library of Congress F2520.1.B76K72

NK 0205906 DLC

Bol
F
Pam

Knoche, Walter Alfred, 1881-1945.
... Algunas observaciones microclimaticas en la mina aguila - Bolivia (5200 m. de altura) ... Buenos Aires, Talleres gráficos "Tomás Palumbo, 1944.
cover-title, p. 145-154. 26.5 cm.
"De los "Anales de la Sociedad Científica argentina" Abril 1944, E. IV, Tomo CXXXVII, pág. 145 y sig."

NK 0205907 DPU

Knoche, Walter Alfred, 1881–
...Der "Austrocknungswert" als klimatischer Faktor, von Walter Knoche... Hamburg, 1929. 47 p. illus. (charts.) sq. 4°. (Germany. Seewarte, Direktion der. Aus dem Archiv der deutschen Seewarte. Bd. 48, Nr. 1.)

1. Humidity. 2. Hygrometry. I. Ser.
N. Y. P. L. April 1, 1931

NK 0205908 NN

Knoche, Walter Alfred, 1881-
Beitrag zum Wesen der andinen Bergkrankheit. 1910.
32371

NK 0205909 DAS

KNOCHE, Walter Alfred, 1881-
Bemerkungen zu einem gewitter in San Carlos de Ancud. n.p., n.d.

Cover serves as title-page.
"From 'Terrestrial Magnetism and Atmospheric Electricity', September, 1913." pp.151-156.

NK 0205910 MH

QH123
.K5

Knoche, Walter Alfred, 1881-
Bio- und medizinisch-geographische Beobachtungen auf einer Reise durch Ecuador. Buenos Aires, 1931.
[135]-247 p. illus. 27 cm.
"Sonderabdruck aus "Phoenix' Zeitschrift des Deutschen Wissenschaftlichen Vereins."
Bibliography: p. 247.
1. Biology - Ecuador. 2. Ecology - Ecuador. i. t.

NK 0205911 NNBG DAS

278

Knoche, Walter Alfred, 1881-
Breve información sobre la ley de la evaporación y su significado para la irrigación, ed. 1916.
(Trabajo pub. en el No. 23 de la Revista chilena de historia y geografía)

NK 0205912 DPU

M86
K72cl

Knoche, Walter Alfred, 1881-1945.
...Clima de las metrópolis y de interiores. (Apartado de La revista meteorologica, año 2, no. 5, enero 1943). ‹Buenos Aires›, A. Monteverde & cia, 1943.
24p. tables, diagrs. 25cm.

NK 0205913 DAS DPU

M/1730
K72co

Knoche, Walter. Alfred, 1881-
Condiciones climáticas en relación a las migraciones melanesio-polinésicas dentro de la Oceanía y hacia Sud América. Buenos Aires. 1939.
p.247-254. tab. 26cm.

(De los Anales de la Sociedad científica argentina, oct. de 1939, e.IV, t.128.)

NK 0205914 DAS

VOLUME 300

M/1730 K72d
Knoche, Walter. Alfred, 1881-
Diferencias de orden climático entre la colonización española y portuguesa. Buenos Aires 1939.
p.175-189. tabs. 26cm.
(De los Anales de la Sociedad científica argentina, sept. de 1939, e.III, t.128.)

NK 0205915 DAS

M/1737 K72
Knoche, Walter. Alfred, 1881-
Der Einfluss von Vegetationsbränden auf die Witterung. Braunschweig. 1937.
p.243-254, tables, diagrs. 30 cm.

NK 0205916 DAS

KNOCHE, Walter Alfred, 1881-
Einige bemerkungen über die Uti-Krag am río Doce (Espirito Santo). [Berlin?,1913?].
pp.(7).
Without title-page. Caption title.
"Aus der Zeitschrift fur ethnologie. Heft. 3,19,13," pp.394-399.

NK 0205917 MH

Knoche, Walter Alfred, 1881–
Einige Messungen luftelektrischer Zerstreuung auf dem Pico de Teyde und in Puerto Orotava (Tenerife). Von Walter Knoche. [Leipzig: S. Hirzel, 1904.] 3 p. Tables. 4°.
Caption-title.
Repr.: Physikalishe Zeitschrift. Jahrg. 6, no. 1.

1. Electricity (Atmospheric), Canary islands: Teneriffe.
N. Y. P. L. October 30, 1917.

NK 0205918 NN

G918.3 K751g
Knoche, Walter Alfred, 1881-1945.
... La geografía de Chile y la agricultura, por el dr. Walter Knoche, con un apéndice que contiene las leyes de colonización agrícola. [Santiago de Chile] Editorial Nascimento, 1933.
39p. 18cm.
At head of title: Departamento de extensión cultural. Ministerio del trabajo.
1. Chile. 2. Agricultural laws and legislation - Chile. I. Chile. Departamento de extensión cultural.

NK 0205919 TxU DAS IU DNAL MH CU

Knoche, Walter Alfred, 1881–
... The ice age problem, by Walter Knoche ... City of Washington, The Smithsonian institution, 1941.
1 p. l., 5 p. 24½cm. (Smithsonian miscellaneous collections, v. 99, no. 22)
Publication 3633.

1. Glacial epoch. I. Title.
Library of Congress Q11.S7 vol. 99, no. 22 41-50990
——— Copy 2. QE697.K67
[10] (506) 551.79

OO OU OCU
NK 0205920 DLC ViU MoU WaS WaWW OrSaW DAS NBuU FU

86 721d
Knoche, Walter Alfred, 1881-
Ideas sobre los fundamentos bioclimaticos y biogeograficos para una colonizacion Europea. Buneos Aires, 1943.
p. 99-111. 26½cm.

NK 0205921 DAS DPU

Knoche, Walter Alfred, 1881-
Jahres-, Januar- und Juli-Niederschlags-karte der Republik Chile. 1929.
p. 208-216. charts. (fold.) 25½ cm.

NK 0205922 DAS

Knoche, Walter. Alfred, 1881-
Karten der Januar- und Juli- Bewölkung in Chile. 1927.
p. 220-224. chart. 26 cm.

NK 0205923 DAS

Knoche, Walter Alfred, 1881-1945.
Klimatische Beobachtungen auf einer Reise in Ecuador. Santiago de Chile, Impr. W. Gnadt [1932?]
46 p. 25 cm.
Cover title.
"Sonderabdruck aus den Verhandlungen des Deutschen wissenschaftlichen Vereins zu Santiago de Chile, n. F., Bd. 2, 1932."

1. Ecuador—Climate. I. Title.
QC988.E2K6 52-58199

NK 0205924 DLC DAS

Knoche, Walter Alfred, 1881-
Liste der Publikationen. Santiago. n.d.
unp. 24½ cm.

NK 0205925 DAS

KNOCHE, Walter. Alfred, 1881-
Meteorologische und luftelektrische messunge während der totalen sonnenfinsternis am 10. oktober 1912, auf der facenda Boã Vista bei Christina, Brazilien. Von W. Knoche und J. Laub. [Chicago, The University of Chicago press, 1916]
Dover serves as title-page.
"From Terrestrial Magnetism and Atmospheric Electricity, Sept. and Dec. 1916."

NK 0205926 MH

Knoche, Walter Alfred, 1881-
...Una nueva representacion grafica de orden antropo y fitoclimatico con ejemplos para la Republica Argentina, por... Walter Knoche. n.p., n.d.
23 p.

NK 0205927 PPC DPU

Arg QC Pam
Knoche, Walter, 1881-
... Observación de un enfriamiento súbito debido a una grandeza fina ... Buenos Aires, Talleres gráficos "Tomás Palumbo", 1942.
cover-title, p. 242-244. table. 27 cm.
"De los "Anales de la Sociedad cienctífica argentina" Octubre 1942, E. IV, Tomo CXXXIV, pág. 242 y sig."

NK 0205928 DPU

Knoche, Walter. Alfred, 1881-
Observaciones en la mina Águila 5.200 m (Cordillera de Quimza Cruz, Bolivia) del 26 abril hasta el 12 de septiembre de 1909. Santiago de Chile: Sección Impresiones del Instituto Meteorológico, 1911. xiii p., 1 l., 243(1) p. f°. (Chile. Instituto Central Meteorológico y Geofísico de Chile. Publ. 1.)
Text and title also in German: Beobachtungen in der Aguila-Mine...

1. Meteorology.—Observations, Bolivia, 1909.
N. Y. P. L. May 11, 1916.

NK 0205929 NN MB

Rhh9 E16 +913
Knoche, Walter, Alfred, 1881-
... Observaciones meteorológicas de la Isla de Pascua. Explicaciones sobre el clima de Isla de Pascua ... [Santiago de Chile, 1913]
23p. 37½cm.
Caption title.
"De la Publicacion no.4 del Instituto central meteorológico de Chile."
Spanish and German text in parallel columns.

NK 0205930 CtY

Knoche, Walter. Alfred, 1881-
... Observaciones microclimáticas en una sala de operaciones. Estudio comparativo del metabolismo basal climático. Conferencias por ... Walter Knoche. Buenos Aires, Caporaletti hnos., 1943.
29 p. plan, tables. 23cm.
At head of title: Instituto de perfeccionamiento médico-quirúrgico ...

NK 0205931 ICJ PPC MnU

KNOCHE, Walter, Alfred, 1881-
Die Osterinsel. Beobachtungen und erkundigungen auf der Osterinsel. Reduzierung psychophysischer messungen auf gleiche perioden. Santiago, Imp. "El Globo", 1921.
1.8°. pp.64.
"Sonderabdruck aus den Verhandlungen des Deutschen Wissenschaftlichen Vereins in Santiago, bd.VII ."

NK 0205932 MH

Knoche, Walter, Alfred, 1881 -
... Die Osterinsel, eine zusammenfassung der chilenischen Osterinsel-expedition des jahres 1911. Concepcion, Wiss. archiv von Chile, 1925.
4 p. l., 319, [1] p. front., illus., plates, maps, facsims. 19½cm.
"Literatur": p. 1-7.
"Zum musik der Osterinsulaner": 1 p. at end.

1. Easter Island. I. Title.
Library of Congress F3169.K7 27-21187
[2]

NK 0205933 DLC NN

KNOCHE, Walter Alfred, 1881-
Los promedios climatéricos por horas (1912-1914) de Valparaiso. (Anuario astronómico 1920) Santiago de Chile, Imprenta universitaria, 1919.
pp.30. Tables.

NK 0205934 MH

Knoche, Walter Alfred, 1881–
Resumen de la organización del servicio meteorológico... (In: Pan Amer. Scientific Congress. 2d, Washington, 1915-16. Proc. Washington, 1917. 8°. v. 2, p. 730-735.)

1. Meteorology, Chile.
N. Y. P. L. September 20, 1918.

NK 0205935 NN

VOLUME 300

Knoche, Walter Alfred, 1881-
Sobre la radiación bio-climatérica.
Inaug. Diss. Chile, 1928 (Santiago De Chile)

NK 0205936 DLC

KNOCHE, Walter, Alfred, 1881-
Sobre la relación numérica de los sexos en Chile. Santiago de Chile, H.A.Maffet, A.Folsch, [1926].

1.8°. pp.12. Map.
("Publicado en la Revista médica de Chile, no.4, 1926.)

NK 0205937 MH

Knoche, Walter Alfred, 1881-
Las "temperatures sentidas" en la Peninsula. Iberica. Madrid. 1936.
12 p. 24 cm.

NK 0205938 DAS

Knoche, Walter Alfred, 1881-
... Tres notas sobre la isla de Pascua: I. Observaciones de algunas pinturas, en sus reproducciones. II. Los últimos tatuajes en la isla de Pascua. III. Un cuento y dos canciones. Santiago de Chile, Imprenta universitaria, 1912.
27 p. plates (part col.) 26cm.

1. Ethnology—Easter Island.

Library of Congress GN671.E2K6 13-10521

NK 0205939 DLC NcU CtY OCl CU DPU MB

Knoche, Walter Alfred, 1881-
Über die Kahl der gewitter in Chile.
Valparaiso. (n.d.) (12p.) 25 cm.

NK 0205940 DAS

KNOCHE, Walter, Alfred, 1881-
Ueber die kulturpflanzen der Osterinsel. Buenos Aires, J.Weiss & Preusche, 1919.

1.8°. pp.24.
Cover serves as title-page.
At head of title:- Sonderabdruck aus Zeitschrift des Deutschen Wissenschaftlichen Vereins zur Kultur- und Landeskunde Argentiniens, jahrgang 1919, heft.3 ."

NK 0205941 MH NcU

Knoche, Walter, Alfred, 1881-
... Ueber die räumliche und zeitliche verteilung des wärmegehalts der unteren luftschicht. Von Walter Knoche ... Hamburg, Gedruckt bei Hammerich & Lesser in Altona, 1905.
1 p. l., 46 p. 2 fold. pl. (incl. charts, diagrs.) 29½ x 23½cm. (Aus dem Archiv der Deutschen seewarte. XXVIII. jahrgang 1905 ... no. 2)

1. Atmospheric temperature.

Library of Congress QC801.H3 1905 8-33487
—— —— Copy 2. Library of Congress QC901.K7

NK 0205942 DLC NN

Knoche, Walter. Alfred, 1881-
Über die räumliche und zeitliche verteilung des wärmegehalts der unteren luftschicht ... [Berlin, Universitätsbuchdruckerei von G. Schade (O. Francke)] 1906.
1 p. l., 46 p., 1 l. 2 fold. pl. (incl. maps) tables. 29 x 24cm.
Inaug.-diss.—Berlin.
Lebenslauf.
Issued also in Aus den archiv der Deutschen seewarte. 1905.

1. Atmospheric temperature.

Library of Congress QC901.K72 7—17706

NK 0205943 DLC PU ICRL CU CtY

Knoche, Walter Alfred, 1881-
El "Valor de desecación" como factor climatológico. Santiago de Chile, Impr. Universitaria, 1919.
91 p.

NK 0205944 DLC-P4 DAS

Knoche, Walter Alfred, 1881-
Verteilung des Niederschlagsüberschusses in Chile.
4 p. diagr. 27½ cm.

NK 0205945 DAS

Knoche, Wilhelm, 1900-
Das verkehrsmonopol als nationalpolitische lösung des wettbewerbs von eisenbahn und kraftwagen im güterfernverkehr ... Von Wilhelm Knoche ... Göttingen, Druck der Göttinger handelsdruckerei, 1934.
viii, 131, [1] p. 21cm.
Inaug.-diss.--Göttingen.
Lebenslauf.
"Literaturverzeichnis": p.[126]-131.

1.Transportation--Germany. I.Title.

NK 0205946 MiU NNC CtY ICRL

HS394 .F73 Knochen, Helmut, 1910-
Das Freimaurerlogen-Museum in Nürnberg. München, Bayerland-Verlag, 1938.

Knochen, Helmut, 1910-
Der dramatiker George Colman ... Göttingen, Buchdruckerei des "Göttinger tageblattes", Gebr. Wurm g.m.b.h., 1935.
83 p. 21cm.
Inaug.-diss.-Göttingen.
Lebenslauf.
"Literaturverzeichnis": p.81-82.

1.Colman, George, 1732-1794.

NK 0205948 MiU OU CtY NjP NN ICRL

Knochen, Muskeln, Sehnen, Sehnenscheiden, Schleimbeutel
see under Albertini, Ambrosius von, 1894-

Knochendöppel, Carl
Neuere Einrichtungen und Ergebnisse auf dem Gebiete der Funkentelegraphie. ... . Ein Beitrag zur Geschichte der Elektrizität von Oberlehrer Dr. C. Knochendöppel. Apolda, vol. 1, Druck von R. Birkner, vol. 2, Druck von H. Blume, 1905-1908.
2 vol. in 1. tables, diagrs. 27½ x 21cm.
Programm — Grossherzogliche Wilhelm und Louis Zimmermanns Realschule, Apolda.

NK 0205950 ICJ

Knochendoeppel, Carl
Ueber den einfluss eines magnetischen feldes auf das entladungspotential in Geissler'schen roehren.
Jena, 1901

QC711 .K7

NK 0205951 DLC CtY PU NN MH ICRL

QA 218 .K72 Knochendöppel, Carl.
Von den Gleichungen dritten und höheren Grades mit zahlreichen Beispielen und Übungsaufgaben nebst ihren Lösungen. Berlin, Volk und Wissen Verlag, 1949.
76 p. diagrs. 23 cm. (Mathematische Lehrhefte)

1.Equations--Numerical solutions. 2.Equations Cubic.

NK 0205952 MiU OrCS InU OU

QA242 .K56 Knochendöppel, Carl.
Von den Kettenbrüchen und den diophantischen gleichungen. Berlin, Vold und Wissen Verlags, 1948.
71 p. 23 cm. (Mathematische Lehrhefte, hrsg. von Prof. Dr. L. Peters)

1. Fractions, Continued. 2. Diophantine analysis. I. Title.

NK 0205953 TU OrCS KU OU MiU InU

968.22 K72g Knochenhauer, Bruno.
Die Goldfelder in Transvaal mit besonderer Berücksichtigung der de Kaap Goldfelder. Fachwissenschaftlich beleuchtet von B. Knochenhauer. Berlin, Walter & Apolant, 1890.
55p. 20cm.

1. Gold mines and mining. Transvaal. 2. Mines and mineral resources. Transvaal. 3. Africa, South. Econ. condit. I. Title.

NK 0205954 IEN

Knochenhauer, Bruno.
... Korea. Vortrag, gehalten in der Abteilung Berlin-Charlottenburg der Deutschen Kolonial-Gesellschaft. Berlin: D. Reimer, 1901. p. 75-124. map. 8°. (Deutsche Kolonial-Gesellschaft. Abt.: Berlin-Charlottenburg. Verhandlungen. [v. 5,] Heft 4.)

1. Korea—Descr. and trav., 1800-1900. 2. Ser.
N. Y. P. L. September 17, 1925

NK 0205955 NN MH

Knochenhauer, Bruno.
Die oberschlesische Montanindustrie. Gotha, Flamberg, 1927.
151 p. ports., fold. map. 23 cm. (Die Deutsche Wirtschaft und ihre Führer, 9. Bd.)

1. Mineral industries—Silesia, Upper (Province) 2. Mines and mineral resources—Silesia, Upper (Province) I. Title.

HD9506.G23S7 55-45205

NK 0205956 DLC NN

Knochenhauer, C.
Grundriss der Weltgeschichte für den Unterricht in Schulen ed. 2. Potsdam, Stein, 1876.
315p. O.

NK 0205957 OO

VOLUME 300

Knochenhauer, C.
Handbuch der weltgeschichte für den unterricht auf höheren lehranstalten. Potsdam, A. Stein, 1860.
3 v. in 1. tables. 21 cm.
Contents.- 1. T. Die alte geschichte.- 2. T. Geschichte des mittelalters. 1862.- 3. T. Geschichte der neueren zeit. 1863.

NK 0205958 OCU

Knochenhauer, C
Handbuch der Weltgeschichte für den Unterricht auf höheren Lehranstalten und zum Selbststudium. Theil 3, Geschichte der neueren Zeit. Potsdam, Riegel, 1863.

NK 0205959 MH

Knochenhauer, Karl Wilhelm, 1805-1875.
Repertorium der physik. Enthaltend eine vollständige zusammenstellung der neuern fortschritte dieser wissenschaft ...
see under title

Knochenhauer, Karl Wilhelm, 1805-1875.
... Über den zusammenhang des magnetismus mit den oscillationen des batteriestroms. 1863?
p. 249-267. tables. 24 cm. (In Physical tracts, v. 5)

NK 0205961 RPB

KNOCHENHAUER, Karl Wilhelm, 1805-
Über die gemeinsame wirkung zweier elektrischer ströme. [Wien, 1855.]

NK 0205962 MH

Knochenhauer, Karl Wilhelm, 1805-1875.
Die undulationstheorie des lichtes. Eine beilage zu den lehrbüchern der physik, von K. W. Knochenhauer. Mit fünf figurentafeln. Berlin, G. Reimer, 1839.
iv p., 1 l., 206 p. 53 diagrs. on V pl. 25 x 20cm.

1. Light, Wave theory of. I. Title.

NK 0205963 ViU NNC MiU NN CU CtY

Knochenhauer, Theodor, 1842-1869.

Chroust, Anton, 1864- ed.
Chroniken der stadt Bamberg ... herausgegeben von Anton Chroust. Leipzig, Quelle & Meyer, 1907-10.

943.22 K72g
Knochenhauer, Theodor, 1842-1869.
Geschichte Thuringens in der karolingischen und sachsischen Zeit. Gotha, F.A. Perthes, 1863.
x, 195p.

Bibliographical footnotes.

1. Thuringia--History. I. Title.

NK 0205965 IEN CU MH

Knochenhauer, Theodor, 1842-1869.
Geschichte Thüringens zur zeit des ersten landgrafenhauses, 1039-1247. Mit anmerkungen herausgegeben von Karl Wenzel. Mit vorwort und einer lebensskizze des verfassers von R. Usinger. Gotha, F. A. Perthes, 1871.
pp. xiv, (2), 375.

NK 0205966 MH CU

Rh10 +G21 v.3
Knochenhauer, W
... Dürre und Dürreperioden 1934 ... Berlin, J.Springer, 1937.
23p.incl.charts,tables,diagrs. 6pl.(1 fold.) 34cm. ([Germany] Reichsamt für Wetterdienst. Wissenschaftliche Abhandlungen, Bd.III, Nr.9)
"Aus dem Geophysikalischen Institut der Universität Leipzig."

NK 0205967 CtY

Knochenhauer, Wolfgang, ed.
Hundert Jahre Victoria Versicherung
see under
Victoria zu Berlin, Allgemeine Versicherungs A.-G.

Knochenhauer, Wolfgang.
... Das Recht der Lebens- und der Unfallversicherung, von Gerichtsassessor Wolfgang Knochenhauer ... Leipzig: F. Meiner [etc., etc.] 1936. 110 p. 23cm. (Die Praxis der Versicherungswirtschaft. Heft 10.)

49414B. 1. Insurance, Life—Jurisp.—Germany. 2. Insurance, Accident—Jurisp.—Germany. I. Ser.
N. Y. P. L. June 4, 1940

NK 0205969 NN

Knochenstiern (Hugo). *Ueber den Keimgehalt der Dorpater Marktmilch, nebst einigen bacteriologischen Untersuchungen von Frauenmilch. 51 pp. 8°. Dorpat, Schnakenburg, 1893.

NK 0205970 DNLM

Knochenwebel (Joh. Godofredus). *De ischiadico malo. 51 pp., 2 l. 4°. Halæ Magdeb., typ. J. C. Hendelii, [1729].

NK 0205971 DNLM PPC

ML 410 .S26K66
Knoch's album; Schubert and Vienna. Der Liederfürst Franz Schubert und Wien [1828-1928, von Dolf Six] Hrsg. von W.J. Knoch. Wien, Kommissions-Verlag Wolfrum [1928]
64 p. illus., port. (Knoch's Informator edition)
English text: p. 43-64.
"Museums": p. 58-64.
1. Schubert, Franz Peter, 1797-1828. 2. Vienna--Galleries and museums. I. Six, Dolf. II. Knoch, W.J., firm, Vienna.

NK 0205972 ICU NNC ICN MiD OBlC

Knoch's opera guide ...
see under Knoch, W J firm, publishers, Vienna.

Knock, A G.
Fine willow basketry, by A. G. Knock ... [Leicester, Eng.] The Dryad press [1929]
69 p. incl. illus., plates. front. 22cm.
On label mounted above imprint: The Manual arts press, Peoria, Illinois.
"First published 1929."

1. Basket making. I. Title: Willow basketry.
Library of Congress TS910.K6 38-7414
[3] 677.543

NK 0205974 DLC CaBVa TU NN ODW OU OCl KMK

TS910 .K6
Knock, A G
Willow basketry. Leicester, The Dryad Press [1946]
41p. incl. illus., plates. front. 22cm.
Label mounted over imprint; The Manual Arts Press.

NK 0205975 NNU-W IaU Or

Knock, A G
Willow basket-work. [4th ed.] Leicester [Eng.], Dryad Press [1951]
54 p. illus. 22 cm.
Label pasted above imprint reads: Chas. A. Bennett Co. Inc., Peoria, Illinois.

NK 0205976 NcRS

TS910 .K66 1953
Knock, A G
Willow basket-work. [5th ed.] Leicester [Eng.] Dryad Press [1953]
53p. illus. 22cm.
On label mounted above imprint: Peoria, Ill., C. A. Bennett.

1. Basket making. I. Title. 3

NK 0205977 PSt CaBVa WaS WaT

Knock, Arthur Wilhelm, 1885-
Personal evangelism; a study guide in how to do personal work, by A. W. Knock ... Minneapolis, Minn., The author; The Lutheran Bible institute [c1934]
4 p. l., 189 p. 20½cm.

1. Evangelistic work. I. Title.
Library of Congress BV3793.K5 35-3559
——— Copy 2.
Copyright A 78777 [2] 269

NK 0205978 DLC InAndC-T

Knock, Barold
... Continens observationes sex ad selecta quaedam juris romani loca ... submittit, Barold Knock ... Groningae, G. Spandaw [1746]
2 p.l., 60, [6] p. 22½cm.
Diss.- Groningen.
Engraved title-page.

NK 0205979 MH-L

Knock, Bernhardus Hermannus
... Exhibens nonnullas juris romani et groningani differentias ... submittit Bernhardus Hermannus Knock ... Groningae, J. Bolt [1761]
3 p.l., 10 p. 26½cm.
Diss.- Groningen.

NK 0205980 MH-L

Knock, Nicolaas Arnoldi, 1759-1794.
... De legum naturalium et civilium natura ... submittit Nicolaus Arnoldi Knock ... Groningae, P. Doekema [1780]
3 p.l., 65, [1] p. 24cm.
Diss.- Groningen.

NK 0205981 MH-L

VOLUME 300

Knock, Nicolaas Arnoldi, 1759-1794.
Dispositien der merkwaardigste kerk-orgelen, welken in de provincie Friesland, Groningen en elders aangetroffen worden. Kunnende dit werk verstrekken tot een vervolg van het werk van den Heer J. Hess. Door Nicolaas Arnoldi Knock ... Groningen, P. Doekema, 1788.
2 p. l., 77, [3] p. 21 x 17cm.

1. Organ—Construction.
13-24939
Library of Congress ML582.A2K7

NK 0205982 DLC

Microfiche
ML
15
Knock, Nicolaas Arnoldi, 1759-1794.
Dispositien der merkwaardigste kerk-orgelen, welken in de provincie Friesland, Groningen en elders aangetroffen worden. Kunnende dit werk verstrekken tot een vervolg van het werk van den Heer J. Hess. Door Nicolaas Arnoldi Knock ... Groningen, P. Doekema, 1788.
2 p. l., 77, [3] p. 21 x 17cm. 2 cards.
Microfiche. Inter Documentation Co., AG, Zug, Switzerland, 1970.

NK 0205983 InU

Knock, Sidney.
"Clear lower deck"; an intimate study of the men of the Royal navy, by Sidney Knock ... [London] P. Allan, 1932.
viii, 280 p. plates. 22cm.

1. Gt. Brit.—Navy—Sea life. 2. Seamen. I. Title.
NN 33-31449
Library of Congress V737.K6
[2] 359.0942

NK 0206001 DLC CaBViP CtY NN

Knock — and ye shall enter —
see under [Heath, William] 1795-1840.

PR
3991
.A1
K72
A knock at the door; or, Worsted works wonders. Acted at Castle Ashby, Jan. 2nd, 1846. Grantham, Printed by S. Ridge [1846?]
1 p.l., iii, 53 p. 20cm.
Manuscript corrections and stage directions throughout.

NK 0206003 MiU

Knock at the door, peep in, open the latch and walk in. [1884]
see under Lewis, Miss Mattie.

*pFB8
N1627
Z805n
A knock down blow in the ocean.!! Or Bonoparte taking french leave.
Pubd at Ackermans gallery 101 Strand London Augt. 4. 1803.
plate. 24x34cm., mounted & bd. to 50x40cm.
George 10073; Broadlly A-527 (ascribed to Woodward).
Engraving (hand-colored), unsigned.
A satire on Napoleon's intended invasion.
No. 99 in a volume lettered on spine: Napoleonic caricatures.

Another copy. 25x35.5cm., mounted & bd. to 66x50cm.
With slightly different coloring.
No. 38b in a volume lettered on spine: Caricatures on Napoleon ...

NK 0206006 MH

CINEMA
SP
K72
1949
Knock on any door. [n.d.]
1v. (various pagings) 29cm.
Text for motion picture.
Mimeographed.
Released by Columbia Pictures Corporation, 1949.
From Willard Motley's work of the same name.

I. Motley, Willard, 1912-

NK 0206007 CLSU

Knockaloe-lager-zeitung; zeitschrift des zivil-gefangenenlagers Knockaloe, Isle of Man. Hrsg. von der früheren schriftleitung der "Stobsiade". 2.- jahrg.; 7. okt. 1916-
[Peel, W. J. Clarke, printer, 1916-
v. 30½cm. Irregular.
"In ihrem titel trägt sie die bezeichnung 'zweiter jahrgang'. Doch ist anzunehmen, dass ein erster jahrgang überhaupt nicht erschienen ist. Die 'Stobsiade' hat wohl als erster jahrgang auch dieser zeitung gegolten."—R. Hellmann, Die deutschen feldzeitungen.
"Die schriftleitung: H. Beckmann, E. Behrens, F. Oberndorfer, H. A. Sierau, F. Roitzsch."
1. European war, 1914-1918—Period. 2. European war, 1914-1918—Prisoners and prisons, British—Knockaloe. I. Stobsiade; zeitung des deutschen kriegsgefange- nen-lagers Stobs.
CA 29-101 Unrev'd
Library of Congress D627.M2A15

NK 0206008 DLC

KNOCKE, C.
Die geisteskranken vor dem schwurgerichte; mit besonderer rücksicht auf die zurechnung nach § 30 und 60 des criminal-gesetzbuches für das herzogthum Braunschweig. Leipzig, 1863.
85 + (1) p.
"Aus der Allgemeinen deutschen strafrechtszeitung ... 1863, besonders abgedruckt."

NK 0206009 MH-L

Knocke (Carolus). De morbis universalibus, quos celebres quidam scriptores nuperrime ex morbosis singulorum locorum affectionibus, præcipue ex inflammatoria conditione cerebri, medullæ spinalis, meningum, cordis, lienis, tunicæ mucosæ stomachi et intestinorum deduxerunt. viii, 69 pp. 4°. *Gottingæ, typ. Dieterichianis*, 1837.

NK 0206010 DNLM

Knocke, Frederick John, 1914-
Orthopaedic nursing, by Frederick J. Knocke and Lazelle S. Knocke. Philadelphia, F. A. Davis Co., 1951.
xix, 682 p. illus. 22 cm.
Includes bibliographies.

1. Orthopedic nursing. I. Knocke, Lazelle S., 1917- joint author.
RD737.K55 617.3073 51—1632

ICJ
NK 0206011 DLC CaBViP OrU OrU-M WaS WaT N DNLM FMU

Knocke, Frederick John, 1914-
Orthopaedic nursing, by Frederick J. Knocke and Lazelle S. Knocke. Philadelphia, F. A. Davis Co., 1954 [°1951]
682 p. illus. 23 cm.

1. Orthopedic nursing. I. Knocke, Lazelle S., 1917- joint author.
RD753.K5 1954 *610.736 617.3073 54-1026 ‡

NK 0206012 DLC Or CaBVaU OU ViU

Knocke, Heinrich
Der honoraranspruch des arztes aus der behandlung eines verunglückten. ... Emsdetten, 1932. 44 p.
Inaug. Diss. -Erlangen, 1932.
Bibliography.

NK 0206013 ICRL

Knocke, Hermann.
Praxis des Eisenbahn-Güterverkehrs. Leitfaden zum praktischen Gebrauch in Handelsschulen und Kontoren. Nach den neugsten amtlichen Quellen bearbeitet und mit Beispielen versehen von H. Knocke. ... Hannover, Berlin, C. Meyer (G. Prior), 1905.
65 p. 23½cm.

NK 0206014 ICJ CU

RD753
.K5
1954
Knocke, Lazelle S., 1917- joint author.
FOR OTHER EDITIONS SEE MAIN ENTRY
Knocke, Frederick John, 1914-
Orthopaedic nursing, by Frederick J. Knocke and Lazelle S. Knocke. Philadelphia, F. A. Davis Co., 1954 [°1951]

Knocke, Belgium
see Knokke, Belgium.

Knocker, Clinker
see Clinker Knocker, pseud.

Knocker, Douglas, *ed.*
Accidents in their medico-legal aspect, by leading medical and surgical authorities, ed. by Douglas Knocker ... London, Butterworth and co.; [etc., etc.] 1910.
xxviii, 1254 p. front., illus., 4 pl. (1 fold.) 25cm.
CONTENTS.—pt. 1. Medico-legal aspect of accidents, by D. Knocker.—pt. 2. Effects of personal injuries.—pt. 3. Case guide.—Index.

1. Accidents. 2. Medical jurisprudence. I. Title.
[Full name: William Douglas Knocker]
11-2121 Revised
Library of Congress RA1121.K6

NK 0206018 DLC WaU-L DNLM TxU PPB PU-L ICJ PPC

Knocker, Douglas, *ed.*
Accidents in their medico-legal aspect, by leading medical and surgical authorities. London, Baillière, Tindall, and Cox, 1912.
xxviii, 1254 p. illus. 25 cm.

1. Accidents. 2. Medical jurisprudence. I. Title.
Full name: William Douglas Knocker.
RA1121.K6 1912 58-52303

NK 0206019 DLC ViU-L MH-L ICRL DNLM

Knocker, Douglas.
Butterworths' digest of leading cases on workmen's compensation, being a second edition of Knocker's digest of workmen's compensation cases, by Sidney Henry Noakes ... consulting editor: His Honour Judge Alfred Hildesley, K. C. London, Butterworth & co. (publishers), ltd.; Toronto, Butterworth & co. (Canada), ltd.; [etc., etc.] 1933. = C + Y
lxxxvi, 479, 30, [2] p. 26cm.
——— Supplement 1938. [London] Butterworth & co., ltd. [1938]
cover-title, vi, [481]-504 p. 24½cm.
With t.-p. to serve as substitute for t.-p. of main work.

——— ... Second cumulative supplement, by R. Marven Everett ... London, Butterworth & co., ltd., 1942.
2 p. l., iii-vii, 18 p. 24½cm.

1. Employers' liability—Gt. Brit. I. Noakes, Sidney Henry, ed. II. Hildesley, Alfred, 1873- III. Everett, Richard Marven Hale. IV. Gt. Brit. Courts. V. Title.
[Full name: William Douglas Knocker]
33-23831 Revised 2
Library of Congress [2] 331.8250942

NK 0206021 DLC MH-L IU CtY

VOLUME 300

Knocker, Douglas, ed.

Butterworths' Workmen's compensation cases ... v. 1– (New series.) Being a continuation of "Minton-Senhouse's Workmen's compensation cases" ⌐1898–1907⌐ containing reports of every case heard in the House of lords and Court of appeal, England, and selected cases heard in the Irish Court of appeal and Scottish Court of session, decided under the Workmen's compensation acts, during the period ⌐September, 1907–
London, Butterworth & co.; ⌐etc., etc.⌐ 1909–

NK 0206023 DLC PU PU-L

Knocker, Douglas.
Workmen's compensation digest, containing every reported decision of present authority in the House of lords and the Supreme court of judicature in England decided up to May 15th, 1912, and in the Court of session in Scotland and the Supreme court of judicature in Ireland reported up to May 15th, 1912, under the Workmen's compensation acts, 1897, 1900, and 1906, by Douglas Knocker ... London, Butterworth & co.; ⌐etc., etc.⌐ 1912.

xxvii, 455, ⌐40⌐ p. 26cm.

1. Employers' liability—Gt. Brit. ⌐1. Workmen's compensation—Gt. Brit.⌐ I. Gt. Brit. Parliament. House of lords. II. Gt. Brit. Supreme court of judicature. III. Scotland. Court of session. IV. Ireland. Supreme court of judicature. V. Title.
⌐Full name: William Douglas Knocker⌐

Library of Congress 13-7446 Revised

NK 0206023 DLC PU PU-L

Knocker, Editha G., 1869-1950.
An analysis of the art of practising; being a complement of The making of a violinist, by Editha G. Knocker. London: Goodwin & Tabb, Ltd.⌐, cop. 1921.⌐ 51 p. 12°.

1. Violin—Instruction and study.
N. Y. P. L. November 15, 1927

NK 0206024 NN

Knocker, Editha G., 1869-1950.
The making of a violinist; the science of violin technique as applied to art. A summary of principles for the use of teachers, by Editha G. Knocker. London: Goodwin & Tabb, Ltd.⌐, 1921?⌐ 32 p. illus. (music.) 12°.

1. Violin—Instruction and study.
N. Y. P. L. November 15, 1927

NK 0206025 NN IU

Knocker, Editha G 1869–
... The violin ⌐by⌐ E. G. Knocker. ⌐Glasgow, etc., Paterson sons & co., ltd, °1922⌐

cover-title, 1 p. l., 15 p. 18½cm. (Festival booklets, ed. by F. H. Bisset. No. 10)

1. Violin—Instruction and study.

Library of Congress MT260.K58 44-25781
⌐2⌐ 787.1

NK 0206026 DLC

Knocker, Editha G., 1869-
The violin. [By] E. G. Knocker.
— [Glasgow. Paterson Sons & Co., Ltd. 1929.] (1), 15 pp. [Festival booklets. No. 10.] 18½ cm.
The title is on the cover.

N8041 — S.r.c. — Violin. Instruction books.

NK 0206027 MB

Knocker, Editha G 1869–1950.
Violinist's vade mecum; an invitation to all students, teachers, and performers. London, J. Curwen; New York, G. Schirmer, 1952.

xiv, 101 p. illus., music. 29 cm. (Curwen edition, 8358)
"The history of the violin," by Martin Johnson: p. 3–8.
Includes exercises for violin.
"Suggested acc. to exercises" (score (19 p.) for violin and piano) laid in.

1. Violin—Instruction and study. 2. Violin—Studies and exercises. I. Johnson, Martin Christopher, 1896– II. Title.

MT260.K582 1952 787.1 54-25164

NK 0206028 DLC CaBVa OrP WaS LU CLSU MoU CU

Knocker, Edward, 1804–1884.
An account of the Grand Court of Shepway, holden on the Bredenstone Hill, at Dover, for the installation of the Right Honourable Henry John Temple, viscount Palmerston ... as constable of H. M. castle of Dover, and warden and keeper of H. M. Cinque Ports, etc. August 28, 1861. By Edward Knocker ... London, J. R. Smith, 1862.

xviii p., 1 l., 164 p. front., illus., pl. 22cm.

1. Cinque Ports. 2. Shepway, Court of. 3. Palmerston, Henry John Temple, 3d viscount, 1784–1865.

3—16476

Library of Congress DA690.C6K7

NK 0206029 DLC N GU-L MdBP PU-L

KNOCKER, EDWIN.
...Juden mit der weissen Weste. Berlin–Schöneberg: Verlag Deutsche Kultur-Wacht, 1936. 56 p. incl. diagr. plates, ports. 21cm.

881847A. 1. Jews in Germany—Anti-Semitic writings.

NK 0206030 NN CtY

Knocker, Edwin.
... Juden mit der weissen weste. Berlin-Schöneberg, Verlag Deutsche kultur-wacht, 1936.

Film copy made in 1943 by the Library of Congress. Negative.
Collation of the original, as determined from the film: 2 p. l., 7–56 p. illus., plates, port.
"1. auflage."

1. Capitalists and financiers—Germany. 2. Banks and banking—Jews. I. Title.

43-19881

Library of Congress Film DS-1 reel 6, no. 7
⌐2⌐

NK 0206031 DLC

Knocker, Mrs. Elsie (Shapter)

SEE

T'Serclaes, Elsie (Shapter) Knocker, baronne de, 1885-

Knocker, Frederic William.
How to judge rubber investments; or, *Hevea brasiliensis* in British Malaya, by Frederic W. Knocker, ... With an introduction by Sir William Hood Treacher, ... Containing many illustrations from photographs by the author, and a map. London, A. Moring, ltd., 1910.

xxii, 85, [1] p. front., 16 pl., 1 fold. map. 22½cm. (*Half-title:* "How to" series. — No. 18.)

NK 0206033 ICJ NN

⌐Knocker, Frederic William⌐
A Malayan miscellany ... Edited by the Palia Dorai. Notes and jottings, reminiscences and anecdotes, stories and essays from the scrap-books of an Englishman resident in British Malaya: illustrated by photographs from the same source and sketches from elsewhere. Kuala Lumpur, F. M. S., Huxley, Palmer & co., ltd., 1924.

1 p. l., vi, 250 p. illus., xxii pl. (incl. front.) on 17 l. 22cm.
Signed: F. K.
"Published for Frederic Knocker."—p. 249.

1. Malay Peninsula—Descr. & trav. 2. Rubber industry and trade—Malay Peninsula. I. Title.

Library of Congress DS592.K6 42-39046

NK 0206034 DLC CtY

Knocker, Gratiana Longworth
"Trebetherick"; a story of North Cornwall as written by one David Rounsevall of the parish of St. Enodoc in that country, by Gratiana Chanter, ⌐pseud.⌐ .... Napoli, F. Giannini & figli, 1913.
1 p. l., 232p.

NK 0206035 MiU PBm

Knocker, Gratiana Longworth.
The witch of Withyford; a story of Exmoor, by Gratiana Chanter...with illustrations by the author. New York: Macmillan and Co., Ltd., 1896. 187 p. front., plates. 12°. (Iris ser.)

Printed in Great Britain.

239254A. 1. Fiction, English. 2. Title.
N. Y. P. L. October 16, 1926

NK 0206036 NN MiEM MH

Knocker, Herbert Wheatley.
The ancient "greenways" of Suffolk. By Herbert W. Knocker. ⌐London, 1928.⌐ 8 p. illus. 20½cm. (Manorial Society. Publications. no. 15.)

"Reprinted from the East Anglian Daily Times."

1. Suffolk, Eng.—Descr. and trav. I. Ser.
N. Y. P. L. February 10, 1934

NK 0206037 NN PU

Knocker, Herbert Wheatley.
... Kentish manorial incidents, by Herbert W. Knocker ... London, The Manorial society, 1912.

12 p. 20½cm. (The Manorial society's publications. no. 7)

1. Land tenure—England—Kent. I. Title.

12-16819

Library of Congress DA26.M3 no. 7

NK 0206038 DLC PU PU-L NN

Knocker, Herbert Wheatley.
Manors and the new acts; the freehold tenement, London, Manorial Society, 1926.
12 p. (The Manorial Society's publications, no. 13)
"Reprinted from the Land Union journal for June, 1926."
1. Manors. Gt. Brit.

NK 0206039 ICU PU NN

DA20 .M3 no.14

Knocker, Herbert Wheatley.
Manors and the new acts; the freehold tenement, extinguishment of incidents. London, Manorial Society, 1926.
7 p. (The Manorial Society's publications, no.14)
"Reprinted from the Law times for 7th August, 1926."

1. Manors--Gt.Brit.

NK 0206040 ICU CSmH NN DLC PU

VOLUME 300

333.32
M285M
no.5

Knocker, Herbert Wheatley.
... The special land tenure bill of 1911; a critical analysis, by Herbert W. Knocker ... together with a preface containing some account of gavelkind and borough English, by the registrar of the Society. London, The Manorial society, 1911.
3 p. l., vi, 35, [1] p. 20½ cm. (The Manorial society's publications, no. 5)

1. Land tenure—Gt. Brit. 2. Inheritance and succession—Gt. Brit.
11-16402
Library of Congress HD595.K6

NK 0206041 DLC PU PU-L NcD

Knocker, William Douglas.
See
Knocker, Douglas.

The Knocker. v. 1; May–Oct. 1901. Philadelphia, The Knocker co., 1901.
1 v. 18cm. monthly.
No more published.
2-19481

NK 0206043 DLC

The Knocker. A journal for cranks. v. -5; Mar. 1904.
Blair, Neb., 19 -04.
v. plates. 16½cm. monthly.
Editor: -Mar. 1904, W. A. Campbell.
No more published.

I. Campbell, Will A., ed.
CA 10-5579 Unrev'd
Library of Congress AP2.K73

NK 0206044 DLC

Knockersmith, Diogenes, *pseud.*
Knocks from the little hammer of Diogenes Knockersmith ... New York, Dodge publishing company [°1907]
[59] p. illus. 19 x 10½cm.

7-11979

NK 0206045 DLC ViU AAP

Knockin, England (Parish).
The register of Knockin [1661–1812]. [London, 1913.] vi, 58, x p. 22½cm. (Shropshire Parish Register Society. Shropshire parish registers. St. Asaph diocese. v. 3, part 2.)
Half-title.
Transcribed by Mrs. Walker and Miss Oldfield; collated by D. R. Thomas; indexes compiled by B. A. Hughes.
Introduction dated 1912.

559284. 1. Parish registers—Gt. Br. —Eng.—Knockin. I. Hughes, Beatrice A. II. Oldfield III. Thomas, David Richard, 1833– 1916. IV. Walker V. Ser.
N. Y. P. L. Revised November 28, 1934

NK 0206046 NN MiD

Knod, Gustav
see Knod, Gustav Carl, 1850-

Knod, Gustav Adolf, 1880-
Die Tatbestände der unerlaubten Handlungen des Bürgerlichen Gesetzbuches, verglichen mit dem gemeinen Recht ... von Gustav Knod ... Düsseldorf, C. Schaab, 1909.
viii p., 1 l., 67 p., 1 l. 21cm.
Inaug.-Diss. - Heidelberg.
"Lebenslauf": leaf at end.
"Literaturverzeichnis": p.[vii]-viii.

NK 0206048 MH-L ICRL MH

Ln18
B4
1

Knod, Gustav Carl, 1850-
Acta Nationis Germanicae Universitatis Bononiensis. Vortrag gehalten auf der Generalversammlung der Gesammtvereins zu Metz am 10. September, 1889 ... Berlin, 1890.
Pamphlet
"Separat-Abdruck aus dem Korrespondenzblatt des Gesammtvereins der deutschen Geschichte-und Alterthumsvereine", 1890.

NK 0206049 CtY

C44
St8Fk
1621-
1793

Knod, Gustav Carl, 1850-
Die alten matrikeln der universität Strassburg. 1621 bis 1793 ... Strassburg, K. J. Trübner, 1897-1902.
3v. (Added t.-p.: Urkunden und akten der stadt Strassburg ... 3.abth.)

1. Strassburg. Universität--Registers.

NK 0206050 IU MH

Z
7128
H9
K72

Knod, Gustav Carl.
Aus der Bibliothek des Beatus Rhenanus; ein Beitrag zur Geschichte des Humanismus. Leipzig, O. Harrassowitz, 1889.
xi, 114 p. 23cm.

1. Bildius (Beatus) Rhenanus, 1485-1547. 2. Humanism--Bibl. I. Bildius (Beatus) Rhenanus, 1485-1547.

NK 0206051 NIC MnU MH PHC ICN NNUT

Knod, Gustav Carl, 1850-
Aus der Bibliothek des Beatus Rhenanus. Ein Beitrag zur Geschichte des Humanismus. Separat-Abdruck aus der Festschrift zur Einweihung des neuen Bibliotheksgebäudes zu Schlettstadt am 6. Juni 1889. Leipzig, Harrassowitz, 1889.
xi, 114 p.
Microfilm (positive) New York, Columbia University Libraries, 1971. 1 reel.
Master negative 0019.

NK 0206052 NNC

Knod, Gustav Carl, 1850- *comp.*
Deutsche studenten in Bologna (1289–1562) Biographischer index zu den Acta nationis germanicae Universitatis bononiensis. Im auftrag der K. Preussischen akademie der wissenschaften bearbeitet von G. C. Knod. [Berlin] R. v. Decker's verlag, G. Schenck, 1899.
xxv p, 1 l., 765, [1] p. 28cm.

1. Germany—Biog. 2. Bologna. Università. I. Acta nationis germanicae Universitatis bononiensis. II. K. Akademie der wissenschaften, Berlin. III. Title.
2—647
Library of Congress LF3273.A2K5

WaU CtY-M DNLM NNC OU NcD
NK 0206053 DLC OrU CU MH IaU TxU IEN CSt IU NIC

Microfilm
Knod, Gustav Carl, 1850- comp.
Deutsche studenten in Bologna (1289-1562) Biographischer index zu den Acta nationis germanicae Universitatis bononiensis. Im auftrag der K. Preussischen akademie der wissenschaften bearbeitet von G. C. Knod. [Berlin] R. v. Decker's verlag, G. Schenck, 1899.
Microfilm copy, made in 1960, of the original in University of California library. Berkeley. Negative.
Collation of the original: xxxv p., 1 l., 765, [1] p.

1. Germany--Biog. 2. Bologna. Università. Natio germanicae. Acta Nationis germanicae Universitatis bononiensis (Indexes). I. Acta nationis germanicae Universitatis bononiensis. II. K. Akademie der wissenschaften, Berlin. III. Title.

NK 0206055 MoSU

PT
1524
G8K72

Knod, Gustav Carl, 1850-
Gottfried von Neifen und seine Lieder; eine literarhistorische Untersuchung. Tübingen, F. Fues, 1877.
66 p. 21cm.

1. Gottfried von Neifen, fl. 1234-1255.

NK 0206056 NIC CU MA

Knod, Gustav Carl, 1850-
Gottfried von Neifen und seine Lieder; eine literarhistorische Untersuchung. Tübingen, F. Fues, 1877.
66 p.
Photocopy.

1. Gottfried von Neifen, fl. 1234-1255.

NK 0206057 CaBVaU

E
5
.S 751

KNOD, GUSTAV CARL, 1850-
Jacob Spiegel aus Schlettstadt. Ein Beitrag zur Geschichte des deutschen Humanismus. Strassburg, R. Schultz & Co., 1884-86.
2 pt. in 1v. 27cm.
Part 2 has imprint: Strassburg, M. DuMont-Schauberg, 1886.
Programm---Schlettstadt Realgymnasium (Beilage)

NK 0206058 ICN NIC

Knod, Gustav Carl, 1850–
Das papsttum und die deutsche landeskirche zur zeit der Ottonen. Historische abhandlung vom oberlehrer dr. Gustav Knod ... Gebweiler, Buchdruckerei von J. Dreyfus, 1881.
1 p. l., 22 p. 25 x 19cm.
"Beilage zum Programm des Realgymnasiums zu Gebweiler."

1. Catholic church—Relations (diplomatic) with the Holy Roman empire. 2. Holy Roman empire—For. rel.—Catholic church. 3. Germany—Hist.—843-1273. I. Gebweiler, Ger. Realgymnasium. II. Title.
42-27075
Library of Congress DD137.5.K6

NK 0206059 DLC DDO PHC

Knod, Gustav Carl, 1850-
Sélestat, Alsace. Bibliothèque municipale.
Die Stadtbibliothek zu Schlettstadt. Festschrift zur einweihung des neuen bibliotheksgebäudes am 6. juni 1889, von Joseph Gény ... [und] dr. Gustav C. Knod ... Strassburg, Buchdruckerei M. Du Mont-Schauberg, 1889.

VOLUME 300

LF3195 S75K6 Knod, Gustav Carl, 1850-
Die Stiftsherren von St. Thomas zu Strassburg, 1518-1548; ein Beitrag zur Strassburger Kirchen- und Schulgeschichte, von Gustav C. Knod. Strassburg, Strassburger Druckerei und Verlagsanstalt, 1892.
59 p.
At head of title: Lyceum zu Strassburg im Elsass.
"Beilage zum Programm des Lyceums zu Strassburg, 514."
1. Strassburg. St. [i.e. Sankt] Thomas (Church) Kollegiatst 2. Strassburg (Diocese) - History. I. Title.

NK 0206061 CU MNS

Knod, Gustav Carl, 1850- ed.
Strassburg.
Urkunden und akten der stadt Strassburg, herausgegeben mit unterstützung der landes- und der stadtverwaltung ... Strassburg, K. J. Trübner, 1879-19

Knod (Hans). Das Bromäthyl und seine Anwendung als Narkoticum in der zahnärztlichen Praxis. 26 pp. 8°. *Essen, H. L. Geck*, 1891.

NK 0206063 DNLM

Knod, Reinhold.
... Devonische faunen Boliviens. Von Reinhold Knod ... Stuttgart, E. Schweizerbart'sche verlagshandlung (E. Nägele) 1908.
1 p. l., 493-600 p. illus., 11 pl. 23cm. (Beiträge zur geologie und palaeontologie von Südamerika ... XIV)
Each plate preceded by leaf with descriptive letterpress.
Separat-abdruck aus dem Neuen jahrbuch für mineralogie etc. Beilage-band XXV.
1. Paleontology—Bolivia. 2. Paleontology—Devonian.
G S 8-354
Library, U. S. Geol. survey 203(400) B39 no. 14

NK 0206064 DI-GS MH

Knode, Jay Carroll, 1885- joint ed.
Nanninga, Simon Peter, 1891- *ed.*
... Articulation of high school and college in New Mexico; report of a conference held at the University of New Mexico, July 21-22, 1933, edited by S. P. Nanninga ... and Jay C. Knode ... Albuquerque, N. M., The University of New Mexico, 1933.

Knode, Jay Carroll, 1885-
Foundations of an American philosophy of education [by] Jay C. Knode, dean of the College of arts and sciences and of the General college, University of New Mexico, and associates. New York, D. Van Nostrand company, inc., 1942.
viii, 553 p. 23½cm.
"Reading list" at end of each chapter.
1. Education—Philosophy. I. New Mexico. University. II. Title.
42-25489
Library of Congress LB875.K7 [10] 370.1

NK 0206066 DLC MtBC OrCS KMK PV PU-Penn OU OCU OO ODW PSt PWcS OrU MtU OrP WaS Or

---

Knode, Jay Carroll, 1885-
An intellectual primer. New York, Philosophical Library [°1955]
88 p. 21 cm.
1. Philosophy. I. Title.
B945.K683 I 6 191.9 55-14030 ‡

NK 0206067 DLC NcD PBa ViU MB TxU NN PP PCC PU CaBVa OrU

Knode, Jay Carroll, 1885-
Orienting the student in college, with special reference to Freshman week, by Jay Carroll Knode ... New York city, Teachers college, Columbia university, 1930.
vi, 140 p., 1 l. 23cm.
Thesis (PH. D.)—Columbia university, 1930.
Vita.
Published also as Teachers college, Columbia university, Contributions to education, no. 415.
Bibliography: p. 137-140.
1. Students—U. S. 2. Universities and colleges—U. S.—Administration. 3. Personnel service in education. I. Title. II. Title: Freshman week.
30-30687
Library of Congress LB2343.K6 1930
Columbia Univ. Libr. [3] 371.214

NK 0206068 NNC DLC MtU WaTC

Knode, Jay Carroll, 1885-
Orienting the student in college, with special reference to Freshman week, by Jay Carroll Knode ... New York city, Teachers college, Columbia university, 1930.
vi, 140 p. 23½cm. (Teachers college, Columbia university. Contributions to education, no. 415)
Published also as thesis (PH. D.) Columbia university.
Bibliography: p. 137-140.
1. Students—U. S. 2. Universities and colleges—U. S.—Administration. 3. Personnel service in education. I. Title. II. Title: Freshman week.
30-30610
Library of Congress LB2343.K6 1930 a
——— Copy 2. LB5.C8 no. 415
Copyright A 29288 [a37k1] 371.214

NK 0206069 DLC OrU OrP KEmT NcD OOxM PU OCU MiU OCl PU PBm PPT MB MH ViU AU

Knode, Jay Carroll, 1885-
... Problems of freshman scholarship in a small state university, by Jay C. Knode ... Albuquerque, N. M., University of New Mexico, 1931.
39 p. tables. 23 cm. (The University of New Mexico bulletin. v. 5, no. 4. Education series. Whole no. 203. Nov. 1, 1931)
1. College freshmen. 2. Ability. 3. New Mexico. University. I. Title.
LB1131.K625 378.789 E 32-128
U. S. Office of Education. Library
for Library of Congress [a66e1]†

NK 0206070 DHEW OrU CaBVaU PSt OU OCU MiU ViU DLC

PQ2635 .E48Z7 **Knodel, Arthur,** 1916-
Jules Renard as critic. Berkeley, University of California Press, 1951.
109-220 p. 24 cm. (University of California publications in modern philology, v. 35, no. 3)
Based on thesis—University of California.
Bibliography: p. 217-220.
1. Renard, Jules, 1864-1910. I. (Series: California. University. University of California publications in modern philology, v. 35, no. 3)
PB13.C3 vol. 35, no. 3 840.81 A 51-9840
——— Copy 2. PQ2635.E48Z72
California. Univ. Libr.
for Library of Congress [5]†

NK 0206071 CU AAP MsU GU NN TxU OCU CU OOxM FTaSU ViU OO OU DLC MB

PQ2635 Re48Z65 Knodel, Arthur, 1916-
Jules Renard, critique littéraire. [Berkeley, Calif., 1948]
317 *l.* 29cm.
Thesis (Ph.D.) - Univ. of California, June 1948.
"Bibliographie": p.306-317.
1. Renard, Jules, 1864-1910.

NK 0206072 CU

Knodel, Arthur, 1916- tr.
ML410 .S932 A13 **Stravinskiĭ, Igor' Fedorovich,** 1882-
Poetics of music in the form of six lessons; tr. by Arthur Knodel and Ingolf Dahl. Cambridge, Harvard Univ. Press, 1947.

Knodel, Hans.
Praktischer Bauholzschutz durch den Baufachmann. Karlsruhe i. B., Bruderverlag, 1955.
48 p. illus. (part col.) 30 cm.
1. Wood—Preservation. 2. Trees—Diseases and pests.
A 56-3796
Ohio State Univ. Libr. TA424
for Library of Congress [3]

NK 0206074 OU DNAL

Knodel, Heinz, 1924-
Möglichkeiten und Probleme konjunkturorientierter Finanzpolitik; ein Beitrag zur wirtschaftspolitischen Gestaltung der Finanzpolitik. [Heidelberg, 1949?]
155 l. 29 cm.
Typescript (carbon copy)
Inaug.-Diss.—Heidelberg.
Vita.
Bibliography: leaves 153-155.
1. Finance, Public.
HJ161.K6 51-26934

NK 0206075 DLC

KNODEL, Karl Wilhelm, 1862-
See KNODEL, Wilhelm, 1862-

Knodel, Rudolf, 1875- Rechtsanw.: Beschränkungen der Vertragsfreiheit durch das Reichsgesetz über den Versicherungsvertrag vom 30. Mai 1908. Calw 1917: Oelschläger. 80 S. 8°
Tübingen, Jur. Diss. v. 15. Febr. 1917, Ref. v. Heck
[Geb. 11. Febr. 75 Nagold; Wohnort: Nagold; Staatsangeh.: Württemberg; Vorbildung: Ev. Sem. Maulbronn Reife 93; Studium: Tübingen 9, Berlin 1 S.; ohne Coll. 9. Dez. 16.] [U 17. 548

NK 0206077 ICRL MH-L

Knoder, C. Eugene.
New game birds for Ohio; outline and plans for upland game bird development and introductions. [Columbus, Ohio, Ohio Division of Wildlife, 1953]
26 p. 28 cm. (Ohio. Dept. of Natural Resources. Division of Wildlife. Technical bulletin no. 1)

NK 0206078 OU OOxM

Knoderer, Charles.
Neue wichtige Erfindung in der Lohgerberei ... Aus dem Französischen von Christian Heinrich Schmidt. Weimar, B. F. Voigt, 1857.
xvi, 99 p. 19 cm. (Neuer Schauplatz der Künste und Handwerke, 234. Bd.)
Translation of Nouvelle tannerie française.
1. Tanning. (Series)
P O 52-233
U. S. Patent Office. Library TS957.F8K7
for Library of Congress [3]

NK 0206079 DP DSI

VOLUME 300

TS 957 F8K7 1856 **Knederer, Charles.**
Nouvelle tannerie française, par Charles Knederer. Deuxième edition. Paris, Leiber et Commelin, 1856.
111 p. 23 cm.

1. Tanning. 2. Hides and skins.

NK 0206080 DSI DP

Knoderer, H G.
The farm wiring problem, as presented at the 30th annual meeting of American society of agricultural engineers, Estes Park, Colorado, June 22nd to 25th, 1936, by H. G. Knoderer... Bridgeport, Conn.: General electric co., c1936. 27 p. incl. tables. illus. (incl. plans.) 27 x 22cm.

1. Electric wiring. 2. Electricity in agriculture. I. General electric company. II. Title.
N. Y. P. L. January 28, 1938

NK 0206081 NN DNAL WaSPS NNC OU

Knodishall, *Eng.*
The register of the parish church of Knodishall, co. Suffolk, 1566–1705; transcribed and ed. by Arthur T. Winn ... London, Bemrose & sons, ltd., 1909.
vii, 78 p., 1 l. front. (facsim.) 25cm.

1. Registers of births, etc.—Knodishall, Eng. I. Winn, Arthur Thomas, ed.
10-8464
Library of Congress CS436.K7

NK 0206082 DLC MH ViU NN

Ia742 840k Knodle, E comp.
A classifying word-book, in some parts of which, words are classed according to ending, and in other parts, according to meaning; ... with Webster's perspicuous definitions annexed ... Baltimore, Printed by J.Murphy, 1840.
273p. 18cm.

NK 0206083 CtY MdBP

Knodt, Cloy Bernard, 1917–
Successful dairying. New York, McGraw-Hill [°1954]
381 p. illus. 24 cm. (McGraw-Hill rural activities series)

1. Dairying. I. Title.
SF239.K73 637 53—5169 ‡

Wa
IdPI MtBC CaBVa CaBVaU OrCS NIC DNAL WaS WaT WaE OrP
NK 0206084 DLC OU TU ICJ NcRS PP PSt MB NcC CaBViP

Div.S. 284.2 K72B **Knodt, Emil,** 1852-1924
Die Bedeutung Calvins und des Calvinismus für die protestantische Welt im Lichte der neueren und neuesten Forschung. Giessen, A. Töpelmann, 1910.
71 p. 21 cm. (Vorträge der theologischen Konferenz zu Giessen, 30. Folge)

Bibliography included in "Anmerkungen" (p. 50-71)
1. Calvin, Jean 1509-1564. 2. Calvinism.

NK 0206085 NcD MH CtY NjPT CLSU PPiPT CtY-D TxFTC IU

Knodt, Emil, 1852-1924.
Bilder aus der wissenschaftlichen Thierfolter... Dresden, 1882.
19p.

AC931 .H3 v.177 [Haverford-Beuer pamphlets, v. 177, no. 4]

NK 0206086 DLC

---

943 Luth.347 H538z K72fe KNODT, Emil, 1852-1924 ed.
Festschrift zur hundertjahr-feier des koeniglicher Theologischen Seminars in Herborn. Herausgeben von E. Knodt. Herborn, Oranien-Verlag, 1918.
285p. front. (illus.), ports. 23.5cm.

Contributors: Emil Knodt, Karl Haussen [et al.]

NK 0206087 MH-AH

922.4 C168KN **Knodt, Emil,** 1852-1924.
Johann Calvin. Mitteilungen aus seinem Leben und seinen Schriften. Herborn, Buchhandlung des Nassauischen Colportagevereins, 1909.
iv, 305 p. 22 cm.

On cover: Johann Calvin; ein Lebensbild.
1. Calvin, Jean, 1509-1564.

NK 0206088 NcD NNUT NjPT CSt MH-AH CtY-D

BV 2957 .W5 K5 **Knodt, Emil, 1852-1924.**
Johann Hinrich Wichern, der Vater und Herold der Inneren Mission. Ein Lebensbild, von E. Knodt. Herborn, Buchhandlung des Nassauischen Colportagevereins, 1908.
259 p. port. (front.) 19 cm.
1.Wichern, Johann Hinrich, 1808-1881.

NK 0206089 MH-AH

Me45 W5243 K7 **Knodt, Emil,** 1852-1924.
D.Johann Westermann, der Reformator Lippstadts, und sein sogenannter Katechismus, das älteste litterarischeDenkmal der evangelischen Kirche Westfalens; ein Beitrag zur Geschichte der westfälischen Reformation und des Katechismus, von E.Knodt ... Gotha, G.Schloessmann, 1895.
2p.l.,170p. 19½cm.
"Westermanns Katechismus im Original": p.[97]-170.

NK 0206090 CtY NjPT

Knodt, Emil, 1852-
Die vivisection vor dem forum der logik und moral. Leipzig, Voigt, 1880.
40p.

AC931 .H3 v.177 [Haverford-Bauer pamphlets, v. 177, no. 1]

NK 0206091 DLC

YAR 275 Knodt, Emil, 1852-1924.
Die von den grafen Albrecht und Philipp im jahre 1576 publizierte Nassau-Saarbrucken'sche kirchenordnung und agende. Herborn, 1905.
161 p.

NK 0206092 DLC MH-AH

Knodt, Emil, 1852-1924.
Zoophilus. Biblische Studien über Thierbestimmung, Thierleben und Thierschutz. Dresden: [J. Wieprecht in Eberbach], 1881.
76p.

NK 0206093 OCH DLC

Knodt, Hermann, 1880- ed
Hessisches Geschlechterbuch
see under title

Knodt, Josef.
Ferdinand der Bulgare; die Balkanmission eines Prinzen aus dem Hause Sachsen-Koburg und Gotha-Kohary, 1887–1918. Bielefeld, L. Bechauf, 1947.
237 p. plates, ports., maps, coat of arms, geneal. tables. 22 cm.
"Benutzte Literatur": p. 219–220.

1. Ferdinand I, Czar of Bulgaria, 1861–1948.
DR87.K6 923.1497 49–16367*

NK 0206095 DLC CtY NcD GU

3418 .529 **Knodt, Josef.**
Reise durch das deutschsprachige Dialekt-Paradies. Vlotho a.d. Weser, Köhler, 1949.
206 p. illus. 21 cm.

"Quellen-Verzeichnis": p.202.

1.German language - Provincialisms.
2.German language - Dialects.

NK 0206096 NjP

Knodt, Josef, 1896- Zahnarzt: Die Anwendung von Salvarsanpräparaten bei Erkrankungen der Mundhöhle. [In Maschinenschrift.] 20, IV S. 4°(2°). — Auszug: Bonn 1921: Rhenania-Dr. 4 S. 8°
Bonn, Med. Diss. v. 28. Febr. 1921, Ref. Krause
[Geb. 23. Febr. 76 Trier; Wohnort: Trier; Staatsangeh.: Preußen; Vorbildung: RG. Trier 93; Studium: Berlin 6, Bonn 2 S.; Coll. 28. Febr. 21; Zahnärztl. Approb. 22. Dez. 99.] [U 21. 2718

NK 0206097 ICRL

KNODT, Karl
Die Gestaltung der Abendmahlsfeier. Goettingen, Vandenhoeck & Ruprecht, 1927.
37p. 24cm. (Das Heilige und die Form. Beihefte zur Monatschrift fuer Gottesdienst und kirchliche Kunst, 3)

NK 0206098 MH-AH

Knodt, Karl Ernst, 1856-1917.
Aus allen Augenblicken meines Lebens; neue Gedichte. Lpz., Eckardt, K.D.
297 s.

NK 0206099 PPG

834K753 K1904 **Knodt, Karl Ernst,** 1856-
Aus meiner waldecke; gedichte mit zeichnungen von G. Rampmann. 2.aufl. Altenburg, S.A., 1904.
202p. illus.

NK 0206100 IU

VOLUME 300

831.8 Knodt, Karl Ernst, 1856-
K72au Aus meiner Waldecke, Gedichte. Mit Zeichnungen von C. Rampmann. 3. Aufl. Altenburg, S.-M., S. Geibel, 1904.
ix,202p. illus. 19cm.

Each section has a special engraved t.p.

Contents.- Heimatläuten.- Tote Sonnen.- Sonnensehnsucht.- Erinnerung.- "Zu dir heb ich die Hände".
I. Title.

NK 0206101 TNJ

Knodt, Karl Ernst, 1856-1917.
Fontes Melusinae, ein Menschheitsmärchen von Karl Ernst Knodt; mit Bildern von G. Kampmann. Altenburg, S.-A., S. Geibel, 1904.
4 p.l., 76 p. incl. illus., plates. 24 cm.

NK 0206102 CtY

PT Knodt, Karl Ernst, 1856-
1229 Die Gott suchen. Eine Sammlung religiöser
.K66 deutscher Dichtungen von den Anfängen bis zur Gegenwart. München, C. H. Beck, 1912.
v, 408p. 19cm.

1. German poetry - Collections. 2. Religious poetry, German - Collections. I. Title.

NK 0206103 TNJ

Knodt, Karl Ernst, 1856-
Ich hatt' einen kameraden ... Requiem von Karl Ernst Knodt ... Stuttgart, Strecker und Schröder, 1916.
2 p. l., 107 p. 19½cm.

1. European war, 1914- —Poetry. 2. Köhler, Paul Ernst, 1889 or 90-1914. I. Title.

20-7637

Library of Congress D526.5.K65

NK 0206104 DLC

Knodt, Karl Ernst, 1856-
Ich hatt' einen kameraden ... Zur erinnerung an Martin Nast, evangelischer vikar in Grulich (Böhmen), gefallen als offizierstellvertreter bei Pont-a-Mousson am 13. Februar 1915. 3. aufl. Stuttgart, Im flugeschriftenverlag dem Ev. Pressverbands (1916?)
56 p. 22 cm.

NK 0206105 DNW

831.8 Knodt, Karl Ernst, 1856-
K72Li "Lichtlein sind wir"; eine Auslese aus allen Liederbänden von Karl Ernst Knodt, Bensheim a,B. München, Müller und Frölich, 1916.
xxvi,170p. front.(port.) 19cm.

Jubiläumsausgabe zum 6. Juni 1916 (Sechzigster Geburtstag)

I. Title.

NK 0206106 TNJ

PT35 Knodt, Karl Ernst, 1856-
B4 Theodor Storm, der Lyriker. Leipzig, Verlag für Literatur,
no. 4 Kunst und Musik, 1906.
27 p. (Beiträge zur Literaturgeschichte, Heft 4)

1. Storm, Theodor, 1817-1888.

NK 0206107 CU PU OU

831.8 Knodt, Karl Ernst, 1856-
K72e Ein Ton vom Tode und win Lied vom Leben. Neue Verse mit 2 Titelbildern von Gustav Kampmann. Giessen, E. Roth [n.d.]
viii,276p. illus. 19cm.

NK 0206108 TNJ

PT
2621 Knodt, Karl Ernst, 1856-1917.
K72t Ein ton vom tode und Ein lied vom leben; neue verse ... Giessen, E.Roth [1905]
viii,276p. illus. 19cm.

I. Title. II. Title: Ein lied vom leben.

NK 0206109 NRU MH

Knodt, Karl Ernst, 1856- comp.
831.808
K72W Wir sind die Sehnsucht; Liederlese moderner Sehnsucht ... Stuttgart, Greiner & Pfeiffer [1902]
xi, 324 p. illus. 20½cm.

1. German poetry. 19th century
I. Title

NK 0206110 NcD

Knodt, Karl Ernst, 1856-*1917*, *comp.*
Wir sind die sehnsucht. Liederlese von Karl Ernst Knodt. 2. veränderte aufl. (3.-4. tausend) Stuttgart, Greiner & Pfeiffer [1912]
336 p. 20cm.
Illus. t.-p. and text within ornamental border.
"Unsere quellen": p. 331-336.

1. German poetry—19th and 20th cent. I. Title.

NK 0206111 ICU CU

4BX Knodt, Manfred.
1087 Das evangelische Darmstadt in Geschichte und Gegenwart. Zum 625jährigen Stadtjubiläum Darmstadts im Auftrag des Evangelischen Dekanats Darmstadt-Stadt verfasst von Manfred Knodt. Darmstadt, 1955.
36 p.

NK 0206112 DLC-P4 MH

Knöbber, Ferdinand, 1912-
... Versuche über die Durchlässigkeit von Zahnzementen für Bakterien und Flussigkeit ... Bielefeld, 1937.
Inaug.-Diss. - Münster.
Lebenslauf.

NK 0206113 CtY

Knoebber, Mary Mildred, sister
see Knoebber, Mildred, sister, 1900-

Knoebber, Mildred, sister, 1900-
The adolescent girl; an analysis of her attitudes, ideals, and problems, from the viewpoint of the girl herself ... [St.Louis, Mo.] 1935.
5 p.l., 279 numb.l., [2] l. tables, form, diagrs. 28cm. (University Microfilms. Pub.no.184)
Abstracted in University Microfilms. Abstracts, v.II, no.2, p.117, 1940.
Thesis (PH.D.)--St.Louis university, 1934.
Vita.
Typewritten copy.
Bibliography: p.254-279.

1.Girls. 2.Adolescence.

NK 0206115 MoSU

Knoebber, Mildred, *sister*.
The self-revelation of the adolescent girl; an analysis of the attitudes, ideals, and problems of the adolescent girl from the viewpoint of the girl herself [by] Sister M. Mildred Knoebber ... New York, Chicago [etc.] The Bruce publishing company [©1937]
xiii p., 1 l., 206 p. illus. (map) diagr. 22cm. (*Half-title:* Science and culture series, Joseph Husslein ... general editor)
Based on questionnaire study.
"Selected bibliography": p. 187-200.

1. Girls. 2. Adolescence. I. Title.

37-1344

Library of Congress HQ798.K55
—— —— Copy 2.
Copyright A 101980 [3] [159.9227364] 136.7354

NK 0206116 DLC NN DCU PPPL OClUr OClND WaSpG MB

4D-1090 Knöbber, Paul.
Festschrift zur Erinnerung an die Enthüllung des Denkmals für die Gefallenen des Füsilier-Regiments von Gersdorff (Kurhessisches Nr. 80) und seiner Kriegstruppenteile: Reserve-Infanterie-Regiment Nr. 80, Landwehr-Infanterie-Regiment Nr. 80 ... Wiesbaden vom 4. bis 6. Oktober 1930.
92 p.
[Hrsg. von Paul Knöbber, Th. Szymanski und R.W. Wolff-Malm.]

NK 0206117 DLC-P4

Knoebel, G C
A complete edition of the papers
see under Evangelical Association of North America. Congress, Chicago, 1894.

Knöbel, Herbert, 1905-
*Die Therapie der idiopathischen Nachhand-Parese des Hundes. Leipzig, 1930.
52 p. 8°.

NK 0206119 DNLM

Knoebel, Jacob Burckhard.
Examen quietismi sive quietis mysticae ...
see under Jaeger, Johann Wolfgang, 1647-1720, praeses. [Supplement]

Knöbel, Schewach
see
Knöbil, Schewach.

VOLUME 300

Knöbil, Schewach.
... גרם המעלות ... תולדותיו, וקורותיו של ... משולם איגרא ... ותולדות צאצאיו ... עד ימינו אלה. ערכתי וחברתי ... שבח קנעביל ... הוצ'. ב' עם הרבה הוספות. וינה, דפוס "אניק," תרפ"א.
Wien, Verlag des verfassers [1921]
66 p., 1 l. 22cm.
(1. Egra, Meshullam, 1752-1801. I. Title.)
Title transliterated: Gerem ha-ma'aloth.
45-44910
Library of Congress BM755.E36K5

NK 0206122 DLC

Knöbl, Adolf.
... Untersuchungen in drei nordmährischen dörfern (Benke, Liebesdorf, Strupschein) von Adolf Knöbl. Prag. Verlag der Deutschen gesellschaft der wissenschaften und künste für die Tschechoslowakische republik. in kommission bei G. Fischer. Jena, 1931.
3 p. l., 5-69 p. incl. illus. (map) tables. XIII pl. on 7 l. 31cm. (Deutsche gesellschaft der wissenschaften und künste für die Tschechoslowakische republik. Anthropologische untersuchungen in den Sudetenländern ... I)
Plates in pocket.
"Schriftennachweis": p. 69.
1. Anthropometry—Moravia. 2. Anthropo-geography—Moravia.
34-9161
Library of Congress GN58.M65K6
[2] 573.6094372

NK 0206123 DLC ICU

---

f
GN 58
.M76
K716

Knöbl, Adolf.
Untersuchungen in weiteren 18 nordmährischen Dörfern. Mit einem Anhang: Neudorf in Nordmähren, von Heimo Gödl. Prag, Verlag der Deutschen Gesellschaft der Wissenschaften und Künste für die Tschechoslowakische Republik, in Kommission bei G. Fischer, Jena, 1934.
181 p. illus., tables. (Anthropologische Untersuchungen in den Sudetenländern 2)
Plates in pocket.
Bibliography: p. 181.
1. Anthropometry--Moravia. 2. Anthropo-geography--Moravia. I. Gödl, Heimo. Neudorf in Nordmähren. II. Series.

NK 0206124 ICU DLC

Knöbl, Emmerich.
Blick auf Österreich: Wien. Mit 8 Vierfarben-Kunstdruck-Blättern nach Aquarellen Wiener Meister als Beilage. Wien, Selbstverlag, °1948.
[3] l., 8 col. plates (in portfolio) 33 cm.
1. Vienna—Descr.—Views. I. Title.
DB855.K57 50-19094

NK 0206125 DLC

Knöbl, Herbert, 1901-
*Experimentelle Untersuchungen über Haftfestigkeit von Stiftverankerungen. Münch, 1934.
26 p. 8°.

NK 0206126 DNLM PPWI CtY

Knöchel, Emma.
Fachwörterbuch für die zuckerindustrie. Deutsch-italienisch und italienisch-deutsch, bearb. von E. Knöchel ... Berlin, Selbstverlag des Instituts für zucker-industrie, 1936.
142 p. 17½cm.
1. German language—Dictionaries. [1. Germany—Language—Dictionaries] 2. Italian language—Dictionaries. [2. Italy—Language—Dictionaries] 3. Sugar trade—[Dictionaries]
Agr 37-171
U. S. Dept. of agr. Library for Library of Congress 205K75 [TP377]

NK 0206127 DNAL PPFr

Knöchel, Emma.
Fachwörterbuch für die zuckerindustrie. Englisch-deutsch und deutsch-englisch, bearb. von E. Knöchel ... Berlin, E. S. Mittler & sohn, 1938.
224 p. 17½cm.
1. German language—Dictionaries. [1. Germany—Language—Dictionaries] 2. Sugar trade—[Dictionaries]
Agr 39-142
U. S. Dept. of agr. Library for Library of Congress 201K75 [TP377]

NK 0206128 DNAL MB PPFr NN ICJ

Knöchel, Gerhard, 1903-
Untersuchungen zur frage der entwicklung des kapital- und warenverkehrs zwischen Mutterland und Kolonien. ... Borna-Leipzig, 1932. 89 p.
Inaug. Diss. -Rostock, 1932.
Lebenslauf.
Bibliography.

NK 0206129 ICRL NNC CtY PU

Knöchel, Wilhelm, 1899- defendant.
[Statement for the prosecution]
see under Germany. Volksgerichtshof. Oberreichsanwalt.

Knoeckel, Charlotte, 1879-
Kinder der gasse, roman von Charlotte Knoeckel. 2. tausend. Berlin, S. Fischer, 1906.
340 p. 19½cm.
8-12819

NK 0206131 DLC

Knoeckel, Charlotte, 1879-
Maria Baumann; roman von Charlotte Knoeckel. Berlin, S. Fischer [1909]
150, [2] p. 18½cm. (*On cover:* Fischers bibliothek zeitgenössischer romane [1. jahrg. 12. bd.])
Title within double line borders.
I. Title.
9-24898
Library of Congress PT2621.N63M3 1909

NK 0206132 DLC PPF TNJ OrU PPL NN

Knoedel, Karl. Side-lights on socialism: women and socialism. 10 pp. (*Fortn. Rev.* n. s. v. 57, 1895, p. 267.)

NK 0206133 MdBP

Knödgen, Hermann, 1910-
... Ueber Beckenabrissfracturen als Sportverletzungen ... Berlin, [1937]
Inaug.-Diss. - Berlin.
Lebenslauf.
"Schrifttum": p. 17.

NK 0206134 CtY

W 4
B51
1905

KNÖDLER, Arthur, 1880-
Die Unterbindung und die Resektion der Vena femoralis unterhalb des Ligamentum Poupartii. Berlin [1905]
30 p.
Inaug.-Diss. - Berlin.

NK 0206135 DNLM NNC PU CtY ICRL

Knoedler, Rev. C
K'afa ka-Temne ka-trotroko traka an'-karandi a-fet ka an-tof a-Temne ro-Afrika ħa ro-pil; or, A Temne primer for the use of Temne schools in West-Afrika. London, C.M. Society, 1865.
20 p. 16°.

NK 0206136 NN

Knoedler, Christiana F
The Harmony Society; a 19th-century American utopia. New York, Vantage Press [1954]
160 p. illus. 22 cm.
1. Harmonists.
HX656.H2K5 335.06273 54-7409 ‡

PPT PBm OO PU PSt OClW PPD PPLT
NK 0206137 DLC OrU NN TU TxU OCl PPEB PP PPAmP PHi

[Knoedler, Edmond L.]
List of mezzotint engravings by S. Arlent-Edwards
see under Knoedler (M.) and Co., Inc.

[Knoedler, Edmond L]
Modern etchers. Short biographical sketches of the leading etchers of the present day. 1891. New York, M. Knoedler & co. [°1891]
182 p. 15cm.
1. Etchers. I. Title.
12-13311
Library of Congress NE2110.K7 1891

NK 0206139 DLC OCl ICJ

Knoedler, E. L. & Orr, C.A.
The effect of salts on the settling of portland cement in the cold. 1905.

NK 0206140 OClJC

Knoedler, Elmer L 1912-
Performance of packed tower operating as cold water vacuum deaerator. [New York] 1952.
40, 16, [136] l. diagrs. (1 fold.) tables. 29cm.
Thesis, Columbia university.
Typescript.
Bibliography: l. [45-46]

NK 0206141 NNC

Knoedler, Elmer L , 1912-
Performance of packed tower operating as cold water vacuum deaerator. Ann Arbor, University Microfilms [1954]
([University Microfilms, Ann Arbor, Mich.] Publication no. 9527)
Microfilm copy of typescript. Positive.
Collation of the original: 40, [6], 16, [136] l. diagrs. (1 fold.) tables.
Thesis—Columbia University.
Abstracted in Dissertation abstracts, v. 14 (1954) no. 10, p. 1654-1655.
Bibliography: leaves [45]-[46]
1. Gases—Absorption and adsorption. 2. Packed towers.
Microfilm AC-1 no. 9527 Mic A 54-2420
Columbia Univ. Libraries for Library of Congress [1]†

NK 0206142 NNC DLC

WY
193
qK72n
1953

KNOEDLER, Evelyn L
The nurse assistant's manual. [Lakewood, Ohio] c1953.
102 p. illus.
Cover title.
1. Nursing

NK 0206143 DNLM OClW

VOLUME 300

Knoedler, Gotthold.
Wirtschafts- und Siedlungsgeographie des nord-östlichen Schwarzwaldes und der angrenzenden Gäulandschaften, von Schulrat G. Knödler... Öhringen: F. Rau, 1930. 143 p. incl. diagrs., tables. illus. (incl. maps), plans, plates. 8°. (Erdgeschichtliche und landeskundliche Abhandl. aus Schwaben und Franken. Heft 11.)
Cover-title.
Bibliography, p. 142-143.

1. Black forest—Economic geography. 2. Regional planning—Germany—Black forest. I. Ser.
N. Y. P. L. May 6, 1931

NK 0206144 NN

Knoedler, M., & company, inc.
Aldegrever, Altdorfer and "The little masters" of Nuremberg (1500-1550) January 6th to 18th, 1936 New York[1936]

NK 0206145 CtY

Knoedler, M. & co., New York.
American paintings of the 18th and early 19th century in our current collection
see its Catalogue: American paintings of the 18th & early 19th century.

Knoedler, M. and Co., New York.
... American portraits by American painters. 1730-1944
see its ... A loan exhibition of American portraits.

Knoedler, M., & company, inc.
Arms' "Handbook" illustrations. New York, M. Knoedler & company, inc., 1934.
4 p. l., 132 p., 1 l. illus. 24cm. (*On cover:* The print-lover's monographs. no. 3)
"Of this book there have been printed ... three hundred fifty copies, of which three hundred are for sale ... no. 17."

1. Engravings. I. Arms, John Taylor, 1887– Handbook of print making and print makers. II. Title.
35-30960
Library of Congress NE900.K55
[2] 769

NK 0206148 DLC PSt NN OC NcU PSt FU

Knoedlor, M., & co., inc., London.
N7633 K6 Beautiful women of the 19th century; loan exhibition in aid of the War service legion ... February 10th to March 11th, 1933. M. Knoedler & company, inc. ... [London, 1933]
[8] p. front., ports. 26cm.
Clippings in enevelope.
1. Women--Portraits. I. Title.

NK 0206149 CSmH

Knoedler, M. & co.
Berthe Morisot (Madame Eugene Manet) 1841-1895; May-June 1936. Lond., [The Author, 1936]
[17] p., mount. illus.

NK 0206150 MiDA

Knoedler, M., & company, inc.
Biographical notes of XVIII & XIX century mezzotinters not mentioned in our two previous brochures. New York, M. Knoedler & co., 1905.
34 p., 1 l. front., pl. 16 x 12½cm.
On cover: Mezzotinters of the 18th & 19th century.

1. Mezzotint engraving—Hist. 2. Mezzotinters. I. Title. II. Title: Mezzotinters of the 18th & 19th century.
42-40479
Library of Congress NE1815.K6

NK 0206151 DLC MiDA NBuU TxU N CtY PP NN

Knoedler, M., & Company, Inc.
British mezzotinto portraits of the XVIII century
see under title

Knoedler, M. & co., inc.
Bronzes and ivories from the old kingdom of Benin. Exhibition from November 25 to December 14 at the galleries of M. Knoedler and co. New York, [1935]
1 v. (unpaged) illus., maps.

NK 0206153 CU MiDA

Knoedler, M., & company, New York
Bronzes and ivories from the old kingdom of Benin. Exhibition from November 25 to December 14,1935, at the galleries of M.Knoedler and company ... [Paris, Dehon & cie,printers, 1935]
[36]p.incl.plates,maps. 27½cm.
"Introduction"signed: Georges-Henri Rivière.
"The royal art of Benin" (p.[4-9]) signed: Louis Carré.
Bibliography: p.[9]
1. Bronzes, African - Exhibitions. 2. Ivories. 3. Sculpture - Benin. 4. Sculpture Primitive. I. Carré, Louis.

NK 0206154 MH NNU-W NRU DDO FMU NNC NjR InU PPT CtY IEN NjP

Knoedler (M.) and Company, inc.
Catalogue: American paintings of the 18th & early 19th century in our current collection. New York, 1948.
[32] p. illus. 26 cm.
Cover title: American painting of the eighteenth and early nineteenth century.

1. Paintings, American—Catalogs. I. Title: American painting of the eighteenth and early nineteenth century.
ND207.K6 759.13 49-6151*

NK 0206155 DLC MH

KNOEDLER, M., & CO., New York.
Catalogue, Loan exhibition of paintings by El Greco and Goya for the benefit of the American Women War Relief Fund and the Belgian Relief Fund. On exhibition at the galleries of M. Knoedler & Company... on view until January 23rd inclusive, 1915. [New York, 1915.] 40 p. 8°.

597709A. 1. Theotocopuli, Dominico, called El Greco, d.1614. 2. Goya y Lucientes, Francisco José de, 1746-1828.

NK 0206156 NN CtY

Knoedler, M., & Company, New York.
Catalogue of a loan exhibition of paintings of "childhood in art," November 29th to December 18th, 1926. New York: M. Knoedler & Co.[, 1926.] 19 p. 8°.

426211A. 1. Children in art.
N. Y. P. L. August 21, 1929

NK 0206157 NN

Knoedler (M.) and Company, inc.
Catalogue of a notable collection of etchings by August Lepère
see under Lepère, Auguste, 1849-1918.

Knoedler, M. and Co, inc. 8067.219
Catalogue of a notable collection of wood-engravings ... Galleries of M. Knoedler & Co. ... New York, commencing October 25th, 1920.
= [New York. 1920.] 38, (1) pp. Portrait. Plates. 18½ cm.
Engravings by Auguste Lepère.

M456 — Wood engravings. Catalogues.

NK 0206159 MB

4NE 60 Knoedler (M.) and Company, inc.
Catalogue of an exhibition of British mezzotinto portraits of the eighteenth century, November 1st to 13th, 1926. New York [1926]
31 p.

NK 0206160 DLC-P4 MH-FA CtY ICU

Jn41 1 Knoedler, M., & company, inc.
Catalogue of an exhibition of dry-points and etchings by Frank W.Benson. March 8th to 26th, 1927. New York,1927.
Pamphlet
1.Benson, Frank Weston, 1862-

NK 0206161 CtY MWiCA

4NE 36 Knoedler (M.) and Company, inc.
Catalogue of an exhibition of early English sporting prints, October 9th to October 27th, 1928. New York, [1928]
19 p.

NK 0206162 DLC-P4

Jnl.1 Knoedler, M., & company, inc.
Catalogue of an exhibition of early engravings Italy, Germany, The Netherlands. January, 1925. New York[1925]

NK 0206163 CtY DLC

Knoedler (M.) and company, inc.
Catalogue of an exhibition of early mezzotints, galleries of M. Knoedler & co. ... New York ... from April 15th, 1918. [New York, 1918]
55, [1] p. front., plates. 20cm.
Cover-title: Early mezzotints.
Errata slip inserted.
142 items.

1. Mezzotints—Exhibitions.
45-49079
Library of Congress NE1815.K62

NK 0206164 DLC OClMA

NE250 .K72 KNOEDLER, M., & COMPANY, INC.
Catalogue of an exhibition of engraved portraits from Dürer to Gaillard, 1519-1886. February 15th to March 5th, 1927. New York [1927]
45 p.

1. Engravings--Catalogs. 2. Portraits--Catalogs.

NK 0206165 ICU MiD CtY OO DLC-P4

VOLUME 300

4NE 61 Knoedler (M.) and Company, inc.
Catalogue of an exhibition of engraved portraits of historical personages, May 1st to June 1st, 1928. New York [1928]
33 p.

NK 0206166 DLC-P4 CtY MiD

ND588 D9.5 K56 1926 Knoedler, M. & Company, inc., New York.
Catalogue of an exhibition of engravings and etchings by Albrecht Dürer, Feb. 8th to 20th, 1926. New York, 1926.
28 p. 22.5cm.

Priced.

NK 0206167 MWiCA MiD CtY

Knoedler (M.) and company, inc.
Catalogue of an exhibition of engravings by "The little masters," October 11th to November 5th, 1927. New York, M. Knoedler & company [1927]
21 p. 22½cm.
Cover-title: "The little masters."

1. Engineers, German—Exhibitions. 2. Little masters (Artists)
45-47774
Library of Congress NE651.K6

NK 0206168 DLC

NE539 W6 K56 Knoedler, M., & Company, inc., New York.
Catalogue of an exhibition of engravings on wood - originals and reproductions of famous paintings. By the late Henry Wolf, N. A. Galleries of M. Knoedler & Co....from October 4th, 1916. [New York, 1916]
3l. 19cm.

Priced.

1. Wolf, Henry, 1852-1916.

NK 0206169 MWiCA

ND497 C35.5 K56 1921 Knoedler, M., & Company, inc., New York.
Catalogue of an exhibition of etchings and dry-points by D. Y. Cameron and James McBey [Exhibition at the] galleries of M. Knoedler & Co.... commencing February 2nd, 1921. [New York, 1921]
16 p. 13.5cm.

Priced.

NK 0206170 MWiCA

ND497 C35.5 K56 1923 Knoedler, M., & Company, inc., New York.
Catalogue of an exhibition of etchings and dry-points by D.Y. Cameron, galleries of M. Knoedler & Co. ... commencing March 27th, 1923. [New York, 1923]
21 p. 20.5cm.

Priced.

NK 0206171 MWiCA

ND237 W5.5 K56 1911 Knoedler, M., & Company, inc., New York.
Catalogue of an exhibition of etchings and dry points by James Abbott McNeill Whistler at the Knoedler Galleries... February, 1911. [New York, 1911]
15 p. 17.5cm.

Priced.

NK 0206172 MWiCA CtY

NE642 M12 K56 1917 Knoedler, M., & Company, inc., New York.
Catalogue of an exhibition of etchings & drypoints by James McBey; galleries of M. Knoedler & Co., ... from November fifth, 1917. [New York, Printed by L.W. Goerck, 1917]
[15] p. 14.5cm.

Priced.

NK 0206173 MWiCA

Knoedler, M., & Co., New York.
Catalogue of an exhibition of etchings & dry points, by James McBey. Galleries of M. Knoedler & Co... from January fifteenth, 1919. [New York,] 1919. 8 l. 8°.

1. M'Bey, James, 1883-
N. Y. P. L. May 14, 1919.

NK 0206174 NN MWiCA

ND497 B58.5 K56 1919 Knoedler, M., & Company, inc., New York.
Catalogue of an exhibition of etchings and dry-points by Muirhead Bone, galleries of M. Knoedler & Co. ... from December 3rd, 1919. [New York, 1919]
[14] p. front. 15cm.

Priced.

NK 0206175 MWiCA CtY InU

ND497 B58.5 K56 1922 Knoedler, M., & Company, inc., New York.
Catalogue of an exhibition of etchings and dry-points by Muirhead Bone, galleries of M. Knoedler & Co. ...from January 30th, 1922. [New York, 1922]
10 p. 14cm.

Priced.

NK 0206176 MWiCA

ND653 R4.5 K56 1921 Knoedler, M., and Company, inc., New York.
Catalogue of an exhibition of etchings and dry-points by Rembrandt, 1606-1669... commencing March 1st, 1921. [New York, 1921]
15 p. 14cm.

Priced.

NK 0206177 MWiCA

4NE 51 Knoedler (M.) and Company, inc.
Catalogue of an exhibition of etchings and dry-points by Rembrandt, 1606 -1669, commencing February 5, 1923. [New York, 1923]
22 p.

NK 0206178 DLC-P4 MWiCA

769.93 W579K6 Knoedler, M. & co., inc.
Catalogue of an exhibition of etchings and dry points by Whistler. April-May, 1925. New York [1925]
iv, 7, [1] p.

1. Whislter, James Abbott McNeill, 1834-1903. 2. Etchings - Catalogs. 3. Drypoints.

NK 0206179 MiDA MWiCA CtY

4NE 58 Knoedler (M.) and Company, inc.
Catalogue of an exhibition of etchings and lithographs by J.-L. Forain. May 4th to May 28th, 1926. New York [19]
16 p.

NK 0206180 DLC-P4 MWiCA CtY MiD

NE642 M12 K56 1915 Knoedler, M., & Company, inc., New York.
Catalogue of an exhibition of etchings and water-color drawings by James McBey, galleries of M. Knoedler & Co. ... October 19th to November 6th, 1915. [New York, Printed by Goerck Art Press, 1915]
[15] p. 16.5cm.

Priced.

NK 0206181 MWiCA

Knoedler, M., & co., inc.
Catalogue of an exhibition of etchings and water colors, by James McBey; October 5th to October 17th, 1925. New York [The Author, 1925]
10 p.

I. McBey, James, 1883-

NK 0206182 MiD MWiCA

Knoedler, M., & Co., New York.
Catalogue of an exhibition of etchings by Alphonse Legros, galleries of M. Knoedler & Co... October 2nd to 16th, 1915. [New York, 1915.] 8 l. 8°.

1. Etchings (French). 2. Legros, Alphonse, 1837-1911.
N. Y. P. L. January 15, 1916.

NK 0206183 NN MWiCA

4NE 29 Knoedler (M.) and Company, inc.
Catalogue of an exhibiton of etchings by Anders Zorn... from January 14th 1918. [New York, 1918]
1 v. (unpaged)

NK 0206184 DLC-P4

4NE 49 Knoedler (M.) and Company, inc.
Catalogue of an exhibition of etchings by Zorn. Galleries of M. Knoedler & Co., 556-558 Fifth Avenue, near 46th St., commencing January 7th, 1921. [New York, 1921]
16 p.

NK 0206185 DLC-P4

4NE 30 Knoedler (M.) and Company, inc.
Catalogue of an exhibition of etchings by Anders Zorn, 1860-1920, October 11th to 30th, 1926. New York [1926]
33 p.

NK 0206186 DLC-P4 CtY MH MiD

VOLUME 300

NE2195 Knoedler, M., & Company, inc.
.Z67 Catalogue of an exhibition of etchings by Anders Zorn (1860-1920) February 5th to 23rd, 1929. New York, M. Knoedler & Company [1929]
40 p. plates. 22 cm.

1. Zorn, Anders, 1860-1920.

NK 0206187 NjR MiDA CU IEN DLC PPPM ICarbS MiD MH CtY

Jn41 1 Knoedler, M., & company, inc.
Catalogue of an exhibition of etchings by Auguste Lepère (1849-1918) March, 1925. New York city[1925]

1.Lepère, Auguste, 1849-1918.

NK 0206188 CtY MWiCA

ND497 C35.5 K56 1914 Knoedler, M., & Company, inc., New York.
Catalogue of an exhibition of etchings by D.Y. Cameron at the galleries of M. Knoedler & Co. ... November 23rd to December 5th inclusive, 1914. [New York, 1914]
16 p. front. 16.5cm.

Priced.

NK 0206189 MWiCA

NE642 M12 K56 1926 Knoedler, M., & Company, inc., New York.
Catalogue of an exhibition of etchings by James McBey, December 1st to 11th, 1926. New York [1926]
15 p. 22.5cm.

Priced.

NK 0206190 MWiCA CtY MiD

4NE 52 Knoedler (M.) and Company, inc.
Catalogue of an exhibition of etchings by Rembrandt, 1606-1669, March -April, 1925. New York [1925]
26 p.

NK 0206191 DLC-P4 MiDA MWiCA

Jn41 1 Knoedler, M., & company, inc.
Catalogue of an exhibition of etchings by Sir D.Y. Cameron ... Beginning on October fifteenth. New York[1924]

On cover: October, nineteen twenty-four.

1.Cameron, Sir David Young, 1865-

NK 0206192 CtY MWiCA

ND497 C35.5 K56 1937 Knoedler, M., & Company, inc., New York.
Catalogue of an exhibition of etchings by Sir D.Y. Cameron, February, 1937. New York [1937]
6 ℓ. 22cm.

NK 0206193 MWiCA

ND237 W5.5 K56 1920 Knoedler, M., & Company, inc., New York.
Catalogue of an exhibition of etchings by Whistler, galleries of M. Knoedler & Co... commencing November 10th, 1920. [New York, 1920]
20 p. 13.5cm.

Priced.

NK 0206194 MWiCA

ND237 W5.5 K56 1922 Knoedler, M., & Company, inc., New York.
Catalogue of an exhibition of etchings by Whistler, galleries of M. Knoedler & Co.... commencing April 3rd, 1922. [New York, 1922]
16 p. 13.5cm.

Priced.

NK 0206195 MWiCA

4NE 27 Knoedler (M.) and Company, inc.
Catalogue of an exhibition of etchings, dry-points, lithographs by J.-L. Forain, February 7th to March 3rd, 1928. New York [1928]
18 p.

NK 0206196 DLC-P4 MiD CtY MWiCA

4NE 48 Knoedler (M.) and Company, inc.
Catalogue of an exhibition of etchings of architecture, April 6th to May 1st, 1926. New York [1926]
28 p.

NK 0206197 DLC-P4 CtY

Knoedler, M., & co., inc.
Catalogue of an exhibition of French & English colour-prints of the 18th century; Old English sporting prints; December 14th, 1925 to January 9th, 1926. New York [The Author, 1925]
36 p.

NK 0206198 MiD CtY

Jn66 01 Knoedler, M., & company, inc.
Catalogue of an exhibition of French & English colour-prints of the 18th century. December 13th, 1926 to January 8th, 1927. New York[1926]

NK 0206199 CtY MiD DLC-P4

Knoedler, M., & company, New York
Catalogue of an exhibition of landscape etchings from Dürer to McBey, April 5th to April 30th,1927. New York, M.Knoedler & co. [1927]
2 p.ℓ.,34p. 21½cm.
Cover-title: Landscape etchings. Dürer to McBey.

1. Etchings - Exhibitions. 2. Landscape.
I. Title: Landscape etchings Dürer to McBey.

NK 0206200 NRU CtY MiD DLC MH

ND237 W5.5 K56 1918 Knoedler, M., & Company, inc., New York.
Catalogue of an exhibition of lithographs by Whistler, galleries of M. Knoedler & Co. ...from February 25th, 1918. [New York, 1918]
[14] p. 14.5cm.

Priced.

NK 0206201 MWiCA

ND237 W5.5 K56 1919 Knoedler, M., & Company, inc., New York.
Catalogue of an exhibition of lithographs by Whistler, galleries of M. Knoedler & Co... from February twenty-fourth, 1919. [New York, 1919]
[19] p. front., plate. 14.5cm.

Priced.

NK 0206202 MWiCA CtY

4NE 55 Knoedler (M.) and Company, inc.
Catalogue of an exhibition of masterpieces of graphic art, illustrating and supplementing "Famous prints," edited by Frank Weitenkampf. November 15th to 27th, 1926. New York [1926-
pt. 1-

Contents.- pt. 1. Etchings and engravings.

NK 0206203 DLC-P4 CtY PSt MH

Jℓ70.01 Knoedler, M., & company, inc.
Catalogue of an exhibition of old and modern drawings at the galleries of M.Knoelder & co. ... from February first, 1924. [New York,1924]

NK 0206204 CtY DSI

Knoedler, M., and Co., inc.
Catalogue of an exhibition of Old English sporting prints
see under Boston. Museum of Fine Arts.

4NE 63 Knoedler (M.) and Company, inc.
Catalogue of an exhibition of one hundred etchings by modern masters, February, 1925. New York [1925]
12 p.

NK 0206206 DLC-P4 CtY

4NE 44 Knoedler (M.) and Company, inc.
Catalogue of an exhibition of one hundred masterpieces of graphic art, November 9th to December 3rd, 1927. New York [1927]
34 p.

NK 0206207 DLC-P4 PSt CtY MH

Knoedler (M.) and company, inc.
A catalogue of an exhibition of paintings and prints of every description, on the occasion of Knoedler, one hundred years, 1846–1946. New York [1946]
[31] p. 22½cm.
Exhibition held April 1 to 27, 1946.

1. Paintings—Exhibitions. 2. Engravings—Exhibitions.

46-20241
Library of Congress N5020.N4183 [2] 759.0838

NK 0206208 DLC

Knoedler, M., & Co., New York.
Catalogue of an exhibition of paintings and sketches, by Alfred Philippe Roll, at the galleries of M. Knoedler & Co.'...from October 2nd to 16th inclusive, 1915. [New York: Goerck Art Press, 1915.] 8 l., 1 pl., 1 port. 8°.

1. Roll, Alfred Philippe, 1847-
N. Y. P. L. January 13, 1916.

NK 0206209 NN

Knoedler (M.) & co., inc.
Catalogue of an exhibition of paintings by G. E Browne; Jan. 10th to...15th... [New York: M. Knoedler & Co. [1910] 2 l. 8°.

1. Paintings (U. S.)—Exhibitions.

NK 0206210 NN

VOLUME 300

4NE 35 Knoedler (M.) and Company, inc.
Catalogue of an exhibition of portrait etchings by Van Dyck, Rembrandt, Whistler, Degas, Rodin and Zorn, together with four lithographs by Jean Auguste Dominique Ingres, October, 1925. New York [1925]
16 p.

NK 0206211 DLC-P4

Jd22 01 Knoedler, M., & co.,inc.
Catalogue of an exhibition of recent work by a group of American artists, with a foreword by Frederick James Gregg, March 15 to March 29 ... 1919. New York[1919?]

I.Gregg, Frederick James

NK 0206212 CtY

N5020 .C737 Knoedler (M.) and Company, inc.

Colorado Springs Fine Arts Center.
Catalogue of an exhibition of 21 great paintings, held in the galleries of the Colorado Springs Fine Arts Center, July 20 through August 30, 1947, through the courtesy of the Knoedler Galleries, New York. [New York? 1947]

ND497 B58 K56 1924 Knoedler, M., & Company, inc., New York.
Catalogue of an exhibition of water colors, pastels and drawings by Muirhead Bone, beginning on November first, galleries of M. Knoedler & Company... New York [1924]
14 p. 23.5cm.

Priced.

NK 0206214 MWiCA

4NE 62 Knoedler (M.) and Company, inc.
Catalogue of an exhibition of woodcuts by Albrecht Dürer, February 24th to March 13th, 1926. New York [1926]
47 p.

NK 0206215 DLC-P4 MWiCA MiD

4NE 28 Knoedler (M.) and Company, inc.
Catalogue of an exhibition of woodcuts by Albrecht Dürer, March 6th to April 7, 1928. New York [1928]
55 p.

NK 0206216 DLC-P4 PSt DSI MH-FA CtY MiD

ND237 W5.5 K56 1914 Knoedler, M., & Company, inc., New York.
Catalogue of drawings, etchings and lithographs by James McNeill Whistler, exhibited at M. Knoedler & Co. galleries ... commencing March 23d, 1914. [New York, 1914]
[13] p. 15cm.

Priced.

NK 0206217 MWiCA

Knoedler, M. & Co., New York.
Catalogue of early Chinese paintings of the T'ang, Sung and Yüan dynasties. A.D. 600-1400. On exhibition at the galleries of M. Knoedler & company...New York [Printed by the Goerck art press] 1914.
1 p.l., [18] p., 2 l. 20 1/2 cm.

NK 0206218 DSI PPPM CtY OClMA

Knoedler, M., & Co.
Catalogue of eighteenth century mezzotints on exhibition at the galleries of Messrs. M. Knoedler & Co... [New York: Goerck Art Press,] 1910. 27(1) p. 8°.

1. Engravings (Mezzotints).— Sales catalogues.
N. Y. P. L. March 6, 1911.

NK 0206219 NN

Knoedler, M., & Company, inc.
Catalogue of eighty-four mezzotinto, stipple and line-engravings, exhibited at the opening of the Springfield museum of fine arts
see under Springfield, Mass. Museum of Fine Arts.

Knoedler (M.) & Co., inc.
[Catalogue of engravings. New York, cop. 1898.]
5 l., 19 pl. f°.

NK 0206221 NN

Knoedler, M., and Co.
Catalogue of etchings, mezzotints, dry points, and aquatints by Sir Frank Short... [New York: Goerck Art Press,] 1915. 11 l. 8°.

One page contains list of prints not mentioned in the Strange catalogue.

1. Short, Sir Frank, 1857–
N. Y. P. L. August 25, 1915.

NK 0206222 NN

Knoedler, M., and co., inc.
Catalogue of line-engravings by the Peintre-Engravers of the XVIIth century and the line-engravers of the XVIIIth century, Estampe l'Age Gallante. November 29th to December 11th inclusive. New York, Goerck art press, 1915.
32 p. [2] illus. 20 cm.

NK 0206223 PPPM

Knoedler, M., & Co.
Catalogue of modern paintings belonging to M. Knoedler & Co...to be sold by absolute auction, to settle the estate of the late John Knoedler on...April 11, 12, 13, and 14...at Chickering Hall...T. E. Kirby, auctioneer. New York: Amer. Art Assoc., 1893. 142 p. 8°.

Priced.
Newspaper clippings, giving account of sale, inserted.

1. Paintings.—Catalogues.
N. Y. P. L. January 22, 1914.

NK 0206224 NN NNC

ND497 B58.5 K56 1914 Knoedler, M., & Company, inc., New York.
Catalogue of original etchings by Muirhead Bone, exhibited at M. Knoedler & Co. galleries... February 2nd, 1914 and following days. [New York, 1914]
[7] p. front. 15cm.

Priced.

NK 0206225 MWiCA

4NE 50 Knoedler (M.) and Company, inc.
Catalogue of original etchings by Rembrandt, exhibited at M. Knoedler & Co. galleries, 556-558 Fifth Avenue between 45th and 46th Streets, New York, commencing March 2nd, 1914. [New York, 1914]

NK 0206226 DLC-P4 MWiCA OClMA

Knoedler, M., & co., inc.
Catalogue of the annual exhibition of engravings, woodcuts, etchings of the XV and XVI centuries... New York, M. Knoedler & co. [ ]
v. fronts.(v.4-5),illus.(incl.ports.) 22cm.
[2nd]-8th,1926-32; 9th-10th,1934-35]

Title varies: Catalogue of the ... annual exhibition [of] engravings and
Cover-titles bound in.

Contents.-

[2nd] Catalogue of an exhibition of engravings and woodcuts of the fifteenth and sixteenth centuries, January 18th to February 6th, 1926.-3rd, January 11th to February 5th, 1927.-4th, January 4th to 28th, 1928.-5th, January 3rd to 26th, 1929.-6th, February 5th to March 8th, 1930 .-7th, Engravings and

etchings, January 6th to 31st, 1931.-8th, Engravings and etchings, February 1932.-9th, Engravings and woodcuts, February 1934.-10th, March 5th to April 6th, 1935.-

13th, April 4th to April 30th, 1938.

NK 0206229 MU NcD DSI DDO MdBJ MWelC PPPM PPAFA NBB MiDA MH CU OO PBm NRU NN OClMA OCl

---

ND237 W5.5 K56 1907 Knoedler, M., & Company, inc., New York.
Catalogue of the celebrated Theobald (London) collection of Whistler etchings comprising 241 examples, on exhibition at the galleries of M. Knoedler & Co., January MCMVII. [New York, 1907]
12 p. 16cm.

Priced.

NK 0206230 MWiCA

Knoedler, M., & Company, inc.
Catalogue of the etchings by Auguste Lepère
see under Lotz-Brissonneau, A.

4NE 34 Knoedler (M.) and Company, inc.
Catalogue of the etchings by Rembrandt. Exhibited... January 9th to 25th inclusive 1913. [New York, 1913]
1 v. (unpaged)

NK 0206232 DLC-P4 NN MWiCA

Knoedler, M., & company, inc.
Catalogue of the ninth annual exhibition of engravings and woodcuts of the XV and XVI centuries, February, 1934. New York, M. Knoedler & company, inc. [1934]
93, [1] p. illus. 22½cm.

1. Engravings—Exhibitions. 2. Wood-engravings—Exhibitions.
34-29137
Library of Congress NE45.N6K6 1934
[2] 760.838

NK 0206233 DLC DDO CU

Jn1 1 Knoedler, M., & company, inc.
Catalogue of the works of painter-etchers and painter-engravers from the XV to XX century. Exhibition at M.Knoedler & co. galleries ... New York, commencing February 19th, 1912. [New York,1912]

On cover: Masters of the burin and needle.

NK 0206234 CtY

VOLUME 300

Knoedler, M., & company, inc.

Claghorn, James L
Catalogue of valuable paintings, the private collection of Mr. James L. Claghorn ... comprising well-chosen examples of the various schools of modern art, by French, German, English, American, Roman, and Spanish masters ... To be sold by auction April 18 and 19, 1877. Robert Somerville, auctioneer. The sale will be under the supervision of Messrs. M. Knoedler & co.... [New York? 1877]

Knoedler, M., & Co., Inc., *London.* Catalogue: old sporting pictures, loan exhibition in aid of the Royal Free Hospital, June 7 to 30, 1928 . . . [London, 1928.] 8vo. N8250 K6

NK 0206236 CSmH

Jk19 Knoedler, M., & company, inc.
01 A century of French painting; exhibition organised for the benefit of the French hospital of New York. 12th November - 8th December, 1928. New York[1928]

NK 0206237 CtY MH-FA CLU OClMA OCU MiD InU CSt

Knoedler (M.) and company, inc.
... The classical period of Renoir. 4th to 24th November, 1929. Knoedler & company ... New York. [New York, 1929]
[29] p. mounted illus. 31 x 24cm.
At head of title: 1875-1886.
Foreword signed: Etienne Bignou.

1. *Renoir, Auguste, 1841-1919. I. Bignou, Etienne. II. Title.
45-45608
Library of Congress ND553.R45K7

NK 0206238 DLC ICU MiD CtY OClMA MH-FA InU NN RPD

Knoedler, M., & co., inc.

Dodgson, Campbell, 1867-
The classics, by Campbell Dodgson. New York, Priv. print., M. Knoedler & company, inc. [c1938]

Knoedler, M., & company, inc.
... Classics of the nude ... New York, M. Knoedler and company [1939]
4 p. l., 7-27 p. 14 pl. on 8 l. 28cm.
At head of title: Loan exhibition. Pollaiuolo to Picasso.
"For the benefit of the Lisa day nursery, April 10 to April 29, 1939."
Includes bibliographies.

1. Human figure in art. 2. Nude in art. 3. Paintings—Exhibitions. 4. Drawings—Exhibitions. I. Title.
42-5281
Library of Congress N7570.K55
[3] 704

NK 0206240 DLC OClMA MA MdBWA DDO CtY PSt CSmH OO

Knoedler (M.) and Company, inc.
Collection of J. P. Morgan; exhibition of paintings
see
Morgan, John Pierpont, 1867-1943.
Exhibition of paintings; collection of J. P. Morgan ...

759.914 Knoedler, (M.) & co., inc.
K75c A collectors' exhibition; impressionist and post-impressionist masterpieces from the collections of members of the advisory committee of the Institute of Fine Arts. February 6 to 25, 1950. New York, 1950.
25, xxxi-xxxii p. illus.

At head of title: New York University. The Institute of Fine Arts.
Includes bibliographic references.

NK 0206242 MiDA

Knoedler (M.) and company, inc.
A collector's taste...
see under Clark, Stephen Carlton, 1882-

759.93 Knoedler (M.) and Co., inc.
L241K5 Commemorative exhibition, paintings by Martin J. Heade (1819-1904) Fitz Hugh Lane (1804-1865) from the private collection of Maxim Karolik and the M. and M. Karolik collection of American paintings from the Museum of Fine Arts, Boston. May 3 through May 28, 1954. New York, 1954.
[20]p. illus.

Introduction by John I. H. Baur.

NK 0206244 MiDA PPPM NN NNMM

Knoedler, M., & company, inc.
Jbt Complete set of Joseph Mallord William
047 Turner's Liber studiorum, published 1807-1819. On exhibition at the galleries of M.Knoedler & co. ... New York, commencing February 16th, 1907.[New York,1907]

NK 0206245 CtY

Knoedler, M., and co., inc.
Concerning Delacroix and Jules Breton, apropos of a special exhibition of their work at the galleries of M. Knoedler and co. New York, [189-?]
8 p. 2 portrs. 8°.

NK 0206246 MB

Knoedler (M.) and company, inc.
Dali. April 14 to May 5, 1943, at the galleries of M. Knoedler and company, inc. ... New York city. [New York, 1943]
11 l. 25 pl. on 13 l. 30½ x 23 cm.
Half-title: An exhibition of drawings and paintings by Dali.
"Published under the supervision of Inez Chatfield for Art aid corporation ... New York."

1. Dalí, Salvador, 1904- 2. Paintings, Spanish—Exhibitions. 3. Drawings, Spanish—Exhibitions. 4. Portraits—Exhibitions. I. Chatfield, Inez, ed. II. Art aid corporation, New York.
ND813.D3K58 759.6 43-7937 rev

NK 0206247 DLC CaBVaU MiEM CSt TU TxU OU OO MB IaU

Knoedler, M., & company, inc.
David and Ingres; paintings and drawings. January 8 to January 27, 1940, M. Knoedler and company ... New York. [New York, 1939?]
[29] p., 1 l. 16 pl. on 8 l. 24½cm.
"Foreword" signed: John Lee Clarke, jr.
Includes bibliographies.

1. David, Jacques Louis, 1748-1825. 2. Ingres, Jean Auguste Dominique, 1780-1867. I. Clarke, John Lee, 1907-
41-4425
Library of Congress ND553.D25K6
[2] [927.5] 759.4

NK 0206248 DLC WaU NcU MdBWA PU-FA NNC PPPM

Knoedler (M.) and company, inc.
Descriptive catalogue of the portraits, etchings, and engravings by H. Herkomer. Exhibited at M. Knoedler's Gallery, New York, November 25., 1882. [*New York: F. Hart & Co.*], 1882. 16 pp. 8°.

NK 0206249 NN

Knoedler (M.) and company, inc.
Dutch masters of the seventeenth century; exhibition February 5-February 24, 1945. New York, M. Knoedler and company [1945]
[18] p. 7 pl. on 4 l. 24½cm.

1. Paintings, Dutch—Exhibitions. I. Title.
A 45-2943
Harvard univ. Library for Library of Congress [3]

NK 0206250 MH NN MdBWA OClMA

Knoedler, M., & company. New York.
Early impressionism. 1868-1883. Exhibition March 31-April 12, 1941, Knoedler...New York. [New York, 1941]
2 l. 23cm.

1. Impressionism in art.
N. Y. P. L. April 21, 1943

NK 0206251 NN

Knoedler (M) and Company, Inc.
Eaux-fortes sur Paris par C. Meryon. New York, M. Knoedler et Cie., 1935
16 p. illus. 23 cm.
Cover title.
Exhibition catalog.

NK 0206252 MH CtY DDO MWiCA

Knoedler (M.) and Company, inc.
Edgar Degas, 1834-1917; original wax sculptures. This is the first exhibition of the original works in wax by Degas from which the series of bronzes were cast by A.-A. Hébrard. November 9th thru December 3rd 1955. London, New York [1955]
[47] p. plates, port. 27 cm.

1. Degas, Hilaire Germain Edgar, 1834-1917. 2. Hébrard, A. A.
A 58-4580
New York Univ. Libraries NB1270 for Library of Congress [2]

NK 0206253 NN MiDA OClMA CU

Knoedler Galleries, New York.
1875-1886, the classical period of Renoir
see its ... The classical period of Renoir.

ND588 Knoedler, M., & Company, inc., New York.
D9.5 Eighty-six engravings and etchings by
K56 Albrecht Dürer. New York, M.
1931 Knoedler, 1931.
80 p. 70 illus. 24cm.

The Print-collector's bulletin, v.2, no.3.
Priced.

NK 0206255 MWiCA

Knoedler (M.) and Company, inc.
An English exhibition to honour Queen Elizabeth II. May 5-May 23, 1953. New York, Knoedler Galleries [1953]
unpaged. illus. 27 cm.

1. Paintings, English—Exhibitions. 2. Elizabeth II, Queen of Great Britain, 1926- I. Title.
ND466.K55 759.2 53-28371 ‡

NK 0206256 DLC NN OClMA

Knoedler, M., & company, inc.
Jn11 Engraved portraits of historical personages,
1 February 2nd to 26th, 1938. New York[1938?]

NK 0206257 CtY

VOLUME 300

NE654 D9K6 Knoedler, (M.) and Company, inc.
Engravings and etchings by Albrecht Dürer, May 1st to May 25th, 1929. New York [1929]
71 p. (chiefly illus.)

1. Dürer, Albrecht, 1471-1528.

CtY NN MiD OC1MA MdBWA
NK 0206258 CU NcD ODW CLSU PSt DLC-P4 NRU NjP PPAFA

Knoedler, M., & Co., inc.
Engravings, etchings and woodcuts of the fifteenth and sixteenth centuries ...
see its Catalogue of the ... annual exhibition.

NE 75 .K 7 1878 Knoedler, M., & co., inc.
Engravings, etchings, photographs, photo-engravings. 1879. General catalogue, M. Knoedler & co., New York. [New York, Trow's printing and bookbinding co., c1878]
2 p.l., 50p. plates. 30 cm.

NK 0206260 DLC

NE650 M5K55 (SA) Knoedler, (M.) and Company, inc.
Etchings and drawings by Charles Meryon from the B.B. MacGeorge Collection. NY, 1917
1 v. 21 cm
Catalogue of an exhibition held at the Galleries of M. Knoedler and Company, April 9, 1917
On cover: MacGeorge Meryon Collection
1. MÉRYON, CHARLES, 1821-1868 I. MacGeorge, Bernard Buchanan

NK 0206261 NjP CtY

Knoedler, M., & Co., inc.
Etchings and drypoints by Rembrandt van Rijn ... 1930
see under Rembrandt Hermanszoon van Rijn, 1607-1669.

Knoedler, M., & Co.
Etchings, drawings by Rajon. November, 1886. New York: M. Knoedler & Co., 1886. 15 p. 12°.

1. Rajon, Paul Adolphe. N. Y. P. L. May 1, 1911.

NK 0206263 NN

Knoedler, M., & Co., inc.
The etchings of J.-L. Forain. 1935.
23 p. illus.

NK 0206264 DDO

Knoedler, M., & company, inc.
Exhibition celebrating Knoedler one hundred years, 1846-1946. April 1 to 27, 1946.
New York, Printed by the Gallery Press, 1946.
pamph.

NK 0206265 PPPM

Knoedler (M.) and Company, inc.
An exhibition of French paintings, February 24 to March 14, 1931, M. Knoedler & Co., Inc., 622 South Michigan Avenue, Chicago. [Chicago, 1931]
[15] p. mounted illus.
Cover title: A century of French painting.

NK 0206266 CLU MiD

Knoedler, M., & company.
... Exhibition of masterpieces through four centuries (1400–1800). In aid of King George's jubilee trust, May 29 – June 29, 1935. At the galleries of M. Knoedler & company, inc. ... London [1935] 8 l. mounted illus. (incl. ports.) 25½cm.

At head of title: Jubilee year.

1. Paintings—Exhibitions – Gt. Br.—Eng.—London. N. Y. P. L. August 29, 1941

NK 0206267 NN CLU

Knoedler, M., & Co.
Exhibition of old masters, for the benefit of the Artists' Fund & Artists' Aid Societies, at the galleries of M. Knoedler & Co., January 11th to 27th inclusive. [New York, 1912.] 54 p., 1 port. 12°.

1. Paintings.—Exhibitions, U. S.: N. Y. City. N. Y. P. L. February 10, 1913.

NK 0206268 NN MH

Knoedler (M.) and Company, inc.
An exhibition of paintings and drawings of Latin America, April 21–May 10, 1947, for the benefit of the Bryn Mawr College Fund. New York, Knoedler Galleries [1947]
[29] p. plates. 23 cm.

1. Paintings, Spanish-American—Exhibitions. 2. Drawings, Spanish-American—Exhibitions.

N6502.K57 709.8 48-383*

NK 0206269 DLC MiDA NIC MdBWA

KNOEDLER, M. & COMPANY.
Exhibition of paintings by Andrew Wyeth, October 26-November 14, 1953. New York[1953] [16]p. illus. 18 x 25cm.

1. Wyeth, Andrew.

NK 0206270 NN

Knoedler, M. & Co., New York.
Exhibition of paintings by Thomas Gainsborough, R. A. and J. M. W. Turner, R. A. for the benefit of the Artists' Fund and Artists' Aid Societies, at the galleries of M. Knoedler & Co... January 14th to 31st inclusive, 1914. [New York: L. W. Goerck,] 1914. 43 p., 1 l. 8°.

1. Gainsborough, Thomas, 1727-88. 2. Turner, Joseph Mallord William, 1775-1851 N. Y. P. L. August 27, 1915.

NK 0206271 NN NIC PPPM

N5020 .N4193 Knoedler (M.) and company, inc.

Morgan, John Pierpont, 1867–1943.
Exhibition of paintings; collection of J. P. Morgan, for the benefit of the Citizens committee for the army and navy, inc. November 23 to December 11, 1943, at the galleries of M. Knoedler and company ... New York. [New York, The William Bradford press, 1943]

KNOEDLER, M., & COMPANY, New York.
...Exhibition of portraits by Savely Sorin. Galleries of M. Knoedler & Company, February 19 to March 5, 1923. [New York, 1923.] 4 l. mounted illus. (ports.) 24cm.

738304A. 1. Sorin, Saveliĭ Abramovich, 1878–

NK 0206273 NN

Knoedler (M.) & Co., inc.
Exhibition of portraits by Van Dyck, from the collections of P.A.B. Widener and H.C. Frick at the galleries of M. Knoedler & Co., New York, Nov.-Dec. 1909. New York, 1909.
8 l. 12°.

NK 0206274 NN

Knoedler, M.& co., London.
Exhibition of sculpture of British champion animals by Herbert Haseltine, held under the auspices of the "Field", July 8th to July 31st, 1925. [London] Knoedler's gallery [1925]

24 p. plates. 21.5 cm.

NK 0206275 MH DDO RPD

Knoedler, M., and Co., Inc.
Exposition de tableaux anciens provenant de collections particulières, 23 avril-10 mai 1913. Paris, 1913.

20 p.

NK 0206276 MH

Knoedler, M., & company, inc., New York.
"Fair women" (1525-1832) January 11th to February 10th, 1934. New York, M. Knoedler & company, inc. c1934?
1 p. l., 3-17 numb. l. O.

NK 0206277 OO

Knoedler, M., & company, inc.
Fifteenth century portraits; loan exhibition, April 15 through April 27, 1935, at the galleries of M. Knoedler and company ... New York city. [New York, The Spiral press, 1935]
[13] p. 18 port. on 9 l. 26½ x 20½cm.
Includes bibliographies.

1. Portraits—Exhibitions. I. Title. 40-25202

Library of Congress ND1301.K6
[2] 757.0638

NK 0206278 DLC NN DDO DSI CSmH OC1MA

Knoedler, M., and Co., inc.
Fifty etchings by Sir D.Y. Cameron
see under Cameron, Sir David Young, 1865-1945.

Knoedler (M.) and Company, inc.
Figure pieces; loan exhibition, March 29 to April 10, 1937, at the galleries of M. Knoedler & Company. [New York, 1937?]
[41] p. 20 plates (incl. ports.) 28 cm.

1. Portraits, French—Exhibitions. 2. Portrait painters, French. I. Title.

ND1316.K5 68-125715

NK 0206280 DLC CtY NNC NN NjR MiDA OC1MA PSt PSC

Knoedler, M., & company.
Fine prints of two centuries, March 12th to April 6th, 1929. New York, 1929. 122 p. illus. 23cm.

1. Engravings—Exhibitions—

MH OC1 OC1MA
NK 0206281 NN OO NjP CtY MiD IU MdBWA CU CLU OrU

Knoedler (M.) and company, inc.

ND665 .B4 Belgium. *Belgian government information center, New York.*
Flemish primitives, an exhibition organized by the Belgian government through the Belgian information center, New York, April 13, 1942 to May 9, 1942 at the galleries of M. Knoedler and company, inc. ... New York city. [New York, 1942]

VOLUME 300

KNOEDLER, M. & COMPANY.
"Flowers" by French painters (XIX-XX centuries) [exhibition] November 1932. New York [1932]
[39] p. 8 plates. 29cm.

1. Painting, Flower, French.

NK 0206283 NN RPD MH CtY MiDA CSt ICU NjR

Knoedler, M., and co., inc.
Forain aquafortiste et lithographe, 1852-1931
see under Dodgson, Campbell, 1867-

Knoedler, M., & co., inc.
Forty etchings by Charles Meryon
see under Meryon, Charles, 1821-1868.

Knoedler, M. & company, inc.
Fourteen masterpieces, Van Gogh; loan exhibition for the benefit of the Home for the Destitute Blind, March 30- April 17, 1948. New York, Knoedler galleries, 1948. 34p. illus. 27cm.

1. Gogh, Vincent van, 1853-1890.

NK 0206286 MWelC MiDA NNC MdBWA

Beinecke Library Za T127 942F
Knoedler (M.) and Company, inc.
Francis Colburn; exhibition of paintings, November 23 to December 12, 1942. New York, Knoedler Galleries [1942]
[3] p. 22 cm.
"... I see Vermont, old, wild and new ... " by Genevieve Taggard.
1. Colburn, Francis - Presentation inscription to F.M. Frost. 2. Frost, Frances Mary, 1905-1959 - Presentation inscription from F. Colburn. I. Colburn, Francis. II. Taggard, Genevieve, 1894-1948.

NK 0206287 CtY

NE1855 K72f GU
Knoedler (M.) and Company, inc.
French colour prints and line engravings of the XVIII century. New York [1930]
80 p. (chiefly illus.) 34cm. (The Print collector's bulletin. v.1, no.1)

At head of title: The print collector's bulletin; an illustrated catalogue for museums and collectors.
Imperfect: p. [3-4] cut away.

1. Color prints French - Catalogs. 2. Engravings - Catalogs. I. Title.

NK 0206288 GU

Knoedler, M. & co.
French engravings of the XVIIIth century. N.Y. [The Author] 1920.
[1] p. [2] plates.

NK 0206289 MiDA

Knoedler (M.) and Company, inc.
Gaston Lachaise, 1882-1935, exhibition, January 20-February 15, 1947. New York [1947]
18 p. plates. 27 cm.

1. Lachaise, Gaston, 1882-1935. 2. Sculpture, American—Exhibitions.

NB237.L26K6 735.73 47-27849*

NK 0206290 DLC NN FMU PP NIC MdBWA MH ViU ICU

Knoedler, M., & company, inc.
... General catalogue, M. Knoedler & co. ... [New York? 1891?]
92 p. 29½ x 24cm.
At head of title: Engravings, etchings, photographs, photo-engravings. 1891.
Priced.

1. Engravings—Catalogs. 2. Photographs—Catalogs. 40-20722

Library of Congress NE70.K6
[2] 760.85

NK 0206291 DLC

Knoedler (M.) and company, inc.
Georges de La Tour. The brothers Le Nain. Edited by Louis Carré. Introduction by Paul Jamot ... New York, M. Knoedler & co. [1936]
[72] p. illus. 28 cm.
Added t.-p.: Loan exhibition of paintings by Georges de La Tour, Antoine Le Nain, Louis Le Nain [and] Mathieu Le Nain, held for the benefit of the Musée de Blérancourt (France) and the Lycée français de New York, November 23–December 12, 1936.
"Printed in France."
Includes bibliographies.
1. La Tour, Georges du Mesnil de, 1593–1652. 2. Le Nain, Antoine, 1588–1648. 3. Le Nain, Louis, 1593–1648. 4. Le Nain, Mathieu, 1607–1677. I. Carré, Louis, ed.

A 41—3968

New York Univ. Wash. Sq. Library ND553
for Library of Congress [a59r55e½]

FMU MiDA DDO CaOTP MWiCA NN
NK 0206292 NNU-W NjR MiU OC1MA OO PSt MdBWA MWelC

Knoedler, M., & company, inc.
El Greco; loan exhibition for the benefit of the Greek war relief association, January 17 to February 15, 1941, commemorating the 400th anniversary of the birth of El Greco, at the galleries of M. Knoedler and company, inc. ... New York city. [New York, Art aid corporation, ©1941]
[29] p. 17 pl. on 9 l. 31cm.
On cover: Δομήνικος Θεοτοκόπολις: El Greco.
"4000 copies were printed."
Introduction signed: Stephan Bourgeois.

1. Theotocopuli, Domenico, called El Greco, d. 1614. I. Bourgeois, Stephan.

41-7093

Library of Congress ND813.T4K6
[2] [927.5] 759.6

PPPM ViU MH-FA DDO WaS MWiCA MtU
NK 0206293 DLC NcU MiU NjR TxSaT MdBWA OO OC1

Knoedler (M.) and company, inc.
Gros, Gericault, Delacroix; loan exhibition of paintings and drawings, November 21 to December 10, 1938, for the benefit of the Sauvegarde de l'art français. New York, M. Knoedler and company [1938]
36 p., 1 l. plates, ports. 31 cm.
"Foreword" signed: Walter Pach.

1. Paintings, French—Exhibitions. 2. Drawings—Exhibitions. 3. Gros, Antoine Jean, baron, 1771–1835. 4. Gericault, Jean Louis André Théodore, 1791–1824. 5. *Delacroix, Eugène, 1798–1863. I. Pach, Walter, 1883-

ND547.K6 759.4 38-37237

OC1MA PSt MB PSC MdBWA CtY WaTC
NK 0206294 DLC DDO IaU NcD ICU NcU MtU NN IU OO

Knoedler, M., & company, inc. *8083.04-590
Herbert Haseltine exhibition of sculpture, Thursday July 10th to Saturday August 9th, 1930. [London, 1930?]
52 p. incl. 23 mounted plates. 27 1/2cm.
Descriptive text opposite each plate.

1. Sculpture—Exhibitions. 2. Haseltine, Herbert, 1877-

NK 0206295 MB NIC OC1MA NNC MH-FA CtY DDO

Knoedler, M., & Company, New York.
Herbert Haseltine, exhibition of sculpture of British champion animals, presented by Mr. Marshall Field to the Field Museum, Chicago. Monday, January 15th, through Saturday, February 3rd, 1934. New York: M. Knoedler & Co. [, 1934.] 23 l. mounted front. (port.), mounted plates. 28 x 23½cm.

Descriptive letterpress on versos facing the plates.

702607A. 1. Haseltine, Herbert, 1877- . 2. Sculpture, British. 3. Sculpture, Animal. I. Field Museum of Natural History, Chicago.
N. Y. P. L. October 2, 1934

NK 0206296 NN MiD NjP MH-FA

N7660 K66
Knoedler (M.) and Company, inc.
Highlights of the turf; exhibition, paintings, bronzes, trophies and books. For the benefit of The New York Infirmary Building Fund, April 20th-May 1st, 1948. New York, Knoedler Art Galleries [1948?]
63 p. illus. 28 cm.

1. Horses - Pictures, illustrations, etc.

NK 0206297 NjR MiDA

Knoedler, M., & Co.
Ideal children's heads in crayon and oil, by S. W. Rowse, on exhibition at the galleries of M. Knoedler & Co., January, 1902. New York: M. Knoedler & Co., 1902. 2 l. 8°.

1. Rowse, Samuel Worcester.
N. Y. P. L. October 29, 1912.

NK 0206298 NN

Knoedler, M., & company, inc.
Illustrated catalogue of a collection of original lithographs by Joseph Pennell. New York, M. Knoedler & co., 1927.
[35] p. incl. illus., plates. 14cm.
Priced.

1. Pennell, Joseph, 1857-1926. 39-3617

Library of Congress NE2415.P5K6
[2] 763

NK 0206299 DLC

Knoedler, M., & Company, inc.
Imaginative paintings by thirty young artists of New York city
see under [Friends of Young Artists, New York]

---

763 K754i
Knoedler, M. & Co., Inc., New York.
Ingres to Forain, a century of lithographs (1815-1915) [Exhibition, beginning October fifth, 1937. New York, 1937.
29p.

1. Lithographs. I. Title.

NK 0206301 MiDA DLC-P4 NNC MH

Knoedler, M., & company, inc.
Italian renaissance portraits; loan exhibition, March 18 through April 6, 1940, for the benefit of Lenox Hill neighborhood association, New York. New York city, M. Knoedler and company [1940]
21, [1] p., 1 l. 11 port. on 6 l. 28cm.
Includes bibliographies.

1. Portraits, Italian—Exhibitions. I. Title. 40-33298

Library of Congress N7606.K6
[2] 757.0945

NK 0206302 DLC NIC NcU DDO CtY PSt PPPM

Knoedler & co., New York.
Jean-Louis Forain (1852-1931) New York, M. Knoedler & company, 1936.
cover-title, 23, [1] p. illus. 22½cm.

1. Forain, Jean Louis, 1852-1931.

NK 0206303 NNC

VOLUME 300

Knoedler (M.) and Company, inc.
Jubilee year exhibition of masterpieces through four centuries (1400-1800)
see its ... Exhibition of masterpieces through four centuries.

Knoedler, M., and Co., inc.
Knoedler booklets
see under title

ND 1356 K72 Knoedler (M.) and Co., inc.
The landscape in French painting, XIX-XX centuries. ⌊Exhibition, October-November 1931. New York, Knoedler Galleries ⌊1931⌋
1 v. (unpaged) plates. 29cm.

1. Landscape painting, French--Exhibitions

NK 0206306 NIC CtY CLU NN MH-FA PSC OU

KNOEDLER, M., & COMPANY, INC.

Landscapes by William Anderson Coffin [exhibited, Mar. 1 to ... 13, 1915, inclusive] Their exhibition catalogues, Mar. 1915)

Verified in: Met. Mus. Art Cat., v. 6, p. 5121

NK 0206307 NNMM

Knoedler, M., and co., inc.
Life masks of noted Americans of 1825
see under Browere, John Henri Isaac, 1792-1834.

Knoedler (M.) & company, inc.
List of mezzotint engravings by S. Arlent-Edwards, on exhibition at the Knoedler galleries ... New York ... ⌊New York, Goerck art press, °1910⌋
cover-title, ⌊21⌋ p., 1 l. illus. (incl. port.) 22½ᶜᵐ.

1. Edwards, Samuel Arlent, 1861-1938.
43-35884
Library of Congress NE642.E4K6

NK 0206309 DLC CtY PP

Knoedler, M., & company, inc.
Loan exhibition in honour of Royal Cortissoz and his 50 years of criticism in the New York herald tribune, December 1 to December 20, 1941, at the galleries of M. Knoedler and company ... New York. ⌊New York, 1941⌋
28 p., 1 l. 10 pl. on 5 l. 28ᶜᵐ.

1. Cortissoz, Royal, 1869- 2. Paintings—Exhibitions.
42-23939
Library of Congress N5020.N7 1941
⌊3⌋ 759.0838

CSmH MdBWA
NK 0206310 DLC WaTC CtY DDO MB OO OClMA NN PPPM

Knoedler (M.) and company, inc.
... A loan exhibition of American portraits by American painters, 1730-1944; 1730-1921 group at Knoedler galleries ... New York; 1921-1944 group at Portraits incorporated ... New York. ⌊New York, The William Bradford press, 1944⌋
⌊28⌋ p. incl. ports. 27ᶜᵐ.
At head of title: April 24 to May 13, 1944.
Cover-title: American portraits by American painters, 1730-1944.

1. Portraits, American—Exhibitions. I. Portraits inc., New York.
44-10652
Library of Congress N7593.K58
⌊3⌋ 757.0838

NK 0206311 DLC WaS DDO IU OO OClMA PPPM ViU

Knoedler, M., & Co., New York.
Loan exhibition of Dutch masters of the seventeenth century, November 16 through 28, 1925. New York⌊, 1925⌋. 14 l. mounted front., plates. 8°.

234109A. 1. Paintings, Dutch and Flemish—Exhibitions—U. S.—N. Y.—New York.
N. Y. P. L. May 5, 1926

NK 0206312 NN MiDA PPPM OClMA MH-FA

Knoedler, M., & company.
...Loan exhibition of English XVIIIth century portraits of children, in aid of the Cheyne hospital for children, 24th April to 23rd May, 1931. ⌊London⌋ M. Knoedler & co. ⌊1931⌋ 32 p. plates. 20cm.

At head of title: Under revision.

1. Portraits of children. 2. Paintings, British, 18th cent.
N. Y. P. L. January 29, 1946

NK 0206313 NN

Knoedler (M.) and Company, inc.
A loan exhibition of fifteen portrait drawings of the 16th century from the Museum of Rheims, organized by the Knoedler Galleries for the benefit of the museums of Rheims, Oct. 29-Nov. 17, 1951. New York, Knoedler Galleries, 1951.
⌊14⌋ p. 15 plates. 27 cm.
On cover: 16th century portrait drawings.
Preface signed: Jakob Rosenberg.
Drawings by Lucas Cranach the elder and the younger, with two drawings attributed to Bartel Bruyn by Rosenberg. Cf. Pref.

1. Drawings, German—Exhibitions. I. Reims. Musée des beaux-arts.
A 53-7041
Temple Univ. Library for Library of Congress NC1055.C7R6
⌊2⌋

NK 0206314 PPT FMU MH WaU

Knoedler, M., & company, New York.
Loan exhibition of figure & landscape paintings by J. B. C. Corot, November 12 through December 1, 1934. M. Knoedler & company...New York. ⌊New York: M. Knoedler & co., 1934⌋ 4 p.l., 24 pl. on 12 l. 27cm.
Mounted col'd illus. on cover.

1. Corot, Jean Baptiste Camille, 1796-1875.
N. Y. P. L. October 6, 1938

NK 0206315 NN DDO NNC MiDA MH FMU

J123 01 Knoedler, M., & company, inc.
Loan exhibition of masterpieces by old and modern painters at the galleries of M.Knoedler & co. ... New York, April 6th to 24th inclusive, 1915. [New York,1915]

NK 0206316 CtY

Knoedler, (M.) and company, New York.
Loan exhibition of masterpieces of drawing for the Musée de Besançon
see under Besançon. Musée des beaux-arts.

Knoedler (M.) and company, inc.
A loan exhibition of naval personages and traditions, 1775-1945, commemorating the centennial of the founding of the United States naval academy at Annapolis, October 10th 1845; September 24th through October 13th, 1945, M. Knoedler & company ... New York. ⌊New York, 1945⌋
15 p. front. (port.) 30½ x 23ᶜᵐ.
Cover-title: United States naval academy centennial, 1845-1945, victory exhibition.

1. Naval art and science—Exhibitions. I. U. S. Naval academy, Annapolis.
46-123
Library of Congress * V13.N42A4
⌊5⌋ 359.074

NK 0206318 DLC PPPM

Knoedler (M.) and company, inc.
Loan exhibition of old masters, for the benefit of the Artists' fund and Artists' aid societies. At the galleries of M. Knoedler & co. ... January 11th to 27th inclusive, 1912. ⌊New York, The Goerck art press, 1912⌋
54 p., 1 l. front., plates. 24ᶜᵐ.
"Two hundred and fifty copies ... privately printed for M. Knoedler & co. The number of this copy being 8."

1. Paintings—Exhibitions.
44-49030
Library of Congress N5020.N4185

OO OClMA
NK 0206319 DLC NN MH RPD IaU CSmH PPPMA PPAFA PU

Knoedler (M.) & Company, inc.
A loan exhibition of paintings and drawings by Ingres
see under Montauban, Musée Ingres.

Knoedler, M., & Co.
Loan exhibition of paintings by El Greco and Goya, at the galleries of M. Knoedler & Co., April 2d to the 20th, inclusive, 1912. The proceeds are to be devoted to the cause of woman's suffrage. ⌊New York,⌋ 1912. 19 p., 2 pl., 1 port. 12°.

1. Theotocopuli, Domenico, called El Greco. 2. Goya y Lucientes, Francisco José de.
N. Y. P. L. February 13, 1913.

NK 0206321 NN

Knoedler, M., & Company, inc.
Loan exhibition of paintings by Georges de La Tour
see its Georges de La Tour.

KNOEDLER, M., & COMPANY, New York.
Loan exhibition of paintings by Goya, under the patronage of His Excellency Señor Don Juan Francisco de Cárdenas, Spanish ambassador, April 9 to April 21, 1934. New York: M.Knoedler & Co. [1934] 4 p. l., 16 pl. on 8 l. 27cm.

847843A. 1. Goya y Lucientes, Francisco José de, 1746-1828.

NK 0206323 NN PPPM NRU MiDA MH RPD

759.93 R118K5 Knoedler, (M.) & Co., Inc., New York.
Loan exhibition of pictures by Raeburn. April 13th through 27th. New York ⌊1926⌋
21p.

1.Raeburn, Sir Henry, 1756-1823.

NK 0206324 MiDA CtY

Knoedler, M., and Co.
Loan exhibition of portraits by Sir Henry Raeburn, for the benefit of the Artists' Fund and Artists' aid societies. ⌊New York:⌋ M. Knoedler & Co., 1913. 28 p., 1 pl. 16°.
Title from cover.

1. Raeburn, Sir Henry.
N. Y. P. L. April 10, 1913.

NK 0206325 NN CSmH

Knoedler, M., & Company, New York.
Loan exhibition of primitives. ⌊New York:⌋ M. Knoedler & Co.⌊, 1929?⌋ 8 l. 4°.
Cover-title.

554281A. 1. Paintings, Italian—Exhibitions—U. S.—N. Y.—New York.
N. Y. P. L. November 4, 1931

NK 0206326 NN MiDA

VOLUME 300

Knoedler, M., & company.
A loan exhibition of sixteen masterpieces, being some paintings which have passed through the hands of M. Knœdler and company during the past year, January 6th – 18th, 1930. New York, M. Knoedler & co. [1930] 36 p. plates (1 col.). 32cm.

1. Paintings—Exhibitions—U. S. N. Y.—New York.
N. Y. P. L. May 24, 1944

NK 0206327 NN

ND547 .R37 Knoedler (M.) and company, inc.

Remarque, Erich Maria, 1898–
Loan exhibition of the collection of pictures of Erich Maria Remarque. October 18 to November 13, 1943, Knoedler galleries ... New York. [New York, William Bradford press, 1943]

Knoedler (M.) and company, inc.
A loan exhibition of the works of Thomas Eakins, 1844–1944, commemorating the centennial of his birth. Through June and July 1944. New York, M. Knoedler & company [1944]
24 p., 1 l. incl. col. front., illus. (facsim.) col. pl. 48 pl. on 24 l. 31 x 23½cm.
Cover-title: Thomas Eakins centennial, 1844–1944.

1. Eakins, Thomas, 1844–1916. 2. Paintings—Exhibitions.
A 44–3442 †
Illinois. Univ. Library for Library of Congress ND237.E15K6
[n45g2]† 759.13

OC1MA NN NcGU DDO DSI NcD WaU FU MsU MWiCA MdBWA
NK 0206329 IU DLC PU-Med PPPM ViU NRU MH-FA OO CU

Knoedler, M., & Company, New York.
A loan exhibition of twelve masterpieces of painting; held at the galleries of M. Knoedler and Company, Incorporated... New York, April 16 to April 28, 1928, for the benefit of the building fund of the Museum of the City of New York. [New York, 1928.] 18 l. mounted illus. 4°.

425241A. 1. Paintings—Exhibitions —U. S.—N. Y.—New York.
N. Y. P. L. August 22, 1929

NK 0206330 NN MtU CtY MdBP OC1MA MdBWA

Knoedler, M., & co., inc.
Loan exhibition. Pollaiuolo to Picasso
see its ... Classics of the nude.

Knoedler, M., and co., inc.
Loan exhibition: 24 masterpieces to commemorate the hundredth anniversary of the Knoedler gallery ...
see its 24 masterpieces.

Knoedler, M. and co.
NE1960 .K7 Luncheon in the harvest field. Le gouter. Salon of 1886 etched by Le Couteux after Jules Breton.
New York, [1887]
1 pan. 16°

NK 0206333 DLC

Knoedler, M., & company, inc., New York.
Martin Schongauer (1445?-1491) April 9th to 27th, 1929. N.Y., M. Knoedler & company, inc., [1929?]
59p. illus. O.

OC1 NBuG CaOTP
NK 0206334 OO OC1MA MiD CtY MdBWA DLC-P4 MH CU InU

Knoedler, M., & company.
Masterpieces by nineteenth century French painters. October — November, 1930. New York: Knoedler galleries [1930] 15 l. illus. 32cm.

"Foreword" signed: Étienne Bignou.

1. Paintings, French, 19th cent. I. Bignou, Étienne.
N. Y. P. L. April 30, 1943

NK 0206335 NN ViU CSt NNC OC1MA NBuG MH

Knoedler, M., & company, New York.
Masterpieces of American historical portraiture. Loan exhibition, November 5 to November 21, 1936, at the galleries of M. Knoedler and company... [New York: Printed at the Spiral press, 1936] 34 p. ports. 28cm.

1. Portrait painting, U. S. 2. Portraits, U. S.
N. Y. P. L. October 13, 1938

NK 0206336 NN DDO MiDA NcD CtY PPPM

ND 1430 K72m Knoedler (M.) and Company, inc.
Masterpieces of Italian religious paintings, XIV to XVIII century; a special loan exhibition. New York [196-?]
[46]p. 20 illus. 26cm.

1. Christian art and symbolism - Exhibitions. 2. Paintings, Italian - Exhibitions. I. Title.

NK 0206337 NRU

Knoedler (M.) and company, inc.
Memorial exhibition, Anne Goldthwaite. New York, M. Knoedler and company [1945]
[24] p. illus. 24½cm.
Illustrations: p. [13]–[24]

1. Goldthwaite, Anne, 1875?–1944. 2. Art, American—Exhibitions.
46–19455
Library of Congress ND237.G6K5
[2] [927.5] 759.13

NK 0206338 DLC NNC PPPM GU MdBWA

Knoedler (M.) and Company, inc.
Mexican painting ...
see under Mexico (City) Galería de Arte Mexicano.

Knoedler, M., and co., inc.
Mezzotinters
see its Biographical notes of XVIII & XIX century mezzotinters.

Knoedler (M.) and Co., Inc.
Mezzotinto engraving, New York, [1903]
7 l. front., illus. 16°.
Cover-title: Some information regarding eighteenth century mezzotinto engravers and their work.

NK 0206341 NN TxU

Knoedler, M., & company, inc.
Mezzotinto engraving. New York, M. Knoedler & co., 1906.
26 p., 1 l. front., illus., plates. 16½cm.

1. Mezzotint engraving. I. Title.
42–44834
Library of Congress NE1815.K65

NK 0206342 DLC MiDA NBuU CtY N NN TxU

Knoedler, M. and co., inc.
Mezzotinto engraving. N.Y. Knoedler, 1908.
26 p. front. pl. s.

NK 0206343 PP

Knoedler, M., & company, inc., New York.
Michael Sweerts, 1624-1664. Portrait of the artist. New York, 1941?
cover-title, [32]p. front. plates, ports.
30 cm.

NK 0206344 OO

Knoedler, M. and co., dealers
Miscellaneous publications and catalogues of exhibitions, 1925-
pamphlets.

NK 0206345 PPPM

4NE 53 Knoedler (M.) and Company, inc.
A notable collection of the works of the peintre-graveur Robert Nanteuil. New York, 1920.
51 p.

NK 0206346 DLC-P4

766 K72n Knoedler (M.) and Company, inc.
Notes on prominent mezzotint engravers of the XVIII century. New York, 1904.
[2] p. plates. 17 cm.

On cover: Prominent mezzotinters of the XVIII century.

1. Mezzotinters. 2. Mezzotint engraving. Hist. I. Title. II. Title: Prominent mezzotinters of the 18th century.

NK 0206347 N TxU NN PP CtY MiDA NBuU

Knoedler, M., & company.
Oils, water colors, pastels & drawings by James McNeill Whistler on exhibition at the galleries of M. Knoedler & co.... commencing April 2nd, 1914. [New York, 1914] 9 l. illus. 21cm.

1. Whistler, James Abbott McNeill, 1834–1903.
N. Y. P. L. April 15, 1943

NK 0206348 NN NNC MWiCA

NE45 .N6 K56 Knoedler (M) and Company, inc.
Old English colour prints [an exhibition, December 1929] New York, 1929.
72p. illus. 23cm.

1. Engravings - Exhibitions.

NK 0206349 PSt NjP MiD CtY OO DLC-P4 MdBWA

Knoedler, M. and Co., inc.
Paintings from the Ambroise Vollard collection, XIX–XX centuries, November — December, 1933. New York: Knoedler galleries [1933] 33 l. plates. 29cm.

"Foreword" signed: Albert C. Barnes.

1. Paintings—Collections, Private —Vollard. I. Barnes, Albert Coombs, 1872– II. Bignou, Étienne. III. Knoedler, M., & company.
N. Y. P. L. May 5, 1943

NK 0206350 NN NjR RPD NNC NjP

VOLUME 300

Knoedler, M., & Company.
Picasso before 1907; loan exhibition for the benefit of the Public education association, Oct. 15–Nov. 8, 1947. New York, Knoedler galleries ₍1947₎ ₍36₎ p. plates. 27cm.

1. Picasso, Pablo, 1881–

NK 0206351 NN NIC ViU NRU NNC IU MiDA MH FMU MWelC

Knoedler, M., & company.
Pictures of people, 1870–1930; a loan exhibition for the benefit of Hope farm, April 6 to 18, 1931, at the galleries of M. Knoedler & co. . . . New York . . . ₍New York, 1931₎ 12 l. mounted illus. 25cm.

1. Portrait painting.
N. Y. P. L. May 24, 1944

NK 0206352 NN MiDA CtY MH PU-FA OClSA

Knoedler, M., & Co., Inc.
The portrait etchings of Anthony van Dyck
see under Dyck, Sir Anthony van, 1599-1641.

Knoedler, M., and company, New York.
A portrait of lady Hylton by Thomas Gainsborough, R.A., 1727-1788. London, N.Y., Paris, M. Knoedler & co., n.d.
₍11₎ p. front.

NK 0206354 OClMA

Knoedler, M., & company, New York.
A portrait of the daughters of Colonel Thomas Cartaret Hardy, by Sir Thomas Lawrence, P.R.A., 1769-1830. London, N.Y., Paris, M. Knoedler & co., n.d.
(9)p. front.

NK 0206355 OClMA

Rare ND 237 S93 K72
Knoedler, (M) and Company, inc.
Portraits by Gilbert Stuart ₍exhibition₎ June 29 to August 1, 1936, at the galleries of M. Knoedler & co., Newport, R. I. ₍Newport? 1936?₎
₍16₎ p. 24cm.

I. Stuart, Gilbert, 1755-1828. II. Title.

NK 0206356 NIC NNC

765 K72
Knoedler, M., & company, inc.
Portraits; line engravings, by Nanteuil and other distinguished engravers. Galleries of M. Knoedler & co. ... commencing November 13th, 1916. [N. Y., Goerck art press, 1916]
[20] p. 2 pl. 21cm.

On cover: Portraits by eminent line engravers.

1. Nanteuil, Robert, 1630?-1678. 2. Engravers. 3. Engravings - Catalogs. I. Title.

NK 0206357 IEN

Knoedler (M.) & company, inc.
Portraits of George Washington and other eighteenth century Americans; loan exhibition, sponsored by the Sons of the American revolution, February 13 to March 4, 1939. New York city, M. Knoedler & company ₍1939?₎
30 p., 2 l. incl. pl. front., ports. 28cm.

1. Washington, George, pres. U. S.—Portraits. 2. U. S.—Biog.—Portraits. 3. Portraits, American—Exhibitions.

43-37554
Library of Congress N7593.K6
₍2₎ 757.8

NK 0206358 DLC MWiCA DDO MA PPAFA NIC CtY MdBWA OClMA MB OO NN CSmH

ND553 P58 K5
Knoedler, M., and Company, inc., New York
Pougny. ₍Exhibition₎ April 21st through May 10, 1952. New York, M. Knoedler & Co. ©1952.
2 l. 21.5cm.

Priced.

1. Pougny, Jean, 1894-1956.

NK 0206359 MWiCA

Jn41 1
Knoedler, M., & company, inc.
Priced catalogue of an exhibition of etchings by contemporary American artists. June 6th to July 6th, 1928. New York[1928]

NK 0206360 CtY

Knoedler, M., & company, New York.
The **Print-collector's** bulletin; an illustrated catalogue for museums and collectors ... v. 1-3; ₍March 1930-1932/34₎ New York, M. Knoedler & company, inc. ₍1930₎-34.

Knoedler , M., & company, inc
Carrington, FitzRoy, 1869– FOR OTHER EDITIONS SEE MAIN ENTRY
A print-lover's hundred, edited by FitzRoy Carrington, M. A. New York, M. Knoedler & company, inc., 1934.

Knoedler (M.) and company, inc.
A print-lover's hundred; second series. One hundred engravings, etchings, woodcuts, mezzotints and lithographs of six centuries. New York, M. Knoedler & company, inc., 1937.
ix, 123 p. illus. 23 cm.

1. Engravings—Catalogs. 2. Etchings—Catalogs. 3. Wood-engravings—Catalogs. 4. Mezzotints—Catalogs. 5. Lithographs—Catalogs. I. Title.
NE390.K6 769 A 39-1100
Rochester. Univ. Libr. for Library of Congress ₍a54c½₎†

NK 0206363 NRU MiDA NcD CSmH CtY DDO ICU CU DLC

Knoedler, M., and Company.
Recent paintings by George Elmer Browne. New York ₍1913₎. 8 l. illus. 12°.
Catalogue of exhibit inserted.
Title from cover.

1. Browne, George Elmer.
N. Y. P. L. May 28, 1913.

NK 0206364 NN

Knoedler (M.) and Co., inc.
The Second Empire by Louis-Jacques Daguerre and his school
see under Bonney, Mabel Therese, 1897-

Knoedler, M., & Company.
Seurat, 1859–1891; paintings and drawings. April 19 to May 7, 1949, loan exhibition for the benefit of the Home for the destitute blind. New York, Knoedler galleries ₍1949₎ ₍46₎ p. plates. 28cm.

1. Seurat, Georges Pierre, 1859–1891.

NK 0206366 NN NjR DDO OClMA NRU NNU-W ViU ICU MiDA FMU MdBWA MWelC

Knoedler (M.) and Co., inc.
Simon Elwes; exhibition of portraits. Dec. 15 to 31, 1938.
Illus.

NK 0206367 DDO

NE 1955 .N4 K7
KNOEDLER (M.) & COMPANY,INC.
Six modern masters ₍exhibition, Jan. 7 to Feb. 1, 1930₎ New York, 1930.
123 p. illus.

Contents: James A. McNeill Whistler; Jean-Louis Forain; Anders L. Zorn; D.Y. Cameron; Muirhead Bone; James McBey.

1. Etchings--Exhibitions. 2. Etchers.

NK 0206368 InU IEN MB OrU DLC-P4 IaU MiD IU OCl OO PBm CtY NBuG MH-FA MdBWA

NE45 N6K75
Knoedler, (M.) and Company, inc.
Sixty masterpieces of engraving and etching. [New York, 1928]
71 p. illus.

1. Engravings - Exhibitions. 2. Etchings - Exhibitions.

NK 0206369 CU MdBWA DLC-P4 MiD NjP ICN ICU OO

Jn4 126d
Knoedler, M., & company, inc.
Sixty masterpieces of engraving, etching and lithography. New York,M.Knoelder & company,inc., 1929.
79p. illus. 23cm.

1.Engravings - Exhibitions.

NK 0206370 CtY NjP OO MdBWA MiD CLSU

Knoedler (M.) and Company, inc.
Some information regarding eighteenth century mezzotinto engravers and their work ...
see its Mezzotinto engraving ...

Knoedler, M., & company, inc.

Thieriot, Charles H.
Sporting paintings from the collection of Charles H. Thieriot, esq. New York, May 1940, M. Knoedler and company. ₍New York, The Spiral press, 1940₎

VOLUME 300

Knoedler (M.) and company, inc.
Stratford; the Lees of Virginia and their contemporaries; a loan exhibition of their portraits ... April 29 through May 18, 1946. New York, Knoedler galleries [1946]
47, [1] p. incl. front., illus. (incl. ports., map) geneal. tab. 28cm.

1. Portraits, American—Exhibitions. 2. Lee family (Richard Lee, 1590?–1663?) 3. Stratford hall, Westmoreland co., Va. I. Title.
46-6067
Library of Congress ND1311.K5
[4] 757.3

NK 0206373 DLC DSI

Knoedler, M., and co., inc.
... Thomas Eakins, 1844-1944
see its A loan exhibition of the works of Thomas Eakins.

Knoedler (M.) and Company, inc.
To honor Henry McBride; an exhibition of paintings, drawings, and water colours, November 29–December 17, 1949. New York [1949]
[42] p. 12 plates. 28 cm.
Facsimile of composition for piano ("Portrait of Henry McBride") by Virgil Thomson: p. [2] and [3] of cover.

1. McBride, Henry, 1867– 2. Art—Exhibitions.
N8375.M3K6 707.4 50-38247

NK 0206375 DLC OC1MA NNC MH DSI MiDA NIC NN MdBWA

Knoedler, M. & company, inc.
Toulouse-Lautrec, 1864-1901; his lithographic work. A loan exhibition of the collection of Ludwig Charell for the benefit of the Musée d'Albi - France, March 22 to April 15, 1950, at the galleries of M. Knoedler & co., inc. New York [1950]
45 p. illus. 26cm.
Bibliography: p. 45-[46]

NK 0206376 NNC MiDA NRU NNU OC1MA NN

Knoedler, M., & company, inc.
Toulouse-Lautrec, paintings and drawings. Loan exhibition for the benefit of the Musée d'Albi, France, January 19th to February 2nd, 1938, at the galleries of M. Knoedler and company, inc. ... [London, n.d.]
1. Toulouse-Lautrec Monfa, Henri Marie Raymond de, 1864-1901.

NK 0206377 CtY

Knoedler, M., & company, inc.
Toulouse-Lautrec, paintings, drawings, posters; loan exhibition for the benefit of the Musée d'Albi, France, November 15 to December 11, 1937, at the galleries of M. Knoedler and company, inc. ... New York city. [New York, The Spiral press, 1937]
37 p. plates, ports. 31cm.
"Editorial note" signed: Louis Carré.
Bibliography: p. 15–17.

1. Toulouse-Lautrec Monfa, Henri Marie Raymond de, 1864–1901. I. Carré, Louis, ed.
38-32536
Library of Congress ND553.T7K6
[3] [927.5] 759.4

NK 0206378 DLC IEN DDO CU ICU NN MdBWA

Knoedler, M., and company, New York.
Travellers in a hilly landscape, with river, by Aelbert Cuyp, 1620-1691. New York, London, Paris, M. Knoedler & co., n.d.
[1]p.

NK 0206379 OC1MA

Knoedler (M.) and Company, inc.
24 masterpieces; loan exhibition to commemorate the hundredth anniversary of the Knoedler Gallery and the seventy-fifth anniversary of the Metropolitan Museum of Art, for the benefit of the Women's Committee of the Metropolitan Museum of Art, November 4 to November 23, 1946. New York [1946]
[64] p. illus. 29 cm.

1. Paintings—Exhibitions. I. New York. Metropolitan Museum of Art.
A 49-3824*
Harvard Univ. Library for Library of Congress [1]

NK 0206380 MH PHC TxU DSI MdBWA

*ND 621 V5K75 Knoedler (M.) and Company, Inc.
Venetian painting of the XVIIIth century; loan exhibition April 6 to April 18, 1936, M. Knoedler and Company, New York. [New York, 1936]
[16]p.

NK 0206381 CLU MdBWA MiDA OC1MA NN

Knoedler (M.) and company, inc.
Venetian paintings of the 15th & 16th centuries; loan exhibition, April 11 through April 30, 1938, at the galleries of M. Knoedler and company ... New York. [New York, The Spiral press, 1938]
29 p., 1 l. 23 pl. on 12 l. 28 cm.

1. Paintings, Italian—Exhibitions. 2. Painters, Italian—Venice. I. Title.
ND621.V5K6 759.5 38-31229 rev
[r58d2]

NK 0206382 DLC CaBVaU PSt MdBWA DSI MiU NcU IU

Knoedler (M.) and company, inc.
Views of Paris, loan exhibition of paintings, January 9 to January 28, 1939 at the galleries of M. Knoedler and company ... New York. [New York, Printed at the Spiral press, 1939?]
4 p. l., 7-26 p., 2 l. plates. 28 cm.
Cover-title: Paintings of views of Paris.
"The end papers of the catalogue are a section of a map of Paris executed in 1739 by Louis Bretez and engraved by Claude Lucas."

1. Paintings—Exhibitions. 2. Paris—Descr.—Views. I. Title.
A 40-1293 rev
Wesleyan Univ. Libr. for Library of Congress [r56c2]

NK 0206383 CtW MWiCA OC1MA CtY DDO MdBWA

KNOEDLER, M.& Co.
Villes et contrees heroïques; exposition de Charles Duvent. L'ouverture aura lieu le 14 avril 1919. [Neuilly-sur-Seine, imp. Roche, 1919].
pp. (40).
Cover serves as title-page.
At head of title: Galerie M. Knoedler & Co.
L'exposition est ouverte du 14 avril au 15 mai 1919."

NK 0206384 MH

Knoedler (M.) and Company, inc.
Washington Irving and his circle; a loan exhibition observing the restoration of "Sunnyside." Oct. 8 through Oct. 26, 1946. New York [1946]
64 p. illus. 24 cm.

1. Irving, Washington, 1783–1859. 2. Paintings, American—Exhibitions.
PS2085.K5 928.1 48-37786*
~~Library of Congress~~ [1]

NK 0206385 DLC WaS IU CU NN ViU MH MdBWA

Knoedler, M., & company, inc.
Water colours by William Blake for Bunyan's The pilgrim's progress; loan exhibition, October 21 to November 8, 1941, at the galleries of M. Knoedler and company ... New York. [New York, The Spiral press, 1941]
[20] p. 20½cm.

1. Blake, William, 1757–1827.
42-23406
Library of Congress ND497.B6K6
[2] 741

NK 0206386 DLC NN RPB

Knoedler, M., & company, inc.
A Whistler centenary, with an introduction by Howard Mansfield; October 16th to November 17th, 1934, M. Knoedler & co., inc. ... New York. [New York? 1934]
15 p. 22½cm.

1. Whistler, James Abbott McNeill, 1834–1903. I. Mansfield, Howard, 1849–1938. II. Title.
41-31627
Library of Congress ND237.W6K6
—— Copy 2. [2] 767

NK 0206387 DLC MiDA DSI CtY DDO NNGr PSt OO

ND497 W24 K6 1922 Knoedler, M., & Company, inc., New York.
William Walcot, etcher, painter, architect. [Exhibition, at the galleries of M. Knoedler & Co., November 13th to 27th, 1922. [New York, 1922]
4l., incl. cover. illus. (mounted port. also on cover) 22cm.
Printed on double leaves folded Chinese style.
Partly priced.
The exhibition covers water-colors, oils and etchings.
1. Walcot, William, 1874-

NK 0206388 MWiCA

Knoedler, Michael, & Co., Inc. *8064.06-990
Winterhalter loan exhibition in aid of the War Service Legion ... December 3–19, 1936. [A catalogue.]
= [London. 1936.] 15 pp. Portraits. 22.5 cm.

E3173 — Winterhalter, Franz Xave. 05–1873. — Paintings. Exhibitions. — Paintings. Catalogues.

NK 0206389 MB

Knoedler, M., & company, New York
A wooded landscape, with figures by Meindert Hobbema, 1638-1709. London, New York, Paris, M. Knoedler & co., n.d.
[1] p.

NK 0206390 OC1MA

Knoedler, M., & company, inc.
Works by Derain, April, 1930
see under Derain, André, 1880-1954.

ND553 L44.5 K6 1914 Knoedler, M., and Company, inc., New York.
Works etched by Auguste Lepère, born in Paris in 1849, pupil of his father, who was a sculptor; [exhibition, commencing January 2, 1914. New York [1914]
[3] p. 20.5cm.
Cover title.
Priced.

NK 0206392 MWiCA

VOLUME 300

Knoedler, T P
Electric stress on dielectric strength.
Thesis 1932.

NK 0206393 OC1W

Knoedler booklets. New York, M. Knoedler & co.
1927-

Analyzed

NK 0206394 DLC OO

Knoef, Jan, 1896-
Cornelis Troost. Amsterdam, H. J. W. Becht [1947]
60 p. illus. 27 cm. (Palet serie; een reeks monografieën over Hollandsche en Vlaamsche schilders. Achttiende en negentiende eeuw)
Bibliography: p. 60.

1. Troost, Cornelis, 1697-1750. (Series)

ND653.T7K5 56-41531

NK 0206395 DLC NIC ICU NcD MH

Knoef, Jan, 1896-
Een eeuw Nederlandse schilderkunst. Amsterdam, E. Querido, 1948.
167 p. illus. 25 cm. [Nederlandsche eeuwreeks]
"Lijst der vermelde kunstenaars met literatuuropgave": p. 143-162.

1. Painting, Dutch—Hist. I. Title.

ND647.K6 49-23618*

NK 0206396 DLC OU CtY ICU

Knoef, Jan, 1896-
Het etswerk van Cornelis Bega, 1620-1664
[Amsterdam, 1920]

p. [289]-295 illus.
Xerox copy made by Library of Congress of article in Elsevier's geillustreerd maandschrift, IX, no.2

NK 0206397 MH-FA

Knoef, Jan, 1896-
Tusschen rococo en romantiek, een bundel kunsthistorische opstellen. 's-Gravenhage, A. A. M. Stols, 1943.
viii, 293 p. illus. 25 cm.

1. Painters, Dutch. I. Title.

ND652.K54 1943 52-55602

NK 0206398 DLC OC1MA NN MH MnU

Knoef, Jan, 1896-
Tusschen rococo en romantiek, een bundel kunsthistorische opstellen. 2. druk. 's-Gravenhage, A. A. M. Stols, 1948.
viii, 293 p. illus. 25 cm.

1. Painters, Dutch. I. Title.

ND652.K54 1948 52-40304

NK 0206399 DLC ICU MH

Knoef, Jan, 1896-
Van romantiek tot realisme; een bundel kunsthistorische opstellen. 's-Gravenhage, A. A. M. Stols, 1947.
viii, 316 p. illus., ports. 25 cm. (Onbetreden gebieden der Nederlandsche kunstgeschiedenis)
Bibliographical footnotes.
CONTENTS.—W. Mol.—C. Kruseman.—De landschapskunst van B. C. Koekkoek.—W. J. J. Nuyen.—J. Tavenraat.—Het grafisch werk van Ch. Rochussen.—Een voorlooper van Jozef Israëls: P. M. Molijn.—P. L. Dubourcq.—Over historieschildering en een historische galerij.—Het grafisch werk van Jan Weissenbruch.—J. J. van der Maaten.—G. A. G. F. Mollinger.—Landschapsteekeningen van A. G. Bilders.—

J. D. Koelman en de jeugd van Willem Maris.—M. Maris en de kunst van zijn tijd.—F. H. Kaemmerer.—W. Verschuur Jr.—Het grafisch werk van A. Allebé.—Register van besproken en afgebeelde kunstwerken, geschriften, enz. (p. 291-309)

1. Art—Netherlands. 2. Artists, Dutch. I. Title. (Series)

N6947.K5 A 48-8424*
Harvard Univ. Library for Library of Congress [1]†

NK 0206401 MH OC1MA OU CtY ICU DLC

Knoefel, August F., 1880-
U. S. *Bureau of mines.*
Advanced first-aid instructions for miners: a report on standardization, by a committee of surgeons: G. H. Halberstadt, A. F. Knoefel, W. A. Lynott, W. S. Rountree, and M. J. Shields. Washington, Govt. print. off., 1917.

Knoefel, August F., 1880-
U. S. *Bureau of mines.* FOR OTHER EDITIONS SEE MAIN ENTRY
... Manual of first-aid instruction for miners by a Committee of surgeons on standardization of first aid. G. H. Halberstadt, A. F. Knoefel, W. A. Lynott, W. S. Rountree, and M. J. Shields. Rev. by R. R. Sayers, passed assistant surgeon, U. S. Public health service. Washington, Govt. print. off., 1922.

W
4
L53
1944

Knöfel, Carl Reinhard, 1916-
Die Präputialklappe. Leipzig, 1944.
31 p.

Inaug.-Diss. - Leipzig.
Bibliography: 29-30.

NK 0206404 DNLM

Knoefel, Georg, 1892-
Die verwendung doppelt epithelisierter temporalislappen zur gesichtsplastik. (Auszug).
Inaug. diss. Koenigsberg, 1920

NK 0206405 ICRL

Knoefel, Henry, joint author.
Knapp, John C.
Erstes deutsches systematisches lesebuch. Mit stoff zu anschauungs- und denkübungen von Johann C. Knapp ... Louisville, Ky., H. Knöfel; New York, E. Steiger [etc.] 1866.

Knoefel, Henry.
... Viertes deutsches lesebuch. Ein lesebuch für die höhern klassen der deutsch-amerikanischen schulen und zur selbstbelehrung. Louisville, Ky., H. Knöfel; New York, W. Radde [1867]
1 p. l., 5-348 p. 20cm.
At head of title: Fourth German reader. Henry Knœfel's series.

1. German language—Chrestomathies and readers.

17-23253

Library of Congress PF3113.K68 4th

NK 0206407 DLC

Knoefel, Henry.
... Vorschule für den ersten unterricht im zeichnen, lesen, schreiben und rechnen. Mit einem vorwort für mütter und angehende lehrer, bearb. von Henry Knöfel. Louisville, Ky., H. Knöfel; New York, W. Radde; [etc., etc., °1867]
iv, [2], 7-36 p. illus. 19cm.
At head of title: German primer. Henry Knœfel's series.

1. Primers, German. I. Title.

17-23254

Library of Congress PF3114.K6

NK 0206408 DLC

Knöfel, Johann, 16th cent.
Cantus choralis
Cantus choralis, musicis numeris quinque vocum inclusus, eo ordine, quo per totum anni curriculum praecipuis diebus festis in ecclesia cantari solet, a Iohanne Knefelio. Noribergae, Gerlach, 1575
4 pts. (altus, tenor, bassus, quinta vox
Microfilm (negative)
Original in Biblioteka Uniwersytecka, Wrockawiu

NK 0206409 MH-I

Knoefel, Johannes Jacobus Wilhelmus.
De signis icteri pathognomonicis.
Witebergae: lit. Tzschiedrichii, [1793].
16 p. 23 cm.

NK 0206410 NNNAM DNLM

KNÖFEL, Julius, 1897-
Ueber die einwirkung von kohlensäure auf calciumphosphate unter hohem druck. Inaug.-diss., Heidelberg. Mosbach (Baden), H. Kirschmer, 1926.

pp. 36+.
"Lebenslauf," at end.

NK 0206411 MH-C ICRL CtY

KNOEFEL, Max.
Die clausula rebus sic stantibus im völkerrecht. Breslau, 1908.

56 p.
Inaug.-diss. --- Breslau.

NK 0206412 MH-L ICRL

RS187
.C3
vol. 1,
no. 15

Knoefel, Peter Klerner, 1906- joint author.
Alles, Gordon Albert, 1901-
Comparative physiological actions of alkyl-trimethylammonium and alkali-metal salts, by Gordon A. Alles and Peter K. Knoefel ... Berkeley, Calif., University of California press, 1939.

Knoefel, Peter Klerner, 1906- joint author.
Alles, Gordon Albert, 1901-
Comparative physiological actions of phenethylamine and of the betahydroxyphenethylamines, by Gordon A. Alles and Peter K. Knoefel ... Berkeley, Calif., University of California press, 1938.

Knöffler, Georg: Ueber die Konstitution des Morphothebains. Synthese des beim Abbau von Morphothebain erhaltenen Tetramethoxyphenanthrens. (Berlin: Ebering 1911.) 25 S. 8°
¶(Ersch. auch als Buch ebd.)
Berlin, Phil. Diss. v. 12. Aug. 1911, Ref. E. Fischer, Nernst
[Geb. 22. Sept. 89 Berlin; Wohnort: Potsdam; Staatsangeh.: Preußen; Vorbildung: Dorotheenstädt. Realgymn. Berlin Reife M. 07; Studium: Berlin 8 S.; Rig. 1. Juni 11.] [U 11.249

NK 0206415 ICRL PU CtY

VOLUME 300

PN6110 .C5G5 1876 Rare Bk. Knöfler, Heinrich, 1824–

₍Gilbert, Rosa (Mulholland)₎ *lady*, 1841–1921.
The first Christmas for our dear little ones. By a member of the Munich school of painting. Richly executed in xylography by H. Knoefler. Ratisbon, New York & Cincinnati, O., Pustet ₍1876₎

NK 0206416 CtY

Knöfler, Johann
Oratio de Caesare Germanico. Wittebergae, 1656.
Diss. - Wittenberg.

NK 0206417 CtY

Knöfler (Oskar [Johannes]) [1863–]. * Ueber ein neues Dilatometer und dessen Verwendung zum Studium der bei der Lösung und bei chemischen Processen auftretenden Volumänderungen. [Erlangen.] 30 pp., 1 pl. 8°. *Leipzig, J. A. Barth*, 1888.

NK 0206418 DNLM ICRL

Knögel, Elsmarie.
Schriftquellen zur kunstgeschichte der Merowingerzeit, von Elsmarie Knögel.
(*In* Bonner jahrbücher. Jahrbücher des Vereins von altertumsfreunden im Rheinlande. Darmstadt, 1936. 27½cm. hft. 140/141, 1. t., p. 1–258)
"Verzeichnis der wichtigeren allgemeinen literatur": p. 237.

1. Art, Medieval—History—Sources. 2. Art, Medieval—Bibliography. 3. Merovingians. I. Title.

A C 40-1022

Metropolitan mus. of art, for Library of Congress — N. Y. Library [DD491.R4B7 hft. 140/141] ₍2₎ (943.42)

NK 0206419 NNMM NNC NN

KNOEGEL, Wilhelm, 1858 -
De retractatione Fastorum ab Ovidio tomis instituta. Diss. Phil. [Münster]. Montaborini 1885.
pp. 35.

NK 0206420 MH PU NjP

Knoegel, W₍ilhelm₎, 1858 - 48576.28
Voss' Luise und die entwicklung der deutschen idylle bis auf Heinrich Seidel. Frankfurt a. M., Reitz & Köhler, 1904.
pp. 45 +.

NK 0206421 MH IaU

Knögel, Wilhelm, 1858-
Was lernen wir aus Horaz fur die gegenwart? Heidelberg, Winter, 1906.
6 p.

From Das humanistische gymnasium, v. 7, p. 176-181

NK 0206422 MNS

Knögel, Wilhelm, 1908–
Der peripatetiker Ariston von Keos bei Philodem, von Wilhelm Knögel. Leipzig, Kommissions-verlag Otto Harrassowitz, 1933.
95 p. 23cm. (*Added t.-p.:* Klassisch-philologische studien, hrsg. von Ernst Bickel und Christian Jensen. hft. 5)
Issued also as author's dissertation, Bonn, 1932.
Bibliographical foot-notes.

1. Ariston, of Chios. 2. Philodemus, of Gadara.

A C 33-836

Columbia univ. Library for Library of Congress ₍2₎

NK 0206423 NNC ICU OC1W OCU IU

Knölcke, Wilhelm: Das Problem der Rechtswidrigkeit auf Grund der Kriegsverbrecherprozesse. [Maschinenschrift.] 114 S. 4°. — Auszug: o. O. (1923). 8 S. 8°
Göttingen, R.- u. staatswiss. Diss. v. 16. Juli 1923 [U 23. 3963

NK 0206424 ICRL

614.8 K754c Knoelk, William Charles, 1881-
Course in school safety ... ₍Milwaukee₎ Milwaukee safety commission ₍1937?₎
7 pts. in 1 v. illus., tables, diagrs.

NK 0206425 WaPS

Knoelk, William Charles, 1881–
Which way is forward? ₍By₎ William C. Knoelk.
(*In* National education association of the United States. Addresses and proceedings, 1933. p. 401–402)

1. Education of children. ₍1. Education and society₎ I. Title.

E 34-114

Library, U. S. Office of Education L13.N212 1933
Library of Congress [L13.N4 1933]

NK 0206426 DHEW

Knoell, Dorothy.
Criteria of B–29 crew performance in Far Eastern combat. Project no. 511–023–0001. Randolph Air Force Base, Tex., 6565th Research and Development Group, Combat Crew Training Research Laboratory, Human Resources Research Center, Air Research and Development Command, 1953–
v. illus. 27 cm. (U. S. Human Resources Research Center, San Antonio. Technical report 53-32)
Bibliography: v. 1, p. 13.
CONTENTS.—1. Ratings, by D. Knoell, R. L. French, and G. Stice.
1. U. S. Air Force—Personnel management. 2. Bombers. I. Title. (Series)
UG633.A3773 no. 53–32, etc. 53–63769

NK 0206427 DLC

LB3999 Knoell, Dorothy
Factor analyses of the performance of twelfth-grade pupils on a battery of language arts tests. 1948.
126 l.

Typewritten.
Thesis--Univ. of Chicago.
Full name: Dorothy Marie Knoell, b.1921.

1. English language--Study and teaching.

NK 0206428 ICU

Knöll, Emil
Der umschlagsplatz ludwigshafen am Rhein. ... Ochsenfurt a. Main, 1932. 111 p.
Inaug. Diss. -Würzburg, 1932.

NK 0206429 ICRL CtY

Knöll, Ernst, Arzt: Beitrag zur Klinik der Pulsionsdivertikel. Aus d. chir. Universitätskl. zu Giessen. Giessen 1920: v. Münchow. 8 S. 8°
Gießen, Med. Diss. v. 30. Aug. 1920, Ref. Poppert
[Geb. 12. Okt. 94 Ettingshausen; Wohnort: Gießen; Staatsangeh.: Hessen; Vorbildung: G. Laubach Reife 13; Studium: Kiel 1, Gießen 8 S.; Coll. 11. Juni 20; Approb. 9. Aug. 20.] [U 20. 1942

NK 0206430 ICRL DNLM CtY

Knöll, Ernst, 1909-
... Anatomische und experimentelle Untersuchungen über die Bilateralität der Leber ... Kiel, 1935.
Inaug.-Diss. - Kiel.
Lebenslauf.
"Literatur": p. 19.

NK 0206431 CtY

Knoell, Gerhard, 1928–
Gebietsänderung und Untergang von Gebietsteilen in Gliedstaaten bei bundesstaatlichen Verfassungen. ₍Mainz? 1953?₎
ii, 131 l. maps. 29 cm.
Diss.—Mainz.
Vita.
Bibliography: leaves i–ii.

1. Federal government. 2. Administrative and political divisions.

56–17813

NK 0206432 DLC

Knöll, Hans, 1913-
... Bakteriologie für jedermann; eine einführung in bakteriologisches arbeiten mit einfachsten mitteln, von Hans Knöll. Stuttgart, Franckh'sche verlagshandlung, 1935.
4 p.l., 47, [1] p. illus. 26 cm. (Handbücher für die praktische naturwissenschaftliche arbeit. bd. 25)
With Mikrokosmos, bd. 28.
1. Bacteriology - Technique.

NK 0206433 CU

4QR-2 Knöll, Hans, 1913-
Bakteriologie für Jedermann; eine Einführung in bakteriologisches Arbeiten mit einfachsten Mitteln. 2. Aufl. Stuttgart, Geschäftsstelle des "Mikrokosmos," Franckh, 1939 [c1935]
48 p. (Handbücher für die praktische naturwissenschaftliche Arbeit, Bd. 25)

NK 0206434 DLC-P4

W 4 F82 1937 KNÖLL, Hans, 1913-
Manometrische Messungen an Einzelplatten zur Anaerobenzüchtung. Frankfurt, a. M., Beck, 1937.
p. ₍230₎-240 illus.
Cover title.
Inaug.-Diss. - Frankfurt.
Reprinted from Zentralblatt für Bakteriologie, Parsitenkunde und Infektionskrankheiten, Bd. 137, 1936.
1. Bacteria - Cultures & culture media

NK 0206435 DLNM

Knöll, Heinrich.
... Herne i. W.
see under Herne, Ger.

---

ar W 53566 no.18 Knöll, Karl, 1873-
Zur Kasuistik und operativen Behandlung der Aneurysmen der unteren Extremitäten. Erlangen, Buchdr. von Junge & Sohn, 1903.
56 p. 22cm.

Inaug.-Diss.--Erlangen.

NK 0206437 NIC ICRL DNLM

Knöll, Karl, d. 1933. 690.2 R004
62100 Die Bauführung. Von K. Knöll, ... Mit 8 Abbildungen im Text. Leipzig, J. J. Weber, 1910.
xi, [1], 224 p. incl. 8 illus., forms. 17cm.
"Benutzte Werke," 1 p. following contents.

NK 0206438 ICJ

Knöll, Karl, d. 1933, joint author.
TH145 .F75 FOR OTHER EDITIONS SEE MAIN ENTRY
Frick, Otto, 1877–
Baukonstruktionslehre ₍von₎ Frick ₍und₎ Knöll. Bearb. von Otto Frick. Leipzig, Teubner ₍1953–54; v. 1, 1954₎

VOLUME 300

Knöll, Karl, *d.* 1933.
... Die darstellung von bauzeichnungen im hochbau für schule und praxis unter berücksichtigung der vom Deutschen normenausschuss ... veröffentlichten normen, mit 153 zum teil farbigen abbildungen und einer farbigen baupolizeizeichnung. 5. aufl., bearbeitet von Karl Schönemann. Görlitz-Biesnitz, H. Kretschmer [1944]
x, 102 p. illus. (incl. plans) forms (1 fold.) diagrs. 29cm.
At head of title: Knöll-Schönemann.
On cover: 1942. Nachdruck 1944.
1. Architectural drawing. I. Schönemann, Karl, ed.
Library of Congress NA2700.K5 1942 46-19512
[2] 744

NK 0206440 DLC IU

Knöll, Ludwig, 1909-
... Krümmungsverhältnisse von niveaulinien in der kreisabbildung einfach-zusammenhängender schlichter gebiete, von Ludwig Knöll ... Giessen, Im selbstverlag des Mathematischen seminars, 1937.
53, [1] p. 23cm. (Mitteilungen des Mathematischen seminars der Universität Giessen ... XXVII. hft.)
"Die arbeit wurde als dissertation eingereicht."
Lebenslauf.
1. Geodesy. 2. Surfaces, Representation of. 3. Map-projection. I. Title.
A C 38-1017
Princeton univ. Library for Library of Congress [QA1.G35 hft. 27]
[2] (510.82)

NK 0206441 NjP ICRL IU DLC

---

881 B.Yk **Knöll, Pius.**
Die babrianischen Fabeln des cod. Bodleianus 2906. [Wien, 1876]
32p. 26cm.
Bibliographical footnotes.
FILM 881 B.Yk ---- ---- Microfilm copy.
1. Babrius. 2. Oxford. University--Bodleian Library--Mss.(2906) I. Title.

NK 0206442 IU

Knöll, Pius.
...Confessionvm libri tredecim...1896
see under Augustinus, Aurelius, Saint, bp. of Hippo. Confessiones. 1896 and later.

Knöll, Pius, ed.
Evgippii Excerpta ex operibvs Avgustini
see under Eugippius.

Knöll, Pius, ed.
Fabularum Babrianarum paraphrasis bodleiana
see under Babrius.
Fabuale Aesopeae. 1877.

Knoell, Pius. *3340.3.95
Das Handschriftenverhältniss der Vita S. Severini des Eugippius. (In Kaiserliche Akademie der Wissenschaften, Vienna. Philosophisch-historische Classe. Sitzungsberichte. Band 95, pp. 445-498. Wien. 1879.)
H5522 — Eugippius, Saint. — Severinus, Saint.

NK 0206446 MB IU

Knöll, Pius.
Neue fabeln des Babrius...
see under Babrius.
Fabulae Aesopeae. 1878.

Knoell, Pius, ed.
Opera. Recensuit et commentario critico instruxit ...
see under Eugippius.

Knoell, Pius, ed. FOR OTHER EDITIONS SEE MAIN ENTRY

Augustinus, Aurelius, *Saint, bp. of Hippo.*
S. Aureli Augustini Confessionum libri tredecim; post Pium Knoell iteratis curis edidit Martinus Skutella. Lipsiae, in aedibus B. G. Teubneri, 1934.

Knöll, Pius, ed.

Augustinus, Aurelius, *Saint, bp. of Hippo.*
Sancti Avreli Avgvstini Contra academicos libri tres, De beata vita liber vnvs, De ordine libri dvo. Recensvit Pivs Knöll. Vindobonae, Lipsiae, Hölder-Pichler-Tempsky a. g., 1922.

Knöll, Pius, ed.

Augustinus, Aurelius, *Saint, bp. of Hippo.*
Sancti Avreli Avgvstini Retractationvm libri dvo. Recensvit et commentario critico instrvxit Pivs Knöll. Vindobonae, F. Tempsky; Lipsiae, G. Freytag, 1902.

Pam. Coll. 34731 Knöll, Pius
[Schriften über Babrius, seine Fabeln und deren Handschriften] Wien, 1876-1909.
6 pieces in 1 v. 25 cm.
Title supplied; various publishers.
Contents.-Die babrianischen Fabeln des Cod. Bodleianus 2906. 1876.-Neue babrianische Fabeln [Rezension der Ausgabe der Fabeln des Babrios von A. Eberhard] 1876.-Neue Fabeln des Babrius. 1878.-Zum Codex Athous und zum ersten Prooemium des Babrios. 1881.-Babrii fabulae recensuit Michael Gitlbauer. [Rezension] 1882.-Die Athoshandschrift des Babrios. 1909.

NK 0206453 NcD

KNÖLL, Wilhelm, 1878 -
Über chlorierte und bromierte molybdänate. Über bromierte molybdänite. . Diss.(Tübingen) Leipzig, 1905.

NK 0206454 MH-C PU DLC

Knöller, Andreas
see
Kneller, Andreas, 1649-1724.

Knöller, Fritz, 1898-
Bataillone des himmels, komödie ... Berlin, Vertriebsstelle des Verbandes deutscher bühnenschriftsteller und bühnenkomponisten [c1928]
62 p. 20cm.
Reproduced from type-written copy.
I. Title.
Library of Congress PT2621.N65B3 42-28380 Brief cataloging

NK 0206456 DLC

Knöller, Fritz, 1898-
Die Fremde vom Meer, Erzählungen. [Bad Wörishofen] Drei-Säulen-Verlag [c1947]
256 p. 19 cm.
I. Title.
PT2621.N65F7 833.91 49-53187*

NK 0206457 DLC NN CU CtY

834K755 Oℓ Knöller, Fritz, 1898-
Liebesqualen; tragikomödie in vier akten ... Berlin, Oesterheld & co., c1929.
60p.
"Als unverkäufliches manuskript vervielfältigt."
Reproduced from typewritten copy.

NK 0206458 IU

Knöller, Fritz, 1898- ed.
... Das muttersöhnchen
see under Goldoni, Carlo, 1707-1793.
[Supplement]

Knöller, Fritz, 1898-
Polter der Menschenfresser; eine Geschichte von Kindern, Greisen und Tieren. [Bad Wörishofen] Drei-Säulen-Verlag [1948]
96 p. illus. 18 cm.
I. Title.
PT2621.N65P6 49-24545*

NK 0206460 DLC

834K755 Os Knöller, Fritz, 1898-
... So und so, so geht der wind; komödie in fünf akten ... Berlin, Oesterheld & co., c1926.
89p.
At head of title: Unverkäufliches manuskript ...
Reproduced from typewritten copy.

NK 0206461 IU

Knöller, Fritz, 1898-
Der trotzige See; zwei Erzählungen. [Wien] K. H. Bischoff, 1942.
96 p. 18 cm. (Die Hundert kleinen Bücher, Bd. 22)
CONTENTS.—Der trotzige See.—Die Seerose.
I. Title. II. Title: Die Seerose. (Series)
PT2621.N65T7 A F 48-3527*
Yale Univ. Library for Library of Congress [1]†

NK 0206462 CtY CU DLC

Knöller, Fritz.
... Wetterleuchten, erzählung. München, A. Langen, G. Müller, 1941.
62, [1] p. 18cm. (*On cover:* Die kleine bücherei. 125)
I. Title.
Library of Congress PT2621.N65W4 1941 41-22623
[2] 833.91

NK 0206463 DLC NN IU CU CtY

Knöller, Fritz, 1898-
... Wetterleuchten, erzählung. München, A. Langen, G. Müller, [1944]
62, [1] p. 18cm. (*On cover:* Die kleine bücherei. 125)
21.-30. Taus.
Feldpostausgabe.

NK 0206464 CtY

VOLUME 300

Knöller, Fritz, 1898–
Wetterleuchten, Erzählung. [Bad Wörishofen] Drei-Säulen-Verlag [°1947]
72 p. port. 18 cm. (Das Kleine Säulenbuch, Bd. 6)

I. Title.
PT2621.N65W4 1947 833.91 49-54419*

NK 0206465 DLC CU CtY

4DD-1633 Knöller, Karl.
Unser Dürrmenz-Mühlacker; ein Ortsbuch für Haus und Schule. Dürrmenz-Mühlacker, K. Elser, 1928.
415 p.

NK 0206466 DLC-P4 MH

Knoellinger, Carl Erik, joint author.

Z7164 .E2H4

Heckscher, Eli Filip, 1879–
De ekonomiska studierna och deras hjälpmedel; en handledning, av Eli F. Heckscher och Carl Erik Knoellinger. Helsingfors, Söderström [1945]

332.7 K72j

Knoellinger, Carl Erik.
Jämförande studier rörande kreditväsendets organisation. Med särskild hänsyn till konkurrensen mellan sparbanker och affärsbanker. Åbo [1935]
xix,411p. tables. 25cm.

Akademisk avhandling - Turku.
Bibliography: p. [xi]-xix.

1. Credit. Finland. 2. Banks and banking. Finland. I. Title.

NK 0206468 IEN

Knoellinger, Carl Erik
Prisregleringens utveckling i Finland. [Åbo, 194-?]

[58]-76 p. (Skriftserie utgiven av Handelshögskolan vid Åbo akademi, B:2)
Saertrykk; Tidsskrift for rettsvittenskap

NK 0206469 MH

WB 718.6 K72a 1943

Knoellinger, Helene
Die Apotheken-Anlernhelferin. Stuttgart, Süddeutsche Apotheker-Zeitung, 1943.
128 p. illus.

1. Pharmacy - Study and teaching - Germany.

NK 0206470 DNLM

QV 704 K72a 1949

KNOELLINGER, Helene
Die Apotheken-Anlernhelferin.
[2. Aufl.] Stuttgart, Wissenschaftliche Verlagsgesellschaft, 1949.
147 p. illus.
1. Pharmacy - Handbooks, manuals, etc. 2. Pharmacy - Germany

NK 0206471 DNLM

QV 704 K72a 1954

KNOELLINGER, Helene.
Die Apotheken-Anlernhelferin. 3., vollständig neubearb. und erweiterte Aufl. Stuttgart, Deutscher Apotheker-Verlag, 1954.
viii, 411 p. illus.
1. Pharmacy - Germany 2. Pharmacy - Handbooks Title

NK 0206472 DNLM

Knoellinger, Hermann, 1883-1914.

Aristoteles.
Aristotelis quae feruntur Problemata physica; edidit Carolus Aemilius Ruelle, recognovit Hermannus Knoellinger, editionem post utriusque mortem curavit praefatione ornavit Iosephus Klek. Lipsiae, in aedibus B. G. Teubneri, 1922.

Knoellinger, Hermann, 1883-1914, ed.

PA6104 .C6D4 1908

Cicero, Marcus Tullius.
De virtutibus libri fragmenta. Collegit Hermannus Knoellinger. Praemissa sunt excerpta ex Antonii de la Sale operibus et commentationes. Lipsiae, In aedibus B. G. Teubneri, 1908.

Knoellinger, Hermann, 1883-1914, ed.

PA6304 .C4 1893

Cicero, Marcus Tullius.
Scripta quae manserunt omnia. Recognovit C. F. W. Mueller. Ed. stereotypa. Lipsiae, In aedibus B. G. Teubneri, 1889-1902.

Knoener, Heinrich, 1847-
Beitraege zu den erkrankungen der harnblase im wochenbett.
Inaug. Diss. Halle, 1874.

NK 0206476 ICRL DNLM

Knoener, Rudolf 1879-
Ueber die chronische ankylosierende entzuendung der wirbelsaeule...
Inaug. Diss. Leipzig, 1903
Bibl.

NK 0206477 ICRL CtY DNLM

Knöös, Emil.
Durchs Rote Kreuz vereint. Ein Spiel in 2 Akten und 1 lebenden Bild in 3 Abteilungen. Heidelberg: J. Hörning, 1913. 26 p. 12°.

1. Drama (German). 2. Red Cross Society. 3. Title.
N. Y. P. L. April 14, 1914.

NK 0206478 NN

Knöös, Emil.
Das Rote Kreuz als Friedenstifter; ein Spiel in 4 Bildern. Heidelberg: J. Hörning, 1913. 24 p. 12°.

1. Drama (German). 2. Red Cross Society. 3. Title.
N. Y. P. L. April 14, 1914.

NK 0206479 NN

Knöpfel, Erwin
... Der eigentumsvorbehalt in der praxis des geschäftslebens von ... Erwin Knöpfel. 2. aufl. Stuttgart, Richard Boorberg [1951?]
41 p. 20½cm. (Schriftenreihe rechtsarchiv der wirtschaft, heft 2)

NK 0206480 MH-L

Knöpfel, Erwin.
Der Eigentumsvorbehalt in der Praxis des Geschäftslebens. 3. Aufl. Stuttgart, R. Boorberg [1951]
41 p. (incl. cover) 21 cm. (Schriftenreihe Rechtsarchiv der Wirtschaft, Heft 2)

1. Sales, Conditional—Germany (Federal Republic, 1949–) I. Title.
55-29661

NK 0206481 DLC

Knöpfel, Erwin.
Der Eigentumsvorbehalt in der Praxis des Geschäftslebens. 4. neubearb. Aufl. Stuttgart, R. Boorberg [1953?]
48 p. 21 cm. (Schriftenreihe Rechtsarchiv der Wirtschaft, Heft 2)

1. Sales, Conditional—Germany (Federal Republic, 1949–) I. Title.
55-29330

NK 0206482 DLC

Knöpfel, Erwin.
Entlassung von Arbeitskräften. Stuttgart, R. Boorberg, 1952.
60 p. 21 cm. (Schriftenreihe Rechtsarchiv der Wirtschaft, Heft 16/17)

1. Employees, Dismissal of—Germany (Federal Republic, 1949–) I. Title.
53-34629

NK 0206483 DLC

Knöpfel, Erwin.
Rechtsfragen um die Einstellung von Arbeitskräften. Stuttgart, R. Boorberg [1951]
36 p. 21 cm. (Schriftenreihe Rechtsarchiv der Wirtschaft, Heft 6)

1. Labor contract—Germany (Federal Republic, 1949–) I. Title.
52-37126

NK 0206484 DLC

Knöpfel, Erwin.
Die Sicherungsübereignung. 3. Aufl. Stuttgart, R. Boorberg [1951?]
32 p. 21 cm. (Schriftenreihe Rechtsarchiv der Wirtschaft, Heft 3)

1. Constitutum possessorium. 2. Security (Law)—Germany (Federal Republic, 1949–) I. Title.
52-29811 ‡

NK 0206485 DLC NNC

Knöpfel, Erwin.
Die Sicherungsübereignung. 4. neubearb. Aufl. Stuttgart, R. Boorberg [1952]
39 p. 21 cm. (Schriftenreiche Rechtsarchiv der Wirtschaft, Heft 3)

1. Constitutum possessorium. 2. Security (Law)—Germany (Federal Republic, 1949–) I. Title.
53-36335

NK 0206486 DLC

Knöpfel, Erwin.
Die Stellung des Gläubigers im Konkurs und im Vergleichsverfahren. Stuttgart, R. Boorberg, 1951.
44 p. 21 cm. (Schriftenreihe Rechtsarchiv der Wirtschaft, Heft 8)

1. Bankruptcy—Germany (Federal Republic, 1949–) 2. Composition (Law)—Germany (Federal Republic, 1949–) I. Title.
55-29318

NK 0206487 DLC MH-L

Knoepfel, Friedrich.
Die zeitlichen Schranken der Verfügungsmacht des Testators im BGB. Darmstadt: E. Roether, 1910. 2 p.l., 79 p. 8°.
Dissertation, Giessen. Bibliography, p. 75-78.

1. Wills.—Jurisprudence, Germany.
N. Y. P. L. February 14, 1912.

NK 0206488 NN MH-L ICRL MH

VOLUME 300

Knöpfel, Gottfried, 1909-
... Zur Frage der Epidermolysis bullosa hereditaria ... Marburg, 1934.
Inaug.-Diss. - Marburg.
Lebenslauf.
"Literaturverzeichnis": p. [31]

NK 0206489 CtY

Knöpfel, Gottfried, 1927-
Die Treupflicht im Recht der GmbH. München, 1954.
iii, 186 l. 30 cm.
Typescript (carbon copy)
Inaug.-Diss.—Munich.
Vita.
Bibliography: leaves 181-186.

1. Private companies—Germany (Federal Republic, 1949-) I. Title.

59-31564

NK 0206490 DLC

Knöpfel, Hans Erwin.
Drei jahre kampf für deutsches recht; ein bericht über die rechtsschöpferische arbeit in den zeitschriften der Deutschen rechtsfront, im auftrage des Presse- und zeitschriftenamtes der Deutschen rechtsfront verfasst von Hans Erwin Knöpfel. Berlin, Deutscher rechts-verlag, 1936.
3 p. l., [5]-85, [1] p. 23cm.
"Anlage 2. Zusammenstellung von sonderheften der zeitschriften der Deutschen rechtsfront über einheitliche rechtsgebiete": p. 84-[86]
1. Law—Germany. 2. Nationalsozialistische deutsche arbeiter-partei. 3. German periodicals. I. Deutsche rechtsfront. Presse und zeitschriftenamt. II. Title.
39-16689

NK 0206491 DLC IaU CtY IEN MH

W 4 Z96 194€
Knoepfel, Hans Konrad, 1919-
Zur Frage der Beziehungen zwischen dyskrinem und schizophrenem Krankheitsgeschehen. Fünf akromegaloide Schizophrene und Psychopathen mit ihren Familien. Berlin, Springer, 1948.
p. [332]-380. illus.
Inaug.-Diss. - Zürich.
"Erschienen im Archiv für Psychiatrie und Nervenkrankheiten, Band 180, Heft 3/4."
Erratum slip tipped in on p. [332]

NK 0206492 DNLM

Knoepfel, Hans Peter.
Die Prokura nach schweizerischem Recht. Aarau, Keller, 1954.
81 p. 23 cm.
Diss.—Zürich.
Bibliography: p. 7-9.

1. Power of attorney—Switzerland. 2. Agency (Law)—Switzerland. I. Title.
55-33733

NK 0206493 DLC MH-L

Knöpfel, Ludwig.
Hesse. *Landesstatistisches amt.*
Landwirtschaftliches gemeindelexikon für das grossherzogtum Hessen. Hrsg. von der Grossh. hessischen zentralstelle für die landesstatistik. Darmstadt, Staatsverlag, 1909.

Knoepfel, Ludwig.
Religionsstatistik. (In: Die Statistik in Deutschland nach ihrem heutigen Stand. München, 1911. 4°. Bd. 1, p. 307-323.)

1. Religion.—Statistics, Germany.
N. Y. P. L. September 27, 1911.

NK 0206495 NN

312.22 R004
Knöpfel, Ludwig.
... Statistik der Säuglingssterblichkeit im Grossherzogtum Hessen in den Jahren 1863 bis 1908, von Regierungsrat Knöpfel ... Darmstadt, Staatsverlag, 1910.
55 p. incl. tables. 24½cm. (Schriften der Grossh. Zentrale für Mutter- und Säuglingsfürsorge in Hessen, Darmstadt. Heft 1)
"Benutzte Literatur": p. [4]

NK 0206496 ICJ

Knoepfel, Rudolf, 1920-
Zur Kenntnis der Verteilung von Legierungselementen in Elektroschweissnähten von legierten Stählen. [Zürich] 1949.
95 p. diagrs. 23 cm.
Promotionsarbeit—Eidgenössische Technische Hochschule, Zürich.
Vita.

1. Electric welding. 2. Welding—Testing.
TK4660.K55 51-29591

NK 0206497 DLC CtY

Knöpfel, Walter
Die Narkose beim Schwein unter besonderer Berücksichtigung des Narconumal-Roche.
Zürich, 1949
Inaug. Diss. - Zürich

NK 0206498 CtY-M

Knöpfel, Walter.
... Untersuchungen zur schall-lokalisation und ihre beziehung zum persönlichkeitstypus. Göttingen, Akademische buchhandlung von Calvör, 1936.
cover-title, [2], 40 p. illus. 23cm. (Untersuchungen zur psychologie, philosophie und pädagogik ... n. f., 11. bd. (1. hft.))
Reproduced from type-written copy.
"Aus dem Psychologischen institut der Universität Göttingen, leitung: Prof. dr. N. Ach."
"Literaturverzeichnis": p. 39-40.
1. Sound, Localization of.
A C 36-2876
Title from Columbia Univ. Printed by L. C.

NK 0206499 NNC

Knoepfel, William H.
An account of Knoepfel's Schoharie cave, Schoharie county, New York: with the history of its discovery, subterranean lake, minerals and natural curiosities. New-York, W. E. & J. Sibell, 1853.
16 p. fold. front., fold. plan. 23½cm.

1. Schoharie cave, Schoharie co., N. Y.
1-14988 Revised
Library of Congress F129.S55K7

NK 0206500 DLC DI-GS OC N TxU OFH PPL PHi NN

*pGB8 V6755R 5.26.48
[Knöpfelmacher, Bernhard]
Die Barrikaden oder der 26. Mai.
[Wien]Gedruckt bei M.Lell.[1848]
broadside. 36.5x24cm.
Another issue has the author's name, "B. Knöpfelmacher", as last line of text.

NK 0206501 MH

*pGB8 V6755R 5.30.48
Knöpfelmacher, Bernhard.
Die Batterien, oder die Übergabe der Kanonen.
[Wien]Gedruckt und zu haben bei U.Klopf sen. und Alex.Eurich.[1848]
broadside. 40x25cm.
Dated: Wien den 30. Mai 1848.

NK 0206502 MH

*pGB8 V6755R 5.30.48
[Knöpfelmacher, Bernhard]
Gedanken am allerhöchsten Namensfeste unsers constitutionellen Kaisers heute am 30. Mai.
[Wien]Gedruckt und zu haben bei U.Klopf sen. und A.Eurich.[1848]
[2]p. 39.5x25cm.
Caption title; imprint on p.[2]; dated & signed: Wien, den 30. Mai 1848. B. Knöpfelmacher.

NK 0206503 MH

*GB8 V6755R 3.21.48
Knöpfelmacher, Bernhard.
Guter Rath. Von Bernhard Knöpfelmacher. Mediziner.
[Wien]Druck von U.Kopf[!] sen.und A.Eurich. [1848]
[2]p. 19.5x12.5cm.
Helfert (Wiener Parnass) 506.
Caption title; imprint on p.[2].
Dated at end: Wien den 21. März 1848.

NK 0206504 MH

*pGB8 V6755R 5.31.48
Knöpfelmacher, Bernhard.
Das Verbrüderungs=Fest im Odeon, oder: Der überraschende Fackelzug mit Musik, gebracht dem Pillersdorf, Pannasch, Füster.
[Wien]Gedruckt bei M.Lell.[1848]
broadside. 48x60cm.
Another copy. 47.5x57.5cm.
Printed on 1 side of a folio sheet; on the other side is printed Joseph Knees, Ehre dem Ehre gebührt! [23 May 1848]

NK 0206505 MH

*GB8 V6755R 6.31.48
Knöpfelmacher, Bernhard.
Wir haben sie begleitet, und haben froh geweint. Von Bernhard Knöpfelmacher, Mediziner.
[Wien]A.Dorfmeister's Buchdruckerei.[1848]
folder([4]p.) 22.5x15cm.
Helfert (Wiener Parnass) 1172.
Caption title on p.[3]; imprint on p.[4]; on p.[1]: Unsern biedern Deputirten nach Frankfurt am Main. Hoch!

NK 0206506 MH

KNÖPFELMACHER, Julius.
Das neue personalsteuergesetz;das novellierte österreichische personalsteuergesetz unter hervorhebung des neuen gesetzestextes und der aufgehobenen gesetzesstellen. 2.aufl. Mähr-Ostrau R.Papauschek,1914.

NK 0206507 MH

Knoepfelmacher, Julius.
Steuer-Freiheiten und Steuer-Begünstigungen bei Bauführungen... Ferner die Steuer- und Gebührenbegünstigungen für Arbeiterhauser und gemeinnützige Bau-Vereinigungen. Herabsetzung der Gebäudesteuer-Grundlagen durch die Zuschlags-Abzugs-Perzente. Mähr.-Ostrau: R. Papauschek, 1913. 3 p.l., 5-346 p., 2 tables. 12°.

1. Land.—Taxation, Germany. 2. Property (Real).—Taxation, Germany. 3. Habitation for working classes, Germany.
N. Y. P. L. October 28, 1913.

NK 0206508 NN

KNÖPFELMACHER, JULIUS.
Wichtige ergänzung zur personalsteuernovelle die wesentlichsten und für den steuerträger wichtigsten bestimmungen aus der vollzugsvorschrift;anhang zu:Das Neue Personalsteuergesetz Mährisch-Ostrau,R.Pap--auscheck,[1914].

NK 0206509 MH

VOLUME 300

Knoepfelmacher (Nathan). *Ueber den Wasserkrebs der Kinder. 28 pp. 8°. *Erlangen, C. H. Kunstmann,* 1837.

NK 0206510 DNLM

Knoepfelmacher (W[ilhelm]). Verdauungsrückstände bei der Ernährung mit Kuhmilch und ihre Bedeutung für den Säugling. 75 pp. 8°. *Wien & Leipzig, W. Braumüller,* 1898.
Forms Hft. 18 of: Beitr. z. klin. Med. u. Chir., Wien & Leipz., 1898.

NK 0206511 DNLM

WG 22821
Knöpfer, Gustav
Beiträge zur Kenntnis der Chinasäure. Wien, 1895.
21 p.

Inaug.-Diss. - Bern.

NK 0206512 CtY DNLM ICRL

Knoepfer, Gustav. *3310.3.117.Abt.2B
Über die Umsetzung von Azinen in Hydrazone.
(In Kaiserliche Akademie der Wissenschaften, Vienna. Mathematisch-naturwissenschaftliche Klasse. Sitzungsberichte. Band 117, Abteilung 2B, pp. 803-812. Wien. 1908.)

H2223 — Azines. — Hydrazones.

NK 0206513 MB

Knoepfke, Friedrich, 1902-
Die wiedergabe von buehnenwerken im rundfunk in ihrer urheberrechtlichen bedeutung.
Inaug. diss. Breslau, 1926.
Bibl.

NK 0206514 ICRL PU CtY

Knöpfle, Franz, 1926-
Die allgemeine Schadenverhütungsklage. München, 1952.
iv, xii, iv, 195 l. 30 cm.
Typescript (carbon copy)
Inaug.-Diss.—Munich.
Vita.
Bibliography: leaves i-xii (2d group of foliation)

1. Interdict (Civil law)—Germany (Federal Republic, 1949-) I. Title.
56-20288

NK 0206515 DLC

Knoepfle, Friedrich.
Beiträge zur frage der widerstandsfähigkeit der obstbäume gegen krankheiten ... München, 1915.
79 p.

NK 0206516 MiEM

Knöpfle, Jakob
Die gefangenenbefreiung durch beamte ... von Jakob Knöpfle ... Burgau, Burgauer Anzeiger, 1933.
vii, 37 p. 23cm.
Inaug.-diss. - Erlangen.
"Literaturverzeichnis": p. v-vii.

NK 0206517 MH-L

Knoepfle, John.
Rivers into islands, a book of poems. Chicago, University of Chicago Press [1965]
viii, 55 p. 21 cm.

I. Title.
PS3561.N6R5 811.54 65-18338

NK 0206518 DLC TNJ

Knöpfle, Ludwig, 1911-
Die konfiguration asymmetrischer a-aminoverbindungen. ... Tübingen, 1935.
Inaug. Diss. - Tübingen, 1935.
Lebenslauf.

NK 0206519 ICRL CtY

W 4 M96 1953
KNÖPFLE, Richard, 1928-
Diagnostik und Therapie mit J131. [München] 1953.
57 l. illus.
Inaug.-Diss. - Munich.
Typewritten copy.
1. Iodine & iodine compounds - Radioactive

NK 0206520 DNLM

Knoepfle, Rudolph J *ed.*
Practice, a pool of teaching experience. Chicago, Loyola University Press, 1952.
354 p. illus. 21 cm.

1. Teaching—Aids and devices. I. Title.
LB1625.K56 371.3082 52-11448 ‡

NK 0206521 DLC WaSpG OU ViU TxU PU-PSW PPLas PPCCH OCIND OCIU WaU PIm

---

Knoepfler, A[lois], 1847-1921.
Der angebliche Kunsthass der ersten Christen. (Festschrift Georg von Hertling zum siebzigsten Geburtstage am 31. Aug. 1913 dargebracht. Kempten, 1913. f°. p. 41-48.)

1. Art (Christian).—History (Early).
N. Y. P. L. January 8, 1914.

NK 0206522 NN

---

232 fK75c
Knöpfler, Alois, 1847-1921.
Das Christusbild und die wissenschaft; rede beim antritt des rektorats der Ludwig-Maximilians-universität, gehalten am 25. November, 1911. Mün. 1911.
39p.

NK 0206523 IU MH

Knöpfler, Alois, 1847-1921, ed.

Hefele, Karl Joseph von, 1809-1893.
Conciliengeschichte. Nach den quellen bearb. von Carl Joseph von Hefele ... Freiburg im Breisgau [etc.] Herder, 1869-90.

Knöpfler, Alois, 1847-1921.
Festgabe Alois Knöpfler zur vollendung des 70. lebensjahres
see under title

Knöpfler, Alois, 1847-1921,ed.

Hefele, Karl Joseph von, 1809-1893.
Histoire des conciles d'après les documents originaux, par Charles Joseph Hefele ... Nouv. traduction française faite sur la 2. éd. allemande, cor. et augm. de notes critiques et bibliographiques, par un religieux bénédictin de l'abbaye Saint-Michel de Farnborough ... Paris, Letouzey et Ané, 1907-

---

Knöpfler, Alois, 1847- **C 1291.2.8**
Johann Adam Möhler; ein gedenkblatt zu dessen hundertstem geburtstag. München, J. J. Lentner, 1896.
pp. ix, 149. Port.

NK 0206527 MH OO

BR358 B3K5
Knöpfler, Alois, 1847-1921.
Die Kelchbewegung in Bayern unter Herzog Albrecht V; ein Beitrag zur Reformationsgeschichte des 16. Jahrhunderts aus archivalischen Quellen, bearb. von Alois Knöpfler. München, E.Stahl Sen., 1891.
vii,223,129 p. 23cm
Bibliographical footnotes.

1.Reformation - Bavaria. 2.Lord's Supper. 3.Albrecht V, Duke of Bavaria, 1528-1579. 4.Bavaria - Church history - Sources. I.Title

NK 0206528 CSt NjPT MH PPeSchw ICU PU

BV 116 .K72
Knöpfler, Alois, 1847-
Lehrbuch der Kirchengeschichte. Freiburg im Breisgau, St. Louis [etc.] Herder, 1895.
xxi, 748 p. 23cm.

NK 0206529 DCU

Knöpfler, Alois, 1847- **C 1831.5**
Lehrbuch der kirchengeschichte. Auf grund der akademischen vorlesungen von Karl Joseph von Hefele. 2e vermehrte und verbesserte aufl. Freiburg im Breisgau, etc., Herder, 1898.
pp. xxxii, 783.
"Die literatur der kirchengeschichte," pp. 14-24.

NK 0206530 MH

Knöpfler, Alois, 1847-1921.
Lehrbuch der Kirchengeschichte... Auf Grund der akademischen Vorlesungen von... Karl Joseph von Hefele... 3te. verm. und verb. Aufl. Freiburg im Breisgau, Herder, 1902.
xxvi, 803 p., 23cm.

"Die Quellen der Kirchengeschichte": p. 5-13.
"Die Litteratur der Kirchengeschichte": p. 13-25.

NK 0206531 NjPT OClJC

BX 77 .K72 1906
Knöpfler, Alois, 1847-1921.
Lehrbuch der Kirchengeschichte ... 4. verm. und verb. Aufl. Freiburg im Breisgau, Herder, 1906.
xxviii, 810 p. 23cm.
"Die Literatur der Kirchengeschichte": p.14-24.
Bibliographical footnotes.

1. Church history.

NK 0206532 DCU

VOLUME 300

Knöpfler, Alois, 1847–
Lehrbuch der kirchengeschichte. Von Alois Knöpfler ... 5., verm. und verb. aufl. Mit einer karte: orbis christianus secc. I–VI. Freiburg im Breisgau, St. Louis, Mo. [etc.] Herder, 1910.
xxviii, 849 p. fold. map. 23½cm.
"Die quellen der kirchengeschichte": p. 5–11.
"Die hilfswissenschaften der kirchengeschichte": p. 11–15.
"Die literatur der kirchengeschichte": p. 15–26.
12–26705
Library of Congress
NK 0206533 DLC CU KAS NN

Knöpfler, Alois, 1847-
Lehrbuch der kirchengeschichte. Von Alois Knöpfler... 6, verm. und verb. aufl. Mit einer karte; orbis christianus secc. I-VI. Freiburg im Breisgau, St. Louis, Mo. [etc.] Herder, [1919.
NK 0206534 OCl

Knöpfler, Alois, Father, 1847-
Lehrbuch der Kirchengeschichte. 6 verm. und verb. Aufl. Freiburg im Br., Herder, 1920.
xxviii, 862 p. fold. map, 23 cm.
Quellen der Kirchengeschichte: p. 5-12.
Hilfswissenschaften der Kirchengeschichte: p.l. 15.
Literatur der Kirchengeschichte: p. 16-26.
1. Church history - Textbooks - 19th century.
NK 0206535 PLatS

Knoepfler, Alois.
Die Namensaenderung der Paepste.
[Compte rendu du iv me congres intern. des Catholiques, V me sect. p. 158-167]
NK 0206536 DCU-H

Knoepfler, Alois. **FR99.K75
Di neuere Franciskuslitteratur.
— (*Cut from* Theologische Revue. Jahrgang 2, Nr. 16, cols. 465–473, Nr. 17, cols. 497–501, Nr. 18, cols. 529–535. Munster i. w. 1903.)
E3476 — Francesco d'Assisi, Saint, 1182–1226. Bibliography.
NK 0206537 MB

KNÖPFLER, Alois, 1847-1921.
Werth und bedeutung des studiums der kirchengeschichte; rede. München, C. Wolf & sohn, 1893.
4°. pp.34.
NK 0206538 MH

Knöpfler (Anton). *Zur Casuistik des Oesophagus-Carcinoms mit Perforation in die Aorta. 23 pp. 8°. *München, Kastner & Lossen,* 1900.
NK 0206539 DNLM

KNÖPFLER, J. FR.
Die Belagerung und Eroberung Kufsteins durch König Maximilian im Jahre 1504; Festschrift zur Erinnerung an die 400ste Wiederkehr dieser denkwürdigen Tage im Auftrage des Stadtmagistrats Kufsteins verfasst. Kufstein, Verlag des Stadtmagistrats [1904] 62 p. illus. 27cm.
Bibliographical references in "Anmerkungen," p. [55]-62.
1. Kufstein, Austria--Hist. 2. Maximilian I, emperor of Germany, 1459-1519. I. Kufstein, Austria. Magistrat. t. 1904.
NK 0206541 NN

Knöpfler, J. Fr.
Mitteilungen aus dem Stadtarchiv Amberg
see under Amberg, Germany. Stadtarchiv.

Knoepfler, Josef
De Vergili Georgicis: quo modo poeta materiam poetico conformaverit. 1, 25p. Salzburg, 1874 Zaunrith, Prog.
Dissertationes in Vergilium, vol. 25, no. 6.
NK 0206543 MiU NjP

Knœpfler, L.
Essai sur la démocratie, l'instruction publique et les universités, par L. Knœpfler. Paris [etc.] Berger-Levrault et c^ie, 1897.
vii, 99 p., 1 l. fold. plan. 22½cm.
1. Education and state—France. 2. Higher education—France.
E 12–1425
Library, U. S. Bur. of Education LC93.F8K7
NK 0206544 DHEW

Knoepfler, Louis .
—. Ophthalmoscope à réfraction pouvant servir de disque optométrique. 10 pp. 8°. *Nancy, [Berger-Levrault & Cie.],* 1889.
NK 0206545 DNLM

Knœpfler (Louis). *Des ruptures bronchiques sans fractures de côtes ou indépendantes de ces fractures dans les traumatismes du thorax. 119 pp., 1 l., 1 pl. 4°. *Nancy,* 1886, No. 220.
NK 0206546 DNLM

Knöpfler, Waldemar, 1914-
Bedeutung und rechtliche grundlagen des anderkontos. ... Borna-Leipzig, 1938. 78 p.
Inaug. Diss. - Jena, 1938.
Lebenslauf.
Benutzte literatur.
NK 0206547 DLC NNC

Knöpfli, Albert,
Geschichte des Heiliggeistspitales zu Bischofszell ... Bischofszell, Salzmann, 1937.
152, [4] p. illus., plate, maps
Bibliography: [4] p. at end.
1. Bischofszell (Switz.) Heiliggeistspital.
NK 0206548 NNC

Knoepfli, Albert.
Die Kapelle St. Gallus in Arbon, von A. Knoepfli und A. Oberholzer, mit einem Vorwort von Josef Hofmann, Pfarrer. Zur Erinnerung an die Restauration in den Jahren 1949/50, hrsg. von der Katholischen Kirchenvorsteherschaft Arbon. [Arbon, Katholischen Kirchgemeinde, 1950]
40, [1] p. 7 plates. 20cm.
DQ 543 .F3 v.2
[Farmington plan pamphlets: St. Gall, v.2, no.1]
"Haupt- sächlichste Literatur: p. 40."
I. Oberholzer, Arnold, joint author.
NK 0206549 MdBJ

Knoepfli, Albert.
N7149 .T4K8
Die Kunstdenkmäler des Kantons Thurgau. Basel, Birkhäuser, 1950–

W 4 B29 1953
KNOEPFLI, Rolf.
Untersuchungen über das Schicksal der Frühgeburten der Jahre 1915-1925. Basel, Karger, 1953.
p. 369-390.
Cover title.
Inaug.-Diss. - Basel.
Reprinted from Gynaecologia, v. 135, no. 6, 1953.
Summary in German, English and French.
1. Infants - Premature
NK 0206551 DNLM

Knœpflin, Édouard. **360.92 K754**
... Les bienfaiteurs des pauvres au XIXe siècle, suivis d'une nomenclature complète des dons faits aux pauvres de Paris depuis 1804 jusqu'à 1860. Paris et Leipzig, E. Jung-Treuttel, 1862.
[4], vi, 379, [1] p. 22½cm.
At head of title: Édouard Knoepflin.
NK 0206552 ICJ MB

Knœpflin, Jacqueline Geneviève, 1917–
... La version dite séparée en obstétrique ... Nancy, Impr nancéienne, 1942.
50 p., 2 l. 24cm. (Nancy. Université. Faculté de médecine. [Thèse, 1941/42. no. 15)
Thèse—Nancy.
1. Version ([Obstetrics])
Med 47–1192
U. S. Army medical library for Library of Congress [W4N17] [2]
NK 0206553 DNLM

Knoepfmacher, Hugo, 1890–
Outer Mongolia; a selection of references, by Dr. Hugo Knoepfmacher. New York, The New York public library, 1944.
13 p. 25½cm.
"Reprinted from the Bulletin of the New York public library of October 1944."
1. Mongolia—Bibl. I. New York. Public library. II. Title.
A 44–5772
New York. Public library for Library of Congress [3]
NK 0206554 NN OCl

VOLUME 300

BM 307 K6.5 Knöpfmacher, Wilhelm.
Religiose Strömungen in der Judenheit der Gegenwart. Wien, 1914.
16 p. 23 cm.
"Separatabdruck aus den Zweimonatsberichten der Humanitätsvereine B'nai B'rith."

1. Judaism--Austria. 2. Reform Judaism. I. Title

NK 0206555 OCH

Knöpke, Horst
Die haftung des kraftfahrzeughalters bei schwarzfahrten. ... München, 1936. 48 p.
Inaug. Diss. - Leipzig, 1936.
Schrifttum.

NK 0206556 ICRL

4U-485 Knöpke, Wilfried.
Der Kriegsbedarf und seine Deckung; unter besonderer Berücksichtigung des Kriegsmaterialbedarfs des Weltkrieges. Borna, 1942.
75 p.

NK 0206557 DLC-P4

Knöpke-Joest, Helga.
Ulla, ein Hitlermädel. Buchschmuck von Willi Engelhardt. Leipzig, F. Schneider [°1933]
80 p. illus., port. 19 cm.

1. Nationalsozialistische Deutsche Arbeiter-Partei. Bund Deutscher Mädel. I. Title.
PZ35.K553 52-45637

NK 0206558 DLC NjP MH ICU NN

KNOEPLE, Johann Baptista.
Dissertatio inauguralis juridica in quaestionem num remedium restitutionis in integrum extraordinarium in processu communi germanico remedium sit mere subsidiarium. Tubingae, 1838.
(2) - 43 p.
Inaug.-diss. --- Tübingen.

NK 0206559 MH-L

Knöpp, Friedrich, *ed.*
Karl und Widukind. Frankfurt am Main, M. Diesterweg, 1935.
50, [1] p. 21 cm. (Grundlagen geschichtlicher Urteilsbildung, Heft 1)
Selections, chiefly from medieval sources.
"Quellen und Literatur": p. 50-[51]

1. Saxony—Hist.—To 1423—Sources. 2. Charlemagne, 742-814. 3. Widukind, fl. 776-785. (Series)
DD801.S361K6 943.21 A F 50-8
Harvard Univ. Library for Library of Congress [1]†

NK 0206560 MH CtY CU NNC NN DLC

Knoepp, Friedrich.
...Die Stellung Friedrichs II. und seiner beiden Söhne zu den deutschen Städten, von Dr. Friedrich Knöpp. Berlin: E. Ebering, 1928. xiv, 87 p. 8°. (Historische Studien. Heft 181.)
Bibliography, p. [ix]-xiv.

1. Frederick II, emperor of Germany, 1194-1250. 2. Cities—Hist.—Germany, Middle Ages. 3. Ser.
N. Y. P. L. June 14, 1929

NK 0206561 NN OU NIC CU WaU MH ICU CtY

Knöpp, Hans.
Das verhältnis zwischen arbeits- und besitzeinkommen, von dr. Hans Knöpp; mit einem vorwort von prof. dr. Paul Arndt. Halberstadt, H. Meyer, 1928.
xii, 113 p. 24cm.
"Schrifttum": p. 111-113.

1. Income. 2. Wages. I. Title.
Library of Congress HB601.K75 30-11274

NK 0206562 DLC

Knöpp, Herbert.
Hydrobiologische Untersuchungen am Rhein-Herne-Kanal. [n. p., 1954]
20 p. illus. 30 cm.
At head of title: Bundesanstalt für Gewässerkunde, Koblenz.

1. Fresh-water biology—Germany—Rhine-Herne Canal. I. Title.
QH96.K6 55-41396 ‡

NK 0206563 DLC

NT K754v Knöpp, Ludwig, 1914-
Die volkskirche auf dem missionsfelde. Die antwort Deutscher evangelischer mission auf die frage nach aufgabe und ziel. Darmstadt, 1938.
142 p. 21 cm.
Diss. - Giessen.
Vita.
Place of publication covered by label: Giessen.
Bibliography: p. 128-132.

NK 0206564 CtY-D MH-AH ICRL MH CtY

Knöppel, Alois, 1863- ed.
Overberg, Bernhard *i. e.* **Heinrich Bernhard, 1754-1826.**
... Bernh. Heinrich Overberg. Bearb. von Al. Knöppel ... Mit dem bildnisse Overbergs. Langensalza, F. G. L. Gressler, 1904.

Knöppel, Alois, 1863-
Bernhard Heinrich Overberg, der lehrer des Münsterlandes. Bearb. von Al. Knöppel ... Mit kirchlicher approbation. Mainz, F. Kirchheim, 1896.
vi p., 1 l., 168 p. 18½cm. (*Added t.-p.:* Lebensbilder katholischer erzieher. Hrsg. von W. E. Hubert. v)

1. Overberg, Bernhard *i. e.* Heinrich Bernhard, 1754-1826.
E 12-1493
Library, U. S. Bur. of Education LB675.O81K7

NK 0206566 DHEW

Knöppel, Al[ois] 1863-
Fénelon und seine abhandlung über die erziehung der mädchen. Von Al. Knöppel ... Halle a. Saale, H. Schroedel, 1903.
2 p. l., [viii]-viii, 62 p. 19cm. (*Added t.-p.:* Die pädagogischen klassiker ... hrsg. von E. Friedrich ... und H. Gehrig ... bd. XI)
On cover: Schroedels pädagogische klassiker ... bd. XI.
"Quellen": p. 1-2.
CONTENTS.—Einleitung.—1. t. Fénelons leben.—2. t. Fénelons abhandlung über die erziehung der mädchen.—3. t. Anhang: Fragen und aufgaben zur ergänzung und vertiefung.

1. Fénelon, François de Salignac de La Mothe-, 1651-1715. 2. Education of women.
Library of Congress LB475.F3K5 6-4190

NK 0206567 DLC

Knöppel, Alois, 1863-
Die kulturhistorischen stufen der Herbart-Ziller-Stoy'schen schule. Eine darlegung nebst beurteilung derselben. Von Al. Knöppel ... Kempten, J. Kösel, 1894.
46, [1] p. 20½cm. (*Added t.-p.:* Pädagogische vorträge und abhandlungen ... 6. hft.)

1. Herbart, Johann Friedrich, 1776-1841. 2. Ziller, Tuiskon, 1817-1882. 3. Stoy, Karl Volkmer, 1815-1885. 4. Education. I. Title.
E 14-108
Library, U. S. Bur. of Education LB648.K75

NK 0206568 DHEW

Knöppel, Alois, 1863-
Der selige Petrus Canisius, zweiter apostel Deutschlands. Bearb. von Al. Knöppel ... Mit kirchlicher approbation. Mainz, F. Kirchheim, 1897.
x, 236 p. 18½cm. (*Added t.-p.:* Lebensbilder katholischer erzieher. Hrsg. von W. E. Hubert. VII)

1. Canisius, Peter, 1521-1597.
E 12-1494
Library, U. S. Bur. of Education LB475.C22K7

NK 0206569 DHEW

Knoeppel, Al[ois], 1863-
Vinzenz Eduard Milde. Langensalza, F. G. L. Gressler, 1909.
xii, 255, (1) p. 12°. (Gresslers Klassiker der Pädagogik. Bd. 26)

NK 0206570 NN

Knöppel, Arvid.
"Barbaren"; eindrücke eines Schweden in Deutschland und an der front im osten, von Arvid Knöppel; übersetzung aus dem schwedischen. Berlin, A. Scherl [1916]
142 p. 19½cm.

1. European war, 1914-1918—Germany. 2. European war, 1914-1918—Campaigns—Eastern. I. Title.
22-7509
Library of Congress D551.K53

NK 0206571 DLC IEN MiU

Knöppel, Arvid.
"Barbarer"; skildringar från Tyskland och fronten i öster, av Arvid Knöppel. Stockholm, P. A. Norstedt & söner [1916]
2 p. l., 243, [1] p. 20cm.
CONTENTS.—Tyskland.—Fångar.—Soldater.—Kämpar vända åter.—I Warszawa.—Förödelse.—Nowo Georgijewsk.—Till storms.—Några av många.—Örnar.—Generalens order.—En spaningspatrull.—Döden knackar.—Preussisk militarism.—Kämpar bakom fronten.—Den döda heden.

1. European war, 1914- —Germany. 2. European war, 1914- —Campaigns—Eastern.
21-14917
Library of Congress D551.K5

NK 0206572 DLC NN

Knöppel, Arvid.
Hjortdjur. Förord av Björn von Rosen. Stockholm, Natur och kultur [1953]
81 p., 151 p. of illus. (part col.) 32 cm.

1. Deer in art. I. Title.
Full name: Gustav Arvid Oskar Knöppel.
NC1175.K5 56-17237

NK 0206573 DLC

VOLUME 300

Knoeppel (C. E.) & Co., Inc., New York.
American Foundrymen's Association. Standard foundry cost system. New York, 1919.
116 (i. e. 120) l. 29cm.
Contains extra numbered leaves 30a, 66a, 69a, 70a.
Leaf number 28 wanting.
Armorial bookplate of Edward T. Miller.

1. Founding—Accounting. I. American Foundrymen's Association. II. Title: Standard foundry cost system.

NK 0206574 ViU

KNOEPPEL, C.E., & Co.
An answer to the question: What is C.E. Knoeppel & co. and what does it do? An analysis of its aims, reason for existence, personnel, standing, and the how and why of its work. [New York, 1917.]

pp.(2),22. Ports. and diagrs.

NK 0206575 MH-BA

Knoeppel, C. E., and Co., Inc., New York.
Industrial efficiency; a consideration of factors necessary in winning the war and in taking our place in world trade after the war... New York: C. E. Knoeppel & Co. [191–?] 80 p. 8°.

Contents: Are you a caretaker or promoter? Reprinted from the American magazine. KNOEPPEL, C. E., and G. S. SMALL. Organizing industrially for war. KNOEPPEL, C. E. American industry! Wake up! HORTON, C. M. The reason for efficiency "expert.ng." KNOEPPEL, C. E. A post-bellum prophesy.

1. Industrial mobilization, United States. 2. European war, 1914–1918—Economic aspects.
N. Y. P. L. November 11, 1924

NK 0206576 NN

KNOEPPEL, C.E., & co., inc.
Questionnaire on organization. A self analysis that conscientiously answered will present an accurate composite picture of organization-efficiency. New York, [1918?].

nar.8°. pp.(7).

NK 0206577 MH-BA

Knoeppel, C. E., & co., inc., *New York.*
What industrial engineering includes; for industrial executives; 101 things to do, 1001 results others secured ... New York, C. E. Knoeppel & co., inc. [°1921]
154 p. 18cm. (Blue book series, no. 3)

1. Efficiency, Industrial. I. Title. II. Title: Industrial engineering.

Library of Congress T58.K67 21-12099

NK 0206578 DLC ICRL ICJ

Knoeppel, C.E., and Co., Inc., New York.

see also Knoeppel, Charles Edward, 1881-

KNOEPPEL, Charles Edward, 1881-
American industry! wake up! A personal word to the American industrial executive in the interests of an American made product. New York, C.E.Knoeppel & co., [1917].

pp.10.

NK 0206580 MH-BA

KNOEPPEL, Charles Edward.
[Constructive outline of steps necessary to secure industrial harmony and efficiency. Based on years of contact with both capital and labor.

Manifold copy. 4°. ff.(31).
By C.E.Knoeppel, I.A.Berndt, J.P.Jordan, and G.S.Small.
Soc 1500.137.11

Supplement. Dated Oct.16th, 1919.
Manifold copy. 4°. ff.(17). 2 blue-prir plans.

NK 0206581 MH

Knoeppel, Charles Edward, 1881–
... "The future of industrial engineering", by C. E. Knoeppel ... an address delivered before Chicago chapter, February 2, and Detroit chapter February 3, 1920. The Society of industrial engineers. [Chicago? 1920]
cover-title, 16 p. $20\frac{1}{2}$cm. (Publications of the Society of industrial engineers, vol. III, no. 5. February, 1920)

1. Efficiency, Industrial. I. Title. II. Title: Industrial engineering, The future of.

Library of Congress HD2326.K5 24-25909

NK 0206582 DLC DL ICJ MiU OU

KNOEPPEL, C[harles] E[dward], 1881-
Graphic production control. [I.] [New York, 1918.]

Contents:- i. Underlying and basic considerations.

NK 0206583 MH-BA

Knoeppel, Charles Edward, 1881–1936.
Graphic production control, by C. E. Knoeppel ... assisted by various members of the author's firm and staff. New York, The Engineering magazine company, 1920.
2 p. l., vii–xxiii, 477 p. illus. (incl. charts, forms) diagrs. (part col.) 23cm.

1. Efficiency, Industrial. 2. Graphic methods. I. Title.

Library of Congress T58.K5 20–8564

MiHM ODW OU ICJ NN MB PU PP TU OrPR CaBVaU IdU
NK 0206584 DLC OKentU FU NcRS ViU OCl OLak OCU MiU

Knoeppel, Charles Edward, 1881–
How to make a time study; reprint of paper before American Foundrymen's Association, American Institute of Metals, Chicago, 1913, by C. E. Knoeppel. Worcester, Mass.: C. E. Knoeppel[, 1913?]. 27 p. incl. form, tables. 8°.
Cover-title.

1. Works management. 2. Foundries.
N. Y. P. L. May 13, 1925

NK 0206585 NN

Knoeppel, Charles Edward, 1881–1936.
...How to plan and control profits, by C. E. Knoeppel. Texts and charts fully describing methods of organizing a business to assure profits, for presentation at Knoeppel profit clinics during 1935–1936... Chicago [etc.] Knoeppel co. [1935] ix, 168 f. illus. 28cm.
Author's autographed presentation copy to F. W. Shibley.

342642B. 1. Management, 1931– 2. Profit.
N. Y. P. L. December 30, 1946

NK 0206586 NN OCU PU-W NNC

Knoeppel, Charles Edward, 1881–
The importance of the human factor in industrial preparedness, by C. E. Knoeppel; delivered before opening session of the national conference on "the human factor in industrial preparedness," under the auspices of the Western efficiency society, Chicago, Ill. May 23, 1917. [Chicago, Holmquist printing co., 1917]
29 p. 23cm.

1. European war, 1914– —Economic aspects—U. S. 2. Efficiency, Industrial. I. Western efficiency society, Chicago. II. Title.

Library of Congress HC106.2.K57 17-21487

NK 0206587 DLC DL

Knoeppel, Charles Edward, 1881–
... Industrial preparedness, by C. E. Knoeppel ... New York, The Engineering magazine co., 1916.
1 p. l., ii, 145 p. 19cm. (Industrial management library)

1. U. S.—Economic policy. 2. Germany—Economic policy. 3. Efficiency, Industrial. 4. European war, 1914–1918—Economic aspects. I. Title.

Library of Congress HC106.2.K6 16—13876

OO OCl OCX NN DW ICJ MiU-C DN PSC PP
NK 0206588 DLC NjP Or IdU WaS OrP OKentU ViU OOxM

Knoeppel, Charles Edward, 1881–1936.
... Installing efficiency methods, by C. E. Knoeppel. New York, The Engineering magazine, 1915.
1 p. l., viii, 258 p. illus. (incl. charts, forms) 26cm. (Works management library)
"As originally prepared the material appeared in a series of articles published in the Engineering magazine during the year 1914."—Introd.

1. Efficiency, Industrial. I. Title.

Library of Congress T58.K6 15—1852

ICJ MB NN PBm PSC PU-Sc MtBC OrCS Or OrP
NK 0206589 DLC WaS CU NcRS OOxM MiU OCX OClW OCU

Knoeppel, Charles Edward, 1881-
... Installing efficiency methods. N.Y., The Engineering magazine, 1917.
258p. illus. (Works management library)

"As originally prepared the material appeared in a series of articles published in the Engineering magazine during the year 1914".—Introd.

NK 0206590 OU MiU OClW PPSteph PU PU-W ICRL

KNOEPPEL, C[harles] E[dward], 1881-
Labor after the war. n.p., [1918].

pp.(16).
"Reprinted from National Efficiency Quarterly Aug.1918."

NK 0206591 MH-BA

Knoeppel, Charles Edward, 1881–1936.
Managing for profit; working methods for profit planning and control, by C. E. Knoeppel ... with the collaboration of Edgar G. Seybold ... 1st ed. New York and London, McGraw-Hill book company, inc., 1937.
xvi, 343 p. incl. front., illus., diagrs., forms. $23\frac{1}{2}$cm.

1. Profit. 2. Business. 3. Efficiency, Industrial. I. Seybold, Edgar G., joint author. II. Title.

Library of Congress HB601.K76 37–1761
——— Copy 2.
Copyright A 101697 [8] 658.01

PP OCU OClCC OU OCl ICJ OrCS WaS OrU
NK 0206592 DLC MB NN IdU OrP NcRS TU CU PPTU PU-W

VOLUME 300

Knoeppel, Charles Edward, 1881–1936.
... Maximum production in machine-shop and foundry, by C. E. Knoeppel. New York, The Engineering magazine, 1911.
1 p. l., vi, 365 p. illus. (forms) diagrs. 19½ cm. (Works management library)
"The material on which the present book is based was most of it contained in three series of articles published originally in the Engineering magazine ... from October, 1908, to May, 1911."—Pref.
1. Machine-shops. 2. Foundries.
TS155.K7 11—29263

NK 0206593 DLC NcD PPF PP PSC OU OOxM MiU OCU OCX OCl MB NN ICJ ICRL CU

Knoeppel, Charles Edward
Most effective type of industrial organization. N. Y., The Author, n. d.
64 p., fold. charts.

NK 0206594 MiD

Knoeppel, Charles Edward, 1881–1936.
Organization and administration, by C. E. Knoeppel ... New York, Industrial extension institute [©1917]
xix, 445 p. illus. (incl. forms.) diagrs. 19½cm. (*Half-title:* Factory management course and service. [v. 6])
Series title in part also on t.-p.
1. Efficiency, Industrial. 2. Factory management. I. Title.
18—8114
Library of Congress TS155.F48
——— Copy 2. TS155.K75

NK 0206595 DLC OCl NN ICRL ICJ

Knoeppel, Charles Edward, 1881–1936.
Organization and administration, by C. E. Knoeppel ... New York, Industrial extension institute, incorporated [©1919]
xix, 445 p. illus., diagrs. 19cm. (*Added t.-p.:* Factory management course and service. [v. 1])
Series title in part on t.-p.
Issued as volume six in an earlier edition of the series.
1. Efficiency, Industrial. 2. Factory management. I. Title.
43-39257
Library of Congress TS155.F482 vol. 1
[2] (658) 658.01

NK 0206596 DLC PP

Knoeppel, C[harles] E[dward], 1881– 658-K
Organization and administration. New York: Industrial Extension Institute, Inc. [cop. 1921.] 445 p. illus. 12°. (Factory management course, v. 1.)
1. Business. 2. Title. 3. Ser.
N. Y. P. L. November 10, 1924

NK 0206597 NN ICRL OCU MiU

KNOEPPEL, C[harles] E[dward], 1881-
Organizing industrially for war, by C.E.Knoeppel and G.S.Small; and A post bellum prophecy, by C.E.Knoeppel. New York, C.E.Knoeppel & company, [1918?]
1.8°. pp.(25.)

NK 0206598 MH-BA

Knoeppel, Charles Edward, 1881-
Organizing industries for economic production, by C.E. Knoeppel. Industrial relations, by Irving A. Berndt... New York, C.E. Knoeppel & co., inc., (1919)
35 p. 23½ cm

NK 0206599 DL

T58
.K64 Knoeppel, Charles Edward, 1881-
The practical introduction of efficiency principles...
[New York, 1914-]
pts. 25 cm.
Reprinted from the Engineering magazine, 1914.

NK 0206600 DLC ICRL

658.155
K754p Knoeppel, Charles Edward, 1881-1936.
Profit control; how to insure steady profits through predetermined costs ... [Cleveland, Ohio? 1932?]
v.p. illus., diagrs.
Reprinted from Factory and industrial management.
1. Profit. 2. Industry - Organization, control, etc. I. Title.

NK 0206601 WaPS

Knoeppel, Charles Edward, 1881–
Profit engineering, applied economics in making business profitable, by C. E. Knoeppel ... with foreword by Fred W. Shibley ... and supplementary chapters by Arthur J. Minor ... [and] E. St. Elmo Lewis ... 1st ed. New York and London, McGraw-Hill book company, inc., 1933.
xvi, 326 p. double col. front., diagrs. 23½ cm.
"Profit bibliography": p. 315.
1. Business. 2. Efficiency, Industrial. 3. Profit. I. Minor, Arthur J. II. Lewis, Elias St. Elmo, 1872– III. Title.
HF5500.K65 658.01 33—6955

NK 0206602 DLC TU PP PU-W OCl MiU ODW OOxM FU NcRS NcD NN MB CU CoU IdU Or OKentU OrP WaS CaBVa OrCS

Knoeppel, Charles Edward, 1881–1936.
The psychology and ethics of wage payment, a lecture on piece work and the bonus system before the class in scientific management, Springfield, Mass., Y. M. C. A., December 11, 1912, by C. E. Knoeppel ... New York [1912?]
25 p. 23cm.
1. Wages. 2. Premium system. 3. Piecework. 4. Efficiency, Industrial. I. Title.
L 13–164 Revised
U. S. Dept. of labor. Libr. for Library of Congress HD4926.K7 [r41b2]

NK 0206603 DL NN

KNOEPPEL, C[harles] E[dward], 1881-
Rebuilding our war machine. Developed from an address before the Cleveland advertising club, Jan.18, 1918, on "Reorganizing for war." New York, C.E.Knoeppel & co., [1918].
pp.12. 1 diagr.

NK 0206604 MH-BA

Knoeppel, Charles Edward, comp.
Standard foundry cost system... Chic., Amer. foundrymen's association, [1919]
65-144 p., forms.
Extract from the Proceedings of the American foundrymen's association, 1919.
Cover title.

NK 0206605 MiD

Knoeppel, Charles Edward, 1881–
Why I am an efficiency engineer, by C. E. Knoeppel; a discussion of some of the causes of industrial inefficiency, with an outline of constructive measures necessary to eliminate them ... [New York, 1915]
16 p. 23cm.
1. Efficiency, Industrial. I. Title.
16-11963
Library of Congress T58.K65

NK 0206606 DLC

Knoeppel, Charles Edward, 1881–
Women in industry, by C. E. Knoeppel; an address based on answers to 1,000 questionnaires on women in industry, delivered before the national conference on "labor problems under war conditions", under joint auspices of the Society of industrial engineers and the Western efficiency society, Chicago, Ill., March, 1918. New York, C. E. Knoeppel & co. [1918?]
1 p. l., 5-123 p. fold. tables. 23cm.
1. Woman—Employment—U. S. 2. European war, 1914-1918—Economic aspects. I. Society of industrial engineers. II. Western efficiency society, Chicago. III. Title.
Library of Congress HD6095.K7 19—6984

NK 0206607 DLC WaS NjP OU OCl ICJ

Knoeppel, Charles Edward, 1881-
see also Knoeppel, C.E., and co., inc., New York.

Knöppel, Gustav Arvid Oskar
see **Knöppel, Arvid.**

Knöppler, Fritz: Beitrag zur Frage der Behandlung der Hundestaupe mit Heilseren. [Maschinenschrift.] 39 S. 4° [Lag nicht vor.] — Auszug: Limburg a. d. L. 1922: Kremer. 3 Bl. 8°
Gießen, Veterinär-med. Diss. v. 29. Jan. 1923 [U 23. 3547

NK 0206610 ICRL

Knör, Hans, 1884-
... Deutsches strafprozessrecht, von amtsgerichtsrat dr. Hans Knör ... München, Bayerischer kommunalschriften-verlag [1931]
132 p. 21cm. (Die studienmappe, unterrichtswerk in heften, hrsg. von J. Jehle ... hft. 25)
"Im vorliegenden heft ist das umfangreiche gebiet des Gerichtsverfassungsgesetzes ... und der Strafprozessordnung ... systematisch niedergelegt."—Vorbemerkung.
1. Criminal procedure — Germany. 2. Courts — Germany. 3. Costs (Law)—Germany. I. Title.
38-39678

NK 0206611 DLC

Knör, Hans, 1884-
Kann bei einer Willensbetätigung eine Verbrechensmehrheit im Sinne der Realkonkurrenz vorliegen? ... von Hans Knör ... Eichstätt, P. Brönner, 1914.
2 p.l., 67 p. 22½cm.
Inaug.-Diss. - Erlangen.
"Verzeichnis der benützten Bücher": p. [66]-67.

NK 0206612 MH-L ICRL NIC

Knoer, Louis Gilhomme de
see Knör, Ludwig Wilhelm von, d. 1754.

Knör, Ludwig Wilhelm von, d. 1754.
Basilius Valentinus redivivus seu Astrum rutilans alchymicum, das ist: Der wieder auffgelebte Basilius Valentinus. Samt beygefügten kurtzen und deutlichen alchyo-physiologischen Reisonement des Autoris. Leipzig, 1716.

NK 0206614 WU

Knör, Ludwig Wilhelm von, d. 1754.
———. Der bey den Frauenzimmer Kranckheiten vernünftig curirende Medicus, welcher alle eigentliche Kranckheiten, die diesem Geschlechte zustossen, deren Kennzeichen und Temperamente richtig untersuchet, und die Curen nach den Hofmann- und Stahlischen Lehrsätzen glücklich ausführet. Dem beygefüget die nach Pflicht und Wissenschaft in und nach der Geburt denen Kreissenden handleistende Hebamme, sammt der vorsichtigen und sorgfältigen Kinderwärterin und guten Amme. 8 p. l., 509 pp., 9 pl., 3 l. 8°
Leipzig, C. F. Gessner, 1747.

NK 0206615 DNLM

VOLUME 300

613.12 K75t
Knör, Ludwig Wilhelm von, d.1754.
Truckne Sauerbrunnen-Cur, vermittelst eines, mit dem solarischen Schwefel vereinigten astralischen Gold-Saltzes, samt: ausführlicher Anweisung, wie die Cur durch dieses Universal-Saltz, mit höchstem Nutzen ... zugebrauchen, darinne man des vielen Wasser-Trinckens überhoben seyn kan ... Wohl meynend angerathen und vorgeschlagen von Louis Gilhome von Knör. Leipzig, J. C. Martini [1719]
48p. 17cm.

NK 0206616 DNLM IU

Knör, Ludwig Wilhelm von, d.1754. Die über den schädlichen Mercurium und Salivation triumphirende Venus, das ist: Naturmässige und in der Erfahrung gegründete Anweisung, wie die Venus-Seuche, samt dem faulartigen Scharbock, der in seinen meisten Zufällen mit der Venus-Seuche überein kömmt, in welchen der Gebrauch des Mercurii noch schädlicher ist, als in dem vorgemeldeten Uebel; nebst einem ausführlichen Unterricht, wie diese beyde angezeigte Seuchen zu unterscheiden, und wenn solche sich mit einander vereiniget befinden, wie sie am füglichsten zu heben. 7 p. l., 244 pp., 2 l. 12°. *Leipzig. C. F. Gessner*. 1753.

NK 0206617 DNLM

Knör, Ludwig Wilhelm von. Venus à la mode, Das ist: Die anietzo im Schwang gehende venerische Moden-Kranckheit, wie solche so wol inn- als äusserlich in allen ihren ereignenden Zufällen gantz sicher und gewiss ohne einigen Gran des Mercurii oder Quecksilber zu curiren, dass man auch währender Zeit allen Verrichtungen unverhindert obliegen könne; alles sowohl theoretice, als practice gantz kurtz und nervös nach spagyrischen Principiis demonstriret, auch die Cur mit vielen probat- und arcanen chymischen Medicamenten angefüllet, nebst einem Anhang verschiedener physicalischer Experimenten und chymischer Medicamenten vom Gold und Antimonio; alles also abgefasset, damit Chirurgi und Benöthigte solches commod im Felde bey sich führen können. 6 p. l., 146 pp. 12°. *Leipzig, J. F. Braun*, 1717.

NK 0206618 DNLM

Knör, Max, Rechtsprakt.: Constitutio Bertholdiana. Eichstätt 1910: Brönner. 56 S. 8°
Erlangen, Jur. Diss. v. 22. Okt. 1910, Ref. Sehling
[Geb. 24. Juni 83 Eichstätt; Wohnort: Eichstätt; Staatsangeh.: Bayern; Vorbildung: Gymn. Eichstätt Reife 03; Studium: München 4, Erlangen 3, Kiel 1 S.; Rig. 3. März 10.] [U 11. 829

NK 0206619 ICRL MH NN CtY NIC

Knoer, Frau R Christine (Dertinger), d. 1809.
Sammlung vieler vorschriften von allerley koch- und backwerk ... [n. p.], 1783.
477 p., 13 l. 17 cm. (8°)

NK 0206620 NNNAM

---

ha TX 709 K72
[Knoer, R Christine d. 1809]
Sammlung vieler Vorschriften von allerley Koch und Backwerk für junges Frauenzimmer; von einer Freundin der Kochkunst. Neue Aufl. Stuttgart, Erhard, 1787.
4p.l., 475p. [29]p.

[Also known as the Goeppinger Kochbuch]

1. Cookery,German. 2. Cookery-Early works to 1800. I. Title: Goeppinger Kochbuch. II.Title.

NK 0206621 NIC NNNAM

Knoerck, Karl Friedrich , 1901-
Zur Kenntnis der alkaloide von corydalis cava. Inaug. diss. Marburg, 1926

NK 0206622 ICRL MH CtY

Knoerich, Friedrich Wilhelm
see Knörrich, Friedrich Wilhelm, 1875-

Knörich, Wilhelm, ed.
Staël-Holstein, Anne Louise Germaine (Necker) *baronne* **de,** 1766-1817.
Corinne, ou, L'Italie, von madame de Staël. Für den schulgebrauch bearbeitet von Wilhelm Knörich ... Berlin, Weidmannsche buchhandlung, 1877.

Knörich, Wilhelm, ed.
Villiers, Claude Deschamps, *sieur* **de,** 1600?-1681.
... De Villiers Le festin de pierre; ou, Le fils criminel. Neue ausg. von W. Knörich. Heilbronn, Gebr. Henninger, 1881.

Knörich, Wilhelm.
Études sur la critique du Cid par Corneille et sur les variantes du premier acte ... Stettin, Impr. A. Bornemann, 1875.
32 p. 20cm.
Inaug.-diss.—Rostock.

1. Corneille, Pierre, 1606-1684. The Cid.

11-19924

Library of Congress PQ1751.K6

NK 0206626 DLC PHC

Knörich, Wilhelm.
Französisches lese- und lehrbuch. 2. verb. aufl. Hannover-List, 1906.
v. 2.

NK 0206627 IU

KNÖRICH, Wilhelm, editor.
Die quellen des Avare von Molière. [Oppeln, etc, 1886.]

pp.(17).
Zeitschrift für neufranzösische sprache und litteratur, 1886, viii. 51-67.

NK 0206628 MH

Knörich, Wilhelm. Zur kritik des Prezioesentums. 10 pp. (*Zeits. f. neufranz. sprache u. lit.* v. 11, pt. 1, 1889, p. 167.)

NK 0206629 MdBP

Knoerin, R. Christine
see Knoer, R. Christine (Dertinger), d. 1809.

WZ 250 K72v 1700
KNÖRING, Frantz Xaver von
Viaticum balneantium; das ist, Neue erholde Bad-Ordnung, in welcher aller denckwürdig in Pusterthall sich befindenden mineralischen Bad-Wässern ... beschriben wird ... Brixen, Joseph Schuechegger, 1700.
[14], 157, [1] p. 15 cm.

NK 0206631 DNLM

KNÖRINGEN, Waldemar, Freiherr von, 1880-
Der begriff des dinglichen rechtes am obligatorischen und dinglichen vorkaufsrecht erläutert. Brückenau, 1908.

58 p.
Inaug.-diss. --- Würzburg.

NK 0206632 MH-L ICRL

Knöringer, Emil
Das recht der kraftfahrlinien in Bayern ... Würzburg, 1933. 71 p.
Inaug. Diss. -Würzburg, 1933.

NK 0206633 ICRL

Knoeringer, Gallus. Aus den Annales Faucenses. 24 pp. (Baumann, F. L., *Quellen zur gesch. d. bauernkriegs in Oberschwaben*, p. 391.)

NK 0206634 MdBP

Knoerk, M, 1883-
Die Negation in der altenglischen Dichtung. Kiel: H. Fiencke. 1907. vi p., 1 l., 79(1) p., 1 l. 8°.

Dissertation, Kiel. Bibliography, p. 75-76.

1. Anglo-Saxon language.—Grammar. 2. Poetry (Anglo-Saxon).—History.
N. Y. P. L. October 9, 1911.

NK 0206635 NN ICRL MiU PU PBm NjP NcD MH DNLM CtY

Knörk, Otto.
Geld-, bank- und börsenkunde; ein ratgeber für den verkehr mit der bank und der börse ... von dr. Otto Knörk ... Berlin, R. Wichert, 1907.
viii, 312 p. incl. forms, tables. 19 cm.
(Added t. p.: Neue kaufmännische bibliothek für den selbstunterricht und die praxis ... bd. 2)
"Benutzte und empfehlenswerte litteratur": p. 312.
1. Money. 2. Banks and banking. 3. Stock-exchange.

NK 0206636 CU

Knörk, Otto, ed.
Wirtschafts- und Verkehrs-Atlas mit besonderer Berücksichtigung Deutschlands ... Berlin, [1911]
2 p.l., 15 fold. maps. 24.5 cm.

NK 0206637 CtY

Knörk, Otto
Wirtschafts- und verkehrs-atlas, mit besender berucksichtigung Deutschlands, fur den gebrauch an gymnasien, realenstalten, fach-und fortbildungsschulen, entworfen und hrsg. von Dr. Otto Knork...Berlin, Gea-verlag 1912.
2 p.l., col. maps 24½ cm
40266

NK 0206638 DNW

Knörk, Otto, 1866-
Untersuchungen über die mittelenglische Magdalenenlegende des ms. Laud 108 ... von Otto Knörk ... Berlin, M. Schorss, 1889.
56 p., 2 l. 22cm.
Inaug.-diss.—Berlin.
Vita.
Bibliographical foot-notes.

1. Mary Magdalene, Saint. Legend. 2. Oxford. University. Bodleian library. Mss. (Laud lat. 108)

42-46317

Library of Congress PR2061.M4K5

NK 0206639 DLC NcD ICRL NNF NjP NIC ICN MH CtY OCl PBm PSC

HE 356 .I3 K69
Knoerle (Joseph K.) and Associates, inc., Baltimore
Engineering report, northern Illinois toll highway, State of Illinois, prepared for the Illinois State Toll Highway Commission. Chicago, 1954.
147 p. illus., fold.diagrs., plans (part fold., part col.) profiles (part fold.) tables. 23 x 29 cm.

1.Toll roads--Illinois. I.Illinois. State Toll Highway Commission. II.Title: Northern Illinois toll highway.

Continued in next column

VOLUME 300

Continued from preceding column

338.2 K75e sup.

---- ---- Supplement. Chicago, 1955. 11p. 4 fold.diagrs. 23x29cm.

1. Toll roads--Illinois. I. Illinois--State Toll Highway Commission. II. Title. III. Title: Northern Illinois toll highway.

NK 0206641 IU

HE356 .I3K5

Knoerle (Joseph K.) and Associates, inc., *Baltimore.*
Feasibility report, toll road program, State of Illinois. Prepared for the Illinois State Toll Highway Commission. Baltimore, 1954.

40 p. illus., maps, diagrs. 29 cm.

Bibliography: p. 37-40.

1. Toll roads—Illinois. I. Illinois. State Toll Highway Commission. II. Title.

A 55-9015

Illinois. Univ. Library for Library of Congress ⌈1⌉

NK 0206642 IU DLC WaS N

Knörlein, Anton, [1808-72]. Beiträge zur Organisirung der landschaftlichen Heil- und Pflege-Anstalt für Seelengestörte zu Niedernhardt. 79 pp. 8°. *Linz, F. Feichtinger's Erben,* 1866.

NK 0206643 DNLM

Knörlein, Anton, 1802-72]. *De induratione textus cellulosi neonatorum. 29 pp., 1 l. 8°. *Vindobonæ, ex typ. vid. Stöckholzer de Hirschfeld,* [1828].

NK 0206644 DNLM

Knoerlein, Anton, 1802-72.

——. Die Irren-Angelegenheiten Ober-Oesterreichs. Ein Vorwort zur Begründung einer Landes-Heilanstalt für Geistes- und Gemüthskranke. 1 p. l., 86 pp., 1 l. 8°. *Linz, V. Fink,* 1851.

For Biography, see Wien. med. Wchnschr., 1872, xxii, 1163.

NK 0206645 DNLM

WY K67p 1849

KNÖRLEIN, Anton, 1802-1872
Die Pflege der Kranken und Verwundeten, und die sichersten Schutzmittel zur Zeit herrschender Epidemien ... Linz, Fink, 1849.
viii, 130 p.

NK 0206646 DNLM

Knoerlein, J. Antonius
see Knörlein, Anton, 1802-1872.

Knörlein, Walter.
Grundbrüche unter Dämmen und ihre Bekämpfung, von Walter Knörlein ⌈und⌉ Kurt Vogl. Berlin, Volk und Reich Verlag, 1939.

41 p. illus., plans. 24 cm. (Forschungsarbeiten aus dem Strassenwesen, Bd. 19)

1. Soil engineering. I. Vogl, Kurt, joint author. (Series)

TA710.K58 50-51249

NK 0206648 DLC

Knoernschild, Eduard
Die strafrechtliche bekaempfung der geschlechtskrankheiten nach dem gesetz vom 18. Februar 1927.
Inaug. diss. Leipzig, 1927
Bibl.

NK 0206649 ICRL

Knoerr, Alvin W
Prospecting for atomic minerals; how to look for and identify atomic ores, stake and protect a claim, evaluate and sell your minerals ⌈by⌉ Alvin W. Knoerr ⌈and⌉ George P. Lutjen. New York, McGraw-Hill ⌈1955⌉

211 p. illus. 20 cm.

Includes bibliography.

1. Uranium ores. 2. Prospecting. I. Lutjen, George P., joint author. II. Title.

TN271.U7K5 622.12 55—11928 ‡

PPT ICJ MiU MsSM WaE WaS CaBVa IdB MtBuM OrP NcD TU OU DI PBm PCM OrAshS TxU PSt NN CU ViU WaSp WaT KEmT CaBViP MtU Or OrU
NK 0206650 DLC OKentU DAU PBL PP NcC IU OOxM OCl

Knörr (Carl [Berthold]) [1864-]. *Zur Lehre der toxischen Psychosen. 25 pp., 1 l. 8°. *Berlin, [G. Reimer],* 1892.

Repr. from: Allg. Ztschr. f. Psychiat. [etc.], Berl., 1892, xlviii.

NK 0206651 DNLM

4QD 619

Knörr, Fritz, 1921-
Reaktionen von Acetylenaldehyden und-Ketonen: Polymerisation, Friedel-Crafts'sche Synthese. [ ] 1953.
92 l.

NK 0206652 DLC-P4

Knoerr, Georg Christian, author and respondent.
Doctrinae orthodoxae de origine mali
see under Buddeus, Johann Franz, 1667-1729, praeses.

W 4 L53 1941

Knörr, Karl, 1915-
Über substernale Strumen im Mittelrheingebiet. Bottrop, Postberg, 1941.
62 p. illus.

Inaug.-Diss. - Bonn.
Bibliography: p. 58.

NK 0206654 DNLM

Sw3 3 K754

Knörrich, Friedrich Wilhelm, 1875-
... Studien über die Ernährungsbedingungen einiger für die Fischproduction wichtiger Mikro-organism des Süsswassers ... Stuttgart[1900]
Inaug.-Diss. - Heidelberg.
Lebenslauf.

NK 0206655 CtY PU DNLM

Knörrich, Horst.
Die Preussische landesrentenbank: vorgeschichte, aufgaben und mitwirkung am deutschen siedlungswerk, von dr. ing. Horst Knörrich. Berlin, Junker und Dünnhaupt, 1937.

83 p. diagr. 24½cm. (*Added t.-p.:* Neue deutsche forschungen. Abt.: Betriebswirtschaftslehre ... hrsg. von Wilhelm Hasenack. bd. 8)

Half-title: Neue deutsche forschungen, hrsg. von Hans R. G. Günther und Erich Rothacker. bd. 117.

"Diese arbeit ist unter gleichem titel als dissertation von der Technischen hochschule zu Berlin, Fakultät für allgemeine wissenschaften, angenommen worden."

"Literaturverzeichnis": p. ⌈82⌉-83.

1. Preussische landesrentenbank. 2. Agricultural credit—Prussia. I. Title.

38-19198

Library of Congress HG2051.G5P83

⌈3⌉ 332.31109431

NK 0206656 DLC

Knoerrlich, Siegfried
Der Heimat Bild; Heimatbuch des Kreises Goldberg-Haynau. Hrsg.im Auftrage der Lehrerschaft des Kreises von S.Knörrlich. Liegnitz, Heinze, 1928

⌈ ⌉,421 p. illus.

NK 0206657 MH

SD664 .F7M3

Knœrtzer, André, joint author.

Marc, Henri.
Le code forestier algérien, par Henri Marc ... ⌈et⌉ André Knœrtzer ... Alger, P. & G. Soubiron ⌈1931⌉

Law

Knœrtzer, André.

Bruno, Henri.
Répertoire alphabétique de la jurisprudence de la Cour d'appel de Rabat, comprenant les matières contenues dans le Recueil des arrêts de la Cour d'appel de Rabat de 1921 au 31 décembre 1944, par Henri Bruno et Paul Moussard. Préf. de André Knoertzer. ⌈Rabat⌉ 1947-55.

Knœrtzer, André, *ed.*
Texte de la Loi du 7 février 1933, sur les garanties de la liberté individuelle. Texte du Décret du 30 juin 1933, rectifié par celui du 7 juillet 1933, rendant applicable à l'Algérie la Loi du 7 février 1933. La Loi du 7 février 1933, sur les garanties de la liberté individuelle telle qu'elle s'applique en Algérie, avec les dispositions spéciales apportées par le Décret du 30 juin 1933, fusion des deux textes en un seul, par André Knœrtzer ... Alger, Éditions P. & G. Soubiron ⌈1934⌉

cover-title, 16 p. 23cm.

1. Liberty. 2. France—Constitutional law. I. France. Laws, statutes, etc. II. Algeria. Laws, statutes, etc. III. Title.

37-34592

NK 0206660 DLC

Knoertzer, Cécile, tr.

Glaeser, Ernst, 1902-
... Classe 22, traduction de Cécile Knoertzer et Joseph Delage ... Paris, Neuchâtel, V. Attinger, 1929.

Knoertzer, Cécile, tr.

Popov, Georgiĭ Konstantinovich.
... La Tschéka; mon emprisonnement et mes aventures à la Loubjanka nº 2; traduit par Cécile Knoertzer. Paris, Plon-Nourrit et cie ⌈1926⌉

Knoertzer, Cécile, 1896-
... Contribution à l'étude de la kératite interstitielle dans la syphilis acquise ...
Lyon, 1937.
Thèse - Univ. de Lyon.
"Bibliographie": p. [41]-44.

NK 0206663 CtY

KNÖRY, Auguste.
Contributions au traitement local des arthrites fongueuses par les injections d'acide phénique. Neuchatel, 1875.

NK 0206664 MBCo DNLM

Knoerzer, Adamus, O.F.M.
Etwas neues für die heutigen gelehrten Kritiker: In Hinsicht des von andern falsch Ungehorsam ausgerufenen Patris Adami Knoerzer, Franziskaners. Im Jahre 1798.
38 p.

NK 0206665 MdSsW

VOLUME 300

Knörzer, Albert.
Temperaturmittel Würzburgs, 1880-1903. [n.p.] 1904.

NK 0206666 DAS

Knoerzer, Albert. *6284.8.22.Teil 3
Die Wärmeinsel am Ostfusse der Vogesen.
— Stuttgart. Engelhorn. 1922. 247-277 pp. Tables. [Forschungen zur deutschen Landes- und Volkskunde. Band 22, Teil 3.] 22 cm., in 8s.

N3369 — T.r. — S.r.c. — Vosges Mountains, France. Meteor.

NK 0206667 MB

Knörzer, Arthur.
Über drei Fälle von Glioma retinae ...
Heidelberg, 1927.
Inaug.-Diss. - Heidelberg.

NK 0206668 CtY

Knoerzer, Guido, ed.

Eckbrecht von Dürckheim-Montmartin, Ferdinand, *graf,* 1811-1891.
Erinnerungen eines elsässischen patrioten, von graf Eckbrecht Dürckheim-Montmartin, herausgegeben von Guido Knoerzer. 2. aufl. Stuttgart, R. Lutz [°1922]

W 6 P3 **KNOERZER, J**
Gesundheit ist Reichtum [Schlachters bei Lindau/B., Wohlmuth-Zentrale, 1954]
31 p.
1. Electrotherapy I. Wohlmuth-Zentrale, Schlachters

NK 0206670 DNLM

Knoes, Anders Erik, 1801-1862.
Skrifter, af Anders Erik Knös. Samlade och utgifna efter författarens död ... Upsala, Essias Edquist, 1863.
188 p.

NK 0206671 PBa

Knös, Anders, 1763-1813, respondent
Fant, Erik Mikael, 1754-1817, *praeses.*
Dissertatio historico-topographica de Alingsâsia veteri et nova ... [Pars 1] Upsaliæ, litteris viduæ direct. J. Edman [1793]

Knös, Anders Erik, 1801-1862, respondent.
De prima notione Scandinaviae ...
see under Geijer, Erik Gustaf, 1783-1847, praeses.

BX8039 **Knös, Anders Erik,** 1801-1862.
.K7 Kurze darstellung der vornehmsten eigenthümlichkeiten der schwedischen kirchenverfassung mit hinblicken auf ihre geschichtliche entwicklung. Von A. E. Knös ... Mit einem vorwort von dr. G. C. A. Harless. Stuttgart, S. G. Liesching, 1852.
ix, [1], 182 p. fold. tab. 22½cm.

1. Lutheran church in Sweden—Discipline and government. 2. Sweden—Church history. 3. Church and state in Sweden.

NK 0206674 ICU PPLT OO

Knoes, Anders Erik
Om aktheten och trovardigheten af de fyra Kanoniska Evangelierna, med hansigt till den mythiska asigten af evangeliska historien. Upsala, Leffler och Sebell, 1842.
1v.

NK 0206675 PBa

BS2203 .K72 Knös, Anders Erik, 1801-1862.
Om revision af Svenska Bibelöfversättningen: med särskildt afseende paa den af Kongl. Bibelcommissionen sednast utgifna Profôfversättningen af Nya Testamentet, jemte naagra historiska uppgifter om den äldsta i Sverige utgifna och hittills obekanta Profôfversättning af naagra bibliska böcker. [Upsala, Tryckt hos Edquist u. K., 1861.]
114p. 25cm. (Uppsala universitets Aarskrift, 1861)

With this is bound: Hultkrantz, Claes Adolf. Den presbyterianska kyrkoförfattningens införande i Skottland.
With this is bound: Hjerpe, Conrad Theodor. Om äktheten af Jacobs Bref, historisk-kritisk undersökning.

With this is bound: Program för Rectorsombytet 1861 af F.F. Carlson, samt Offentliga förläsningar 1861.

1. Bible. N.T. Swedish--History and criticism. 2. Bible. N.T.--Versions, Swedish--History. I. Title. (Series)

NK 0206678 IEG MH

Knös, Anders Erik, 1801-1862, ed.

BV4010 .H33 1839 **Harms, Claus,** 1778-1855.
Pastoraltheologie, af d:r Claus Harms ... Öfwersättning ifrån 2. oförändrade uppl. Stockholm, Hörbergska boktryckeriet, 1839.

Knös, Anders Erik, 1801-1862, respondent.
Platonis Euthyphron Graece et Svethice ...
see under Höijer, Joseph Otto, praeses.

Knoes, Anders Olofsson, 1721-1799.
Anmärkningar öfwer then, i afseende på grundläggningen til. en biblisk och Practisk Christendom, högwigtiga St. Pauli Epistel till the Romare; författade, underjämförelse af Nya Profôfwer sättningeen med Grundtexten, och wär gamala, samt andra versioner, af Andreas Knös... Upsala, Edman, 1776.
558 p.

NK 0206681 PBa

Knoes, Anders Olofsson, 1721-1799.
Bref til Herr N.N. om religionen och den sanna moralen, i anledning af en nyligen pa Fransoska i Stockholm tryckt skrift, efter anmodan till tryck lämnadt af Anders Knös. Stockholm, Kumblinska tryckeriet, 1784.
83 p.

NK 0206682 PBa

Knoes, Anders Olofsson, 1721-1799.
Cathechetiska Foreläsninger i afsiga uppa en Biblisk och Practisk Cateches, eller Larobok i Christendoms Kunskapen; hallne pa Kongl. Larosatet, ofwer D. Lutheri Lilla Cateches, tilliska med Arkebisk D. Swebilii Forklaring efter begaran widare utforde, och till Trycket lemnade, af Andres Knös. Upsala, Johan Edman, 1779-1780.
2v.

NK 0206683 PBa

Knös, Anders Olofsson, 1721-1799.
*Dissertatio academica, characteres veri philosophi breviter delineans. *Upsaliae,* 1740. 2 p.l., 40 pp., 1l. 12°.
In: YAM p. v. 1.

NK 0206684 NN

Knös, Anders Olofsson, 1721-1799.
Institutions theologiae practicae, in praelectionibus publicis breviter propositae, et auctae, quae in praefatione indicantur, una cum dissertatione praeliminari, de veritate ac divinitate scripturae sacrae & religionis Christianae, adversus objectiones hostium Christianismi immota; et duplici indice, Holmiae, Hessalbergii, 1768.
1010 p.

NK 0206685 PBa

Knös, Anders Olofsson, 1721-1799.
Nödige Paminnelser wid en Skrift kallad Behörigt Svar på obehörige och ogrundade Anmärkningar, af Dom-Probsten Doctor A.O. Knös i Skara, tui thez utigifna Catechetiska Forelasningar, m.m. Gifne af Theza Forelasningars Fofattare. Upsala, Edman, 1782.
148 p.

NK 0206686 PBa

Knös, Andreas Ericus
see Knös, Anders Erik, 1801-1862.

Knös, Andreas Olavus
see Knös, Anders Olofsson, 1721-1799.

Knös (Arvid). Hvad bör kunna göras för att bättre tillgodose de hygieniska fordringarne i våra boningsrum beträffande ventilation och uppvärmning medels vanliga kakelugnar? [What can be done to better the care of the hygienic changes in the rooms of our dwelling houses as to ventilation and heating by the common stoves?] 1 p. l., 23 pp., 2 pl. 8°. *Stockholm, A. L. Norman,* 1895.
Repr. from: Teknisk Tidskr. Afd. för Byggnadskonst, Stockholm, 1895, 3. Hft.

NK 0206689 DNLM

CT1118 L33K59 **Knös, Börje,** 1883-
Un ambassadeur de l'hellénisme, Janus Lascaris, et la tradition gréco-byzantine dans l'humanisme français. Uppsala, Almquist & Wiksells, 1945.
225 p. 25cm. (Collection d'histoire de l'humanisme)
Bibliographical footnotes.

1. Lascaris, Janus, 1445?-1535. 2. Hellénisme. 3. Renaissance - France. I. Title.

NK 0206690 CLU ICN MH MiU WaU CSt IU AU CtY ICU RPB NcU NNC CU InU

Knös, Börje, 1883-
Codex graecus XV upsaliensis ... Uppsala, 1908.
Pamphlet
Akademische abhandlung - Uppsala.

NK 0206691 CtY PU OClW IU MH NjP

Knös, Börje, 1883-

Sandberg, Fredrik, 1881-
Education and scientific research in Sweden, by Fr. Sandberg and Börje Knös. Stockholm, Printed by A. Bonniers boktryckeri, 1938.

VOLUME 300

Knös, Börje.
Guillaume Budé och den franska humanismens renässans, av Börje Knös. Stockholm, P.A Norstedt & Söners Förlag [1939]
194 p. illus., facsims., plates, ports. 23 cm. (Svenska Humanistiska Förbundet, 48)
"Litteratur": p. 193.
1. Budé, Guillaume, 1468-1540. 2. Humanism. 3. Philosophy, French.

NK 0206693 TU NIC CSt MH NjP NcU

Knös, Börje, 1883-
Nygrekisk medeltids- och renässansdiktning. Stockholm, Norstedt [1952]
97 p. 19 cm. (Humanistisk kultur: Studier och essäer, 3)
Bibliography: p. [91]-97.
1. Byzantine literature—Hist. & crit. 2. Greek literature, Modern—Hist. & crit. (Series)
Full name: Börje Anders Olof Knös.
A 53-2136
Cincinnati. Univ. Libr. for Library of Congress PA5010.K6 [1]

NK 0206694 OCU NN MnU MH

4PQ Fr.-1275 Knös, Börje, 1883-
Rabelais; humanisten, humoristen, patrioten. Stockholm, Fahlcrantz & Gumaelius [1943]
237 p.

NK 0206695 DLC-P4

Knös, Börje, 1883-
J406 .R15 1939:16 Sweden. *Sakkunnig angående fortsatt förstatligande av kommunala mellanskolor.*
... Utredning och förslag angående fortsatt förstatligande av kommunala mellanskolor, avgivna av för nämnda ändamål tillkallad sakkunnig. Stockholm, I. Hæggströms boktryckeri a. b., 1939.

Knös, Carl Johan, 1767-1835, respondent.
Fant, Erik Mikael, 1754-1817, *praeses.*
Observationes historicæ de Carolo Canuti, ejusque administratione regni ... Upsaliæ, litteris viduæ direct. J. Edman [1791]

Knoes, Carl Johan, 1767-1835, respondent
Vita Jesperi Swedberg...
see under Fant, Erik Mikael, 1754-1817, praeses.

Knös, Gunnar.
Wereld federatie van alle landen met nationale ontwapening en internationale politiemacht; vier radiolezingen. Utrecht, W. de Haan, 1946.
29 p. 24 cm.
1. International organization. I. Title.
JX1954.K55 57-51671 ‡

NK 0206699 DLC

Knös, Gustaf, 1773-1828.
Chrestomathia syriaca, maximam partem e codicibvs manv scriptis collecta. Ed. Gustavus Knös. Gottingae, sumtibus Vandenhoek et Ruprecht, 1807.
viii, 119, [1] p. 17cm.
1. Syriac language—Chrestomathies and readers.
11-19108
Library of Congress PJ5495.K6

NK 0206700 DLC CaBVaU TNJ-R CtY OCl PBm PBa DCU-H

Knös, Gustaf, 1773-1828.
Försök att utreda några wigtiga frågor. Upsala, Palmblad, 1827.
454 p.

NK 0206701 PBa

Knös, Gustaf, 1773-1828
... Paulinam dictionem
see under Dahl, Christoph, praeses.

Knös, Gustaf, 1773-1828.
Samtal med mig sjelf om werlden, menniskan och Gud. Upsala, Palmbald, 1824.
288 p.

NK 0206703 PBa

Knoes (Gustav). *Geschichte der Forschungen über den Geburtsmechanismus von der Mitte des 16. bis zur Mitte des 17. Jahrhunderts. 1 p.l., 83 pp. 8°. *Giessen, M. Merck,* 1854.

NK 0206704 DNLM ICRL

Knös (Johannes Petrus), Medaillen (E.) *and* **Schroder (O.)**
*Epistola Philippi ad Athenienses et de eadem oratio Demosthenis. Parts I-III. *Upsaliae,* 1813. 3 pts. 4°.
In: NBN p. v. 1.

NK 0206705 NN

Knös, Olaus Vilhelmus.
see
Knös, Olof Vilhelm, 1838-1907.

Knös, Olavus Andreas
see Knös, Olof Andreas. 1756-1804.

Knös, Olavus Petri, respondent.
Dissertatio gradualis de divisione civili veteris imperii Sviogothici...
see under Fant, Erik Mikael, 1754-1817, praeses.

Knös, Olof Andreas, 1756-1804.
Analecta epistolarum, in primis, historiam et res litterarias Sveciae illustrantium. Specimen VIII; venia ampliss. facult. philos. Ups. exhibent Olavus Andreae Knös ... et Carolus Petrus Wenström ... Upsaliae, J.F. Edman, 1796.
6 p.

NK 0206708 PBa

Beinecke Library X345 K75 805 Knös, Olof Andreas, 1756-1804.
Catalogus collectionis librorum quam reliquit Olavus Andreae Knös ... quaeque publica auctione Skaris d. 11 septemb. vendenda est. Skara, litteris F.J. Leverentz, 1805.
2 p.ℓ., 224 p. 18 cm.
1. Schröder, Johan Henrik, 1791-1857 - Autograph. 2. Hammer, Christian, 1818-1905. Bibliothèque - Bookplate. I. Title(1)

NK 0206709 CtY

Knös, Olof Andreas, 1756-1804.
Lefvernes-beskrifning om D. Joh. Loccenius ... och D. Joh. Thore Helstadius ... af M. Olof A. Knös ... Stockholm, 1807.
20 p. 16 cm.
Supplement to Gjörwell's Brefväxling, v. 4. [Bound with Gjörwell, C.C. Brefväxling. 4. bandet. Stockholm, 1806]

NK 0206710 CtY

PA4206 .D5K7 **KNÖS, OLOF VILHELM, 1838-1907.**
De digammo homerico quæstiones... Scripsit Olaus Vilelmus Knös... Upsaliæ, typis exscripserunt Edquist et Berglund, 1872-78.
3 v. in 1. 24½cm. (Upsala universitets Årsskrift. 1872-79. Philosophi, språkvetenskap och historiska vetenskaper)
Paged continuously.
1. Homerus--Versification.

ICRL IU MH
NK 0206711 ICU MiU OrU NjP PU CU OU NIC CtY OCU

Knös, Olof Vilhelm, 1838-1907.
De digammo Homerico quaestiones. Upsalae, 1878-83.

NK 0206712 MdBP

---

881 H8.Ykn Knös, Olof Vilhelm, 1838-1907.
Prolegomena ad quaestiones de digammo homerico instituendas. Upsaliae, 1869.
31p.

NK 0206713 IU CtY NjP ICRL

KNÖS, Rudolf, 1876-
Anatomische untersuchungen über die blattspreite der einheimischen Farne. Inaug.-diss. [Erlangen], 1902.

NK 0206714 MH ICRL NN CtY

Knös, Teodor. 4909b.182
Berättelser ur fäderneslandets historia. Läsebok för folkskolan och menige man. 4. upplagan.
— Stockholm. Norstedt. [1906.] (7), 273 pp. 17½ cm., in 8s.
H8919 — Sweden. Lang. Works in Swedish. — Sweden. Hist. — T.r.

NK 0206715 MB

Knös, Teodor
Bo93 61 Skildringar från Korsika jemte några reseminnen fran Nordafrika af Teodor Knös. Efter författarens död utgifna af C.T. Odhner ... Stockholm, Albert Bonnier [1880]
3p.ℓ., [3]-138, [2]p. 1 illus., plates. 22½cm. (Bibliotek för resebeskrifningar. VIII)
Two of the plates misbound as fronts.

NK 0206716 CtY

VOLUME 300

Knös, Thekla. Ragnar Lodbrok. Skaldestycke. Skrift, som vunnit Akademiens stora pris, år 1851. *Extr. fr.* Svenska Akademiens Handlingar. XXVII. delen. Stockholm, 1853. 8°. pp. 11-89. IcP1K721

NK 0206717 NIC

PA 6752 K72 Knös, Wilhelm.
De dativi finalis qui dicitur usu Taciteo commentariolum. Upsaliae, I. Edquist, 1878.
44 p. 22cm.

1. Tacitus, Cornelius--Language--Grammar.

NK 0206718 NIC PU MH

WG 30534 Knoesel, Christian,
Die Einwirkung einiger Antiseptika (Calciumhydroxyd, Natriumarsenit und Phenol) auf alkoholische Gärung. Jena, 1902.
27 p. illus.

Inaug.-Diss. - Erlangen.

NK 0206719 CtY DNLM ICRL PU

Knösel, Georg, 1889-
... Über Endothelien im Kapillenblute bei Endokarditis septika ... Stolp i. P., [1921]
15, [1] p. 21 cm.
Inaug.-Diss. - Greifswald.
Lebenslauf.

NK 0206720 CtY

Knösel, Karl, 1856-
Das altfranzösische Zahlwort ... Erlangen, 1884.
69, [1] p. 23.5 cm.
Bibliography: p. [5]-9.

NK 0206721 CtY NjP

Knoesel, Karl, 1856-
Ueber altfranzoesische zahlwoerter.
Inaug. diss. Goettingen, 1883.

NK 0206722 ICRL PHC PBm

Knösel, Th., ed.

Schubert, Max, *d.* 1901.
Die cellulosefabrikation (zellstofffabrikation). Praktisches handbuch für papier- und cellulosetechniker, kaufmännische direktoren werkführer, sowie zum unterricht in fachschulen. Mit 135 illustrationen von Max Schubert ... 3. umgearb. und vervollständigte aufl. von Th. Knösel ... Berlin, M. Krayn, 1906.

Knösel, Th., ed.

Schubert, Max, *d.* 1901.
Die holzstoff- oder holzschliff-fabrikation. Vom technischen sowie geschäftlichen standpunkte aus, unter erwähnung der berechnung der herstellungskosten und der wasserkräfte, abwässer- und fabrikationswasser-reinigung. Mit 107 illustrationen, von Max Schubert ... 2., verm. und verb. aufl. von Th. Knösel ... Berlin, M. Krayn, 1909.

Knösel, Walter: Über Futtervergiftungen unserer Haustiere durch Befall der Futtermittel mit Rost- und Brandpilzen, sowie mit Peronosporaarten. [Maschinenschrift.] 78 S. 4° [Lag nicht vor.] — Auszug: München 1923: Gotteswinter. 7 S. 8°
Leipzig, Veterinär-med. Diss. v. 21. Mai 1924 [U 24. 6771

NK 0206725 ICRL DNLM

891.86 K754 Om Knoesl, Bohuslav, 1873-
Martyrium touhy; básně. Praha, Moderní revue, 1896.
24p. 22cm. (Knihovna Moderní revue, 7)

NK 0206726 IU

Knoesl, Bohuslav, 1873- Slav 7946.64.22
Oblaka a krystaly; básně proscu. [V Praze] Zátiší srdce i ducha, 1925
83 p. (Klikova sbírka puvodní prosy, 2)

NK 0206727 MH

Knoesl, Bohuslav, 1873- Slav 7946.64.110
Ozvěny a nápěvy; basně. V Praze, Nakl. J.Otto, 1919
41 p. illus.

NK 0206728 MH

Knöss, Conrad.
... Fachkunde für das friseurhandwerk, von C. Knöss ... 7. aufl. Mit 93 bildern und 2 tafeln. Leipzig und Berlin, B. G. Teubner, 1943.
v, 109 p. incl. illus., 2 pl. on 1 l., diagrs. 22½cm. (Teubners berufs- und fachbücherei, hft. 83)

1. Hair-dressing. 2. Hair-work.

46-19420
Library of Congress TT957.K6 1943
[2] 646.7

NK 0206729 DLC

Knöss, Conrad.
Der Friseur, ein Hand- und Nachschlagebuch für Damen- und Herrenfriseure, Haarfärber, Schönheitspfleger und Perückenmacher, hrsg. und bearb. von Conrad Knöss und Ludwig Ross. Nordhausen am Harz, H. Killinger [1936]
ix, 565 p. illus., plates (part col.) 26 cm.
Bound with: Schoefer, Günther. Kleines Rechtslexikon für Beruf und Leben. Nordhausen am Harz [1937] Copy 2.
Bibliography: p. [542]-543.

1. Hairdressing. I. Ross, Ludwig, joint author. II. Title.

TT957.K62 1936 52-56063
[3]

NK 0206730 DLC

Knöss, Conrad.
Der Friseur, ein Hand- und Nachschlagebuch für Damen- und Herrenfriseure, Haarfärber, Schönheitspfleger und Perückenmacher, hrsg. und bearb. von Conrad Knöss und Ludwig Ross. 2., neubearb. und ergänzte Aufl. Nordhausen am Harz, H. Killinger [1938]
ix, 622 p. illus., plates (part col.) 26 cm.
Bound with: Schoefer, Günther. Kleines Rechtslexikon für Beruf und Leben. Nordhausen am Harz [1940] Copy 2.
Bibliography: p. [598]-599.
1. Hairdressing. I. Ross, Ludwig, joint author. II. Title.

TT957.K62 1938 52-56062

NK 0206731 DLC

Knöss, Conrad.
Der Friseur; ein Hand- und Nachschlagebuch für Damen- und Herrenfriseure, Haarfärber, Kosmetiker und Perückenmacher, von Conrad Knöss und Karl Olig. 3. neubearb. und erweiterte Aufl. Giessen, Pfanneberg [1951]
xiv, 758 p. illus., 14 plates (part col.) 2 diagrs. (in pocket) 26 cm.

1. Hairdressing. I. Olig, Karl, joint author. II. Title.

TT957.K62 1951 54-24110

NK 0206732 DLC NN

Knöss, Conrad.
Der Friseur; ein Hand- und Nachschlagebuch für Damen- und Herrenfriseure, Haarfärber, Kosmetiker und Perückenmacher, von Conrad Knöss und Karl Olig. 4., neubearb. und erweiterte Aufl. Giessen, Pfanneberg [1954]
808 p. illus. 26 cm.

1. Hairdressing. I. Olig, Karl, joint author. II. Title.

TT957.K62 1954 54-37308 ‡

NK 0206733 DLC

Knöss, Fritz. Die zwangsbefugnisse des Völkerbundes... 1927.
JX1975 K72
Diss. - Giessen.

NK 0206734 CSt-H ICRL PU

Knötel, A F R.
Atlantis und das volk der Atlanten; ein beitrag zur 400 jährigen festfeier der entdeckung Amerikas, von A. F. R. Knötel. Leipzig, F. W. Grunow, 1893.
viii, 418 p., 1 l. 19cm.

1. Atlantis.

Library of Congress GN761.K7 5-28871

NK 0206735 DLC MiU CtY

---

881 H8.Ykno Knötel, A F R
Homeros, der blinde von Chios, und seine werke. Leipzig, 1894-95.
2v.

NK 0206736 IU CaBVaU PHC NjP MB NN

DT 85 K78 Knötel, August.
Cheops der Pyramidenerbauer und seine Nachfolger. Leipzig, Dyk, 1861.
x, 130 p. 24cm.

1. Cheops, King of Egypt.

NK 0206737 NIC RPB MH NN

DT 86 K78 Knötel, August.
De pastoribus qui Hyc-sos vocantur deque regibus pyramidum auctoribus; commentatio historico-chronologica. Lipsiae, Dyk, 1856.
49 p. 24cm.

With this is bound Junker, P. J. Untersuchungen über die ägyptischen Sothisperioden. Leipzig, 1859.

1. Hyksos.

NK 0206738 NIC RPB

VOLUME 300

KNÖTEL, A[ugust].
Der Niger der alten und andere wichtige fragen der alten geographie Afrikas. Glogau, Verlag von C.Flemming,1866.
pp.48. Map.

NK 0206739 MH

Knötel, August.
Der opisch-lateinische Volksstamm, seine Einwanderung und Verbreitung in Italien. n.p., 1853.

NK 0206740 NjP

Knötel, August.
Das Sühnfest zu Iguvium. Glogau, Zimmermann in Comm., 1862.
iv, 68 p.

NK 0206741 NjP

Knötel, August.
System der ägyptischen chronologie ... nebst einem kurzen abrisse der ältesten ägyptischen geschichte ... von August Knötel ... Leipzig, Dyk'sche buchhandlung [1857]
vi p., 1 l., 123, [1] p. 22½cm.

1. Egypt—Hist.—Chronology.

Library of Congress DT83.K72 5-8999†

NK 0206742 DLC OCH NIC

Knötel, Herbert, 1893-
Das Deutsche Heer. Uniformenkunde. Friedensuniformen bei Ausbruch des Weltkrieges. Im Auftrag der Gesellschaft für Heereskunde e. V. bearb. von Herbert Knötel d. J. in Gemeinschaft mit Paul Pietsch und Egon Jantke. Textband von Major a. D. Baron Collas. Hamburg, V. Diepenbroick-Grüter & Schulz, 1935-
v. (v. 1-2, portfolios of col. plates) illus. 26 cm.

CONTENTS.—1. Bd. Generale, Generalstab und Kriegsministerium. Infanterie, Jäger und Schützen. (Tafelband)—2. Bd. Kavallerie. (Tafelband)—

4. Bd. 1. T. Generale, Generalstab und Kriegsministerium. Infanterie, Jäger und Schützen. Kavallerie. Textband. 2. T. Artillerie, Ingenieur- und Pionierkorps, Verkehrstruppen usw. Textband.

1. Germany. Heer—Uniforms. I. Collas, Wern, Baron. II. Title. III. Title: Uniformenkunde.

UC485.G3K6 55-49960

NK 0206744 DLC NN

Knötel, Herbert, 1893- illus.

UA712 .L46 1936

Lezius, Martin, 1884-1941.
... Die entwicklung des deutschen heeres von seinen ersten anfängen bis auf unsere tage, mit einem geleitwort des generals der infanterie Karl Litzmann. 1.-5., tausend volksaug. (14.-18. tausend der gesamtaufl.) Berlin-Fürstenwalde, Verlag, für militärgeschichte und deutsches schrifttum [1936]

Knötel, Herbert, 1893- ed.

Knötel, Richard, 1857-1914.
Handbuch der uniformkunde; die militärische tracht in ihrer entwicklung bis zur gegenwart, begründet von prof. Richard Knötel, grundlegend überarbeitet, fortgeführt und erweitert von Herbert Knötel d. j. und Herbert Sieg. Mit 1600 uniformdarstellungen nach zeichnungen von Richard Knötel und Herbert Knötel d. j. Hamburg, Von Diepenbroick-Grüter & Schulz [°1937]

UC485 .G3U62

Knötel, Herbert, 1893- illus.

Uniformen des deutschen Heeres im Juli 1914; zugleich Erläuterungen zu den Bildkarten zur Uniformenkunde gezeichnet von Herbert Knötel d. J. [et al.] Hamburg, H. G. Schulz, 1954-

---

Knötel, Herbert, 1893-
Uniformenkunde
see his Das Deutsche Heer.

Uzk23 1

Knötel, Herbert, 1893-
Uniformfibel, von Geschichtsmaler Knötel d.j. Berlin,Verlag "Offene Worte"[1933]
3p.ℓ.,9-55,[1]p. incl.col.plates. 13x19cm.

NK 0206749 CtY DLC-P4

DD 89 K72+

Knötel, Paul, 1858-
Bilderatlas zur deutschen Geschichte. Bielefeld, Velhagen & Klasing, 1895.
xii, 160 p. illus. 27cm.

1. Germany--Hist.--Pictorial works.

NK 0206750 NIC OOxM CtY MH

CR482 K57 1922

Knötel, Paul, 1858-
Bürgerliche Heraldik. 3. verb. und erweiterte Aufl. Breslau, W. John, 1922.
37 p. illus.

1. Heraldry - Europe. I. Title.

NK 0206751 CU

KNOETEL, Paul, 1858-
Die figurengrabmäler Schlesiens. Inaug.-diss Jena. Kattowitz,1890.
pp.51.

NK 0206752 MH PU ICRL

4DD 3354

Knötel, Paul, 1858-
Geschichte Oberschlesiens für weitere Kreise dargestellt. Kattowitz, O.-S., Gebr. Böhm, 1906.
163 p.

NK 0206753 DLC-P4 PPeSchw

4PT Ger.- 2607

Knötel, Paul, 1858-
Im Kampf um die Heimat; eine Geschichte aus schweren Tagen. Mit Bildern von Richard Knötel. Leipzig, K. Siwinna, 1904.
171 p.

NK 0206754 DLC-P4

N7950 K6

Knötel, Paul, 1858-
Kirchliche Bilderkunde Schlesiens. Ein Hilfsbuch zur Geschichte und Kunstgeschichte Schlesiens. Glatz, Gebrüder Jenkner, 1929.
137 p. 8 plates.

Bibliographical footnotes.

1. Christian art and symbolism. 2. Church decoration and ornament - Silesia. 3. Art - Silesia.

NK 0206755 CU

DD491 S53K56 1910

Knötel, Paul, 1858-
Oberschlesien einst und jetzt. Kurzgefasste Geschichte des Regierungsbezirks Oppeln für Schule und Haus. Kattowitz, Böhm, 1910.
vii,109 p. illus.

1. Silesia, Upper (Province) - Hist.

NK 0206756 CU

Knötel, Paul, 1858-
Oberschlesische Sagen; nacherzählt von Paul und Hildegard Knötel; mit Bildern von Paul Knötel. Leipzig und Kattowitz, C. Siwinna, Phonix-Verlag, 1907.
120p.

NK 0206757 OCl

Knötel, Richard, 1857-1914, illus.
Deutschlands Ruhmeshalle im 19 Jahrhundert
see under Kittel, Paul, ed.

Knoetel, Richard, 1857-1914.
Die eiserne Zeit vor hundert Jahren; Heimatbilder aus den Tagen der Prüfung und der Erhebung, 1806-1813. Bild und Wort von R. Knötel. Kattowitz: C. Siwinna [1906]. 32 l. illus. ob. 4°.

Mutilated.

1. Germany.—History, 1806-13. 2. Napoleonic wars, 1806-13.
N. Y. P. L. November 13, 1911.

NK 0206759 NN

Knoetel, Richard. *2821.48
Die eiserne Zeit vor hundert Jahren. [1806-1813.] Heimatbilder aus den Tagen der Prüfung und der Erhebung. Bild und Wort von Richard Knötel.
— Kattowitz. Siwinna. [1907.] (5) pp. (34) ff. Illus. 34 plates. L. 8°, obl.

G6672 — Germany. Hist. 1806-1813. — T.r.

NK 0206760 MB PP

Knötel, Richard, 1857-1914.
L'Europe sous les drapeaux; uniformes et scènes de la vie militaire des armées européennes de terre et de mer. Paris, Librairie de T. Lefèvre [18-?]
1 v. (chiefly illus.)

1. Uniforms, Military--Pictorial works.

NK 0206761 CaOTP

Knötel, Richard, 1857-1914.
Handbuch der Uniformkunde. Von Richard Knötel ... Leipzig: J. J. Weber, 1896. viii, 488 p. illus. 17cm. (J. J. Webers illustrierte Handbücher.)

"Quellen," p. [480]-488.

NK 0206762 NN MB ICN OCl MH

FILM 355.14 K75h

Knötel, Richard, 1857-1914.
Handbuch der uniformkunde. Leipzig, J. J. Weber, 1896.
(Webers illustrirte Katechismen [155])

Microfilm copy (negative)
Collation of the original: viii, 488p. illus.
Bibliography: p. [480]-488.

1. Uniforms, Military. (Series: Webers illustrirte Katechismen, 155)

Uniforms-Military||AcS 232814

NK 0206763 IU

VOLUME 300

Knötel, Richard, 1857–1914.
Handbuch der uniformkunde; die militärische tracht in ihrer entwicklung bis zur gegenwart. begründet von prof. Richard Knötel. grundlegend überarbeitet. fortgeführt und erweitert von Herbert Knötel d. j. und Herbert Sieg. Mit 1600 uniformdarstellungen nach zeichnungen von Richard Knötel und Herbert Knötel d. j. Hamburg. Von Diepenbroick-Grüter & Schulz [°1937]
4 p. l., 438 p. illus. 24½cm.
First edition published 1896.
1. Uniforms, Military. I. Knötel, Herbert, 1893– ed. II. Sieg, Herbert, joint ed. III. Title.
38-9707
Library of Congress UC480.K5 1937
Copyright A—Foreign 38012
[3] 355.14

TNJ
NK 0206764 DLC OrHi CtY NN MiD CaBVaU NNMM AMAU

Knötel, Richard, 1857-1914. *8193.02-110
Heerschau über die kriegsvölker Europa's; mit 118 illustrationen in feinstem farbendruck und 48 illustrationen in tondruck von Richard Knötel und mit erläuterndem texte von Fodor von Köppen ... [Leipzig? 189-?]
152 columns illus., col. double pl. 26cm.
Illustrated t.-p.

1. Uniforms, Military. I. Köppen, Fedor von, 1830-1904, ed. II. Title.

NK 0206765 MB

Knötel, Richard, illus.
Das Militärbilderbuch
see under Vogt, Hermann.

Knötel, Richard
Mittheilungen zur geschichte der militarischen tracht; beilagen zum V bis XIV banden der "Uniformenkunde". Rathenow, Babenzien, 1894-1909.
3 v.

NK 0206767 PP

UA714 .K75 1970 Knötel, Richard, 1857-1914.

Krippenstapel, Friedrich.
Die preussische Armee von den ältesten Zeiten bis zur Gegenwart. Geschichte unseres Heeres in Wort u. Bild. Bearb. von Friedrich Krippenstapel u. Richard Knötel. (1.) Die preussischen Husaren. Berlin, Selbst-Verlag Fr. Krippenstapel, 1883.
GDB 71-A4-232

[Knötel, Richard] 1857–1914.
Soldaten aller Staaten Europas. [Berlin: H. Toussaint & cie, 1889?] folder of 15 col'd pl. 17 x 20½cm.
Cover-title.
Plates signed: R. Knötel.

DEWITT CLINTON FALLS COLL.
1. Military uniforms. I. Title.
N. Y. P. L. September 28, 1939

NK 0206769 NN

Knoetel, R[ichard].
Die türkische Armee und Marine in ihrer gegenwärtigen Uniformirung dargestellt auf 12 Tafeln mit Abbildungen von Offizieren und Soldaten. Gezeichnet von R. Knötel. Nebst ... Mittheilungen über Organisation ... der türkischen Armee und Marine. Rathenow, M. Babenzien [1897]
19, (1) p. obl. 16°.

NK 0206770 NN

[Knötel, Richard] 1857–1914.
Die Uniformen der deutschen Armee; 8 systematische Farbentafeln mit Erläuterungen, nebst Angabe sämmtlicher Truppentheile, ihrer Standquartiere und des Errichtungsjahres. Berlin: A. Thümecke Nachf. [1897] 78, 25 p. col'd pl. 21cm.
Text signed: W. Kuske.

——— ——— Fünfte Auflage. Berlin: A. Thümecke Nachf. [1899]

94421. 1. Military uniforms, German. I. Kuske, W II. Title.

NK 0206771 NN CtY

Knoetel, Richard, 1857–1914.
Uniformenkunde. Lose Blätter zur Geschichte der Entwickelung der militärischen Tracht in Deutschland. Hrsg., gezeichnet und mit kurzem Texte versehen von Richard Knötel. Rathenow: M. Babenzien, 1890–1912. 17 v. plates. 4°.

1. Military uniforms.
N. Y. P. L. August 9, 1924

NK 0206772 NN DLC-P4 ICJ PP MH NBuG

Knötel, Richard, 1857-1914.
Uniformenkunde; lose Blätter zur Geschichte der Entwicklung der militärischen Tracht: Gesamtverzeichnis. Hrsg., gezeichnet und mit kurzem Text versehen von Richard Knötel; fortgesetzt von Herbert Knötel. Hamburg, H. v. Diepenbroick-Grüter, 1932.
50 p.

NK 0206773 CaOTP

Knötel, Richard, 1857-1914.
Unsere feldgrauen und blaujacken
see under Fernau, Peter.

Law Knötgen, Paul, ed.

Germany (*Democratic Republic, 1949–*) *Laws, statutes, etc.*
Die Bildung und Verwendung des Direktorfonds für das Planjahr 1953 im volkseigenen Handel. Gesetzliche Bestimmungen mit Erläuterungen von Paul Knötgen und Rolf Meyer. Berlin, Deutscher Zentralverlag [1954]

PL 539 .K72 KNOETSEN, John F
Japansche taal voor Hollandsch en Maleisch sprekende toeristen, Hollandsch-Japansch-Maleisch-Engelsch. Batavia, De Pertoendjoengan [1912?]
202 p.

"Also for English and Japanese people to learn Dutch and Malay language."

1. Japanese language--Conversation and phrase books. I. Title.

NK 0206776 InU

Wason Pamphlet PL Indonesia 101 Knoetsen, John F
Java tourists; how to speak Malay, Javanese, and Sundanese, by John F. Knoetsen, Tan Giem Hok [and] M.B. Sastro Widjojo. 3d ed. Batavia, Pertoendjangan [193-?]
70 p. 19cm.

NK 0206777 NIC

Knoettge, Rebecca Whitehill (Vaille) 1890–
How shall I punctuate it? By Rebecca W. Vaille and Mabel Van Duzee ... New York, Farrar & Rinehart, inc. [°1937]
viii, [5], 113 p. 23cm.
"Exercises": p. [49]–113.

1. English language—Punctuation. I. Van Duzee, Mabel, joint author. II. Title.
38–1622 Revised
Library of Congress PE1450.K64
[r45i2] 421.9

NK 0206778 DLC OrCS WaS NN

Knötzke, Fritz, 1903-
... Bemerkungen zur Wirbelsäule des Chondrodystrophen ... [Naumburg a. S.], 1928.
Inaug.-Diss. - Freiburg.
Lebenslauf.
"Abdruck aus der "Beiträgen zur pathologischen Anatomie und zur allgemeinen Pathologie', begründet von Ziegler, herausgegeben von Aschoff. (Bd. LXXXI, H. 3, 1929)"
"Literaturverzeichnis": p. 567.

NK 0206779 CtY

KNOETZSCH, Arthur, 1871–
Ueber γ-ketonsauren. Halle, 1897.

NK 0206780 MH-C NN PU

Knoevenagel, Claudia, 1909-
Azidoverbindungen in eiweiss und zuckerchemie und versuche zu Dipeptid und disaccharidsynthesen. ... Coburg, 1937.
Inaug. Diss. - Heidelberg, 1937.
Lebenslauf.

NK 0206781 ICRL CtY

WG 28200 Knoevenagel, Emil, 1865-
Beiträge zur Kenntnis der negativen Natur organischer Radikale. Göttingen, 1889.
35 p.

Inaug.-Diss. - Göttingen.

NK 0206782 CtY ICRL CU

QD481 .K65 Knoevenagel, Emil, 1865–
Beitraege zur kenntniss des asymmetrischen kohlenstoffatoms.
Berlin, 1892.
47p.
Habilitationsschrift, Heidelberg, 1892.

NK 0206783 NjP PPC

Knoevenagel, Emil, 1865– 546 Q001
Praktikum des anorganischen Chemikers. Einführung in die anorganische Chemie auf experimenteller Grundlage. viii,332, [4] p. 37 il. 7 tables. O. Leipzig: Veit & Co., 1901.

NK 0206784 ICJ NjP PPF PU OClW NNU-W

Knoevenagel, Emil, 1865– 546 Q900
Praktikum des anorganischen Chemikers. Einführung in die anorganische Chemie auf experimenteller Grundlage, von Dr. Emil Knoevenagel, ... Zweite, vollständig veränderte Auflage, mitbearbeitet von Dr. Erich Ebler, ... Mit zahlreichen Figuren, vier Tabellen und neun Tafeln. Leipzig, Veit & Co., 1909.
xxiv, 386, [2] p. 50 illus., VIII (*i.e.* 9) fold. pl. (incl. tables). 23cm.

NK 0206785 ICJ NcWsW ICRL NIC

VOLUME 300

Knoevenagel, Emil, 1865-
Praktikum des anorganischen chemikers, einführung in die anorganische chemie auf experimenteller grundlage ... dritte auflage ... Berlin und Leipzig, Vereinigung wissenschaftlicher verleger, 1920.
xxviii, 386 p., [7 l.] tables, diagrs.

NK 0206786 WaPS NcD

Knoevenagel, Julius, 1832-1914.
Redezeichenkunst und deutsche Kurzschrift. Eine Paralelle zwischen den Stenographien von F. X. Gabelsberger und Wilhelm Stolze. Hannover: Th. Schäfer, 1864. viii, 79(1) p., 16 l. 2. ed. 8°.

1. Shorthand.—Systems (German). 2. Gabelsberger, Franz Xavier. 3. Stolze, Wilhelm. BEALE SHORTHAND COLL.
N. Y. P. L. September 30, 1912.

NK 0206787 NN

Knoevenagel, Julius, 1832–1914, and W. Ryssel.
Vollstaendiges, practisches Lehrbuch der Stolze'schen Stenographie. Für Schulen und zum Selbstunterricht, bearbeitet von Julius Knoevenagel...und Wilhelm Ryssel... Hannover: C. Meyer, 1877. viii, 48 p. facsims. 5. ed. 8°.

458827A. 1. Shorthand—Systems, German, 1877. I. Stolze, Wilhelm, 1798–1867. II. Ryssel, Wilhelm, jt. au.
N. Y. P. L. May 27, 1930

NK 0206788 NN

ar W 4629
Knoevenagel, Kurt, 1911-
Die Zerfallsgeschwindigkeiten einiger sechsfach substituierter Aethane. Leipzig, Frommhold & Wendler, 1938.
42 p. illus. 23cm.

Diss.- Halle.

1. Ethanes.

NK 0206789 NIC MH CtY PU

Knoevenagel, Oskar.
Ueber die verbindungen des phenylhydrazins mit acrolein, mesityloxyd und allybromid.
Inaug. diss. Wuerzburg, 1887.

NK 0206790 ICRL PPAN

QZ K72e 1907
KNOEVENAGEL, Otto
Erkältung, eine dunkle, unklare Vorstellung gegenüber chemischen und physikalischen, biologischen, und meteorologischen Vorgängen. München, Aerztliche Rundschau, 1907.
94 p.

NK 0206791 DNLM

Knözinger, Anton
Das rechtsmittel des nebenklägers. München, J. Schreiber, 1933.
32 p. 22cm.
Inaug.-diss. - Erlangen.
"Literatur-Verzeichnis": p. 6-7.

NK 0206792 MH-L ICRL

Knözinger, Otto.
Möglickeiten staatlicher Regelung der Arbeitszeit. München, 1927.
60 p.
Diss. - Munich.

NK 0206793 PU CtY

Knof, Edwin.
... Die steuerliche revision der unternehmungen des handels und der industrie, von dr. Edwin Knof ... Leipzig, G. A. Gloeckner, 1921.
3 p. l., 90 p. 23½cm. (Betriebs- und finanzwirtschaftliche forschungen ... hft. 12)
"Benutzte literatur": verso of t.-p.

1. Taxation—Germany.

Library of Congress HJ2687.K5 21-17773

NK 0206794 DLC NN

Knof, Rudolf.
Die Preisbewerbung. Borna-Leipzig: R. Noske, 1912. viii, 39 p. 8°.
Dissertation, Erlangen.
Bibliography, p. vii-viii.

1. Rewards.—Jurisprudence, Germany.
N. Y. P. L. December 17, 1913.

NK 0206795 NN ICRL CtY NIC

[**Knoff, Christoffer,**] d. 1611.
Dagbog over Daniel Rantzovs Vinterfelttog i Sverig fra den 20de Oktober 1567 til den 14de Februar 1568. (In: Rørdam, H. F., editor. Monumenta historiæ Danicæ... Kjøbenhavn, 1884. 8°. Række 2, Bind 1, p. [1-]350.)
Bibliographical footnotes.

1. Denmark — Hist., 1563–1570. 2. Sweden—Hist., 1563–1570. 3. Rantzau, Daniel, 1529–1569. 4. Title.
N. Y. P. L. January 7, 1925

NK 0206796 NN

Knoff, Gerald E
Christian education and present tensions ... [Chicago, Ill., International council of religious education, 1944]
(On cover: Document prepared for the study of Christian education, October 23, 1944)
Mimeographed.

NK 0206797 NNUT

Knoff, T.H.
T.H. Mennesket. 1912.

NK 0206798 NdU

Pamph. v.446
KNOFF, Thomas Hans, 1848-1929.
Studier over sandheten. Oslo, Olaf Norli [1925]
276p. 24cm.

NK 0206799 MH-AH

YA9451
Knoflach, Augustin.
French simplified...especially intended for self instruction. New York, 1884.
20p.

NK 0206800 DLC

Knoflach, Augustin.
German simplified. Being a concise and lucid explanation of the principles of the German language ... By Augustin Knoflach ... New York, A. Knoflach, 1885.
iv, 207 p. 20cm.

1. German language—Grammar—1870- 10-25050†

Library of Congress PF3111.K55 1885 a

NK 0206801 DLC

Knoflach, Augustin.
German simplified. Being a concise and lucid explanation of the principles of the German language ... By Augustin Knoflach ... New York, A. Knoflach, 1885.
iv, 207, [72] p. 19½cm.
"Key to 'German simplified no. [1-11]'" inserted.

1. German language—Grammar—1870- 10-25051†

Library of Congress PF3111.K55 1885

NK 0206802 DLC

Knoflach, Augustin.
German simplified. Being a concise and lucid explanation of the principles of the German language, accompanied by numerous examples and exercises, and forming a complete course of instruction for the purposes of reading, business, and travel... By Augustin Knoflach... New York: Univ. Pub. Co., 1891. iv, 207 p. 12°.

177690A. 1. German language—Grammar.
N. Y. P. L. September 14, 1925

NK 0206803 NN MH Or

Knoflach, Augustin.
Graded exercises for translation from German into English and from English into German. By Augustin Knoflach ... San Francisco, J. A. Hofmann, 1884.
83, [1] p. 17cm.

1. German language—Composition and exercises. 10-24798†

Library of Congress PF3111.K57

NK 0206804 DLC

Knoflach, Augustin.
A manual of the German language. By Augustin Knoflach. San Francisco, The author [1879]
119 p. 17½cm.

1. German language—Grammar—Outlines, syllabi, etc. 10-27431†

Library of Congress PF3118.K7

NK 0206805 DLC CU

Knoflach, Augustin
Manual of the German language. Phil., Potter, 1882.
119 p.

NK 0206806 PU

Knoflach, Augustin.
Sound-English. A language for the world, by Augustin Knoflach ... New York [etc.] Sold for the author by G. E. Stechert [1890]
iv, 5-63 p. 20½cm.

1. Spelling reform. 2. Language, Universal. 11-12799

Library of Congress PE1150.K5

NK 0206807 DLC PPL CU MH NN

VOLUME 300

Knoflach, Augustin.
A sound-English primer, by Augustin Knoflach ... New York [etc.] Sold for the author by G. E. Stechert [°1890]
iii, 68 p. 19cm.

1. Spelling reform. I. Title.
11—11817
Library of Congress PE1152.K5

NK 0206808 DLC

Knoflach, Augustin.
Spanish simplified. Being a concise and lucid explanation of the principles of the Spanish language ... By Augustin Knoflach. New York, A. Knoflach, 1884.
16 p. 20½cm.

1. Spanish language—Grammar—1870-
10—30273
Library of Congress PC4111.K6

NK 0206809 DLC

Knoflach, Augustin.
Spanish simplified. Being a concise and lucid explanation of the principles of the Spanish language... For use in the class-rooms of public and private schools, academies and business colleges. By Augustin Knoflach... New York: Newson & Co. [cop. 1887.] iv, 192 p. 12°. (Newson's modern language series.)

1. Spanish language.—Grammar.
N. Y. P. L. November 20, 1917.

NK 0206810 NN CtY MH ViU

KNOFLACH, Augustin. 3096.14
Spanish simplified. Being a concise and lucid explanation of the Spanish language, accompanied by numerous examples and exercises. [With Key.]
N. Y. University publishing company. 1892. iv, 192 pp. 12 parts in 1 v. 12°.
The Key, which forms part 12 of this work, is in 11 parts, each paged by itself, and is dated 1888.

NK 0206811 MB

Knoflach, Augustin.
Spanish simplified; being a concise and lucid explanation of the principles of the Spanish language, accompanied by numerous examples and exercises, and forming a complete course of instruction for the purposes of reading, business and travel. For use in the class-rooms of public and private schools, academies, and business colleges. New York, University publishing co., 1899.

NK 0206812 MH MiU

Knoflach, Augustin.
Spanish simplified; being a concise and lucid explanation of the principles of the Spanish language, accompanied by numerous examples and exercises, and forming a complete course of instruction for the purposes of reading, business, and travel. For use in the class-rooms of public and private schools, academies, and business colleges. New York, University publishing co., 1906.

NK 0206813 MH

Knoflach, Maria Nussbaumer-
see
Nussbaumer, Maria.

Knoflach, Valentin
Lehrgang der kalkulation nebst zahlreichen aufgaben fuer gewerbliche schulen sowie zum selbstunterrichte. Wien, Deuticke, 1909.
170 p.

NK 0206815 PU

Knofler (Joannes Paulus). * De sterilitate. 32 pp. 12°. *Viennæ, J. T. de Trattnern,* [1769].

NK 0206816 DNLM

Knogler, Elias, fl. 1610, respondent.
Disputationis De confusione lingvarum...
see under Crinesius, Christoph, 1584-1629, praeses.

Knogler, Gabriel.
Die Meteorologie zum Gebrauche bey seinen Vorlesungen. Landshut, In der F. Hagen'schen Buchhandlung, 1803.

NK 0206818 MH

Knogler (Martinus). * De hydrocephalo. 32 pp. 4°. *Halæ Magdeb., typ. J. C. Hendelii,* [1725].

NK 0206819 DNLM

Knohl, Dov, *ed.*
גוש עציון במלחמתו; יומנים, מכתבי-לוחמים, דינים-וחשבונות, סקירות, פרקי מלחמה, יזכור. ירושלים, המדור הדתי במחלקת לעניני הנוער והחלוץ של ההסתדרות הציונית, תשי"ד.
[Jerusalem, 1953/54]
31, 621 p. illus., maps. 25 cm. (משגב, ב)

1. Israel-Arab War, 1948—Personal narratives. I. Title. (Series: Misgav, 2) *Title transliterated:* Gush 'Etsyon be-milḥamto.
DS126.4.K55 55-46049

NK 0206820 DLC

Knohl, Johann Georg. 1808-78.
— Russia. London, 1844. 8°. 3464

NK 0206821 MdBP

Knoke, Adolf, Medizinalprakt. am städt. Krankenh. zu Hildesheim: Aus d. chir. Klinik d. Univ. Kiel. Nagelextension bei komplizierten Knochenbrüchen. Kiel 1913: (Gerstenberg, Hildesheim). 41 S. 8°
Kiel, Med. Diss. v. 9. März 1914, Ref. Anschütz
[Geb. 25. Febr. 87 Hildesheim; Wohnort: Kiel; Staatsangeh.: Preußen; Vorbildung: G. Andreanum Hildesheim Reife 07; Studium: Marburg 1, Leipzig 7, Kiel 4 S.; Coll. 31. Mai 13; Approb. 16. Febr. 14.] [U 14. 2132

NK 0206822 ICRL CtY DNLM MH

Knoke, Albert.
"Der Naumburger Dom: Frühgotik und heroische Monumentalität." Jahresarbeit des Oberprimaners Albert Knoke. [n. p., n. d.]
1 v. (unpaged) plates (part col.) photos. 41 cm.

1. Naumburg an der Saale. Dom.
NA5586.N3K6 726.6 48-39544*‡

NK 0206823 DLC

Knoke, Anton: Ausländische Wanderarbeiter in Deutschland. Leipzig: Deichert 1911. 108 S. 8° ¶(Im Buchh. ebd.)
Leipzig, Phil. Diss. v. 30. Mai 1911, Ref. Stieda, Schmid
[Geb. 15. März 85 Germete; Wohnort: Marienbronn, Kr. Pleschen; Staatsangeh.: Preußen; Vorbildung: Gymn. Warburg Reife O. 06; Studium: Leipzig Handelshochsch. 6, Univ. 4 S.; Rig. 24. Febr. 11.] [U 11. 3232

NK 0206824 ICRL OU IU CU PU CtY MH

Knoke, Arnold comp.
Deutsche kulturgeschichte in tabellen; eine übersicht über die gesamte entwickelung des deutschen volkes. Weisbaden, Kunzes, 1902. (16)p. F.

NK 0206825 OClW

HD 6059 G3 K58 **Knoke, Arnold**
Was kann unsere Tochter werden? Frauenbildung - Frauenberufe. Leipzig, Quelle & Meyer, 1929. 202p. 23cm.

1. Woman - Employment - Germany 2. Occupations 3. Education of women - Germany I. Title

NK 0206826 WU

Knoke, Arnold, 1869-
Das Zuchtmittel der Drohung im Eide ... von Arnold Knoke ... Hannover, Buchdruckerei des Stephansstifts, 1896.
55, [1] p. 21cm.
Inaug.-diss. - Erlangen.
"Lebenslauf": p. [56]
"Benutzte Litteratur": p. [5]

NK 0206827 MH-L ICRL PU OO

Knoke, Carl
see Knoke, Karl.

Knoke, Eberhard Theodor August Karl
see Knoke, Karl, 1873-

Knoke, Eduard, ed.
Lehzen, Georg Heinrich.
Die hauptstücke aus der betriebsweise der Lüneburger bienenzucht. Verfasst von Georg Heinrich Lehzen. Neu bearbeitet von Eduard Knoke ... Vierte auflage. Hannover, Verlag des Bienenwirtschaftlichen centralvereins, 1922.

DD 121 .K72 Knoke, Friedrich, 1844-1929?
Armin der Befreier Deutschlands, eine quellenmässige Darstellung. Berlin, Weidmann, 1909.
80 p. front., maps. 22 cm.

1. Arminius, Prince of the Cherusci. 2. Germany --Hist.--Early period to 843.

NK 0206831 MiU MH MnU NjP

PA 3903 Z8 K5 Knoke, Friedrich, 1844-
Begriff der Tragödie nach Aristoteles, von F. Knoke. Berlin, Weidmannsche Buchhandlung, 1906.
83 p. 24 cm.

Includes bibliographical references.

1. Aristoteles. 2. Tragedy. I. Title.

NK 0206832 CtY NNC CU-S MiU NjP PBm PU ICRL MA OCU IU MH

VOLUME 300

Knoke, Friedrich, 1844-
Bemerkungen zu dem sprachgebrauch des Tacitus, von dr. Friedrich Knoke ... Berlin, Weidmann, 1925.
36 p. 20½cm.

1. Tacitus, Cornelius—Language.

NK 0206833 MiU CU MA NIC OCU MH ICU

KNOKE, Friedrich.
Der christliche glaube nach Paulus. Osnabrück, 1922.
47 p. 21.5 cm.

NK 0206834 MH-AH

Gntl +cy2 K755e
Knoke, Friedrich, 1844-1929?
Eine Eisenschmelze im Habichtswalde bei Stift Leeden ... Mit 1 Tafel Abbildungen ... Berlin, 1901.
cover-title, 30p. 1 fold.map. 23cm.

1. Germany - Antiq.
2. Habichtswald, Germany

NK 0206835 CtY

Knoke, Friedrich, 1844-1929?
...Der gebrauch von plures bei Tacitus...
Zerbst, Schnee, 1890.
19 p. (Dissertationes Taciteae. v. d. v.2, no. 3)

NK 0206836 PBm NjP CtY

Knoke, F[riedrich], 1844- Ger 370.2
Gegenwärtiger stand der forschungen über die Römerkriege im nordwestlichen Deutschland. Berlin, Weidmann, 1903.
pp. 80. Plate.

Germany-Antiq.|Do.- Hist. B. C. 12-A. D. 16

NK 0206837 MH CtY

KNOKE, Friedrich, 1844-1929?
Der Investiturstreit nach den Streitschriften der Zeit. - Inaugural dissertation. Dessau, 1874.
sm.8°. pp.51.

NK 0206838 MH

Knoke, Friedrich, 1844-
Die kriegszüge des Germanicus in Deutschland, von dr. Friedrich Knoke ... mit 5 karten. Berlin, R. Gaertner, 1887.
ix p., 1 l., 566, [2] p. v maps (4 fold.) 23cm.
MH "Wiederholt erwähnte schriften": p. [vii]-ix.
——— Nachtrag. Berlin, R. Gaertner, 1889.
215, [1] p. illus. (map) 22½cm.
——— Zweiter nachtrag ... Berlin, R. Gaertner, 1897.
95, [1] p. pl. 23½cm.
1. Germany—Hist.—Early period to 843. 2. Germanicus Caesar.

Library of Congress DD121.K68 13—18565-7

NK 0206839 DLC PBm CaBVaU MH CtY MB

DD121 .K68
Knoke, Friedrich, 1844-
Die kriegszüge des Germanicus in Deutschland, von dr. Friedrich Knoke ... 2., mehrfach umgearb. aufl. Berlin, Weidmann, 1922.
x, [1], 512 p. viii pl., fold. map. 23cm.
"Wiederholt erwähnte schriften": p. [vii]-x.

1. Germany—Hist.—Early period to 843. 2. Germanicus Caesar, B.C. 15-A.D. 19.

NK 0206840 ICU OCU NcD PU MiU CtY IU NjP

Knoke, F[riedrich], 1844- Ger 370.3
Neue beiträge zu einer geschichte der Römerkriege in Deutschland. Berlin, Weidmann, 1907.
pp. 62. 2 plates.

Germany-Hist. B. C. 12-... D. 16||AcS 232821

NK 0206841 MH NjP

913.43 K755r 1927
Knoke, Friedrich, 1844-
Der römische Tumulus auf dem Schlachtfelde des Teutoburger Waldes. Berlin, Weidmann, 1927.
42p. plates. 22cm.

1. Germany. Antiquities, Roman. 2. Mounds. Germany. Teutoburger Wald.

NK 0206842 KU CU NcD IU

Knoke, Friedrich, 1844-
Die römischen forschungen im nordwestlichen Deutschland...
Berlin, 1900.
1 v. 8°
DD53.K72

NK 0206843 DLC CtY MH

TG 16 K72
Knoke, Friedrich, 1844-
Die römischen Moorbrücken in Deutschland.
Berlin, R. Gaertner, 1895.
136 p. illus., maps. 25cm.

1. Bridges--Hist. 2. Germany--Antiquities, Roman.

NK 0206844 NIC NjP CU

Knoke, Friedrich, 1844-1929.
Das Schlachtfeld im Teutoburger Walde ...
Berlin, 1899.
46 p., 1 l. 23.5 cm.
1. Teutoburger Wald, Battle of, A.D.9.

NK 0206845 CtY

Knoke, Friedrich.
Ueber die Katharsis der Tragodie bei Aristoteles; eine Erwiderung. Osnabruck, 1908, J. Kisling.

NK 0206846 MA NjP PU

Knoke, Friedrich, 1844-
Ueber hic und nunc in der Oratio obliqua.
Bernburg, Druck von O. Dornblüth, 1881.
11 p. 25 cm.
"Programm" - Herzogliche Karl Gymnasium, Bernburg.

NK 0206847 NIC MH

Knoke, Friedrich, 1844-1929.
Ein Urteil über das Varuslager im Habichtswalde ... Mit 1. Tafel Abbildungen ... Berlin, 1901.
cover-title, 28 p. plate. 23.5 cm.
1. Habichtwalde - Germany.
2. Varus, Publius Quinctilius.

NK 0206848 CtY

Knoke, F[riedrich], 1844- Ger 370.19
Das Varuslager bei Iburg. Berlin, R. Gaertner, 1900.
pp. 30 +. 3 plates and map.

Teutoburger Wald, Battle of, A. D. 9||AcS 232824

NK 0206849 MH

Knoke, F[riedrich], 1844- Ger 370.10F
Das Varuslager im Habichtswalde bei stift Leeden. Berlin, R. Gaertner, 1896.
f°. pp. 20. 2 plates.

Teutoburger Wald, Battle of, A. D. 9||AcS 232823

NK 0206850 MH NjP PU

Knoke, Friedrich, 1913-
Die nichtgeographische Interpolation von Caesars Bellum Gallicum. Düsseldorf, Dissertations-Verlag G. H. Nolte, 1940.
102 p. 21 cm.
Inaug.-Diss.—Cologne.
Bibliographical footnotes.
Vita.

1. Caesar, C. Julius. De bello Gallico. I. Title.

PA6246.K6 51-47949

NK 0206851 DLC OCU ICU

FILM 12605 PA
Knoke, Friedrich, 1913-
Die nichtgeographische Interpolation von Caesars Bellum Gallicum. Düsseldorf, Dissertations-Verlag G. H. Nolte, 1940.
102 p. On film (Negative)
Inaug.-Diss.—Cologne.
Bibliographical footnotes.
Vita.
Microfilm. Original in Universitäts- und Stadtsbibliothek, Cologne.

NK 0206852 CU

Knoke, Georg, 1884-
De 'Charitio' mimo Oxyrhynchio ... Kiliae, 1908.
Pamphlet
Diss. inaug. - Kiel.
Vita.

NK 0206853 CtY PU MH NjP NN

Knoke, Georg Wilhelm, 1904-
Der eigentumserwerb des kommittenten bei der wareneinkaufskommission
Inaug. Diss. Gottingen, 1928
Bibl.

NK 0206854 ICRL

KNOKE, HEINZ, 1921-
Die grosse Jagd; Bordbuch eines deutschen Jagdfliegers. [Federzeichnungen: Willi Ostermeyer] Rinteln, C. Bösendahl [1952]
176 p. illus. 21cm.

1. World war, 1939-1945—Personal narratives, German. 2. World war, 1939-1945—Aerial operations. I. Title.

NK 0206855 NN MH

VOLUME 300

Knoke, Heinz, 1921-
I flew for the Führer; the story of a German airman. Translated by John Ewing. London, Evans Bros. [1953]
187 p. illus. 22 cm.

1. World War, 1939-1945—Aerial operations, German. I. Title.

D787.K613 940.544943 53-4439 ‡

MiD NN
NK 0206856 DLC CaBViP CaBVa CU OKentU OCl NcD PP

Knoke, Heinz, 1921-
I flew for the Führer; the story of a German fighter pilot. Translated by John Ewing, with an introd. by E. R. Quesada. [1st American ed.] New York, Holt [1954]
213 p. illus. 22 cm.

1. World War, 1939-1945—Aerial operations, German. I. Title.

D787.K613 1954 940.544943 54-5450 ‡

OO Or WaS WaE
NK 0206857 DLC Wa PPG IU NcC OEac TxU PP PSt TU Vi

Knoke, Heinz, 1921-
I flew for the Führer; the story of a German fighter pilot Translated by John Ewing, with an introd. by E. R. Quesada. New York, Holt [1954]
213 p. illus. 22 cm.

NK 0206858 MiU

---

ar W
50999 Knoke, J Oskar, 1855-
Die Kraftmaschinen des Kleingewerbes. Berlin, J. Springer, 1887.
xi, 355 p. illus. 24cm.

NK 0206859 NIC CU

Knoke, J Oskar, 1855-
Die kraftmaschinen des kleingewerbes.. 2.,verb.und verm.aufl.... Berlin, Springer, 1899.
12,529 p. diagrs. 24 cm.

1.Machinery. I.Main cd.(ST)

NK 0206860 NjP MiU ICJ

Knoke, K. Alb. Paul, 1874-
see
Knoke, Paul, 1874-

Knoke, Karl, 1841-1920.
Ausgaben des Lutherischen Enchiridions bis zu Luthers Tode und Neudruck der Wittenberger Ausgabe 1535. Stuttgart, Greiner & Pfeiffer, 1903.
40 p.

NK 0206862 PPeSchw

Knoke, Karl, 1841-1920.
Ein bild vom kirchlichen leben Göttingens aus dem jahre 1565. Beschwerdeschrift des prädikanten Hartmann Henremann an den Rat über den bürger Steffen Ramme, mitgeteilt von d. K. Knoke ...
(*In* Archiv für reformationsgeschichte ... Berlin, 1905. 23½cm. nr. 8. 2. jahrg., p. [363]-384)

1. Göttingen—Church history. 2. Ramme, Steffen. I. Henremann, Hartmann.
[*Full name:* Hans Georg Wilhelm Karl Knoke]
A C 34-1966
Title from Union Theol. Sem.
Library of Congress [BR300.A5 jahrg. 2]

NK 0206863 NNUT OU OCl OO

Knoke, Karl, 1841-1920.
Grundriss der pädagogik und ihrer geschichte seit dem zeitalter des humanismus. Vom evangelischen standpunkte dargestellt von D. K. Knoke ... 2. verb. und erweiterte aufl. Berlin, Reuther & Reichard, 1902.
viii, 240 p. 23cm.

1. Education—Hist.
[*Full name:* Hans Georg Wilhelm Karl Knoke]
2-19075 Revised
Library of Congress LA91.K7

NK 0206864 DLC PU ICJ MB

Knoke, Karl
Grundriss der praktischen theologie. Ein hülfsmittel beim studium der praktischen theologie für studierende und kandidaten der theologie. Aufl. 2, ungearbeitet. Göttengen, Vanderhoeck, 1889.
168p.

Bound with Lüttie, Friedrich. Das wesen der religion. 1889. no. 8.

NK 0206865 OClW

YAR Knoke, Karl, 1841-1920.
247 Grundriss der praktischen theologie. 3. erweiterte aufl. Goettingen, 1892.
197 p.

NK 0206866 DLC PPPD

Knoke, Karl, 1841-1920
Grundriss der praktischen theologie; ein huelfsmittel beim studium der praktischen theologie fuer studierende und kandidaten der theologie. 4...aufl. Goettingen, Vandenhoeck, 1896.
232 p.

NK 0206867 PPLT

Knoke, Karl, 1841-1920.
Heimat und Jugendzeit; Erinnerungen eines Siebzigjährigen an die Zeit um 1850. Hildesheim, A. Lax, 1948.
144 p. ports. 21 cm.

I. Title.
Full name: Hans Georg Wilhelm Karl Knoke.
A 50-6194
Harvard Univ. Library for Library of Congress [1]

NK 0206868 MH

Knoke, Karl, 1841-1920.
Niederdeutsches schulwesen zur zeit der französisch-westfälischen herrschaft 1803-1813, von d. Karl Knoke ... Berlin, Weidmann, 1915.
xvi, 431, [1] p. 25½cm. (*Added t.-p.:* Monumenta Germaniae paedagogica ... bd. LIV)
Bibliography: p. [xi]-xvi.

1. Education—Westphalia (Kingdom)
[*Full name:* Hans Georg Wilhelm Karl Knoke]
21-8253
Library of Congress LA720.M8 bd. 54

NK 0206869 DLC NcD MiU OU PU ICJ NN

Knoke, Karl, 1841-1920.
Paedagogische ideale und irrtuemer des 17. jahrhunderts... 23p.

AC931 [Haverford-Bauer pamphlets, v. 140, no. 7]
.H3
v.140

NK 0206870 DLC

FP50 **Knoke, Karl, 1841-1920.**
K755p **Praktisch-theologischer kommentar zu den Pastoralbriefen des apostels Paulus.** Göttingen, Vandenhoeck & Ruprecht, 1887-89.
2 v. 23 cm.

Includes bibliography.
Contents.- 1. t. Der zweite Brief an Timotheus.- 2. t. Der erste Brief an Timotheus und der Brief an Titus.

NK 0206871 CtY-D MH NjPT

822.8 KNOKE, Karl, 1841-1920.
K72re Recht und Pflicht der evangelischen Kirche hinsichtlich der religioesen Unterweisung ihrer heranwachsenden Jugend. Guetersloh, Bertelsmann, 1912.
192p. 22cm.

NK 0206872 MH-AH

Knoke, Karl, 1841-1920.
Rede zur feier der geburtstages seiner majestät des Kaisers und Königs am 27. januar 1891 ... gehalten von Karl Knoke. Göttingen, Druck der Dieterichschen universitäts-buchdruckerei, W. F. Kaestner, 1891.
17 p. 30 cm. [Göttingen. Universität. Dissertationen. v. 31, no. 12]

NK 0206873 CU

KNOKE, Karl, 1841-1920.
Zur methodik der biblischen geschichte. Eine historisch-genetische untersuchungen. Ier theil. 2^e ausg. Hannover, 1878.
270 p.

NK 0206874 MH-AH IU

Knoke, Karl, 1873-
Beitrag zur kenntnis der wirkung des strychnin. Inaug.-diss. Kiel, 1898

NK 0206875 ICRL CtY DNLM MH

Knoke, Karl Ludwig Friedrich
see Knoke, Friedrich, 1844-1929?

Knoke, L Werner.
Some aspects of the current gold situation. Text of speech at the Annual Meeting of the Bankers' Association for Foreign Trade, Colorado Springs, Colorado, May 15, 1951. [n.p., 1951]
13l. 30cm.

Caption title.

1. Gold. I. Title.

NK 0206877 OrU

Knoke, Paul, 1874- comp.
Jherings jahrbücher für die dogmatik des bürgerlichen rechts ... 1.-12. bd., 1857-73; 13.-36. bd. (neue folge, 1.-24. bd.) 1874-96; 37.- bd. (2. folge, 1.- bd.) 1897-
Jena, F. Mauke [etc.] 1857-77; G. Fischer, 1878-

VOLUME 300

Knoke, Paul, 1874–
Das recht der gesellschaft nach dem Bürgerlichen gesetzbuch für das Deutsche reich. Von dr. jur. Knoke ... Jena, G. Fischer, 1901.
viii, 141, [1] p., 1 l. 24cm. (*Added t.-p.: Abhandlungen zum privatrecht und civilprozess des Deutschen reiches ...* 7. bd., 3. hft.)

1. Association and associations—Germany. 2. Corporation law—Germany. I. Title.

34-12220

NK 0206879 DLC CtY MH-L

Knoke, Rud.
C. Sallustius Crispus, Coniuratio Catilinae; Kommentar. 4. Aufl. Heidelberg, Quelle & Meyer [1950]
40 p. 19 cm. (Scriptores Latini, n. F.)

1. Sallustius Crispus, C. Catilina.

PA6653.A4K6 1950 57-26580 ‡

NK 0206880 DLC

Knoke, Theodor Friedrich Arnold
see Knoke, Arnold, 1869-

Knoke (Wilhelm). *Subnormale Temperatur bei Geisteskranken. Ein Beitrag zur Symptomatologie der Geisteskrankheiten. 41 pp. 8°. *Göttingen, W. F. Kaestner,* 1890.

NK 0206882 DNLM ICRL CU

Knoke (Wilhelm) [18-]. *Zur Statistik der Pneumonie. 43 pp., 1 l. 8°. *Kiel, L. Handorff,* 1894.

NK 0206883 DNLM CtY ICRL MH

Knokes, John.
See
Knox, John, 1505-1572.

Knokh, Karl
see
Knoch, Carl, 1864–

Knokke van der Meulen, W G
de
... De adoptione secundum codicem civilem ... submittit W.G. de Knokke van der Meulen ... Schoonhoviae, S.E. van Nooten, 1837.
3 p.l., 79, [5] p. 21cm.
Diss.- Utrecht.
Bibliographical footnotes.

NK 0206886 MH-L

Knokke, Belgium. Casino communal.
L'impressionnisme en Belgique avant 1914; [exposition] sous le haut patronage de M. Léo Collard, 3 juillet - 28 aout, 1955. [Bruxelles] Éditions de la connaissance [1955]
55 p. illus.
At head of title: VIII. Festival belge d'été.

NK 0206887 MH-FA

759.4
M433Zk
Knokke, Belgium, Casino communal.
Matisse; [exposition] Knokke, Le Zoute, Albert Plage, Grande salle des expositions de "La Réserve", 12 juillet-31 août 1952. Bruxelles, Éditions de la connaissance [1952]
35p. illus., ports. 25cm.

"Cet ensemble d'oeuvres d'Henri Matisse a été réuni et le present catalogue redigé par E.L.T. Mesens".

NK 0206888 IEN

759.4
P586Zk
Knokke, Belgium. Casino communal.
Picasso; [catalogue de l'exposition] Knokke Le Zoute, Albert Plage, grande salle des expositions de "La Réserve," 15 juileet-27 août 1950. Bruxelles, Éditions de la connaissance [1950]
23p. illus. 25cm.

"L'exposition'Picasso' a été organisée et le present catalogue rédigé par E. L. T. Mesens... avec la collaboration de J.-M.

de Vlieger... et de P. G. Van Hecke."

1. Picasso, Pablo, 1881- I. Mesens, Edouard L. T. 1903-

NK 0206890 IEN MH

759.06
K72s
Knokke, Belgium. Casino communal.
75 [i.e. Soixante-quinze] oeuvres du demi-siècle, 14 juil.-9 sept.,1951. Knokke-Le Zoute-Albert Plage, grande salle des expositions de "la Réserve." Bruxelles, Éditions de la connaissance,1951.
64p. plates. 24cm.
"... organisée par E.L.T. Mesens.

NK 0206891 IEN MH

Knol, Hendrik Dirk Michiel.
Beginselen van het privaatrecht. 8., herziene en verm druk. Wassenaar, G. Delwel [1943]-48.
2 v. 24 cm.
Vol. 2: 6. herziene druk, 1943.
"Literatuur": v. 1, p. [339]-341. v. 2, p. [290]-291.

1. Civil law—Netherlands. 2. Commercial law—Netherlands.

49-22849*

NK 0206892 DLC

Knol, Hendrik Dirk Michiel.
Beginselen van het privaatrecht. 10. herziene druk. 's-Gravenhage, V/h G. Delwel, 1952-57.
2 v. 24 cm.

1. Civil law—Netherlands. 2. Commercial law—Netherlands.

53-38959 rev ‡

NK 0206893 DLC

Knol, Hendrik Dirk Michiel.
Belasting- en sociale wetgeving. 's-Gravenhage, V/h G. Delwel, 1953.
171 p. 23 cm.

1. Taxation — Netherlands — Law. 2. Insurance, Social — Netherlands. I. Title.

54-26479 ‡

NK 0206894 DLC

Knol, Hendrik Dirk Michiel.
Civielrechtelijke aansprakelijkheid van directie en commissarissen van naamlooze vennootschappen volgens nederlandsch recht, door mr. H. D. M. Knol. Zwolle, W. E. J. Tjeenk Willink n. v. [1936]
viii, 359 p. 23cm.
"Geraadpleegde literatuur": p. 353-359.

1. Stock companies—Netherlands. 2. Corporation law—Netherlands. 3. Legal responsibility—Netherlands. I. Title.

42-1667

NK 0206895 DLC MH-L

Ng€32
948k
Knol, Hendrik Dirk Michiel
Leidraad bij beleggingen. 's-Gravenhage, G. Delwel,1948.
162p. 24cm.

1. Investments. 2. Securities.

NK 0206896 CtY

Knol, Hendrik Dirk Michiel.
De philosophie der accountancy. 's-Gravenhage, V/h G. Delwel [1951]
42 p. 21 cm.

1. Accounting.

A 54-3076

New York Univ. Libraries HF5625.K6
for Library of Congress [1]

NK 0206897 NNU NN

Knol, Hendrik Dirk Michiel.
Recht voor het middenstandsexamen. 's-Gravenhage, V/h G. Delwel, 1950.
168 p. 23 cm.

1. Commercial law—Netherlands—Compends. 2. Law—Netherlands—Compends. I. Title.

53-34591 ‡

NK 0206898 DLC

Knol, Hendrik Dirk Michiel.
Vragen naar aanleiding van de beginselen van het privaatrecht. 's-Gravenhage, V/h G. Delwel, 1950.
99 p. 23 cm.

1. Civil law—Netherlands—Examinations, questions, etc.

55-33854 ‡

NK 0206899 DLC

Knol,Kornelis Swier.
On the atomic scattering factor for X-rays in the region of anomalous dispersion ... door Kornelis Swier Knol ... Groningen [etc.] J.B. Wolters' uitgevers-maatschappij n.v., 1934.
4 p.l.,46,[2] p.incl.tables,diagrs. 24cm.
Proefschrift--Groningen.
Foreword and "Stellingen" ([2] p.at end) in Dutch.

1.X-rays. 2.Absorption spectra. I.Title: Atomic scattering factor for X-rays.

NK 0206900 MiU ICRL CtY NNC

VOLUME 300

Knol, Kornelius Swier.
... Ueber ein verfahren zur messung komplexer leitwerte im dezimeterwellengebiet, von K. S. Knol und M. J. O. Strutt. Gepubliceerd in: Physica 9, 577-590, Juni 1942.

At head of title: Laboratoria N. V. Philips' gloeilampenfabrieken, Eindhoven (Holland), separaat 1617.

NK 0206901 MCM

Knol', M
see
Knoll, Max, 1897-

Knol, Petar, 1873- ed.

Zagreb. Strossmayerova galerija.
Akademijska galerija Strossmayerova. 6. izd., priredio dr. Petar Knoll, izdala Jugoslavenska akademija znanosti i umjetnosti. Zagreb, 1922.

Knoles, George Harmon.
The jazz age revisited; British criticism of American civilization during the 1920's. Stanford, Calif., Stanford University Press, 1955.
vii, 171 p. 23 cm. (Stanford University publications. University series. History, economics, and political science, v. 11)
Bibliography: p. 139-164.

1. U. S.—Civilization. 2. National characteristics, American. 3. Public opinion—Gt. Brit. I. Title. (Series: Stanford University. Stanford University publications. University series. History, economics, and political science, v. 11)

E169.1.K6 973.91 55—10016
——— Copy 2. AS36.L54 vol. 11

PP PSC WaSpG WaTC MiU OU OKentC PHC PSt FMU NN Wa OrSaW NcGW OrU OCU TU OOxM OO OC1W NcD ViU MB TxU
NK 0206904 DLC IU DAU CaBVaU OrAshS MtBC OrP OrPR

Knoles, George Harmon.
... The presidential campaign and election of 1892, by George Harmon Knoles ... Stanford University, Calif., Stanford university press; London, H. Milford, Oxford university press, 1942.
268 p. front. (map) 25½ cm. (Stanford university publications. University series. History, economics, and political science. Vol. v, no. 1)
"Bibliography of works cited": p. 248-252.

1. U. S.—Pol. & govt.—1889-1893. I. Title.

E705.K57 329.01 42—17328
——— Copy 2. AS36.L54 vol. 5, no. 1

OFH PBm PHC DS PU NcGW TxU CU
NK 0206905 DLC WU WaS CaBVaU OrPR WaTC OU OCU OCl OO

Knoles, George Harmon, *ed.*
Readings in Western civilization, selected and edited by George H. Knoles and Rixford K. Snyder. Philadelphia, Lippincott [1951]
xi, 896 p. 26 cm.

1. Civilization, Occidental—Hist.—Sources. I. Snyder, Rixford Kinney, 1908- joint ed. II. Title.

CB245.K6 901 51-4103

NK 0206906 DLC FMU IU MtBC Or OrPS

Knoles, George Harmon, *ed.*
Readings in Western civilization, selected and edited by George H. Knoles and Rixford K. Snyder. Rev. Philadelphia, Lippincott [1954]
922 p. 26 cm.

1. Civilization, Occidental—Hist.—Sources. I. Snyder, Rixford Kinney, 1908- joint ed. II. Title.

CB245.K6 1954 901 53-11275 rev ‡

NcGW PV NcRS
NK 0206907 DLC WaWW OrPS MtBC MeB MiU PU OU

Knoles, Tully Cleon, 1876-
Agencies contributing to general education—abstract [by] Tully C. Knoles.
(*In* National education association of the United States. Addresses and proceedings, 1931. p. 616-618)

1. Education—U. S. I. Title.

E 33-581

Library, U. S. Office of Library of Congress — Education L13.N212 1931 [L13.N4 1931]

NK 0206908 DHEW

Knoll (A. P.). *Untersuchungen über die normale Pulsfrequenz der Rinder und Schweine nebst vergleichenden physiologischen kritischen Studien über die normale Pulsfrequenz des Menschen und der Haussäugetiere. [Zürich.] 75 pp. 8°. Dresden, O. Franke, 1911.

NK 0206909 DNLM

Knoll, Albert. *De senio. 21 pp., 1 l. 8°. *Viennæ, typ. vid. A. Stoeckholzer de Hirschfeld,* [1833].

NK 0206910 DNLM

PT2383 K352G4 1845
[Knoll, Albert]
Gedichte eines Oesterreichers. Leipzig, F.A.Brockhaus, 1845.
xii,156 p. 17cm.
Ascribed to A.Knoll. Cf. Deutsches Anonymen-Lexikon.

NK 0206911 CSt

Knoll, Albert
Zur kenntniss der B-nitrosalicylsaeure und der B-nitrobenzamido-benzoesaeure und abkoemmlinge...
Goettingen, 1878
Inaug. diss. Goettingen.

QD341 .A7K6

NK 0206912 DLC

Div.S. 271.3 K72E
Knoll, Albert , pater, 1796-1863.
Esposición de la Regla de los frailes menores de nuestro padre S. Francisco de Asis, escrita en latín por Alberto de Bulsano. Traducida por Juan B. Díaz. Santiago, Imprenta Gutenberg, 1882.
viii, 707 p. 25 cm.

1. Francesco d'Assisi, Saint, 1182-1226. Regula. 2. Franciscans. I. Title.
Secular name: Joseph Knoll.

NK 0206913 NcD

[Knoll, Albert] 1796-1863.
Expositio Regulae F.F.Minorum S.P. Francisci Ass. ex delcarationibus Romanorum Pontificum, Sancto Bonaventura, aliisque probatis auctoribus congesta, a Reverendissimo P.Alberto a Bulsano ... Oeniponte, F.Rauch, 1850.
xiv, 518, [2] p.

NK 0206914 MdSsW

Knoll, Albert, pater, 1796-1863.
Institutiones theologiae dogmaticae generalis seu fundamentalis. Oeniponti, 1852.

NK 0206915 MiD

BX1751 K59 1864
Knoll, Albert, pater, 1796-1863.
Institutiones theologiae dogmaticae generalis seu fundamentalis conscriptae a reverendissimo p. Alberto a Bulsano ... Editio tertia ab auctore revisa et aucta. Taurini Petri, Hyac. Filii, Marietti, 1864.
526 p.
"Praefatio ad editionem secundam" signed: Fr. Albertus Knoll.

1. Catholic church - Doctrinal and controversial works - Catholic authors. 2. Theology, Doctrinal. I. Title.

NK 0206916 CU KAS

Knoll, Albert, pater, 1796-1863
Institutiones theologiae dogmaticae generalis seu fundamentalis. Ed. 4. Augustae Taurinorum, P. Marietti, 1868.
526p. 22cm.

NK 0206917 KAS OClStM

Knoll, Albert, pater, 1796-1863.
Institutiones theologiae dogmaticae generalis seu fundamentalis. Ed. 5. Augustae Taurinorum, P. Marietti, 1871.
526p. 22cm.

NK 0206918 KAS

Knoll, Albert, *pater,* 1796-1863.
Institutiones theologiae dogmaticae generalis seu fundamentalis conscriptae a reverendissimo p. Alberto a Bulsano ... Editio sexta. Augustae Taurinorum, ex typographia pontificia et archiepiscopali eq. Petri Marietti, 1877.
3 p. l., [3]-526 p., 1 l. 21cm.
"Praefatio ad editionem secundam" signed: Fr. Albertus Knoll.

1. Catholic church—Doctrinal and controversial works. 2. Theology, Doctrinal. I. Title.
[*Secular name:* Joseph Knoll]

40-17687

Library of Congress BX1751.K677 1877
[2] 230.2

NK 0206919 DLC DHN

Knoll, Albert, pater, 1796-1863.
Institutiones theologiae dogmaticae generalis seu fundamentalis. Ed. 7. Augustae Taurinorum, P. Marietti, 1880.
526p. 22cm.

1. Apologetics - 19th cent.

NK 0206920 KAS

Knoll, Albert, pater, 1796-1863.
Institutiones Theologiae Dogmaticae Generalis. Taurini, 1882.

NK 0206921 OClStM DHN

---

31 K71 in 1853 Law Lib.
Knoll, Albert, pater, 1796-1863.
Institutiones theologiae theoreticae seu dogmatico-polemicae concinnatae, a Alberto a Bulsano ... Taurini, ex typis Hyacinthi Marietti, 1853-55.
4 v.

Contents.- pars 1. De Deo in se spectato.- pars 2. De Deo in relatione ad universum consideratio.- pars 3. De Deo lapsi humani generis redemptore.- pars 4. De Deo hominum sanctificatore.

NK 0206922 CU MiD PLatS

VOLUME 300

Knoll, Albert, pater, 1796-1863.
Institutiones theologiae theoreticae seu dogmatico-polemicae ab auctore in compendium redactae. Augustae Taurinorum, P. Marietti, 1865.
2v.in 1. 21cm.

1. Theology, doctrinal.

NK 0206923 KAS MH-AH DHN

Knoll, Albert, pater, 1796-1863.
Institutiones theologiae theoreticae seu Dogmatico-polemicae concinnatae a ... P. Alberto a Bulsano ... Ed. 3a. Augustae Taurinorum, Petrus, H. Filius, Marietti, 1865.
v. 1 and 3.

NK 0206924 MdSsW

Knoll, Albert, pater, 1796-1863.
Institutiones theologiae theoreticae seu dogmatico-polemicae. Ed.4. Augustae Taurinorum, P. Marietti, 1868.
6v. 22cm.

1. Theology, doctrinal.

NK 0206925 KAS PLatS OClStM

Knoll, Albert, pater, 1796-1863.
Institutiones Theologiae Theoreticae. 2 v. Oeniponti, 1872.

NK 0206926 OClStM

Mpn30 K75 Knoll, Albert, father, 1796-1863.
Fr.Alberti Knoll a Bulsano institutiones theologiae theoreticae seu dogmatico-polemicae ab auctore in compendium redactae ... Augustae Taurinorum, ex typographia pontificia et archiepiscopali eq.Petri Marietti, 1881.
2v. 21cm.

NK 0206927 CtY KAS

X BJ 1249 K72 v.1-2 Knoll, Albert, pater, 1796-1863.
... Institutiones theologiae theoreticae seu dogmatico-polemicae ab auctore in compendium redactae. Augustae Taurinorum, ex typographia pontificia et archiepiscopali eq. Petri Marietti 1884.
2 v.

NK 0206928 NSyL

Knoll, Albert, O.F.M.Cap., 1796-1863.
Institutiones theologiae theoreticae seu dogmatico-polemicae, ab auctore in compendium redactae et a sac. Eugenio Morandi recognitae, auctae, emendatae. Augustae Taurinorum, P. Marietti, 1892.
2 v. 22 cm.

NK 0206929 PLatS

Knoll, Albert, O.F.M.Cap., 1796-1863.
Predigten für die festtage des kirchenjahres. Brixen, A. Weger, 1870.

vi, 780 p. front. (port.) 21 cm.

NK 0206930 PLatS

Knoll, Albert, pater, 1796-1863.
Predigten für die Festtage des Kirchenjahres; 2. Auflage. Brixen, A. Weger, 1874.
780p 22cm

NK 0206931 MnCS

Knoll, Albert, pater, 1796-1863.
Predigten für die Sonntage des Kirchenjahres; 2. Auflage. Brixen, A. Weger, 1871.
viii, 615p 22cm

NK 0206932 MnCS

Knoll, Albert, O.F.M.Cap., 1796-1863.
Sonntags predigten für das katholische kirchenjahr. Gesammelt aus dem handschriftlichen nachlass des A. Knoll. Brixen, A. Weger, 1867.

6-615 p. 21 cm.

NK 0206933 PLatS

Knoll, Albert Joseph
see Knoll, Albert, pater, 1796-1863.

Knoll, Alexander.
Geschichte der Steinsetzerbewegung. Leipzig, Zentralsverband der Steinarbeiter Deutschlands, etc., etc. [1925] 1913.

2 v. illus. 23 cm.
Contents: - 1. Geschichte der Strasse und ihrer Arbeiter. - 2. Die Berliner Steinsetzergesellenschaft, 1732-1893.

NK 0206935 MH NNC

Knoll, Alexander.
Geschichte der Strasse und ihrer Arbeiter. Leipzig, Zentralverband der Steinarbeiter Deutschlands [1925]

590 p. illus. 23 cm. (His Geschichte der Steinsetzerbewegung, 1)

NK 0206936 MH

Knoll, Alexander, 1900-
Zur bewertung einiger reflexerscheinungen des fruehen kindesalters.
Inaug. diss. Leipzig, 1926 (Dresden)
Bibl.

NK 0206937 ICRL CtY

Knoll, Alexander Felix, 1901-

Taggart, Arthur Fay, 1884-
... Chemical reactions in flotation, by Arthur F. Taggart, T. C. Taylor and A. F. Knoll ... New York, American institute of mining and metallurgical engineers, inc., ©1930.

Knoll, Alexander Felix, 1901-
Reaction of organic compounds at the surface of heavy metal sulphides. Reaction of galena with aqueous solutions of potassium xanthate ... [By] Alexander F. Knoll. New York city [Pandick press] 1932.

3 p. l., 54 p. illus., diagrs. 23½cm.

Thesis (PH. D.)—Columbia university, 1933.
Vita.
Bibliography: p. 52-53.

1. Chemical reactions. 2. Chemistry, Organic. 3. Sulphides. 4. Galena. 5. Potassium xanthate.

33-12890

Library of Congress QD501.K76 1933
Columbia Univ. Libr. (2) 541.39

NK 0206939 DLC CU MiU OU NNC

Knoll, Arthur Franklin
The mechanical delay of speech... Cincinnati 1930.
37 l.

NK 0206940 OCU

Knoll, August Maria, 1900- ed.
Dominicus a Jesu Maria, ord. Carm. disc.: Seine Persönlichkeit und sein Werk
see under title

Knoll, August Maria, 1900-
Das Kapitalismus-Problem in der modernen Soziologie. Wien, Verlag Herold, 1953.

66 p. 21 cm. (Soziologische Schriftenreihe, Heft 1)
Bibliographical references included in "Anmerkungen" (p. 35-62)

1. Capitalism. I. Title. (Series)

HB501.K57 55-19894

NK 0206942 DLC CU ICU InU MH NN LU

4BX-11 Knoll, August Maria, 1900-
Kardinal Fr. G. Piffl und der österreichische Episkopat zu sozialen und kulturellen Fragen, 1913-1932, Quellensammlung von August M. Knoll. Einband von Rose Reinhold. Wien, Reinhold-Verlag, 1932.
264 p. (Kleine historische Monographien, Nr. 35)

NK 0206943 DLC-P4 CU

Knoll, August Maria, 1900-
Der soziale gedanke im modernen katholizismus ... von August M. Knoll, mit ... bildtafeln. Einband von Rose Reinhold. Wien [etc.] Reinhold-verlag [1932-

v. front., ports. 15 cm. (Added t.-p.: Kleine historische monographien, beilage der Berichte zur kultur- und zeitgeschichte; hrsg. von Nikolaus Hovorka ... nr. 34.

Contains bibliographies.

CONTENTS.—I. bd. Von der romantik bis Rerum novarum.

1. Socialism and Catholic church. 2. Catholic church. Pope, 1878-1903 (Leo XIII) Rerum novarum (15 May 1891) 3. Labor and laboring classes.

A C 33-77 rev

New York. Public Libr. for Library of Congress [r51c2]

NK 0206944 NN

HN18 .W45 1954 Knoll, August Maria, ed.

Wiener Soziale Woche. *1st, Vienna, 1954.*
Sozialpolitik an der Wende; Vorträge und Ergebnisse der Ersten Wiener Sozialen Woche. Hrsg. von August M. Knoll und Karl Kummer. [Wien, Verein für Sozial- und Wirtschaftspolitik] 1955.

Knoll, August Maria, 1900-
Von den drei Wesenstheorien der Gesellschaft; Individualismus, Totalismus, Personalismus. Ein Vortrag. Wien, Manzsche Verlags- und Universitätsbuchhandlung, 1949.

20 p. 21 cm.

1. Personalism. 2. Individualism. 3. Totalitarianism.

B828.5.K57 51-30757

NK 0206946 DLC NN

VOLUME 300

Knoll, Carl.
Taschenbuch zum abstecken der kurven an eisenbahnen und strassen. Mit 28 holzschnitten und 6 tabellen. Für ingenieure, geometer, bauunternehmer und techniker überhaupt, von Carl Knoll ... Stuttgart, A. Kröner, 1873.
viii, 185 p. incl. tables, diagrs. 17½cm.

1. Curves in engineering. 2. Railroads—Curves and turnouts. 3. Roads. I. Title.

NK 0206947 ViU

Knoll, Carl. 625.11 Q200
Taschenbuch zum Abstecken der Kurven an Strassen und Eisenbahnen. Von C. Knoll. Zweite Auflage. Neu bearbeitet von W. Weitbrecht, ... Mit 41 Figuren und 11 Zahlentafeln. Stuttgart, A. Bergsträsser. 1902.
xii, 180, 207 p. 41 diagrs. 17½cm.

NK 0206948 ICJ NN

Knoll, Carl.
Taschenbuch zum abstecken der kurven an strassen und eisenbahnen ... 4. aufl. neu bearb. von W. Weitbrecht ... und M. Knoblich ... Leipzig, 1924.
2 v. in 1. diagrs., tables. 18 cm.

NK 0206949 RPB

Knoll, Carl, of Glogau.
Das beneficium divisionis des Bürgen ... von Carl Knoll ... Glogau, Glogauer Druckerei-Verein, 1895.
vi, 63 p. 21½cm.
Inaug.-diss. - Breslau.
Bibliographical footnotes.

NK 0206950 MH-L ICRL

Knoll, Carl, writer on decoration and ornament.
Die kunst des schmückens; eine klärung des schmuckproblems durch wort und bild für schaffende und geniessende, von Carl Knoll und dr. Fritz Reuther; mit 217 teils farbigen abbildungen. Dresden, G. Kühtmann, 1910.
4 p. l., 146, [4] p. 74 pl. (partly col.) 24cm. M. 12
Descriptive letterpress on verso of each plate.

1. Clothing and dress. 2. Decoration and ornament. I. Reuther, Fritz, joint author.

Library of Congress TT507.K7 10-28019

NK 0206951 DLC CaOTP MB ICJ

Knoll, Carl Adolf Felix Willy, 1878-
see Knoll, Willy, 1878-

Knoll (Charles). *De la fièvre et des antipyrétiques dans le typhus abdominal. 1 p. l., 30 pp. 4°. *Strasbourg*, 1872.

NK 0206953 DNLM PPC

Knoll, Christian Gottlob.
Mittelmeerorient. Reise-Eindrücke und Betrachtungen über die Stätten der Heiligen Schrift von Ch. G.K. ... Zürich, Knoll [1935]
107 p. 19 pl. + 2 maps. 8°.

NK 0206954 PPDrop

Knoll, Constantin, 1799-1865.
Die Münz- u.Medaillen-Sammlung des verstorbenen C.Knoll in Nürnberg. Behufs öffentlicher, zu Nürnberg stattfindender Versteigerung geordnet und beschrieben von J.R.und H.A.Erbstein. Nürnberg, J.A.Stein (A.Köllner), 1866.

NK 0206955 MH

Knoll, Curt
see Knoll, Kurt.

Knoll, Denys W.
Climatology Asiatic station, prepared for the use of the United States Navy by Denys W. Knoll and Asiatic Fleet, Aerological Unit. Washington, U. S. Govt. Print. Off., 1941.
v, 97 p. illus., charts. 30 cm. (H. O. [publication] no. 219)
"Supplement[s]: Asiatic Fleet information bulletin no. 3-39."
Bibliography: p. 97.

1. Meteorology, Maritime—Pacific Ocean. 2. Meteorology, Maritime—Indian Ocean. 3. Asia—Climate. I. U. S. Navy. Asiatic Fleet. (Series: U. S. Hydrographic Office. Publication no. 219)

QC982.K6 551.5 50-47294

NK 0206957 DLC PP NN

Knoll, Denyse, 1914-
... Contribution à l'étude du parasitisme intestinal au cours de la première enfance ... Paris, Vigot frères, 1937.
63, [1] p. tables, diagr.

Thèse, Lille.
"Bibliographie": p. [55]-63.

1. Worms, Intestinal and parasitic. 2. Children - Diseases

NK 0206958 NNC CtY

Knoll, Ernst. Bericht ueber die auf die geschichte der kunst im altertum bezuegliche litteratur der jahre 1880-92. 53 pp. (*Jahresb. ueber fortschr. der class. alterth.* v. 81, 1895. p. 1.)

NK 0206959 MdBP

Knoll, Ernst.
Studien zur ältesten kunst in Griechenland. Bamberg, 1890.

NK 0206960 NjP

Knoll, Ernst, 1889– Referendar: Der Begriff der Ehe nach heutigem Recht. Karlsruhe i. B.: Braun 1913. XIV, 114 S. 8° ¶ Im Buchh. ebd.
Würzburg, Rechts- u. staatswiss. Diss. v. 23. Juni 1913, Ref. Mayer
[Geb. 9. Aug. 89 Magdeburg; Wohnort: Magdeburg; Staatsangeh.: Preußen; Vorbildung: König-Wilhelms-G. Magdeburg Reife 07; Studium: München 3, Berlin 3, Halle 1 S.; Rig. 20. Dez. 12.] [U 13. 1381

NK 0206961 ICRL MH-L CtY

Law
Knoll, Ernst, 1889- ed.

Germany. *Reichsgericht.*
Entscheidungen des Reichsgerichts in Zivilsachen; Sammlung der noch wichtigen Entscheidungen nach Fachgebieten geordnet, hrsg. von L. Auerbach [et al.] Berlin, W. de Gruyter, 1950-

---

Law
Knoll, Ernst, 1889- ed.

Germany. *Reichsversicherungsamt.*
Die grundsätzlichen Entscheidungen des Reichsversicherungsamts; hrsg. von Ernst Knoll [und] Horst Peters. Stuttgart, W. Kohlhammer, 1952-53.

Knoll, Ernst, 1889-
Grundsätzliches zur deutschen Wohnungs- und Siedlungspolitik. Eberswalde, R. Müller, 1939.
211 p. 22 cm. (Handbücherei des Wohnungs- und Siedlungswesens, Heft 28)

1. Housing—Germany. (Series)
HD7339.A3K6 331.833 A F 49-1068 rev*
Harvard Univ. Library for Library of Congress [r49b2]†

NK 0206964 MH CU ICU NN DLC NNC CtY NSyU

Knoll, Ernst, 1889– ed.
Der neuaufbau der sozialversicherung; grundlagen und grundfragen des Gesetzes vom 5. juli 1934 über den aufbau der sozialversicherung, von dr. E. Knoll ... Stuttgart-Berlin, W. Kohlhammer, 1934.
vii, 93 p. 20½cm. (*On cover:* Die sozialgesetzgebung des neuen staates ... bd. 5)

1. Insurance, Industrial—Germany. 2. Insurance, State and compulsory—Germany. 3. Insurance law—Germany. I. Germany. Laws, statutes, etc. II. Title.

Library of Congress HD7179.K57 36-11293
[2] 331.25440943

NK 0206965 DLC NN

Knoll, Ernst, 1889 – ed.
Die neuordnung der kranken- und knappschaftsversicherung, von dr. E. Knoll ... Stuttgart, W. Kohlhammer, 1933.
86 p. 20½cm. (*On cover:* Die sozialgesetzgebung des neuen staates. bd. 1)

1. Insurance, Health—Germany. 2. Insurance law—Germany. I. Germany. Laws, statutes, etc. II. Title.

34-41664

NK 0206966 DLC MH NN

Law
Knoll, Ernst, 1889- ed.

Das **Recht** des städtebaues, des siedlungswesens und der wohnungswirtschaft; sammlung der geltenden bestimmungen ... herausgegeben von dr. Knoll ... prof. dr. Schmidt ... Scholtz ... [u. a.] Eberswalde-Berlin-Leipzig, Verlagsgesellschaft Rudolf Müller [1939-

---

Knoll, Eugen: Die Organisation des Handwerks im Reichsland Elsaß-Lothringen. Strassburg: Strassb. Dr. u. Verlagsanst. 1913. 197 S. 8° ¶ Vollst. im Buchh. ebd.
Straßburg, Rechts- u. staatswiss. Diss. v. 5. Juli 1913, Ref. Sartorius Frh. v. Waltershausen
[Geb. 5. Dez. 64 Frankfurt a. O.; Wohnort: Straßburg; Staatsangeh.: Elsaß-Lothringen u. Preußen; Vorbildung: G. Saargemünd Reife 86; Studium: Straßburg 9 S.] [U 13. 1284

NK 0206968 ICRL PU MH CtY

Knoll (Eugène) [1840-1902]. *Quelques considérations sur la saignée dans le traitement de la pneumonie. 1 p. l., 32 pp. 4°. *Strasbourg*, 1869, 3. s., No. 225.
For Biography, see Arch. f. öff. Gsndhtspflg., Strassb., 1901-2, xxi, 339 (Seck).

NK 0206969 DNLM PPC

583.951 Knoll, F
K75b Die Brennhaare der euphorbiaceen-gattungen dalechampia und tragia. Wien 1905.
20p. diagrs.

NK 0206970 IU

Knoll, Felix.
Rechtsfreunde. Schauspiel in 3 Aufzügen. Berlin, E. Bloch [1907]
2 p.l., (1), 8-104 p. 8°.

NK 0206971 NN

VOLUME 300

Knoll (François-Joseph). *I. Quelle est l'utilité des tisanes et des apozèmes; quel est leur mode de préparation? II. [etc.] 51 pp. 4°. *Strasbourg*, 1838, No. 6, v. 3.

NK 0206972 DNLM

HS539 O7M8 K5 Knoll, Frank W
How masonry came to Oregon; a brief history of Multnomah Lodge no. 1, A. F. & A. M., Oregon City, Oregon, 1846-1948. [Multnomah? Or., 1948?]
[35] p. illus. 16cm.

1. Freemasons. Oregon City, Or. Multnomah Lodge no. 1.

NK 0206973 CU-B

Knoll, Franz, ed.

Reger, Anton, 1845–
A. Reger's militärdienstgesetzgebung des Deutschen Reiches. Mit den für das reich und das königreich Bayern gültigen vollzugsbestimmungen (wehrordnung und heerordnung) unter beifügung erläuternder bemerkungen in 2. und erweiterter 3. aufl. hrsg. und nunmehr unter mitwirkung von Franz Knoll ... in 4. aufl. neu bearb. von Heinrich Jolas ... Ansbach, C. Brügel & sohn, 1914.

Knoll, Franz: Die Geschichte des Dorfes Gutenfeld m. bes. Berücks. seiner Betriebsverhältnisse. [In Maschinenschrift.] 89 S., 1 Pl. 4°(2°). — Auszug in: Inaug.-Dissertationen d. phil. Fak. Königsberg i. P. (Königsberg [1921]: Ostpr. Dr.) S. 121—123. 8°
Königsberg, Phil. Diss. v. 18. März 1921, Ref. Hansen
[Geb. 3. Okt. 92 Harnowen, Kr. Wehlau; Wohnort: Königsberg i. P.; Staatsangeh.: Preußen; Vorbildung: RG. Insterburg Reife 14; Studium: Königsberg 7 S.; Rig. 22. Febr. 21.] [U 21. 7152

NK 0206975 ICRL

Knoll, Friedrich, 1752-1786
see Knoll, Heinrich Christoph Friedrich, 1752-1786.

Knoll, Friedrich Josef
see Knoll, Fritz, 1883-

Knoll, Friedrich Otto.
Die rolle der Maria Magdalena im geistlichen spiel des mittelalters. Ein beitrag zur kultur- und theatergeschichte Deutschlands, von Friedrich-Otto Knoll. Berlin und Leipzig, W. de Gruyter & co., 1934.
122 p. 23cm. (*Half-title:* Germanisch und deutsch; studien zur sprache und kultur, 8. hft.)
"Die vorliegende arbeit ist von der ... Universität Greifswald als doktor-dissertation angenommen worden."
"Aufstellung der benutzten literatur": p. 12-18.
1. Mary Magdalene, Saint—Drama. 2. Mysteries and miracle plays, German. 3. German drama—Medieval—History and criticism.
A C 34-1816
Title from Yale Univ. Printed by L. C.

NK 0206978 CtY NIC InU CU OCU PSt OU

Knoll, Fritz, joint ed.

Swoboda, Heinrich, 1856-1926, *ed.*
... Denkmäler aus Lykaonien, Pamphylien, und Isaurien. Ergebnisse einer im auftrage der gesellschaft von Julius Jüthner, Fritz Knoll, Karl Patsch und Heinrich Swoboda durchgeführten forschungsreise, herausgegeben von Heinrich Swoboda, Josef Keil und Fritz Knoll. Brünn, Wien [etc.] R. M. Rohrer, 1935.

Knoll, Fritz.

Reisch, Emil, 1863–
... Die Marienkirche in Ephesos [von Emil Reisch, Fritz Knoll und Josef Keil] Mit 3 tafeln in farbenlichtdruck, 1 tafel in lichtdruck und 96 abbildungen im texte.
(*In* Österreichisches archäologisches institut, Vienna. Forschungen in Ephesos. Wien, 1932. 40 x 30½cm. bd. IV, hft. 1. 1 p. l., ii, 106 p., 1 l. illus., IV pl. (part col., part fold.; incl. plan; in pocket) diagrs.)

Knoll, Fritz, 1883-
Die feierliche Rektorsinauguration der Universität Wien, 1943
see under Vienna. Universität.

Knoll, Fritz, 1883–
... Insekten und blumen; experimentelle arbeiten zur vertiefung unserer kenntnisse über die wechselbeziehungen zwischen pflanzen und tieren, von dr. Fritz Knoll ... Wien, Zool.-botan. gesellschaft, 1921-26.
3 v. illus., plates (part col.) 28cm. (Abhandlungen der Zool.-botan. gesellschaft in Wien. bd. XII)
CONTENTS.—hft. 1. I. Zeitgemässe ziele und methoden für das studium der ökologischen wechselbeziehungen. II. *Bombylius fuliginosus* und die farbe der blumen. 1921.—hft. 2. III. Lichtsinn und blumenbesuch des falters von *Macroglossum stellatarum*. 1922.—hft. 3. IV. Die *Arum*-blütenstände und ihre besucher. V. Über den blütenbesuch der honigbiene. VI. Die erfolge der experimentellen blütenökologie. 1926.
1. Insects. 2. Flowers. [1, 2. Insects and flowers]
Agr 25-178 Revised
Library, U. S. Dept. of Agriculture 410.9V67A bd.12

NK 0206982 DNAL MiU OU PU-B ICJ

Knoll, Fritz, 1883– *3310.3.117.Abt.1
Über netzartige Protoplasmadifferenzierungen und Chloroplastenbewegung. Plate.
(In Kaiserliche Akademie der Wissenschaften, Vienna. Sitzungsberichte. Mathematisch-naturwissenschaftliche Klasse. Band 117, Abteilung 1, pp. 1227-1241. Wien. 1908.)

H1447 — Histology. Vegetable.

NK 0206983 MB

Knoll, Fritz, 1883–
Die Wissenschaft im neuen Deutschland. Wien, Ringbuchhandlung A. Sexl, 1942.
38 p. 21 cm. (Wiener wissenschaftliche Vorträge und Reden, Heft 1)
"Vortrag gehalten im Rahmen der Vorträge des Deutschen wissenschaftlichen Institutes in Bukarest am 23. Mai 1941."
1. Learning and scholarship—Germany. I. Series.
Full name: Friedrich Josef Knoll.
AZ667.K5 A F 48-619*
Yale Univ. Library for Library of Congress [1]†

NK 0206984 CtY IU MH ICU NN DLC

ar V 3809 Knoll, G
Catalogue d'une collection de livres rétoromans d'une richesse fort rare et à un prix extrêmement modéré. Coire [1903]
16 p. 19cm.

1. Raeto-Romance literature--Bibl.--Catalogs. I. Title.

NK 0206985 NIC

W 4 F82 1938 Knoll, Gebhard, 1913-
Perifokale Entzündung und Allergie. Gelnhausen, Kalbfleisch [1938?]
35 p.
Inaug.-Diss. - Frankfurt am Main.
Bibliography: p. 34-35.

NK 0206986 DNLM

KNOLL, Georg.
Poesie und prosa. 1.Sammlung. [Gesühnt, erzählung.] São Leopoldo und Cruz Alta, Rio Grande do Sul, Rotermund & co., [192-.].
3 vol. Port.
Half-title:- Südamerikanische literatur, 19-21.

NK 0206987 MH

Knoll, Georg, respondent.
De relatis, sex posterioribus categoriis
see under Strauch, Aegidius, 1583-1657, praeses.

[**Knoll, Georg Friedrich**]
Die humanitäre Erneuerung; Grundlage und Grundzüge eine neuen Kulturgestaltung. [Von Friedrich von Frankfurt, pseud.] Herausgeber: Humanitheon-Collegium, Basel-Lörach. [1. Aufl.] Frankfurt, Die Neue Zeit, Humanitheon-Edition [1946]
64 p. 24 cm. (Die Bücher der Neuen Zeit. Schriften aus dem Humanitheon der Humanitären Erneuerung. Humanitheon-Bücher)
1. Humanism. I. Humanitheon. II. Title.
B821.K6 48-27558*

NK 0206989 DLC

Knoll, Gottfried.
... Der deutsche regierungsentwurf zu einer Völkerbundssatzung vom april 1919; zugleich betrachtungen zur Völkerbundsverfassung und zu ihrer reform, von dr. iur. Gottfried Knoll ... Leipzig, T. Weicher, 1931.
xv, [1], 98 p. 26cm. (Leipziger rechtswissenschaftliche studien, hrsg. von der Leipziger juristenfakultät. hft. 61)
"Vorschläge der deutschen regierung für die errichtung eines Völkerbundes": p. [86]-94.
"Literaturverzeichnis": p. [x]-xv.
1. League of nations. 2. League of nations—Germany. 3. European war, 1914-1918—Influence and results. I. Title.
32-31813
Library of Congress [2] 341.1

NK 0206990 DLC NN MH-L CU-L

KNOLL, Hans.
Experimentelle untersuchungen über die aktivität bei geisteskranken. Inaug.-diss., Basel. Berlin, W.de Gruyter & Co., 1924.
pp.36.
Cover serves as title-page.
"Sonderabdruck aus der Allgemeinen zeitsch. für Psychiatrie, bd.80, 1924."

NK 0206991 MH DNLM CtY MiU

Knoll (Hans). *Zur Differentialdiagnose zwischen Pankreas- und Magencarcinom. 27 pp. 1 l. 8°. *München, C. Wolf & Sohn*, 1901.

NK 0206992 DNLM

PT2047 C6K72 Knoll, Hans, 1890-
Theorie der Schauspeilkunst. Darstellung und Entwicklung ihres Gedankens in Deutschland von Lessing zu Goethe. Greifswald, Druck von J. Abel, 1916.
126 p. 23cm.
Cover title.
Inaug.-Diss. - Greifswald.
Vita.
Bibliography: p.[124]
1.Drama - Hist. & crit. - 18th cent.

NK 0206993 CSt IU CtY PU NNU

VOLUME 300

W 4
M96
1951
KNOLL, Hans, 1922-
Die Klinische und genealogische Stellung einer Gruppe um das Klimakterium und um die Involution auftretender Wahnerkrankungen. ⌈München⌉ 1951.
105 ℓ.
Typewritten copy.
Inaug.-Diss. - Munich.
1. Climacteric 2. Mental disorders

NK 0206994 DNLM

W 4
B52
1952
KNOLL, Hans Christoph.
Was bedeuten kurzfristige Kapillarresistenz-Änderungen? Basel, 1952.
22 p. illus.
Inaug.-Diss. - Bern.
Reprinted from the Helvetica medica acta, v. 16, 1949.
1. Capillaries

NK 0206995 DNLM

W 4
M96
1954
KNOLL, Hedwig, 1924-
Beitrag zur Geschichte der Epilepsie. München, 1954.
40 ℓ.
Inaug.-Diss. - Munich.
1. Epilepsy

NK 0206996 DNLM

Knoll, Heinrich.
Allgemeine Bilanzkunde. München, etc., C.H.Beck, 1938.

vii, 110 p. (Arbeit und Wissen, 4)

NK 0206997 MH NNC

Knoll, Heinrich.
Allgemeine Bilanzkunde. ⌈Herausgeber: R. Sellien⌉ Wiesbaden, T. Gabler ⌈Vorwort 1949⌉
208 p. table. 21 cm.
Bibliography: p. ⌈4⌉

1. Bookkeeping. I. Title.

HF5645.K63 657 50-31410

NK 0206998 DLC

Knoll, Heinrich
Der ostdeutsche holzhandel.
Inaug. diss. Zuerich, 1915 (Posen)
Bibl.

NK 0206999 ICRL

Knoll, Heinrich Christoph Friedrich, 1752-1786, supposed author.

Ehrenrettung der hermetischen kunst, durch solche chymisch-physikalische beweise dargethan, die jeder, auch nur mittelmässige kenner und künstler leicht einsehen, selbst nachmachen, und dadurch zugleich überzeugt werden kann und soll: dass alchymie und chrysopoeia keine leere einbildung müssiger köpfe sey, und noch weniger in die zauber-höhle gelehrter windmacher gehöre ... Erfurt, G. A. Keyser, 1785-86.

PT 2383 Knoll, Heinrich Christoph Friedrich, 1752-1786.
.K353 L9 Die Luftschlösser; oder, Die Hirngespinnste. Leipzig, Weygand, 1783.
132 p.

NK 0207001 InU KyB

[Knoll, Heinrich Christopher Friedrich]
Sommer-Nächte philosophischen und moralischen Inhalts in Dialogen und Erzählungen. Erfurt, G.A.Keyser, 1778.
110 p.

NK 0207002 MH InU

551
K75u
Knoll, Heinrich Christoph Friedrich.
Unterhaltende Naturwunder. Erfurt, G. A. Keyser, 1786-88.
2v. in 1. 20cm.
Vol.2 issued after the author's death with notes and a biography of the author by Johann Christian Wiegleb.

I. Wiegleb, Johann Christian, 1732-1800.

NK 0207003 IU OkU DAS

⌈Knoll, Heinrich Christoph Friedrich⌉ 1752-1786
Die Zauberhoehle in Schottland. Wine wundervolle Anecdote aus der Goldmacher-Zeit des Doctor Price. Weimar, 1783.

With Ettner, J.C. von - Rosetum chymicum. 1724.

NK 0207004 WU CoU

RM171
.S35
Knoll, Heinz, 1909- , joint author.
Schürch, Otto, 1896-
Blutkonservierung und transfusion von konserviertem blut, von dr. O. Schürch ... dr. H. Willenegger ... und dr. H. Knoll ... Mit 80, darunter 3 farbigen abbildungen. Wien, Springer, 1942.

Knoll, Heinz, 1909-
... Experimenteller Beitrag zur Frage der Bluttransfusion mit Heparin ... Zürich, 1938.
Inaug.-Diss. - Zürich.
Lebenslauf.
"Literatur": p. [18]

NK 0207006 CtY

KNOLL, HELLI, ed.
Walter Kolb; dargestellt von Leo Brandt [et al.] Mit einem Geleitwort von Fritz von Unruh. Berlin-Grünewald, Arani [1953] 51 p. plates, port. 19cm. (Köpfe der Zeit)

1. Kolb, Walter, chief burgomaster. I. Brandt, Leo.

NK 0207007 NN WU MH

W 4
M22
1951
KNOLL, Helmut, 1922-
Faktoren der hämorrhagischen Diathesen. ⌈Mainz⌉ 1951.
60 ℓ.
Inaug.-Diss. - Mainz.
1. Diathesis - Hemorrhagic

NK 0207008 DNLM

Knoll, Henry Albert, 1922-
The effect of low levels of luminance and freedom from optical stimulation of accommodation upon the refractive state of the eye ... 1950.
71 numb. l.
Thesis (Ph.D.) - Ohio state university, 1950.

NK 0207009 OU

Knoll, Henry Albert, 1922
Mechanical and ophthalmic optics laboratory manual. Los Angeles, Los Angeles College of Optometry, c1952.
44 ⌈i.e., 71⌉ l. illus.

1. Optics - Laboratory manuals. I. Los Angeles College of Optometry. II. Title.

NK 0207010 NNC-M InU

Knoll, Hermann.
Das Elektrizitätswerk in der Rocktasche. ⌈Graz, Buchverlag vorm. Leykam, 1946⌉
77 p. illus. 17 cm.

1. Electric batteries. I. Title.
QC603.K67 A F 49-662*
Illinois. Univ. Library
for Library of Congress †

NK 0207011 IU MCM DLC

LD4673
.A25
no. 4
Knoll, Horton Budd, ed.
Purdue University, *Lafayette, Ind.*
A record of a university in the war years, 1941-1945. Ed. by H. B. Knoll. ⌈Lafayette⌉ 1947.

LD4673
.A25
no. 3
Knoll, Horton Budd, ed.
Purdue University, *Lafayette, Ind.*
The roll of honor of Purdue University, 1941-1945. ⌈H. B. Knoll, editor⌉ ⌈Lafayette⌉ 1947.

Knoll, Ilse, 1899-
Ueber ein aneurysma mycoticum nach grippe.
Inaug. diss. Bonn, 1926.
Bibl.

NK 0207014 ICRL

Knoll (Jean-Georges). *I. Quels sont les caractères des pièces d'argent contenant du plomb? II. [etc.] 48 pp. 4°. *Strasbourg,* 1838, No. 1, v. 3.

NK 0207015 DNLM

Knoll (Joh. Daniel.) *De delirio febrili phrenitis dicto. 36 pp. 4°. *Wittenbergæ, lit. vid. Gerdesiæ,* [1721].

NK 0207016 DNLM

PA6516
.Z8K6
1728
Knoll, Johann
Iohannis Knollii...Lexicon Cornelii Nepotis tripartitvm,qvo secvndvm excellentivm imperatorvm vitas,I. Vocabvla simplicia,II.Phrases atqve formvlae,III.Vocvm difficiliorvm evcleationes continentvr... Editio novissima,plvribvs locis tertium avcta et emendata. Lipsiae,svmtibvs J.F.Gleditsch,1728.
⌈8⌉,403,⌈11⌉ p. 17cm.

1.Nepos,Cornelius--Dictionaries,indexes,etc.

NK 0207017 ICU

VOLUME 300

Knoll, Johann,
Lexicon Cornelii Nepotis tripartitum, quo secundum excellentium imperatorum vita, I. Vocabula simplicia; II. Phrases atque formulae; III. Vocum difficiliorum enucleationes continentur. In eum fidem ita digestum, ut inde usque a primis studiorum initiis ad auctorem hunc mature cognoscendum imitandumque pueris expeditior pateat aditus. Editio novissima, pluribus locis quintum aucta et emendata. Lipsiae, Jo. Frid. Gleditsch. 1761.
[6], 403, [1] p. 17 cm.

1. Nepos, Cornelius - Glossaries, vocabularies, etc.

NK 0207018 PLatS

BS 2312 .K77 1717
Knoll, Johann
... Vocabularium Biblicum Novi Testamenti, ita secundum seriem capitum atque versuum adornatum, ut in lectione sacrorum Novi Testamenti graeci librorum usum praevere possit extemporalem. Editio novissima ... Lipsiae, sumpt. Jo. Fr. Gleditschii, 1717.
686p. 17cm.

1. Bible. N.T. - Dictionaries. I. Title.

NK 0207019 DGU PPLT MBU-T

Knoll, Johann
Johannis Knollii Vocabularium biblicum Novi Testamenti... 10. ed..... Lipsiae, Gleditschium, 1739.
687 p.

NK 0207020 PPLT MH

XR BS2312 .K6 1751
Knoll, Johann.
Vocabvlarivm biblicvm Novi Testamenti, ita secvndvm seriem capitvm atqve versvvm adornatvm, vt in lectione sacrorvm Novi Testamenti Græci librorvm vsvm præbere possit extemporalem. Ed. nova, prioribvs longe avctior atqve emendatior, additis svbinde præter analysin grammaticam vocvmqve themata locorvm difficiliorvm explicationibvs. Lipsiae, In officina Gleditschiana, 1751.
600p. 18cm.

1. Bible. N. T. - Dictionaries 2. Greek language - Dictionaries - Latin I. Title.

NK 0207021 NBC

KNOLL, Johann.
Vocabvlarivm.biblicvm Novi Testamenti, secvndvm Seriem Capitvm atqve Versvvm adornatvm. Ed nova. Lipz., 1777.

pp.600 -.

NK 0207022 MH

Knoll, Johann Christian Gerhard, 1726-1757.
*De medicamentis traumaticis eorumque usu legitimo.
Halae Magd.: typ. J.C. Hilligeri.
[1746] 38 p. 20 cm.

RBS. 13819C

NK 0207023 NNNAM PPC DNLM

610.4 K754
Knoll, Johann Christian Gerhard, 1726-1757.
... Fortsezung der Gedanken über einige Materien aus der Arzneiwissenschaft. Quedlinburg, G. H. Schwan, 1754.
[16], 190 p. 18cm.

At head of title: Joh. Christian Gerhard Knoll.

NK 0207024 ICJ

Knoll, Johann Christian Gerhard, 1726-1757.
——. Gedanken von der Lage der Kranken in einem Sendschreiben. 11 pp. sm. 4°. Quedlinburg, G. H. Schwan, 1752.

NK 0207025 DNLM

Knoll, Johann Christiatian Gerhard, 1726-1757.
——. Lettre à un ami sur les opérations du caffé. 20 pp. sm. 4°. Quedlinbourg, G. H. Schwan, 1752.

NK 0207026 DNLM

TP559 G3K6 Case B ★
[Knoll, Johann Paul]
Der curiöse und offenhertzige Wein-Artzt; das ist: Allerhand bewährte Mittel, wie der Wein von der Kelter an sorgfältig zu warten ... mitgetheilet von Sincero Philalethe. Dresden, J.J. Wincklern, 1700.
237,136 p. front.

Has bound with: [De la Croyx, Andreas] Deliciae & arcana florum ... 1700.
Foreword signed: J.P.K.

NK 0207027 CU MH-A

Knoll, Josef, 1898-
*Fussosteomyelitis. Würzburg, 1930.
33 p. 8°.

NK 0207028 DNLM CtY

Knoll, Josef Gabriel, 1899-
Die pflanzenbestandsverhältnisse der dauerwiesen in der umgebung von Alm mit besonderer berücksichtigung der vorherrschenden Grasarten. ...
54 p.
Inaug. Diss. - Landw. Hochschule Hohenheim, [1925]
Lebenslauf.
Benutzte Literatur.

NK 0207029 ICRL

Knoll, Josef Gabriel, 1899-
... Die pflanzenbestandsverhältnisse des süddeutschen grünlandes. I. Die wiesentypen des württembergischen unterlandes ... Von dr. J. G. Knoll ... Berlin, Deutsche landwirtschaftsgesellschaft, 1932.
84 p. $24\frac{1}{2}$cm. (Added t.-p.: Arbeiten der Deutschen landwirtschafts-gesellschaft. hft. 386)

At head of title: Aus der Grünlandabteilung des Instituts für pflanzenbau und pflanzenzüchtung der Landwirtschaftlichen hochschule Hohenheim.
"Literaturverzeichnis": p. 83-84.

1. Meadows.

Agr 33-585 Revised

Library, U. S. Dept. of Agriculture 18D48 hft. 386
Library of Congress [S7.D35 hft. 386]

NK 0207030 DNAL MH

---

60 K75
Knoll, Josef Gabriel, 1899-
Umwelt, Futter und Leistung; eine kritische Betrachtung der Futterwirtschaft Südbadens. [Donaueschingen, 1953]
40 p. (Wartenberg-Hefte. Heft 1)

1. Forage plants. Germany. 2. Cattle, Dairy. Nutrition. I. Wartenberg-Hefte. no.1.

NK 0207031 DNAL

Knoll, Joseph, 1796-1863
see Knoll, Albert, pater, 1796-1863.

DB203 K5
Knoll, Joseph Leonard, 1775-1841.
Mittelpunkte der Geschichtsforschung und Geschichtschreibung in Böhmen und Mähren, als Einleitung in die sieben Bücher mährischer Geschichten. Olmütz, Gedruckt bey A.Skarnitzl, 1821.
viii,140 p. 18cm.

1.Bohemia - Historiography. 2.Moravia - Historiography. I.Title.

NK 0207033 CSt

Knoll, Joseph Leonard, 1775-1841.
Thuiscon, oder Das Lied der Weihe. Gesungen am acht und vierzigsten Gedächtnisstage der Geburt Seiner Majestät, des allerdurchlauchtigsten Kaisers von Osterreich, Franz des Ersten. Brünn, Druck und Lettern von Gastl, 1816.

[8] p. 23 cm.

NK 0207034 MH

Knoll, Karl.
Das beneficium divisionis des bürgen
see Knoll, Carl, of Glogau.

Knoll, Karl: Das Geltungsgebiet staatlichen Strafrechts im Verhältnis zum Völkerrecht (sogen. internationales Strafrecht) unt. Berücks. d. Entwurfs zu einem Deutsch. Strafgesetzbuch v. 1919. [Maschinenschrift.] 114 S. 4°. — Auszug: Berlin [1924]: Ebering. 2 Bl. 8° [Dazu] Juristische Thesen ... zur Erwerbung des Grades eines Dr. juris ... Berlin (1924): Ebering. 2 Bl. 8°
Berlin, Jur. Diss. v. 4. März 1924 [1925] [U 25. 19

NK 0207036 ICRL

---

ar W 24032
Knoll, Karl, 1920-
Die Gesellung der deutschen Jugend in der Gegenwart. [München?] 1962.
viii,310 p. 21cm.

Inaug.-Diss.--Munich.

1. Youth--Germany. 2. Youth movement--Germany.

NK 0207037 NIC

Knoll, Konrad, joint ed.

Arnold, Xaver, 1848- ed.
Sammlung von initialen, band 1. Hrsg. von Arnold u. Knoll. Leipzig, L. Denicke [1867-68]

VOLUME 300

Knoll, Konrad.
Arnold, Xaver, 1848- ed.
Sammlung von initialen aus werken vom 11.-17. jahrhundert hrsg. von Xaver Arnold ... 1. bd. 2. aufl. Leipzig, J. Brehse [1889-90]

LA678.7 K58 **Knoll, Kurt**
Die Geschichte der schlesischen akademischen Landsmannschaft "Oppavia" in Wien; im Rahmen der allgemeinen studentischen Entwicklung an den Wiener Hochschulen. Zum 90 semestrigen Stiftungsfeste der Landsmannschaft in ihrem Auftrage verfasst. Wien, Buchdruckerei Schöler, 1923-1924.
2v. 23cm.
Includes bibliographical references.
1. Oppavia. 2. Students' societies - Austria - Vienna. I. Title. II. Title: Der schlesischen akademischen Landsmannschaft "Oppavia."

NK 0207040 IaU MH

371.8309436 K72g Knoll, Kurt.
Die Geschichte der wehrhaften Vereine deutscher Studenten in der Ostmark von den Anfängen bis an die Gegenwart. Wien, Schlesische Akademische Landsmannschaft "Oppavia", 1924.
608 p.
"Sonderdruck aus dem Werke: Die Geschichte der schlesischen akademischen Landsmannschaft 'Oppavia' in Wien im Rahmen der allgemeinen studentischen Entwicklung and de Wiener Hochschulen."
1. Students' societies--Austria--Hist. 2. Students--Austria. 3. Oppavia, Vienna. I. Title. II. Title: Vereine deutscher Studenten in der Ostmark.

NK 0207041 ICarbS

Knoll, Kurt.
London im mittelalter, seine wirtschaftliche, politische und kulturelle bedeutung für das britische volk, von dr. Kurt Knoll ... mit 4 karten. Wien und Leipzig, W. Braumüller, 1932.
vi p., 1 l., 219 p. fold. map. 24cm.
"Eine parallelausgabe dieses werkes erschien als LVI. bd. der 'Wiener beiträge zur englischen philologie'."
1. London—Hist. I. Title.
Library of Congress DA680.K7 32-9957
942.1

NK 0207042 DLC MB OrU FU TU MU MiU OCU OC1W OC1

Knoll, Kurt.
London im mittelalter, seine wirtschaftliche, politische und kulturelle bedeutung für das britische volk, von dr. Kurt Knoll ... mit 4 karten. Wien und Leipzig, W. Braumüller, 1932.
vi p., 1 l., 219 p. fold. map. 24 cm. (Added t.-p.: Wiener beiträge zur englischen philologie ... LVI. bd.)
"Die vorliegende arbeit erschien in einer gleichlautenden sonderausgabe als selbständige broschüre."
1. London—Hist. I. Title.
PR13.W5 bd. 56 942.1 32—9958

NK 0207043 DLC MH ICU NN PHC PBm PU NcD

Knoll, Kurt.
Eine offene Schuld Amerikas an 3 1/2 Millionen Deutsche in der Tschecho-Slowakei. Eine historische Darstellung und Aufklärung für alle Freunde der Wahrheit und des wirklichen Völkerfriedens. Von Prof. Dr. Kurt Knoll... Wien: Verlag der Sudetendeutschen Verlagsbuchhandlung, 1927. 51 p. map. 23cm.
"Bibliographie," p. 51.
1. Germans in Czecho-Slovakia. 2. Czecho-Slovakia—Economic relations with foreign countries.
N. Y. P. L. December 20, 1943

NK 0207044 NN CSt-H CtY DLC-P4

Knoll (Léon-Fernand) [1877-]. *Traitement des kystes de l'ovaire compliquant la grossesse. 55 pp. 8°. Lille, 1902, No. 98.

NK 0207045 DNLM

Knoll, Leonhard.
... Brochado; aplicaciones, proyecto y fabricación de las agujas de brochar. Defectos que pueden presentarse en el trabajo, por Leonhard Knoll. Brochado exterior, por el ing. Artur Schatz. Aserrado de los metales; estudio de las hojas de sierra y de sus condiciones de trabajo. Selección de las máquinas, por el ing. H. Hollaender. Con 339 figuras. Barcelona [etc.] Editorial Labor, s. a., 1943.
340 p. illus., diagrs. 21½cm. (Trabajos de taller, guía práctica del mecánico moderno ... 14)
1. Drilling and boring. 2. Saws. 3. Metal-work. I. Schatz, Artur. II. Hollaender, H. III. Title.
44-32039
Library of Congress TJ1250.K58
621.95

NK 0207046 DLC

Knoll, Leonhard.
... Innenräumen; anwendung, konstruktion und herstellung der räumnadeln. Fehler beim räumen. Von Leonhard Knoll ... 2., erweiterte aufl. des bisher unter dem titel "Räumen" erschienenen heftes (8. bis 14. tausend) Mit 142 abbildungen im text. Berlin, Springer, 1942.
61, [1] p. illus., diagrs. 22½cm. (Werkstattbücher für betriebsbeamte, konstrukteure und facharbeiter. Herausgeber: dr.-ing. H. Haake ... Hft. 26)
1. Broaching machines. 2. Saws. 3. Metal-work. I. Title.
TJ1250.K56 1942 621.95 46-44097

NK 0207047 DLC DBS NNE CoU IU

TJ1260 K55 1951 **Knoll, Leonhard**
Innenräumen, von Artur Schatz. 3., völlig umgearb. und erweiterte Aufl. des vorher von L. Knoll bearb. Heftes. Berlin, Springer, 1951.
58 p. illus. (Werkstattbücher für Betriebsangestellte, Konstrukteure und Facharbeiter. Heft 26)
1. Broaching machines. I. Schatz, Artur.

NK 0207048 CU

Knoll, Leonhard.
...Raeumen; Anwendung, Konstruktion und Herstellung der Räumnadeln. Fehler beim Räumen, von Leonhard Knoll... Berlin: J. Springer, 1926. 57 p. diagrs., illus. 8°. (Werkstattbücher für Betriebsbeamte, Vor- und Facharbeiter. Heft 26.)
1. Broaches. 2. Ser.
N. Y. P. L. January 6, 1928

NK 0207049 NN

Knoll, Mrs. Mabel Marie (Miller)
see Miller, Mabel Marie, 1899-

Knoll, Manja H
Redeema, a novel. [1st ed. New York] Pageant Press, 1954.
321 p. 24 cm.
I. Title.
PZ4.K74Re 54-12352 ‡

NK 0207051 DLC NN

Knoll, Maria, 1912-
Flächen mit einer schar geodätischer krümmungslinien und flächen mit einer schar kongruenter krümmungslinien ... Nördlingen, C.H. Beck, 1938.
34 p., 1 l.
Thesis - Würzburg.
Lebenslauf.

NK 0207052 CtY MH ICRL

Knoll, Maria, 1912-
Flächen mit einer schar geodätischer krümmungslinien und flächen mit einer schar kongruenter krümmungslinien ... Nördlingen, C.H. Beck, 1938.
34 p., 1 l.
Film copy of the original at Harvard. Negative.
Thesis - Würzburg.
Lebenslauf.

NK 0207053 RPB

Knoll (Marie-Xavier-Désiré-Léon). *Des affections charbonneuses chez l'homme et de leur traitement. 116 pp. 4°. Paris, 1883, No. 182.

NK 0207054 DNLM PPC

FILM 647 K75e **Knoll, Marjorie May.**
Economic contributions given to and received from individual members of families and households in relation to their financial situation. Ann Arbor, University Microfilms [1954]
([University Microfilms, Ann Arbor, Mich.] Publication no.10,591)
Microfilm copy (positive) of typescript. Collation of the original: 220 l. tables.
Thesis--Cornell University.
Abstracted in Dissertation abstracts, v.15 (1955) no.1, p.114-115.
Vita.
Bibliography: leaf 209.
1. Home economics. 2. Home. 3. Family.

NK 0207056 IU OU NIC DNAL OrU OrCS

Knoll, Max, joint author.
Law
Pamperl, Hans, 1884-
Handbuch für Kraftfahrer, Fuhrwerkslenker und Radfahrer; eine zusammenfassende Darstellung aller österreichischen Gesetze und Verordnungen über das Kraftfahrwesen und die strassenpolizeilichen Vorschriften für den praktischen Gebrauch, verfasst von Hans Pamperl, Karl Müller [und] Max Knoll. Wien, 1937.

621.3 K75a Knoll, Max, 1897-
Anleitungen zum arbeiten im röhrenlaboratorium. Berlin, J. Springer, 1937.
67p. diagrs.
"Dritter teil der Anleitungen zum arbeiten im elektrotechnischen laboratorium, von E. Orlich."
Includes bibliographies.
1. Electric engineering--Laboratory manuals. 2. Electric conduits. I. Title. II. Orlich, Ernest Max, 1868- Anleitungen zum arbeiten im elektrotechnischen laboratorium.

NK 0207058 IU NcU OrCS

VOLUME 300

Knoll, Max, 1897–
Gasentladungstabellen; tabellen, formeln und kurven zur physik und technik der elektronen und ionen, von M. Knoll, F. Ollendorff, und R. Rompe, unter mitarbeit von A. Roggendorf. Mit 196 textabbildungen. Berlin, J. Springer, 1935.
x, 171, ⌊1⌋ p. incl. tables, diagrs. 25cm.
1. Electric discharges through gases. 2. Ions. 3. Electrons. 4. Gases—Tables, calculations, etc. I. Ollendorff, Franz, joint author. II. Rompe, Robert, joint author. III. Roggendorf, A. IV. Title.
35-6805
Library of Congress QC711.K715
Copyright A—Foreign 27006
537.53

NK 0207059 DLC NcU NcD CtY PPF OO OU OC1L NRU IU

Knoll, Max, 1897–
Gasentladungstabellen; tabellen, formeln und kurven zur physik und technik der elektronen und ionen, von M. Knoll, F. Ollendorff, und R. Rompe, unter mitarbeit von A. Roggendorf. Mit 196 textabbildungen. Berlin, J. Springer, 1935.
Ann Arbor, Mich., Edwards Brothers, 1944.
x, 171, ⌊1⌋ p. incl. tables, diagrs. 25cm.

NK 0207060 ICJ

Knoll, Max, 1897–
Storage tubes and their basic principles ⌊by⌋ M. Knoll ⌊and⌋ B. Kazan. New York, Wiley ⌊1952⌋
143 p. illus. 24 cm.
1. Storage tubes. I. Title.
TK7872.S7K6 *621.34 621.38 52—9368 ‡

OrP WaT MtBC OrPS Or WaWW
ViU NIC NcRS OCU PBL CU OC1U NcD IEN OrCS WaS CaBVaU
NK 0207061 DLC DSI MiHM NBuC OC1W TU NN TxU ICJ MB

Knoll, Max, 1897– joint author.

Espe, Werner.
Werkstoffkunde der hochvakuumtechnik; eigenschaften, verarbeitung und verwendungstechnik der werkstoffe für hochvakuumröhren und gasgefüllte entladungsgefässe, von W. Espe ... und M. Knoll ... Mit 405 textabbildungen und einer mehrfarbigen tafel. Berlin, J. Springer, 1936.

Knoll, Max, 1897–
Zur begrenzung des auflösungsvermögens der Braunschen röhre (mitteilung aus dem Laboratorium für elektronenforschung telefunken) von M. Knoll.

Photostat reproduction, positive (3 1. 28 1/2 cm.) from Telegraphen-, fernsprech-funk-und fernsprecht- technik. Berlin, 1942. bd. 31, hft. 8, p. 213-215. illus.

NK 0207063 CU

Knoll (Oskar). *Ueber die Resection des Kniegelenks. 31 pp. 8°. *Leipzig, Huethel u. Legler,* [1866].

NK 0207064 DNLM

Knoll, Oskar, *d.* 1875.
Beiträge zur italienischen historiographie im vierzehnten jahrhundert. Von Dr. Oskar Knoll. Göttingen, R. Peppmüller, 1876.
viii, 84 p. 21½ cm.
Ed. by Joh. Heller.
CONTENTS.—1. Zur chronologie des Matteo Villani.—2. Zum Polistore.—3. Annales mediolanenses, eine ableitung des Chronicon placentinum.—4. Eine verlorne Pisaner chronik von 1353.
1. Italy—Hist.—Historiography. I. Heller, Johann, ed.
DG465.K72 4—29961

NK 0207065 DLC NSyU OCU NNC IEN ICJ OO

Knoll, Otto Hans Rudolf, 1902–
Untersuchung der eigenschaften und des verhaltens von sperrschichtzellen ... 1936. 141 p.
Inaug. Diss. - Techn. Hochschule Karlsruhe, 1936.
Lebenslauf.

NK 0207066 ICRL CtY

Knoll, Paul.
Die ansiedlungen der Athener im fünften jahrhundert ... Rostock, Universitäts-buchdruckerei von Adler's erben, 1875.
36 p. 20½cm.
Inaug.-dis.—Rostock.
1. Athens—Colonies.
5-4410†
Library of Congress DF251.K72

NK 0207067 DLC NjP

Knoll, Paul.
Die photographie im dienste der presse. Von Paul Knoll ... mit 26 abbildungen auf 13 tafeln. Halle a. S., W. Knapp, 1913.
xii p., 2 l., 91 p. XIII pl. 22cm. (*Half-title:* Encyklopädie der photographie. hft. 82)
1. Photography. 2. Journalism. I. Title.
14-493
Library of Congress TR820.K7

NK 0207068 DLC ICJ NN

Knoll, Paul Xenophon, 1896– joint author.

Wells, Earl William, 1898–
The extempore speech, a textbook of practical analysis and adaptation, by Earl W. Wells ... and Paul X. Knoll ... New York, The Ronald press company ⌊1942⌋

Knoll, Petar
see
Knol, Petar, 1873–

KNOLL, Philipp, 1841-1900.
Alois Brinz. Denkrede gehalten am 29ten november 1887 im Deutschen Vereine zu Prag. Prag, verlag des Deutschen Vereines, 1888.
pp. 24.

NK 0207071 MH

325.243 Knoll, Philipp, 1841-1900.
K75b Beiträge zur heimischen Zeitgeschichte. Mit einer Gedenkrede auf den Verfasser von Gustav C. Laube. Hrsg. von der Gesellschaft zur Förderung deutscher Wissenschaft, Kunst und Literatur in Böhmen. Prag, J. G. Calve, 1900.
xlvii, 593p. port. 20cm.
1. Germans in Bohemia. I. Gesellschaft zur Förderung deutscher Wissenschaft, Kunst und Literatur in Böhmen, Prague. II. Title.

NK 0207072 IU ICU MH

Knoll, Philipp, 1841-1900. **612.2 O200**
Beiträge zur Lehre von der Athmungsinnervation. Von Prof.
110845 Dr. Philipp Knoll. Erste–[vierte] Mittheilung. [Wien, K. k. Hof- und Staatsdruckerei], 1882–[1883].
4 pts. in 1 vol. 15 fold. pl. 24cm.
"Aus dem LXXXV.–[LXXXVIII.] Bande der Sitzb. der K. Akad. der Wissensch. III. Abth. ... 1882–1883."

NK 0207073 ICJ MiU

591.11
1
Knoll, Philipp, 1841-1900.
[Collected papers on physiology, especially of the respiratory
168890 **and circulatory systems.]**

NK 0207074 ICJ

Knoll, Philipp, 1841-1900, ed.

Lotos. Naturwissenschaftliche zeitschrift. Herausgegeben vom Deutschen naturwissenschaftlich-medizinischen verein für Böhmen "Lotos" in Prag. 1.– jahrg. Prag, 1851–19

Knoll (Philipp). Ueber den Einfluss des Halsmarkes auf die Schlagzahl des Herzens. 26 pp., 2 pl. 8°. [*n. p.*, 1872.]

NK 0207076 DNLM MiU

Knoll, Philipp, 1841-1900.
Ueber die folgen der herzcompression, von prof. dr. Knoll ... Prag, Haase, 1881.
1 p.l., 34 p. IV fold. diagrs.
"Sonderabdruck aus dem naturwissenschaftlichen jahrbuch 'Lotos', bd. II ..."
1. Blood - Circulation. 2. Heart.

NK 0207077 NNC

Knoll, Philipp
——. Ueber die Veränderungen des Herzschlages bei reflectorischer Erregung des vasomotorischen Nervensystemes, so wie bei Steigerung des intracardialen Druckes überhaupt. (Aus dem physiologischen Institute zu Prag.) 56 pp., 4 pl. 8°. [*n. p.*, 1872.]

NK 0207078 DNLM MiU

Knoll, Philipp, 1841-1900.
Über die wirkung von chloroform und äther auf athmung und blutkreislauf ... [1876-78]
2 pts. in 1 v. 1 illus., 8 fold. diagrs.
From Sitzungsb. der Kais. akads. d. w. Math. naturw. cl. LXXIV. bd. III, abth. 1876. p. 233-269; LXXVIII. bd. III, abth. 1878, p. 223-252.
1. Chloroform - Physiological effect.
2. Ether - Physiological effect.

NK 0207079 NNC MiU

Knoll, Philipp, 1841-1900.
Ueber eine methode zur Verzeichnung der volumschwankunger der herzens. Ueber reflexe auf die Athmung bei Zufuhr einiger fluechti ger substanzen. (Bound with Knoll, Philipp. Beitraegeate)

NK 0207080 MiU

VOLUME 300

13545
Y
v.58
Knoll, Philipp, 1841-1900.
Über Protoplasmaarme und Protoplasmareiche Musculatur. ₍Wien, K.K. Hof- und Staatsdruckerei, 1891₎
633-700 p. 9 plates. 29cm. (Akademie der Wissenschaften, Vienna. Mathematisch-naturwissenschaftliche Klasse. Denkschriften, Bd. 58)

1. Muscles. 2. Protoplasm.

NK 0207081 NIC

Knoll (Philipp) [1841-1900]. Ueber Reflexe auf die Athmung bei Zufuhr einiger flüchtiger Substanzen zu den unterhalb des Kehlkopfes gelegenen Luftwegen. 29 pp., 4 pl. 8°. [*Wien, J. Wagner*, 1874.] A. L. A.
Repr. from: Sitzungsb.d.k.Akad.d.Wissensch. Math.-naturw. Cl., Wien, 1873, lxviii.

NK 0207082 DNLM

Knoll, Pius
see Knoell, Pius.

48
K752
Knoll, Richard.
Všestranný ohař; jehó výcvik á vedení. ₍Vyd.1.₎ Praha, Naše vojsko, 1953.
213 p.

1. Hunting dogs. I. Báča, Jan, joint author.

NK 0207084 DNAL

Knoll, Robert
Hermann Conring als historiker
Inaug. Diss. Rostock, 1889

NK 0207085 ICRL

Knoll, Robert E *ed.*
Contrasts: idea and technique. New York, Harcourt, Brace ₍°1955₎
575 p. 22 cm.
Includes bibliography.

1. English literature (Selections: Extracts, etc.) 2. American literature (Selections: Extracts, etc.) I. Title.

PR1109.K55 820.82 55-575 ‡

NK 0207086 DLC IdPI NIC FTaSU AAP

Knoll, Roman.
Bemerkungen über die polnische Politik 1939. Uwagi o polskiej polityce 1939. Dienstliche Uebersetzung der Publikationsstelle in Berlin-Dahlem, ausgeführt von Paul Kluke. ₍Berlin₎ 1939.
22 l. 30 cm. (₍Publikationsstelle Berlin-Dahlem. Polnische Reihe. Bücher und grössere Aufsätze₎ 182)
"Nur für den Dienstgebrauch!"
In German.

1. Poland—Pol. & govt.—1918-1945. I. Title. (Series: Germany. Publikationsstelle Berlin-Dahlem. Polnische Reihe. Bücher und grössere Aufsätze, 182)

DK441.K6 55-45837

NK 0207087 DLC

DK
441
.K6
Knoll, Roman
Uwagi o polskiej polityce 1939. Warszawa, Instytut Wydawn. "Biblioteka Polska", 1939,
39 p.

1. Poland - Politics and government - 1915-1945. I. Title.

NK 0207088 NNG

Knoll, Romedius, fl. ca. 1774.
Die verbesserte Bettmaschine und der Fahrsessel für die Kranke ... Augsburg, bey Nicolaus Doll, 1789.

NK 0207089 NNNAM

Knoll, Rosi.
... Kinder im garten, eine geschichte für kinder, mit vielen bunten bildern von Berta Tappolet. Zürich, Morgarten-verlag aktiengesellschaft ₍1941₎
₍35₎ p. illus. (part col.) 25 x 20½cm.

I. Title.

Library of Congress PZ33.K56 42-3206

NK 0207090 DLC

Knoll, Rudolf. 662.2 Q800
Das Knallquecksilber und ähnliche Sprengstoffe, sowie deren Verwendung zur Erzeugung von Sprengkapseln, Zündhütchen und Flobertpatronen. Geschichte, Fabrikation, Eigenschaften und Prüfung. Nach den neuesten Erfahrungen bearbeitet von Ing. chem. Dr. R. Knoll, ... Mit 39 Abbildungen und 1 Tafel. Wien und Leipzig, A. Hartleben, 1908.
viii, 191, [1] p. 39 illus., 1 fold. plan. 19½cm. (*On cover:* Chemisch-technische Bibliothek. Band 312.)
"Literaturangabe," p. viii.

NK 0207091 ICJ ICRL CU

Knoll, Rudolf
Synthetische und isolierte riechstoffe und deren darstellung, von dr. Rudolf Knoll ... Halle, Knapp, 1908.
x p., 1 l., 133 p. illus., diagrs. 24½ cm. [Monographien über chemisch-technische fabrikationsmethoden, bd.X]
Added series t.-p.
"Benutzte literatur und behelfe": 1 p. following p.x.

NK 0207092 NNCoCi PPL ICJ OU NN OC1W

Knoll, Rudolf.
Synthetische und isolierte riechstoffe und ihre herstellung, von dr. Rudolf Knoll ... 2., vollständig neu bearb. und erweiterte aufl., von direktor Alfred Wagner ... Mit 27 in den text gedruckten abbildungen. Halle (Saale) W. Knapp, 1928.
6 p. l., 257, ₍1₎ p. illus., diagrs. 24½ cm. (*Added t.-p.:* Monographien über chemisch-technische fabrikationsmethoden ... hrsg. von L. M. Wohlgemuth ... bd. x)
"Benutzte literatur": 6th prelim. leaf.

1. Perfumes, Synthetic. 2. Essences and essential oils. I. Wagner, Alfred, ed. LC.

TP983.K6 1928 28—21146

NK 0207093 DLC OC1W ICJ PPF CLSU

KNOLL, Rudolph Johann
Untersuchungen über ogier's schwefeloxychlorid und einwirkung von schwefeloxytetrachlorid auf benzol und homologe. Rostock, 1894.
32p.
Inaug.-Diss.

NK 0207094 MH-C

3781
S78
K72
Knoll, Samson Benjamin.
Herder and the French revolution. ₍Stanford, Calif.₎ 1952.
xv, 440 l.
Thesis (Ph.D.) - Dept. of History, Stanford University.
Bibliography: l.421-440.

1. Herder, Johann Gottfried von, 1744-1803.

Brief cataloging

NK 0207095 CSt

Knoll, Simon.
Die Apostelgeschichte in kanzelvorträgen für das christliche volk erklärt. Schaffhausen, Fr. Hurter, 1863.
xvi, 448 p. 22 cm.

NK 0207096 PLatS

Knoll, Simon.
Die laurentanische Litanei. Dem christlichen volke erklärt von Simon Knoll. Regensburg & New York, F. Pustet, 1867.
vi, 754 p. front., 18 cm.

NK 0207097 PLatS MnCS

Knoll, Simon.
Das leben derkirche, dargestellt in liturgischen predigten. Schaffhausen, Fr. Hurter, 1863-69.
5 v. 20 cm.
Each volume has special title page.

NK 0207098 PLatS

Knoll, Simon.
Predigten auf alle sonn- und festtage des katholischen kirchenjahres für stadt und land, gehalten von Simon Knoll ... Schaffhausen, F. Hurter, 1862.
2 v. in 1. 22½cm.

1. Church year sermons. 2. Festival-day sermons. 3. Catholic church—Sermons. 4. Sermons, German.

Library of Congress BX1756.K64P7 37-20663
252.02

NK 0207099 DLC MnCS

Knoll, Simon.
Das Salve Regina in einunddreissig vorträgen erklärt von S.Knoll. Regensburg, G.J. Manz, 1860.
vi, 432 p. 19 cm.

NK 0207100 PLatS

Knoll, Ulrich, 1888-
Über einen beitrag zum blutbild des gesunden pferdes, unter berücksichtigung der gesamten einschlägigen literatur ... Prenzlau, Druck C. Vincent, 1924.
24 p. 22½cm.
Inaug.-diss.—Giessen.
Lebenslauf.
"Literaturverzeichnis": p. 21-23.

1. Blood—Analysis and chemistry. 2. Blood—Horses.

Library, U. S. Dept. of Agriculture 444K752 Agr 26-1543

NK 0207101 DNAL ICRL DNLM

VOLUME 300

Knoll, Waldemar: Der Warenkreditschutz im Grosshandel in systematischer Darstellung. [Maschinenschrift.] x, 182 S. m. Anl. 4°. — Auszug: Breslau 1923: Bresl. Genoss.-Buchdr. 2 Bl. 8°
Breslau, R.- u. staatswiss. Diss. v. 5. März 1924 [U 24. 1475

NK 0207102 ICRL

Knoll, Werner, 1896-
Ueber die konstitution des lichenins. Berlin, 1926.
In. Diss.

NK 0207103 ICRL CtY

Knoll, Werner, 1903-
Die klärung der breitungsfrege mit hilfe der spannungsflächenhypothese.
Inaug. Diss. Breslau, 1931.
7 p.

NK 0207104 ICRL

W 4
M96
1953

KNOLL, Werner, 1928-
Die Prolapsoperationen und ihre Methoden und Ergebnisse an der I. Universitätsfrauenklinik in München, 1945-1950. München, 1953.
39 ℓ.
Inaug.-Diss. - Munich.
1. Genitals - Female - Prolapse

NK 0207105 DNLM

Knoll, Wilhelm, 1876- *ed.*
Der bewegungsablauf bei sportlicher arbeit; eine wissenschaftliche gemeinschaftsarbeit des Instituts für leibesübungen der Hamburgischen universität, unter mitarbeit von K. Büsen ... H. Ebbe ... [u. a.] herausgegeben von prof. dr. Wilhelm Knoll ... mit 57 abbildungen im text. Leipzig, J. A. Barth, 1936.
2 p. l., 114 p. illus., diagrs. 22½cm.

1. Athletics. 2. Animal locomotion. I. Hamburg. Universität. Institut für leibesübungen. II. Title.
38-25714
Library of Congress GV705.K5
Copyright A—Foreign 31654
796.4

NK 0207106 DLC NN

Knoll, Wilhelm, 1876-
Die embryonale Blutbildung beim Menschen. St. Gallen, Zollikofer, 1950.
99 p. diagrs., col. plates. 23 cm.
"Separatabdruck aus Band 73 der Berichte (Jahrbuch) der St. Gallischen Naturwissenschaftlichen Gesellschaft."
Bibliography: p. 91-99.

1. Blood. 2. Embryology, Human. I. Title.
A 53-1021
Temple Univ. Library for Library of Congress QM611.K58

NK 0207107 PPT OU DNLM NIC KPT

L616.03
S800 v.15

Knoll, Wilhelm, 1876-
Fortschritte der Sportmedizin, von W. Knoll ...
(*In* Neue deutsche Klinik. Berlin, 1938. 26cm. Bd. 15 (Erg. Bd. 5) p. [153]-174. diagrs.)

NK 0207108 ICJ

Knoll, Wilhelm, 1876-
...Leistung und Beanspruchung; Erfahrungen aus 30jähriger sportärztlicher Arbeit. St. Gallen, Zollikofer & C., 1948. 416 p. illus. 21cm.

Bibliography, p. 399-411.

534761B. 1. Physical education. 2. Sports—Physical effects. 3. Athletics—Physical effects.

NK 0207109 NN IU DNLM

Knoll, Wilhelm, 1876- *ed.*
Normale und pathologische physiologie der leibesübungen, bearb. von A. Arnold ... M. Bürger ... [u. a.] hrsg. von Wilhelm Knoll ... und Arno Arnold ... mit 67 abbildungen im text. Leipzig, J. A. Barth, 1933.
viii, 316 p. illus., diagrs. 25cm.
"Bibliographie für jeden abschnitt, von Arno Arnold": p. [270]-312.

1. Physiology. 2. Exercise. 3. Physical education and training. I. Arnold, Arno, 1897- joint ed. II. Title.
33-35409
Library of Congress QP301.K6
Copyright A—Foreign 21882
612.7661

NK 0207110 DLC DNLM CtY-M ICU

Knoll, Wilhelm, 1876-
Skiwettläufer; eine sportärztliche Monografie. Bern, P. Haupt, 1923.
218 p. plates. 21 cm.
"Literaturverzeichnis": p. [217]-218.

1. Skis and skiing. I. Title.
GV854.K57 50-48339

NK 0207111 DLC

Knoll, Willi
Die angeborenen und erworbenen missbildungen des unterkiefers ... Berlin, Ebering [1922]
[4] p.
Abstract, thesis, Berlin, 1922.

1. Jaws - Abnormities and deformities.

NK 0207112 NNC ICRL

Knoll, Willi.
Wohin am Sonntag? Wanderführer für Berlin und Potsdam. [Berlin] Das Neue Berlin [°1953]
142 p. illus. 19 cm.

1. Berlin—Environs. 2. Potsdam—Environs. I. Title.
DD881.K6 54-25307 ‡

NK 0207113 DLC

Knoll, Willi, 1902-
Die deutsche zigarettenindustrie ... von Willi Knoll ... Erlangen, Buch- und akzidenzdruckerei Höfer & Limmert, 1929.
vii, [1], 151 p. 21cm.
Inaug.-diss.—Frankfurt am Main.
Lebenslauf.
"Literaturverzeichnis": p. v-vii.

1. Cigarette manufacture and trade—Germany.
44-37958
Library of Congress HD9149.C42G35

NK 0207114 DLC MiU

Knoll (Willy). *Zwei Fälle von Ruptur-Aneurysma der Aorta. Beiträge zur Histologie der Aneurysmen. [Zürich.] 51 pp., 4 pl., 4 l. 8°. Frauenfeld, Huber & Co., 1904.

NK 0207115 DNLM

Knoll, Willy 1875-
Ein beitrag zur geschichte der lepra.
Inaug. Diss. Berlin, 1898

NK 0207116 ICRL DNLM

Knoll, Willy, 1878-
... Uber traumatische magenerweiterungen ... Berlin, Schade [1903]
38, [2] p.
Inaug.-diss., Berlin, 1903.
Lebenslauf.
"Litteratur": p. [39]
1. Stomach - Wounds and injuries.

NK 0207117 NNC DNLM ICRL CtY

Knoll, Wolfgang F
Flugmodelle; Anleitung zum Selbstbau von Flugmodellen mit Gummimotorantrieb unter Anwendung der vom NSFK. empfohlenen Leisten-Normen sowie einfachste Darstellung der wichtigsten Grundbegriffe und Gesetze des Modellflugs. 5., neu bearb. Aufl. Leipzig, H. Beyer [1939]
32 p. diagrs., fold. plan (in pocket) 21 cm. (Wie baue ich mir selbst? Bd. 85)
L. C. copy imperfect: fold. plan wanting.

1. Aeroplanes—Models. (Series)
TL770.K58 1939 50-49276

NK 0207118 DLC

PT
2621
.N65
A48

Knoll, Wolfgang Friedrich.
Atherus. Dramatischer Gesang in drei Teilen [von] Wolf-Fried. [Lörrach, Baden] Humanitheon, 1948.
152p. 19cm.

NK 0207119 TNJ DLC-P4

Knoll A.G., Ludwigshafen am Rhein.
Cardiazol: D.R.P. name geschützt. Analeptikum und allgemeines stimulans, insbesondere für kreislauf und atmung; vollkommen wasser- und lipoidlöslich, überraschend schnell wirksam, grosse therapeutische breite, frei von unangenehmen nebenwirkungen. Ludwigshafen, Knoll, 1937.
3 p.l., 9-301, [1] p. 21.5 cm.
1. Metrazol.

NK 0207120 NNC OClW

QV
103
K72c
1937

KNOLL A.-G., Ludwigshafen am Rhein
Cardiazol, nome registado. Analeptico e estimulante geral, especialmente da circulação e da respiração; absolutamente soluvel em agua e nos lipoides, de acção surpreendentemente rapida, grande margem terapeutica, isento de efeitos secundarios desagradaveis. Ludwigshafen s. o Rheno, 1937.
315 p.
1. Metrazol

NK 0207121 DNLM

VOLUME 300

Knoll a.-g., Ludwigshafen am Rhein .
Diuretin-Knoll,/a true diuretic.
[Reports from various hospitals on a large number of cases treated with diuretin-Knoll.]
16 pp. 8°. *London, Danks & Son,* [1894, *vel subseq.*].

NK 0207122 DNLM

Knoll A. G., Ludwigshafen
Diuretin-Knoll, diuretic, heart tonic and vascular remedy. Ed. 1911. New York, Knoll & Co., 1911.
79p.

NK 0207123 ICRL CU MiU

Knoll A.-G., Ludwigshafen.
Die Knoll a.-g und ihre erzeugnisse. Ludwigshafen, Knoll ₍1934?₎
4 p. l., 7-166 p. illus., ports. 17½cm.

NK 0207124 NNC

Knoll A.-G., Ludwigshafen am Rhein.
Informaciones médicas Knoll
see under title

Knoll A.G., Ludwigshafen am Rhein.
Knoll's Mitteilungen für Ärzte ... 1912-1914
see under title

W 5 K72k 1936
Knoll A.-G., Ludwigshafen am Rhein.
Knoll's Mitteilungen für Ärzte; Jubiläumsausgabe, 1886-1936. [Ludwigshafen am Rhein, 1936?]
288 p. illus.
Includes bibliographies.
1. Medicine - Collected works.
2. Therapeutics - Collected works.

NK 0207127 DNLM

Knoll A-G., *Ludwigshafen a/Rhein.* 615.1 R106
Knoll's Pharmaka./ Ludwigshafen a/Rhein. Knoll & C°, 1911.
189597 xiii, 373 p. illus., diagrs. 23½cm.
Bibliography at end of most chapters.

NK 0207128 ICJ MiU PPJ CtY PPC OClW MH IU-M

WB 750 K72s 1941
Knoll A.-G., Ludwigshafen am Rhein
Spezialpräparate "Knoll." Ausgabe 1941. Ludwigshafen am Rhein ₍1941?₎
116 p. illus.

1. Drugs 2. Therapeutics

NK 0207129 DNLM

W 5 K72v 1936
KNOLL A.-G., Ludwigshafen am Rhein
Vom Wirken berühmter Ärzte aus vier Jahrhunderten. Ludwigshafen a. Rh., 1936.
261 p. illus., ports.
Consists of bio-bibliographical introductions and excerpts from the works of Theophrast von Hohenheim (Paracelsus) William Harvey, Leopold Auenbrugger and Carl Gustav Carus.
1. Medicine - Collected works
2. Physicians Biog. Title

NK 0207130 DNLM CtY-M WU MH NNC NNU-B

NK 2408 .K72
Knoll Associates, Inc., New York.
₍Catalog of furniture and textiles. New York, ©1950₎
79 p. (chiefly illus.) 31 cm.
"This book is designed by Herbert Matter, edited and produced by Hockaday Associates, Inc."

1. Furniture--U.S.

NK 0207131 MiU

---

749 A-K755c
₍Knoll Associates, Inc.₎
A condensed guide to the Knoll international furniture collection. ₍New York, n.p., n.d.₎
29 p. (chiefly illus.)

Cover title: Knoll furniture guide.

1. Furniture - Catalogs. I. Title. II. Title: Knoll furniture guide.

NK 0207132 WAU MtBC

745.2 K755
Knoll Associates, inc.
₍Knoll fabric color guides₎ New York ₍195-₎
12 folders on ring. illus., col. mounted samples. 21cm.

1. Textile industry and fabrics. 2. Textile design.

NK 0207133 OrU

Knoll Associates, Inc.
Knoll furniture guide
see its A condensed guide to the Knoll international furniture collection.

Knoll Associates, inc.
Knoll index of contemporary design. ₍New York, 1954₎
63 p. illus., maps. 31 cm.
Published in 1950 under title: Knoll index of designs.

1. Furniture. 2. Textile industry and fabrics. I. Title.

NK2265.K6 1954 749.245 54—12139

NK 0207135 DLC OrCS IU CU NIC ViU TU CLSU TxU NcGU OCl OClSA OCU PPMoI NcRS MB OrU WaT WaS CaBVaU IdU MtBC MiD PP

Knoll Associates, inc.
Knoll index of designs. ₍New York, ©1950₎
79 p. illus. 31 cm.

1. Furniture. 2. Textile industry and fabrics. I. Title.

NK2265.K6 749.245 51-5964 ‡

NK 0207136 DLC NIC ViU NcGU NcU MB NN NIC TU MiD GAT OrU WaS

NK2260 qK5 pam
Knoll Associates, inc.
Knoll office planned furniture. ₍n.p., n.d.₎
23 p. illus. (part col.) 31cm.

"Printed in Germany."

1. Office furniture. I. Title.

NK 0207137 OrCS

QV 772 K75
KNOLL Pharmaceutical Company, Orange, N. J.
[Catalogs of drugs and pharmaceuticals]

A file of these publications will be found on the shelves under the call number.
1. Drugs - U. S. - catalogs

NK 0207138 DNLM

Knoll & Co., Ludwigshafen
see Knoll, A.G. Ludwigshafen am Rhein.

Knolle, Armin, 1906-
... Die Serumbaktericide bei Diabetes mellitus ... Marburg, 1935.
Inaug.-Diss. - Marburg.
Lebenslauf.
"Literaturverzeichnis": p. 27-29.

NK 0207140 CtY

Knolle, Dorothy Nell, *ed.*
Adventures in reading. Philadelphia, J. C. Winston Co. ₍1946-48₎
3 v. illus. (part col.) 22 cm.
Vol. 3 by Dorothy Nell Knolle and Dora E. Palmer.
Includes bibliographies.
CONTENTS.—1. Discovery.—2. Exploration.—3. Treasures.

1. Readers and speakers—1870- I. Palmer, Dora E., joint ed. II. Title.

PE1117.K6 808.8 47-1540 rev*

NK 0207141 DLC Or ICU

Knolle, Dorothy Nell, *ed.*
Adventures in reading; illustrated by Rafaello Busoni ₍and others₎ Philadelphia, Winston ₍1950-
v. illus. (part col.) 22 cm.
Includes bibliographies.
CONTENTS.—1. Discovery.—

1. Readers and speakers—1870- I. Title.

PE1117.K62 808.8 50-4732

NK 0207142 DLC

Knolle (Fredericus). *De artis obstetriciæ historia. 23 pp. 4°. *Argentorati, ex prelo J. H. Heitzii,* 1773.

NK 0207143 DNLM PPC

Knolle, Fridericus Augustus Gottlob.
*De obstructione alvina diaeteticis auxiliis tollenda.
RBS. 138249
Lipsiae, ex off. Langenhemia, 1772.
42 p. 22 cm.

NK 0207144 NNNAM

VOLUME 300

Knolle, Fridericus Augustus Gottlob.
Plantas venenatas umbelliferas indicat. 19 pp. 4°. *Lipsiæ, ex off. Langenhemia*, [1771].

NK 0207145 DNLM

Knolle, Heinz, 1877–
... Beiträge zur kenntnis der hals- und schwanzwirbel der haussäuger und ihnen verwandten arten für forensische und fleischbeschauzwecke ... Hannover, M. & H. Schaper, 1911.
2 p. l., 26 p. XIII fold. pl. 22½cm.
Inaug.-diss.—Bern.
Lebenslauf.
"Literaturverzeichnis": p. [13]
1. Domestic animals—Anatomy and physiology. 2. Vertebrae.
[Full name: Heinrich Friedrich Wilhelm Knolle]
Agr 11-2257
U. S. Dept. of agr. Library for Library of Congress 444K75 [a41b1]

NK 0207146 DNAL PU

Knolle, Herbert.
Konjunkturengewinn im verhältnis zum unternehmergewinn, von Herbert Knolle ... Jena, G. Fischer, 1931.
3 p. l., 103 p. 24½cm. (*Added t.-p.:* Untersuchungen zur theoretischen nationalökonomie ... hft. 8)
"Literaturverzeichnis": p. 100-103.
1. Profit. I. Title.
Library of Congress HB601.K77 33-1797
339.2

NK 0207147 DLC ICJ NN MH CU

Knolle, Johannes Fridericus.
*De ossium carie venerea.
Lipsiae, ex off. Langenhemia, [1763].
48 p. 1 pl. 20 cm.
RBS. 138162

NK 0207148 DNLM

Knolle (Johannes Fridericus). Decas librorum anatomicorum rariorum. Comment. 12 pp. 4°. *Lipsiæ, ex off. Langenhemia*, [1761].

NK 0207149 DNLM

KNOLLE, Theodor, 1885-
Bindung und Freiheit in der Gestaltung; Vortrag auf der vierten Haupttagung der Liturgischen Konferenz Niedersachsens zu Flensburg 1931. Goettingen, Vandenhoeck & Ruprecht, 1932.
20p. 24cm. (Das Heilige und die Form. Beitraege zur Monatschrift fuer Gottesdienst und kirchliche Kunst, 12)

NK 0207150 MH-AH

Knolle, Theodor, 1885– *ed.*
... Luther in der deutschen kirche der gegenwart; eine übersicht, herausgegeben im auftrag der Luther-gesellschaft von ihrem zweiten präsidenten, d. Theodor Knolle. Gütersloh, C. Bertelsmann, 1940.
80 p. front. (port.) plates. 22cm. (Schriftenreihe der Luther-gesellschaft, hrsg. von Paul Althaus und Theodor Knolle. Hft. 14)
"Literatur zur Lutherforschung": p. 77-79.
1. Luther, Martin, 1483–1546. 2. Luther, Martin—Societies, periodicals, etc. I. Title.
BR334.K57 922.443 A F 46-519
Union theol. sem. Library for Library of Congress †

NK 0207151 NNUT DLC NcD NN FU IU MH CtY

Knolle, Theodor, 1885- comp.
Das lutherische Hamburg; Aufsätze zu Geschichte und Gegenwart des Luthertums in Hamburg. Hamburg, 1928.
149 p. illus.,ports. 24cm
"Festschrift zur XX. Haupttagung des lutherischen Einigungswerkes in Hamburg-Altona 1928."
1.Lutheran Church in Hamburg. I.Title.
BX8023 H3K5

NK 0207152 CSt

Div.S. 270.6 L973SC Hft.10
Knolle, Theodor, 1885-
Luthers Glaube; eine Widerlegung. Weimar, H. Böhlaus Nachf., 1938.
70 p. 23 cm. (Schriftenreihe der Luther-Gesellschaft, Hft. 10)
Includes bibliographical references.
1. Luther, Martin, 1483-1546. Theology. I. Title. II. Series: Luther-Gesellschaft, Wittenberg. Schriftenreihe, Hft. 10.

NK 0207153 NcD

Knolle, Theodor, 1885- ed.
Luther, Martin, 1483–1546.
... Luthers glossen zum Alten Testament in auswahl nach der ordnung seiner lehre. München, C. Kaiser, 1935.

Knolle, Theodor Louis Georg Albert
see Knolle, Theodor, 1885-

Knolle, Ulrich Walter: Die Entwicklung des Zinsfusses bei den ländlichen Spar- und Darlehnskassen des Verbandes der landwirtschaftlichen Genossenschaften der Provinz Sachsen und der angrenzenden Staaten zu Halle a. S. von 1913 bis 1918. [Maschinenschrift.] 89 S. m. Taf. 4°. — Auszug: Halle 1922. 2 Bl. 8°
Halle, R.- u. staatswiss. Diss. v. 12. Aug. 1922 [1923] [U 23. 4864

NK 0207156 ICRL

SB129 .R5 1943
Knolle, Wilhelm, 1900-
Ries, Ludwig Wilhelm, 1891–
Die maschinelle Bewältigung der Ernte von Getreide, Heu und Hackfrüchten, ein Ratgeber für die Praxis, von L. W. Ries, C. H. Dencker [und] W. Knolle. 2., neubearb. Aufl. Berlin, P. Parey, 1943.

Knolle, Wilhelm, 1900-
... Untersuchungen an breitdresch-trommeln, von dr.-ing. Wilhelm Knolle. Berlin, Beuth-verlag, 1930.
55, [1] p. illus., fold. tables, diagrs. 21cm. (RKTL; schriften des Reichskuratoriums für technik in der landwirtschaft, hft. 7)
"Schriftennachweis": p. 54-55.
1. Threshing-machines.
Library of Congress S699.K5 32-19947

NK 0207158 DLC

Knollenberg, Bernhard, 1892–
Franklin and William Pitt, Franklin's letter of January 21, 1775. Bloomington, 1949.
24 p. 24 cm. (Indiana University Library publications, no. 1)
Rev. ed., 1949, ascribing the letter to Jonathan Williams, has title: Franklin, Jonathan Williams and William Pitt: a letter of January 21, 1775.
Bibliographical references included in "Notes" (p. 22-24)
1. U. S.—Pol. & govt.—Revolution. 2. Franklin, Benjamin, 1706-1790. 3. Pitt, William, 1st Earl of Chatham, 1708-1788. The speech of the Right Honourable the Earl of Chatham, in the House of Lords, on Friday the twentieth of January, 1775. I. Title. (Series)
E211.K7 1949 973.311 49-49518*

NK 0207159 DLC TxU

Knollenberg, Bernhard, 1892–
Franklin, Jonathan Williams and William Pitt: a letter of January 21, 1775. Bloomington, 1949.
24 p. 24 cm. (Indiana University Library publications, no. 1)
Rev. ed. of the author's Franklin and William Pitt, Franklin's letter of January 21, 1775, ascribing the letter to Jonathan Williams.
Bibliographical references included in "Notes" (p. 22-24)
1. U. S.—Pol. & govt.—Revolution. 2. Franklin, Benjamin, 1706-1790. 3. Pitt, William, 1st Earl of Chatham, 1708-1778. The speech of the Right Honourable the Earl of Chatham, in the House of Lords, on Friday the 20th of January, 1775. I. Williams, Jonathan, 1750-1815. (Series)
E211.K7 1949a 973.311 49-48250 rev*

NK 0207160 DLC NN ICU PHi TxU MiU-C

Knollenberg, Bernhard, 1892-
... Guy T. Helvering, commissioner of internal revenue, petitioner, vs. Walter C. Janney and Pauline F.M. Janney ...
see under Helvering, Guy Tresillian, 1878- petitioner.

Knollenberg, Bernhard, 1892- ed.
Hawaiian Citations
see under Finley, Elizabeth, comp.

E172 .A35 vol. 56
Knollenberg, Bernhard, 1892- ed.
Adams, John, *Pres. U. S.*, 1735–1826.
John Adams, Knox, and Washington.
(*In* American Antiquarian Society, Worcester, Mass. Proceedings. Worcester, 1947. 25 cm. v. 56, p. [207]-238)

Knollenberg, Bernhard, 1892–
Pioneer sketches of the upper Whitewater valley, Quaker stronghold of the West, by Bernhard Knollenberg. Indianapolis, Indiana historical society, 1945.
171 p. front. (map) plates. (*Half-title:* Indiana historical society. Publications, v. 15, no. 1)
"Sources": p. [147]-155.
1. Whitewater valley, Ind.—Hist. 2. Friends, Society of. Indiana. I. Title.
F521.I 41 vol. 15, no. 1 977.2 46-4455

NK 0207164 DLC ViU PPAmP PHC NN WaTC CaBVaU

---

503 Y27 1
[Knollenberg, Bernhard] 1892-
Three Washington letters.
(In The Yale university library gazette. [New Haven,Conn.,1940] 26½cm. v.15,p.5-8)
Signed: B.K.
The first two letters, which were written to Lund Washington, are dated Oct.6,1776 and Dec.10 and 17,1776; the third was written to Bushrod Washington, and dated Feb.10,1796.

NK 0207165 CtY

Knollenberg, Bernhard, 1892–
Washington and the revolution, a reappraisal; Gates, Conway, and the Continental congress, by Bernhard Knollenberg. New York, The Macmillan company, 1940.
xvi p., 1 l., 269 p. front. (port.) 22cm.
"First printing."
"Table of books cited": p. 232-250. "Manuscript collections cited": p. 251.
1. Washington, George, pres. U. S., 1732-1799. 2. U. S.—Hist.—Revolution. I. Title.
Library of Congress E312.25.K64 40-35489
——— Copy 2.
Copyright 923.173

NK 0207166 MiU-C ViU WaTC Or OrPR WaSp OrU WaS CaBVaU MtU OrSaW DLC OrP MiU NcRS PSC PU PPD ODW OCU OCl

VOLUME 300

Knollenberg, George H., co.
Knollenberg's souvenir pictorial history of the city of Richmond, Indiana... «Richmond, Nicholson print.» 1904.

NK 0207167 OOxM

Knollenberg, William E.
Knollenberg's tables for the use of cigar manufacturers and cigar makers. Computed by W. E. Knollenberg ... [Jacksonville? Ill.] 1896.

128 p. 16cm.

1. Cigar manufacture and trade—Tables and ready-reckoners.

9-2355†

Library of Congr... TS2251.K72

NK 0207168 DLC

Knoller, Chaim, 1847-1927.
דבר יום ביומו. יכיל לכל יום ויום מימי השנה דברים חשוים לכל נפש. פרעמישלא, תרס"ז-ע. [Przemyśl, 1907-09]

2 v. 28 cm.

1. Jewish devotional literature (Selections, extracts, etc.) 2. Jews---Rites and ceremonies. 3. Fasts and feasts---Judaism. I. Title.

Title transliterated: Devar yom be-yomo.

BM700.K55 1907 53-49660

NK 0207169 DLC

Knoller, Chaim, 1847-1927.
דבר יום ביומו. יכיל לכל יום ויום מימי השנה דברים חשוים לכל נפש. ועתה נדפס מחדש ע"י דוד הכהן ויוסף וואקס. ברוקלין, "שרנא" פאבלישינג, תש"ו. [Brooklyn, 1946]

2 v. in 1. 23 cm.

[1. Chronology] 2. Jews—Rites and ceremonies. 3. Fasts and feasts—Judaism. I. Title.

Title transliterated: Devar yom be-yomo.

BM700.K55 1946 A 53-1677

New York. Public Libr. for Library of Congress †

NK 0207170 NN CLU DLC MH

Knoller, Chaim, 1847-1927.
כבוד חכמים. פרעמישלא, בדפוס זופניק, קנאללער עם וואלף [19—]-1898.

2 v. 23 cm.

Vol. 2, בדפוס ח. קנאללער

CONTENTS.—חלק א. חמשה חומשי תורה.—חלק ב. נביאים וכתובים

1. Bible. O. T.—Commentaries. I. Title.

Title transliterated: Kevod ḥakhamim.

BS1158.H4K5 A 51—1324

New York. Public Libr. for Library of Congress [a65b½]†

NK 0207171 NN DLC

Knoller, Chaim, 1847-1927.
Megilat Ester
see under Bible. O. T. Esther. Hebrew. 1894.

Knoller, Chaim, 1847-1927.
Megilat Kohelet
see under Bible. O. T. Ecclesiastes. Hebrew. 1896?

Knoller, Gabriel: Verlauf der Gewichtskurve bei acuten Infektionskrankheiten der Kinder. Aus d. Univ.-Kinderkl. zu Berlin. [In Maschinenschrift.] 33 S. 4°(2°). — Auszug: Berlin (1921): Blanke. 2 Bl. 8°

Berlin, Med. Diss. v. 15. Febr. 1921, Ref. Czerny

[Geb. 9. März 92 Krefeld; Wohnort: Berlin; Staatsangeh.: Preußen; Vorbildung: Friedrichs-G. Berlin Reife 11; Studium: Berlin 2, Würzburg 1, Berlin 4, Würzburg 1, Berlin 2 S.; Coll. 11. Febr. 21; Approb. 23. Sept. 19.] [U 21. 2418

NK 0207174 ICRL

Knoller, Jacob, 1887-
...Adams Tod. Von Jacob Knoller. New York, 1945. 14 p. 28cm.

318507B. 1. Adam—Fiction. 2. Fiction, German-American.
N. Y. P. L. October 4, 1945

NK 0207175 NN

Knoller, Jacob, 1887-
...Anthem: "America ahead." Words and music by Jacob Knoller... New York, c1943. 2 l. 34cm.

For bass voice with piano accompaniment.
First line: America, thy wings are rising.
Black-line print from autograph manuscript.

1. Songs, English—U. S. composers. 2. National music—U. S. 3. Autographs—Music—Knoller, J.—Facsimiles.
N. Y. P. L. November 30, 1945

NK 0207176 NN

Knoller, Jacob, 1887-
The beauty of N. Y. Central park, and other drawings and paintings, by Jacob Knoller. New York, 1947. 21 pl. 28 x 35cm.

Title from label.

NK 0207177 NN

Knoller, Jacob, 1887-
...Ein besserer Herr. Einakter, von Jacob Knoller. New York, c1946. 14 f. 28cm.

Typescript.

356853B. 1. Drama, German-American. I. Title.
N. Y. P. L. January 10, 1947

NK 0207178 NN

Knoller, Jacob, 1887-
Besuch im Prager Ghetto, von Jakob Knoller. Berlin: Kaskaden Verlag, c1936. 10 p. illus. 22cm.

Original imprint changed to: Copyright 1936 by the author: Prof. Jac. Knoller, New York city.

164706B. 1. Jews in Czecho-Slovakia—Prague. 2. Ghetto—Prague.
N. Y. P. L. May 19, 1942

NK 0207179 NN

Knoller, Jacob, 1887-
...The burning thornbush. One-act play, by Jacob Knoller. New York, 1941. 8 f. 27cm.

1. Moses—Drama. 2. Drama, American. I. Title.
N. Y. P. L. May 17, 1944

NK 0207180 NN

Knoller, Jacob, 1887-
...The death of Adam. By Jacob Knoller. [New York, 1945] 12 f. 28cm.

327345B. 1. Adam and Eve—Fiction. I. Title.
N. Y. P. L. October 9, 1947

NK 0207181 NN

Knoller, Jacob, 1887-
Dream in the dawn. Traum in der Dämmerung. Words and music by Jacob Knoller. [New York, J. Knoller, c1944]

Reproduced from autograph manuscript.
Song with piano accompaniment.
First line: Where, oh, where is she. (Eine, nur Eine, für die ich lebe).

1. Songs, U. S. 2. Autographs (Music)—Knoller, J.—Facsimiles.
I. Song index (4).
N. Y. P. L. February 7, 1951

NK 0207182 NN

Knoller, Jacob, 1887-
...Du bist wie eine Blume. (Heine.) Berlin: Kaskaden-Verlag, c1930. 4 l. 32cm.

For 1 voice with piano acc.
Below imprint, part in ms.: Copyright 1930 by Prof. Jacob Knoller, New York city.

1. Songs, German. I. Heine, Heinrich, 1797-1856.
N. Y. P. L. July 17, 1942

NK 0207183 NN

Knoller, Jacob, 1887-
[Esther. Libretto. German]
Esther. Oper in 5 Akten. Libretto und Musik von Jacob Knoller. New York, c1946. 41 p. 28cm.

NK 0207184 NN

Knoller, Jacob, 1887-
[Esther. Vocal score. English & German]
...Esther; opera in five acts. Libretto and music by Jacob Knoller. [New York, 1946, c1941] 10 p.l., 175 [i. e. 185] f. 28cm.

Reproduced from autograph manuscript; t.-p. and notes typewritten.
Autograph of composer on flyleaf.

529853B. 1. Operas—Vocal scores. 2. Autographs (Music)—Knoller, J.—Facsimiles. 3. Autographs (Signatures, etc.)—Knoller, J.

NK 0207185 NN

Knoller, Jacob, 1887-
[Esther. Libretto. English]
Esther. Opera in five acts. Libretto and music by Jacob Knoller. New York, c1946. 48 p. 28cm.

NK 0207186 NN

Knoller, Jacob, 1887-
...Die Ferien des Malers Anton van Dyck; oder, Der Freund als Neffe. Eine Novelle von Jacob Knoller. [New York, c1941] 158 f. 28½cm.

Reproduced from typewritten copy.

164702B. 1. Dyck, Sir Anthonie van, 1599-1641—Fiction. 2. Fiction, German-American. I. Title.
N. Y. P. L. July 28, 1942

NK 0207187 NN

VOLUME 300

Knoller, Jacob, 1887–
Free will or destiny. One act play around Frederick Chopin, by Jacob Knoller. New York, J. Knoller, 1950. 13 f. 29cm.

Typescript.

532937B. 1. Drama, German-American. 2. Chopin, Frédéric, 1810-1849—Drama. I. Title.
N. Y. P. L. July 25, 1950

NK 0207188 NN

Knoller, Jacob, 1887–
...Der fremde Herr. Eine Erzählung von Jacob Knoller. New York, 1945. 13 f. 28cm.

318506B. 1. Fiction, German-American. I. Title.
N. Y. P. L. October 4, 1945

NK 0207189 NN

Knoller, Jacob, 1887–
...Gedichte und Bekenntnisse, 1948–1951, von Jacob Knoller. New York, 1951. 29 f. port. 28cm.

With author's autograph.

NK 0207190 NN

Knoller, Jacob, 1887–
The general manager...by Jacob Knoller. New York, J. Knoller [1950] 43, 26, 18 f. 28cm.

Also issued in German.

529145B. 1. Drama, German-American. I. Title.
N. Y. P. L. September 13, 1950

NK 0207191 NN

Knoller, Jacob, 1887–
...Der General-Direktor...von Jacob Knoller. [New York, 1950] 83 f. 28cm.

Also issued in English.

529144B. 1. Drama, German-American. I. Title.
N. Y. P. L. September 26, 1950

NK 0207192 NN

Knoller, Jacob, 1887–
...Im Facett-Spiegel des Lebens. Gedichte, Gedanken und Erzählungen, von Jacob Knoller. New York, c1946. 200 f. illus. 29cm.

NK 0207193 NN

Knoller, Jacob, 1887–
...Im Schein der Feuersäule. Gedichte, Sentenzen und Erzählungen, von Jacob Knoller. [New York, 1942] 118 f. mounted illus. (incl. port.) 27cm.

Reproduced from typewritten copy.

187809B. 1. German literature—Misc. I. Title.
N. Y. P. L. August 19, 1942

NK 0207194 NN

Knoller, Jacob, 1887–
The impractical profession; one act play, by Jacob Knoller. New York, J. Knoller, 1950. 8 f. 29cm.

Typescript.

532938B. 1. Drama, German-American. I. Title.
N. Y. P. L. June 28, 1950

NK 0207195 NN

Knoller, Jacob, 1887–
...Jonah and the storm. One-act play, by Jacob Knoller. New York, 1941. 13 f. 26cm.

1. Jonah, the prophet—Drama. 2. Drama, American. I. Title.
N. Y. P. L. May 17, 1944

NK 0207196 NN

Knoller, Jacob, 1887–
...Landscapes and flowers. New York, J. Knoller, 1952. 2 p. l., 36 pl. 18 x 26cm.

Title from mounted strip.
Imprint at head of t.-p.
Photo-reproductions.

NK 0207197 NN

Knoller, Jacob, 1887–
...Little Eva and her brother's soul; or, How I proved the existence and the home-return of our soul. By Jacob Knoller. New York, 1941. 12 f. 26cm.

1. Immortality. I. Title.
N. Y. P. L. December 28, 1945

NK 0207198 NN

Knoller, Jacob, 1887–
...The magic island; drama...by Jacob Knoller. New York, c1948. 72 f. 28cm.

Typescript.
"Last changed and authorized wording of October 1, 1948."—*Label on t.-p.*

482283B. 1. Drama, German—Translations into English. I. Title.
N. Y. P. L. July 20, 1949

NK 0207199 NN

Knoller, Jacob, 1887–
...Mein Leben. Bilder und Dokumente... My life... New York, c1948. 88 f. incl. facsims., ports. (part mounted) 28cm.

Text typewritten.

528693B. 1. Musicians—Correspondence, reminiscences, etc.
N. Y. P. L. June 14, 1950

NK 0207200 NN

Knoller, Jacob, 1887–
...Mein Leben (Selbst-Biographie), von Jacob Knoller... New York, c1949. 3 v. in 2. 29cm.

Typewritten.
With autograph of author.
"Werke," Teil 3, 3 l. at end.

525141-2B. 1. Musicians—Correspondence, reminiscences, etc.
N. Y. P. L. June 19, 1950

NK 0207201 NN

Knoller, Jacob, 1887–
Palestine-journey in pictures, by Jacob Knoller. [New York, 1939?] album of 19 mounted pl. (incl. port.) 18 x 26cm.

Title from label on cover.

1. Palestine—Views. I. Title.
N. Y. P. L. June 4, 1940

NK 0207202 NN

KNOLLER, JACOB, 1887–
Palestine-journey in pictures, by artist-painter, Professor Jacob Knoller... [New York] The author, c1941. 1 p.l., 20 mounted pl. (incl. 3 ports.) 26cm.

"Painted and drawn directly from nature in Palestine."

1. Palestine—Views.

NK 0207203 NN

Knoller, Jacob, 1887–
The peacock and the nightingale. Der Pfau und die Nachtigall. Words and music by Jacob Knoller. [New York, J. Knoller, c1946]

Reproduced from autograph manuscript.
Song with piano accompaniment.

1. Songs, U.S. 2. Autographs (Music)—Knoller, J.—Facsimiles. I. Song index (2).
N. Y. P. L. February 7, 1951

NK 0207204 NN

Knoller, Jacob, 1887–
Phantom on the journey. Words and music by Jacob Knoller. [New York, J. Knoller, c1944]

Reproduced from autograph manuscript.
Song with piano accompaniment.
First line: Clouds and hazy veils.

1. Songs, U.S. 2. Autographs (Music)—Knoller, J.—Facsimiles. I. Song index (2).
N. Y. P. L. February 7, 1951

NK 0207205 NN

Knoller, Jacob, 1887–
...Portraits and groups; drawings, paintings and etchings in photo-reproductions. New York, J. Knoller, 1952. 1 p. l., 40 figs. on 36 l. 38cm.

Caption-title from mounted leaf of typescript.
Imprint at head of t.-p.

NK 0207206 NN

Knoller, Jacob, 1887–
[Esther. Act 4. Prelude]
Prelude to act IV, opera "Esther," by Jacob Knoller. [New York, c1941] 15 p. 39cm.

Full score, with piano score above.
Reproduced from manuscript copy.

1. Orchestra—Score—1800- I. Title: Esther.
N. Y. P. L. August 25, 1943

NK 0207207 NN

VOLUME 300

Knoller, Jacob, 1887 -
...Question to God, by Jacob Knoller. New York, c1944. 3 p. 32cm.

For piano.

488329B. 1. Piano. I. Title. October 24, 1949
N. Y. P. L.

NK 0207208 NN

Knoller, Jacob, 1887–
A refined gentleman; one act play, by Jacob Knoller. New York, J. Knoller, 1950. 12 f. 29cm.

Typescript.

532939B. 1. Drama, German-American. I. Title. June 28, 1950
N. Y. P. L.

NK 0207209 NN

Knoller, Jacob, 1887 -
...Rund um die Welt. Gedichte, Sinnsprüche und Erzählungen, von Jacob Knoller. [New York, 1942] 228 f. front. (port.), plates. 27½cm.

Reproduced from typewritten copy.

187808B. 1. German literature—Misc. I. Title. August 25, 1942
N. Y. P. L.

NK 0207210 NN

Knoller, Jacob, 1887 -
...Salomo (Heine). Berlin: Kaskaden-Verlag, c1930. 4 p. 31½cm.

For high voice with piano acc.
First line: Verstummt sind die Pauken.
Below imprint, part in ms.: Copyright 1930 by Prof. Jacob Knoller, New York city.

——— ——— Medium voice.

——— ——— Low voice.

1. Songs, German. I. Heine, Heinrich, 1797-1856. July 22, 1942
N. Y. P. L.

NK 0207211 NN

Knoller, Jacob, 1887 -
...Die Schlacht im Warschauer Ghetto, Drama...von Jacob Knoller. The battle in the Warsaw ghetto. [New York, J. Knoller, 1946] 87 f. 28cm.

Text in German.

351080B. 1. Warsaw ghetto, Battle of, 1943—Drama. 2. Drama, German-American. I. Title. August 30, 1946
N. Y. P. L.

NK 0207212 NN

Knoller, Jacob, 1887 –
Der Sinn der Neunten Symphonie von Beethoven. Von Jacob Knoller. [New York, 1945] 15 p. 27cm.

Typewritten.

343195B. 1. Beethoven, Ludwig van. Symphony no. 9. September 30, 1946
N. Y. P. L.

NK 0207213 NN

Knoller, Jacob, 1887 -
...Song of the victory workers, by Jacob Knoller... New York, c1944. 2 l. 34cm.

For bass voice with piano accompaniment.
First line: The hammer rattles, the auger hums.
Black-line print from autograph manuscript.

1. Songs, English—U. S. composers. 2. World war, 1939- —U. S. 3. Autographs—Music—Knoller, J.—Facsimiles. November 30, 1945
N. Y. P. L.

NK 0207214 NN

Knoller, Jacob, 1887 -
...Der unpraktische Beruf. Einakter von Jacob Knoller. New York, c1946. 12 f. 28cm.

Typescript.

356857B. 1. Drama, German-American. I. Title. January 8, 1947
N. Y. P. L.

NK 0207215 NN

Knoller, Jacob, 1887 -
...Verheissung, Schuld und Sühne. Vier Biblische Scenen um Jacob. Von Jacob Knoller... New York: J. Knoller, c1941. 32 f. 27cm.

1. Jacob, the patriarch—Drama. 2. Drama, German-American. I. Title. July 19, 1943
N. Y. P. L.

NK 0207216 NN

Knoller, Jacob, 1887 -
...Die verzauberte Insel. Drama... Von Jacob Knoller. [New York, c1948] 72 p. 28cm.

At head of title: Copyright 1948...

449543B. 1. Drama, German-American. I. Title. July 13, 1948
N. Y. P. L.

NK 0207217 NN

Knoller, Jacob, 1887 -
Visit to the Prague ghetto. By Jacob Knoller. New York, N. Y., c1941. 9 f. front., port. 28cm.

Reproduced from typewritten copy.

164598B. 1. Ghetto—Prague. 2. Jews in Czecho-Slovakia—Prague. December 21, 1942
N. Y. P. L.

NK 0207218 NN

Knoller, Jacob, 1887 -
...Von hoher Warte. From the high watch tower. Gedichte, Lieder, Gedanken und Erzählungen, von Jacob Knoller. [New York, 1948] 65 l. 28cm.

Text in German or English.

472737B. 1. German-American literature—Misc. I. Title. March 4, 1949
N. Y. P. L.

NK 0207219 NN

Knoller, Jacob, 1887 -
...Von Liebe, Liebe und Liebe. Gedichte. New York, 1941. 46 p. front. 27cm.

NK 0207220 NN

Knoller, Jacob, 1887 -
...Wanderers Nachtlied (Goethe). Berlin: Kaskaden-Verlag, c1930. 2 p. 32cm.

For 1 voice with piano acc.
First line: Über allen Gipfeln ist Ruh'.
Below imprint, part in ms.: Copyright 1930 by Prof. Jacob Knoller, New York city.

1. Songs, German. I. Goethe, Johann Wolfgang von. July 22, 1942
N. Y. P. L.

NK 0207221 NN

Knoller, Jacob, 1887 -
...Wille oder Schicksal. Einakter, von Jacob Knoller. New York, c1946. 18 f. 28cm.

Typescript.

356856B. 1. Drama, German-American. I. Title. January 8, 1947
N. Y. P. L.

NK 0207222 NN

Knoller, Jacob, 1887–
Words and their meanings; one act play, by Jacob Knoller. New York, J. Knoller, 1950. 10 f. 28cm.

Typescript.

532940B. 1. Drama, German-American. I. Title. July 26, 1950
N. Y. P. L.

NK 0207223 NN

Knoller, Jacob, 1887 -
...Ein Wort—ein Wort! Einakter, von Jacob Knoller. New York, c1946. 12 f. 28cm.

Typescript.

356854B. 1. Drama, German-American. I. Title. January 10, 1947
N. Y. P. L.

NK 0207224 NN

Knoller, Jacob, 1887 -
...Young 'Hamlet'; or, The man in the box. By Jacob Knoller. New York, 1941. 18 f. 28cm.

NK 0207225 NN

4BM 352 Knoller, Lesser, 1860-
Das Problem der Willensfreiheit in der älteren jüdischen Religionsphilosophie des Mittelalters. Leipzig, 1884.
95 p.

NK 0207226 DLC-P4 CtY ICRL NjP

W 4 B52 1947 Knoller, Otto
Die Bedeutung der tödlichen Verkehrsunfälle der Kinder und der Jugendlichen in der Schweiz. Schwarzenburg, Gerber, 1947.
30 p. illus.

Inaug.-Diss. - Bern.
Bibliography: p. 26.

NK 0207227 DNLM CtY

VOLUME 300

Knoller, Richard, 1869–
Flüssigkeitswiderstand und propellertheorie. Von ing. R. Knoller. Wien, Verlag des Österr. flugtechnischen vereines, 1909.
32 p. diagrs. 23cm.

1. Hydrodynamics. 2. Propellers. I. Title.

Library of Congress QA911.K6 34-10672
——— Copy 2. 532.58

NK 0207228 DLC

Knoller, Richard, 1869–
Die gesetze des luftwiderstandes, von ing. R. Knoller ... Wien, Verlag des Österr. flugtechnischen vereines, 1909.
14 p. diagrs. 23cm.
"Separatabdruck aus 'Flug- und motor-technik' ... nummer 21 und 22, III. jahrgang."

1. Air resistance. I. Title.

Library of Congress TL570.K6 34-11487
629.13234

NK 0207229 DLC OkU

Knoller, Richard, 1869 -
Die stabilität der drachenflieger. Von ingenieur Richard Knoller ... Wien, Verlag des vereines "Flugmaschine", 1908.
32 p. incl. front., diagrs. 23cm.
"Separat-abdruck aus den Mitteilungen des vereines 'Flugmaschine', II. jahrgang, 1908."

1. Stability of aeroplanes. I. Title.

31-29332
Library of Congress TL574.S7K6 629.13

NK 0207230 DLC OkU

Knoller, Richard, 1869–
... Vorlesungen über luftschiffahrt. Vom vortragenden selbst durchgesehene ausgabe der lehrkanzel. 2. aufl. Wien, Druckerei Stiw, 1920.
2 p. l., 89 p., 1 l. illus., VII fold. pl., diagrs. 25½cm.
On label mounted on cover: Mit eingeklebten korrekturen.
CONTENTS.—Eigenschaften der atmosphäre.—Aerodynamik.—Aerostatik.—Die wichtigsten formelzeichen. — Geschichtlicher überblick.—Biographische daten.—Einschlägige literatur (p. [88]–89)—Berichtigungen.

1. Aeronautics. 2. Aerodynamics. 3. Aerostatics.

34-11486
Library of Congress TL570.K63 1920 629.1323

NK 0207231 DLC OkU

Knoller, Rudolf, 1908-
Die begehung strafbarer handlungen durch benutzung von organen der strafrechtspflege zu amtshandlungen gegen einen unschuldigen
Inaug. Diss. Greifswald, 1931.

NK 0207232 ICRL

Knoller, Rudolf.
Die begehung strafbarer handlungen durch benutzung von organen der strafrechtspflege zu amtshandlungen gegen einen unschuldigen. Von Rudolf Knoller. Breslau, Schletter, 1931.
xx, 127 p. 24cm. (*Added t.-p.:* Strafrechtliche abhandlungen ... hft. 294)
"Schrifttum": p. [VI]–XX.

1. Malicious prosecution. 2. Justice, Administration of. 3. Criminal procedure—Germany. I. Title.

32-4955

NK 0207233 DLC MH-L

Knolles, Richard, 1550?–1610. Ott 150.5.8
d'Algemeene historie der Turken, van hun eerste oorspronk af tot den opgangh van't Ottomannisch Huys, nevens der Christen-prinssen aanmerkens-waerdige optochten tegens de zelve. Eertijts in't Engelsch beschreven. En nu vertaalt door J. G. t'Amstelredam, J. Benjamin, 1670.]
sm. 4°. pp. (10), 198. Plates.

NK 0207234 MH

Knolles, Richard, 1550?-1610.
A continuation of the Turkish historie ...
see under Roe, Sir Thomas, 1581?-1644.

Knolles,Richard,1550?-1610.
The generall historie of the Turkes,from the first beginning of that nation to the rising of the Othoman familie; with all the notable expeditions of the Christian princes against them. Together with The lives and conquests of the Othoman kings and emperours faithfullie collected out of the best histories,both auntient and moderne,and digested into one continuat historie untill this present yeare 1603: by Richard Knolles. London, Printed by A.Islip, 1603.
5 p.*l*.,1152,[38] p.,1 *l*. illus.(ports.) 32½cm.

Title within architectural border ornamented with arms of England,etc.
"The lives of the Othoman kings and emperors" has special t.-p.
"A brief discourse of the greatnesse of the Turkish empire ... " (caption title): p.[1-15] at end.

1.Turkey--Hist.

PHC DFo NN
NK 0207237 MiU NNC NjP ICN CU CtY ViU CSmH MH PBL

DR439
.K7
Knolles, Richard, 1550?-1610.
The generall historie of the Turkes from the first beginning of that nation to the rising of the Othoman familie ... Together with the lives and conquests of the Othoman kings and emperours ... London, A. Islip, 1603.
6 l., 1167, [23] p. illus. (ports.) 31 cm.

Head and tail pieces; initials.
Lettered on spine: Knolles's Turkey.
Imperfect: first two leaves, incl. t.-p., wanting.
1. Turkey - Hist.

NK 0207238 NjR

FILM
Knolles,Richard,1550?-1610.
The generall historie of the Turkes,from the first beginning of that nation to the rising of the Othoman familie: with all the notable expeditions of the Christian princes against them. Together with the lives and conquests of the Othoman kings and emperours. Faithfullie collected out of the best histories,both auntient and moderne,and digested into one continuat historie vntill this present yeare 1603. London, Printed by A.Jslip, 1603.

In 2 pts.,the 2d with special t.p.: The lives of the Othoman kings and emperors ...
"A briefe discourse of the greatnesse of the Turkish empire": p.[1]-[15] at end.
University Microfilms no.20370 (carton 763)
Short-title catalogue no.15051.

1.Turkey--Hist.

NK 0207240 MiU

Knolles, Richard, 1550?-1610.

The generall historie of the Turkes from the first beginning of the nation to the rising of the Othoman familie ... Together with the lives and conquests of the Othoman kings and emperours ... London, Printed by A. Islip, 1609.
3 p.l., 1303, [38] p. illus. (incl. ports.) 33cm.
"The lives of the Othoman kings and emperors ..." has special t.-p. with imprint: London, Printed by A. Islip, 1609.
Imperfect: Title-page and several prelim. leaves wanting.
1. Turkey—Hist.

NK 0207241 ViU MWA

Ag
K755
+603gb
Rare
Books
Col
Knolles, Richard, 1550?-1610.
The generall historie of the Turkes, from the first beginning of that nation to the rising of the Othoman familie: with all the notable expeditions of the Christian princes against them. Together with the lives and conquests of the Othoman kings and emperours unto the yeare 1610. Written by Richard Knolles ... The 2d ed. [London] Printed by Adam Islip. 1610.
5p.*l*.,1303,[38]p. incl. illus.(incl. ports.) geneal. tables. 34cm.
Title within ornamental border.

"The lives of the Othoman kings and emperors": p.[129]-1303.
"A briefe discourse of the greatnesse of the Turkish empire": p.[1]-[15] at end.
Armorial bookplate of Hickman Barr?

1. Turkey - Hist.

CtY DFo
NK 0207243 TxU ViU PPL OClW OCU CSmH MoU CSt WaU IEN

FILM
Knolles,Richard,1550?-1610.
The generall historie of the Turkes,from the first beginning of that nation to the rising of the Othoman familie: with all the notable expeditions of the Christian princes against them. Together with the lives and conquests of the Othoman kings and emperours vnto the yeare 1610. The 2d ed. [London] Printed by A.Islip, 1610.
In 2 pts.,the 2d with special t.p.: The lives of the Othoman kings and emperors ... London,

Printed by A.Jslip, 1609.
"A briefe discourse of the greatnesse of the Turkish Empire": p.[1]-[15] at end.
University Microfilms no.20371 (carton 764)
Short-title catalogue no.15052.

1.Turkey--Hist.

NK 0207245 MiU

Knolles, Richard, 1550?–1610.
The generall historie of the Turkes, from the first beginning of that nation to the rising of the Othoman familie: with all the notable expeditions of the Christian princes against them. Together with the lives and conquests of the Othoman kings and emperours unto the yeare 1621. Written by Richard Knolles ... The 3d ed. [London] Printed by Adam Islip. 1621.
5 p. l., 1396, [39] p. incl. illus. (incl. ports.) geneal. tables. 34cm.
Title within ornamental border.
"The lives of the Othoman kings and emperors": p. [129]–1396.
"A briefe discourse of the greatnesse of the Turkish empire": p. [1]–[15] at end.

1. Turkey—Hist.

DR439.K74 1621 47-36212

MB NNC DFo MeB
NK 0207246 DLC InU CtY NjP MWA CLU MH MWiW-C CSmH

VOLUME 300

FILM

Knolles,Richard,1550?-1610.
The generall historie of the Turkes,from the first beginning of that nation to the rising of the Othoman familie: with all the notable expeditions of the Christian princes against them. Together with the lives and conquests of the Othoman kings and emperours vnto the yeare 1621. The 3d ed. [London] Printed by A.Islip, 1621.
In 2 pts.,the 2d with special t.p.: The lives of the Othoman kings and emperors ... London, Printed by A.Islip, 1620.

"A continuation of this historie ... to the end of this present yeare 1620. By Edvvard Grimston": p.1297-1396.
"A briefe discourse of the greatnesse of the Turkish Empire": p.[1]-[15] at end.
University Microfilms no.20372 (carton 764)
Short-title catalogue no.15053.

NK 0207248 MiU

Knolles, Richard, 1550?–1610.
The generall historie of the Turkes, from the first beginning of that nation to the rising of the Othoman familie: with all the notable expeditions of the Christian princes against them. Together with the lives and conqvests of the Othoman kings and emperours. Written by Richard Knolles ... With a new continuation, from ẏ yeare of our Lord 1621. vnto the yeare 1629. faithfully collected. The 4th ed. [London] Printed by A. Islip, 1631.
5 p. l., 1511, [47] p., 1 l. illus. (ports.) tables. 34cm.

Engraved t.-p.
"A continvation of the Tvrkish historie, from the beginning of the yeare ... 1620. vntill the ending of the yeare ... 1628. Collected ovt of the papers and dispatches of Sir Thomas Roe ... by M. B.": p. [1397]–1511.
"A briefe discourse of the greatnesse of the Turkish empire ... By Richard Knolles": p. [1–15] at end.

1. Turkey—Hist. I. Roe, Sir Thomas, 1581?–1644. II. B., M. III. M. B.

5-9252

Library of Congress DR439.K74

NK 0207250 DLC IaU ViU DFo MB PPAmP

FILM

Knolles,Richard,1550?-1610.
The generall historie of the Turkes,from the first beginning of that nation to the rising of the Othoman familie: with all the notable expeditions of the Christian princes against them. Together with the lives and conqvests of the Othoman kings and emperours. With a new continuation from ẏ yeare of our Lord 1621.vnto the yeare 1629.faithfully collected. The 4th ed. [London] Printed by A.Islip, 1631.
In 2 pts.,the 2d with special t.p.: The lives

of the Othoman kings and emperors ... London, Printed by A.Islip, 1630.
"A continuation of this present historie (... since the yeare ... 1609,vnto the yeare, 1617,&c.) By Edward Grimston": p.1297-1396.
"A continvation of the Tvrkish historie,from the beginning of ... 1620 ... vntill the ending of ... 1628. Collected ovt of the papers and

dispatches of Sir Thomas Roe ... by M.B.": p.1397-1511.
"A briefe discourse of the greatnesse of the Turkish Empire": p.[1]-[15] at end.
University Microfilms no.20373 (carton 765)
Short-title catalogue no.15054.
1.Turkey--Hist. I.Grimestone,Edward,fl.1604-1635. II.Roe,Sir Thomas,1581?-1644.

NK 0207253 MiU

Knolles, Richard, 1550?–1610.
The generall historie of the Turkes, from the first beginning of that nation to the rising of the Othoman familie: with all the notable expeditions of the Christian princes against them. Together with The lives and conqvests of the Othoman kings and emperours; written by Richard Knolles ... With a new continuation, from ẏ yeare of Our Lord 1629 vnto the yeare 1638 faithfully collected. The 5th ed. [London] Printed by A. Islip, 1638.
5 p. l., 1500, [20], 31, [3] p. illus. (ports.) 32½cm.

Continued in next column

Continued from preceding column

Engr. t.-p.
"A continvation of the Tvrkish history, from the beginning of the yeare ... 1620, vntill the ending of the yeare ... 1628. Collected ovt of the papers and dispatches of Sr Thomas Rowe ... And since by him re-viewed and corrected": p. 1397–1500, [1]
"A briefe discourse of the greatnesse of the Turkish empire ... By Richard Knolles": [15] p.
"A continvation of the Tvrkish historie, from the yeare ... 1628, to the end of the yeare 1637. Collected out of the dispatches of Sr Peter Wyche ... and others: by Thomas Nabbes": 31 p.

1. Turkey—Hist. I. Roe, Sir Thomas, 1581?–1644. II. Nabbes, Thomas, fl. 1638.

16-9127

Library of Congress DR439.K74 1638

PPL OCl CSmH ICN DFo VtMiM
NK 0207255 DLC PU NcD PSt WU CSt NcGU CtY MnU MH

FILM

Knolles,Richard,1550?-1610.
The generall historie of the Turkes,from the first beginning of that nation to the rising of the Othoman familie; with all the notable expeditions of the Christian princes against them. Together with the lives and conqvests of the Othoman kings and emperours. With a new continuation,from ẏ yeare of Our Lord 1629 vnto the yeare 1638 faithfully collected. The 5th ed. [London] Printed by A.Islip, 1638.
Engraved t.p.
"The lives of the Othoman kings and

emperours" has a special t.p.,engr.
"A continvation of the Tvrkish history,from the beginning of ... 1620,vntill the ending of ... 1628. Collected ovt of the papers and dispatches of Sr Thomas Rowe": p.1397-[1501]
Appended: A briefe discourse of the greatnesse of the Turkish empire ... By Richard Knolles; and A continvation of the Tvrkish historie from ... 1628,to the end of ...

1637. Collected out of the dispatches of Sr Peter Wyche ... and others: by Thomas Nabbes.
Short-title catalogue no.15055 (carton 964)

1.Turkey--Hist. I.Roe,Sir Thomas,1581?-1644. II.Nabbes,Thomas, fl.1638.

NK 0207258 MiU

N
949.6
qK72

Knolles, Richard, 1550? - 1610?
The lives of the Othoman kings and emperors. Faithfvlly gathered ovt of the best histories both antient and moderne, and digested into one continuat[!] historie. [Quotation:] Eccles. 10. 4. ... London, Printed by Adam Islip, 1630.
1 p.ℓ.,1504,[55] p. ports.,tables. 34cm.

Occasional errors in page-numbering.
Lacks p. 130.
1. Turkey. Hist. I. Title.

NK 0207259 N

Knolles, Richard, 1550?-1610, tr.

Bodin, Jean, 1530–1596.
The six bookes of a commonweale. Written by I. Bodin ... Out of the French and Latine copies, done into English, by Richard Knolles. London, impensis G. Bishop, 1606.

Knolles, Richard, 1550?–1610.
The Turkish history, from the original of that nation, to the growth of the Ottoman empire, with the lives and conquests of their princes and emperors, by Richard Knolles ... With a continuation to this present year. MDCLXXXVII. Whereunto is added The present state of the Ottoman empire. By Sir Paul Rycaut ... The 6th ed., with the effigies of all the kings and emperors ... London, Printed for T. Basset, 1687–1700.
3 v. pl., 27 port. (incl. fronts.) 38½cm.

Continued in next column

Continued from preceding column

Vol. 1 and the first part of v. 2 paged continuously; v. 1: 4 p. l., 740 p.; v. 2: 1 p. l., 741–990 p. The remainder of v. 2 has two separate pagings (2 p. l., 338 p.; 3 p. l., 104, [28] p., 1 l., [8] p., 1 l.) with special title-pages.
Vol. 2 has title: The Turkish history. The second volume. Beginning from Mahomet III. and continued to the present year 1687. The sixth edition. London, Printed for T. Basset, 1687.
"A continuation of this present history [1609–1620] ... by Edward Grimston": v. 2, p. 897–962.
"A continuation of the Turkish history, from ... 1620, until ... 1628. Collected out of the papers and dispatches of Sir Thomas Roe ... By M. B.": v. 2, p. 963–980.

"A brief discourse of the greatness of the Turkish empire ... By Richard Knolles": v. 2, p. 981–990.
"The history of the Turkish empire, from the year 1623, to the year 1677. Containing the reigns of the three last emperors ... By Sir Paul Rycaut ... London, Printed by J. D. for T. Basset, R. Clavell, J. Robinson, and A. Churchill, 1687": v. 2 [pt. 2] 2 p. l., 1–262 p.
"The history of the Turkish empire continued [1676–1686] ... By Sir Roger Manley, knight": v. 2 [pt. 2] p. [263]–338.
"The present state of the Ottoman empire. Containing the maxims of the Turkish polity; the most material points of the Mahometan religion ... their military discipline ... In three books. By Sir Paul Rycaut ... London, Printed by J. D., 1687": v. 2 [pt. 3] 3 p. l., 104 p.

Vol. 3 has title: The history of the Turks. Beginning with the year 1679. Being a full relation of the last troubles in Hungary, with the sieges of Vienna, and Buda, and all the several battles both by sea and land, between the Christains, and the Turks, until the end of the year 1698, and 1699. In which the peace between the Turks, and the confederate Christain princes and states, was happily concluded at Carlowitz in Hungary ... With the effigies of the emperors and others of note ... which compleats the sixth and last edition of the History of the Turks ... By Sir Paul Rycaut ... London, Printed for R. Clavell, and A. Roper, 1700.
Articles of the treaty of peace at Carlowitz, Latin and English: v. 3, p. 567–602.
1. Turkey—Hist. 2. Mohammedanism. 3. Vienna—Siege, 1683. 4. Carlowitz, Peace of, 1699. I. Rycaut, Sir Paul, 1628–1700, contin. II. Grimestone, Edward. III. Roe, Sir Thomas, 1581?–1644. IV. Manley, Sir Roger, 1626?–1688.

5—9249

Library of Congress DR439.K75

NcD CtY OO OCU ODW NN MdAN CtU NjP
NK 0207264 DLC CU-S DDO PU PP MWA NjN LU PPL OrU

Knolles, Richard, 1550?–1610.
The Turkish history, from the original of that nation, to the growth of the Ottoman empire, with the lives and conquests of their princes and emperors, by Richard Knolles ... With a continuation to this present year. MDCLXXXVII. Whereunto is added The present state of the Ottoman empire. By Sir Paul Rycaut ... The 6th ed., with the effigies of all the kings and emperors ... London, Printed for Robinson, 1687–1700.
3 v. pl., 27 port. (incl. fronts.) 38½cm.

NK 0207265 WaTC Wa

Knolles, Richard, 1550?–1610.
The Turkish history, comprehending the origin of that nation, and the growth of the Othoman empire, with the lives and conquests of their several kings and emperors. Written by Mr. Knolles, and continu'd by the Honourable Sir Paul Rycaut, to the peace at Carlowitz, in the year 1699. And abridged by Mr. Savage. Revis'd and approv'd by the late Sir Paul Rycaut, and adorn'd with nine and twenty copper-plates, of the effigies of the several princes, &c. ... London, Printed for I. Cleave, A. Roper, A. Bosvile, and R. Basset, 1701.

2 v. pl., 28 port. (incl. fronts.) 20cm.

"The history of the present state of the Ottoman empire ... In three books. By Sir Paul Rycaut, &c. London, Printed for I. Cleave, A. Roper, R. Basset, and A. Bosvile, 1701": v. 2, 70 p. at end.

1. Turkey—Hist. 2. Mohammedanism. I. Rycaut, Sir Paul, 1628–1700, contin. II. Savage, John, 1673–1747, ed.

5--9248

Library of Congress DR439.K76

NK 0207267 DLC PU CtY CaOTP MiU DFo CLU-C

Knolles, Richard, 1550?-1610.
The Turkish history, comprehending the origin of that nation, and the growth of the Ottoman empire, with the lives and conquests of their several kings and emperors. Written by Mr. Knolles, and continued by Sir Paul Rycaut, to the peace at Carlowitz in the year 1699. And abridg'd by Mr. Savage. Revised and approved by the late Sir Paul Rycaut, and adorn'd with nine and twenty copper-plates, of the effigies

Continued in next column

VOLUME 300

Continued from preceding column

of the several princes, &c... London, Printed for I. Cleave, A. Roper, A. Bosvile, and R. Basset, 1704-01.
2 v. pl., 28 ports. (incl. fronts.) 20cm.

"The history of the present state of the Ottoman empire..... In three books. By Sir Paul Rycaut, &c. London, Printed for I.

Cleave, A. Roper, R. Basset, and A. Bosvile, 1704": v. 2, 70 p. at end.
Second edition.
Title within double line border.

1. Turkey - History. 2. Mohammedanism. I. Rycaut, Sir Paul, 1628-1700, contin. II. Savage, John, 1673-1747, ed.

NK 0207270 FU

F 59 .467 KNOLLES, RICHARD, 1550?-1610.
The Turkish history, comprehending the origin of that nation, and the growth of the Othoman Empire, with the lives and conquests of their several kings and emperors. Written by Mr. Knolls, continued by Sir Paul Rycaut to the Peace of Carlowitz in the year 1699. And Abridg'd by Mr. Savage. Rev. and approved by the late Sir Paul Rycaut... 2d ed. carefully corr., improv'd and brought down to the present year, 1704. With an addition of the life of the impostor Mahomet, by the same author... London, I. Cleave[etc.] 1704.
2v. ports.

"The history of the present state of the Othoman Empire... In three books. By Sir Paul Rycaut, &c. London, I. Cleave [etc.] 1703": v.2, 70p. at end.
Imperfect: v.2, p.408-448, numbered p.208-248.
Bookplates of Thomas Pitman and Edward Francis Searles.

NK 0207272 ICN

Knollin, A. J.

U. S. *Congress. Senate. Committee on finance.*
Reciprocity with Canada. Remarks of Frank J. Hagenbarth, Arthur Sterecker, and A. J. Knollin before the Committee on finance, United States Senate, May 19 and 22, 1911, on House bill 4412. An act to promote reciprocal trade relations with the Dominion of Canada and for other purposes. Washington, Govt. print. off., 1911.

Knollin, Ernesto Ray, 1886-

Oregon. *Office of superintendent of public instruction.*
Course of study. State of Oregon. High schools. Physical education for boys. Prepared by Ernesto R. Knollin, professor in the School of physical education, University of Oregon. Edited by D. A. Emerson, state department of education. Issued by C. A. Howard, superintendent of public instruction. Salem, Or., State printing department, 1934.

Knollius, Joannes
see Knoll, Johann, 1694-1701.

QE129 .A2 no. 64 Knollman, Harry John, 1889-

Mississippi. *Geological, Economic and Topographical Survey.*
Itawamba County mineral resources: Geology, by Franklin Earl Vestal; Tests, by Harry J. Knollman. University, 1947.

Knollmann, Albert, 1900-
Die Vereinheitlichung des Handelsraumes in den europäischen Ländern ... Bochum-Langendreer, 1935.
Inaug. diss.-Köln.

NK 0207277 CtY

Knollmann, Erich, 1902 -
Der staat als unternehmer in der nachkriegszeit
Inaug. Diss. Giessen, 1931.
Bibl.

NK 0207278 ICRL PU PBm MH CtY

Knolls Atomic Power Laboratory.
Corrosion of reactor structural materials in high-temperature water II. Static corrosion behavior at 600 to 680 degrees F.
see under Fowler, R., Jr.

621.48 G326 Knolls Atomic Power Laboratory.
Nuclear engineering course, 1947-1948. [Schenectady ? 1948]
8 pts. in 1 v. 27cm.
KAPL-PC-148 - 155.
Notes on lectures by various men.
Contents.-Nuclear physics I-IV. - Pile neutron physics II, V-VI. - Pile control I.

1.Atomic power. 2. Nuclear physics. I. Title. II. Title: Pile neutron physics.

NK 0207280 CSt

Knoll's Mitteilungen für Aerzte. v. 1-3, 1912-1914. 8°. Ludwigshafen a. Rh.

NK 0207281 DNLM ICRL PCC

Knoll's Mitteilungen für Ärzte; Jubiläumsausgabe, 1886-1936
see under Knoll A.-G., Ludwigshafen am Rhein.

Knoll's Pharmaka
see under Knoll A.-G., Ludwigshafen am Rhein.

Knollwood Country Club, White Plains, N. Y.
Constitution and by-laws, officers and members . . .
1
White Plains, N. Y., 1 16°.
no. plates.

1. Country clubs—U. S.—N. Y.— White Plains.
N. Y. P. L. March 7, 1928

NK 0207284 NN

Knollys, Beatrice
The gentle art of good talking. James Bowden, N.Y., Mansfield, 1900. London.
149 p.

NK 0207285 PPL PPT MB

KNOLLYS, CHARLES, called 4th earl of Banbury, 1662-1740, defendant
The arguments of the Lord Chief Justice Holt and Judge Powell, in the controverted point of peerage: in the case of the King and Queen against Charles Knowles, otherwise earl of Banbury. London, Printed for J. Brown and sold by J. Roberts, 1716.
2 p.l., 19 p. fol

NK 0207286 InU

Knollys, Sir Clement Courtenay, 1849-1905.

Trinidad. *Commission of enquiry into the water riots of 1903.*
The Commission of enquiry into the water riots of Monday, March 23rd, 1903 ... Port-of-Spain, Printed at the "Diocesan press," 1903.

Lmd75 R8 873k Knollys, Clement Courtenay, 1849 - 1905 ed.
Oxford university challenge races, together with a list of the crews which have rowed in the head boats of the river, and in the trial eights, and some account of the Henley regatta, &c.,&c., from 1816 to the present time. Collected and edited by C.C.Knollys ... Oxford, T.Shrimpton & son[etc.,etc.]1873.
xiip., 2l., 111p. 18½cm.
Relates to racing between the colleges of Oxford.

NK 0207288 CtY

Knollys, George.
Ledgers & literature; by George Knollys. London, J. Lane; New York, J. Lane company, 1907 [1906]
175, [1] p. 19½cm.

CONTENTS.—The romance of book-keeping.—A panegyric of dining.—A professor of sentiment.—Vespertina quies.—Lunching in the city.—The brother of the twilight.—On the advantages of living in a lunatic asylum.—An officer of the boy's brigade.—On the cultivation of the spirit of Greek archaeology.—A week on the Thames.—Chalfont St. Giles.—The three ship-owners.—L'envoi.

Washington, D. C. Public Library W 6-332

NK 0207289 DPW NN PPL

---

*EC65 K7555 667a [Knollys, Hanserd, 1599?-1691]
Apocalyptical mysteries, touching the two witnesses, the seven vials, and the two kingdoms, to wit, of Christ, and of antichrist, expounded. Wherein is contained some things necessary for the saints in this present generation to know. And therein is also shewed, what the Israel of God ought to do in this day. By H. K. ...
London, Printed in year, 1667.
4p.l., 35p., 1l., 45p., 1l., 18p. 14cm.
Parts 2 and 3 have each special t.-p. and separate paging.

NK 0207290 MH ICU

[KNOLLYS, Hanserd,] 1599?-1691.
The baptists answer, to Obed. Wills, his Appeal against H. Danvers. L., 1675.

pp. (2), 14.
(Appended to D'Anvers, Henry. A second reply, 1675.)

NK 0207291 MH NNUT-Mc

VOLUME 300

KNOLLYS, Hanserd. Christ Exalted: | A | Lost Sinner | Sought, and saved by Christ: | Gods people are an Holy people. | Being the summe of divers Sermons Preached | in Suffolk; | By Hanserd Knollys. | Who for this Doctrine had the Meeting-house doores | shut against him, and was stoned out of the Pulpit (as he was | preaching) by a rude multitude; who were gathered to- | gether, and set on by a Malignant High- | Constable. | Which hath been proved by divers Witnesses of good | reputation, before the Honourable Committee of Examination | at London. | . . . (9 lines).
London, Printed by Jane Coe, according to Order. 1646. | Border. 18.2x14.2 cm. (2),38p.

NK 0207292 NNUT-Mc CtY CSmH

British Tracts 1645 K75
Knollys, Hanserd, 1599?-1691.
Christ exalted: in a sermon begun to be preached at Debenham in Suffolk, upon the 14. day of Febr. last ... by Hanserd Knollys. Who was stoned out of the pulpit ... Also, another sermon preached at Stradbrooke in Suffolk, the 13. day of Febr. last ... London,1645.
1p.ℓ.,22p. 19cm.

NK 0207293 CtY

Knollys, Hanserd, 1599-1691.
An exposition of the 11th Chapter of Revalation. n.p., 1679.
48 p. 4°

NK 0207294 MWA

Rare Books Dept.
Knollys, Hanserd, 1598-1691.
An exposition of the first chapter of the Song of Solomon. Wherein the text is analysed, the allegories are explained, and the hidden mysteries are unveiled ... With spiritual meditations upon every verse ... London, Printed by W. Godbid, and are to be sold by Livewel Chapman, 1656.
3 p.ℓ., 78 p. 18cm.
Wing K-709.

NK 0207295 CU

[Knollys, Hanserd] 1599?-1691.
An exposition of the whole book of the Revelation. Wherein the visions and prophecies of Christ are opened and expounded: shewing the great conquests of Our Lord Jesus Christ for his church over all his and her adversaries, pagan, Arian and papal; and the glorious state of the church of God in the new heavens and new earth, in these latter days. By H. K. ... London, Printed for the author; and are to be sold by W. Marshall, M DC LXXXIX.
3 p. l., 244 p. 21 x 16½ cm.
1. Bible. N. T. Revelation—Commentaries. 2. Bible—Commentaries—N. T. Revelation. I. K., H. II. Title.
BS2825.A2K6 40—23182

NK 0207296 DLC MeB CtY CLU-C

Knollys, Hanserd, 1599?-1691, supposed author.
A glimpse of Sions glory
see under Goodwin, Thomas, 1600-1680.

Knollys, Hanserd, 1599?-1691.
The gospel minister's maintenance vindicated
see under title

Knollys, Hanserd, 1598-1691.
Grammaticae Latinae, Graecae, & Hebraicae. Compendium. Rhetoricae adumbratio. Item Radices Graecae & Hebraicae omnes quae in Sacra Scriptura Veteris & Novi Testamenti occurrunt. Opera & studio Hanserdi Knollys. Londini, Typis Tho. Roycroft ... 1665.
6 pt. in 1 v. fold.table. 13½cm.
Signatures: A^6 (A_1 blank? wanting); A-C^{12}, A^6; B-C^{12}, D^6; A^{12}, B^3; 1 leaf unsigned, B^{12}; A-B^{12}, C^2 (A_3. A_5, incorrectly signed C_3, A_4)

NK 0207299 CLU-C RPB

Film 318
Knollys, Hanserd, 1599?-1691.
Grammaticae Latinae, Graecae, & Hebraicae compendium. Rhetoricae adumbratio. Item radices Graecae & Hebraicae omnes quae in Sacra Scriptura Veteris et Novi Testamenti occurrunt. Londini, Tho. Roycroft, 1665.

Microfilm copy, made by British Museum. 1952. Negative.
Collation of the original, as determined from the film: [8] 70, 58, 52, 12, 27, 23 p.

Contents.--Grammaticae Latinae compendium; or, an introduction to the Latin tongue. 1664.--Grammaticae Graecae compendium. 1664.--Radices Hebraicae omnes quae in S. Scriptura, Veteris Testamenti occurrunt. 1664.--Rhetoricae adumbratio. 1663.--Radices simplicium vocum, flexi lium maxime, Novi Testamenti. 1664.--Linguae Hebraicae delineatio. 1664.
Each part has separate title-page.

NK 0207302 NIC

Knollys, Hanserd, 1599-1691.
The life and death of H. K. ...written with his own hand to the year 1672 and continued in general, in an epistle by Mr. William Kiffin: to which is added his last legacy to the church. Lond., E. Huntington, 1812.
67 p., port.

NK 0207303 MiD NRAB

Case E 5 .K 757
KNOLLYS, HANSERD, 1599?-1691.
The life and death of the old disciple of Jesus Christ, and eminent minister of the gospel, Mr. Hanserd Knollys, who dyed in the ninety third year of his age. Written with his own hand to the year 1672. and continued in general, in an epistle by Mr. William Kiffin. To which is added, his last legacy to the church. London, Printed for J.Harris,1692.
[6],50p. port. 16cm.

STC II K 715.
Bound by Malt- by, Oxford.

NK 0207304 ICN

Knollys, Hanserd, 1599?-1691.
The life and death of that old disciple of Jesus Christ, and eminent minister of the gospel... Hanserd Knollys, who died in the ninety-third year of his age, written with his own hand to the year 1672, and continued in general in a epistle by... William Kiffin, to which is added his last legacy to the church... London, E. Huntington, 1812.
163 p. 20cm.
I Kiffin, William, 1616-1701

NK 0207305 NjPT NcWsW

*EC65 Sa153 645f
Knollys, Hanserd, 1599?-1691.
A moderate answer vnto Dr. Bastvvicks book; called, Independency not Gods ordinance. Wherein, is declared the manner how some chvrches in this city were gathered, and upon what tearmes their members were admitted ... By Hanserd Knollys ...
London,Printed by Iane Coe.1645.
1p.ℓ.,20p. 19.5cm.
Page 2 unnumbered; p.4, 19 misnumbered 6,13.
Bound with John Sadler's Flagellum flagelli ... 1645.

NK 0207306 MH DFo

Film 14123
Knollys, Hanserd, 1599?-1691.
A moderate answer unto Dr. Bastwicks book; called, Independency not Gods ordinance. Wherein is declared the manner how some churches in this city were gathered, and upon what tearmes their members were admitted; that so both the Dr. and reader may judge how near some beleevers who walk together in the fellowship of the Gospell do come in their practice to these apostolicall rules which are propounded by the Dr. as Gods method in gathering churches and admitting members. By Hanserd Knollys. London, Printed by I.Coe, 1645.
20p.

Microfilm (negative) Cambridge, Harvard University Library, 1971. 1 reel.
On reel with Sadler, John. Flagellum flagelli. London, 1645.

1. Bastwick, John, 1593-1654, Independency not Gods ordinance. 2. Church polity. 3. Gt.Brit. - Hist. - Puritan Revolution, 1642-1660. I. Title.

NK 0207308 IaU

Mhc8 1679 K76
Knollys, Hanserd, 1599?-1691.
Mystical Babylon availed. Wherein is proved, I. That Rome-papal is mystical-Babylon. II. That the Pope of Rome is the beast. III. That the church of Rome is the great whore. IV. That the Roman-priests are the false prophet. Also A call to the people of God to come out of Babylon ... [n.p.]1679.
3p.ℓ.,31p. 20cm.
Portrait of the author, dated 1810, inserted as frontispiece.

NK 0207309 CtY MH MWA

*EC65 K7555 674p
Knollys, Hanserd, 1599?-1691.
The parable of the kingdom of heaven expounded. Or, An exposition of the first thirteen verses of the twenty fifth chapter of Matthew ... By Han. Knollis.
London,Printed for Benjamin Harris,and are to be sold at the Stationers Armes in Sweetings rents,in Cornhill,near the Royal Exchange.1674.
2p.ℓ.,135p. front.(port.) 14.5cm.

NK 0207310 MH CtY MWA ICU

*EC65 K7555 648r
Knollys, Hanserd, 1599?-1691.
The rudiments of the Hebrew grammar in English. Published for the benefit of some friends, who being ignorant of the Latine, are desirous to understand the Bible in the originall tongue. By Hanserd Knollys ...
London,Printed by M.B.1648.
8°. 1p.ℓ.,27p. fold.table. 15.5cm.
Signatures: A-D^4.
Leaf D_4 is a variant t.-p., presumably intended for a cancel, with imprint: London, Printed by Moses Bell, for William Larner at the Blackmore neere Bishopsgate, and George Whittington at the blew Anchor in Cornhill near the Exchange. 1648.
Wing does not record the variant t.-p.

NK 0207311 MH CSmH ICU

VOLUME 300

Knollys, Hanserd, 1599?-1691
The shining of a flaming fire in Zion; or, A clear answer unto 13. exceptions, against the grounds of new baptism; (so called) in Mr. Saltmarsh his book, intituteled, The smoke in the temple ... London,Printed by Jane Coe,1646.
2p.l.,17p. 18cm.

1. Saltmarsh, John, d.1647. The smoke in the temple.

NK 0207312 CtY CLU-C CU-A CSmH NNUT-Mc

Knollys, Sir Henry, 1840-
The elements of field-artillery, designed for the use of infantry and cavalry officers. Edinburgh, W. Blackwood, 1877.
x, 180 p. illus. 19cm.

1. Artillery.

NK 0207313 NIC NN

Knollys, *Sir* **Henry,** 1840-
English life in China, by Major Henry Knollys ... London, Smith, Elder, & co., 1885.
ix, 333 p. 21cm.

1. British in China. 2. China—Descr. & trav. I. Title.

A 13-637

Title from Univ. of Chicago DS707.K72 Printed by L. C.

NK 0207314 MB ICU CU FTaSU IaU MSaE NcD PPL OCl DN ICJ

Knollys, Henry, 1840 -
From Sedan to Saarbruck, via Verdun, Gravelotte and Metz; by an officer of the royal artillery. Lond., Kerby and Endean, 1872.
275 p.

NK 0207315 MiD PPL

Knollys, Sir Henry, 1840- comp.
Incidents in the China war of 1860
see under Grant, Sir James Hope, 1808-1875.

Knollys, Henry, ed.

Grant, *Sir* **James Hope,** 1808-1875.
Incidents in the Sepoy war, 1857-58, compiled from the private journals of General Sir Hope Grant ... together with some explanatory chapters by Henry Knollys ... Edinburgh and London, W. Blackwood and sons, 1873.

Knollys, Henry, ed.

Grant, Sir James Hope, 1808-1875.
Life of General Sir Hope Grant; with selections from his correspondence. Edited by Henry Knollys. Edinburgh, W. Blackwood, 1894.

Knollys, Henry, 1840 -
Sketches of life in Japan, by Major Henry Knollys ... London, Chapman and Hall, limited, 1887.
x p., 1 l., 327 p. front., plates. 20cm.

1. Japan—Soc. life & cust.

4-29657

Library of Congress DS809.K72

NK 0207319 DLC MH OCl DN WaS NIC CU NNC

Knollys, William, 1763-1834, petitioner.

Nicolas, *Sir* **Nicholas Harris,** 1799-1848.
A treatise on the law of adulterine bastardy, with a report of the Banbury case, and of all other cases bearing upon the subject. By Sir Harris Nicolas ... London, W. Pickering, 1836.

Knollys, Sir William Thomas, 1797-1883, tr.

Montesquiou-Fezensac, Raymond Aymery Philippe Joseph, *duc* **de,** 1784-1867.
A journal of the Russian campaign of 1812. Tr. from the French of Lieut.-General de Fezensac, with an introductory notice of some passages connected with the campaign, by Colonel W. Knollys ... London, Parker, Furnivall, and Parker, 1852.

Knollys, *Sir* William Thomas, 1797 - 1883, ed.
Papers relating to Mary, Queen of Scots.
98 pp. (Philobiblon Soc. Miscel. v. 14.)

NK 0207322 MdBP PU

KNOLLYS,W[illiam] W[allingford],1833-
For queen and country;battles of Her Majesty's reign. London,etc.,R.Tuck & sons,ltd.,[1897?]

obl.8°. pp.16,incl.covers. Port and other illustr.(partly colored).
Cover serves as title-page.

NK 0207323 MH

Knollys, William Wallingford, 1833-
Hand-book of field fortification, intended for the guidance of officers preparing for promotion, and especially adapted to the requirements of beginners, by Major W.W. Knollys ... London, Strahan & co., 1873.
ix, 273p. illus.,diagrs. 18½cm.

1. Fortification.

NK 0207324 TxU NN

Knollys, William Wallingford, 1833-
Hand-book of field fortification, intended for the guidance of officers preparing for promotion, and especially adapted to the requirements of beginners, by Major W. W. Knollys ... Philadelphia, G. Gebbie, 1873.
ix, 273 p. illus., diagrs. 18½cm.

1. Fortification. I. Title.

12-36042

Library of Congress UG403.K72

NK 0207325 DLC PU NN

Knollys, William Wallingford
Hand-book of field fortification, intended for the guidance of officers preparing for promotion, and especially adapted to the requirements of beginners, by Major W.W. Knollys... London, Lockwood & co., 1875.
273p. illus., diagrs.

NK 0207326 MiHM

Knollys, William Wallingford, 1833-
A handy dictionary of military terms, by Major W. W. Knollys. London, E. & F. N. Spon, 1873.
3 p. l., 95 p. 15cm.

1. Military art and science - Terminology.

NK 0207327 DSI

Knollys, William Wallingford, 1833-
Heroes of the battlefield, by Lieut.-Col. Knollys and Major Elliott. London, Dean [1895?]
440 p. illus.

1. Gt. Brit.—History, Military.
2. Gt. Brit. Army—Biog.
I. Elliott, William John, joint author.
II. Title.

NK 0207328 CaOTP

Knollys, William Wallingford, 1833- joint author.

Combermere, Mary Woolley (Gibbings) Cotton, *viscountess, d.* 1889.
Memoirs and correspondence of Field-Marshal Viscount Combermere, G. C. B., etc., from his family papers. By the Right Hon. Mary, viscountess Combermere, and Capt. W. W. Knollys ... London, Hurst and Blackett, 1866.

(Roberts, F.)

KNOLLYS, WILLIAM WALLINGFORD, b. 1833.
The story of Earl Roberts...told by Col. W. W. Knollys ... [London, etc.: R. Tuck & sons, ltd., 190-] 6 l. illus. (part col'd.) 27cm.

Cover-title.
Text also on inside of covers.
"Printed in Germany."

1. Roberts, Frederick Sleigh Roberts, 1st earl, 1832-1914.

NK 0207330 NN

KNOLTON, J. Daniel
Dissertatio inauguralis, de pertussi ... Edinburgi, Balfour et Smellie, 1773.
22 p. 23 cm.
Diss. - Edinburgh.

NK 0207331 DNLM

KNOLZ, Joseph Johann
Darstellung der Brechruhr-Epidemie in der k. k. Haupt- und Residenzstadt Wien, wie auch auf dem flachen Lande in Oesterreich unter der Enns, in den Jahren 1831 und 1832, nebst den dagegen getroffenen sanitäts-polizeylichen Vorkehrungen. Wien, Mayer, 1834.
x, 366 p.

NK 0207332 DNLM

VOLUME 300

Knolz, Joseph Johann
Darstellung der Humanitäts- und Heilanstalten im Erzherzogthume Oesterreich unter der Enns, als Staatsanstalten und Privatwerke, nach ihrer dermaligen Verfassung und Einrichtung. Wien, Verlag der Mechitaristen Congregation, 1840
viii, 320 p.
Cover title: Wien's Humanitäts und Heil-Anstalten.

NK 0207333 MH MiU PPC

W 32 GA8 K7d 1829 KNOLZ, Joseph Johann
Darstellung der Medicinal-Verfassung in den k. k. Staaten Oesterreichs, in Beziehung auf den Wirkungskreis der Kreiswundärzte, der Civil-, Stadt- und Landwundärzte, und der Landesthierärzte. Zum Gebrauche für Kreis-, Civil-, Stadt- und Landwundärzte, öffentliche Sanitäts-Individuen, Ärzte, Dominien, Kreisämter und Behörden überhaupt. Wien, Mechitaristen-Congregation, 1829.
xx, 560 p.

NK 0207334 DNLM CtY MH

Knolz, Joseph Johann
Darstellung der verfassung und einrichtung der baumwoll-spinnerei-fabriken in Niederosterreich... 1843.

NK 0207335 MiU

WB K72i 1835 KNOLZ, Joseph Johann
Institutiones medicae hygienes et semiotices generalis usui academico adcommodatae. Viennae, Typis Congregationis Mechitaristicae, 1835.
xii, 375 p.

NK 0207336 DNLM

Knonau, Gerold Ludwig Meyer von
SEE
Meyer von Knonau, Gerold Ludwig, 1804-1858.

Knonau, Gerold Meyer von
see
Meyer von Knonau, Gerold, 1843-1931.

Knonau, Ludwig Meyer von
see
Meyer von Knonau, Ludwig, 1769-1841

193 G927Bk Knoodt, Franz Peter, 1811-1889.
Anton Günther; eine Biographie. Wien, W. Braumüller, 1881.
2v.

1. Günther, Anton, 1783-1863.

NK 0207340 ICarbS MH

KNOODT, Franz Peter, 1811-1889.
Günther und Clemens; offene briefe. Wien, W. Braumüller, 1853-54.
3 vol.

NK 0207341 MH IU

KJ85 K756r Knoodt, Franz Peter, 1811-1889.
Reden der Herren Prof. Dr. Knoodt und Bischof Dr. Reinkens, gehalten im Altkatholiken-Verein in Düsseldorf, am 24. März 1876. Düsseldorf, P. Ritter [n.d.]
30 p. 22 cm.

1. Old Catholic Church. I. Reinkens, Joseph Hubert, Bp., 1821-1896. II. Title.

NK 0207342 CtY-D NcD

Knoodt, Peter
see Knoodt, Franz Peter, 1811-1889.

Gk32 51 Knook, Pieter Cornelis
De overgang van metrisch tot rythmisch proza bij Cyprianus en Hieronymus ... Purmerend, J. Muusses, 1932.
5p.ℓ., [3]-90p. incl. tables. 22½cm.
Proefschrift - Amsterdam.
"Résumé [in French]": p. [88]-90.
"Stellingen", [4]p., laid in at end.

NK 0207344 CtY ICU ICRL MiU

Knoop, Mrs. No. 26 in 8050a.232
The flowers of Andalusia. Al campo della gloria. Arranged for the guitar.
= [Baltimore?] Peters. 1850. 3, 4 pp. F°.

[This work is kept on the Special Libraries Floor.]

G3331 — T.r. (2). — Guitar. Music.

NK 0207345 MB

Knoop, Anna, d. 1889, tr.

[Holbach, Paul Henri Thiry, *baron* d', 1723-1789.
Glaube und vernunft, oder Le bon sens des römisch-katholischen priesters Jean Meslier [*pseud.*] Nach dem französischen original übersetzt von fräulein Anna Knoop. New York, Fräulein Anna Knoop [1880]

BL2773 .H74 Knoop, Anna, d. 1889, tr. FOR OTHER EDITIONS SEE MAIN ENTRY

[Holbach, Paul Henri Thiry, *baron* d'] 1723-1789.
Superstition in all ages; a dying confession by Jean Meslier, a Roman Catholic priest, who at his death left as his "Last will and testament" this now famous manuscript as contained herein, entitled Common sense ... Tr. from the French original by Miss Anna Knoop; arranged for publication in its present form and manner with new title page and preface by Dr. L. W. de Laurence. Same to now serve as "text-book" number five, for "The Congress of ancient, divine, mental and Christian masters." Chicago, Ill., De Laurence, Scott & co., 1910.

Knoop, August, 1877-
Studien ueber das wesen der paranitranilin-vergiftung mit besonderer beruecksichtigung des blutes.
Inaug. diss. Wuerzburg, 1908.
Bibl.

NK 0207348 ICRL CtY DNLM

Knoop, Bernhard, 1908-
Hegel und die Franzosen. Stuttgart, W. Kohlhammer, 1941.
vi, 127 p. 23 cm. (Frankreich, sein Weltbild und Europa; Gemeinschaftsarbeit der deutschen Romanistik)
Bibliographical footnotes.

1. Hegel, Georg Friedrich Wilhelm, 1770-1831. 2. Philosophy, French. I. Series.
B2948.K58 A F 48-724*
Columbia Univ. for Library of Congress Libraries †

NK 0207349 NNC DLC ICU TNJ IEN WU IaU

Knoop, Bernhard, 1908-
Victor Cousin, Hegel und die französische Romantik. Einflüsse und Wirkungen... von Bernhard Knoop... Oberviechtach (Opf.): I. Forstner, 1932. 101 p. 21cm.
Inaugural-Dissertation — München, 1932.
Lebenslauf.
"Literatur," p. [99]-101.

1. Cousin, Victor, 1792-1867. 2. Hegel, Georg Wilhelm Friedrich, 1770-1831. 3. Romanticism—France.
N. Y. P. L. September 9, 1940

NK 0207350 NN PU CtY MH PBm MiU

Knoop, Carl.
Wetterauische gesellschaft für die gesamte naturkunde, *Hanau.*
Bericht.
Hanau, Druck der Waisenhausbuchdruckerei, 18

Knoop (Carlos). Beitrag zur Therapie der Nabelschnurbrüche.
In Samml. klin. Vortr., n. F., Leipz., 1903, No. 348 (Gynäkol., No. 129, 863-882).

NK 0207352 DNLM

Knoop, Carlos, 1875-
Ueber exostosis cartilagines.
Inaug. diss. Bonn, 1897.
Bibl.

NK 0207353 ICRL CtY DNLM

Knoop, Douglas, 1883-
American business enterprise, a study in industrial organisation; a report to the electors of the Gartside scholarships on the results of a tour in the United States in 1906-7, by Douglas Knoop ... Mancheser, The University press, 1907.
xi p., 1 l., 112 p. 23cm. (*Half-title:* Publications of the University of Manchester. Economic series, no. VIII. Gartside reports on industry and commerce, no. 5)
On verso of t.-p.: University of Manchester publications, no. xxx.
1. U. S.—Indus. 2. U. S.—Comm.
8-6075
Library of Congress HC106.K72

NK 0207354 MiU ODW OClW OCl OU PBm PU ICJ NN MB DLC CU NjP OrP OKentU CLSU MB FU PPAmP

308 Z Box 558 Knoop, Douglas, 1883-
Begemann's history of freemasonry, by Douglas Knoop and G.P. Jones. Printed for private circulation, 1941.
15 [1] p. 21½cm.

Caption-title.
"Printed in Great Britain by Butler & Tanner ltd., Frome and London."

1. Freemasons. 2. Begemann, Wilhelm, 1843-1914. Vorgeschichte und anfänge der freimaurerei. I. Jones, G P

NK 0207355 NNC MH

VOLUME 300

Knoop, Douglas, 1883-

DA664 The Bolsover castle building account, 1613.
B65K6 By Douglas Knoop and G. P. Jones. [London, The Quatuor coronati lodge, no. 2076, 1936]

56 p. illus. (map) 27 cm.

Half-title.
On cover: "Issued in advance of 'Ars quatuor coronatorum' vol. XLIX part 1. 1936".
Bibliographical foot-notes.

1. Bolsover castle. I. Jones, Gwilym Peredur, 1892- joint author. II. Title.

NK 0207356 CSmH CtY NN CU

Knoop, Douglas, 1883-
The building of Eton college, 1442-1460; a study in the history of operative masonry, by Douglas Knoop ... and G. P. Jones ... [1933]
47 p. map, facsim., diagr. 28½cm.

From "Trans. Quatuor Coronati lodge, vol.xlvi., 1933, pp. 70-114."
Bibliographical foot-notes.
1. Stone-masons. 2. Eton college. I.Jones, Gwilym Peredur, 1892- jt. au.

NK 0207357 NNC

Knoop, Douglas, 1883-
... Colour impressions. A report to the Albert Kahn trustees on the results of a journey round the world, July 21, 1913, to July 24, 1914, by Douglas Knoop... London, University of London press, 1914.
99, [1]p. 22cm. (Albert Kahn travelling fellowships)
1. Race problems. I. Title. II. London. University. Albert Kahn travelling fellowships.

NK 0207358 CU

Knoop, Douglas, 1883-
Jr25.01 The decline of the mason-architect in England, by Douglas Knoop and G.P.Jones.
Pamphlet
"Reprinted from the Journal of the Royal institute of British architects, vol.44, third series, no.19, Sept. 1937."

I.Jones, Gwilym Peredur, 1892- joint author

NK 0207359 CtY

Knoop, Douglas, 1883- ed.
The early masonic catechisms, transcribed and edited by Douglas Knoop ... G. P. Jones ... and Douglas Hamer ... [Manchester, Eng.] Manchester university press, 1943.
viii, 200 p. diagrs. 22cm. (Half-title: Publications of the University of Manchester, no. CCLXXXV)
"Five hundred copies have been printed."

1. Freemasons. I. Jones, Gwilym Peredur, 1892- joint ed. II. Hamer, Douglas, joint ed. III. Title.
A 44-523
Harvard univ. Library for Library of Congress HS405.K6
† 366.1

NK 0207360 MH CaQML CU PU OCl DLC

Knoop, Douglas, 1883- ed.
Early masonic pamphlets, reprinted and edited by Douglas Knoop ... G. P. Jones ... and Douglas Hamer ... [Manchester, Eng.] Manchester university press, 1945.
x, 346 p. 22 cm. (Half-title: Publications of the University of Manchester, no. CCLXXXVII)
"Five hundred copies have been printed."

1. Freemasons—Addresses, essays, lectures. I. Title.
HS371.K6 366.1082 A 46—531
New York. Public Libr. for Library of Congress [a59c1]†

NK 0207361 NN DLC CaQML

Knoop, Douglas, 1883-
Ndy60 The English medieval quarry, by Douglas
G5 Knoop and G.P.Jones ... [n.p.,1938]
1 Pamphlet
1938 Cover-title.
"Reprinted from the Economic history review, November, 1938."
Bibliographical foot-notes.

NK 0207362 CtY

Knoop, Douglas, 1883-
Nrb18 The evolution of masonic organisation; being
+1 a re-examination of the old charges and of the
1932 earlier documents relating to operative masonry. By Douglas Knoop ... and G.P.Jones ...
Pamphlet
From "(Trans.Quatuor coronati lodge, vol.xlv., 1932, pp.267-301.)"

NK 0207363 CtY

Knoop, Douglas, 1883-
The first three years of the building of Vale Royal abbey, 1278-1280; a study in operative masonry, by Douglas Knoop ... and G. P. Jones ... [1932?]
cover-title, 43 p. fold. table. 28½cm.

Reprinted from Transactions Quatuor Coronati lodge, vol. xliv, 1931, p. 5-47.
1.Vale Royal, Eng. (Cistercian abbey) I.Jones, Gwilym Peredur, 1892- jt.au.

NK 0207364 NNC

Knoop, Douglas, 1883-
Freemasonry and the idea of natural religion, by Douglas Knoop and G. P. Jones ... [Frome and London, Printed by Butler & Tanner ltd.] 1942.
15, [1] p. 21½cm.
"Printed for private circulation."

1. Freemasons—Addresses, essays, lectures. 2. Natural theology. I. Jones, Gwilym Peredur, 1892- joint author. II. Title.
43-48630
Library of Congress HS397.K63
366.1

NK 0207365 DLC

Knoop, Douglas, 1883-

Berthélemy, Henry, 1857-
Gemeindebetriebe in Frankreich und England. Von H. Berthélemy ... und Douglas Knoop ... Im auftrag des Vereins für socialpolitik hrsg. von Carl Johannes Fuchs. Leipzig, Duncker & Humblot, 1910.

366.1 KNOOP, DOUGLAS, 1883-
K7551.2
The genesis of freemasonry; an account of the rise and development of freemasonry in its operative, accepted, and early speculative phases, by Douglas Knoop and G.P.Jones. [Manchester] Manchester University Press, 1947.
x, 334p. 22cm. (Publications of the University of Manchester. No. CCXCIX)

Bibliographical foot-notes. "Bibliographical note:" p.325-326.

NK 0207367 PU NN TxU OCl CaQML NBC CaBViP

366.1 Knoop, Douglas, 1883-
K72g The genesis of freemasonry; an account of the rise and development of freemasonry in its operative, accepted, and early speculative phases, by Douglas Knoop and G.P. Jones. [Manchester, Manchester University Press, 1949.
x, 334 p. 22 cm. (Publications of the University of Manchester, no. 299)
Based on their Short history of freemasonry to 1730.
Includes bibliographical footnotes.

NK 0207368 N NNC NcD NIC ICN

Knoop, Douglas, 1883-
The genesis of speculative masonry, by Douglas Knoop ... [Frome and London] Printed for private circulation, 1941.
31, [1] p. 21½cm.
"Select list of references": p. [32]

1. Freemasons. I. Title.
A 41-4450
Harvard univ. Library for Library of Congress

NK 0207369 MH CtY DLC

Knoop, Douglas, 1883-
A handlist of masonic documents, compiled by Douglas Knoop ... and G. P. Jones ... [Manchester, Eng.] Manchester university press, 1942.
viii, 55, [1] p. 19cm.
Revised and enlarged edition. The first edition was appended to the authors' The nomenclature of masonic mss. cf. Pref.

1. Freemasons—Bibl. I. Jones, Gwilym Peredur, 1892- joint author. II. Title.
A 42-3038
Harvard univ. Library for Library of Congress Z5993.K68
† 016.3661

NK 0207370 MH DLC CtY NcD CU OCU NNC PU

Knoop, Douglas, 1883-
Henry Yevele and his associates, by Douglas Knoop and G. P. Jones. [1935]
20 p. 28cm.

Reprinted from the Journal of the Royal institute of British architects, Vol. 42, Series 3, No. 14, 1935.

1.Yevele, Henry, fl. 1330-1390. I.Jones, Gwilym Peredur, 1892- jt.au.

NK 0207371 NNC

Knoop, Douglas, 1883 -
Industrial conciliation and arbitration, by Douglas Knoop ... With an introduction by Sydney J. Chapman ... London, P. S. King & son, 1905.
xxiv, 241 p. 19cm.
Bibliography: p. [197]-233.

1. Arbitration, Industrial.
5-29066
Library of Congress HD5481.K6

NK 0207372 DLC ICJ NN MB OCl ODW OCU MiU CtY NjP NcU ICRL CU CaBVaU

Knoop, Douglas, 1883-
An introduction to freemasonry, by Douglas Knoop ... and G. P. Jones ... [Manchester] Manchester university press, 1937.
vii, 136 p. 19cm.
"Short bibliography": p. [129]-132.

1. Freemasons. I. Jones, Gwilym Peredur, 1892- joint author.
38-2007
Library of Congress HS395.K55
366.1

NK 0207373 DLC CU MU IEN NN PU CtY OrPR WaS CaBVa

Knoop, Douglas, 1883-
London bridge and its builders; a study of the municipal employment of masons mainly in the fifteenth century, by Douglas Knoop ... and G. P. Jones ... [London? 1934]
cover-title, 40 p. diagr. 28½cm.

"Trans. Quatuor coronati lodge, vol xlvii., 1934, pp. 5-44."

1.London bridge. 2.Stone-masons. I.Jones, Gwilym Peredur, 1892- , jt. au.

NK 0207374 NNC

VOLUME 300

Knoop, Douglas, 1883–
The London mason in the seventeenth century, by Douglas Knoop ... and G. P. Jones ... Manchester [Eng.] The Manchester university press; London, The Quatuor coronati lodge, no. 2076, 1935.
2 p. l., 92 p. 26½cm.
"Issued in advance of 'Ars quatuor coronatorum', vol. XLVIII, part I, 1935."
"Sources": p. 7–9; "Short bibliography": p. 66–67.
1. Stone-masons. 2. Building—London. I. Jones, Gwilym Peredur, 1892– joint author. II. Title.
36–13820
Library of Congress HD6461.M3K5
331.88193

NcD MB
NK 0207375 DLC OrPR CU DFo CtY OCl MiU PU CSmH NN

KNOOP, Douglas, 1883-
The London Masons' Company. By Douglas Knoop and G.P.Jones. [Bungay, Suffolk, R.Clay and Co., Ltd., 1939].
25 cm. pp.10.
Paper cover serves as title-page.
"Reprinted from Economic History, February, 1939," pp.[157]-166.

NK 0207376 MH

Knoop, Douglas, 1883–
The mason word. The Prestonian lecture for 1938, by Douglas Knoop ... [Frome and London] Printed for private circulation, 1938.
35, [1] p. 21½cm.
1. Freemasons—Rituals. I. Title.
A 41–1165
Yale univ. Library for Library of Congress

NK 0207377 CtY OCl CSmH

Knoop, Douglas, 1883–
Masonic history old and new, by Douglas Knoop and G. P. Jones. (Printed for private circulation, 1942) [Frome and London, Printed by Butler & Tanner, ltd., 1942]
15, [1] p. 21½cm.
Caption title.
"This paper is to be communicated very shortly to the Q. C. lodge."—p. [16]
1. Freemasons. Gt. Brit.—Hist. I. Jones, Gwilym Peredur, 1892– joint author. II. Title.
A 43–477
Harvard univ. Library for Library of Congress

NK 0207378 MH CtY NNC

Ndy60
G5
1
1939
Knoop, Douglas, 1883-
... Master Walter of Hereford, cementarius. By Douglas Knoop and G.P.Jones ... [n.p., 1939]
Pamphlet
"Reprinted from Miscellanea Latomorum, December, 1939."
I.Jones, Gwilym Peredur, 1892- joint author.

NK 0207379 CtY MH

Knoop, Douglas, 1883–
The mediæval mason; an economic history of English stone building in the later middle ages and early modern times, by Douglas Knoop ... and G. P. Jones ... [Manchester, Eng.] Manchester university press, 1933.
xii, 294 p. diagr. 22cm. (*Half-title:* Publications of the University of Manchester, no. CCXXVII. Economic history series, no. VIII)
"Short bibliography": p. 279–283.
1. Stone-masons. 2. Building—Gt. Brit. 3. Building—Hist. I. Jones, Gwilym Peredur, 1892– joint author. II. Title.
34–13440
Library of Congress TH57.K55
——— Copy 2. 690.942

NcD PSC PU PPAmP OU OCl OClW OO MiU MB ViU
NK 0207380 DLC OrCS OrU ScCleU MU MH-BA CU OrPR WaU

338.4769
K72m
Knoop, Douglas, 1883-
The mediaeval mason; an economic history of English stone building in the later Middle Ages and early modern times, by Douglas Knoop and G.P. Jones. [Manchester, Eng.] Manchester University Press, 1949 [1933]
294p. illus. (Publications of the University of Manchester, no.227. Economic history series, no.8)
First published 1933; reprinted.
Includes bibliography.
1. Stone-masons - Great Britain. 2. Building - Great Britain. I. Jones, Gwilym Peredur, 1892- jt. auth. II. Title. III. Victoria University of Manchester. Publications Economic history series, no.8.

NK 0207381 FTaSU PBm PKsL CaQML LU IEN CaBVaU IdPI

Knoop, Douglas, 1883–
The nomenclature of masonic mss. and handlist of the mss., by Douglas Knoop and G. P. Jones. [Frome and London] Printed for private circulation [by Butler & Tanner ltd.] 1941.
iv, 59, [1] p. 18½cm.
"This paper is to be communicated very shortly to the Quatuor coronati lodge, and should appear in A. Q. C., liv."—Prefatory note.
"Bibliographical note": p. 59.
1. Manuscripts. 2. Freemasons — Bibl.—Manuscripts. I. Jones, Gwilym Peredur, 1892– joint author. II. Title.
41–23812
Library of Congress Z6611.F8K6
016.3661

NK 0207382 DLC OCl CtY MH CSmH NNC

Jr25.1
Knoop, Douglas, 1883-
... A note on the position and the number of foundation stones, by Douglas Knoop and G.P. Jones. [n.p., 1936]
"Reprinted from Miscellanea Latomorum, June 1936."
I. Jones, Gwilym Peredur, 1892- joint author.

NK 0207383 CtY

Jr25.1
Knoop, Douglas, 1883-
Notes on three mediaeval master masons. By Douglas Knoop and G.P.Jones.
Pamphlet
"Reprinted from Miscellanea latomorum, November, 1937."
I.Jones, Gwilym Peredur, 1892- joint author

NK 0207384 CtY

Nrb40
935k
Knoop, Douglas, 1883-
On the connection between operative & speculative masonry ... The inaugural address delivered to the Quatuor coronati lodge, no.2076, London, on his installation as master, 8 November, 1935. [Sheffield, J.W.Northend ltd., printers, 1935]
59p., 1l. 17½cm
Bibliography: p.49-59.

NK 0207385 CtY

Knoop, Douglas, 1883–
Outlines of railway economics, by Douglas Knoop ... London, Macmillan and co., limited, 1913.
xvi, 274 p. 19cm.
"Authorities": p. [267]–269.
"This book owes its origin to a course of lectures on 'Economics with special reference to railways' ... at the Midland railway institute, Derby, and at the University of Sheffield, during the past winter."—Pref.
1. Railroads — Finance. 2. Railroads — Gt. Brit. 3. Railroads and state—Gt. Brit. 4. Railroads—Gt. Brit.—Rates.
A 13–2041
Title from Bureau of Railway Economics Library of Congress HE1031.K6

OCU OU OOxM MiU NjP ICJ MB NN
NK 0207386 DBRE IdU-SB OrP NIC ICRL CU PU PSC PPT

KNOOP, Douglas, 1883 –
Outlines of railway economics. [2nd ed.] London, Macmillan and co., ltd., 1923. [c1923].
274 p.

NK 0207387 MH-BA CtY IU

Ndv57
B9
1
1938
Knoop, Douglas, 1883-
Overtime in the age of Henry VIII, [by] ... Douglas Knoop and G.P.Jones ... [n.p., 1938]
Cover-title.
"Most of our illustrations relate to masons."
"Reprinted from Economic history (Supplement), February, 1938."
Bibliographical foot-notes.

NK 0207388 CtY

Knoop, Douglas, 1883 –
Principles and methods of municipal trading, by Douglas Knoop ... London, Macmillan and co., limited, 1912.
xvii, 409 p. incl. tables. 22½cm.
"Bibliographical note": p. 389–393.
1. Municipal ownership.
12—22620
Library of Congress HD4431.K6

MiU OClW OU OCl OO MB NN ICJ NjP PP PU PPT
NK 0207389 DLC Or OrP OrPR CU FMU ICRL NcU CtY OCU

KNOOP, Douglas, 1883-
Prolegomena to the Mason Word. By Douglas Knoop and G.P.Jones. London, Quatuor Coronati Lodge, No.2076, 1939.
28 cm. pp.12.
Paper cover serves as title-page.
"Issued in advance of 'Ars Quatuor Coronatorum' Vol.LII, part 1, 1939."

NK 0207390 MH

366.1
K7567
Knoop, Douglas, 1883-
Pure antient masonry, by Douglas Knoop ... [London?] Printed for private circulation, 1939.
62 p., 1 l. 21½cm.
1. Freemasons. 2. Masonry, English.

NK 0207391 NNC CtY OCl CSmH MH

VOLUME 300

Knoop, Douglas, 1883-
... The repair of Beaumaris town wall, 1536-1538. By Douglas Knoop ... and G.Peredur Jones ... Liverpool,1935.

At head of title: Anglesey antiquarian society and field club, 1935.
"Reprinted from the Anglesey antiquarian society's Transactions (1935)"

NK 0207392 CtY

Knoop, Douglas, 1883–
The riddle of unemployment, by Douglas Knoop ... London; Macmillan and co., limited, 1931.
viii, 192 p. 19 cm.

1. Unemployed. 2. Economic history—1918–1945. I. Title.

HD5706.K65 331.137 32—1851

NK 0207393 DLC NN MB ViU OCl OCU CtY OrPR

Knoop, Douglas, 1883-
The rise of the mason contractor, by Douglas Knoop and G. P. Jones. [London, Loxley, 1936]
24 p. 26cm.

"Reprinted from the Journal of the Royal institute of British architects, Vol. 43, series 3, no. 20, 1936."
"This article gives the substance of a paper read to the Economic history section of the Anglo-American historical conference in July 1936."

1. Contractors. 2. Stone-masons. I. Jones, Gwilym Peredur, 189 2- jt. au.

NK 0207394 NNC CtY

Knoop, Douglas, 1883–
... The scope and method of masonic history, by Douglas Knoop & G. P. Jones. Oldham [Eng.] Printed for the Association by F. & G. Pollard (Oldham) ltd., the Wellington press, 1944.
16 p. 21cm.
At head of title: Manchester association for masonic research.

1. Freemasons—Hist.—Historiography. I. Jones, Gwilym Peredur, 1892– joint author. II. Manchester association for masonic research. III. Title.
A 45-3675

Harvard univ. Library
for Library of Congress

NK 0207395 MH CtY NNC

Knoop, Douglas, 1883–
The Scottish mason and The mason word, by Douglas Knoop ... and G. P. Jones ... [Manchester, Eng.] Manchester university press, 1939.
x, 113, [1] p. incl. front. (map) 22½cm.
The second study is the Prestonian lecture for 1938, issued for private circulation in the spring of 1938. cf. Pref.
Bibliography: p. ix–x.

1. Stone-masons. 2. Building—Scotland. 3. Freemasons. Scotland. I. Jones, Gwilym Peredur, 1892– II. Title. III. Title: The mason word.
40-11503

Library of Congress HD8039.M35G74
331.76930941

NK 0207396 DLC CU MU MB CaQML MiU CtY PU

Knoop, Douglas, 1883-
Second thoughts on Masonic history old and new; being the 'Reply' of Douglas Knoop and G.P.Jones to the comments on their paper "Masonic history old and new", communicated to the Q.C.lodge, 2nd October 1942. [Frome, etc., Butler & Tanner ltd.] 1943.

15 p. 21.5 cm.
Caption-title.
"Printed for private circulation."

NK 0207397 MH

Knoop, Douglas, 1883–
A short history of freemasonry to 1730, by Douglas Knoop ... and G. P. Jones ... [Manchester, Eng.] Manchester university press, 1940.
ix, 148 p., 1 l. incl. tables. 19cm.
"Bibliographical note": p. 140. "Select list of references": p. 141–142.

1. Freemasons. Gt. Brit.—Hist. I. Jones, Gwilym Peredur, 1892– joint author. II. Title.
A 41-1740

Harvard univ. Library
for Library of Congress

NK 0207398 MH CaQML FU NcD OO OU OCU PPWe ICU DLC

Knoop, Douglas, 1883–
The sixteenth century mason, by Douglas Knoop and G. P. Jones. [London, The Quatuor coronati lodge, no. 2076, 1937]
20 p. 27½cm.
"Issued in advance of 'Ars quatuor coronatorum' vol. I. part III. 1937."

1. Stone-masons. 2. Building—Gt. Brit. I. Jones, Gwilym Peredur, 1892– joint author. II. Title.

Library of Congress HD8039.M35G75 39-12156
331.76930942

NK 0207399 DLC CtY CSmH NNC

Knoop, Douglas, 1883–
The story of the Royal Brunswick lodge, Sheffield, 1793–1943, by Douglas Knoop ... Printed for the lodge for the 150th anniversary of its first meeting, 10th July, 1793. [Sheffield, Pawson & Brailsford ltd., printers, 1943]
51, [1] p. ports., facsims. 26½cm.

1. Freemasons. Sheffield, Eng. Royal Brunswick lodge.
A 43-3480

Harvard univ. Library
for Library of Congress HS598.S52R6
† 366.1

NK 0207400 MH DLC NNC CtY

Knoop, Douglas, 1883- ed.

Freemasons. *Constitutions.*
The two earliest masonic mss.: the Regius ms. (B. M. Bibl. reg. 17 A1) the Cooke ms. (B. M. Add. ms. 23198) transcribed and edited by Douglas Knoop ... G. P. Jones ... and Douglas Hamer ... [Manchester, Eng.] Manchester university press, 1938.

Knoop, Douglas, 1883–
University masonic lodges. Sheffield [Eng.] Printed for private circulation by J. W. Northend, 1945.
21 p. 23 cm.

1. Freemasons. I. Title.
A 49-6887*

Harvard Univ. Library
for Library of Congress [1]

NK 0207402 MH NNC

Knoop, Douglas, 1883- ed.

The **Wilkinson** manuscript, transcribed and edited by Douglas Knoop ... G. P. Jones ... [and] Douglas Hamer ... [Sheffield] Printed for private circulation [by Pawson & Brailsford ltd.] 1946.

Knoop, Emil, 1910-
Das problem der nachträglichen vereinbarung des eigentumsvorbehalts ... von Emil Knoop ... Würzburg, K. Triltsch,1935.
vi, 32 p., 1 l. 22½cm.

Inaug. - diss. - Köln.
"Lebenslauf": 1 l. at end.
"Literaturverzeichnis": p. iv-vi.

NK 0207404 MH-L

Knoop (Ernst Conrad Wilhelm). *Ueber die qualitative Bestimmung der Meconsäure und der Alkaloide des Opiums im Magen- und Darminhalt sowie im Harn in Vergiftungsfällen. 15 pp. 4°. *Kiel, C. F. Mohr*, 1868.
In: SCHRIFT. d. Univ. zu Kiel. xv. 1868. vii. med. iv.

NK 0207405 DNLM

Knoop, Faith Yingling.
Arkansas: yesterday and today; a history of Arkansas for elementary grades, by Faith Yingling Knoop ... and James R. Grant ... Chicago, Philadelphia, J. B. Lippincott company [°1935]
viii, 350 p. front. (fold. map) illus. (1 col.) 19cm.

1. Arkansas—Hist. I. Grant, James Richard, 1880– joint author. II. Title.
36-279

Library of Congress F411.K66
——— Copy 2.
Copyright A 90111 976.7

NK 0207406 DLC OkU

Knoop, Faith Yingling.
Arkansas: yesterday and today; a history of Arkansas for elementary grades, by Faith Yingling Knoop and James R. Grant. Philadelphia, J. B. Lippincott Co. [1947]
viii, 350 p. illus., ports., fold. map. 20 cm.

1. Arkansas—Hist. I. Grant, James Richard, 1880– joint author. II. Title.

F411.K66 1947 976.7 48-1077*

NK 0207407 DLC TxU

Knoop, Faith Yingling.
Lars and the Luck Stone; illustrated by John Moment. [1st ed.] New York, Harcourt, Brace [1950]
182 p. illus. 21 cm.

I. Title.

PZ7.K75Lar 50-9394

NK 0207408 DLC WaSp WaS Or

Knoop, Faith Yingling.
Quest of the cavaliers; De Soto and the Spanish explorers, by Faith Yingling Knoop. Illustrated by William Merritt Berger. New York, Toronto, Longmans, Green and co., 1940.
vi, 202 p. illus. 22½cm.
Title vignette.
Illustrated lining-papers.
"First edition."
Bibliography: p. 185–186.

1. Soto, Hernando de, 1500 (ca.)–1542. 2. America—Disc. & explor.—Spanish. I. Title.
40-10866

Library of Congress E125.S7K7
——— Copy 2.
Copyright 923.9

NK 0207409 DLC OCl OClh PPD PPGi ViU WaSp WaS OrLgE Or

VOLUME 300

Knoop, Faith Yingling
Zebulon Pike; illustrated by Armstrong Sperry. Row, c1950.
36 p. illus. (Real people)

NK 0207410 WaSp OrLgE OrP

Knoop, Franz, 1875-
Der Abbau aromatischer Fettsäuren im Tierkörper. Aus dem physiologisch-chemischen Institut in Strassburg und der medizinischen Abteilung des chemischen Institutes in Freiburg i.B... Freiburg(Baden),E.Kuttruff, 1904.
44p. 23cm.
1.Acids, Fatty - Physiological effect.

NK 0207411 CtY-M DNLM CtY

Knoop, Franz, 1875-
Lebenserscheinungen und Chemie. Öffentliche Antrittsrede. Freiburg, Speyer, 1921.
28 p. 24 cm.

NK 0207412 MBCo PPC

Knoop, Franz, 1875–
... Oxydationen im tierkörper; ein bild von den hauptwegen physiologischer verbrennung von Franz Knoop ... Stuttgart, F. Enge, 1931.
37 p. 25 cm. (Sammlung chemischer und chemisch-technologischer vorträge ... n. f., hft. 9)
1. Oxidation, Physiological.
QD1.S2 n. f., hft. 9 612.01536 32—5524

NK 0207413 DLC CoU NcD NBuU ViU PU OU MiU

Knoop, Franz, 1875-
Ueber sehnenplastik ... Freiburg in Baden, Speyer, 1900.
30 p.
Inaug.-diss., Freiburg im Breisgau, 1900.
"Litteraturverzeichnis": p. [29]-30.
1. Tendons - Transplantation.

NK 0207414 NNC DNLM DLC ICRL

Knoop, Frederick, joint author.

Herschman, Harry Kurtz, 1899–
... Influence of grinding treatments on the surface hardness of intaglio printing plates of 0.33-percent carbon steel, by Harry K. Herschman and Frederick Knoop ...
(R P 1374, *in* U. S. National bureau of standards. Journal of research of the National bureau of standards. Washington, U. S. Govt. print. off., 1941. 23½cm. March, 1941, v. 26, no. 3, p. 261–272. 3 pl. on 2 l., tables, diagrs.)

Knoop, Frederick.
... A sensitive pyramidal-diamond tool for indentation measurements, by Frederick Knoop, Chauncey G. Peters, and Walter B. Emerson ...
(R P 1220, *in* U. S. National bureau of standards. Journal of research of the National bureau of standards. Washington, U. S. Govt. print. off., 1939. 23½cm. July, 1939, v. 23, no. 1, p. 39–61 incl. illus., tables, diagrs. plates)
Running title: Sensitive pyramidal indenter.
1. Measuring instruments. I. Peters, Chauncey George, 1887– joint author. II. Emerson, Walter Bradbury, joint author. III. Title. IV. Title: Sensitive pyramidal indenter.
39-26890
Library of Congress QC1.U52 v. 23, no. 1
T1.U42 v. 23, no. 1
(506.173) 620.1123

NK 0207416 DLC OU

KNOOP,Fritz,1901-
Der arbeitsmarkt der bergischen textilindustrie unter besonderer berücksichtigung seiner nachkriegskonjunktur. Inaug.-diss. Münster i. Westf. [Gütersloh i. W.,H.Franke],1928.
"Lebenslauf",following p.129.
"Literaturverzeichnis",pp.VIII-X.
Charts inserted.

NK 0207417 MH

Knoop, Gerhard, 1920– , comp.
Studentlyrikk, samlet av Gerhard Knoop, Ingvar Hauge og Øivind Holter. Med bidrag av Reidar Andersen-Næss...[og 19 andre] Oslo, E. G. Mortensen, 1947. 100 p. 21cm.
"Biografiske notiser," p. 97–100.
1. College verse—Oslo universitet. I. Hauge, Ingvar, 1921– , jt. comp. II. Holter, Øivind, 1918– , jt. comp.
N. Y. P. L. March 17, 1949

NK 0207418 NN MiU

PT2621 .N77A7 1915 **Knoop, Gerhard J Ouckama, 1861-1913.**
Das A und das Q; Roman [von] Gerhard Ouckama Knoop. München, Delphin-Verlag, 1915.
355 p. 20 cm.

NK 0207419 ViU ICU InU CU RPB NN NjP OrU PU CU

834K75 Oa **Knoop, Gerhard J. Ouckama, 1861-1913.**
... Das A und das Q; roman. München, 1925.
355p.

NK 0207420 IU

PT2621 .N7A8 1909 Knoop, Gerhard J Ouckama, 1861-1913.
Aus den Papieren des Freiherrn von Skarpl, hrsg. von Gerhard Ouckama Knoop. Berlin, E. Fleischel [1909]
188 p.

NK 0207421 ICU CtY InU

Knoop, Gerhard J. Ouckama, 1861-1913.
Aus des Papieren des Freiherrn von Skarpl.
6. Aufl. Egon Fleischel, 1911.

NK 0207422 OrU

[Knoop, Gerhard Julius Ouckama,] 1861–1913.
Die Dekadenten. Psychologischer Roman, von Gerhard Ouckama [pseud.]. München: Piloty & Loehle, 1898. 316 p. 12°.
152195A. 1. Fiction (German). 2. Title.
N. Y. P. L. October 15, 1924

NK 0207423 NN NjP CU OrU MH

Hkp K756 E5 **Knoop, Gerhard J Ouckama, 1861-1913.**
Das Element, Roman. Leipzig, Insel-Verlag, 1901.
191p. 21cm.

NK 0207424 CtY CU OClW NN NjP InU ICU OrU

Knoop, Gerhard J. Ouckama, 1861-1913.
Die Erlosende Wahrheit. Munchen, Piloty & Loehle, 1899.

NK 0207425 OrU

Knoop, Gerhard J. Ouckama, 1861-
Gedichte ... Leipzig, 1904.

NK 0207426 NjP

PT 2621 .N77 A17 1914 **KNOOP, GERHARD J OUCKAMA, 1861-1913**
Gedichte. Leipzig, Insel-Verlag, 1914.
51 p.

NK 0207427 InU OrU

PT2621 .N7G3 1907 Knoop, Gerhard J Ouckama, 1861-1913.
Der Gelüste Ketten; Novellen. Berlin, E. Fleischel, 1907.
233 p.

NK 0207428 ICU OrU NjP InU

PT2621 .N7G8 1903 Knoop, Gerhard J Ouckama, 1861-1913.
Die Grenzen. Leipzig, Im Insel-Verlag, 1903-05.
2 v.
Contents.—v.1. Sebald Soekers Pilgerfahrt.—v.2. Sebald Soekers Vollendung.

NK 0207429 ICU OO InU CtY

KNOOP,Gerhard J. Ouckama,1861-1913.
Hermann Osleb;roman. Berlin,E.Fleischel & co.,1904.

NK 0207430 MH CtY NjP OrU NNC

PT 2621 N77 H6 **Knoop, Gerhard J Ouckama, 1861-1913**
Die Hochmögenden; Roman. Berlin, E. Fleischel, 1912.
375p. 19cm.

NK 0207431 WU IU NjP MH ICU

Knoop, Gerhard J. Ouckama, 1861-1913.
Die Hochmögenden. Egon Fleishel & Co., 1913.

NK 0207432 OrU

834K75 Ok **Knoop, Gerhard Ouckama, 1861-1913.**
Die Karburg. Fremde Erlebnisse, eigene Betrachtungen. Aus einem Tagebuche. Von Gerhard Ouckama. München, Piloty & Loehle, 1897.
283p. 19cm.

NK 0207433 IU OrU

Knoop, Gerhard J. Ouckama, 1861-1913.

M1619 .5 .K6B6 **Bode, Rudolf,** 1881–
[Knoop-Lieder]
Knoop-Lieder (Gerhard Ouckama Knoop) Berlin-Lichterfelde, C. F. Vieweg [194-?] Pl. no. V. 2238.

VOLUME 300

Knoop, Gerhard [J] Ouckama, 1861-1913.
Nadeshda Bachini. Roman. Berlin, 1906.
19.5cm.

NK 0207435 CtY OrU

Knoop, Gerhard J. Ouckama, 1861-1913.
Outsider Novellen. Leipzig, Pierson, 1901.

NK 0207436 OrU

PT 2621 N77 P7
Knoop, Gerhard J Ouckama, 1861-1913
Prinz Hamlets Briefe. München, Delphin [19—?]
208p. 17cm.

1. Shakespeare, William, 1564-1616. Hamlet I. Title

NK 0207437 WU ICU MU

Knoop, Gerhard J. Ouckama, 1861-1913.
Prinz Hamlet's Briefe. Berlin, Reichl & Co., 1909.

NK 0207438 OrU

Knoop, Gerhard Julius Ouckama, 1861-1913.
Sebald Soekers pilgerfahrt; ein roman. Leipzig, Insel, 1903.
540 p.

NK 0207439 PBm

3465 .14 .383
Knoop, Gerhard Julius Ouckama, 1861-1913
Sebald Soekers Pilgerfahrt; Roman. [2.Aufl.] Leipzig, Insel, 1911
453 p. 19 cm

NK 0207440 NjP OrU MH OO NN IU

Knoop, Gerhard Julius Ouckama, 1861-1913.
Sebald Soekers vollendung. Leipzig, Insel, 1905.
162 p. (His Die grenzen, 2d bd.)

NK 0207441 PBm

Knoop, Gerhard Julius Ouckama, 1861- 1913
Sebald Soekers Vollendung. München-Pasing: Die Heimkehr, 1921. 130 p. 12°. (His: Die Grenzen.)

1. Fiction (German). 2. Title.
N. Y. P. L. March 30, 1923.

NK 0207442 NN OrU OO IU

Knoop, Gerhard J Ouckama, 1861-1913.
Unter könig Max; Münchener roman, von Gerhard Ouckama Knoop. Berlin, E. Fleischel & co., 1913.
2 p. l., 283 p. 20½cm. M. 3.50

I. Title.

Library of Congress PT2621.N77U6 1913 13-25774

NK 0207443 DLC ICU CU InU CtY OCl NjP OrU WaS

Knoop, Gerhard J Ouckama, 1861-1913.
Verfalltag, roman von Gerhard Ouckama Knoop. Berlin, E. Fleischel & co., 1911.
3 p. l., 279 p. 20½ cm.

I. Title.

Library of Congress PT2621.N77V4 1911 11—10777

NK 0207444 DLC OrU

Knoop, Gertrud Ouckama, tr.

PG3328 .D633
Dostoevskaia, Lîubov' Fedorovna, 1869–
Dostojewski, geschildert von seiner tochter A. Dostojewski. Erlenbach-Zürich, E. Rentsch, 1920.

Film 1414
Knoop, Gisela, 1924-
Gesamtdarstellungen der deutschen Literatur bis zu Wilhelm Scherer. Münster Westfalia, 1952.
Microfilm copy of the original
Collation of the original: 137p.
Thesis (Ph.D.) - Wilhelmsuniversität zu Münster, Westfalia, 1952.
Bibliography: p. 120-137.
Vita.

1. German literature - History and Criticism. I. Title.

NK 0207446 TNJ

Knoop, H D , Caldwell, H. F. and Shaw, R. A.
Investigation of automobile springs... [1924]
Thesis, University of Cincinnati, Mechanical Engineer, 1924.

NK 0207447 OCU

Knoop, Hans.
Der Mehrwerth... Bremen, R. A. Ordemann Söhne, 1883.
30 p. 21cm.

I. Value.

NK 0207448 NN

Knoop, Hedwig, 1908-
... "Familienmord oder erweiterter Selbstmord" mit kasuistischen Beiträgen ... Bielefeld, 1935.
Inaug. diss.-München.
Lebenslauf.

NK 0207449 CtY

Knoop, Helmut
Das problem der clausula rebus sic stantibus im BGB in schrifttum und rechtsprechung unter berücksichtigung der neuen entwicklung. ... Eisfeld/Thür., 1937. 96 p.
Inaug. Diss. - Erlangen, 1937.
Schrifttum.

NK 0207450 DLC

Knoop, Hendrik. 3753.85
De aanleg vorm en verbreiding der glandulae en noduli lymphatici in den oesophagus van den mensch en de apen. Proefschrift . . . Utrecht . . .
= Middelburg. Van Straaten. [1916.] (7), 192 pp. Plates. 24½ cm., in 8s.
Literatuur, pp. 170-184.

L8925 — Lymphatic glands. — Primates.

NK 0207451 MB ICRL PPAN IU NjP

Knoop, Herman.
Een theater in Dachau, door ds Herm. Knoop ... Goes, Oosterbaan & Le Cointre [1946]
183 p. 23cm.

and prisons, German. 3. World war, 1939-1945—Personal narratives, Dutch. 4. World war, 1939-1945—Religious aspects. I. Title.
D805.G3K6 A F 47-2090
Harvard univ. Library for Library of Congress †

NK 0207452 MH DLC

KNOOP, Herman, 1891-
Zaligverklaarde dooden; preek gehouden Zondag 23 Maart 1952, de sterfdag van K. Schilder, in de Geref. Kerk van Barendrecht en Rotterdam-Z., over Openbaring 14: 13 en op verzoek uitgegeven. [Barendrecht, Drukkerij Barendrecht, 1952]
16p. front. 22cm.

NK 0207453 MH-AH

Knoop (Hermann) [1864-]. *Gallensteine im Nabel. 42 pp., 1 l. 8°. *Marburg, R. Friedrich*, 1892.

NK 0207454 DNLM

KNOOP, Jac.
Anleitung zur angelfischerei. Leipzig, A.O. Paul, [1903].

32°. pp.55. Illustr.
(Miniatur-bibliothek, 440.)

NK 0207455 MH

Knoop, Jeanne Siebentje Anne Margaretha.
Hygiene der vrouw... met voorwoord van Dr. Cath. van Tussenbroek... Amsterdam, Scheltens & Giltay, n.d.
[152p. illus.]

NK 0207456 OCl

RG163 .K7
Knoop, Jeanne Siebentje Anne Margaretha.
De invloed van geestelijken arbeid op de specifiek vrouwelijke functies ... Leiden, S. C. van Doesburgh, 1919.
[7], 113, 5 p. incl. tables. 23cm.
Proefschrift—Amsterdam.

1. Education of women. 2. Woman—Diseases.

NK 0207457 ICU DNLM MH

VOLUME 300

Knoop, Joannes Sebastianus
... Exhibens quaedam ad legem Corneliam de sicariis & veneficis ... submittit Joannes Sebastianus Knoop ... Groningae, J. Dikema, 1782.
2 p.l., 36, [2] p. 25½cm.
Diss. - Groningen.

NK 0207458 MH-L

Knoop, Johann Hermann. 18th cent. Beknopte huishoudelyke hovenier. 3 dln. Amsterdam. [1760?–62.] 8°.
i. Ooft-vrugten. 2e druk. [1760?] pp. x, 294.—ii. Bloem-gewassen. [1760.] pp. [8], 415.—iii. Medicinaale planten. [1762.] pp. [8], 362, [42].

NK 0207459 MH-A

Knoop, Johann Hermann, 18th cent.
Beschouwende en werkdadige hovenier-konst; of, Inleiding tot de waare oeffening der planten. Waarin aangewezen word al't gene een hovenier en aan andere tuin-oeffenaars dienstig en nodig zyn kan te weeten, om niet alleen met gewenscht voordeel, maar ook met vermaak allerley boom-, heester-, kruid-, en bloem-gewassen te cultiveeren ... Dienende verders sowel voor de veldt- als tuin-oeffenaars. Door Johann Hermann Knoop. Leeuwarden, A. Ferwerda, 1753.
14 p. l., 594 p. xvi fold. pl. (incl. plan) 26cm.
1. Gardening—[Early works to 1800. [1. Horticulture]
Agr 23-656
Library, U. S. Dept. of Agriculture 90K75

NK 0207460 DNAL MH-A

Knoop, Johann Hermann, 18th cent. **L634.2 F1**
123147 Beschrijving en afbeeldingen van de beste soorten van appelen en peeren, meest geacht en zorgvuldigst aangekweekt in Duitschland, in Frankrijk, in Engeland, en in de XVII. Provintien, door Johann Hermann Knoop, met eene voorreden van Johannes Florentius Martinet, ... Amsterdam en Dordrecht, Allart, Holtrop, De Leeuw en Krap, 1790.
viii, 36 p. 20 col. fold. pl. 33½cm.
Half-title: J. H. Knoop over vruchten en gewassen.
Also published under title: Pomologia.

NK 0207461 ICJ CtY

Knoop, Johann Hermann, 18th cent.
Beschryving van de moes- en keuken-tuin, zo van alle vrugten, planten en kruiden die men in dezelve plant ... Waar by derzelver differente benamingen, groeiplaats, zoorten, voorteeling, cultuur, broeijing, vervroeging en huishoudelyk gebruik, als mede hoe men dezelve inleggen kan, als ook derzelver kragten in de medicynen, en voor wie gemelde vrugten gezond of ongezond zyn. Waar agter nog gevoegt zyn verscheide registers ... Door een veeljarige ondervinding opgestelt, door Johann Hermann Knoop ... Leeuwarden, A. Ferwerda en G. Tresling, 1769.
1 p. l., 235 p. 36cm.
1. Gardening. [1. Horticulture]
Agr 19-507
Library, U. S. Dept. of Agriculture 97K75

NK 0207462 DNAL MiU MH-A

Knoop, Johann Hermann, 18th cent. **L634.2 F1**
123149 Beschrijving van plantagie-gewassen, die men in hoven aankweekt, zo om te dienen tot sieraad bij het maaken van laanen, cingels, heggen, berceaux, kabinetten, pyramiden, slinger-boschjes enz., als tot huishoudelijk gebruik. Nevens derzelver verschillende naamen, groei-plaatzen, aankweeking, onderhoud en onderscheiden gebruiken, opgesteld, volgens eene veeljarige ondevinding, door Johann Hermann Knoop. Amsterdam en Dordrecht, Allart, Holtrop, De Leeuw en Krap, 1790.
[4], 87, [4] p. 33½cm.
Also published under the title: Dendrologia.
With his Beschrijving en afbeeldingen van de beste soorten van appelen en peeren. 1790.

NK 0207463 ICJ CtY

Knoop, Johann Hermann, 18th cent. **L634.2 F1**
123148 Beschrijving van vruchtboomen en vruchten, die men in hoven plant en onderhoudt, met derzelver verschillende naamen, voortteeling, groei-plaatzen, aankweeking, huishoudelijk gebruik, wijze van uitleggen, en toebereiding. Na eene veeljarige ondervinding opgesteld door Johann Hermann Knoop, met naar het leven geteekende en gekoleurde afbeeldingen. Amsterdam en Dordrecht, Allart, Holtrop, De Leeuw en Krap, 1790.
[4], 70 p. XIX col. fold. pl. 33½cm.
Also published under title: Fructologia.
With his Beschrijving en afbeeldingen van de beste soorten van appelen en peeren. 1790.

NK 0207464 ICJ CtY

Knoop, Johann Hermann, *18th cent.*
Dendrologia, of beschryving der plantagie-gewassen, die men in de tuinen cultiveert, zo wel om te dienen tot cieraad om daar van allées, cingels, heggen, berçeaux, cabinets, pyramiden, plaizier-bosschen, enz., als tot huishoudelyk gebruik, te planten. Waar by derzelver differente benamingen, groei-plaatzen, aankweeking, en verdere onderhouding, en vervolgens haar tuin- en huishoudelyke gebruiken, nauwkeurig beschreeven en aangewezen worden. Alles door een eige veeljarige ondervinding, ten dienste en vermaak der tuin-beminnaars opgestelt, door Johann Hermann Knoop. Leeuwarden, By A. Ferwerda en G. Tresling, boekverkopers [n. d.]
2 p. l., 87, [4] p. 33½cm. [*With his* Pomologia. Leeuwarden, n. d.]
First published in 1763.

1. Trees. I. Title.
Agr 2-78 Revised
Library, U. S. Dept. of Agriculture 90K75
Library of Congress SB361.K7

NK 0207466 DNAL MiU IU NIC

Knoop, Johann Hermann, *18th cent.*
Dendrologia, of beschryving der plantagie-gewassen, die men in de tuinen cultiveert, zo wel om te dienen tot cieraad, om daar van allèes, cingels, heggen, berçeaux, cabinets, pyramiden, plaisier-bosschen, enz., als tot huishoudelyk gebruik, te planten. Waar by derzelver differente benamingen, groeyplaatzen, aankweeking en verdere onderhouding, en vervolgens haar tuin- en huishoudelyke gebruiken, nauwkeurig beschreeven en aangewezen worden. Alles door een eige veeljarige ondervinding, ten dienste en vermaak der tuin-beminnaars opgestelt, door Johann Hermann Knoop. Leeuwarden, Gedrukt by A. Ferwerda en G. Tresling, boekverkopers, 1763.
2 p. l., 168, [4] p. 37cm. [*With his* Pomologia. Leeuwarden, 1758]
1. Trees.
Agr 2-81 Revised
U. S. Dept. of agr. Library 93K75
for Library of Congress [r37b2]

NK 0207467 DNAL CU MBH MH-A NIC

Knoop, Johann Hermann, *18th cent.*
Fructologia, of beschryving der vrugtbomen en vrugten die men in de hoven plant en onderhout: waar by derzelver differente benamingen, voortteeling, groei-plaatzen, cultuur, en huishoudelyk gebruik, als mede het confyten en meer andere toebereidingen der vrugten, enz., nauwkeurig aangewezen worden. Alles door een veeljarige ondervinding opgestelt, ten dienste en vergenoegen der tuin-liefhebbers, door Johann Hermann Knoop. Leeuwarden, By A. Ferwerda en G. Tresling, boekverkopers [n. d.]
2 p. l., 70 p. XIX fold. col. pl. 33½cm. [*With his* Pomologia. Leeuwarden, n. d.]
First published in 1763.
1. Fruit-culture. [1. Pomology] I. Title.
Agr 2-77 Revised
Library, U. S. Dept. of Agriculture 90K75 [r29c2]
Library of Congress SB361.K7

NK 0207468 DNAL MiU IU

Knoop, Johann Hermann, 18th cent
Fructologia ... Leeuwarden, 1758.

Bound with his Pomologia.

NK 0207469 NjN

Knoop, Johann Hermann, 18th cent.
—— Fructologia; of, Beschryving der vrugtbomen en vrugten die men in die hoven plant en onderhout. Leeuwarden. [1763.] f°. pp. [4], 70. 19 colored plates.

NK 0207470 MH-A

Knoop, Johann Hermann, *18th cent.*
Fructologia, of beschryving der vrugtbomen en vrugten die men in de hoven plant en onderhoud: waar by derzelver differente benamingen, groey-plaatzen, voortteeling, cultuur, en huishoudelyk gebruik, als mede het confyten en meer andere toebereidingen der vrugten, enz., nauwkeurig aangewezen worden. Alles door een veeljarige ondervinding opgestelt, ten dienste en vergenoegen der tuin-liefhebbers, door Johann Hermann Knoop. Met platen, vertonende alle vrugten naar het leven, die in dit werk vervat zyn. Leeuwarden, Gedrukt by A. Ferwerda en G. Tresling, boekverkopers, 1763.
2 p. l., 132 p. XIX col. pl. 37cm. [*With his* Pomologia. Leeuwarden, 1758]
1. Fruit-culture. [1. Pomology]
Agr 2-80 Revised
U. S. Dept. of agr. Library 90K75
for Library of Congress [r40b2]

NK 0207471 DNAL NIC MH-A MBH CU

SB Knoop, Johann Hermann, 18th cent.
361 Fructologie ou Description des arbres
K7 fruitiers ainsi que des fruits que l'on plante
1768 et qu'on cultive ordinairement dans les jardins
\+ ... par Jean Herman Knoop. Avec figures représentant au naturel toutes les sortes de fruits contenuës dans cet ouvrage. A Amsterdam Chez la veuve K. van Tongerlo & fils, 1768.
2p.l., 205, [1]p. XIX fold.col.plates 31cm.
With this is bound his Pomologie ... 1768.

1. Fruit-culture. I. Title.

NK 0207472 MU CU

Knoop, Johann Hermann, *18th cent.*
Fructologie, ou Description des arbres fruitiers; ainsi que des fruits. Que l'on plante et qu'on cultive ordinairement dans les jardins. Avec une explication detaillée de leurs différentes dénominations, de leur païs natal, de leur propagation, de leur culture & de leur usage oeconomique, ainsi que de la manière de consire & diverses façons de préparer les fruits, &c. ... par Jean Herman Knoop ... Amsterdam, M. Magérus, 1771.
1 p. l., 205, [1] p. XIX fold. col. pl. 34cm. [*With his* Pomologie. Amsterdam, 1771]
1. Fruit-culture. [1. Pomology]
Agr 12-89 Revised
U. S. Dept. of agr. Library 93K75
for Library of Congress [r40b2]

NK 0207473 DNAL MBH MH-A OU

Knoop, Johann Hermann, 18th cent.
Jongmans-onderwyser, leerende op een korte, dog klare, en bevattelyke wyze, de voornaamste wetenschappen die voor een jongman, van een goede educatie, voor eerst't nodigst om te weten en te leeren zyn. Namelyk: I. De arithmetica of rekenkonst. II. Het gemeen, en italiaansch boekhouden. III. De hoofd-regels om wel gestyliseerde brieven te schryven ... IV. Formulieren van obligatien en contracten &c. V. De eerste beginzels der geometrie of meetkonst ... VI. De practicale geometrie of 't meeten van landen en andere platte gedaantens ... VII. De stereometrie of lighamelyke meting ... VIII. De geographie of aardryks-kunde. IX. Verscheidene staatstafels, tot verklaring dienende van veele staatsen andere zaken. X. De chronologie of tyd-rekenings-kunde, zo wel de borgerlyke als historische ... door Johann Hermann Knoop ... Te Leeuwarden, gedrukt by Abraham Ferwerda; en 's Hage, by Pieter van Thol, 1756.
12 p. l., 878, 50 p. plates. 20½cm.

NK 0207475 NNC CtY

Knoop, Johann Hermann, *18th cent.*
Pomologia, dat is, beschryvingen en afbeeldingen van de beste zoorten van appels en peeren, welke in Nederen Hoog-Duitschland, Frankryk, Engeland en elders geagt zyn, en tot dien einde gecultiveert worden. Beschreven, door Johann Hermann Knoop ... Leeuwarden, By A. Ferwerda en G. Tresling, boekverkopers [n. d.]
1 p. l., 36 p. 20 fold. col. pl. 33½cm.
First published in 1758.
1. Fruit-culture. 2. Apple. 3. Pear. I. Title.
Agr 2-76 Revised
Library, U. S. Dept. of Agriculture 90K75
Library of Congress SB361.K7

NK 0207476 DNAL MiU IU MH-A

VOLUME 300

Knoop, Johann Hermann, *18th cent.*
Pomologia; dat is, Beschryvingen en afbeeldingen van de beste soorten van appels en peeren, welke in Nederen Hoog-Duitsland, Frankryk, Engelland en elders geagt zyn, en tot dien einde gecultiveert worden. Beschreven, naar het leven geteikent, en met de natuurlyke coleuren afgezet door Johann Hermann Knoop ... Leeuwarden, By A. Ferwerda, boekverkoper, 1758.
2 p. l., 86 p., 1 l. 20 col. pl. 37cm.
1. Apple. 2. Pear. I. ₍Title₎
Agr 2-79 Revised
U. S. Dept. of agr. Library 93K75
for Library of Congress [SB361.K]

NK 0207477 DNAL MBH NjN MoU NIC CU MH-A MH NjR

Knoop, Johann Hermann, *18th cent.*
Pomologia, das ist beschreibungen und abbildungen der besten sorten der aepfel und birnen, welche in Holland / Deutschland / Franckreich / Engeland und anderwårts in achtung stehen, und deswegen gebauet werden. Beschrieben, nach dem leben abgebildet und mit ihren natůrlichen farben erleuchtet, von Johann Hermann Knoop ... Aus dem holländischen in das deutsche ůbersetzet / von d. Georg Leonhart Huth. Nůrnberg, J. M. Seligmann, 1760–66.
2 v. in 1. 44 col. pl. 39cm.
Pt. 2 has title: Pomologia, das ist beschreibungen und abbildungen der besten arten der aepfel, birnen, kirschen und einiger pflaumen, welche in- und ausserhalb Deutschland in achtung stehen und gebauet werden ... Nůrnberg, Im verlag der Seligmånnischen erben. Anno 1766.
1. Fruit-culture. ₍1. Pomology₎ I. Huth, Georg Leonhardt, 1705–1761, tr.
Agr 11-15 Revised
U. S. Dept. of agr. Library 90K75P
for Library of Congress ₍r40b2₎

NK 0207479 DNAL CU MH-A MoSB

SB357 Knoop, Johann Hermann, 18th cent.
K54 Pomologie; ou, Description des meilleures
1768 sortes de pommes et de poires que l'on estime & cultive le plus, soit aux Pais-Bas, soit en Allemagne, en France, en Anglettere, &c ... Amsterdam, La Veuve K. van Tongerlo, 1768.
339₍i.e.139₎ p. fold.plates.
Last page misnumbered 339.
With this is bound: His Fructologie ... 1768.

NK 0207480 CU MU

Knoop, Johann Hermann, *18th cent.*
Pomologie, ou Description des meilleures sortes de pommes et de poires, que l'on estime & cultive le plus, soit aux Pais-Bas, soit en Allemagne, en France, en Angleterre, &c., par Jean Herman Knoop ... Amsterdam, M. Magérus, 1771.
2 p. l., 339 (*i. e.* 139) p. xx fold. col. pl. 34cm.
Paging irregular: p. 139 numbered 339.
1. Apple. 2. Pear.
Agr 12-90 Revised
U. S. Dept. of agr. Library 93K75Po
for Library of Congress ₍r40b2₎

NK 0207481 DNAL MH-A MBH OU

Knoop, Johann Hermann, 18th cent.
Pylaar der algemene mathesis of wis-kunde, of de arithmetica ... Amsterdam, J. Sluyter, 1768.
2 v. 21 cm.
Paged continuously.
Vol. 2 has half title only, Tweede stuk, of Vervolg van de arithmetica.
1. Arithmetic--Before 1846.

NK 0207482 CtY

K756
Knoop, Johann Hermann, 18th cent.
Tegenwoordige staat of historische beschryvinge van Friesland. Waarin deszelfs legging, gesteldheid, natuur, vrugtbaarheid, de oorsprong, voortgang, aart, zeeden en gebruiken der inwoonders ... enz. vervolgens de werelklyke en geestelyke regeerings-form, de oorsprong en genealogie van het doorlugtige Huis van Orangien en Nassauw, enz. ... duidelyk aangeweezen worden ... Te Leeuwarden, By A. van Linge, 1763.
₍16₎, 539, ₍25₎ p. map, geneal. table.

NK 0207483 NNC CU

Knoop, Johann Hermann,18th cent.
*NC7 Verhandeling van de sphaerische of klootsche
K7567 zonne-wysers; namelyk, hoe men op een sphaera
761v convexa, of ronde kloot, allerley zonnewysers meetkonstig beschryven kan. Als mede om in een sphaera concava of halve holle kloot, veelerley uur- en andere cirkels te beschryven. Mitsgaders een berigt, hoe men de sphaera armillaris gnomonica, of hemel-kringzonnewyser toestellen kan. Gedaan, door Johann Hermann Knoop mathematicvs. Met kopere platen.
Te Leeuwarden,By H.A.de Chalmot.1761.
8°. 5p.ℓ.,244,[8]p. 21 fold.plates. 22.5cm.
Title vignette, engr.

NK 0207485 MH

Knoop, Käte.
Die erzählungen Eduard von Keyserlings; ein beitrag zur deutschen literaturgeschichte, von Käte Knoop. Marburg a. L., N. G. Elwert, 1929.
38 p. 23cm.
"Teildruck."
Inaug.-Diss.--Marburg.

NK 0207486 NIC DLC CtY MH PU ICRL

Knoop, Käte.
Die erzählungen Eduard von Keyserlings; ein beitrag zur deutschen literaturgeschichte, von Käte Knoop. Marburg a. L., N. G. Elwert, 1929.
4 p. l., 94 p. 24cm. (*Added t.-p.:* Beiträge zur deutschen literaturwissenschaft ... nr. 37)
"Literatur-verzeichnis": 3d–4th prelim. leaves.
1. Keyserling, Eduard Heinrich Nikolaus, graf von, 1855–1918.
30-10189
Library of Congress PT2621.E93Z7

PU MiU LU NN ICU InU MoU
NK 0207487 DLC CU CaBVaU NBuU MH TU CU-S OrU OU PBm

Knoop, L.
Die zwergrindformen aus der umgebung von Börssum im herzogtum Braunschweig. illus.
Landw. jahrb. bd. 48, p. 791-803. Berlin, 1915.
1. Cattle—History.
Agr 20-2060
Library, U. S. Dept. of Agriculture 18L23 bd. 48

NK 0207488 DNAL

Knoop, Ludwig August
see Knoop, August, 1877-

4BF Knoop, M
293 Leren studeren; de techniek van het knapper worden. Zutphen, W. J. Thieme, 1951.
98 p.

NK 0207490 DLC-P4 NNC-T

Knoop, M
Sexuele opvoeding. Lochem, 1951

NK 0207491 MH

Knoop, M
Voer het woord; spreken in het openbaar, gesprekstechniek en groepsdiscussie. 's-Gravenhage, Nijgh & Van Ditmar, 1954.
viii, 86 p. illus., ports. 21 cm.
Bibliography: p. 82–86.
1. Oratory. I. Title.
A 55-5496
Northwestern Univ. Library
for Library of Congress

NK 0207492 IEN

Knoop, M., joint author.
BF128
.D8H65
Hoogwerf, P A
Wat leert u de zielkunde; een boek voor allen, die belang stellen in psychologie, door P. A. Hoogwerf en M. Knoop. Met een voorbericht van Ph. Kohnstamm. Utrecht, Erven J. Bijleveld, 1951.

Knoop, O₍tto₎, 1853– 26274.64.5
Allerhand scherz, neckereien, reime und erzählungen über pommersche orte, und ihrer bewohner. Stettin, F. Hessenland, 1891.
pp. (1), 105.
Folklore-Germany-Pomerania||AcS 232836

NK 0207494 MH

Knoop, Otto, ed.
Blätter für pommersche volkskunde. Monatsschrift für sage und märchen, sitte und brauch, schwank und streich, lied, rätsel und sprachliches in Pommern ...
1.- jahrg.;
okt. 1892-
Stettin, J. Burmeister, 1893-

Knoop, Otto, 1853-
Die deutsche Walthersage und die polnische sage von Walther und Helgunde. 18p. Posen, J. Jolowicz, 1887.
"Vortrag gehalten in der Historischen gesellschaft zu Posen am 8. september, 1885."
"Separatabdruck aus Am urds-brunnen, 1887."

NK 0207496 OCl IU MH

VOLUME 300

PT919 Knoop, Otto, 1853- comp.
.P8K57 Ostmärkische sagen, märchen und erzählungen. Gesammelt und hrsg. von professor Otto Knoop. Stolp (Pomm.) O. Eulitz [1909?]
vii, 193 p. 19½cm.

1. Legends—Posen (Province)

NK 0207497 ICU OCl MH IU

Knoop, Otto, 1853-
Plattdeutsches aus Hinterpommern... 2v. in 1. Posen, Hofbuchdruckerei W. Decker & co., 1890-91.

Programm - Königliche gymnasium zu Gnesen.
Contents.-v.1. Sprüchwörter und redensarten.-v.2. Fremdsprachliches im hinterpommerschen platt, nebst einer anzahl von fischer-ausdrücken und ekelnamen.

NK 0207498 OCl IU MH CU

Knoop, Otto, 1853-
Posener dämonensagen; ein beitrag zur sagengeschichte der provinz Posen. 15p. Rogasen, J. Alexander's wwe., 1912.

Programm - Königl. gymnasium in Rogasen.

NK 0207499 OCl

Film 2730 Reel 192 Item 8
Knoop, Otto, 1853-
Posener Geld- und Schatzsagen. Ein Beitrag zur Heimat- und Volkskunde der Provinz Posen. Lissa i.P., Comenius, 1908.
45p. 20cm.
"Wissenschaftliche Beilage zum Programm des Kgl. Gymnasiums zu Rogasen. 1908. Prog. Nr. 224."
Microfilm. Lexington, Ky., Erasmus Press; available from General Microfilm Co., Cambridge, Mass. 1 reel (various items) 35mm.
Title on micro- film box label: Literature of folklore.

NK 0207500 TxU UU OCl MH

Film 2730 Reel 192 Item 7
Knoop, Otto, 1853-
Posener Märchen; ein Beitrag zur Heimat- und Volkskunde der Provinz Posen. Lissa i.P., Comenius, 1909.
29p. 27cm.
"Wissenschaftliche Beilage zum Programm des Kgl. Gymnasiums zu Rogasen. 1909. Progr. Nr. 236."
Microfilm. Lexington, Ky., Erasmus Press; available from General Microfilm Co., Cambridge, Mass. 1 reel (various items) 35mm.
Title on micro- film box label: Literature of folklore

NK 0207501 TxU InU OCl MH

Knoop, Otto, 1853- ed.
Sagen der provinz Posen, gesammelt und herausgegeben von professor Otto Knoop ... Berlin-Friedenau, H. Eichblatt [°1913]
xvi, 183, [1] p. front., illus., plates. 19½cm. (*Half-title:* Eichblatts Deutscher sagenschatz. bd. 3)
"Quellen": p. 175-181.

1. Legends—Posen (Province) 2. Folk-lore—Posen (Province)

A C 37-1397

Chicago. Univ. Library for Library of Congress PT915.E34 vol. 3

NK 0207502 ICU OCl IU

Knoop, Otto, ed.
Sagen der provinz Posen, mit abbildungen. Berlin-Friedenau H. Eichblatt [1919]
xvi, 183, [1] p. front. illus., plates. (Eichblatts Deutscher sagenschatz, 3.)

NK 0207503 OCl

Knoop, Otto, 1853-
Sagen, erzählungen und schwanke aus dem kreise Begenwalde. Labes, A. Straube & sohn, 1924.
xi, [1], 110p.

NK 0207504 OCl

PT919 Knoop, Otto, 1853- ed.
.P71N3K7 Sagen und erzählungen aus dem kreise Naugard, unter mitwirkung von rektor H. Gosch in Daber gesammelt und hrsg. von professor Otto Knoop. Stargard in Pommern, O. Plath, 1925.
98 p. 19½cm.

1. Legends—Pomerania—Naugard. 2. Folk-lore—Pomerania—Naugard.

NK 0207505 ICU OCl NBuG MH

GR167 .P8K72
KNOOP, OTTO, 1853- comp.
Sagen und erzählungen aus der provinz Posen. Posen, Eigenthum der Gesellschaft, 1893. 20+364p. (Historische gesellschaft für die provinz Posen. Sonder-veröffentlichungen. 2)

NK 0207506 InU NBuG CU OCl NN

Film 2730 Reel 225 Item 4
Knoop, Otto, 1853- comp.
Sagen und Erzählungen aus der Provinz Posen. Gesammelt von Otto Knoop. Posen, Eigenthum der [Historischen] Gesellschaft [für die Provinz Posen] 1895.
xix, 363p. 20cm. (Sonder-Veröffentlichungen der Historischen Gesellschaft für die Provinz Posen, 2)
Microfilm. Lexington, Ky., Erasmus Press; available through General Microfilm Co., Cambridge, Mass. 1 reel (various items) 35mm.
Title on micro- film box label: Literature of folklore

NK 0207507 TxU CtY ICJ

GR167 Knoop, Otto, 1853-
.P71S8K7 Stargarder sagen, überlieferungen und geschichten, mit einem anhang: Die sagen der Madüe. Gesammelt und hrsg. von professor Otto Knoop. Stargard in Pommern, O. Plath, 1924.
109 p. 19cm.

1. Legends—Pomerania—Stargard. 2. Folk-lore—Pomerania—Stargard.

NK 0207508 ICU MH OCl

GR 167 P7 K72
Knoop, Otto, 1853-
Volkssagen, Erzählungen, Aberglauben, Gebräuche und Märchen aus dem östlichen Hinterpommern. Posen, J. Jolowicz, 1885.
xxx, 240 p. 22cm.

1. Folk-lore--Pomerania. 2. Pomerania--Soc. life & cust. I. Title.

NK 0207509 NIC PU IU NN MB OCl MH IaU CU

2730 Reel 186 Item 3
Knoop, Otto, 1853-
Volkssagen, Erzählungen, Aberglauben, Gebräuche und Märchen aus dem östlichen Hinterpommern. Posen, J. Jolowicz, 1885.
xxx, 240p. 20cm.
Microfilm. Lexington, Ky., Erasmus Press; available from General Microfilm Co., Cambridge, Mass. 1 reel (various items) 35mm.
Title on microfilm box label: Literature of folklore.

NK 0207510 TxU UU

PT919 Knoop, Otto, 1853- ed.
.P71D8K7 Volkssagen, erzählungen und schwänke aus dem kreise Dramburg. Unter mitwirkung von konrektor A. Heller ... gesammelt und hrsg. von professor Otto Knoop. Köslin, C. G. Hendess, 1926.
xi, 116 p. 21cm. (*Half-title:* Ostpommerscher sagenschatz. bd. 3)

1. Legends—Pomerania—Dramburg. 2. Folk-lore—Pomerania—Dramburg.

NK 0207511 ICU MH OCl

PT919 Knoop, Otto, 1853- ed.
.P71L3K7 Volkssagen, erzählungen und schwänke aus dem kreise Lauenburg, gesammelt und hrsg. von professor Otto Knoop. Köslin, C. G. Hendess, 1925.
xii, 104 p. 19½cm. (*Half-title:* Ostpommerscher sagenschatz. bd. 2)

1. Legends—Pomerania—Lauenburg. 2. Folk-lore—Pomerania—Lauenburg.

NK 0207512 ICU OCl

GR167 Knoop, Otto, 1853-
.P7K7 Volkssagen und erzählungen aus der stadt und dem landkreis Stolp, gesammelt und hrsg. von professor Otto Knoop. Stolp, O. Eulitz, 1925.
viii, 84, [6] p. 20cm.

1. Folk-lore—Pomerania.

NK 0207513 ICU OCl MH

Film 2730 Reel 270 Item 9
Knoop, Otto, 1853-
Volkstümliches aus der Pflanzenwelt.
(In Deutsche Gesellschaft für Kunst und Wissenschaft in Posen. Zeitschrift der Naturwissenschaftlichen Abteilung. v.11 (1904), p.52-59, 72-88; v.12 (1905), p.13-17)
Microfilm. Lexington, Ky., Erasmus Press; available through General Microfilm Co., Cambridge, Mass. 1 reel (various items) 35mm. (Literature of folklore, 270)

NK 0207514 TxU UU

Film GR 10 L5 reel 148
Knoop, Otto, 1853- ed.
Volkstümliches aus der tierwelt. Rogasen, Im selbstverlage des herausgebers, 1905.
68p. (Beiträge zur volksunde der Provinz Posen, I)
Microfilm (positive. Literature of folklore, reel 148)

1. Folk-lore--Posen. 2. Posen--Social life and customs. 3. Animals in literature. I. Title.

.5/72

NK 0207515 UU MH

VOLUME 300

W 4 R831 1938 KNOOP, Rolf, 1912-
Die Veränderungen am bleibenden Gebiss nach Überstehen einer Säuglings-rachitis. Rostock, 1938.
20 p.
Inaug.-Diss. - Rostock.
1. Rickets 2. Teeth - Diseases

NK 0207516 DNLM CtY:

Knoop, Rudolf, 1901-
Feinmessungen fuer Druck und Zug an beton-betonbalken mit mikrokomparator.
Inaug. diss. Braunschweig, techn. hochs. 1926.

NK 0207517 ICRL MH DBS

Knoop, Ulrich, 1886-
Der betrieb kleinerer und mittlerer werften.
Inaug. diss. Berlin, tech. hoch. 1926. (1928)

NK 0207518 ICRL PU

325.91 K75p Knoop, W J
Het probleem Nederland-Indonesie; hoe kan de band tusschen Nederland en Indonesië behouden blijven? s'-Gravenhage, N.V. "Adi-Poestaka," 1925.
x, 199p. 25cm.

1. Netherlands--Colonies--Dutch East Indies.

NK 0207519 IU CtY CSt-H WU CLU MH HU NN

KNOOP, WALTER
Die politische Aufgabe der Gegenwart. Leipzig, G. Heinig, 1943.
167,[1]p. 19cm.

1. Germany - Pol. & govt. - 1933-1945.
2. National socialism.

NK 0207520 TxU IaU NcD OCU

Knoop, Walter.
Die politische Aufgabe der Gegenwart. 2. Aufl. Leipzig, "Der Nationale Aufbau" Verlag, 1944.
167 p. 19 cm.

1. Germany—Pol. & govt.—1918-1933. 2. Germany—Pol. & govt.—1933-1945.
DD240.K52 943.085 A F 49-1044 rev*
Harvard Univ. Library for Library of Congress [r50b2]†

NK 0207521 MH LU IEN DLC MnU IU TxU NcD NN CSt

HJ8710 .K7 Knoop, Walter A 1879-
Die verzinsliche russische staatsschuld ... Berlin, F. Ledermann, 1907.
vii, 176 p. tables (part. fold.) 22cm.
Inaug.-diss.—Würzburg.
"Literatur-verzeichnis": p. [vi]-vii.

NK 0207522 ICU CtY IEN DLC MH

Knoop, Walter A 1879-
Die verzinsliche russische staatsschuld, von Walter A. Knoop ... (Mit vier tabellen) Berlin, Dr. F. Ledermann, 1907.
vii, 176 p. 4 tab. (3 fold.) 22cm.
"Literatur-verzeichnis": p. [vi]-vii.

1. Debts, Public—Russia. I. Title.
36-21755
Library of Congress HJ8714.K6 1907 a 336.30947

NK 0207523 DLC

Knoop, Wilhelm.
... Frauen um Michael, novelle. Berlin, W. Limpert [1943]
84 p. illus. 18cm.
"Feldpost-ausgabe."

I. Title.
45-20262
Library of Congress PT2621.N78F7
833.91

NK 0207524 DLC

DJ187 K5 Knoop, Willem Jan, 1811-1894.
Krijgs- en geschiedkundige beschouwingen over Willem den derde. Schiedam, Roelants, 1895.
3v. 21cm.

1. William III, king of Gt. Brit., 1650-1702.
2. Netherlands. History. 1648-1714.

NK 0207526 IaU CLSU MB MiU

DH 113 .K72 1861 Knoop, Willem Jan, 1811-1894.
Krijgs- en geschiedkundige geschriften.
Schiedam, H.A.M.Roelants, 1861-67.
8 v. 19 cm. fold.map (v.6)
Vol.5-6 have also special t.p.: Seelig op de citadel van Antwerpen. (1830-1832); v.7-8 have also special t.p.: Verspreide geschriften.

1.Netherlands--History,Military. 2.Belgium--History,Military.

NK 0207527 MiU MH

Knoops, Carl: Die Umgrenzung des Rücktrittsbegriffes im deutschen Reichsrechte. Borna-Leipzig 1916: Noske. X, 78 S. 8°
Breslau, Jur. Diss. v. 31. Mai 1916, Ref. Leonhard, Schott
[Geb. 8. April 90 Krefeld; Wohnort: Krefeld; Staatsangeh.: Preußen; Vorbildung: RG. Krefeld Reife 08; Studium: Heidelberg 3, Berlin 1, München 1, Bonn 3 S.; Rig. 20. Febr. 14.] [U 16. 189

NK 0207528 ICRL

Knoops, Fr.
Untersuchung ueber leistung und wirkungsgrad elektrischer widerstandsoefen ...(Auszug).
Inaug. diss. Freiburg, 1923

NK 0207529 ICRL

N5298 K648 1922 Knoops-Terhoeven, M
Jade; verzameling M. Knoops-Terhoeven Amsterdam. Catalogus door A.J. Kleykamp [n.p.] 1922.
32 p. 5 plates. 22cm.

Cover title: Jade; collectie Knoops.
Bibliography: p. [19]

NK 0207529-1 MWiCA

Knoote,
Holland; praktischer Reiseführer
see under Grieben, firm, publishers, Berlin.

Knop, Adolf, 1828-1893.
Der Kaiserstuhl im Breisgau, eine naturwissenschaftliche studie, von dr. Adolf Knop ... Mit 8 lichtdruckbildern, 89 figuren im text und einer geologischen karte. Leipzig, W. Engelmann, 1892.
vii, 538 p. 8 col. pl., fold. map, diagrs. 24cm.

1. Geology—Germany.
G S 15-819
Library, U. S. Geological Survey 203(530) K75

NK 0207531 DI-GS

548 K72 Knop, Adolf, 1828-1893.
Molekularconstitution und wachsthum der krystalle. Von dr. Adolf Knop...Leipzig, H.Haessel, 1867.
viii, 2 ℓ., 96 p. illus., diagrs. 22 cm.

NK 0207532 MiU OkU CtY NjP

G552.4 K757 Knop, Adolf, 1828-1893.
Studien über Stoffwandlungen im Mineralreiche besonders in Kalk- und Amphiboloid-Gesteinen. Leipzig, Haessel, 1873.
xii, 144 p. illus. 23cm.
1. Rocks, Crystalline and metamorphic.
I. Title.

NK 0207533 MnU CtY MiHM MA MH

Knop, Adolf, 1828-1893.
System der anorganographie als grundlage für vorträge an hochschulen, von dr. A. Knop ... Mit 120 in den text gedruckten holzschnitten und 2 in lichtdruck ausgeführten tafeln. Leipzig, H. Haessel, 1876.
xxviii, 296 p. II pl., diagrs. 22½cm.

1. Crystallography. I. Title: Anorganographie.

NK 0207534 MiU CtY CU NN

Knop, August.
Ueber das einwirkungsprodukt von phosphorpentasulfid auf anilin.
Inaug. Dis. Freiburg, 1888.

NK 0207535 ICRL

Knop, C J
... Engels, door C. J. Knop ... Amsterdam, J. M. Meulenhoff [1941]
128 p. 19cm. (De Vreemde talen op het mulo-examen)

1. English language—Text-books for foreigners—Dutch.
PE1129.D8K5 A F 47-4535
Newberry library for Library of Congress †

NK 0207536 IEN DLC MH

VOLUME 300

Knop, Friedrich .
Kycm und herz.

Inaugural dissertation, 1928.

NK 0207537 PPWI CtY

Knop, Fritz, 1889-
Die Libri Carolini und die Epistola Hadriani papae de imaginibus als Quellen für das Verhältnis Karls des Grossen zum griechischen Kaiser und römischen Papst auf Grund der augustinischeschatologischen Anschauungen ... Greifswald,H.Adler,1914.
54p.,1l. 24cm.
Inaug.-Diss. - Greifswald.
Lebenslauf.
"Quellen und Literatur": p.[6]-8.

NK 0207538 CtY PU

Knop, Georg, 1911-
... Über Zusammenhänge zwischen Sekundärdentin und Zementapposition ... Freiburg im Breisgau, 1937.
Inaug. diss.-Freiburg im Breisgau.
Lebenslauf.
"Schrifttum" p. 19.

NK 0207539 CtY

Knop, Gerrit.
Brandarisflitsen, een vacantieuitstapje van twee Amsterdammers naar het eiland Ter-Schelling. Leiden, Burgersdijk & Niermans, 1948.
180 p. illus., maps. 21 cm.

1. Terschelling (Island) I. Title.
DJ401.T4K59 49-18416*
Library of Congress

NK 0207540 DLC MH NN OrP

PF1497
.T4K5

Knop, Gerrit.
Fersen yn de Schylger tongslach. Boalsert, A. J. Osinga, 1949.
136 p. port. 21 cm.

A 50-2988
Harvard Univ. Library
for Library of Congress

NK 0207541 MH NN NNC DLC

Knop, Gerrit
Schylge, Schylger tael en Schylger minsken. Rede, ûtspritsen yn de Kanselarije to Ljouwert op 2 Aug., 1932 en fan deselde: De sjongende wein, liêdtsies en gedichten yn de Westerschylger tongslach. Boalsert, Osinga, 1933
64 p. illus.

NK 0207542 MH PU

Knop, Gerrit.
Schylgeralân; een beschrijving van land en volk van het eiland Ter-Schelling, door Gerrit Knop. Leiden, Burgersdijk & Niermans, 1946.
vii, 346 p., 1 l. illus. (incl. plans) plates (1 col.) ports., maps, diagrs. 25cm. (Added t.-p.: Nederlands volksleven, onder redactie van dr P. J. Meertens ... en dr Win. Roukens ... I)
"Literatuurlijst": p. 337-341.

1. Terschelling (Island) I. Title.
DJ401.T4K6 A F 47-1884
Harvard univ. Library
for Library of Congress †

NK 0207543 MH WaU NN CLU ICU DLC OrP

Knop, Gerrit.
Schylgerlaner leisboek. Tekst fan G. Knop, D. F. en C. Roggen. Boekforsiering fan Fr. Lieuwen. Dokkum, J. Kamminga, 1935.
100 p. illus. 29.5 cm.

NK 0207544 PU

Knop, Gerrit.
De spraakkunst der Terschellinger dialecten. Assen, Van Gorcum, 1954.
xxvi, 270 p. port. 25 cm. (Taalkundige bijdragen van Noord en Zuid, 6)
"Bibliographie": p. xxiii-xxvi.

1. Dutch language—Dialects—Terschelling (Island)
A 55-5379
Harvard Univ. Library
for Library of Congress

NK 0207545 MH TU CU CSt NN PU

Knop, Heinrich.
De enuntiatorum apud Isaeum condiccionalium et finalium formis et usu... quam ... scripsit Henricus Knop. Cellis, typis expressit y Grossgebauer, 1892.
35 p. 24.5 cm.
Dissertation (Ph.D.)-1892.

NK 0207546 NcD MH NjP

Knop (Heinrich) [1874-]. *Zur Kasuistik der Noma. [München.] 22 pp. 8°. Erlangen, E. Th. Jakob, 1909.

NK 0207547 DNLM

Knop, Johan August Hermann.
Het verschil in reactiesnelheid bij additie aan cis- en trans-dichlooraetheen in tegenwoordigheid van aluminiumchloride ... Purmerend, 1938.
Academisch proefschrift - Amsterdam.

NK 0207548 CtY

56.4
K75

Knop, Johann August Ludwig Wilhelm, 1817-1891.
Ackererde und Culturpflanze. Leipzig, Haeffer, 1883.
133 p.
1. Soil. 2. Fertilizers.

NK 0207549 DNAL CtY

Knop, Johann August Ludwig Wilhelm, 1817-1891.
Agricultur-chemische versuche ausgeführt auf der versuchs-station zu Möckern.
Landw. vers. stat. bd. 1, p. 3-21. Dresden, 1859.

1. Agricultural chemistry.
Agr 4-2412
Library, U. S. Dept. of Agriculture

NK 0207550 DNAL

Knop, Johann August Ludwig Wilhelm, 1817-1891.
Analysen vom Nilabsatz.
Landw. vers. stat. bd. 17, p. 65-70. Chemnitz, 1874.

1. Nile alluvium.
Agr 4-2413
U. S. Dept. of agr. Library
for Library of Congress [S7.L293 bd. 17]

NK 0207551 DNAL

Knop, Johann August Ludwig Wilhelm, 1817-1891.
Arbeiten aus dem laboratorio der versuchsstation zu Möckern.
Landw. vers. stat. bd. 7, p. 436-450. Chemnitz, 1865.

1. Lichens.
Agr 4-2414
U. S. Dept. of agr. Library
for Library of Congress [S7.L293 bd. 7]

NK 0207552 DNAL

Knop, Johann August Ludwig Wilhelm, 1817-1891.
Arbeiten der versuchsstation Möckern.
Landw. vers. stat. bd. 7, p. 54-62. Chemnitz, 1865.

1. Plant nutrition.
Agr 4-2415
Library, U. S. Dept. of Agriculture

NK 0207553 DNAL

Knop, Johann August Ludwig Wilhelm, 1817-1891.
Beiträge zur kenntniss der ackererden.
Landw. vers. stat. bd. 17, p. 401-408. Chemnitz, 1874.

1. Soil analysis.
Agr 4-2417
Library, U. S. Dept. of Agriculture

NK 0207554 DNAL

Knop, Johann August Ludwig Wilhelm, 1817-1891.
Beitrag zur beantwortung der frage: athmet eine gesunde pflanze ammoniak aus?
Landw. vers. stat. bd. 1, p. 162-164. Dresden, 1859.

1. Ammonia in plants. 2. Plant respiration.
Agr 4-2416
Library, U. S. Dept. of Agriculture

NK 0207555 DNAL

Knop, Johann August Ludwig Wilhelm, 1817-1891.
Bemerkung zu der abhandlung von J. Fittbogen über Phragmites communis.
Landw. vers. stat. bd. 7, p. 434-435. Chemnitz, 1865.

1. Reed.
Agr 4-2419
Library, U. S. Dept. of Agriculture

NK 0207556 DNAL

VOLUME 300

Knop, Johann August Ludwig Wilhelm, 1817–1891.
Bemerkungen zu der abhandlung von Dr. Baumann über ammoniak-bestimmung im boden, band 33, seite 247.
Landw. vers. stat. bd. 33, p. 435–445. Berlin, 1887.

1. Soils, Ammonia in. Agr 4–2418
Library, U. S. Dept. of Agriculture

NK 0207557 DNAL:

Knop, Johann August Ludwig Wilhelm, 1817–1891.
Bereitung einer concentrirten nährstofflösung für pflanzen.
Landw. vers. stat. bd. 30, p. 292–294. Berlin, 1884.

1. Plant food. Agr 4–2420
Library, U. S. Dept. of Agriculture
2 (e)

NK 0207558 DNAL

Knop, Johann August Ludwig Wilhelm, 1817-1891.
Die bonitirung der ackererde. Von dr. W. Knop... Leipzig, H.Haessel, 1871.
2 p.l.,126p. 18cm.

1. Soils - Analysis.

NK 0207559 DP NjR

S593 .K5 Knop, Johann August Ludwig Wilhelm, 1817-1891.
Die Bonitirung der Ackerede. 2. verm. Ausg. Leipzig, Haessel, 1872.
iv, 164 p. tables (1 fold.) 19 cm.

1. Soils--Analysis. I. Title.

NK 0207560 TU

QD1 .C7 Knop, Johann August Ludwig Wilhelm, 1817-1891, ed.
Chemisches Zentralblatt.
Berlin, Akademie-Verlag [etc.]

Knop, Johann August Ludwig Wilhelm, 1817–1891.
Einige analysen von sommerrübsen.
Landw. vers. stat. bd. 1, p. 170–175. Dresden, 1859.

1. Rape. Analysis. Agr 4–2422
Library, U. S. Dept. of Agriculture

NK 0207562 DNAL

Knop, Johann August Ludwig Wilhelm, 1817–1891.
Einige bemerkungen zur analyse der ackererden.
Landw. vers. stat. bd. 31, p. 155–158. Berlin, 1885.

1. Soil analysis. Agr 4–2423
Library, U. S. Dept. of Agriculture

NK 0207563 DNAL

Knop, Johann August Ludwig Wilhelm, 1817–1891.
Einige bestimmungen der quantitäten wasser, welche die pflanzen durch die blätter verdunsten.
Landw. vers. stat. bd. 6, p. 239–260. Chemnitz, 1864.

1. Plant transpiration. Agr 4–2424
Library, U. S. Dept. of Agriculture

NK 0207564 DNAL

Knop, Johann August Ludwig Wilhelm, 1817–1891.
Einige versuche über endosmose vegetirender pflanzenorgane. illus.
Landw. vers. stat. bd. 7, p. 146–153. Chemnitz, 1865.

1. Endosmose. Agr 4–2425
Library, U. S. Dept. of Agriculture

NK 0207565 DNAL

Knop, Johann August Ludwig Wilhelm, 1817-1891.
Grasuntersuchungen
see under Arendt, Rudolf Friedrich Eugen, 1828-1902.

QD K72h 1859 KNOP, Johann August Ludwig Wilhelm, 1817-1891
Handbuch der chemischen Methoden. Leipzig, Voss, 1859.
iv, 506 p.

NK 0207567 DNLM PBL

Knop, Johann August Ludwig Wilhelm, 1817–1891.
Körpermolecule. Nachweisung der thatsache, dass die molecule der neueren chemie durch zusammenlegen von tetraedern und oktaedern atomistisch nachgebildet werden können, von prof. Wilhelm Knop. Leipzig, Commissionsverlag von L. Staackmann, 1876.
1 p. l., ii, 46 p. 24cm.

1. Molecular theory. I. Title.
29–8092
Library of Congress QD461.K5

NK 0207568 DLC

S585 .K7 **Knop, Johann August Ludwig Wilhelm,** 1817–1891.
Der kreislauf des stoffs. Lehrbuch der agricultur-chemie (C) von dr. Wilhelm Knop ... Leipzig, H. Haessel, 1868.
2 v. in 1. illus., diagrs. 21cm.
Bibliographical foot-notes.

1. Agricultural chemistry.

NK 0207569 ICU NNC TU OU ICJ CtW ViU

Knop, Johann August Ludwig Wilhelm, 1817–1891.
Künstlicher boden zu vegetationsversuchen.
Landw. vers. stat. bd. 7, p. 341–344. Chemnitz, 1865.

1. Soils, Artificial. 2. Vegetation experiments. Agr 4–2426
Library, U. S. Dept. of Agriculture

NK 0207570 DNAL

Knop, Johann August Ludwig Wilhelm, 1817–1891.
Methode der chemischen analyse der ackererden.
Landw. vers. stat. bd. 17, p. 70–87. Chemnitz, 1874.

1. Soil analysis. Agr 4–2428
Library, U. S. Dept. of Agriculture

NK 0207571 DNAL

Knop, Johann August Ludwig Wilhelm, 1817–1891.
Mittheilungen über einen fütterungsversuch.
Landw. vers. stat. bd. 1, p. 250–256. Dresden, 1859.

1. Feeding stuffs. Agr 4–2429
Library, U. S. Dept. of Agriculture

NK 0207572 DNAL

Knop, Johann August Ludwig Wilhelm, 1817–1891.
Notiz über die bedeutung der kieselsäure für die gramineen.
Landw. vers. stat. bd. 2, p. 268–269. Dresden, 1860.

1. Silica in cereals. Agr 4—2430
U. S. Dept. of agr. Library for Library of Congress [S7.L293 bd. 2]

NK 0207573 DNAL

Knop, Johann August Ludwig Wilhelm, 1817–1891.
Quantitativ-analytische arbeiten über den ernährungsprocess der pflanzen.
Landw. vers. stat. bd. 3, p. 295–324; bd. 4, p. 173–187; bd. 5, p. 94–109. Dresden, 1861–63.

1. Plant nutrition. Agr 4–2431
Library, U. S. Dept. of Agriculture

NK 0207574 DNAL

Knop, Johann August Ludwig Wilhelm, 1817–1891.
Quantitative untersuchungen über den ernährungsprocess der pflanze.
Landw. vers. stat. bd. 7, p. 93–107. Chemnitz, 1865.

1. Plant nutrition. Agr 4–2432
Library, U. S. Dept. of Agriculture

NK 0207575 DNAL

Knop, [Johann August Ludwig] Wilhelm, 1817–1891.
Ueber das verhalten einiger wasserpflanzen zu gasen ... Leipzig, Druck von J. B. Hirschfeld, 1853.
1 p. l., 63 p. fold. pl. 21cm.
[Botanical pamphlets, v. 17, no. 15]
Habilitationsschrift—Leipzig.

1. Plants, Effect of gases on. 2. Fresh water flora.
5–36608†
Library of Congress QK3.B77

NK 0207576 DLC CtY

VOLUME 300

Knop, Johann August Ludwig Wilhelm, 1817-1891.
Ueber das vorkommen der salpetersäure in wässern, ackererden und das verhalten des ammoniaks und der salpetersauren salze in der ackererde.
Landw. vers. stat. bd. 5, p. 137-160. Dresden, 1863.

1. Soils, Ammonia in. 2. Soils, Nitric acid in. Agr 4-2433
Library, U. S. Dept. of Agriculture

NK 0207577 DNAL

Knop, Johann August Ludwig Wilhelm *and* **Wolf, Wilhelm.**
Ueber das vorkommen und verhalten des ammoniaks in der ackererde.
Landw. vers. stat. bd. 4, p. 67-89. Dresden, 1862.

1. Soils, Ammonia in. Agr 4-2446
Library, U. S. Dept. of Agriculture

NK 0207578 DNAL

Knop, Johann August Ludwig Wilhelm, 1817-1891.
Ueber das zurückgehen des superphosphates.
Landw. vers. stat. bd. 30, p. 287-291. Berlin, 1884.

1. Superphosphates. Reversion. Agr 4-2434
Library, U. S. Dept. of Agriculture

NK 0207579 DNAL

Knop, Johann August Ludwig Wilhelm, 1817-1891.
Ueber den grünsteinboden von Berneck im Fichtelgebirge und berichtigungen zu den analysen der ackerkrume von Dr. Frey.
Landw. vers. stat. bd. 23, p. 191-201. Berlin, 1879.

1. Soil analysis. Agr 4-2435
Library, U. S. Dept. of Agriculture

NK 0207580 DNAL

Knop, Johann August Ludwig Wilhelm, 1817-1891.
Ueber die bedeutung des humus (analyse des Nilschlamms).
Landw. vers. stat. bd. 15, p. 13-21. Chemnitz, 1872

1. Humus. 2. Nile alluvium. Agr 4-2436
Library, U. S. Dept. of Agriculture

NK 0207581 DNAL

Knop, Johann August Ludwig Wilhelm, 1817-1891.
Ueber die ernährung der pflanzen durch wässrige lösungen bei ausschluss des bodens.
Landw. vers. stat. bd. 2, p. 65-99, 270-293. Dresden, 1859-60

1. Plant nutrition. 2. Water culture. Agr 4-2437
Library, U. S. Dept. of Agriculture

NK 0207582 DNAL

Knop, Johann August Ludwig Wilhelm, 1817-1891.
Ueber ein phosphorhaltiges oel der erbsen.
Landw. vers. stat. bd. 1, p. 26-30. Dresden, 1859.

1. Pea, Oil in. Agr 4-2438
Library, U. S. Dept. of Agriculture

NK 0207583 DNAL

Knop, Johann August Ludwig Wilhelm, 1817-1891.
Ueber eine bedingung der fruchtbarkeit der ackererde.
Landw. vers. stat. bd. 5, p. 110-116. Dresden, 1863.

1. Soil fertility. 2. Soil physics. Agr 4-2439
Library, U. S. Dept. of Agriculture

NK 0207584 DNAL

Knop, Johann August Ludwig Wilhelm, 1817-1891.
Ueber einige beziehungen zwischen luft und pflanze.
Landw. vers. stat. bd. 1, p. 147-162. Dresden, 1859.

1. Photosynthesis. 2. Plant nutrition. Agr 4-2440
Library, U. S. Dept. of Agriculture

NK 0207585 DNAL

Knop, Johann August Ludwig Wilhelm *and* **Wolf, Wilhelm.**
Ueber einige vorgänge beim keimen der samen unter normalen und abnormen umständen.
Landw. vers. stat. bd. 4, p. 137-146. Dresden, 1862.

1. Germination. Agr 4-2447
Library, U. S. Dept. of Agriculture

NK 0207586 DNAL

Knop, Johann August Ludwig Wilhelm, 1817-1891.
Ueber ernährungsverhältnisse des zuckerrohrs.
Landw. vers. stat. bd. 30, p. 277-287. Berlin, 1884.

1. Cane sugar. Agr 4-2441
Library, U. S. Dept. of Agriculture

NK 0207587 DNAL

Knop, Johann August Ludwig Wilhelm, 1817-1891.
Ueber regelmässigkeiten in der condensation des wasserdampfes durch poröse körper, insbesondere durch ackererden.
Landw. vers. stat. bd. 6, p. 281-301. Chemnitz, 1864.

1. Soil hygroscopicity. Agr 4-2442
Library, U. S. Dept. of Agriculture

NK 0207588 DNAL

Knop, Johann August Ludwig Wilhelm *and* **Wolf, Wilhelm.**
Ueber wasser- und landwurzeln.
Landw. vers. stat. bd. 7, p. 345-351. Chemnitz, 1865.

1. Roots. Agr 4-2448
Library, U. S. Dept. of Agriculture

NK 0207589 DNAL

Knop, Johann August Ludwig Wilhelm, 1817-1891.
Untersuchung über das vorkommen und verhalten des ammoniaks in der ackererde.
Landw. vers. stat. bd. 3, p. 109-127, 207-236. Dresden, 1861.

1. Soils, Ammonia in. Agr 4-2443
Library, U. S. Dept. of Agriculture

NK 0207590 DNAL

Knop, Johann August Ludwig Wilhelm, 1817-1891.
Untersuchungen über die aufnahme der mineralsalze durch das pflanzengewebe.
Landw. vers. stat. bd. 6, p. 81-107. Chemnitz, 1864.

1. Plant nutrition. Agr 4-2444
Library, U. S. Dept. of Agriculture

NK 0207591 DNAL

Knop, Johann August Ludwig Wilhelm, 1817-1891
Ein vegetationsversuch.
Landw. vers. stat. bd. 1, p. 181-202. Dresden, 1859.

1. Plant nutrition. Agr 4-2421
Library, U. S. Dept. of Agriculture

NK 0207592 DNAL

Knop, Johann August Ludwig Wilhelm, 1817-1891.
Vorschlag zu feldversuchen.
Landw. vers. stat. bd. 6, p. 265-275. Chemnitz, 1864.

1. Agriculture. Experimentation. Agr 4-2445
Library, U. S. Dept. of Agriculture

NK 0207593 DNAL

Szy32 3 E757
Knop, Johannes, 1891-
Bakterien und Bakteroiden bei Oligochaeten... Berlin, 1926.
Inaug.-Diss. - Greifswald.
Lebenslauf.
"Sonderabdruck aus der Zeitschrift für Morphologie und Okologie der Tiere, Bd.6, Heft.3."
"Literaturverzeichnis": p.623-624.

NK 0207594 CtY ICRL

VOLUME 300

Knop, Josef.
...O gravimetrickém poměru mezi antimonem a antimontetroxydem. Observations on gravimetric proportion between antimony and antimony-tetroxyde. Brno: Vysoká škola zemědělská, 1924. 10 p. incl. tables. 8°. (Vysoká škola zemědělská, Brno. Sborník. Sign. C 2.)

Cover-title.
Summary in English, p. 10.
Bibliography, p. 9.

1. Antimony. 2. Ser.
N. Y. P. L. January 11, 1928

NK 0207595 NN OU

386
K75 **Knop, Josef.**
Obecná chemie. Praha, Státní pedagogické nakl.,
(Učební texty vysokých škol)

1. Chemistry. Textbooks. I. Brünn. Vysoká škola zemědělská. Fakulta agronomická.

NK 0207596 DNAL

Knop, Josef.
...Oxydimetrické studie o antimonu. Oxyditric studies on antimony... Brno: Vysoká skola zemědělská, 1924. 22 p. incl. diagrs. tables. 8°. (Vysoká škola zemědělská, Brno. Sbornik. Sign. C 1.)

Cover-title.
Summary in English, p. 22.
Bibliography, p. 20–21.

1. Antimony. 2. Ser.
N. Y. P. L. January 10, 1928

NK 0207597 NN OU

Knop, Josef.
Příručka anorganické analytické chemie kvalitativní. [Vyd. 1.] Praha, Státní pedagogické nakl., 1953.
129 p. illus. 29 cm. (Učební texty vysokých škol)
At head of title: Vysoká škola zemědělská v Brně. Fakulta agronomická.
Includes bibliography.

1. Chemistry, Analytic—Qualitative. 2. Chemistry, Inorganic. I. Title.
QD81.K5 59–17959 ‡

NK 0207598 DLC

Knop, Josef.
Spektrální analysa a její použití. [Vyd. 1.] Praha, Nákl. Československé společnosti chemické; v komisi L. Součka, 1949.
71 p. illus. 25 cm. (Chemická technologie, sv. 6: Technické rozbory, díl 1., kapitola 3)
Includes bibliographies.
With, as issued, Šandera, Karel. Konduktometrie. Praha, 1949. Hála, Miloš. Drahé kovy. Praha, 1949, and Fanderlik, M. Rozbory sklářské. Praha, 1949.

1. Spectrum analysis. I. Title. (Series)
QD95.K75 53–37155

NK 0207599 DLC

Knop (Joseph Adalbert) *De inflammatione ex typho carbunculoso animalium contagiosa. 63 pp. 8°. *Olsnæ, J. C. S. Ludwig*, [1831].

NK 0207600 DNLM

Knop, Joseph Adalbert
Die paradoxie des willens; oder, Das freiwillige handeln bei innerem widerstreben vom standpunkte der forensischmedicinischen Praxis. Lpz., Pernitzsch, 1863.
96 p.

NK 0207601 PU

Knop, Leo, 1885-
Friedrich Bouterwek als dramatiker und romanschriftsteller ... Von Leo Knop. Leipzig, A. Hoffmann, 1912.
128 p. 23^{cm}.
Inaug.-diss.—Griefswald.
Lebenslauf.
"Quellen und literatur": p.6-9.

1. Bouterwek, Friedrich, 1766-1828.
[Full name: Leo Hermann Albert Knop]

NK 0207602 MiU NjP PU MH IU NNU DLC CtY ICRL

Knop, Lydia (Kath)
see **Kath, Lydia, 1906–**

Knop, Martin, 1903-
Fortbildung des seeverkehrsrechtes nach dem weltkriege. ... Berlin, 1935. 86 p.
Inaug. Diss. - Halle-Wittenberg, 1935.
Lebenslauf.
Verzeichnis der benutzten schriften.

NK 0207604 ICRL NN CtY MH

Knop, Martin, 1903–
... Landratten im seewind. 3. und 4. aufl., 9.–18. tausend. Dülmen i. Westf., A. Laumman [1941]
3 p. l., 9–173 p. plates. 21^{cm}.

1. Voyages and travels. 2. Merchant marine—Germany. 3. Ships. I. Title.
Library of Congress G540.K58 1941 41-20322
910.4

NK 0207605 DLC NNA

Knop, Victor de.
Essai de traitement de la fièvre typhoïde par un complexe colloïde-antigène microbien. Docteur Victor de Knop. Liége, Impr. E. Corombelle, 1923.
33 p. illus. (incl. diagrs.) $23\frac{1}{2}^{cm}$.
"Index bibliographique": p. 33.

1. Typhoid fever.
Agr 25-217
Library, U. S. Dept. of Agriculture 448K752

NK 0207606 DNAL

MC
631 Knop, Werner
Der kostenerstattungsanspruch. ... Düsseldorf, 1936. 63 p.
Inaug. Diss. - Erlangen, 1936.
Literatur.

NK 0207607 ICRL

Knop, Werner Gustav John, 1911–
For works written in collaboration with Peter Ferdinand Drucker, under the name Germanicus
see
Germanicus, *pseud.*

Knop, Werner Gustav John, 1911– *comp.*
Beware of the English! German propaganda exposes England; with a foreword by Stephen King-Hall. London, H. Hamilton [1939]
xviii, 304 p. illus. 23 cm.
Articles and illustrations pub. in representative German newspapers during the past nine months.

1. Propaganda, German. 2. Caricatures and cartoons—Germany. 3. Germany—For. rel.—Gt. Brit. 4. Gt. Brit.—For. rel.—Germany. I. Title.
DD119.5.K55 1939a 940.5488743 41-5380 rev*

NK 0207609 DLC CtY ICN NN NcD NIC DAU GU CaBVaU

Knop, Werner Gustav John, 1911– joint comp.
DD253
.S74
Strachey, Celia, *comp.*
Fascist Germany explains, by Celia Strachey and John Gustav Werner [pseud.] New York, Covici, Friede [1934]

DD253 Knop, Werner Gustav John, 1911-
A1F97 ...Germany's economic situation in 1939 and
v.71 her challenge to the world, by W.G.J. Knop. With a foreword by Captain Oliver Lyttelton... London, Friends of Europe [1939]
cover-title, 32 p. $21\frac{1}{2}^{cm}$. ("Friends of Europe" publications, no.71)

1. Germany - Economic policy. 2. Germany - Econ. condit. 1933- I. Title.

NK 0207611 CSt ViU

Knop, Werner Gustav John, 1911–
Prowling Russia's forbidden zone; a secret journey into Soviet Germany. [1st ed.] New York, A. A. Knopf, 1949.
viii, 200, iv p. map. 20 cm.
Appeared serially in part in the Saturday evening post.

1. Germany—Pol. & govt.—1945– 2. Germany (Territory under Allied occupation, 1945– Russian Zone) I. Title.
DD257.4.K6 1949 943.086 49-8731*
Library of Congress

NK 0207612 DLC ViU ICU DS MB WaU OU PP CaOTP OrP CaBVaU Or OrU WaE WaS WaT

Knop, Wilhelm, 1817-1891
see
Knop, Johann August Ludwig Wilhelm, 1817-1891

Knop, Wilhelm, 1905-
Untersuchungen über aktive aschefreie zuckerkohle ...62 p.
Inaug. Diss. -Berlin, [1933]
Lebenslauf.
Bibliography.

NK 0207614 ICRL CtY

VOLUME 300

Knop, Willy Julius Erich, ed.
Das Wohnungswesen der freien Hansestadt Bremen
see under Bremen.

W 4 C53 1951
KNOPEL LEUSCHNER, Federico
La reacción de Pagniez y el antígeno cardiolipina en el serodiagnóstico de la sífilis. [Santiago, 1951?]
18 p. illus. (Chile. Universidad, Santiago. Facultad de Biología y Ciencias Médicas. Tesis de licenciatura, 1951/52, I, no. 55)
1. Syphilis - Diagnosis

NK 0207616 DNLM

Knopf, Aaron A
Secrets of taking good pictures. [1st ed.] Garden City, N. Y., Hanover House [1955]
144 p. illus. 22 cm.

1. Photography—Handbooks, manuals, etc. I. Title.

TR146.K56 770.2 55—6487 ‡

NK 0207617 NcD Or Wa WaS WaT CaBVa CaBViP IdB WaSp DLC MB TxU PP NN NcC ViU PWcT OU OCl

Knopf, Adolph, 1882–
The age of the earth and the age of the ocean, by Adolph Knopf ...
(In Smithsonian institution. Annual report, 1932. Washington, 1933. 23cm. p. 193–206)
"Reprinted ... from Bulletin of the National research council, no. 80, June, 1931."
"References": p. 205–206.

1. Earth—Age. 2. Ocean. I. Title.

Library of Congress Q11.S66 1932 34-4390

NK 0207618 DLC OCl OClMN ODW OU WaS

Knopf, Adolph, 1882–
... An alteration of Coast Range serpentine. By A. Knopf. [Berkeley, The University press, 1906]
p. [425]–430. 27cm. (University of California publications. Bulletin of the Department of geology. vol. 4, no. 18)
Issued in single cover with vol. 4, no. 17 of the series.

1. Serpentine. 2. Petrology—California.

A 12-553

Title from Univ. of Calif. Library of Congress

NK 0207619 MtBuM CU MoU MiU OU OCl OO PPAmP MU NN OrU

Knopf, Adolph, 1882–
The antimonial silver-lead veins of the Arabia district, Nevada, by Adolph Knopf... Washington: Gov. Prtg. Off., 1918. iii, 249–255 p. 8°. (United States. Geological Survey. Bull. no. 660-H.)
At head of title: Department of the Interior...
Contributions to economic geology. 1917, part I.

1. Antimony, U. S.: Nev. 2. Silver, U. S.: Nev. 3. Lead, U. S.: Nev. 4. Series.
N. Y. P. L. March 28, 1918.

NK 0207620 NN PPAN

Knopf, Adolph, 1882– comp.
Bibliography of isostasy, comp. by Adolph Knopf. Issued in mimeographed form by the Division of geology and geography, National research council. Washington, D. C., 1924.
2 p. l., 39 numb. l. 28cm.
465 titles.
Based on the bibliography compiled by William Bowie published in his "Investigations of gravity and isostasy" in 1917 (U. S. Coast and geodetic survey, Special publication, no. 40)

1. Isostasy—Bibl. I. National research council. Division of geology and geography. II. Title.

27—3707

Library of Congress Z6033.I 8K7

NK 0207621 DLC CtY IU NN DNO OCl OCU PPAmP GU

Knopf, Adolph, 1882–
... Biographical memoir of Edward Salisbury Dana, 1849–1935, by Adolph Knopf. Presented to the academy at the autumn meeting, 1937.
(In National academy of sciences, Washington, D. C. Biographical memoirs. City of Washington, 1938. 23cm. vol. XVIII, 15th memoir, 1 p. l., p. 349–365. front. (port.))
Issued also separately.
"Bibliography of Edward S. Dana": p. 359–365.

1. Dana, Edward Salisbury, 1849–1935.

40–11682

Library of Congress Q141.N2 vol. 18, 15th memoir
(925) 925.49

NK 0207622 DLC

.N2 vol. 27, 15th memoir
Knopf, Adolph, 1882–
Charles Schuchert, 1858–1942.
(In National Academy of Sciences, Washington, D. C. Biographical memoirs. Washington. 23 cm. v. 27 (1952) [15th memoir] p. 363–389. port.)
Bibliography of Charles Schuchert, prepared by Carl Owen Dunbar: p. 377–389.

1. Schuchert, Charles, 1858–1942. (Series: National Academy of Sciences, Washington, D. C. Biographical memoirs, v. 27, 15th memoir)

Q141.N2 vol. 27, 15th memoir 925.6 55–2852

NK 0207623 DLC CtY-M

Knopf, Adolph, 1882 –
The Darwin Silver-Lead mining district, California. Washington: Gov. Prtg. Off., 1914. ii, 18 p. 8°. (United States. Geological Survey. Bull. 580 — A.)
Contributions to economic geology, 1913, part 1 — A.

1. Silver.—Mines, etc., U. S.: Cal. 2. Lead.—Mines, etc., U. S.: Cal. 3. Geology, U. S.: Cal.
N. Y. P. L. May 9, 1916.

NK 0207624 NN MdBJ MB

Knopf, Adolph, 1882– *7872.55.715
The Divide silver district, Nevada.
(In United States. Geological Survey. Bulletin. 715. Contributions to economic geology. 1920, part I. Pp. 147–170. Map. Geological section. Washington. 1921.)

M4270 — Divide district, Nev. — S... Mining, etc. — Nevada. Mines and mining.

NK 0207625 MB

Knopf, Adolph, 1882–
... The Eagle river region, southeastern Alaska, by Adolph Knopf. Washington, Govt. print. off., 1912.
61 p. 2 pl., 3 fold. maps (2 in pocket) diagrs. 23½cm. (U. S. Geological survey. Bulletin 502)

1. Geology—Alaska. I. Title.

G S 13—251

U. S. Geol. survey. Library for Library of Congress (200) E no. 502 QE75.B9 no. 502
[a40b1]

NK 0207626 MiU ODW OCl OO ICJ NN MB PPAmP DLC PPAN DI-GS CaBViP WaWW WaS NBuU CU-B DNW OU

Knopf, Adolph, 1882– joint author.
Paige, Sidney, 1880–
... Geologic reconnaissance in the Matanuska and Talkeetna basins, Alaska, by Sidney Paige and Adolph Knopf. Washington, Govt. print. off., 1907.

Knopf, Adolph, 1882–
... A geologic reconnaissance of the Inyo range, and the eastern slope of the southern Sierra Nevada, California, by Adolph Knopf, with a section of the stratigraphy of the Inyo Range, by Edwin Kirk. Washington, Govt. print. off., 1918.
130 p. XXIII pl. (part fold., incl. 2 maps (in pocket)) diagrs. 29 cm. (U. S. Geological survey. Professional paper 110)
At head of title: Department of the interior.
Many plates printed on both sides of leaf.
Bibliography: p. 15–16.
1. Geology—California—Sierra Nevada mountains. I. Kirk, Edwin, 1884–

QE75.P9 no. 110 G S 19—33
——— Copy 2. QE89.K7
U. S. Geol. Survey. Libr. for Library of Congress [66m½]†

NK 0207628 CU WaWW OrU OrCS CaBVaU DI-GS DLC ICJ MB OCl OO OU ODW MiU PPAmP

LD3915 .J4T6 3d ser.
Knopf, Adolph, 1882-
The geologic records of time.
(In New York university. James Arthur foundation. Time and its mysteries. 1949. ser.III, p.[31]-59)
Lecture given April 16,1941.

NK 0207629 NNU-W

Knopf, Adolph, 1882- joint author.
Westgate, Lewis Gardner, 1868–
... Geology and ore deposits of the Pioche district, Nevada, by Lewis G. Westgate and Adolph Knopf. Washington, U. S. Govt. print. off., 1932.

Knopf, Adolf, 1882–
... Geology and ore deposits of the Rochester district, Nevada, by Adolph Knopf. Washington, Govt. print. off., 1924.
ix, 78 p. illus., IV pl. (incl. 2 fold. maps) 23cm. (U. S. Geological survey. Bulletin 762)
At head of title: Department of the interior.
Bibliographical references.

1. Ore-deposits—Nevada. 2. Geology—Nevada. I. Title.
QE75.B9 no. 762 G S 24-349
——— Copy 2. TN24.N3K55
U. S. Geol. survey. Library for Library of Congress [a40m1]†

NK 0207631 DNW DI-GS ViU CU OU OO OCl ODW ICJ DLC PP

Knopf, Adolph, 1882–
... Geology and ore deposits of the Yerington district, Nevada, by Adolph Knopf. Washington, Govt. print. off., 1918.
68 p. illus., V pl. (part fold., part col., incl. map (in pocket) profile) diagrs. 29cm. (U. S. Geological survey. Professional paper 114)
At head of title: Department of the interior.

1. Geology—Nevada. 2. Ore-deposits—Nevada.
G S 19—31
U. S. Geol. survey. Library for Library of Congress (200) B no. 114 QE75.P9 no. 114
TN443.N3K6

NK 0207632 ODW OO PP DLC ICJ MB PPAN DI-GS CaBVaU WaWW OrU OrCS MiU OU OCl

VOLUME 300

Knopf, Adolph, 1882–
... Geology of the Berners Bay region, Alaska, by Adolph Knopf. Washington, Govt. print. off., 1911.
58 p. illus., II fold. maps (in pocket) diagrs. 23½cm. (U. S. Geological survey. Bulletin 446)
"Recent survey publications on Alaska": p. 49–55.
Issued also as House doc. no. 1053, 61st Cong., 3d sess.

1. Geology—Alaska.

G S 11-55

Library, U. S. Geol. survey (200) E no. 446

OU OCl OO ICJ MB NN PPAN
NK 0207633 DI-GS WaWW WaS CaBViP NBuU NjP MiU ODW

Knopf, Adolph, 1882 –
... Geology of the Seward Peninsula tin deposits, Alaska, by Adolph Knopf. Washington, Govt. print. off., 1908.
71 p. illus., IX pl. (incl. fold. map) diagrs. 23½cm. (U. S. Geological survey. Bulletin 358)
Issued also as House doc. no. 1033, 60th Cong., 2d sess.

1. Tin ores—Alaska.

G S 9-6

Library, U. S. Geol. survey (200) E no. 358

OCl ICJ NN PPL PBa
NK 0207634 DI-GS WaSp WaWW WaS NBuU MiU OU ODW OO

Knopf, Adolph, 1882–
A gold-platinum-palladium lode in southern Nevada. Washington: Gov. Prtg. Off., 1915. 1 p.l., 18 p., 1 map. 8°. (United States. Geological Survey. Bull. 620 — A.)

1. Gold, U. S.: Nev. 2. Platinum, U. S.: Nev. 3. Palladium, U. S.: Nev.
N. Y. P. L. July 27, 1916.

NK 0207635 NN MB DLC

HD7264 .U6 1928

Knopf, Adolph, 1882–

U. S. *Public health service.*
... The health of workers in dusty trades ... Prepared by direction of the surgeon general. Washington, U. S. Govt. print. off., 1928–41.

---

memoir

Knopf, Adolph, 1882–
Louis Valentine Pirsson, November 3, 1860–December 8, 1919.
(*In* National Academy of Sciences, Washington, D. C. Biographical memoirs. New York. 24 cm. v. 34 (1960) ⌊10th memoir⌋ p. ⌊228⌋–248. port.)
Bibliography: p. 244–248.

1. Pirsson, Louis Valentine, 1860–1919. (Series: National Academy of Sciences, Washington, D. C. Biographical memoirs, v. 34, 10th memoir)

Q141.N2 vol. 34, 10th memoir 61–152

NK 0207637 DLC

QE75 .B9 no. 417

Knopf, Adolph, 1882–

Moffit, Fred Howard, 1874–
... Mineral resources of the Nabesna-White river district, Alaska, by F. H. Moffit and Adolph Knopf, with a section on the Quaternary, by S. R. Capps. Washington, Govt. print. off., 1910.

Knopf, Adolph, 1882–
... The Mother lode system of California, by Adolph Knopf. Prepared in cooperation with the California State mining bureau. Washington, U. S. Govt. print. off., 1929.
viii, 88 p. incl. illus., tables, diagrs. 12 pl. (part fold., incl. maps (1 col.)) 29cm. (U. S. Geological survey. Professional paper 157)
At head of title: Department of the interior.
Map folded in pocket.

1. Ore deposits. 2. Gold mines and mining—California. I. California. State mining bureau. II. Title.

G S 29-83

U. S. Geol. survey. Library for Library of Congress (200) qB no. 157
QE75.P9 no. 157
TN423.C2K6

OrU OrCS WaWW CaBVaU
NK 0207639 DI-GS DLC OO ODW OCl OU MiU PU PPAN MB

Knopf, Adolph, 1882–
... Notes on the foothill copper belt of the Sierra Nevada. By A. Knopf. ⌊Berkeley, The University press, 1906⌋
p. ⌊411⌋–423. 27cm. (University of California publications. Bulletin of the Department of geology. vol. 4, no. 17)
Issued in single cover with vol. 4, no. 18 of the series.

1. Copper mines and mining—California.

A 12-554

Title from Univ. of Calif. Library of Congress

MtBuM
NK 0207640 CU MU MoU PPAmP MiU OU OCl OO NN OrU

Knopf, Adolph, *1882*– *7872.55-725
Ore deposits of Cedar Mountain, Mineral County, Nevada. (*In* United States. Geological Survey. Bulletin no. 725. Contributions to economic geology, 1921, part I. Pp. 361–382. Map. Geologic sections. Washington. 1922.)

N811 — Ores. Deposits. — Nevada. Mines and mining. — Cedar Mountain, Nev. Mines and mining. — Mineral County, Nev. Mines and mining.

NK 0207641 MB

Knopf, Adolph, 1882–
... Ore deposits of the Helena mining region, Montana, by Adolph Knopf. Washington, Govt. print. off., 1913.
143 p. illus., plates, fold. maps, diagrs. 23cm. (U. S. Geological survey. Bulletin no. 527)
Some of the plates printed on both sides of leaf.
"Literature": p. 18–19.

1. Mines and mineral resources—Montana. 2. Geology—Montana.

G S 13-376

Library, U. S. Geol. survey (200) E no. 527

OCl OO ICJ NN MB
NK 0207642 DI-GS WaSp WaS WaWW NBuU PPAN OU MiU ODW

QE26 .T42 1944

Knopf, Adolph, 1882– joint author.
FOR OTHER EDITIONS SEE MAIN ENTRY

Longwell, Chester Ray, 1887–
... Outlines of physical geology, by Chester R. Longwell ... Adolph Knopf ... and Richard F. Flint ... ⌊Madison, Wis.⌋ Pub. for the United States Armed forces institute by J. Wiley & sons, inc. ⌊1944⌋

QE501 .L65

Knopf, Adolph, 1882– joint author.

Longwell, Chester Ray, 1887–
Physical geology, by Chester R. Longwell, Adolph Knopf ⌊and⌋ Richard F. Flint. 3d ed. New York, J. Wiley ⌊1948⌋

Knopf, Adolph, 1882–
... The probable Tertiary land connection between Asia and North America. By Adolph Knopf. Berkeley, The University press, 1910.
cover-title, ⌊413⌋–420 p. 27cm. (University of California publications. Bulletin of the Department of geology, vol. 5, no. 28)
Bibliographical foot-notes.

1. Geology—Alaska—Seward peninsula.

QE1.C15 vol. 5, no. 28 A 10-640
——— Copy 2. QE83.K6

California. Univ. Libr. for Library of Congress ⌊a47b1⌋†

MtBuM OrU CaBVaU
NK 0207645 CU DLC NN OU OO OCl MiU PPAmP MoU MU

Knopf, Adolph, 1882–
... The quantitative determination of quartz ("free silica") in dusts, by Adolph Knopf, professor of physical geology, Yale university, and consultant, United States Public health service ... Washington, U. S. Govt. print. off., 1933.
1 p. l., 8 p. incl. tab. 23cm.
Reprint no. 1560 from the Public health reports, v. 48, no. 8, February 24, 1933 (p. 183–190)
Running title: Determination of quartz in dusts.

1. Dust. 2. Quartz. 3. Silica. I. U. S. Public health service. Public health reports. Reprint 1560. II. Title. III. Title: Determination of quartz in dusts.

33-26296

Library of Congress HD7264.K6
——— Copy 2. 614.71

NK 0207646 DLC MiU CaBVaU

TN24 .C6K6

Knopf, Adolph, 1882 –
... Recent developments in the Aspen district, Colorado.
Wash., 1926.
1 pam. 8°

NK 0207647 DLC PPAN

QE431 .P68 1947

Knopf, Adolph, 1882–
FOR OTHER EDITIONS SEE MAIN ENTRY

Pirsson, Louis Valentine, 1860–1919.
Rocks and rock minerals. 3d ed., rev. by Adolph Knopf. New York, J. Wiley ⌊1947⌋

Knopf, Adolph, 1882–
... The Sitka mining district, Alaska, by Adolph Knopf. Washington, Govt. print. off., 1912.
32 p. illus., fold. map. 23 cm. (U. S. Geological survey. Bulletin 504)

1. Mines and mineral resources—Alaska. 2. Geology, Economic—Alaska. I. Title.

QE75.B9 no. 504 G S 12-77
——— Copy 2. TN24.A4K5

U. S. Geol. Survey. Libr. for Library of Congress ⌊a57c⌋†

ODW ICJ DLC MB PPAmP PPAN NBuU DLC
NK 0207649 DI-GS CaBViPA WaWW WaS OCl OO MiU OU

Knopf, Adolph, 1882–
... Sketch of the geology of Mineral King, California, by A. Knopf and P. Thelen. Berkeley, The University press, 1905.
cover-title, p. ⌊227⌋–262. pl. 28–30 (incl. map) 27cm. (University of California publications. Bulletin of the Department of geology. vol. 4, no. 12)

1. Geology—California. 2. Sierra Nevada Mountains. I. Thelen, Paul, 1881– joint author.

A 12-555

Title from Univ. of Calif. Library of Congress

PPGeog
NK 0207650 CU OrU MtBuM MU MoU MiU OU OCl OO NN

Knopf, Adolph, 1882– *7842.55.620
Some cinnabar deposits in western Nevada.
(In United States. Geological Survey. Bulletin 620. Contributions to economic geology, 1915, part I. Pp. 59–68. Washington. 1916.)

L7642 — Cinnabar. — Nevada. Mines and mining.

NK 0207651 MB

F847 E8K5

Knopf, Adolph, 1882–
Some cinnabar deposits in western Nevada. Washington, Govt. Print. Off., 1915.
ii, 59–68 p. 23cm. (U.S. Geological survey. Bulletin 620-D)

Reprinted from Contributions to economic geology, 1915, part I.

NK 0207652 CU-B NN MdBJ PPAN

VOLUME 300

TN 23 .K72 Knopf, Adolph, 1882-
Strategic mineral supplies, by Adolph Knopf ... [n.p., 1946]
cover-title, 5-14 p. diagrs. 25cm.
"From an address before the Yale chapter of Sigma xi, April, 1945."--Foot-note, p.5.
"Reprinted from the Scientific monthly, January, 1946, vol. LXII."

1. Mines and mineral resources--U.S. I. Title.

NK 0207653 MiU

Knopf, Adolph, 1882-
Strontianite deposits near Barstow, California, by Adolph Knopf... Washington: Gov. Prtg. Off., 1918. ii, 257-270 p., 1 fold. map. 8°. (United States. Geological Survey. Bull. no. 660-I.)

Contributions to economic geology, 1917, part 1.

1. Strontium, U. S.: Cal.: Barstow. 2. Series.
N. Y. P. L. September 16, 1918.

NK 0207654 NN PPAN

QE26 .T412 Knopf, Adolph, 1882- FOR OTHER EDITIONS SEE MAIN ENTRY
A **Textbook** of geology ... 2d (rev.) ed. New York, J. Wiley & sons, inc.; London, Chapman & Hall, limited, 1939-41.

Knopf, Adolph, 1882- *7842.55.640
Tin ore in northern Lander County, Nevada.
(In United States. Geological Survey. Bulletin 640. Contributions to economic geology, 1916, part 1. Pp. 125-138. Map. Washington. 1917.)

L7642 — Tin. — Nevada. Mines and mining.

NK 0207656 MB PP

F868 I6K65 Knopf, Adolph, 1882-
Tungsten deposits of northwestern Inyo County, California. Washington, Govt. Print. Off., 1917.
ii, 229-249, viii, 251-255 p. diagrs., maps. 23cm. (U.S. Geological Survey. Bulletin 640-L)

Reprinted from Contributions to economic geology, 1916, part 1.

NK 0207657 CU-B NN MB PPAN

Knopf, Albert A 1908-
... Eingriffe an der Vorsteherdrüsenvergrösserung von der Harnröhre aus einst und jetzt ... Berlin, n.d.
Inaug. diss.-Berlin.
Lebenslauf.
"Literatur" p. [13]-15.

NK 0207658 CtY

Knopf, Alfred, 1890-
Jules Lemaitre als dramatiker.
Inaug. diss. Leipzig, 1926.
Bibl.

NK 0207659 ICRL CU CtY

Knopf, Alfred, 1890-
Jules Lemaitre als Dramatiker, von Dr. Alfred Knopf. Leipzig[: R. Pries], 1926. 133 p. 8°.

Bibliography, p. 131-133.

340136A. 1. Lemaître, Jules, 1833-1914.
N. Y. P. L. March 30, 1928

NK 0207660 NN PU IEN OC1W IU MH

Knopf, Alfred, 1890-
Wickersdorf einst und jetzt. Jena, Neuenhahn, 1938
136 p. illus.

NK 0207661 MH

Collection S913k Knopf, Alfred A 1892-
Joseph Conrad, the romance of his life and of his books, by Alfred A. Knopf. [Garden City, New York, Doubleday, Page & co., 1913]
24p. incl. plate, ports., facsim. 18½cm. In case 23cm.
Portrait of Conrad on verso of cover.
"Joseph Conrad, a pen portrait, by James Huneker": p.[1]; "Bibliography": p.19-23.

NK 0207662 CtY PPF NN LU

Knopf, Alfred A 1892-
On making a few books.
(*In* The New colophon. New York. 28 cm. v. 2, pt. 6 (1949) p. 120-134)

1. Publishers and publishing.
[Z1007.C72 vol. 2, pt. 6] A 52-4112

Grosvenor Library for Library of Congress

NK 0207663 NBuG

Knopf, Alfred A 1892-
Some random recollections; an informal talk made at the Grolier Club, New York, 21 October 1948. New York, The Typophiles, 1949.
41 p. illus. 19 cm. (Typophile chapbook, 22)
"An abridgment of the text appeared in the New colophon, part VI, under the title 'On making a few books.'"

I. Title. (Series: The Typophiles, New York. Typophile chap books, 22)
Z473.K72A3 655.473 50-4175

CaBVaU NcU MB PSC
NK 0207664 DLC NNC MH OC1 OU MeB MoU MiU CSt KyU

---

* PS3543 .A653T319 1924 Knopf, Alfred A , 1892-
The tattooed countess, by Carl Van Vechten. [review]
(In Alfred A. Knopf presents the new Borzoi books. New York. 18½cm. (Fall, 1924) Rev. ed. p. 22, illus.)

1. Van Vechten, Carl, 1880-1964. The tattooed countess. I. Alfred A. Knopf presents the New Borzoi books.

NK 0207665 ViU

---

*BROADSIDE 1940 .K667 Knopf, (Alfred A.) inc., New York.
Alfred A. Knopf has the honor to announce the forthcoming publication of one of the great biographies of our generation, Shelley, by Newman Ivey White. [New York, 1940]
broadside ([8] p.) illus., ports. (1 col.) facsim. 24cm.

1. White, Newman Ivey, 1892- . Shelley. 2. Shelley, Percy Bysshe, 1792-1822.

NK 0207666 ViU

Knopf, (Alfred A.) inc., New York.
Angela Thirkell; an autobiographic sketch, some American appreciations, a selection of poetry written to announce the publication of some of Mrs. Thirkell's books an abridged bibliography. [New York] A. A. Knopf [1952] 8 l. port. 17cm.

"All of the poetry was written by Frances Lindley."

1. Thirkell, Angela (Mackail), 1890- I. Lindley, Frances.

NK 0207667 NN

Knopf (Alfred A.) inc., *New York.*
The Borzoi 1920; being a sort of record of five years' publishing. New York, 1920.
xiv, 143 p. illus., facsim., ports. 19 cm.
"A bibliography of all Borzoi books published from 25 September, 1915 to 25 September, 1920": p. [103]-131.

I. Title.
Z473.K72 21-335 rev

CLSU
OrU NIC NcU TxU NBuU MiU PP OC1 OU NjP ICJ NcD LU
NK 0207668 DLC ViU MiD OC1WHi MB NN IaU MiU-C TxU

Knopf (Alfred A.) inc., *New York.*
The Borzoi 1925; being a sort of record of ten years of publishing. New York [1925]
xii, 351 p. ports. (1 col.) 20 cm.
"A bibliography of all Borzoi books published from the beginning to June 30th, 1925": p. 271-351.

I. Title.
Z473.K72 1925 26-539 rev

NbU GU WHi MoSW PSt WaSpG OrP KU OrU MB CaBVaU
ViU OC1RC OC1 MiU OEac OC1W OO PV NcU OU TxU CoU LU
NK 0207669 DLC ScU OKentU NcD NN CSmH NjP NcD PSC

Knopf (Alfred A) inc., New York.
Clarence Day
see under title

Knopf, (Alfred A.) inc, New York. 4559-453
Francis Brett Young.
= New York. [1928.] 11, (1) pp. Portrait. Map. Facsimile. 15.5 cm.
Contains a bibliography of Young's works.

D4682 — Young, Francis Brett, 1884-

NK 0207671 MB

Knopf, (Alfred A.) inc., New York.
H. L. Mencken. New York, 1920.
32 p. illus., ports. 19 cm.
Contents.--Fanfare, by Burton Rascoe.--The American critic, by Vincent O'Sullivan.--Bibliography, by F. C. Henderson.
1. Mencken, Henry Louis, 1880-
2. Mencken, Henry Louis, 1880- - Bibl.

NK 0207672 MdBP IU

VOLUME 300

Knopf, (Alfred A.) inc., New York.
The history of a book which is making history; with notes on its author... New York: A. A. Knopf[, 1927]. 16 p. illus. (ports.) 16°.

Brief sketch of Oswald Spengler, with a comment on his work: The decline of the West.

571577A. 1. Spengler, Oswald, 1880- : Der Untergang des Abendlandes. I. Title.
N. Y. P. L. February 24, 1932

NK 0207673 NN MB

---

*BROAD-SIDE 1955 .K66 **Knopf, (Alfred A.) inc., New York.**
Introducing ... a great writer, from one of the world's rich but hitherto almost unknown literatures. [n. p., 1955]
broadside (6 l.) 28 x 22cm.
Reproduced from type-written copy.

1. Tanizaki, Jun'ichirō, 1886-

NK 0207674 ViU

CT99 .H2325K7 **Knopf, (Alfred A.) inc., New York.**
Knut Hamsun. [New York, A. A. Knopf, 1928]
[4] p. illus. (port.) 21cm.

Caption title.
"Authorized translations of works by Knut Hamsun": p. [4]

1. Hamsun, Knut, 1859-

NK 0207675 DLC

Knopf, (Alfred A.) inc., New York.
Menckeniana; a Schimpflexikon
see under title

Knopf, (Alfred A.), inc., New York.
Notes for The ivory tower
see under James, Henry, 1843-1916.

Knopf (Alfred A.) inc., *New York.*
Sigrid Undset ... [a critical appreciation, with some account of her life. New York, Knopf, 1932]
15 p. illus., ports. 20 cm.
Cover title.

1. Undset, Sigrid, 1882-1949.

PT8950.U5Z7 66-43258

NK 0207678 DLC WaPS OO

Knopf (Alfred A.) inc., New York.
Thomas Mann, Nobel prize winner of 1929. A critical estimate
see under title

Knopf (Alfred A.) inc., New York.
Tromboners, or musical anecdotage
see under title

Knopf (Alfred A.) inc., New York.
Willa Cather; a biographical sketch, an English opinion, an American opinion, reviews and articles, and an abridged bibliography. New York [n.d.]
31 p. port. 19cm.

1. Cather, Willa Sibert, 1875-1947. I. Title.

NK 0207681 NN

Knopf (Alfred A.) inc., *New York.*
Willa Cather; a biographical sketch, an English opinion and an abridged bibliography. New York [1927]
16 p. port. 20 cm.
Cover-title.
"An English opinion ... by Alexander Porterfield": p. 4-14.

1. Cather, Willa Sibert, 1873-1947. 2. Cather, Willa Sibert, 1873-1947—Bibl. I. Title.

Z8155.65.K72 27-12839 rev

NK 0207682 DLC ViU PPD MB PBm PU OO Or ODW OU OClW

Ex 3670 .29 .761 **Knopf, (Alfred A.) inc., New York.**
Willa Cather; a biographical sketch, an English opinion, reviews and articles concerning her later books and an abridged bibliography. New York, A.A. Knopf [1933]
28 p. illus. 19 cm.

1. Cather, Willa Sibert, 1873-1947. 2. Cather, Willa Sibert, 1873-1947 - Bibl.

NK 0207683 NjP OU

---

*AC85 C8507 C925 Knopf, (Alfred A.) inc., New York.
The work of Stephen Crane, edited by Wilson Follett ...
Alfred A.Knopf,730 Fifth avenue.New York. [1925]
folder (3,[1]p.) 19cm.
Includes an order form.
Laid into the first volume of a set of the work.
A prospectus.

NK 0207684 MH

Za B995 Q940k **Knopf, (Alfred A.) inc., New York.**
The works of Witter Bynner. Biographical sketch and critical bibliography. [New York, 1940]
[12]p. 20cm.

NK 0207685 CtY RPB

W 4 S89 1941 **Knopf, Anne Margot, 1917-**
Sur une forme souvent méconnue de la paralysie infantile: la forme polio-pyramidale, ses types cliniques, son pronostic. Clermont-Ferrand [etc.] Vallier, 1941.
52 p. (Strasbourg. Université. Faculté de médecine. Thèse. 1941. no. 20)

NK 0207686 DNLM

Knopf (Armin). *Zur Osteotomie. 50 pp. 8°. *Jena, A. Neuenhahn,* 1875.

NK 0207687 DNLM ICRL

Knopf, C. L.
...Methods for testing automobile gear lubricants. N. Y., Amer. petroleum inst., 1928.
[21] l., fold. diagrs.

At head of title: American petroleum institute
"Before 9th annual meeting, American petroleum institute, Dec. 3-6, 1928."

NK 0207688 MiD

Knopf, Carl Sumner, 1889-1942.
An ancient inscribed cone of Sin-gashid, king of Erech, by Carl S. Knopf ... Los Angeles, University of Southern California press [°1930]
v, 11 p. 1 illus. 23cm. (*Half-title:* Semicentennial publications of the University of Southern California, 1880-1930)
On cover: University of Southern California. Studies. Language and literature series. no. 2.
"The ancient object herein described is in the private collection of President R. B. von KleinSmid."—Foreword.
1. Singashid, king of Erech. 2. Cuneiform inscriptions, Sumerian. I. KleinSmid, Rugus Bernhard von, 1875-
30-23066
Library of Congress PJ4071.S5K6
—— Copy 2.
A 27155 [a37d1] 492.1917

OCU OCl OU MH CSmH
NK 0207689 DLC OrPR CoU NIC NcD OrU MoU PBm PU MiU

Knopf, Carl Sumner, 1889-1942.
Ask the prophets, a Bible study manual [by] Carl Sumner Knopf ... New York, Cincinnati [etc.] The Abingdon press [°1938]
149 p. illus. (maps) 17½cm.
"About books and the Book": p. 13-18; bibliography at end of some of the chapters.

1. Bible. O. T. Prophets — Study — Text-books. 2. Bible—Study—Text-books—O. T. Prophets. I. Title.
38-5983
Library of Congress BS1506.K55
—— Copy 2.
Copyright A 115011 224

OrSaW IdB
NK 0207690 DLC NcD PCC OClTem ODW OLak WaTC Or OrCS

Knopf, Carl Sumner, 1889-1942.
... Bible poetry and inspired song; an introductory manual for the study of the Psalms, by Carl Sumner Knopf ... Los Angeles, J. R. Miller, 1928.
39 p. 15cm. (Chapbook religious series)

1. Bible. O. T. Psalms—Criticism, interpretation, etc. I. Title.
28-7291
Library of Congress BS1433.K6

NK 0207691 DLC

Knopf, Carl Sumner, 1889-1942.
... Bible youth in modern times; a study in permanent values, by Carl Sumner Knopf ... New York, Cincinnati, The Methodist book concern [°1927]
134 p. 19½cm. (Christian comradeship series, W. E. J. Gratz, editor)
"Approved by the Committee on curriculum of the Board of education of the Methodist Episcopal church."

1. Bible—Biog. I. Title.
28-7297
Library of Congress BS571.K6

NK 0207692 DLC

---

f016.33 K72b Knopf, Carl Sumner, 1889-1942.
Bibliography of the works of Professor John Bates Clark of Columbia University, compiled and arranged by Carl S.Knopf and Frank M.Toothaker. [Los Angeles] University of Southern California, 1914.
9 l. 33cm.

1.Clark, John Bates, 1847-1938 - Bibl. I.Toothaker, Frank M.

NK 0207693 CLSU

VOLUME 300

Knopf, Carl Sumner, 1889-1942.
... Comrades of the way; a study of the New Testament writers and their message for today, by Carl Sumner Knopf ... New York, Cincinnati, The Methodist book concern [c1928]
131, [1] p. 19½cm. (Christian comradeship series, W. E. J. Gratz, editor)
"Approved by the Committee on curriculum of the Board of education of the Methodist Episcopal church."

1. Bible. N. T.—Criticism, interpretation, etc. I. Title.
28-16769
Library of Congress BS2361.K6

NK 0207694 DLC

Knopf, Carl Sumner, 1889-1942.
... Comrades of the way; a study of the New Testament writers and their message for today, by Carl Sumner Knopf ... Rev. ed. New York, Cincinnati [etc.] The Methodist book concern [c1936]
151, [1] p. 19½cm. (Christian comradeship series, W. E. J. Gratz, editor)
"Approved by the Committee on curriculum of the Board of education of the Methodist Episcopal church."

1. Bible. N. T.—Introductions. 2. Bible—Introductions—N. T. I. Title.
37-30393
Library of Congress BS2330.K58 1936
Copyright AA 229532 225.6

NK 0207695 DLC

F
Assyr.
100m
Knopf, Carl Sumner, 1889-1942.
Items of interest from miscellaneous neo-Babylonian documents ...
(In Bulletin of the Southern California Academy of sciences, vol.XXXII, May-August, 1933. Part 2, p.41-76. illus. 23cm.)
"Some of this material is an abridged form of a dissertation presented to ... Yale university ... for the degree of doctor of philosophy." - 1931.
A detached copy.

NK 0207696 CtY

Knopf, Carl Sumner, 1889-1942.
... Items of interest from miscellaneous neo-Babylonian documents, by Carl Sumner Knopf ... [Los Angeles, 1933]
41-76 p. illus. (incl. facsims.) 23cm.
Caption title.
"Some of this material is an abridged form of a dissertation presented to ... Yale university ... for the degree of doctor of philosophy [1931]"—p. 42.
Detached from Bulletin of the Southern California academy of sciences, v. 32, pt. 2, May/Aug. 1933.
Bibliographical foot-notes.

1. Babylonia—Hist. 2. Assyro-Babylonian language—Texts. 3. Cuneiform inscriptions.
43-48260
Library of Congress DS74.K58
935.4

NK 0207697 DLC

OO4
LDJ
K72m
Knopf, Carl Sumner, 1889-1942.
Miscellaneous Neo-Babylonian documents, chiefly from Erech. [n.p.] 1931.
v, 295 p. 28 cm.

Thesis—Yale.
Library copy xerographic copy.

1. LDJ. 2. WWGC5. 3. JTHbwcIR.
I. Title.

NK 0207698 CCSC

Knopf, Carl Sumner, 1889-1942.
The Old Testament speaks, by Carl Sumner Knopf ... New York, T. Nelson and sons, 1933.
2 p. l., iii-xviii p., 1 l., 19-372 p. illus. (incl. facsims.) maps. 21½ cm. (*Half-title:* Nelson's religious series)
Bibliography: p. 361-372.

1. Bible. O. T.—History of Biblical events. 2. Jews—Hist.—To 70 A. D. I. Title.
BS1197.K6 221.95 33—28385

ScCleU WaWW OrSaW Or OrU OrP
NK 0207699 DLC CoU NcD ODW OO OCl OOxM PSC PHC

BS
1197
.K6
1946
Knopf, Carl Sumner, 1889-1942.
The Old Testament speaks. New York, Ronald Press Co. [1946,c1933]
xviii, 388 p. (Nelson's religious series)
Bibliography: p. 361-372.

1. Bible. O. T. - History of Biblical events. 2. Bible. - History of Biblical events. 3. Jews - Hist. - To 70 A. D.
I. Title.

NK 0207700 NBuU MH OCIW KyWAT MtU

Knopf, Carl Sumner, 1889-1942.
The student faces life; a study of solutions; lectures delivered at the University of Redlands, March, 1931, by Carl Sumner Knopf, PH. D. Philadelphia, Boston [etc.] The Judson press [c1932]
8 p. l., 3-222 p. 20cm.

1. Students. 2. Religion—Philosophy. I. Redlands, Calif. University. II. Title.
32-11210
Library of Congress LB3605.K55
—— Copy 2.
Copyright A 49612 [201] 371.8

NK 0207701 DLC PCC MtU NcD NRAB

Knopf (Christianus Carolus). *De herniis abdominis. 46 pp., 1 l. 8°. *Jenæ, typ. Branii,* [1843].

NK 0207702 DNLM

Knopf, Diederich Carl.
De ornatu oris, nasi et aurium apud populos americanos ... Cum septem tabulis lithographicis. Gottingæ, typis Dieterichianis, 1832.
63 p. 7 pl. 20cm.
Inaug.-diss.—Göttingen.
Includes bibliographies.

1. Deformities, Artificial. 2. Indians—Costume and adornment. I. Title.
41-32100
Library of Congress GN477.6.K55

NK 0207703 DLC

Knopf, Eduard, 1878-
Ueber einen neuen augenspiegel fuer Studenten und Aerzte.
Inaug. Diss. Leipzig, 1902 (Berlin)
Bibl.

NK 0207704 ICRL DNLM CtY

Knopf, Mrs. Eleanora Frances (Bliss) 1883-

Maryland. *Geological survey,* 1896-
... Baltimore county. Baltimore, The Johns Hopkins press, 1929.

Knopf, Eleanora Bliss. *7872.55.725
Chrome ores of southeastern Pennsylvania and Maryland.
(*In* United States. Geological Survey. Bulletin no. 725. Contributions to economic geology, 1921, part 1. Pp. 85-99. Map. Washington. 1922.)

N810 — Chromite. — Maryland. M[ines] and mining. — Pennsylvania. Mines and mining.

NK 0207706 MB PPAN

Knopf, Eleanora Frances (Bliss) 1883-
... Geology of the McCalls Ferry-Quarryville district, Pennsylvania, by Eleanora Bliss Knopf and Anna I. Jonas. Washington, U. S. Govt. print. off., 1929.
xiii, 156 p. incl. illus., tables, diagrs. 8 pl. (incl. fold. map in pocket) fold. tab. 23 cm. (U. S. Geological survey. Bulletin 799)
At head of title: Department of the interior.
Bibliographical foot-notes.

1. Geology—Pennsylvania. I. Stose, Anna Isabel (Jonas) 1881- joint author. II. Title.
QE75.B9 no. 799 G S 29-128
—— —— Copy 2. QE158.M3K5
U. S. Geol. Survey. Libr. for Library of Congress [a63k½]†

ODW ICJ MB PP
NK 0207707 DI-GS DLC ViU PPAN WaWW MiU OCl OU OO

Knopf, *Mrs.* Eleanora Frances (Bliss) 1883-
Relation of the Wissahickon mica-gneiss to the Shenandoah limestone and to the Octoraro mica-schist, of the Doe Run-Avondale district, Coatesville, quadrangle, Pennsylvania ... by Eleanora F. Bliss and Anna I. Jonas ... [n. p., 1914]
2 p. l., 66 p. v pl. (4 fold. in pocket) fold. tab. 24cm.
Thesis (PH. D.)—Bryn Mawr college, 1912.
Vita.

1. Gneiss. 2. Limestone. 3. Petrology—Pennsylvania. I. Jonas, Anna Isabel, 1881-
14-13399 Revised
Library of Congress QE475.K73 1912
Bryn Mawr College Libr. [r34b2]

ViU CU NIC DLC
NK 0207708 PBm RPB PU PHC ICJ MiU OU ODW OCU OO

Knopf, Mrs. Eleanora Frances (Bliss), 1883-

Relation of the Wissahickon mica gneiss to the Shenandoah limestone and Octoraro schist of the Doe Run and Avondale region, Chester county, Pennsylvania, by Eleanora F. Bliss and Anna I. Jonas... Washington: Gov. Prtg. Off., 1916. ii, 9-34 p., diagr., map, pl., table. 4°. (United States. Geological Survey. Professional paper no. 98 — B.)
Shorter contributions to general geology, 1916.

1. Gneiss, U. S.: Pa. 2. Limestone, U. S.: Pa. 3. Jonas, Anna Isabel, 1881- . 4. Series.
N. Y. P. L. August 25, 1919.

NK 0207709 NN MiU MB OU MiU

Knopf, *Mrs.* Eleanora Frances (Bliss) 1883-
Some problems of international readjustment of mineral supplies as indicated in recent foreign literature. [By] Eleanora F. Bliss ...
(*In* Smithsonian institution. Annual report, 1918. Washington, 1920. 23½cm. p. 251-269. illus.)
"Reprinted ... from Economic geology, vol. XIV, no. 2, March-April, 1919."

1. Mines and mineral resources. I. Title.
20-18972 Revised
Library of Congress Q11.S66 1918

NK 0207710 DLC ICJ MiU OO OCl OU ODW

Knopf, Mrs. Eleanora Frances (Bliss) 1883-

Stose, George Willis, 1869-
... Southern Pennsylvania and Maryland, by George W. Stose, Anna I. Jonas [and] George H. Ashley. Washington, U. S. Govt. print. off., 1932.

QE431
.K58
Knopf, Eleanora Frances (Bliss) 1883-
... Structural petrology, by Eleanora Bliss Knopf and Earl Ingerson. [New York] Published by the Society, 1938.
xv, 270 p. illus., 27 pl. (incl. col. front.) on 17 l., diagrs. 26 cm. (Geological society of America. Memoir 6)
Bibliographical foot-notes.
CONTENTS.—pt. I. Principles of structural petrology, by E. B. Knopf.—pt. II. Laboratory technique of petrofabric analysis, by Earl Ingerson.

1. Petrology. 2. Rocks—Analysis. I. *Ingerson, Earl, 1906- joint author. II. Title.
[QE431.K] G S 39—18
U. S. Geol. Survey. Libr. for Library of Congress G(200)G29m no. 6 [a51m1]

CaBVaU WaTC IdU OrP ViU MiHM PU OCl OO OU PPAN
NK 0207712 DI-GS NcD OKentU OU CoU MoU DLC MtBuM

VOLUME 300

KNOPF, Erich, 1904-
Versuche über zucker und insulin. Inaug.-diss. Heidelberg. n.p., 1928.
Manifold copy. pp.(4), 31 f.
"Lebenslauf", at end.

NK 0207713 MH-C ICRL CtY

Knopf, Ernst
see Altkirch, Ernst, 1873-1926.

Knopf, Eugen, 1909-
... Über eine natürliche Zahnmarkentzündung der Schneidezähne beim Kaninchen ... Heidelberg, 1937.
Inaug. diss.-Heidelberg.
Lebenslauf.
"Verzeichnis des Schrifftums" p. 14.

NK 0207715 CtY DNLM

Knopf, Eugene.
The spit and image. New York, Exposition Press ₍1949₎
31 p. 22 cm.

1. Religion and science—1900- I. Title.

BL241.K59 215 49-9088*

NK 0207716 DLC NcD

Knopf, Filip, ed.

Bohemia. *Laws, statutes, etc.*
Obce právo a moc; nezbytná pomůcka pro starosty obcí, členy zastupitelstev obecních, korporace samosprávné, úřady hospodářské, lesnické a j. Sest. Filip Knopf. V Praze, I. L. Kober, 1904.

Knopf, Franz Eduard Ludwig Walther
see Knopf, Walther, 1889-

₍**Knopf, Frederick**₎ 1866-
Coast manual of lettering and designs. ₍Los Angeles, Cal., F. Knopf and J. M. Mahaffey₎ ©1907.
3 p. l., ₍5₎-95, ₍1₎ p. illus. (partly col.) 22½ x 31cm.
By Fred Knopf and J. M. Mahaffey.

1. Lettering. I. Mahaffey, James Marion, 1871- joint author.

7-14247

NK 0207719 DLC PPStePh CU ICJ CLU ICRL

Knopf, Fredericus Arminius
Diss. inauguralis medica exhibens novum lithopaedii exemplum. Jenae, Schreiberi, 1845.
38 p.

NK 0207720 PPC

Knopf, Frieda Wenger-
see **Wenger-Knopf, Frieda.**

Knopf, Gustav.
Die stromversorgung der telegraphen- und fernsprechanstalten, von G. Knopf ... mit 210 eingedruckten abbildungen und vier tafeln. Braunschweig, F. Vieweg und sohn, 1910.
xiv, 241 p. illus., fold. tables. 24cm. (*Added t.-p.:* Telegraphen- und fernsprech-technik in einzeldarstellungen unter mitwirkung anderer fachmänner hrsg. von T. Karrass ... IX)

1. Telegraph—Current supply. 2. Telephone—Current supply.

Library of Congress TK5371.K6 10-15413

NK 0207722 DLC MiU ICJ

Knopf (Hans) [1882-]. *Ueber die Behandlung der varikösen Unterschenkelgeschwüre mit Berücksichtigung der Entstehung von Varizen. [Freiburg i. Br.] 32 pp. 8°. Berlin, W. Axt, 1906.

NK 0207723 DNLM ICRL

Knopf, Harry, 1887-
Genehmigung im B.G.B. unter dem Gesichtspunkte der §§182ff und ihre rechtliche Bedeutung ... von Harry Knopf ... Berlin, W. Rohr, 1912.
5 p.l., 100 p. 22cm.
Inaug.-Diss. - Erlangen.
"Literaturverzeichnis": 4th-5th prelim. leaves.

NK 0207724 MH-L ICRL MH NN NIC

Knopf, Heinrich: Welche Aenderungen verursacht die Berieselung mit Spüljauche in der Zusammensetzung des Bodens, mit besonderer Berücksichtigung des Kalkgehaltes? (Berlin: Ebering 1911.) 59 S. 8° ¶ (Ersch. auch als Buch ebd.) Berlin, Phil. Diss. v. 30. März 1911, Ref. Orth, Gabriel
[Geb. 27. Sept. 84 Sorau; Wohnort: Charlottenburg; Staatsangeh.: Preußen; Vorbildung: Joachimsth. Gymn. Berlin Reife O. 03; Studium: Breslau 2, Berlin Landw. Hochsch. 4, Univ. 2 S.; Rig. 27. Febr. 11.] [U 11. 250

NK 0207725 ICRL CtY PU

1949 Knopf, Henry A 1911-
Survey of the library of the College of physicians and surgeons (the Medical Library) Columbia university. ₍New York, 1949₎
63 l. tables, diagrs., charts.
Bibliography: l. ₍64-65₎

1. Columbia university. College of physicians and surgeons Medical library.

NK 0207726 NNC-M

Knopf, Herbert.
Die chemischen vorgaenge bei der vergasung von rohbraunkohle.
Inaug. diss. Muenchen, 1927.

NK 0207727 ICRL

Knopf, Herm Eman *ed.*
Der weg zur gesundheit; ein ärztliches hausbuch für gesunde und kranke beiderlei geschlechts, bearb. und hrsg. von dr. med. H. E. Knopf unter mitarbeit der herren dr. Bach ... ₍u. a.₎ Mit vielen hundert abbildungen und 24 tafeln. Ulm a. D., J. Ebner ₍©1911₎
xv, ₍1₎, 917 p. col. front., illus., plates (partly col.) 24½cm. M. 11

1. Medicine, Popular. 2. Hygiene.

Library of Congress RC81.K826 12-17641

NK 0207728 DLC

ha
TX
721
K73
Knopf, Johann D
Braunschweigisches Kochbuch für angehende Köche, Köchinnen und Haushälterinnen. 3te Aufl. Braunschweig, In der Schulbuchhandlung, 1812.
xv, 664p. 3 fold.pl.

1. Cookery, German. 2. Cookery-Early works, 1800-1850. I. Title.

NK 0207729 NIC

ha
TX
709
K73
₍Knopf, Johann D ₎
Neues Hannöverisches Kochbuch; von einem praktischen Koche. Neueste Ausg. Hannover, Hahn, 1800.
xxxii, 264p.

1. Cookery, German. 2. Cookery - Early works to 1800. I. Title: Hannöverisches...

NK 0207730 NIC

Knopf, Julius, 1863-1935
Der nervöse redakteur; lustspiel in 3 akten von Julius Knopf ... Berlin, E. Bloch, ©1912.
68 p. 19½cm.
"Als manuskript vervielfältigt."

I. Title.

Library of Congress PT2621.N82N4 1912 20-13968
Copyright D 33444

NK 0207731 DLC CaBVaU

Knopf, Julius, 1863-1935
Der nervöse Redakteur; Lustspiel in 3 Akten. Berlin, E. Bloch, c1912.
68p.
Microcard edition.
"Als Manuskript vervielfältigt."

NK 0207732 ICRL

Knopf, Julius, 1863-1935.
... Der seiltänzer. Komödie in 3 akten ... Berlin, ©1912.
60 p. 34cm.
Reproduced from type-written copy.

I. Title.

Library of Congress PT2621.N82S4 43-19852 Brief cataloging

NK 0207733 DLC

Knopf, Karl.
Das erzgebirge als klimafaktor.
Inaug. diss. Tech., Hoch. Dresden, 1929.
Bibl.

NK 0207734 ICRL

855
K72
Knopf, Karl.
Deutsches land und volk in liedern deutscher dichter. Beiträge zur vaterländischen erdkunde gesammelt und hrsg. von Karl Knopf. Braunschweig, E. Appelhans & comp. ₍1907₎
10 p.l., 440 p. front.(port.) plates. 20cm.

NK 0207735 CU NcD

VOLUME 300

Knopf, Kenyon Alfred.
The location of the rubber tire and inner tube industry.

Thesis - Harvard, 1949.

NK 0207736 MH

Knopf, Kurt, 1907-
Die romantische struktur des denkens Richard Wagners ... von Kurt Knopf ... Jena, Neuenhahn, 1932.
66 p. 21 cm.

Thesis, Jena.
Bibliography: p. ⌊67⌋

1. Wagner, Richard, 1813-1883. 2. Romanticism in music.

NK 0207737 NNC PU CU ICRL InU

Knopf, Kurt, 1920-
Messungen der Adsorptionszeit an Platin, Nickel und Glas durch die Strömungsmethode. ⌊Heidelberg, 1950⌋
44 l. diagrs. 30 cm.
Typescript (carbon copy)
Inaug.-Diss.—Heidelberg.
Vita.

1. Gases — Absorption and adsorption. 2. Platinum. 3. Nickel. 4. Glass.

QC182.K58 78-221275

69 ⌊1½⌋

NK 0207738 DLC

Knopf (L.) * Contribution à l'étude de l'étiologie de la fièvre typhoïde à propos d'une épidémie observée à Vallerysthal (Meurthe), dans le cours de l'hiver 1874-5. 1 p. l., 65 pp., 1 l. 4°. *Nancy,* 1875, 1. s., No. 23.

NK 0207739 DNLM

⌊**Knopf, Leo**⌋
A first tour of France, by Leo. London and New York, Transatlantic Arts ⌊1946⌋
31 p. illus. (part col.) map. 25 cm.

1. France—Descr. & trav.—1919- I. Title.

DC28.K6 914.4 48-14631*

NK 0207740 DLC

Knopf, Leo, 1876- . Anatomische Untersuchung von zwei Fällen von Syringomyelie. Leipzig 1909: Lehmann. 43 S. 8°
Leipzig, Med. Diss. v. 17. Juli 1909, Ref. Marchand
[Geb. 4. April 76 Neuweier; Wohnort: Leipzig; Staatsangeh.: Baden; Vorbildung: Gymn. Lörrach Reife Juli 96; Studium: Straßburg 1, Heidelberg 1, Würzburg 2, Heidelberg 5 S.; Coll. 24. Juli 09; Approb. 24. Juli 01.]
[U 09. 2803

NK 0207741 ICRL DNLM CtY

Knopf (Leo E.) [1870–]. *Beitrag zur Frage der unblutigen Behandlung der kongenitalen Hüftgelenkverrenkung. 30 pp. 8°. Giessen, Heppeler & Meyer. 1912.

NK 0207742 DNLM ICRL MBCo

Knopf, Ludwig Wilhelm Bernhard, 1877-
... Beiträge zur kenntnis des phlorhizindiabetes ... Marburg, 1902.
25, ⌊2⌋ p. 22cm.
Inaug.-diss.—Marburg.
Lebenslauf.

1. Diabetes. 7-30390†

Library of Congress RC909.K72

NK 0207743 DLC DNLM CtY

M1503
K595D3
1910

Knopf, Martin, 1876-
[Die Dame von Moulin Rouge. acc. arr. piano]
Die Dame von Moulin Rouge; Operette in einem Akt von Louis Taufstein. Klavierauszug mit Text. Leipzig, A. Cranz [c1910]
31 p.

Vocal score with piano accompaniment, and instrumental cues.
German words.

I. Taufstein, Louis. II. Title.

NK 0207744 CU

Knopf, Martin, 1876-
⌊Duett im Grünen. Libretto. German⌋

Duett im Grünen; Lustspiel mit Musik in drei Akten nach dem gleichnamigen Lustspiel Hans Kasper Francops von Bruno Hardt-Warden. Berlin, Vertriebsstelle des Verbandes Deutscher Bühnenschriftsteller und Bühnenkomponisten, ©1930.
84 p. 20 cm.
⌊1. Musical revues, comedies, etc.—Librettos⌋ I. Hardt-Warden, Bruno. Duett im Grünen. II. Title.

ML50.K71D8 1930 51-54945 rev

NK 0207745 DLC

M1503
K595K4

Knopf, Martin, 1876-
[Das kleine Fräulein Li; acc. arr. piano]
Das kleine Fräulein Li; Operette in 2 Akten mit einem Vor- und Nachspiel von Bruno Hardt-Warden und Hermann Feiner. Berlin, Verlag und Vertrieb A.-G., c1930.
138 p.

Vocal score with piano accompaniment and instrumental cues.
German words.

NK 0207746 CU

M1503
K595K5

Knopf, Martin, 1876-
[Die kleine Hoheit; acc. arr. piano]
Die kleine Hoheit; Operette in 3 Akten, von Hans Gaus, nach dem gleichnamigen Lustspiel von Dora Duncker und Hans Gaus. Berlin, Bibliothek für Dramatik und Musik Verlagsges. [c1919]
152 p.

Vocal score with piano accompaniment. German words.

NK 0207747 CU

KNOPF, MARTIN, 1876-
[DIE MÄDELS VON DAVOS. LIBRETTO. ENGLISH]
The little girls of Davos; operetta in three acts, by Hans Bühler; text by Theo Halton; music by Martin Knopf. [London] Marshall's [n.d.]
40,39,12 l. 26cm.

Typescript.

1. Musical comedies--Librettos. The little girls of Davos. I. Bühler, Hans. Die Mädels von Davos. II. Halton, Theo. III. Title.

NK 0207748 NN

M1503
K595P3

Knopf, Martin, 1876-
[Pariser Luft, acc. arr. piano]
Pariser Luft; musikalischer Schwank in drei Akten, von Alexander Engel und Julius Horst [i M. A. Beĭkone] Gesangstexte von Louis Taufstein [i M. A. Beĭkone] Klavier-Auszug mit Text. München, Drei Masken-Verlag [c1912]
134 p.

Instrumental cues. German words.
Beĭkone's name transliterated from Cyrillic.

NK 0207749 CU

M1503
K595T7

Knopf, Martin, 1876-
[Der Traum vom Glück, acc. arr. piano]
Der Traum vom Glück; Singspiel in drei Akten, von Eduard von der Becke. Klavierauszug mit Text. Berlin, Paragon Musik-Verlag [c1921]
84 p.

Instrumental cues. German words.

NK 0207750 CU

M1503
K595S8

Knopf, Martin, 1876-
[Suzette; acc. arr. piano]
Suzette; Operette in 3 Akten. Text von Max Epstein. Berlin, Ed. Bote & G. Bock [c1910]
109 p.

Vocal score with piano accompaniment. German words.

NK 0207751 CU

M1503
K595U5

Knopf, Martin, 1876-
[Die ungeküsste Eva; acc. arr. piano]
Die ungeküsste Eva; Operette in 3 Akten (nach einer Idee von Max Kempner-Hochstädt) von Pordes-Milo. Gesangstexte von Fritz Rotter und Otto Stransky. Berlin, Vertriebsstelle des Verbandes Deutscher Bühnenschriftsteller und Bühnenkomponisten, c1928.
74 p.

Vocal score with piano accompaniment. German words.

NK 0207752 CU

Knopf, Martin, 1887- Ueber Dibenzalaceton und seine Umsetzung mit Methylamin. (Berlin: Ebering 1912.) 29 S. 8° ¶(Im Buchh. ebd.)
Berlin, Phil. Diss. v. 3. Juli 1912, Ref. E. Fischer, Nernst
[Geb. 6. Dez. 87 Sorau; Wohnort: Berlin-Wilmersdorf; Staatsangeh.: Preußen; Vorbildung: Dorotheenstädt. Realgymn. Berlin Reife M. 07; Studium: München 2, Berlin 8 S.; Rig. 6. Juni 12.] [U 12. 277

NK 0207753 ICRL CtY PU

Knopf, Matthäus Ferdinand. **M912.43131 F3**
Mappa geographica exhibens principatvm Brandenbvrgico-Onols-
150982 bacensem, una cum finitimis regionibus terrisque, delineata a Matthæo Ferdinand Cnopf et edita cura Homañianorum heredum. [Norimbergæ], 1763.
1 map. 45½ x 56cm.
Scale, 10.2cm. = 3milliaria Germ.
Hand-tinted.

NK 0207754 ICJ

Knopf, Matthäus Ferdinand. **M912.43131 F2**
Principatus Brandenbvrgico-Cvlmbacensis vel Barvthini. Tabula
150981 geographica quoad partem inferiorem expresſus, et in ſuas ditiones atque præfecturas divisus unacum finitimis regionibus delineata a Matthaeo Ferdinand; Cnopf et edita cura Homannianorum heredum. [Norimbergæ], 1763.
1 map. 41¼ x 53½cm.
Scale, 12.2cm. = 2Meilen.
Hand-tinted.

NK 0207755 ICJ

VOLUME 300

Knopf, Mildred O 1895–
The perfect hostess cook book. Introd. by June Platt. New York, Knopf, 1950.
xxx, 499, xxii p. 22 cm.

1. Cookery, American. I. Title.

TX715.K699 1950✓ 641.5 50-9591

CaBViP NcGU PP
NK 0207756 DLC NN MB WaS Wa OrP OrCS Or CaBVa

Knopf, Olga, 1888–
The art of being a woman, by Olga Knopf; edited by Alan Porter. Boston, Little, Brown, and company, 1932.
vii p., 2 l., 3–307 p. diagr. 22½ cm.

1. Woman. 2. Woman—History and condition of women. I. Porter, Alan, 1899–1942, ed. II. Title.

HQ1221.K6 396 32—26097

OrU
OClW MiU OLak OEac OCl WaS OrU KMK OrCS WaE MtU Wa
NK 0207757 DLC NcC MCR PPPL NN NIC MH CU MB ODW

HQ1221 .K6 1932a Knopf, Olga, 1888-
The art of being a woman. Edited by Alan Porter. New York, Blue Ribbon Books ᶜc1932ᶟ 307p.

1. Woman. 2. Woman - History and condition of women. I. Porter, Alan, ed. II. Title.

NK 0207758 NcU MiEM PU-Penn OU OO OCU

Knopf, Olga, 1888–
Women on their own, by Olga Knopf, M. D.; edited by Alan Porter. Boston, Little, Brown, and company, 1935.
4 p. l., 3–306 p. diagrs. 22½cm.

1. Woman—Social and moral questions. 2. Woman—History and condition of women. I. Porter, Alan, ed. II. Title.
Library of Congress HQ1206.K55 35–27074

NcC OkU CU MH OEac OLak OO OCl OClW MB NN PPPL
NK 0207759 DLC WaS Wa WaE Or CaBVa OrCS OrU MiU NcU

I 747 .455 no.7 KNOPF, OTTO HEINRICH JULIUS, 1856-1945.
Die Astronomie an der Universität Jena von der Gründung der Universität im Jahre 1558 bis zur Entpflichtung des Verfassers im Jahre 1927. Jena, G. Fischer, 1937.
xiv, 226p. plates. 22cm. (Zeitschrift des Vereins für Thüringische Geschichte und Altertumskunde. N.F. 19. Beiheft)

"Beiträge zur Geschichte der Universität Jena. Heft 7."
Bibliographical foot-notes.

NK 0207760 ICN NN NjP CU CBPac

Knopf, Otto Heinrich Julius, 1856–
... Beobachtungen veränderlicher sterne und bestimmung ihrer grössen, von Otto Knopf, mit 48 abbildungen im text. Jena, G. Fischer, 1944.
2 p. l., 118 p. diagrs. 29cm. (Veröffentlichungen der Universitäts-sternwarte zu Jena, nr. 4)

1. Stars, Variable. 2. Stars—Magnitudes.

QB835.K58 523.82 47-22237

NK 0207761 DLC MH ICU

519.1 K757w-S 1942 Knopf, Otto Heinrich Julius, 1856-1945.
Cálculo de probabilidades. Con 10 figuras. Traducido directamente de alemán por Francisco Cebrián. 3. edición. Barcelona [etc.] Editorial Labor, s.a., 1942.
230 p. 19 cm.
"Bibliografía," p. [7]-8.

1. Probabilities. I. Title. II. Title: Wahrscheinlichkeitsrechnung.

NK 0207762 MoSU NNC

Knopf, Otto Heinrich Julius, 1856–
... Christentum oder wissenschaft, von dr. Otto Knopf ... Leipzig, J. Dörner, 1936.
176 p. 21cm. (Aktuelle bücherei; schriften zur kultur- und zeitgeschichte)

1. Christianity—Controversial literature. 2. Religion and science—1900– I. Title.
36-31745
Library of Congress BL2775.K63

NK 0207763 DLC CSt-H

Knopf, Otto Heinrich Julius, 1856 -
Ernest Abbe. Von Otto Knopf.
Leipzig, 1905.
14 p. port. 24 cm.

(From Jahresbericht der deutschen mathematiker vereinigung. v. 14, p. 217-230. Leipzig, 1905.)

NK 0207764 DN-Ob

Knopf, Otto Heinrich Julius, 1856–
... Die geographischen koordinaten von Jena, von Otto Knopf ... Jena, 1927.
4 p. l., 104 p. incl. tables, diagrs. pl. 31½cm. (Veröffentlichung der Universitäts-sternwarte zu Jena)

1. Geographical positions—Germany—Jena. I. Title.
29-6756
Library of Congress QB205.G5J4

NK 0207765 DLC MH MsU

Knopf, Otto Heinrich Julius, 1856–
... Mathematische himmelskunde, von dr. phil. Otto Knopf ... Mit 30 figuren im text. Leipzig und Berlin, B. G. Teubner, 1925.
48 p. diagrs. 18½cm. (Mathematisch-physikalische bibliothek ... [bd.] 63)

1. Astronomy. I. Title.
26-10574
Library of Congress QB43.K6

NK 0207766 DLC

Knopf, Otto [Heinrich Julius] 1856–
Die Schmidt'sche sonnentheorie und ihre anwendung auf die methode der spektroskopischen bestimmung der rotationsdauer der sonne ... Jena, Druck von B. Vopelius, 1893.
44 p. diagrs. 28½ x 22½cm.
Habilitationsschrift—Jena.

1. Sun.
5—29505
Library of Congress QB521.K72

NK 0207767 DLC ViU CU DNLM NjP OCU MiU PU CtY NN

Knopf, Otto [Heinrich Julius] 1856–
Über die methoden zur bestimmung der mittleren dichtigkeit der erde ... Jena, Druck von A. Neuenhahn, 1880.
58 p. diagrs. 21½cm.
Inaug.-diss.—Jena.

1. Earth, Density of.
6–11055†
Library of Congress QB341.K7

NK 0207768 DLC MH

Knopf, Otto Heinrich Julius, 1856–
... Wahrscheinlichkeitsrechnung, von dr. Otto Knopf ... Berlin und Leipzig, W. de Gruyter & co., 1923.
v. 16cm. (Sammlung Göschen. [508])

1. Probabilities.
42-46134
Library of Congress QA273.K55

ICU ICRL MH NjP
NK 0207769 DLC MiU OCU ODW MB CoU MtU CtY DBS

Knopf (Paul [Eduard]) [1851–]. * Ueber Nierenexstirpation. 28 pp., 2 l. 12°. Berlin, G. Schade, 1886.

NK 0207770 DNLM

Knopf, Philip, *vs.* City of Chicago. 352.0773 C774
In the Supreme Court of Illinois. February term, A. D. 1900. Philip Knopf, county clerk of Cook county, Illinois, Plaintiff in error, vs. the City of Chicago .... Chicago Board of Education .... Sanitary district of Chicago, defendant in error. .... Argument for plaintiff in error. 76 p. O. Chicago [1900].
'The suits in question are proceedings by mandamus to compel the county clerk of Cook County to compute the rates and extend the taxes in accordance with the law, claiming that section 49 of that certain act of the legislature entitled "An Act for the assessment of property, providing the means therefor and to repeal a certain act therein named," under which the county clerk was acting, is unconstitutional and void.' *Statement.*
No title-page. Title taken from inside cover.

NK 0207771 ICJ

Knopf, Richard C., ed.

E83 794 W3 Wayne, Anthony, 1745–1796.
Campaign into the wilderness; the Wayne-Knox-Pickering-McHenry correspondence. Edited by Richard C. Knopf. Columbus, Anthony Wayne Parkway Board, Ohio State Museum, 1955.

Knopf, Richard C
The re-discovery of Fort Washington, October, 1952, Cincinnati, Ohio ᶜby Richard C. Knopf, Raymond S. Baby, and Dwight L. Smith. Transcribed by: the Anthony Wayne Parkway Board; The Ohio Historical Society. ᶜColumbus? 1953?ᶟ
6l.

Cover-title.
"This report appeared in the January, 1953 issue of the Bulletin of the Historical and Philosophical Quarterly of Ohio."

NK 0207773 OCl

977 K757t Cov. Coll. Knopf, Richard C., ed.
Two journals of the Kentucky Volunteers, 1793 and 1794. Edited by Richard C. Knopf. Columbus, Ohio, Anthony Wayne Parkway Board [1953?]
47l. 28cm.

Journals of an unidentified officer in the Kentucky Volunteers.
Reprinted from Filson Club history quarterly v.27, no.3, July 1953.
Mimeographed.

NK 0207774 OOxM

VOLUME 300

Knopf, Richard C
The West Point orderly books
see under
U.S. Army. Legion.

Knopf, Rudolf. 26275.14.5
Westpreussische volkssagen. Graudenz, J. Gaebel, 1891.
5 nos.
Contents: — 1. Die teufelskanzel zu Sartowitz. — 2. Die pfingstglocken vom Klostersee. — 3. Der schwedenschimmel von Stuhm. — 4. Der kaplan vom Hagelsberge. — 5. Das festungsgespenst von Graudenz.

Folklore–Germany–Prussia||AcS 232845

NK 0207776 MH

Knopf, Rudolf, 1874–1920, *ed.*
... Ausgewählte märtyreracten, hrsg. von lic. Rudolf Knopf ... Tübingen und Leipzig, Mohr, 1901.
ix, 120 p. 21½cm. (Sammlung ausgewählter kirchen- und dogmengeschichtlicher quellenschriften ... II. reihe, 2. hft.)
"Literatur zur geschichte der verfolgungen und der märtyrer": p. vii–ix.
CONTENTS.—Martyrium des Polykarp.—Acten des Karpus, Papylus, und der Agathonike.—Martyrium des Ptolemäus und Lucius.—Acten des Justin und seiner genossen.—Die lugdunensischen märtyrer.—Acten der scilitanischen märtyrer.—Acten des Apollonius.—Martyrium der Perpetua und Felicitas.—Martyrium der Potamiäna und des Basilides.—Martyrium des Pionius.—Acten des Cyprian.—Martyrium des Marinus.—Acten des Maximilianus.—Acten des Marcellus.—Acten des Felix.—Martyrium des Dasius.—Acten der Agape, Chionia, und ihrer genossinnen.—Acten des Euplius.—Brief des Phileas.—Acten des Phileas und Philoromus.—Das testament der vierzig märtyrer.—Indices.
1. Martyrs. I. Title.
3–21451
Library of Congress BR45.S3 reihe 2, hft. 2

NK 0207777 DLC OO OC1W MH MoU NcD NjP

BR
1604
.K72
1913

Knopf,Rudolf,1874-1920,ed.
Ausgewählte Märtyrerakten. 2.neu bearb.Aufl. Tübingen, J.C.B.Mohr, 1913.
viii,114 p. 21 cm. (Sammlung ausgewählter kirchen- und dogmengeschichtlicher Quellenschriften. 2.Reihe. 2.Heft)
Bibliography: p.v-viii.
CONTENTS.--Martyrium Polykarps.--Akten des Karpus,Papylus und der Agathonike.--Martyrium des Ptolemäus und Lucius.--Akten Justins und seiner Genossen.--Die Lugdunensischen Märtyrer.--Akten der Scilitanischen Märtyrer.--Akten des Apollonius.--Martyrium der Perpetua und Felicitas.--Martyrium der Potamiäna und des Basilides.--Martyrium des Pionius.

--Akten Cyprians.--Martyrium des Marinus.--Akten des Maximilianus.--Akten des Marcellus.--Akten des Felix.--Martyrium des Dasius.--Martyrium der Agape,Eirene,Chione und Genossen.--Akten des Euplius.--Brief des Phileas an die Thmuiten.--Akten des Phileas und Philoromus.--Das Testament der vierzig Märtyrer.

1.Martyrs.

NK 0207779 MiU CtY NjNbS

270.1
K72a
1929

Knopf, Rudolf, 1874-1920, ed.
Ausgewählte Märtyrerakten. 3., neubearbeitete Aufl.von Gustav Krüger. Tübingen, J.C.B.Mohr, 1929.
xi,135p. 23cm. (Sammlung ausgewählter kirchen- und dogmengeschichtlicher Quellenschriften; neue Folge, 3)

Text in Greek and Latin, notes in German.
Bibliography: p.vi-xi.
1.Martyrs. I.Krüger, Gustav, 1862- joint ed. II.Title.

NK 0207780 CLSU PPLT RPB MsU InStme PBm CtY DDO

Knopf, Rudolf, 1874–1920.
... Die briefe Petri und Judä, völlig neu bearb. von d. Rud. Knopf ... Göttingen, Vandenhoeck & Ruprecht, 1912.
2 p. l., 329 p. 24½cm. (Kritisch-exegetischer kommentar über das Neue Testament, begründet von H. A. W. Meyer. 12. abt., 7. aufl.)
"Literatur": p. 25–26.

1. Bible. N. T. Peter—Commentaries. 2. Bible. N. T. Jude—Commentaries. 3. Bible—Commentaries—N. T. Peter. 4. Bible—Commentaries—N. T. Jude.
12–13250
Library of Congress BS2344.M45 N. T. abt. 12, 1912
Copyright A—Foreign 5166
[a34b1] (225.7) 227.9

NK 0207781 DLC OC1JC OO CtY-D DCU PPiPT MH-AH IEG MoSCS

Knopf, Rudolf, 1874 - 1920. 3425.174
Clemens an die Korinther. [Kommentar.]
(In Hennecke, Edgar. Handbuch. . . . Pp. 173–190. Tübingen. 1904.)

G3381 — Bible. N. T. Apocrypha. Epistles of Clement. Commentaries.

NK 0207782 MB

BS2330
.K72
(Ha)

Knopf,Rudolf,1874- 1920.
...Einführung in das Neue Testament;**Bibelkunde** des Neuen Testaments,geschichte und **religion des** urchristentums von d.Rudolf Knopf... **Giessen,A.** Töpelmann,1919.
xii,394 p. 23cm. (Sammlung Töpelmann. **1.gruppe**:Die theologie im abriss. bd.2)

1.Bible.N.T.-Criticism,interpretation,etc.

NK 0207783 ICU MH PPWe OO NjNbS PPPD

BS2330
.K73

Knopf, Rudolf, 1874- 1920.
... Einführung in das Neue Testament; Bibelkunde des Neuen Testaments, geschichte und religion des urchristentums, von Rudolf Knopf ... 2. aufl. sorgfältig durchgesehen und vielfach verm., unter mitwirkung von professor d. Hans Lietzmann bearb. von professor d. dr. Heinrich Weinel. Giessen, A. Töpelmann, 1923.
xiv, [1], 406 p. 23cm. (Sammlung Töpelmann. 1. Gruppe: Die theologie im abriss. bd. 2)

1. Bible. N. T.—Introductions.

NK 0207784 ICU PPLT PCC OO MH NjP IU

BS2330
.K731

KNOPF,RUDOLF,1874-1920.
...Einführung in das Neue Testament;Bibelkunde des Neuen Testaments, geschichte und religion des urchristentums,von Rudolf Knopf... 3.aufl.,unter mitwirkung von professor d.Hans Lietzmann bearb.von professor d. dr.Heinrich Weinel. Giessen,A.Töpelmann,1930.
xvi,408 p. 23cm. (Sammlung Töpelmann. 1.gruppe: Die theologie im abriss. bd.2)

1.Bible. N.T.--Introductions.

NK 0207785 ICU

Knopf, Rudolf, 1874–1920.
... Einführung in das Neue Testament; Bibelkunde des Neuen Testaments; geschichte und religion des urchristentums, von Rudolph Knopf ... 4. aufl., unter mitwirkung von professor d. Hans Lietzmann neu bearb. von professor d. dr. Heinrich Weinel. Giessen, A. Töpelmann, 1934.
xvi, 408 p. 23 cm. (Sammlung Töpelmann; die theologie im abriss: bd. 2)
Bibliographies interspersed.
1. Bible. N. T.—Introductions. I. *Lietzmann, Hans, 1875– joint ed. II. Weinel, Heinrich, 1874– III. Title.
BS2330.K6 1934 225 35—11563

NK 0207786 DLC OCH

FD
K72
1945

Knopf, Rudolf, 1874- 1920.
Einführung in das Neue Testament. Bibelkunde des Neuen Testaments Geschichte und Religion des Urchristentums, von Rudolf Knopf ... New York,N.Y.,Nachgedruckt von der Amerikanischen Hilfs-Kommission des Okumenischen Rates der Kirchen[1945?]
2p.l.,[ix]-xvi,408p. 21.5cm.
Contains bibliographies.

NK 0207787 NNUT NjPT

BS2330
.K733

Knopf, Rudolf, 1874-1920.
Einführung in das Neue Testament; Bibelkunde des Neuen Testaments; Geschichte und Religion des Urchristentums [von] Rudolf Knopf, Hans Lietzmann [und] Heinrich Weinel. 5. Aufl. Berlin, A. Töpelmann, 1949.
xvi, 444 p. (Sammlung Töpelmann; die Theologie im Abriss, Bd.2)

1. Bible. N.T.--Introductions. I. Lietzmann, Hans, 1875- ed. II. Weinel, Heinrich, 1874-

NK 0207788 ICU DDO NcD OrU IEG IaU CtY-D

Knopf, Rudolf, 1874-1920, ed.

Clemens *Romanus.*
Der erste Clemensbrief, untersucht und herausgegeben von lic. Rudolf Knopf. Leipzig, J. C. Hinrichs, 1899.

Knopf, Rudolf, 1874-1920.

Weiss, Johannes, 1863–1914.
The history of primitive Christianity, by Johannes Weiss ... completed after the author's death by Rudolf Knopf ... translated by four friends and edited by Frederick C. Grant. New York, Wilson-Erickson, incorporated, 1937.

Knopf, Rudolf, 1874-1920.
Laodicenerbrief... Tübingen, 1904
see under Bible. N. T. Apocryphal books. Epistle of Paul to the Laodiceans. German. 1897.

Knopf, Rudolf, 1874–1920, *ed.*
... Die lehre der zwölf apostel. Die zwei Clemensbriefe. Erklärt von d. Rudolf Knopf ... Tübingen, J. C. B. Mohr (P. Siebeck) 1920.
1 p. l., 184 p. illus. 25cm. (Handbuch zum Neuen Testament. Ergänzungs-band ... Die apostolischen väter, I)
Published also as Handbuch zum Neuen Testament, neubearbeitung, bd. 17.

I. Clemens Romanus. II. Teaching of the twelve apostles.
A C 37–1394
Yale univ. Library
for Library of Congress

NK 0207792 CtY OO OCH NjNbS MH NjP MoSCS NcD

BR165 **Knopf, Rudolf,** 1874- 1920.
.K74 Das nachapostolische zeitalter, geschichte der Christlichen gemeinden vom beginn der Flavierdynastie bis zum ende Hadrians, dargestellt von lic. Rudolf Knopf ... Tübingen, J. C. B. Mohr (P. Siebeck) 1905.
xii, 468 p. 24cm.
"Literatur": p. 466–468.

1. Church history—Primitive and early church.

NK 0207793 ICU MiU TxFTC MB MH CU PCC PPWe DDO IEG NcD InU CtY MiU OO ICN NjPT

VOLUME 300

PT30 Knopf, Rudolf, 1874-1920.
K757p Paulus. Leipzig, Quelle & Meyer, 1909.
123 p. 19 cm. (Wissenschaft und bildung; einzeldarstellungen aus allen gebieten des wissens, 48)

Bibliography: p. [118]

NK 0207794 CtY-D MH CU PP OU MiD PPWe ICU

BS2505 **Knopf, Rudolf,** 1874-1920.
.K726 Probleme der Paulusforschung. Von d. Rudolf Knopf ... Tübingen, J. C. B. Mohr (P. Siebeck) 1913.

[4], 41 p. 22½cm. (*On cover:* Sammlung gemeinverständlicher vorträge und schriften aus dem gebiet der theologie und religionsgeschichte. 77)

1. Paul, Saint, apostle.

NcD MoSCS
NK 0207795 ICU PPWe MH CtY NNUT OCH NIC CtY-D IEG

BS2360 **Knopf, Rudolf,** 1874-1920.
.K72 ... Der text des Neuen Testaments; neue fragen, funde und forschungen der neutestamentlichen textkritik, von lic. Rudolf Knopf ... Giessen, A. Töpelmann (vormals J. Ricker) 1906.

48 p. 20cm. (Vorträge der Theologischen konferenz zu Giessen. 25. folge)

1. Bible. N. T.—Criticism, Textual.

NK 0207796 ICU MH NjPT CtY TxFTC

BS2410 Knopf, Rudolf, 1874-1920.
.W28
Weiss, Johannes, 1863-1914.
Das urchristentum, von d. Johannes Weiss ... Nach dem tode des verfassers herausgegeben und am schlusse ergänzt von d. Rudolf Knopf ... Mit einem bildnis von Johannes Weiss ... Göttingen, Vandenhoeck & Ruprecht, 1917.

Knopf, Rudolf, 1874- 1920 .
... Die völker Österreich-Ungarns, von dr. Rud. Knopf ... Bonn, F. Cohen, 1914.

19 p. 22cm. (Bonner vaterländische reden u. vorträge während des krieges. IV)
"Zum besten der invaliden und der hinterbliebenen gefallener krieger."

1. Austria—Nationality.

26-22026

Library of Congress D509.B6 vol. IV

NK 0207798 DLC CtY NN

Knopf, Rudolf, 1874-1920.
Die zukunftshoffnungen des urchristentums, von professor lic. Rudolf Knopf-Marburg a/L. 1.-10. tausend ... Tübingen, J. C. B. Mohr (P. Siebeck) 1907.

1 p. l., 64 p. 20cm. (Religionsgeschichtliche volksbücher für die deutsche christliche gegenwart. 1. reihe, 13. hft. Hrsg. von F. M. Schiele)
"Literatur": p. 63.

1. Eschatology—History of doctrines. I. Title.

8-20744

Library of Congress BL25.R4 reihe 1, hft. 13

CBPac CBDP IaU
NK 0207799 DLC CtY OCl OCH MiU NcD IEG CSaT CBSK

Knopf, Rudolf Hermann, 1893- Die Wirkungen der Kartelle der Textil- und Bekleidungsindustrie auf die Abnehmer. Mit e. Anh.: Krieg u. Konventionen. Karlsruhe i. B.: Braun 1915. x, 116 S. 8°
Heidelberg, Phil. Diss. v. 29. Dez. 1915, Ref. Gothein
[Geb. 11. Nov. 93 Karlsruhe i. B.; Wohnort: Heidelberg; Staatsangeh.: Baden; Vorbildung: Goethesch. Karlsruhe Reife 12; Studium: München 2, Berlin 1, Heidelberg 3 S.; Rig. 24. Juli 15.] [U 15. 1902

NK 0207800 ICRL CtY

Knopf, Rudolf Hermann, 1893-
Die wirkungen der kartelle der textil- und bekleidungsindustrie auf die abnehmer. Mit einem anhang: Krieg und konventionen. Von dr. Rudolf Knopf. Karlsruhe i. B., G. Braun, 1915.

x, 116 p. 23½cm.
Issued also as inaugural dissertation, Heidelberg.
"Literaturverzeichnis": p. [ix]-x.

1. Textile industry and fabrics—Germany. 2. Clothing trade—Germany. 3. Trusts, Industrial—Germany.

45-28863

Library of Congress HD9863.5.K6 1915

NK 0207801 DLC PU MH

Knopf (Samuel). * Die visceralen Neuralgien im Verlaufe der Tabes dorsualis. 2 p. l., 40 pp. 8°. *Breslau, F. W. Jungfer*, 1877.

NK 0207802 DNLM

Knopf, Siegmund Adolph

SEE

Knopf, Sigard Adolphus, 1857- 1940 .

W 6 KNOPF, Sigard Adolphus, 1857-1940
P3 The alarming increase in the morbidity and mortality of tuberculosis among young women. [Chicago? 1928]
19 p. illus.
Reprinted, with additions and changes, from the Journal of the American Medical Association. Feb. 18. 1928.
DLC: YA 23000

NK 0207804 DNLM DLC PPPHC

Knopf, Sigard Adolphus, 1857- 1940 .
Alleged mental abnormality in pulmonary tuberculosis. 1927.
10 p.

NK 0207805 PPPHC

Knopf, Sigard Adolphus, 1857-1940.
... Aspects of birth control [by] Adolphus Knopf. Girard, Kans., Haldemann-Julius co., [1921?]
57 p. 13 cm. in cover 15 cm. (Ten cent pocket series no. 209)
1. Birth control.

NK 0207806 CU OO MH

HQ766 **Knopf, Sigard Adolphus, 1857-1940.**
.K69 Aspects of birth control. Girard, Kansas, Haldeman-Julius [1928?]
59 p. (Little blue book, no.209)
Electrostatic prints made by the Planned Parenthood Federation of America in 1966.

1. Birth control. Series.

NK 0207807 ICU

HQ 763 **Knopf, Sigard Adolphus, 1857-1940.**
. P3 Birth control as it confronts the medical profession in the United States ... New York, 1927.
[8] p. (Pamphlets on birth control no. 21)
"Reprinted from Clinical medicine and surgery, October 1927."

NK 0207808 DLC

Knopf, Sigard Adolphus, 1857- 1940 .

Birth control, its medical, social, economic, and moral aspects, by S. Adolphus Knopf ... [New York:] A. R. Elliott Pub. Co., cop. 1916. 19(1) p. 12°.

Caption-title.
Address delivered...at the forty-fourth annual meeting of the Amer. Public Health Assoc., Cincinnati, Octobre 27, 1916.
Repr.: New York medical jour. November 18, 1916.

1. Conception.—Prevention of.
N. Y. P. L. August 29, 1917.

NK 0207809 NN

HQ 763 **Knopf, Sigard Adolphus, 1857-1940.**
. P3 ... Birth control in its medical, social, economic and moral aspects ... with the discussion by Drs. Ira S. Wile, J. H. Landis, W. L. Holt, Louis I. Dublin, John W. Trask, and the closing remarks by Dr. Knopf. New York, The Birth control review [1917]
24 p. [Pamphlets on birth control no. 22]
"Reprinted from The American journal of public health, February, 1917."

NK 0207810 DLC NN

Knopf, Sigard Adolphus, 1857- 1940 .
Birth control in its medical, social, economic and moral aspects, by S. Adolphus Knopf ... with the discussion by Drs. Ira S. Wile, J. H. Landis, W. L. Holt, Louis I. Dublin, John W. Trask, and the closing remarks by Dr. Knopf. 2d ed., rev. by the author and reprinted with his permission. New York, New York women's publishing co., inc., 1919.

42 p. 20½cm.

1. Birth control. I. Title.

34-16956

Library of Congress HQ766.K6 1919 613.94

NK 0207811 DLC

HQ 763 **Knopf, Sigard Adolphus, 1857-1940.**
. P3 Birth control laws, their unwisdom, injustice and inhumanity ... Supplement to Various aspects of birth control, medical, social, economic, legal, moral and religious. With President Herbert Hoover's "The child's bill of rights" and a description of the Brush foundation for the betterment of the human stock, etc. ... Preface by Professor Charles De M. Sajous ... 4th ed. rev. and enl. ... New York, The

American birth control league, inc. [c1929]
21 p. [Pamphlets on birth control. no. 23]
Revised and reprinted from Medical journal and record of February 20, 1929.

NK 0207813 DLC

Knopf, Sigard Adolphus, 1857- 1940 .

Blinded soldiers as masseurs in hospitals and sanatoria for reconstruction and rehabilitation of disabled soldiers, by S. Adolphus Knopf ... New York: W. Wood & Co. [1918?] 9 p. 12°.

Cover-title.
"Reprinted from the Medical record, October 26, 1918."

1. Disabled.—Rehabilitation, etc. 2. Masseurs. 3. Title.
N. Y. P. L. May 28, 1919.

NK 0207814 NN

VOLUME 300

Knopf, Sigard Adolphus, 1857-1940.

Blinded soldiers as masseurs in hospitals and sanatoria for reconstruction and rehabilitation of disabled soldiers.
= [Philadelphia. 1918.] 6 pp. [American Academy of Political and Social Science. Publication no. 1236.] 25 cm.
Reprinted from the Annals of the American Academy of Political and Social Science, vol. 80 [*3565.109.80].

L6377 — S.r. — Blind, The. — European War, 1914- . Soldiers and sailors. Disabled.

NK 0207815 MB

Knopf, Sigard Adolphus, 1857-1940
3794.249
Ce que le soldat américain, qui combat actuellement en France, devrait savoir sur la tuberculose.
= [Montreal. 1918.] 23 pp. Illus. [Institut Bruchési antituberculeux de Montreal.] 12°.
Reprinted from L'union médicale du Canada.
Contains a preface by Jos. E. Dube, and an introduction by William H. Welch.
There is no title-page.

L6381 — S.r. Pubs. — Tuberculosis. — Welch, William Henry, pref., 1850-. — Dube, Joseph E., pref.

NK 0207816 MB

Knopf, Sigard Adolphus, 1857-1940.
Child labor and the nation's health; ratification of the Child labor amendment would decrease tuberculosis, increase the nation's health in general and lead to adoption of medical examination of old and young, and the creation of a Ministry of public health. By S. Adolphus Knopf ... Boston, The Christopher publishing house [°1937]
viii, 9-32 p. illus. (incl. ports.) 19cm.
1. Children—Employment—U. S. 2. Hygiene, Public—U. S. I. Title.
37-23803
Library of Congress HD6250.U3K6
——— Copy 2.
Copyright A 110032 331.30973

NK 0207817 DLC DL

HQ 766 .K58 Knopf, Sigard Adolph, 1857-1940.
[Collected papers, reprints, etc. on birth control]
7 pam.
[1] Some modern medico-sociologic conceptions of the alcohol, venereal diseases and tuberculosis problems. 34 p. (From Amer. practitioner, Feb., March and April, 1913) [2] Legalization of birth control, with special reference to the tuberculosis problem in the United States. 7 p. (Repr. Woman's med. journ., Sept., 1915) [3] Birth control, in its medical, social, economic and moral aspects. 24 p. (Repr. Amer. journ. pub. health, Feb. 1917) [4] The rights of the wife and mother. 24 p. (Repr. Woman's med. journ. Feb. 1917) [5] Preventive medicine and birth control. 15 p. (Repr. Med. times, April, 1917) [6] The dilemma of the family physician regarding conception and sterilization for race betterment. 14 p. (Ibid. April, 1930)

NK 0207819 DLC

WZ 100 qK722 KNOPF, Sigard Adolphus, 1857-1940
A collection of miscellaneous biobibliographical material on this person, together with abstracts, résumés, etc. of his works, may be found on the shelves under the above call number.

NK 0207820 DNLM

W 7 qK72 KNOPF, Sigard Adolphus, 1857-1940
[Collection of papers]
The library has a collection of miscellaneous papers by this author kept as received. These papers are not listed nor bound separately.

NK 0207821 DNLM

WF 7 K72c KNOPF, Sigard Adolphus, 1857-1940
[Collection of reprints, mainly on tuberculosis. New York [etc.] 1889-
v. illus.
1. Tuberculosis - Collected works

NK 0207822 DNLM ICJ DL

Knopf, Sigard Adolphus, 1857-1940.

Constructive suggestions toward the control of tuberculosis in times of peace and in times of war, by S. Adolphus Knopf... New York, 1917. 14 p., 1 l. 8°.
Cover-title.
Repr.: New York medical jour. June 23, 1917.

1. Tuberculosis.—Prevention.
N. Y. P. L. May 9, 1919.

NK 0207823 NN

Knopf, Sigard Adolphus, 1857-1940.
Dental hygiene for the pupils of public schools. N.Y., City Club of N.Y., 1912.
5 p.
"Reprinted from N.Y. medical journal, Sept. 28, 1921"

NK 0207824 OO

Knopf, Sigard Adolphus, 1857-1940.

Dental hygiene for the pupils of public schools. (In: Internat. Congress on Hygiene and Demography. 15. Washington, 1912. Transac. Washington, 1913. 8°. v. 3, p. 350-359.)

1. Teeth.—Hygiene of. 2. School children.—Medical inspection of.
N. Y. P. L. October 8, 1917.

NK 0207825 NN

Knopf, Sigard Adolphus, 1857-1940.
The dilemma of the family physician regarding contraception and sterilization for race betterment... (New York, 1930)
14 p. 31cm.

NK 0207826 DL

Knopf, Sigard Adolphus, 1857-1940.

The duties of the individual and the government in the combat of tuberculosis. [New York, 1903].

NK 0207827 MBCo

Knopf, Sigard Adolphus, 1857-1940
The duties of the school teacher in the combat of tuberculosis as a disease of the masses. By S. A. Knopf ... [Philadelphia, 1903]
p. 65-72. illus. 29cm.
From American medicine. July 11, 1903.

1. Tuberculosis.
7-29827 Revised
Library of Congress RC311.K715

NK 0207828 DLC

Knopf, Sigard Adolphus, 1857-1940.

Fragmentary notes on how to preserve and increase the physical, mental and moral vigor of our school children. (In: Internat. Congress on School Hygiene. 4. Buffalo, 1913. Transac. Buffalo, 1914. 8°. v. 3, p. 405-412.)

1. Schools.—Hygiene.
N. Y. P. L. June 25, 1917.

NK 0207829 NN

Knopf, Sigard Adolphus, 1857-1940

The health officer and the tuberculosis problem in rural communities, by S. Adolphus Knopf... New York: W. Wood & Co. [1914?] 12 p. 12°.
Cover-title.
Repr.: Medical record. Oct. 10, 1914.

1. Tuberculosis.—Prevention. 2. Hygiene (Rural).
N. Y. P. L. January 27, 1919

NK 0207830 NN

Knopf, Sigard Adolphus, 1857-1940.
Heart disease and tuberculosis; efforts including methods of diaphragmatic and costal respiration to lessen their prevalence [by] S. Adolphus Knopf ... New York, N. Y., 1936.
vii, 108 p. illus., diagrs. 20½ cm.
"This book issued by the patients at Potts memorial hospital for the rehabilitation of the tuberculous. For sale by the Livingston press, Livingston, Columbia county, New York."
"Revised from contributions in the Medical record of January 2nd, April 17th and June 19th, 1935."—Foot-note, p. 1.
"References": 73-74.
1. Heart—Diseases. 2. Tuberculosis. 3. Oxygen therapy.
RC683.K68 [616.246] 616.12 36—22333

NK 0207831 DLC DNLM OU NIC ICJ WU-M

Knopf, Sigard Adolphus, 1857-1940.
Herbert Maxon King - in memoriam, by S. A. Knopf.
n. p., n. pub., 1917.
Cover-title: 4 p., front. (port.)

Reprint from the Journal of outdoor life, Aug. 1917.

NK 0207832 MiDW NN

Knopf, Sigard Adolphus, 1857-1940.
A history of the National tuberculosis association; the anti-tuberculosis movement in the United States, by S. Adolphus Knopf, M. D. New York city, National tuberculosis association, 1922.
xii, 505 p. illus., plates, ports. 24cm.
Contains bibliographies.

1. National tuberculosis association. 2. Tuberculosis—Prevention.
22—21807
Library of Congress RC306.N4K6

NK 0207833 CaBVaU Wa OrP MtU Or WaS NIC NcD NcD-MC ICRL FTaSU DLC NN ICJ PP PU DNLM OU OClW OCl OrU-D

VOLUME 300

Knopf, Sigard Adolphus, 1857-1940.
The hygiene of public conveyances. By S. Adolphus Knopf. New York: W. Wood & Company, 1911. 19 p. 12°.
Repr.: The Medical Record, March 18, 1911. Title from cover.

1. Vehicles (Public).—Hygiene.
N. Y. P. L. August 23, 1911.

NK 0207834 NN

Knopf, Sigard Adolphus, 1857-1940.
The hygienic, educational, and symptomatic treatment of pulmonary tuberculosis, with a plea for sanatoriums for the poor. New York, Publishers' Printing co., 1897.
16 p. 1 pl. 8°.
Repr. The Medical Record, Feb. 13, 1897.

NK 0207835 NN

Knopf, Sigard Adolphus, 1857-1940.
In memoriam Warren G. Harding, president of the United States, 1920–1923, honorary vice-president of the National Tuberculosis Association, 1921–1923...by S. Adolphus Knopf... New York [1923] 2 l. port. 22½cm.
Cover-title.
"Reprinted from the New York medical journal and medical record, September 5, 1923."

743131A. 1. Harding, Warren Gamaliel, 29th pres. U. S.
N. Y. P. L. January 24, 1935

NK 0207836 NN

Knopf, Sigard Adolphus, 1857-1940.
Kampen mod tæring, med tillæg omhandlende sundhedsregler for hjemmet og skolen, tilstelning af sanatorium-behandling i hjemmet samt en historisk oversigt over kampen mod tæring i de Forenede Stater ... Et prisbelønnet skrift af S. Adolphus Knopf ... Bemyndiget udgave for norske og danske. Oversat fra engelsk af A. C. Amundson ... Madison, Wis., Amerika publishing company, 1908.
96 p. illus. 21½cm.
1. Tuberculosis. I. Amundson, Albert Christian, 1855-1919, tr. II. Title.
8-30729 Revised
Library of Congress RC311.K717

NK 0207837 DLC ICJ

WZ 309 K72k 1917
KNOPF, Sigard Adolphus, 1857-1940
The Knopf anthology; a collection of selected quotations from the addresses and writings of Dr. S. Adolphus Knopf. [n. p.] 1917.
59 l.
Contains author's bookplate.
Title

NK 0207838 DNLM

Knopf, Sigard Adolphus, 1857-1940.
The marriage of the tuberculous and the size of the family in their bearing on the tuberculosis problem. n. t.-p. [Philadelphia, 1906.] 4 p. 8°.
Repr.: Amer. medicine. v. 11, no. 1.

1. Tuberculosis.—Statistics.
N. Y. P. L. October 1, 1913.

NK 0207839 NN

Knopf, Sigard Adolphus, 1857-1940.
Medical essays. [New York? 1906–32.] 26 pams. in 1 v. illus., plan, ports. 31½cm.
Binder's title.
Bibliographies included.
Contents: The patient's duty. 12½cm. Early diagnosis of tuberculosis. 19cm. The relation of the medical profession to the housing problem. 18½cm. Robert Koch and the golden anniversary of his discovery of the tubercle bacillus. 20½cm. Some notes on the etiology, prophylaxis and therapeutics of laryngeal tuberculosis. 20cm. The mission of the municipal or state sanatorium for the tuberculous. 18cm.
Some newer problems...of the anti-tuberculosis warfare in the United States. 20cm. Birth control laws, their unwisdom, injustice and inhumanity. 20cm. Tuberculosis, drug addiction and the negro within our gates. 20½cm. How may the medical and teaching professions cooperate to improve the moral, mental and physical conditions of the young? 19½cm. In memoriam of Professor J. J. Grancher. 20½cm. Alleged mental abnormality in pulmonary tuberculosis. 20½cm. Sunlight and tuberculous disease. 20½cm. Climate in tuberculosis and the prevention of relapses. 21½cm. A plea for cremation in tuberculosis and similarly infectious diseases. 21½cm. The only effective famine relief. 23cm. In memoriam [Dr. Abraham Jacobi]. 23cm. In memoriam, James Freyer Cooper. 23cm. Halving the tax rate on buildings.
25½cm. The medical care of tuberculous thoracoplastic cases. 25½cm. The tuberculosis nurse and the tuberculosis problem. 25cm. What someone else thinks of us. 28cm. The future of medicine. 28cm. Birth control in tuberculosis and other serious disease. 28cm. An open letter on maternal mortality. 27½cm. The dilemma of the family physician regarding contraception and sterilization for race betterment. 30½cm.

617671A. 1. Tuberculosis. 2. Medicine—Essays and misc.
N. Y. P. L. June 30, 1933

NK 0207842 NN

Knopf, Sigard Adolphus, 1857-1940.
The medical, social, economic, moral and religious aspects of birth control, by S. Adolphus Knopf ... 3d ed., rev. and enl.; based upon an address delivered on December 21, 1925, at the New York academy of medicine before the Medical association of the greater city of New York, and printed in the Medical journal and record of January 6, 1926. New York, °1926.
4 p. l., 7-66 p. illus. 20cm.
First and second editions have title: Birth control in its medical, social, economic, and moral aspects.
"References": p. 66.
1. Birth control. I. Title.
26-12916 Revised
Library of Congress HQ766.K6 1926

NK 0207843 DLC ICJ MH DNLM

Knopf, Sigard Adolphus, 1857–1940.
Modern medicine in the United States; past achievements and solution of present day problems, by S. Adolphus Knopf ... Livingston, N. Y., Printed by tuberculous patients at the Potts memorial hospital for rehabilitation [1939]
40 p. 20½cm.

1. Medicine—U. S. I. Title.
A 41-3103
Columbia univ. Libraries for Library of Congress R152.K65
614.20973

NK 0207844 NNC NN

Knopf, Sigard Adolphus, 1857-1940.
Modern prophylaxis of pulmonary tuberculosis and its treatment in special institutions and at home. [New York, 1898.]
268 p.

NK 0207845 PPC

Knopf, Sigard Adolphus, 1857-1940
The modern warfare against tuberculosis as a disease of the masses. By S. Adolphus Knopf... [New York: A. R. Elliott Pub. Co., cop. 1914.] 28(1) p. 8°.
Cover-title.
Repr.: New York medical jour., Oct. 3, 1914.

1. Tuberculosis.—Prevention.
N. Y. P. L. September 19, 1916.

NK 0207846 NN

Knopf, Sigard Adolphus, 1857-1940.
The need of the hour, a united progressive medical profession with enough of the nation's wealth to further the nation's health [by] S. Adolphus Knopf... [New York: Medical jour. and record pub. co., inc., 1938] 22 p. 20½cm.
Cover-title.
"Reprinted from the Medical record, January 5, 1938."

1. Medicine—Social and economic aspects. 2. Medicine, State. I. Title.
N. Y. P. L. September 25, 1940

NK 0207847 NN

Knopf, Sigard Adolphus, 1857-1940
...Official provision for the tuberculous soldier and what he should know about his disease, by S. Adolphus Knopf... [New York:] A. R. Elliott Pub. Co., cop. 1919. 25(1) p. illus. 12°.
Caption-title.
"Reprinted from the New York medical jour. for March 15, 1919."

1. Tuberculosis.—Treatment. 2. European war, 1914- .—Medical and sanitary affairs.
N. Y. P. L. January 3, 1920.

NK 0207848 NN

HQ 763 .P3
Knopf, Sigard Adolphus, 1857-1940.
The only effective famine relief ... [1928]
[4] p. [Pamphlets on birth control. no. 24]
Caption title.
"Reprinted from The Medical critic and guide for December, 1928."

NK 0207849 DLC

Knopf, Sigard Adolphus, 1857-1940.
Open-air schools and open-air instructions with breathing exercises in schools and colleges to prevent tuberculosis and other diseases. (In: Internat. Congress on Hygiene and Demography, 15. Washington, 1912. Transac. Washington, 1913. 8°. v. 3, p. 22–38, 2 pl.)

1. Schools (Open air). 2. Tuberculosis.—Prevention.
N. Y. P. L. October 8, 1917.

NK 0207850 NN

Knopf, Sigard Adolphus. 1857-1940.
The Owen bill for the establishment of a federal department of health, and its opponents. [New York, 1910] p. 373-378. 8°.
Repr.: Popular Science Monthly. October, 1910.

1. Health boards, U. S., 1910.
N. Y. P. L. June 13, 1911.

NK 0207851 NN

R489.Os5 K75
Knopf, Sigard Adolph, 1857-1940.
... Personal reminiscences of Sir William Osler ... by S. Adolphus Knopf ... 1926.
cover-title, 8 p. 3 ports. on 2 l. 23cm.
At head of title: In memoriam.
"Reprinted from the memorial number of the International association of medical museums, 1926".
Presentation copy with author's inscription and signature.

NK 0207852 NNC PPHPI

VOLUME 300

Knopf, Sigard Adolphus, 1857-1940.

5079a.207

Ἡ φυματίωσις. Μετὰ πολλῶν εἰκόνων. Κατα μετάφρασιν Μιλτιάδου Θάλη.
Ἐν Ἀθήναις. 1906. 109 pp. Illus. [Σύλλογος πρὸς διάδοσιν ὠφελίμων βιβλίων. Ἐκδόσεις. 78.] 17 cm., in 8s.
A Modern Greek translation of the author's Tuberculosis as a disease of the masses [3794.92].

K2081 — Greece. Lang. Modern Greek. Works in Modern Greek. — Tuberculosis. — Thales, Miltiades, tr. — S.r.

NK 0207853 MB OCU OCl NN

Knopf, Sigard Adolphus, 1857-1940.
The physical, mental, and moral vigor of our school children. By S. Knopf... (New York? 1913?)
cover-title, 48 (1) p. 23 cm.
"Reprinted from the New York medical journal... December 13, 1913".

NK 0207854 DL

Knopf, Sigard Adolphus, 1857-1940

A plea for justice to the consumptive. A reply etc. New York,[1904].

NK 0207855 MBCo

Knopf, Sigard Adolphus, 1857-1940.

Pneumonia among soldiers in camps, cantonments, and at the front. Causes, prevention, treatment, and aftercare. By S. Adolphus Knopf... [New York: A. R. Elliott Pub. Co., cop. 1918.] 27(1) p. 8°.

Caption-title.
Repr.: New York medical jour., Jan. 26, 1918.

1. Pneumonia. 2. European war. 1914- .—Medical and sanitary affairs.
N. Y. P. L. June 21, 1918.

NK 0207856 NN

Knopf, Sigard Adolphus, 1857-1940.
Present status of preventative means against the spread of tuberculosis in the various States of the Union critically reviewed. N.Y., 1897.

pamph.

NK 0207857 PPHa

Knopf, Sigard Adolphus, 1857-1940.

Prevention of relapses in cases of arrested tuberculosis among soldiers and sailors [by] S. Adolphus Knopf... [Chicago: Amer. Medical Assoc., cop. 1919.] 31 p. illus., fold. pl. 8°.

"Reprinted from the Jour. of the Amer. Medical Assoc., Feb. 22, 1919, v. 72, p. 539-546."

1. Tuberculosis.—Treatment. 2. European war, 1914- .—Medical and sanitary affairs.
N. Y. P. L. January 3, 1920.

NK 0207858 NN

Knopf, Sigard Adolphus, 1857–1940.

Pulmonary tuberculosis; its modern prophylaxis and the treatment in special institutions and at home; Alvarenga prize essay of the College of physicians of Philadelphia for the year 1898; rev. and enl., by S. A. Knopf ... with descriptions and illustrations of the most important sanatoria of Europe, the United States, and Canada. Philadelphia, P. Blakiston's son & co., 1899.

2 p. l., ix-xvi, 17-343 p. incl. illus., plates, tables. double pl. 24cm.

1. Tuberculosis. I. Title.

99—2941

Library of Congress RC311.K72

PP ICRL NcD CaBVaU
NK 0207859 DLC ICJ DNLM NBuG MB OClW-H MiU OU PU

Knopf, Sigard Adolphus, 1857–1940.

Report to the United States government on tuberculosis, with some therapeutic and prophylactic suggestions [by] S. Adolphus Knopf, M. D. Revised and enlarged report submitted to the State department, War department and War veterans bureau, as government delegate to the International union against tuberculosis held at the Hague, Sept. 6–9, 1932 by S. Adolphus Knopf ... New York city, The National tuberculosis association [1933]

xiii, 59 p., 1 l. front. (port.) plates. 23½cm.
Bibliography at end of one chapter (p. 53)
1. Tuberculosis. 2. Tuberculosis—Hospitals and sanatoriums. 3. International conference against tuberculosis. 8th Hague, 1932. I. U. S. Dept. of state. II. U. S. War dept. III. U. S. Veterans' administration. IV. Title.
Library of Congress RC311.K725 33—23639
—— —— Copy 2.
Copyright A 65099 [a41n2] 616.246

OClW-H ICJ ViU
NK 0207860 DLC PPT-M OrU WaS PPHa PPCI MiU OU OCl

Knopf, Sigard Adolphus, 1857-1940.
Rest and exercise for the tuberculous and the predisposed child at school...by S. Adolphus Knopf... New York, W. Wood & company (1913)
cover-title, 32 p. illus., fold, pl., fold. plans. 20 cm.

"The architecture of open-air schools, by John V. Van Pelt". p.23-32

NK 0207861 DL

Knopf, Sigard Adolphus, 1857-1940.

Rest and exercise for the tuberculous and the predisposed child at school, with practical demonstrations of breathing exercises and a device combining open-air study and window-tent. (In: Internat. Congress on School Hygiene, 4. Buffalo, 1913. Transac. Buffalo, 1914. 8°. v. 5, p. 439–447.)

1. School children.—Medical inspection. 2. Tuberculosis in school children.
N. Y. P. L. June 6, 1917.

NK 0207862 NN

Knopf, Sigard Adolphus, 1857-1940.

...The rights of the wife and mother, by S. Adolphus Knopf ... [New York? 1917] 24 p. 20½cm.

Caption-title.
"Reprint from the Woman's medical journal, February, 1917."
"Address delivered...before the Philadelphia County Medical Society, January 10, 1917."

818977A. 1. Birth control.
N. Y. P. L. May 7, 1936

NK 0207863 NN

19th cent RC309 K56 1895

KNOPF, Sigard Adolphus, 1857-1940.
Les sanatoria: traitement et prophylaxie de la phtisie pulmonaire, par S. A. Knopf. Paris, G. Carré, 1895.
206p. illus. 25cm.
Thèse - Paris.
Bound with Tuffier, Th. Chirurgie du paumon. Paris, 1897.

1. Tuberculosis - Hospitals and sanatoriums 2. Tuberculosis - Prevention I. Title

NK 0207864 CtY-M DNLM PPC

WFA K72s 1895

KNOPF, Sigard Adolphus, 1857-1940
Les sanatoria, traitement et prophylaxie de la phtisie pulmonaire.
Paris, Carré, 1895.
206 p. illus.
Issued also as thesis, Paris.

NK 0207865 DNLM

WFA qK72s 1900

KNOPF, Sigard Adolphus, 1857-1940
Les sanatoria, traitement et prophylaxie de la phtisie pulmonaire.
2. éd. Paris, Carré et Naud, 1900.
xv, 495 p. illus.
Author's autograph presentation copy. Signed.

NK 0207866 DNLM PPC CtY-M

W 6 P3

KNOPF, Sigard Adolphus, 1857-1940
The social aspect of tuberculosis.
[n. p., 1908?]
16 p. illus.
Caption title.
Address delivered before the State Medical Association of Alabama, Montgomery, April 27, 1908.

NK 0207867 DNLM

WFA qK72se 1901

[KNOPF, Sigard Adolphus] 1857-1940
State control of tuberculosis. [New York, 19--?]
74 l. illus.
Contains author's bookplate.
Title

NK 0207868 DNLM

Knopf, Sigard Adolphus, 1857-1940

The statue of Edward Livingstone Trudeau, by S. Adolphus Knopf... [New York, 1918.] 4 p., 1 l. illus. 8°.

Cover-title.
Repr: New York medical jour. Aug. 24, 1918.

1. Trudeau, Edward Livingston, 1848-1915.
N. Y. P. L. March 8, 1919.

NK 0207869 NN

Knopf, Sigard Adolphus, 1857-1940

The teachers' part in the tuberculosis problem, by S. A. Knopf. New York: W. Wood & Co., 1906. 44 p. 12°.

Cover-title.
Repr.: Medical record, Feb. 17, 1906.

1. Tuberculosis.—Prevention.
N. Y. P. L. March 12, 1921.

NK 0207870 NN

Knopf, Sigard Adolphus, 1857-1940

——. The tenement and tuberculosis; an address delivered before a conference held under the auspices of the tenement house committee of the Charity Organization Society, New York, Feb. 20, 1900. 7 pp. 8°. [*New York*, 1900.]

NK 0207871 DNLM

VOLUME 300

Film 979 no. 2 KNOPF, Sigard Adolphus, 1857-1940
La tisis ó tuberculosis como enfermedad popular y el modo de combatirla ... Tr. libremente del idioma alemán al castellano, cuidadosamente arreglado con alcunos aumentos ... por Ernesto Sánchez y Rosal. Berlín, 1901.
55 p. illus.
"Folleto de concurso laureado por el Congreso Internacional para Combatir la Tisis ó Tuberculosis como Enfermedad Popular ... Berlin ... 1899."
Translation of Die Tuberkulose als Volkskrankheit und deren Bekämpfung.

NK 0207873 DNLM

RC311 K7524 Knopf, Sigard Adolph, 1857-1940.
... A tuberculose como doença popular e meios de combatel-a ... pelo dr. S. A. Knopf ... Traduzido e ampliado com um capitulo sobre "O problema da tuberculose em Portugal e no Brasil" pelo dr. Clemente Ferreira ... Sao Paulo, Escola typographica Salesiana, 1901.
52 p., 1 l. illus.
At head of title: Publicações da "Revista medica de Sao Paulo".
Some pages mutilated in trimming.

NK 0207874 NNC DNLM

WFA K72t 1902 KNOPF, Sigard Adolphus, 1857-1940
La tuberculose considérée comme maladie du peuple, des moyens de la combattre. Tr. et annoté par G. Sersiron. Paris, Naud, 1902.
93 p. illus.
Translation of Die Tuberkulose als Volkskrankheit und deren Bekämpfung.
"Ouvrage ayant obtenu le prix de 5000 francs proposé par le Congrès de Berlin pour la lutte contre la tuberculose considérée comme maladie du peuple."

NK 0207876 DNLM

Knopf, Sigard Adolphus, 1857-1940.
La tuberculosis ... San Salvador, centro editorial Melendez. (n.d.)

NK 0207877 DPU

WF 200 K72t 1900 Knopf, Sigard Adolphus, 1857-1940
Tuberculosis. (Diagnosis, prognosis, prophylaxis, and treatment) [New York, 1900]
p. [187]-358. illus.
Reprinted from Twentieth century practice, v. 20, 1900, ed. by T. L. Stedman.
Bibliography: p. 350-358.
Author's autograph presentation copy. Signed; contains also his book-plate.

NK 0207878 DNLM

Knopf, Sigard Adolphus, 1857-1940.
Tuberculosis a preventable and curable disease; modern methods for the solution of the tuberculosis problem, by S. Adolphus Knopf ... New York, Moffat, Yard and company, 1909.
xxxii, 3-394 p. incl. front. (port.) illus. col. pl. 20½cm.

1. Tuberculosis. 2. Tuberculosis—Prevention.
9-17599 Revised
Library of Congress RC311.K77

NK 0207879 PU PPL WaS Wa MtHi DNLM NcD ICRL DLC OC1W-H OU OC1 OC1W OO ViU ICJ NN PP

Knopf, Sigard Adolphus, 1857-1940.
Tuberculosis a preventable and curable disease; modern methods for the solution of the tuberculosis problem, by S. Adolphus Knopf ... 2d ed. New York, Moffat, Yard and company, 1910.
xiii, 3-394 p. incl. front. (port.) illus., col. pl. 20cm.

1. Tuberculosis. 2. Tuberculosis—Prevention.
25-15220 Revised
Library of Congress RC311.K77 1910

NK 0207880 DLC PPHa PPHPI NN OU MiU

Knopf, Sigard Adolphus, 1857-1940.
Tuberculosis a preventable and curable disease; modern methods for the solution of the tuberculosis problem. 2d ed. New York, Moffat, Yard and company, 1913.
394p. illus.

NK 0207881 ICRL

Knopf, Sigard Adolphus, 1857-1940.
Tuberculosis a preventable and curable disease; modern methods for the solution of the tuberculosis problem ... New ed. New York, 1916.
xxxii, 3-394 p. incl. front. (port.) illus. col. pl. 21 cm.

NK 0207882 RPB

Knopf, Sigard Adolphus, 1857-
Tuberculosis as a disease of the masses, and how to combat it ... Prize essay by S. A. Knopf ... New York, M. Firestack, 1901.
86 p. illus. 23½cm.
"The 'International congress to combat tuberculosis as a disease of the masses', which convened at Berlin, May 24th to 27th, 1899, awarded the international prize to this work through its committee on July 31st, 1900."

1. Tuberculosis. I. Title.
3-5277 Revised
Library of Congress RC311.K74

NK 0207883 DNLM ICJ MB NN NjP DLC PPC PPL PPT-M ICRL OU OC1W-H OC1

WFA K72t 1905 KNOPF, Sigard Adolphus, 1857-1940
Tuberculosis as a disease of the masses, and how to combat it. American ed. New York, Firestack, 1905.
86 p. illus.
Translation of Die Tuberkulose als Volkskrankheit und deren Bekämpfung.
"The 'International Congress to Combat Tuberculosis as a Disease of the Masses,' which convened at Berlin, May 24th to 27th, 1899, awarded the International prize to this work through its Committee on July 31st, 1900."
Author's autograph presentation copy. Signed.

NK 0207885 DNLM PPC NjP

Knopf, Sigard Adolphus, 1857-1940.
Tuberculosis as a disease of the masses and how to combat it. 5th ed. rev. & illus... N.Y., Flori. 1906.
104p. O.

NK 0207886 OO

RC312 .K7 Knopf, Sigard Adolphus, 1857-1940.
Tuberculosis as a disease of the masses, and how to combat it. 4th issue rev. and illustrated, with supplement on home hygiene, school hygiene, installation of the sanatorium treatment at home, and a historical review of the anti-tuberculosis movement in the United States... Prize essay by S.A. Knopf... New York, F.P. Flori [etc.] 1907.
104 p. illus. (incl. diagrs.) 22½cm.
The "International congress to combat tuberculosis as a disease of the masses"...Berlin, 1899, awarded the International prize to this work.

NK 0207888 ICU CtY-M DNLM Mi MoU PPC PPJ ICJ NN

Knopf, Sigard Adolphus, 1857-1940.
Tuberculosis as a disease of the masses and how to combat it. 5th ed., rev. and illus., with supplement on home hygiene, school hygiene, installation of the sanatorium treatment at home, and a historical review of the anti-tuberculosis movement in the United States... Prize essay... New York, Flori, 1908.
104p. illus. O.

NK 0207889 IaU ICRL IU-M PPC OC1W

RC311 K752 1909 Knopf, Sigard Adolph, 1857-1940
Tuberculosis as a disease of the masses and how to combat it. 5th ed. rev. and illustrated, with supplement on home hygiene, school hygiene, installation of the sanatorium treatment at home, and a historical review of the anti-tuberculosis movement in the United States ... prize essay by S. Adolphus Knopf ... New York, Flori, 1909.
104 p. illus. 23cm.
Presentation copy to New York society library with author's inscription and signature.
"List of translations": p. [2]
1. Tuberculosis. 2. Tuberculosis, Pulmonary.

NK 0207890 NNC

Knopf, Sigard Adolphus, 1857-1940.
Tuberculosis as a disease of the masses and how to combat it. 7th American ed., enl. and rev. With 64 illustrations ... Prize essay, by S. Adolphus Knopf ... New York, The Survey, 1911.
124 p. illus. (incl. port.) 23cm.
"The 'International congress to combat tuberculosis as a disease of the masses', which convened at Berlin, May 24th to 27th, 1899, awarded the International prize to this work through its committee on July 31st, 1900."
"List of translations": p. [2]
1. Tuberculosis. I. Title.
13-22054 Revised
Library of Congress RC311.K74 1911

NK 0207891 DLC DNLM DL ICJ PPC Or OrU-M

WFA K72t 1913 KNOPF, Sigard Adolphus, 1857-1940
Tuberculosis as a disease of the masses and how to combat it. 7th American ed., enl. and rev. New York, The Survey, 1913.
124 p. illus.
Translation of Die Tuberkulose als Volkskrankheit und deren Bekämpfung.
"The 'International Congress to Combat Tuberculosis as a Disease of the Masses,' which convened at Berlin, May 24th to 27th, 1899, awarded the International prize to this work through its committee on July 31st, 1900."
Author's autograph presentation copy. Signed.

NK 0207893 DNLM DL PU PP PPJ

VOLUME 300

K7628
Knopf, Sigard Adolph, 1857-1940.
... La tuberculosis es una enfermedad del pueblo, medios de combatirla ... folleto premiado escrito por S. A. Knopf ... Traducido del texto inglés por D. Vergara Lope ... precedido de un prólogo escrito por el sr. dr. E. Licéaga ... Mexico, D. F., Publicado por la Antigua imprenta de Murguia, 1902.
111 p. illus.

At head of title: Ministerio de gobernacion. Consejo superior de salubridad.

NK 0207894 NNC DNLM

Knopf, Sigard Adolphus, 1857-1940.
... The tuberculosis problem in rural communities: its modern aspect and the duty of health officers, by S. Adolphus Knopf, M. D., New York, N. Y. ... Washington, Govt. print. off., 1915.
11 p. 23cm.
At head of title: United States Public health service. Rupert Blue, surgeon general.
Reprint no. 243 from the Public health reports, v. 29, no. 51, December 18, 1914.
1. Tuberculosis—Prevention. I. U. S. Public health service. Public health reports. Reprint 243.
15-26089 Revised
Library of Congress RA644.T7K7

NK 0207895 DLC NN DL OC1W MiU DNLM

RC311
K7522
Knopf, Sigard Adolph, 1857-1940.
Tuberkuloosi kansantautina ja sen ehkäisceminen ... kilpakirjotus, sommitellut S. A. Knopf ... Asianomaisella luvalla suomentaneet Johannes Hoving ja Lauri Rosendal ... [New York?] Pohjan Tähden kirjapainossa, 1906.
61, [1] p. illus.

I. Hoving, Johannes, tr.
II. Rosendal, Lauri, tr.

NK 0207896 NNC MnHi

Knopf, Sigard Adolphus, 1857-1940.
טובערקולאזע (אויסצעהרונג—שווינדזוכט) אַלס אַ קראַנק־הייט צווישען דאָס פאָלק און וויא עס צו בעקעמפפען ... פרעמיום־ווערק, איבערזעצט און אַרויסגעגעבען אין אידיש פון דר. ל. וו. צבי׳זאהן. L. W. Zwisohn, M. D. ... ניו יאָרק, דרוק פון א. צונזער, 1902.
100 p. illus. 21cm.
1. Tuberculosis. I. Zwisohn, Lazarus W.
2-19187 Revised
Library of Congress

NK 0207897 DLC

Knopf, Sigard Adolphus, 1857-1940.
Die tuberkulose als volkskrankheit und deren bekämpfung ... Preisschrift, gekrönt mit dem preise des Kongresses zur bekämpfung der tuberkulose als volkskrankheit, Berlin 24.-27. mai 1899. Von dr. S. A. Knopf ... Herausgegeben vom Deutschen central-komite zur errichtung von heilstätten für lungenkranke. Berlin [Druck der buch- und kunstdruckerei Rares & co.] 1900.
48 p. illus. 23cm.
"Vorwort" by Prof. B. Fränkel.
1. Tuberculosis. I. Deutsches zentral zur bekaempfung der tuberkulose, komitee lungenkranke, Berlin.
6-17711 Revised
Library of Congress RC311.K73

NK 0207898 DLC MiU DNLM NcU

RC311
K7523
1901
Knopf, Sigard Adolph, 1857-1940.
Die tuberkulose als volkskrankheit und deren bekämpfung. Preisschrift, gekrönt mit dem preise des Kongresses zur bekämpfung der tuberkulose als volkskrankheit, Berlin 24.-27. mai 1899, von dr. S. A. Knopf ... Hrsg. vom heilstätten für lungenkranke. Berlin [Druck von Trowitzsch & sohn] 1901.
48 p. illus.

NK 0207899 NNC

RC
311
.K519
Knopf, Sigard Adolphus, 1857-1940
Tuberkulosen såsom folksjukdom ock dess bekämpande; prisskrift, av S. A. Knopf ... Bemyndigad översättning till svenska av Johannes Hoving. New York, Tryckt i Finska Amerikanaren, 1905.
72 p. illus. 20 cm.

Translation of Tuberculosis as a disease and how to combat it.

NK 0207900 MnHi

Knopf, Sigard Adolphus, 1857-1940.
Um berklaveiki sem þjóðarmein og ráð til að útrýma henni. Verðlaunarit. Íslenzk þýðing með ýmsum breytingum eftir Guðmund Björnsson. Gefin út á landssjóðs kostnað. Reykjavík, 1903. 8°. pp. vii + 56, *illustr.*

NK 0207901 NIC

Knopf, Sigard Adolphus, 1857-1940
Various aspects of birth control: medical, social, economic, legal, moral and religious, by S. Adolphus Knopf ... 4th ed., rev. and enl. New York, °1928.
92, [1] p. illus. 20cm.
First and second editions have title: Birth control in its medical, social, economic and moral aspects.
"References": p. 85.

1. Birth control. I. Title.
28-13469 Revised
Library of Congress HQ766.K6 1928

NK 0207902 DLC NcD-L CU MiU OC1W ICJ PPC PPJ NN

Knopf, Sigard Adolphus, 1857-1940.
What may be done to improve the hygiene of the city dweller. By S. Adolphus Knopf. New York: W. Wood & Company, 1910. 40 p. 12°.
Repr.: Medical Record, January 8, 1910. Title from cover.

1. Hygiene (Public).
N. Y. P. L. August 22, 1911.

NK 0207903 NN

Knopf, Sigard Adolphus, 1857-1940.
What the American soldier now fighting in France should know about tuberculosis, by S. Adolphus Knopf...with an introduction by William H. Welch... Published by authority of the surgeon general of the United States army. [New York? 1918. 6 p., 1 l. illus. 8°.
Cover-title.
Repr.: Jour. of the outdoor life, New York. Jan. 1918.

1. Tuberculosis. 2. European war. 1914- —Medical and sanitary affairs. 3. Title.
N. Y. P. L. April 4, 1918.

NK 0207904 NN MB

WF
200
K72w
1918
KNOPF, Sigard Adolphus, 1857-1940
What the American soldier now fighting in France should know about Tuberculosis. Rev. ed. New York, 1918.
20 p. illus.

NK 0207905 DNLM

WO
212
M7
K72
RB
Knopf, Sigard Adolphus, 1857-1940.
William T G. Morton, the discoverer and revealer of surgical anesthesia, at last in the Hall of Fame -- a vindication. n.p. [1921].
16 p., illus., 20 cm.
Reprinted from the Medical Record, January 29, 1921.

1. Morton, William Thomas Green, 1819-1868.
2. Ether Controversy

NK 0207906 IParkA PPWD

Knopf, Sigard Adolphus, 1857-1940
Woman's duty in the antituberculosis crusade. By S. Adolphus Knopf... New York: W. Wood & Co. [1916.] 9 p. 12°.
Repr.: Medical record, July 8, 1916.

1. Tuberculosis.—Prevention. 2. Woman in sociological work.
N. Y. P. L. February 26, 1919.

NK 0207907 NN

Knopf, Thomas Hans Henrich. Insviae Islandiae delineatio, prout haec solenni negotio mensurandi sub auspiciis potentissimi regis Daniae facto, & a 1734 demum per Cnopfium ad finem producto . . . Edita studio et impensis Homanniorum Heredum, Norimbergae, 1761. *Map, col. Size:* 59 x 45 cm. IcC3M296

NK 0207908 NIC

Knopf, Thomas Hans Henrich. Minning efter ett samtal med ingenieur capitainen Hans Henric Christopher Knoff, om Island, sedan han tillika med sin broder, på kongl. dansk befallning afmått samma landskap och ö, åhren . . . *Rotograph copy of MS. in* Kungl. Biblioteket, Stockholm, ff. (7). IcC9K725
Inserted a letter from O. Wieselgren.

NK 0207909 NIC

Knopf, Walther, 1889-
Untersuchungen zur wirkung der kampfderivate "camphenilon" und "camphenon".
Inaug. diss. Bonn, 1916.

NK 0207910 ICRL DNLM CtY

Knopf, Werner.
... Die entwicklung der religionsvergehen seit Anselm von Feuerbach, von dr. Werner Knopf. Leipzig, A. Klein, 1936.
123 p. 22cm. (Völkisches erwachen, hrsg. von Gustav von Reinkirch. hft. 9)
"Schrifttum": p. 115-123.

1. Feuerbach, Paul Johann Anselm, ritter von, 1775-1833. 2. Sacrilege. 3. Blasphemy. 4. Germany — Religion. 5. Criminal law — Germany. I. Title.
39-2847

NK 0207911 DLC NNC MH

VOLUME 300

Hie26
80
Knopf, Wilhelm, 1876-
Zur Geschichte der typischen Zahlen in der deutschen Litteratur des Mittelalters ... Leipzig,E.Glausch,1902.
vi,96p.,1ℓ. 22½cm.
Inaug.-Diss. - Leipzig.
Lebenslauf.
"Litteraturangabe": p.[v]-vi.

1.Numerals. 2.Middle High German literature - Hist. & crit.

NK 0207912 CtY ICRL GEU MdBJ IaU PU CSt

Diss.
378
N.U.
1950
Knopf, William C 1910-
A study of the infra-red spectrum of iron I
Evanston, 1950.
55ℓ. illus.,graphs. 28cm.

Thesis - Northwestern Univ.
Vita.
Bibliography: leaves 52-53.

1. Spectrum, Infra-red. 2. Iron.

NK 0207913 IEN

VM
2079
E 9
K 72g
KNOPFEL, GUSTAV C.
Grand Te Deum in B♭... New York,W.A.Pond & co.,c1872.
23p.

Vocal score with organ accompaniment.
English words.
Plate no.: 8230.
Composer's autograph presentation copy to Otto Lob.

NK 0207914 ICN

Knöpfel, Gustav C
see Knopfel, Gustav C

Knopff, Christianus Alardus, *praeses.*
... De sponsione inæqvali; Von ungleicher wette, præside Christiano Alardo Knopff, J. U. D., publice disputabit Ernestus Carolus Wahlfeldt, Osnabr. Westph., in auditorio jctorum ad d. jul. anno M.DC.LXXXVI. Jenæ, typis J. D. Wertheri [1686?]
[28] p. 19½cm.
At head of title: Dei et superiorum permissu.

1. Wagers. I. Wahlfeldt, Ernestus Carolus, respondent. II. Title.

34-15160

Library of Congress 347.4

NK 0207916 DLC

Knopff, Christian Alard, praeses
... Nullitatem conditionis de assumenda religione pontificia heredi vel legatario adscriptae in foro romano ... Jenae, G.H. Müller [1687]
[24] p. 19½cm.

Diss. - Jena (Andreas Eggertt, respondent)

NK 0207917 MH-L

Knopff, Heinz, Landwirtschaftslehrer: Der Einfluss der Kriegswirtschaft auf Milchleistung und Form der ostpreussischen Rinder. [In Maschinenschrift.] 140 S. 4°(2°). — Auszug in: Inaug.-Dissertationen d. phil. Fak. Königsberg i. P. S. 61—63. o. O. [1921]. 8°
Königsberg, Phil. Diss. v. 29. Juli 1921, Ref. Hansen
[Geb. 25. März 94 Seesken, Kr. Oletzko; Wohnort: Königsberg i. P.; Staatsangeh.: Preußen; Vorbildung: Löben-RG. Königsberg Reife 12; Studium: Königsberg 1, Jena 2, Königsberg 4 S.; Rig. 19. Juli 21.] [U 21. 7153

NK 0207918 ICRL DLC

Knopff (Joannes Petrus). * Diss. sistens pathologiam renum. 3 p. l., 58 pp. 8°. *Jenæ, typ. Etzdorfii et soc.*, [1800].

NK 0207919 DNLM

Knopff (Joh. Jacobus). * Diss. phys. de corpore humano. 11 pp. 4°. *Ratisponæ, typ. A. Hanckwitz*, 1681.

NK 0207920 DNLM

Knopff, Johann Georg, respondent.
... De legibus in genere et specie
see under Bechmann, Johann Volkmar, 1624-1689, praeses.

Knopff, Paul.
Darstellung der ablautverhältnisse in der schottischen schriftsprache, mit vergleichungen in bezug auf abweichungen der anderen mittelenglischen dialekte ... von Paul Knopff ... Würzburg, Druck von Memminger, 1904.
111, [1] p., 1 l. 21cm.
Inaug.-diss.—Bern.
"Verzeichnis der im text erwähnten werke": p. [112]

1. English language—Dialects—Scotch. 2. English language—Middle English (1100-1500)—Vowel gradation.

5-11114

Library of Congress PE2114.K7

NK 0207922 DLC NcD PBm PU NN

Knopfli (Emil). * Ueber angeborene Defecte der Kammerscheidewand des Herzens. 49 pp., 3 pl. 8°. *Zürich, Polygraphisches Inst.* 1901.

NK 0207923 DNLM

J8
.P72
Knopfli, Josué, ed.
Mozambique.
Boletim oficial.
Lourenço Marques, Impr. Nacional.

KNOPFLI, JOSUÉ, ed.
Sinopse das matérias oficiais publicadas no "Boletim oficial" da colónia de Moçambique referiola ao ano de 1944. Lourenço Marques, Imprensa nacional de Moçambique, 1945. 92 p. 24cm.

Microfiche (neg.) 2 sheets. 11 x 15cm. (NYPL FSN-02356)

1. Government publications--Mozambique--Bibl. I. Mozambique. Boletin oficial (Indexes)

NK 0207925 NN

Knopfli, Josue, *ed.*
Sinopse das matérias oficiais publicadas no "Boletim oficial" da Colónia de Moçambique referida ao ano de 1949. Lourenço Marques, Impr. Nacional de Moçambique, 1950.
160 p. 25 cm.

1. Mozambique—Government publications—Bibl. 2. Mozambique. Boletim oficial.

Z3884.G68K55 015.679 53-20403

NK 0207926 DLC NSyU

Knopfli, Walter,
Beitraege zur morphologie und entwicklungsgeschichte des brustschulterskelettes...
Inaug. diss. Zurich,1918.
Bibl.

NK 0207927 ICRL

Knopfli, Walter, 1889-
Echte Möwen: [Larinae (Unterfamilie Laridae). n.p., 1946]
3531-3786p. (Die Vögel der Schweiz ("Katalog der Schweizerischen Vögel von Studer und Fatio") Lieferung XVIII)

NK 0207928 InLP

Knopfli, Walter, 1889-
Methoden der tiergeographie. Von Knopfli ...
(*In* Abderhalden, Emil, ed. Handbuch der biologischen arbeitsmethoden ... Berlin, 1920- 25cm. abt. VII, Methoden der vergleichenden morphologischen forschung. t. 1 (1930) p. [33]-76. illus., diagrs.)
"Literaturverzeichnis": p. 74-76.

1. Zoology—Geographical distribution.

A C 36-3208

Title from Ohio State Univ.
Library of Congress [QH324.A3 1920 abt. 7, t. 1]

NK 0207929 OU

Knopfmacher, Heinz Paul, 1913-
A genetical study of rabbit blood groups ... [Providence, 1942]
iv, 36 (i. e. 37) [1] numb. l. incl. tables. 27 cm.
Thesis (Ph. D)--Brown university, 1942.
Typewritten.
Vita.
Bibliography: l. 34-36.

NK 0207930 RPB

Knopfmacher, Heinz Paul, 1913-
A study of four antigenic components of rabbits' erythrocytes, by H. P. Knopfmacher ... [n. p., 1942]
cover-title, 121-128 p. incl. tables. 25½cm.
Part of thesis (PH. D.)—Brown university, 1942.
"Reprinted from the Journal of immunology, vol. 44, no. 2, June, 1942."
"References": p. 128.

1. Antigens and antibodies. 2. Blood groups. 3. Rabbits.

A 45-1380

Brown univ. Library for Library of Congress QR185.K6

NK 0207931 RPB DLC

Knopfmacher, Walter, 1899-
Wege zum selbsttätigen auffinden und einregeln von Maxima und Minima-bedingungen physikalischer Grössen. ... Bückeburg, 1936.
Inaug. Diss. - Techn. Hochschule Berlin, 1936.
Lebenslauf.
Literatur-Verzeichnis.

NK 0207932 ICRL

VOLUME 300

[Knoph, L]
Veiledning for emigranter til Amerika, forsaavidt angaar befordring pr. dampskib over Hull og Liverpool till New-York og videre indgjennem landet pr. jernbane. Christiania, Lehmannske bogtrykkeri, 1869.
31 p. 17cm.
Signed: L. Knoph, af firma Blichfeldt, Knoph & co., autoriserede emigrations-agenter.
1. U. S.—Description and travel. I. Title.
A 30-223
Title from Minnesota Hist. Soc. Printed by L. C.

NK 0207933 MnHi

Knoph, Ragnar, 1894-1938.
Åndsretten. Oslo, Nationaltrykkeriet, 1936.
xv, 643 p. 24 cm.
Bibliography: p. [634]-637.
1. Copyright—Norway. 2. Patent laws and legislation—Norway. 3. Trade-marks—Norway. 4. Business names—Norway. 5. Competition, Unfair—Norway.
Full name: Ragner Johan Gyth Knoph.
655.6481 43-29024 rev*

NK 0207934 DLC ICU

Knoph, Ragnar, 1894-1938
... Funksjonæropfinnelsen. Oslo, H. Aschehoug & co., 1928.
4 p. l., 101 p. 20cm.
1. Patent laws and legislation—Norway. [1. Patents—Norway] 2. Patent laws and legislation. 3. Contracts. [3. Contracts — Norway] I. Title.
[Full name: Ragnar Johan Gyth Knoph]
30-16190

NK 0207935 DLC

Knoph, Ragnar, 1894-1938, ed.
Lov om motorvogner av 20. februar 1926, med trafikkregler, forskrifter m. m.; kommentar-utgave ved Ragnar Knoph ... og A. Rørholt ... Oslo, Grøndahl & søn, 1927.
4 p. l., 120 p. illus. (incl. plans) 20cm.
Amendments, 1928-1930 (Norwegian and Norwegian landsmål in parallel columns): [2], 4, 14, 2 p. laid in.
1. Automobiles—Laws and regulations—Norway. 2. Highway law—Norway. 3. Traffic regulations—Norway. I. Rørholt, Arnold, 1884- joint ed. II. Title.
[Full name: Ragnar Johan Gyth Knoph]
36-29360
Library of Congress HE5679.K5
388.309481

NK 0207936 DLC

Knoph, Ragnar, 1894-1938.
... Norsk arverett. Oslo, H. Aschehoug & co., 1929.
278 p. 23.5 cm.

NK 0207937 CtY

Knoph, Ragnar, 1894-1938.
... Norsk arverett. Oslo, H. Aschehoug & co., 1930.
xvi, 441 p. 23½cm.
Bibliography: p. [438]-439.
1. Inheritance and succession—Norway. I. Title.
[Full name: Ragnar Johan Gyth Knoph]
36-3705
Library of Congress [347.6] 349.481076

NK 0207938 DLC

Knoph, Ragnar, 1894-1938.
Norsk arverett. 2. utg ved Hans Lütken. Oslo, H. Aschehoug, 1944.
xvi, 433 p. 24 cm.
"Forkortelser" (bibliography): p. [432]-433.
1. Inheritance and succession—Norway. I. Lütken, Hans, 1882- ed. II. Title.
Full name: Ragnar Johan Gyth Knoph.
48-32338*

NK 0207939 DLC MnU

Knoph, Ragnar, 1894-1938.
... Norsk sjørett. Oslo [Nationaltrykkeriet] 1931.
xvi, 390 p. 23cm.
"Annen utgave ... trykt som manuskript."—Forord.
"Forkortelser" (bibliography): p. [378]-379.
1. Maritime law—Norway. I. Title.
[Full name: Ragnar Johan Gyth Knoph]
36-3702
Library of Congress [347.709481] 349.481077

NK 0207940 DLC

Knoph, Ragnar, 1894-1938.
... Oversikt over Norges rett. Oslo, Nationaltrykkeriet, 1934.
xxii, 458 p., 1 l. 23½cm.
1. Law—Norway. I. Title.
[Full name: Ragnar Johan Gyth Knoph]
36-5534
Library of Congress [347.09481] 349.481

NK 0207941 DLC CtY

293r
S4
K72
1937
Law
Library
Knoph, Ragnar, 1894-1938.
Oversikt over Norges rett. 2.utgave. Oslo, Nationaltrykkeriet, 1937.
xxii,470 p.

NK 0207942 CU

Knoph, Ragnar, 1894-1938.
Oversikt over Norges rett. 3. utg. ved Sverre Grette. Oslo, Nationaltrykkeriet, 1949.
xxii, 481 p. 24 cm.
1. Law—Norway. I. Grette, Sverre, ed.
Full name: Ragnar Johan Gyth Knoph.
49-53163*
Library of Congress

NK 0207943 DLC IU NNC

Knoph, Ragnar, 1894-1938.
Rett og rettsbevissthet. Kristiania, O.Norli, 1923.
29 p. 20 cm. (Det Norske studentersamfunds folkeskrifter, 5)
Paper-cover: Utgit med bidrag av Universitetets jubilaeumsfond.

NK 0207944 MH NN

Knoph, Ragnar, 1894-1938.
... Rettslige standarder, særlig Grunnlovens § 97. Oslo, I kommisjon hos Grøndahl & søn, 1939.
3 p. l., [v]-xiii, [1], 296 p. front. (port.) 23½cm.
"Forord" signed: F. Schjelderup.
1. Law—Interpretation and construction. 2. Law—Norway—Interpretation and construction. 3. Retroactive laws. 4. Limitation of actions—Norway. I. Schjelderup, Thorleif Ferdinand, 1886- ed. II. Title.
[Full name: Ragnar Johan Gyth Knoph]
43-28223

NK 0207945 DLC

Knoph, Ragnar, 1894-1938.
... Rettslige standarer, saerlig Grunnlovens §97. Oslo, Grøndahl, 1948.
3 p.l., [v]-xiii, [1], 296 p. front. (port.) 22½cm.
"Litteraturen": p. 14-16.
"Forord" signed: F. Schjelderup.
First published in 1939.

NK 0207946 MH-L CU

Knoph, Ragnar, 1894-1938, ed.
... Trustloven av 1926, med kommentarer. [Oslo] Norges industriforbund [1926]
193 p. 21½cm.
1. Trusts, Industrial—Norway—Law. I. Norway. Laws, statutes, etc. II. Title.
[Full name: Ragnar Johan Gyth Knoph]
36-4214
Library of Congress 338.809481

NK 0207947 DLC

Canon Law
BV
104
.C35
n.16
Knopke, Roch Francis, 1906-
... Reverential fear in matrimonial cases in Asiatic countries; Rota cases; a historical synopsis ... Washington, D.C., The Catholic University of America, 1948.
iii, 20numb. leaves. 28cm. (The Catholic university of America. Canon law studies [J.C.L. theses, no. 16])
Thesis (J.C.L.) --C.U.A., 1948.
Bibliography: leaves 25-27.
Vita.
1. Marriage - Cases (Canon law) I. Title.

NK 0207948 DCU

Knopke, Roch Francis, 1906-
Reverential fear in matrimonial cases in Asiatic countries: Rota cases; a historical synopsis and a commentary. Washington, Catholic University of America Press, 1949 [©1950]
xi, 112 p. 23 cm. (The Catholic University of America. Canon law studies, no. 294)
Thesis—Catholic University of America.
Vita.
"Chronological listing of the Rota cases cited": p. 91-94.
Bibliography: p. 86-89.
1. Marriage (Canon law) 2. Marriage—China. 3. Duress (Canon law) 4. [Marriage—Cases] I. Catholic Church. Rota Romana. II. Title. (Series)
173.1 A 51—116
Catholic Univ. of America. Library for Library of Congress [a60d½]†

NK 0207949 DCU DLC NIC

KNOPKEN, Andreas, d.1539
In epistolam ad Romanos Andreae Knopken Costerinēsis interpretatio ... [Wittenberg] M. D. XXV.
[160]p. 15.5cm.
Signatures: A-K8.
Colophon: Excvdebarvr Anno Domini M. D. XXV
Title within ornamental borders.

NK 0207950 MH-AH

VOLUME 300

Knopl, Michael P.
The dragon's smile; novel by Michael Knopl. [Los Angeles, Eastern printing company] 1926.
55 p. 21½cm.

I. Title.

26-22409

Library of Congress PZ3.K757Dr

NK 0207951 DLC

Knopp, Ernst Heinrich Otto
see Knopp, Otto, 1883-

Knopp, Friedrich August, *ed.*
Die sudetendeutschen preisvorschriften, herausgegeben von oberregierungsrat F. A. Knopp ... und dr. G. Goedecke ... fortgesetzt von regierungsrat dr. Fritz Thiel ... Reichenberg, Sudetenland, Sudetendeutscher verlag F. Kraus, 1939-40.
2 v. 16½cm.
Loose-leaf.
Volume 2 has title: Die sudetendeutschen preisvorschriften, bearbeitet von regierungsrat dr. Fritz Thiel ... und oberregierungsrat F. A. Knopp ...

1. Prices—Sudetenland. I. Goedecke, Gerold, joint ed. II. Thiel, Fritz, joint ed. III. Title.

42-28363

Library of Congress HB236.C05S84

338.509437

NK 0207953 DLC

Knopp, Gerhard, 1900-
Paläobotanische studien über das Albert- und das Augustens freudeflöz der lazisker schichten (Westfal B) in Polnisch-Oberschlesien ...
Inaug. Diss. -Techn. Hochsch. Berlin, [1932]
Lebenslauf.
Bibliography.

NK 0207954 ICRL

Knopp, Gerhard, 1900-
... Paläobotanische studien über das Albert- und das Augustensfreudeflöz der Lazisker schichten (Westfal B) in Polnisch-Oberschlesien, von dipl.-ing. G. Knopp ... hierzu 7 textabbildungen und tafel 12 u. 13.
(*In* [Prussia. Geologische landesanstalt] Arbeiten aus dem Institut für paläobotanik und petrographie der brennsteine. Berlin, 1933. 25cm. bd. 3, hft. 1, p. [151]-192 incl. illus., tab., diagrs. pl. 12-13)
"Literatur": p. [191]-192.

1. Paleobotany—Carboniferous. 2. Paleobotany—Silesia, Upper. I. Title.

G S 36-292

Library, U. S. Geological Survey (530.1) In7a bd. 3, hft. 1 [QE919.P]

NK 0207955 DI-GS

Knopp, Hermann, 1901-
Das zurechnungsproblem der Wiener schule ... von Hermann Knopp ... Borna-Leipzig, Universitätsverlag von R. Noske, 1932.
2 p. l., 90 p., 1 l. diagrs. 21cm.
Inaug.-diss.—Hamburg.
Lebenslauf.
"Berichtigung": leaf inserted.
"Verzeichnis der benutzten literatur": p. 89-90.

1. Cost. 2. Value. 3. Marginal utility.

42-28237

Library of Congress HB201.K67

NK 0207956 DLC CtY

DD205
W4K5

Knopp, J N
Ludwig Windthorst; ein Lebensbild, von J.N.Knopp. Dresden, C.Reissner, 1898.
293 p. port. 20cm (Männer der Zeit, 7)

1. Windthorst, Ludwig Josef Ferdinand Gustav, 1812-1891. I.Ser.

NK 0207957 CSt CtY NIC IaU

Knopp, J N.
Ludwig Windthorst; ein lebensbild, von J. N. Knopp. Leipzig, H. Seemann nachfolger [1898]
3 p. l., 293 p. port. 20cm. ([Männer der zeit, 7. bd.])

Subject entries: Windthorst, Ludwig Josef Ferdinand Gustav, 1812-1891.

3-5616

NK 0207958 DLC

Knopp, Johannes: Über Albuminurie bei Blasenmole. [Maschinenschrift.] 69 S. 4°. — Auszug: Bonn 1922: Ludwig. 2 Bl. 8°
Bonn, Med. Diss. v. 28. Juni 1923 [U 23. 841

NK 0207959 ICRL

RBC
497.2051
K72p

Knopp, John M.
[Prayer in Mopan Maya by John M. Knopp, S.J. Accompanied by a literal translation in English. 1946?]
[21.] 22 cm
Translation in manuscript.
1. Mayan languages - Texts. I. Title: Mopan Maya prayer.

NK 0207960 LNHT

Knopp, Josef.
Martin Luther und der Christ von heute, zum 400. Todestag am 18. Februar 1546, Vortrag im Linzer "Katholischen Bildungswerk" am 27. März 1946. Linz, Verlag: Katholische Schriftenmission, 1946.
32 p. 21 cm. (Wort in der Zeit, Schriftenreihe des Katholischen Bildungswerkes Linz, 3. Heft)

1. Luther, Martin, 1483-1546. (Series)

BR334.K58 922.443 48-27937*

NK 0207961 DLC DCU CtY

Knopp, Konrad, 1882-
...Asymptotische Formeln der additiven Zahlentheorie, von Konrad Knopp. Berlin: Deutsche Verlagsgesellschaft für Politik und Geschichte m.b.H., 1925. 30 p. diagr. 4°. (Koenigsberger gelehrte Gesellschaft. Naturwissenschaftliche Klasse. Schriften. Jahr 2, Heft 3.)

1. Numbers—Theory. 2. Ser.
N. Y. P. L. December 1, 1927

NK 0207962 NN PU PU-Math IU PBm PSC OCU

Knopp, Konrad, 1882-
... Aufgabensammlung zur funktionentheorie, von dr. Konrad Knopp ... Berlin und Leipzig, W. de Gruyter & co., 1923-28.
2 v. 16cm. (Sammlung Göschen. [877-878])
Each volume in 2 parts: Aufgaben und Lösungen.
"Vorbemerkungen" contain bibliographical references.
CONTENTS.—I. teil. Aufgaben zur elementaren funktionentheorie.—II. teil. Aufgaben zur höheren funktiontheorie.

1. Functions. I. Title.

A 32-1157

Michigan. Univ. Library for Library of Congress QA331.K72a QA331.K66

[a38c1] 517.5

NcD FMU CoU IU NN PBm
NK 0207963 DLC MiU MtU CtY ODW OCU OClW MH ViU

QA331
.K701

KNOPP, KONRAD, 1882-
...Aufgabensammlung zur funktionentheorie, von dr. Konrad Knopp... 2.verb.aufl. Berlin, W.de Gruyter & co., 1931-
v. 16cm. (Sammlung Göschen [nr.877-

1. Functions.

NK 0207964 ICU CU NN CtY OO ViU

QA331
.K702

Knopp, Konrad, 1882-
Aufgabensammlung zur Fundtionentheorie. 3. durchgesehene Aufl. Berlin, W. de Gruyter, 194 - 1944.
2 v. (Sammlung Göschen, Bd.877-878)
Each volume in 2 parts: Aufgaben and Lösungen.
"Vorbenerkungen" contain bibliographical references.
Contents.—T.1. Aufgaben zur elementaren Funktiontheorie. T.2. Aufgaben zur höheren Funktionentheorie.
1. Functions.

NK 0207965 ICU NBuU PU-Math

QA331
.K702
1949

Knopp, Konrad, 1882-
Aufgabensammlung zur Funktionentheorie. 4. Aufl. Berlin, W. de Gruyter, 1949.
2 v. in 1. (Sammlung Göschen, Bd.877-878)
Each vol. in 2 parts: Aufgaben und Lösungen.
"Vorbemerkungen" contain bibliographical references.
Contents.--T.1. Aufgaben zur elementaren Funktionentheorie.--T.2. Aufgaben zur höheren Funktionentheorie.
1. Functions.

NK 0207966 ICU TU MiU PPT OU

QA37
.M318

Knopp, Konrad, 1882- ed.

FOR OTHER EDITIONS SEE MAIN ENTRY

Mangoldt, Hans Carl Friedrich von, 1854-1925.
Einführung in die höhere Mathematik für Studierende und zum Selbststudium. Vollständig neu bearb. und erweitert von Konrad Knopp. 9. Aufl. Stuttgart, S. Hirzel, 1948.

Knopp, Konrad, 1882-
... Elemente der funktionentheorie, von prof. dr. Konrad Knopp ... Mit 23 figuren. Berlin, Leipzig, W. de Gruyter & co., 1937.
144 p. diagrs. 16cm. (Sammlung Göschen. 1109)
"Literatur": p. 5.

1. Functions.

37-38232

Library of Congress QA331.K68

517.5

NK 0207968 DLC NcD CU NN OCU PU-Math ICU

Knopp, Konrad, 1882-
... Elemente der funktionentheorie, von prof. dr. Konrad Knopp ... Mit 23 figuren. 2., durchgesehene aufl. Berlin, W. de Gruyter & co., 1944.
144 p. diagrs. 16cm. (Sammlung Göschen, bd. 1109)
"Literatur": p. 5.

1. Functions.

46-20945

Library of Congress QA331.K68 1944

517.5

NK 0207969 DLC RPB ICU

VOLUME 300

Knopp, Konrad, 1882–
... Elemente der funktionentheorie, von prof. dr. Konrad Knopp ... Mit 23 figuren. Berlin, Leipzig, W. de Gruyter & co., 1949.
144 p. diagrs. 16cm. (Sammlung Göschen. 1109)
"Literatur": p. 5.

NK 0207970 TU

QA 331 K72e 1955
Knopp, Konrad, 1882-
Elemente der Funktionentheorie. 4.Aufl. Berlin, W.de Gruyter, 1955.
144p. diagrs. 16cm. (Sammlung Göschen, Bd.1109)
Bibliography: p.5.

1. Functions.

NK 0207971 NRU RPB NIC

Knopp, Konrad, 1882–
Elements of the theory of functions; translated by Frederick Bagemihl. [1st American ed. New York] Dover Publications [1953, °1952]
140 p. illus. 21 cm.

1. Functions.

QA331.K6814 517.5 53-7031 ‡

MU CaBVaU CaBVa OrPS OrSaW PSC OO MsU MiHM IEN WaS NN NcD OC1W KEmT ODW DSI ScCleA FTaSU NBuU OrPR NbU
NK 0207972 DLC FMU MoU OC1L PU MB CU IU ViU NNC TU

---

no.19,35
Knopp, Konrad, 1882-
Fonksiyonlar teorisi. Yazan: Konrad Knopp, Çeviren: Nazim Terzioğlu. Istanbul, Maarif Matbaasi, 1940-43.
2 v. diagrs. (Istanbul Üniversitesi Ana ilim kitaplari, Tercüme serisi, Genel no. 19, 35; Fen no. 5)

NK 0207973 NNC

Knopp, Konrad, 1882–
Fonksiyonlar teorisine başlangiç, yazan: prof. dr. Konrad Knopp, türkçeye ceviren: dr. Nazim Terzioğlu ... İstanbul, Maarif matbaasi, 1939–
v. diagrs. 24cm. (İstanbul üniversitesi. Ana ilim kitaplari tercüme serisi, genel no. 9, Fen no. 1)

1. Functions. I. Terzioğlu, Nazim, tr. II. Title.

Library of Congress QA331.K682 40-24405

NK 0207974 DLC NNC

Knopp, Konrad, 1882-
Functional Nörlund methods, by K. Knopp and B. Vanderburg. Cincinnati, University of Cincinnati. Mathematics Division, 1954.
2 pts. in 1. 28cm.

Reproduced from typewritten copy.

1. Functions. I. Vanderburg, B jt. auth. I. Title: Nörlund methods.

NK 0207975 NcU

Knopp, Konrad, 1882–
... Funktionentheorie, von dr. Konrad Knopp ... Berlin und Leipzig, G. J. Göschen, 1913.
2 v. diagrs. 16cm. (Sammlung Göschen. [668, 703])
"Literatur": v. 1, p. [5]–6; v. 2, p. 4.
CONTENTS.—1. t. Grundlagen der allgemeinen theorie der analytischen funktionen.—2. t. Anwendungen der theorie zur untersuchung spezieller analytischer funktionen.

1. Functions.

Library of Congress QA331.K7 13-12264

NK 0207976 DLC NjP CU MiU OC1W MB

KNOPP, KONRAD, 1882-1957.
Funktionentheorie. Berlin, W. de Gruyter, 1913-1931. 2 v. 16cm. (Sammlung Göschen, Bd. 668,703)

Includes bibliographies.
CONTENTS.--v. 1. Grundlagen der allgemeinen Theorie der analytischen Funktionen.--v. 2. Anwendungen und Weiterführung der allgemeinen Theorie. 4. verb. Aufl.

1. Functions. t.1913.

NK 0207977 NN

Knopp, Konrad, 1882–
... Funktionentheorie, von dr. Konrad Knopp ... 2., vollständig neu bearb. aufl. Berlin und Leipzig, G. J. Göschen, 1918–20.
2 v. diagrs. 16cm. (Sammlung Göschen. [668, 703])
"Literatur": v. 1, p. [2]; v. 2, p. [4]
CONTENTS.—1. t. Grundlagen der allgemeinen theorie der analytischen funktionen.—2. t. Anwendungen und weiterführung der allgemeinen theorie.

1. Functions.

Library of Congress QA331.K7 1918 43-42989

NK 0207978 DLC MoU MtU OU MiU MH NN CtY

Knopp, Konrad, 1882-
... Funktionentheorie, von dr. Konrad Knopp ... 2. vollständig neu bearb. aufl. Durchgesehener neudruck. Berlin, Gruyter, 1926.
2 v. diagrs. 16 cm. (Sammlung Göschen [no. 668, 703])

Bibliography: v.1, p. [2]; v.2. p. [4]
Contents.--1.t. Grundlagen der allgemeinen theorie der analytischen funktionen.--2.t. Anwendungen und weiterführung der allgemeinen theorie.
1. Functions.

NK 0207979 NNC OC1JC CoU CtY PBm ODW NcD

QA 331 K7114
Knopp, Konrad, 1882-
Funktionentheorie. 4., verb. Aufl. Berlin, W. de Gruyter, 1930-31.
2 v. illus. 16 cm. (Sammlung Göschen [668, 703)
Includes bibliographies.
Contents.- 1. T. Grundlagen der allgemeinen Theorie der analytischen Funktionen.- 2. T. Anwendungen und Weiterführung der allgemeinen Theorie.
1. Functions. I. Title.

MiEM NcU CU OCU CtY
NK 0207980 CU-S NcD FMU MH OC1ND OC1W OO MiU ViU

AC-S QA331 .K72f 1937
Knopp, Konrad, 1882-
... Funktionentheorie, von prof. dr. Konrad Knopp ... Berlin, W. de Gruyter & co., 1937, '31.
2v. diagrs. 16cm. (Samnlung Göschen. [668]-703)

Bibliography: v.1, p.[5]; v.2, p.[4]
CONTENTS.--1.t. Grundlagen der allgemeinen theorie der analytische funktionen. 5. vollständig neu bearb. aufl. 1937.--2.t. Anwendungen und weiterführung der allgemeinen theorie. 4. verb. aufl. 1931.
Sir Owen Richardson Collection on the Atom.

1. Functions. Br.: Richardson Collection.

NK 0207982 TxU NcRS OC1W IU ICU NcD CtY NIC

Knopp, Konrad, 1882–
... Funktionentheorie, von prof. dr. Konrad Knopp ... 5., vollständig neu bearb. aufl. Berlin, W. de Gruyter & co., 1937–41.
2 v. diagrs. 16 cm. (Sammlung Göschen. [668; 703])
Bibliography: v. 1, p. [5]; v. 2, p. [4]
CONTENTS.—1. t. Grundlagen der allgemeinen theorie der analytische funktionen.—2. t. Anwendungen und weiterführung der allgemeinen theorie.

1. Functions.

QA331.K7115 517.5 39-9657 rev

NK 0207983 DLC PU-Math RPB ICU

QA331 K65 1949
Knopp, Konrad, 1882-
Funktionentheorie. 7. Aufl. Berlin, de Gruyter, 1949-
v. diagrs. (Sammlung Göschen, Bd.668

Bibliography: v.1, p.[5]

Contents.- 1.T. Grundlagen der allgemeinen Theorie der analytischen Funktionen.

NK 0207984 CU OrU OU PPTU MH

QA331 K7 1955
Knopp, Konrad, 1882-
Funktionentheorie. 8. Aufl. Berlin, de Gruyter, 1955.
2 v. diagrs. 16cm. (Sammlung Göschen, bd. 668, 703)

Contents.--1. t. Grundlagen der allgemeinen Theorie der analytischen Funktionen.--2. t. Anwendungen und Weiterführung der allgemeinen Theorie.

NK 0207985 RPB LU

Knopp, Konrad, 1882–
Grenzwerte von reihen bei der annäherung an die konvergenzgrenze ... von Konrad Knopp ... [Göttingen, Druck der Dieterich'schen univ.-buchdruckerei (W. F. Kaestner) 1907]
50 p., 1 l. 24cm.
Inaug.-diss.—Berlin.
Lebenslauf.

1. Series, Infinite.

Library of Congress QA295.K7 9-20692

NK 0207986 DLC CtY CU PU NjP

Knopp, Konrad, 1882–
Problem book in the theory of functions. [1st American ed.] New York, Dover Publications [1948–53; v. 2, °1952]
2 v. 17 cm.
CONTENTS.—v. 1. Problems in the elementary theory of functions, translated by L. Bers.—v. 2. Problems in the advanced theory of functions, translated by F. Bagemihl.

1. Functions. I. Title.

QA331.K663 517.5 49-7400 rev*

WaTC WaWW MtBuM MtBC KEmT CaBVaU MtU IdU OrPS OrU OrSaW WaS WaSpG CU DSI NBuC OU TU OO ICN TxU PU-Math PPT PSC MB
NK 0207987 DLC ViU PPD KEmT OrU MiHM CaBVa NN AU

VOLUME 300

QA295 **Knopp, Konrad,** 1882–
.K7 Theorie und anwendung der unendlichen reihen, von dr. Konrad Knopp ... Berlin, J. Springer, 1922.

x, 474 p. diagrs. 24cm. (*Added t.-p.:* Die grundlehren der mathematischen wissenschaften ... bd. II)

"Literatur": p. [468]

1. Series, Infinite.

NK 0207989 ICU CU CSt CtY PBm MiU OCU NjP MH

Knopp, Konrad, 1882–

Theorie und anwendung der unendlichen reihen, von dr. Konrad Knopp ... 2. erweiterte aufl. Mit 12 textfiguren. Berlin, J. Springer, 1924.

x, 526, [2] p. diagrs. 24½cm. (*Added t.-p.:* Die grundlehren der mathematischen wissenschaften in einzeldarstellungen ... bd. II)

"Literatur": p. 520.

1. Series, Infinite.

Library of Congress QA295.K73 1924 24-32189

NN ICJ OU PU PPTU PSC MH NjP NjR
NK 0207990 DLC CU MtU MeB NcD MiU OCU OClW OCX IU

Knopp, Konrad, 1882–

Theorie und anwendung der unendlichen reihen, von dr. Konrad Knopp ... 3., verm. und verb. aufl., mit 14 textfiguren. Berlin, J. Springer, 1931.

xii, 582 p. diagrs. 24½cm. (*Added t.-p.:* Die grundlehren der mathematischen wissenschaften in einzeldarstellungen mit besonderer berücksichtigung der anwendungsgebiete ... bd. II)

"Literatur": p. [575]

1. Series, Infinite. I. Title.

Library of Congress QA295.K73 1931 31-32918
Copyright A—Foreign 13034
512.4

PU
NK 0207991 DLC CoU CU NcD IdU MiU OCU OU IU MH NBC

Knopp, Konrad, 1882–

Theorie und Anwendung der unendlichen Reihen. 4. Aufl. Berlin, Springer, 1947 [i. e. 1948]

xii, 582 p. diagrs. 25 cm. (Die Grundlehren der mathematischen Wissenschaften in Einzeldarstellungen, Bd. 2)

"Literatur": p. [575]

1. Series, Infinite. (Series)

QA295.K73 1948 512.4 50-15366

ICU NRU FTaSU NNC OU
NK 0207992 DLC MH NcD CU-S MtBC OrU NjP CtY TU NN

Knopp, Konrad, 1882–

Theory and application of infinite series, by Dr. Konrad Knopp ... translated from the second German edition by Miss R. C. Young, L. ès SC. London and Glasgow, Blackie & son limited, 1928.

xii, 571 p. diagrs. 24cm.

To this edition has been added a chapter on "Euler's summation formula and asymptotic expansions", translated by W. M. Deans. *cf.* Pref. to the English edition.

Bibliography: p. 564.

1. Series, Infinite. I. Young, R. C., tr.

Library of Congress QA295.K74 29-9871

IU NN NjP PBm PPPCPh
TxU CtY NcD NcRS OClU OU OCU MiU ODW PSC ViU ICJ TU
NK 0207993 DLC OrPS CaBVaU MtBC OrPR OrU WaSpG WaWW

514.3
K757tTy
1928r KNOPP, KONRAD, 1882-

Theory and application of infinite series, by Dr. Konrad Knopp ... translated from the second German edition by Miss R.C. Young, L. ès SC. London and Glasgow, Blackie & son limited [1946]

xii, 571p. diagrs. 24cm.

"First issued 1928. Reprinted ... 1946."

To this edition has been added a chapter on "Euler's summation forumula and asymptotic expansions", trnalsted by W.M. Deans.—cf. Pref. to the English edition.

Bibliography: p.564.

1. Series, Infinite. I. Young, R.C., tr.

NK 0207994 TxU

514.3
K757tTy
1928r
Physics
Lib'y

KNOPP, KONRAD, 1882-

Theory and application of infinite series, by Dr. Konrad Knopp ... translated from the second German edition by Miss R.C. Young, L. ès SC. London and Glasgow, Blackie & son limited [1948]

xii, 571p. diagrs. 24cm.

"First issued 1928. Reprinted ... 1948."

To this edition has been added a chapter on "Euler's summation formula and asymptotic expansions", translated by W.M. Deans.—cf. Pref. to the English edition.

Bibliography: p.564.

1. Series, Infinite. I. Young, R.C., Tr.

NK 0207995 TxU CU

Knopp, Konrad, 1882–

Theory and application of infinite series. Translated from the 2d German ed. by R. C. Young. New York, Hafner Pub. Co. [1949]

xii, 571 p. 23 cm.

With a new chapter on Euler's summation formula and asymptotic expansions, translated by W. M. Deans.
Bibliography: p. 564.

1. Series, Infinite.

QA295.K74 1949 512.4 49-9067*

NK 0207996 DLC PPT MB

Knopp, Konrad, 1882-

511.9
K72ta
ed.2

Theory and application of infinite series. [2d ed.] Translated from the 2d German ed. and rev. in accordance with the 4th by R.C.H. Young. New York, Hafner Pub. Co. [1950]

xii,563 p. 23cm.

With a chapter on Euler's summation formula and asymptotic expansions, translated by W.M. Deans.

Bibliography: p.556.

1. Series, Infinite. 2. Euler, Leonhard, 1707-1783.

NK 0207997 CSt MiU OrU OU MnU NcGU WU WaTC IU CU

Knopp, Konrad, 1882–

Theory and application of infinite series. [2d ed.] Translated from the 2d German ed. and rev. in accordance with the 4th by R. C. H. Young. London, Blackie [1951]

xii, 563 p. diagrs. 23 cm.

Bibliography: p. 556.

1. Series, Infinite.

QA295.K74 1951 512.4 51-7902

NN IU NNC TxU CaQMM MU MoU WaU MiHM CU
NK 0207998 DLC TU IdPI MiU IdU MtU OrU OrSaW NcU

Knopp, Konrad, 1882–1957.

Theory of functions, by Dr. Konrad Knopp ... translated by Frederick Bagemihl ... New York, Dover publications, 1945–47.

2 v. diagrs. 17 cm.

Part 1 is translated with minor changes in text, from the 5th German edition; pt. 2 is translated from the 4th German edition.
"First American edition."
Bibliography: v. 1, pt 141–142; v. 2, pt 147.

CONTENTS.—pt. 1. Elements of the general theory of analytic functions.—pt. 2. Applications and continuation of the general theory.

1. Functions of complex variables. I. Bagemihl, Frederick, tr.
Translation of Funktionentheorie.

QA331.K713 517.5 45—6381

WaT WaWW OrSaW TNJ
CaBVa IdPI IdU MtBC MtU MtBuM OrCS OrPR WaSpG
NcD NcRS MiHM NBuT MoU KEmT WU MH MU WaS CaBVaU
ViU TxU AU CU MB MiU NIC DSI OClW PLT PBL PPLas
NK 0207999 DLC MB OO TU PBm PHC PSC OU OClJC OCU

Knopp, Leslie.

Practical navigation for yachtsmen, by Leslie Knopp ... With an introduction by Maurice Griffiths ... London, The Technical press ltd., 1935.

xv, 183 p. illus., diagrs. 22½cm.

1. Navigation. 2. Yachts and yachting.

Library of Congress VK555.K55 38-9700
[3] 527

NK 0208001 DLC CaBVa NN

Knopp, Manfred, joint author.

HF5716
.S6M63

Mohrberg, Wilhelm.

Handbuch englisch-amerikanischer Papierformate mit Umrechnungen in das cgs-System, hrsg. von Wilhelm Mohrberg und Manfred Knopp. [1. Aufl.] Darmstadt, E. Roether, 1954.

Knopp, Nikolaus, 1814-1856.

Der katholische Seelsorger als Zeuge vor Gericht. Eine kirchenrechtliche-pastoralistische Abhandlung. Regensburg, Georg Joseph Manz, 1849.

76p. 18cm.

1. Confessors (Canon Law) I. Title.

NK 0208003 PLatS

Knopp, Nikolaus, 1814–1865.

Vollständiges katholisches Eherecht, mit besonderer Rücksicht auf die practische Seelsorge. Regensburg, G. J. Manz, 1850–52.

2 v. 21 cm.

Also issued in the same years, in 6 parts, under title: Ausführliche Darstellung der kirchlichen Lehre von den Ehehindernissen.

1. Marriage (Canon law) I. Title.

76-283760

NK 0208004 DLC ICJ

Knopp, Nikolaus, 1814–1865.

Vollständiges katholisches eherecht. Mit besonderer rücksicht auf die practische seelsorge bearbeitet von Nikolaus Knopp ... 3., verm. und verb. aufl. Regensburg, G. J. Manz, 1864.

x, 584 p. 22cm.

Cover-title: Eherecht.
First edition published under title: Ausführliche darstellung der kirchlichen lehre von den ehehindernissen. 2 v. 1850–52.

1. Marriage (Canon law) 2. Catholic church—Discipline. 3. Marriage law—Germany. I. Title. II. Title: Eherecht.

36-22431

Library of Congress HQ1024.K68 1864 173.1

NK 0208005 DLC DCU CU

4K
7542

Knopp, Nikolaus, 1814-1865.

Vollständiges katholisches Eherecht mit besonderer Rücksicht auf die practische Seelsorge. 4., verm. und verb. Aufl. Regensburg, G. J. Manz, 1873.

590 p,

NK 0208006 DLC-P4 MH-L OClStM OClJC

26274.64.5 **Knopp,** Otto. Allerhand scherz, neckereien, reime und erzählungen über pommersche orte, und ihrer bewohner. Stettin. 1891. 8°.

NK 0208007 MH

VOLUME 300

Film 2730 Reel 148 Knopp, Otto, ed.
Volkstümliches aus der Tierwelt. Rogasen, 1905.
68p. 20cm. (Beiträge zur Volkskunde der Provinz Posen, 1)

Microfilm. Cambridge, Mass., Filmed by General Microfilm Co. for Erasmus Press, Lexington, Ky. 1 reel (various items) 35mm.
Title on microfilm box label: Literature of folklore.

NK 0208008 TxU

WE 4389 Knopp, Otto, 1883-
Untersuchungen über Thermoelemente. Halle a. S., 1909.
34 p. illus. (Mitteilungen der Physikalischen Versuchs-Station Halle-Cröllwitz, no. 15)

Inaug.-Diss. - Halle-Wittenberg.

NK 0208009 CtY ICRL MH PU

HV9158 .N3 Knopp, W.

Nationalsozialistische deutsche arbeiter-partei. *Reichsjugendführung.*
... Kriminalität und gefährdung der jugend, lagebericht bis zum stande vom 1. januar 1941. Herausgegeben vom jugendführer des Deutschen reichs, bearbeitet von bannführer W. Knopp, unter mitarbeit von stammführer amtsgerichtsrat dr. Rätz. [Berlin, W. Limpert, 1941?]

QD543 .K7 Knopp, Werner, 1880-
Ueber die loeslichkeitsbeeinflussung von wasserstoff und stickoxydul in waessrigen loesungen verschieden dissociierter stoffe.
Berlin, 1903.
32p.
Inaug. diss. Berlin.

NK 0208011 DLC ICRL PU

Knopp, Wilhelm, 1905-
... Die gerichtsärztliche Bedeutung des Tierfrasses an freiliegenden Leichen ... Düsseldorf, 1934.
Inaug. diss.-Münster.
Lebenslauf.

NK 0208012 CtY

Knoppe, A. D., *pseud.*
see
Lacey, Joseph Berry, 1842-

Knoppe, Hugo.
Drechslerkunst; Meistertechniken alter und neuer Zeit, von Hugo Knoppe... Leipzig-Gohlis: F. E. Steiger, 1926. 150 p. front. (port.), illus. 8°.

1. Lathework.
N. Y. P. L. January 6, 1928

NK 0208014 NN ICJ

W 6 P3 KNOPPERS, A Th.
Chemotherapie; ontwikkeling en perspectief. Amsterdam, Scheltema & Holkema, 1950.
20 p.
Lecture given at the Univ. of Amsterdam, Oct. 27, 1950.
1. Chemotherapy

NK 0208015 DNLM

W 4 L68 1941 KNOPPERS, A Th.
De rattestaart als proefobject voor de beoordeeling van de bloeddoorstrooming in perifere organen. Amsterdam, Bakker, 1941.
119 p. illus.
Proefschrift - Leyden.
1. Blood circulation - Experimental studies 2. Body temperature

NK 0208016 DNLM CtY

Wason LA2255 K72+ Knoppers, B A
Het hoger onderwijs in Indonesië. Rapport uitgebracht naar aanleiding van een oriëntatiereis naar Indonesië in opdracht van het Nederlands Comité voor World Student Relief van 19 Augustus tot 28 September 1948. Leiden, Nederlands Comité voor World Student Relief, 1948.
43 p. 33cm. (Het Nederlands Comité voor World Student Relief. Uitgave no.1)

Cover-title.

NK 0208017 NIC

Knoppers, B. A.
Was Jezus een socialist? Eenige opmerkingen aan het adres van Karl Kautzky, door B. A. Knoppers... Kampen: J. H. Kok, 1921. 46 p. 12°.

1. Kautsky, Karl, 1854- : Der Ursprung des Christentums. 2. Jesus Christ.
N. Y. P. L. December 26, 1922.

NK 0208018 NN

Knopping, Roubin.
Islam und judaismus, populär-wissenschaftliche Koranstudien von Roubin Knopping ...
Leipzig, M. W. Kaufman; [etc., etc.] 1900.
v. 20 cm.
1. Mohammedanism. 2. Jews--Religion.

NK 0208019 CU CtY OCH CU MH

Knopping, Roubin.
Der katechismus für Zionisten. Kamenets-Podol'sk, 1901-
pt. 1-
1. Jews--Restoration.

NK 0208020 NjP

Knopping, Roubin.
Wie soll das Judentum seiner Zukunft entgegen Gehen? ... Berlin, Poppelauer, 1901.
22 p. 22 cm.
1. Jewish question.

NK 0208021 NNJ

326.3 K75a Knops, Arnold, 1880-
Die aufhebung der leibeigenschaft (eigenbehörigkeit) im nördlichen Münsterlande (den vormals arenbergischen und bergischen teilen des Französischen kaiserreiches) ... Münster i. Westf., Druck der Westfälischen vereinsdruckerei, 1906.
vii, 63p.
Inaug.-diss.--Münster.
Lebenslauf.
"Fortsetzung im hft.IX der 'Münsterschen beiträge zur geschichtsforschung'."
"Literatur- und quellenangabe": p.[v]-vii.

NK 0208022 IU PU ICRL MH

Knops, Arnold, 1880- Ger 39.2.3 (9)
Die aufhebung der leibeigenschaft, eigenbehörigkeit, im nördlichen Münsterlande. Münster, Westf., Coppenrath, 1906.
pp. v, (1), 110. (Münstersche beiträge zur geschichtsforschung, neue folge, 9.)

Serfdom|Münster, Germ.||Series|AcS 232846

NK 0208023 MH

WG 22400 Knops, Carl, 1861-
Ueber die Molecularrefraction der Isomerien Fumar-Maleïnsäure, Mesacon-Citracon-Itaconsäure und des Thiophens und ihre Beziehung zur chemischen Constitution dieser Substanzen. Bonn, 1887.
54 p. illus.
Inaug.-Diss. - Bonn.

NK 0208024 CtY CU ICRL MiU

Knops, Eberhard, 1908-
Der persönliche geltungsbereich des tarifvertrags und tarifbeteiligung ... von ... Eberhard Knops ... Aachen, Westdeutsche druckerei-gesellschaft m.b.h., 1934.
41 p. 22½cm.

Thesis, Köln.
Bibliography: p. 40-41.

1.Wages - Germany. 2.Labor contract.

NK 0208025 NNC

Knops (Franciscus Guilelmus) [1838-]. *De therapia mercuriali in iis, qui vocantur "dyscrasiæ chronicæ" morbis, imprimis in syphilide. 32 pp. 8°. *Berolini, G. Schade,* [1863].

NK 0208026 DNLM

Knops (Heinrich). *Zur Statistik der geburtshülflichen Operationen im Regierungsbezirk Cassel in den Jahren 1867, 1871, 1872. 15 pp., 8 l. 8°. *Marburg, J. A. Koch,* 1874.

NK 0208027 DNLM ICRL

B 430 .A6 062 K72 Knops, Jan Pieter Hubert.
Études sur la traduction française de la morale à Nicomache d'Aristote par Nicole Oresme. 's-Gravenhage, Uitgeverij Excelsior [1952?]
132 p. 24 cm.
Proefschrift--Groningen.
"Stellingen": [2] p. inserted.
Bibliography: p.132.

1.Aristoteles. Ethica. 2.Oresme, Nicolas, Bp., d.1382.

NK 0208028 MiU ICU NIC MH CtY NNC TxU DLC-P4

VOLUME 300

Knops, Johann: Der Wandel des zwischenvokalischen r zu z im Französischen. [Handschrift.] 139 S. m. Kt. 4°. — Auszug: Bonn 1923. 7 S. 8°
Bonn, Phil. Diss. v. 9. März 1923 [1924] [U 24.1292

NK 0208029 ICRL

Knops, Johann Karl Stephon, 1861-
Ueber die molecularrefraction der isomerien fumar-maleinsaeure,...
Bonn, 1887
Dissert.

QD305 .A2-

NK 0208030 DLC

SB 734 K72

Knops, Karl.
Die wichtigeren Pflanzenkrankheiten.
Essen, G.D. Baedeker, 1894.
22 p. 26cm.

At head of title: Realgymnasium zu Essen. Einladung zu der am 21. März vormittags 9 Uhr in der Aula der Realschule stattfindenden Entlassung der reifen Zöglinge.
From 1894. Prog. Nr. 479.

NK 0208031 NIC

BF241 K6 Biological Sciences Library

Knops, L
Contribution à l'etude de la "naissance et de la "permanence" phénoménales dans le champ visuel. Louvain, Institut supérieur de philosophie, 1947.
[562]-610p. illus. 24cm.
"Extrait des Miscellanea psychologica Albert Michotte."
Cover-title.
Bibliographical footnotes.

1. Perception. 2. Sight.

NK 0208032 RPB

Knops (Leonardus) [1821-]. *De sectionis cæsareæ historia, methodis uterique cicatrice critica quædam. 31 pp. 8°. *Berolini, G. Schade,* [1845].

NK 0208033 DNLM

MY37 K757b

Knops, Pierre, 1898-
Bij de oermenschen van Boven-Ivoorkust. Door Pater P. Knops, van de Sociëteit der Afrikaansche Missiën. [Cadier en Keer?] Missiehuis Blitterswijk [1929]
97 p. illus., port. 25 cm.

1. Ghana - Missions. 2. Catholic Church - Missions - Ghana. 3. Society of African Missions. Afr

NK 0208034 CtY-D IEN

Knopse, Max, 1871-
Beitrag zur entstehung centraler dammrisse bei hinterhauptslage.
Inaug. diss Greifswald, 1898

NK 0208035 ICRL

Knopstück-Rowel. Tod dem Scheintode. Absolut sichere Verhütung des Lebendigbegrabenwerdens durch Behandlung des Toten mit Kälte, Finsternis und Einsamkeit. Unfehlbares Schutzverfahren gegen das spontan Wiedererwachen scheintoter Personen im Grabe. 15 pp. 8°. *Dresden, F. Flechtner,* 1902.

NK 0208036 DNLM

Knopwood, Robert, 1761–1838.
Bobby Knopwood and his times; from the diaries of 1804–8, 1814–17, by the Rev. Robert Knopwood... Edited with introduction and notes by Mabel Hookey. Hobart, Australia: W. E. Fuller, 1929. 152 p. front., plates, ports. 12°.

"Some of the matter contained in this book has already appeared in The Australasian."

489570A. 1. Tasmania—Hist. I. Hookey, Mabel, editor.
N. Y. P. L. August 20, 1930

NK 0208037 NN MH CtY

Knopwood, Robert, 1761-1838.
Hudspeth memorial volume: an introduction to the diaries of the Rev. Robert Knopwood ...
see under Hudspeth, Wilfrid Hugh, 1874-

Knor, Antonín.
Dolní věstonice
see under Československá akademie věd.

Knor, Johann B Father,
Ausgeführte Christenlehren. Rottenberg a N., Wilhelm Bader, 1921.

3 v. 21 cm.
2 verm. und verb. Aufl.
Contents: 1 Teil: Glaubenslehre. 2 Th: Sittenlehre; 3 Teil: Die Gnadenlehre.

1. Religious education. I. Title.

NK 0208040 PLatS

Knor, Peter, 18th cent.
Liber de fundatione et abbatibus monasterii S. Viti Martyris in Gladbach. Coeln, 1856.
fo. (Fahne, A., Dynasten ... von Bocholtz, v. 3: Chronica abbatiae Gladbacensis)

NK 0208041 MdBP

Knorin, Vil'gel'm Germanovich, 1890-

Piatnitskii, Osip Aronovich, 1882–
... Beiträge zur geschichte der Kommunistischen Internationale. Moskau-Leningrad, Verlagsgenossenschaft ausländischer arbeiter in der UdSSR, 1934.

Knorin, Vil'gel'm Germanovich, 1890– *ed.*
Communist Party of the Soviet Union, a short history written by B. Ponomaryev (group leader), N. Voitinsky, F. Anderson, G. Krovitsky and A. Kuchkin. Edited by W. Knorin. Moscow, Co-operative Publishing Society of Foreign Workers in the U. S. S. R., 1935.
xxiv, 516 p. 22 cm.
"Translated and edited by I. B. Lasker, from the second Russian edition."
Errata slip inserted.
Bibliography: p. [514]–516.
1. Kommunisticheskaia partiia Sovetskogo Soiuza. I. Title.

JN6598.K7K53 38—1150*

NK 0208043 OOxM CU ViU NcGU NcD DLC CtY NN NNC NBC CU-S IaU MiU NIC TxU

Knorin, Vil'gel'm Germanovich, 1890– *ed.*
Communist Party of the Soviet Union, a short history written by B. Ponomaryev (group leader), N. Voitinsky, F. Anderson, G. Krovitsky and A. Kuchkin. Edited by W. Knorin. Moscow, Co-operative Publishing Society of Foreign Workers in the U. S. S. R., 1935.
xxiv, 516 p. 22 cm.
"Translated and edited by I. B. Lasker, from the second Russian edition."
Errata slip inserted.
Bibliography: p. [514]–516.
Reproduced by Duopage process by Micro Photo Div., Bell & Howell Co., Cleveland, Ohio, 1967.

NK 0208044 NBuU CNoS

335 K757f

Knorin, Vil'gel'm Germanovich, 1890-
Fascism, social-democracy and the communists. London, Modern Books [1934?]
52p. 19cm.

Cover title.
At head of title: Thirteenth plenum of the E.C.C.I.

1. Fascism. 2. Communism. 3. Socialism in Germany.

NK 0208045 DLC

Knorin, Vil'gel'm Germanovich, 1890–
...Fascism, social-democracy and the Communists; speech by V. Knorin. Moscow [etc.] Co-operative Pub. Soc. of Foreign Workers in the U.S.S.R., 1934. 52 p. 18cm.

At head of title: Thirteenth plenum of the Executive Committee of the Communist International — December 1933.

816842A. 1. Socialism—Germany, 1933. I. The International. 3rd, formed 1919.
N. Y. P. L. April 29, 1936

NK 0208046 NN

Knorin, Vil'gel'm Germanovich, 1890–
... Fascism, social-democracy and the communists. Speech by V. Knorin. New York city, Workers library publishers, 1934.
47, [1] p. 18cm. [Thirteenth plenum series]
At head of title: Thirteenth plenum of the Executive committee of the Communist International—December, 1933.

1. Fascism. 2. Communism. 3. Socialism in Germany.
A 35-407 Revised
Illinois. Univ. Library for Library of Congress HX40.K6
[r44d2]† 335

NK 0208047 IU TxU PPT MH DLC

Knorin, Vil'gel'm Germanovich, 1890–
Фашизм, соціал-демократія і комуністи; промова на XIII пленумі ВККІ 6 грудня 1933. [Харків] Партвидав, 1934.
39 p.
At head of title: XIII пленум ВККІ. В. Кнорин.
Microfilm. 1 reel. 35 mm.
1. World politics—Addresses, essays, lectures. I. Title.
Title romanized: Fashyzm, sotsial-demokratiia i komunisty.

Microfilm Slavic 7883 D Mic 53–528

NK 0208048 DLC

Knorin, Vil'gel'm Germanovich, 1890– 1938.
К итогам чистки Московской организации ВКП(б) [Москва] Моспартиздат, 1933.
81 p. illus. 18 cm.

1. Kommunisticheskaia partiia Sovetskogo Soiuza—Purges.
I. Title.
Title transliterated: K itogam chistki Moskovskoi organizatsii VKP(b)

JN6598.K7K516 60–55490 ‡

NK 0208049 DLC

VOLUME 300

HX314 .L354 Knorin, Vil'gel'm Germanovich, 1890- 1938, ed.

Lenin, Vladimir Il'ich, 1870–1924.
... Коммунистический интернационал; статьи, речи, документы, 1914–1923, под редакцией В. Кнорина ... ₍Москва₎ Партиздат, 1934–

JN6598 .K7K52 1936 Knorin, Vil'gel'm Germanovich, 1890- 1938 ed.
Краткая история ВКП(б). Составлена бригадой Историко-партийного института красной профессуры: Б. Пономарев ₍и др.₎ 2. изд. ₍Москва₎ Партиздат, 1936.
411 p. 23 cm.

1. Kommunisticheskaia partiia Sovetskogo Soiuza. I. Ponomarev, Boris Nikolaevich. II. Title.
Title transliterated: Kratkaia istoriia VKP(b)

JN6598.K7K52 1936 57-55090

NK 0208051 DLC

Knorin, Vil'gel'm Germanovich, 1890- *ed.*
קורצע געשיכטע פון אלקפ (ב) צונויפגעשטעלט דורך ב. פאנאמאריאוו ₍און אנדערע₎ קיעוו, פארטפארלאג צק קפ(ב)או.
₍Kiev₎ 1934.
435 p. illus., ports., facsims. 24 cm.

Errata slip inserted.
Russian bibliography at end of each chapter.

1. Kommunisticheskaia partiia Sovetskogo Soiuza. I. Ponomarev, Boris Nikolaevich. II. Title.
Title transliterated: Kurtse geshikhte fun ALKP(B)

JN6598.K7K538 A 57-952

New York. Public Libr. for Library of Congress

NK 0208052 NN DLC

HX312 K723 ed.2 Knorin, Vil'gel'm Germanovich, 1890- ed.
Kurze Geschichte der KPdSU(b) ₍Verfasst von einer Brigade des Instituts für Parteigeschichte an der roten Professur in Moskau, bestehend aus B. Ponomarow (Brigadier) N. Wojtinski, F. A. Anderson, et al. Die deutsche Ausgabe wurde nach der zweiten russischen Ausgabe _ von M. Ignatowitsch besorgt₎ Moskau, Verlagsgenossenschaft Ausländischer Arbeiter in der UdSSR, 1935.
537 p. 21cm.

1. Vsesoiuznaia kommunisticheskaia partiia (bol'shevikov) I. Ignatovich, M ed.

NK 0208053 CSt-H OrU IU MH

PN2724 .P3 1927 Knorin, Vil'gel'm Germanovich, 1890-1938.

Partiinoe soveshchanie po voprosam teatra, Moscow? 1927.
Пути развития театра; стенографический отчет и решения Партийного совещания по вопросам театра при Агитпропе ЦК ВКП (б) в мае 1927 г. Со вступ. статьей В. Г. Кнорина. Под ред. С. М. ₍i. e. Н.₎ Крылова. Москва, Кинопечать, 1927.

HX13 .C6 1920a Knorin, Vil'gel'm Germanovich, 1890- 1938 joint ed.

Communist International. *2d congress, Petrograd and Moscow,* 1920.
... Второй конгресс Коминтерна июль-август 1920 г. Под редакцией О. Пятницкого, Д. Мануильского, В. Кнорина ₍и др.₎ Москва, Партийное издательство, 1934.

Knork, Otto
see Knörk, Otto.

Knorozov, IUrii Valentinovich
La antigua escritura de los pueblos de América Central ₍por₎ Y. V. Knorozov. México, Fondo de Cultura Popular ₍1954₎
37 p. illus. (Biblioteca obrera, 5)

"De la revista 'Etnografía soviética', número 3 de 1952."
"Versión que el 'Boletín de Información de la Embajada de la U.R.S.A.', de esta ciudad, dió a conocer en su número 20 (484) correspondiente al 16 de mayo de 1953."

NK 0208057 NNC MH-P

G497 K757b Knorozov, IU V
A brief summary of the studies of the ancient Maya hieroglyphic writing in the Soviet Union. Moscow, Publishing House of USSR Academy of Sciences, 1955.
53p. illus. 20cm.

Russian and English; added t.-p. in Russian.

1. Maya language. 2. Hieroglyphics, Maya.

NK 0208058 TxU

PM3962 K72 S1955 Knorozov, IU V
La escritura de los antiguos mayas. Moscú, 1955.
53-94 p. 22 cm.
At head of title: Academia de Ciencias de la URSS. Instituto de Etnografía.
Photocopy of the Spanish text of Sistema pis'ma drevnikh maiia, originally issued in Russian and Spanish.
1. Picture-writing, Maya. I. Akademiia nauk SSSR. Institut etnografii. II. Knorozov, IU V Sistema pis'ma drevnikh maiia. III. Title.

NK 0208059 DSI

Knorozov, IU V
Краткие итоги изучения древней письменности майя в Советском Союзе. Москва, Изд-во Академии наук СССР, 1955.
53 p. illus. 20 cm.

Russian and English.
Added t. p.: A brief summary of the studies of the ancient Maya hieroglyphic writing in the Soviet Union.
On cover: Доклады советской делегации на x международном конгрессе историков в Риме.

1. Mayas—Writing. I. Title. II. Title: A brief summary of the studies of the ancient Maya hieroglyphic writing.
Title transliterated: Kratkie itogi izuchenia drevnei pis'mennosti maiia.

PM3962.K6 56-27294 ‡

NK 0208060 DLC

.K63 Knorozov, IU V
Система письма древних майя. ₍Перевод на испанский Л. Купер₎ Москва, Изд-во Академии наук СССР, 1955.
94 p. 22 cm.

At head of title: Академия наук СССР. Институт этнографии им. Н. Н. Миклухо-Маклая.
Russian and Spanish. Added t. p.: La escritura de los antiguos mayas.

1. Mayas—Writing. I. Title. II. Title: La escritura de los antiguos mayas. *Title transliterated:* Sistema pis'ma drevnikh maiia.

PM3962.K63 56-44167 ‡

Library of Congress

NK 0208061 DLC

F1376 L258 Knorozov, IUrii Valentinovich, ed.

Landa, Diego de, 1524–1579.
Сообщение о делах в Юкатане. ₍Написано в₎ 1566 г. Перевод со старо-испанского. Вводная статья и примечания Ю. В. Кнорозова. Москва, Изд-во Академии наук СССР, 1955.

KNORPP, Gustav, 1904-
Untersuchungen über den keimgehalt der trächtigen und nichtträchtigen gebärmutter beim rinde. Inaug.-diss., München. Lucka (Bez. Leipzig), R. Berger, 1923.

pp.38-.
"Lebenslauf", at end.
"Literaturverzeichnis", pp.[36]-38.

NK 0208063 MH PPWI CtY

Knorpp, Karl, 1888-
Sf22.051 ... Untersuchungen über die Hauttemperatur bei der Ziege und beim Schafe ...
Stuttgart, 1911
(Arbeiten aus der Medizinischen Veterinärklinik der Universität Giessen.)
Inaug.-Diss. - Giessen.
Lebenslauf.
"Literatur": pp.[73]-75.

NK 0208064 CtY ICRL MH PU DNLM

Knorpp, Richard, 1906-
... Der biologische Nachweis des C-Vitamins im Nateina ... Borna-Leipzig, 1934.
Inaug. diss.-Tübingen.
Lebenslauf.
"Literatur" p. [13]

NK 0208065 CtY

Knorr, Alajos, 1828-1911.
Csődtörvény (1881. XVII. t.-cz.)
see under Hungary. Laws, statutes, etc.

Knorr, Alajos, 1828-1911.
Házassági perek és eljárás a házassági perekben. Irta Knorr Alajos ... Budapest, Az Athenaeum irod. és nyomdai r. t. kiadása, 1899.
viii, 252 p. 17½cm.
Includes legislation.
Bibliographical footnotes.

NK 0208067 MH-L

Knorr, Alajos, 1828-1911.
A magyar büntető jog és eljárás. Kérdések és feleletekben. Szerkesztette Knorr Alajos ... Pest, Eggenberger-féle akad. könyvkereskedés, 1871.
2 p.l., 216 p. 18½cm.

NK 0208068 MH-L

Knorr, Alajos, 1828-1911.
A magyar magánjog. Különös tekintettel a gyakorlati élet igényeire is. Irta Knorr Alajos ... Pest, Eggenberger-féle akad. könyvkereskedés, 1873.
4, ₍v₎-xviii, 528 p. 17cm.
"A magyar magánjog irodalma": p. 16-18.
_____. Függelék ... Budapest, Az Eggenberger-féle könyvkereskedés kiadása, 1878.
16+ p. 17cm. (With main work)
Imperfect: p. 17+ lacking.

NK 0208069 MH-L

VOLUME 300

Law
Knorr, Alajos, 1828-1911, comp.

Hungary. *Laws, statutes, etc.* (*Indexes*)
A Magyar törvénytár betürendes tárgymutatója. 1.- köt.; 1847/48-1880—
Budapest, Ifjabb Nágel O.

Knorr, Alajos, 1828-1911.
Ügyvéd, vagyis Gyakorlati útmutatás jogügyletek elintézésére, okiratok s beadványok szerkesztésére. A legujabb törvények alapján 450 irományi-példával felvilágosítva ... Szerkesztette Knorr Alajos ... 5. ujra átdolgozott kiad. Budapest, Ifj. Nagel O., 1894.
xv, 1015 p. incl. forms. 22½cm.

NK 0208071 MH-L

Knorr, Alajos, 1828-1911.
Ügyvéd vagyis gyakorlati utmutatás jogügyletek elintézésere. Okiratok és beadványok szerkeztésére. A legujabb törvények alapjan 378 iromány-példával felvilágositva Birák, ügyvedek, jegyzök és felek hasznalatara szerkesztette. Budapest, 1901.
839 p.

NK 0208072 PPB NjP

Z593 .H8
Knorr, Alajos, 1828-1911, ed.

Hungary. *Laws, statutes, etc.*
A szerzői jog (1884. xvi. törvényczikk) magyarázata. Írta Knorr Alajos ... Budapest, Ifj. Nagel O., 1890.

Knorr, Alfred.
Beiträge zur Erklärung einiger Stellen aus Horaz und Vergil ... Belgard, Klemp, 1900.
28 p. O. (Vergil ... Pamphlets, no. 29)

NK 0208074 NcD PU

PA 6826 K72
Knorr, Alfred.
Beiträge zur Erklärung einiger Stellen der Aneide. Belgard, G. Klemp, 1898.
27 p. 25cm.

"Beilage zum Jahresbericht des städtischen Gymnasiums zu Belgard."

1. Vergilius Maro, Publius. Aeneis.

NK 0208075 NIC CU MiU NjP

---

ar X 2838 no.16
Knorr, Alfred.
Die Parasiten bei den Griechen. Die Parasitennamen bei Alciphron. Belgard, A. Klemp, 1875.
20 p. 24cm.

Accompanies "Programm"--Gymnasium, Belgard, 1874/75.
No.16 in a vol. lettered: Programmes: Greek antiquities.

1. Priests, Greek. I. Title.

NK 0208076 NIC NjP PU

Knorr, Alfred.
De parasitis Graecorum. [n.p.] 1873.

NK 0208077 NjP

Knorr, Alfred, 1875-
Über ein angeborenes Teratoma sacrale und einen nach dessen Operation zur Entwicklung gelangten Hydrocephalus. Leipzig 1909: Hoffmann. 25 S. 8°
Leipzig, Med. Diss. v. 22. Juli 1909, Ref. Marchand
[Geb. 20. Dez. 75 Leipzig; Wohnort: Leipzig; Staatsangeh.: Sachsen; Vorbildung: Realgymn. Leipzig Reife O. 04; Studium: Leipzig 11 S.; Coll. 24. Juli 09.] [U 09. 2804

NK 0208078 ICRL CtY DNLM

Knorr, Alfred Julius
see Knorr, Alfred, 1875-

Knorr (Angelo) [1864-99]. *Experimentelle Untersuchungen über die Grenzen der Heilungsmöglichkeit des Tetanus durch Tetanusheilserum. Habilitationsschrift. 31 pp., 8 tab. 8°. *Marburg, C. L. Pfeil*, 1895.

NK 0208080 DNLM

Knorr (Angelo) [1882-]. *Chinoide und teilchinoide Verbindungen. 76 pp., 1 l. 8°. München, V. Höfling, 1909.

NK 0208081 DNLM CtY MH PU

Knorr, Artur Friedrich Wolfram von, 1880- tr.

Japan. *Admiral staff.*
Der japanisch-russische seekrieg, 1904/1905, amtliche darstellung des Japanischen admiralstabes, auf veranlassung der schriftleitung der marine-rundschau, übersetzt von kapitänleutnant v. Knorr ... Berlin, E. S. Mittler und sohn, 1911.

Knorr, August, 1900-
Beiträge zur Kenntnis des Lidschlages unter normalen und pathologischen Verhältnissen ... Leipzig, 1928.
Inaug.-Diss. - Göttingen.
Lebenslauf.
"Sonderdruck aus Würzburger Abhandlung aus dem Gesamtgebiet der Medizin Bd. XXV."
"Verzeichnis der benutzten Literatur": p. 222-223.

NK 0208083 CtY DNLM

Knorr, August E.
Examination of meats.
(*In* U. S. Dept. of agriculture. Report, 1886, p. 355-357. 23cm. Washington, 1887)

1. Meat—Analysis.

Agr 13-1022
Library, U. S. Dept. of Agriculture 1Ag84 1886

NK 0208084 DNAL OO

KNORR, Balthasar.
Compendium juris exiomaticum, ex jure divino caninico, civili, feudali, recessibus item et constitutionibus imperii jureq. novissimo. Ratisbonae, 1680.

NK 0208085 MH-L

Knorr, Bernhard.
Die therapeutische beeinflussung ulceroser prozesse der mundhöhle durch silargetten.

Inaugural dissertation, Universitat zu München, 1933.

NK 0208086 PPWI CtY

WY K72i 1883
KNORR, C
Instruktion für militärische Krankenwärter. Berlin, Mittler, 1883.
vii. 121 p.

NK 0208087 DNLM

Knorr, Carl, 1901-
Untersuchungen ueber das verhalten von sommerweizen sorten und kreuzungen bei kuenstlicher infektion mit steinbrand. (Tilletia tritici.)
Inaug. diss. Halle, 1928.
Bibl.

NK 0208088 ICRL MH CtY

Knorr, Carl Gottlieb
see Knorre, Carl Gottlieb, d. 1753.

Knorr ([Carolus] Ludovicus) [1831-]. *De epitheliomate, præsertim labii inferioris. 31 pp. 8°. *Berolini, typ. frat. Schlesinger*, 1855.

NK 0208090 DNLM

FILM 4333 PT Reel 153
Knorr, **Caspar.**
Signaculum Dei, Das ist: Der hochschätzbare Pitschafft-Ring Gottes...Bey des Wol-Edlen, Gross-Achtbaren und Hochgelahrten Hn. Andreae Gryphii ...Beerdigung...d. 27. Jul. ... bey der Grufft in der Evangel. Lutherischen Kirchen von Gross Glogau, In einer Station gezeiget...von Caspar Knorren, Diac. daselbst. [1664]
68p. 17cm.
With Gryphius' portrait.
First edition.
(German Baroque Literature, No.638, reel No. 153 Research Publications, Inc.)
Microfilm.

NK 0208091 CU

Knorr, Catherine Lindsay, *comp.*
Marriage bonds and ministers' returns of Brunswick County, Virginia, 1750-1810. [Pine Bluff, Ark.] 1953.
138 p. illus. 28 cm.

1. Marriage licenses—Brunswick Co., Va. 2. Registers of births, etc.—Brunswick Co., Va.

F232.B9K6 929.3 54—2737 ‡

NK 0208092 DLC KyHi OCH NcD Vi ViU NN NNBG IHi TxU Or WaS WaSp

VOLUME 300

Knorr, Catherine Lindsay.
Marriage bonds and ministers' returns of Charlotte County, Virginia, 1764–1815. [Pine Bluff? Ark.] 1951.
119 p. illus. 28 cm.
Cover title: Marriages of Charlotte County, Virginia, 1764–1815.

1. Registers of births, etc. — Charlotte Co., Va. 2. Charlotte Co., Va.—Geneal.—Sources.
F232.C4K6 929.3 51-37440 ‡

NK 0208093 DLC KyHi Vi NN ViU Or MiD TxU WaS WaSp NBuG

F234 .F8K45 Knorr, Catherine Lindsay, ed.

King, George Harrison Sanford.
Marriage bonds and ministers' returns of Fredericksburg, Virginia, 1782–1850; also, tombstone inscriptions from St. George Cemetery, 1752–1920. Edited and published by Catherine Lindsay Knorr. [Pine Bluff, Ark.] 1954.

Knorr, Catherine Lindsay.
Marriage bonds and ministers' returns of Greensville County, Virginia, 1781–1825. [Pine Bluff, Ark.] 1955.
100 p. illus. 28 cm.

1. Marriage licenses—Greensville Co., Va. I. Title. Sp.: Littlefield Fund.
F232.G87K6 929.3 55-28329 ‡

NK 0208095 TxU NN NcD NcU ICN PHi ViU Vi KyHi C OCH Or WaS DLC

Knorr, Catherine Lindsay.
Marriage bonds and ministers' returns of Prince Edward County, Virginia, 1754–1810. [Pine Bluff? Ark.] 1950.
109 p. map. 28 cm.
Cover title: Marriages of Prince Edward County, Virginia, 1754–1810.

1. Marriage licenses—Prince Edward Co., Va.
F232.P83K5 929.3 50-11730

NK 0208096 DLC Vi CU PHi TxU ViU NBuG NcU Or WaS WaSp

Knorr, Catherine Lindsay.
Marriage bonds and ministers' returns of Southampton County, Virginia, 1750–1810. Rev. & enl. [i. e. 2d] ed. [Pine Bluff, Ark., 1955]
145 p. 28 cm.
Cover title: Marriages of Southampton County, Virginia, 1750–1810.
First ed., by B. A. Chapman and C. L. Knorr, published in 1948 under title: Marriage bonds of Southampton County, Virginia, 1750–1800.

1. Marriage licenses—Southampton Co., Va. I. Chapman, Blanche (Adams) 1895– Marriage bonds of Southampton County, Virginia, 1750–1800.
F232.S7K59 1955 929.3 56-223

NK 0208097 DLC KyHi AU ViU PHi ICN Vi NcD TxU NN WaS

Knorr, Catherine Lindsay, *comp.*
Marriage bonds and ministers' returns of Sussex County, Virginia, 1754–1810. [Pine Bluff, Ark.] 1952.
111 p. 28 cm.

1. Registers of births, etc.—Sussex Co., Va.
F232.S96K5 929.3 53-1774 ‡

NK 0208098 DLC TxU NcD NN Vi IHi ICN NBuG ViU OClWHi C Or WaS WaSp

---

F232 .S7C5 Knorr, Catherine Lindsay, joint author.

Chapman, Blanche (Adams) 1895–
Marriage bonds of Southampton County, Virginia, 1750–1800, compiled and published by Blanche Adams Chapman and Catherine Lindsay Knorr. [Richmond] 1948.

Knorr, Catherine Lindsay.
Marriages of Culpeper County, Virginia, 1781–1815. [Pine Bluff, Ark.] 1954.
127 p. illus., map. 28 cm.

1. Marriage licenses—Culpeper Co., Va. I. Title.
F232.C9K5 929.3 A 55-1158

NK 0208100 TxU NcD OClWHi PHi Vi MiD-B DLC KyHi NN Or WaS

W 4 M96 1951 KNORR, Dietrich, 1923-
Über das Verhalten der Phosphorsäure in fluoridvergifteter Hefe im Vakuum. [München] 1951.
34 l. illus.
Inaug.-Diss. - Munich.
1. Yeast - Chemistry

NK 0208101 DLNM

Knorr, E 540.2 Q906
Leitfaden der Chemie für Brauer und Mälzer. Von Dr. E. Knorr. Leipzig, Eisenschmidt & Schulze G.m.b.H., [1909].
viii, 390 p. incl. illus., tables, diagrs. 21cm.

NK 0208102 ICJ ICRL CU-A

SD397 .B4K7 Knorr, E August.
Studien über die buchen-wirthschaft. Von E. A. Knorr... Nordhausen, F. Förstemann, 1863.
vi, [1], 252 p. 22½cm.

1. Beech.

NK 0208103 ICU

Knorr, Elfride. L746 K75
Neue Muster für Macrame-Knüpfarbeit von Elfride Knorr, Barmen. Leipzig, G. Hedeler, 1910.
[24] p. 12 pl. 33x25½cm.
Printed on only one side of the leaves.

NK 0208104 ICJ

Knorr, Elfriede, 1910-
... Der zellige Aufbau des normalen menschliche Knochenmarks (Untersuchungen an Sternalpunktaten beim Lebenden): I. Anatomie des Knochenmarks; II. Untersuchungsmethoden und Ergebnisse früherer Autoren; III. eigene Untersuchungen ... Bleicherode am Harz, 1937.
Inaug.-Diss. - Leipzig.
Lebenslauf.
"Diese Dissertation ist gleichzeitig als Broschüre im Verlag Carl Nieft, Bleicherode, erschienen."

NK 0208105 CtY

Knorr, *Mrs.* **Elizabeth H.,** *pseud.*
see
Melch, Jessie.

Knorr, Emil.
Entstehung und Enwickelung der geistlichen Schauspiele in Deutschland und das Passionspiel im Ober-Ammergau. Zwei Vorträge...von Emil Knorr... Leipzig: T. Scheibel, 1872. 151 p. front. (port.) 8°.

1. Drama, Religious, German—Hist. and crit. 2. Passion plays—Germany—Oberammergau.
N. Y. P. L. July 1, 1930

NK 0208107 NN PU OU IU

QD341 A2K688 Knorr, Emil.
Ueber (4)nitro-m-xylol(2)sulfonsaeure. Freiburg, 1887.
43p. 8°
Inaug. diss. Freiburg.

NK 0208108 DLC

Knorr, Emil, 1884-
Ueber die perforation des pericholecystitischen abszesses im gefolge von cholecystitis calculosa in den herzbeutel... 1914.

NK 0208109 MiU CtY PPWI DNLM

UH K72e 1880 KNORR, Emil, d. 1904.
Entwickelung und Gestaltung des Heeres-Sanitätswesens der europäischen Staaten, vom militärisch-geschichtlichen Standpunkte. Hannover, Helwing, 1880.
982, x p.
Issued 1877-79 in six parts with title Ueber Entwickelung und Gestaltung des Heeres-Sanitätswesens der europäischen Staaten; each part has special title page.

A supplementary study, with title Das russische Heeres-Sanitätswesen während des Feldzugs 1877-78, was published by the author in 1883.

NK 0208111 DNLM

Knorr, Emil, d. 1904.
Das erste deutsche Parlament und die wehrfragen unter benutzung archival - Quellen. Berlin, 1887.

NK 0208112 MH

4DK Pol. 475 Knorr, Emil, d. 1904.
Die polnischen Aufstände seit 1830 in ihrem Zusammenhange mit den internationalen Umsturzbestrebungen; unter Benutzung archivalischer Quellen. Berlin, E. S. Mittler, 1880.
431 p.

NK 0208113 DLC-P4 NcU MH

---

4 UH 25 Knorr, Emil, d. 1904.
Das russische Heeres-Sanitätswesen während des Feldzugs 1877/78. Hannover, Helwing, 1883.
227 p.

NK 0208114 DLC-P4 DNLM

Knorr, Emil, d. 1904.
Ueber Entwickelung und Gestaltung des Heeres-Sanitätswesens der europäischen Staaten
see his Entwickelung und Gestaltung des Heeres-Sanitätswesens ...

VOLUME 300

4 UA Ger. 42 Knorr, Emil, d. 1904.
Von 1807 bis 1893; zur Entwickesungs-geschichte unserer Heeresverfassung. Berlin, H. Peters, 1893.
141 p.

NK 0208116 DLC-P4

[KNORR, Emil] d. 1904
Von Alsen bis zum frieden; eine skizze vom kriegstheater. Schluss des "Von der Eider bis Düppel" und "Von Düppel bis zur waffenruhe Voneinem officier. Hamburg, Perthes-Besser & Mauke, 1865.

NK 0208117 MH

[Knorr, Emil] d. 1904.
Von der Eider bis Düppel. Eine Skizze vom Kriegstheater, von einem Officier. 3. unveränderts Ausg. Hamburg, Perthes-Besser & Mauke, 1864.
88 p. 21 cm.
Bound with the author's Von Düppel bis zur Waffenruhe. Hamburg, 1864.

1. Schleswig-Holstein War, 1864. I. Title.

DL236.K6 1864 55-48849

NK 0208118 DLC

[Knorr, Emil] d. 1904.
Von Düppel bis zur Waffenruhe. Eine Skizze vom Kriegstheater. Fortsetzung des "Von der Eider bis Düppel." Von einem Officier. Hamburg, Perthes-Besser & Mauke, 1864.
152 p. 21 cm.
Bound with the author's Von der Eider bis Düppel. Hamburg, 1864.

1. Schleswig-Holstein War, 1864. I. Title.

DL236.K6 1864 55-48850

NK 0208119 DLC

Knorr, Emil Richard, 1877-
De Apollonii Rhodii Argonauticorum fontibus quaestiones selectae ... Lipsiae, 1902.
46 p. 23.5 cm.
Inaug.-Diss. - Leipzig.
Vita.

NK 0208120 CtY

Knorr, Erich.
Beitraege zur kenntnis der pyrazol-homologen, 1897.

Jena Univ. Ph.D. Diss.

NK 0208121 PU DNLM MH

280.2 K75 Knorr, Erich.
Ungarns Produktionsgenossenschaften zeigen den werktätigen Bauern den Weg zum besseren Leben. Berlin, Deutscher Bauernverlag [1952]
31 p.

1. Agriculture, Cooperative. Societies. Hungary.

NK 0208122 DNAL

Knorr, Erich, 1884-
Vormerkung zur Sicherung des Anspruchs auf Löschung einer Hypothek (§ 1179 B.G.B.) ... von Erich Knorr ... Berlin, C. Kuhn & Söhne [1908]
4 p.l., [7]-73 p., 2 l. 21cm.
Inaug.-diss. - Heidelberg.
"Lebenslauf": 2d leaf at end.
"Literaturverzeichnis": 1st leaf at end.

NK 0208123 MH-L ICRL NN

Knorr, Ernst, b. 1805.
Disquisitiones quaedam de aestu maris. Dissertatio quam ... publice defendet auctor Ernestus Knorr ... Berolini, Typis Fratrum Unger [1830]
1 p. l., 23, [2] p. 24cm.

NK 0208124 NNC NN NIC

Knorr, Ernst, 1878-
Beitraege zur primaeren zahnfleischtuberkulose und zu den infektionswegen der halsdruesen-tuberkulose. Breslau, 1917.
Inaug. diss. - Breslau.
Bibl.

NK 0208125 ICRL DNLM

---

4 M 377 Knorr, Ernst Lothar Karl von, 1896-
Auf einer Burg; Suite für Klavier. Köln, P.J. Tonger.
8 p.
Pl. no. P.J.T. 8624.

NK 0208126 DLC-P4

---

4 M 376 Knorr, Ernst Lothar Karl von, 1896-
Aus dem Leben der Kinder; Suite für Klavier. Köln, P.J. Tonger.
8 p.
Pl. no. P.J.T. 8603.

NK 0208127 DLC-P4

Knorr, Ernst Lothar von, 1896-

Drei gemischte Chöre auf Worte von Walther von der Vogelweide... Köln, P.J. Tonger [1954]
6 p. 29cm.

Score: SATB.
Contents.—Was ist Minne? "Sag mir einer."—Zu Dank "Kann noch wer zu Danke singen?"—

Sängers Klage "Weh dir, höfisch edles Singen."

1. Choral music, Secular (Mixed, 4 pt.)—Unacc.
I. Walther von der Vogelweide, 12th cent.

NK 0208129 NN

Knorr, Ernst Lothar Karl von, 1896-
[Lieder der Arbeit, unison voices & piano]

Lieder der Arbeit; für einstimmigen Gesang mit Klavier und Vorspielen. Hamburg, Hanseatische Verlagsanstalt [c1937]
11 p. 23 x 29 cm. (Lobeda-Spielhefte. Reihe B: Zum Singen und Spielen, Heft 3)
Contents.—Wir schreiten, Kolonnen (Ferdinand Oppenberg).—Schwinge, Hammer! (Ferdinand Oppenberg).—Pack zu! (Georg Zemke)

1. Choruses, Secular (Unison) with piano. I. Title.

M1609.K 52-49443

NK 0208130 DLC NN

Knorr, Ernst Lothar Karl von, 1896-
Lieder zur Weihnacht; eine Folge der schönsten Weihnachtslieder in Wort und einstimmiger Melodie. Stuttgart, Reclam-Verlag [1954]
63p. 10x16cm.

NK 0208131 PSt

Knorr, Ernst Lothar von, 1896-

...Der Lohn des Fleisses; Lehrstück nach Worten von Wilhelm Busch für eine Singstimme, Chor <Sopran, Mezzosopran und Alt> und Instrumente im G-Schlüssel, einzeln oder chorisch zu besetzen. Leipzig: J. Rieter-Biedermann [etc., etc., c1932] Publ. pl. no. 11024–11026. 1 v. 27cm. (Neue Schulkantaten... Nr. 3.)

Score (12 p.): solo voice, 3-part women's chorus and violin I-III. Choral part and 3 string parts. German words.

1. Cantatas, Secular—Instr. acc. I. Busch, Wilhelm, 1832-1908. II. Title.
N. Y. P. L. February 15, 1943

NK 0208132 NN

M1580 .H28N4 Knorr, Ernst Lothar Karl von, 1896- joint ed.

Hannemann, Carl, 1890- ed.
Neues singebuch für männerchor, in verbindung mit dem Amt Feierabend der NS gemeinschaft Kraft durch freude herausgegeben von Carl Hannemann, unter mitarbeit von Walter Rein und Ernst Lothar von Knorr. Hamburg, Hanseatische verlagsanstalt [1940]

Knorr, Ernst Lothar Karl von, 1896- joint ed.

M1734 .P17S6 1940 Pallmann, Gerhard, 1906- ed.
FOR OTHER EDITIONS SEE MAIN ENTRY
Soldaten, Kameraden; Liederbuch für Wehrmacht und Volk. [Notenausg.] 3. Aufl. Hrsg. von Gerhard Pallmann und Ernst Lothar v. Knorr. Hamburg, Hanseatische Verlagsanstalt, 1940.

M786.4 K757s Knorr, Ernst Lothar Karl von, 1896-

Sonatine für Klavier. Köln, E.Risping [1947]
[8]p. 31cm. (Neue Hausmusik)

1. Sonatas (Piano) 2. Piano music. I. Series.

NK 0208135 OrU

Knorr, Ernst Lothar Karl von, 1896-
[Sonatina, piano, A]

Sonatine in A. Piano solo. Hamburg, N. Simrock [c1948]
11 p. 31 cm. (Elite Edition, No. 261)

1. Sonatas (Piano)

M23.K72S6 1961 M 61-900

NK 0208136 DLC

Knorr, Ernst Lothar von, 1896-

...Die Strafe der Faulheit; Lehrstück nach Worten von Wilhelm Busch für Einzelstimmen, Sprechchor, Singchor <Sopran, Mezzosopran und Alt> und Streich-Quartett <3 Violinen und Viola>, einzeln oder chorisch zu besetzen. Leipzig: J. Rieter-Biedermann [etc., etc., c1932] Publ. pl. no. 11027–11029. 1 v. 27cm. (Neue Schulkantaten... Nr. 4.)

Score (7 p.): solo voice, 2-part women's chorus, violin I-III and viola. Choral part and 4 string parts. German words.

1. Cantatas, Secular—Instr. acc. I. Busch, Wilhelm, 1832-1908. II. Title.
N. Y. P. L. February 15, 1943

NK 0208137 NN

VOLUME 300

Knorr, Ernst Rudolph.
A few words on international co-operation in maritime hydrography. By E. R. Knorr ... Washington, Judd & Detweiler, printers, 1884.
24 p. 23½cm.

1. Hydrographic surveying.
13—14155
Library of Congress VK593.K72

NK 0208138 DLC NcD DN-Ob DN

Knorr, Ernst Rudolph.
... Memoranda on running surveys, with remarks on chronometer errors and rates. By E. R. Knorr ... Washington, Govt. print. off., 1872.
21 p. 24cm. (U. S. Hydrographic office. Bureau of navigation. [Publication] no. 36)

1. Hydrographic surveying.
13—14194
Library of Congress VK593.K73

NK 0208139 DLC NN

Knorr, Ernst Rudolph, tr.

U. S. *Hydrographic office.*
... Papers on the eastern and northern extensions of the Gulf stream. From the German of Dr. A. Petermann, Dr. W. von Freeden, and Dr. A. Mühry. Tr. in the United States Hydrographic office ... by E. R. Knorr. Washington, Govt. print. off., 1871.

Knorr, Ernst Rudolph, tr.

Kropp, Wilhelm.
... Physical geography of the Red sea; with sailing directions. By Captain W. Kropp, Imperial Austrial navy. Tr. from the German by E. R. Knorr, with the addition of a translation by authority of the Meteorological committee, London, of a paper issued by the Meteorological society of the Netherlands [entitled] Routes for steamers from Aden to the straits of Sunda, and back. Washington, Gov't print. off., 1872.

Knorr, Ernst Rudolph.
Standard time for the United States, Canada and Mexico. A review of the propositions published by the American society of civil engineers ... By E. R. Knorr ... Washington, Judd & Detweiler, printers, 1882.
16 p. fold. map, fold. diagr. 22½cm.

1. Time—Systems and standards.
11—32488
Library of Congress QB223.K6

NK 0208142 DLC DN NN

[Knorr, F.]
Wandervogel-Kochbuch; hrsg. vom Wandervogel Verein zur Förderung des Jugend-Wanderns in Bayern (E. V.). München: J. F. Lehmann [1910]. 27(1) p. 16°.

1. Cookery (Camp). 2. Wandervogel Verein zur Förderung des Jugend-Wanderns in Bayern (E. V.). 3. Title.
N. Y. P. L. May 16, 1911.

NK 0208143 NN

Knorr, Felicitas, 1907-
... Die Histologie der alternden Quadrizeps-Sehne mit einem Beitrag zu ihrer Spontanruptur ... Berlin [n. d.]
Inaug.-Diss. - Berlin.
Lebenslauf.
"Schrifttum": p. [14]

NK 0208144 CtY

KNORR, Ferdinand.
Germanische namengebung; ein versuch der lösung des namenrätsels. Berlin, E. Frowein, [1912].

NK 0208145 MH

Knorr, Ferdinand.
Die Natur und Funktion der Vorzugsrechte. Eine rechtsvergleichende Studie ... von Ferdinand Knorr. München, C. Wolf & Sohn, 1891.
2 p.l., 114 p. 22cm.
Inaug.-Diss. - Erlangen.
Bibliographical footnotes.

NK 0208146 MH-L ICRL CU

Knorr, Frederick, arr.

Cowboy dance tunes, arranged by Frederick Knorr to accompany Lloyd Shaw's book Cowboy dances. Foreword by Lloyd Shaw. Caldwell, Idaho: The Caxton printers, ltd., 1940. 24 p. 22½cm.

For piano with letter notation for guitar.

1. Cowboys. 2. Dancing—U. S. I. Shaw, Lloyd, 1890- Cowboy dances. II. Title.
N. Y. P. L. June 25, 1942

NK 0208147 NN Or WaSp OrCS

Knorr, Frederick, arr.
Cowboy dance tunes; arranged by Frederick Knorr, to accompany Lloyd Shaw's book Cowboy dances. Foreword by Lloyd Shaw. Caldwell, Idaho, The Caxton printers, ltd. 1941. 24p.

NK 0208148 OCl

Knorr, Frederick.

GV1767 .S5

Shaw, Lloyd, 1890-
Cowboy dances; a collection of western square dances, by Lloyd Shaw; with a foreword by Sherwood Anderson. Caldwell, Id., The Caxton printers, ltd., 1939.

Knorr, Friedrich, 1872-
... Deutsche sprachwissenschaft, von dr. Friedrich Knorr. Freiburg i. Br., H. F. Schulz, 1942.
39, [1] p. 23½cm. (Wissenschaftskunde in einzeldarstellungen, hrsg. von dr. Wolfgang Strauss und Hans Ferdinand Schulz. Hft. 2)
"Unveränderte wiedergabe eines vortrages, den ich im frühjahr 1939 auf einer tagung der wissenschaftlichen buchhändler gehalten habe."—p. 3.

1. German language. I. Title.
46-38076
Library of Congress PF3071.K57
430

NK 0208150 DLC TxU MnU MH NcD CtY

Knorr, Friedrich, 1872- ed.
Die epischen dichtungen des deutschen mittelalters
see under title

Knorr, Friedrich, 1872-
Friedhöfe der älteren eisenzeit in Schleswig-Holstein, von Friedr. Knorr. Hrsg. von dem Schleswig-Holsteinischen museum vaterländischer altertümer. Kiel, Kommissionsverlag von Lipsius & Tischer, 1910-
v. plates. 25½cm.

1. Iron age—Schleswig-Holstein. 2. Schleswig-Holstein—Antiq. I. Title.
22-1822
Library of Congress GN780.S4K6

NK 0208152 DLC CU

Knorr, Friedrich, 1872- tr.

PT1682 .P6K52

Wolfram *von Eschenbach, 12th cent.*
Der junge Parzival. [Aus dem Mittelhochdeutschen übertragen von Friedrich Knorr und Reinhard Fink. Frontbuchhandelsausgabe für die Wehrmacht] Jena, E. Diederichs [1944, °1943]

Knorr, Friedrich, 1872-
Der meister des Neukirchener altars ... Kiel, Schmidt & Klaunig, 1903.
46, [2] p. plates. 26½cm.
Inaug.-diss.—Kiel.
Vita.

7-16663

NK 0208154 DLC CtY PU CU NN

Knorr, Friedrich, 1872-
... Die mittelhochdeutsche dichtung. Jena, Eugen Diederichs verlag [°1938]
2 p. l., 7-209 p., 1 l. 21cm.

1. German poetry—Middle High German—History and criticism. I. Title.
A C 39-1323
Illinois. Univ. Library for Library of Congress [2]

NK 0208155 IU NcU NcD CU InU PSC OCl OO OCU NN NjP PHC CtY CaBVaU

Knorr, Friedrich, 1872- ed.

PA3 .N62

Neue jahrbücher für deutsche wissenschaft. 1.-13. jahrg.; 1925-37. Leipzig und Berlin, B. G. Teubner [1925-37]

Knorr, Friedrich, 1872- tr.

Wolfram *von Eschenbach, 12th cent.*
... Parzival; aus dem mittelhochdeutschen übertragen von Friedrich Knorr und Reinhard Fink. Jena, E. Diederichs [°1940]

VOLUME 300

Knorr, Friedrich, 1872–
Shakespeares Mass für Mass. [Coburg] 1955. 45 p. 24cm. (Coburger Dienstagsgesellschaft. Jahresgabe. 1955)

1. Shakespeare, William. Plays. Measure for measure. I. Coburger Dienstagsgesellschaft. Jahresgabe.

NK 0208158 NN DLC-P4 CtY

DD1 .Z43 Knorr, Friedrich, 1872– ed.

Zeitschrift für deutsche Geisteswissenschaft. 1.–6. Jahrg.; Apr. 1938–1943/44. Jena, E. Diederichs.

Div.S. 831.64 K72P Knorr, Friedrich, 1904–
Das Problem der menschlichen Philosophie bei J. G. Herder. Marburg, 1930.
167 p. 23 cm.
Inaug.-Diss.--Marburg.
Vita.
Bibliography: p. 163-165.
1. Herder, Johann Gottfried von, 1744-1803. I. Title.
dcb

NK 0208160 NcD CtY MH PU

Knorr, Fritz.
... Experiments with crops under fall irrigation at the Scottsbluff reclamation project experiment farm. By Fritz Knorr. [Washington, Govt. print. off.] 1914.

17 p. incl. tables, diagrs. 23cm. (U. S. Dept. of agriculture. Bulletin no. 133)

Contribution from Bureau of plant industry.

1. Irrigation—Nebraska. 2. [Scotts Bluff field station, Mitchell, Neb.]

Agr 14–1448 Revised

Library, U. S. Dept. of Agriculture 1Ag84B no. 133

NK 0208161 DNAL WaWW OU OC1MN OO OC1 PPAN NN

Knorr, Fritz.
Irrigated field crops in western Nebraska. Lincoln [1914]. 32 p. 8°. (Nebraska. Agricultural Experiment Station. Bull. 141.)

Scottsbluff substation bull. 1.

1. Irrigation, U. S.: Neb.
N. Y. P. L. May 24, 1915.

NK 0208162 NN

Knorr, Fritz.
Work of the Scotts Bluff field station ...
see under U.S. Bureau of plant industry.

WG 32168 Knorr, Fritz, 1909–
Beiträge zum biologischen Abbau der organischen Substanz einiger Wirtschaftsdüngemittel im Ackerboden. Göttingen, 1933.
50 p.
Inaug.-Diss. - Göttingen.

NK 0208164 CtY

Knorr, Georg.
Die bayerischen Provinzen, ihre Selbstverwaltung und Aufgaben. München, Verlag: Buchdr. A. Waldbaur Nachf. [1928?]

9 p. 29 cm.

"Vortrag, gehalten ... bei der gemeinsamen Tagung der Preussischen Landerhauptleute und der Bayerischen Kreistagpräsidenten im Landhause des Provinz Brandenburg in Berlin am 18. Oktober 1928."

1. Local government—Bavaria.

JS5471.B42K6 49–36786*

NK 0208165 DLC

Knorr, Georg.

Popitz, Johannes, 1884–
... Finanzausgleichsprobleme; I. von staatssekretär im Reichsfinanzministerium professor dr. Popitz, II. von oberbürgermeister Knorr ... III. wechselrede in der sitzung des vorstandes und des arbeitsausschusses des Vereins für kommunalwirtschaft und kommunalpolitik e. v. in München am 8. januar 1927. Berlin-Friedenau, Deutscher kommunal-verlag g. m. b. h., 1927.

Knorr, Georg Wolfgang, 1705–1761.
Allgemeine Künstler-Historie, oder, Berühmter Künstlere Leben, Werke und Verrichtungen, mit vielen Nachrichten von raren alten und neuen Kupferstichen beschrieben, von Georg Wolfgang Knorr. Nürnberg: Zu finden bey dem Author, Gedruckt, bey A. Bieling, 1759. 282 p. ports. 21cm.

The portraits of artists are line engravings, two of them by G. N. Knorr.

150705B. 1. Artists—Biog.
N. Y. P. L. April 3, 1942

NK 0208167 NN CtY

---

f x QH 41 K7214 1779 Knorr, Georg Wolfgang, 1705-1761.
Delices de la nature; ou, Choix de tout ce que les trois regnes de la nature, renferment de plus digne des recherches d'un curieux pour en former un cabinet; ouvrage communiqué di-devant au public par George Wolfgang Knorr. Continue par ses héritiers avec les descriptions et remarques de Philippe Louis Statius Müller. Revu, corrigé et augmenté d'une préface par Mr. Jean Ernest Emanuel Walch. Traduit del'allemand par

Jaques Frederic Isenflamm. Nuremberg, Ches les Héritiers de feu G.W. Knorr, 1779.
2v. illus.,pl.
1. Natural history--Pictorial works.
2. Natural history--Pre-Linnean works.
I. Müller, Philipp Ludwig Statius, 1725-1776.
II. Walch, Johann Ernst Immanuel, 1725-1778.
III. Isenflamm, Jaques Frederic, tr.
IV. Title.

NK 0208169 UU NN

Knorr, Georg Wolfgang, 1705–1761.
Les delices des yeux et de l'esprit, ou Collection generale des differentes especes de coquillages que la mer renferme, communiquée au public par Georg Wolffgang Knorr ... Nuremberg, 1760–73.

6 v. 190 pl. (180 col.) 26 x 21cm.

Added t.-p., illus., in colors: Collection des differentes espèces de coquillages qu'on trouve dans les mers ...

1. Shells. 6–18544†

Library of Congress QL404.K72

NK 0208170 DLC CtY

Knorr, Georg Wolfgang, 1705-1761.
Deliciae naturae selectae oder Auserlesenes Naturalien-Cabinet welches aus den drey Reichen der Natur zeiget... Nürnberg, 1754.

f°. illum.title & 30 col.plates. [No text.]

NK 0208171 MH-Z

Knorr, Georg Wolfgang, 1705-1761
Deliciae naturae selectae; oder, Auserlesenes naturalien Cabinet ... beschrieben von Philipp Ludwig Müller ... & in das Französische übersetzet von Matthäus Verdier de la Blaquiere. Nürnberg, 1766.

NK 0208172 PPL

Knorr, Georg Wolfgang, 1705–1761.
Deliciae naturae selectae: oder, Auserlesenes naturaliencabinet, welches aus den drey reichen der natur zeiget, was von curiösen liebhabern aufbehalten und gesammlet zu werden verdienet. Ehemahls hrsg. von Georg Wolfgang Knorr ... fortgesetzet von dessen erben, beschrieben von Philipp Ludwig Statius Müller ... und in das französische übersetzet von Matthäus Verdier de la Blaquiere ... Nürnberg, 1766–67.

2 v. in 1. 91 col. pl. (1 fold.) 57 cm.

Added t.-p., engraved, dated 1754. Added t.-p. (printed) in French. Text in German and French.

"Verzeichniss derer schriftsteller, welche man bey verfertigung des textes mehrentheils zu rathe gezogen": v. 1, 8 p. preceding p. i.

1. Natural history—Pictorial works. 2. Natural history—Pre-Linnean works. I. Müller, Philipp Ludwig Statius, 1725–1776. II. Verdier de La Blaquière, Mathieu, tr., d. 1769. III. Title.

QH41.K72 7—40989

NK 0208174 DLC PPAN MWiW-C

QH 46 .K728 Knorr,Georg Wolfgang,1705-1761.
Deliciae naturae selectae,of,Uitgeleezen kabinet van natuurlyke zeldzaamheden; welke de drie ryken der natuur aanbieden,om door keurige liefhebberen verzameld te worden,wel eer uitgegeven door George Wolfgang Knoor ... en vervolgd door zyne erven; eerst in de hoogduitsche taal beschreeven,en nu in het nederduitsch overgezet en met aanmerkingen vermeerderd door Philip Ludwigh Statius Muller

... Dordrecht, A.Blussé en zoon, 1771.
2 v. 91 col.plates. 47 cm.
Added t.-p.,engraved and illustrated in colors.
"Alphabetische lyst der autheuren,van welke men eenig gebruik gemaakt heeft in het toestellen van dit werk":v.1,p.[xvii]-xxxii.
1.Natural history--Pictorial works.
I.Müller,Philipp Ludwig Statius,1725-1776. II.Title.

NK 0208176 MiU ICJ PPAN

Knorr, Georg Wolfgang, 1705-1761.
Die Naturgeschichte der Versteinerungen ...
see under Walch, Johann Ernst Immanuel, 1725-1778.

QE709 f.K7 Rare bk Knorr, Georg Wolfgang, 1705-1761.
Recveil de monvmens des catastrophes qve le globe de la terre a éssviées, contenant des pétrifications et d'avtres pierres cvrievses, dessinées, gravées et enlvminées par George Wolfgang Knorr. Nvremberg [1768-78]
4 v. plates (part col.) port. 40cm.
Added title page, engraved, in Latin and German.
After the death of Knorr, continued by J. E. I. Walch.
1. Paleontology--Early works to 1800. I. Walch Johann Ernst Immanuel, 1725-1778.

NK 0208178 ICU MH NN DI-GS CU IU

VOLUME 300

Knorr, Georg Wolfgang, 1705–1761.
Sammlung von merckwürdigkeiten der natur und alterthümern des erdbodens, welche petrificirte cörper enthält aufgewiesen und beschrieben, von Georg Wolffgang Knorr ... Nürnberg, Gedruckt bey A. Bieling, 1755–73 [v. 3, '69]
3 v. in 2. front. (port.) fold. plates (part col.) 38½cm.
Vol. 1 has also engraved t.-p. in Latin and German, 1750. Latin title: Lapides, ex celeberrimorum virorum sententia diluvii universalis testes, quos in ordines ac species distribuit, suis coloribus exprimit, æriq; incisos in lucem mittit et alia naturae miranda addit Georg Wolffgang Knorr Norimbergensis.
After the death of Knorr, the work was continued by J. E. I. Walch.

Zweiter theil (designated on t.-p. "erster theil") [1. abschnitt] and 2. theil, 2. abschnitt, have special t.-p.: Die naturgeschichte der versteinerungen zur erläuterung der Knorrischen Sammlung von merkwürdigkeiten der natur, herausgegeben von Johann Ernst Immanuel Walch ...
Each of the two parts has also special engraved t.-p.
Zweiter theil. 1. abschnitt, has imprint: Nürnberg. Gedruckt mit Felsseckerischen schrifften, 1773; 2. abschnitt: Nürnberg, Gedruckt bey P. J. Felssecker, 1769.

1. Paleontology—Early works to 1800. I. Walch, Johann Ernst Immanuel, 1725–1778. II. Title.

G–1984 Revised

Library of Congress QE709.K74

NK 0208180 DLC NjP NN MH-A CtY MdBP IU DI-GS N

Knorr, Georg Wolfgang, 1705-1761.
Schnecken und Muscheln welche im Meere gefunden werden.

NK 0208181 PPAN

1850 K75 Knorr, George Wolfgang 1705-1761.
Thesaurus rei Herbariae Hortensis Universalis. Nürnberg, G.W. Knorr, 1750.[1770-1772, Text by Philipp F. Gmelin, con't by Georg R. Boehmer.] 2 vols.

Vol.I: T.p. in color (Regnum florae das reich der Blumen...), Pref.4pp.; 119 handcol. engr. pls. arranged alphabetically by name, (A-Q). Text pp.1-30; 1-26; 1-236 (Latin & German)

$A_2-G_2;H_2;A_2-G_2;A_2-Z_2;Aa_2-Zz_2;Aaa_2-Nnn_2;Ooo_1$.

VolII, Part I: T.p. (Latin & German) 80 engr. handcol. pls. arranged alphabetically, (R-Z). Text, in Latin & German, pp.1-24; 1-54; 1-34. [2pp.] tables.
$A_2-F_2;A_2-N_2;O_1;A_2-I_2$.

Part II: T.p. (Lat. & Ger.). 101 handcol. engr. pls. arranged alphabetically, (A-V). Text, in Latin & German, pp.1-130. Index, part 2 [4pp.] General indexes (17pp.) in Latin, German, Greek, Italian, French, English & Belgic.

$A_2-Z_2;Aa_2-Ii_2;Kk_1;$,o(2;$(x)_2-(xxxx)_2;(xxxxx)_1$.

Folio, full calf, gilt, marbled endpapers. 16 1/4" x 10 1/4".

NK 0208184 DDO

Knorr, Georg Wolfgang, 1705–1761.
Thesavrvs rei herbariae hortensisqve vniversalis, exhibens figvras florvm, herbarvm, arborvm, frvticvm, aliarvmqve plantarvm prorsvs novas, et ad ipsos delineatas depictasqve archetypos nativis coloribvs, atqve idiomate tam Latino qvam Germanico describens eorvndem partes, formam et habitvm, nec non vsvm in officinis pharmacevticis, vita commvni, et medicina, provt singvla haec nova docvit applicata observatio et archetyporvm exacta contemplatio ... Apud Georgii Wolfgangi Knorrii haeredes ... Allgemeines blumen- kräuter- frucht- und garten-buch ... Nürnberg, Gedruckt bey P. J. Felssecker, 1770–72.
2 v. front. (port., v. 2) col. plates. 39cm.

Text by Philipp Friedrich Gmelin, continued by Georg Rudolph Boehmer.
Latin and German in parallel columns.
[Vol. 2] has title: Regnum florae. Das reich der blumen mit allen seinen schönheiten, nach der natur und ihren farben vorgestellt ...

CONTENTS.—[v. 1] Text.—[v. 2] Plates.

1. Gardening. [1. Horticulture] I. Böhmer, Georg Rudolph, 1723–1803. II. Gmelin, Philipp Friedrich, 1721–1768. III. Title.

Agr 16–1071

Library, U. S. Dept. of Agriculture 90K753

NK 0208186 DNAL

Knorr, Georg Wolfgang, 1705-1761,
Thesaurus rei Herbariae, Hortensisque universalis, a G.W. Knorrio. Wittenberg, 1788-9.
2 pts.

NK 0208187 PPL

Knorr, Georg Wolfgang, 1705 - 1761
Vergnügen der Augen & des Gemüthes in vorstellung einer allgemeinen sammlung von Muscheln & und andern Geschöpfen welche im Meere gefunden werden, herausgegeben von G. Wolfgang Knorr in Nurnberg. 1757-1772.
4 v. in 6 theile.

NK 0208188 PPAN MH DSI

Knorr, George Washington.
... Consolidated rural schools and organization of a county system. By George W. Knorr ... Washington, Govt. print. off., 1910.
99 p. incl. tables, diagrs. illus. 23cm. (U. S. Dept. of agriculture. Office of experiment stations. Bulletin 232)
Issued by the Office of experiment stations in cooperation with the Bureau of statistics.
1. Rural schools. I. Title.

Agr 10–1583

Library, U. S. Dept. of Agriculture 1Ex6B no. 232

NK 0208189 DNAL Or WaS WaSp MiU ODW OCl OO PP MB NN

Knorr, George Washington.
... A study of 15 consolidated rural schools; their organization, cost, efficiency, and affiliated interests, by George W. Knorr. Washington, D. C., Southern education board, 1911.
55 p. illus., diagrs. 23½cm. (Publication no. 6)

1. Rural schools. 2. Schools—Centralization.

E 13–1366

Library, U. S. Bur. of Education LB1567.K75

NK 0208190 DHEW Or ODW

KNORR, Gerhard *Die Bestimmung der tödlichen und der die Leistungsfähigkeit nicht vermindernden Gaben einiger Mittel bei Brieftauben. 12p. 8° Lpz., 1934.

NK 0208191 DNLM

Knorr, Mrs. H A
See
Knorr, Catherine Lindsay.

Knorr (Hans) [1887–]. *Beitrag zur Kenntnis der Trichinellen-Krankheit des Menschen. [München.] 23 pp., 2 pl. 8°. Leipzig, F. C. W. Vogel, 1912.

NK 0208193 DNLM

Knorr, Harry Virgil, 1896-
A photometric study of the appearance of spectral lines in condensed sparks... [Columbus, The Ohio state university, 1931. Thesis (PH.D.)-The Ohio state university.

NK 0208194 OU

Knorr, Heinrich Hardwick
Dissertatio de principvm Germaniae legationibv Jenae, [1868]

[Diplomatic pamphlets, v. 8:1]

NK 0208195 OOC

Knorr, Heinz, 1914-
Oeffentliches und privates recht im umbruch des rechtsdenkens. ... Würzburg, 1938.
Inaug. Diss. - Halle-Wittenberg, 1938.
Lebenslauf.
Literaturverzeichnis.

NK 0208196 ICRL

Knorr, Heinz Arno.
... Die slawische keramik zwischen Elbe und Oder; einteilung und zeitansetzung auf grund der münzgefässe, mit einem kurzen abriss der frühmittelalterlichen keramik, von dr. Heinz A. Knorr ... Mit 167 abbildungen im text und 36 tafeln. Leipzig, Curt Kabitzsch, verlag, 1937.
4 p. l., 222 p., 1 l. illus. (incl. maps) 37 pl. (1 fold.) on 19 l. 25cm. (Mannus-bücherei ... 58)
Issued also in part as the author's thesis, Berlin.
Bibliographical foot-notes.
1. Pottery, Slavic. 2. Pottery, Primitive. I. Title.

A C 39–2249

Columbia univ. Library
for Library of Congress [GN705.M3 no. 58]
[2] (571.082)

NK 0208197 NNC CLU MoU CtY MH DLC PU-Mu

Knorr, Helmut.
Abessinische Impressionen, erlebt und gezeichnet von Helmut Knorr; nacherzählt von Peter Hall. Zürich, W. Classen [°1950]
1 v. (unpaged) illus. 29 cm.

1. Ethiopia—Descr. & trav.—Views. I. Hall, Peter, of Zürich? II. Title.

NC293.K6H3 51–31093

NK 0208198 DLC CtY NN

Knorr, Helmut, illus.

PT2647 .I 35C5 Rare Bk. Coll. **Wilczynski, Karl,** 1887–
Choräle zwischen Nacht und Morgen. Mit 8 handkolorierten Originallithographien von Helmut Knorr. [Zürich, W. Classen, 1948]

WB 16391 Knorr, Helmut.
Durch Steppe und Urwald. Solothurn, Schweizer Jugend-Verlag[c1952]

1. Africa, French West - Descr. & trav.

NK 0208200 CtY

916.3 K72m Knorr, Helmut.
Meine Abenteuer in Abessinien. [Bearb. und hrsg. von Josef Specker. 2. Aufl.]
Solothurn, Schweizer Jugend-Verlag [1952]
153p. illus. 22cm.

1.Ethiopia. Descr. & trav. I.Title.

NK 0208201 IEN

VOLUME 300

916.61
K72q Knorr, Helmut.
Quer durch die Sahara. [Bearb. und hrsg. von Josef Specker] Solothurn, Schweizer Jugend-Verlag [1952]
182p. illus. 22cm.

1. Sahara. Descr. & trav. I. Title.

NK 0208202 IEN

Knorr, Helmut.
Unterwegs in Afrika. Zürich, Artemis-Verlag [1954]
68 p. illus. 24 cm.

1. Africa, French West—Descr. & trav. I. Title.

DT527.K56 55-22287 ‡

NK 0208203 DLC IEN CtY NN

Knorr (Henricus Eduardus) [1829-]. *De gangliis synovialibus. 28 pp., 2 l. 8°. Berolini, F. G. Nietack, [1856].

NK 0208204 DNLM

D
534.3
.K72 Knorr, Herbert, ed.
Einser-Bilderbuch; 200 Aufnahmen aus der Geschichte des K.B.I. Infanterie-Regiments König im Weltkrieg, zusammengestellt und erläutert. München, Verlag Bayerisches Kriegsarchiv, 1926
1 v. 200 illus. (Erinnerungsblätter deutscher Regimenter. Bayerische Armee, Heft 8a)

1. Germany. Heer. Bayerisches 1. Infanterie-Regiment König. 2. European War, 1914-1918--Regimental histories--Germany--Bayerisches 1. Infanterie-Regiment König. I. Title.

NK 0208205 MiU

Knorr, Herbert.
Querdurch und rundherum; bilder aus dem alten Braunschweig ... Braunschweig, Graff [1920]
2 v. in 1. plates. 26.5 cm.
Cover-title.
In portfolios.
1. Brunswick (City)--Descr.--Views.

NK 0208206 NjP

KNORR, HERBERT, 1910-
Ausgewählte Kapitel der Grossraumtriangulation [von] Herbert Knorr [und] Willy Sander. Bamberg, Meisenbach, 1952. 125 p. diagrs., tables. 21cm. (Institut für angewandte Geodäsie, Frankfurt am Main. Veröffentlichungen. [Nr.] 15)

Added t. p., and summaries in English.

1. Triangulation, 1952. I. Sander, Willy, 1878- II. Series.

NK 0208207 NN

Knorr, Hermann.
Our political and social organism. A critical review of our conditions, also, a national and patriotical monitor and sound of alarm. Elaborated from the ideas and suggestions of Hermann Knorr, by P. Reiselt. Philadelphia, Globe printing house, 1892.
2 p. l., 3-85 p. fold. front. 17cm.

1. Social sciences—Miscellanea. I. Reiselt, P., ed.

Library of Congress HN64.K7 8-33089†

NK 0208208 DLC

Knorr, Hermann.
Politisch-sozialer Organismus. Kritische Streifzüge durch unsere Zustände. Zugleich ein national-patriotischer Weck- und Mahnruf. Nach den Ideen und Anleitungen von H. Knorr bearbeitet von P. Reiselt. Philadelphia, Pa., Druck vom Globe Printing House, 1892.
2 p.l., 3-90 p. 1 pl. 16°.

NK 0208209 NN

Knorr, Iwan, 1853–1916.
Aufgaben für den Unterricht in der Harmonielehre, für die Schüler des Dr. Hoch'schen Konservatoriums in Frankfurt a. M., zusammengestellt von Iwan Knorr. Leipzig: Breitkopf & Härtel, 1903. v(i), (1)8–78 p. 8°.

1. Harmony.
N. Y. P. L. June 16, 1916.

NK 0208210 NN MH

Knorr, Iwan, 1853–1916.
Aufgaben für den unterricht in der harmonielehre für die schüler von dr. Hoch's konservatorium in Frankfurt a. M., zusammengestellt von Iwan Knorr. 2., durchgesehene aufl. Leipzig, Breitkopf & Härtel, 1913.
v, [2], 8-78 p. illus. (music) 23½cm.

1. Harmony.

16-15273 Revised

Library of Congress MT50.K71

NK 0208211 DLC

Knorr, Iwan, 1853–1916.
Aufgaben für den unterricht in der harmonielehre für die schüler des dr. Hoch'schen konservatoriums in Frankfurt a. M., zusammengestellt von Iwan Knorr. 4. u. 5. aufl. Leipzig, Breitkopf & Härtel, 1921.
v, [2], 8-78 p. illus. (music) 23½cm.

1. Harmony.

22-22352

Library of Congress MT50.K72

NK 0208212 DLC

Knorr, Iwan, 1853–1916.
Festschrift zur feier des hundertjährigen bestehens der Frankfurter museumsgesellschaft 1808 bis 1908, von Iwan Knorr. Frankfurt am Main, Druck von A. Osterrieth, 1908.
1 p. l., 47 p. xv pl. (incl. ports.) 26½ x 19½cm.

1. Frankfurter museumsgesellschaft, Frankfurt am Main.

9-9292 Revised

Library of Congress ML279.8.F84

NK 0208213 DLC

Knorr, Iwan, 1853–1916.
Die Fugen des "Wohltemperierten Klaviers" von Joh. Seb. Bach in bildlicher Darstellung. Als Anhang und Ergänzung zu seinem Lehrbuch der Fugenkomposition hrsg. von Iwan Knorr. Leipzig: Breitkopf & Härtel, 1912. 5 p.l., 48 p. diagr. 8°. (Lehrgänge an Dr. Hochs Konservatorium in Frankfurt a. M.)
German, English and French text.

1. Bach, Johann Sebastian, 1685–1750. 2. Fugue.
N. Y. P. L. June 17, 1916.

NK 0208214 NN NSyU

Knorr, Iwan, 1853–1916.
Die fugen des "Wohltemperierten klaviers" von Joh. Seb. Bach in bildlicher darstellung, als anhang und ergänzung zu seinem Lehrbuch der fugenkomposition herausgegeben von Iwan Knorr. 2. aufl. Leipzig, Breitkopf & Härtel, 1926.
5 p. l., 48 p. diagrs. 24cm.

Added t.-p.: Diagrams of the fugues in the "Welltempered clavichord" by Joh. Seb. Bach; an appendix and supplement to Iwan Knorr's Textbook of fugal composition. Les fugues du "Clavecin bien tempéré" de J. S. Bach; diagrammes ... 2. éd.
Text in German, English, and French.

1. Bach, Johann Sebastian. Das wohltemperierte clavier. 2. Fugue.

28-24529

Library of Congress MT59.B2K7 1926

NK 0208215 DLC MB

---

*Knorr, Iwan, 1853-1916.

Morin, August, 1849-
Johannes Brahms. Erläuterung seiner bedeutendsten werke, von C. Beyer, R. Heuberger, prof. J. Knorr, dr. H. Riemann, prof. J. Sittard, K. Söhle und musikdir. G. H. Witte. Nebst einer darstellung seines lebensganges mit besonderer berücksichtigung seiner werke. Von A. Morin. Frankfurt a. M., H. Bechhold [1897]

Knorr, Iwan, 1853-1916. No. 16 in **M.217.12.6
Johannes Brahms. Serenade für grosses Orchester (D-dur, Op. 11) Erläutert von Iwan Knorr.
Frankfurt a/M. Bechhold. [1898.] 14 pp. [Der Musikführer No. 142.] 16°.

E2767 — Brahms, Johannes. — Serenades.

NK 0208217 MB

Knorr, Iwan, 1853-1916. No. 16 in **M.217.12.1
Johannes Brahms. Serenade für kleines Orchester. Op. 16, erläutert von Iwan Knorr.
Frankfurt a/M. Bechhold. [1895.] 25 pp. [Der Musikführer. No. 16.] 16°.

Jan. 3, 1902
E2767 — Brahms, Johannes — Serenades.

NK 0208218 MB

Knorr, Iwan, 1853-1916. No. 5 in **M.217.12.3
Johannes Brahms, Sextett für Streichinstrumente. (No. 2, G-dur, Op. 36) Erläutert von Iwan Knorr.
Frankfurt a/M. Bechhold. [1897.] 22 pp. [Der Musikführer. No. 57.] 16°.

Jan. 3, 1902
E2767 — Brahms, Johannes. — Chamber music. String sextets.

NK 0208219 MB

Knorr, Iwan, 1853-1916. No. 23 **M.217.12.1
Johannes Brahms. Sextett in B-dur, Op. 18, erläutert von Iwan Knorr.
Frankfurt a/M. Bechhold. [1895.] 20 pp. [Der Musikführer. No. 23.] 16°.

E2767 — Brahms, Johannes. — Chamber music. String sextets.

NK 0208220 MB

4
Music
2434 Knorr, Iwan, 1853-1916.

Johannes Brahms; Symphonien und andere Orchesterwerke. Erläutert von I. Knorr, H. Riemann, J. Sittard, nebst einer Einleitung: Johannes Brahms' Leben und Schaffen von A. Morin. Berlin, Schlesinger'sche Buch- und Musikhandlung (R. Lienau) [ ]

158 p.

(Schlesinger'sche Musik-Bibliothek, Meisterführer, Nr. 3)

NK 0208222 DLC-P4 MB PP TxFTC OU ViFreM TxFTC OCl

VOLUME 300

Knorr, Iwan, 1853-1916. No. 17 in **M.217.12.6
Johannes Brahms, Triumphlied für achtstimmigen Chor und Orchester. Op. 55. Erläutert von Iwan Knorr.
Frankfurt a. M. Bechhold. [1898.] 9 pp. [Der Musikführer. No. 143.] 16°.

E2764 — Brahms, Johannes.

NK 0208223 MB

Knorr, Iwan, 1853-1916. No. 3 in **M.217.12.1
Johannes Brahms. Variationen über ein Thema von J. Haydn für Orchester, Op. 56a, erläutert von Jwan Knorr.
Frankfurt a/M. Bechhold. [1894.] 21 pp. [Der Musikführer. No. 3.] 16°.

E2767 — Variations. Orchestra. — Brahms, Johannes.

NK 0208224 MB

Knorr, Iwan. 1853-1916. No. 8 in **M.217.12.4
Johannes Brahms, Zweite Symphonie (D-dur). Op. 73. Erläutert von Iwan Knorr.
Frankfurt a. M. Bechhold. [1898.] 16 pp. [Der Musikführer. No. 86.] 16°.

E2767 — Brahms, Johannes. — Symphonies.

NK 0208225 MB

Knorr, Iwan.
Jugendbibliothek für zwei pianaforte zu achthänden. Kürzere stücke aus werken alter und neuer meister zum gebrauche beim unterricht, bearbeitet von Ivan Knorr. Leipzig, Breitkopf & Hartel, n.d.
2 v.

NK 0208226 PBa

Knorr, Iwan, 1853-1916.
Lehrbuch der fugenkomposition, von Iwan Knorr. Leipzig, Breitkopf & Härtel, 1911.
vii, [1], 162 p., 1 l., 28 p. illus. (music) 23½cm. (*Added t.-p.: Lehrgänge an dr. Hochs konservatorium in Frankfurt a. M.*) M. 3
"Anhang. Fugenbeispiele": 28 p. at end.

1. Fugue.
Library of Congress MT59.K68 11-18068 Revised

NK 0208227 DLC NN MH CU

Knorr, Iwan, 1853-1916.
Peter Jljitsch Tschaikowsky, von Iwan Knorr. Berlin, "Harmonie," verlagsgesellschaft für literatur und kunst, 1900.
91, [1] p. front. (port.) illus. (incl. music) pl., facsims. (part fold., incl. music) 26cm. (*Half-title:* Berühmte musiker ... hrsg. von Heinrich Reimann. xi)

1. Chaĭkovskiĭ, Petr Il'ich, 1840-1893.
3-17426 Revised
Library of Congress ML410.C4K7

NK 0208228 DLC TxU MoU OO MiU PPCI MB

Knorr, Iwan. 1853-1916. No. 17 in **M.217.12.1
Peter Tschaikowsky, Serenade für Streichorchester. Op. 48 erläutert von Jwan Knorr.
Frankfurt a/M. Becchold. [1895.] 16 pp. [Der Musikführer. No. 17.] 16°.

E2768 — Tchaikovski, Petr Iliitch. — Serenades.

NK 0208229 MB

Knorr, Iwan, 1853-1916. No. 5 in **M.217.12.1
Peter Tschaikowsky, Suite No. 3 (in G-dur für Orchester, Op. 55, erläutert von Jwan Knorr.
Frankfurt a/M. Bechhold. [1894.] 21 pp. [Der Musikführer. No. 5.] 16°.

E2768 — Tchaikovski, Petr Iliitch. — Suites.

NK 0208230 MB

[Knorr, Iwan,] 1853-1916.
Sechs Kinderstücke für Pianoforte und Violine. (Die Pianofortestimme im Violinschlüssel, die Violinstimme in der 1. Position.) Componirt von J. O. Armand [pseud.]. Op. 11. No. 1. Tema con variazioni. No. 2. Gavotte. No. 3. Ländler. No. 4. Polonaise. No. 5. Serenata. No. 6. Ungarisch... Leipzig: Breitkopf & Härtel [1885] Publ. pl. no. 16877. 2 parts. f°.

1. Violin and piano. 2. Children. —Music for.
N. Y. P. L. June 27, 1921

NK 0208231 NN

VM 1045 K 72s
KNORR, IWAN, 1853-1916.
[Symphonische Phantasie, orchestra, op.12]
Symphonische Phantasie für grosses Orchester. Op.12. Partitur. Frankfurt a/M, B.Firnberg [189-?]
score(135p.) 34cm.
Plate no.: 211.

60-273

NK 0208232 ICN

VM 1003 K 72v
KNORR, IWAN, 1853-1916.
[Variations, orchestra, op.7] Variationen über ein ukrainisches Volkslied, für Orchester. Op.7. Partitur. Leipzig, Breitkopf & Härtel [1891]
score(27p.) 34cm. (Breitkopf & Härtels Partitur-Bibliothek)

NK 0208233 ICN MH

KNORR, IWAN, 1853-1916.
Variationen und Fuge über ein Russisches Volkslied, für 2 Pianoforte zu 4 Händen, Op. 8. Leipzig, Breitkopf & Härtel [1928?] Pl. no. V.A.3321. 27 p. 31cm. (Edition Breitkopf. Nr. 3321)

Score: piano I-II.
Issued from plates of ca. 1910.
1. Piano (2 pianos). 2. Folk songs, Russian (Instrumental settings).

NK 0208234 NN

Knorr, Iwan Otto Armand
see Knorr, Iwan, 1853-1916.

Knorr, James.
The cadet of temperance; being a collection of dialogues, scenes, recitations, songs, odes, etc. designed for the use of sections in their public and private exhibitions... Philadelphia, T.B. Peterson [1848]
148p.

NK 0208236 OCl

Knorr, James.
The two roads; or, The right and the wrong. By James Knorr. Philadelphia, Lippincott, Grambo & co., 1854.
xi, 25-372 p. 19cm.
Temperance stories, poems and sketches.

1. Temperance—Exercises, recitations, etc. I. Title.
10—1625
Library of Congress HV5071.K6

NK 0208237 DLC KEmT PSt OU PPPrHi

FILM 4274 PR v.2 reel K7
Knorr, James,
The two roads; or, The right and the wrong ... Phila., Lippincott, Grambo, 1854.
372 p. (Wright American fiction, v.II, 1851-1875, no.1494, Research Publications Microfilm, Reel K-7)

1. Temperance - Exercises, recitations, etc.
I. Title.

NK 0208238 CU

Knorr (Joannes Godofredus). * Observationes chemicæ miscellæ. 25 pp., 1 l. 4°. *Gottingæ, lit. Hagerianis,* [1768].

NK 0208239 DNLM

Knorr, Johann Friedrich, respondent.
... De poenitentia ecclesiastica. Von der kirchen-busse ... Jenae, typis Joh. Jacobi Bauhoferi, 1678.
1 p.l., 164, [2] p. 19.5 cm.
Discursus - Jena (P. Müller, praeses)
Pages 161-[166] damaged.

NK 0208240 CtY

Knorr, Johann Friedrich.
... De poenitentia ecclesiastica. Von der Kirchen-Busse ... nunc recognitus & auctior ed. A Joh. Friderico Knorren ... Jenae, S. Schmidt, 1700.
186, [14] p. 19cm.
First published as dissertation (Jena, 1678) with Peter Müller as praeses.

NK 0208241 MH-L

Knorr, Johann Friedrich, respondent.
Exercitationem moralem de jure naturae, gentium et civili...
see under Cortrejus, Adam, 1637-1706, praeses.

Knorr, Johann Max
see Knorr, Max, 1908-

VOLUME 300

Knorr, Johannes Leopold Oscar, 1865- *3762.121
Experimentelle Untersuchungen über den Streptococcus longus.
(In Behring. Gesammelte Abhandlungen zur ätiologischen Therapie von ansteckenden Krankheiten. Theil 2, pp. 193-266. Leipzig. 1893.)

F6872 — Biological experimentation. — Streptococci.

NK 0208244 MB

Knorr (Johannes [Leopold Oscar]), 1865-
"Ueber congenitale Enchondrome der Halsgegend. 28 pp., 1 l. 8°. Greifswald, C. Sell, 1889.

NK 0208245 DNLM

PT2383 K355A76 Knorr, Josephine, Freiin von, 1827-1908.
Abendgedanken. Wien, Daberkow [1906]
24 p.

NK 0208246 CU

PT2383 K355A88 Knorr, Josephine, Freiin von, 1827-1908.
Aus späten Tagen, Gedichte. Mit Vorwort von Marie von Ebner-Eschenbach. Stuttgart, J.G. Cotta, 1897.
x,130 p.

NK 0208247 CU

Knorr, Josephine, *freiin* von, 1827-1908.
Gedichte von Josephine freiin v. Knorr. Wien, J. Dirnböck, 1872.
2 p. l., 3-151, [1] p., 1 l. 15cm.

21-22351

Library of Congress PT2383.K355

NK 0208248 DLC

Knorr, Josephine, Freiin von, 1827-1908.
Gedichte. Stuttgart, Cotta, 1902.
ix,249 p.

NK 0208249 CU

Knorr, Josephine, Freiin von, 1827-1908. 4879a.136
Pensées du soir. [Traduites avec une introduction par Louise Read.]
= Paris. Lemerre. 1903. (1), vii, 60, (1) pp. 16°.

F5289 — T.r. — Read, Louise, tr.

NK 0208250 MB

PT2383 K355S6 Knorr, Josephine, Freiin von, 1827-1908.
Sommerblumen und Herbstblätter, Gedichte. (Dritte Sammlung) Wien, L. Rosner, 1885.
166 p.

NK 0208251 CU

VM 201 D 85 v.2 KNORR, JULIUS, 1807-1861, ed.
Anfangs-Studien im Pianofortespiel als Vorläufer zu der musikalischen Chrestomathie aus Mozart, Haydn, Clementi und Cramer. Herausgegeben von Julius Knorr. Heft I. Für 4 Hände auf 5 Tasten. 2. Ausgabe. Leipzig, C.F. Kahnt [18--]
11p. 34cm.

Binder's title: Duets. v.2.

NK 0208252 ICN

MT225 .C896 1850 Knorr, Julius, 1807-1861, ed.

Cramer, Johann Baptist, 1771-1858.
[Studies. Selected]

The celebrated studies of J. B. Cramer, with new fingering & explanatory notes by Julius Knorr. Boston, O. Ditson; N[ew] York, Berry & Gordon; [etc., etc., 185-]

Knorr, Julius, 1807-1861.
Collection d'exercices, gammes et passages, pour le piano...
see under Herz, Henry, 1803-1888.

KNORR, JULIUS, 1807-1861.
Erklärendes verzeichniss der hauptsächlichtsen musikkunstwörter ... Leipzig, Breitkopf & Härtel, 1854.
60 p.

NK 0208255 NB

Knorr, Julius, 1807-1861.
Führer auf dem Felde der Clavierunterrichts-Literatur. Nebst allgemeinen und besonderen Bemerkungen. Hrsg. v. J. Knorr. Leipzig: C. F. Kahnt [1861]. 2 p.l., 108 p. 16°.

Interleaved, with manuscript notes.

1. Piano.—Bibliography.
N. Y. P. L. September 12, 1913.

NK 0208256 NN NNC

Knorr, Julius, 1807-1861.
Führer auf dem felde der clavierunterrichts-literatur, mit allgemeinen und besonderen bemerkungen, von Julius Knorr. 2. vielfach veränderte und bedeutend verm. aufl. Hrsg. von mehreren tüchtigen fachmännern. Leipzig, C. F. Kahnt [1861]
120 p. 17cm.

1. Pianoforte music—Bibl. 2. Pianoforte—Instruction and study.

10-9348

Library of Congress ML132.P3K7

NK 0208257 DLC

KNORR, Julius, 1807-1861.
Materials for the mechanical part of pianoforte playing collected and arranged complete. B. [cop. 1852].

f.(1). pp.59 Mus 460.4

NK 0208258 MH

KNORR, Julius, 1807-1861.
Knorr's Materials for the mechanical part of piano-forte playing... Boston, O. Ditson & co., etc., etc., cop. 1868.

pp.59.

NK 0208259 MH NBuG

Knorr, Julius, ed.
Methodischer leitfaden für clavier lehrer; 4. verb. aufl. Leipzig, Breitkopf, 1857.
viii, 64 p. illus. (music), diagrs. S.

NK 0208260 PP

R785.7 K757m Knorr, Julius, 1807-1861.
Methodischer Leitfaden für Clavierlehrer. 5. verbesserte Aufl. Leipzig, Breitkopf und Härtel, 1861.
viii, 64 p. music

1. Piano - Instruction and study I. T.

NK 0208261 MiD

Knorr, Julius, 1807-1861.
Methodischer Leitfaden für Clavierlehrer. Hrsg. von J. Knorr. 6th ed. Leipzig, Breitkopf and Härtel, 1869.
viii, 64 p. 12°.

NK 0208262 NN

Knorr, Karl.
Über Ulrich von Lichtenstein. Historische und litterarische untersuchungen, von Karl Knorr. Strassburg, K. J. Trübner; [etc., etc.] 1875.
3 p. l., 104 p. 22½cm. (*Added t.-p.:* Quellen und forschungen zur sprach- und culturgeschichte der germanischen völker ... 9)

1. Lichtenstein, Ulrich von, fl. 1255. I. Title.

1-7413

Library of Congress PD25.Q4 hd. 9

NK 0208263 MdBP MU MB PU PBm ViU NN NjP GU CU NBuU DLC CLSU INS CU LU NcD MiU OCU OU OC1W

Knorr, Karl Gottlieb
see Knorre, Carl Gottlieb, d. 1753.

W 4 M961 1954 KNORR, Klaus, 1925-
Neuzeitliche Gelenkverbindungen und ihre Verarbeitung. München, 1954.
40 l. illus.
Inaug.-Diss. - Munich.
1. Dentistry - Mechanical
2. Teeth - Prosthetic

NK 0208265 DNLM

Knorr, Klaus Eugen, 1911-
Access to raw materials in the postwar world, by K. E. Knorr ... [Chicago, A.W. Shaw company] 1943.
Cover-title, 385-396 p.
"Reprinted from Harvard business review, spring 1947."
Label mounted on cover has note: "A contribution from Food research institute, Stanford university, Stanford university, California."
1. Commercial policy. 2. Raw materials.

NK 0208266 CSt-H MH

VOLUME 300

Knorr, Klaus Eugen, 1911–
... The American trade proposals, by Klaus E. Knorr ... New Haven, Conn., 1946.
3 p. l., 22 numb. l., 1 l. 28½ x 22cm. (Yale institute of international studies ... Memorandum no. 19)
Bibliographical foot-notes.

1. U. S.—Commercial policy. I. Title.
HF1455.K67 337 47-2520
© 28Oct46; 2c 18Dec46; Yale institute of international stud-

NK 0208267 DLC OkU AAP DAU CaBVaU ViU DS

Knorr, Klaus Eugen, 1911–
Basic principles of economics. Washington, National War College [1952?]
177 p. 27 cm.

1. Economics.
HB171.5.K632 330 60-42100 ‡

NK 0208268 DLC

JV9999 Knorr, Klaus Eugen.
British colonial theories 1570-1850. 1941.
503 numb.l.

Typewritten.
Thesis(Ph.D.)--University of Chicago.

1.Gt.Brit.--Colonies.

NK 0208269 ICU

JV1011
.K6
Knorr, Klaus Eugen, 1911–
... British colonial theories, 1570–1850 ... by Klaus E. Knorr. Chicago, Ill., 1944.
1 p. l., 22 p. 23cm.
Part of thesis (PH. D.)—University of Chicago, 1941.
Reproduced from type-written copy.

1. Gt. Brit.—Colonies. I. Title.
A 44-5953
Chicago. Univ. Library for Library of Congress JV1011.K6

NK 0208270 ICU

Knorr, Klaus Eugen, 1911–
British colonial theories, 1570–1850, by Klaus E. Knorr ... With a foreword by H. A. Innis. Toronto, The University of Toronto press, 1944.
xix, 429 p. 23½cm.
Issued also in part as the author's thesis (PH. D.) University of Chicago.
"Index of names, books, and periodicals": p. [415]–423.
Bibliographical foot-notes.

1. Gt. Brit.—Colonies. I. Title.
A 45-831 †
New York. Public library for Library of Congress JV1011.K6 1944 a
[a45e3]† 325.342

WaS CaBVa CaBVaU MtBC MtU DLC
ViU MB NcGU KEmT OClU Or OrPR NcD MoU OrPS OrCS
NK 0208271 NN NcU OU CaBViP PU PBm PPTU OClW OO LU

Knorr, Klaus Eugen, 1911–
A critique of the Randall Commission report on United States foreign economic policy. Prepared by Klaus Knorr and Gardner Patterson on the basis of a conference held at Princeton University, February 4 and 5, 1954. [Princeton, N. J., International Finance Section, Princeton University,

65 p. 23 cm.
1. U. S. Commission on Foreign Economic Policy. Report to the President and the Congress. 2. U. S.—Foreign economic relations. I. Patterson, Gardner, joint author.
HC106.5.A57533 338.973 54—2637

OClW CU PU TxU PLF NN PSt PHC
OCl OU PBL CaBViP OrCS OrP WaWW CaBVaU Or OrU OrPR
NK 0208272 DLC NBuC DNAL NIC CLSU NNC ICU IU DS TxU

Knorr, Klaus Eugen, 1911–
A critique of the Randall Commission report on United States foreign economic policy. Prepared by Klaus Knorr and Gardner Patterson on the basis of a conference held at Princeton University, February 4 and 5, 1954. [Princeton, N. J., International Finance Section, Princeton University, 1954] [Photocopy. Ann Arbor, Univ. Microfilms,
65 p. 23 cm.

NK 0208273 NcGU DAU MiU

Knorr, Klaus Eugen, 1911- joint tr.

JN3953
1941
.F7
Fraenkel, Ernst, 1898–
The dual state; a contribution to the theory of dictatorship [by] Ernst Fraenkel, translated from the German by E. A. Shils, in collaboration with Edith Lowenstein and Klaus **Knorr.** New York, London [etc.] Oxford university press [c1941]

Knorr, Klaus Eugen, 1911-
Economics and international relations: a problem in teaching. New York, Academy of Political Science, 1947.
552-568 p.

"Reprinted from Political science quarterly, Vol. LXII, no. 4, December 1947."

1. Economics - Study and teaching. I. Title

NK 0208275 NNC

Knorr, Klaus Eugen, 1911–
Passive defense for atomic war. [Princeton] Center of International Studies, Princeton University, 1954.
32 p. 28 cm. ([Princeton University. Center of International Studies] Memorandum no. 6)

1. Atomic weapons—Safety measures. 2. Air defenses, Civil. I. Title. (Series: Princeton University. Center of International Studies. Policy memorandum no. 6)
UF767.K67 *355.232 54-14459 rev ‡

OU AAP CaBVaU
NK 0208276 DLC WaU NN DS ViU NcD OO PBL PPT OrU ICU

Knorr, Klaus Eugen, 1911- FOR OTHER EDITIONS SEE MAIN ENTRY

Chicago. University. *University extension division. Home-study dept.*
... Political science 203 (comparative government) by Klaus E. Knorr. [Chicago] The University of Chicago, c1940.

JX1311
.C5
Knorr, Klaus Eugen, 1911-
Chicago. University. *University extension division. Home-study dept.*
... Political science 261 (international relations) by Klaus E. Knorr. [Chicago] The University of Chicago, c1939.

Knorr, Klaus Eugen, 1911-

JX1975
.A25
1946.
II.A.2
League of nations. *Secretariat. Economic, financial and transit dept.*
... Raw-material problems and policies ... **Geneva, League of nations, 1946.**

Knorr, Klaus Eugen, 1911–
... Rubber after the war [by] K. E. Knorr ... Stanford University, Calif., Food research institute, Stanford university, 1944.
2 p. l., 46 p. 23cm. ([Leland Stanford junior university. Food research institute] War-peace pamphlets. [No. 4])
"A revision of a series of articles in the India rubber world, July-October 1943."

1. Rubber industry and trade—U. S. 2. Rubber, Artificial. I. Title.
A 44-2168 Revised
Hoover library, Stanford for Library of Congress univ. HD9161.U52K6
[r45q5]† 338.47678

OU DPU DLC MH-BA ViU PSC PU
NK 0208280 CSt-H CaBViP OrP NcRS FMU DS MB OOxM OO

Knorr, Klaus Eugen, 1911–
Strengthening the free world economy; a report of a conference held at Princeton on December 16–17, 1952. [Princeton] Center of International Studies, Princeton University, 1953.
45 l. 29 cm. (Princeton University. Center of International Studies. Memorandum no. 3)

1. Europe—Comm. 2. Balance of trade. 3. U. S.—Commercial policy. I. Title. (Series: Princeton University. Center of International Studies. Policy memorandum no. 3)
HF3496.K55 382 53-1101 rev

NK 0208281 DLC OrU WaU ICU OU MH MiU DS ViU TxU NN

Knorr, Klaus Eugen, 1911–
Tin under control, by K. E. Knorr. Stanford University, Calif., Food research institute, Stanford university [1945]
xi, 314 p. incl. illus. (map) tables, diagrs. 2 maps on 1 l. 23½ cm. [Leland Stanford junior university. Food research institute. Commodity policy studies, no. 5]

1. Tin industry.
HD9539.T5A312 338.2745 A 45—1107
Stanford University. Libraries for Library of Congress [a64o½]†

PPTU TxU DS MB CaBVaU Or OrCS OrPR WaS DLC
NK 0208282 CSt OCl OOxM OClW OCU ViU ViU-L PSt PBm

Knorr, Klaus Eugen, 1911–
Union of western Europe, a third center of power? Draft memorandum. New Haven, Yale Institute of International Studies, 1948.
iii, 118 l. 28 cm.

1. European federation. 2. World politics—1945– I. Title.
D840.K58 940.55 48-4148*‡

NK 0208283 DLC MH CU DS NcU

Knorr, Klaus Eugen, 1911–
World rubber and its regulation; by K. E. Knorr. Stanford University, Calif., Stanford university press [c1945]
x, 265 p. incl. tables, diagrs. 24cm. [Leland Stanford junior university. Food research institute. Commodity policy studies, no. 6]
"Annotated bibliography": p. 257–260.

1. Rubber industry and trade. 2. Rubber, Artificial. I. Title.
A 45-5353
Stanford univ. Library for Library of Congress [4]

OrPR WaS
OClW OOxM ViU MB PBm PSC PP MiHM TxU CaBVaU Or OrCS
NK 0208284 CSt NcGU CU OAk NcRS NNUN DS OCl OCU

4K
Ger.
170
Knorr, L
Das Executionsverfahren nach gemeinem Rechte vom gesetzlichen und gesetzgeberischen Gesichtspunkte aus betrachtet, in Verbindung damit wie sich solches im Grossherzogthum Hessen diesseits des Rheins ausgebildet hat. 2. Ausg. Giessen, J. Ricker, 1851.
59 p.
[With, as issued, Schweppe, Albrecht. Das System des Concurses der Gläubiger. Göttingen, 1829]

NK 0208285 DLC

VOLUME 300

Knorr, L W.
L.W.Knorr's Praktische grammatik der englischen sprache. Mit einer vollständigen anleitung zur aussprache und accentuirung der englischen wörter, und zahlreichen uebungsstücken. 5. aufl., durchgesehen und verbessert von dr.F.E. Feller. Leipzig, T.O.Weigel, 1847.
x,422 p. 22cm.

1.English language--Grammar. I.Feller,Friedrich Ernst,1802-1859,ed.

NK 0208286 MiU

---

ar W 17414 Knorr, Leopold.
Die Jungfrau von Orléans. Fraustadt, L.S. Pucher, 1875.
19 p. 24cm.

Accompanies "Programm"--Realschule zu Fraustadt ₍Ger.₎

1. Jeanne d'Arc, Saint, 1412-1431.

NK 0208287 NIC InU

---

ar X 1034 Knorr, Leopold.
Der Nationalcharakter der Engländer. Fraustadt ₍1870₎
20 p. 26cm.

No. 6 in vol. lettered: Programmes. Great Britain. History.
Detached from Fraustadt, Ger. Programm ... 1870. Fraustadt ₍1870₎

1. National characteristics, English.

NK 0208288 NIC

Knorr, Levin, freiherr von Wintzingeroda-
See
Wintzingeroda-Knorr, Levin, freiherr von

KNORR, LORENZ.
Gedanken zur sozialistischen Erziehung; eine Einladung zur Diskussion über Theorie und Praxis. Bonn, Verlag Schaffende Jugend [1954?] 170 p. 21cm. (Schriftenreihe zum Problem der sozialistischen Erziehung. Bd. 1)

1. Socialism, 1945- 2. Education-- Social and economic aspects. I. Schriftenreihe zum Problem der sozialistischen Erziehung.

NK 0208290 NN CtY

Knorr, Louis.
Markenmüller. Philatelistische Berichte. Leipzig, Gebr. Senf ₍1893₎
132 p. 19 cm.

1. Postage-stamps—Collectors and collecting. I. Title.

HE6200.K6 53-51389 ‡

NK 0208291 DLC CtY

Thesis 1945 K71 Knorr, Louis Carl, 1914-
Research on the bacterial ring rot of potatoes. ₍Ithaca, N. Y.₎ 1945.
135 l. illus., photos., tables. 28 cm.

Thesis (Ph. D.) - Cornell University, Oct. 1945.

1. Potatoes - Diseases and pests. 2. Potato-rot. ₍I. Title.₎ II. Title: Bacterial ring rot of potatoes.

NK 0208292 NIC

Knorr, Ludovicus
see Knorr, Carolus Ludovicus.

QD261 K55 1904 Biochem. Library Knorr, Ludwig.
Anleitung zum Praktikum in der organischen Chemie, zusammengestellt von L. Knorr und P. Duden. 2. Aufl. Jena, Chemisches Universitätslaboratorium, 1904.
73 ℓ.

Recto of each leaf of text is blank.
Includes bibliographies.

1. Chemistry - Organic - Laboratory manuals. I. Duden, Paul, joint author.

NK 0208294 CU OClW

QD401 .K723 Knorr, Ludwig.
Ueber das piperyl-hydrazin. Muenchen, 1882.
21p.
Inaug. diss. Erlangen.

NK 0208295 DLC DNLM

QD401 .K724 Knorr, Ludwig.
Ueber die bildung von kohlenstoff-stickstoffringen durch einwirkung von amin- und hydrazinbasen auf acetessigester und seine derivate. Erlangen, 1886.
100p.
Habilitationsschrift. Erlangen.

NK 0208296 DLC DNLM MH

HX 271 S52 2 21 Knorr, Ludwig, social democrat.
Sozial-demokratischer Katechismus für das arbeitende Volk. München, 1893.
59p. 21-25cm. (Socialism in Germany; miscellaneous pamphlets, v.2, no.21)

NK 0208297 WU

HX276 .K6 1894 Knorr, Ludwig, social democrat.
Sozial-demokratischer katechismus für das arbeitende volk, von Ludwig Knorr. ₍4.durchgesehene und verm.aufl.₎ ... Nürnberg, Wörlein & comp., 1894.
62, ₍2₎ p. 18cm.

1.Socialism.

NK 0208298 OCU

KNORR, Ludwig Karl.
See KNORR, Karl.

Knorr, M
Bericht der gymnastisch-orthopädischen und elektrischen Heilanstalt in München
see under Munich. Gymnastisch-orthopädische und elektrische Heilanstalt.

QB 216 K72 Knorr, Martinus, praeses.
Dissertationem astronomicam de crepusculis ... tuebitur M. Frieder. David. Stubnerus ... Ad D. April. A. C. MDCIIC. ... Wittenbergae, Typis Christiani Kreusigii ₍1698₎
₍14₎ l. fold. pl., fold. table. 18cm.

Diss.--Wittenberg (F. D. Stubnerus, respondent.
Signatures: A-C^4, D^2.

NK 0208301 NIC

Knorr, Mary.
A program planning institute
see under
Artesia, N. M. Public Library.

Knorr, Max.
Was soll man bei Einrichtung einer Zentralheizung beachten? Halle a. S., C. Marhold, 1909.
24 p. 8°.
Repr. Haustechnische Rundschau, Jahrg. xiv, Heft 2, 3 and 4, 1909.

NK 0208303 NN

---

871 P5n.Yk Knorr, Max, 1908-
Das griechische vorbild der Mostellaria des Plautus ... Coburg, Druck: A. Rossteutscher, 1934.
60p.

Inaug.-diss.--München.
Lebenslauf.
Bibliographical foot-notes.

NK 0208304 IU MiU CtY

Microfilm 2371 Knorr, Max, 1908-
Das griechische Vorbild der Mostellaria des Plautus, von Max Knorr. Coburg, A. Rossteutscher, 1934.
60 p.

Inaug. Diss. - München.
Microfilm. [N.p., n.d.] 1 reel. 35mm.

1. Plautus, Titus Maccius. Mostellaria. I. Title.

NK 0208305 CoU PBm

Knorr, Otto.
Der Grossvenediger in der Geschichte des Alpinismus. München, Gesellschaft alpiner Bücherfreunde, 1932. 60 p. illus., ports., maps.

"Schrifttum": p. 53-58.

1. Mountaineering 2. Alps I. Title.

NK 0208306 NN

VOLUME 300

Knorr, Otto.
Die Rabenschüssel am Eichberg bei Maua, Natur- und Kletterführer; Gestein, Pflanzen und Tiere einer Buntsandsteinlandschaft bei Jena, von O. Knorr. Naturkundliche Abhandlungen von K. Mägdefrau und E. Uhlmann. Jena, G. Fischer, 1954.
94 p. illus. 20 cm.

1. Natural history—Germany—Eich-Berg. 2. Eich-Berg. I. Title.
QH149.K55 57-43762 ‡

NK 0208307 DLC MH NIC

Knorr, Richard.
Die cystoskopie und urethroskopie beim weibe. Von dr Richard Knorr ... Mit 145 zum teil farbigen abbildungen im text, 1 schwarzen und 2 farbigen tafeln. Berlin [etc.] Urban & Schwarzenberg, 1908.
xii, 286 p. illus., III pl. (2 col.) 25½cm.
Colored plates accompanied by guard sheets with descriptive letterpress.

1. Bladder—Exploration. 2. Genito-urinary organs—Diseases—Diagnosis.
Library of Congress RC920.K7 8-18290

NK 0208308 DLC ICRL DNLM CtY PPC ICJ MH

Knorr, Richard.
Zur Diagnose und Therapie der Nieren-Blasentuberkulose bei der Frau. 46 pp. 8°. Halle a. S., C. Marhold, 1908.
Forms 7 Heft, v. 7, of Samml. zwangl. Abhandl. a. d. Geb. d. Gravenh. u. Geburtsh.

NK 0208309 DNLM

Knorr, Robert, 1865-
Südgallische terra-sigillata-gefässe von Rottweil... Stuttgart, Kohlhammer, 1912.
50 p. 30 pl.

1.Pottery,Roman. 2.Rottweil,Ger.-Antiquities,Roman.

NK 0208310 NjP CtY IU MH MdBWA

NK 3850 .K5 Knorr, Robert, 1865-
[Terra sigillata] Stuttgart, W. Kohlhammer, 1905-19.
5 v in 1. illus.

Made-up set; title from spine.
CONTENTS.--[1] Die verzierten terra sigillata-Gefässe von Cannstatt und Köngen-Grinario .--[2] Die verzierten terra-sigillata-Gefässe von Rottweil.--[3] Die verzierten terra-sigillata-Gefässe von Rottenburg-Sumelocenna.--

[4] Südgallische terra-sigillata-Gefässe von Rottweil.--[5] Töpfer und Fabriken verzierter terra-sigillata des ersten Jahrhunderts.

#Pottery, Roman.
#Cannstatt, Ger.--Antiq.
#Köngen, Ger.--Antiq.
#Rottweil, Ger.--Antiq.
#Rottenburg, Ger.--Antiq.

NK 0208312 MoU

Knorr, Robert, 1865-
Terra-Sigillata-Gefässe des ersten Jahrhunderts, mit Töpfernamen. Stuttgart, W. Kohlhammer [pref. 1952]
xvi p. 83 plates, map. 25 cm.

1. Pottery, Roman. I. Title.
A 53-1291
Cincinnati. Univ. Lib. for Library of Congress NK3850.K58 [2]

NK 0208313 OCU TU NcU DLC DDO NjP CtY IaU ICU ViU

---

738 K757te **Knorr, Robert,** 1865-
Die terra-sigillata-gefässe von Aislingen ... Dillingen, 1913.
cover-title, 77p. illus., XVIII plates.

NK 0208314 IU

Knorr, Robert, 1865-
Töpfer und Fabriken verzierter Terra-Sigillata des ersten Jahrhunderts, von Robert Knorr... Stuttgart: W. Kohlhammer, 1919. 1 p.l., x, 140 p. illus., 100 pl. 8°.

I. Pottery (Ancient).
N. Y. P. L. July 9, 1920.

NK 0208315 DDO ICJ IU OCU NN NNU MiDA CtY PPAmP OCU OClW MH NjP

Knorr, Robert, 1865-
Die verzierten Terra Sigillata-Gefässe von Cannstatt und Köngen-Grinario. Hrsg. von der Württembergischen Kommission für Landesgeschichte. Stuttgart, W. Kohlhammer, 1905.
49 p. illus., 47 plates. 25 cm.

1. Pottery, Roman. 2. Germany—Antiquities, Roman. 3. Cannstatt, Ger. 4. Köngen, Ger. I. Title: Terra Sigillata-Gefässe.
NK3850.K7 6-35609 rev*

NK 0208316 DLC PBm NjP

Knorr, Robert, 1865-
Die verzierten terra-sigillata-gefässe von Rottenburg-Sumelocenna... Stuttgart, Kohlhammer, 1910.
72 p. illus.,22 pl.
"Literatur": p.[vii]-x.

1.Pottery,Roman. 2.Rottenburg,Ger.-Antiq.,Roman.

NK 0208317 NjP MH MdBWA

Knorr, Robert, 1865-
Die verzierten Terra-Sigillata-Gefässe von Rottweil. Hrsg. vom Altertumsverein Rottweil. Stuttgart, W. Kohlhammer, 1907.
ix, 70 p. 32 pl. 8°.

NK 0208318 NN PBm

Knorr, Robert, 1865-
...Die westpfälzischen sigillata-töpfereien von Blickweiler und Eschweilerhof, von R.Knorr und Fr.Sprater... Speier, am Rhein, 1927.
120 p. front.,illus.,104 pl. (Spires, Ger. Historisches museum. Veröffentlichungen. 3.bd.)

1.Pottery,Roman. 2.Eschweilerhof,Ger.-Antiquities,Roman. 3.Blickweiler,Ger.-Antiquities,Roman. I.Sprater,Friedrich, 1884-

NK 0208319 NjP PU MH

Knorr, Theodor Ferdinand Albert, 1873- tr.

Whistler, James Abbott McNeill, 1834-1903.
James McNeill Whistler's Zehnuhr-vorlesung (Ten o'clock); deutsch von Theodor Knorr. Strassburg, Heitz, 1904.

Knorr, Walter Emil, 1888-
Pupura teleangiectodes annularis (Majocchii)... 1915.
Inaug.-diss.-München.

NK 0208321 MiU CtY DNLM PPWI

CS 2549 L9K72+ Knorr, Wilhelm, 1827-
Die Familiennamen des Fürstenthums Lübeck. Eutin, G. Struve, 1876-82.
2 v. in 1. 27cm.

1. Names, Personal--Germany--Lübeck.

NK 0208322 NIC MH

Knorr, Wilhelm, b. 1827.
Reinaert de Vos und Reineke Vos, von collab. Knorr. Eutin,G.Struve, 1857. 89p. 22cm. (Öffentlichen prüfung sämmtlicher klassen der vereinigten gelehrten und bürgerschule zu Eutin, ladet ergebenst ein Ch. Pansch)
"Worte bei entlassung der Abiturienten Ostern 1854" p.69-74.
"Schulnachrichten" p.75-88.

NK 0208323 MWelC NIC PU NjP CU

Knorr, Wilhelm, b. 1827, ed.
Reinardus Vulpes, emendavit et adnotavit Guilelmus Knorr. Utini, 1860
see under Reinaert de Vos. Latin.

---

ar W 3153 Knorr, Wilhelm, 1827-
Über besonders bemerkenswerte Personen- und Geschlechtsnamen in Schleswig-Holstein. [about 1880]
p. 137-200. 22cm.

1. Names, German.

NK 0208325 NIC

VOLUME 300

KNORR, Wilhelm, 1827-
Die zwanzigste Branche des Roman de Renart und ihre Nachbildungen nebst einem kurzen Nachtrage zum Reinandus Vulpes. Separatabdruck aus dem Osterprogramm des eutiner Gymnasiums. Eurtin. 1866.

f(1). pp. 42. 28.5 cm. 27285.2 1/2

NK 0208326 MH NN OCl NjP

Knorr, Wilhelm, 1870–
Die Donau- und die meerengenfrage; ein völkerrechtsgeschichtlicher rückblick und ein rechtspolitischer ausblick von dr. jur. Wilhelm Knorr ... 1.–3. tausend. Weimar, G. Kiepenheuer, 1917.

5 p., 1 l., 191, [1] p. fold. map. 21ᶜᵐ. (*Half-title:* Deutsche Orientbücherei hrsg. von Ernst Jäckh. XXIV)

"Schrifttum": p. 189–191.

1. Eastern question (Balkan) 2. Danube river. 3. Dardanelles. 4. Bosporus. 5. Black sea. I. Title.

19—7063

Library of Congress D375.K6

NK 0208327 DLC CU FMU ICJ

Knorr, Wilhelm, 1870–
Das ehrenwort kriegsgefangener in seiner rechtsgeschichtlichen entwicklung von dr. Wilhelm Knorr. Breslau, M. & H. Marcus, 1916.

xii, 136 p. 23½ᶜᵐ. (*Added t.-p.:* Untersuchungen zur deutschen staats- und rechtsgeschichte, hrsg. von O. v. Gierke ... 127. hft.)

Also issued as author's inaugural dissertation, Rostock. Breslau, 1916.
"Schrifttum": p. [127]–133.

21–20464

NK 0208328 DLC NcU PU CtY MB NN DNW

Knorr, Willy, 1878-
Der erbvertrag nach dem buergerlichen gesetzbuche. Inaug. Diss. Leipzig, 1903,
Bibl.

NK 0208329 ICRL MH-L

Knorr, Willy, 1878– joint author.

Sanftenberg, Gustav.
... Das staats- und verwaltungsrecht des herzogtums Anhalt, von G. Sanftenberg ... und W. Knorr ... Hannover, M. Jänecke, 1909.

Knorr, Willy, 1878-
Das verordnungsrecht des Bundesrats des Deutschen Reiches nach staats- und verfassungsrechtlicher seite hin betrachtet. Ein beitrag zur lehre Adolf Arndts vom formellen gesetz ... Dessau, Buchdr. Gutenberg, 1906.

xii, 62 p. 22ᶜᵐ.

Inaug.-diss.—Würzburg.
"Literaturverzeichnis": p. [vii]–xii.

1. Germany—Constitutional law. 2. Germany. Bundesrat. 3. Arndt, Adolf, 1849–

9—18998

Library of Congress JN3641.K6

NK 0208331 DLC MiU

Knorr, Wolfgang, 1911-
Die kinderreichen in Leipzig. ... 53 p. Inaug. Diss. - Leipzig, [1935]
Lebenslauf.

NK 0208332 ICRL

Knorr, Wolfgang, 1911–
... Die kinderreichen in Leipzig. Mit 7 zeichnungen. Heidelberg–Berlin, K. Vowinckel verlag g. m. b. h., 1936.

53, [1] p. diagrs. 20½ᶜᵐ. (*Half-title:* Beihefte zur Zeitschrift für geopolitik, hft. 13)

"Eine parallelpublikation erscheint als inaugural-dissertation bei der philologisch-historischen abteilung der Philosophischen fakultät der Universität Leipzig."
"Quellenangabe": p. [54]

1. Children. 2. Leipzig—Population. 3. Family. I. Title.

A 43–819

Ohio state univ. Library for Library of Congress D410.Z42 hft. 13
[3]† (940.5082) 362.7

NK 0208333 OU McD MB NN CU OU DLC NNC

Knorr, Wolfgang, 1911–
Vergleichende erbbiologische Untersuchungen an drei asozialen Grossfamilien. Berlin, W. de Gruyter, 1939.

51 p. fold. table (in pocket) 23 cm.

1. Heredity, Human. 2. Defective and delinquent classes. I. Title.

QH431.K56 56–52775

NK 0208334 MdBP DLC CtY NcD MnU CU NNC PBL NcD

Knorr, Wolfram von
see Knorr, Artur Friedrich Wolfram von, 1880-

Knorr und Zoeltschen, Johann Heinrich von, respondent.
De iure statvvm imperii
see under Treuer, Gottleib Samuel, 1683-1743, praeses.

Knorr von Rosenoth, Caspar
see Knorr, Caspar.

Speck Collection
Tr
K72
930

Knorr von Rosenroth, Christian, 1636-1689.
... Aesch Mezareph or purifying fire; a chymico-kabalistic treatise collected from the Kabala denudata of Knorr von Rosenroth. Translated by a Lover of Philalethes, 1714. Preface, notes and explanations by "Sapere Aude" New York, Occult research press [ca. 1930]
vi, [7]-60p. 18cm. (Collectanea Hermetica)

NK 0208338 CtY UU

[Knorr von Rosenroth, Christian] 1636-1689.
A genuine explication of the visions of the book of Revelation: full of sundry new Christian considerations: wherein true and false Christendom is briefly and nakedly represented, and the time of each of them, after a mathematical manner, demonstrated; and all confronted with good history; both shewing the accomplishment of things past, and thence ascertaining the fulfilling of things yet to come. By the learned and pious A. B. Peganivs. English'd out of High-Dutch by H. O London, Printed by W. G. and are to be sold by Moses Pitt, at the White Hart in Little-Britain [1670?]
4 p.l., 360p. 14½cm.

Errors in paging.

1. Bible--N.T.--Revelation. I. O., H., tr. II H. O., tr. III. Title.

NK 0208340 IU

Zg17
K75
677

[Knorr von Rosenroth, Christian] 1636-1689
Conjugium Phöebi & Palladis; oder, Die durch Phöebi und Palladis Vermählung erfundene Fortpflantzung des Goldes bey des ... Herrn Leopold des Ersten, erwählten Römischen Keysers ... mit der ... Frauen Eleonara Magdalena Theresia, Pfaltzgrävin bey Rhein ... vollzogener drittmahliger Vermählung ... in ein chymisches Pracht-Spiel verfasset ... durch Ch.K.v.R.a.H. F.P S. H R. Sultzbach, Gedruckt durch Abraham Lichtenthaler, 1677.
[56]p. 1 illus.(port.) 21x17cm.

Signatures:)(^{4}A-F^4.
In verse.

NK 0208342 CtY CU

Witchcraft
BF
1600
K72

[Knorr von Rosenroth, Christian] 1636-1689.
Kabbala denudata seu Doctrina Hebraeorum transcendentalis et metaphysica atqve theologica opus antiquissimae philosophiae barbaricae variis speciminibus refertissimum. In qvo ante ipsam translationem libri difficillimi atque in literatura Hebraica summi, commentarii nempe in Pentateuchum, & quasi totam Scripturam V. T. Cabbalistici, cui nomen Sohar tam veteris, quam recentis, ejusque Tikkunim seu supplementorum tam veterum, quam recentiorum, praemittitur apparatus cujus pars prima continet locos communes Cabbalisticos, secundum ordinem alphabeticum concinnatos, qui lexici Cabbalistici instar esse possunt ... Pars secunda verò constat è tractatibus variis, tam didacticis, quam polemicis ... Adjectusque est index Latinus, & locorum Scripturae ... Sulzbaci, Typis Abrahami Lichtenthaleri, Prostat Francofurti apud Zunnerum, 1677-84.

K72

2 v. in 3. front., fold. plates. 21cm.

Vol. 2 has title: Kabbalae denudatae tomvs secvndvs: Id est Liber Sohar restitutus ... Cui adjecta Adumbratio Cabbalae Christianae ad captum Judaeorum. Francofvrti, Sumptibus Joannis Davidis Zunneri, Typis Balthasar. Christoph. Wustii Sen., 1684.
Text of Zohar in Latin and Hebrew.

K72

Appended to vol. 1, with special t. p. and separate paging, is: Apparatus in Librum Sohar pars tertia et quarta, quarum prior est שער השמים seu Porta coelorum ... autore R. Abraham Cohen Irira ... Altera vero continet arbores seu tabulas Cabbalisticas universales ... hic typis aeneis expressa figuris 16. Cum praefatione de applicatione dogmatum Cabbalisticorum ad Scripta N. T. ... Solisbaci, Typis Abrahami Lichtenthaleri, 1678.
"Apparatus in Librum Sohar pars tertia et quarta ..." is misbound in both copies: in copy 1, t. p. and preface are bound between pars 3. and 4.; in copy 2, "pars quarta" precedes "pars tertia".
Appended to vol. 2, with special t. p. and separate paging, is: Adumbratio Kabbalae Christianae, Id est Syncatabasis Hebraizans, sive Brevis applicatio doctrinae Hebraeorum Cabbalisticae ad dogmata Novi Foederis; pro formanda hypothesi, ad conversionem Judaeorum proficua. Francofvrti ad Moenvm, Sumtu Johannis Davidis Zunneri, cassitero Joh. Phil. Andreae, 1684.
Copy 2 of vol. 1 has imprint: Sulzbaci, Typis Abrahami Lichtenthaleri, 1677. This copy is imperfect: some plates are wanting and two plates misbound.

NK 0208348 NIC ICU MH NN NjP OCH OU PU

VOLUME 300

KNORR von Rosenroth, Christian, 1636-1689
Kabbala Denudata...Sulzbach, var. Publishers, 1684-1678.) var. pag. fold. tables 20.5cm Title page missing
4 pts.Special title of the third: ...Porta Coelorum...Autoro R. Abraham Cohen Irira, lusitano...Sulzbach, Lichtenthaler, 1678.
1.Cabbalah. 2.Irira.3.Title.

NK 0208349 NNJ NRCR

Knorr von Rosenroth, Christian, 1636-1689.
Kabbala denudata ... London
see under Mathers, S. Liddell MacGregor.

Knorr von Rosenroth, Christian, 1636-1689.
The Kabbalah unveiled ...
see under Mathers, S. Liddell McGregor, comp.

[Knorr von Rosenroth, Christian] 1636–1689, *ed.*
Kabbalæ denudatæ tomvs secvndvs: id est Liber Sohar restitutus ... opus omnibus genuinæ antiquitatis, & sublimiorum hebraicæ gentis dogmatum indagatoribus, nec non hebraicæ & chaldaicæ linguæ, & in specie idiomatis terræ israëliticæ, tempore Christi & apostolorum usitati, studiosis, aliisque curiosis utilissimum, & verè kabbalisticum. Cui adjecta Adumbratio Cabbalæ Christianæ ad captum Judæorum. Francofvrti, sumptibus J. D. Zunneri, 1684.
2 v. in 1. front., fold. pl. 21½ x 17cm.

"Adumbratio Cabbalæ Christianæ" wanting in this copy.
Appended: Apparatus in librum Sohar pars tertia & quarta, quarum prior est liber ... Porta cœlorum ... Autore r. Abraham Cohen Irira ... Altera verò continet arbores seu tabulas cabbalisticas universales ... Solisbaci, typis A. Lichtenthaleri, 1678.

1. Cabala. 2. Occult sciences. I. Zohar. Latin. II. Herrera, Abraham Cohen, ca. 1570-ca. 1639. III. Title.
45-51261
Library of Congress BM525.A2K2

NK 0208353 DLC OCH OCIW CtY CLU NN

Case 3A 387 [KNORR VON ROSENROTH, CHRISTIAN] 1636-1689.
Neuer Helicon mit seinen neun Musen; das ist, Geistliche Sitten-Lieder ... von einem Liebhaber christlicher Übungen [sic] ... theils neu gemacht, theils übersetzet, theils aus andern alten ... geändert. Nunmehro aber zusammen geordnet und von einem guten Freunde zum Druck befödert. Sampt einem Anhang von etlichen geistlichen Gedichten desselben, darunter des Herrn Fouqet in frantzösischen Versen ... geschriebene ... in Teutsch übersetzet. Wie auch ein geistliches Lust-Spiel, von der Vermählung Christi mit der Seelen. Nürnberg, Verlegts J.J.Felsseder, 1684.
[4]l.,262p. 17x7cm.
For solo voice and continuo.

NK 0208355 ICN

KNORR-BREMSE A.G.
Fünfzig Jahre Knorr-Bremse, 1905-1955. [Verfasst von Franz Ludwig Neher unter Mitarbeit der Fachleute der Knorr-Bremse AG und ihrer Tochterwerke] Berlin [1955] 193 p. illus. (part col.), ports. 26cm.

Bibliography, p. 187.
1. Neher, Franz Ludwig.

NK 0208356 NN MH-BA

Knorr & Hirth, G.m.b.H., Munich.
Rückblicke und Erinnerungen, anlässlich ihres 25jährigen Jubiläums herausgegeben von der Buch- und Kunstdruckerei Knorr & Hirth, Verlag der Münchner Neuesten Nachrichten. München: Druck von Knorr & Hirth, G.m.b.H., 1900. 101 p. front., illus. (incl. facsims.), plates, ports. 30½cm.

797576A. 1. Printing—Germany—Munich.
N. Y. P. L. July 9, 1936

NK 0208357 NN NNC MH

Knorre, Carl Gottlieb, 1696-1753, praeses.
Ad tit. XIV. ord. prov. anh. de eo quod iustum
see under Claep, Leopold Ludwig, respondent.

4K 4375 Knorre, Carl Gottlieb.
Anleitung zu Referirung der Acten; mit nützlichen Anmerkungen erläutert und mit einen Anhange von Extracten, Relationen und Urtheilen nebst einen dienlichen Register versehen, von Ernst Friedrich Knorren. Halle im Magdeburgischen, C.H. Hemmerde, 1755.
482 p.

NK 0208359 DLC-P4 MH-L

Knorre, Carl Gottlieb, praeses.
... De alimentis a matre liberis praestandis ... Halae Magdeburgicae, Typis J.C.Hilligeri [n.d.]
45 p. 21cm.
Diss. - Halle, 1725 (C.M.Krieger, respondent)
FL6 D613 v.8 no.16 Vol.8,no.16 of a collection with binder's title: Dissertationes juridicae.

1.Parent and child. I.Krieger,Christian Michael,respondent. II.Title.

NK 0208360 MiU-L MH-L

Knorre, Carl Gottlieb, 1696-1753
... De alimentis a matre liberis praestandis. Halae Salicae, J.F. Grunert, 1756.
46 p. 22½cm.
First published as dissertation (Halle, 1725) with Christian Michael Krieger as respondent.

NK 0208361 MH-L

Knorre, Carl Gottlieb, 1696-1753, praeses
... De differentiis iuris romani & germanici in nobilitate adoptiva ... Halae Venedorvm, J. Gruner [1721]
3 p.l., 30 p. 19cm.
Diss. - Halle (Polycarp Dreysig, respondent)

NK 0208362 MH-L

HQ1018 .D7K7 Knorre, Carl Gottlieb, 1696-1753, praeses.
...De dote filiae locupletis... Halae Magdebvrgicae, 1724.
28 p. 21x17cm.
Diss.-Halle(Joannes Victor Bandau,respondent and author)

1. Dower.

NK 0208363 ICU MH-L

Knorre, Carl Gottlieb, 1696-1753
... De dote filiae locvpletis. Halae Salicae, J.F. Grunert, 1756.
32 p. 20½cm.
First published as dissertation (Halle, 1724) with J.V. Bandau as respondent.

NK 0208364 MH-L MiU-L

Knorre, Carl Gottlieb, 1696-1753, praeses
... De familiae condvctitiae foro competente inprimis in Saxonia Electorali ... Halae Magdebvrgicae, J.F. Grunert [1748]
2 p.l., 29, [7] p. 19cm.
Diss. - Halle (J.G. Funckler, respondent)

NK 0208365 MH-L

Knorre, Carl Gottlieb, 1696-1753, praeses
... De jvre conivgis nvptias iterantis in bonis propriis et a priori conivge qvaesitis ad L. VI. C. de secvnd. nvpt. ... Halae Magdebvrgicae, J.C. Hilliger [1726]
35 p. 18cm.
Diss. - Halle (J.F. Hartmann, respondent)

NK 0208366 MH-L

Knorre, Carl Gottlieb.
De iure coniugis nuptias iterantis in bonis propriis et a priori coniuge quaesitis. Ad L.VI. Cod. De secund.nupt. Halae Salicae, Recusa impensis I.F.Grunerti, 1756.
40 p. 20cm.
FL6 D613 v.47 no.7 Vol.47,no.7 of a collection with binder's title: Dissertationes juridicae.

1.Husband and wife. I.Title: De secundis nuptiis.

NK 0208367 MiU-L MH-L

Knorre, Carl Gottlieb, 1696-1753, praeses
... De obsignatione ivdiciali. Von der gerichtlichen Versiegelung ... Ed. altera priore multo auctior. Halae Magdebvrgicae, Litteris Hendelianis, 1738.
55 p. 18½cm.
Diss. - Halle (Friedrich Ernst Knorre, respondent)
First published in 1722.

NK 0208368 MH-L

Knorre, Carl Gottlieb, praeses.
... De recto dilationum usu ... Halae Salicae, Typis I.H.Grunerti [n.d.]
42 p. 20cm.
Diss. - Halle, 1739 (J.F.Dreysig, respondent)
FL6 D613 v.42 no.37 Vol.42,no.37 of a collection with binder's title: Dissertationes juridicae.

1.Time. I.Dreysig,Johann Friedrich, respondent. II.Title.

NK 0208369 MiU-L MH-L

VOLUME 300

Knorre, Carl Gottlieb, 1696-1753
... De transactione non rescindenda propter laesionem vltra dimidivm. Halae Salicae, J.F. Grunert, 1756.
32 p. 23cm.
First published as dissertation (Halle, 1723) with Johann Friedrich Goldhammer as respondent.

NK 0208370 MH-L

Knorre, Carl Gottlieb, 1696-1753.
De tvtela pactitia romanis incognita disserit simvlqve recitationes pvblicas per menses hibernos habendas stvdiosae ivventvti in Regia fridericiana indicit Carol. Gottlieb Knorrivs ... Halae Salicae, J.C. Hilliger [1736]
18 p. 18½cm.

NK 0208371 MH-L CtY-L

Knorre, Carl Gottlieb, 1696-1753, praeses.
... De vsu practico doctrinae ivris romani de praetore et judice pedaneo ... Halae Magdeburgicae, J.C. Hilliger [1725]
40 p. 19cm.
Diss. - Halle (J.F. Bollmann, respondent)

NK 0208372 MH-L

Knorre, Carl Gottlieb.
De usu practico doctrinae iuris Romani de praetore et iudice pedaneo. Halae Salicae, Recusa impensis I.F. Grunerti, 1756.
38 p. 20cm.
FL6 D613 v.43 no.1 Vol.43, no.1 of a collection with binder's title: Dissertationes juridicae.
1. Judges. I. Title: De praetore et iudice pedaneo.

NK 0208373 MiU-L CtY-L MH-L

Knorre, Carl Gottlieb, 1696-1753.
... Diatriba de festinata vrbis obsessae deditione. Von frühzeitiger Übergabe der Vestungen ... Halae Salicae, Ex Officina Hendeliana, 1740.
62 p. 18½cm.

NK 0208374 MH-L MiU-L

Knorre, Carl Gottlieb, praeses.
Dissertatio inauguralis de differentiis juris marchici et magdeburgici in successione conjugum. Halae Magdeburgicae, n.d.
(6), 38, (2) p. 12°
Diss. --- Halle, 1745.
F.W. Ockel, respondent.

NK 0208375 MH-L

Knorre, Carl Gottlieb, praeses.
Dissertatio juridica de refutatione feudi poenae loco imperata. Halae Magdeburgicae, n.d.
(4), 32, (11) p. 12°.
Diss. --- Halle, 1743.
F.C. Foerster, respondent.

NK 0208376 MH-L

KNORRE, Carl Gottlieb.
... Felicitatem Abrahamicam, in adipiscendo spiritvs promisso maxime positam, civibvs academicis meditandam commendans solemnia Pentecostos indicit. Halae Magdebvrgicae, Impensis Orphanotrophei [1738]
20p. 19cm.

NK 0208377 MH-AH

KL 44 v.23 no.1 Knorr, Carl Gottlieb, d. 1753.
... Observationes ad prooemivm Institvtionvm f. Ivstiniani imp. ... Halae, impensis Ioh. Christ. Hendelii [1748]
80p. 20cm.

NK 0208378 CtY-L MiU-L MH-L

Knorre, Carl Gottlieb, 1696-1753
... Observationes selectae ad Lvdovici Doctrinam pandectarvm, qvas ex schedis paternis edidit et indicibvs instrvxit filivs d. Ernestvs Fridericvs Knorre ... Halae Magdebvrgicae, Impensis Carol. Herman Hemmerde, 1757.
4 p.l., 525, [47] p. 17cm.
With this is bound his Rechtliche abhandlungen und gutachten. Halle im Magdeburgischen, 1757.

NK 0208379 MH-L

4K 7742 Knorre, Carl Gottlieb,
Rechtliche Abhandlungen und Gutachten. Hrsg. von Ernst Friedrich Knorre. Halle im Magdeburgischen, C. H. Hemmerde, 1757.
367 p.

NK 0208380 DLC-P4 MH-L

Knorre, Carl Gottlieb, 1696-1753
Usum paroemiae iuris Germanici, Der Letzte thut die Thür zu, in successione coniugum demonstrat simulque praelectiones iuris Germanici per semestre hibernum habendas studiosae iuventuti in regia Fridericiana indicit Carolus Gottlieb Knorre ... Halae Magdeburgicae, Litteris I.C. Hendelii [1741]
12 p. 20 cm.
FL6 D613 v.44 no.2 Vol.44, no.2 of a collection with binder's title: Dissertationes juridicae.
1. Husband and wife.

NK 0208381 MiU-L MH

Knorre (Carolus Adolphus). *De vesicula umbilicali. 78 pp. 8°. *Dorpati Livonorum, ex off. acad. typ. J. C. Schünmanni*, 1822.

NK 0208382 DNLM

Knorre (Conradus). *De glaucomate. 18 pp. 4°. *Heidelbergæ, typ. Reichardianis*, 1833.

NK 0208383 DNLM

W 4 M22 1948 KNORRE, Dieter, 1923-
Untersuchungen zur Klaerung der Frage des Ueberganges der Hepatitis epidemica in einen haemolytischen Ikterus. [Mainz] 1948.
23 l.
Inaug.-Diss. - Mainz.
Typewritten copy.
1. Hepatitis - Infectious 2. Jaundice - Hemolytic

NK 0208384 DNLM

Knorre, É. V., ed.
TE145 .M83 Moscow. Gosudarstvennyĭ nauchno-ėksperimental'nyĭ institut grazhdanskikh, promyshlennykh i inzhenernykh sooruzheniĭ.
Городские улицы и их благоустройство; сборник статей по вопросам прокладки и ремонта подземных сооружений на городских улицах; под ред. Э. В. Кнорре и В. К. Некрасова. Москва, Гострансиздат, 19

Knorre, Ernst Friedrich, d. 1771, ed.
Anleitung zu referirung der acten ...
see under Knorre, Carl Gottlieb, 1696-1753.

KNORRE, Ernst Friedrich, d. 1771.
Dissertatio inauguralis de probatione nobilitatus per instrumenta. Halae Magdeb., n. d.
(2) + 74 p.
Inaug.-diss., --- [Halle], 1751.

NK 0208387 MH-L

KNORRE, Ernst Friedrich, Praeses.
Dissertatio juris cambialis de filiofamilias cambiante. Halae Magdeb. [n. d.]
20 p.
Inaug.-diss., --- [Halle], 1754. Respondent, J.D. Adluhg.

NK 0208388 MH-L

KNORRE, Ernst Friedrich, d. 1771.
Exercitatio juris cambialis de vera natura ac indole contractus cambialis in cambio trassato. Halae ad Salam, 1752.
24 p.

NK 0208389 MH-L

Knorre, Ernst Friedrich, d. 1771, praeses.
Dissertatio juris feudalis de successione adoptivorum in feuda. Halae Magdeburgicae, n.d.
(2), 26 p. 12°
Diss. --- Halle? 1753.
J.C. Meyn, respondent.

NK 0208390 MH-L

Knorre, Ernst Friedrich, ed.
... Observationes selectae ...
see under Knorre, Carl Gottlieb, 1696-1753.

VOLUME 300

Knorre, Ernst Friedrich, d. 1771, ed.
... Rechtliche abhandlungen und gutachten
see under Knorre, Karl Gottlieb, 1696-1753.

NK 0208392 DLC

Knorre, Fedor Fedorovich, 1903-
Рассказы. Москва, Советский писатель, 1953.
417 p. 21 cm.
Title transliterated: Rasskazy.
PG3476.K557A15 1953 54-37911 ‡

NK 0208392 DLC

Knorre, Fedor Fedorovich, 1903-
Рассказы. Москва, Советский писатель, 1955.
352 p. 21 cm.
Title transliterated: Rasskazy.
PG3476.K688A15 1955 56-45815 ‡

NK 0208393 DLC

PG3476 .K557A15 Knorre, Fedor Fedorovich, 1903-
Stories. Moscow, Foreign Languages Pub. House ‹1953?›
141p. 17cm. (Library of Soviet short stories)
Contents.-The mother; translated by Eugene Felgenhauer.-Morning; translated by Eugene Felgenhauer.-Auntie Pasha; translated by Lev Navrozov.
I.Title: The mother. II.Title: Morning. III.Title: Auntie Pasha.

NK 0208394 AAP MdU MH

Knorre, Fedor Fedorovich, 1903-
Твоя большая судьба. Москва, Советский писатель, 1948.
237 p. 17 cm.
CONTENTS. — Твоя большая судьба. — Неизвестный товарищ. — Встреча в темноте. — Жена полковника. — Новый дом. — Деревянная морда.
I. Title. *Title transliterated:* Tvoia bol'shaia sud'ba.
PG3476.K557T9 49-19629*
Library of Congress ‹1›

NK 0208395 DLC

Knorre, Fedor Fedorovich, 1903-
Встреча в темноте; пьеса в четырех действиях, семи картинах. Москва, Искусство, 1944.
127 p. 14 cm.
I. Title. *Title transliterated:* Vstrecha v temnote.
PG3476.K557V8 56-50177 ‡

NK 0208396 DLC

Knorre, Friedrich Ernst, respondent.
... De obsignatione ivdicali ...
see under Knorre, Carl Gottlieb, 1696-1753, praeses.

Knorre (Georg). *Casuistische Studien über Schädelfracturen. 50 pp., 1 l., 2 pl. 8°. *Dorpat, C. Mattiesen*, 1890.

NK 0208398 DNLM CU

QD181 W1K7 **Knorre, Georg von.**
Beitraege zur kenntniss der wolframverbindungen. Leipzig, 1883.
52p.
Inaug. diss. Jena.

NK 0208399 DLC MH-C ICRL

‹Knorre, Georg von,› 1906-
Die Nachkommen des Michael Ehrenreich Kauzmann (1768.—1816.)... Riga‹: Buchdr. H. Schütze›, 1932. 48 p. incl. geneal. tables. 22cm.
"Als Manuskript gedruckt."
"Zur Einführung" signed: Georg v. Knorre.
1. Kauzmann family. I. Title.
N. Y. P. L. January 17, 1935

NK 0208400 NN

Knorre, Georgiĭ Fedorovich.
Что такое горение? Научно-популярное изложение физических основ процесса. Москва, Гос. энерг. изд-во, 1955.
223 p. illus. 23 cm.
Errata slip inserted.
1. Combustion. I. Title.
Title transliterated: Chto takoe gorenie?
QD516.K55 55-57675

NK 0208401 DLC

TJ320 .M65 Knorre, Georgiĭ Fedorovich, ed.
FOR OTHER EDITIONS SEE MAIN ENTRY
Moscow. Moskovskoe vysshee tekhnicheskoe uchilishche. *Kafedra "Kotel'nye ustanovki."*
Исследование котельно-топочных процессов. Под общей ред. Г. Ф. Кнорре. Москва, Гос. научно-техн. изд-во машиностроит. лит-ры, 1955.

KNORRE, Heinrich VON. *Klinische Erregbarkeitsstudien (Chronaxie) 52p. 8° Jena, 1930.
Also Deut. Arch. klin. Med., 1930, 168:

NK 0208403 DNLM CtY

Knorre, Ingeborg von, 1905-
Die Taiga Sibiriens; versuch einer gliederung (teildruck) ... vorgelegt von Ingeborg von Knorre ... Zeulenroda, B. Sporn, buchdruckerei und verlagsanstalt, 1935.
87 p. fold. map. 21cm.
Inaug.-diss.—Thüringischen landesuniversität, Jena.
Lebenslauf.
Literaturverzeichnis: p. 5-13.
1. Siberia—Description and travel. 2. Physical geography—Siberia. I. Title.
G S 36-135
Library, U. S. Geological Survey 590(690) K75t ‹DK755.K ›

NK 0208404 DI-GS ICRL CtY

W 4 M96 1953 KNORRE, Josef, 1918-
Die Sterblichkeit der Stadt Bayreuth von 1701-1875. ‹München› 1953.
‹57› l.
Inaug.-Diss. - Munich.
1. Mortality - Germany

NK 0208405 DNLM

B524 Z
‹Knorre, Karl Friedrich› 1801-1883.
Der Ort des sterns δ Ursae minoris für jeden Tag des Jahre 1823-1830 berechnet aus Bessels Tafeln. Nicolajew, Gedruckt im Charten-Depot der Flotte des schwarzen Meeres, 1824.
36 p. 21cm. in 24cm.
Signed: K. Knorre.
Volume of pamphlets.

NK 0208406 NNC DN-Ob

KNORRE, Karl Friedrich, 1801-1883.
Verzeichniss der von Bradley, Piazzi, Lalande und Bessel beobachteten sterne berechnet und auf 1800 reducirt. Berlin, 1835.
f°.

NK 0208407 MH

Knorre, M E ed.
Erdrutsche und ihre Bekämpfung. ‹Übersetzung aus dem Russischen: Georg Uhl› Berlin, Verlag Technik, 1953.
141 p. illus. 21 cm. (Schriftenreihe des Verlages Technik, Bd. 89)
Includes bibliographies.
1. Landslides. I. Title.
QE599.A2K614 56-57209 ‡

NK 0208408 DLC MiU

Knorre, M E
Опытный кессон Волгоярстроя; сборник статей. Под общей ред. М. Е. Кнорре. Москва, Госстройиздат, 1938.
143 p. illus., diagrs. 22 cm.
At head of title: М. Е. Кнорре ‹и др.›
Errata slip inserted.
1. Caissons. 2. Volgoîarstroĭ (Projected) I. Title.
Title transliterated: Opytnyĭ kesson Volgoîarstroia.
TC199.K6 54-53640

NK 0208409 DLC

Rare K D593 Knorre, Otto Friedrich.
Lectiones inaugurales ad L. Querela 12. C. ad L. Corneliam de falsis. De praescriptione criminum. Quas ... in ... Universitate Fridericiana pro impetranda juris utriusque licentia ... habuit d. XIX. et XX. Junii a. o. r. MDCXCV. Otto Fridericus Knorre ... Cum programmate Dn. Samueli Strykii ... Hallae Magdeburgicae, Impensis Simon. Johann. Hübneri haered., literis viduae Salfeldianae, 1696.
‹12›, 68 p. 20cm.
No. 11 in vol. lettered: Disputat. variae.

NK 0208410 NIC

Knorre (Otto Henricus). * De prognosi in hydrope. 50 pp. 4°. *Gottingæ, lit. J. H. Schulzii*, [1781].

NK 0208411 DNLM

VOLUME 300

Knorre, Victor ⌜**Carl**⌝ 1840–
Additamenta in usum commodiorem et tutiorem methodorum, quae ad orbitas planetarum paucis observationibus determinandas inserviunt ... Berolini, typis C. Schultzii ⌜1867⌝
29, ⌜1⌝ p. 24½ x 21cm.
Inaug.-diss.—Berlin.
Vita.

1. Orbits.

Library of Congress QB355.K7 6-11054†

NK 0208412 DLC NjP NIC

Knorre, Victor Carl, 1840– ****E.5121.17.6
Doppelsternbeobachtungen mit dem doppelbrechenden Mikrometer.
(In his Ueber ein neues mikrometrisches Beobachtungsverfahren.
Pp. 12–25. Berlin. 1892.)

H5003 — Stars. Double.

NK 0208413 MB

Knorre, Victor Carl, 1840–
... I. Ueber ein neues mikrometrisches beobachtungsverfahren mit doppelbrechenden prismen nach den von dr. V. Wellmann unter mitwirkung von dr. M. Brendel und prof. dr. V. Knorre gemachten vorschlägen und über die bearbeitung der nach demselben angestellten beobachtungen, von V. Knorre, nebst anhängen, enthaltend a) Doppelstern-beobachtungen mit dem doppelbrechenden mikrometer von V. Knorre. b) Ebensolche beobachtungen von T. J. J. See. c) Ebensolche beobachtungen von V. Wellmann. II. Ueber die brechung des lichtes in prismen aus einaxigen kristallen und über deren anwendung zu mikrometrischen messungen, von Martin Brendel. III. Ueber den einfluss der temperatur auf die messungen mit doppelbrechenden prismen und über die bei solchen beobachtungen auftretenden chromatischen abweichungen, von V. Wellmann. Berlin, F. Dümmler, 1892.
1 p. l., 79 p. diagrs. 29 x 23cm. (Beobachtungs-ergebnisse der Königlichen sternwarte zu Berlin. hft. n. 6)
1. Micrometer. 2. Stars, Double. I. See, Thomas Jefferson Jackson, 1866– II. Wellmann, Victor Carl Paul, 1861– III. Brendel, Martin i. e. Otto Rudolf Martin, 1862–
9-19443
Library of Congress QB4.B51
——— Copy 2. QB113.K7

NK 0208415 DLC MB

Knorre, Victor Carl, 1840-
Ueber graphische Aufzeichnung mikrometrischer Messungen.
Berlin, 1881
7 p. 27 cm.

Zs. Instrumentenk., Berlin, 1, 1881, p. 213-219.

NK 0208416 DN-Ob

Knorre, Victor Carl, 1840-
Untersuchungen über schraubenmikrometer.
Von V. Knorre... [Mit einer tafel.] [Berlin, 1890?]
columns [321]-360.

NK 0208417 ViU

Knorre, Victor Carl, 1840– ****E.5121.17.9
Zonenbeobachtungen angestellt am Berliner Aequatoreal vermittelst des Registrirmikrometers.
— Berlin. Dümmler. 1901. 61 pp. [Beobachtungs-Ergebnisse der Königlichen Sternwarte zu Berlin. No. 9.] 31 cm., in 4s.

H5001 — Astronomical observations. — Micrometer. Self-registering. — S.r.c.

NK 0208418 MB PU ICU

Knorrek, Friedrich, 1881–
Das gefecht bei Arbedo am 29. juni 1422; eine studie zur kriegsgeschichte des mittelalters ... von Friedrich Knorrek ... ⌜Berlin, G. Nauck (F. Rühe) 1910⌝
2 p. l., 68 p. map. 23cm.
Inaug.-diss.—Berlin.
Lebenslauf.
"Literatur": p. ⌜65⌝–66.

1. Arbedo, Battle of, 1422. I. Title.
43-38739
Library of Congress DQ98.K58

NK 0208419 DLC ICRL MH PU CtY

Knorrek, Marianne.
Der einfluss des rationalismus auf die englische sprache; beiträge zur entwicklungsgeschichte der englischen syntax im 17 und 18. jahrhundert, von Marianne Knorrek. Breslau, Priebatsch, 1938.
3 p. l., v–xiii, 128 p. 24½cm. (*Added t.-p.:* Sprache und kultur der germanischen und romanischen völker ... A. Anglistische reihe ... bd. 30)

Bibliography: p. vii–xiii.

1. English language—Syntax. I. Title.
39-7406
Library of Congress PE1361.K6
425.2

NK 0208420 DLC CtY MH OCU NcD PU

Knorrenschild, Wilhelm.
... Die geschichtlichen grundlagen der revolutionsdramen Romain Rollands, von dr. Wilhelm Knorrenschild. Münster, Selbstverlag des Romanischen seminars; ⌜etc., etc.⌝ 1934.
4 p. l., 67 p. 23cm. (Arbeiten zur romanischen philologie, hrsg. von Eugen Lerch. Nr. 20)
Issued also as inaugural dissertation, Münster.
"Bibliographie": p. 66.

1. Rolland, Romain, 1866–
41-21450
Library of Congress PQ2635.O5Z74 1934
⌜2⌝ 842.91

NK 0208421 DLC OrU CtY NN ICU

De knorrepot, of De gestoorde doctor
see under [Pinto, Isaac de]

Knorring, F I
Через Америку и Японію; путевые очерки. Петербургъ, Изд. Н. М. Лагова, 1904.
316 p. illus. 19 cm.

1. U. S.—Descr. & trav.—1865–1900. I. Title.
Title transliterated: Cherez Ameriku i I͡Aponii͡u.

E168.K708 54-53365 ‡

NK 0208423 DLC

Knorring, Frans Peter von, 1792-1875
Gamla Finland, eller Det fordna wiborgska gouvernementet. 1.afd. Abo, Hjelt, 1833
viii, 269 p. illus., 6 tables
No more published

1. Vyborg, Russia (Government) - Historical geography.
X refs.: Viipuri, Finland; Wiborg, Finland (Län);
Vyborg, Finland (to Vyborg, Russia)

NK 0208424 MH

Knorring, Frans Peter von, 1792-1875.
Språk-forskningar. Stockholm, Norstedt, 1844-57.
2 v.

NK 0208425 MH

Knorring, Gleb Mikhaĭlovich.
Проектирование электрического освещения. Ленинград, Гос. энерг. изд-во, 1950.
416 p. illus. 23 cm.
Bibliography: p. ⌜411⌝

1. Electric lighting. I. Title.
Title romanized: Proektirovanie ėlektricheskogo osveshcheni͡a.

TK4175.K6 50-39450

NK 0208426 DLC

Knorring, Gleb Mikhaĭlovich.
Справочник для проектирования электрического освещения. Изд. 3., перер. Ленинград, Гос. энерг. изд-во, 1952.
168 p. illus. 21 cm.

1. Electric lighting. I. Title.
Title romanized: Spravochnik dli͡a proektirovani͡a ėlektricheskogo osveshcheni͡a.

TK4164.K5 1952 54-18397

NK 0208427 DLC

Knorring, Gleb Mikhaĭlovich.
Цеховые электрические сети; вопросы построения и выполнения. Ленинград, Гос. энерг. изд-во, 1952.
133, ⌜3⌝ p. illus. 23 cm.
At head of title: Г. М. Кнорринг, М. К. Харчев.
Bibliography: p. 133–⌜134⌝

1. Factories—Electric equipment. I. Kharchev, M. K., joint author. II. Title.
Title romanized: T͡Sekhovye ėlektricheskie seti.

TK4035.F3K5 54-18049

NK 0208428 DLC

Knorring, Irina.
Окна на сѣверъ; вторая книга стиховъ. Парижъ ⌜c1939⌝
58 p. 17 cm. (Серія Русскіе поэты, вып. 10)

I. Title. *Title transliterated:* Okna na si͡ever.

PG3476.K5575O4 61-57381 ‡

NK 0208429 DLC

Knorring, L *baron* **de.**
Mémoire confidentiel concernant des mesures préventives à adopter contre l'infiltration de la propagande faite par la IIIe Internationale de Moscou. Berne, 1924.
⌜8⌝ p. 29 cm.

1. Propaganda, Russian. I. Title.

DK266.5.K6 63-30400

NK 0208430 DLC

VOLUME 300

Knorring, N., illus.

PZ68 .V623 Voronkova, Lûbov' Fedorovna.
Неделька. Рисунки Н. Кнорринг. Москва, Правда, 1954.

NK 0208431 ...

Knorring, N N
Сфаять; очерки изъ жизни Морского корпуса въ Африкѣ. Парижъ [1935]
204 p. 21 cm. (Библiотека "Иллюстрированной Россiи." 1935 г. Приложение № 42)

1. Russia—Hist.—Revolution, 1917–1921—Refugees. 2. Russians in Tunisia. I. Title.
Title transliterated: Sfaât.

DK265.9.R3K6 68–34323

NK 0208432 DLC ViU

Knorring, Oscar von. Scan 3000.9
Genom Lappland, Skåne, och Seeland; reseskildringar. Stockholm, P. A. Norstedt & söner, 1874.
pp. 396 +. Illus.

Lapland|Scania, Sweden|Seeland||AcS 232850

NK 0208433 MH NN CtY

Knorring, Oscar von. Afr 3978.73
Två månader i Egypten. [Stockholm], P. A. Norstedt & söner, [1873].
l. 8°. pp. vii, 331 +. Ports., maps, and other illus.

Egypt-Descr. 1840–1889||AcS 232851

NK 0208434 MH CtY

[Knorring, Sofia Margareta (Zelow) friherrinna von, 1797-1848]
Axel, af författaren till Cousinera. Stockholm, Z.Haeggström, 1836.
3 v. in 1.

NK 0208435 MA

Knorring, Sofia Margareta (Zelow) friherrinna von, 1797-1848.
Cousinerna. 2. uppl. Stockholm, Z. Haeggström, 1836.
3 v. in 1.

NK 0208436 WaU RPB

Knorring, Sofia Margareta (Zelow), Friherrinna von, 1797-1848.
Cousinerna
see also her Kusinerna.

[Knorring, Sofia Margaretha (Zelow), friherrinna von,] 1797–1848.
Forhaabninger. [Kjøbenhavn, 1844.] 4 v. in 2. 18cm.
Half-title.

Translated by J. H. Halvorsen.
Imperfect: title-pages wanting; translator note and imprint from Svensk Boklexikon, 1883.

531851–2A. 1. Fiction, Swedish. I. Halvorsen, Johan Hendrik, b. 1812, translator. II. Title.
N. Y. P. L. September 19, 1934

NK 0208438 NN

[KNORRING, Sofia Margaretha (Zelow) friherrinna von, 1797-1848]
Gunnar, of De gevolgen van een enkelen misstap. Een tafereel uit het Zweedsche volksleven. Haarlem, 1845.
2 vol. Vign.

NK 0208439 MH

KNORRING, Sofia Margareta, friherrinna von.
Illusionerna. [Anon.]
— Stockholm. Hæggström. 1836. viii, 291 pp. Sm. 12°

NK 0208440 MB

Knorring, Sofia Margareta (Zelow) friherrinna von, 1797-1848.
Der Käthner und seine Familie. Stuttgart, Franckh'schen Buchhandlung, 1846.
2v. in 1. (Das belletristische Ausland)
Bound with Thomson's Die weisse Maske. Stuttgart, 1846.

NK 0208441 ICRL NN ICU PPG

PT9758 K5K8 1928 Knorring, Sofia Margareta (Zelow), friherrinna von, 1797-1848.
Kusinerna. Stockholm, A. Bonnier [c1928]
238 p.

NK 0208442 CU MH

Knorring, Sofia Margareta (Zelow), friherrinna von, 1797-1848.
Kusinerna
see also her Cousinerna.

839.73 K72m Knorring, Sofia Margareta (Zelow) friherrina von,
Marie Gellert, der schützende engel der Armuth. Aus dem schwedischen der Freyin A. v. Knorring. Grimma und Leipzig, Verlags-Comptoir, 1851.
2 v. 16cm. (Europäische bibliothek der neuen belletristischen literatur ... Der ganzen sammlung. 406. -407. bände. V. Serie. 6.-7.)

Mansfeld Sanders collection.

NK 0208444 AzU

Knorring, Sofia Margareta (Zelow) friherrinna von, 1797–1848.
The peasant and his landlord. By the Baroness Knorring. Translated [from the Swedish] by Mary Howitt ... London, R. Bentley, 1848.
2 v. 20½cm.

I. Howitt, Mary (Botham) "Mrs. W. Howitt," 1799–1888, tr. II. Title.
Library of Congress PZ3.K758P 7–14181 Revised

NK 0208445 DLC MH PPL

Knorring, Sofia Margareta (Zelow) Friherrinna von. 418.9
The peasant and his landlord. Translated by Mary Howitt. New York. Harper. 1848. 12°.

NK 0208446 MB CtY MH

Beinecke Library 1973 173 [Knorring, Sofia Margareta Zelow, Friherrinna von] 1797-1848.
The peasant and his landlord; or, Life in Sweden. Translated by Mary Howitt ... London, Richard Bentley, 1849.
2 v. 21 cm.

1. Libraries, Subscription. 2. Parnell (J.) Stationer & bookseller - Bookplate. I. Howitt, Mary Botham, 1799-1888, tr. II. Title.

NK 0208447 CtY

839.78 K72t.H 1855 Knorring, Sofia Margareta (Zelow) friherrinna von, 1797-1848.
The peasant and his landlord, tr. by Mary Howitt. New York, Harper, 1855.
351p. D.

NK 0208448 IaU PSt NN

Knorring, Sofia Margareta (Zelow) friherrinna von, 1797-1848.
Skizzen von Frau A. von Knorring. Stuttgart, Franckh'schen Buchhandlung, 1847.
2v. in 1. (Das belletristische Ausland)
Bound with A. L. G. Tousaint's Das Haus Lauernesse. Stuttgart, 1847.

In the MIDWEST INTER-LIBRARY CENTER

NK 0208449 ICRL PPG

KNORRING, Sofia Margareta (Zelow) friherrinna. 490
Stånds-paralleler. Tecknade af forfattaren till Cousinerna.
— Stockholm. Hæggström. 1838. 3 parts in 1 v. 16°.

NK 0208450 MB RPB

KNORRING, Sofia Margareta (Zelow) friherrinna von. No. 2 in 4
Tante Lisbeths 19:de testamente. Nouvell. [Anon.]
— Stockholm. Hæggström. 1838. 226 pp. Sm. 12°.

NK 0208451 MB

Knorring, Sofia Margareta (Zelow) friherrinna von, 1797-1848.
Torparen och hans omgivning; en skildring. Stockholm, L. J. Hjerta, 1843.
2 v.

NK 0208452 WaU

VOLUME 300

Knorring, Sofia Margareta (Zelow) friherrinna von, 1797-1848.
Torparen och hans omgifning; en skildring ur folklifvet. Med en inledande uppsats of Johan Mortensen. Stockholm, Bonnier [1906]
2 v. in 1 (Svenska klassiker. 3)

NK 0208453 WaU

Knorring, Sofia Margaretha (Zelow), friherrinna von, 1797-1848.
Vännerna. Stockholm, 1836.
3 v. in 1. D.

NK 0208454 RPB

*GC8 B4574 804d
Knorring, Sophie (Tieck) 1775-1836.
Dramatische Fantasieen von Sophie Bernhardi geb. Tieck.
Berlin. In der Realschulbuchhandlung. 1804.
4p.l.,[5]-361p. 16cm.
Contents: Die Alte vom Bach.--Die Brüder.--Frühlingszauber.
With this is bound Caroline Behrends's Veilchen, Magdeburg, 1820.

NK 0208455 MH

*GC8 B4574 836e
[Knorring, Sophie (Tieck)] 1775-1836.
Evremont. Ein Roman. Herausgegeben von Ludwig Tieck ...
Breslau, im Verlage bei Josef Max und Komp. 1836.
3v. 17.5cm., in case 18.5cm.
"Dieser Roman, welchen ich dem Publikum übergebe, ist die letzte Arbeit meiner verstorbenen Schwester Sophia ..."--Vorrede in v.1, signed: Ludwig Tieck.
Original printed gray-green wrappers; in cloth case.

NK 0208456 MH NjP PPG OCU

Knorring, Sophie (Tieck) 1775-1836.
Flore und Blanscheflur. Ein episches Gedicht ...
see under Floire and Blancheflor. German.

Knorring, Sophie (Tieck) 1775-1836.
St. Evremont; ein roman; hrsg. von Johnn Ludwig Tieck. 2., verbesserte aufl. Breslau, Max, 1845.
3 vols.

NK 0208458 OClW

Tieck, Sophie (Tieck) 1775-1836.
St. Evremont; een Roman. Sneek, 1847.
2 v.

NK 0208459 NjR

Knorring, Sophie (Tieck), 1775-1836.
Wunderbilder und Träume in eilf Mährchen.
Königsberg, Nicolovius, 1802.
374 p.

NK 0208460 NNC

WB 54320
[Knorring, Th de]
La Russie et la Pologne; esquisse historique par Th. de K. Berlin, Nauck, 1834.
390 p.

1. Poland - Hist. 2. Poland - For.rel. - Russia. 3. Russia - For.rel. - Poland. I. Title.

NK 0208461 CtY

Knorring, Wilhelm von, respondent.
... An modus adquirendi dominium originarius praesidium inveniat in jure patrio
see under Hernbergh, Andreas, praeses.

Knorringa, Heiman.
Emporos; data on trade and trader in Greek literature from Homer to Aristotle ... Amsterdam, H. J. Paris, 1926.
4 p. l., 144 p. 24½cm.
Proefschrift—Utrecht.
Published also without thesis note.
"Stellingen": [3] p. laid in.

1. Greece—Comm.—Hist. 2. Greek literature—Hist & crit. I. Title. II. Title: Trade and trader in Greek literature from Homer to Aristotle.

28-16607

Library of Congress HF375.K6 1926

NK 0208463 DLC OrU CaBVaU

Knorringa, Heiman.
Emporos; data on trade and trader in Greek literature from Homer to Aristotle, by Dr. H. Knorringa. Amsterdam, H. J. Paris, 1926.
3 p. l., 144 p. 24½cm.
Presented as author's proefschrift, Utrecht, 1926.

1. Greece—Comm.—Hist. 2. Greek literature—Hist. & crit. I. Title. II. Title: Trade and trader in Greek literature from Homer to Aristotle.

28-11827

Library of Congress HF375.K6

NK 0208464 DLC CU CtY MiU OClW OCU ICU PU MH IU NjP NN

DE1 .H4
Knorringa, Heiman, ed.
Hermeneus; maandblad voor de antieke cultuur. 1.- jaarg.; 15 sept. 1928-
Zwolle, W. E. J. Tjeenk Willink.

PT5850 .K57H4
Knorringa, Heiman.
Herodotus lacht. [Zeven verhalen. Tekeningen van Leo Gestel] Amsterdam, De Spieghel, 1953.
115 p. illus. 25 cm.

I. Herodotus. II. Title.

A 54-4547

Harvard Univ. Library for Library of Congress

NK 0208466 MH NN NNC DLC

DE71 .A63 v.25-26
Knorringa, Heiman.
Latijns leesboek, door H. Knorringa en C. R. van Paassen. Groningen, J. B. Wolters, 1952.
2 v. illus. (Antieke cultuur [v.25-26])

1. Latin language--Chrestomathies and readers. I. Paassen, Carl Richard van, joint author.

NK 0208467 ICU

Knorrius, Carolus Gottlieb
see Knorre, Carl Gottlieb, 1696-1753.

Knors, Clemens, 1885-
Experimentelle untersuchungen über den lernprozess ... Leipzig, W. Engelmann, 1910.
3 p. l., 65, [1] p. diagrs. 23cm.
Inaug.-diss.—Münster.
"Sonderdruck aus dem 'Archiv für die gesamte psychologie' bd. XVII, hft. 3/4."
Lebenslauf.
"Literaturverzeichnis": p. 65.

1. Study, Method of. 2. Educational psychology.

E 10-2135

Library, U. S. Bur. of Education LB2395.K75

NK 0208469 DHEW MiU

243 197 G69 K76
Knors, Franz,
Katechetisches Handbuch zur Erklärung der Evangelien des Kirchenjahrs; mit Berücksichtigung des Katechismus und des Lesebuchs für den Schulgebrauch. Paderborn, F. Schöningh, 1864.
viii, 494p 21cm

NK 0208470 MnCS

Knorst, William James, 1888-
A glossary of traffic terms and abbreviations and their explanations. [Chicago, Traffic Service Corp., 1945]
24 p. 18 cm.

1. Transportation—Dictionaries. 2. Freight and freightage—Dictionaries. I. Title.

HE147.K55 385.03 46-5670 rev*

NK 0208471 DLC CU MoU OrP OOxM NN TxU ICJ IU DS

Knorst, William James, 1888-
A glossary of traffic terms and abbreviations and their explanations. [Washington, D. C., Traffic Service Corporation, °1953]
vi, 22 p.

NK 0208472 MiU MiD

656 K721
Knorst, William James, 1888- ed.
Interstate commerce law and practice. Chicago, College of Advanced Traffic, 1953-54 [i.e. 1955]
4 v. (1700p.) illus., maps. 24cm.
Vol. 4 is supplementing vols. 1,2,3.

1. Shipment of goods. 2. Freight & frieghtage - U.S. I. Title.

NK 0208473 NcU

Knorst, William James, 1888- *ed.*
Interstate commerce law and practice. Chicago, College of Advanced Traffic, 1953-54 [i. e. 1955]
3 v. (xxiv, 1920 p.) 24 cm.

1. Interstate commerce. I. Title.

385 54-1290 rev

NK 0208474 DLC CoU MoU TxU TU NIC IU MiD NcD OCl OU WaS WaSp OClJC FMU

VOLUME 300

Knorst, William James, 1888- ed.
Interstate commerce law and practice. Chicago
College of Advanced Traffic, 1953-57.
4v. 24cm.

NK 0208475 OClU

385
K721 Knorst, William James, 1888-
Interstate commerce law and practice.
Chicago, College of Advanced Traffic, 1953-1958.
4v. (xxiv, 2530p.) 24cm.
Vol. 4 supplements v. 1-3 recording changes and proposed changes in both the I. C. Act and the general rules of practice of the I. C. C., since the publication of the 3 previous vols.

1. Interstate commerce.

NK 0208476 ICarbS

Knorst, William James, 1888-
Transportation and traffic management. Chicago, College of Advanced Traffic, 1947-49.
4 v. illus., maps. 24 cm.
—— Complete and authoritative problem review of text covering transportation and traffic management. Chicago, College of Advanced Traffic, 19
v. 30 cm.
HF5761.K612
1. Shipment of goods. 2. Freight and freightage—U. S. I. College of Advanced Traffic. II. Title.
HF5761.K6 656 47-6870 rev 2*

NK 0208477 DLC IaU TU OrU ICJ

HF
5761
K72 **Knorst, William James, 1888-**
Transportation and traffic management.
Chicago, College of Advanced Traffic, 1948-50.
4 v. illus., maps. 24cm.

Vol. 1-2, 2nd ed.

1. Shipment of goods. 2. Freight and freightage—U.S. I. College of Advanced Traffic. II. Title.

NK 0208478 NIC

Knorst, William James, 1888-
Transportation and traffic management. 2d ed. Chicago, College of Advanced Traffic, 1949-51.
4 v. (1700 p.) illus., maps. 24 cm.

1. Shipment of goods. 2. Freight and freightage—U. S.
HF5761.K62 656 49-6918 rev*

NK 0208479 DLC WaSp OU PPT OCl CU

HF5761
K62 Knorst, William James, 1888-
Transportation and traffic management. Chicago, College of Advanced Traffic, 1950-[55]
4 v. illus., maps.

1. Shipment of goods. 2. Freight and freightage - U. S. I. Title.

NK 0208480 CU

Knorst, William James, 1888-
Transportation and traffic management. 3d ed. Chicago, College of Advanced Traffic, 1950 [i. e. 1951]-55.
4 v. (1700 p.) illus., maps. 24 cm.

1. Shipment of goods. 2. Freight and freightage—U. S. I. Title.
HF5761.K622 656 51-1992 rev

NK 0208481 DLC WaSpG CU TxU ViU

Knorst, William James, 1888-
Transportation and traffic management. 4th ed. Chicago, College of Advanced Traffic, 1952-
v. illus. 24 cm.

1. Shipment of goods. 2. Freight and freightage—U. S. I. Title.
HF5761.K623 *385.1 656 53-1274 ‡

NK 0208482 DLC OU TxU ViU

Knorst, William James, 1888-
Transportation and traffic management. 5th ed. Chicago, College of Advanced Traffic, 1955-
v. illus. 24 cm.

1. Shipment of goods. 2. Freight and freightage—U. S. I. Title.
HF5761.K623 1955 *385.1 656 55-43499 ‡

NK 0208483 DLC PSt ViU FMU

Knortz, Karl. 1841-1918. **G.74.7=**T.97.242
An American Shakespeare-bibliography.
= Boston. Schoenhof & Moeller. [1876.] (2), 16 pp. 19 cm.

J327 — Shakespeare, William. Bibl.

NK 0208484 MB NcU NjP MiU PU-F MH NN

F
83941
.467 KNORTZ, KARL, 1841-1918, tr.
Amerikanische Gedichte der Neuzeit. Frei ins Deutsch übertragen. Leipzig, E. Wartig, 1883.
viii, 128p. 19cm.

NK 0208485 ICN MB

---

4 DS
291 **Knortz, Karl, 1841-1918.**
Das amerikanische Judentum. Leipzig, G. Engel, 1914.
43 p.

NK 0208486 DLC-P4 NjP ICN PPCS OCH MH PPDrop NN

Knortz, Karl, 1841-
Amerikanische lebensbilder. Skizzen und tagebuchblätter von Karl Knortz ... Zürich, Verlags-magazin (J. Schabelitz) 1884.
2 p. l., 208 p. 21½cm.
CONTENTS.—Skizzen aus Pennsylvanien.—Die deutsche einwanderung früher und jetzt.—Das deutsche lied in Amerika.—Die ansiedlung der Rappisten in Economy, Pennsylvanien.—Aus den erinnerungen eines deutsch-amerikanischen geistlichen.—Die deutsche turnerei in Amerika.—Entdeckung Amerika's durch die Isländer.—Die Deutschen in Amerika zur zet des unabhängigkeitskrieges.—Tagebuchblätter.—Ursachen des temperenzthums vieler Amerikaner.—Die pioniere der deutschen einwanderung.
1. U. S.—Soc. life & cust. 2. Germans in the U. S. 3. Economy, Pa.—Hist. 4. Harmonists. I. Title.
5-14182
Library of Congress E168.K71

NK 0208487 DLC UU TxU MsU MoU FMU MiU ICJ NN

Knortz, Karl, 1841-
Amerikanische redensarten und volksgebräuche, von professor Karl Knortz ... Mit dem anhang: Folkloristisches in Longfellow's "Evangeline". Leipzig, Teutonia verlag, 1907.
82 p. 22½cm.

1. Americanisms. 2. U. S.—Social life and customs. 3. Longfellow, Henry Wadsworth, 1807-1882. Evangeline. I. Title.
A 21-1203
Title from Stanford Univ. Printed by L. C.

NK 0208488 CSt NcU IdU CtY MH NN MB

H
8683
.467 **KNORTZ, KARL, 1841-1918.**
Der amerikanische Schutzzoll. Zürich, J. Schabelitz, 1892.
60p. 22cm.

NK 0208489 MnHi

917.3
K72a Knortz, Karl, 1841-1918.
Amerikanische Skizzen. Halle, H. Gesenius, 1876.
311p.

1. U. S.—Descr. & trav. 2. Indians of North America—Religion and mythology. 3. Mormons and Mormonism. I. Title.

NK 0208490 ICarbS IU ICN DI-GS NN OCU RPB OCl PPG

Knortz, Karl, 1841-1918.
Der amerikanische sonntag. Kulturhistorische skizze von Karl Knortz ... Zürich, J. Schabelitz, 1891.
36 p. 19½cm. [With his Rom in Amerika ... Zürich, 1891]

1. Sunday. 2. Sunday legislation—U. S. I. Title.
3-17175
Library of Congress BX1770.K7

NK 0208491 DLC ICJ PPG

Knortz, Karl, 1841- 379.73 II
51384 Die amerikanische Volksschule. Von Karl Knortz, ... Tübingen, H. Laupp'sche Buchhandlung, 1904.
49 p. 24cm.

NK 0208492 ICJ NN

Knortz, Karl, 1841-
Amerikanischer aberglaube der gegenwart, ein beitrag zur volkskunde, von prof. Karl Knortz ... Leipzig, T. Gerstenberg, 1913.
156 p. 20½cm.

1. Superstition. 2. Folk-lore—U. S. I. Title.
26-4759
Library of Congress GR105.K7

NK 0208493 DLC NIC CtY OCl MB NjP ICJ OCl NN

Knortz, Karl, 1841-
Ein amerikanischer Diogenes (Henry D. Thoreau). Von Karl Knortz ... Hamburg, Verlagsanstalt und druckerei A.-G. (vormals I. F. Richter) 1899.
32 p. 21½cm.

Subject entries: Thoreau, Henry David, 1817-1862.
2-20462

NK 0208494 DLC TNJ IU NN MB NIC

VOLUME 300

Knortz, Karl, 1841-1918.
Aus dem wigwam. Uralte und neue märchen und sagen der nordamerikanischen Indianer. Wiedererzählt von Karl Knortz. Mit vier anfangsvignetten und sechs tonbildern. Leipzig, O. Spamer, 1880.
xii, 214 p. front., illus., plates. 20½cm. (*Added t.-p.*: Otto Spamer's Illustrirte jugend- und hausbibliothek ...)
Mounted colored illustrated cover-title.
CONTENTS.—1. abt. Vierzig sagen. Mitgetheilt vom häuptling Ma-to-toh-pa —2. abt. Vierzig sagen. Mitgetheilt von Chingorikhoor.—3. abt. Noch vierzig sagen. Mitgetheilt vom Navajoehäuptling El Sol.—4. abt. Zwanzig sagen. Mitgetheilt von Kah-geh-ga-gah-bah.
1. Folk-lore, Indian. 2. Indians of North America—Legends.

NK 0208495 MiU WaS OCl ICN

Knortz, Karl, 1841–
Aus der alten & neuen Welt. Bunter Kram, von Karl Knortz ... München: M. Poessl, 1892. 309 p. 12°.

Contents: Tagebuchblätter aus der alten und neuen Welt. Aus dem amerikanischen Westen. Geistliches und weltliches.

237352A. 1. Essays, Germany. 2. Title.
N. Y. P. L. November 1, 1926

NK 0208496 NN

F
8394
.4579
KNORTZ, KARL, 1841-1918.
Aus der Mappe eines Deutsch-Amerikaners. Frommes und Gottloses. Bamberg, C. Schneider, 1893.
124p. 20cm.

Author's autograph copy.

NK 0208497 ICN PU ICJ

Knortz, Karl, 1841-1918.
Aus der transatlantischen Gesellschaft. Nordamerikanische Kulturbilder, von Karl Knortz. Mit dem Bildnisse James A. Garfield's. Leipzig, B. Schlicke, 1882.
4 p. l., 304 p. front. (port.) 20cm.

1. U. S.—Descr. & trav. 2. U. S.—Soc. life & cust. 3. Germans in the U. S.
2—3382
Library of Congress E168.K72

NK 0208498 DLC PU PPG NN ICU PP NcD MiEM ICU MiU OCl

Knortz, Karl, 1841-1918.
Brook Farm und Margaret Fuller; Vortrag gehalten im Deutschen Gesellig-Wissenschaftlichen Verein von New York am 11. März 1885. New York, Druck von H. Bartsch, 1886.
29 p. 24 cm. (Vorträge hrsg. vom Deutschen Gesellig-Wissenschaftlichen Verein von New York, No. 11)

1. Brook Farm. 2. Ossoli, Sarah Margaret (Fuller) marchesa d', 1810-1850. (Series: Deutscher Gesellig-Wissenschaftlicher Verein von New York. Vorträge, No. 11)

AC30.D4 No. 11 50-54542

NK 0208499 DLC NIC ICJ ICN

Knortz, Karl, 1841–
Brook farm und Margaret Fuller. Ein nordamerikanisches kulturbild. Von Karl Knortz. 2. aufl. Hamburg, G. A. Rudolph, 1900.
28 p. 21½cm.

1. Brook farm. 2. Ossoli, Sarah Margaret (Fuller) marchesa d', 1810-1850.
G-1308
Library of Congress PS2506.K6

NK 0208500 DLC

Knortz, Karl, 1841-1918, *comp.*
Das buch des lebens; sprüche der weisheit für freie und unfreie von Karl Knortz. Leipzig, Klinkhardt & Biermann, 1908.
311, [1] p. 19½cm.

1. Quotations, German. I. Title.
8-11430
Library of Congress PN6333.K6

NK 0208501 DLC PPeSchw NN

Knortz, Karl, 1841-1918.
Christentum und Kirchentum! Vortrag von K. Knortz. Leipzig, Teichmann & Co., [1909?]
24 p. 8°.

NK 0208502 NN

4A
8844
KNORTZ, KARL, 1841-1918.
Die christlich-kommunistische Kolonie der Rappisten in Pennsylvanien und neue Mitteilungen über Nikolaus Lenau's Aufenthalt unter den Rappisten. Vortrag von Dr. Karl Knortz... Leipzig, E. Wiest, 1892.
31p. 22cm.

NK 0208503 ICN MoSCS NjPT NN PPG PU-Mus

Knortz, Karl, 1841- 1918.
Deutsche in Amerika, von prof. Karl Knortz. Leipzig, C. L. Hirschfeld, 1906.
48 p. 23cm.

1. Germans in the U. S.
10-20288
Library of Congress E184.G3K6

NK 0208504 DLC ICN CtY PU NN

Knortz, Karl, 1841-1918.
Das deutsche volkslied. n.t.p., n.p., 1891.
12 p. (Verein fuer kunst und wissenschaft - Gedenkblaetter ... 1891)

NK 0208505 PU

Knortz, Karl, 1841-1918.
Die deutschen volkslieder und märchen. Zwei vorträge von Karl Knortz ... Zürich, Verlags-magazin (J. Schabelitz) 1889.
117 p. 21½cm.
"Anhang. Volkslieder aus Yorkshire. Aus 'The ballads and songs of Yorkshire', by C. J. D. Ingledew (London, 1860), frei übersetzt."

1. Folk-songs, German—Hist. & crit. 2. Folk-songs, English—Yorkshire. 3. English poetry—Translations into German. 4. German poetry—Translations from English. I. Title.
22-18967
Library of Congress PT507.K65

NK 0208506 DLC NIC OCl MH MB

810.9
K75d
Knortz, Karl, 1841-1918.
Deutsches und Amerikanisches. Glarus, Vogel, 1894.

179 p. 19cm.
1. American literature. History and criticism. I. Title.

NK 0208507 MnU NcU CU PPPM PPCJ MH

Knortz, Karl, 1841-1918.
Die deutschfeindlichkeit Amerikas, von prof. Karl Knortz ... Leipzig, T. Gerstenberg [1915?]
63 p. 22½cm.

1. European war, 1914-1918. 2. U. S.—Relations (general) with Germany. 3. Germany—Relations (general) with U. S. I. Title.
15—10258
Library of Congress D619.K6

NK 0208508 DLC NN OU CtY

Tz
325.243
K758d
Knortz, Karl, 1841-1918.
Das Deutschthum der Vereinigten Staaten. Hamburg, Verlagsanstalt und Druckerei A.-G. (vormals J.F. Richter) 1898.
83p. 21cm.

1. Germans in the U.S. I. Title.

NK 0208509 TxU NIC ICN PPG MB

Knortz, Karl, 1841-1918, ed.
Eines deutschen Matrosen Nordpolfahrten. Wilhelm Nindemann's Erinnerungen an die Nordpol-expedition der "Polaris" und "Jeanette." Zürich, 1885.
48 p. 21.5 cm.

NK 0208510 CtY

Knortz, Karl, 1841-1918.
Epigramme. Lyck, Wiebe, 1878.

47 p.

NK 0208511 MH

Knortz, Karl, 1841-1918.
Folklore, von Karl Knortz ... mit dem anhange: Amerikanische kinderreime. Dresden, Glöss, 1896.
87 p. 23½cm.

1. Folk-lore—New York. 2. Folk-lore—Indiana.

NK 0208512 ViU PU-Mus MH RPB LNHT

GR71
.K7
KNORTZ, KARL, 1841-1918.
Folkloristische streifzüge, von prof. Karl Knortz... 1.bd. Oppeln und Leipzig, G. Maske, 1899.
431 p. 19½cm.
No more published.

1. Folk-lore.

NK 0208513 ICU DLC CU OCl ICJ NN ICN RPB

Film
2730
Reel
192
Item
2
Knortz, Karl, 1841-1918.
Folkloristische Streifzüge. 1. Bd. Oppeln-Leipzig, G. Maske, 1900.
431p. 20cm.
Microfilm. Lexington, Ky., Erasmus Press; available from General Microfilm Co., Cambridge, Mass. 1 reel (various items) 35mm.
Title on microfilm box label: Literature of folklore.
1. Folk-lore - Germany. 2. Superstition. I. Title. II. Series: Literature of folklore. Reel 192.

NK 0208514 TxU UU

VOLUME 300

F 83941 .46707 KNORTZ, KARL, 1841-1918.
Die fonografische Literatur in den Vereinigten Staaten Nordamerikas. [Leipzig, 1874?]
25p. 24cm.

Reprinted from Panstenographikon, v.1, no.3-4.
Paper signed, and dated: 1. Juni 1870.
Bibliographical footnotes.

NK 0208515 ICN

---

ar W 3152 Knortz, Karl, 1841-1918
Fremdwörterei, Vortrag gehalten im allgemeinen deutschen Sprachverein zu New-York. Hannover, Hahn, 1909.
25 p. 23cm.

1. German language.

NK 0208516 NIC PPeSchw MH OCICC NcD IEN NjP CtY NN

4B 1616 Knortz, Karl, 1841-1918.
Friedrich Nietzsche, der Unzeitgemässe; eine Einführung. Mit einer Nietzsche- Bibliographie. Annaberg, Sachsen, Grafers Verlag, 1909.
93 p.

NK 0208517 DLC-P4 PPeSchw CLSU UU

KNORTZ, KARL, 1841-1918.
Friedrich Nietzsche und sein Uebermensch. Zürich, Verlag von Stern's literarischem Bulletin der Schweiz, 1898. 40 p. 24cm.

Film reproduction. Negative.

1. Nietzsche, Friedrich Wilhelm, 1844-1900.
2. Superman.

NK 0208518 NN NIC

LB1162 K6 Knortz, Karl, 1841-1918.
Der fröbel'sche Kindergarten, und seine Bedeutung für die Erhaltung des Deutschthums im Auslande. Glarus, Schweizerische Verlagsanstalt, 1895.
47 p. 21 cm.

Author's presentation copy.

NK 0208519 MeB CtY CU DHEW

834K758 K1875 Knortz, Karl, 1841-1918.
Gedichte. Leipzig [1875?]
51p. (Universal bibliothek)

NK 0208520 IU RPB MH NN

Knortz, Karl, 1841-1918.
Geschichte der nordamerikanischen literatur. Von Karl Knortz ... Berlin, H. Lüstenöder, 1891.
2 v. 19cm.

1. American literature—Hist. & crit.

1-18631

Library of Congress PS106.K6

OCl NN
NK 0208521 DLC NcU UU OKentU CoFS CtY OU OCU OO MiU

KNORTZ, Karl, 1841-1918.
Goethe und die Wertherzeit. Ein vortrag, Mit dem anhange; Goethe in Amerika. Zurich, 1885

pp. 56.

NK 0208522 MH CtY PU NIC ICN

Knortz, Karl, 1841-1918, tr.

Whitman, Walt, 1819-1892.
... Grashalme. Gedichte. In auswahl übersetzt von Karl Knortz und T. W. Rolleston ... Zürich, Verlags-magazin (J. Schabelitz) 1889.

CC115 .S5K7 Knortz, Karl, 1841–
Gustav Seyffarth. Eine biographische skizze von Karl Knortz. New York, E. Steiger & co., 1886.
121, [1] p. front. (port.) 22cm.
"Chronologisches verzeichniss der schriften und abhandlungen": p. 107-119; "Nachgelassene manuskripte": p.120-121.

1. Seyffarth, Gustav, 1796-1885.

NK 0208524 ICU ICN DLC NN MH PPLT CtY NIC

PR2958 M3K5 Knortz, Karl, 1841-1918
Hamlet und Faust. Zürich, Verlags-Magazin, 1888.
55p. 22cm.

Contents.- Hamlet.- Christopher Marlove und seine Faustdichtung.

1. Shakespeare, William. Hamlet. 2. Marlowe, Christopher, 1564-1593. Tragical history of the life and death of Doctor Faustus.

NK 0208525 IaU LU PU-F MA CtY ICN NN

Knortz, Karl, 1841–
Der Handfertigkeits-Unterricht. Ein amerikanisches Gutachten. Arnsberg: J. Stahl, 1904. 20 p. 8°. (J. Stahls Sammlung zeitgemässer pädagogischer Vorträge und Abhandlungen. Heft 4.)

1. Manual training, United States.
N. Y. P. L. January 23, 1911.

NK 0208526 NN

Knortz, Karl, 1841-1918.
Hexen, teufel und blocksbergspuk in geschichte, sage und literatur. Allen anmutigen blocksberghexlein und munteren teufelsbrüdern des Harzgebirges gewidmet, von professor Karl Knortz. Annaberg, Sachsen, Grasers verlag (R. Liesche) [1913]
1 p. l., 169 p. 18½cm.
Bibliographical foot-notes.

1. Witchcraft. 2. Folk-lore. 3. Supernatural in literature.

NK 0208527 MiU NIC ICarbS CU MH OCl OClW IaU

Knortz, Karl, 1841-1918.
Humoristische gedichte, von Karl Knortz ... Baltimore, Rossmässler und Morf; [etc., etc., °1877]
104, iii p. 14½cm.

Library of Congress PT3919.K64H7 1877 21-21470

NK 0208528 DLC ICN MH

Knortz, Karl, 1841-1918
Humoristische gedichte. Ed. 2, enl. Glarus, Vogel, 1889.
141 p.

NK 0208529 PU CU MeB

Knortz, Karl, 1841-1918.
Individualität. Pädagogische betrachtungen von Karl Knortz... Leipzig, E.H. Mayer, 1897.
46p.

NK 0208530 MiU

Film GR 10 L5 reel 166 Knortz, Karl, 1841-1918.
Die Insekten in Sage, Geschichte und Literatur. Annaberg (Sachsen), Grasers Verlag (Richard Liesch), 1910.
[3],151p.

Microfilm (positive. Literature of folklore, reel 166)

1. Insects. 2. Legends--Germany. I. Title.

NK 0208531 UU PPeSchw ICJ NN OCl WaWW TxU

PB 1445 K72 Knortz, Karl, 1841-1918.
Irländische Märchen wiedererzählt. Zürich, Verlags-Magazin, 1886.
iv, 134 p. 21cm.

1. Folk-lore, Irish. 2. Tales, Irish. I. Title.

NK 0208532 NIC MH ICN

KNORTZ, Karl, 1841-1918.
Kapital und arbeit in Amerika; vortrag gehalten in der Zionskirche zu Johnstown. Pa., Zürich, C. Schmidt, 1880.

pp. 43.

NK 0208533 MH ICN MU NN

Knortz, Karl, 1841-1918.
Kapital und Arbeit in Amerika; Vortrag gehalten in der Zionskirche zu Johnstown, Pa. ... Zürich, 1881.

NK 0208534 CtY

Knortz, Karl, 1841–
Kindeskunde und häusliche erziehung. Von prof. Karl Knortz ... Altenburg, A. Tittel, 1900.
62 p. 22½cm.

1. Child study. 2. Domestic education.

E 10-2481

Library, U. S. Bur. of Education LB1119.K75

NK 0208535 DHEW OO

VOLUME 300

Knortz, Karl, 1841-1918.
Kulturhistorisches aus dem Dollar-Lande.
Basel, Schweiz. Verlags-Druckerei, 1892.
171 p.

1. U. S. - Social life and customs.

NK 0208536 NNC ICN

Knortz, Karl, 1841-
Lesebuch für deutsch-amerikanische Volkschulen.
Boston, K.H.Heintzemann, 1896.

NK 0208537 MH WaS

PN6104
K59 Knortz, Karl, 1841-1918, tr.
Lieder aus der Fremde; freie Uebersetzungen
von Karl Knortz. Clarus, T. Vogel, 1887.
111 p. 18 cm.

Author's autograph presentation copy to the
Bowdoin College Library.

1. Poetry - Translations into German. I.
Title.

NK 0208538 MeB MB NN ICN CLU PU CtY NIC TU

KNORTZ, Karl, 1841-1918, tr.
Lieder und Romänzen Alt-Englands.
Cöthen. Schettler. 1872. (8), 262 pp. 16°.

NK 0208539 MB PU MH IU ICN

Knortz, Karl, 1841-1918, ed.

Seyffarth, Gustav, 1796-1885.
The literary life of Gustavus Seyffarth ... An autobiographical sketch. New York, E. Steiger & co., 1886.

Knortz, Karl, 1841-
Longfellow. Literar-historische studie von Karl Knortz. Hamburg, H. Grüning, 1879.
2 p. l., 123 p. 22½cm.

Library of Congress 5-10442

NK 0208541 DLC OClW PU

Knortz, Karl. 1841-1918.
Macbeth. Eine Shakespeare-Studie. Essen-Ruhr: Literatur-Verlag. 1911. 44 p. 8°.

1. Shakespeare (William).—Single plays: Macbeth.
N. Y. P. L. January 9, 1911.

NK 0208542 NN NcU PU-F PPeSchw

Knortz, Karl, 1841-
Märchen und sagen der nordamerikanischen Indianer.
Von Karl Knortz ... Jena, H. Costenoble, 1871.
viii, 285 p. 19cm.

Subject entries: 1. Folk-lore, Indian. 2. Indians of North America—Legends.
3-24753

Library of Congress, no. E98.F6K7.

NK 0208543 DLC MdBP PP OCl OCH PU PPL

Knortz, Karl, 1841-
Der menschliche körper in sage, brauch und sprichwort. Von prof. Karl Knortz ... Würzburg, C. Kabitzsch (A. Stuber) 1909.
2 p. l., 240 p. 19½cm.

1. Folk-lore. 2. Proverbs.

Library of Congress GR489.K6 11-12291

NK 0208544 DLC TxU CU ICRL CtY PPC OCl ICJ NN

---

ar V
6144 Knortz, Karl, 1841-1918, ed.
Modern American lyrics. Edited by Karl
Knortz and Otto Dickmann. Leipzig, F. A.
Brockhaus, 1880.
ix,308 p. 19cm.

1. American poetry--19th cent. I. Dickmann, Otto, joint ed.

NK 0208545 NIC MtU MB NjP NNU-W

Knortz, Karl, 1841-1918.
Mythologie und civilisation der nordamerikanischen Indianer. Zwei abhandlungen von Karl Knortz. Leipzig, P. Frohberg, 1882.
1 p. l., 76 p. 22½cm.

1. Indians of North America. Civilization of. 2. Indians of North America—Religion and mythology.
3-24620

Library of Congress E98.R3K7

NK 0208546 DLC PU OCl NN

Knortz, Karl, 1841-
Nachklänge germanischen glaubens und brauchs in Amerika. Ein beitrag zur volkskunde, von Karl Knortz ... Halle a. S., H. Peter, 1903.
1 p. l., 122 p. 19½cm.

1. U. S.—Soc. life & cust. 2. Folk-lore, Germanic. 3. Germans in America.
4-8094

Library of Congress E168.K723

NK 0208547 DLC ICN CtY PU OCl NN MB

Beinecke
Library
Zg19
K761
884e

Knortz, Karl, 1841-1918.
Neue Epigramme von Dr. Karl Knortz. Zürich,
Verlags-Magazin (J. Schabelitz), 1884.
49 p. 20 cm.

NK 0208548 CtY

Beinecke
Library
Zg19
K761
884

Knortz, Karl, 1841-1918
Neue Gedichte von Karl Knortz. Glarus, J.
Vogel, 1884.
135 p. 16 cm.

NK 0208549 CtY MiU PPG

Knortz, Karl, 1841-1918.
Neue Gedichte. 2. verb. Aufl.
Glarus, J. Vogel, 1893.
121 p.

NK 0208550 MH OCU ODW

Knortz, Karl, 1841-1918.
Das Nibelungenlied und Wilhelm Jordan. Mit dem anhange: Richard Wagner in Amerika. Von Karl Knortz ... Glarus und Leipzig, Schweizer verlags-anstalt [1897]
132 p. 17½cm.

1. Jordan, Wilhelm, 1819-1904. Nibelunge. 2. Nibelungenlied.
3. Wagner, Richard, 1813-1883.
30-13472

Library of Congress PT2370.J4N4

NK 0208551 DLC MeB OCl OCU CtY MiU NN

Knortz, Karl, 1841-
Nietzsche und kein Ende, von Prof. Karl Knortz... Torgau: Torgauer Druck- und Verlagshaus G.m.b.H., 1913. 68 p. 8°.

516442A. 1. Nietzsche, Friedrich Wilhelm, 1844-1900.
N. Y. P. L. February 20, 1931

NK 0208552 NN IEN

B
3313
.A44
K72

Knortz,Karl,1841-1918.
Nietzsche's Zarathustra. Eine einführung von
professor Karl Knortz. Halle a.S., H.Peter,
1906.
1 p.ℓ.,66 p. 20cm.

1.Nietzsche,Friedrich Wilhelm,1844-1900. Also sprach
Zarathustra.

NK 0208553 MiU UU MA CtY

Knortz, Karl, 1841-1918.
Nokomis. Märchen und sagen der nordamerikanischen Indianer. Wiedererzählt von Karl Knortz. Zürich, J. Schabelitz, 1887.
2 p. l., 121 p. 21cm.

1. Folk-lore, Indian. 2. Indians of North America—Legends.
I. Title.
3-24756

Library of Congress E98.F6K71

NK 0208554 DLC InU OCU

Knortz, Karl, 1841-1918.
Die Notwendigkeit des religionslosen Moralunterrichts in der Volksschule. Ein amerikanisches Gutachten ... Leipzig, Teichmann & Co. [1909]
47 (1) p. 8°.

NK 0208555 NN

VOLUME 300

Knortz, Karl, 1841–
... Die notwendigkeit einer organisation der freidenker. Von prof. Karl Knortz ... Milwaukee, Wis., Verlag des Bundes-vororts, 1910.
16 p. 23½cm. (Bibliothek des Bundes der freien gemeinden und freidenker-vereine von Nord-Amerika, no. 11)
11-8301

NK 0208556 DLC

Knortz, Karl, 1841–1918.
Parzival. Litterarhistorische skizze, von Karl Knortz ... Mit dem anhange: Der einfluss und das studium der deutschen litteratur in Nordamerika. Glarus und Leipzig, Schweizerische verlags-anstalt [1896]
60 p. 17½cm.

1. Wolfram von Eschenbach, 12th cent. Parzival. 2. Literature, Comparative—German and American. 3. Literature, Comparative—American and German.
30-13473
Library of Congress PT1688.K6

NK 0208557 DLC ODW OCU NN CU MeB

4 PS 274 **Knortz, Karl, 1841-1918.**
Der Pessimismus in der amerikanischen Literatur. Wien. Verlag "Lumen," 1909.
45 p

NK 0208558 DLC-P4 NjP NN NcU

ar W 25759 Knortz, Karl, 1841-1918.
Plauderelen eines Deutsch-Amerikaners. Basel, G. L. Kattentidt [1898?]
126 p. 22cm.

NK 0208559 NIC

Knortz, Karl, 1841–1918.
Poetischer hausschatz der Nordamerikaner. Hrsg. von prof. Karl Knortz ... Oldenburg und Leipzig, Schulze [1902]
269, [1] p. 20cm.
Translations of poems by American authors.
"Quellen": p. [3]
"Biographische notizen": p. [250]–265.

1. American poetry—Translations into German. 2. German poetry—Translations from English.
3—11117
Library of Congress PS619.G3K5

NK 0208560 DLC OCl

BR515 .K7 **Knortz, Karl,** 1841–
Religiöses leben in den Vereinigten Staaten. Ein unerbaulicher bericht von Karl Knortz ... Jugenheim a. d. Bergstrasse, Sueviaverlag, 1909.
260 p. 19cm.

1. U. S.—Religion.

NK 0208561 ICU NcD NN

Knortz, Karl, 1841– *ed.*
Representative German poems, ballad and lyrical; original texts with English versions by various translators, ed. with notes by Karl Knortz. New York, H. Holt and company [etc.]; Boston, C. Schoenhof, 1885.
xix, [1], 352 (*i. e.* 692) p. 22cm.
Added t.-p. in German.
p. 1–[340] numbered in duplicate.
"Translators and sources": p. xvii–xix.

1. German poetry (Collections) 2. German poetry—Translations into English. 3. English poetry—Translations from German.
4-14015/4
Library of Congress PT1155.K67

NK 0208562 DLC NIC NBuG OClW OCU PU PPGi MH

831.08 K72 **Knortz, Karl, 1841-1918, ed.**
Representative German poems, ballad and lyrical; original texts with English versions by various translators, edited with notes by Karl Knortz. New York, H. Holt and company [etc.] Boston, C. Schoenhof, 1889.
xix, [1] 352 (i.e.692) p. 22 cm.
Added t.-p. in German.
Pages 1-[340] numbered in duplicate.
"Translators and sources": p. xvii-xix.
1. German poetry. Collections. 2. German poetry. Translations into English. 3. English poetry. Translations from German.

NK 0208563 N

Knortz, Karl, 1841-
Reptilien und Amphibien in Sage, Sitte und Literatur. (4),90 p. Annaberg,Sachsen,Grasers Verlag,1911.

NK 0208564 OCl TxU PPeSchw ICJ

Film GR 10 L5 reel 237 Knortz, Karl, 1841-1918.
Reptilien und Amphibien in Sage, Sitte und Literatur. Annaberg, Grasers Verlag, 1911.
90p.
Microfilm (positive. Literature of folklore, reel 237)

1. Reptiles. 2. Amphibians. 3. Animal lore. I. Title.

NK 0208565 UU

Knortz, Karl, 1841-1918.
Robert Owen und seine Weltverbesserungsversuche. Leipzig: E. Demme [1910?]. 45(1) p. 8°.

1. Owen, Robert. 2. Communism, U. S.
N. Y. P. L. February 23, 1911.

NK 0208566 NN TxU ICJ MiU ICN PPeSchw MH

KNORTZ, KARL 1841-1918.
Römische Taktik in den Vereinigten Staaten Berlin, C.U. Schwetschke und sohn, 1904.
30 p. 22½ cm.

NK 0208567 PPCS

Knortz, Karl, 1841–
Rom in Amerika. Ein vortrag von Karl Knortz ... Zürich, J. Schabelitz, 1891.
59 p. 19½cm.
8-17174

NK 0208568 DLC ICN

Knortz, Karl, 1841-1918.
Schiller der Dichter der Freiheit. Vortrag gehalten am 23. März 1905 vor der Deutschen Gesellschaft in Evansville, Indiana. Evansville, Ind., 1905.
24 p. 8°.
Mounted clippings from the Evansville Demokrat 24.-26. März 1905.

NK 0208569 NN

Knortz, Karl, 1841- ed. & tr.
Schottische balladen. Halle, Waisenhaus, 1875.
116p. D.

Most of the ballads have been taken from Aytoun's Ballads of Scotland.

NK 0208570 IaU IEN MH OCl

820 S527 eKNO **Knortz, Karl, 1841-1918.**
Shakespeare in Amerika; eine literarhistorische Studie. Berlin, T.Hofmann, 1882.
85p. 20cm.

1.Shakespeare, William - Criticism and interpretation. I.Title.

NK 0208571 NNUT PU-F ICN CLSU MA PU MiU NcD MB MH NIC NcU MH NjP

4A 8839 KNORTZ, KARL, 1841-1918.
Staat und Kirche in Amerika. Vortrag gehalten in der Zionskirche zu Johnstown, Pa., von Karl Knortz. Gotha,Stollbergsche Verlagsbuchhandlung,1882.
52p. 21cm.

NK 0208572 ICN MnHi

Knortz, Karl, 1841–1918.
Streifzüge auf dem gebiete amerikanischer volkskunde. Altes und neues, von Karl Knortz. Leipzig, E. Wartigs verlag, E. Hoppe, 1902.
2 p. l., 284 p. 23½cm.
CONTENTS.—Ostergebräuche.—Sitten, aberglaube, sprache und litteratur der Deutsch-Pennsylvanier.—Sprüchweisheit.—Teufelsgeschichten.—Weihnachten.—Amerikanische volksrätsel.—Allerlei lieder und reime.

1. Folk-lore—America. 2. Folk-lore. 3. Proverbs, German-American. I. Title.
3—12712
Library of Congress GR105.K45

NK 0208573 DLC ICN PHC CtY OCl ICJ MiU MB NN

Knortz, Karl, 1841–
Sudermanns Dramen. Vortrag, gehalten unter den Auspizien der Germanistischen Gesellschaft von Amerika, von Karl Knortz. Halle a. S.: M. Grosse, 1908. 80 p. 8°.
With autograph of author.

1. Sudermann, Hermann, 1857–
N. Y. P. L. February 8, 1927

NK 0208574 NN IaU DLC-P4 NcD CtY CU MH

Knortz, Karl, 1841-1918. 2879.30
Ueber den Einfluss und das Studium der deutschen Litteratur in Amerika.
(In his Parzifal. Pp. 51–60. Glarus. [1898?])

L42 — Germany. Lit. Hist.

NK 0208575 MB

VOLUME 300

Knortz, Karl, 1841-1918.
Die Vereinigten Staaten von Amerika. Mit 17 Illustrationen. Berlin, H. Hillger [1907]
96 p. 16°. (Hillgers illustrierte Volksbücher. Bd. 81)

NK 0208576 NN

GR735 .K7 KNORTZ, KARL, 1841-
Die vögel in geschichte, sage, brauch und literatur, von professor Karl Knortz...mit buchschmuck von Hans Berthold. München, F. Seybold [c1913]
[3], 296 p. illus. 23cm.
Title and text within green line border.

1. Birds--Legends and stories. 2. Folk-lore of birds.

NK 0208577 ICU DSI OCl TxU MH

F 83941 .4676 KNORTZ, KARL, 1841-1918.
Die wahre Inspirations-Gemeinde in Iowa; ein Beitrag zur Geschichte des christlichen Pietismus und Communismus. Leipzig, O. Wigand, 1896.
88p. 21cm.

NK 0208578 ICN IaHi NN MB

Knortz, Karl, 1841-1918.
Walt Whitman. Vortrag gehalten im Deutschen gesellig-wissenschaftlichen verein von New York am 24. märz 1886. Von Karl Knortz. New York, Druck von H. Bartsch, 1886.
49 p. 22cm. (On cover: Vortraege; hrsg. vom Deutschen gesellig-wissenschaftlichen verein von New York. No. 14)

1. Whitman, Walt, 1819-1892.
43-30502
Library of Congress AC30.D4 no. 14

NK 0208579 DLC NcD ICN NIC CtY NN ViU CSt MH MB MiU

Knortz, Karl, 1841-
Walt Whitman, der dichter der demokratie. Von Karl Knortz ... 2. aufl. Mit den beilagen: 1. Neue uebersetzungen aus "Grashalme." 2. Dreizehn originalbriefe Whitman's. Leipzig, F. Fleischer, 1899.
95, [1] p. 22cm.
Imprint covered by R. Voigtländer's label.

Subject entries: Whitman, Walt, 1819-1892.
2-20461
Library of Congress, no.

NK 0208580 DLC NIC ViU CtY NN IEN OClW OCU MB NN

Knortz, Karl, 1841-1918.
Walt Whitman und seine nachahmer, ein beitrag zur literatur der edelurninge, von Karl Knortz. Leipzig, W. Heichen, 1911.
1 p. l., 159 p. front. (port.) 18cm.

1. Whitman, Walt, 1819-1892. 2. Carpenter, Edward, 1844-1929. 3. Crosby, Ernest Howard, 1856-1907. 4. Traubel, Horace, 1858-1919.
PS3236.K54 47-36903

NK 0208581 DLC NjP IU NSyU CSt

GR 46 K72 1900 Knortz, Karl, 1841-1918.
Was ist Volkskunde und wie studiert man dieselbe? Altenburg, A. Tittel, 1900.
211 p. 20cm.
"(Zugleich als bedeutend erweiterte zweite Auflage eines in nur wenigen Exemplaren in Amerika erschienen Privatdruckes.)"

NK 0208582 NIC NN MH

Knortz, Karl, 1841-1918 398.01 K75
Was ist Volkskunde und wie studiert man dieselbe? Von Karl Knortz. Dritte Auflage. Jena, H. W. Schmidts Verlagsbuchhandlung, G. Tauscher, 1906.
[6], 211, [1] p. 19cm.
Contains numerous extracts from M. Friedrich Zieglers "Heilige Seelen-Vergnügung im Grünen", Leipzig 1692.

NK 0208583 ICJ ICN MB NN OCl MnU MiU CtY

Knortz, Karl, 1841-1918.
Washington Irving in Tarrytown. Ein beitrag zur geschichte der nordamerikanischen literatur, von prof. Karl Knortz ... Nürnberg, C. Koch, 1909.
57 p. 21½cm.

1. Irving, Washington, 1783-1859. 9-14174
Library of Congress PS2084.K6

NK 0208584 DLC PU

Knortz, Karl, 1841-1918.
Eine Weltanschauung in Citaten. Leipzig, M. Spohr, 1892.

NK 0208585 MH OCl

Knortz, Karl, 1841- 325.73 P400
Wie kann das Deutschtum im Auslande erhalten werden? Von Karl Knortz, ... Bamberg, Handels-Druckerei zu Bamberg, [1894].
25 p. 24cm.

NK 0208586 ICJ ICN DLC-P4

Knortz, Karl, 1841-1918.
Zkasky severo-americkych Indianu; ceske mladezi; vypravuje Vaclav Petru. Praze, Hynka, 1882.
[120p.]
Bohemian

NK 0208587 OCl

Knortz, Karl, 1841-1918.
Zur amerikanischen volkskunde. Von prof. Karl Knortz ... Tübingen, H. Laupp'sche buchhandlung, 1905.
73 p. 23½cm.

1. Folk-lore—U. S. 7-24146
Library of Congress GR105.K5

NK 0208588 DLC CtY MiU ICJ NN

Knorz (August). *Ein Fall von Sarkomatose des Peritoneums, mit grösserer Tumorenbildung im Netz und Ovarium. 24 pp. 8°. München, Kastner & Lossen, 1900.

NK 0208589 DNLM

Knorz, Ernst: Studien über die Regenverhältnisse Italiens. Wetzlar 1918: Schnitzler. 60 S. 8°
Gießen, Phil. Diss. v. 18. Mai 1918, Ref. Sievers
[Geb. 6. Mai 90 Wetzlar, gest. 20. Nov. 14; Wohnort: Wetzlar; Staatsangeh.: Preußen; Vorbildung: G. Wetzlar Reife 08; Studium: Gießen 1, Marburg 2, Erlangen 3, Gießen 1, Berlin 1, Gießen 4 S.; Rig. 2. Dez. 13.] [U 18. 1425

NK 0208590 ICRL DAS CtY PU MH

Knorz, Franz.
Ein beitrag zur bestimmung der absoluten muskelkraft.
Inaug. Diss. Marburg, 1865

NK 0208591 ICRL DNLM

Knorz (Joh. Eduard Franz). *De pili structura et genesi. 46 pp., 1 l. 8°. Marburgi Cattorum, typ. Elwerti, [1842].

NK 0208592 DNLM PPC

Knös, Karl: Ein Fall von Fibroma des Dickdarms. 30p. 8°. Münch., 1928.

NK 0208593 DNLM PPWi CtY

Knos, Carl Johan
see Knös, Carl Johan, 1767-1835.

4 BV 5049 Knos, Katheryn.
52 short devotional programs. Cincinnati, Standard Pub. Co., c1949.
216 p.

NK 0208595 DLC-P4

Knos, Olaf Vilhelm
see Knoes, Olaf Vilhelm, 1838-1907.

Knosalla, Johannes, 1893- Selbstverstümmelung bei Soldaten im Kriege mit bes. Berücks. d. chir. Seite. Aus d. chir. Kl. d. Univ. Breslau. Breslau: Hochschulverl. [1921]. 23 S. 8°
Breslau, Med. Diss. v. 10. Nov. 1921, Ref. Küttner
[Geb. 27. Nov. 93 Wreske, Kr. Oppeln; Wohnort: Wreske; Staatsangeh.: Preußen; Vorbildung: G. Oppeln Reife 13; Studium: Breslau 15 S.; Coll. 29. April 20; Approb. 12. Mai 20.] [U 21. 2975

NK 0208597 ICRL CtY DNLM

AP85 .K55 Κνωσός; μηνιαῖον δελτίον. Ἔτος 1- Τεῦχος 1- Ἰούλ. 1953-
Ἀθῆναι.
v. 25cm.

NK 0208598 OCU

VOLUME 300

Knosp, Gaston, 1874-1942. *4042.162
Bibliographia musicæ exotica.
= Berlin. Hornhostel. 1910. 19 pp. 24 cm.
Supplément à la revue S. I. M. du 15 novembre, 1910 [*4042.234.6].
Mostly a bibliography of the music of the East.

H7274 — East, The. Fine arts. Music. Bibl. — Music. Bibl.

NK 0208599 MB

Knosp, Gaston, 1874–1942.
La Birmanie.
(In Encyclopédie de la musique et dictionnaire du Conservatoire. Paris [°1913]–31. 30 cm. 1. ptie. [v. 5] (1922) p. [3094]–3099. illus., music)

1. Music—Burma—History and criticism.
ML100.E5 pt. 1, vol. 5 A 44–2440

NK 0208600 ICN DLC

Knosp, Gaston, 1874–1942.
Franz Lehár; une vie d'artiste. Bruxelles, Schott Frères, °1935.
70 p. illus., music, ports. 21 cm.
At head of title: G. Knosp.

1. Lehár, Ferenc, 1870–1948.
A C 36–2431
Newberry Library for Library of Congress [r69c2] rev

NK 0208601 ICN PP

Knosp, Gaston, 1874–1942.
G. Puccini. Bruxelles, Schott Frères [1937]
238 p. facsims., plates, ports. (1 mounted) 22 cm.
Cover title.
Includes dates of "premières," characters and plots of Puccini's operas.

1. Puccini, Giacomo, 1858–1924. 2. Operas—Stories, plots, etc.
ML410.P89K72 927.8 38–35361

NK 0208602 DLC MB

Knosp, Gaston, 1874–1942.
Historie de la musique dans l'Indo-Chine.
(In Encyclopédie de la musique et dictionnaire du Conservatoire. Paris [°1913]–31. 30 cm. 1. ptie. [v. 5] (1922) p. [3100]–3146. illus., music)

1. Music—Indochina, French—History and criticism. 2. Musical instruments—Indochina, French.
ML100.E5 pt. 1, vol. 5 A 44–2441
Newberry Library for Library of Congress rev [r71c2]† MN

NK 0208603 ICN DLC

Knosp, Gaston, 1874–1942.
Les îles Canaries.
(In Encyclopédie de la musique et dictionnaire du Conservatoire. Paris [°1913]–31. 30 cm. 1. ptie. [v. 5] (1922) p. [3234]–3244. music)

1. Music—Canary Islands—History and criticism.
ML100.E5 pt. 1, vol. 5 A 44–2446
Newberry Library for Library of Congress rev [r71c2]† MN

NK 0208604 ICN DLC

KNOSP, GASTON, 1874-
Mârouf, savetier du Caire; opéra-comique en cinq actes de Henri Rabaud & Lucien Népoty. Glossaire de Gaston Knosp. Bruxelles, E. de Saedeler & E. Possoz, 1919. 33 p. 23cm.

Microfiche (neg.) 1 sheet. 11 x 15cm. (NYPL FSN 14,729)

1. Rabaud, Henri, 1873-1949. Mârouf. 2. Népoty, Lucien, 1878- Mârouf. I. Title.

NK 0208605 NN

Knosp, Gaston, 1874–1942.
La musique des Indiens de l'Amérique du Nord.
(In Encyclopédie de la musique et dictionnaire du Conservatoire. Paris [°1913]–31. 30 cm. 1. ptie. [v. 5] (1922) p. [3333]–3336. illus., facsim., music)

1. Indians of North America—Music. 2. Musical instruments, Primitive.
ML100.E5 pt. 1, vol. 5 A 44–2448
Newberry Library for Library of Congress [r69c2]† rev

NK 0208606 ICN DLC

Knosp, Gaston, 1874-
Parsifal; drame sacré de Richard Wagner; guide analytique et thématique, par Gaston Knosp. Bruxelles: Schott frères, 1913. 50 p. illus. (music.) 12°.

1. Wagner, Richard, 1813–1883: Parsifal.
N. Y. P. L. June 13, 1928

NK 0208607 NN

Knosp, Gaston, 1874–1942.
Rapport sur une mission officielle d'étude musicale en Indochine, par G. Knosp. Leyde, E. J. Brill [1912?]
[141 p. illus., 2 col. plates. 33 cm.
"Tirage à part des Archives internationales d'ethnographie. Tome xx/xxi."

1. Music—Indochina, French.
ML345.I 48K78 14–11297

NK 0208608 DLC

Knosp, Gaston, 1874–1942.
Les tziganes.
(In Encyclopédie de la musique et dictionnaire du Conservatoire. Paris [°1913]–31. 30 cm. 1. ptie. [v. 5] (1922) p. [2646]–2655. music)

1. Folk music, Gipsy—History and criticism.
ML100.E5 pt. 1, vol. 5 A 44–2432
Newberry Library for Library of Congress rev [r71c2]†

NK 0208609 ICN DLC

VM 1503 K 72y
KNOSP, GASTON, 1874-
[Le yakounine. Piano-vocal score. French]
Le yakounine, drame japonais. Paroles de Lucien Métivet. Musique de Gaston Knosp. Bruxelles, L'Art belge [19--?]
score (54p.) 36cm.
Composer's autograph copy.
Plate no.: A. B. 150.

NK 0208610 ICN

Knospe, Erich: Beitrag zur Klinik der Lyssa. [Maschinenschrift.] 21 Bl. 4°. — Auszug: o. O. [1923]. 1 Bl. 8°
Breslau, Med. Diss. v. 18. Juli 1923 [U 23. 1280

NK 0208611 ICRL

KNOSPE, FRANZ.
Selbst-Schutz Ober-Schlesien. [Berlin, Verlag Deutscher Kultur-Wacht, 1923] 88 p. illus., port. 21cm.

1. Silesia, Upper, Germany--Hist.--Partition, 1919-1921.

NK 0208612 NN MH

Knospe, Hans, 1899-
Beitrag zur kenntnis ploetzlicher todesfaelle aus natürlichen Ursachen. Berlin, 1925.
In. Diss. Bibl.

NK 0208613 ICRL DNLM CtY

Knospe, Heinz, 1901-
Implantationsmetastasen nach operiertem unteruscarcinom.
Inaug. diss. Berlin, 1927.
Bibl.

NK 0208614 ICRL CtY

Knospe (Max) [1871-]. *Beitrag zur Entstehung centraler Dammrisse bei Hinterhauptslage. 30 pp. 8°. Greifswald, J. Abel, 1898.

NK 0208615 DNLM

Knospe, Paul.
Arbeitsstoffe zur erdkunde; Europa (ohne Deutsches Reich) Mit 95 skizzen und graphischen darstellungen. 2., durchgesehene aufl. Breslau, F. Hirt, 1927.
131 p. incl. illus., maps, tables, diagrs. 22½cm.
"Jugendschriften": p. [120]–122.

1. Geography—Study and teaching. 2. Europe—Descr. & trav. I. Title.
28–28373
Library of Congress G126.K59 1927

NK 0208616 DLC

Knospe, Paul.
Die bedeutung Herbarts im lichte der schulgeographie der gegenwart. Von Paul Knospe ... Langensalza, H. Beyer & söhne, 1913.
17, [1] p. 21½cm. (Pädagogisches magazin, hft. 545)

1. Herbart, Johann Friedrich, 1776–1841. 2. Geography—[Study and] teaching. I. Title.
E 24–522
Library, U. S. Bur. of Education LB648.K75

NK 0208617 DHEW NN

Knospe, Paul.
Der erdkundliche unterricht in der arbeitsschule. Von Paul Knospe ... Langensalza, H. Beyer & söhne, 1912.
39 p. 21½cm. (Pädagogisches magazin, hft. 503)

1. Geography—[Study and] teaching. 2. [Arbeitsschule] I. Title.
E 24–498
Library, U. S. Bur. of Education LB1583.K75

NK 0208618 DHEW NN

VOLUME 300

Knospe, Paul.
Die geologie im erdkundlichen unterrichte. Ein beitrag zu den reformbestrebungen auf dem gebiete des erdkundlichen unterrichts. Von Paul Knospe ... Langensalza, H. Beyer & söhne, 1912.
60 p. tab. 21½cm. (Pädagogisches magazin, hft. 485)
"Literatur-nachweis": p. 55-60.

1. Geology—(Study and) teaching. 2. Geography—(Study and) teaching. I. Title.
E 24-492
Library, U. S. Bur. of Education LB1655.K75

NK 0208619 DHEW NN

970.1 K75i
[Knospe, Paul] ed.
Indianer – Breslau, F. Hirt [1931]
79p. incl.front.(port.) illus., maps. (Added t.-p.: Hirts deutsche sammlung. Sachkundliche abt. Länder- und völkerkunde. Gruppe III: Mensch und volkstum. bd.5)
"Inhalts- und quellenverzeichnis": p.[78]-79.

1. Indians of North America. 2. Indians of South America. I. Title.

NK 0208620 IU

Knospe, Paul.
Der Kinematograph im Dienste der Schule. Unter besonderer Berücksichtigung des erdkundlichen Unterrichts. Halle a. d. S.: Verlag der Buchhandlung des Waisenhauses, 1913. 34 p. 12°.

1. Moving pictures.—Kinematograph. 2. Geography.—Study and teaching, 1913.
N. Y. P. L. December 17, 1913.

NK 0208621 NN

910.7 K75n2
Knospe, Paul.
Neue ziele und wege des erdkundlichen unterrichts. Ein einführung in die reformbestrebungen der gegenwart. 2.verb. aufl. Langensalza, 1925.
190p. (Half-title: Die neue deutsche schule ... VIII.bd)

NK 0208622 IU

Knospe, Robert Herman, 1929–
Some aspects of the electrical effects of the sulfone group. Ann Arbor, University Microfilms [1955]
([University Microfilms, Ann Arbor, Mich.] Publication no. 11,687)
Microfilm copy of typescript. Positive.
Collation of the original: xliv, 105 l. diagrs., tables.
Thesis—Purdue University.
Abstracted in Dissertation abstracts, v. 15 (1955) no. 5, p. 701-702.
Vita.
Includes bibliographies.
1. Sulphones. 2. Electrochemistry.
Microfilm AC-1 no. 11,637 Mic A 55-930
Purdue Univ. Library for Library of Congress [1]†

NK 0208623 InLP DLC

KNOSPE, Sigmar.
Aristipps erkenntnistheorie im platonischen Theätet. Gross-Strehlitz, [1902]
pp.11.
(Progr. d. Kgl. Gym. "1902. nr.232.")

NK 0208624 MH PU

Knospen und Blüten. Erzählungen und Märchen für junge Mädchen... Mülheim a.d. Ruhr: J. Bagel [, 1896]. 111 p. col'd front., col'd plates. 12°

167547A. 1. Fairy tales, German.
N. Y. P. L. June 10, 1925

NK 0208625 NN

Knossalla, Arnold: Die Regelung der Eigentumsverhältnisse bei einem Schatzfund in herrenlosen Sachen, zugl. ein Beitr. z. Lehre d. Schatzrechtes u. d. Altertumsfundes. [Maschinenschrift.] IV, 28 S. 4°. — Auszug: (Breslau [1925]: Schles. Volkszeit.). 2 Bl. 8°
Breslau, R.- u. staatswiss. Diss. v. 20. Juli 1925 [U 25. 722

NK 0208626 ICRL

DD 901 .H68 K72
Knossalla, Josef.
Geschichte der Stadt Hindenburg O/S. (Zabrze) aus Anlass der Stadtwerdung in Einzelbildern dargestellt. Katowice, Ksieg.i Druk.Katolicka, 1929.
318 p. 24 cm.
Bibliography: p.311-313.

1.Hindenburg,Ger.--Hist.

NK 0208627 MiU

Knossalla, Joseph.
Der pseudo-justinische λόγος παραινετικὸς πρὸς Ἕλληνας.
(In Kirchengeschichtliche Abhandlungen. Vol. 2, pp. 107-190. Breslau. 1904.)

G9106 — Justinus, Martyr. — Λόγος παραινετικὸς πρὸς Ἕλληνας.

NK 0208628 MB NNUT DDO NjPT PPPD MB

Knossington
see under [Mowbray, A B de]

Knost, Friedrich: Das Grundeigentum im mittelalterlichen Osnabrück. [Maschinenschrift.] 85 S. 4°. — Auszug: o. O. (1921). 8 S. 8°
Göttingen, R.- u. staatswiss. Diss. v. 6. Dez. 1921 [1922] [U 22. 5812

NK 0208630 ICRL

Knost, Friedrich August.
Feststellung und nachweis der abstammung; systematische darstellung mit sämtlichen durchführungsbestimmungen zum abstammungsnachweis und den gebührenvorschriften, von dr. Friedrich A. Knost ... Berlin, F. Vahlen, 1939.
x, 160 p. front. 19cm. (On cover: Sammlung Vahlen)
"Schrifttum": p. [v]

1. Germany—Race question. 2. Jews—Legal status, laws, etc.—Germany. 3. Illegitimacy—Germany. I. Title.
41-16392

NK 0208631 DLC IEN NNC CtY MH

Knost, Friedrich August, ed.

Law

Germany. *Laws, statutes, etc.*
Das neue Personenstands- und Familienrecht, nebst den Staatsangehörigkeitsvorschriften für die neuen deutschen Gebiete. Textausgabe der neuen Gesetzgebung mit Verweisungen und Sachverzeichnis für den standesamtlichen Handgebrauch, hrsg. von Friedrich A. Knost [und] Franz Massfeller. Berlin, Verlag für Standesamtswesen, 1940.

Knost, Friedrich August, joint ed.

FOR OTHER EDITIONS SEE MAIN ENTRY

Germany. *Laws, statutes, etc.*
Die Nürnberger gesetze, mit den durchführungsverordnungen und den sonstigen einschlägigen vorschriften, herausgegeben und erläutert von dr. Bernhard Lösener ... [und] dr. Friedrich A. Knost ... 5. aufl. (14./15. tausend) Berlin, F. Vahlen, 1942.

Knost, Wilhelm.
Das blankoindossament im wechselrecht. Inaug. Diss. Leipzig, 1903
Bibl.

NK 0208634 ICRL

Knostman, Carol Susan.
Percentage yield of available meat from the cuts of yearling beef carcasses, by C.S. Knostman & A.H. Mustard. Wash., A.H.E.A., n.d.
3 p.

NK 0208635 PPD

Knot, Antoni.
Finis Poloniae; legenda maciejowicka. Lwów, Krawczyński, 1938.
104 p.
"Praca przedstawiona na posiedzeniu naukowym Oddziału Lwowskiego Polskiego Towarzystwa Historycznego dnia 18 grudnia 1936 r."

NK 0208636 MH

Knot, Antoni, *ed.*
Galicyjskie wspomnienia szkolne. Kraków, Wydawn Literackie [1955]
lviii, 520 p. 24 cm.
Errata slip inserted.

1. Schools—Galicia. I. Title.
LA688.G3K6 56-57321

NK 0208637 DLC KU WaU OU IU MiDW NN MH

Knot, Antoni, ed.

Law

Poland. *Laws, statutes, etc.*
Polskie prawo biblioteczne; zbiór przepisów prawnych dotyczących bibliotek, zebrał i wydał Antoni Knot. Wrocław, Książnica-Atlas, 1947.

D16 .4 .P6W5
Knot, Antoni, ed.
Wiadomości historyczno-dydaktyczne. rocz. 1-7, no. 1-1933-39. Lwów.

H 172.4 K75oD
Knot, J
Onder de wapenen. J. Knot, Doopsgezind Predikant. Uitgave van de Commissie tot behartiging van de belangen van Doopsgezinde militairen. [Kollum, Firma T. Banda, n.d.]
28p. 16 1/2cm. (Brochure voor Doopsgezinde Dienstplichtigen)

NK 0208640 ViHarEM

VOLUME 300

Knot-Rab, *pseud.*
see
Barton, K.

NK 0208644?

A knot of blue and gray
see under [Weckert, John C] comp.

A knot of fooles
see under [Brewer, Thomas] fl. 1624.

*
PS1260
.C7E83
1896
A knot of white and blue. Words by Guy Wetmore Carryl. Arranged by Arthur D. Woodruff.
(In Columbia University. Columbia college song book. Boston. 1896. 27cm. p. 16)

1. Songs with piano. I. Carryl, Guy Wetmore, 1873-1904. A knot of white and blue. II. Woodruff, Arthur D , 1853-1934, arr. III. Columbia University. Columbia college song book.

NK 0208644 ViU

A knot untied: or, Allegiance sworn to the King, no breach of allegiance due unto God ... London, H. Eversden, 1660.
36 p. 19cm.

From the Isaac Foot collection.

Wing K-727

NK 0208645 CLU-C NNUT-Mc

The knot unty'd: or, The association disbanded ...
see under [Ferguson, Robert] d. 1714.

Knote, Anna Caroline.
The geography of West Virginia, with accurate maps and definitions. Wheeling, 1872.
55 p. maps (1 fold.) 20 cm.

1. West Virginia—Descr. & trav.

F241.K72 1-7888*

NK 0208647 DLC

Knote, A[nna] C[aroline]
The geography of West Virginia, with accurate illustrations, maps and definitions Wheeling, W. Va., A[nna] C. Knote [1878]
55 pp. illus., map. 12°.
F241.K74 1-7889—M 1

NK 0208648 DLC

Knote, A[nna] C[aroline]
The geography of West Virginia, with accurate illustrations, maps and definitions . . . Wheeling, W. Va., A[nna] C. Knote [1883]
56 pp. illus., pl., map. 12°.
F241.K75 1-7890—M 1

NK 0208649 DLC

Knote, A[nna] C[aroline]
The geography of West Virginia, with accurate maps and definitions . . . Wheeling, W. Va., A[nna] C. Knote [1888]
104 pp. illus., pl., map. 12°.
F241.K76 1-7891—M 1

NK 0208650 DLC

Knote, A[nna] C[aroline]
The geography of West Virginia, with accurate maps and definitions . . . Wheeling, W. Va., A[nna] C. Knote, 1895.
106 pp. illus., pl., map. 12°.
F241.K78 1-7892—M 1

NK 0208651 DLC

Knote, Henry: Krieg und Säuglingssterblichkeit. [Maschinenschrift.] 33 S. 4° [Lag nicht vor.] — Auszug: (Rostock 1923). 1 Bl. 8° Rostock, Med. Diss. v. 15. Juni 1924 [1925] [U 25. 7831

NK 0208652 ICRL

Knote, John McBride.
... Some chemical and physical changes in clays due to the influence of heat, by J. M. Knote ... Urbana, The University, 1910.
1 p. l., 39 p. diagrs. 23½cm. (*At head of title:* University of Illinois Bulletin. vol. VII, no. 30 ... Bulletin no. 15, Department of ceramics)
"Reprinted from Transactions of American ceramic society, vol. XII. Paper read at Pittsburgh meeting, February, 1910."

1. Pottery.

A 11-1812 Revised

Title from Illinois Univ. Printed by L. C.

NK 0208653 IU CU OrU Or OO OU MiU ICJ NN MB

Knote, Manfred.
... Im fluge durch literatur und kunst in der weltgeschichte; ein buch für den bildungshungrigen im volke. [München, "Im fluge durch", °1929]
1 p. l., 5-108, [2] p. 22½cm.
"Druckfehlerberichtigung" slip inserted.

1. Literature—Hist. & crit. 2. Art—Hist. I. Title.
30-10830
Library of Congress PN554.K6

NK 0208654 DLC PPG

Knote (Paul) [1888-]. *Zur Kasuistik der Knochenbildungen in Laparotomiennarben. 30 pp. 8°. Breslau, Breslauer Genossenschafts-Buchdruckerei, 1918.

NK 0208655 DNLM ICRL

Hk[l]
y358d
Knote, Walter, 1909-
Hermann Lingg und seine lyrische Dichtung ... Würzburg, 1936.
4p.l., 102p., 1l. 22cm.
Inaug.-Diss. - Würzburg.
Lebenslauf.
"Eine Auswahl aus Hermann Linggs lyrischer Dichtung": p.[65]-98.
Bibliography: p.101-102.

NK 0208656 CtY ICRL CU

Knote. Berlin.

NK 0208657 NjP

Knotek, František.
. . . Hannibal; historická studie. Praha, J. Albert, 1946.
121 p. illus., map. 26cm.
1. vyd.
Bibliography, p. [124]

1. Hannibal.

NK 0208658 NN DLC-P4

Knotek, Fritz.
Die anlage und bewirtschaftung kleiner waldbaumschulen zur erziehung von nadelholzpflanzen. Eine kurze anleitung für land- u. forstwirtschaftliche vereine. Bearb. von Fritz Knotek ... Prag, Verlag der Deutschen sektion des Landeskulturrates für das königreich Böhmen, 1907.
2 p. l., [7]-22 p. illus., pl. 25½cm. (*On cover:* Arbeiten der Deutschen sektion des Landeskulturrates für das königreich Bohmen. hft. IX)

1. Forest nurseries.

Agr 9-913

Library, U. S. Dept. of Agriculture 19B634 no. 9

NK 0208659 DNAL ICJ

Knotek, Fritz.
... Anleitung zur korbweidenzucht, bearb. von ing. Fritz Knotek ... Prag, Verlag der Deutschen sektion des Landeskulturrates für das königreich Böhmen, 1914.
21 p. illus. 26cm. (Arbeiten der Deutschen sektion des Landeskulturrates für das königreich Böhmen. hft. XVIII)

1. Osier. [1. Basket willow]

Agr 14-1391

Library, U. S. Dept. of Agriculture 19B634A no. 18

NK 0208660 DNAL

Knotek, Ladislav.
Československý státní zaměstnanec, jeho práva a povinnosti. Dle platných zákonů, nařízení a výnosů sestavili L. Knotek a B. Vávra ... V Praze, Nákladem vlastním, 1924.
264, [1] p., 1 l. tables. 21cm.

NK 0208661 MH-L DL

Knoth, Alexander.
[Three compositions for the pianoforte] by A. Knoth. New York, A. Buchbaum, c1901.
3 pms. f°.
Marche des rois. Prés de la fontaine. Valse caprice de concert.

NK 0208662 NN

VOLUME 300

Knoth, Bärbel.
Die Entwicklung der Lehre vom Schutzumfang des Patents. Hamburg, Rechts- und Staatswissenschaftlicher Verlag [1948]
87 p. 21 cm. (Abhandlungen der Rechts- und Staatswissenschaften)
Bibliography: p. 4-6.

1. Patent laws and legislation—Germany. I. Title. (Series)
49-12961*

NK 0208663 DLC NN

Knoth, Carolus Ludovicus Alexander
see Knoth, Louis.

BX4705 U2K5 **Knoth, Ernst**, 1874-
Ubertino von Casale; ein Beitrag zur Geschichte der Franziskaner an der Wende des 13. und 14. Jahrhunderts. Marburg, N.G. Elwert, 1903.
viii, 162, [1] p.
"Verzeichnis der Schriften Ubertino's": p. [163] Bibliographical footnotes.

1. Ubertinus, de Casali, 1259-1330. 2. Franciscans.

NK 0208665 CU DHN ICN MB CtY

Knoth, Ernst, *1874-*
Ubertino von Casale. Ein Beitrag zur religiösen Litteratur des Franziskanerordens . . .
Darmstadt. Otto. 1901. (4), 50, (1) pp. 22 cm., in 8s.
Inaugural — dissertation . . . Universität Marburg.
Die . . . Dissertation ist der erste Teil von des Verfassers Abhandlung: „Ubertino von Casale, sein Leben und seine Schriften."
Contains a MS. note by Sabatier.

E3634 — Ubertino, of Casale, 1259-1330? — Franciscans. Lit.

NK 0208666 MB ICRL PU MH

Knoth, Ervin Arthur.
Methods in physical education, by E. A. Knoth ... Manhattan, Kan. [Printing dep't., K. S. A. C.] °1923.
111 p. 16cm.

1. Physical education and training. 2. Exercise.
23-5291
Library of Congress GV363.K6

NK 0208667 DLC

Knoth, Heinz.
Platon im Lichte lebensnaher Pädagogik; über die volkserzieherischen Gedanken in Platons "Gesetzen." Frankfurt/Main, 1952.
73 p. 21 cm.

1. Plato. Leges. 2. Education, Greek.
LB85.P7K6 52-36044 ‡

NK 0208668 DLC

Knoth, Johann Samuel, respondent.
Dissertationem ... qua stabilito vero sensu verborum Hoseae IX ...
see under Stiebritz, Johann Friedrich, 1707-1772, praeses.

Knoth, Karl Ludwig Alexander.
see Knoth, Louis.

Knoth, Johannes Paul.
Der strafzweck im militärstrafrecht, von dr. jur. Johannes Paul Knoth. Dresden, Buchdruckerei M. Dittert & co., 1935.
54 p. 20½cm.
Issued also as inaugural dissertation, Leipzig.
"Literatur-verzeichnis": p. 5-6.

1. Military law—Germany. 2. Punishment—Germany. I. Title.
39-24140
Library of Congress UB785.G3K55
[2] 355.13

NK 0208671 DLC ICRL

Knoth, Lieselotte.
Das gärvermögen der pombehefe. ... Dresden, 1937.
Inaug. Diss. - Techn. Hochschule Dresden, 1937.
40 p. 8°.

NK 0208672 ICRL

---

*pGB8 V6755R 5.18.48 Knoth, **Louis.**
An den Herrn Advokaten Dr. Wildner Ed.en von Maithstein und V.....i.
[Wien, 1848]
Signed Ludwig Knoth.
broadside. 42.5x52.5cm.
Dated: Wien, am 18. Mai 1848.

NK 0208673 MH

Knoth, Louis.
[... Aufgeklärte Mosaische] Archi-Geschichte ... New York [1881-87]
34.5 cm.
Cover-title.
Issued in 9 parts.
A cryptogram. Lithographed.
Contents.-1. Hft. Einleitung und die 4 ersten

NK 0208674 CtY MiU

Knoth, Lou:
Codicill zum social-reformatorischen stamm-buch. Endes-gefertigt von dr. Knoth, (no. 3 Essex street) in New York, anno nati Domini 4000+1887. New York, J. Ottmann, 1887.
cover-title, 343-350 p. 33½cm.
Autographed from manuscript copy.
A communication in German, addressed to Dr. John B. Hamilton, secretary general of the Ninth international medical congress, in Washington, D. C

1. Medicine—Curiosa and miscellany.

NK 0208675 MiU

Knoth, Louis.
De paedopneumotetano. Viennae, A. Benko, 1838.
184 p., 3 l. 8°.
Author's name given as Carolus Ludovicus Alexander Knoth.

NK 0208676 DNLM PPC

---

*pGB8 V6755R 5.7.48 Knoth, **Louis.**
Mitbürger! Justitia regnorum fundamentum. Indem ihr jetzt für Freiheit und Vaterland so vielfach in Anspruch genommen seid ...
[Wien, 1848]
broadside. 41.5x53cm.
Dated: Wien am 7. Mai 1848.
Signed: Ludwig Knoth.

NK 0208677 MH

[**Knoth, Louis**]
Offener brief an den deutschen reichskanzler Bismarck [!] New York, Braeunlich & co., photo-lithographers [1879?]
cover-title, 12 facsim. 35cm.
Title vignette (portrait)

1. Bismarck-Schönhausen, Otto Eduard Leopold, fürst von, 1815-1898. I. Title.
24-31948
Library of Congress DD218.8.K5

NK 0208678 DLC MH MiU

Knoth, Louis.
Offener Brief erlassen zum (4000+) 1879...
New York [1879]
port. f°

NK 0208679 NN

Knoth, Louis.
Das social-reformatorische Stamm-Buch mit ursächlichem Inhalts-Verzeichniss verbindlich gefertiget von Dr. Knoth... [New York: Braeunlich & Co.,] 1886. 12 f., 350 p. f°.
Lithographed.
Contents: Offener Brief an den deutschen Reichskanzler Bismarck. Erstes [-achtes] Heft der aufgeklärten mosaischen Archi-Geschichte. Codicil zum social-reformatorischen Stamm-Buch.

NK 0208680 NN

---

*pGB8 V6755R 9.27.48 Knoth, **Louis.**
Volks=Vertreter!
[Wien]Gedruckt und zu haben bei U.Klopf sen. und Alexander Eurich.[1848]
broadside. 42x53cm.
Dated: Wien, am 27. September 1848.
Signed: Ludwig Knoth.

NK 0208681 MH

Knoth, Ludwig
see Knoth, Louis.

WB 22 GG4 K7b 1955 KNOTH, M ed.
Bäder und Kurorte in der Deutschen Bundesrepublik. Rehau, Frankonia-Verlag [1955]
110 p. illus.
1. Health resorts - Germany - Direct.

NK 0208683 DNLM

Knoth, Max: Untersuchungen über Beschälseuchetrypanosomen ⟨Trypanosoma equiperdum⟩ m. Berücks. d. Lebensfähigk. außerh. d. Tierkörpers u. d. Übertrag. ohne Deckakt. [Maschinenschrift.] 37 S. 4° [Lag nicht vor.] — Auszug: o. O. (1923). 7 S. 8°
Leipzig, Veterinär-med. Diss. v. 3. Aug. 1923 [1924] [U 24. 6772

NK 0208684 ICRL

VOLUME 300

Z6956
G3Z36

Knoth, Max, ed.

Zeitschriften-Almanach. 1954–55—
Rehau, Oberfranken, Frankonia-Verlag.

Knoth, Max, 1863-
Ueber die methoden zum ersatz von knochen-defecten ... Greifswald, Abel, 1891.
31 p.

Inaug.-diss., Greifswald, 1891.
Lebenslauf.
"Literatur": p. 29.

1. Bone-grafting.

NK 0208686 NNC DNLM

Knoth, Max, 1898-
Neue versuche zur züchtung der im pansen von wiederkäuern lebenden ophryoscoleciden (Ciliata)
Inaug. Diss. Rostock, 1928

NK 0208687 ICRL CtY

Knoth, Richard.
Zur kasuistik der traumatischen leukaemie.
Inaug. diss. Jena, 1896.
Bibl.

NK 0208688 ICRL DNLM

Knoth, Rolf, 1899-
Das laienelement in der verwaltungsgerichtsbarkeit von Thüringen und Hamburg
Inaug. Diss. Jena, 1930.

NK 0208689 ICRL CtY

Knoth, Walter Henry, 1930–
Spectroscopic evidence against low-energy reaction intermediates ... containing pentacovalent silicon. Synthetic approaches to 1-silabicyclo-[2,2,1]-heptanes. Further studies on aliphatic organo-functional silanes. Ann Arbor, University Microfilms [1955]

([University Microfilms, Ann Arbor, Mich.] Publication no. 11,725)

Microfilm copy of typescript. Positive.
Collation of the original: iii, 132 l. illus.
Thesis—Pennsylvania State University.
Abstracted in Pennsylvania. State University. Abstracts of doctoral dissertations, v. 17 (1954) p. 191–194.
Bibliography: leaves 129–132.
1. Silicon organic compounds. I. Title.
Microfilm AC–1 no. 11,725 Mic 56–5036
Pennsylvania. State University. Library
for Library of Congress [1]†

NK 0208690 PU DLC

Knothe (Benjamin Gotthelf). *Partus cujusdam singularis historiam cum trium insimul natorum puerorum descriptione tradit. 14 pp. 4°. *Lipsiæ, lit. Waltherianis,* [1779].

NK 0208691 DNLM NNNAM

Knothe, Benjamin Gotthelf.
——. *Sylloge observationum quarundam chirurgico-medicarum. 3 p. l., 26 pp. sm. 4°. *Lipsiæ, ex off. Büschelia,* 1781.
Also [Abstr.], *in:* Weiz (F. A.) Neue Ausz. [etc.] 12°. *Frankf. u. Leipz.,* 1782. xv. 42–59.

NK 0208692 DNLM PPC

Knothe (Carolus Sigismundus Gottlob.) *De atrophia infantum. 25 pp. sm. 4°. *Halæ, lit. Michaelis,* [1786].

NK 0208693 DNLM

Knothe, Edwin, 1853–
Angelsächsisch oder englisch? ... [Von] Edwin Knothe ... Greifswald, Druck der Universitäts-buchdruckerei von F. W. Kunike, 1877.

3 p. l., 43 p. 21½cm.

Inaug.-diss.—Greifswald.
Lebenslauf.

1. Anglo-Saxon language. I. Title.

45–26048

Library of Congress PE115.K6

NK 0208694 DLC NcU CtY NjP

Knothe, Emil Paul, 1867–
Bestimmung aller untergruppen der projectiven gruppe des linearen complexes ... Kristiania, Det Mallingske bogtrykkerei, 1892.

2 p. l., 68 p. 23cm.

Inaug.-dis.—Leipzig.
Lebenslauf.

1. Complexes. 2. Groups, Continuous.

Library of Congress QA608.K72 5–3168†

NK 0208695 DLC NjP

Knothe, Erich, 1878-
Vergleichende anatomie der unbenetzbaren blaetter.
Inaug. diss. Heidelberg, 1902 (Berlin)

NK 0208696 ICRL CtY

Knothe, Felix, 1887-
Untersuchungen zu Redgauntlet von Walter Scott. Görlitz, Görlitzer Nachrichten und Anzeiger, 1913.
xi,100p. table. 23cm.

Inaug.-Diss. - Kiel.
Lebenslauf.
"Literatur": p.[vi]-xi.

1. Scott, Sir Walter, Bart., 1771-1832. Redgauntlet.

NK 0208697 IEN MH CtY PU MiU ICU ICRL NcD

Knothe, Franz.
Die Markersdorfer mundart. Ein beitrag zur dialectkunde Nordböhmens. Von Franz Knothe. Leipa, Im verlage des Nordböhmischen excursions-clubs [1895]

128 p. 24cm.

"Verzeichnis der hilfsmittel": p. 17–18.

1. German language—Dialects—Markersdorf. 2. German language—Dialects—Silesian.

27–15762

Library of Congress PF5544.M3K6

NK 0208698 DLC IU

Knothe, Franz.
Wörterbuch der schlesischen mundart in Nordböhmen... Hohenelbe, 1888. 21cm.

Sonderabdruck der in zeitschrift Das Riesengebirge in wort und bild von demselben verfasser unter dem titel Die schlesische mundart in Nordböhmen veröffentlichten artikelreihe.

NK 0208699 CU

PT5585
.K7

Knothe, Gerhard, 1877–
Untersuchungen über den wortschatz von Reinaert I u. II ... Strassburg i. E., Druck von M. D. Schauberg, 1907.

cover-title, [iii]–xii, 91 p. 22cm.

Inaug.-diss.—Strassburg.
Vita.
"Literaturangabe": p. [vii]–viii.

1. Reinaert de Vos. 2. Reinaerts historie. 3. Reynard the Fox. Flemish. 4. Flemish language—Glossaries, vocabularies, etc. 5. Flemish language—Words—Hist.

NK 0208700 ICU IU MH NcU MiU ICRL NjP

W 1
BE341
Heft 7
1955

KNOTHE, Hans.
Über die Epidemiologie der Tularämie. Leipzig, Barth, 1955.
viii, 122 p. (Beiträge zur Hygiene und Epidemiologie, Heft 7)
1. Tularemia Series

NK 0208701 DNLM InU

Knothe, Heino Arnold, 1911-
Das problem des betriebsrisikos ... Breslau, 1934. 60 p.
Inaug. Diss. - Breslau, 1934.
Lebenslauf.

NK 0208702 ICRL

Knothe, Herbert.
Das schlesische Sommerhochwasser, 1938, von Herbert Knothe. Mit 39 Karten, 5 Diagrammtafeln, 3 Tabellen auf 52 Blättern in besonderer Mappe und 1 Karte, 1 Diagrammtafel, 6 Abbildungen und 3 Tabellen im Textband. Breslau: Priebatschs Buchhandlung, 1939. xv, 79 p. charts, illus. (map), tables. 24½cm. and atlas of 1 l., 52 pl. 45 x 65cm. (Schlesische Gesellschaft für Erdkunde. Veröffentlichungen. Heft 28.)

"Literaturverzeichnis," p. [77]–79.

1. Floods—Germany—Silesia, 1938. I. Ser.
N. Y. P. L. October 3, 1939

NK 0208703 NN KU

Knothe, Herbert.
Tarnung und Verdunklung als Schutz gegen Luftangriffe, Zweiggebiete des baulichen Luftschutzes. 2. Aufl. Berlin, W. Ernst, 1936.

44 p. 22 cm. (Baulicher Luftschutz, Heft 1)

1. Camouflage (Military science) 2. Blackouts in war. I. Title. (Series)

UG630.K65 1936 49–32074*

NK 0208704 DLC DN

DD732
.2
.F7

Knothe, Herbert, ed.

Vom deutschen Osten; Max Friederichsen zum 60. geburtstag, herausgegeben von Herbert Knothe. Mit 13 textfiguren sowie 28 tafeln. Breslau, Verlag von M. & H. Marcus, 1934.

VOLUME 300

Knothe, Herbert, 1898–
Spitzbergen; eine landeskundliche studie, von dr. Herbert Knothe ... Mit literaturverzeichnis, 1 karte und 14 abbildungen auf tafeln. Gotha, J. Perthes, 1931.
109, [1] p. 8 pl. (incl. fold. map, charts, fold. diagrs.) 27½cm. (On cover: Dr. A. Petermanns mitteilungen ... ergänzungsheft nr. 211)
"Literaturverzeichnis": p. 98–102.

1. Spitsbergen.
35-30274
Library of Congress G1.P44 nr. 211
[2] (910.82) 919.8

NK 0208706 DLC ViU MoU OCU MiU OU DS ICN ICJ NN TxU

863 K92 K72 Knothe, Hermann, 1821-1903.
Carl Friedrich Kretschmann (der barde Rhingulph) Ein beitrag zur geschichte des bardenwesens. Von dr. Hermann Friedrich Knothe. Zittau, W.Pahl, 1868
1 p.l., 32p. 24cm.

NK 0208707 CU

Knothe, Hermann, 1821-1903
Geschichte des Oberlausitzer adels und seiner güter vom xiii. bis gegen ende des xvi. jahrhunderts. Leipzig, Breitkopf & Härtel, 1879.
pp. viii, 686.

Lusatia, Upper||AcS 22110

NK 0208708 MH CU PPeSchw

KNOTHE, Hermann, 1821-1903
Die Oberlausitz während der jahre 1623 bis 1631, von der pfandübergabe an Kursachsen bis zum beginn des krieges mit dem kaiser. [Görlitz, 188-].

pp. 71.

NK 0208709 MH

+ DD801 .S32 .C6 t.2, bd.7 Knothe, Hermann, 1884- ed.
Urkundenbuch der städte Kamenz und Löbau... hrsg. von Hermann Knothe... Leipzig, Giesecke & Devrient, 1883.
xli, 350, [1] p. 1 plate. 29cm. (Codex diplomaticus Saxoniae regiae, 2. hauptheil 7. bd.)

1. Kamenz, Saxony. 2. Löbau, Saxony.

NK 0208710 NNU-W NN MH MB

Knothe, Hermann, 1821-1903.
... Die verschiedenen klassen slavischer höriger in den wettinischen landen der zeit vom 11. bis zum 14. jahrhundert. Von Hermann Knothe. Dresden. W. Baensch, n.d.
36 p. 20 cm.
Caption title.
Bibliographical foot-notes.
Separatabdruck aus dem neuen archiv für sächsische geschichte und alterthumskunde. Bd. IV. H.1.2.
1. Serfdom--Saxony.

NK 0208711 CU

Knothe, Hermann, 1884–
Die gemeindegesetzgebung der französischen revolution ... Borna-Leipzig, Buchdr. R. Noske, 1910.
viii, 87 p. 22cm.
Inaug.-diss.—Erlangen.
"Literaturverzeichnis": p. [vii]–viii.

1. Local government—France. 2. France—Hist.—Revolution. I. Title.
17-14607
Library of Congress JS4851.K7

NK 0208712 DLC NIC CtY CU NN

Knothe, Hermann Friedrich
see Knothe, Hermann, 1821-1903.

NK 0208713

Knothe, Max: I. Einwirkung von Ammoniak auf Säuredichloride. II. Zur Kenntnis der Azoxyverbindungen. Weida i. Th. 1912: Thomas & Hubert. 64 S. 8° ¶(Auszugsweise in: Berichte d. Dtsch. Chem. Ges. Bd 45.)
Leipzig, Phil. Diss. v. 17. Sept. 1912, Ref. Paal, Hantzsch
[Geb. 9. Okt. 84 Eilenburg; Wohnort: Leipzig; Staatsangeh.: Preußen; Vorbildung: Realgymn. Dessau Reife O. 05; Studium: Kiel 1, Leipzig 8 S.; Rig. 31. Juli 12.] [U 12. 6189

NK 0208714 ICRL MH OCU PU CtY

Knothe, P.
Einfache ... untersuchung der krümmung der mondbahn gegen die sonne. Prag, 1904.

NK 0208715 NjP

GW24 B327 Xk75 Knothe, Paul.
Siegmund Jakob Baumgarten und seine stellung in der aufklärungstheologie. Gotha, L. Klotz, 1928.
46 p. 22 cm.
Inaug.-diss. - Königsberg Pr.
Vita.
"Sonderdruck aus der Zeitschrift für kirchengeschichte, XLVI. band. Neue folge IX, 4. heft!
Bibliograph- ical footnotes.

NK 0208716 CtY-D MH PU CtY ICRL

Knothe, Paul, 1877-
Kants lehre vom inneren sinn und ihre auffassung bei Reininger ... Diesdorf bei Gäbersdorf, Buchdruckerei der Schreiberhau-Diesdorfer rettungsanstalten [n.d.]
64, [1]p. diagrs. 21cm.
Thesis (Ph.D.) - Friedrich-Alexanders-universität, 1905.
Vita.

NK 0208717 CLSU IEN ICRL CtY PU

Knothe, Rudolf: Volkswirtschaftliche Betrachtungen zur Umsatzsteuer im Anschluß an das Gesetz vom 24. 12. 1919. [Maschinenschrift.] 238 Bl. 4°. — Auszug: Neustadt O.-S. 1921: Reichelt. 8 S. 8°
• Breslau, R.- u. staatswiss. Diss. v. 10. Jan. 1922 [U 22. 1101

NK 0208718 ICRL

Knothe, W
Erste geographische darstellung der schutzländer und colonieen des deutschen reiches ... Schwiednitz [n.d.]
iv p., 1 l., 88 p. 21 cm. (Deutsche colonieen)

NK 0208719 CtY

TP881 .K8 Knothe, Walter, joint author.
Kühl, Hans, 1879–
Die chemie der hydraulischen bindemittel; wesen und herstellung der hydraulischen bindemittel, von dr. Hans Kühl ... und dr. Walter Knothe ... Mit 51 abbildungen. Leipzig, S. Hirzel, 1915.

NK 0208720

Knothe, Walter: Die Überführungszahl der Schwefelsäure in verdünnten wässrigen Lösungen. Greifswald 1910: Adler. 47 S. 8°
Greifswald, Phil. Diss. v. 31. März 1910, Ref. Roth, Auwers
[Geb. 9. Sept. 83 Kottbus; Wohnort: Kottbus; Staatsangeh.: Preußen; Vorbildung: Gymn. Kottbus Reife O. 03; Studium: Greifswald 2, Heidelberg 1, Greifswald 9 S.; Rig. 8. Dez. 09.] [U 10. 1022

NK 0208721 ICRL PU MH NN CtY

Knothe, Werner.
Die dickdarmschleimhaut; ihre normale und pathologische funktion im röntgenbilde, von priv.-doz. dr. Werner Knothe ... Mit 113 abbildungen. Leipzig, G. Thieme, 1932.
4 p. l., 56 p. illus. 26cm.
"Literaturverzeichnis": p. 54–56.

1. Colon (Anatomy)—[Mucous membrane] 2. [Colon (Anatomy)—Diseases—Diagnosis, Radiologic] I. Title.
S G 32-80
Library, U. S. Surgeon-General's Office

NK 0208722 DNLM PPC ICJ

Knothe, Wilhelm, 1926–
Todesursachen-Statistik und durchschnittliche Lebensdauer der Bovölkerung der Stadt Beckum in Westfalen von 1900–1945. [Mainz?] 1951.
75 l. diagrs. 30 cm.
Typescript (carbon copy)
Inaug.-Diss.—Mainz.
Vita.
Bibliography: leaves 74–75.

1. Beckum, Ger. (North Rhine-Westphalia)—Statistics, Vital. I. Title.
HB3596.B4K6 52-35793

NK 0208723 DLC

Knothe, Zygmunt.
Toruń, stolica Pomorza; przewodnik po mieście. Toruń, Nakł. Instytutu Bałtyckiego; skł. gł.: Kasa im. Mianowskiego, 1934.
123 p. illus. 18 cm. (Biblioteczka bałtycka)

1. Toruń, Poland.
DK651.T63K6 55-49314 ‡

NK 0208724 DLC WU NN CaBVaU

Knotius, Christianus Fridericus, respondent.
... De erroribvs circa cavsas mortis svbitae ...
see under Heucher, Johann Heinrich, 1677-1747, praeses.

NK 0208725

Knotius, Christianus Fridericus, respondent.
De praesagiis vitae et mortis ...
see under Vater, Christian, 1651-1732, praeses.

NK 0208726

VOLUME 300

Knott, Adolf,
Die sogenannte tätige reue im deutschen reichsstrafgesetzbuch und in der reichstagsvorlage von 1927... 1932. 93 p.
Inaug. Diss. Erlangen, 1932.
Bibliography.

NK 0208727 ICRL

SHAW COLL. Knott, Alfred.
The three spirits and other poems. London, Groombridge, 1856.
96p.

Author's presentation copy to his niece Mary Ann Knott.

NK 0208728 FTaSU

PR4889 .K4W4 1854 KNOTT,ALFRED.
War echoes:being poems for the time. By Alfred Knott... London,Dalston & Stoneman,1854.
12 p. 19½cm.

1.Crimean war--Poetry.

NK 0208729 ICU

Knott, Aloysius Leo, 1829-
Address of Hon. A. Leo Knott delivered at St. Mary's Seminary, Baltimore, on 3d. of Oct. 1891, on the occasion of the celebration of the Centennial Anniversary of St. Mary's College and Seminary. [Baltimore, St. Mary's Seminary, 1917.]
p. 36. 17 cm.

NK 0208730 DCU-H

Pam. Coll. 21378 Knott, Aloysius Leo, 1829-
Address to the graduating class of Rock Hill College, Ellicott City, Md., delivered at the annual commencement of the institution, June 27, 1872 ... Published by the faculty. Baltimore, Kelly, Piet & Co., 1872.
22 p. 22 cm.

1. Baccalaureate addresses. Rock Hill College. Ellicott City, Maryland.

NK 0208731 NcD PPL

Knott, Aloysius Leo, 1829-
... A history of Maryland, its agriculture, products, commerce, manufactures and statistics. By A. Leo Knott. By permission of the publishers. ₍Baltimore? 19—?₎
₍11₎ p. front. (port.) 26cm.
At head of title: Encyclopedia americana.
In double columns. Caption title.

1. Maryland—Hist.

Library of Congress F181.K72 4-33564 Revised

NK 0208732 DLC

Knott, Aloysius Leo, 1829-
Valuable miscellaneous library of the Hon. A. Leo Knott ... Sold, 1909. Baltimore, Pattison & Gahan, 1909.
135 p. 8°.

NK 0208733 NN

Knott, Arthur Reynolds, 1894-
Life saving and artificial respiration, by Arthur R. Knott. ₍Cooperstown, N. Y., Printed by Freeman's journal co., °1915₎
1 p. l., 41 p. illus. 14½cm. $0.25

1. Respiration, Artificial. 2. Life-saving.

15-20565

Library of Congress RC87.K6

NK 0208734 DLC DNLM Or ICJ

Knott, Aubrey Kirk.
A study of the status of orientation procedures for college freshmen. 1941₍i.e.1940₎
iv,173 l.

Bibliography: l.₍143₎-152.
Thesis, Doctor of education, Oregon, School of education.

1. Students. U.S. 2. Colleges and universities. U.S. 3. Personnel service in education.

NK 0208735 OrU

Knott, Cargill Gilston, 1856-1922.
The abacus, in its historic and scientific aspects. By Cargill G. Knott ...
(*In* Asiatic society of Japan. Transactions. Yokohama, 1886 ₍*i. e.* 1907₎ 23cm. v. 14, pt. 1, p. ₍18₎-73. diagrs.)
Originally issued in 1886.
"Reprinted February, 1907."

1. Abacus. A C 38-3291

Chicago. Univ. Library for Library of Congress AS552.A83 vol. 14 [AS552.Y8 vol. 14] (068.52)

NK 0208736 ICU NcD OU DLC

Knott, Cargill Gilston, 1856- ed.
Collected scientific papers of John Aitken ...

SEE UNDER

Aitken, John, 1839-1919.

551.22 Z v.1 Knott, Cargill Gilston, 1856-1922.
Earthquake frequency, by C. G. Knott ... ₍1886₎
20 p. 4 fold. diagrs., 2 tables. 22½cm.
VOLUME OF PAMPHLETS
Caption title.
"Read May 21st 1884 ₍i.e. 1885₎"
From Transactions of the Seismological society of Japan, vol. IX, part 1, 1886.
Presentation copy to Prof. J. A. Ewing, with author's inscription.
1. Earthquakes.

NK 0208738 NNC

Knott, Cargill Gilston, 1856- ed.

Edinburgh. Committee for the meeting of the British association, 1921.
Edinburgh's place in scientific progress, prepared for the Edinburgh meeting of the British association by the local Editorial committee. Edinburgh and London, W. & R. Chambers, limited, 1921.

Knott, Cargill Gillston. 1856-
Electricity and magnetism. Elementary course adapted to the syllabus of the South Kensington science department.
London. Chambers. 1893. 239 pp. Illus. Sm. 8°.

H7635 — Electricity. Theory and history. — Magnetism.

NK 0208740 MB

Knott, Cargill Gilston, 1856-
Electricity and magnetism, elementary course by C. G. Knott ... Philadelphia, J. B. Lippincott company, 1894.
239p. illus. (incl. maps) diagrs. 18cm.

1. Electricity. 2. Magnetism.

NK 0208741 CtW MiD OCl PPAp

QA55 K5 1905 Knott, Cargill Gilston, 1856-1922.
Four-figure mathematical tables. New and enl. ed. London, W. & R. Chambers ₍1905?₎
40 p.

Cover title.

1. Mathematics - Tables, etc.

NK 0208742 CU PU-El

Knott, Cargill Gilston, 1856-1922.
Four-figure mathematical tables; new and enl. ed. .... London and Edinburgh, W. & R. Chambers, ltd. [1933]
Cover-title. 40 p. 19 cm.
"Original edition, June 1905, latest reprint, July 1933."

NK 0208743 RPB

Knott, Cargill Gilston, 1856-1922
Further studies on earthquake waves. (Scot.geogr.mag.,Edinb. v.33. Sept.,1917. p.406-422.)

NK 0208744 DAS

Knott, Cargill Gilston, 1856-1922.
Inō Chūkei, the Japanese surveyor and cartographer. By Cargill G. Knott ...
(*In* Asiatic society of Japan. Transactions. Yokohama, 1889. 23cm. v. 16, pt. 2, p. 173-178)

1. Ino, Tadataka, 1745-1818. A C 38-3316

Chicago. Univ. Library for Library of Congress AS552.A83 vol. 16 [AS552.Y8 vol. 16] ₍4₎ (068.52)

NK 0208745 ICU DLC OU NcD

Knott, Cargil Gilston, 1856- ed.

Kelland, Philip, 1808-1879.
Introduction to quaternions, by the late professors Philip Kelland ... and Peter Guthrie Tait ... 3d ed. Prepared by C. G. Knott ... London, Macmillan and co., limited; New York, The Macmillan company, 1904.

VOLUME 300

Knott, Cargill Gilston, 1856–1922.
Life and scientific work of Peter Guthrie Tait, supplementing the two volumes of Scientific papers published in 1898 and 1900, by Cargill Gilston Knott ... Cambridge, University press, 1911.
ix, [1], 379 p. front., ports., diagrs. 30cm.
Bibliography: p. [351]–365.

1. Tait, Peter Guthrie, 1831–1901.
A 12–755
Stanford univ. Library for Library of Congress QC16.T3K5

OKentU NBuU MU
ICJ MB NN PSC PHC PU-P CaBVaU OrCS OrPR UU DSI LU
NK 0208747 CSt InU CU NjP NIC CtY OCU OU ODW OO DLC

Knott, Cargill Gilston, 1856-1922.
Knott's mathematical tables (four-figure)
see his Four-figure mathematical tables.

Knott, Cargill Gilston, 1856–1922, *ed.*
Napier tercentenary memorial volume; ed. by Cargill Gilston Knott. London, New York [etc.] Pub. for the Royal society of Edinburgh, by Longmans, Green and company, 1915.
xi, 441, [1] p. front. (col. port.) illus., plates (1 col.) facsims., diagrs. 26cm.
"Bibliography of books exhibited at the Napier tercentenary celebration, July 1914": p. [177]–242.

1. Napier, John, 1550–1617. 2. Napier, John, 1550–1617—Bibl. 3. Logarithms. 4. Trigonometry.
16—17916
Library of Congress QA29.N2K5

OrU CaBVaU
CSmH ICJ IU ViU DN KMK OrU CU NBuU NcD MtU OrCS
NK 0208749 DLC ICRL NcU CtY OC1W OU OO OOxM MiU OC1W

Knott, Cargill Gilston.
The new seismology. Edinburgh, 1899.
(Scottish geog. mag. v. 5, p. 1-13.)

NK 0208750 PPAmP

Knott, Cargill Gilston, 1856–1922.
Notes on the summer climate of Karuizawa. By Cargill G. Knott ...
(*In* Asiatic society of Japan. Transactions. Tōkyō, 1891. 23cm. v. 19, pt. 3, p. [565]–577)

1. Karuizawa, Japan—Climate.
A C 38-3551
Chicago. Univ. Library for Library of Congress AS552.A83 vol. 19 [AS552.Y8 vol. 19]
(068.52)

NK 0208751 ICU NcD OU DLC

KNOTT, Cargill Gilston.
On certain thermoelectric effects of stress in iron. n.p., 1891.

By C.G. Knott and S. Kimura.

NK 0208752 MH

KNOTT, Cargill Gilston.
Physics. An elementary text-book for university classes.
— Phila. Lippincott. 1897. vi, 351 pp. Illus. Pls. Sm. 8°.

NK 0208753 MB PPD ICJ

Knott, Cargill Gilston.
Physics, an elementary text-book for university classes. Lond., Chambers, 1904.
355 p.

NK 0208754 PU-Med

---

530 Knott, Cargill.Gilston.
K75p3 Physics: an elementary text-book for university classes. 3d ed. thoroughly rev. and amplified, and containing an entirely new chapter on the electron theory and radio-activity. London, 1913.
370p.

NK 0208755 IU CaBVaU

Knott, Cargill Gilston, 1856–1922.
The physics of earthquake phenomena, by Cargill Gilston Knott ... Oxford, Clarendon press, 1908.
xii, 283, [1] p. illus., 2 pl., diagrs. 22½ cm.

1. Earthquakes.
QE534.K6 GS8–443 †
U. S. Geol. Survey. Libr. for Library of Congress [a48e1]†

DLC PPUnC NN MB MiHM ICJ NcU PSt ICRL
NK 0208756 DI-GS DAS CtY PPAmP PP OC1 OC1W OU MiU

Knott, Cargill Gilston, 1856- ed.

[Pryde, James] 1802–1879.
Practical mathematics. New [3d] ed., rev. under the supervision of C. G. Knott ... and J. S. Mackay ... New York, D. Van Nostrand company [1904]

Knott, Cargill Gilston.
The propagation of earthquake waves through the earth, and connected problems. (Proc.roy.soc.Edinburgh, Edinb. v.39. pt.2 1918-19. p.157-208.)

NK 0208758 DAS

Knott, Cargill Gilston, 1856–1922.
Remarks on Japanese musical scales. By C. G. Knott ...
(*In* Asiatic society of Japan. Transactions. Tōkyō, 1891. 23cm. v. 19, pt. 2, p. [373]–391)

1. Musical intervals and scales. 2. Music, Japanese.
A C 38-3544
Chicago. Univ. Library for Library of Congress AS552.A83 vol. 19 [AS552.Y8 vol. 19]
[4] (068.52)

NK 0208759 ICU NcD DLC OU

Knott, Cargill Gilston, 1856-1922, tr.

[Good, Arthur] 1853–
Scientific amusements, by Tom Tit [*pseud.*] Translated from the French and adapted by Cargill G. Knott ... London, New York [etc.] T. Nelson and sons, ltd. [1935?]

Knott, Cargill Gilston.
Seismic radiations. Pt.2. (Proc.roy.soc.,Edib. v.30. pt.1. 1909-10 p.23-37.)

NK 0208761 DAS

Knott, Charles.
Marseilles. Marseilles, [n.d.] ~~cover-title~~, 24p., illus., map, 17cm.
Cover title.

1.Marseille --Description and travel-Guide-books.

NK 0208762 TU

Knott, E E *comp.*
Ready reference manual of the statute laws of the states and territories in the United States and the provinces of Canada, along with national, international laws, and miscellaneous information. A plain, common sense synopsis of laws in daily use that every person wants to know ... Comp. by E. E. Knott ... Burlington, Vt., International publishing co., 1889.
viii, [9]–381 p. illus. 22½cm.

1. Law—U. S. 2. Law—Canada. I. Title.
12-34866

NK 0208763 DLC

Knott, E E comp.
... Ready reference manual of the statute laws of the states and territories in the United States and the provinces of Canada, with references to national and international laws, and miscellaneous information ... Compiled by E. E. Knott. Sytacuse, N.Y., C.W. Bardeen, 1890.
381 p. incl. illus., forms. 22.5 cm.

NK 0208764 CtY

Knott, Edward, pseud.
see Wilson, Matthew, 1582?-1656.

Knott, Edward E.
Job and occupational analyses, their methods and end products, including a discussion on the research activities and organization of your employment service, by Edward E. Knott, jr. Jefferson City, Mo., Missouri State employment service, a Division of the Unemployment compensation commission of Missouri, 1941.
4 p. l., 47 numb. l. incl. tab., diagrs. (part fold.) forms. 26½cm.
Reproduced from type-written copy.
"This paper has been prepared, on invitation, for the 1941 joint session of the Missouri academy of science and the Missouri section of the Society for the promotion of engineering education."—4th prelim. leaf.
"List of references": leaf 47.
1. Occupations. 2. Employment agencies. 3. Missouri. State employment service. I. Title.
Library of Congress HD5861.K5 41-46004
[2] 371.425

NK 0208766 DLC OC1 PP

Knott, Eleanor, ed.

O'Huiginn, Tadhg Dall, 1550?–1591.
A bhfuil aguinn dár chum Tadhg Dall O'Huiginn (1550–1591) idir mholadh agus marbhnadh aoir agus ábhacht iomarbháigh agus iomchasaoid. Eleanor Knott do chuir i n-eagar agus d'aistrig go Béarla Saxan ... Lúndain, Simpkin, Marshall, Hamilton, Kent & co., ltd., d'fhoillsigh ar son Chumainn na sgríbheann Gaedhilge ⟨1920⟩ 1922–⟨1921⟩ 1926.

VOLUME 300

Y 8285 .0 445 v.1
KNOTT, ELEANOR.
Foclóir d'Eisirt... Baile áta cliat,Brún agus O'Nólain,teor.[n.d.]
56p.
Binder's title: Miscellaneous works. O'Leary. 1.

NK 0208768 ICN

KNOTT,Eleanor.
Foclóir d'Eisirt. Eleanor Knott,do cuir le céile. Baile Áta Cliat,Muintir na Leabar Gaedilge,The Irish Book Co.,1910.
18.5 cm. pp.56.

NK 0208769 MH

Knott, Eleanor.
An introduction to Irish syllabic poetry of the period, 1200–1600, with selections, notes and glossary, by Eleanor Knott. Cork: Cork Univ. Press, 1928. viii, 135 p. 12°.
Printed in Belgium.
438699A. 1. Irish literature—Texts and translations. N. Y. P. L. October 17, 1929

NK 0208770 NN CU ODW CtY IU ICN ICU MH

Knott, Eleanor.
An introduction to Irish syllabic poetry of the period 1200–1600, with selections, notes and glossary, by Eleanor Knott. 2d ed. Cork and Dublin, Cork university press [etc.] 1934.
viii, 135 p. $18\frac{1}{2}$cm.
"Appendix: Manuscript sources": p. 134-135.
1. Irish poetry (Collections) 2. Irish language—Versification. I. Title.
46-36350
Library of Congress PB1347.K58 1934 [2] 891.621

NK 0208771 DLC NcU MB OCl PBm CtY

Knott, Eleanor, ed.
An Irish seventeenth-century translation of the Rule of St. Clare
see under Poor Clares.

Knott, Eleanor, ed.
Togail bruidne Da Derga.
Togail bruidne Da Derga, edited by Eleanor Knott. Dublin, Stationery office, 1936.

Knott, (Frau) Elisabeth (Hartmann) 1912-
... Über die Fiebererzeugung mittels Ultrakurzwellem beim Menschen ... Gelnhausen, 1937.
Inaug.-Diss. - Frankfurt am Main.
Lebenslauf.
"Literaturverzeichnis": p. 19.

NK 0208774 CtY DNLM

Knott, Elizabeth May, 1902–
... A quantitative study of the utilization and retention of vitamin B by young children ... Philadelphia, Pa., The Wistar institute press [1936]
cover-title, p. 597-611. diagrs. $25\frac{1}{2}$cm.
Condensation of thesis (PH. D.)—University of Iowa, 1936.
Thesis note on label mounted on cover.
"Reprinted from the Journal of nutrition, vol. 12, no. 6, December, 1936."
"Literature cited": p. 611.
1. Vitamins. 2. Children—Nutrition.
37-11448
Library of Congress QP801.V5K6 1936
Univ. of Iowa Libr.
——— Copy 2. [2] 612.39

NK 0208775 DLC

TL702 .C3M6
Knott, Ernest Walter, 1890–
Molloy, Edward, ed.
... Aeroplane carburettors ... General editor: E. Molloy. Advisory editor: E. W. Knott ... Compiled by a panel of experts ... New York, N. Y., Chemical publishing co., inc., 1940–

TL589 .M6
Knott, Ernest Walter, 1890–
Molloy, Edward, ed.
... Aeroplane instruments ... General editor: E. Molloy. Advisory editor: E. W. Knott ... Compiled by a panel of experts ... New York, N. Y., Chemical publishing co., inc., 1940–

TL693 .M64
Knott, Ernest Walter, 1890–
Molloy, Edward, ed.
... Aeroplane radio equipment; dealing with Marconi, standard, and North American radio equipment, with special notes on direction finding equipment, Lorenz equipment, and bonding and screening. General editor: E. Molloy. Advisory editor: E. W. Knott ... Compiled by a panel of experts. With fifty-nine illustrations. Brooklyn, N. Y., Chemical publishing company, inc., 1941.

Knott, Ernest Walter, 1890–
Molloy, Edward, ed.
... Airframes ... General editor: E. Molloy. Advisory editor: E. W. Knott ... Compiled by a panel of experts ... Brooklyn, Chemical publishing company, inc., 1941.

Knott, Ernest Walter
Molloy, Edward, ed.
... Airscrews ... General editor: E. Molloy. Advisory editor: E. W. Knott ... Compiled by a panel of experts ... New York, N. Y., Chemical publishing co., inc., 1940–

Knott, Ernest Walter, 1890–
Molloy, Edward, ed.
... Auxiliary equipment; dealing with fire-extinguishing equipment, care and maintenance of batteries and sparking plugs, ignition screening harness, de-icing equipment, and the maintenance of parachutes. General editor: E. Molloy. Advisory editor: E. W. Knott ... Compiled by a panel of experts. With one hundred and four illustrations. Brooklyn, N. Y., Chemical publishing company, inc., 1941.

Knott, Ernest Walter.
The book of the Douglas; a complete guide for owners and prospective purchasers of Douglas motor-cycles...dealing with every phase of the subject, including chapters on driving, touring, legal matters, insurance, tracing faults, and overhauling. Pitman, 1925.
98 p., illus., diagrs. (Motor-cyclist's library)

NK 0208782 MiD

Knott, Ernest Walter
...The book of the Douglas; a complete guide for owners and prospective purchasers of Douglas motor-cycles, by Ernest W. Knott... London: Sir I. Pitman & Sons, Ltd., 1928. xii, 92 p. incl. diagrs., tables. illus. 2. ed. 12°. (The motor-cyclist's library.)
381160A. 1. Motor-cycles. N. Y. P. L. November 27, 1928

NK 0208783 NN

629.13135 K75b 1941
Knott, Ernest Walter, 1890-
Boost control for aero engines, dealing with the latest types of apparatus used for the control of boost pressure and mixture strength for pilots, ground engineers and students of aeronautical engineering, by E. W. Knott ... Rev.ed. London, G. Newnes, limited [1941]
40p. illus., diagrs.
"First published April 1939 ... Revised ... October 1941."
1. Aeroplanes--Motors. I. Title.

NK 0208784 IU NjP

Knott, Ernest Walter
Carburettor handbook; a book of reference written avowedly for the non-technical motorist and mechanic, and including a detailed description of many popular types with instructions for their installation and adjustment, by Ernest W. Knott ... London, New York [etc.] Sir I. Pitman & sons, ltd., 1925.
vii, 403 p. illus. $28\frac{1}{2}$cm.
1. Carbureters.
Library of Congress TJ787.K6 25—10748

NK 0208785 DLC CU MiU DSI

Knott, Ernest Walter, 1890–
Molloy, Edward, ed.
... Engines ... General editor: E. Molloy. Advisory editor: E. W. Knott ... Compiled by a panel of experts ... Brooklyn, N. Y., Chemical publishing company, inc., 1941.

Knott, Ernest Walter, 1890–
Molloy, Edward, ed.
... Fuel and oil systems; dealing with the maintenance and repair of the fuel and oil systems on representative types of aeroplane fuel. General editor: E. Molloy. Advisory editor: E. W. Knott ... Compiled by a panel of experts. With one hundred and three illustrations. Brooklyn, N. Y., Chemical publishing company, inc., 1941.

TL697 .H9M6
Knott, Ernest Walter, 1890–
Molloy, Edward, ed.
... Hydraulic equipment; dealing with the operation, inspection, and maintenance of Lockheed, Dowty, and other representative types of hydraulic equipment, with a summary of retractable undercarriages and operating systems. General editor: E. Molloy. Advisory editor: E. W. Knott ... Compiled by a panel of experts. With eight-four illustrations. Brooklyn, N. Y., Chemical publishing company, inc., 1941.

VOLUME 300

Knott, Ernest Walter.

Molloy, Edward, *ed.*
... Landing legs, wheels, and brakes; dealing with the maintenance and repair of the Lockheed airdraulic oleo leg, the Vickers oleo-pneumatic shock absorber strut, the Turner oleo-pneumatic and pneumatic landing legs, and the Dowty oleo-pneumatic shock absorbers and tail-wheel units, Dunlop, Bendix, and Palmer brakes. General editor: E. Molloy. Advisory editor: E. W. Knott ... Compiled by a panel of experts. With one hundred and twenty-nine illustrations. New York, N. Y., Chemical publishing co., inc., 1940.

Knott, Ernest Walter, 1890–

Molloy, Edward, *ed.*
... The link trainer; dealing in a comprehensive manner with the installation, maintenance, and adjustment of the link trainer used for the training of pilots in instrument flying. General editor: E. Molloy. Advisory editor: E. W. Knott ... Compiled by a panel of experts. With sixty-one illustrations. Brooklyn, N. Y., Chemical publishing company, inc., 1941.

Knott, Ernest Walter, 1890–

Molloy, Edward, *ed.*
... Magnetos; dealing with the maintenance and repair of the Scintilla, Rotax, and the British Thomson-Houston types of magnetos. General editor: E. Molloy. Advisory editor: E. W. Knott ... Compiled by a panel of experts. With eighty-two illustrations. Brooklyn, N. Y., Chemical publishing company, inc., 1941.

Knott, Ernest Walter, 1890–

Molloy, Edward, *ed.*
... Starters and generators; dealing with the operation and maintenance of Rotax starters and generators, B. T. H. and Armstrong-Siddeley starters, and notes on the construction, operation, and maintenance of gas starters. General editor: E. Molloy. Advisory editor: E. W. Knott ... Compiled by a panel of experts. With sixty-seven illustrations. Brooklyn, N. Y., Chemical publishing company, inc., 1941.

Knott, Eustace Reynolds, 1880–
Knott's pop-corn book ... comp. by E. R. Knott. Boston, Mass., E. R. Knott machine co. [c1915]
2 p. l., 3-51, [1] p. illus. (1 col.) 23cm. $1.00
Contains advertising matter.
"The tested and true pop-corn machines": p. [33]-51.

1. Pop-corn.

Library of Congress TX799.K7 15-9664

NK 0208793 DLC ICJ

Knott, Eustace Reynolds, 1880–
Knott's pop-corn book ... comp. by E. R. Knott. Boston, Mass., E. R. Knott machine co. [c1920]
59, [1] p. illus. (1 col.) 23cm.
Contains advertising matter.

1. Pop-corn.

Library of Congress TX799.K7 1920 20-4633

NK 0208794 DLC

Knott, Felize, 1910–
Dudo erobert Dalmatien; eine Ferienreise an die Adria. Reutlingen, Ensslin & Laiblin [1952]
168 p. illus. 22 cm.

I. Title.

PZ33. K563 52-42058 ‡

NK 0208795 DLC

Knott, Frank Alexander, 1889–
Clinical bacteriology, by F. A. Knott ... With 60 illustrations including 12 plates. Philadelphia, P. Blakiston's son & co. inc., 1939.
viii, 426 p. illus., plates. 22cm.
"Printed in Great Britain."

1. Bacteriology. 2. Immunity. 3. Contagion and contagious diseases. I. Title.

Library of Congress QR46.K6 40-4481
[4] 616.01

NK 0208796 DLC ICRL CU OrU-M PPC

Knott, Frank Alexander, 1889–

Hurst, *Sir* **Arthur Frederick,** 1879–
Medical diseases of war, by Sir Arthur Hurst ... with the co-operation of H. W. Barber ... F. A. Knott ... and T. A. Ross ... London, E. Arnold & co. [1940]

Knott, Frederick.
Dial "M" for murder. New York, Random House [1953]
182 p. illus. 21 cm. (A Random House play)

I. Title.

PS3521.N66D5 812.5 53—5031

WaTC OrStbM OrPS WaWW WaE WaS WaSp WaT WaSpG CaBVa CaBVaU NcWil MiU IdB OrCS OrP Or OrPS Wa PPT OC1W OC1 OO PPPSW TxU TU OOxM PLFM NcU NBuU
NK 0208798 DLC VtU CoU MnU OU MeB ViU MsSM PP PU

Knott, Frederick.
Dial "M" for murder, play in three acts. [Acting ed. New York] Dramatists Play Service [1954]
79 p. illus. 20 cm.

I. Title.

PS3521.N66D5 1954 812.5 55-15729 ‡

NK 0208799 DLC MtU CaBVaU MtBuM MtU WaT PBL NcGU

Knott, Frederick.
Dial "M" for murder, a play in three acts. [Rev. acting ed.] London, French [1955]
71 p. illus. 22 cm. (French's acting edition, no. 477)

I. Title.

PS3521.N66D5 1955 812.5 55-44159

NK 0208800 DLC

Knott, Frederick.
Dial 'M' for murder; screenplay
see under title

KNOTT, FREDERICK.
Dial "M" for murder, written and adapted for television by Frederick Knott. [New York, 195-]
1 v. (various pagings) 29cm.

Typescript.
A Milberg production for the Hallmark hall of fame program.

1. Drama, Television, English. 2. Television—Scripts. I. Hallmark hall of fame (Television program). II. Title.

NK 0208802 NN

Knott, G H.
... Mr. John Burns, M. P. By G. H. Knott, M. A. London, H. J. Drane, 1901.
90 p. front. (port.) 12½cm. (Bijou biographies, no. IV)

Subject entries: Burns, John, 1858- 2-24026

Library of Congress, no.

NK 0208803 DLC PPL

Knott, George, 1835–1894.
... Micrometrical measures of double stars. By George Knott, esq. [London, 1877]
32 p. 28 x 22cm.
Reprinted from the "Memoirs of the Royal astronomical society," vol. XLIII.

1. Stars, Double.

Library of Congress QB821.K72 7-6890†

NK 0208804 DLC

Knott, George, 1835-1894.
Observations of twenty-three variable stars... ed. by H. H. Turner... London, Royal astronomical society, 1899.
1 p. l., vii.-xxii, p., 1 l., 310p. diagrs.

NK 0208805 OO

Knott, George, 1835–1894.
On the method of observing variable stars. By George Knott ... and Joseph Baxendell ... London, Printed for private circulation [Harrild, printer] 1863.
16 p., 1 l. diagrs. 21½cm. [With The Astronomical register. London, 1864. vol. II]

1. Stars, Variable. I. Baxendell, Joseph, 1815-1887.

Library of Congress QB1.A35 8-5466

NK 0208806 DLC MH

KNOTT, George, 1835-1894.
On the variable star R vulpeculae. London, 1867.

1 pam.

NK 0208807 MH

Law Knott, George H., d. 1924, ed. FOR OTHER EDITIONS SEE MAIN ENTRY

Casement, *Sir* **Roger,** 1864–1916, *defendant.*
Trial of Sir Roger Casement, edited by George H. Knott ... 2d ed. Edinburgh and London, W. Hodge & company, limited [1926]

VOLUME 300

Law **Knott, George H., d. 1924, ed.** FOR OTHER EDITIONS SEE MAIN ENTRY

Palmer, William, 1824–1856, *defendant.*
Trial of William Palmer, edited by George H. Knott. [3d ed.] rev. by Eric R. Watson. London, W. Hodge [1952]

Knott, Harold Elkin.
How to prepare a sermon, by H. E. Knott ... introduction by Jesse R. Kellems ... Cincinnati, O., The Standard press [°1927]
135 p. 19½cm.

1. Homiletics. I. Title.

Library of Congress BV4211.K6 27-11599

NK 0208810 DLC TNDC

Knott, Harold Elkin.
How to prepare an expository sermon, by Harold E. Knott ... Cincinnati, O., The Standard publishing company [°1930]
138 p. 20cm.

1. Preaching. I. Title.

Library of Congress BV4211.K58 30-19600
Copyright A 26398 [2] [252.8] 251

NK 0208811 DLC NcC InAndC-T KyLxCB

Knott, Henry.
The destroyer; man to demon, the devastation of a life by strong drink, by Henry Knott ... Chicago, Ill., W. R. Vansant & co., °1908.
222 p. incl. front. 7 pl. 20½cm.

I. Title.

Library of Congress PZ3.K759D 8-35964

NK 0208812 DLC

Knott, Henry N., joint comp.

Minneapolis. *Charters.*
Minneapolis city charter and ordinances. Court and board acts, park ordinances, rules of City council, etc. Published by authority of the City council of the city of Minneapolis. Compiled under direction of City council by Frank Healy ... L. A. Lydiard ... Wm. H. Morse ... Henry N. Knott ... [Minneapolis, 1905.

Knott, Heribert, 1880-
Die Bestimmungen des Bürgerlichen Gesetzbuches über die Haftung des Verkäufers für Mängel der verkauften Sachen, verglichen mit den allgemeinen Bestimmungen über die Unmöglichkeit der Leistung ... von Heribert Knott ... Opponenten: ... Georg Wolff ... Georg Sperlich. Halle a.S., Druck der Buchdruckerei des Waisenhauses, 1903.
viii, 98 p., 1 l. 22cm.

Inaug.-diss. - Halle-Wittenberg.
"Lebenslauf": leaf at end.
"Benutzte Literatur": p.[vii]-viii.

NK 0208815 MH-L ICRL

Knott, J. Ger 10039.95
Stockenfels die alte ritterveste und geisterburg in Regenthale; auszug aus der Chronik der pfarrei Fischbach. Stadtamhof, J. Mayr, 1880.
pp. 62 +. Front.

Stockenfels||AcS 22113

NK 0208816 MH

Thesis 1926 K72 Knott, James Edward, 1897-
Catalase in relation to growth and other changes in plant tissue. [Ithaca, N.Y.] 1926.
105 l. illus. 27cm.

Thesis (Ph.D.)--Cornell University, March, 1926.

NK 0208817 NIC

Knott, James Edward, 1897–
Catalase in relation to growth and to other changes in plant tissue ... by J. E. Knott ... [Ithaca, N. Y., 1927]
63 p. illus. 23cm.
Thesis (PH. D.)—Cornell university, 1926.
Reprinted from New York. Agricultural experiment station. Memoir 106, May 1927.
"Literature cited": p. 59–63.

1. Catalase. 2. Growth (Plants)

Library of Congress QK896.K6 1926 28—9042

NK 0208818 DLC NIC MiU OU OCU ICJ

Knott, James Edward, 1897- joint author.

Boswell, Victor Rickman, 1900–
... Descriptions of types of principal American varieties of cabbage. Prepared jointly by specialists of the United States Department of agriculture and of the Agricultural experiment stations of California, Pennsylvania, South Carolina, Texas, Virginia, and Wisconsin. [By Victor R. Boswell ... and W. C. Edmundson ... O. H. Pearson ... J. E. Knott ... and C. E. Myers ... R. A. McGinty ... W. H. Friend ... H. H. Zimmerley ... J. C. Walker ...] Washington [U. S. Govt. print. off.] 1934.

Knott, James Edward, 1897–
... Production of head lettuce in California [by] J. E. Knott and A. A. Tavernetti ... Berkeley, Calif., The College of agriculture, University of California [1944]
51 p. incl. illus., tables, diagrs. 24cm. (California agricultural extension service. Circular 128, September, 1944)
"This circular supersedes extension Circular 105, Head-lettuce production in California, by A. A. Tavernetti and John B. Schneider."—Footnote, p. 3.

1. Lettuce. I. Tavernetti, Achilles Alfred, 1893– joint author.

California. Univ. Libr. for Library of Congress [S39.C4 no. 128] A 44-5702

NK 0208820 CU

Knott, James Edward, 1897–
Vegetable growing, by James Edward Knott ... illustrated with 62 engravings. Philadelphia, Lea & Febiger, 1930.
xvi, [17]–352 p. illus. 21cm.
"Suggested reading" at end of most of the chapters.

1. Vegetable gardening.

Library of Congress SB321.K5 30-1964

NK 0208821 DLC MBH NN MtBC WaS PPeSchw PP MB OCl NN CaBVaU OrP

Knott, James Edward, 1897–
Vegetable growing, by James Edward Knott ... 2d ed., thoroughly rev. Illustrated with 70 engravings. Philadelphia, Lea & Febiger, 1935.
361 p. illus. 20½cm.
"Suggested reading" at end of most of the chapters.

1. Vegetable gardening.

Library of Congress SB321.K5 1935 35-4959
—— Copy 2.
Copyright A 82216 [3] 635

NK 0208822 DLC NcRS MB MtU WaS ViU OLak OEac OCl PP TU OrP OrCS

Knott, James Edward, 1897–
Vegetable growing, by James Edward Knott ... 3d ed., thoroughly rev. Illustrated with 80 engravings. Philadelphia, Lea & Febiger, 1941.
356 p. incl. illus., tables. 20½cm.
"Suggested reading" at end of most of the chapters.

1. Vegetable gardening.

Library of Congress SB321.K5 1941 41-18160
[3] 635

NK 0208823 DLC NcD CU NIC PSt OCl OEac OLak ICJ OOxM OCU OClW OrP WaS Or OrCS CaBVa

---

Knott, James Edward, 1897–
Vegetable growing. 4th ed., thoroughly rev. Philadelphia, Lea & Febiger, 1949.
314 p. illus. 25 cm.
"Suggested reading" at end of most of the chapters.

1. Vegetable gardening.

SB321.K5 1949 635 Agr 49-17*
U. S. Dept. of Agr. Libr. for Library of Congress 91.15K75 Ed. 4 [3]†

NK 0208824 DNAL PSt OU DLC CU MtBC OrCS WaS WaT NcSal

Knott, James Edward, 1897–
Vegetable growing. 5th ed., thoroughly rev. Philadelphia, Lea & Febiger, 1955.
358 p. illus. 24 cm.
Includes bibliography.

1. Vegetable gardening.

SB321.K5 1955 635 55-7846 ‡

NK 0208825 DLC AAP NcU OrCS DNAL NIC MB PP IU C Or CaBVaU MtBC WaS WaTC OClU

---

428 X752 [Knott, James I.]
Mosquito control, Suva. What you should know about filariasis. [Suva, Smith government printer, 1944]
16 p.

NK 0208826 DNAL

Knott (J[ames] J[errold]) [1839–]. Phosphorus. The cause of yellow fever; its prevention and cure. 27 pp. 12°. *Atlanta, S. W. Postell,* [1893].

NK 0208827 DNLM

VOLUME 300

Knott, James Proctor. 1830–1911. Address.
18 pp. (Scotch-Irish Soc. of Am. *Proc. at Columbia*, p. 72.)

NK 0208828 MdBP

Knott, James Proctor, 1830-1911.
Andrew Jackson, an address delivered before the Andrew Jackson League at Chicago, Illinois, January 8th, 1890. Louisville, Ky., John P. Morton, 1890.
16 p.

NK 0208829 KyHi

Knott, James Proctor.
Argument in re Varney Hatfield et al. Louisville, Courier journal publishing co., 1888.

NK 0208830 KyBgW KyU

Knott, James Proctor, 1830–1911.
The constitution vs. the test oath. Speech of Hon. J. Proctor Knott, of Kentucky, in the House of representatives, February 1, 1868. [n. p., 1868?]
8 p. 23½cm.
Caption title.

1. Oaths—U. S. 2. U. S. Congress. I. Title: Test oath.
44-38210
Library of Congress JK1067.K6

NK 0208831 DLC

Knott, James Proctor, 1830-1911.
Duluth! Speech of Hon. J. Proctor Knott, of Kentucky, delivered in the House of representatives, on the St. Croix and Superior land grant, January 27, 1871 ... Washington, F. & J. Rives & G. A. Bailey, 1871.
8 p. 24½cm.
Reprinted from the Congressional globe, 41st Cong., 3d sess., App., p. 66-68, 1871.
1. Duluth, Minn. I. Title: St. Croix and Superior land grant.

NK 0208832 MiU NN DLC ICN OClWHi PHi PPL MH NIC

Knott, James Proctor, 1830-1911.
Duluth! Speech of Hon. J.Proctor Knott, of Kentucky. Delivered in the House of Representatives, on the St. Croix and Superior land grant, January 27, 1871. [n.p., 1872?]
1 *l*. 25 x 62 cm.

Verso of New 30-7 gold loan of the Nor'-Nor'-West-by-North Pacific & Hudson Bay Railroad Company.

NK 0208833 MH-BA

Knott, James Proctor, 1830-1911.
... Duluth! Speech ... on the St.Croix and Superior land grant, delivered in the House of representatives, January 27, 1871 ... Washington,D.C.,Solomons & Chapman,1876.
16p. 24cm.
At head of title: Authorized edition.
Original wrappers.

NK 0208834 CtY

Microcard
F 614 D8 K6
Knott, James Proctor, 1830-1911.
Duluth! Speech of Hon. J. Proctor Knott, of Kentucky, on the St. Croix and Superior land grant, delivered in the House of Representatives, January 27, 1871. Washington, D.C., J.J. Chapman, 1879.
16p.
Micro-opaque. (Nineteenth century American literature on microcards. Series A: The Ohio Valley)

NK 0208835 UU NNC ICRL OOxM IU OClW

Knott, James Proctor, 1830-1911.
Duluth. The zenith city of the unsalted seas. A little booklet in which is presented the speech of Hon. J. Proctor Knott, delivered in Congress in 1871, and the correspondence of W.E. Curtis in the Chicago Record Herald, concerning Duluth in 1907 times, thus showing what years have brought forth. Duluth,1908. 23l., 2 pl. 16°.

NK 0208836 NN

Knott, James Proctor, 1830-1911.
The Fourteenth amendment from a legal stand-point—The late rebels not disfranchised. Speech of Hon. J. Proctor Knott, of Kentucky, delivered in the House of representatives, January 23, 1869. Washington, F. & J. Rives & G. A. Bailey, printers, 1869.
15 p. 23½cm.

1. Amnesty—U. S. 2. U. S. Constitution. 14th amendment.
12-30827
Library of Congress E668.K72

NK 0208837 DLC ICU OClWHi

Knott, James Proctor.
Free elections - no armed interference at the polls - ... Speech...April 3, 1879. Wash., 1879.

YA5000 J 17 (Congressional speeches,by author)

NK 0208838 DLC

Knott, James Proctor.
Green River island. Supreme court of the United States, October term, 1889. No. 2 original. The state of Indiana, complainant, vs. the state of Kentucky, respondent, in equity, Brief for respondent. Frankfort, Ky., Capital printing co., 1889.
86p.

NK 0208839 OClWHi

Knott, James Proctor.
Kentucky. An address delivered...at the annual commencement of the agricultural and mechanical college...New York [1887]. YA10928
16p.

NK 0208840 DLC

Knott (J[ames] Proctor) [1830-]. Kentucky School of Medicine; doctorate address, 1890. 8 pp. 8°. *Louisville, Courier-Journal Job Print. Co.*, 1890.
Repr. from: N. York M. J., 1890. lii.

NK 0208841 DNLM

Knott, James Proctor, 1830-1911.
"Knott on Duluth"; speech of Hon. J. Proctor Knott, of Kentucky. <Delivered in the House of representatives, Feb., 1871.> [Chicago, Poole bros., printers and engravers, 1887?]
[13] p. col. illus. 21½ x 10cm.
In folder of Northern Pacific railway company, which has title: Northern Pacific R. R., the Yellowstone Park and dining car route to the Pacific coast.
Caption title.
Title on back cover of folder: "Duluth, the zenith city of the unsalted sea."
Notes interspersed throughout speech, giving commercial statistics of Duluth for 1886, etc.
1. Duluth, Minn. I. Northern Pacific railway company.

NK 0208842 MiU

Knott, James Proctor, 1830-1911.
Presidential Title. Views of Hon. J.P. Knott ... on the bill to provide a mode for trying and determining by the Supreme Court of the United States the title of the President and Vice-President of the United States ... Washington, 1878.
14 p. 8°.

NK 0208843 NN

Knott,James Proctor,1830-1911.
Proctor Knott on Duluth;a reprint of the speech delivered in Congress by the Hon.J.Proctor Knott of Kentucky,1871. Issued by the Convention & publicity bureau,Chamber of Commerce of Duluth. [Duluth, Stewart Taylor company, 1920?]
1 p.*l*.,5-30 p. double map. 19cm.

1.Duluth,Minn. 2.Lake Superior and Mississippi Railroad. 3.St.Croix and Bayfield Railroad. 4. Kentuckiana. I.Title.

NK 0208844 MiU-C

Knott, James Proctor
Public expenditures---paving of Pennsylvania Avenue. Speech...in the House of representatives May 20 1870

Washington 1870? 8p

YA5000 J 17 (Congressional speeches,by author)

NK 0208845 DLC

Knott, James Proctor, 1830-1911.
Steckler association.
Samuel Sullivan Cox. Memorial service, Cooper union, Thursday evening, October 10, 1889. Under the auspices of the Steckler association. Memorial address by J. Proctor Knott. New York, Press of De Leeuw & Oppenheimer, 1889.

KNOTT, James Proctor.
[Speech in regard to extending the time to construct a railroad from the St. Croix river or lake to the west end of Lake Superior,etc.]
(In Watterson. Oddities of Southern life and character, 7th edition. Pp. 265-284. Boston, 1893.)

NK 0208847 MB

VOLUME 300

AC901
P75
v.8
no.3
Knott, James Proctor, 1830-1911.
Speech of Hon. J. Proctor Knott, of Kentucky, in the House of Representatives, February 13 and 14, 1880, on the bill to regulate the removal of causes from state courts to the circuit courts of the United States. [Washington, D.C., Rufus H. Darby, book and job printer, 1880]
15 p. 22 cm.
Caption title.

NK 0208848 ICHi

Knott, James Proctor, 1830–1911.
Speech of Proctor Knott on Duluth with statistical comments up to date. Duluth, Minn., The Chamber of commerce [°1893]
14, [2] p. 15cm.
Caption title: "Knott on Duluth." Speech of Hon. J. Proctor Knott, of Kentucky. ⟨Delivered in the House of representatives, Feb. 1871⟩ The speech was delivered on Jan. 27, 1871. *cf.* Congressional record (of that date)

1. Duluth. I. Duluth. Chamber of commerce.
6-37684
Library of Congress F614.D8K4

NK 0208849 DLC

Knott, James Proctor.
Speech delivered in the House of representatives, Jan. 23, 1869. Washington, F. & J. Rives & G. A. Bailey, 1869.

NK 0208850 KyBgW

3A
504
KNOTT, JAMES PROCTOR, 1830-1911.
Speeches of Proctor Knott delivered in Congress ... and at Duluth ... also our reasons why Duluth and vicinity is the best place in which to invest. Duluth, Evening Herald, 1890.
38 p. fold. map. 14 cm.
"Our Reasons Why" (pp. 17- 28) by Elisha R. Brace.

NK 0208851 ICN

Knott, James Proctor, 1822-1908.
Speeches of Hons. Eppa Hunton, of Virginia and J. Proctor Knott, of Kentucky ...
see under Hunton, Eppa, 1822-1908.

Knott, James Proctor, 1830-1911.
Term of presidential office. Speech of Hon. J. Proctor Knott, of Kentucky, in the House ... Washington, 1876.
11 p.

NK 0208853 ViU PHi

Knott, James Proctor, 1830-1911.

Russell, Morris Craw, 1840–
Uncle Dudley's odd hours, being the vagaries of a country editor. By M. C. Russell. Also, as an appendix, J. Proctor Knott's famous speech on Duluth. Duluth, Minn., Comp. and pub. by Susie M. Russell, 1882.

Knott, John, 1753-1818.
The distinguishing principles and practice of the Baptists vindicated; in seven dialogues: or, An answer to Mr. Shrubsole's Plain Christian Shepherd's Defence of his flock. Rochester [Eng.] C. Etherington [etc] 1794.
63p. 21 1/2cm.

NK 0208855 NRAB RPB

Knott, John.
The army and the man; an examination of human problems in military life. Foreword by Sir Ronald Adam. London, S. Low, Marston [1947]
xi, 175 p. 21 cm.

1. Gt. Brit. Army—Military life. I. Title.
U767.K5 355.115 48-12299*

NK 0208856 DLC

BR301
E38
Knott, John.
Calvin and Servetus: an episode in the history of religious persecution and scientific suppression. By John Knott ... [New York? 1912] p.552-561. 24cm. [Henry Morse Stephens collection. Pamphlets on the reformation. no.3:

Extract from: American medicine. Oct. 1912, n.s. vol.VII, no. 10.

1. Calvin, Jean, 1509-1564. 2. Servetus, Michael 1509 or 11-1553.

NK 0208857 CU

Knott, John.
The last illness of Lord Byron. A study in the borderland of genius and madness, or cosmical inspiration and pathological psychology. By John Knott. ... St. Paul, Volkszeit Ptg. Co., 1912.
43 p. O. (In Collected monographs, v. 274)

NK 0208858 NcD

HE2712
.C64D3
Knott, John A., et al., plantiffs.
Chicago, Burlington and Quincy railroad company, et al., *defendants.*
(John A. Knott, et al., *plaintiffs*)
The cases known as the Missouri, Minnesota (and other) state rate cases.

WI
K72e
1878
KNOTT, John F
An essay on the pathology of the oesophagus. Dublin, Fannin, 1878.
v, 225 p. illus.
"Awarded the Gold Medal of the Pathological Society at the close of the session of 1876-77."

NK 0208860 DNLM OClW-H

Knott, John F An essay on the pathology of the œsophagus. v (1 l.), 225 pp. 8°. *Dublin, Fannin & Co.; London, Longmans, Green & Co.,* 1878.

NK 0208861 DNLM NcD PPC

Knott, John F
Note on the "fatigue fever" of M. Peter. 5 pp. 8°. *Dublin, J. Falconer,* 1889.

NK 0208862 DNLM

Knott, John F
——. The old Venetian "bleeding-glass". 12 pp. 8°. *Dublin, J. Falconer,* 1889.

NK 0208863 DNLM

Knott, John F
——. On the use of certain organic acids in the gouty rheumatic and allied diatheses. 19 pp. 8°. *London, J. Bale & Sons.* 1888.

NK 0208864 DNLM

Knott, John Francis, 1878–
War cartoons, by John F. Knott ... [Dallas, Southwestern printing co.] °1918.
1 p. l., [100] p. of illus. front. 28cm.
Part of cartoons reprinted from Dallas news.

1. European war, 1914– —Humor, caricatures, etc. I. Title.
19-681
Library of Congress D526.2.K7

NK 0208865 DLC TxU WaS

Knott, John M
The Bank of England charter act, 1844, and the Manchester commercial association ... London, Seeley; [etc., etc.] 1855.
55, [1] p.

NK 0208866 MH-BA IEN CtY

D
245
.4673
[KNOTT, JOHN M]
Church defence. The session of 1864. [Roxeth, 1864]
7p. 19cm.
Letters signed: John M. Knott.
Caption title.

NK 0208867 ICN

D
245
.1725
KNOTT, JOHN M.
Church rates. The paper read...before the Congress at Cambridge, November, 1861. London, Seeley, Jackson and Halliday, 1861.
8p. 23cm.
Binder's title: Church rates.

NK 0208868 ICN

D
245
.1725
[KNOTT, JOHN M]
Church rates. The present state of the question calmly considered. London, Seeley, Jackson and Halliday [1861]
18p. 16cm.
Signed: John M. Knott.
Binder's title: Church rates.

NK 0208869 ICN

VOLUME 300

HG939 .P2 v.2 ⌈Knott, John M⌉
The currency and the late Sir Robert Peel. ⌈n.p.,1850?⌉
23 p. 22cm.
Caption title.
⌈Pamphlets on banking and currency in Great Britain,v.2,no.3⌉

1.Currency question--Gt.Brit.

NK 0208870 ICU

Knott, John M.
The established church and the political non conformists of 1866 ... With notes & illustration. L., Rivington ... 1866.
20 p.

NK 0208871 CtY

D 245 .K675 KNOTT, JOHN M.
The established church and the subdivision of parishes. The paper...read at the Bristol Church Congress, on Wednesday the 12th of October, 1864. With notes mainly suggested by the recent meetings of the Baptist Union and the Congregational Union. London, Seeley,Jackson and Co.,1864.
15p. 22cm.

NK 0208872 ICN CtY

Knott, John Olin, 1859–
Behind closed doors, by John Olin Knott. New York, Authors & publishers corporation ⌈°1927⌉
viii, 9-331 p. 19½cm.

I. Title.
Library of Congress PZ3.K7592Be 27-28082

NK 0208873 DLC TxU NcD

Knott, John Olin, 1859–
... Denominational schools. Comp. by J. O. Knott ...
(*In* U. S. Bureau of education. Report, 1914, v. 1, chap. XXVI, p. 597-613)

1. Parochial schools. 2. Denominational schools.
Library, U. S. Bur. of Education E 15-2665
——— Reprint. LC375.K75

NK 0208874 DHEW MiU OCl OO

Knott, John Olin.
U. S. *Bureau of education.*
... Educational work of the churches.
(*In* U. S. Bureau of education. Report, 1914, v. 1, chap. XXVI, p. 597-613; 1915, v. 1, chap. xxiii, p. 559-581; 1916, v. 1, chap. XXV, p. 413-428;)

Knott, John Olin, 1859–
The remaking of man and nations ... sermonic-address by Rev. John O. Knott, PH. D. ⌈Washington?⌉ Printed by J. P. Sontag, 1944.
14 p. 23½cm.
"Facing the far future ⌈poem⌉ by John O. Knott": ⌈3⌉ p. inserted.

1. Providence and government of God. 2. Reconstruction (1939–) I. Title. II. Title: Facing the far future.
Library of Congress BT96.K55 45-3135
⌈3⌉ 231.7

NK 0208876 DLC

Knott, John Olin, 1859–
Seekers after soul, by John O. Knott, PH. D. Boston, Sherman, French & company, 1911.
5 p. l., 208 p. 21cm.
"The chapter on 'The persistence of ideas' is the essence of a thesis presented a few years ago to the faculty of Washington and Lee university for the degree of doctor of philosophy." The chapters on Job and Browning were published in a somewhat different form in the "Methodist review," Nashville, Tenn.
CONTENTS.—Job: the soul's pathfinder.—Plato: intimations of immortality.—Kant: a protest against materialism.—Hegel: theistic evolution.—Persistence of ideas: the spirit in the trend of thought.—Robert Browning: the subtle assertor of the soul.
1. Bible. O. T. Job—Criticism, interpretation, etc. 2. Plato. 3. Kant, Immanuel, 1724-1804. 4. Hegel, Georg Wilhelm Friedrich, 1770-1831. 5. Browning, Robert, 1812-1889. 6. Bible—Criticism, interpretation, etc.—O. T. Job.
Library of Congress B823.K5 11-13128
⌈a44b1⌉

NK 0208877 DLC NIC NN ViU

Knott, John Olin, 1859–
A sketch of the Knott family from researches made by John O. Knott ... ⌈n. p., 19—⌉
cover-title, ⌈3⌉ p. illus. (port.) 22½cm.

1. Knott family.
Library of Congress CS71.K729 19— 38-14710

NK 0208878 DLC

BF191 K5 Knott, John Russell, 1911–
An outline of neuro-psychology: part one. ⌈Iowa City, Dept. of Psychology, University of Iowa, 1942.
76,A31*l*. diagrs. 28cm.

"An outline of neuroanatomy for students": Appendix A.
No more published?

1. Psychology, Physiological. 2. Nervous system. I. Title: Neuropsychology.

NK 0208879 IaU

Knott, John Russell, 1911–
Some effects of mental set upon the electrophysiological processes of the human cerebral cortex ⌈by⌉ John R. Knott ... ⌈Lancaster, Pa., Lancaster press, inc., 1939⌉
cover-title, ⌈1⌉, 384-405 p. diagrs. 25cm.
Main content of thesis (PH. D.)—University of Iowa, 1938.
"Reprinted from the Journal of experimental psychology, vol. 24, no. 4 ... April, 1939."
"References": p. 404-405.

1. Brain. 2. Electrophysiology.
Library of Congress QP376.K55 1938 40-11084
Univ. of Iowa Libr.
——— Copy 2.
⌈2⌉ 612.8223

NK 0208880 IaU DLC

MICROFORMS CENTER Film 3056 Knott, John William.
A letter to the parishioners of S. Saviour's, Leeds, from their vicar. London, J. Masters, 1851.
23p.
Microfilm (negative) London, British Museum, 1969. 1 reel.
Filmed with Rev. George Pierce Grantham, B. A. London, 1885.
I. Leeds, Eng. Saint Saviour's Church II. Title

NK 0208881 WU

⌈**Knott, Josef**⌉
Das buch der kochkunst; eine sammlung mustergültiger kochrezepte aus dem erfahrungsschatz der prominenten köche Österreichs. Offizielles kochbuch des Verbandes der köche Österreichs. Wien, J. Knott ⌈1934⌉
xii, 476 p. illus. 24cm.
Advertising matter interspersed.
Ruled pages for "Notizen" (475-476)

1. Cookery, Austrian. I. Verband der köche Österreichs. II. Title.
Library of Congress TX721.K6 35-4518
Copyright A—Foreign 26773
⌈2⌉ 641.59436

NK 0208882 DLC

Knott, Joseph, respondent.
In the Supreme court, State of Oregon ...
Points and brief of appellant
see under Stephens, James B., appellant.

KNOTT, JOSEPH, *respondent.*
In the Supreme Court, State of Oregon. | September term, 1868. | James B. Stephens, Appellant | vs. | Joseph Knott, Respondent. | [*Filet*] | Appeal from Multnomah County. | [*Filet*] | Points and brief of Respondent. | [Salem? 1868.]
3 p. 17 x 23.5 cm.
No imprint.

NK 0208884 OrCS

Knott,Joseph,1909–
... Über den einfluss der monohalogenessigsäure auf die muskeltätigkeit ... Kallmünz, 1933.
Diss. - Munich.

NK 0208885 MiU PPWi CtY

630.73 W27ec no.23 Knott, Joseph Carlton, 1893–
... Alfalfa hay an economical feed for dairy cows ⌈by⌉ J. C. Knott and C. C. Hampson ... Pullman, Wash., State college, 1935.
⌈4⌉ p. tables, diagrs. (State college of Washington. Extension service. Circular no. 23)

On cover: Divisions of Dairy husbandry and Agricultural economics.

1. State college of Washington authors, Works of. 2. Alfalfa as a feeding stuff. 3. Cows, Dairy. 4. Alfalfa hay. I. Hampson, Chester C 1895– joint author.

NK 0208886 WaPS

PNC 636.2342 K759a Knott, Joseph Carlton, 1893–
An analysis of the State college of Washington Holstein herd ... ⌈Pullman, Wash., Author, 1936?⌉
49*l*. tables, diagrs.

Processed.

NK 0208887 WaPS

Knott, Joseph Carlton, 1893– joint author
Hodgson, Ralph Edward, 1906–
Apparent digestibility of, and nitrogen, calcium, and phosphorus balance of dairy heifers on, artificially dried pasture herbage. By R. E. Hodgson ... and J. C. Knott ...
(*In* U. S. Dept. of agriculture. Journal of agricultural research. v. 45, no. 9. Nov. 1, 1932, p. 557-563. 23½cm. Washington, 1932)

E630.73 W27eb no.217 Knott, Joseph Carlton, 1893–
... Apple pomace for dairy cows ⌈by⌉ J. C. Knott, R. E. Hodgson and O. J. Hill ... Pullman, Wash., State college, 1926 ⌈?⌉
⌈4⌉ p. illus., tables (State college of Washington. Extension service. Extension bulletin 217)

"The State college of Washington and U. S. Department of agriculture co-operating."

1. State college of Washington authors, Works of. (three cards, one for each author) 2. Cows, Dairy - Feeding. 3. Apple pomace as a feeding stuff. I. Hodgson, Ralph Edward, 1906– joint author. II. Hill, Otto Julius, 1901– joint author.

NK 0208889 WaPS

VOLUME 300

Knott, Joseph Carlton, 1893- joint author.

Hodgson, Ralph Edward, 1906–
The calcifying properties of green, artificially dried, and sun-cured pasture herbage. By R. E. Hodgson ... and J. C. Knott ...
(*In* U. S. Dept. of agriculture. Journal of agricultural research. v. 48, no. 5, Mar. 1, 1934, p. 439–446. 23cm. Washington, 1934)

Knott, Joseph Carlton, 1893–
The determination of the apparent digestibility of green and cured grass by modified procedures. By J. C. Knott ... and H. K. Murer ... and R. E. Hodgson ...
(*In* U. S. Dept. of agriculture. Journal of agricultural research. v. 53, no. 7, Oct. 1, 1936, p. 553–556. 23cm. Washington, 1936)
Contribution from Washington Agricultural experiment station (Wash.—25)
Scientific paper no. 341, College of agriculture and Experiment station, State college of Washington.
Published Dec. 3, 1936.
"Literature cited": p. 556.
1. Grasses. 2. Forage plants. 3. Nutrition. [1-3. Grasses and forage plants—Nutritive value] I. Hodgson, Ralph Edward, 1906– joint author. II. Murer, Harvey K., 1911– joint author.
Agr 36-923
U. S. Dept. of agr. Library for Library of Congress 1Ag84J vol. 53, no. 7 [S21.A75 vol. 53, no. 7]

NK 0208891 DNAL

PNC 639.73 W27b no.362 Knott, Joseph Carlton, 1893-
... The digestibility and feeding value of apple and apple-alfalfa silage, by J. C. Knott, H. K. Murer, R. E. Hodgson, and E. L. Overholser ... Pullman, Wash., State college, 1938.
20 p. tables, diagrs. (Washington (State) Agricultural experiment station. Bulletin no. 362)
On cover: The Division of animal husbandry, the Western Washington experiment station and the Bureau of dairy industry, U. S. Department of agriculture.
"Literature cited": p 20.

NK 0208892 WaPS

Knott, Joseph Carlton, 1893- joint author.

Hodgson, Ralph Edward, 1906–
Effect of temperature of artificial drying on digestibility and availability of nutrients in pasture herbage. By R. E. Hodgson ... J. C. Knott ... R. R. Graves ... and H. K. Murer ...
(*In* U. S. Dept. of agriculture. Journal of agricultural research. v. 50, no. 2, Jan. 15, 1935, p. 149–164. illus. 23cm. Washington, 1935)

636.08452 K759f Knott, Joseph Carlton.
Feeding dairy cows. [Pullman, Wn., n.p., n.d.
8 l., 6 tables.
Mimeographed.
1. Cows, Dairy - Feeding. 2. State College of Washington authors, Works of. I. Title. II. PNC sh. cd.

NK 0208894 WaPS

E630.73 W27eb no.164 Knott, Joseph Carlton, 1893-
... Feeding dairy cows, by J. C. Knott ... Pullman, Wash., State college, 1931.
12 p. illus., tables (State college of Washington. Extension service. Extension bulleti no. 164)
"The State college of Washington and U. S. Department of agriculture co-operating."
1. State college of Washington authors, Works of. 2. Cows, Dairy - Feeding. I. Title.

NK 0208895 WaPS

E630.73 W27eb no.164 Rev. Knott, Joseph Carlton, 1893-
... Feeding dairy cows, by J. C. Knott and O. J. Hill ... Pullman, Wash., State college, 1935.
14 p. illus., tables (State college of Washington. Extension service. Extension bulletin no. 164, revised April 1935)
"The State college of Washington and U. S. Department of agriculture co-operating."
1. State college of Washington authors, Works of. (two cards, one for each author) 2. Cows, Dairy - Feeding. I. Hill, Otto Julius, 1901- joint author. II. Title.

NK 0208896 WaPS

E639.73 W27b no.270 Knott, Joseph Carlton, 1893-
... The feeding value of dried apple pomace for dairy cows, by J. C. Knott, R. E. Hodgson, and E. V. Ellington ... [Pullman, State college] 1932.
18p. illus., tables. (Washington (State) Agricultural experiment station. Bulletin no. 270)
On cover: Division of dairy husbandry and Western Washington experiment station.
"Literature cited": p. 18.

NK 0208897 WaPS

E639.73 W27b no.287 Knott, Joseph Carlton, 1893-
... The feeding value of pea feed and other pea by-products for dairy cows, by J. C. Knott, J. O. Trotsven and R. E. Hodgson ... [Pullman, State college] 1933.
20p. tables. (Washington (State) Agricultural experiment station. Bulletin no. 287)
On cover: Division of dairy husbandry, Western Washington experiment station and Bureau of dairy industry, United States Department of agriculture.
"Literature cited": p. 19-20.

NK 0208898 WaPS

Knott, Joseph Carlton, 1893–
Growth, reproduction, production and the economy of growth and production by dairy cattle fed rations of roughage alone and roughage with added concentrates ... by Joseph Carlton Knott ... [n. p., 1942]
cover-title, 7 l. 27½ x 21½cm.
Summary of thesis (PH. D.)—University of Minnesota. 1941.
Reproduced from type-written copy.
"Published as Scientific paper number 507, College of agriculture and Agricultural experiment station, State college of Washington, Pullman, Wash."
From Proceedings of the 27th annual meeting of the Western division of the American dairy science association, 1941, with addition of cover having thesis note and Vita.
1. Cows. 2. Feeding and feeding stuffs.
43-10597
Library of Congress SF203.K7

NK 0208899 DLC

E639.73 W27b no.295 **Knott, Joseph Carlton, 1893-**
... Method of measuring pasture yields with dairy cattle, by J. C. Knott, R. E. Hodgson and E. V. Ellington ... [Pullman, State college] 1934.
20p. tables. (Washington (State) Agricultural experiment station. Bulletin no. 295)
On cover: The Western Washington experiment station, the Division of dairy husbandry and the Bureau of dairy industry, U. S. Department of agriculture.
"Literature cited": p. 12.

NK 0208900 WaPS

E630.73 W27eb no.214 Knott, Joseph Carlton, 1893-
... Pea feed and other pea by-products for dairy cows, by J. C. Knott, R. E. Hodgson and O. J. Hill ... Pullman, Wash., State college, 1936.
[4] p. tables (State college of Washington. Extension service. Extension bulletin no. 214)
"The State college of Washington and U. S. Department of agriculture co-operating."
1. State college of Washington authors, Works of. (three cards, one for each author) 2. Cows, Dairy - Feeding. 3. Peas as a feeding stuff. I Hodgson, Ralph Edward, 1906- joint author. II Hill, Otto Julius, 1901- joint author. III. Title.

NK 0208901 WaPS

E639.73 W27b no.273 **Knott, Joseph Carlton, 1893-**
... Raising dairy calves with dried skimmilk ... [Pullman, State college] 1932.
19 [1] p. illus., tables, diagrs. (Washington (State) Agricultural experiment station. Bulletin no. 273)
On cover: Division of dairy husbandry and Western Washington experiment station.
1. State college of Washington authors, Works of. 2. Calves - Feeding. 3. Milk as feeding stuff. 4. Milk powder. I. Title. II. Washington (State) Agricultural experiment station.

NK 0208902 WaPS

Knott, Joseph Carlton, 1893-
... Raising dairy calves [by] J. C. Knott, O. J. Hill and R. E. Hodgson ... Pullman, Wash., State college, 1938.
27 p. illus., tables (State college of Washington. Extension service. Extension bulletin 239)
"The State college of Washington and U. S. Department of agriculture co-operating."
1. State college of Washington authors, Works of. 2. Calves--feeding. 3. Cattle, Dairy. I. Hill, Otto Julius. 1901- joint author. II. Hodgson, Ralph Edward, 1906- joint author. III. Title.

NK 0208904 WaPS

Z 636.082455 K759s Thesis **Knott, Joseph Carlton**, 1893-
A study of the gestation period of Holstein-Friesian cattle, 1930.

NK 0208905 WaPS

Knott, Justina (Kuipers) Spencer-
see **Spencer-Knott, Justina (Kuipers)** 1915–

Knott, L. E., apparatus company, *Boston.*
A catalogue of physical instruments Boston,
1 v. illus. 27cm.
Only latest number received is kept on shelf.
1. Physical instruments—Catalogs.
Library of Congress QC53.K6 CA 12-701 Unrev'd

NK 0208907 DLC

Knott, L.E., apparatus company, Boston.
A catalogue of scientific instruments. Catalogue 21. Boston, Knott apparatus co. [c1916]
507 p. 29cm.

NK 0208908 PPT

Knott, L.E., apparatus company, Boston.
Chemistry - biology. Boston, Knott [c1918]
128 p. 29cm.

NK 0208909 PPT

VOLUME 300

Knott, L. E., apparatus company, *Boston.*
Current electricity; [catalogue of] L. E. Knott apparatus company (incorporated) Boston, Mass. Proprietors of E. S. Ritchie & son's apparatus, 1853 ... Boston, L. E. Knott apparatus company [1902]
1 p. l., 902-997 p. illus. 26cm.
2-22494

NK 0208910 DLC

KNOTT, L.E., APPARATUS COMPANY
Harcourt equipment for chemistry. Author c1929.
214 p.

NK 0208911 Or

Knott, L. E., Apparatus Company.
Harcourt equipment for physics; standard for education since 1895... Cambridge, Mass.: L. E. Knott Apparatus Co.[, cop. 1928.] 230 p. incl. tables. illus. 4°.
"Catalogue 33R, 1928."
470444A. 1. Physics—Instruments and apparatus—Catalogues. 2. Title.
N. Y. P. L. June 5, 1930

NK 0208912 NN Or

Knott L. E., Apparatus Company, Boston.
Influence machine; surgical and educational.
4. ed. 16 pp. roy. 8°. *Boston, [n. d.].*

NK 0208913 DNLM

Knott, L. E., apparatus company, Boston.
...Order list of physics laboratory equipment. Boston, [1905]
QC53
.K72

NK 0208914 DLC

Knott, L.E., Apparatus Company, Boston.
Order list of physics laboratory equipment. Boston, L.E. Knott Apparatus Co. [1907]
144 p. 23cm.

NK 0208915 NIC

Knott, L. E., Apparatus Company, Boston
Scientific instruments. Catalogue no. 26. Boston, 1921.
326 p.

NK 0208916 PPF PPPCo

KNOTT, Laura Anna.
Educational aims; an address delivered by Miss Laura A. Knott at a reception given her by the trustees of Bradford Academy, on the twenty-ninth of October, nineteen hundred and one, Bradford, Mass. [Holyoke, Mass., Griffith, Axtell & Cady Co., printers, 1902].
nar.12°. pp.(14).
At head of title: Bradford Academy.

NK 0208917 MH

KNOTT, Laura Anna.
Educational aims; an address delivered by Miss Laura A. Knott at a reception given her by the trustees of Bradford Academy, on the twenty-ninth of October, nineteen hundred and one, Bradford, Mass. 2d ed. [Boston, Mass., Griffith-Stillings Press, 1904].
nar.12°. pp.(14).
At head of title: Bradford Academy.

NK 0208918 MH

Knott, Laura Anna.
... Student's history of the Hebrews, by Laura A. Knott ... New York, Cincinnati, The Abingdon press [1922]
413 p. incl. illus., maps. 20cm. (The Abingdon religious education texts, D. G. Downey, general editor. Community training school series, N. E. Richardson, editor)
Bibliography: p. 397.
1. Jews—Hist.—To A. D. 70. I. Title.
Library of Congress DS121.K7 22—9067

NK 0208919 DLC MU NcD IdU ODW OC1W OCH OO

Knott, Laura Anna. 2298.144
Student's history of the Hebrews.
— New York. The Abingdon Press. [1931.] 413 pp. Illus. Plates. Maps, some colored. [The Abingdon Religious education texts. Community training school series.] 19½ cm.
Bibliography, p. 397; Biblical sources at the end of each chapter.
D2113 — S.r. — Jews. Hist.

NK 0208920 MB

Knott, Laura Anna.
... Student's history of the Hebrews. N.Y., The Abingdon press [1936].
413p. (The Abingdon religious education texts. D.G. Downey, general editor. Community training school series, N.E. Richardson, editor.)

NK 0208921 OC1W

*LA304
.A35
no.6
Knott, Laura Anna.
... The teaching of English in the State normal school at Lowell, Massachusetts [by] Laura A. Knott ... Boston, Mass., Wright & Potter printing company [1900]
40 p. 23cm. ([Massachusetts. Board of education] The public schools of Massachusetts, U. S. A. Eight educational monographs, VI)
At head of title: Paris exposition of 1900. The public schools of Massachusetts, U. S. A. Eight educational monographs.
1. English language—Study and teaching. Normal schools. I. Paris. Exposition universelle, 1900—Massachusetts. II. Massachusetts. Board of education.

NK 0208922 MB MH

Knott, Laura Anna.
Vesper talks to girls, by Laura A. Knott. Boston and New York, Houghton Mifflin company, 1916.
5 p. l., 188, [2] p. 20cm. $1.50
"Talks which the author has given on Sunday afternoons to the students of Bradford academy."—Pref.
CONTENTS.—New starts in life.—School friendships.—The art of living with others.—Enduring hardness.—The rhythm of life.—The uses of trouble.—School spirit.—Making the best of things.—Conflicting loyalties.—The value of discipline.—The successful life.—The progress of woman.—Sources of happiness.—After graduation.
1. Conduct of life. 2. Students. I. Title.
Library of Congress BJ1681.K6 16—6728

NK 0208923 DLC NcC Or OO PPFr PU PPCCH NN MB

j
F5497.1
K6
Knott, Leonard Lewis, 1905-
The children's book of the Great Lakes. Illus. by Walter Ferrier. Montreal, Editorial Associates [1946]
[29] p. illus. 29 cm.
1. Great Lakes - Juvenile literature.

NK 0208924 CaBVaU

372.6
K759ch
Knott, Leonard Lewis, 1905-
The children's book of the Saguenay. Illustrations by Jaques Gagnier. Montreal, Editorial Associates Limited, [c1945]
[29] p. col. illus.

NK 0208925 WaU InU WaSp

Knott, Leonard Lewis, 1905-
The children's book of trees; pictures by Jacques Gagnier. Montreal, Editorial associates [1949?]
[28] p.

NK 0208926 CaBVaU

Knott, Leonard Lewis.
The children's guide to Canada's capital ... Pictures by Jacques Gagnier. Brunswick press [1952]
unpaged, illus.
Prepared with the editorial co-operation of the Ottawa board of trade.

NK 0208927 Or

Knott, Leonard Lewis, 1905-
Harnessing the giant. [n.p. Northern Electric company ltd., c1952]
32 p. illus. D. (Forward with Canada series, no. 6)

NK 0208928 CaBViP

Pamph
HC
N
Knott, Leonard Lewis, 1905-
Highways of history. (In [Northern Electric Company]-Forward with Canada. No.7. [1954].)
1. Canada - Canals, rivers, etc.

NK 0208929 CaOTU

Knott, Leonard Lewis, 1905-
The PR in profit; a guide to successful public relations in Canada. Toronto, McClelland & Stewart [1955]
254 p. illus. 24 cm.
1. Public relations. I. Title.
HM263.K6 1955 56-21110 ‡
*301.152 301.154

NK 0208930 DLC CaBVa CaBViP CaBVaU CaOTU

VOLUME 300

Knott, Leonard Lewis.
This is a business ... Montreal, Editorial associates[c1946].
28p.illus.O.

NK 0208931 CaBViP

Knott, *Mrs.* Lucy Pierce, 1856–
The exalted name, a study of the name "Lord Jesus Christ", by Lucy P. Knott; introduction by Dr. George A. McLaughlin, M. A. Kansas City, Mo., Nazarene publishing house [°1929]
328 p. front. 19½cm.

1. Jesus Christ. I. Title.

Library of Congress BT590.N2K6 30-30117
Copyright A 30046 [2] 232

NK 0208932 DLC

Knott, *Mrs.* Lucy Pierce, 1856–
Salvation life lines and spiritual life preservers ... Arranged by Lucy P. Knott. [Los Angeles, Cal., Nazarene pub. house, 1899]
3 p. l., [6]–76 p. 15½cm.

I. Title.

0-6416 Revised

NK 0208933 DLC

Knott, Lucy Pierce, 1856-
Student's Bible text-book
see under Bible. English. Selections. 1913. Authorized.

Knott, Luella (Pugh) 1871–
The garden I love best [by] Luella Knott. Boston, White-Smith music publishing co. [°1937]
2 p. l., 3–42 p. 20cm.
Poems.

I. Title.

38-1432 Revised
Library of Congress PS3521.N67G3 1937
[r46c2] 811.5

NK 0208935 DLC

Knott, Luella (Pugh) 1871–
Keys to Christian living. Boston, W. A. Wilde Co. [1951]
248 p. 21 cm.

1. Christian life. I. Title.

BV4501.K593 248 51-14498 ‡

NK 0208936 DLC

Knott, Luella (Pugh) 1871–
Life-lore poems, by Luella Knott. Boston, Sherman, French & company, 1912.
6 p. l., 3–161 p. 19½cm.

I. Title.

12-5575 Revised
Library of Congress PS3521.N67L5 1912
[r46b2]

NK 0208937 DLC MiU

---

*
PS3521
.N67M3
1933
Knott, Luella (Pugh) 1871–
Mary Magdalene by Luella Knott. Boston, White-Smith Pub. Co., 1933.
[32] p. (incl. blank pages) 16½cm.
Poem.
Inscribed Bessie Randolph from Miss Maud Schivalmeyer, 1933.
Bookplate of Bessie Carter Randolph.

NK 0208938 ViU

Knott, Luella (Pugh) 1871–
Reading backward, by Luella Knott. Macon, Ga., The J. W. Burke company, 1941.
8 p. l., 222 p. incl. front., illus., pl., ports., coats of arms. 23½cm.
"Letters ... written primarily for the Knott grandchildren."—Pref.
"Leaves from the family album": p. [163]–219.
Bibliography: 6th prelim. leaf.

1. Pugh family (James Pugh, d. 1724) 2. Rees family (Sir David Rhys, fl. 1700) I. Title.

46-36859
Library of Congress CS71.P979 1941

NK 0208939 DLC NcD WHi PHi NN

Knott, Luella (Pugh) 1871–
Uncle Abe says.... by Luella Knott. Macon, Ga., The J. W. Burke company [°1938]
5 p. l., 78 p. 19½cm.
Poems.

I. Title.

39-543 Revised
Library of Congress PS3521.N67U6 1938
[r46c2] 811.5

NK 0208940 DLC ViU FTaSU

Knott, Luella (Pugh) 1871–
Where we call each other honey, by Luella Knott. Macon, Ga., The J. W. Burke company [1940]
5 p. l., 66 p. front. 19½cm.
Poems.

I. Title.

40-5261 Revised
Library of Congress PS3521.N67W5 1940
[r46c2] 811.5

NK 0208941 DLC FTaSU

Knott, Lulu.
More life beyond, by Lulu Knott ... [Niles, Mich., °1936]–
v. 17½cm.

1. New thought. I. Title.

37-612
Library of Congress BF639.K67
——— Copy 2.
Copyright A 101022 [3] [159.91324] 131.324

NK 0208942 DLC

Knott, Maple.
Canadian homes; or the mystery solved, a Christmas tale. Montreal, John Lovell, 1858.
136p.T.

NK 0208943 CaBViP

BV3415
.K7
KNOTT, MARGARET C.
The light approaching, China and the L.M.S., by Margaret C.Knott...with epilogue by Cyril W.Knott ... Westminster, Livingstone press[1928]
142 p. front., plates, ports., map. 18cm.
Plates printed on both sides.

1.Missions--China. 2.London missionary society.

NK 0208944 ICU CtY

Knott, Margaret C
Trek to the west; a story of modern China. London, London Missionary Society, 1946.
63 p. illus. 19 cm.

I. Title.

PZ7.K76Tr 48-20289*

NK 0208945 DLC NNUT

Knott, Mary John.
Two months at Kilkee, a watering place in the County Clare, near the mouth of the Shannon, with an account of a voyage down that river from Limerick to Kilrush, and sketches of objects of interest in the neighbourhood, which will serve as a guide to the coast scenery. By Mary John Knott ... Dublin, W. Curry jun. and co.; [etc., etc.] 1836.
1 p. l., 9, [1], [xi]–xii, [13]–255, [2] p. front., illus., 3 pl., fold. map. 18cm.
Added t.-p., engraved.
1. Kilkee, Ire.—Descr. I. Title.

Library of Congress DA995.K4K7 2—28673

NK 0208946 DLC PPL

Knott, May B.
see
Coe, Alice Rollit

M2190
K6
Knott, Maybelle.
... Pilgrims of the night; a pageant service for Christmas, by Maybelle Knott, A. B. Dorsey [and] C. D. Lowden ... Philadelphia, Hall-Mack co., °1928.
cover-title, 15p. 21½cm.

NK 0208948 NBuG

Knott, Middleton O'Malley.
Gone away with O'Malley; seventy years with horses, hounds and people. By M. O'Malley Knott, with Page Cooper. Illustrated by Paul Brown. Garden City, New York, Doubleday, Doran and company, inc., 1944.
viii, 280 p. incl. front., illus. 21½cm.
"First edition."

1. Veterinarians—Correspondence, reminiscences, etc. 2. Horses. I. Cooper, Page. II. Title.

44-9781
Library of Congress SF613.K6A4
[40] [926.19] 926.36

PU-V PP PPA TxU CaBVa Or OrP WaS
NK 0208949 DLC KyU CU FTaSU ViU OClUr OCl OLak OEac

VOLUME 300

Knott, Middleton O'Malley.
Gone away with O'Malley. Seventy years with horses, hounds and people. By M. O'Malley with Page Cooper. Illus. by Paul Brown. London, New York, Hurst & Blackett [1946]
183 p. illus. 22 cm.

1. Veterinarians—Correspondence, reminiscences, etc. 2. Horses. I. Cooper, Page, joint author. II. Title.
[SF613.K6A] [926.19] 926.36 A 48-2983*
New York. Public Libr. for Library of Congress [1]

NK 0208950 NN CaBVaU

Knott, Middleton O'Malley.
A hunting holiday in County Cork
see under title

Knott, Nora Frances
see **Grensted, Nora Frances (Knott)**

Knott, O'Malley.
See
Knott, Middleton O'Malley.

888.9 P783sYk Knott, Otto.
De fide et fontibus Polyaeni. Lipsiae, 1883.
96p.

Dissertatio--Jena.

1. Polyaenus. Strategemata. I. Title.

NK 0208954 ICarbS DDO ICRL NjP

PA 25 J51 v.3 no.2 Knott, Otto,
De fide et fontibus Polyaeni.
Lipsiae, B. G. Teubner, 1884.
51-96 p. 23cm. (Jena. Universität. Commentationes philologae Ienenses. v.3, no.2)

1. Polyaenus.

NK 0208955 NIC

Knott, Rachel Thayer.
A Morro miscellany [by] Rachel Thayer Knott. [Pirmo, Calif., Printing press of the Pirmo times, °1933]
1 p. l., 5-55 p. 18cm.
"Vignettes in prose and verse which have appeared from time to time in the Morro Bay news and the San Luis Obispo county sun, 1930-33."

1. Morro Bay, Calif. I. Title.
Library of Congress F868.S18K7 34-2609
Copyright A 66110 [2] 917.9478

NK 0208956 DLC CU-B CtY

Knott, Richard W
A currency catechism in which coin's financial school is contrasted with the school of experience. Louisville, Ky. Evening post co., 1885.
15p.

[Reprinted from the Louisville Evening post.]

NK 0208957 OClWHi

Knott, Richard W., ed.
The Southern bivouac: a monthly literary and historical magazine. v. -5; -May 1887. Louisville, Ky., E. H. & W. N. McDonald [etc.] 18 -87.

4BF 835 Knott, Robert Rowe.
The new aid to memory; containing the most remarkable events and a complete summary of the history of Greece. London, Printed for the author by M. Mason [ ]
107 p.

NK 0208959 DLC-P4

Knott, Robert Rowe.
The new aid to memory: containing the most remarkable events of the history of England. Illustrated by one hundred and twenty symbolical engravings. By the Rev. Robert Rowe Knott ... 7th ed. London, J. Field [185-]
xxviii, 68 p. 12 pl. 19cm.
6th edition was published London, 1848.

1. Mnemonics.
10-19592
Library of Congress BF383.K73

NK 0208960 DLC TxU OO

4BF 845 Knott, Robert Rowe.
The new aid to memory; containing the most remarkable events of the history of Rome. Illustrated by eighty symbolical engravings. 5th ed. London, J. Field [1845?]
71 p.

NK 0208961 DLC-P4

Krf3 839k v.1 [Knott, Robert Rowe]
A new aid to memory. Part the first, containing the most remarkable events of the history of England. Illustrated by one hundred and twenty symbolical engravings. By a Cambridge M.A. London: Pub. by Whittaker and co.,1839.
2p.ℓ.,ix-xxxi,63p. 12plates. 20cm.

NK 0208962 CtY PP

Knott, Robert Rowe.
The new aid to memory. Part the second: containing the most remarkable events of the history of Rome. Illustrated by eighty symbolical engravings. By the Rev. Robert Rowe Knott ... 2d ed. London, Whittaker and co., 1841.
xxviii, 68 p. 8 pl. 19½cm.

1. Mnemonics.
CA 11-1418 Unrev'd
Library of Congress BF383.K6

NK 0208963 DLC CtY

Knott, Robert Rowe.
The new aid to memory. Part the third: adapted to scripture history. Containing a chronology of the patriarchs, kings, rulers, prophets, and the most remarkable epochs from the creation to the destruction of Jerusalem. Illustrated in connexion with facts by one hundred and forty-two symbolical engravings. By the Rev. Robert Rowe Knott ... London, Whittaker and co., 1842.
xxviii, 68 p. 13 pl. 19cm.

1. Mnemonics.
CA 11-1419 Unrev'd
Library of Congress BF383.K63

NK 0208964 DLC CtY

4BF 636 Knott, Robert Rowe.
The new aid to memory, part the third, adapted to Scripture history; containing a chronology of the patriarchs, kings, rulers, prophets and the most remarkable epochs from the Creation to the destruction of Jerusalem. 2d ed. London, Whittaker, 1843.
68 p.

NK 0208965 DLC-P4 CaBVaU OO

Knott, Robert Rowe.
The new aid to memory. Part the fourth. Adapted to the New Testament, containing a chronology of the most remarkable events of that sacred volume. Illustrated by forty-eight symbolical engravings. By the Rev. Robert Rowe Knott ... London, Whittaker and co., 1844.
xxi, [22]-95 p. VI pl. 19cm.

1. Mnemonics.
10-19593
Library of Congress BF383.K7

NK 0208966 DLC CtY PU OO

4BF 834 Knott, Robert Rowe.
The new aid to memory: part the fourth, adapted to the New Testament, containing a chronology of the most remarkable events of that sacred volume. Illustrated by forty-eight symbolical engravings. 2d ed. London, Sold by Souter and Law, 1846.
95 p.

NK 0208967 DLC-P4

Knott, Rudolf
Michel Stüeler; ein Lebens- und Sittenbild aus der Zeit des dreissigjährigen Krieges. Teplitz, C.Weigend [18-]
37 p.
Cover title
"Sonderabdruck aus dem Jahresberichte des k.k. Staats- Real- und Obergymnasiums in Teplitz-Schönau"

NK 0208967-1 MH

F 58986 .46 KNOTT, RUDOLF.
...Ueber die geschichtliche entwicklung der badestadt Teplitz-Schönau... Berlin,Vogel, 1903.
cover-title,18p.

"Sonderabdruck aus dem reisebericht des comités zur veranstaltung ärztlicher studienreisen in bade- und kurorte. II. band 1902."

NK 0208968 ICN

VOLUME 300

GC1 W83 53-44 Knott, S T
Design of depth meters for use with cable suspended hydrophones. Woods Hole, Mass., 1953.
[2], ii, 13 l. plates, diagrs. (1 fold.), tables. 29 cm. (Woods Hole, Mass. Oceanographic Institution. Reference no. 53-44)
"Submitted to the Bureau of Ships under contract NObsr-43270 (NE 120221, Task 2)"
Bibliography: l. 12.
1. Ocean. 2. Scientific aparatus and instruments. 3. Depth meters. I. U.S. Bureau of Ships. II. Title: Hydrophones, Cable suspended. (Series)

NK 0208970 DI

Knott (Samuel). * De animi in morbis et gignendis et sanandis potestate. 3 p. l., 30 pp. 8°. Edinburgi, 1831.

NK 0208971 DNLM

Knott, Stratton C.
Meteorological observations at Mojanga, Madagascar, during 1892-1894. London. 1895.
p. 21-27. 24½ cm.

NK 0208972 DAS

385.13 K759 Knott, Stuart R., 1859-1907?
Argument of Stuart R. Knott before the Senate of Kentucky in Committee of the Whole, Tuesday, February 21, 1888.
[n.p., n.d.]
13 p. 24 cm.
Cover title;
"...to correct some misstatements relative to railway management in our State..."

NK 0208973 KyU

Knott, Stuart R., 1859-1907?

Northrop, Claudian Bellinger, 1864- *comp.*
Replies of Judge Baxter, Messrs. Stuyvesant Fish, E. P. Ripley, Henry Fink and S. R. Knott to questions involving valuation of railway property and reasonableness of rates together with extracts from certain decisions of the courts supporting said replies. Compiled by Claudian B. Northrop, special attorney, Southern railway company. [Washington? 1906]

W 4 M79 1932/33 Knott, Szymon, 1904-
Contribution à l'étude du mécanisme de quelques fractures du membre inférieur par arrachement musculaire (rôle des travées osseuses dans la direction du trait de fracture) Montpellier, Mari-Lavit, 1933.
63 p. illus. (Montpellier, France. Université. Faculté de médecine. Thèse. Doct. de l'univ. 1932/33. no. 18)
Bibliography: p. 59-63.

NK 0208976 DNLM CtY

Knott, T H.
Sonnets [by] T. H. Knott. [New York city, The author, 1927]
cover-title, 2 p. l., 10 numb. l. 15 x 12cm.
Printed on one side of leaf only.

31-19150

Library of Congress PS3521.N6986 1927

NK 0208977 DLC

Knott, Thomas.
The speech...delivered at the anniversary meeting of the Bible society...Manchester, [1816?]

NK 0208978 PHC

Knott, Thomas.
Speech delivered at the Turk's Head long room, Newcastle-upon-Tyne, Dec. 4, 1816, at the anniversary meeting of the British and Foreign Bible Society. L, Hutton, 1817.

NK 0208979 MH

Knott, Thomas Albert, 1880-1945, joint author.
The elements of old English
see under
Moore, Samuel, 1877-

Knott, Thomas Albert, 1880-1945.
... An essay toward the critical text of the A-version of "Piers the Plowman" ... by Thomas A. Knott ... Chicago, 1915.
1 p. l., p. 129-161. diagrs. 24cm.
Thesis (PH. D.)—University of Chicago, 1912.
"Reprinted with additions from Modern philology, vol. XII, no. 7."
I. Langland, William, 1330?-1400? II. Title: Piers the Plowman.

15-5961

Library of Congress PR2016.K5
Univ. of Chicago Libr.

NK 0208981 NjP DLC WaWW OrU NIC NcU NcD MiU OC1W OU PHC

Knott, Thomas Albert. joint author.

Carpenter, Millington Farwell.
Handbook of correct writing, by Millington F. Carpenter ... William S. Maulsby ... Thomas A. Knott ... New York, Harcourt, Brace and company [°1927]

Knott, Thomas Albert, 1880-1945 joint author.

Carpenter, Millington Farwell.
Minimum essentials of correct writing, by Millington F. Carpenter ... and George Carver, William S. Maulsby, Thomas A. Knott ... New York, Harcourt, Brace and company [°1924]

PE1625 .W3 1945 Knott, Thomas Albert, 1880-1945 joint ed.
FOR OTHER EDITIONS SEE MAIN ENTRY

Webster, Noah, 1758-1843.
Webster's New international dictionary of the English language. 2d ed., unabridged. An entirely new book utilizing all the experience and resources of more than one hundred years of genuine Webster dictionaries. A Merriam-Webster ... William Allan Neilson ... editor in chief; Thomas A. Knott ... general editor; Paul W. Carhart, managing editor. Springfield, Mass., G. & C. Merriam company, 1945.

Knott, Thomas Albert, 1880-1945, ed.
Piers the Plowman
see under
Langland, William, 1330?-1400?

PE1137 .K37 1953 Knott, Thomas Albert, 1880-1945, joint ed.
FOR OTHER EDITIONS SEE MAIN ENTRY

Kenyon, John Samuel, 1874- *ed.*
A pronouncing dictionary of American English, by John Samuel Kenyon and Thomas Albert Knott. Springfield, Mass., G. & C. Merriam Co. [°1953]

Knott, Thomas Albert, joint author

Kirby, Thomas Joseph, 1877-
Pupil activity, English series ... [by] Thomas J. Kirby ... Millington F. Carpenter ... Thomas A. Knott ... illustrated by R. M. Brinkerhoff. New York, Chicago, Harcourt, Brace and company [°1930-

---

Knott, Thomas Albert, 1880- ed.
Stylebook of the Middle English dictionary. [Ann Arbor, Mich., 1936?]
1 p.l., ii, 48 numb.l. 28½cm.
Lithographic reproduction of typewritten copy.
1. English language--Lexicography. 2. English language --Middle English (1150-1500)--Dict. I. Title. II. Title: Middle English dictionary.

NK 0208988 MiU

PR2065 .G308K7 [Knott, Thomas Albert] 1880-1945.
The text of Sir Gawayne and the Green knight [Baltimore, The Johns Hopkins press 1915]
[7] p. 27½cm.
Caption title.
Signed: Thomas A. Knott.
"Reprint from Modern language notes, April, 1915."
1. Gawain and the Grene knight.

NK 0208989 ICU

Knott, Thomas Albert, 1880-1945, joint author.

Carver, George, 1888-
Writing and rewriting, by George Carver, William S. Maulsby [and] Thomas A. Knott ... New York, Harcourt, Brace and company [°1923]

VOLUME 300

Knott, Thomas B.
Pianoforte fingering, its principles and applications, by Thomas B. Knott. London: Oxford Univ. Press[, 1928]. 23 p. illus. (music.) 8°.

493717A. 1. Piano playing. N. Y. P. L. August 29, 1930

NK 0208991 NN CtY OCl CoU KyLoS TNJ-P

MT 232 .K66 Knott, Thomas B.
Pianoforte fingering; its principles and applications, by Thomas B. Knott. [London] Oxford University Press [1946]
23 p. music.
First published 1928.

1. Piano - Instruction and study. I. Title.

NK 0208992 AMob

MT232 .K7 KNOTT,THOMAS B
Pianoforte fingering; its principles and applications. London, New York, Oxford university press [1950]
23 p. music.

1. Piano--Instruction and study. I. tc.

NK 0208993 InU

Knott, Thomas Henry.
Hongkong. *Committee on the Medical department.*
... Report of the Committee appointed by His Excellency Sir William Robinson ... to enquire into the Medical department and other matters relative thereto together with the evidence taken before the Committee. Hongkong, Printed by Noronha & co., government printers, 1895.

Knott, Tina (Kuipers) Spencer
see Spencer-Knott, Justina (Kuipers) 1915–

Knott, Van Buren, 1871– 617.04 K75
[Collected papers on surgery.]
126623 Reprinted from various medical serials.

NK 0208996 ICJ

Knott, Virginia M (Bergstresser) 1913–
Physical measurement of young children: a study of anthropometric reliabilities for children three to six years of age, by Virginia Bergstresser Knott ... Iowa City, Ia., The University of Iowa press, 1941.
99 p. illus., diagrs. 23½cm. ([Iowa. University] University of Iowa studies. Studies in child welfare, vol. XVIII, no. 3)
University of Iowa studies. New series, no. 394.
Thesis (PH. D.)—University of Iowa, 1938.
Without thesis note.
"References": p. 96–99.
1. Anthropometry. 2. Children. I. Title. 41—46103
—— Library of Congress LB3423.A2K5
—— —— Copy 2. Thesis note on label mounted on t.-p.
[a43l2] 573.6

ODW OO OCl OU PPTU ICU
NK 0208997 DLC CaBVaU OrU-M OrLgE NBuU CU NcD OCU

Knott, W V as comptroller of the state of Florida, *appellee.*
(Pullman company, *appellant*)
Action brought to test the constitutionality of the Florida laws imposing the gross receipts tax and advalorem tax upon sleeping and parlor car companies.
Briefs and other records in this case, 1914– not separately listed or cataloged are to be found on shelf: HE1075.F6K6
1. Railroads—Florida—Taxation. 2. Railroads—Florida—Sleeping-cars. 3. Taxation—Florida. I. Florida, appellee. II. Pullman company, appellant.
CA 16-296 Unrev'd
Library of Congress HE1075.F6K6

NK 0208998 DLC

Knott, W. V.
Florida. *Laws, statutes, etc.*
Insurance laws of the state of Florida in force July 1st, 1909. W. V. Knott, state treasurer, supervising officer. Tallahassee, Capital publishing co., state printer, 1909.

F856 .G5 Knott, Walter.
Ghost town news.
[Buena Park, Calif., W. Knott, 19

Knott, Walter, 1905–
Die Behandlung operativer Wunden in der Mundhöhle mit der Heidelberger Radiumsole ... [Heidelberg] 1932.
Inaug.-Diss. - Heidelberg.
Lebenslauf.
"Literatur": p. 8.

NK 0209001 CtY

Knott, Widnell Dimsdale, 1893–
The influence of tax-leeway on educational adaptability; a study of the relationship of residual or potential economic ability, expressed as tax-leeway, to educational adaptations in the state of New York, by Widnell Dimsdale Knott ... New York city, Teachers college, Columbia university, 1939.
x p., 1 l., 84 p., 1 l. incl. tables, diagrs. 23cm.
Thesis (PH. D.)—Columbia university, 1939.
Vita.
Published also as Teachers college, Columbia university, Contributions to education, no. 785.
"One of a series of studies of adaptability of public school systems carried forward by students of the Advanced school of education, Teachers college, Columbia university, under the sponsorship of Professor Paul R. Mort."
Bibliography: p. 81–84.
1. Education and state—New York (State) 2. Public schools—New York (State)—Finance. 3. Taxation—New York (State) I. Title.
40-8542
Library of Congress LB2826.N7K6 1939
Columbia Univ. Libr. [2] 379.1309747

DLC
NK 0209003 NNC KEmT OCU OOxM OU ViU WaTC PPT PPD

Knott, Widnell Dimsdale, 1893–
The influence of tax-leeway on educational adaptability; a study of the relationship of residual or potential economic ability, expressed as tax-leeway, to educational adaptations in the state of New York, by Widnell Dimsdale Knott ... New York city, Teachers college, Columbia university, 1939.
x p., 1 l., 84 p. incl. tables, diagrs. 23½cm. (Teachers college, Columbia university. Contributions to education, no. 785)
Issued also as thesis (PH. D.) Columbia university.
"One of a series of studies of adaptability of public school systems carried forward by students of the Advanced school of education, Teachers college, Columbia university, under the sponsorship of Professor Paul R. Mort."
Bibliography: p. 81–84.
1. Education and state—New York (State) 2. Public schools—New York (State)—Finance. 3. Taxation—New York (State) I. Title.
Library of Congress LB2826.N7K6 1939 a 40-8541
—— —— Copy 2. LB5.C8 no. 785
Copyright A 136159 [8] 379.1309747

NK 0209004 DLC MtU OrU CaBVaU

KNOTT, WILLIAM T., b. 1822.
Hisory of Marion county, Kentucky. [Frankfort, Ky., Kentucky historical society, 1952] vi, 115 l.
Film reproduction. Positive.
A copy of a scrapbook of clippings from the Lebanon, Ky., newspaper.
1. Marion county, Ky.--Hist. 2. Marion county, Ky.--Geneal.

NK 0209005 NN KyHi

BX8947 .K4K7 Knott, William T 1822–
History of the Presbyterian church in what is now Marion County and city of Lebanon, Kentucky. By W. T. Knott ... From the year 1789 to 1895 ... [Frankfort? 1895?]
iv, 5–52 p. ports. 22½cm.
"Erratum" slip at end.
1. Presbyterian church in Kentucky.

NK 0209006 ICU KyHi PPPrHi

Knott, William T 1822–
Report on the geology of Marion County
see under Kentucky. State Geologist.

Knott, William T., b. 1822.
Washington and Marion Counties [, Kentucky]
see under Kentucky. State Geologist.

Knott, William Wilson.
"Old sport;" or, A sketch of the life of Peter Napoleon Campana. A life history of indomitable pluck, tireless energy, famous achievements and wide acquaintance with celebrities of the ring and race-track. By William Wilson Knott ... Chicago, The Bow-knot publishing co. [c1891]
49 p. front. (port.) 20cm.
LC copy replaced by microfilm
1. Campana, Peter Napoleon, 1828– 2. Walking.
CA 7-6247 Unrev'd
Library of Congress [GV1071.K7]

NK 0209009 DLC

Knott, William Wilson.
Stolen sweets, or, W. W. W. and W. A romance with a moral--the acme of realistic fiction. Chicago, Bow-Knot pub. co., c 1891.
368 p. D.

NK 0209010 NcD

Knott, Y.
Conservative socialism, or socialism for the middle classes, by Y. Knott. London, S. Sonnenschein & co., 1909.
159 p. 18½cm.
1. Socialism. I. Title.
A 10-627
Title from Leland Stanford Jr. Univ. Printed by L. C.

NK 0209011 CSt NcU ICJ NN

Knott Corporation
see Knott Hotels Corporation.

VOLUME 300

Knott Hotels Corporation.
Incorporated Sept. 9, 1927 as Knott Corporation. Name changed in March 1950 to Knott Hotels Corporation.

NK 0209013 CtY

Knott Hotels Corporation.
Report.
[New York]
v. illus. 28 cm. annual.

TX941.K6A34 55-23711 ‡

NK 0209014 DLC CtY

Knott reminiscences; early history of Nevada in the 1850s
see under Hamlin, Herbert Skyhawk, comp.

DD163 .5 .K72 Knotte, Ernst, 1877-
Untersuchungen zur chronologie von schriften der Minoriten am hofe kaiser Ludwigs des Bayern...
Wiesbaden, 1903
Inaug. diss. Bonn.
Lebenslauf.

NK 0209016 DLC CtY MH PU NjP

Knotte, Ernst, 1882-
Ueber einen fall von schwerer allgemein tuberkulose mit herz und gallenblasentuberkulose.
Inaug. diss. Leipzig, 1907.

NK 0209017 ICRL CtY

Knotte (W[ilhelm]). *Ueber Vergiftung durch Seifen. 23 pp. 8°. *Würzburg, F. Fromme,* 1890.

NK 0209018 DNLM

Knottenbelt, A.
Ouderlijke nacht en voogdij. Behnopte mededeelingen over de wijzigingen van het burgerlijk wetboek, door A. Knottenbelt.
Vlaardingen, 1905.
32 p.

NK 0209019 PU-L

Knorring, A. von, freyin
see Knorring, Sofia Margareta (Zelow) friherinna von, 1797-1848.

Knottenbelt, Anthony.
Verpanding en zekerheidstelling in den Oost-Preanger. Bandoeng, 1934.
135 p. 25 cm.
Proefschrift—Rechtshoogeschool, Djakarta.
"Stellingen": [2] leaves inserted.
Bibliography: p. [131]-132.

1. Mortgages (Adat law) 2. Pledges (Adat law) I. Title.
60-58895

NK 0209020 DLC CtY NIC

Knottenbelt, Gulielmus Christianus
see Knottenbelt, Willem Christian, 1813-1875.

Knottenbelt, J 330.2 N204
Volkshuishoudkunde. Een leesboek voor de leerlingen der burgerscholen door Mr. J. Knottenbelt, ... Arnhem, J. Voltelen, 1872.
[8], 229 p. 20½cm.

NK 0209021 ICJ

Knottenbelt, J. W., ed.

Netherlands (*Kingdom, 1815- *) *Laws, statutes, etc.*
Kinderrecht; wettelijke voorschriften met betrekking tot het kinderrecht en de kinderbescherming, door J. W. Knottenbelt. Vuga-boekerij. [Arnhem, G. W. van der Wiel, 1953-

---

Knottenbelt, Johannis Hendrik.
... De divortio ... defendet Johannis Hendricus Knottenbelt ... Lugduni Batavorum, J.C. Cyfveer, 1833.
3 p.l., 73, [4] p. 21cm.
Diss.- Leiden.
Bibliographical footnotes.

NK 0209023 MH-L

W 4 L68 1947 KNOTTENBELT, Nelly.
Stollingremmende behandeling van thrombose. 's-Gravenhage, Boucher, 1947.
106 p. illus.
Proefschrift - Leyden.
Summary in Dutch, English, French, and German.
1. Bishydroxycoumarin 2. Heparin 3. Thrombosis

NK 0209024 DNLM ICU

Me35 C728 839k Knottenbelt, Willem Christiaan, 1813-1875.
Disputatio historico-theologica de Columbano, quam ... submittit Gulielmus Christianus Knottenbelt ... Lugduni Batavorum, H.W.Hazenberg et socii,1839.
4p.ℓ.,111p. 22½cm.
Diss. - Leiden.

1.Columbanus, Saint, abbot of Luxeuil and Bobbio, ca.540- 615.

NK 0209025 CtY MH MdBP CPFT

Knottenbelt, Willem Christiaan, 1813-1875.
Geschiedenis der staatkunde van Johan de Witt. Door W. C. Knottenbelt ... Bekroond door de Hollandsche maatschappij van fraaije kunsten en wetenschappen in den jare 1860. Amsterdam, Van Bonga & comp., 1861.
cover-title, 1 p. l., 220 p. 23½cm.

1. Witt, Johan de, 1625-1672. 2. Netherlands—Foreign relations. 3. Netherlands—Hist.—1648-1714.
31-30192
Library of Congress DJ173.W7K5 923.2492

NK 0209026 DLC IaU

Knotting ... Lond.C.Arthur Pearson ltd.1933. 108p.illus.D. (The Gilcraft series,no.7)

NK 0209027 CaBViP

[Knotting, by Gilcraft... London, C. Arthur Pearson, ltd. [1939]
108 p. illus.
"First published 1929"

NK 0209028 PPL

Knotting, England (parish).
The parish register of Knotting (1592-1812). (In: Bedfordshire, England. County Records Committee. Bedfordshire parish registers. Bedford, 1933. 34cm. v. 7, B. ii, 14 p.)
Reproduced from typewritten copy.

696926A. 1. Parish registers— Gt. Br.—Eng.—Knotting. I. Ser.
N. Y. P. L. April 19, 1934

NK 0209029 NN

Knottnerus-Meyer, Hermann.
Der unbekannte Löns; gespräche und erinnerungen von Hermann Knottnerus-Meyer. 1. bis 5. tausend. Jena, E. Diederichs, 1928.
1 p. l., v-vii, 177, [1] p. 2 port. (incl. front.) facsim. 20½cm.

1. *Löns, Hermann, 1866-1914. I. Title.
Library of Congress PT2623.O36Z7 29-13812
Copyright A—Foreign 2408

NK 0209030 DLC WU CU OCl

Knottnerus-Meyer, Theodor Christian Bernhard, 1876-
Birds and beasts of the Roman Zoo; some observations of a lover of animals, by Th. Knottnerus-Meyer ... translated by Bernard Miall. London, G. Allen & Unwin ltd. [1927]
vi p., 2 l., 3-378 p. front., plates, port. 22cm.
"Printed in U. S. A."

1. Animals, Habits and behavior of. 2. Birds. 3. Rome (City) Giardino zoologico. I. Miall, Bernard, tr. II. Title. III. Title: Beasts of the Roman Zoo.
Library of Congress QL791.K48 28-3443

NK 0209031 DLC CaBVaU CU

Knottnerus-Meyer, Theodor Christian Bernhard, 1876-
Birds and beasts of the Roman zoo; some observations of a lover of animals, by Th. Knottnerus-Meyer ... translated by Bernard Miall. New York & London, The Century co. [°1928]
vi p., 2 l., 3-378 p. front., plates, port. 21½cm.

1. Animals, Habits and behavior of. 2. Birds. 3. Rome (City) Giardino zoologico. I. Miall, Bernard, 1876- tr. II. Title. III. Title: Beasts of the Roman zoo.
28-5646
Library of Congress QL791.K48 1928

OEac OCl Or OrU
NK 0209032 DLC WHi OrU MB IEN INS PP ICJ NN OOxM

SF430 .K55 Knotterus-Meyer, Theodor Christian Bernhard
Hunderassen-rassenlunde.
Zuerich,[c1929.]
1 v. 12°

NK 0209033 DLC

VOLUME 300

Knottnerus-Meyer, Theodor, 1876-
...Tiere im Zoo; Beobachtungen eines Tierfreundes... Leipzig: W. Klinkhardt, 1925. 262 p. front., plates. 2. ed. 4°.

250189A. 1. Animals, Wild. 2. Zoological gardens.
N. Y. P. L. August 25, 1926

NK 0209034 NN NcD

Knottnerus-Meyer, Theodor Christian Bernhard, 1876-
Über das Tränenbein der huftiere; vergleichend-anatomischer Beitrag zur Systematik der rezenten Ungulata. Berlin, 1907.
Inaug.-Diss. - Kiel.

NK 0209035 MH CtY DNLM PU ICRL

Knottnerus-Meyer, Theodor Christian Bernhard, 1876-
...Zoologisches Wörterbuch, von Dr. phil. Theodor Knottnerus-Meÿer. Leipzig: B. G. Teubner, 1920. iv, 217 p. 12°. (Teubners kleine Fachwörterbücher. Bd. 2.)

499604A. 1. Zoology—Dictionaries. I. Ser.
N. Y. P. L. April 17, 1931

NK 0209036 NN CU PBL NcD

Knotts, Armanis F.
The dunes of northwestern Indiana, by A. F. Knotts .. "Photos taken by H. H. Daugherty, Gary, Ind." [Gary 1917]
20 p. illus. (incl. maps) 23cm.
"Prepared for and published in Indiana geological report, 1916." [Forty-first annual report of Department of geology and natural resources, Indiana, p. 11-27]

1. Sand-dunes. 2. Michigan, Lake. 3. Geology—Indiana. I. Title.
Library of Congress GB635.I 6K6 CA 19-73 Unrev'd

NK 0209037 DLC ICJ

NK2002
.N47
Knotts, Benjamin.
New York. Metropolitan museum of art.
I remember that; an exhibition of interiors of a generation ago. The Index of American design. [New York] The Metropolitan museum of art [1942]

NK1530
.P47
Knotts, Benjamin.
Pennsylvania German designs, a portfolio of silk screen prints. The Index of American design, the National gallery of art, research by the Pennsylvania WPA art project. [New York] The Metropolitan museum of art [1943]

[Knotts, D J]
... The parentage of Lincoln. An examination into the family history of the famous president.—"Nancy Hanks" and her South Carolina connections. Columbia, S. C., The State, 1911.
30 l. 23cm.
Articles and letters signed: D. J. Knotts.
Photostat facsimiles of four articles extracted from "The State, Columbia, S. C., Sunday morning, April 9, 1911" to Nov. 26, 1911, and of two letters from the author.
Facsimiles of newspaper clippings in double columns.
1. Lincoln, Mrs. Nancy (Hanks) 1784-1818. I. Title. II. Title: "Nancy Hanks" and her South Carolina connections.
A 31-926
Title from H. E. Huntington Libr. Printed by L. C.

NK 0209040 CSmH

F1234
V7K73
Knotts, E Franklin, 1868-1934.
Pancho Villa, the bandit, the soldier, the man. [n.p., n.d.]
76 l. 27cm.
Caption title.
Xerox copy.

1. Villa, Francisco, 1877-1923. 2. Mexico - Hist. - Revolution, 1910-1929. I. Title.

NK 0209041 CSt-H

Knotts, John Duren.
The poetical works of John D. Knotts ... Orangeburg, S. C., The author, R. L. Berry, printer, 1897.
179, [5] p. front. (port.) 17½cm.
CONTENTS.—pt. 1. Hymns for the use of churches, Sunday-schools and other religious meetings.—pt. 2. Poems for the young.

1. Hymns, American.
Library of Congress PS2197.K12 27-25708

NK 0209042 DLC ViU

Knotts, Mrs. Minnie Prey, ed.
Nebraska territorial pioneers' association, *Lincoln.*
Reminiscences and proceedings. v. 1-
Lincoln, 1917-

Knotts, Raymond.
And the deep blue sea, by Raymond Knotts. New York, Toronto, Farrar & Rinehart incorporated [1944]
5 p. l., 3-246 p. 19cm.

I. Title.
Library of Congress PZ3.K75924An 44-3162

NK 0209044 DLC OCl CaBVa WaSp PP

Knotts, Raymond.
Meeting by moonlight, by Raymond Knotts. Garden City, New York, Pub. for the Crime club by Doubleday & company, inc., 1946.
5 p. l., [9]-222 p. 19cm.
"First edition."

I. Title.
PZ3.K75924Me 46-8189

NK 0209045 DLC PP

Knotts, Walter Ernest.
Swift and politics, 1701-1714
Thesis - Harvard, 1952

NK 0209046 MH

C979.44
S193kn
Knott's Berry Farm, Buena Park, Calif.
Calico, ghost town; S. California's greatest silver camp. [Ghost Town, Calif., c1952]
56p. photos., ports., maps. 22cm.
Cover title.
1.Calico, Calif. 2.Mining camps. California

NK 0209047 CoD CU-S CU-B

Knotty problems of baseball.
St. Louis, The Sporting news.
v. illus., ports. 17 cm. (A Spink sports publication)
Began in 1949.
Originally compiled by John B. Foster and W. G. Evans in 1920-39 under title Knotty problems.

1. Baseball. I. Sporting news.
GV877.K5 65-5843 rev

NK 0209048 DLC

76-01
KN9236
Harris Collection
Knotty Walk; a ghostly idyl, by the Local Philosopher. [Quincy? Mass., 19--?]
10 l. 14cm.
Caption title.
Printed on one side of leaf only
In verse.
I. The Local Philosopher

NK 0209049 RPB

Knotzinger, Franz.
Der Rückgang des Gebirgsbauerntums in Niederösterreich; eine siedlungskundliche Darstellung seiner Grundlagen an Hand der Entwicklung im oberen Schwarzatal. Berlin, F. Vahlen, 1938.
111 p. illus., maps (part fold.) 24 cm. (Südostdeutsches Bauerntum, Bd. 1)
1. Beiheft des Geographischen Jahresberichtes aus Österreich.
"Literatur": p. [109]-111.
1. Land settlement—Schwarza Valley, Austria. 2. Schwarza Valley, Austria. I. Title. (Series. Series: Geographischer Jahresbericht aus Österreich. Beiheft 1)
HD640.S35K6 333.7 50-49852

NK 0209050 DLC DNAL NN ICRL

Knouf, Clyde E.
Log scaling, by R. W. McIntyre, Bernard Brereton, Emanuel Fritz, Clyde E. Knouf [and] E. I. Karr. Portland, Or., San Francisco, Calif., The Timberman, 1936.

[Knouf, Clyde E.]
... Trade course in log scaling for Idaho woods. State board for vocational education, Boise. [Boise, Idaho, 1924]
iv, 119, [1] p. illus., diagrs., tables. 23 cm. (At head of title: Idaho, Bulletin of vocational education. v.7, no.5, May, 1924)

NK 0209052 CaBVaU

Geneal.
Case
fE
7
.W 927
KNOUF, OSEE (JOHNSON) 1897-
Wright family history. La Grange, Ill., 1951-
v. 29cm.
Typewritten copy (carbon)
Contents.--v.l. Genealogy of Benjamin Wright, sr.

NK 0209053 ICN

Knouff, Al
see
Knouff, Alfred H.

Knouff, Alfred H., joint author.
Swift, Robert K.
A practical course in flying, by Bob Swift and Al Knouff. Athens, O., The Aircraft directory [1938]

VOLUME 300

QL999 Knouff, Ralph Albert.
.K71 ... The origin of the cerebral ganglia of rana ... By Ralph Albert Knouff. Chicago, 1927.
iii numb. l., 1 l., 3-148, 11 numb. l. incl. vi pl. 29cm.
Typewritten.
Thesis (PH. D.)—University of Chicago, 1927.
"Literature cited": l. 128-134.
"Abstract": 11 l. at end.

1. Nervous system, Sympathetic. 2. Frogs.

NK 0209056 ICU

Knous, Caroline Boardman (Shultas) b. 1841.
Ancestry sketches. Compiled for the children, by C. B. S. K. [Hartford? Conn.] Hartford Press, 1900.
88 p. geneal. table. 21 cm.
"Limited to 100 copies."

1. Glover family. I. K., C. B. S. II. Title.

CS71.G566 1900 65-72794

NK 0209057 DLC NN

F689 Knouse, Charles A comp.
.O8K7 A town between two rivers; an informal narrative of the settling, founding and growth of the city of Osawatomie, Kansas, any [!] many of the events that have transpired during the past one-hundred years. Osawatomie, Kan., Osage Valley Centennial, 1954.
96 p. illus., ports.

1. Osawatomie, Kan.—Hist. I. Title.

NK 0209058 ICU KU MiD

Knouse, Frederick L
... Cristal de rocha, no estado do Espirito Santo, por Frederick L. Knouse. Rio de Janeiro, 1944.
3 p. l., [11]-16 p. plates (1 fold.) fold. map, fold. tab. 23½cm. (Brazil. Departamento nacional da produção mineral. Divisão de fomento da produção mineral. Avulso n. 55)
At head of title: Republica dos estados unidos do Brasil. Ministério da agricultura. ... Departamento nacional da produção mineral ... Divisão de fomento da produção mineral ...

1. Quartz. 2. Petrology—Brazil—Espirito Santo (State) I. Title.
GS 44-106
U. S. Geol. survey. Library for Library of Congress [TN41.A35 no. 55]
[3] (622.0981)

NK 0209059 DI-GS

Knouse, Frederick L
Deposits of quartz crystal in Espirito Santo and eastern Minas Gerais, Brazil.
(In Mining technology. York, Pa., 1937-48. 23 cm. v. 10, no. 2, Mar. 1946. 12 p.)
American Institute of Mining and Metallurgical Engineers. Technical publication no. 1962 (Class A, Metal mining, no. 184; Class H, Industrial Minerals Division, no. 142)

1. Quartz. I. Title.
[TN1.A5256 vol. 10, no. 2] P O 51-6
U. S. Patent Office. Library for Library of Congress [1]

NK 0209060 DP

Knout, David.
D765
.2
.W3B34 ... La Bataille du ghetto de Varsovie, vue et racontée par les Allemands. Paris, Éditions du Centre, 1946.

Knout, David.
Contribution à l'histoire de la résistance juive en France 1940-1944. Paris, Éditions du Centre, 1947.
181 p. illus., ports., facsims. 22 cm. (Centre de documentation juive contemporaine. Série "Études et monographies," no 3)

1. World War, 1939-1945—Jews. 2. World War, 1939-1945—Underground movements—France. 3. Jews in France. (Series)

D810.J4K6 940.5344 48-11400*

NK 0209062 DLC CU OU NcU NNUN CSt-H InU NcU IU TU IEN NIC ICU MB MiU

---

4 PQ Knout, Elisabeth.
Fr. La ronde des mouches [récits] Paris, J.
594 Vigneau, 1947.
117 p.

NK 0209063 DLC-P4

The knout, a tale of Poland. Tr. from the French, by Mrs. J. Sadlier. Philadelphia, P. F. Cunningham [°1856]
260 p. 17cm.

1. Poland—Hist.—Revolution, 1830-1832—Fiction. I. Sadlier, Mary Ann (Madden) "Mrs. James Sadlier," 1820-1903, tr.

7-14182†
Library of Congress PZ3.K7593

NK 0209064 DLC PU OCl

The knout, a tale of Poland. Tr. from the French, by Mrs. J. Sadlier. Philadelphia, P. F. Cunningham [°1865]
260 p. 17½cm.

1. Poland—Hist.—Revolution, 1830-1832—Fiction. I. Sadlier, Mary Ann (Madden) "Mrs. James Sadlier," 1820-1903, tr.

7-14183†
Library of Congress PZ3.K7593 2

NK 0209065 DLC

Know. v. 1-
1st quarter 1939-
[Norfolk, Va., Norfolk Advertising Board]
v. in illus., ports. 28-31 cm.

1. Norfolk, Va. I. Norfolk Advertising Board.

F234.N8K6 49-40794*

NK 0209066 DLC Vi NN

Know
... The navy and post-war Norfolk. Norfolk, Va., c1945.
233, [1] p., illus., plates, ports.,

"A special edition...vol. VII, no. 1, July, 1945"
Caption-title.

NK 0209067 OCl

KNOW all men. A Doctor's fallacy on smoking and smokers, etc., 1857.

NK 0209068 MH

Know all men by these presents, that have constituted, ordained, and made, and in stead and place put ... to be true, sufficient and lawful attorney ... Anno Domini, one thousand seven hundred and and in the year of His Majesty's reign. Signed, sealed and delivered ... [n. p., 17--?]

facsim. broadside. 24 x 21cm.

Blank form conferring power of attorney.

NK 0209069 MiU-C

---

*AB7 Know all men by these presents, that
A100 held and firmly bound into in the
733k full and just sum of to be paid to the said his certain attorney, executors, administrators, or assigns. For the which payment well and truly to be made and done bind heirs, executors, administrators, firmly by these presents. Sealed with seal dated this day of in the year of H Majesty's reign; annoque Domini. 17

Philadelphia: [Printed and] sold [by B. Franklin] at the New printing-office near the Market. [1733?]
broadside. 31x20cm.

Blank form for a bond, filled out in ms. for Mondnogo Thomas and Richard Treats as obligors and Humphrey Marry as obligee; dated 20 November 1733. Signed by Amy Lawrence and Joseph Lawrence as sureties and by the obligors.

NK 0209072 PU

Know all men, by these presents that held and firmly bound unto in the sum of lawful money of to be paid to the said certain attorney, executors, administrators or assigns ... Philadelphia [1767]
Loan form filled out in ms.

NK 0209073 PU

... Know all men by these presents, that held and firmly bound unto in the sum of money of to be paid to the said certain attorney, executors, administrators, or assigns: to which payment well and truly to be made, bind ... Dated the day of in the year of our Lord, one thousand seven hundred and ...
At head of l.1: Philadelphia: Printed and sold by William and Thomas Bradford. [ca. 1771].
2 l. 33x21cm.
Leaf 2 begins: To attorney of the Court of common pleas at

Leaf 1 is a bond from Joseph Wharton and William Parr to Ann Okill, 15 June 1771; Leaf 2 is Wharton's power of attorney to Daniel Clymer of the same date.
Unbound; filed with broadsides.
Ms. catalogued separately.

NK 0209075 PPRF

---

79. Know all men by these presents, that——held and firmly bound unto——in the sum of lawful money——to be paid to the said——. Dated the——day of——in the year of our Lord one thousand seven hundred and . . . Wilmington, Printed and sold by James Adams [1774?]. § Broadside; 32 by 20 cm.
Forms, filled in and dated in ink: Oct. 14, 1774; another copy dated: August 1, 1775.
Hawkins C:4.
Copies:

NK 0209076 DeHi

VOLUME 300

80. Know all men by these presents, that——held and firmly bound unto John Head, of the city of Philadelphia, and province of Pennsylvania, merchant, in the sum of——. Dated the——day of——in the year of our Lord one thousand seven hundred and——and in the year of the reign of our Sovereign Lord . . . Wilmington, Printed by James Adams, 1774. § Broadside; 31 by 19.5 cm.
Bristol, p. 226; Hawkins C:5.
Copies: DeHi.

NK 0209077 DeHi

---

bD695 K73a Know all Men by these presents, That [I Cornelis Joosten of the Citty of new yorke Carpenter am] Holden and firmly Bound unto [Coll: Abraham De Peyster of the Citty of new york merch^t] in the Pænal Sum of [Sixty pounds ———] lawful Money of the Province of [new yorke] ... [New York, William Bradford, ca. 1695]
Broadside. 29 x 19.5cm. 1/2°
Blank form completed in manuscript as indicated within brackets.

Title from beginning of text.
Dated 26 June 1695, with day, month, and last digit of year completed in ms.

NK 0209079 RPJCB

Know all men by these presents, that ⌊I Isaac Zane Jun. ...⌋ Held and firmly bound unto ⌊Daniel Wister⌋ ...
Philadelphia, by William Goddard, ⌊1770⌋
broadside.

NK 0209080 RPJCB

Know all men by these presents, that ⌊I John Buchanan...⌋ held and firmly bound unto ⌊Joseph Chambers...⌋
⌊Philadelphia, 1760⌋ broadside

NK 0209081 RPJCB

Know all men by these presents, that I John Webster of Abington, in the county of Philad^a ... am held and firmly bound unto Stephen Jenkins of the same place yeoman in the full and just sum of three hundred pounds ...⌊Signed⌋ John Webster, William Lyewell ⌊and⌋ Jonathan Beere. Philadelphia: Printed by B.Franklin, and D.Hall, at the New Printing-Office, near the Market ⌊174-⌋
Broadside. 31 x 21cm.
Dated in manuscript: September 4, 1751; a copy in Yale University Library is dated 1749.
Underlined portions in manuscript.
Endorsement on back: Arbitration bond. John Webster to Stephen Jenkins.

NK 0209082 MiU-C

Know all men by these presents, that we and master of the vessel or called the and are held and firmly bound to the United States of America, in the full and just sum of $11,100 ... ⌊n.p., 1813?⌋
Broadsides. 33 x 20.5cm.
Underlined portions in manuscript.
In manuscript at head of title: "Given the 3th January 1813." However, the body of the text refers to an act of December 17, 1813.
Relates to the embargo of 1813.
1.Broadsides.2.Embargo, 1813.

NK 0209083 MiU-C

Know all men by these presents, that I ⌊Theobold End of Germantown...⌋ have made...my trusty and loving Friend ⌊Lewis Stephen...⌋ My true and lawful Attorney...
Philadelphia, ⌊1742-43⌋
broadside.

NK 0209084 RPJCB

---

411. Know all men by these presents, that we are held and firmly bound unto Maxwell Bines, Esq. High Sheriff of the aforesaid county of New Castle——. Dated the——day of——in the year of our Lord one thousand seven hundred and ninety——. Newcastle, Printed by S. & J. Adams [1796?]. § Broadside; 32 by 22 cm.

NK 0209085 DeHi

Know all men by these presents, that ⌊We Jost Dubst... and Conrad Waldeker...⌋ held and firmly bound unto ⌊Michael Israel⌋ ...
Philadelphia, ⌊1742-43⌋
broadside.

NK 0209086 RPJCB

028.1 K76 Know America; a reading list. [New York, R. R. Bowker co., 1940]
23p.

"Prepared for observance of America month (February, 1940)"- p.2.

1. Bibliography--Best books. 2. U.S.--Bibl.

NK 0209087 IU

Oversize DS558 A6K66 Know Angkor, the magnificent capital of the ancient empire of the Khmers, one of the most amazing civilizations the world has ever known ... Paris, Editions "Tel" [1931]
[6] l., 42 plates. 38cm.
Title page and text in French and English.

1. Angkor, Cambodia. I. Éditions Tel, Paris.

NK 0209088 CoU

Know Florida
see under Florida. Bureau of Immigration.

Know-how.

New York.

"Official publication of the Associated Public School Systems".

1. Education. Period. 2. Public Schools. U.S. I. Associated Public School Systems.

NK 0209090 IaU

Know how to make your will; how to put your affairs in legal order, by a barrister. For the man or woman with little as well as for those possessed of great wealth, a complete guide for executors and administrators of estates, with many specimen wills and a special section appertaining to Scots law. London, New York, W. Foulsham ⌊1953⌋
128 p. 19 cm. (The Know how books)

1. Wills—Gt. Brit. 2. Wills—Scotland. I. A barrister.
347.6 54-26614 ‡

NK 0209091 DLC

Know Knoxville news
see under Knoxville, Tenn. Chamber of Commerce.

Know New York State.
v.

New York, 192 17½cm.
nos.

Published by the New York State Committee on Public Utility Information.
Ceased publication with v. 3.

1. New York (state)—Stat. 2. E... nomic history—U. S.—New York. 3. Corporations, Public service—U. S.—New York. I. New York State Committee on Public Utility Information, New York.
N. Y. P. L. April 28, 1933

NK 0209093 NN

The Know nothing? Boston, J. P. Jewett & company; [etc., etc.] New York, Sheldon, Lamport, & Blakeman, 1855.
347 p. 20^{cm}.

Library of Congress PZ3.K7597 7-14184†

NK 0209094 DLC WU OClW MnU ViU CtY NcD OU NcU IU CU InU MiEM

Know nothing: a poem, for natives and aliens
see under [Phillips, Samuel R] 1824-1880.

KNOW NOTHING almanac, and true Americans' manual for 1855. N. Y. DeWitt & D. [185 12°.

NK 0209096 MB DLC PPL

... The Know-Nothing delusion exposed! The warning voice of the great men of the nation! Opinions of distinguished democrats.
32 p. O.

NK 0209097 NcD

Know-Nothing Party
see
American Party.

JK2341 .A7 1854a Know Nothing platform: containing an account of the encroachments of the Roman Catholic hierarchy, on the civil and religious liberties of the people in Europe, Asia, Africa and America, showing the necessity of the order of Know Nothing. Philadelphia ⌊1854⌋
100 p.

1. American Party. 2. Church and state--Catholic church.

NK 0209099 ICU ICarbS

Know-nothing songster. Compiled and composed by "a native." Boston, Press of the Franklin printing house, 1854.
64 p. 14^{cm}.
Without music.
Copyrighted by Charles Sinclair.

1. American party. 2. Political ballads and songs, American. I. Sinclair, Charles.
29-25818

Library of Congress JK2341.A7.1854.K6

NK 0209100 DLC

VOLUME 300

Know-nothing token
see Wide-awake gift.

Know nothingism: illustrated with "cuts": the portraits drawn from life. Hornby, 1855.
8 p. O.
Unbound.
In cover.

NK 0209102 RPB

... Know-nothingism and the A. P. A. [New York? 1894] 21 p. 23cm.

Caption-title.
At head of title: "Religious toleration the best fruit of the last four centuries." In the liberty of a congress of religions.
"Issued by a committee of liberal-minded representative clergymen of all denominations."
Imperfect: p. 1-2 mutilated.

1. Liberty, Religious—U. S. 2. American party, 1852-1860. 3. American protective association of the United States.
N. Y. P. L. March 20, 1940

NK 0209103 NN

Know nothingism; or, the American party
see under Franklin, pseud.

The Know nothings. An expose of the secret order of Know nothings ... By a Know something ... New York, Stearns & company, 1854.
32 p. incl. 3 pl. 22cm.

1. American party.
Library of Congress JK2341.A7 1854 9—32706

NK 0209105 DLC CaBViP ICU OO ViU TU

The Know-nothings. Cause and effect
see under [Dex, pseud.]

A Know nothing's defence of American workingmen's rights. [185-?]

NK 0209107 IaU

"Know Ohio."
see under [Clifton, John Leroy] 1881-

... Know popery; or, Are all these conversions nothing to me? ... London, Burns and Lambert; [etc., etc.] 1851.
16 p. 16 cm. [Catholic tracts. no. 9]
At head of title: Entertaining and instructive library.
1. Conversion.

NK 0209109 CU

Know Ohio league
A buckeye symposium. Columbus, Ohio., The "Know Ohio" leabue, nd
12p.

NK 0209110 OClWHi

Know Rhode Island. [1st]- ed.
[Providence] 1927-
v. illus. 21-23 cm.
First-5th ed. issued by the State Bureau of Information of Rhode Island; 6th- ed. by the Dept. of State of Rhode Island.

1. Rhode Island—Descr. & trav. I. Rhode Island. State Bureau of Information. II. Rhode Island. Dept. of State.
F84.K5 917.45 28-27111 rev*

NK 0209111 DLC MH

Know Rochester; civic weekly and buyers' guide. Rochester, Minn, 1925?

NK 0209112 MnHi

Know Ross county
see under [Keeler, Fred R.]

A Know something.
The Know nothings. An expose of the secret order of the Know nothings ...
see under title

The know-something. Down with proscription! Equal rights forever!! "Eternal vigilance is the price of liberty." ... [185-?]
7 p. 23cm.

Signed: Julian.
"By Isaac Seely, Jr.": manuscript note.

1. Aliens - U. S. I. Seely, Isaac

NK 0209115 NNC

Know the Americas. no.1- June 1952-
Washington, D.C., Pan American Union.
no. in v. 25cm.
Some numbers accompanied by supplements.

1. Latin America. I. Pan American union.

NK 0209116 TxU DLC

Pam 972.511 (282) Cathedral
Know the Cathedral of Mexico. Conozca la Catedral de Mexico. [n.p.,1953]
60p. illus. (part col.) 20 cm.
Cover title.
Foreword (Preambulo) signed: Phil.
English and Spanish.
1. Mexico (City) Catedral.

NK 0209117 LNHT

Know the truth. Statement from the entire colored delegation of the National Progressive Convention, Chicago, Aug. 7, 1912. [That colored delegates participated in the convention. New York: Mail and Express Job Print, 1912.] 2 l. 8°.

In: IO (1912) p. v. 1, no. 14.

1. United States.—Politics, 1912. 2. Negro, U. S., 1912.
N. Y. P. L. March 31, 1913.

NK 0209118 NN

Know then, my brethren. Song [S. or T.].
(In Smith. Musica antiqua. P. 56. London. [1812.])

E8334 — Songs. With music.

NK 0209119 MB

Know thyself. v. 1-2; Sept. 1923 - Feb. 1925 Girard, Kansas.
2 v. illus. 27cm.

Monthly.
Edited by W. J. Fielding and E. Haldeman-Julius.
Absorbed by Haldeman-Julius monthly, March 1925.

1. Freethinking—Per. and soc. publ. I. Fielding, William John, 1886- ed. II. Haldeman-Julius, Emanuel, 1889- , ed.

NK 0209120 NN

Know thyself; or, Nature's secrets revealed; a word at the right time to the boy, girl, young man, young woman, husband, wife, father and mother, also timely counsel, help and instruction for every member of every home; including important hints on social purity, heredity, physical manhood and womanhood, by noted specialists; introduced by Bishop Samuel Fallows ... one of the collaborators ... medical department by W. J. Truitt ... Marietta, O., The S. A. Mullikin company, 1911.
602 p. col. front., illus., col. plates. 20½cm. $2.25
1. Medicine, Popular. 2. Marriage. I. Fallows, Samuel, bp., 1835- II. Truitt, William J.
Library of Congress RC81.K83 11-11207

NK 0209121 DLC IU NB NcGU

Know your allies
see under Supreme Headquarters, Allied Powers, Europe.

Know your ally; a brief record of Gt. Britain's contributions to the cause of democracy and liberty
see under Dixon, William Macneile, 1866-1945.

917.3 K76
Know your America program. [no.1-
Garden City, N.Y., N. Doubleday.
no. illus. (part col.) 21cm.

Prepared with the cooperation of the American Geographical Society.

1. U.S. - Descr. & trav. I. American Geographical Society of New York.

NK 0209124 TxU DLC

Know your boro; entering Kinnelon, New Jersey
see under Kinnelon League of Women Voters.

VOLUME 300

Know your cheese and how to sell it. New York, 1947
see under [Borden company]

Know your California; what to see on and off the highways
see under [Van Tuyle, Bert] comp.

Know your community as a basis for understanding the schools' problems
see under [Goodykoontz, Bess] 1894-

Know your Congress.
[Washington, Capital Publishers, etc.] 19
v. illus. 23-31 cm.
"Originally published in 1920."
Title varies: Pictorial directory of Congress (varies slightly)
Vols. called Inaugural ed.
L. C. set includes a v. 81 without edition designation, published by Hal. J. Miller News Service.

1. U. S. Congress.
JK1051.K6 53-976 rev ‡

NcD Or OrCS OCl NBuU DS MB LU NN P
NK 0209129 DLC TxU IU NN INS WHi ViU NRU DL AU

Know your county
see under [Greenough, Katharine (Croan)] 1889-

Know your destiny. Anonymous. New York [J. F. Tapley co.] 1918.
102 p. 19cm.
Attributed to Carolyn Spencer Halsted.

Library of Congress BF1773.K6 19-1661

NK 0209131 DLC OKentU NN

Know your fighting men: a hand-book of timely information with...description of the insignia marking the ranks of officers and the divisions and subdivisions of branches of the United States army and navy... Lynn, Mass., G. H. & A. L. Nichols, inc. [c1917]
59 p.

NK 0209132 MiD-B

Know your horses and jockeys
see under [Evans, Ben Taylor] 1918-

... Know your navy ...

[Portland, 33cm.

Weekly.
Caption-title.
Reproduced from typewritten copy.
Radio programs presented over Station KOIN by the Portland Navy recruiting station in cooperation with the Portland civic theatre; prepared by the Oregon Writers' project of the Work projects administration.

1. No subject. I. United States. Navy recruiting service. II. United States. Works progress administration. Oregon.
N. Y. P. L. August 6, 1942

NK 0209134 NN

Know your presidents; from George Washington to Franklin D. Roosevelt
see under [Perks, Catharine Agnes]

M-10
5880
KNOW your navy.
Washington. v. illus., ports. 29cm.

Monthly, Jan.-Oct. 1950; quarterly, 1951-Aug. 1952.
Suspended publication between Apr. 1951 and Aug. 1952.
Published by the Navy league of the United States.
Ceased publication with Aug. 1952.

1. Navy, U.S.--Per. and soc. publ. I. Navy league of the United States.

NK 0209136 NN DLC

Know your own mind; a comedy
see under Murphy, Arthur, 1727-1805.

Know your own state. Virginia
see under [Standard oil company]

Know your packaging materials: foils, paper, films, boxboard, foam plastics

see under

American Management Association.

... Know your school child ...
see under [Davis, Mary Dabney] 1884-

Know your school. Know your teacher
see under [Deffenbaugh, Walter Sylvanus] 1872-

Know your school. Know your school library
see under [Beust, Nora Ernestine] 1888-

... Know your school principal ...
see under [Deffenbaugh, Walter Sylvanus] 1872-

Know your state. [New York? 1950]
see under Garden Club of America. Conservation Committee.

... Know your state educational program ...
see under [Deffenbaugh, Walter Sylvanus] 1872-

... Know your superintendent ...
see under [Deffenbaugh, Walter Sylvanus] 1872-

... Know your teacher ...
see under [Deffenbaugh, Walter Sylvanus] 1872-

T791.9
K76s
Know your Texas (Radio program)
[A series of radio scripts written by Joe Murphy and Marye Benjamin and produced by the University of Texas Radio House]
no.1- Oct. 9, 1951-
[Austin, Tex.]
v. 28cm.

I. Murphy, Joe Virgil. II. Benjamin, Marye, joint author. III. Texas. University. Radio House.

NK 0209148 TxU

Know your Texas state hospitals and special schools. [Assembled by Staff members of the various institutions. Austin, Tex., Hogg Foundation for Mental Hygiene, 1954]
30p. 26cm.

1. Hospitals - Texas. 2. Asylums - Texas. 3. Public welfare - Texas. I. Texas. Bard for Texas State Hospitals and Special Schols. II. Texas. University. Hogg Foundation.

NK 0209149 TxU

R533.565
K76
KNOW your war planes.
[Atlanta, Ga. Coca-Cola Company. c1943] unp. illus.(part col.)

NK 0209150 WaS

Know your weapons.
no.

London: Nicholson & Watson [194 18cm.
nos. illus.

1. Guns. 2. Ordnance.
N. Y. P. L. November 6, 1942

NK 0209151 NN DLC

Know your weeds
see under Nebraska. Dept. of Agriculture and Economic Development.

Know your woolfacts...1953-1954

see under

Wool bureau, inc., New York.

VOLUME 300

HQ1 .K5

Know-yourself; life mysteries explained with pictures. v.1 June 1938- ₍New York, Popular medicine, ᶜ1938₎- v. illus. 23½cm. monthly. (irregular)

Editor: June 1938- Hugo Gernsback.

1. Hygiene, Sexual--Period. I. Gernsback, Hugo, 1884- ed.

NK 0209154 DLC

Knower, Daniel.

The adventures of a forty-niner. An historic description of California, with events and ideas of San Francisco and its people in those early days. By Daniel Knower. Albany, Weed-Parsons printing co., 1894.

200 p. plates, port., facsim. 19cm.

1. California—Gold discoveries. 2. California—Descr. & trav. 3. San Francisco, Cal. I. Title.

Library of Congress F865.K7 1-Rc-801

NK 0209155 DLC CaBViPA CaBVaU MiU PU NN FTaSU MsU TxU MU InU GU CU-A OkU MoU

Microcard 1007

Knower, Daniel.

The adventures of a forty-niner, an historic description of California, with events and ideas of San Francisco and its people in those early days. Albany ₍N.Y.₎ Weed-Parsons Print Co., 1894.

200 p. 19cm.

Micro-opaque. 6 cards. (Nineteenth century American literature and history. Ser. C: The Trans-Mississippi West)

1. Calif. - Gold discoveries. 2. Calif. - Description. 3. San Francisco, Calif. I. Title.

NK 0209156 CSf

Knower, Daniel.

Ceremonies of laying the corner-stone of the monument to David Williams, one of the captors of Major Andre. At Schoharie court house, September 23, 1876. Albany, Weed, Parsons and company, printers. 1876.

Knower, Daniel

Homestead of David William:

4 pp. (Mag. Am. Hist. v. 17, 1887, p. 163.)

NK 0209158 MdBP

Knower, Edward Cronin, d. 1897, ed.

Gilchrist, James Grant.

A manual for infantry officers of the national guard ... comp. by Col. J. G. Gilchrist ... rev. by Lieut. E. C. Knower ... Chicago, A. C. McClurg & company, 1887.

Knower, Franklin Hayward, 1901–

An experimental study of the effect of argument on changes of attitude ... by Franklin Hayward Knower ... ₍Minneapolis? 1936₎

cover-title, p. 315-347, 522-532, 114-127. 25cm.

Thesis (PH. D.)—University of Minnesota, 1933.

Vita.

Parts 2 and 3 (23cm) incorrectly bound in front of pt. 1.

Pt. 1 offprinted from the Journal of social psychology, 1935, 6, 315-347; pt. 2 reprinted from the Journal of abnormal and social psychology, vol. XXX, no. 4, January–March, 1936; pt. 3 reprinted from Applied psychology, vol. XX, no. 1, p. 114-127, February, 1936.

CONTENTS.—I. A study of the effect of oral argument on changes of attitude.—II. A study of the effect of printed argument on changes in attitude.—III. Some incidence of attitude changes.

1. Attitude (Psychology) I. Title: Argument, An experimental study of the effect of.

Library of Congress HM291.K6 1933 38-6089

Univ. of Minnesota Libr.

——— Copy 2. ₍2₎ 301.15

NK 0209160 MnU DLC

PN4121 .B315

Knower, Franklin Hayward, 1901- joint author.

Baird, Albert Craig, 1883–

General speech, an introduction; by A. Craig Baird and Franklin H. Knower. 1st ed. New York, McGraw-Hill Book Co., 1949.

Knower, Franklin Hayward, 1901-

A preliminary outline of a course of study in fundamentals of speech for Minnesota high schools proposed for the consideration of students and teachers of speech. n.p.₍1938₎

ii p.,₍1₎ 118 l. 28cm.

Prepared with the assistance of workers supplied by the Works progress administration, University of Minnesota research project, W.P.5209, Sub-project,231

NK 0209162 OrU MiEM

Knower, Franklin Hayward, 1901- joint author.

Gilkinson, Howard, 1898–

Psychological studies of individual differences among students of speech ₍by₎ Howard Gilkinson ... and Franklin H. Knower ... ₍Minneapolis₎ H. Gilkinson and F. H. Knower, 1939.

Knower, Franklin Hayward, 1901–

Speech education in Ohio; a research survey of speech education in Ohio schools for the year of 1948–49, conducted with the cooperation of the Ohio Association of College Teachers of Speech. Columbus, Dept. of Speech, Ohio State University ₍1950₎

v, 157 p. 22 cm.

1. Speech—Study and teaching. I. Title.

PN4092.O4K5 808.5 51-62045

NK 0209164 DLC CaBVaU TxU

Z6514 .S7S7

Knower, Franklin Hayward, 1901-

Speech Association of America.

Table of contents of the Quarterly journal of speech, 1915–1952, Speech monographs, 1934–1952, and the Speech teacher, 1952; with a revised index compiled through 1952, by Franklin H. Knower. ₍Iowa City, Iowa, 1953₎

QL801 .A4

Knower, Henry McElderry, 1868- ed.

The **American** journal of anatomy. v. 1– Nov. 7, 1901– Philadelphia ₍etc.₎ Wistar Institute of Anatomy and Biology.

Knower, Henry McElderry, 1868- ed.

Sabin, Florence Rena, 1871–

An atlas of the medulla and midbrain, by Florence R. Sabin, M. D. A laboratory manual, illustrated with seven colored plates, one black plate and fifty-two figures; ed. by Henry McE. Knower ... Baltimore, Md., The Friedenwald company, 1901.

Knower (H[enry] McE[ldery]). A comparative study of the development of the generative tract in termites. 3 pp., 2 pl. 8°. *Baltimore, 1901.*

Repr. from: Johns Hopkins Hosp. Bull., Balt., 1901, xii.

NK 0209168 DNLM

KNOWER, Henry McElderry, 1868-

Effects of early removal of the heart and arrest of the circulation on the development of frog imbryos. Baltimore, 1907.

NK 0209169 MH

Knower, Henry McElderry, 1868–

The embryology of a termite eutermes (rippertii?) (I) (Including a contribution to the discussion as to the primitive type of development, and the origin of embryonic membranes ₍amnion₎ and of the mesoderm in the *Insecta*) Boston, Ginn & co., 1899.

1 p. l., 64 p., 1 l. fold. pl. 8°.

Inaug.-diss.—Johns Hopkins university.

Reprinted from vol. XVI of the Journal of morphology.

1. Eutermes rippertii. 2. Embryology—Insects. 1—1568

Library of Congress QL958.K7

NK 0209170 DLC NIC NjP MiU MB MH OU OClW

Knower, Henry McElderry, 1868–

A resurvey of the development of lymphatics and associated blood vessels in anuran *Amphibia* by the method of injection ₍by₎ Henry McElderry Knower ... Five text figures and nineteen plates (forty figures) ... Philadelphia, The Wistar institute of anatomy and biology, 1939.

125 p., 1 l. incl. illus., 19 pl. 25½cm. (American anatomical memoirs. no. 18)

Bibliography: p. 84-87.

1. Lymphatics. 2. Embryology—Batrachia. 3. Frogs. 40-1565

Library of Congress QL841.K7

₍4₎ 611.4

NK 0209171 DLC CaBVaU TxU CU NcD PU OO OU ViU

A Knowing Hand.

The horse, his beauties and defects

see under title

Knowing how to stop, a technique for the prevention of th wrong use of the self, an introduction to the work of F Matthias Alexander. London, Chaterson ltd. ₍1946₎

v, 61, ₍1₎ p. 18½cm.

"First published 1946."

CONTENTS.—Instinct and functioning in health and disease, by Peter Macdonald.—The F. Matthias Alexander technique and its relation to education, by I. G. Griffith.—End-gaining and means-whereby, by Aldous Huxley.—F. Matthias Alexander and the problem of animal behaviour, by A. Rugg-Gunn.—The work of F. M. Alexander and the Medical white paper, by D. S. Radcliffe Drew.—Knowing how to stop, by Winfred Barlow.—The F. Matthias Alexander technique, by F. P. Jones.—Some objections answered, by Wilfred Barlow.

1. Alexander, Frederick Matthias, 1869– 2. Self. 3. Mind and body. 4. Mental healing.

BF145.A59K58 131.3 46-22090

NK 0209173 DLC ICJ DNLM

Knowing people; graphology, scientific character analysis and self development. v. 1– Aug. 15, 1919– ₍Philadelphia, D. B. Lucas₎ 1919–24; ₍Detroit, Mich., D. B. Lucas₎ 1924–

v. illus. 27½-29cm.

Monthly, Aug. 1919–July 1920; quarterly, Oct. 1920–

Title varies: Aug. 1919–June 1920, Now, a magazine of the present; graphology, scientific character analysis and self development. July 1920– Knowing people ...

Editor: Aug. 1919– D. B. Lucas.

1. Graphology—Period. I. Lucas, De Witt Bannister, 1876– ed

Library of Congress BF889.K6 28-9921

NK 0209174 DLC OCl

Knowland, Helen Davis (Herrick)

Madame Baltimore. ₍A novel of suspense₎ New York, Dodd, Mead, 1949.

210 p. 22 cm. (Red badge detective)

I. Title.

PZ3.K7599Mad 49-2535*

NK 0209175 DLC WaE OrP TxU

VOLUME 300

TT 595 .K73 Knowland, J., sr.
Key to the J. Knowland combination coat and vest system. It contains all the matter explanatory of the draughts contained in the book entitled as above. By J. Knowland, sr. Kansas City, Tiernan-Havens printing co., 1890.
24 p. 22.5 cm.

NK 0209176 DLC

Knowland, Joseph Russell, 1873–1966
California, a landmark history; story of the preservation and marking of early day shrines ... by Joseph R. Knowland ... [Oakland, Calif., Tribune press, °1941]
xviii, 245 p. illus., plates, ports. 22½ cm.

1. California—Hist. 2. California—Historic houses, etc.

Library of Congress F862.K68 42-5610
[18] 979.4

Or
NK 0209177 DLC WaS IdU OrP OrU CaBViP CU-S CU PPD

F856 C2266K5 Knowland, Joseph Russell, 1873-1966.
The California Historic Landmarks League: what it has accomplished in three years; what it hopes to accomplish. [San Francisco] 1905.
14 p. illus. 26cm.

Cover title.
Signed copy.

1. California Historic Landmarks League. 2. Historic landmarks - California.

NK 0209178 CU-B

Knowland, Joseph Russell, 1873–1966

U. S. *Congress. House. Committee on interstate and foreign commerce.*
... Operation of Panama canal ... Report. <To accompany H. R. 21969.> [Washington, Govt. print. off., 1912]

F851 K6 Knowland, Joseph Russell, 1873-1966
Pacific Coast terminals and a review of recent legislation by Congress for the development and encouragement of water transportation. Speech of Hon. Joseph R. Knowland of California before the tenth Annual convention of the National Rivers and Harbors Congress ... December 4, 1913. [Washington, Govt. Print. Off., 1913]
8 p. 24cm.

Caption title.

NK 0209180 CU-B

Knowland, Joseph Russell, 1873-1966

Wagner, Harr, 1857–
Pacific history stories, arranged and retold for use in the public schools, by Harr Wagner, assisted by Alice Rose Power San Francisco, Harr Wagner publishing company. 1918.

Knowland, Joseph Russell. 1873-1966

U. S. *Congress. House. Committee on interstate and foreign commerce.*
... [Panama canal tolls] Section 5 of an act to provide for the opening, maintenance, protection, and operation of the Panama canal, etc. ... Report. <To accompany H. R. 14385.> [Washington, Govt. print. off., 1914]

Knowland, Joseph Russell, 1873–1966, *comp.*
Panama canal tolls. Symposium of views protesting against a surrender of American rights and upholding the side of the United States in the toll controversy. A discussion of the Hay-Pauncefote treaty, of the right of foreign nations to interfere in our domestic affairs, and of the influences back of the effort to repeal the sections of the Panama canal act beneficial to American commerce. Extracts from Congressional record and public documents comp. by Hon. Joseph R. Knowland ... 1912-1913. Washington [Govt. print. off.] 1913.
134 p. 23½ cm.
1. Panama canal—Rates and tolls. 2. Hay-Pauncefote treaty, 1901. I. Title.

Library of Congress HE537.9.T7K62 13-35490

NK 0209183 DLC CU-B NN ViU CU ICJ

Knowland, Joseph Russell, 1873-1966.
A permanent Tariff Board ... Speech of Hon. Joseph R. Knowland of California in the House of Representatives, Thursday, May 4, 1911. Washington [Government Printing Office] 1911.
15 p. 4°. Bound in Maroon Cloth.

NK 0209184 CSmH

HE2710 A2K5 Knowland, Joseph Russell, 1873-1966.
Railroad bill - its many meritorious provisions - future stifling of water competition by railroads prevented; speech in the House of Representatives Tuesday, April 19, 1910. Washington, 1910.
13 p. 23cm.

1. Railroad law - U.S. 2. Railroad and state - U.S. 3. Interstate commerce. I. Title.

NK 0209185 CU-B

Knowland, Joseph Russell, 1873–1966
"The right of the United States to control the Panama canal." Address by Congressman Joseph R. Knowland, of California, to be delivered before the Lake Mohonk conference on international arbitration, Mohonk Lake, N. Y., on Friday, May 16, morning session. [Washington? 1913]
13 p. 23½ cm.

1. Panama canal.

Library of Congress HE537.9.T7K6 13-11502

NK 0209186 DLC

F855 .5 K62 Knowland, Joseph Russell, 1873–1966
[Speeches of the Hon. Joseph R. Knowland of California in the House of representatives of the United States] [Washington, 1906-12]
5 pamphlets in 1 v. 25cm.

Contents: Our naval shipbuilding policy. May 3, 1906.- The importance of the cruise of the battle-ship fleet to the Pacific ... a reply to Mr. Lilley's criticism of the Mare Island navy-yard. Speeches ... April 10, and ... April 16, 1908.- A permanent tariff board. May 4, 1911.- Operation of the Panama canal. May 16, 1912.- The white slave traffic act. June 15, 1912.

NK 0209187 CU-B

F855 .5 K59 Knowland, William Fife, 1908-
Address delivered by United States Senator William F. Knowland, Port of Oakland Day luncheon, Thursday noon, October 27, 1949, Outer Habor [!] Terminal of the Port of Oakland, under the joint auspices of Oakland Board of Port Commissioners [and the] Oakland Junior Chamber of Commerce. [Oakland? 1949?]
[8] p. 23cm.

NK 0209188 CU-B

Knowland, William Fife, 1908–
Republican Congress, seven months' progress. Review of the first session of the Eighty-third Congress, January 3, 1953–August 3, 1953, together with a summary of legislation. Washington, U. S. Govt. Print. Off., 1953.
33 p. 23 cm. (83d Cong., 1st sess. Senate. Document no. 75)

1. U. S. 83d Cong., 1st sess., 1953. 2. U. S.—Pol. & govt.—1945– (Series: U. S. 83d Cong., 1st sess., 1953. Senate. Document no. 75)

JK1059 83d.K57 53-63447

NK 0209189 DLC DS N

Knowland, William Fife, 1908–
The Republican record, security and welfare of American people advanced; review of achievements of the Eighty-third Congress, January 3, 1953–August 20, 1954, together with a summary of legislation. Washington, U. S. Govt. Print. Off., 1954.
65 p. 24 cm. (83d Cong., 2d sess. Senate. Document no. 156)

1. U. S. 83d Cong., 1953–1954. 2. U. S.—Pol. & govt.—1953– I. Title. (Series: U. S. 83d Cong., 2d sess., 1954. Senate. Document no. 156)
JK1059 83d.K58 54-60738

NK 0209190 DLC DS N

Knowland, William Fife, 1908–
Republican report on the first session of the 84th Congress, together with Republican achievements, January 1953 to July 1955. Washington, U. S. Govt. Print. Off., 1955.
50 p. 24 cm. (84th Cong., 1st sess. Senate. Document no. 86)

1. U. S. 84th Cong., 1st sess., 1955. 2. U. S.—Pol. & govt.—1953– (Series: U. S. 84th Cong., 1st sess., 1955. Senate. Document no. 86)
JK1059 84th.K6 55-63307
Library of Congress [2]

NK 0209191 DLC

Knowle, Eng.
The records of Knowle
see under Downing, Thomas William, 1864– comp.

Knowle, Eng. Gild.
The register of the guild of Knowle in the county of Warwick. 1451–1535. From the original manuscript in the Public reference library, Birmingham. Transcribed and ed. by W. B. Bickley for the archaeological section of the Birmingham and Midland institute. Walsall, W. H. Robinson, 1894.
xlii, [1], a–c p., 1 l., 272, [i]–xxxix p. illus., facsim. 28½ cm.
Title vignette.
This copy "no. 63."
I. Bickley, W. B. II. Birmingham and Midland institute.

A 13-1116

Title from Peabody Inst., Baltimore. Printed by L. C.

NK 0209193 MdBP CaBViP NN CtY PU

Knowle Mental Hospital, Fareham, Eng.
see Fareham, Eng. Knowle Mental Hospital.

Knowledge. v. 1–
Oct. 1903–
New York, The Business and finance publishing co., 1906–
v. in 30 cm. monthly.
Title varies: Oct. 1903–June 1909, Business and finance.
July 1909– Knowledge.
Editor: July 1909– Robert Ruxton.
Official organ of the American brokers' association, Nov. 1906–June 1909.

1. Business—Period. I. Ruxton, Robert, ed. II. American brokers' association, New York.

9-34821†

Library of Congress HF5001.K7

NK 0209195 DLC

VOLUME 300

Knowledge. A journal of information, advice and suggestion for the direct-by-mail advertiser. Philadelphia. no. 1-109, 1915-Jan, 1926.
Subtitle varies.

NK 0209196 MiU ICJ

Knowledge ... A monthly record of science. v. 1-8, Nov. 1881-Oct. 1885; v. 9-26 (new ser., v. 1-18) Nov. 1885-Jan. 1904; v. ⌊27⌋-40 (new ser., v. 1-14) Feb. 1904-Oct./Dec. 1917. London, Wyman & sons ⌊etc.⌋ 1882-1917.
40 v. in 39. illus., plates, facsims. 29cm.
Weekly, Nov. 1881-Oct. 1885; monthly, Nov. 1885-Dec. 1916.
Vol. 40 consists of 2 no. (Jan./Sept. and Oct./Dec. 1917)
Title varies: Nov. 1881-Jan. 1904, Knowledge; an illustrated magazine of science ... (later "of science, literature & art")
Feb. 1904-Apr. 1910, Knowledge & illustrated scientific news (caption title: Knowledge & scientific news)
May 1910-Dec. 1917, Knowledge ... A monthly record of science.

Editors: 1881-88, R. A. Proctor.—1889-94, A. C. Ranyard.—1904-Apr. 1910, B. F. S. Baden-Powell, E. S. Grew.—May 1910-Dec. 1917, W. M. Webb, E. S. Grew.
Absorbed Illustrated scientific news in Feb. 1904, Hardwicke's science gossip in 1910.
No more published.

1. Science—Period. I. Proctor, Richard Anthony, 1837-1888, ed II. Ranyard, Arthur Cowper, 1845-1894, ed. III. Baden-Powell, Baden Fletcher Smyth, 1860- ed. IV. Grew, Edwin Sharpe, 1867- ed V. Webb, Wilfred Mark, 1868- ed.
18-9853 Revised

Library of Congress Q1.K7

OO NjP ICJ MB
NK 0209198 DLC ICN CaBVaU WaS NIC NNE ICRL DSI

Knowledge. A monthly record of science.
Aeronautics ... v. 1-21; Dec. 1907-July 28, 1921. London ⌊King, Sell & Olding, ltd., etc., 1907-21⌋

Knowledge: a weekly magazine. Supplementing all cyclopedias. v. 1; June-Dec. 1890. New York, J. B. Alden, 1891.
1 p. l., 586 p. 19½ x 11cm.
Cover-title: The Knowledge annual. 1890.

Library of Congress AG5.K7 7-19878†

NK 0209200 DLC OClWHi

Knowledge; an illustrated magazine of science
see Knowledge ... A monthly record of science.

Knowledge. Being a journal of common sense on the subject of advertising
see Knowledge. A journal of information, advice and suggestion for the direct-by-mail advertiser.

Knowledge; the magazine of scientific progress
see
Scientific progress; the news magazine of science.

Knowledge and choice literature, an illustrated weekly paper. New York, John B. Alden, 1892.
[3] v.

NK 0209204 N

... **Knowledge** and foreknowledge. The symposia read at the joint session of the Aristotelian society and the Mind association at the University, Bristol, July 9th-11th, 1937. London, Harrison and sons, ltd., 1937.
2 p. l., 245 p. 21½cm. (Aristotelian society. Supplementary vol. XVI)
CONTENTS.—The inaugural address—The teaching of philosophy, by G. C. Field.—Symposium: Induction and hypothesis. I. By Margaret MacDonald. II. By G. Ryle. III. By I. Berlin.—Symposium: Is there an absolute good? I. By W. G. de Burgh. II. By J. Laird. III. By C. A. Campbell.—Symposium: Does philosophy analyse common sense? I. By A. E. Duncan Jones. II. By A. J. Ayer.—The philosophical implications of foreknowledge. By C. D. Broad.—The philosophical implications of precognition. By C. D. Broad and H. H. Price.
1. Knowledge, Theory of. I. Aristotelian society for the systematic study of philosophy, London. II. Mind association.
A 38-516

Virginia. Univ. Librar
for Library of Congress [B11.A7 suppl. vol. 16]
⌊a2⌋ (106.242)

NK 0209205 ViU CaBVaU UU OCU OU DLC

Knowledge & illustrated scientific news
see Knowledge ... A monthly record of science.

The Knowlege and practice of Christianity made easy to the meanest capacities
see under Wilson, Thomas, Bp. of Sodor and Man, 1663-1755.

... **Knowledge** and society; a philosophical approach to modern civilization, by G. P. Adams, W. R. Dennes, J. Loewenberg, D. S. Mackay, P. Marhenke, S. C. Pepper ⌊and⌋ E. W. Strong ... New York, London, D. Appleton-Century company, incorporated ⌊©1938⌋
xiii, 417 p. 23 cm. (The Century philosophy series)

1. Civilization—Philosophy. I. Adams, George Plimpton, 1882- II. Dennes, William Ray, 1898-
38-9890

Library of Congress CB19.K55
⌊49q1⌋ 901

MiU NcD LU CU OrU CaBVaU WaWW
OClW OU DAU IdPI OrCS OrSaW WaTC PPD IdU TU KyLxT
NK 0209208 DLC MtU WaS OrPR TU PU PHC NN OO OCU

Knowledge and society.

... **Selected** writings in philosophy, a companion volume Knowledge and society, compiled by G. P. Adams, W. R. Dennes, J. Loewenberg, D. S. Mackay, P. Marhenke, S. C. Pepper ⌊and⌋ E. W. Strong ... New York, London, D. Appleton-Century company incorporated ⌊©1939⌋

The **Knowledge** annual. 1890
see
Knowledge: a weekly magazine.

The **knowledge** book; science, invention, discovery, progress ... supplemented by a series of review questions for students ... by Ferdinand Ellsworth Cary ... Emory Adams Allen ... Thomas H. Russell ... Embellished and illuminated with over six hundred photographic half-tone illustrations and color plates ... Marietta, O., The S. A. Mullikin company, 1915.
764 p. col. front., illus., col. plates, ports. (1 col.) 24cm.

1. Encyclopedias and dictionaries. I. Cary, Ferdinand Ellsworth, 1848- ed. II. Allen, Emory Adams, 1853- joint ed. III. Russell, Thomas Herbert, 1862- joint ed.
16-738

Library of Congress AG105.K6 1915

NK 0209211 DLC ViU

Knowledge diary and scientific handbook. London, Knowledge Office.
v. illus. annual.

Began 1901.

NK 0209212 ICRL ICJ RPB NN

... **Knowledge,** experience and realism. The symposia read at the joint session of the Aristotelian society and the Mind association at the University college, Nottingham, July 12th-15th, 1929. London, Harrison and sons, ltd., 1929.
iii, 225 p. 21½cm. (Aristotelian society. Supplementary vol. IX)
CONTENTS.—The inaugural address: Probability and paradox, by F. Granger.—Symposium: Indirect knowledge. I. By G. E. Moore. II By H. W. B. Joseph.—Symposium: Negation. I. By J. D. Mabbott. II By G. Ryle. III. By H. H. Price.—Symposium: Realism and modern physics. I. By J. Laird. II. By C. E. M. Joad. III. By L. S. Stebbing.—Address: Logical form, by F. Wittgenstein.—Symposium: Immediate experience. I. By G. Dawes Hicks. II. By B. Edgell. III. By G. C. Field.
1. Knowledge, Theory of. 2. Experience. 3. Realism. I. Aristotelian society for the systematic study of philosophy, London. II. Mind association.
A 33-408

Virginia. Univ. Library
for Library of Congress [B11.A7 suppl. vol. 9]
⌊a40d1⌋

NK 0209213 ViU CaBVaU CU OCU OU OClW ICN DLC

Knowledge for every child
see under [Tuttle, George] 18?4-1872.

Knowledge for free men ... ⌊Essays by Carl M. White, and others, on the Bicentennial theme at Columbia University. New York, 1954.
23, 26, 22, 24 l.

Reproduced from typewritten copy.
Never published. Cf. first leaf.
Contents.--The open door to knowledge, by C. M. White.--Knowledge on the job, by H. J. Carman.--The open paths to knowledge, by Allan Nevins.--Knowledge for the free man, by R. M. MacIver.

NK 0209215 NNC

[Knowledge for the people: or, The plain why and because
see under [Timbs, John] 1801-1875.

Knowledge in a nut-shell; or, Repository of valuable information
see under [Byrn, Marcus Lafayette]

KNOWLEDGE in a nutshell. Pearl English dictionary,Atlas of the world, Gazetteer of the world,and Book of general information. New York,F.A.Stokes Co.,[18-].

4 vol.

NK 0209218 MH

Knowledge is gold!
see under [Frederick, John]

Knowledge is the door; a forerunner.
121 Privately printed. [London, J. & E.
K73N Bumpus, 1937]
73 p. 18 cm.
The name of author and printer supplied in presentation letter on flyleaf: "This little book was compiled by Charlotte F. Shaw and privately printed for her by J. Girslow [?]"
1. Knowledge, Theory of. I. Shaw, Charlotte Frances Payne-Townshend.

NK 0209219 NcD

VOLUME 300

The **knowledge** library; science, invention, discovery, progress ... supplemented by a series of review questions for students, by Ferdinand Ellsworth Cary ... Emory Adams Allen ... Thomas H. Russell ... Embellished and illuminated with nearly six hundred and fifty photographic half-tone illustrations and color plates ... Marietta, O., The S. A. Mullikin company, 1918.
764 p. col. front., illus., col. plates, ports. (1 col.) 24½cm.
Published in 1915 under title: The knowledge book.
1. Encyclopedias and dictionaries. I. Cary, Ferdinand Ellsworth, 1848- joint ed. II. Russell, Thomas Herbert, 1862- ed. III. Allen, Emory Adams, 1853- joint ed.
18-14844 Revised
Library of Congress AG105.K6 1918

NK 0209220 DLC

[The Knowledge (!)] of Christ recommended
see under Pemberton, Ebenezer, 1704-1777.

The Knowledge of Divine Things from Revelation, not from Reason or Nature
see under Ellis, John, D.D.

Knowledge of general science ...
see under [Philp, Robert Kemp] 1819-1882.

The knowledge of medals ...
see under [Jobert, Louis] 1637-1719.

Knowledge of natural history ...
see under [Philp, Robert Kemp] 1819-1882.

Knowledge of one another in the future state. Philadelphia, Henry Perkins, 1838.
47 p. 24°.

NK 0209226 DLC

Knowledge of the Bible ...
see under [Philp, Robert Kemp] 1819-1882.

The knowledge of the heavens and the earth made easy
see under Watts, Isaac, 1674-1748.

The knowledge of the world: or, The art of well-educating youth ...
see under [Chévremont, Jean Baptiste de] 1640-1702, supposed author.

The knowledge of things unknown
see under Godfridus, astronomer.

Knowledge Office, London.
Knowledge diary and scientific handbook
see under title

Knowledge Organization Bureau, *London.*
[Pamphlets on the Knowledge Organization Bureau. **London,** 1905.]
78912
12 pamphlets in 1 vol. 25½cm.
Secretary: Marshall Bruce Williams.

NK 0209232 ICJ

Knowledge the soul of freedom. [Verse.]
Broadside. Boston. Printed by N. Coverly. [178-?] Size, 10 × 8½ inches. Vignette.

L.7313 — Broadsides. — Coverly, Nathaniel, printer.

NK 0209233 MB

FILM 4468
Knowler, A E
Interm report on an experimental 2-1/4 in. high speed tunnel of the injector type. [n. p.] 1944.
Microfilm copy (negative)—University of Virginia.
Collation of the original: 4 l., illus., tables.

1. Tunnels.

NK 0209234 ViU

629.1306 G798r no.1933 Engin Lib'y
KNOWLER, A E
... On the drag of circular cylinders at high speeds, by A.E. Knowler ... and F.W. Pruden ... London, H.M. stationery off. [1944]
cover-title, 10p. incl. plates, diagrs. 30½cm. ([Gt. Brit. Air ministry] Aeronautical research committee. Reports and memoranda. R. & M. no. 1933 (7483) A.R.C. technical report)
At head of title: Ministry of aircraft production.
"References": p.4.
1. Air resistance. 2. Cylinders. I. Pruden, F.W., joint author. II. Title. III. Series (contents)

NK 0209235 TxU

Knowler, Bethel O
The little Australian's first book of English ... Perth, Australia, Carroll's ltd., c1941.
32 p.

NK 0209236 MiEM

Knowler, Lloyd A.
Quality control by statistical methods ...
see under Iowa. University. College of engineering.

Knowler, Lloyd A.

Iowa. *Old age assistance commission.*
Revision of rating system in use by the Iowa Old age assistance commission. Prepared for the Iowa Old age assistance commission by Lloyd A. Knowler and Donald A. Trauger. January, 1937. Iowa Old age assistance commission. Des Moines, Ia. [1937]

Knowler, William, 1699-1773, ed.

Strafford, Thomas Wentworth, *1st earl of,* **1593-1641.**
The Earl of Strafforde's letters and dispatches, with an essay towards his life, by Sir George Radcliffe. From the originals in the possession of his great grandson ... Thomas, earl of Malton, knight of the Bath. By William Knowler ... London, Printed for the editor by W. Bowyer, 1739.

Knowler, William, 1699-1773.

DA20 .C17 new ser. no. 53
Firth, *Sir* **Charles Harding, 1857-1936,** *ed.*
Papers relating to Thomas Wentworth, first earl of Strafford. From the mss. of Dr. William Knowler. Edited by C. H. Firth ... [Westminster] The Camden society, 1890.

Knowles,
Naughty Clara
see Knowles, W

Knowles, Canon
see Knowles, John Harris, 1832-1908.

Knowles, Mrs.
Dialogue between Mrs. Knowles and Dr. Johnson
see Knowles, Mary (Morris) 1733-1807.

Knowles, A.
A. Knowles' improvements in machinery and apparatus for cutting and getting coal... Manchester: G. Falkner, 1871.
10 p. 4 pl. 8°.

405122A. 1. Coal—Mines and mini —Machinery.
N. Y. P. L. December 27, 1929

NK 0209244 NN

Knowles, A Edgar
... The manufacture of oxygen, with special reference to its production electrolytically. London, Pub. by the Institution, 1925.
29p. illus.
At head of title: The Institution of welding engineers.

NK 0209245 OU

---

652 K761
Knowles (A.W.) & Co., Detroit.
Real pen work, self-instructor in penmanship... Detroit, Mich. [c1884]
1v.(chiefly illus.,part col.) 23x29cm.
On cover: Self-instructor in pencil, pen work, penmanship.
1. Penmanship. I. Title. II. Title: Self-instructor in pencil, pen work, penmanship.

NK 0209246 OrU

Knowles, Alan.
The trade of West Africa. London, Sheldon Press [1943]
15 p. 17 cm. (African home library, 26)
"Talks ... first prepared for broadcasting in Africa through local stations."

1. Africa, West—Comm. I. Series.
HF3876.K56 382 48-33163*
[1]

NK 0209247 DLC

VOLUME 300

Knowles, Almon.
...Song book...
see under Boy Scouts of America. Brooklyn Council.

KNOWLES, Andrew and Co. v. McADAM, J.K.
Colliery Income Tax Appeal Report of Income Tax Appeal Case under the Act 37 & Vict., c. 16. High Court of Justice, Exchequer Division, 1877. London, n. d.
80 p. 12 mo.
"Reprinted from 'The Colliery Guardian'".

NK 0209249 MH-L

Knowles, Antoinette.
Oral English; or, The art of speaking, by Antoinette Knowles ... Boston, New York [etc.] D. C. Heath & co. [c1916]
vi, 361 p. 19cm.
Bibliography: p. [344]-353.

1. Oratory. 2. Elocution. 3. English language—Rhetoric. I. Title.
16—20918
Library of Congress PN4121.K9

NK 0209250 OCl NN DLC Wa NcRS PP MiU OClUr OO OClh OOxM

*PS3521 .N72A4 1913
Knowles, Archibald Campbell, 1865-
Adventures in the Alps. London, Skeffington, 1913.
xi, 175 p. 19cm.
Inscribed by the author.

NK 0209251 ViU NN

Knowles, Archibald Campbell. 1865-
Adventures in the Alps.
— Philadelphia. Jacobs & Co. [1913.] xi, 175, (1) pp. Plates. 19 cm., in 8s.

K646 — T.r. — Alps. Geog. — Mountain climbing.

NK 0209252 MB CtY

Knowles, Archibald Campbell, 1865-
Balsam boughs, being Adirondack and other stories; by Archibald Campbell Knowles ... Philadelphia, Porter & Coates, 1893.
4 p. l., 200 p. front., plates. 19cm.
CONTENTS.—The signor.—Old Grumps.—Little Tim's Christmas.—Love victorious.—A romance of Eden.—The lake of the Broken Heart.—Her mistake.—Lost in the Indian pass.—A mountain ramble.—A jolly good time.—A mother's love.—I'm going home.—The guide's story.—Balsam boughs.

7—14185
Library of Congress PZ3.K761B

NK 0209253 DLC NcD CtY CU PU PPL

Knowles, Archibald Campbell, 1865-
The belief and worship of the Anglican church Phila., 1894.
108p. 32°

NK 0209254 NBuG

Knowles, Archibald Campbell, 1896-
The belief and worship of the Anglican church with an explanation of her teaching and ritual ... 2nd ed., rev. and enl. With an introduction by ... Isaac Lea Nicholson ... Philadelphia, 1896.
xix, 319 p. 13 cm.

NK 0209255 RPB DLC PPPD PV

Knowles, Archibald Campbell, 1865-
The church and the greater sacraments. With a sketch concerning early church buildings. By Archibald Campbell Knowles. Milwaukee, The Young churchman co., 1894.
69 p. fold. tab. 17cm.

1. Sacraments—Anglican communion.
3-1875
Library of Congress BX5949.A1K6

NK 0209256 DLC

Knowles, Rev. Archibald Campbell, 1865-
Church unity. Philadelphia: G. W. Jacobs & Company [190-?]. 24 p. 8°.

1. Church unity.
N. Y. P. L. March 28, 1911.

NK 0209257 NN

Knowles, Archibald Campbell, 1865-
Come unto me; a manual of instructions and devotions for confirmation, holy communion and other occasions; written and comp. by ... A. C. Knowles. New York, E. P. Dutton & co. [1901]
xiii p., 1 l., 269 p. front., pl. 14½cm.

1. Protestant Episcopal church in the U. S. A.—Prayer-books and devotions—English. 2. Devotional exercises. I. Protestant Episcopal church in the U. S. A. Liturgy and ritual. II. Title.
1-24613
Library of Congress BX5940.K6

NK 0209258 DLC PU

Knowles, Archibald Campbell, 1865-
The doctrine, discipline and worship of the Anglican church, written and compiled by the Reverend Archibald Campbell Knowles ... Philadelphia and London, G. W. Jacobs & company [c1907]
3 p. l., 97 p. front., plates. 14cm.
To take the place of the author's "The belief and worship of the Anglican church," now withdrawn. cf. Pref.

7-18808

NK 0209259 DLC

Knowles, Archibald Campbell, 1865-
Franklin Delano Roosevelt, the great liberal [by] Archibald Campbell Knowles ... Burlington, N. J., Enterprise publishing co. [c1936]
64 p. 19cm.

1. Roosevelt, Franklin Delano, pres. U. S., 1882- 2. U. S.—Pol. & govt.—1933-
37-4312
Library of Congress E807.K66
——— Copy 2. [5] 923.173

NK 0209260 DLC PU PPT PBm

Knowles, Archibald Campbell, 1865-
The holy Christ-child; a devotional study of the incarnation of the Son of God... New York: T. Whittaker, 1905. vii(i), 154 p., 1 l. 12°.

1. Jesus Christ.—Incarnation. 2. Jesus Christ.—Birth. 3. Title.
N. Y. P. L. September 24, 1914.

NK 0209261 NN GEU PU PP

Knowles, Archibald Campbell, 1865-
Joscelyn Vernon. A story of the days of King Charles the first. By Archibald Campbell Knowles ... Philadelphia, G. W. Jacobs & co., 1898.
140 p. 18½cm.

1. Gt. Brit.—Hist.—Stuarts, 1603-1714—Fiction. I. Title.
98-1843 Revised
Library of Congress PZ3.K761J

NK 0209262 DLC OCl PU PPL

FILM Knowles, Archibald Campbell, 1865-
Joscelyn Vernon. A story of the days of King Charles the first. By Archibald Campbell Knowles ... Philadelphia, G. W. Jacobs & co., 1898.
140 p. 18½cm.
(Wright American Fiction, v. III, 1876-1900, no. 3181, Research Publications, Inc. Microfilm. Reel K-19)

NK 0209263 NcD CU

Knowles, Archibald Campbell, 1865-
A layman's Lent. An argument for its observance from an historical, Scriptural, and practical standpoint, by Archibald Campbell Knowles ... with a commendatory preface, by the Rt. Rev. Isaac Lea Nicholson ... Philadelphia, G. W. Jacobs & co., 1897.
138 p. 15cm.

1. Lent. I. Title.
37-16714
Library of Congress BV85.K6
Copyright 1897: 11123 [2] 248

NK 0209264 DLC PPD

Knowles, Archibald Campbell, 1865-
The life of offering; meditations upon the passion and resurrection of Our Blessed Lord, arranged for use during Lent and Holy week and for the Fridays throughout the year, by the Reverend Archibald Campbell Knowles ... Milwaukee, The Young churchman co., 1906.
5 p. l., 78 p. 17½cm.

1. Jesus Christ—Passion—Meditations. I. Title.
6-5697 Revised
Library of Congress BT430.K7
[r41b2] 232.96

NK 0209265 DLC CU IEG PU

Knowles, Archibald Campbell, 1865-
Lights and shadows of the sacred ministry. West Park, N. Y., Holy Cross Press, 1947.
xii, 160 p. 20cm.

1. Theology, Pastoral—Anglican communion. I. Title.
BV4010.K6 250 47-24956*

NK 0209266 DLC

Knowles, Archibald Campbell, 1865-
On wings of fancy, by Archibald Campbell Knowles ... Philadelphia, G. W. Jacobs & co., 1895.
103 p. 17cm.
Poems.

I. Title.
33-32478
Library of Congress PS3521.N72O6 1895
Copyright 1895: 30548 811.5

NK 0209267 DLC PU NBuG DAU

VOLUME 300

Knowles, Archibald Campbell, 1865-
The practice of religion, a short manual of instructions and devotions ... by the Reverend Archibald Campbell Knowles ... 3d ed. With a preface by the Right Reverend the Bishop of Fond du Lac. New York, E. S. Gorham, 1911.
xiv, 181 p. front., plates. 14cm.

Library of Congress BX5930.K63 11-1429

NK 0209268 DLC ViU

Knowles, Archibald Campbell, 1865-
The practice of religion, a short manual of instructions and devotions ... by the Reverend Archibald Campbell Knowles ... 12th ed. With a preface by the Right Reverend Charles Chapman Grafton ... New York, E. S. Gorham, 1918.
xii p., 1 l., 200 p. front., plates. 14cm.

I. Title.
Library of Congress BX5947.K6 1918 18-15371

NK 0209269 DLC

Knowles, Archibald Campbell, 1865-
The practice of religion, a short manual of instructions and devotions ... by the Reverend Archibald Campbell Knowles ... 19th ed., with a preface by the Right Reverend Charles Chapman Grafton ... New York, E. S. Gorham, 1922.
xiv p., 1 l., 240 p. incl. front. plates. 14cm.

I. Title.
Library of Congress BX5948.K6 1922 22-15680

NK 0209270 DLC

Knowles, Archibald Campbell, 1865-
The practice of religion, a short manual of instructions and devotions ... by the Reverend Archibald Campbell Knowles ... 28th ed. With a preface by the Right Reverend Charles Chapman Grafton ... New York, E. S. Gorham, 1926.
xiv p., 1 l., 256 p. incl. front. plates. 14cm.

I. Title.
Library of Congress BX5948.K6 1926 26-7064

NK 0209271 DLC NcD

Knowles, Archibald Campbell, 1865-
The practice of religion; a short manual of instructions and devotions ... by the Reverend Archibald Campbell Knowles ... 38th ed. With a preface by the Right Reverend Charles Chapman Grafton ... New York, E. S. Gorham, inc., 1930.
xiv p., 1 l., 256 p. incl. front. plates. 13½cm.

I. Title.
Library of Congress BX5948.K6 1930 30-7734

NK 0209272 DLC PPDio

Knowles, Archibald Campbell, 1865-
The practice of religion; a short manual of instructions and devotions ... by the Reverend Archibald Campbell Knowles ... Milwaukee, Wis., Morehouse publishing co., 1935.
xiii p., 1 l., 256 p. front., plates. 13½cm.

Continued in next column

Continued from preceding column

1. Protestant Episcopal church in the U. S. A.—Prayer-books and devotions—English. I. Title.
Library of Congress BX5930.K63 1935 35-4613
Copyright A 81083 [3] 264.03

NK 0209273 DLC NcU PU TNJ-R

Knowles, Archibald Campbell, 1865-
The practice of religion; a short manual of instructions and devotions. By the Rev. Archibald Campbell Knowles. [7th ed.] New York, Morehouse-Gorham Co. [1939]
xiii, 256 p. illus. 14 cm.
1. P.E.C.U.S.A. Prayer-books and devotions. I. Title.

NK 0209274 IEG

Knowles, Archibald Campbell, 1865-
Reminiscences of a parish priest, by the Reverend Archibald Campbell Knowles ... with a commendation by the Bishop of Milwaukee ... New York, Milwaukee, Morehouse publishing co., 1935.
viii p., 2 l., 212 p. front., plates, ports. 19cm.

I. Title.
Library of Congress BX5995.K55A3 35-12049
——— Copy 2.
Copyright A 85268 [2] 922.373

NK 0209275 DLC OKentU PU PP PPA

Knowles, Archibald Campbell, 1865-
"A rendezvous with destiny," by the Reverend Archibald Campbell Knowles ... Philadelphia, David McKay company, 1946.
96 p. incl. front. 19cm.
Cover-title: A rendezvous with destiny (Franklin Delano Roosevelt)

1. Roosevelt, Franklin Delano, pres. U. S., 1882-1945. I. Title.
Library of Congress E807.K67 46-2223
[4] 923.173

NK 0209276 DLC NcD FMU PU OrSaW

Knowles, Archibald Campbell, 1865-
The triumph of the cross; a devotional study of the passion, crucifixion and resurrection of Our Blessed Lord and Redeemer Jesus Christ ... New York, E. & J.B. Young & co., [pref., 1899.]
281 p.

NK 0209277 PPT IEG

Knowles, Archibald Campbell
Triumph of the cross; a devotional study of the passion, crucifixion & resurrection of our blessed Lord & Redeemer, Jesus Christ. Lond., Skeffington, 1900.
281 p.

NK 0209278 PU

17
1750
Knowles, Archibald Campbell, 1865-
Turning points. With an introduction by ... rt. rev. Leighton Coleman, d.d. lld. bishop of Delaware. Philadelphia, G.W. Jacobs & co., 1898.
112 p. 18°.

NK 0209279 DLC PP

Knowles, Arthur James.
Road-bridges over the Nile at Cairo. London, The Institution, 1909.
21 (1) p. 1 pl. 8°.
Repr.: Minutes of Proceed. of the Inst. of Civ. Eng. v. 177, pt. 3.

NK 0209280 NN

Knowles, Asa Smallidge, 1909-
Industrial management; principles and problems, by Asa S. Knowles ... Boston, Mass., Northeastern university, ©1940.
2 p. l., 190 numb. l. incl. diagrs., forms. 28 x 23½cm.
"Revised edition."

1. Factory management. 2. Efficiency, Industrial. I. Title.
Library of Congress T56.K582 1940 41-456
[a44d1] 658.01

NK 0209281 DLC

Knowles, Asa Smallidge, 1909-
Industrial management, by Asa S. Knowles ... & Robert D. Thomson ... New York, The Macmillan company, 1944.
xiv p., 1 l., 791 p. illus. (incl. plans) tables, forms, diagrs. 22cm.
Part of the illustrative material is folded.
"Selected bibliography and readings": p. 763-769.

1. Factory management. 2. Employment management. 3. Factories—Accounting. I. Thomson, Robert Douglas, 1884- joint author.
Library of Congress T56.K58 44-2181
658

NK 0209282 WaS WaSp WaSpG GAT AU PV CU DNAL CaBVaU MiHM ViU ViU TxU PHC PSt PU IdPI IdU MtU OrCS OrU DLC CtY TU OCU OU OO OEac OLak OCl OClh

Knowles, Asa Smallidge, 1909-
Industrial management, by Asa S.Knowles & Robert D.Thomson. New York, The Macmillan co., 1945.
791 p. illus. 22 cm.
"Selected bibliography and readings": p. 763-769.

NK 0209283 MH PJA

658.31243
K761i
1944r
KNOWLES, ASA SMALLIDGE, 1909-
Industrial management, by Asa S. Knowles ... & Robert D. Thomson ... New York, The Macmillan company, 1946 [c1944]
xivp., 1l., 791p. illus.(incl. plans) tables, forms, diagrs. 22cm.
"Reprinted December, 1946."
Part of the illustrative material is folded.
"Selected bibliography and readings": p.763-769.
1. Factory management. 2. Employment management. 3. Factories - Accounting. I. Thomson, Robert Douglas, 1884- joint author.

NK 0209284 TxU NcD

Knowles, Asa Smallidge, 1909-
Job evaluation for hourly and salaried workers ... by Asa S. Knowles ... New York, N. Y., Supervision publishing company, inc. [1943]
23 p. incl. forms. 28 x 21½cm.
"Reprinted ... as originally published in Supervision, the magazine of industrial relations and operating management, 1942-1943."

1. Job analysis. I. Title.
Library of Congress T58.K69 43-8628
[3] 658.511

NK 0209285 DLC ICU MB OCl OEac PPD TU

VOLUME 300

Knowles, Asa Smallidge, 1909–
Management of manpower, by Asa S. Knowles ... & Robert D. Thomson ... New York, The Macmillan company, 1943.
ix, 248 p. illus., tables (1 fold.) diagrs., forms (1 fold.) 22cm.
"Part of a larger volume on Industrial management." cf. Pref.
Bibliographical foot-notes.

1. Employment management. 2. Job analysis. I. Thomson, Robert Douglas, 1884– joint author. II. Knowles, Asa Smallidge, 1909– Industrial management. III. Title.
43-11830
Library of Congress T58.K693
[10] 658.!

PU PPT OC1W OCU OU OC1 TxU ViU
NK 0209286 DLC NcRS CoU Wa WaS WaSpG OrCS MtU TU

Knowles, Asa Smallidge, 1909-
Merit rating and labor management, by Asa S. Knowles ... New York, American management association, c1940.
16 p. diagrs. 23cm.

"Reprinted from Personnel, volume 17, number 1."

1. Employment management. 2. Efficiency, Industrial. I. Title: Rating and labor management II. Title.

NK 0209287 NNC OU

Knowles, Asa Smallidge, 1909–
... Merit rating in industry, by Asa S. Knowles ... Boston, Mass., Northeastern university, College of business administration, Bureau of business research [1940]
cover-title, 4 p. l., 3-36, 5 p. incl. diagrs. forms. 22½cm. (Northeastern university publications. Bulletin no. 1, February, 1940)
At head of title: College of business administration, Bureau of business research.

1. Efficiency, Industrial. 2. Ability. I. Northeastern university, Boston. College of business administration. Bureau of business research. II. Title.
40-33469
Library of Congress HF5549.K57

NK 0209288 DLC IU PU-W PPT MB

Knowles, Asa Smallidge, 1909–
Merit rating of supervisors, foremen and department heads, by Asa S. Knowles ... [Boston, Mass., Northeastern university] °1940.
19 p. incl. double form. 22½cm. (On cover: Northeastern university publications. Bulletin, no. 4, November, 1940)
On cover: College of business administration. Bureau of business research.
"Reprinted from Personnel, volume 17, number 2, American management association, New York."
1. Employment management. 2. Executive ability. 3. Efficiency, Industrial. I. Northeastern university, Boston. College of business administration. Bureau of business research. II. Title.
41-7335
Library of Congress HF5549.K58
[3] 658.31243

NK 0209289 DLC MB PPD PU-W

Knowles, Asa Smallidge, 1909–
Production control, by Asa S. Knowles ... & Robert D. Thomson ... New York, The Macmillan company, 1943.
x p., 1 l., 271 p. illus., forms (part fold.) diagrs. (part fold.) 22cm.
"Reproduction of part v (Production control) and part vi (Cost control) of a larger volume on Industrial management."—Pref.

PBm
1. Factory management. I. Thomson, Robert Douglas, 1884– joint author. II. Knowles, Asa Smallidge, 1909– Industrial management. III. Title.
43-13249
Library of Congress T56.K6
[6] 658.5

ViU PBm ScU NcRS CU CoU MtU OrU Wa WaSpG
NK 0209290 DLC OrCS NcD TU PP PPT OCU OC1 OU OLak

Knowles, Asa Smallidge, 1909–
Salary evaluation, by Asa S. Knowles ... and Thomas M. McAuley ... [Boston, Northeastern university] °1941.
33 p. incl. forms, diagrs. 22½cm. (On cover: Northeastern university publications. Bulletin no. 7, November, 1941)
On cover: College of business administration. Bureau of business research.
"Reprinted from Personnel, volume 18, number 3, American management association, New York."

1. Wages. 2. Employees, Rating of. I. McAuley, Thomas M., joint author. II. Northeastern university, Boston. College of business administration. Bureau of business research. III. Title.
43-13923
Library of Congress HD4909.K6
[4] 658.32

NK 0209291 DLC MB PU-W PPD OU NNC MH-BA NN ViU

Knowles, Asa Smallidge, 1909-
A survey of job evaluation as used by industry in determining base rates, by Asa S. Knowles ... and Frederic C. Means... [1938]
1 p.l., 381-416 p., 1 l. tables, diagrs. 22½cm.
(National association of cost accountants bulletir vol.XX, no.7. Sect.1, December 1, 1938)

Caption title.

I. title: Job evaluation. II. Means, Frederic C (jt au)

NK 0209292 NNC

Knowles, Atherton.
Text-book of Anglican service-music: tracing its development from Thomas Tallis to Samuel Sebastian Wesley. By Atherton Knowles ... London, E. Stock, 1895.
ix p., 1 l., 55 p. 18cm.

1. Church music—Church of England. 2. Church music—England—Hist. & crit. I. Title.
17-5210
Library of Congress ML3166.K77

NK 0209293 DLC OO MB

Knowles, Ava Beatrice, 1881-
The beginning of the church. n.p., [c1924]
[12] l. 28 cm.
Cover title.
Typewritten copy.

NK 0209294 RPB

Knowles, Ava Beatrice, 1881-
The prodigal son. New York, c1924.
[10] l. 28 cm.
Cover title.
Typewritten copy.

NK 0209295 RPB

KNOWLES, AVA BEATRICE, 1881-
The prodigal son, The beginning of the church, by Ava Beatrice Knowles. New York: The Womans Press[, 1925]. 32 p. 17½cm.

Two one-act plays.
First published in 1924.

652414A. 1. Drama, Religious. 2. Drama, American. I. Title. II. Title: The beginning of the church.

NK 0209296 NN

Knowles, Ava Beatrice, 1881–
The saint; a play in one act, by A. Beatrice Knowles ... New York, N. Y., Los Angeles, Calif., S. French; London, S. French, ltd.; [etc., etc.] °1936.
33, [1] p. diagr. 19cm.
"First prize winner 1935–1936 play writing contest sponsored by the religious drama council of the greater New York federation of churches."

1. Christmas plays. I. Title.
37-33794 Revised
Library of Congress PN6120.C5K59
[r45d2] 812.5

NK 0209297 DLC OrP Or OC1

Knowles, Benjamin, 1885–1933, *defendant.*
Trial of Benjamin Knowles, edited by Albert Lieck ... Edinburgh and London, W. Hodge & company, limited [1933]
6 p. l., 215 p. front., ports., plan. 22 cm. (Half-title: Notable British trials)
Trial of Dr. Knowles within the Chief commissioner's court of Ashanti, Kumasi, November, 1928, for the murder of his wife, Harriet Louise Knowles, and appeal to the King in Council.
Appendices: I. Laws of Ashanti—Ashanti administration. Laws of the Gold coast colony.—II. Reprints of press comments.
1. Knowles, Harriet Louise, d. 1928. I. Lieck, Albert Henry, ed. II. Ashanti. Chief commissioner's court. III. Gt. Brit. Privy council. Judicial committee.
34—1609

TxU PP PPB NN NNC
NK 0209298 DLC PSt WaU-L CaBVaU OU NcD CLU ViU-L

Knowles, Benjamin L.

Longshore, Joseph Skelton, 1809–1879.
The centennial liberty bell. Independence hall; its traditions and associations. The Declaration of independence and its signers. With an appendix embracing the opening ceremonies of the International exhibition, and of the centennial celebration of July 4th, 1876. By Jos. S. Longshore, M. D. and Benjamin L. Knowles, esq. ... Philadelphia, Claxton Remsen & Haffelfinger, 1876.

Knowles, Bernard.
Southampton, the English gateway. Pref. by the Duke of Wellington, with a foreword by Arthur Bryant. London, New York, Hutchinson, 1951.

Knowles, Bernard Dawson, 1890–
Britain's problem, by B. D. Knowles. London, John Lane [1941]
64 p. 22cm.
"First published 1941."

1. Currency question—Gt. Brit. 2. Gt. Brit.—Economic policy. 3. Gt. Brit.—Econ. condit.—1918– I. Title.
A 41-4945
Harvard univ. Library for Library of Congress HG939.K6
[2] 330.942

NK 0209301 MH CU CtY DLC

781.3 **Knowles, C H G**
K76r **Rhymes on the rules of harmony. Founded on Dr. Prout's "Harmony." London, Augener [1898.**
23p. music. 19cm. (Augener's edition no. 10110)

1. Harmony. I. Prout, Ebenezer, 1835-1909. Harmony.

NK 0209302 IU

Knowles, C. H. G.
...Rhymes on the rules of harmony. Founded on Dr. Prout's "Harmony." By C. H. G. Knowles... London: Augener & Co.[, 1904.] 23 p. illus. (music.) 12°.
At head of title: Augener's edition, no. 10,110.

1. Harmony. 2. Prout, Ebenezer, 1835-1909: Harmony.
N. Y. P. L. November 22, 1927

NK 0209303 NN

VOLUME 300

Knowles, Charles.
Notes on the libel suit of Knowles v. Douglas in the Superior Court of Judicature, 1748 and 1749
see under Noble, John, 1829-1909.

Knowles, Sir Charles, bart., 1704?-1777. supposed author.
FOR OTHER EDITIONS SEE MAIN ENTRY
An account of the expedition to Carthagena, with explanatory notes and observations ... The 2d ed. London, Printed for M. Cooper, 1743.

Knowles, Sir Charles, Bart., 1704?-1777.
Authentick papers, concerning a late remarkable transaction
see under title

[Knowles, *Sir* Charles, *bart.*] 1704?-1777.
The conduct of Admiral Knowles on the late expedition set in a true light ... London, Printed for J. Clarke [etc.] 1758.
30 p. fold. pl. 20½cm.
Signed: Charles Knowles.

1. Rochefort expedition, 1757. I. Title.
6-20539
Library of Congress DA87.5.1757.K5

NK 0209307 DLC KU PU NIC MH CU CU-A CtY PHi NN

Knowles, Charles, 1704-1777.
An essay on the duty and qualifications of a sea-officer. London, 1765.

NK 0209308 DN

Knowles, Charles, bart., 1704-1777.
Minutes of the proceedings at the trial of rear-admiral Knowles, before a court martial...
see under Fearne, Charles.

Knowles, Sir Charles, bart., 1704?-1777.
A refutation of the charge brought against Admiral Knowles in a pamphlet entitled "The conduct and treatment of John Crookshanks, Esq." London, 1759.
36 p. 8°.

NK 0209310 MdAN MiU-C RPJCB CSmH

Knowles, Sir Charles, Bart., 1704?-1777.
The speech of ... Kingston [1755]

NK 0209311 RPJCB

Knowles, Charles Edward, 1865–
History of the Bank for savings in the city of New York, 1819–1929, by Charles E. Knowles; introduction and illustration by Herbert Manchester. New York, The Bank for savings [°1929]
191 p. incl. front., illus. (incl. ports., facsims.) 26cm.

1. Bank for savings in the city of New York.
29-8934
Library of Congress HG2613.N5K6

NK 0209312 DLC WaS OU OCIFRB OCI MWA MB

Knowles, Charles Edward, 1865-
History of the Bank for Savings in the City of New York, 1819-1929; introduction and illustration by Herbert Manchester. [2d ed.] 1936.
197 p. illus., port.

1. Bank for Savings in the City of New York.

NK 0209313 NNC N ViU

Knowles, Charles Edward, 1865–
In quest of gold; being a romance dealing with the remarkable expedition of Ferdinand De Soto and his cavaliers to Florida in the year 1539, by Charles E. Knowles; illustrations by Howard M. Nesmith. New York, John Lane company, 1912.
3 p. l., [5]-228 p. front., plates. 19 cm.

I. Title.
PZ3.K7615 I 12—5156

NK 0209314 DLC

[**Knowles, Charles Edwin,** *comp.*
Edward Howard Hutchinson; eighty years of activity. [Buffalo? 1932?]
8 p. l., 181 p. front. (port.) plates. 23½cm.
Signed: Charles Edwin Knowles, compiler.
"The record here presented ... consists for the most part of carefully selected newspaper articles written at the time of the various happenings, arranged in chronological order."

1. Hutchinson, Edward Howard, 1852–
S 33-240
Library, Smithsonian Institution

NK 0209315 DSI NN NBuHi

Knowles, Charles H.
... The banana in Fiji. By Charles H. Knowles ... and Frank P. Jepson ... Suva, Printed by E. J. March, government printer, 1912.
17 p. VI pl. on 3 l. 24½cm. (Fiji Islands. Dept. of agriculture. Bulletin no. 4)
"References": p. 16.

1. Banana. 2. Banana. Pests. I. Jepson, Frank P., joint author.
Agr 13-1696
Library, U. S. Dept. of Agriculture 25F47B no. 4

NK 0209316 DNAL

Knowles, Charles H.
... Coconut experiments. By Charles H. Knowles ... Suva, S. Bach, government printer, 1915.
1 p. l., 8 p. incl. 2 pl. on 1 l. 25cm. (Fiji Islands. Dept. of agriculture. Bulletin no. 8)

1. Coconut.
Agr 16-595
Library, U. S. Dept. of Agriculture 23F47B no. 8

NK 0209317 DNAL

Knowles, Charles H.
... Hurricanes in Fiji. Hints to the observers at barometer observing stations, together with remarks upon the atmospheric conditions most suitable to the formation of hurricanes, and a list of storms recorded in Fiji. By C. H. Knowles ... Suva, A. G. Griffiths, 1911.
14 p. III tab. (1 fold.) fold. diagr. 23cm. (Fiji Islands. Dept. of agriculture. Bulletin no. 2)

1. Fiji Islands. Climate. 2. Hurricanes.
Agr 13-1697
Library, U. S. Dept. of Agriculture 25F47B no. 2

NK 0209318 DNAL DAS

Knowles, Charles H.
... Notes on a lemon-grass from Fiji. By Charles H. Knowles ... Suva, S. Bach, government printer, 1913.
1 p. l., 4 p. 25cm. (Fiji. Dept. of agriculture. Bulletin no. 6)

1. Cymbopogon coloratus.
Agr 13-1948
Library, U. S. Dept. of Agriculture 25F47B no. 6

NK 0209319 DNAL

Knowles, Charles H.
... Sisal hemp in Fiji. By C. H. Knowles ... Suva, Printed by E. J. March, government printer, 1911.
1 p. l., 16 p. plates. 25cm. (Dept. of agriculture, Fiji. Bulletin no. 1)

1. Sisal hemp.
Agr 11-1115
Library, U. S. Dept. of Agriculture 25F47B no. 1

NK 0209320 DNAL

Knowles, Charles Matthew.
Knowles, *Mrs.* Lilian Charlotte Anne (Tomn) 1870–1926.
The economic development of the British overseas empire, by L. C. A. Knowles ...
London, G. Routledge & sons, ltd., 1924–

331.83 Knowles, Charles Matthews.
K76h The housing problem in London. London, n.d.
19p. (London reform union pamphlet: no.80)

NK 0209322 IU

Knowles, Charles Matthews.
The housing problem in London.
= London. London Reform Union. 1899. 21 pp. [London Reform Union. Pamphlet No. 81.] 8°.
Bibliography, p. 21.

F8472 — T.r. — S.r. — Houses for workingmen.

NK 0209323 MB

331.83 Knowles, Charles Matthews.
K761ho The housing problem in the towns. Manchester, Eng., 1901.
37p. illus. ("Eighty" club pamphlet)
At head of title: "Eighty" club.

NK 0209324 IU

Knowles, Charles Matthews.
The housing problem in the towns. Plates. Tables.
(In Co-operative Wholesale Societies Limited, England and Scotland. Annual for 1901. Pp. 309-344. Manchester. 1901.)

K1714 — T.r. — Houses for workingmen.

NK 0209325 MB

VOLUME 300

4K Gt. Brit. 250 Knowles, Charles Matthew
The law relating to compensation for injuries to workmen: being an exposition of the Workman's compensation act, 1906, and of the case law relevant thereto. London, Stevens, 1907.
278 p.

NK 0209326 DLC-P4

331.2 K76112 Knowles, Charles Matthews, ed.
The law relating to compensation for injuries to workmen; being an exposition of the Workmen's compensation act, 1906, and of the case law relevant thereto, and including the workmen's compensation rules and forms, 1907, with the whole of the regulations and forms made under the provisions of the act by the Home office, Treasury, and Chief registrar of friendly societies. 2d ed. London, 1907.
460p.

NK 0209327 IU PPB

Knowles, Charles Matthew, *ed.*
The law relating to compensation for injuries to workmen: being an exposition of the Workmen's compensation act, 1906, together with the Workmen's compensation (Anglo-French convention) act, 1909, and certain relevant provisions of the National insurance act, 1911, and including the Workmen's compensation rules and forms and all other appropriate statutory rules and orders. By C. M. Knowles ... 3d ed. London, Stevens and sons, limited, 1912.
lxi, 590 p. 22½cm.
1. Employers' liability—Gt. Brit. [1. Workmen's compensation—Gt. Brit.] I. Gt. Brit. Laws, statutes, etc. II. Title: Compensation for injuries to workmen.
13-10835 Revised

NK 0209328 DLC OU PU-L MH

Knowles, Charles Matthew.
The law relating to compensation for injuries to workmen: being an exposition of the Workmen's compensation acts, 1906 and 1923, together with other relevant statutory provisions and including the Workmen's compensation rules and all other appropriate statutory rules and orders. By C. M. Knowles ... 4th ed. London, Stevens and sons, limited, 1924.
lxxi, 502 p. 25cm.
1. Employers' liability — Gt. Brit. [1. Workmen's compensation — Gt. Brit.] I. Gt. Brit. Laws, statutes, etc. II. Title: Compensation for injuries to workmen.
25-22352

NK 0209329 DLC CtY PU-L NN

Knowles, Charles Matthews, ed.

Gt. Brit. *Laws, statutes, etc.*
The law relating to the generation, distribution and use of electricity, including electric traction ... By C. M. Knowles ... London, Stevens and sons, limited, 1911.

[**Knowles, Charles Matthew**]
... Municipal water ... [London, The Fabian society] 1898.
4 p. 22cm. (Fabian tract no. 81)
Caption title.
Ascribed to C. M. Knowles by E. R. Pease, History of the Fabian society, London, 1925, p. 292.

1. Water-supply—Gt. Brit. 2. Municipal ownership—Gt. Brit. I. Title.
36-2887
Library of Congress HX11.F25 no. 81
[2] (335.106242) 628.10942

NK 0209331 DLC CU-S INS IaU NcD MH

Knowles, Charles Matthew, ed FOR OTHER EDITIONS SEE MAIN ENTRY

Smith, Charles Manley, 1819–1902.
A treatise on the law of master and servant, by Charles Manley Smith ... The 8th ed., by C. M. Knowles ... London, Sweet & Maxwell, limited; Toronto, The Carswell company, limited: [etc., etc.] 1931.

Knowles, Chester Lewis.
The preparation of para diphenyl propiolic acid and some new and interesting reactions of diphenyl and its derivatives. Theses submitted ... for the degree of Doctor of philosophy [1920] Providence, [1920]
63 p. table, diagr. 29 cm.
Typewritten ms.

NK 0209333 RPB

Knowles, Christine.
A visit to Switzerland in war-time. By Christine Knowles... London: Published in aid of the British Prisoners of War Food Parcels and Clothing Fund [1917]. 19(1) p. illus. 8°.

1. European war, 1914– —Prisoner and prisons (German). 2. British Prisoners of War Food Parcels and Clothing Fund. 3. Title.
N. Y. P. L. May 13, 1918.

NK 0209334 NN NjP

KNOWLES, CLARENCE RICHARD, 1880–
The care and operation of track motor cars, by C. R. Knowles... [New York:] Simmons-Boardman Pub. Co., 1931. 67 p. incl. diagrs., forms, tables. illus. 30½cm.

On cover: A series of 15 articles.
Repr.: Railway engineering and maintenance. Jan.–May, 1930–1931.

730173A. 1. Cars, Motor.

NK 0209335 NN MiD

TF 290 .K5 Knowles, Clarence Richard, 1880–
... "Railway water supply," by C.R. Knowles. [New York, printed by Edwin C. Bruen, inc., c1917]
12 p. 23 cm.
Caption title.
At head of title: New York Railroad Club.
Advance copy of paper to be presented at the meeting of Friday, April 20, 1917.

NK 0209336 DLC

Knowles, Daniel Clark, 1836–1913
Chapel talks, by Daniel Clark Knowles. New York, Eaton & Mains; Cincinnati, Jennings & Graham [c1910]
210 p. front. (port.) 20cm. $1.00
10-3021
Library of Congress

NK 0209337 DLC

BX8495 .W7K7 **Knowles, Daniel Clark,** 1836–1913.
A life that speaketh; a biography of Rev. George P. Wilson. By Daniel Clark Knowles ... New York, Nelson & Phillips; [etc., etc.] [c1874]
229 p. 17½cm.

Wilson, George Pickering, 1830–1873.

NK 0209338 ICU DLC CSmH IU MBNMHi

Knowles, Daniel Emerson, 1892– joint author.

Bailey, Warren G.
Accounting procedures for public utilities, with special reference to electric light, gas, water, and electric railway utility companies, by Warren G. Bailey ... and D. E. Knowles ... Chicago & New York, A. W. Shaw company; London, A. W. Shaw and company, limited, 1926.

Knowles, Daniel Emerson, 1892–
... The departmental monthly statement as a business barometer, by Daniel E. Knowles ... [Chicago?] Society of Industrial Engineers [1923]
7 p. 24cm. (Society of Industrial Engineers. Department of publications. vol. VI, no. 2. August, 1923)

NK 0209340 ICJ OU DLC

Knowles, Darline McCreery
Preservation of fruits and vegetables in cold storage lockers. 1940.
12 p., tables. (North Dakota. Agricultural college. Circular, no.169)

NK 0209341 MiD

Knowles, David, Father, 1896-
Abbot Butler: a memoir. Bath, England, 1934.
125 p. illus., 21 cm.

NK 0209342 OrStbM

Knowles, David, *father,* 1896–
The American civil war; a brief sketch by David Knowles. Oxford, The Clarendon press, 1926.
x, [2], 223 p. incl. front., illus. (maps) 19 cm.
"Books about the war": p. [213]–219.
"Suggested short course of reading on the war": p. [220]

1. U. S.—Hist.—Civil war. I. Title.
Secular name: Michael Clive Knowles.
E468.K73 26-23695 rev 2

NK 0209343 OO OCl OU PPGi MB NN Ok DLC NcRS ViU MtU WaS NIC PPiU PPL MiU

Knowles, David, *Father,* 1896–
Archbishop Thomas Becket, a character study.
(*In* British Academy, London (Founded 1901) Proceedings, 1949. London [1952] v. 35, p. [177]–205)
Raleigh lecture on history, read 13 July 1949.
Bibliographical references included in "Notes" (p. 198–205)

1. Thomas à Becket, Saint, Abp. of Canterbury, 1118?–1170. (Series: British Academy, London (Founded 1901) Annual Raleigh lecture, 1949)
Secular name: Michael Clive Knowles.
AS122.L5 vol. 35 A 53–2925
Wisconsin. Univ. Libr. for Library of Congress [2]†

NK 0209344 TNJ-R MtBC CaBVaU DLC MH WaU MdBJ NN CU-I WU ViU IEN KEmT RP WU MsSM NNC CU-S MB NBuT OrPR IMunS CtY

Knowles, David, 1896-
The Benedictines. Sheed & Ward, 1922.

NK 0209345 PRosC

VOLUME 300

Knowles, David, *Father*, 1896–
The Benedictines, by Dom David Knowles ... London, Sheed & Ward [1929]
3 p. l., 9–112 p. 17½ cm. (The "Many mansions" series)

1. Benedictines. *Secular name:* Michael Clive Knowles.

BX3002.K6 1929. 30–5611 rev

NK 0209346 DLC PPGi InStme

Knowles, David, *father*, 1896–
The Benedictines, by Dom David Knowles ... with an introduction by J. Hugh Diman, o. s. b. New York, The Macmillan company, 1930.
ix, 90 p. 17½ cm. (The "Many mansions" series)

1. Benedictines. *Secular name:* Michael Clive Knowles

BX3002.K6 1930 30–3327 rev 2

NK 0209347 MiU OCX NN OrMonO DLC OrStbM PPL IU PPDrop PV OCl OLak

---

Knowles, *David, Father, 1896–*
C. W. Previte-Orton, 1877-1947 [Obituary notice] (In Proceedings of the British academy, v. 33, 1947, p. [351]-360. port.)

Signed: M. D. Knowles.

NK 0209348 NNC

Knowles, David, 1896- , ed.
Cambridge air surveys
see under title

Knowles, David, *Father*, 1896–
The censured opinions of Uthred of Boldon.
(*In* British Academy, London (Founded 1901) Proceedings, 1951. London [1953] 26 cm. v. 37, p. [305]–342)
Bibliographical footnotes.

1. Uthredus Bolton, 1315?–1396. I. Title. *Secular name:* Michael Clive Knowles.

AS122.L5 vol. 37 A 54–1563
Wisconsin. Univ. Libr. for Library of Congress [2]†

NK 0209350 WU CaBVaU NNC DLC

Knowles, *David, Father, 1896–*
The censured opinions of Uthred of Boldon. L [1951]

From The proceedings of the British Academy, vol.37, p.[305]-342

NK 0209351 MH

Knowles, David, *Father*, 1896–
Charterhouse, the medieval foundation in the light of recent discoveries [by] David Knowles and W. F. Grimes. London, New York, Longmans, Green [1954]
xiii, 95 p. illus., plans. 26 cm.
Bibliographical footnotes.

1. Charterhouse. I. Grimes, William Francis, joint author. *Secular name:* Michael Clive Knowles.

DA687.C4K6 54–14524

NK 0209352 OU TxU PPPD DLC CaBViP CaBVa MB ICU TU PP NcD NN

Knowles, David, 1896–
Cistercians & Cluniacs; the controversy between St. Bernard and Peter the Venerable. London, New York, Oxford University Press, 1955.
32 p. 22 cm. (Friends of Dr. Williams's Library, 9th lecture, 1955)
Bibliographical footnotes.

1. Cistercians. 2. Cluniacs. I. Title. (Series: Friends of Dr. Williams's Library, London. Lecture, 1955) *Secular name:* Michael Clive Knowles.

A 56–2918
General Theol. Sem. for Library of Congress Library [2]

NK 0209353 MiU NcD IMunS OU CtY-D MB MH NN NjPT KyLxCB NNG TxFTC CU KMK CaBVaU OrStbM NNC ICU

Knowles, David, 1896–

BX2592 .S6 **Smith, Reginald Anthony Lendon, 1915–1944.**
Collected papers. With a memoir by David Knowles and a foreword by the Master of Trinity. London, New York, Longmans, Green [1947]

Knowles, David, *father*, 1896–
The English mystics, by Dom David Knowles ... London, Burns, Oates & Washbourne, ltd. [1927]
ix, 210 p. 19 cm.
CONTENTS.—Introduction.—The nature of mysticism.—The mystical experience.—The epoch of the mystics.—The Ancren riwle.—Richard Rolle.—The cloud of unknowing.—Walter Hilton.—Margery Kempe and Dame Julian.—Father Baker.—Characteristics of the English mystics.—Appendix A—Bibliography (p. 189–197)—Appendix B—Dean Inge and Miss Underhill.—Appendix C—Dame Gertrude More and Father Benet Fitch.

1. Mysticism—Gt. Brit. I. Title. *Secular name:* Michael Clive Knowles.

BV5077.G7K6 28–14861 rev 2

NK 0209355 OCl OCX NN DLC TxU CtY PHC PRosC PU MiU OClStM

Knowles, David, *Father*, 1896–
The Episcopal colleagues of Archbishop Thomas Becket. Cambridge [Eng.] University Press, 1951.
190 p. 20 cm. (Ford lectures, 1949)

1. Thomas à Becket, Saint, Abp. of Canterbury, 1118?–1170. 2. Gt. Brit.—Church history—Medieval period. 3. Gt. Brit.—Hist.—Henry II, 1154–1189. 4. Bishops—Gt. Brit. I. Title. (Series: Oxford. University. Ford lectures, 1949) *Secular name:* Michael Clive Knowles.

BR750.K6 283.42 51–10527 rev

NK 0209356 N OKentC TxU DCU MB IEN NIC LU CtY GU NcU MH TU ViU MsU PRosC KAS OrStbM WaSpG OrU OrPR CaBVa CaBVaU DLC OClW TxHR NcRS MoU DAU NBuT FTaSU

Knowles, David, 1896–
Great historical enterprises. II. The Maurists.
(*In* Royal Historical Society, London. Transactions. London. 22 cm. 5th ser., v. 9 (1959) p. 169–187)
Presidential address, read 13 December 1958.
Bibliographical footnotes.

1. Benedictines. Congrégation de Saint-Maur. I. Title. *Secular name:* Michael Clive Knowles.

DA20.R9 ser. 5, vol. 9 A 59–6083
Newberry Library for Library of Congress [2]†

NK 0209357 ICN DLC TxU MiU

Knowles, David, *Father*, 1896–
The historian and character; inaugural lecture delivered at Cambridge, 17 November 1954. Cambridge [Eng.] University Press, 1955.
21 p. 19 cm.

1. Historiography. I. Title. *Secular name:* Michael Clive Knowles.

D13.K57 55–14212 ‡

NK 0209358 PPAN PP PPT IEN IaU GU InStme PU OCl KAS CU MdBJ Wa DLC WaSpG IdPI NNC TxU RPB IU MH PPD

---

*Knowles, David, 1896- ed.

Matthew, *Sir* **Tobie,** 1577–1655.
The life of Lady Lucy Knatchbull, by Sir Tobie Matthew. Now first printed from the original manuscript, with an introduction by Dom David Knowles. London, Sheed and Ward, 1931.

Knowles, David, *Father*, 1896–
Medieval religious houses, England and Wales, by David Knowles and R. Neville Hadcock. London, New York, Longmans, Green [1953]
xxiii, 387 p. fold maps. 23 cm.
"The nucleus of this volume was a handlist compiled by Dom David Knowles, with the title: The religious houses of medieval England, and published in 1940, to which additions and corrections were made in the English historical review of September 1945."
Bibliographical footnotes.
1. Monasticism and religious orders—England. 2. Monasticism and religious orders—Wales. I. Hadcock, Richard Neville, joint author. II. Title. *Secular name:* Michael Clive Knowles.

BX2592.K56 271 53—12742

NK 0209360 MH-AU MdBWA WaSpG CaBViP OrU MnCS TxU TU NcD IaU ViU NN PSt IEN IEG MoU WaS ICU NN MB NcU OClW PPLT OU ScCleU GU CaBVaU MtU DLC OrPR Or CSt N MiD NNC MH NIC CU

Knowles, David, 1896–
The monastic order in England; a history of its development from the times of St. Dunstan to the Fourth Lateran council, 943-1216, by Dom David Knowles. Cambridge [Eng.] The University press, 1921.
xix p., 2 l., [3]-764 p. front, tables. 26cm.

Bibliography: p. [727]-743.
1. Monasticism and religious orders - England. 1. Title. [Full name: Michael David Knowles]

NK 0209361 PSt PSC PPPD

Knowles, David, *father*, 1896–
The monastic order in England; a history of its development from the times of St. Dunstan to the Fourth Lateran council, 943–1216, by Dom David Knowles. Cambridge [Eng.] The University press, 1940.
xix p., 2 l., [3]–764 p. front., tables. 26 cm.
Bibliography: p. [727]–743.

1. Monasticism and religious orders—England. I. Title. *Secular name:* Michael Clive Knowles.

BX2592.K57 271.0942 40–32853 rev

NK 0209362 OrU OOxM NcGU WaS WaSpG NcU NcD NIC OrStbM CaBVa OrPS DLC TU CtY PU OClW PHC PBm OCl OU OO ViU

BV 2023 K5 1941 **Knowles, David, 1896–**
The monastic order in England; a history of its development from the times of St Dunstan to the Fourth Lateran council, 943-1216. Cambridge [Eng.] University Press, 1941.

xix, 764 p. front., tables. 25 cm.

Bibliography: p. 727-743.

1. Monasticism and religious orders—England. I. Title.

NK 0209363 MBtS

Knowles, David, 1896-
The monastic order in England; a history of its develo ment from the times of St. Dunstan to the fourth Lateran council, 942-1216. Cambridge [Eng.] Univ. Press, 1949.

xix, 764 p. illus.

NK 0209364 MH CaBVaU MtU PPLas NBC MH-AH MiU

VOLUME 300

14087 Knowles, David, 1896-
.529
.11 The monastic order in England; a history of its development from the times of St.Dunstan to the fourth Lateran council, 943-1216... Cambridge [Eng.] University press, 1950.
764 p. illus. 25½ cm.

Reprinted with corrections, 1949.
Bibliography: p.[727]-743.

NK 0209365 NjP CtY FTaSU WaU MoSU

Knowles, David, *Father*, **1896–**
Monastic sites from the air, by David Knowles and J. K. S. St. Joseph. Cambridge [Eng.] University Press, 1952.
xxvii, 282 p. illus., map, plans. 28 cm. (Cambridge air surveys, 1)
Bibliographical footnotes.

1. Monasteries—England. I. St. Joseph, John Kenneth Sinclair, joint author. II. Title. (Series)
Secular name: Michael Clive Knowles.

BX2592.K575 271 52—12370

CtY MU ICU CSt KyLxCB ICarbS KyU AAP WaU KMK FMU OClSA OU OClW NBC OrU CaBVaU MtBC OrStbM GU PPiU
NK 0209366 DLC CaBVa IU NNC MH NN N TxU PU PRosC

Knowles, David, *Father*, **1896–**
The prospects of medieval studies. An inaugural lecture delivered on 29 October 1947. Cambridge [Eng.] University Press, 1947.
22 p. 18 cm.

1. Middle Ages—Hist.—Study and teaching. I. Title.
Secular name: Michael Clive Knowles.

D119.K6 940.107 48–1179 rev*

OAU
NK 0209367 DLC CaBVaU OrStbM OrU MBtS MiU MH TxU

Knowles, David, 1896-
The reforming decrees of Peter the Venerable.

(In Petrus Venerabilis 1156-1956. Studies and texts commemorating the 8th centenary of his death edited by Giles Constable and James Kritzeck, pp. 1-20) (Studia Anselmiana, fasc. 40).

NK 0209368 PLatS

Knowles, David, 1896-
Les relations monastiques entre la Normandie et l'Angleterre.

(In Congrès scientifique du XIII centenaire de Jumièges, Rouen, 1954. vol. 1, pp. [261]-267).

NK 0209369 PLatS

Knowles, David, *father*, **1896–**
The religious houses of medieval England, by Dom David Knowles. London, Sheed & Ward, 1940.
viii, 167 p. 5 double maps. 22 cm.
Bibliographical references in "Introduction" (p. 2–9) "Books quoted in notes": p. 148–151.
CONTENTS.—Preface.—Introduction.—Essay on the origins and development of the religious life in England.—Catalogue of the religious houses of England and Wales.—Appendices.

1. Monasticism and religious orders—England. 2. Monasticism and religious orders—Wales. I. Title.
Secular name: Michael Clive Knowles.

BX2592.K58 271.0942 A 41–1496 rev

Harvard Univ. Library for Library of Congress [r53d¾]†

OrStbM
NK 0209370 MH DLC NIC CLSU PHC PU OCU OU CtY NcU

Knowles, David, 1896–
The religious orders in England. Cambridge [Eng.] University Press, 1948–59.
3 v. fronts. 26 cm.
Includes bibliographies.
CONTENTS.—[v. 1] The old orders, 1216–1340. The friars, 1216–1340. The monasteries and their world.—v. 2. The end of the Middle Ages.—v. 3. The Tudor age.

1. Monasticism and religious orders—England.
Secular name: Michael Clive Knowles.

BX2592.K583 271.0942 48–10465 rev 3*

PPT CtY-D PU PBL OO
MH-AH MoSU ViU ICU OCl MiEm NcGU OU PP PU TxU OOxM
NK 0209371 DLC GU NRCR MsSM WU NN OCU AAP NNC IEG

BX
2592
K583
LC Coll.

Knowles, David, 1896–
The religious orders in England. Cambridge [Eng.] University Press, 1948–61.
3 v. fronts. 26 cm.
Includes bibliographies.
CONTENTS.—[v. 1] The old orders, 1216–1340. The friars, 1216–1340. The monasteries and their world.—v. 2. The end of the Middle Ages.—v. 3. The Tudor age.
Printings vary.

NK 0209372 COSA

BX
2592
K583
1950

Knowles, David, Father, 1896-
The religious orders in England. Cambridge [Eng.] University Press, 1950-
v. fronts. 26 cm.

Vol. 1 first published in 1948.
Bibliography: v. 1, p. [327]-338; v. 2, p. 376-388.
Contents. - v. 1. [1216-1340] - v. 2. The end of the Middle Ages.

1. Monasticism and religious orders - England. I. Title.
Secular name: Michael Clive Knowles.

InStme NN MB
NK 0209373 Vi NcD PBm OCU NcU DFo MB IEN MiU PHC

Knowles, David, Father, 1896-
The religious orders in England. Cambridge [Eng.] University Press, 1955.
xvi, 348 p. front. 26 cm.
Bibliography p. [327]-338.
1. Monasticism and religious orders--England.
Secular name: Michael Clive Knowles.

NK 0209374 PRosC NcU ScU

Knowles, David, 1896-

Caussade, Jean Pierre de, *d.* 1751.
Self-abandonment to divine providence, a posthumous work, by Father J. P. de Caussade, S. J., revised and edited by Father P. H. Ramière, S. J.; a new translation by Algar Thorold, with an introduction by Dom David Knowles ... London, Burns, Oates & Washbourne, ltd. [1933]

Knowles, David, *Father*, **1896–**
Some developments in English monastic life, 1216–1336, by Dom David Knowles ...
(*In* Royal historical society, London. Transactions. London, 1944. 22 cm. 4th ser., vol. XXVI, p. 37–52)
Bibliographical foot-notes.

1. Monasticism and religious orders—Gt. Brit. I. Title.
***Secular name:* Michael Clive Knowles.**

DA20.R9 ser. 4, vol. 26 (942.0062) A 44–1388 rev

Newberry Library for Library of Congress [r53d¾]†

NK 0209376 DLC ICN CaBVaU OU NcD

---

q539.211 Knowles, Dewey Deforest, 1899-
K76t Theory and application of the grid-glow tube by D. D. Knowles and S. P. Sashoff. East Pittsburgh, Pa., Westinghouse Electric & Manufacturing Co.[1930]
15p. illus. 30cm.
"Reprinted from the February, April and August 1930 issues of the Electric journal.
Bibliography: p.7.
1. Vacuum-tubes. 2. Electric discharges through gases. I. Sashoff, Stephan Pencheff, joint author. II. Title: The grid-glow tube.

NK 0209377 IU

Knowles, Dorothy.
The censor, the drama and the film, 1900–1934, by Dorothy Knowles ... preface by Hubert Griffith. London, G. Allen & Unwin ltd. [1934]
2 p. l., 294 p., 1 l. 19cm.
Bibliography: p. 277–286.
Errata slip inserted.

1. Theater—Censorship. 2. Moving-pictures—Censorship. I. Title.

Library of Congress PN2042.K6 34–37615
[3] 323.446

CtY OU NN
NK 0209378 DLC GU MB OrAshS CSt OrU NcU TxU CLSU

Knowles, Dorothy.
... La réaction idéaliste au théâtre depuis 1890. Paris, E. Droz, 1934.
3 p. l., 558 p. 25cm. [Bibliothèque de la Société des historiens du théâtre, IV]
"Bibliographie": p. [505]–543.

1. French drama—19th cent.—Hist. & crit. 2. French drama—20th cent.—Hist. & crit. 3. Idealism in literature. I. Title.

Library of Congress PQ558.K6 35–10181
[2] 842.809

OCU MiU OO NN
NK 0209379 DLC NIC NNC OrU IdU NcU OU PU CU PHC

Knowles, Douglas B
The effects of hail injury on wheat and other grain crops. Saskatoon, Saskatchewan, University of Saskatchewan [1941]
23 p.

NK 0209380 KMK

Knowles, Doyle B., 1924-
Ground-water resources of Ector County

see under

Texas. Board of Water Engineers.

Knowles, Doyle B., 1924-
Ground-water resources of the Odell sand hills

see under

Texas. Board of Water Engineers.

GB1025 Knowles, Doyle B., 1924-
.T4A5
1947a
Texas. *Board of Water Engineers.*
Preliminary report on the geology and ground water resources of Reeves County, Texas, by D. B. Knowles and Joe W. Lang. Prepared in cooperation with the Geological Survey, and the Bureau of Reclamation, United States Dept. of the Interior. [Austin] 1947.

VOLUME 300

BX 5037 K58 LC Coll.
[Knowles, E H]
Twelve hundred questions on the history of the Church of England; with some answer-hints, and with tabular annals of the reigns of Henry VIII., Edward VI., Mary, Elizabeth, James I., and Charles I. By a lecturer [pseud.] London, Rivingtons, 1888.
318 p. 19cm.

1. Church of England--History--Questions and answers. I. Title.

NK 0209384 CBBD

Knowles, E J *comp.*
Christmas chimes. Ed. by Mrs. E. J. Knowles. With an introduction by J. F. Hurst, D. D. Illustrated by Mary A. Lathbury. New York, Nelson & Phillips; [etc., etc.] 1878.
vi, 220 p. incl. front. illus. 22½cm.

1. Christmas—Poetry. I. Title.

13—17841

Library of Congress PN6110.C5K5

NK 0209385 DLC

Knowles, Edward Hadarezer
The Castle of Kenilworth, a hand-book for visitors. Warwick, Cooke, 1872.
240p.

NK 0209386 OCl CtY

[Knowles, Edward Peck] 1805-1881.
The cove lands and proprietors' rights; [ed. by Frederic Denison] [Providence, 1877]
[6] p. 22 cm.
Caption-title.
Clippings from the Providence journal of May, 1877.

NK 0209387 RPB

Knowles, Edward Randall, 1861–
Ecce regnum! By Edward Randall Knowles ... [Worcester, Mass., The Messenger print] °1891.
2 p. l., 7-33 p. 14½cm.
On cover: Author's edition.

I. Title.

33-32479

Library of Congress PS3521.N74E3 1891
Copyright 1891: 39704 811.5

NK 0209388 DLC RPB NBuG

Knowles (Edward Randall) [1861-]. Memorial. Joshua Bartlett Rich. 6 pp. 8°. [Worcester, Mass.], 1896.

NK 0209389 DNLM MH DLC MWA OCIWHi

Knowles, Edward Randall, 1861-
The nature of the existence of matter. Lately published in the Kansas City Review. Pascoag, R.I., 1881.
Pamphlet

NK 0209390 CtY RPB

Knowles, Edward Randall, 1861–
Selections from the writings of Edward Randall Knowles ... Boston, J. S. Smith & co., 1893.
43 p. 19½cm.
Verse and prose.

Library of Congress PS2197.K15A6 32-16276
Copyright 1893: 24714 818.5

NK 0209391 DLC MWA MB NN NNUT

PS3521 .N74S6 1891
Knowles, Edward Randall, 1861-
Songs of the life eternal; and other writings. By Edward Randall Knowles. Boston, 1891.
2 p. l., 3-38 p. 19cm.

NK 0209392 DLC NNUT PBa MB MH NBuG NN RPB

Knowles, Edward Randall, 1861-
...The supremacy of the spiritual. [n.p., c] c1892.
7p.
(From Religio-Philosophical journal, March 5 & 12)
YA 19048

NK 0209393 DLC PBa NNUT

Knowles, Edward Randall, 1861–
The supremacy of the spiritual, by Edward Randall Knowles, LL. D. Boston, Arena publishing company, 1895.
1 p. l., 61 p. 19cm.

1. Metaphysics.

11-6673

Library of Congress BD331.K6

NK 0209394 DLC RP MB OCl OU MWA NBuG NcD

Knowles, Edward Randall, 1861–
The supremacy of the spiritual. By Edward Randall Knowles, LL. D. [Boston, Arena publishing company, 1895]
1 p. l., 61 p. 19cm.

1. Metaphysics.

11-6674

Library of Congress BD331.K6 1895a

NK 0209395 DLC

Knowles, Edward Randall, 1861-
The true christian science. Worcester, Mass., 1891.
13p.
DLC: YA 25533

NK 0209396 DLC

Knowles, Edwin Blackwell, 1903-
Don Quixote abridged, by Edwin B. Knowles. (In Bibliographical society of America. Papers. New York, 1955. 24.5cm. v.49, first quarter, 1955, p.19-36. illus. (incl. facsim.))

A full description of 4 English chapbook editions of Don Quijote published in London between 1686 and 1700(?) and recorded in Wing STC as C1771-C1773, C1778.

NK 0209397 MH

Knowles, Edwin Blackwell, 1903–
... Four articles on Don Quixote in England [by] **Edwin B.** Knowles, jr. ... New York, 1941.
12, [573]-586, 252-265, 103-115 p. 23cm.
Selections from thesis (PH. D.)—New York university, 1939.
"The first piece ... amounts to a condensed survey of the major portions of my thesis ... The second selection, an offprint from Philological quarterly, vol. XX, no. 4 (October, 1941) ... The third article, an offprint from Hispanic review, vol. IX, no. 2 (April, 1941) ... The last piece, an offprint from Hispania, vol. XXIII, no. 2 (May, 1940)"—Foreword.
Bibliographical foot-notes.

CONTENTS.—Don Quixote in England before 1660.—Allusions to Don Quixote before 1660.—The first and second editions of Shelton's Don Quixote part I: a collation and dating.—Don Quixote through English eyes.

1. Cervantes Saavedra, Miguel de. Don Quixote. 2. Literature, Comparative—Spanish and English. 3. Literature, Comparative—English and Spanish. I. Title: Don Quixote in England.

A 42-2143

New York univ. Wash. sq. library
for Library of Congress PQ6353.K5
[5]† 863.32

NK 0209399 NNU-W OrU PBm MNS MH DLC

KNOWLES, EDWIN BLACKWELL, 1903-
Notes on the Madrid, 1605, editions of Don Quijote.
[Philadelphia, 1946.]
p.47-58. 23½cm.
Caption title; signed at end: Edwin B. Knowles, jr.
Detached from Hispanic review, v.14, 1946.
Inscribed: To Dr. Rosenbach, with the author's compliments. Edwin B. Knowles Jr. 3/8/46.

NK 0209400 PPRF

Knowles, Edwin Blackwell, 1903–
Some textual peculiarities of the first English Don Quixote, by Edwin B. Knowles, jr.
(In Bibliographical society of America. Papers. New York, 1943. 23½cm. v. 37, third quarter, 1943, p. 203–214. illus. (facsim.))

1. Cervantes Saavedra, Miguel de. Don Quixote.

45-3258

Library of Congress Z1008.B51P vol. 37

NK 0209401 DLC MH PPT OU OCU

Knowles, Edwin Blackwell, 1903- joint author

Shaw, Harry, 1905–
Workbook for A complete course in freshman English [by] Harry Shaw [and] E. B. Knowles ... [New York] Harper & brothers [°1941]

Knowles, Edwin Chandler.
... Substituted phenylacetonitriles and derivatives. 1-phenyl-1-cyanocyclopropane, alpha-phenyl-gamma-hydroxybutyronitrile, alpha-phenyl-gamma-chlorobutyronitrile and alpha-phenylcrotononitrile, by Edwin C. Knowles and John B. Cloke. Troy, N. Y. [1934]
cover-title, 24 p. 22cm. (Rensselaer polytechnic institute bulletin. Engineering and science series. no. 49)
"Constructed from the first part of a thesis presented by Edwin Chandler Knowles in June 1931 to the Graduate school of the Rensselaer polytechnic institute ... for the degree of doctor of philosophy."
1. Phenylacetonitriles. I. Cloke, John Benjamin, 1897- joint author.

35-11884

Library of Congress QD341.N7K57 1931
——— Copy 2. [3] 547.1

NK 0209403 DLC PPT MiU OU ViU IU

Knowles, Eleanor Elaine, 1906-
Posture and other physiological responses of the worker in relation to the height of working surface used in household ironing. [Ithaca, N. Y., 1944.
441 l. illus. 27cm.

Thesis (Ph. D.)--Cornell University, Oct. 1944.

1. Posture. 2. Laundry workers.

NK 0209404 NIC

VOLUME 300

Knowles, Elise, 1908-
Die forschungsmethode im mathematischen unterricht als mittel der erziehung zu autonomie und gemeinschaft ... 1933. 133 p.
Inaug. Diss. -Jena, 1933.
Lebenslauf.
Bibliography.

NK 0209405 ICRL RPB CtY IU

Knowles, Ellin J (Toy) *"Mrs. J. H. Knowles,"* 1835-1929
Heart talks on Bible themes, by Mrs. J. H. Knowles ... New York, Chicago [etc.] Fleming H. Revell company [1911]
3 p. l., 5-237 p. front. 19½cm.
"These Heart talks are selections from those originally written by me for the Sunday school journal and Bible magazine."—Foreword.

Library of Congress 11-10946

NK 0209406 DLC NNUT

Knowles, Ellin J (Toy) 1835-1929.
Spirit and life; selections from Bible readings. Boston, New York [etc.] Silver, Burdett and company, 1899.
xiv p., 1 l., 287 p. front. (port.) 18cm.

1. Christian life. I. Title.
99-1244 Revised
Library of Congress BV4501.K596

NK 0209407 DLC NN

BF 1141 K73b Knowles, Elmer E
..The basic principles of suggestion, hypnotism, telepathy, personal magnetism, character building ... and the development of the dormant faculties. Brussels, Psychology Foundation, 1926.
14 p., 28 cm. (Branch 1 of the Elmer E. Knowles System of Personal Influence and Healing).
At head of title: A correspondence course.

1. Hypnotism.

NK 0209408 IParkA

Knowles, Elmer E.
Clairvoyance; how to develop psychic powers, by Elmer E. Knowles ... New York, N.Y.: Modern science pub. co., c1906. 24 p. 15cm.

1. New thought. 2. Clairvoyance. May 4, 1942
N. Y. P. L.

NK 0209409 NN

4BF 846 **Knowles, Elmer E**
Complete system of personal influence and healing. [London, National Institute of Sciences]
6 pts. in 1.

NK 0209410 DLC-P4 TxU IU

BF 1141 K73h Knowles, Elmer E
Hypnotism, telepathy, personal magnetism, personal influence. Brussels, Psychology foundation, 1926.
42 p., illus., 28 cm. (Branch 2 of the Elmer E. Knowles System of Personal Influence and Healing).
At head of title: A correspondence course.

1. Hypnotism.

NK 0209411 IParkA

Knowles, Elmer Nyler, 1920-
Kindergarten children's control and acceptance of same sex peers and their parents' control and acceptance of them. [Ithaca, N.Y.] 1952.
178 l. illus., plates. 27cm.
Thesis (Ph.D.)—Cornell Univ., Sept., 1952.

NK 0209412 NIC

F1074 .5 .S3P4 **Knowles, Eric, joint author.**
Peel, Bruce Braden, 1916-
The Saskatoon story, 1882-1952 [by Bruce Peel and Eric Knowles] Saskatoon, Printed by General Print. and Bookbinding, 1952.

Knowles, Eusebius.
"Although." An address on England's present fiscal position. London, Simpkin ... & Co., 1903.
22 p., 1 l. 8°.

NK 0209414 NN

Knowles, F., tr.
Rooses, Max, 1839-1914, *ed.*
Dutch painters of the nineteenth century. With biographical notices. Ed. by Max Rooses ... tr. by F. Knowles. With six etchings by Ph. Zilcken, six photogravure plates and over 200 other illustrations. London, S. Low, Marston & company, limited, 1898-1901

KNOWLES, F W
Recipes for cooking frozen foods and directions for freezing fresh foods Everett, Wash Kane & Harcus c1939,1940
32p

NK 0209416 WaT

Knowles, Frances Ivens-
see Ivens-Knowles, Frances.

Knowles, *Sir* Francis, *bart.*, 1915-
see
Knowles, *Sir* Francis Gerald William, *bart.*, 1915-

Kress Room Knowles, Sir Frances Charles, bart.
"The monetary crisis considered"; being incidentally a reply to Mr. Horsley Palmer's pamphlet "on the action of the Bank of England, &c." and a defence of the joint-stock banks against his accusations ... London, P. Richardson, 1837.
90 p. 22.5 cm.

1.Currency question - Gt.Brit. 2.Banks and banking - Gt.Brit. 3.Banks and banking - Early works to 1850. I.Palmer, John Horsley, 1779-1858.

NK 0209419 MH-BA PPL PU CtY NNC

Knowles, Sir Francis Charles, bart,
A proposal for heating large towns with pyrogen gas... By Sir Francis C. Knowles... London, Wyman & sons, 1874.
1 p.l.,20p. 21cm.

1. Gas manufacture and works. 2. Gas as

Library. U.S. Patent Office. TP761.P98K7

NK 0209420 DP

Knowles, *Sir* Francis Gerald William, *bart.*, 1915-
Biology and man. London, Harrap [1950]
304 p. illus., ports. 19 cm. (Harrap's torch books)

1. Biology. I. Title.
QH307.K55 574 50-14337 rev

NK 0209421 DLC WaU OkU MiU NcD

QH 307 K73d 1950 KNOWLES, Francis Gerald William, bart., 1915-
Diagrams of human biology. London, Harrap [1950]
108 p. illus.
1. Biology

NK 0209422 DNLM

Knowles, Francis Gerald William, bart., 1915-
Freshwater and salt-water aquaria. With 11 plates in half-tone and with 70 illus. in line by the author. London, Harrap [1953]
174 p. illus. 20 cm.
Includes bibliography.

1. Aquariums. I. Title.
QL78.K59 590.74 53-8787 ‡
Library of Congress [55m3]

NK 0209423 WaTC PP TU TxU InU CaBVaU CaBVa Wa OrLgE OrMonO OrP WaS DLC CSt LU CaBViP Or TxU OU MB OCl PSt

---

Knowles, *Sir* Francis Gerald William, *bart.*, 1915-
The living organism; a preliminary course in biology. With illus. in line by the author and 28 plates in half-tone. London, Harrap [1948]
289 p. illus. 23 cm.

1. Biology. I. Title.
QH308.5.K49 574 48-23115 rev*

NK 0209424 DLC

Knowles, Francis Gerald William, bart., 1915-
Man and other living things; an introduction to human biology, by Francis G. W. Knowles ... with illustrations in line by the author and thirty-two plates in half-tone. London, Toronto [etc.] G. G. Harrap & co. ltd. [1945]
2 p. l., 3-355 p. illus., plates, ports. diagrs. 22cm.
"First published 1945."
"Errata": slip inserted.
"Books for further reading": p. 312-317.

1. Biology. I. Title.
46-17805
Library of Congress QH308.5.K5
[3] 574

NK 0209425 DLC CU ICU

VOLUME 300

Knowles, Francis Howe Seymour, 1886–
... The glenoid fossa in the skull of the Eskimo, by F. H. S. Knowles. Ottawa, Government printing bureau, 1915.
cover-title, 14 p., 16–24 numb. l. incl. iv pl. 24½cm. (Canada. Geological survey. Museum bulletin no. 9. Anthropological series, no. 4)
At head of title: Canada. Department of mines ...
The guard sheets are included in the pagination.
"References to literature consulted": p. 14.
1. Craniology. 2. Eskimos. I. Title.
Library of Congress QH1.C13 no. 9 16–1071
CaBVa
OrPR CU PP PU MiU OO OU OClMN OCl OClW MB NN CtY
NK 0209426 DLC OrU MU MtBuM CaBVaU OrCS CaBViPA

Knowles, *Sir* Francis Howe Seymour, *bart.*, 1886–
The manufacture of a flint arrow-head by quartzite hammer-stone. Oxford, Printed at the University Press, 1944.
36 p. illus. 24 cm. (Pitt Rivers Museum, University of Oxford. Occasional papers on technology, 1)
1. Arrow-heads. I. Title.
GN498.B78K5 571.15 53–52569 ‡
[2]
NK 0209427 DLC CaBViP ICN MH PU NN

Knowles, Francis Howe Seymour, 1886–
... Physical anthropology of the Roebuck Iroquois with comparative data and other Indian tribes, by Sir Francis H. S. Knowles. Ottawa, J. O. Patenaude, printer, 1937.
viii, 75 p. front. (map) illus., tables. 24½cm. (Canada. National museum of Canada. Bulletin no. 87. Anthropological series no. 22)
At head of title: Canada. Department of mines and resources ... Mines and geology branch ... National museum of Canada ...
Bibliographical foot-notes.
1. Iroquoian Indians—Antiquities. 2. Indians of North America—Anthropometry. I. Title.
S 37–32
U. S. Bur. Amer. eth. Libr. for Library of Congress E51.C2 no. 22 [QH1.C13 no. 87]
PPAN CtY PU PP OClW OClWHi DLC
NK 0209428 DSI MU NBuU CaBVaU CaBVa OrPR DNLM CU

Knowles, *Sir* Francis Howe Seymour, *bart.*, 1886–1953.
Stone-worker's progress; a study of stone implements in the Pitt Rivers Museum. Edited by T. K. Penniman and B. M. Blackwood. Oxford, Printed at the University Press, 1953.
120 p. illus. 24 cm. (Pitt Rivers Museum, University of Oxford. Occasional papers on technology, 6)
Bibliography: p. 108–111.
1. Stone implements. I. Title. (Series: Oxford. University. Pitt Rivers Museum. Occasional papers on technology, 6)
A 55–7265
Minnesota. Univ. Libr. for Library of Congress [1]
PU-Mu MiU
NK 0209429 MnU ICU CaBViP CSt PPT CtY MH-P NN PSt

Knowles, Frank.
A practical course in agricultural chemistry for senior students of agriculture, dairying, horticulture and poultry husbandry, by Frank Knowles ... and J. Elphin Watkin ... With a foreword by Sir John Russell ... London, Macmillan and co., limited, 1937.
ix, 188 p. illus., diagrs. 22½cm.
1. Agricultural chemistry. I. Watkin, Job Elphin, joint author.
37–19470
Library of Congress S585.K6 [5] 630.24
NK 0209430 DLC CaBVaU OrCS CaBVa NcRS NNBG NN

Knowles, Frank.
A practical course in agricultural chemistry, for senior students of agriculture, dairying, horticulture and poultry husbandry, by Frank Knowles and J. Elphin Watkin, with a foreword by Sir John Russell. [2d ed.] London, Macmillan, 1947.
xi, 216 p. illus. 22 cm.
1. Agricultural chemistry. I. Watkin, Job Elphin, joint author.
S585.K6 1947 630.24 48–19933*
NK 0209431 DLC CaBVaU OrCS TU MiU PSt

Knowles, Frank Crozer, 1881–
[Collected papers, chiefly on skin diseases]
NK 0209432 ICJ

Knowles, Frank Crozer, 1881-
Collected reprints. Phila., 1906-1931.
NK 0209433 PPC

Knowles, Frank Crozer, 1881–
Diseases of the skin, including the acute eruptive fevers, by Frank Crozer Knowles ... with 199 illustrations and 14 plates. Philadelphia and New York, Lea & Febiger, 1914.
xiv, [17]–546 p. illus., xiv pl. (2 col., incl. front.) 24½cm.
1. Skin—Diseases. 14–14887
Library of Congress RL71.K5
Copyright A 379211 [a36b1]
NK 0209434 ICRL DLC DNLM PPC PU PPJ ICJ ViU

Knowles, Frank Crozer, 1881–
Diseases of the skin, by Frank Crozer Knowles ... 2d ed., thoroughly rev., with 229 illustrations and 14 plates. Philadelphia and New York, Lea & Febiger, 1923.
xv, [17]–595 p. illus., xiv pl. (2 col.; incl. front.) 24½cm.
1. Skin—Diseases.
Library of Congress RL71.K5 1923 23–12589
NK 0209435 DLC OrU-M PPJ CtY-M PPC PPHa DNLM ICJ

Knowles, Frank Crozer, 1881–
Diseases of the skin, by Frank Crozer Knowles ... 3d ed., thoroughly rev., with 240 illustrations and 11 plates. Philadelphia, Lea & Febiger, 1935.
640 p. illus., xi pl. 24½cm.
1. Skin—Diseases. 35–18799
Library of Congress RL71.K5 1935
Copyright A 86503 [3] 616.5
PLF ViU CtY-M ICRL
NK 0209436 DLC MiU PPC PU-Med OU NNC-M OrU-D

Knowles, Frank Crozer, 1881–
Diseases of the skin, by Frank Crozer Knowles ... Edward F. Corson ... and Henry B. Decker ... 4th ed., thoroughly rev., with 272 illustrations. Philadelphia, Lea & Febiger, 1942.
621 p. illus. 24cm.
1. Skin—Diseases. I. Corson, Edward Foulke, 1883– joint author. II. Decker, Henry Bristol, 1893– joint author.
42–11255
Library of Congress RL71.K5 1942 [2] 616.5
PPJ DNLM
NK 0209437 DLC OrU-M IdPI CtY-M NcU-H PPHa OU ICJ

Knowles, Frank Crozer, 1881-
External origin of eczema.
pamph.
NK 0209438 PPHa

Knowles, Frank Crozer, 1881-
Eruptions of unusual type caused by absorption from belladonna plaster and from ocular instillation of atropine.
pamph.
NK 0209439 PPHa

Knowles, Frank Crosier, 1881-
Multiple areas of pigmentation in a girl of 12.
pamph.
NK 0209440 PPHa

Knowles, Frank Crozer, 1881-
Psoriasis families.
pamph.
NK 0209441 PPHa

Knowles, Frank Crozer, 1881- joint author.
Gittings, John Claxton, 1874–
Tuberculosis in infancy and childhood; lectures delivered at the Children's hospital, Philadelphia, under the auspices of the Philadelphia pediatric society, by J. Claxton Gittings ... Frank Crozer Knowles ... and Astley P. C. Ashhurst ... with 23 illustrations. Philadelphia & London, J. B. Lippincott company [c1922]

Knowles, Frank Crozer, 1881-
Varicella of hemorrhagic type.
pamph.
NK 0209443 PPHa

Lilly
PN 6110
.C 7 K 73
1906
KNOWLES, FREDERIC LAWRENCE, 1869-1905, comp.
Cap and gown, a treasury of college verse selected by Frederic Lawrence Knowles ... Boston, L.C. Page & Company, 1906.
4 p.ℓ., vii.-xxii p., 1 ℓ., xxiii-xxiv p., 1 ℓ., 368 p. front, ports. 19 cm
"Tenth impression, February, 1906."
Bound in blue pictorial cloth; top edge gilt.
NK 0209444 InU WaSp

Knowles, Frederic Lawrence, 1869–1905, *comp.*
Cap and gown, a treasury of college verse. Selected by Frederic Lawrence Knowles ... Boston, L. C. Page & company [1910?]
4 p. l., vii–xxii p., 1 l., xxiii–xxiv p., 1 l., 368 p. front., ports. 19½cm.
1. College verse. 2. American poetry (Collections) I. Title.
A 24–704
John J. Halsey memorial libr. for Library of Congress [a38c1]
NK 0209445 NN MiD WU MdBP ScU

VOLUME 300

[Knowles, Frederic Lawrence] 1869-1905, supposed ed.
Cap and gown in prose; short sketches selected from undergraduate periodicals of recent years
see under Paget, R.L., pseud., ed.

Knowles, Frederic Lawrence, 1869-1905, *comp.*
Cap and gown. Second series, selected by Frederic Lawrence Knowles. Boston, L. C. Page and company (incorporated) 1897.
xxiv p., 1 l., 368 p. front. 17½cm. (Cap and gown series)
Cover-title: Cap and gown, the second series of collge (!) verse.

1. College verse. 2. American poetry (Selections) I. Title.

Library of Congress PN6110.C7K6 1897 12-14836

NK 0209447 DLC Wa MiD NcD WU MB MiU OU OO OCl ODW PSt MB PV PPD PP Nh CaBViP WaS MsSM NIC NcU ICarbS OrU

Knowles, Frederic Lawrence, 1869-1905, supposed comp.
Cap and gown; some college verse
see under Paget, P.L., pseud., comp.

Knowles, Frederick Lawrence, 1869-1905, supposed comp.
Cap and gown ... third series
see under Paget, R.L., pseud., comp.

Knowles, Frederic Lawrence, 1869-1905, supposed author.
The cocktail book
see under Paget, R.L., pseud.

Knowles, Frederic Lawrence, 1869-1905, ed.
The golden treasury of American songs and lyrics ... London, n.d.
332 p. 16 cm.

NK 0209451 RPB

Knowles, Frederick Lawrence, 1867-1905, ed.
Golden treasury of American songs and lyrics.
L, Page, 1897.

NK 0209452 PPAp

Knowles, Frederic Lawrence, 1869-1905, *ed.*
The golden treasury of American songs and lyrics, ed. by Frederic Lawrence Knowles. Boston, L. C. Page & company (incorporated) 1898.
xix p., 1 l., 319 p. front. 17½cm.

1. American poetry (Collections) I. Title.

Library of Congress PS593.L8K6 1898 4-13826
Copyright 1897: 65436 (a36h1) 811.0822

NK 0209453 DLC WaSpG PV PPD OCl PPSJ MH MiU MB Nh KyLx

Knowles, Frederic Lawrence, 1869-1905, *ed.*
The golden treasury of American songs and lyrics, ed. by Frederic Lawrence Knowles. New rev. ed. Boston, L. C. Page and company (incorporated) 1901.
xix p., 1 l., 330 p. front. 17cm. (*On verso of half-title:* The Cap and gown series)

1. American poetry (Collections) I. Title.

Library of Congress PS593.L8K6 1901 1-15161

NK 0209454 DLC WaS WaT Or MoU NjP NIC PP MB

KC 1786
Knowles, Frederic Lawrence, 1869-1905, ed.
The golden treasury of American songs and lyrics. Popular ed. Boston, L.C.Page and co., inc., 1904.

"Golden treasury series."

NK 0209455 MH ViU WaSp

Knowles, Frederic Lawrence, 1869-1905, ed.
The golden treasury of American songs and lyrics, edited by Frederic Lawrence Knowles ... Portrait ed. Boston, L. C. Page & company, 1905.
xxii p., 1 l., 332 p. front., ports. 19½cm.

1. American poetry (Collections) I. Title.

PS593.L8K6 1905 46-45060

Library of Congress (2)

NK 0209456 DLC NN OCl MB

811.08 K76g 1906 Knowles, Frederic Lawrence, 1869-1905, comp.
The golden treasury of American songs and lyrics London, G. Routledge & sons, limited [1906-?]
331p. (Half-title: The new universal library)

1. American poetry (Collections) I. Title.

NK 0209457 IU CSmH

Coll K731g 1908 **Knowles, Frederic Lawrence, 1869-1905, ed.**
The golden treasury of American songs and lyrics, edited by Frederic Lawrence Knowles. Boston, L.C. Page & company, 1908.
xix p., 1 l., 319p. front. 18cm.

NK 0209458 RPB

Knowles, Frederic Lawrence, 1869-1905, ed.
The golden treasury of American songs and lyrics, ed. by Frederic Lawrence Knowles. Portrait ed. Boston, L.C. Page and co., inc., c1911
332p.

NK 0209459 MiU PSC

Knowles, Frederic Lawrence, 1869-1905, *ed.*
The golden treasury of American songs and lyrics, ed. by Frederic Lawrence Knowles. ... Boston, L. C. Page & company c1914.
xxii p., 1 l., 332 p. 31 ports. (incl. front.) 20cm.

NK 0209460 ViU NN

Knowles, Frederic Lawrence, 1869-1905.
A Kipling primer; including biographical and critical chapters, an index to Mr. Kipling's principal writings, and bibliographies, by Frederic Lawrence Knowles ... Boston, Brown and company, 1899.
219 p. front. (port.) 18½cm.
Bibliography: p. 200-215.

1. Kipling, Rudyard, 1865- —Dictionaries, indexes, etc. I. Title.

Library of Congress PR4856.A26 99-4253 Revised

NK 0209461 DLC OrU OClJC ICU NjP OCl OCU OClRC OO ViU PBm MB TxU Nh CaBVaU IdU PWcS PSt PP PV MH CLSU NcD PPD CtY IEN AAP FTaSU

---

*EC9 K6287 S899ka Knowles, Frederic Lawrence, 1869-1905.
A Kipling primer, including biographical and critical chapters, an index to Mr. Kipling's principal writings, and bibliographies, by Frederic Lawrence Knowles ...
London, Chatto & Windus, 1900.
219p. ports.(incl.front.) 19cm.
Original red cloth.

NK 0209462 MH INS

Knowles, Frederic Lawrence, 1869-1905.
Love triumphant, a book of poems, by Frederic Lawrence Knowles ... Boston, D. Estes & company [1904]
xii p., 1 l., 168 p. 18½cm.

I. Title.

Library of Congress PS3521.N75L6 1904 4-27340

NK 0209463 DLC ViU Wa WaS ICU ODW MiU NN MB PSC TNJ WaWW

Knowles, Frederic Lawrence, 1869-1905.
Love triumphant, a book of poems, by Frederic Lawrence Knowles ... Boston, D. Estes & company [1906]
193 p. 19cm.
"Fifth revised edition" ...

NK 0209464 FU MH

Knowles, Frederic Lawrence, 1869-1905
Love triumphant, a book of poems. 5th rev. ed., containing "Sunset poems," now first collected since the author's death, also an appreciation by Prof. C. T. Winchester.
Boston, Page Co. [1914]
xiii p., 1 l., 193 p. 19 cm.
"Fifth impression, May, 1914."

I. Winchester Caleb Thomas, 1847-1920.

NK 0209465 RPB CLSU MH NjP

Knowles, Frederic Lawrence, 1869-1905.
McKinley, William, *pres. U. S.*, 1843-1901.
McKinley's masterpieces; selections from the public addresses in and out of Congress, of William McKinley. Ed. by R. L. Paget [*pseud.*] Boston, Joseph Knight company, 1896.

Knowles, Frederic Lawrence, 1869-1905.
On life's stairway, by Frederic Lawrence Knowles. Boston, L. C. Page & company, 1901.
126 p. 17½cm.
Poems.

I. Title.

Library of Congress PS3521.N75O5 1901 0-6260 Revised
Copyright 1900 A 25186 (r34b2) 811.49

NK 0209467 DLC TNJ NcD IU NcU OClW MB

VOLUME 300

Knowles, Frederic Lawrence, 1869–1905.
On life's stairway, by Frederic Lawrence Knowles. Boston, D. Estes & company [1905]
xii p., 1 l., 126 p. 19cm.
Poems.
First published 1901.
CONTENTS.—Nature and life.—Steps toward faith.

I. Title.

Library of Congress PS3521.N75O5 1905 5—13177

NK 0209468 DLC WaS TNJ MiU OCl OU ODW

[**Knowles, Frederic Lawrence**] 1869–1905, *comp.*
Poems of American patriotism, 1776–1898; selected by R. L. Paget [*pseud.*] Boston, L. C. Page and company (incorporated) 1898.
3 p. l., vii–xvi p., 1 l., 414 p. 18cm.

1. National songs, American. 2. American poetry (Collections) I. Title.

Library of Congress PS595.H5K6 C—171

OClWHi WaU NN MB PCC PPCS
NK 0209469 DLC OrMonO MH OU KyLx MB PP OO OCl OClW

[Knowles, Frederic Lawrence] 1869–1905, ed.
Poems of American patriotism, 1776–1898; selected by R.L. Paget [pseud. New rev. ed.] Boston, L. C. Page and company (incorporated) 1898.
3p. l.,vii–xvi p., 1 l.,421p. 18cm.

NK 0209470 RPB PU MnHi NN MH NjP WaSp NNC

Knowles, Frederic Lawrence, 1869–1905, ed.
Poems of American patriotism, selected by Frederic Lawrence Knowles ... Boston, The Page company [1918]
xiii, [1] p., 1 l., [xv]–xvi, 421 p. front., plates. 19cm.
"Ninth impression, September, 1918."

1. National songs, American. 2. American poetry (Collections). I. Title

NK 0209471 ViU MB ICN

Knowles, Frederic Lawrence, 1869–1905, *ed.*
Poems of American patriotism from the time of the revolution to the present day, edited by Frederick Lawrence Knowles ... New ed., revised and edited by R. L. Paget [*pseud.*] ... Boston, L. C. Page & company [c1926]
5 p. l., ix–xiv p., 2 l., 393 p. front., plates, ports. 19½cm.

1. National songs, American. 2. American poetry (Collections) I. Paget, R. L., pseud. II. Title.

Library of Congress PS595.H5K6 1926 26–14559

NK 0209472 DLC CaBVa PWcS PP OCl MB

Knowles, *Frederic Lawrence, 1869-1905, comp.*
Poetry of American wit and humor.
n.p.

NK 0209473 PPAp

[**Knowles, Frederic Lawrence**] 1869–1905, *comp.*
The poetry of American wit and humor; selected by R. L. Paget [*pseud.*] Boston, L. C. Page and company (incorporated) 1899.
xii, 367 p. front. 18 cm. (*On verso of half-title:* The cap and gown series)

1. American wit and humor. 2. American poetry (Collections) I. Title.

Library of Congress PS595.H8K6 99—4936
[a48q1] -817.0822

DAU PP OClU
NK 0209474 DLC PV PPPD MB ODW OLak MiU OO PPL MH

Knowles, Frederic Lawrence, *1869-1905, comp.*
The poetry of American wit and humor. Selected by R. L. Paget [pseud.].
Boston. Page & Co. [1907.] xiii, 367 pp. Portraits. 19½ cm.

H4498 — Wit and humor. — United States. Lit. Poetry. Colls.

NK 0209475 MB

Knowles, Frederic Lawrence, *1869-1905, comp.*
The poetry of American wit and humor, selected by R. L. Paget, pseud. Boston, Page, 1910. 367p.

NK 0209476 OCl

810.18 Knowles, Frederic Lawrence, 1869-1905,
K73p comp.
Poetry of American wit and humor...
Boston, Page [1918]
367p. front.,ports. D.

NK 0209477 IaU ViU

Knowles, Frederic Lawrence, 1869–1905.
Practical hints for young writers, readers and book buyers, by Frederic Lawrence Knowles. Boston, L. C. Page and company (incorporated) 1897.
xii p., 1 l., [15]–73 p., 2 l. 18½cm.

1. Authorship—Handbooks, manuals, etc.

Library of Congress PN158.K5 8–14808

NK 0209478 DLC TxU MiU OCl Nh NN MB

Knowles, Frederic Lawrence, *1869-1905*
Practical hints for young writers, readers, and book buyers. Concord, N. H., 1897.
39p.
DLC: YA 25223

NK 0209479 DLC

Knowles, Frederic Lawrence, 1869–1905, *ed.*
A treasury of humorous poetry; being a compilation of witty, facetious, and satirical verse selected from the writings of British and American poets; ed. by Frederic Lawrence Knowles ... Boston, D. Estes & company [c1902]
xxiv, 407 p. front. (port. group) plates. 19cm.

1. English wit and humor. 2. American wit and humor. 3. English poetry (Collections) 4. American poetry (Collections) I. Title.

Library of Congress PN6110.H8K6 2—24319
Copyright
808 [s26t2] Yo

OO OCl PP NN ViU Or CLSU KyLx FMU WaE
NK 0209480 DLC WaS WaT NcC PPL CaBVa OEac OClh

Knowles, Frederic Lawrence, 1869–1905, *ed.*
A treasury of humorous poetry; being a compilation of witty, facetious, and satirical verse selected from the writings of British and American poets; ed. by Frederic Lawrence Knowles ... Boston, **The Page company [1919]**
xxiv, 407 p. front. (port. group) plates. 19cm.

NK 0209481 ViU OOxM PP MH

Knowles, Frederic Lawrence, 1869–1905, *ed.*
The value of courage; ed. by Frederic Lawrence Knowles. Boston, H. M. Caldwell co., 1905.
xi, 172 p. 22½cm.
Ornamental borders and end-papers in green.

1. Courage. I. Title.

Library of Congress BJ1533.C8K6 5—26239

NK 0209482 DLC PP PCC MB

Knowles, Frederic Lawrence, 1869–1905, *ed.*
The value of friendship, ed. by Frederic Lawrence Knowles. Boston, H. M. Caldwell co., 1904.
2 p. l., 119 numb. l. 22½cm.
Decorations in green.
Printed on one side of leaf only, the printed pages facing each other.

1. Friendship. I. Title.

Library of Congress BJ1533.F8K7 4—25390

NK 0209483 DLC WaWW ixU ViU OCl NN MB

177.6 Knowles, Frederic Lawrence, 1869-1905, ed.
K762v The value of friendship. New York, H. M. Caldwell [c1904]
127 p. illus.
Printed on one side of leaf only, the printed pages facing each other.

1. Friendship. 2. Poetry - Collections. I. Title.

NK 0209484 MsSM

Knowles, Frederic Lawrence, *editor.*
The value of friendship.
— New York. Dodge Publishing Co. [1904.] 13–100 pp. [Best value series.] 17 cm.
A book of quotations.

D5493 — T.r. — S.r. — Friendship. — Quotations.

NK 0209485 MB

Knowles, Frederic Lawrence, 1869–1905, *ed.*
The value of love, ed. by Frederic Lawrence Knowles; introduction by Louise Chandler Moulton. Boston, H. M. Caldwell co., 1906.
3 p. l., v–xi, 178 p. 23½cm.
Ornamental borders.

6–26089

NK 0209486 DLC

Knowles, Frederic Lawrence, 1869–1905, ed
The value of love, ed. by Frederic Lawrence Knowles. New York [etc.] H. M. Caldwell co. [c1906] 84 p. 17cm.

331085B. 1. Love in literature. I. Title.
N. Y. P. L. May 8, 1946

NK 0209487 NN RPB PP

VOLUME 300

811.08
K762w Knowles, Frederic Lawrence, 1869-1905, ed.
Wesleyan verse, selected from the undergraduate publications of Wesleyan University. Middletown, Conn. [Case, Lockwood & Brainard Co., Printers] 1894.
111 p. 17cm.

1. College verse--Wesleyan University, Middletown, Conn. I. Title.

NK 0209488 AU RPB PU CtY

Knowles, Frederic Lawrence, 1869-1905.
What are the best fifty American poems? (From Literary Digest, May 3, 1902. 15 cm. 5 l. port.)

NK 0209489 RPB

Knowles, Frederic Lawrence, 1869-1905, *ed.*
A year book of famous lyrics: selections from the British and American poets, arranged for daily reading or memorising, ed. by Frederic Lawrence Knowles ... Boston, D. Estes & company [1901]
xix p., 1 l., 392 p. 16 port. (incl. front.) 19 cm.

1. English poetry (Selections: Extracts, etc.) 2. Poetry—Yearbooks. I. Title.
PR1176.K5 1—22877
[50c1]

NK 0209490 DLC MtU NcD OCl KyLx PP ViU NN WaS OrP

[Knowles, Frederic Lawrence] 1869-1905
See also
[Paget, R.L.] pseud.

Knowles, Frederick.
With the Dinkums. no. 1. Sydney, N. S. W. Bookstall co., 1918. 40 p. (chiefly illus.) 31cm.
Ceased publication.

1. European war, 1914-1918—

NK 0209492 NN

Knowles, Frederick L
DDT residual house spray, a method of malaria control in rural areas, by Frederick L. Knowles and Clinton S. Smith ... [Washington, U. S. Govt. print. off., 1946]
1 p. l., 6 p. 23cm. ([U. S. Public health service; Public health reports. Reprint no. 2688)
"References": p. 6.

1. DDT (Insecticide) 2. Malarial fever—Prevention. I. Smith, Clinton S., joint author.
Library of Congress RA644.M2K56 46-25993
[3] 614.53

NK 0209493 DLC CaBVaU PP

Knowles, Frederick L
DDT water emulsion in rice fields as a method of controlling larvae of *Anopheles quadrimaculatus* and other mosquitoes, by Frederick L. Knowles and Frank W. Fisk ... [Washington, U. S. Govt. print. off., 1945]
16 p. incl. tables, diagrs. pl. 23cm. ([U. S. Public health service; Public health reports. Reprint no. 2650)
"References": p. 16.

1. Mosquitoes—Extermination. 2. DDT (Insecticide) I. Fisk, Frank Wilbur, joint author.
Library of Congress RC116.K54 46-25377
[3] 614.43

NK 0209494 DLC PP

Knowles, Frederick L
Observations on the use of "phenol" larvicides for mosquito control, by Frederick L. Knowles, Wiley V. Parker, and H. A. Johnson ... [Washington, U. S. Govt. print. off., 1941]
1 p. l., 5 p. 23½cm. ([U. S. Public health service; Public health reports. Reprint no. 2303)

1. Mosquitoes—Extermination. 2. Larvae. I. Parker, Wiley Vernon, 1886- joint author. II. Johnson, Henry Adams, 1888- joint author. III. Title: "Phenol" larvicides for mosquito control.
41-46326
Library of Congress RC116.K55
[4] 614.43

NK 0209495 DLC

Knowles, F[rederick] M[ilton]
A cheerful year book, for the recording of engagements and other serious matters, accompanied by philosophic and moral aphorisms ... by F. M. Knowles; the same being illustrated with tasteful and illuminating pictures by C. F. Lester, and the whole introduced and concluded with profound and edifying remarks by Carolyn Wells. New York, H. Holt and company, 1906.
[144] p. illus. 18½cm.

6-37877

NK 0209496 DLC ViU

Knowles, F[rederick] M[ilton]
A cheerful year book, for the recording of engagements and other serious matters, accompanied by philosophic and moral aphorisms ... by F.M. Knowles; the same being illustrated with tasteful and illuminating pictures by C. F. Lester, and the whole introduced and concluded with profound and edifying remarks by Carolyn Wells. New York, H. Holt and co., 1907.
vii, 134 p. 1 pl., illus. 19 cm.

NK 0209497 RPB NRCR

JS.10
5361 **Knowles, Freeman,** 1846-1910.
Free homesteads. Speech ... in the House ... March 10, 1898. Washington [Gov't print. off.] 1898.
7 pp. map. 8°.
1-4473

NK 0209498 DLC

HG533
.K65 **Knowles, Freeman,** 1846-1910.
National bankers and "national honor." Speech ... in the House ... January 31, 1898. Washington [Gov't print. off.] 1898.
7 pp. 8°.
1-4472

NK 0209499 DLC

JO
.KN Knowles, Freeman, 1846-1910
"Our press censorship. The case of Freeman Knowles of the Lantern." Deadwood, S.D. [n.d.]
16 p. 15cm.

Cover title.

1. Liberty of the press.
2. The Lantern, Deadwood, S.D.

NK 0209500 WHi

UA25
.K7 **Knowles, Freeman,** 1846-1910
Volunteers vs. regulars. Remarks ... in the House ... April 23, 1898. Washington [Gov't print. off.] 1898.
4 pp. 8°.
1-4471

NK 0209501 DLC

HJ8114
.K7 **Knowles, Freeman,** 1846-1910
War taxes—Divinity of courts—Bonds vs. greenbacks. Speech ... in the House ... April 27, 1898. Washington [Gov't print. off.] 1898.
8 pp. 8°.
1-4530

NK 0209502 DLC

Knowles, G W.
The book of dogs, by G. W. Knowles ... London and Edinburgh, T. C. & E. C. Jack, ltd. [1924]
ix, 11-132 p. front., illus., plates. 19½cm.
The plates are printed on both sides.

Dogs. I. Title.
Library of Congress SF427.K5 25-15361

NK 0209503 DLC

Knowles, Gaye.
The islanders follow a clue; illustrated by the author. London, Heinemann [1952]
198 p. illus. 19 cm

I. Title.
PZ7.K762 Is 52-43295 ‡

NK 0209504 DLC MiU

Knowles, Gaye.
The islanders in danger; illustrated by the author. London, Heinemann [1953]
189 p. illus. 19 cm.

I. Title.
PZ7.K762 It 53-36514 ‡
Library of Congress [2]

NK 0209505 DLC

Kress
Room Knowles, George
Railroads. Observations on the expediency of making a line of railroad from York to Scarbrough ... Scarbrough, Printed by C.R.Todd, 1841 [i.e. 1844]
8, 9 p. 21.5 cm.

Cover-title: Railroads. Observations on the expediency of making a line of railroad from York to Scarborough ... together with a supplement ... 1844.

1.Railroads - Gt.Brit. 2.Railroads - Early works to 1850.

NK 0209506 MH-BA NNC CSmH

Knowles, George.
Road-side spraying
see under
Canada. Experimental farms service.

Knowles, George Beauchamp, 1829-1852, ed.

The **Floral** cabinet, and magazine of exotic botany. Conducted by G. B. Knowles ... and Frederic Westcott. vol. I-III. London, W. Smith, 1837-40.

VOLUME 300

Knowles, George Hogan.
In the grip of the jungles, by George Hogan Knowles ... London, Wright & Brown [1932]
xx, 320 p. front. (port.) plates. 22½cm.
"Contains contributions made previously to the Cornhill magazine, the Tatler, the Autocar, and to other magazines."—p. xv.

1. Hunting—India. 2. Animals, Habits and behavior of. I. Title.
32-20132
Library of Congress SK235.K65
[3] 799.2954

NK 0209509 DLC CU NN

KNOWLES, GEORGE HOGAN.
Jungle haunts, by George Hogan Knowles... London: Wright & Brown [1934] xxii, 295 p. front., plates, ports. 22cm.

746967A. 1. Hunting—India. 2. India—Descr. and trav., 1910- . I. Title.

NK 0209510 NN

KNOWLES, GEORGE HOGAN.
Terrors of the jungle, by George Hogan Knowles... London: Wright & Brown[, 1932]. 320 p. front. (port.), plates. 21½cm.
"Two stories in this book were contributed to the 'Cornhill' magazine."

645151A. 1. Hunting—India. 2. India—Descr. and trav., 1910- 3. Adventure. I. Title.
March 23, 1933

NK 0209511 NN

Knowles, George Parker, *b.* 1797.
A genealogical account of the Rosses of Dalton, in the county of Dumfries, from their first settlement in Scotland, in the twelfth century, to the year of Our Lord 1854. By George Parker Knowles ... London, Printed for private circulation only, by Harrison and sons, 1855.
8 p. illus. (coat of arms) fold. geneal. tab. 25cm.
"Only seventy-five copies printed."
"Coulthart, of Coulthart, Collyn, and Ashton-under-Lyne. Derived from the family muniments, and brought down to A. D. 1853, by Alexander Cheyne ... of Ashton-under-Lyne, co. Lancaster ... and George Parker Knowles, of Manchester": geneal. tab.
1. Ross family. 2. Coulthart family.
15-23251
Library of Congress CS479.R83

NK 0209512 DLC NN

Knowles, George Parker, *b.* 1797.
A genealogical and heraldic account of the Coultharts of Coulthart and Collyn, chiefs of the name, from their first settlement in Scotland, in the reign of Conarus, to the year of our Lord 1854; to which are added, the pedigrees of seven other considerable families, that, through heiresses, became incorporated with the house of Coulthart. By George Parker Knowles ... Derived from the family muniments. London, Printed for private circulation only by Harrison and sons, 1855.
23 p., 1 l. front. (coat of arms) illus., fold. geneal. tab. 25cm.

Only seventy-five copies printed.
Printed on vellum.
CONTENTS.—Coulthart of Coulthart and Collyn.—Ross of Renfrew.—Macknyghte of Macknyghte.—Glendonyn of Glendonyn.—Carmichael of Carspherne. — Forbes of Pitscottie. — Mackenzie of Craig hall. — Gordon of Sorbie.

1. Coulthart family. 2. Ross family. 3. Mc Knight family. 4. Glendonyn family. 5. Carmichael family. 6. Forbes family. 7. Mackenzie family. 8. Gordon family.
12-22091
Library of Congress CS479.C85

NK 0209514 DLC NN

Knowles, George Shaw, 1882- ed.

Australia. *Laws, statutes, etc.*
The acts of the Parliament of the commonwealth of Australia (except appropriation and supply acts) passed from 1901 to 1911, and in force on 1st January, 1912, to which is prefixed the Commonwealth of Australia constitution act (63 & 64 Vict. ch. 12) as altered to 1st January, 1912: with tables and indexes ... Comp. and annotated by George S. Knowles ... Melbourne, Victoria, Printed for the government of the commonwealth of Australia by A. J. Mullett, government printer for the state of Victoria; and pub. by C. F. Maxwell (G. Partridge & co.) 1913.

Knowles, George Shaw, 1882- **comp.**

Australia. *Constitution.*
The Commonwealth of Australia constitution act (as altered to 1st July, 1936), and the acts altering the Constitution. With notes, tables, indexes and appendixes. Compiled and annotated by George S. Knowles ... Canberra, L. F. Johnston, commonwealth government printer [1936?]

Knowles, George William, 1879- *ed.*
Friends; some Quaker peace documents, 1654–1920 ... With an introduction and notes by G. W. Knowles ... London, Peace book company [1939]
2 p. l., 52 p. 21cm. (Peace classics. vol. IV)
First published (London, 1427) under title: Quakers and peace.
Bibliography: p. 15-18.
CONTENTS.—Letter of George Fox to Oliver Cromwell (1654)—Selection from an epistle of G. Fox to "all Friends everywhere" (1660?)—Selection from a declaration by Quakers (1660) — Selection from the Yearly meeting epistle (1693)—Selection from the works of Isaac Penington.—Selection from R. Barclay's Epistle to the ambassadors.—Selection from the Apology by R. Barclay.—Selection from An essay on the peace of Europe by W. Penn.—W. Penn's address to American Indians (1682)—Selection from Governor Gordon's speech to American Indians (giving heads of Penn's treaty of friendship) (1728)—Selection from an essay on war by J. Dymond.—Message to men and women of goodwill (1914)—Selection from The true way of life by E. Grubb.—Selection from The Christian and war by W. Blair Neatby.—Selection from London Yearly meeting epistle (1915) — Selection from "Friends and war" (adopted by the Conference of all Friends, 1920)

1. Friends, Society of. 2. Peace. I. Title.
A 41-818
Northwestern univ. Libr. for Library of Congress [BX7748.W2K]

NK 0209518 IEN CtY MH

Knowles, George William, 1879- joint author

Aggs, William Hanbury.
Handbook on education, being the education act, 1921, with full notes and an introduction and index, by W. H. Aggs ... and G. W. Knowles ... London, Sweet & Maxwell, ltd. [etc.] 1922.

Knowles, George William, 1879- joint author

Aggs, William Hanbury.
Handbook on railways, being the Railways act, 1921, with full notes and an introduction and index by W. H. Aggs ... and G. W. Knowles ... London, Sweet & Maxwell, ltd.; Stevens & sons, ltd., 1922.

Knowles, George William, 1879-
Junior labour exchanges (A plea for closer co-operation between labour exchanges and education authorities). With a preface by S. J. Chapman. London: Sherratt & Hughes, 1910. 32 p. 8°.

1. Employment bureaus, Gt. Br. 2. Education (Industrial and technical), Gt. Br. 3. Chapman, Sidney John. N. Y. P. L.
December 21, 1911.

NK 0209521 NN DL MiD

Law Knowles, George William, 1879- FOR OTHER EDITIONS SEE MAIN ENTRY

Wurtzburg, Edward Albert, 1850–1921.
... The law relating to building societies. 9th ed., by G. W. Knowles ... London, Stevens & sons, limited [etc.] 1946.

Knowles, George William, 1879- *ed.*
... Quakers and peace, with an introduction and notes by G. W. Knowles ... London, Sweet & Maxwell, limited, 1927.
iii, 52 p. 21½cm. (The Grotius society publications. Texts for students of international relations. No. 4)
Bibliography: p. 15-18.
CONTENTS.—Letter of George Fox to Oliver Cromwell (1654)—Selection from an epistle of G. Fox to "all Friends everywhere" (1660?)—Selection from a declaration by Quakers (1660)—Selection from the Yearly meeting epistle (1693)—Selection from the works of Isaac Penington.—Selection from R. Barclay's Epistle to the ambassadors.—Selection from the Apology by R. Barclay.—Selection from An essay on the peace of Europe, by W. Penn.—W. Penn's address to American Indians (1682)—Selection from Governor Gordon's speech to American Indians (giving heads of Penn's treaty of friendship) (1728)—Selections from an essay on war, by J. Dymond.—Message to men and women of goodwill (1914)—Selection from The true way of life, by E. Grubb.—Selection from The Christian and war, by W. Blair Neatby.—Selection from London Yearly meeting epistle (1915)—Selection from "Friends and war" (adopted by the Conference of all Friends, 1920)
1. Friends, Society of. 2. Pacifism. I. Title.
27-24164
Library of Congress BX7748.W2K6

NK 0209524 DLC WaU-L DS PU-L PPB PHC OU MB

Knowles, George William, 1879- ed.

Simpson, Archibald Henry, 1843–1918.
A treatise on the law and practice relating to infants, by Archibald H. Simpson ... 4th ed., by George W. Knowles ... London, Sweet & Maxwell, limited; [etc., etc.] 1926.

Knowles, George William, 1879- ed. FOR OTHER EDITIONS SEE MAIN ENTRY

Wurtzburg, Edward Albert, 1850–1921.
Wurtzburg's Law relating to building societies. 8th ed., by G. W. Knowles ... London, Stevens & sons, ltd. [etc.] 1940.

q615.32 K73m Knowles, Gilbert, fl.1723.
Materia medica botanica; in qua symptomata variorum morborum describuntur, herbæque iisdem depellendis aptissimæ apponuntur, tam quæ in nostris hic sponte oris, quam quæ in aliis orbis regionibus nascuntur: plantæ exoticæ, sive alienigenæ, numero plùs quadrigentæ quantùm ad omnes partes ex peritissimis botanices authoribus, ut Raio, Tournefortio, &c. accuratissimè describuntur. Variæ episodiæ, ornatûs causâ, intertextuntur. Octingentis, præter propter, carminibus latinis hexametris totum opus constat ... Authore G. Knowles. Londi- ni, typis G. Bowyer, 1723. 256p.

NK 0209527 IU

Knowles, Guy, tr.

Cassagnac, Paul de, 1881-
French wines, by Paul de Cassagnac, translated by Guy Knowles. London, Chatto & Windus, 1930.

Knowles, H. L.
Dielectric constant of ethyl alcohol vapor and possible effect of conductivity [1932?] Thesis (Ph.D.)-University of Kansas. Reprinted from the Journal of physical chemistry, vol XXXVI pp. 2554-2566, October, 1932.

NK 0209529 OU

GB55 .G313 Knowles, Harold L., joint author.

Gaddum, Leonard William, 1890-
Our physical environment, a problem approach [by] Leonard W. Gaddum [and] Harold L. Knowles. Boston, Houghton Mifflin [1953]

VOLUME 300

Knowles, Helen C.

Songs and pictures for little folks; words and music by Helen C. Knowles, photographs by Ruth Alexander Nichols. New York, A. S. Barnes and company, incorporated, 1938.

[31] p. illus. 29 x 22cm.

1. Children's songs. 2. Photography of children. I. Nichols, Mrs. Ruth Alexander, illus. II. Title.

39-22605

Library of Congress M1990.K885

——— Copy 2.

Copyright A 120977 [7] 784.624

NK 0209531 DLC OrLgE Or OClh OEac PPT PSt

PJA OCl OOxM NcD NN

Knowles, Helen K

Making money for your church, library, hospital, social, or welfare organizations. Portland, Me., Bond Wheelwright Co. [1955]

225 p. 21 cm.

1. Fund raising. I. Title.

HV41.K58 361.73 55—6259 ‡

NK 0209532 DLC IdB Or PJA OCl OOxM NcD NN NcC CaBVa CaBViP OrP Wa WaS WaSp WaT

Knowles, Henry.
Barton-upon-Irwell Union
see under title

Knowles, Henry
Voice, its culture & preservation.
Lond., Renshaw, 1886.
80 p.

NK 0209534 PU

Knowles, Herbert M.

Dead fish on the coast of Rhode Island. By Herbert M. Knowles.

(*In* Bulletin of the United States fish commission for 1886. Washington, 1887. 22½cm. vol. VI, p. 194-195)

1. Fishes—[Mortality]

F 18-571

Library, U. S. Bur. of Fisheries

NK 0209535 DI CaBVaU OO

Knowles, Horace Greeley, 1863-1913.

La amarga protesta del pueblo dominicano, por Horace C. [!] Knowles ... "Hombre de cien puntos"; publicados por A. Patiño. La Vega, R. D., Imp. de J. Cardona Ayala [1921]

26 p. 17½cm.

1. Dominican republic—For. rel.—U. S. 2. U. S.—For. rel.—Dominican republic. I. Patiño, Aristides. II. Title.

43-30255

Library of Congress F1931.K728

NK 0209536 DLC

Knowles, Horace J comp.
A book of thoughts on hope. Illustrated and decorated by Horace J. Knowles.
London, E. Mathews & Marrot, 1932.
[24]p. illus. 20cm.

1. Quotations, English. I. Title.

NK 0209537 TxU

Knowles, Horace J *comp.*

Countryside treasures; quotations selected, decorated and illustrated by Horace J. Knowles. London, Francis James publishing company [1946]

5 p. l., [7]-40, [3] p. incl. front., illus. 28½ cm.

"First published 1946."

1. Nature in literature. 2. Quotations, English. I. Title.

PN6084.N2K6 808.8 47-25247

[2]

NK 0209538 DLC

Knowles, Horace J., illr

Parr, Harriet, 1828-1900.

Legends from fairy land, narrating the history of Prince Glee & Princess Trill, the cruel persecutions & condign punishment of Aunt Spite, the adventures of the great Tuflongbo, & the story of the blackcap in the giant's well; by Holme Lee [pseud.] With illustrations by Reginald L. Knowles & Horace J. Knowles, & an introduction by Effie H. Freemantle. London, Chatto & Windus; Philadelphia, J. B. Lippincott co., 1908.

Knowles, Horace J.
Peeps into fairyland. n.p.

NK 0209540 PPAp

Knowles, Horace J., illus.
The Sermon on the Mount... London, Nicholson & Watson, 1935
see under Bible. N. T. Matthew. V-VII. English. 1935. Authorized.

Knowles, Howard Brabrook, 1888- joint author.

Lundell, Gustav Ernst Frederick, 1881-

... A contribution to the chemistry of rhenium, by G. E. F. Lundell and H. B. Knowles ...

R P 999, *in* U. S. Bureau of standards. Journal of research of the National bureau of standards. Washington, U. S. Govt. print. off., 1937. 23½cm. May, 1937, v. 18, no. 5, p. 629-637 incl. tables, diagr.)

Knowles, Howard Brabrook, 1888-

Burgess, George Kimball, 1874-1932.

... Manufacture and properties of steel plates containing zirconium and other elements, by George K. Burgess, physicist [and] Raymond W. Woodward, physicist, Bureau of standards. February 2, 1922 ... Washington, Govt. print. off., 1922.

Knowles, Howard Brabrook, 1888-

... The use of α-benzoinoxime in the determination of molybdenum, by H. B. Knowles ...

(R P 453, *in* U. S. Bureau of standards. Bureau of standards journal of research. Washington, U. S. Govt. print. off., 1932. 23½cm. July, 1932, v. 9, no. 1, 7 p. incl. tables)

Running title: Benzoinoxime for determining molybdenum.

1. Molybdenum. 2. Benzoin. I. Title. II. Title: Benzoinoxime for determining molybdenum.

32-26843

Library of Congress QC1.U52 vol. 9, no. 1

——— Copy 2. T1.U42 vol. 9, no. 1

[7] (506.1) 546.77

NK 0209544 MiU DLC OU OCl

Knowles, Howard Brabrook, 1888-

... Use of 8-hydroxyquinoline in determinations of aluminum, beryllium, and magnesium, by Howard B. Knowles ...

(R P 813, *in* U. S. Bureau of standards. Journal of research of the National bureau of standards. Washington, U. S. Govt. print. off., 1935. 23½cm. July, 1935, v. 15, no. 1, p. 87-96 incl. tables)

Running title: Determinations of Al, Be, and Mg.

1. Hydroxyquinoline. 2. Aluminium. 3. Beryllium. 4. Magnesium. 5. Chemistry, Analytic—Quantitative. I. Title. II. Title: Determinations of Al, Be, and Mg.

35-26591

Library of Congress QC1.U52 vol. 15, no. 1

——— Copy 2. T1.U42 vol. 15, no. 1

[6] (506.173) 546.66

NK 0209545 DLC MiU OU

Knowles, Howard Brabrook, 1888- joint author

Lundell, Gustav Ernst Fredrick, 1881-

... Use of 8-hydroxyquinoline in separations of aluminum, by G. E. F. Lundell and H. B. Knowles ...

(R P 86, *in* U. S. Bureau of standards. Bureau of standards journal of research. Washington, U. S. Govt. print. off., 1929. 23½cm. July, 1929, v. 3, no. 1, p. 91-96 incl. tables)

Knowles, Hulda, joint author

BF637 .L4K57

Knowles, Malcolm Shepherd, 1913-

How to develop better leaders, by Malcolm and Hulda Knowles. New York, Association Press [1955]

Knowles, J. F.

Retail shoe salesmen's institute, *Boston.*

Stockkeeping, by the staff editors, Retail shoe salesmen's institute, in collaboration with A. O. Day ... J. F. Knowles ... William Livingston [and others] ... Boston, Retail shoe salesmen's institute [°1920]

Knowles, Mrs. J. H.
see Knowles, Ellin J., 1835-1929.

---

41 K76

Knowles, Jack O
Fracture repair by bone pinning. [Croydon, Eng., 1949]
5 p.

1. Fractures. 2. Veterinary surgery. I. National Veterinary Medical Association of Great Britain and Ireland. II. Title: Bone pinning.

NK 0209550 DNAL

Knowles, James, 1759-1840.

A critical pronouncing dictionary of the English language, incorporating the labours of Sheridan and Walker ... also a key to the pronunciation of classical and Scripture proper names, by James Knowles. 7th ed. London, H. G. Bohn, 1851.

v, [6], 790, [1] p. front. (port.) 24cm.

1. English language—Dictionaries. I. Title.

27-1076

Library of Congress PE1625.K6 1851

NK 0209551 DLC OC OO MdBP CU

Knowles, James, 1759-1840.
A critical pronouncing dictionary of the English language. 9th ed. London, 1861.
port. 8°

NK 0209552 NN MWA

VOLUME 300

Knowles, James, 1759-1840.
A critical pronouncing dictionary of the English language. London, [187- ?]
8°

NK 0209553 NN

Knowles, James, 1759-1840.
Orthoepy and elocution; or, The first part of a philosophical and practical grammar of the English language, for the use of teachers, academies, and public speakers. By James Knowles ... In which, also, the principles of elocution are ... developed ... Glasgow, Printed for the author, 1829.
iv, vii, [9]-228 p. 18cm.

The first section (24 p.) of the author's Examination of Mr. Walker's 559 "Principles of pronunciation" is appended.

NK 0209554 NNC

898 K735 cri 1835 Knowles, James, 1759-1840.
A pronouncing and explanatory dictionary of the English language, founded on a correct developement of the nature, the number, and the various properties of all its simple and compound sounds ... to which is added a vocabulary of Greek, Latin, and Scripture proper names, with their correct pronunciations. London, F. de Porquet and Cooper, 1835.
790, xxiii p.

Later ed. published under title: A critical pronouncing dictionary of the English language.

1. English language - Dictionaries.

NK 0209555 CU CtY MH MB

Knowles, James, 1759-1840.
A pronouncing and explanatory dictionary of the English language, to which is added a vocabulary of Greek, Latin and Scripture proper names. London, 1837; 4th ed. 8°

NK 0209556 NNUT

Knowles, James, 1759-1840
A pronouncing and explanatory dictionary of the English language ... to which is added a vocabulary of Greek, Latin, and scripture proper names ... a new ed. London, Moxon, 1845.
viii, 8, 791 p. O.

NK 0209557 PP

KNOWLES, James (1759-1840)
A pronouncing and explanatory dictionary of the English language. To which is added, A vocabulary of Greek, Latin, and Scripture proper names. New ed. London, H.G.Bohn, 1847.
1.8°. pp. viii,(8). 790-. Port.

NK 0209558 MH

Knowles, James, 1811-1886.
Gathering jewels
see under Young, Duncan McNeill, 1838-1891.

Knowles, Sir James, 1831-1908.
see
Knowles, Sir James Thomas, 1831-1908.

Microfilm 01104 no. 95-96 AP Knowles, James Davis, 1798-1838, ed.
The Columbian star. v. 1-4; Feb. 2, 1822-Dec. 31, 1825. Washington, Anderson & Meehan [etc.]

Knowles, James Davis, 1798-1838.
Importance of theological institutions. An address, delivered before the trustees, students and friends of the Newton theological institution, November 14, 1832. By James D. Knowles ... Boston, Lincoln & Edmands, 1832.
24 p. 24½cm.

1. Theological seminaries. 2. Theology—Study and teaching. I. Title.
35-22546
Library of Congress BV4022.K53 207

NK 0209562 DLC MH-AH MWA NcD IaU PPPrHi PPAmP NN OClWHi MH

Knowles, James Davis, 1798-1838.
Life of Mrs. Ann H. Judson, late missionary to Burmah; with an account of the American Baptist mission to that empire. Prepared for the American Sunday school union; by James D. Knowles ... Revised by the committee of publication. Philadelphia, American Sunday school union, 1830.
266 p. front. (port.) plates. 15cm.

1. Judson, Mrs. Ann (Hasseltine) 1789-1826.
3-7918
Library of Congress BV3271.J81K6

NK 0209563 DLC CtY PPL-R PPeSchw OO PHi

BV 3271 J81 1843 Knowles, James Davis, 1798-1838
Memoir of Ann H. Judson, late missionary to Burmah.... A new ed. Boston, Gould, Kendall, and Lincoln, 1843.
392, 4, 12 p. illus.

JUDSON, MRS. ANN HASSELTINE, 1789-1826
MISSIONS--BURMA
MISSIONARIES, WOMEN
BAPTISTS--MISSIONS
Title: Memoir

NK 0209564 KMK NcD MB

Knowles, James Davis, 1798-1838.
Memoir of Ann H. Judson, late missionary to Burmah; including a history of the American Baptist mission in the Burman empire, by James D. Knowles ... A new ed., with a continuation of the history of the mission to the present time. Boston, Gould, Kendall, and Lincoln, 1844.
viii, [9]-392 p. front.(port.)fold.map. 18cm.

NK 0209565 CU MWA MH

KNOWLES, James Davis, 1798-1838.
Memoir of Ann H. Judson, late missionary to Burmah; including a history of the American Baptist Mission in the Burman Empire. A new ed., with a continuation of the history of the mission to the present time. Boston, Gould, Kendall, and Lincoln, 1845.
viii,392p. illus.,map. 19cm.

NK 0209566 MH-AH MB OClWHi

Knowles, James Davis, 1798-1838.
Memoir of Ann H. Judson, missionary to Burmah. By James D. Knowles. ... Boston, Gould, Kendall, and Lincoln, 1846.
viii, [9]-354 p. incl. front. (port.) 16½cm.

1. Judson, Mrs. Ann (Hasseltine) 1789-1826.

NK 0209567 NjR MH MiU

E 5 .J 92335 Knowles, James Davis, 1798-1838.
Memoir of Ann H.Judson, missionary to Burmah... Boston,1847.

NK 0209568 ICN MH

Knowles, James Davis, 1798-1838.
Memoir of Ann H. Judson, missionary to Burmah. By James D. Knowles ... Boston, Gould, Kendall, and Lincoln, 1848.
1 p. l., [iv]-viii, [9]-354 p. front. (port.) 16cm.

1. Judson, Mrs. Ann (Hasseltine) 1789-1826.
37-25845
Library of Congress BV3271.J81K7 1848 a
[2] 922.6591

NK 0209569 DLC

BV3271 .J91K71 Knowles, James Davis, 1798-1838.
Memoir of Ann H. Judson, missionary to Burmah. By James D. Knowles ... Boston, Gould, Kendall, and Lincoln, 1849.
viii, [9]-354 p. incl. front. (port.) 16½cm.

1. Judson, Mrs. Ann (Hasseltine) 1789-1826.

NK 0209570 ICU

BV 3271 J81 K7 1850 Knowles,James Davis,1798-1838.
Memoir of Ann H.Judson,missionary to Burmah, by James D.Knowles. Boston, Gould,Kendall,and Lincoln, 1850.
[iv]-viii,354 p. port.

1.Judson,Mrs.Ann (Hasseltine) 1789-1826.

NK 0209571 NSyU

Knowles, James Davis, 1798-1838
Memoirs of Ann H. Judson, missionary to Burmah. Boston, N.Y., 1855.
354p. S.

NK 0209572 OClW

Knowles, James Davis, 1798-1838.
Memoir of Ann H.Judson, missionary to Burmah. Boston, Gould and Lincoln, etc., etc., 1856.

NK 0209573 MH MB

VOLUME 300

Wason Knowles, James Davis, 1798–1838.
BV3271 Memoir of Ann H. Judson, missionary to Burmah. By
J81 James D. Knowles ... Boston, Gould and Lincoln; New
K73 York, Sheldon and company, [etc., etc.,] 1861.
1861 1 p. l., [v]–viii, [9]–354 p. front. (port.) 17½ cm.

NK 0209574 NIC

Knowles, James Davis, 1798–1838.
Memoir of Mrs. Ann H. Judson, late missionary to Burmah. Including a history of the American Baptist mission in the Burman empire. By James D. Knowles ... Boston, Lincoln & Edmands, 1829.
viii, [9]–324 p. front. (port.) fold. map. 19cm.

1. Judson, Mrs. Ann (Hasseltine) 1789–1826.

Library of Congress BV3271.J81K7 1829 3–7916

NK 0209575 DLC NcD NcU NjNbS MWA NN PPAmS MU NNC NcWsW MiEM

Knowles, James Davis, 1798–1838.
Memoir of Mrs. Ann H. Judson, late missionary to Burmah. Including a history of the American Baptist mission in the Burman empire. By James D. Knowles ... 2d ed. Boston, Lincoln & Edmands, 1829.
viii, [9]–324 p. front. (port.) fold. map. 19cm.

1. Judson, Mrs. Ann (Hasseltine) 1789–1826.

Library of Congress BV3271.J81K7 1829 a 3—7917

NK 0209576 DLC CtY-D NN OO PCC PPL PPLT

BV3271 .J81K7 1829 Knowles, James Davis, 1798–1838.
Memoir of Mrs. Ann H. Judson, late missionary to Burmah. Including a history of the American Baptist mission in the Burman empire. By James D. Knowles ... Boston, Lincoln & Edmands, 1829. 3d ed.
viii, [9]–324 p. front. (port.) fold. map. 19cm.

NK 0209577 AAP PHC NRCR ViU CtY-D KyLx CtY

Knowles, James Davis, 1798–1838.
Memoir of Mrs. Ann H. Judson, wife of the Rev. Adoniram Judson, missionary to Burmah. Including a history of the American Baptist Mission, in the Burman empire. By James D. Knowles... Third edition. London: Wightman and Co., [etc., etc.,] 1830. viii, 10–324 p. front. (port.), map. 19cm.

1. Judson, Ann (Hasseltine), 1789–1826. 2. Missions, Foreign—India—Burma.
N. Y. P. L. Revised November 28, 1934

NK 0209578 NN NBuU

Knowles, James Davis, 1798-1838.
Memoir of Mrs. Ann H. Judson... Phil., 1830.

NK 0209579 NjNbS

MU 14 J921 K762 Knowles, James Davis, 1798-1838.
Memoir of Mrs. Ann H. Judson, late missionary to Burmah. Including a history of the American Baptist mission in the Burman empire. 4th. ed. Boston, Lincoln & Edmands, 1831.
406 p. port., fold. map.

1. Judson, Mrs. Ann (Hasseltine) 1789-1826.

NK 0209580 KyWAT KyU MWA MH NcWsW MB

MU14 J921 Xk76 1832 Knowles, James Davis, 1798-1838.
Memoir of Mrs. Ann H. Judson, late missionary to Burmah. Including a history of the American Baptist mission in the Burman empire. 5th ed. Boston, Lincoln & Edmands, 1832.
408 p. illus., port., map. 16 cm.

NK 0209581 CtY-D

Knowles, James Davis, 1798-1838.
Memoir of Mrs. Ann H. Judson, late missionary to Burmah; including a history of the American Baptist mission in the Burman empire. By James D. Knowles ... 6th ed. with a continuation of the history of the mission. Boston, Gould, Kendall, & Lincoln, 1835.

viii, [9]-394 p. front.(port.) pl., fold. map. 16cm.
1. Judson, Mrs. Ann (Hasseltine) 1789-1826. 2. Missionaries.

NK 0209582 MnU TxFTC PPPD ODW OO PPT

Knowles, James Davis, 1798-1838.
Memoir of Mrs. Ann H. Judson, wife of the Rev. Adoniram Judson, missionary to Burmah: including a history of the American Baptist mission, in the Burman empire. 9th ed. London, G. Wightman, 1838.
xii,382p. ports.map.

NK 0209583 ScU

Knowles, James Davis, 1798-1838.

Memoir of Mrs. Ann H. Judson, late missionary to Burmah; including a history of the American Baptist mission in the Burman Empire. 10th ed.

Boston, Gould, Kendall & Lincoln, 1838.
395 p. map. port.

NK 0209584 MCR

Knowles, James Davis, 1798-1838.
Memoir of Mrs. Ann H. Judson. Boston, 1845.
345 p. 16°.

NK 0209585 MWA

Knowles, James Davis, 1798-1838.
Memoir of Mrs. Ann H. Judson, late missionary to Burmah. Including a history of the American Baptist mission in the Burman empire. Boston, 1853.
viii, [9]-324 p. front. (port.), fold., map. 19 cm.

NK 0209586 RPB MB

Knowles, James Davis, 1798–1838.
Memoir of Roger Williams, the founder of the state of Rhode-Island. By James D. Knowles ... Boston, Lincoln, Edmands and co., 1834.
xx, [21]–437 p. front. (facsim.) 19cm.

1. Williams, Roger, 1604?–1683. 2. Rhode Island—Hist.—Colonial period.

Library of Congress F82.W785 13—33610

NK 0209587 DLC NBuHi ICRL CU MdBP PU PLF PPG NIC MeB OrU NcD NN MB RPJCB MWA OO OClW OClWHi ViU MiU-C PNt PHC PU NcU

KNOWLES, James Davis, 1798-1838.
Memoiren der Mrs. Anna H. Judson, etc., Nach der 10en ausg. Aus dem englischen. Hamb. [18-]

11 x 16.

NK 0209588 MH-AH

Knowles, James Davis, 1798–1838.
Oration, delivered at the Columbian college, in the District of Columbia, July 4, 1823; by James D. Knowles, member of the Enosinian society. Washington city, J. S. Meehan, 1823.
20 p. 22cm.
[Miscellaneous pamphlets, v. 277, no. 6]

1. Fourth of July orations. I. George Washington university, Washington, D. C. Enosinian society.

Library of Congress AC901.M5 vol. 277 19–17291
——— Copy 2. [Moore pamphlets, v. 35, no. 23] AC901.M7 vol. 35

NK 0209589 DLC CtY ViU NcU

Knowles, James Davis, 1798–1838.
Perils and safeguards of American liberty. Address, pronounced July 4, 1828, in the Second Baptist meeting-house in Boston, at the religious celebration of the anniversary of American independence, by the Baptist churches and societies in Boston. By James D. Knowles, pastor of the Second Baptist church. Boston, Printed by Lincoln & Edmands [1828]
27, [1] p. 21½cm.

1. Fourth of July orations. I. Title.

Library of Congress E286.B74 1828 k 37-9972
[2] 973.361

NK 0209590 DLC PHi RPJCB RPB N MB MH NN

BR1 .R356 Knowles, James Davis, 1798–1838, ed.
Religious intelligencer, and Christian monitor. v. 1, no. 1-26; May 13-Nov. 4, 1820. Providence.

Knowles, James Davis, 1798-1838.
... Sermon II. n.p. n. pub. 1829.

v. 3, no. 2 of the Baptist preacher, November, 1829.

NK 0209592 MeWC

Knowles, James Davis, 1798–1838.
Spirituous liquors pernicious and useless. An address delivered in the Second Baptist Meeting-House, Boston, April 9, 1829, the day of the annual fast. By James D. Knowles... Boston: Printed by Lincoln & Edmands, 1829. 24 p. 16°.
In: VTZ p. v. 57, no. 6.

1. Temperance.—Addresses, essays, lectures.
N. Y. P. L. February 16, 1918.

NK 0209593 NN MWA RPB MB

KNOWLES, James Davis, 1798-1838.
What is call to the ministry. New York, n. d.

NK 0209594 MH PPPrHi RPB

VOLUME 300

Knowles, James Hinton.
A dictionary of Kashmiri proverbs & sayings, explained and illustrated from the rich and interesting folklore of the valley. Bombay, Education Society's Press, 1885.
viii, 263 p. 19 cm.

1. Proverbs, Kashmiri. 2. Folk-lore—Kashmir. I. Title.

PN6519.K3K6 55-47018

NK 0209595 CU MH MdBP NcU InU IU OU DLC NSyU ICN NN NNCoCi OCl PU NIC NcD

Knowles, J[ames] Hinton.
Folk-tales of Kashmir. London, Trübner & Co., 1888.
pp. xii, 510. (Trübner's Oriental series.)

NK 0209596 MH OCH PU MdBP

Knowles, James Hinton.
Folk-tales of Kashmir. By the Rev. J. Hinton Knowles ... 2d ed. London, K. Paul, Trench, Trübner & co., l[td], 1893.
xii, 510 p. 20½cm. (Half-title: Trübner's oriental series)
"Glossary": p. 505-506.

1. Folk-lore—Kashmir.

Library of Congress GR305.K5 5-12162

NK 0209597 ICU ICN PPL KMK NIC DLC NcD PPT CU PP MiU OCl OO NjP NN

---

33 Knowles, James Hinton.
Not changed but glorified; and other verses with a preface by canon Knowles. New York, J. Pott & co., 1896.
1 p.l., 38 p. 12°.

NK 0209598 DLC RPB

[**Knowles, James O**]
Rockton. A story of springtime recreations. By Kel Snow, esq. [pseud.] Cincinnati, Cranston & Stowe; New York, Hunt & Eaton, 1891.
280 p. 19cm.

Library of Congress PZ3.K762R 7-14187†

NK 0209599 DLC OrU NcD ViU CU

Knowles, James Purdie.
Samuel A. Purdie, his life and letters, his work as a missionary and Spanish writer and publisher in Mexico and Central America, by James Purdie Knowles, with an introduction by Allen Jay ... Plainfield, Ind., Publishing association of Friends [1908]
xvi, [17]-251 p. 23cm.

1. Purdie, Samuel Alexander, 1843-1897. 2. Friends, Society of—Missions.

Library of Congress BX7795.P85K55 43-44590

NK 0209600 DLC CU-B NcD PSC CtY

---

822 Knowles, James Sheridan, 1784-1862.
K76 Works. [London, J. Ridgway, 1823-39]
1823 2v. 22cm.

Binder's title.
Each play has special t.p. and paging.
Vol.2 and last two plays of v.1 are published by E. Moxon.

NK 0209601 IU

---

822 Knowles, James Sheridan, 1784-1862.
K76t Alexina; or, True unto death. A drama in two
1866 acts. London, Adams & Francis, 1866.
48p. 15cm.

First produced at the Strand Theatre, May 21, 1866.
Bound with the author's The beggar of Bethnal Green. London, 1834; Brian Boroihme. London [n.d.]; The daughter. London, 1837. The bridal. London [n.d.]

NK 0209602 IU

KNOWLES, James Sheridan, 1784-1862.
Alfred the Great, or The patriot king; an history play. Baltimore, J. Robinson, 1829.

24°. pp. 72.

NK 0209603 MH CtY

PR4889 **Knowles, James Sheridan, 1784-1862.**
.K5A8 Alfred the Great; or, The patriot king: a drama, in five
1831 acts. As performed with enthusiastic applause at the Theatre Royal Drury Lane on the 28th April, 1831. By J. S. Knowles ... Glasgow, Atkinson & co.; [etc., etc., 1831]
[5]-93 p. 23cm.

1. Alfred the Great, king of England, 849-901—Drama.

NK 0209604 ICU MH

---

x822 Knowles, James Sheridan, 1784-1862.
K76a Alfred the Great; or, The patriot king. An historical play London, J Ridgway, 1831.
85p 22cm.

Bound by Riviere in light brown calf

1 Alfred the Great, King of England, 849-901--Drama I Title.

NK 0209605 IU NjP CSmH NN MH CtY CU-A NIC InU CSt

Knowles, James Sheridan, 1784-1862.
Alfred the Great; or, The patriot king. An historical play, in five acts, by James
PO 1269 S. Knowles ... [London, J. Dicks, 1880?]
.D 55 24 p. 19½cm. (Dicks' standard plays,
no. 314 no. 314)

Caption title.

1. Alfred the Great, King of England, 849-901 - Drama. I. Title.

NK 0209606 MdBJ InU

DG262 **Knowles, James Sheridan, 1784-1862.**
.5 **Appendix to Rudiments of gesture; consisting**
.K6 **of a debate on the character of Julius Cæsar.**
1830 **By James Sheridan Knowles. Designed for practical exercise in declamation. [Boston? 1830?]**
1 p. l., L p. 17 1/2cm.

1. Cæsar, Caius Julius.

NK 0209607 MB NN MH PPL PPAmP

Knowles, James Sheridan, 1784-1862.
The beggar of Bethnal Green, a comedy. In three acts. Altered from The beggar's daughter of Bethnal Green. By J. S. Knowles... London: E. Moxon, 1834. 4 p.l., 108 p. 8°.
In verse.
In: NCO p. v. 393, no. 4.

1. Drama (English). 2. Title.
N. Y. P. L. October 30, 1915.

NK 0209608 ICU CU InU NN CtY PP CSt MH WU CSt PU IU NjP ICRL

Knowles, James Sheridan, 1784-1862.
The beggar of Bethnal Green, a play, in three acts. Altered from the Beggar's daughter of Bethnal Green. By J. S. Knowles ... (In: Alexander's modern acting drama. Philadelphia, 1835. v. 2, p. [157-]228.)

334948A. 1. Drama, English. 2. Title.
N. Y. P. L. February 17, 1928

NK 0209609 NN

Lilly Library
PR 4859 KNOWLES, JAMES SHERIDAN, 1784-1862
.K5 B49 The beggar's daughter of Bethnal Green. A comedy, in five acts. By James Sheridan Knowles. First performed at the Theatre Royal, Drury Lane, Nov. 22, 1828. [London, J. Dicks, n.d.]
26 p. 1 illus. 18.5 cm. (Dicks' Standard plays, no. 695)

Copy 1 in brown, copy 2 in green printed paper wrappers. Both copies have series advts. to no. 632.

NK 0209610 InU OClW

PR4889 **Knowles, James Sheridan, 1784-1862.**
.K5B4 The beggar's daughter of Bethnal Green. A comedy.
1828 By James Sheridan Knowles ... London, B. Stewart, and J. Ridgway; [etc., etc.] 1828.
[7], 92 p. 21cm.

NK 0209611 ICU NjP CSmH IU MH InU OrU

Knowles, James Sheridan, 1784-1862.
Book of the play
see his Mr. John McCullough's authorized version ...

Knowles, James Sheridan, 1784-1862.
Brian Boroihme, or, The maid of Erin, a historical Hibernian melo-drama, in three acts, as performed at the Theatres Royal, Dublin, and Belfast; also at the Philadelphia and New-York theatres. Now first printed. By James S. Knowles ... New-York, E. M. Murden, 1828.
40 p. 15cm.
An adaptation of Daniel A. O'Meara's drama of the same name.

1. Brian Boroimhe, king of Ireland, 926-1014—Drama. I. O'Meara, Daniel A. II. Title.

25-15283

Library of Congress PR4859.K5B7 1828

NK 0209613 DLC MH NN

Knowles, James Sheridan, 1784-1862
Brian Boroihme: or, the maid of Erin. A historical Hibernian melodrama, in three acts. Added, a description of the costumes, cast of the characters . . .
New York. French. [1853?] 27 pp. [French's American drama. No. 118.] 16°.

F8013 — T.r. — S.r.

NK 0209614 MH NN MB

VOLUME 300

828 K762b Knowles, James Sheridan, 1784-1862.
Brian Boroihme; or, The maid of Erin. A drama, in three acts. London, T. H. Lacy [1856?]
42 p. 19 cm.

An adaptation of Daniel A. O'Meara's drama of the same name.

1. Brian Boroihme, king of Ireland, 926-1014 - Drama. I. O'Meara, Daniel A. II. Title.

NK 0209615 LU IU

Knowles, James Sheridan, 1784–1862.
... Brian Boroihme: or, The maid of Erin. A historical Hibernian melo-drama, in three acts. By James Sheridan Knowles ... To which are added, a description of the costume—cast of the characters ... and the whole of the stage business. As performed at the New York theatres. New-York, S. French [1856?]
27 p. 18½cm. (French's American drama. The acting edition. no. 23)
An adaptation of Daniel A. O'Meara's drama of the same name.
1. Brian Boroimhe, king of Ireland, 926–1014—Drama. I. O'Meara, Daniel A. II. Title.
27-22900
Library of Congress PR4859.K5B7 1856

NK 0209616 DLC CSt MiU OCl ViU

Knowles, James Sheridan, 1784–1862.
... Brian Boroihme: or, The maid of Erin. A historical Hibernian melo-drama, in three acts. By James Sheridan Knowles ... To which are added, a description of the costume—cast of the characters ... and the whole of the stage business. As performed at the New York theatres. New-York, S. French [1856?] ; [Louisville, Falls City Microcards, 1965?]
27 p. 18½cm. (French's American drama. The acting edition. no. 23 ; FCM 2991)
An adaptation of Daniel A. O'Meara's drama of the same name.
Microcard ed. 1 card. 7 1/2 x 12 1/2 cm.

NK 0209617 RPB

Knowles, James Sheridan, 1784–1862.
Brian Boroihme; or, The maid of Erin. A drama in three acts. By James Sheridan Knowles. [London, 1885] 16 p. illus. 18cm. (Dicks' standard plays. no. 670.)
Caption-title.
An adaptation of Daniel A. O'Meara's drama of the same name.
"Acted at Covent Garden theatre...April 20th, 1837."

227267B. 1. Brian Boroimhe, king of Ireland, 926–1014—Drama. 2. Drama, English. I. O'Meara, Daniel A. Brian Boroimhe.
N. Y. P. L. April 14, 1944

NK 0209618 NN InU OClW

Knowles, James Sheridan, 1784-1862.
FOR OTHER EDITIONS SEE MAIN ENTRY
Beaumont, Francis, 1584–1616.
The bridal. A tragedy, in five acts. Adapted for representation (with three original scenes, written by James Sheridan Knowles, esq.) from the Maid's tragedy, of Beaumont and Fletcher, as performed at the Theatre Royal Haymarket ... London, Chapman and Hall [1837?]

Lilly Library PR 4859 .K5 B9 1841 KNOWLES, JAMES SHERIDAN, 1784-1862
The bridals of Messina; or, John of Procida. A tragedy, in five acts. By James Sheridan Knowles ... Third edition. London, G. Routledge, 1841.
vi p., 1 ℓ., 116 p. 20.5 cm.

NK 0209620 InU MH TxU

Knowles, James Sheridan, 1784–1862.
Caius Gracchus: a tragedy, in five acts, by James Sheridan Knowles ... Printed from the acting copy, with remarks, biographical and critical, by D.—G. ... As performed at the Theatres Royal ... London, J. Cumberland [n. d.]
80 p. incl. front. 15cm. (Cumberland's British theatre. London, ca. 1825–55. v. 6 [no. 4])
Remarks by George Daniel, editor of the series.
1. Gracchus, C. Sempronius—Drama. I. Title.
21-14529
Library of Congress PR1243.C8 vol. 6
——— Copy 2. (Davidson's shilling volume of Cumberland's plays. London, ca. 1849–55. 15cm. v. 27 [no. 2]) PR1243.C82 vol. 27 [2]

NK 0209621 DLC OO OCl PU-F

Wn K762 823c KNOWLES, JAMES SHERIDAN, 1784-1862.
Caius Gracchus: a tragedy. In five acts. As performed at the Theatre-Royal, Drury-Lane. By James Sheridan Knowles ...
Glasgow:Printed for J.Ridgway,and Hurst, Robinson,& Co.London;Constable & Co.Edinburgh; Reid & Henderson,Glasgow;and R.Milliken,Dublin. 1823. 101,[1]p. 22cm.
Printed slip inserted at p.[5].

NK 0209622 NcD InU TxU ICU NN ICN IU MiU CtY NjP CSmH ViU

---

ar U 277 Knowles, James Sheridan, 1784-1862.
Caius Gracchus, a tragedy in five acts. Printed from the original edition, with remarks. As now performed at the Theatres Royal, London. Embellished with a wood engraving, from an original drawing made expressly for this work, by I. R. Cruikshank, and executed by Mr. White. London, T. Dolby [1824?]
79 p. illus. 15 cm. (Dolby's British theatre)
No. 2 in vol. lettered: Plays. Knowles and Sheridan.

NK 0209623 NIC NNC PU-F CtY NN MH InU DLC MiU OCU

KNOWLES, James S[heridan], 1784-1862.
Caius Gracchus; a tragedy, in five acts. New York, E. M. Murden, 1824.
24°. pp.58.

NK 0209624 MH NN

An K762 883c Rare Books Col KNOWLES, JAMES SHERIDAN, 1784-1862.
... Caius Gracchus. By J.S. Knowles ... London; J. Dicks, 313, Strand; and all booksellers [1883?] cover title, 27p. 1 illus. 18cm in envelope in folder 23cm. (Dicks' standard plays. no.298)
Title vignette.
In double columns.
Advertisements: inside front cover, [2]p. at end.
I. Gracchus, C. Sempronius - Drama. I. Title.

NK 0209625 TxU InU

DG262 .5 .K6 Knowles, James Sheridan, 1784-1862.
The character of Julius Cæsar: a debate. By James Sheridan Knowles ... Boston, T. B. Wait & son, printers, 1826.
52 p. 18 1/2cm.
"Reprinted for the elocution school, at the Pantheon hall."

1. Cæsar, Caius Julius.

NK 0209626 MB MH

KNOWLES, James Sheridan, 1784-1862.
A collection of ana illustrating the life of James Sheridan Knowles to which are added his autograph letters and those of his friends, portraits, views, etc., collected for James McHenry by Francis Harvey. 1874.
3 vol. f°.

NK 0209627 MH

Knowles, James Sheridan, 1784–1862.
A collection of poems on various subjects, by James Sheridan Knowles. Waterford, Printed for the author, by John Bull, 1810.
4 p. l., 72 p. 18cm.
25-24739
Library of Congress PR4859.K5A17 1810

NK 0209628 DLC IEN

Knowles, James Sheridan, 1784-1862
The daughter, a play in five acts. 1837.

NK 0209629 ViU

KNOWLES, James Sheridan, 1784-1862.
The daughter; a play, in five acts. Berlin, B. Behr, 1837.
pp.69.

NK 0209630 MH

822.89 K73DE Knowles, James Sheridan, 1784–1862.
The daughter. A play, in five acts. By James Sheridan Knowles ... London, E. Moxon, 1837.
4 p. l., 108 p. 22cm.

NK 0209631 NcD CtY MH TxU ViU ICU CU

Knowles, James Sheridan, 1784–1862.
The daughter. A play, in five acts. By James Sheridan Knowles ... 2d ed. London, E. Moxon, 1837.
4 p. l., 108 p. 22cm.
I. Title.
31-23543
Library of Congress PR4859.K5D3 1837 822.72

NK 0209632 DLC NN PU InU IU MB MH WU NjP TxU

---

37 5423 Knowles, James Sheridan, 1784-1862
A debate on the character of Julius Caesar. [Boston, 1838]
[In Russell, William. Rudiments of gesture, p. 73-120]

NK 0209633 DLC ODW

Knowles, J[ames] Sheridan, 1784–1862.
A debate upon the character of Julius Cæsar, adapted from J. Sheridan Knowles; designed as a practical exercise in declamation, and as a model for juvenile debating clubs ... Boston, Crosby, Nichols & co., 1856.
69 p. 19cm.
1. Caesar, C. Julius.
4-35234†
Library of Congress DG262.K7

NK 0209634 DLC PPeSchw

VOLUME 300

Knowles, James Sheridan, 1784-1862.
The debater's handbook, including A debate upon the character of Julius Cæsar; adapted from J. Sheridan Knowles ... Boston, Lee and Shepard [1887]
114 p. 17½cm.
"Questions for debate": p. 83-111.

1. Debating. 2. Caesar, C. Julius.

Library of Congress PN4181.K6 13-18304
Copyright 1887: 19501

NK 0209635 DLC OrU OCl MB

Knowles, James Sheridan, 1784-1862.
The dramatic works of James Sheridan Knowles. London, New York, G. Routledge and sons [n. d.]
2 v. in 1. 19cm. (*On cover:* Routledge's Poets for the people)

17-30865
Library of Congress PR4859.K5A19 1883

NK 0209636 DLC CaBVa PPD PBm PRosC OClW PV NcD TU FTaSU OOxM

Knowles, James Sheridan, 1784-1862.
The dramatic works of James Sheridan Knowles ... London, E. Moxon, 1841.
2 v. front. (v. 1, port.) 19cm.
CONTENTS.—v. 1. Caius Gracchus. Virginius. William Tell. Alfred the Great; or, The patriot king. The hunchback.—v. 2. The wife: a tale of Mantua. The beggar of Bethnal green. The daughter. The love-chase. Woman's wit; or, Love's disguises.

25-24740
Library of Congress PR4859.K5A19 1841

NK 0209637 DLC WaSp NcD CSmH NN NjP

822.8
K73 Knowles, James Sheridan, 1784-1862.
The dramatic works of James Sheridan Knowles...London, E.Moxon, 1841-43.
3 v. front.(port.) 19½ cm.
Contents:-v.1.Caius Gracchus. Virginius. William Tell. Alfred the Great. The hunchback.-v.2.The wife. The beggar of Bethnal Green. The daughter. The love-chase. Woman's wit.-v.3.The maid of Mariendorpt. Love. John of Procida. Old maids. The rose of Arragon.

NK 0209638 MiU MH ViU CtY PPT OCU OU MH ICN InU ICU MdBP FU OrU NN PBa

---

Knowles, James *Sheridan, 1784-1862.*
Dramatic works. London, 1847.
3 v. 8°

NK 0209639 NN

Knowles, James Sheridan, 1784-1862.
Dramatic works. London, New York, G. Routledge, 1856.
2 v. port. 19 cm.
CONTENTS.—v. 1. Caius Gracchus. Virginius. William Tell. Alfred the Great; or, The patriot king. The hunchback. The wife; a tale of Mantua. The beggar of Bethnal Green. The daughter.—v. 2. The love-chase. Woman's wit; or, Love's disguises. The maid of Mariendorpt. Love. John of Procida; or, The bridals of Messina. Old maids. The rose of Arragon. The secretary.

PR4859.K5A19 1856 54-50151

NK 0209640 DLC MdBP NNC PPL PHC PPYH CLSU CtY OCl ViU MB NIC OU OO OClW InU MiU ODW MWA OrU

Knowles, James Sheridan, *1784-1862*
Dramatic works... L. Routledge, 1858.
2v. in 1.

NK 0209641 OClW PRosC ICN CoU

Knowles, James Sheridan, 1784-1862.
The dramatic works of James Sheridan Knowles ... A new ed. in one volume. London, New York, Routledge, Warnes, & Routledge, 1859.
vi p., 1 l., 448, 457 p. 19cm.
CONTENTS.—pt. I. Caius Gracchus. Virginius. William Tell. Alfred the Great; or, The patriotic king. The hunchback. The wife: a tale of Mantua. The beggar of Bethnal green. The daughter.—pt. II. The love-chase. Woman's wit; or, Love's disguises. The maid of Mariendorpt. Love. John of Procida; or, The bridals of Messina. Old maids. The rose of Arragon. The secretary.

34-20451
Library of Congress PR4859.K5A19 1859 822.

NK 0209642 DLC CaBVaU PU NN MH WaU RPB CSt

Knowles, James Sheridan, 1784-1862.
The dramatic works of J. S. Knowles. [Pt. 1-2] London, G. Routledge & Sons, [186-?]
2 v. in 1 port. 8°.
v. 1. Caius Gracchus. Virginius. William Tell. Alfred the Great. The hunchback. The wife. The beggar of Bethnal Green. The daughter. v. 2. The love chase. Woman's wit. The maid of Mariendorpt. Love. John of Procida. Old maids. The rose of Arragon. The secretary.

NK 0209643 NN NBuG PU

Knowles, James Sheridan, 1784-1862.
The dramatic works of James Sheridan Knowles ... London, New York, Routledge, Warne, & Routledge 1864.
2 v. front. (port.) 18½cm.
CONTENTS.—v. 1. Caius Gracchus. Virginius. William Tell. Alfred the Great. The hunchback. The wife. The beggar of Bethnal Green. The daughter.—v. 2. The love-chase. Woman's wit. The maid of Mariendorpt. Love. John of Procida. Old maids. The rose of Arragon. The secretary.

NK 0209644 MiU PU PV I NN

PN 4145 KNOWLES, JAMES SHERIDAN, 1784-1862.
.K73 The elocutionist; a collection of pieces in prose and verse, peculiarly adapted to display the art of reading.... Preceded by an introduction, in which an attempt is made to simplify Walker's system, and ... to reduce the number of his rules. 7th ed., greatly enlarged. Belfast, Simms and M'Intyre, 1831.
384 p.

1. Elocution. 2. Reading. 3. English language—Inflection. I. Title.

NK 0209645 InU NN

KNOWLES, James Sheridan, 1784-1862.
The elocutionist; a collection of pieces in prose and verse adapted to display the art of reading, preceded by an introductio . 14th ed. Belfast, Simms and M'Intyre, etc., etc., 1838.

NK 0209646 MH

Knowles, James Sheridan, *compiler, 1784-1862.*
The elocutionist, a collection of pieces in prose and verse; peculiarly adapted to display the art of reading . . . 16th edition. — London. Simms & McIntyre. 1844. xxxvi, 384 pp. 17½ cm., in 12s.

N8822 — T.r. — Speakers.

NK 0209647 MB

Knowles, James Sheridan, 1784-1862.
Knowles's elocutionist; a first-class rhetorical reader and recitation book ... By James Sheridan Knowles ... Altered and adapted to the purposes of instruction in the United States, by Epes Sargent. New York, J. Mowatt & co., 1844.
xiii, [15]-322 p. 18cm.

1. Elocution. I. Sargent, Epes, 1813-1880, ed.

Library of Congress PN4111.K6 11-16320

NK 0209648 DLC IaU MH

Knowles, James Sheridan, 1784-1862.
(Knowles') elocutionist; a first-class rhetorical reader and recitation book, containing the only essential principles of elocution, directions for managing the voice, etc., simplified and explained on a novel plan, with numerous pieces for reading and declamation. Designed for the use of school and colleges, Sargent, Epes, ed. Ed. 5. N.Y., Saxton, 1844.
322p. D.

NK 0209649 OO NBuG

808.8
K73e
1846 Knowles, James Sheridan, 1784-1862.
The elocutionist, a collection of pieces in prose and verse, peculiarly adapted to display the art of reading, in the most comprehensive sense of the term. Preceded by an introduction, in which an attempt is made to simplify Walker's system, and, by referring his illustrations to more general principles, to reduce the number of his rules. 17th ed. London, Simms and M'Intyre, 1846.
xxxvi, 384 p. 18cm.
1. Readers and speakers - 1800-1870. 2. Elocution. I. Title.

NK 0209650 FU

Knowles, James Sheridan, 1784-1862.
Knowles' elocutionist; a first-class rhetorical reader and recitation book. Containing the only essential principles of elocution, directions for managing the voice, etc., simplified and explained on a novel plan. With numerous pieces for reading and declamation. Designed for the use of schools and colleges. By James Sheridan Knowles. Enlarged and adapted to the purposes of instruction in the United States. By Epes Sargent. Stereotype edition. Revised by S. S. Randall... New York: J. C. Riker, 1847. xiii, 16-322 p. front. 12°.

72517A. 1. Elocution. 2. Recitations. 3. Sargent, Epes, 1813-80, editor. 4. Randall, Samuel Sidwell, 1809-81, editor.
N. Y. P. L. February 23, 1923.

NK 0209651 NN

Knowles, James Sheridan, 1784-1862.
The elocutionist; a collection of pieces in prose and verse ... including a debate upon the character of Julius Caesar. Preceded by an introd. in which Walker's system is simplified. 18th ed., rev. and improved. London, Simms and M'Intyre, 1852.
xxxvi, 378 p. 19cm.

1. Readers and speakers. 2. Elocution. I. Title.

NK 0209652 MiDW MH

Knowles, James Sherican, 1784-1862.
Elocutionist; a collection of pieces in prose and verse. Ed. 26. London, Mullan, 1879.
tab.
Contents--Promiscuous selections in prose. Pulpit eloquence. Ancient and modern oratory. Promiscuous selections of verse. Sacred extracts.

NK 0209653 OrP

VOLUME 300

Knowles, James Sheridan, 1784-1862
The elocutionist; a collection of pieces in prose and verse... 28th ed. enl. Ed. by Robert Mullam. London, 1879.

NK 0209654 ODW

Knowles, James Sheridan, 1784–1862.
The elocutionist, a collection of pieces in prose and verse, peculiarly adapted to display the art of reading; with an introduction on the principles of elocution. 28th ed., greatly enl. London, Gall & Inglis [1883]
xxxvi, 417 p. 19 cm.

1. Readers and speakers—1800–1870. 2. Elocution. I. Title.
PN4201.K65 1883 49–55945*

NK 0209655 DLC

Knowles, James Sheridan, 1784-1862.
Fortescue, a novel. New York, Harper, 1846.
126 p. 23 cm.

NK 0209656 MdBP NjP

Knowles, James Sheridan, 1784–1862.
Fortescue. A novel. By James Sheridan Knowles ... London, E. Moxon, 1847.
3 v. 19½cm.

Library of Congress PZ3.K763F 7–14188†

NK 0209657 DLC GEU CtY

Knowles, James Sheridan, 1784-1862
Fortescue.
New York. Harper. 1874. 228 pp. [Library of select novels. No. 92, 94.] 8°.

NK 0209658 MB CU

Knowles, James Sheridan, 1784–1862.
George Lovell. A novel. By James Sheridan Knowles ... London, E. Moxon, 1847.
3 v. 19½cm.

Library of Congress PZ3.K763G 7–14189†

NK 0209659 DLC NcU CtY CSmH PU

In K763 847b
Knowles, James Sheridan, 1784-1862.
George Lovell. A novel ... New York:Burgess, Stringer, & co.,1847.
159p. 22cm.

NK 0209660 CtY NN

KNOWLES, JAMES SHERIDAN, 1784-1862.
George Lovell. A novel. By James Sheridan Knowles... London: E.Moxon, 1852. 3 v. 20½cm.

814733-5A. 1. Fiction, English. I. Title.

NK 0209661 NN

Knowles, James Sheridan, 1784–1862.
T. Sheridan Knowles' great Hibernian melo-drama, Brian Boroihme, newly arranged to suit amateur performers, by Rev. L. Griffa. Oswego, N. Y., R. J. Oliphant, job printer, 1883.
16 p. 17½cm.

I. Griffa, Lewis, ed. II. Title: Brian Boroihme.
25–21471
Library of Congress PR4859.K5B7

NK 0209662 DLC

Knowles, James Sheridan, 1784–1862.
Hertuginden af Mantua, et drama i fem acter, af James Sheridan Knowles. Oversat af engelsk ved forfatteren af skuespillet: "Navnet, eller Det hurtige frieri;" udg. af C. Molbech ... [Kjøbenhavn, Schubothe, 1834]
33 p. 22cm. (Kongelige theaters repertoire, no. 64)
Caption title.
Translation of The wife: a tale of Mantua, by Sille Beyer.
No. 4 in a collection of pamphlets lettered: Nyt repetorium [!]

I. Beyer, Sille Henrikke Christine, 1803–1861, tr. II. Molbech, Christian, 1783–1857, ed. III. Title.
22–11062
Library of Congress PT8000.K6 no. 64

NK 0209663 DLC NN

Knowles, James Sheridan, 1784–1862.
The hunchback: a play, in five acts, by James Sheridan Knowles ... Printed from the acting copy, with remarks, biographical and critical, by D.—G. ... As performed at the Theatres Royal ... London, G. H. Davidson [n. d.]
76 p. front. 15cm. (Davidson's shilling volume of Cumberland's plays. London, ca. 1849–55. v. 4 (no. 1))
Reissue of an earlier edition, by Cumberland.
Remarks by George Daniel, editor of the original series.
"Performed at Covent Garden, April 5, 1833."

I. Title.
20–14596
Library of Congress PR1243.C82 vol. 4
——— Copy 2. PR1243.C8 vol. 42
(Cumberland's British theatre. London, ca. 1825–55. 15cm. v. 42 (no. 1))
Imperfect: frontispiece wanting.

NK 0209664 DLC CSt OCU OO PU-F NIC

Lilly PR 4859 .K5 H89
KNOWLES, JAMES SHERIDAN, 1784-1862
The hunchback. A play, in five acts. By J. Sheridan Knowles. [London, J. Dicks, n. d.]
26 p. 1 illus. 18 cm. (Dicks' Standard plays, no. 206)

Copy 1 in cream printed paper wrappers; series advts. to no. 204.
Copy 2 in green printed paper wrappers; series advts. to no. 914.
Copy 3 in purple printed paper wrappers; series advts. to no. 1062.

NK 0209665 InU

822.8 K73hun
Knowles, James Sheridan, 1784-1862.
...The hunchback. The love-chase. By James Sheridan Knowles. New York, Cassell & co. [n.d.]
192 p. 14 cm. (Cassell's national library)

NK 0209666 MiU WaU

Knowles, James Sheridan, 1784-1862.
... The hunchback. A play in five acts... With the author's latest corrections... The only unmutilated edition... N.Y., M. Douglas, n.d. [8]-82p.

NK 0209667 MiU

PR 4859 K5 H8 1800
Knowles, James Sheridan, 1784-1862
The hunchback; a play in five acts.
London, Cumberland [18--?]
76p. 16cm.

NK 0209668 WU

808.82 P69 v.2
Knowles, James Sheridan, 1784-1862.
The hunchback. A play, in five acts. With a portrait of the author, and remarks by D.-G. London, T.H. Lacy [18--]
78 p. illus. 19 cm. (Plays, v.2)

Remarks by George Daniel.
"First performed at the Theatre Royal, Covent Garden on the 5th of April, 1832."- cf. Verso of t.p.

NK 0209669 LU MH

Knowles, James Sheridan, 1784-1862.
The hunchback: a play in five acts ... London, The Music Pub. Co., [18--]
76 p. 1 port. 24°.
Prompter's copy, interleaved. Ms. notes.

NK 0209670 NN

PR4889 .K5H9 18-
Knowles, James Sheridan, 1784-1862.
...The hunchback. A play in five acts. By James Sheridan Knowles. With the author's latest corrections. All the stage business...&c. As performed by Mr.Knowles, Mr.and Miss Kemble, Mr.and Mrs.Charles Kean. The only unmutilated ed. ... New York, S.French[18-]
v,[7]-82 p. 19cm. (No.XV. French's standard drama)

NK 0209671 ICU CtY NN MB OrP MH MiU PPWI MWA

Knowles, James Sheridan, 1784-1862.
The hunchback. A play, in five acts. [London? 183-?]
3-14 p., 2 l., 91-170 p. 16°.
Prompter's copy, interleaved. Ms. notes.
T.-p. missing.

NK 0209672 NN

Knowles, James Sheridan, 1784-1862
The hunchback. A play, in five acts ... Baltimore, J. Robinson, 1832.

NK 0209673 PU

[Knowles, James Sheridan, 1784–1862.
The hunchback; a play in five acts. London, pref. 1832.]
iv, iv–v, 10–82 p. 12°.
t.-p. lacking.
Interleaved, with ms. notes.

385986A. 1. Drama, English. 2. Promptbooks. 3. Title.
N. Y. P. L. April 21, 1927

NK 0209674 NN

Lilly Library PR 4859 .K5 H9 1832
KNOWLES, JAMES SHERIDAN, 1784-1862
The hunchback. A play, in five acts. By James Sheridan Knowles. London, E. Moxon, 1832.
viii p., 1 ℓ., 118 p. 21 cm.

First edition.
Author's inscribed presentation copy to Miss Taylor, who created the part of Helen in the play; text is marked for the part of Helen. and has numerous ms.

Continued in next column

VOLUME 300

Continued from preceding column

amendments and directions; inserted is ms. poem by Knowles.
Bound in full polished calf, with bookplates of Coningsby Disraeli and Henry Irving.
Copy 2 bound in half morocco, has publisher's advertising leaf preceding title, and following p. 118 of text.

NK 0209676 InU NjP IU MH NN PPRF NIC IEN ICN ICU

Lilly Library
PR 4859 .K5 H9 1832c
KNOWLES, JAMES SHERIDAN, 1784-1862
The hunchback. A play, in five acts. By James Sheridan Knowles ... Fourth edition. London, E. Moxon, 1832.
viii p., 1 ℓ., 118 p. 20.5 cm.

One leaf publisher's advts. at end.

NK 0209677 InU NNCoCi

Ln K762 832he
Knowles, James Sheridan, 1784-1862.
The hunchback. A play, in five acts. By James Sheridan Knowles ... 5th ed. London;E.Moxon,64,New Bond Street.1832.
viiip.,1ℓ.,118p. 21½cm.
Autograph of Mrs. Copper.
Ms. annotations marking omissions for stage production.
With this is bound Jacob Jones's Regulus. London, 1841.

NK 0209678 TxU MB

812.1 K73h 1832
Knowles, James Sheridan, 1784-1862
The hunchback; a play in five acts 6th ed. London, Moxon, 1832.
118p. O.

In case. Subscription list to Leigh Hunt's Poetical works [2p.] is bound in at back.

NK 0209679 IaU MH NN InU CtY WU

Knowles, James Sheridan, 1784-1862.
The hunchback, a play, in five acts. By James Sheridan Knowles ... New-York, Peabody & co., 1832.
76 p. 23½cm.

I. Title.

46-35548

Library of Congress PR4859.K5H8 1832

NK 0209680 DLC MB NN PPL LNHT MH

Knowles, James Sheridan, 1784-1862.
...The hunchback; a play...by James Sheridan Knowles... Printed from the acting copy, with stage directions. New-York, O. Phelan [1832?] vi, 78 p. 15cm.

Prompt-book; interleaved, with cast of characters.
At head of title: Phelan's edition.
With autograph of John Procter.

255694B. 1. Drama, English. 2. Prompt-books. June 19, 1944
N. Y. P. L.

NK 0209681 NN CtY MH

Knowles, James Sheridan. 1784-1862.
The hunchback: a play, in five acts. With the London and Philadelphia casts.
Philadelphia. Turner. 1832. 70 pp. [Turner's American stage.] 15½ cm., in 18s.

H6786 — S.r.

NK 0209682 MB PPL

Knowles,James Sheridan,1784-1862.
The hunchback. A play,in five acts. By James Sheridan Knowles,author of "Virginius." [Second edition] Baltimore: Printed and published by J.Robinson,circulating library and dramatic depository. 1833.
78 p. 16.5cm.
"Dramatis personae. Covent Garden,1832.": p.[2]

1.Drama. I.Title.

NK 0209683 MiU-C CtY MH

Knowles, James Sheridan, 1784-1862.
The hunchback. A play, in five acts. By James Sheridan Knowles... 7. ed. London, E. Moxon, 1833. viii, 118 p. 22cm.

Prompt-book.
Contains original cast.
With autographs of T. Fredericks and Isaac Cohen.

1. Drama, English. I. Title. November 19, 1947
N. Y. P. L.

NK 0209684 NN NcU MH IU InU

---

822 K76h 1834
Knowles, James Sheridan, 1784-1862.
The hunchback, a play in five acts.
8th ed. London, E. Moxon, 1834.
viii, 118p. 23cm.

NK 0209685 IU ICU MH

Knowles, James Sheridan, 1784-1862.
The hunchback, a play — in five acts. By James Sheridan Knowles... (In: Alexander's modern acting drama. Philadelphia, 1835. 24°. v. 1, p. [117-]203.)

Partly in verse.

334948A. 1. Drama, English. 2. Title. February 17, 1928
N. Y. P. L.

NK 0209686 NN

Lilly Library
PR 4859 .K5 H9 1836
KNOWLES, JAMES SHERIDAN, 1784-1862
The hunchback. A play in five acts. By James Sheridan Knowles ... Berlin, B. Behr's Library, 1836.
88 p. 18 cm.

First German edition (in English.)
Printed in Berlin by C. Feister.
Bound in marbled boards, with cloth spine.

NK 0209687 InU

Knowles, James Sheridan, 1784-1862.
The hunchback. A play in five acts. By James Sheridan Knowles... 9th ed. London, E.Moxon, 1836.
vii, 77, [1] p. 21½ cm.

Interleaved.
Fanny Kemble's prompt book with the signature of her husband, Pierce Butler, on the t.-p.

1. Prompt books. I. Title. II. Kemble, Frances Anne, 1809-1893.

NK 0209688 PU-F InU MoU WU IU CtY NN PU

---

822 K76h 184-?
Knowles, James Sheridan, 1784-1862.
The hunchback. A play, in five acts With a portrait of the author and remarks by D.-G. London, T. H. Lacy [184-?]
77p. front.(port.) (On cover: Lacy's acting edition)

"First performed on the 5th of April,1832 [and in May, 1847]"

I. Daniel, George, 1789-1844. II. Title.

NK 0209689 IU

RA822.7 K73h 1841
Knowles, James Sheridan, 1784-1862.
The hunchback. A play, in five acts, by James Sheridan Knowles ... London: Charles Cumberland [1841]
76p.port.(plate)14cm.

NK 0209690 OC

Lilly
PR 4859 .K5 H9 1841
KNOWLES,JAMES SHERIDAN,1784-1862
The hunchback. A play, in five acts, by James Sheridan Knowles ... Printed from the acting copy, with remarks ... As performed at the Theatres Royal, London ... London, J. Cumberland [1841]
76 p. front. 15 cm. (Cumberland's British theatre, no. 336)

Copy 1 in grey printed paper wrappers; series advts. to no. 137.
List of author's works following name on title page differs in each copy; publisher's address also differs.

NK 0209691 InU MH DLC

Lilly
PR 4859 .K5 H9 1845
KNOWLES,JAMES SHERIDAN,1784-1862
The hunchback. A play, in five acts ... the only edition in print, with alterations and additions, as recently revised and corrected by the author ... Philadelphia, New York, Turner & Fisher, 1845.
79 p. front. 15 cm. (Turner's dramatic library)

Prompt copy.
Ms. note tipped in preceding p. 33.
In later wrappers.

NK 0209692 InU IU CtY MH

Knowles, James Sheridan, 1784-1862.
... The hunchback; a play in five acts. By James Sheridan Knowles. With the author's latest corrections. All the stage business, cast of characters, costumes, relative positions, &c. as performed by Mr. Knowles, Mr. and Miss Kemble, Mr. and Mrs. Charles Kean. The only unmutilated edition ... New York, W. Taylor; Baltimore, Taylor, Wilde, & co., 1846.
iv, [iii]-v, [1], [9]-82 p. 19cm. (Modern standard drama, edited by Epes Sargent. [vol. II] no. XV)

I. Title.

A 34-2231

Rochester. Univ. Library for Library of Congress PR1243.M68 no. 15 [a40b1]

NK 0209693 NRU WaS MB MH ViU PU

PR 4859 K5 H8 1847
Knowles, James Sheridan. 1784-1862.
The hunchback: a play. A new and rev. ed. London, E. Moxon, 1847.
65 p.

NK 0209694 CaBVaU

---

822 K76h 1848
Knowles, James Sheridan, 1784-1862.
The hunchback. A play in five acts. With the author's latest corrections. All the stage business, cast of characters, costumes, relative positions, &c., as performed by Mr. Knowles, Mr. and Miss Kemble, Mr. and Mrs. Charles Kean. The only unmutilated ed. With the stage omissions carefully marked with inverted commas. New York, Douglas, 1848.
82p. 18cm. (Modern standard drama, no.15)

Bound with the author's The hunchback. Boston [1889]; Love, New York [n.d.]; Virginius. New York, 1882; The wife. New York, 1846; The wife. New York [1833?]

NK 0209696 IU MH

VOLUME 300

Lilly Library
PR 4859 .K5 H9 1865
KNOWLES, JAMES SHERIDAN, 1784-1862
The hunchback. A play, in five acts. By James Sheridan Knowles ... London, T. H. Lacy [1865]
76 p. front. 17.5 cm. (Lacy's Acting edition, no. 1000)
Imperfect: lacks at least 2 pages at end.

NK 0209697 InU

PR4859 .K5 H8 1870
Knowles, James Sheridan, 1784-1862.
The hunchback, a play in five acts. With a portrait of the author and remarks by D. G. London, T. H. Lacy [1870?]
78p. illus.

NK 0209698 NcU

PR 4859 K5 H8 1870
Knowles, James Sheridan, 1784-1862
The hunchback. A play in five acts. [Acting ed.] New York, Crest [c1870]
76p. 19cm.

NK 0209699 WU

Knowles, James Sheridan, 1784-1862.
... The hunchback. A play in five acts. By James Sheridan Knowles. With the author's latest corrections ... The only unmutilated ed. With the stage omissions carefully marked with inverted commas. New York, S. French [ca. 1870]
v, [8]-82 p. $18\frac{1}{2}$cm. (French's standard drama. no. xv)

I. Title.

25-21472

Library of Congress PR4859.K5H8

NK 0209700 DLC NIC NNG MB CtY IaU MiU NcD

---

822 K76h 1832a
Knowles, James Sheridan, 1784-1862.
The Hunchback. A play in five acts. Sydenham, Crystal Palace Co., 1874.
55p. 21cm.
Bound with the author's The hunchback. 2d ed. London, 1832.

NK 0209701 IU InU

Knowles, James Sheridan, 1784-1862.
The hunchback. A play, in five acts. By James Sheridan Knowles ... From the original text ... An entirely new acting ed. ... Ed. by John B. Kingdom ... Chicago, The Dramatic publishing company, c1876.
69 p. 18.5 cm. (On cover: Sergel's acting drama, no. 197)

NK 0209702 OU

Knowles, James Sheridan, 1784-1862.
The hunchback. A play, in five acts. By James Sheridan Knowles ... From the original text ... An entirely new acting ed. ... Ed. by John M. Kingdom ... New York, R. M. De Witt, °1876.
69 p. $18\frac{1}{2}$cm. (On cover: De Witt's acting plays. no. 197)

I. Kingdom, John M., ed. II. Title.

12-34951

Library of Congress PR4859.K5A7 1876

NK 0209703 DLC NcD NN

PR 1245 N53+ v.4
Knowles, James Sheridan, 1784-1862.
The hunchback: a play, in five acts.
(In The New York drama. New York, c1879. 26cm. v. 4, p. 321-344)

NK 0209704 NIC

KNOWLES, JAMES SHERIDAN, 1784-1862.
...The hunchback. A play in five acts. By James Sheridan Knowles. With the author's latest corrections... The only unmutilated ed. With the stage omissions carefully marked with inverted commas. New York, W. Taylor & co. [1882]
iv,[iii]-v,[1],[9]-82 p. $19\frac{1}{2}$cm. (Modern standard drama; edited by E. Sargent. no. 15)

757258A. 1. Drama, English. I. Title. II. Ser.

NK 0209705 NN PU MH

An K762 883h Rare Books Col
KNOWLES, JAMES SHERIDAN, 1784-1862.
... The hunchback. By J.S. Knowles ... London: J. Dicks, 313, Strand; and all booksellers. New York: Samuel French & son, 122, Nassau Street-sole agents [1883?] cover title, 26p. 1 illus. 18cm. in envelope in folder 23cm. (Dicks' standard plays. no.206)
Title vignette.
In double columns.
Advertisements: inside front cover, [2]p. at end.
I. Title.

NK 0209706 TxU

Rare PR 4859 K5 H9 1883
Knowles, James Sheridan, 1784-1862.
The hunchback: a play in five acts. London, New York, S. French [1883?]
76 p. 19cm. (French's Acting edition (late Lacy's) no. 1000)

NK 0209707 NIC OClW

Drama Library PR4859 K56 H8 1887 (LC)
Knowles, James Sheridan, 1784-1862.
The hunchback [and] The love-chase. London, Cassell, 1887.
192 p. 15 cm. (Cassell's national library)

I. Knowles, James Sheridan, 1784-1862. The hunchback. II. Knowles, James Sheridan, 1784-1862. The love-chase. III. Title.

NK 0209708 CtY NcU

---

822 K76h 1848
Knowles, James Sheridan, 1784-1862.
The hunchback. A play in five acts. With the author's latest corrections. Unmutilated ed. With the stage omissions carefully marked with inverted commas. Boston, W. H. Baker [1889]
72p. 19cm.
Bound with the author's The hunchback. New York, 1848.
I. Title.

NK 0209709 IU OrPR MtU KyU CLSU OrP MH NcD

Knowles, James Sheridan, 1784-1862.
The hunchback, by Sheridan Knowles. Prepared for Daly's Theatre. n. p. [189-?] 68 l. 8°.
Leaves cut, mounted, and bound.
t.-p. missing.
Prompter's copy, with ms. notes.
First produced at Daly's Theatre, New York, Nov. 1892.

1. Drama (English). 2. Prompt books. 3. Daly, Augustin, 1838-99. 4. Title.
N. Y. P. L. January 11, 1916.

NK 0209710 NN

Knowles, James Sheridan, 1784-1862.
... The hunchback. The love-chase. By James Sheridan Knowles. London, Paris [etc.] Cassell & company, limited, 1891.
1 p.l., [5]-192 p. 14cm. (Cassell's national librar

I. Title. II. Title: The love-chase. III. Ser.

NK 0209711 ViU KyU

Knowles, James Sheridan, 1784-1862.
The hunchback; a comedy in five acts, by Sheridan Knowles. As first produced at Daly's theatre, New York, November 29, 1892, and here printed from the prompt-book as then used. [New York] Privately printed [by Trow directory prtg. and bookbinding co.] for Augustin Daly, 1893. 71 p. front. (port.) 27cm.

962296A. 1. Drama, English.
N. Y. P. L. October 3, 1939

NK 0209712 NN MiEM InU NNC PU MiU CSmH IaU MH

---

822 K76h 190-
Knowles, James Sheridan, 1784-1862.
The hunchback. A play, in five acts ... From the original text as first produced at the Theatre Royal, Covent Garden, London, April 5,1832; the Park theatre, New York, 1832 and 1845; and the Union square theatre, New York, October 26, 1874. An entirely new acting edition. (Preserving the author's text entire.) With full stage directions, accurately marked ... Edited by John M. Kingdom ... Chicago, The Dramatic publishing company [190-?]
69p. (On cover: Sergel's acting drama. number 197)

NK 0209713 IU

[Knowles, James Sheridan] 1784-1862.
"The hunchback"... [New York, 190-?] 8 parts in 1 v. 28cm.
Cover-title.
Typewritten.
Play in five acts by J. S. Knowles; sides only for eight characters.
First produced at the Covent garden theatre, London, April 5, 1832.

947252A. 1. Drama, English.
N. Y. P. L. January 24, 1939

NK 0209714 NN

---

822 K76h 1901
KNOWLES, JAMES SHERIDAN, 1784-1862.
"The hunchback," a play in five acts, by James Sheridan Knowles. A complete acting version, for modern stage use, as arranged by Fred. Williams. New York, London, Samuel French, c1901.
96p. 23cm. (American academy of dramatic arts' edition of standard plays. no.1)

NK 0209715 TxU OCl MH

Knowles, James Sheridan, 1784-1862.
The hunchback
see also Glover, Lyman Beecher, 1846-1915.
Viola Allen as Julia in The hunchback.

KNOWLES,James Sheridan, 1784-1862
The idol demolished by its own priest; an answer to Cardinal Wiseman's lectures on transubstantiation. Edinburgh, A.& C.Black, 1851.
pp.310. 16.5cm.

NK 0209717 MH-AH PPL

VOLUME 300

265.3 Knowles, James Sheridan, 1784-1862
K76i The idol demolished by its own priest. An answer to Cardinal Wiseman's lectures on transubstantiation ... London, 1852.
318p.

NK 0209718 IU NN DLC

Knowles, James Sheridan, 1784-1862.
The idol demolished by its own priest: an answer to Cardinal Wiseman's lectures on transubstantiation. 2d thousand [edition] London, J. Blackwood, 1852.
318 p. sm. 8°.

NK 0209719 MB DLC

Lilly Library
PR 4859 .K5 J49 KNOWLES, JAMES SHERIDAN, 1784-1862
John of Procida; or, The bridals of Messina. A tragedy, in five acts. By James Sheridan Knowles. First performed at Covent Garden Theatre, Sept. 19, 1840. London, J. Dicks, n. d.
24 p. 1 illus. 18.5 cm. (Dicks' Standard plays, no. 691)

In blue printed paper wrappers.

NK 0209720 InU

Knowles, James Sheridan, 1784-1862.
John of Procida; or, The bridals of Messina: a tragedy...by James Sheridan Knowles... Philadelphia [etc.] Turner & Fisher [18—?] 81 p. 19cm.

In verse.

1. Drama, English. I. Title.
N. Y. P. L. February 7, 1949

NK 0209721 NN MH CtY

PR 4859 .K5 J6 Knowles, James Sheridan, 1784-1862.
John of Procida; or, The bridals of Messina. A tragedy. In five acts. By James Sheridan Knowles ... London, E. Moxon, 1840.
vi p., 1 l., 116 p. 22cm.

"Also played as The bride of Messina."--Nicoll, A. A history of early nineteenth century drama.

NK 0209722 MiU InU NIC NjP CSmH IaU NN MH IU NjR TxU CSt

PR 4859 K5 .J55 Knowles, James Sheridan, 1784-1862.
John of Procida, or, The bridals of Messina; a tragedy in five acts. London, E. Moxon, 1840.
vi, 128 p.

I. Title. II. Title: The bridals of Messina.

NK 0209723 WaU

KNOWLES, James Sheridan, 1784-1862.
John of Procida, or The bridals of Messina; a tragedy, in five acts. New York, J. Winchester, 1840.

pp.68.

NK 0209724 MH

KNOWLES, James Sheridan, 1784-1862.
John of Procida, or The bridals of Messina; a tragedy in five acts. Berlin, B. Behr, 1841.

pp.74.

NK 0209725 MH

Lilly Library
PR 4859 .K5 J5 KNOWLES, JAMES SHERIDAN, 1784-1862
John of Procida; or, The bridals of Messina. A tragedy. In five acts. By James Sheridan Knowles ... London, E. Moxon, 1841.
vi p., 1 l., 116 p. 22 cm.

First edition.
Copy 1 is in drab printed paper wrappers; printed paper label on cover.
Copy 2, uncut, in quarter red morocco, with original drab printed paper wrappers bound in.
Copy 3, cut, in quarter red morocco.

NK 0209727 InU

Knowles, James Sheridan, 1784-1862.
Kathleen. Opera in 2 acts
see under Barnett, John, 1802-1890.

822.7 K73 C2 Knowles, James Sheridan, 1784-1862.
Knowles & Buckstone's plays. London, J. Cumberland, 18--
70, 86, 79, 25, 35, 48p. plates. 15cm.

Binder's title.
Each play has special t.p. and pagination, with front. from drawings by R. Cruikshank.
Edited by George Daniel.
Contents.—Virginius, by J.S. Knowles.—William Tell, by J.S. Knowles.—Caius Gracchus, by J.S. Knowles.—Popping the question, by J. B. Buckstone.—The happiest day of my life, by J. B. Buckstone.—Snakes in the grass, by J. B. Buckstone.

I. Buckstone, John Baldwin, 1802-1879. II. Daniel, George, 1789-1864, ed.

NK 0209730 ICarbS

Knowles, James Sheridan, 1784-1862.

Brown, Calvin Smith, 1866- ed.
The later English drama, edited with an introduction and notes by Calvin S. Brown. Students' ed. New York, A. S. Barnes and company, 1898.

Knowles, James Sheridan, 1784-1862.
Lectures on dramatic literature, delivered by James Sheridan Knowles during the years 1820-1850. Privately printed for J. McHenry. London, 1873. 228 p. illus. 32cm.

"Revised and edited by Francis Harvey."
One of 25 copies printed at the Chiswick press.
CONTENTS.—The Greek drama.—Hamlet; Julius Caesar.—Unity of action, climax of action, unity of character, &c.—First-[Second] act of Macbeth.—Shakespeare.

255194B. 1. Drama, Greek—Hist. and crit. 2. Shakespeare, William—Commentaries and criticism. I. Harvey, Francis, 1830-1899, ed. II. McHenry, James.
N. Y. P. L. March 30, 1944

NK 0209732 NN GU InU TxHU CtY CSt PBL IU

Knowles, James Sheridan, 1784-1862.
Lectures on dramatic literature, by James Sheridan Knowles. (Never before published): Macbeth ... London, F. Harvey, 1875.
2 p. l., 82 p., 1 l. 21½cm.

1. Shakespeare, William. Macbeth. I. Title.

21-15625

Library of Congress PR2823.K6

NK 0209733 DLC MB NN CtY PP PU-F MiU

Knowles, James Sheridan, 1784-1862.
Lectures on oratory gesture and poetry to which is added a correspondence with four clergymen in defence of the stage. By James Sheridan Knowles. [Revised and edited by Francis Harvey] London, Priv. print. for J. McHenry [at the Chiswick press] 1873.
4 p.l., 249 p. facsims. 32½cm.
Floriated initials, head and tail-pieces.
"Only twenty-five copies printed."
Bound in green morocco, gold tooled; inside borders; gilt edge.
1.Gesture. 2.Oratory. 3.Poetry - Addresses essays, lectures. 4.Theater - Moral and religious aspects.

NK 0209734 CSt NcU CtY InU NN IU MoU TxHU PBL

Knowles, James Sheridan, 1784-1862.
Love. A play in five acts... London, J. Cumberland, n.d.
74p. (Bell, J. British theatre, v. 28, no.3)

NK 0209735 OU

Lilly Library
PR 4859 .K5 L 46 KNOWLES, JAMES SHERIDAN, 1784-1862
Love. A play, in five acts. By James Sheridan Knowles. London, J. Dicks, n.d.
26 p. 1 illus. 18.5 cm. (Dicks' Standard plays, no. 364)

Copies 1 and 2 in pink printed paper wrappers. Copy 1 has series advts. to no. 606; copy 2 has series advts. to no. 364.

NK 0209736 InU

Knowles, James Sheridan, 1784-1862.
Love; a play in five acts ... London, G. H. Davidson [18--]
74 p., 1 p.l. nar. 24°.
Prompter's copy, interleaved. Ms. notes.

NK 0209737 NN

PR 4859 .K5 L9 18-- Knowles, James Sheridan, 1784-1862.
... Love: a play in five acts. By James Sheridan Knowles. With the stage business, casts of characters ... etc. New York, S. French & son; London, S. French [18--]
v, [7]-69 p. 19cm. (French's standard drama. no. LXV)
"Produced at Drury Lane theatre on the 4th November, 1839."--p. [iii]

NK 0209738 MiU MH NN InU IaU

Knowles, James Sheridan, 1784-1862.
...Love. A play, in five acts. By James Sheridan Knowles... 1. Amer. ed. [Philadelphia, etc.] Turner & Fisher [18—] [1]-78 p. 19cm. (Turner's dramatic library.)

Prompt-book, made from printed edition, with ms. corrections and notes.
First London production at the Theatre Royal, Covent Garden, Nov. 4, 1839; first New York production at the Park theatre, Jan. 17, 1840.
Imperfect: t.-p. wanting; title from another copy.

1. Drama, English. 2. Prompt-books. I. Title.
N. Y. P. L. January 5, 1945

NK 0209739 NN MH

VOLUME 300

PR4889 .K5L7 1839 Rare bk
Knowles, James Sheridan, 1784-1862.
Love. A play, in five acts. 1st American ed. Boston, J. Fisher, [1839]
78 p. (Turner's Dramatic library)

NK 0209740 ICU MH

Lilly Library PR 4859 .K5 L 5 1839
KNOWLES, JAMES SHERIDAN, 1784-1862
Love: a play, in five acts. By James Sheridan Knowles ... Third edition. London, E. Moxon, 1839.
vi p., 1 l., 116 p. 22 cm.

Bound in drab printed paper wrappers; printed paper label on cover; one leaf publisher's advts. precedes title page.

NK 0209741 InU NN PU IU WU MnU CtY

PR4889 .K5L7 1839a Austrian
Knowles, James Sheridan, 1784-1862.
Love; a play in five acts ... 4th ed. London, E. Moxon, 1839.
vi, [1], 116 p. 23 cm.

NK 0209742 ICU MH CSmH

Knowles, James Sheridan, 1784-1862.
... Love; a play in five acts... N.Y., London, French [1839?]
69p.

NK 0209743 OCl

Knowles, James Sheridan, 1784-1862.
... Love. A play, in five acts. By James Sheridan Knowles ... 1st American ed. Baltimore, H. A. Turner; New York, Turner & Fisher; [etc., etc., 184-]
2 p. l., [11]-78 p. 14½ cm. (Turner's dramatic library)

I. Title.

PR4859.K5L57 47-40212

NK 0209744 DLC MH

Knowles, James Sheridan, 1784-1862.
Love: a play, in five acts, by James Sheridan Knowles ... Printed from the acting copy, with remarks, biographical and critical, by D.—G. ... As performed at the Theatres Royal ... London, G. H. Davidson [184-]
74 p. front. (port.) 15cm. (Cumberland's British theatre. London, ca. 1825-55. v. 40 [no. 1])
Remarks by George Daniel, editor of the series.
Reissue of Cumberland's earlier edition.

I. Title.

Library of Congress PR1243.C8 vol. 40 21-14530

NK 0209745 DLC PU-F OU OCU InU

Knowles, James Sheridan, 1784-1862.
... Love. A play, in five acts. By James Sheridan Knowles ... 1st American ed. Philadelphia, New York, Turner & Fisher [184-]
2 p.l., [11]-78 p. 14.5 cm. (Turner's dramatic library)

NK 0209746 ViW

Knowles, James Sheridan, 1784-1862.
Love. A play, in five acts ... [and in verse] printed from the acting copy, with remarks, biographical and critical, by D.-G. [i. e., G. Daniel] ... As performed at the Theatres Royal, London. Embellished with a portrait of Mr. Anderson, in the character of Huon. Engraved on steel by Mr. Hall, from an original drawing by Mr. E. Walker. London: J. Cumberland [1840]. 74 p., 1 port. 24°. (Cumberland's British theatre. v. 40.)

Bound with his: The love-chase; a comedy ... London, 1840. 24°.

1. Drama (English). 2. Daniel, George. 3. Hall, engraver. 4. Walker, E., illustrator. 5. Title.
N. Y. P. L. May 13, 1914.

NK 0209747 NN MiU OCU CtY IU InU

Lilly PR 4859 .K5 L5 1840
KNOWLES, JAMES SHERIDAN, 1784-1862
Love: a play in five acts. By James Sheridan Knowles ... London, E. Moxon, 1840.
vi p., 1 l., 116 p. 21.5 cm.

Copy 1 bound in half purple morocco by Maclehose. Copy 2, trimmed to 20 cm., bound in quarter red morocco. Both copies have at foot of p. 116: London, Bradbury and Evans, Printers.
Copy 3, bound in quarter red morocco, has at foot of p. 116: London, Bradbury and Evans, Printers to the Queen.
Each copy has 1 leaf publisher's advts. preceding title page.

CSmH FTaSU
NK 0209748 InU MoU NN NcD IU MH AU CaBVaU CtY TxU

Lilly Library PR 4859 .K5 L 5 1840a
KNOWLES, JAMES SHERIDAN, 1784-1862
Love: a play. In five acts. By James Sheridan Knowles ... Fifth edition. London, E. Moxon, 1840.
5 p. l., 116 p. 21 cm.

One leaf publisher's advts. precedes title page.

NK 0209749 InU IU

Knowles, James Sheridan, 1784-1862.
... Love; a play in five acts, by James Sheridan Knowles. With the stage business, casts of characters, costumes, relative positions, etc. New York, M. Douglas, 1848.
v, [6]-69 p. 19cm. (Modern standard drama, ed. by John W. S. Hows. [vol. IX] no. LXV)

I. Title. A 40-1279

Virginia. Univ. Library for Library of Congress

NK 0209750 ViU PU NIC MH NN MB

Lilly PR 4859 .K5 L 49 1848
KNOWLES, JAMES SHERIDAN, 1784-1862
Love: a play, in five acts. [New York, M. Douglas, 1848]
6 p.l., [7]-69 p. front.(port.) 15.9 cm.

Prompt copy.
Title from t.p. clipping on upper cover.
Disbound from vol. ix of Modern Standard Drama. New York, M. Douglas, 1848.
Stitched in later wrappers.

1. Prompt books

NK 0209751 InU NN

Knowles, James Sheridan, 1784-1862.
... Love; a play in five acts. By James Sheridan Knowles ... New York: W. Taylor & Co., [, 185-?] 69 p. 12°. (Modern standard drama. no. 65.)

1. Drama, English. 2. Title. 3. Ser.
N. Y. P. L. August 8, 1928

NK 0209752 DLC NN MB MH IU

Rare PR 4859 K5 L8 1860
Knowles, James Sheridan, 1784-1862.
Love: a play in five acts. With the stage business, casts of characters, costumes, relative positions, etc. New York, S. French [186-?]
69 p. 20cm. (French's standard drama. no. 65)

NK 0209753 NIC IU

Lilly PR 4859 .K5 L 5 1867
KNOWLES, JAMES SHERIDAN, 1784-1862
Love. A play, in five acts. By James Sheridan Knowles ... London, T. H. Lacy [1867]
74 p. front. 17.5 cm. (Lacy's Acting edition, no. 1107)

With 2-line imprint; no printer.

NK 0209754 InU CtY

Lilly Library PR 4859 .K5 L58
KNOWLES, JAMES SHERIDAN, 1784-1862
... The love-chase. A play in five acts. By James Sheridan Knowles ... Correctly printed from the most approved acting copy ... As now performed in the London and American theatres ... Boston, J. Fisher [etc., etc., n. d.]
67 [1] p. 15.5 cm. (Turner's Dramatic library of acting plays, v. 5, no. 35)

In brown printed paper wrappers.

NK 0209755 InU MB

Knowles, James Sheridan, 1784-1862.
The love chase. A comedy in five acts. London, T.H. Lacy [18--?]
62 p., 1 l. pl. 12°.
Prompter's copy. Interleaved. Ms. notes.

NK 0209756 NN

Knowles, James Sheridan, 1784-1862.
The love-chase. A comedy, in five acts. By James Sheridan Knowles ... London, E. Moxon, 1837.
3 p. l., 111 p. 20½cm.

I. Title. 15-16671

Library of Congress PR4859.K5L6

NK 0209757 DLC InU IU WU CtY TxU CSmH MH

Knowles, James Sheridan, 1784-1862.
The love-chase. A comedy, in five acts. By James Sheridan Knowles ... 2d ed. London, E. Moxon, 1837.
4 p. l., 111 p. 22½cm. [With Lytton, E. G. E. L. Bulwer-Lytton, 1st baron. The Duchess de la Vallière. London, 1836]
Imperfect: half-title wanting.

I. Title. 15-22900

Library of Congress PR4922.D7 1836
——— Copy 2. [Hazlitt tracts, v. 31, no. 1] AC911.H3 vol. 31

NK 0209758 DLC MnU InU

KNOWLES, James Sheridan, 1784-1862.
The love-chase; a comedy, in five acts. Berlin, B. Behr, 1838.

pp. 71.

NK 0209759 MH

VOLUME 300

Lilly Library PR 4859 .K5 L 6 1838a KNOWLES, JAMES SHERIDAN, 1784-1862
The love-chase. A comedy, in five acts, by James Sheridan Knowles ... Printed from the acting copy, with remarks ... As performed at the Theatres Royal, London, ... London, J. Cumberland [1838?]
64 p. front. 14.5 cm. (Cumberland's British theatre, no. 326)

Copy 2 is without other works by D. G. after his name on title page.

NK 0209760 InU OO MiU CtY

Lilly Library PR 4859 .K5 L 6 1838 KNOWLES, JAMES SHERIDAN, 1784-1862
The love-chase. A comedy, in five acts. By James Sheridan Knowles ... Third edition. London, E. Moxon, 1838.
4 p.ℓ., 111 p. 21.5 cm.

Copy 2, bound in quarter red morocco, and trimmed slightly, is author's inscribed presentation copy.

NK 0209761 InU RPB PU MH MoU TxU

PR4889 .K5L8 1838 Knowles, James Sheridan, 1784-1862.
The love-chase. A comedy in five acts ...
New York, G. Dearborn and Adlard & Saunders, 1838.
116 p.

NK 0209762 ICU CtY PU MH TxU NNC

Knowles, James Sheridan, 1784–1862.
The love-chase. A comedy, in five acts. By James Sheridan Knowles... New York: G. Dearborn & Co., 1838. 116 p. 2. ed. 12°.

In verse.
Interleaved, with ms. notes.

285987A. 1. Drama, English. 2. Promptbooks. 3. Title.
N. Y. P. L. April 22, 1927

NK 0209763 NN NcU MB MH

Knowles, James Sheridan, 1784-1862.
... The love-chase. A play ... Philadelphia [etc.] Turner & Fisher [etc.] [1838]
[1]-[68] p. 6 in.
At head of title: Turner's Dramatic Library.

NK 0209764 PKsL MH

Knowles, James Sheridan, 1784–1862.
The love-chase : a comedy, in five acts, by James Sheridan Knowles ... Printed from the acting copy, with remarks, biographical and critical, by D.—G. ... As performed at the Theatres Royal ... London, G. H. Davidson [184–]
64 p. front. (port.) 15cm. (Cumberland's British theatre. London, ca 1825–55. v. 41 [no. 1])
Remarks by George Daniel, editor of the series.
Reissue of Cumberland's earlier edition.
I. Title.

21-18551
Library of Congress PR1243.C8 vol. 41

NK 0209765 DLC InU CtY PU-F NN

Knowles, James Sheridan. 1784–1862.
The love-chase. A comedy in five acts. With the stage business ... costumes, &c. ...
New-York. Taylor & Co. [184–?] 67 pp. [Modern standard drama. No. 22.] 18 cm.
A programme is inserted in the copy on shelf-number **T.97.314.

NK 0209766 MB MWA PPL

PR 1243 P72 v.5 Knowles, James Sheridan, 1784-1862.
The love-chase, a comedy in five acts. Printed from the acting copy, with remarks, biographical and critical, by D.--G.... As performed at the Theatres Royal, London. With a portrait of Miss Elphinstone in the character of Constance, engraved on steel by Mr. Hall, from the original drawing by E. Walker. London, J. Cumberland [1840]
64 p. illus. 15cm.
Remarks by George Daniel.
Vol. 5, no. 2 in a set lettered: Plays.

NK 0209767 NIC

PR 1271 P73 Knowles, James Sheridan, 1784-1862.
The love-chase. A comedy, in five acts. Printed from the acting copy, with remarks, biographical and critical, by D.--G. [i. e., George Daniel] As performed at the Theatres Royal, London. With a portrait of Miss Elphinstone...engraved on steel by Mr. Hall, from an painting by Mr. E. Walker. London, The Music-Pub. [1840?]
64 p. illus. 15 cm.

No. 1 in vol. lettered: Plays. Knowles and other.

I. Title.

NK 0209768 NIC NN

---

828 K73ℓc Knowles, James Sheridan, 1784-1862.
... The love-chase; a comedy in five acts. By James Sheridan Knowles. With the stage business, cast of characters, costumes, relative positions, &c. as played at the Park theatre. New York, Samuel French, [1842?]
iv, [2], [7]-67p. 19cm. (French's standard drama. [vol. 3] no.22)

NK 0209769 LNHT MH NN InU CSmH MB NIC IaU

Lilly PR 4859 .K5 L6 1842 KNOWLES, JAMES SHERIDAN, 1784-1862
The love-chase. A comedy in five acts ... New York, William Taylor & Co. [1842?]
67 p. 16.1 cm. (Modern standard drama, no. 22)

Imprint date from author's preface.
Prompt copy, some leaves bound in.
In later wrappers.

1. Prompt books.

NK 0209770 InU NN

Knowles, James Sheridan, 1784–1862.
... The love-chase; a comedy in five acts. By James Sheridan Knowles. With the stage business, cast of characters, costumes, relative positions, &c. as played at the Park theatre. New York, Philadelphia [etc.] W. Taylor & co., 1846.
iv, [2], [7]–67 p. 19cm. (Modern standard drama, edited by Epes Sargent. [vol. III] no. XXII)

I. Title.

A 34-2236
Rochester. Univ. Library for Library of Congress PR1243.M68 no. 22 [PR4859.K5L] [a38b1]

NK 0209771 NRU WaS DLC MH NcD NcU IU PU ViU

Knowles, James Sheridan, 1784–1862.
... The love-chase. A comedy in five acts. By James Sheridan Knowles. With the stage business, cast of characters, cosumes [!] ... &c. As played at the Park theatre. New York, S. French [185–?]
iv, [2], [7]–67 p. 17½cm. (French's standard drama. No. XXII)
No. 2 in a volume lettered: Standard drama.

I. Title.

44-12962
Library of Congress PR1271.S8 no. 2 [2]

NK 0209772 DLC

Knowles, James Sheridan, 1784-1862.
... The love-chase ... N. Y., Taylor [1852?]
67 p. 12°.

NK 0209773 CtHT-W

Lilly Library PR 4859 .K5 L 6 1865 KNOWLES, JAMES SHERIDAN, 1784-1862
The love chase. A comedy, in five acts. By James Sheridan Knowles ... London, T. H. Lacy [1865]
64 p. front. 17.5 cm. (Lacy's Acting edition, no. 1007)

NK 0209774 InU CtY MiU

Knowles, James Sheridan, 1784–1862.
... The love-chase. A comedy in five acts. By James Sheridan Knowles. With the stage business, cast of characters, cosumes [!] relative positions, &c. As played at the Park theatre. New York, S. French & son; London, S. French [187–?]
iv p., 1 l., [7]–67 p. 18½cm. (French's standard drama. No. XXII)

I. Title.

42-27286
Library of Congress PR4859.K5L6

NK 0209775 DLC

812.1 K73ℓ Knowles, James Sheridan, 1784-1862
The love chase. A comedy, in five acts. London, French [1870?]
64p. S. (On cover: French's acting edition, 1007)

NK 0209776 IaU

PR 1245 N53+ v.2 Knowles, James Sheridan, 1784-1862.
The love-chase: a comedy, in five acts.
(In The New York drama. New York, c1876. 26cm. v. 2, p. 257-276)

NK 0209777 NIC CtY MB

---

v. 2, no. 21
KNOWLES, JAMES SHERIDAN, 1784-1862.
The love chase; a comedy in five acts.
(IN: New York drama. Library edition. New York. 26cm. v. 2, no. 21(1876) p. [1]-20)

Film reproduction. Positive.

1. Drama, English.

NK 0209778 NN

Knowles, James Sheridan, 1784-1862
Love-chase, a comedy in five acts.
Wash., Wheat, c1876.
20 p.

NK 0209779 PU

Lilly Library PR 4859 .K5 L 6 1883 KNOWLES, JAMES SHERIDAN, 1784-1862
The love case. A comedy, in five acts. By James Sheridan Knowles. [London, J. Dicks, 1883]
22 p. 1 illus. 18.5 cm. (Dicks' Standard plays, no. 322)

Copy 1 in pale green, copy 2 in pale blue printed paper wrappers.

NK 0209780 InU

VOLUME 300

PR4889 Knowles, James Sheridan, 1784-1862.
.K5L8 ... The love-chase. A comedy in five acts, by James
1896 Sheridan Knowles. With the stage business ... &c. as played at the Park theatre. New York [etc.] S. French [1896?]
iv, [5]-67 p. 19cm. (No. XXII. French's standard drama)

NK 0209781 ICU MH CtY

KNOWLES, JAMES SHERIDAN, 1784-1862.
...The love-chase (1837); a comedy in five acts, by James Sheridan Knowles. (In: The Malvern Festival plays, MCMXXXIII. London, 1933. 19cm. p.211-276.)

664218A. 1. Drama, English. I. Title.

NK 0209782 NN

3816 Knowles, James Sheridan, 1784-1862.
.7
.361 The Magdalen, and other stories... London, Moxon, 1832.
199 p. 17½ cm.

NK 0209783 NjP CtY OClW PU MH

Knowles, James Sheridan, 1784-1862.
The Magdalen, and other tales ... Philadelphia, Carey, Lea, and Blanchard, 1833.
1 p.l., [7]-192 p. 15.5 cm.
Contents. The Magdalen. Love and authorship. Old Adventures. Therese. The lettre-de-cachet. The portrait: a sketch.
Imperfect: end-leaves wanting.

NK 0209784 CtY

Knowles, James Sheridan, 1784-1862.
The Magdalen, and other tales. By James Sheridan Knowles ... New York: Wallis & Newell, 1835. 44 p. 12°. (Franklin library edition.)
Contents: The Magdalen. Love and authorship. Old adventures.

1. Fiction (English). 2. Title. 3. Title: Love and authorship. 4. Title: Old adventures.
N. Y. P. L. March 3, 1920.

NK 0209785 NN MiU CtY

[KNOWLES, James Sheridan] 1784-1862
The maid of Mariendorpt. n.p., n. d.

Proof copy.
Presentation copy from the author.

NK 0209786 MH

Knowles, James Sheridan, 1784-1862.
... The maid of Mariendorpt. A play, in five acts ... Correctly printed from the most approved acting copy, with a description of the costume ... and the whole of the stage business; to which are added, properties and directions, as now performed in the principal theatres. Boston, J. Fisher; Philadelphia, Turner & Fisher; [etc., etc., 1838?]
72p. 14cm. (Turner's dramatic library)

NK 0209787 CtY PU MH MB NN

Lilly Library
PR 4859 .K5 M29 KNOWLES, JAMES SHERIDAN, 1784-1862
The maid of Mariendorpt. A play, in five acts. By Sheridan Knowles. First performed at the Theatre Royal, Haymarker, October 9th, 1838. [London, J. Dicks, n.d.]
22 p. 1 illus. 18.5 cm. (Dicks' Standard plays, no. 496)

In pink printed papor wrappers; series advts. to no. 504.

NK 0209788 InU

KNOWLES, J[ames] Sheridan, 1784-1862.
The maid of Mariendorpt. a play, in five acts. Baltimore, J. Robinson, [1838?]

24°. pp. 60.
At head of title: Robinson's edition.

NK 0209789 MH NN

[Knowles, James Sheridan] 1784-1862.
[The maid of Mariendorpt: a play in five acts]
[London? ded. 1838]
1 p.l., 5-60 p. 24°.
Prompter's copy, interleaved. Ms. notes.
Title-page missing.

NK 0209790 NN

---

x822 Knowles, James Sheridan, 1784-1862
K76m The maid of Mariendorpt A play, in five acts London, E Moxon, 1838
111p. 22cm.

"To Miss Porter's novel of 'The village of Mariendorpt' I am indebted for the plot of this drama."--Advertisement.
Author's presentation copy to George Daniel
Bound by Riviere in light brown calf

NK 0209791 IU CSmH MB MH NN ViU TxU CSt InU IaU PU NcD DLC CtY NjP WaU PU

Knowles, James Sheridan, 1784-1862.
[The maid of Mariendorpt] a play, in five acts. By J. Sheridan Knowles ... Correctly printed from the acting copy, with cast of the characters, entrances and exits, relative positions, and the whole of the stage business; to which are added, properties and directions, as performed at the Theatre Royal, Haymarket, London. Baltimore: Published by Jos. Robinson [1839?]
60 p. 13cm

Vol. 9, no. 2 in a set of nine volumes lettered: Miscellaneous plays.
First produced in 1838.
Upper part of title-page cut away.

NK 0209793 PU-F

Knowles, James Sheridan, 1784-1862.
... The maid of Mariendorpt. A play, in five acts. By J. Sheridan Knowles, esq. ... Correctly printed from the most approved acting copy ... Philadelphia, New York, Turner & Fisher [1839?]
72 p. 15cm. (Turner's dramatic library of acting plays. no. 47)
Series title in part at head of t.-p.
"To Miss Porter's novel of 'The village of Mariendorpt' I am indebted for the plot of this drama."—Advertisement.

I. Porter, Anna Maria, 1780-1832. The village of Mariendorpt. II. Title.
Library of Congress PR4859.K5M3 1839 40-23537

NK 0209794 DLC DeGE

Knowles, James Sheridan, 1784-1862.
The Malvern festival plays, MCMXXXIII, arranged for production by H. K. Ayliff. With an introduction by Hugh Walpole, and a preface by Sir Barry Jackson. London, Heath Cranton ltd., 1933.

Knowles, James Sheridan, 1784-1862.
Mariana; Schauspiel in fünf Aufzügen
see under Treitschke, Georg Friedrich, 1776-1842.

---

x822 Knowles, James Sheridan, 1784-1862
K76ma A masque; as represented at the Theatre-Royal, Covent-Garden London, E Moxon, 1832.
14p. 22cm.

On the death of Sir Walter Scott
Author's presentation copy to Miss E Tree
Bound by Riviere in light brown calf

1. Scott, Sir Walter, bart- -Drama I Title

NK 0209797 IU CSmH MiD

Knowles, James Sheridan, 1784-1862.
Miscellaneous dramatic works and poems of James Sheridan Knowles. Now first collected and privately printed for J. McHenry. London, 1873-74. 2 v. illus. 32cm.
Title of v. 2 varies slightly.
"Revised and edited by Francis Harvey."
One of 25 copies printed at the Chiswick press.
CONTENTS.—v. 1. Hersilia; Fragment of a Spanish play; Vaccination; The storm; Leo; Brian Boroihme; A masque; The bridal; Alexina (opera)—v. 2. The Duke of London. The Duke of London; another draft of the first act of this play. Fragment of a play (The Widow). Fragment of an anonymous play. An unpublished scene from "Caius Gracchus". An unpublished scene from "William Tell". Biographical notice on Professor Marc-Monnier. Guillaume Tell.

253550-1B. 1. Drama, English. I. Harvey, Francis, 1830-1899, ed. II. McHenry, James.
N. Y. P. L. March 31, 1944

NK 0209798 NN CtY

Knowles, James Sheridan, 1784-1862.
...Mr. John M'Cullough's authorised version of James Sheridan Knowles' tragedy, Virginius. Mise en scène by Mr. Augustus Harris... London: Letts, Son & Co., Ltd. [1881.]
45 p. 8°.
At head of title: Theatre Royal, Drury Lane.

1. Drama (English). 2. Harris, Sir Augustus Henry Glossop Harris, 1825-96. 3. McCullough, John Edward, 1832-85. 4. Title: Virginius.
N. Y. P. L. November 29, 1921.

NK 0209799 NN MH

---

822 Knowles, James Sheridan, 1784-1862.
K76h Mr. John McCullough's authorized version of
1848 J. S. Knowles' tragedy, Virginius. Philadelphia, Ledger Job Print, 1882.
45p. 21cm.

Bound with the author's The hunchback. New York, 1848.
Cover title.
At head of title: Book of the play.

I. Title: Virginius.

NK 0209800 IU MH NcU CtY

Lilly Library
PR 4859 .K5 O 59 KNOWLES, JAMES SHERIDAN, 1784-1862
Old maids. A comedy, in five acts. By James Sheridan Knowles. First performed at Covent Garden Theatre, Oct. 28th, 1841. [London, J. Dicks, n. d.]
27 p. 1 illus. 18.5 cm. (Dicks' Standard plays, no. 629)

In pink printed paper wrappers; series advts. to no. 632.

NK 0209801 InU

VOLUME 300

Knowles, James Sheridan, 1784–1862.
...Old maids. A play, in five acts, by James Sheridan Knowles... Correctly printed from the most approved acting copy. Philadelphia: Turner & Fisher [, 184–?]. 84 p. 24°. (Turner's dramatic library.)

334765A. 1. Drama, English. 2. Title. March 30, 1928
N. Y. P. L.

NK 0209802 NN MB ICU ViU MH DeGE

---

x822 K76o Knowles, James Sheridan, 1784-1862.
Old maids: a comedy In five acts. As performed at the Theatre Royal, Covent Garden. London, E. Moxon, 1841.
128p. 22cm.
Author's presentation copy to George Daniel, Esq.
Bound by Rivieri in light brown calf

NcD WaS InU
NK 0209803 IU TxU CtY ICN RPB MH CSmH IaU MnU WU

Z825K76 OP **Knowles, James Sheridan, 1784-1862.**
Plays. [London, E. Moxon, 1833-41]
5 v. in 1. 22cm.
Binder's title.
Contents.- [1] The wife.- [2] The love-chase.- [3] Woman's wit.- [4] Love.- [5] Old maids.

NK 0209804 MnU

Knowles, James Sheridan, 1784-1862.
Plays. London, E. Moxon, 1838.
4 v. in 1. 22 cm.
Each play has separate paging and t.p.
CONTENTS.-The hunchback.-The wife.-The beggar of Bethnal-Green.-The daughter.

NK 0209805 CaBVaU

Lilly PR 4859 .K5 A19 1838 KNOWLES, JAMES SHERIDAN, 1784-1862
Plays by James Sheridan Knowles. The hunchback. The wife. The daughter. London, E. Moxon, 1838.
5 p. ℓ., 77, [1], [8], 72, [8], 108 p. 21.5 cm.
First edition of the collection.
Comprising the ninth, seventh, and second editions respectively of the plays.
Author's inscribed presentation copy, bound in quarter red morocco.

NK 0209806 InU CSmH OrSaW

Lilly Library PR 4859 .K5 R59 KNOWLES, JAMES SHERIDAN, 1784-1862
The rose of Arragon. A play, in five acts. By James Sheridan Knowles. Originally performed at the Theatre Royal, Haymarket, May 30th, 1842.
[London, J. Dicks, n.d.]
24 p. 1 illus. 18.5 cm. (Dicks' Standard plays, no. 689)
Copy 1 in green; copy 2 in pink printed paper wrappers.

NK 0209807 InU

Wn K762 842r KNOWLES, JAMES SHERIDAN, 1784-1862.
The rose of Arragon: a play. In five acts. As performed at the Theatre-Royal, Haymarket. By James Sheridan Knowles.
London: Edward Moxon, Dover Street. 1842.
4p.ℓ., 120p. 22cm., in case 25½cm.

ICU WaU WU
NK 0209808 TxU IaU MiU CtY MH CSmH NN InU IU OC

Knowles, James Sheridan, 1784-1862.

Russell, William, 1798–1873.
Rudiments of gesture, comprising illustrations of common faults in attitude and action. By William Russell. 2d ed., improved. With fifty-six engravings. To which is added an appendix ... consisting of a debate on the character of Julius Cæsar. By James Sheridan Knowles. Boston, G. W. Palmer & company, 1838.

Lilly Library PR 4859 .K5 S39 KNOWLES, JAMES SHERIDAN, 1784-1862
The secretary. A play, in five acts. By James Sheridan Knowles. First produced at Drury Lane Theatre, April 24, 1843. [London, J. Dicks, n. d.]
23 p. 1 illus. 18.5 cm. (Dicks' Standard plays, no.665)
In orange printed wrappers.

NK 0209810 InU

PR4889 .K5S4 1843 Knowles, James Sheridan, 1784–1862.
The secretary. A play, in five acts. By James Sheridan Knowles ... London, E. Moxon, 1843.
[8], 68 p. 20½cm.

NK 0209811 ICU IU InU CSmH MH CtY

KNOWLES, James Sheridan, 1784-1862.
The secretary; a play in five acts. 1st American ed. New York, Wilson & co., [1843]
f°. pp.16.
At head of title: Mr. Knowles' new play complete.
"Brother Jonathan, extra shut, no.27."

NK 0209812 MH NNC CtY

Toner Knowles, James Sheridan, 1784–1862.
Select dramatic works of James Sheridan Knowles. With a memoir by R. Shelton Mackenzie, LL. D. Baltimore, E. J. Coale & co., 1835.
1 p. l., xi p., 3 l., [7]-395 p. 16cm.
CONTENTS.—Virginius.—William Tell.—The hunchback.—The wife: a tale of Mantua.

31-25880
Library of Congress PR4859.K5A19 1835 822.72

NK 0209813 DLC ViU OClW CSmH MH

In K763 C833 Knowles, James Sheridan, 1784-1862.
Select works of James Sheridan Knowles. Consisting of his most popular tales and dramas, with an original notice of his life and writings ... Boston, Carter, Hendee and co. [etc.] 1833.
2v. in 1. 16½cm.
Contents. - v.1. Love and authorship. Old adventures. Therese. The Magdalen. The lettre-de-cachet. The portrait. Virginius. - v.2. William Tell. The hunchback. The wife; a tale of Mantua.

NK 0209814 CtY PPL ICU AU MB MH OClStM

Knowles, James Sheridan, 1784-1862.
Select works ... 2d ed. Boston, 1836.
2 v. in 1.

NK 0209815 NjP

Knowles, James Sheridan, 1784-1862.
A sermon occasioned by the death of James Sheridan Knowles
see under Thomas, Alfred C.

Knowles, James Sheridan, 1784–1862.
Tales and novelettes, by James Sheridan Knowles. Collected and privately printed for J. McHenry. London, 1874. 365 p. 32cm.
"Revised and edited by Francis Harvey."
One of 25 copies printed at the Chiswick press.
CONTENTS.—The Magdalen.—Love and authorship.—Old adventures.—Therese.—The lettre de cachet.—The portrait.—The widowed bride.—The wrecker.—The blacksmith of Clonmel.—The guerilla.—Glorvina, the maid of Meath.—An Indian tradition.—Woman's love.—My grandfather's dream.

255195B. I. No subject. I. Harvey, Francis, 1830-1899, ed. II. McHenry, James. March 29, 1944
N. Y. P. L.

NK 0209817 NN InU PBL MH CSt IU CtY TxHU

Ms.L K73h Knowles, James, Sheridan, 1784-1862
To [Leigh] Hunt. [n.p., n.d.]
Concerning his appointment with Hunt. Mounted and bound. Typed copy follows.
A.L.S. [1] fold.ℓ. 0.

NK 0209818 IaU

Knowles, James Sheridan, 1784-1862

Mason, J A.
A treatise on the climate and meteorology of Madeira; by the late J. A. Mason ... ed. by James Sheridan Knowles. To which are attached a review of the state of agriculture and of the tenure of land; by George Peacock ... and An historical and descriptive account of the island, and guide to visitors; by John Driver ... London, J. Churchill, 1850.

KNOWLES, James Sheridan, *1784-1862*
True unto Death. A Drama in Two Acts. B. [186-]
pp.37. (SPENCER'S Universal Stage, No.35)
11435.5

NK 0209820 MH

Lilly Library PR 4859 .K5 T8 KNOWLES, JAMES SHERIDAN, 1784-1862
True unto death: a drama in two acts. By Sheridan Knowles. London, Adams & Francis [etc.] 1866.
4 p.ℓ., 88 p. front. (port.) 18 cm.
First edition.
"First produced at the Royal Strand Theatre, May 21, 1866."
Bound in green cloth.

NK 0209821 InU NN CSmH MiU NRU

Knowles, James Sheridan, 1784–1862.
...True unto death. A drama in two acts. By J. Sheridan Knowles. Boston: G. M. Baker & Co. [187–?] 37 p. 12°. (Spencer's universal stage. no. 35.)

1. Drama (English). 2. Title. June 30, 1921.
N. Y. P. L.

NK 0209822 NN

VOLUME 300

KNOWLES, J[ames] Sheridan, 1784-1862.
True unto death; a drama in two acts. Boston, W.H.Baker & co., [cop. 1889].

pp.37.
Cover:- Baker's edition of plays.

NK 0209823 MH IU

Knowles, James Sheridan, 1784-1862.
Various dramatic works of James Sheridan Knowles now first collected and privately printed for James McHenry. [Revised and edited by Francis Harvey] London [Printed at the Chiswick press] 1874.
2 v. facsim. 32½cm.
Floriated initials; head and tail-pieces.
"Only twenty-five copies printed."
Bound in green morocco, gold tooled; inside borders; gilt edges.
Contents.-I.Hersilia; a fragment. Fragment of a Spanish play. accination; a dramatic CSt poem. The storm; a dramatic fragment. Leo; or, The gipsy; a fragment. Brian Boroihme; or, The maid of Erin. A masque. The bridal. Alexina.- II.The Duke of London. Fragment of a play (The widow) Fragment of an anonymous play. An unpublished scene from "Caius Gracchus". An unpublished scene from "William Tell". Biographical notice on Professor Marc-Monnier. Guillaume Tell...traduction de Marc-Monnier.
I.Harvey, Francis. 1830-1889, ed. II.Monnier, Marc, 1827-1885, tr. III.Chiswick press, London.

NK 0209825 CSt IU TxHU PBL InU

Lilly Library PR 4859 .K5 V59

KNOWLES, JAMES SHERIDAN, 1784-1862
Virginius: a tragedy, in five acts, by James Sheridan Knowles ... Printed from the acting copy, with remarks ... As now performed at the Theatres Royal, London ... London, J. Cumberland, [n. d.]
70, [2] p. incl. front. 14 cm. (Cumberland's British Theatre, no. 38)

Copy 3 has: "As performed."
Address of publisher varies in the three copies; other variations in title pages.

NK 0209826 InU OrU CtY

Knowles, James Sheridan, 1784-1862
Virginius, a tragedy in five acts. N.Y., French, n.d.
72p. (In French's standard drama. The acting edition, v. 29)

NK 0209827 OClW

Knowles, James Sheridan, 1784-1862.
Virginius; a tragedy in five acts. n.p. [18--]
9-72 p. 12°.
Prompter's copy, interleaved. Ms. notes.
T.-p. wanting. Title taken from another copy.

NK 0209828 NN

KNOWLES, James Sheridan, 1784-1862.
Virginius; a tragedy in five acts. Baltimore: H.Turner, etc., etc., [18-]

24°. pp.(6). [13]-76. Front.
"Turner's dramatic library"
This copy cut for acting.

NK 0209829 MH

Knowles, James Sheridan, 1784-1862.
Virginius: a tragedy in five acts ... [London? 18--]
1 p.l., 9-82 p. 8°.
Prompter's copy. Ms. notes.
Beginning of play missing, supplied by leaf of 24° copy; pages missing at end, play finished in ms.
Title-page missing, except fragment.

NK 0209830 NN

Knowles, James Sheridan, 1784-1862.
...Virginius; a tragedy in five acts, by James Sheridan Knowles... New York: S. French, [18—?]. iv, 5-72 p. 12°. (French's standard drama. no. 25.)

In verse.

1. Drama, English. 2. Title.
N. Y. P. L. December 17, 1926

NK 0209831 NN PU PPL MH

PR 10 J7 C6 1820 V5

Knowles, James Sheridan, 1764-1862.
Virginius: a tragedy, by James Sheridan Knowles. Epilogue by Barry Cornwall. 1820.

Item in the Colbeck Collection; enquire at the Information Desk.

I. Cornwall, Barry, 1787-1874, contributor.

NK 0209832 CaBVaU

Knowles, James Sheridan, 1784-1862
Virginius: a tragedy. In five acts. As performed at the Theatre Royal, Covent Garden. By James Sheridan Knowles ... London, Printed for J. Ridgway, 1820.
85 p. 21 cm.

TxU CaBVaU CtY
NK 0209833 NNCoCi ViU NN MdU MH IU RPB IEN ICU InU

Knowles, James Sheridan, 1784-1862.
Virginius: a tragedy. In five acts. As performed at the Theatre Royal, Covent Garden. By James Sheridan Knowles, esq. 3d ed. London, J. Ridgway, 1820.
85 p. 23½cm.

1. Virginia, daughter of Virginius—Drama. I. Title.
38-21241
Library of Congress PR4859.K5V5 1820
[2] 822.72

NK 0209834 DLC

KNOWLES, James Sheridan, 1784-1862.
Virginius; a tragedy, in five acts. 4th ed. London, printed for J. Ridgway, 1820.

pp.85, (1).

NK 0209835 MH CtY

Knowles, James Sheridan, 1784-1862
Virginius: a tragedy in five acts... N.Y., French, pref. 1820.
72p. (French's standard drama)

NK 0209836 OClW

Knowles, James Sheridan, 1784-1862.
Virginius, a tragedy. In five acts. By James Sheridan Knowles, esq. From the second London edition. New-York: T. Longworth, 1820. 70+ p. 24°.

Imperfect: all after p. 70 wanting.

1. Drama (English). 2. Title.
N. Y. P. L. June 18, 1919.

NK 0209837 NN MH PU CtY IU

Lilly Library PR 4859 .K5 V6 1823a

KNOWLES, JAMES SHERIDAN, 1784-1862
Virginius: a tragedy. In five acts. As performed at the Theatres Royal, Covent Garden and Drury Lane. By James Sheridan Knowles, esq. Sixth edition. London, J. Ridgway, 1823.
4 p.ℓ., [7]-85, [1] p. 21 cm.

In this copy the original leaf of the cast at Covent Garden is present as well as the cancel leaf with the casts of Drury Lane and Covent Garden.

NK 0209838 InU NN NjP

Lilly Library PR 4859 .K5 V6 1824

KNOWLES, JAMES SHERIDAN, 1784-1862
Virginius: a tragedy, in five acts. As performed at the Theatre Royal, Covent Garden. By James Sheridan Knowles. Sixth edition. Glasgow, Reid & Henderson [etc., etc.] 1824.
86 p., 1 ℓ. 21 cm.

NK 0209839 InU CSmH

Knowles, James Sheridan, 1784-1862.
... Virginius, a tragedy, in five acts. By James Sheridan Knowles, esq. Printed under the authority of the managers, from the prompt book. With notes, critical and explanatory. Also an authentic description of the costume, and the general stage business. As performed at the Theatres Royal, London ... London, Printed and pub. by T. Dolby [1824?]
vi, [4], [9]-69, [1] p. front., 2 diagr. 14½cm. (Dolby's British theatre)
[Broadhurst, J. Plays. v. 12, no. 3]
Reissued with different preliminary matter as no. 38 (v. 6, no. 3) in Cumberland's British theatre.
1. Virginia, daughter of Virginius—Drama. I. Title.
21-15045
Library of Congress PR1271.B7 vol. 12
[2]

NK 0209840 DLC InU NNC MH

Knowles, James Sheridan, 1784-1862.
Virginius; a tragedy in five acts... N.Y., London, French [1824?]
72p.

NK 0209841 OCl

Knowles, James Sheridan, 1784-1862.
Virginius; a tragedy in five acts, as performed at the London and Baltimore theatres. Baltimore, J. Robinson [1825]
77 p. 15 cm.
No. 12 in a volume lettered: Plays, II.
L. C. copy imperfect: lower part of t. p. (containing imprint date?) cut away.

1. Virginia, daughter of Virginius—Drama. I. Title.
PR1245.P63 no. 12 54-53823
Library of Congress [3]

NK 0209842 DLC NN

VOLUME 300

Knowles, James Sheridan, 1784-1862.
Virginius. A tragedy, in five acts. From the second London edition. Boston, B. Davenport, 1826.
72 p. nar. 12° bd. in nar. 8°.

NK 0209843 NN MH MB

NCOF p.v.171
Knowles, James Sheridan, 1784–1862.
Virginius: a tragedy, in five acts, by James Sheridan Knowles ... Printed from the acting copy, with remarks... To which are added, a description of the costume, cast of the characters... and the whole of the stage business. As now performed at the theatres royal, London... London, J. Cumberland [1826?]
70, [2] p. front. 15cm.
Prompt-book.

NK 0209844 NN MH NIC InU OCl PU-F IU

Knowles, James Sheridan, 1784-1862
Virginius: a tragedy, in five acts...[and in verse] printed from the acting copy, with remarks, biographical and critical, by D.-G. [i. e., G. Daniel]... As performed at the Theatres Royal, London. [With prologue by J. H. Reynolds, and epilogue by B. Cornwall.] Embellished with a fine engraving, by Mr. White, from a drawing taken at the theatre, by R. Cruikshank. London: G. H. Davidson [1826]. 2 p.l., 7-70 p., 1 l., 1 pl. 24°. (Cumberland's British theatre. v. 6.)
Bound with his: The love-chase; a comedy... London, 1840. 24°.
1. Drama (English). 2. Daniel, George. 3. Reynolds, John Hamilton. 4. Cornwall, Barry, pseud. of B. W. Procter. 5. White, engraver. 6. Cruikshank, R., illustrator. 7. Title.
N. Y. P. L. May 14, 1914.

NK 0209845 NN

Knowles, James Sheridan, 1784-1862.
Virginius, a tragedy in five acts. Baltimore, J. Robinson, 1832.
72 p. 16°.

NK 0209846 NN

KNOWLES, James Sheridan, 1784-1862.
Virginius; a tragedy in five acts. Berlin, E. Behr, 1836.
pp. 79.

NK 0209847 MH

*PR4859 .K5V5 1837
Knowles, James Sheridan, 1784-1862.
... Virginius, a tragedy, in five acts. By J. Sheridan Knowles ... Correctly printed from the most approved acting copy, with a description of the costume, cast of the characters, entrances and exits, relative positions, and the whole of the stage business; to which are added, properties and directions, as now performed in the principal theatres. Embellished with a fine wood engraving. Philadelphia, New-York, Turner & Fisher [1837?]
3 p. l., [13]-76 p. front. 15cm. (Turner's dramatic library)
1. Virginia, daughter of Virginius—Drama. I. Title. II. Series.

NK 0209849 MB MH MnU

*PR4859 .K5V5 1840
Knowles, James Sheridan, 1784-1862.
... Virginius, a tragedy, in five acts. By J. Sheridan Knowles ... Correctly printed from the most approved acting copy, with a description of the costume, cast of the characters, entrances and exits, relative positions, and the whole of the stage business; to which are added, properties and directions, as now performed in the principal theatres. Embellished with a fine wood engraving. Boston, J. Fisher; Philadelphia, NewYork, Turner & Fisher [184-?]
3 p. l., [13]-76 p. front. 15 1/2cm. (Turner's dramatic library [New ser. vol. VIII, no. 52])
1. Virginia, daughter of Virginius—Drama. I. Title. II. Series.

NK 0209851 MB

KNOWLES, JAMES SHERIDAN, 1784-1862.
Virginius; a tragedy in five acts. With the stage business, cast of characters, costumes, relative positions, etc. New York, W. Taylor [184-] 72 p. 18cm. (Modern standard drama. no. 25)
Promptbook, interleaved.
1. Drama, English. 2. Drama--Promptbooks and Typescripts. I. Title

NK 0209852 NN NIC NNC PU MB MH

Knowles, James Sheridan, 1784-1862
Virginius, a tragedy; ed. with notes by C.S. Brown.
(see his Dramatic works. 1841. v.1, p.83-154)

NK 0209853 OrP

Knowles, James Sheridan, 1784-1862
...Virginius. A tragedy, in five acts... New York, French [1842]
72p. D. (French's standard drama, no.XXV)

NK 0209854 IaU CtY

Rare PR 4859 K5V8 1843
Knowles, James Sheridan, 1784-1862.
Virginius: a tragedy in five acts. With the stage business, cast of characters, costumes, relative positions, &c. As performed by Mr. Forrest, Mr. Macready, and other eminent tragedians. New York, M. Douglas [1843?]
72 p. 18cm. (Modern standard drama. Edited by Epes Sargent. No. 25)
Interleaved, with ms. additions; size of leaf: 18 cm.
With autograph: A. W. Fenno.

NK 0209855 NIC PU MH

KNOWLES, James Sheridan, 1784-1862.
Virginius. (SARGENT, Epes. Modern Standard Drama, 1846. etc., 12°. Vol. IV. No. 25).

NK 0209856 MH

Knowles, James Sheridan, 1784-1862.
... Virginius; a tragedy in five acts. By James Sheridan Knowles. With the stage business, cast of characters, costumes, relative positions, &c. as performed by Mr. Forrest, Mr. Macready, and other eminent tragedians. New York and Baltimore, W. Taylor & co.; Boston, Redding and company; [etc., etc.] 1846.
iv, 5-72 p. 19cm. (Modern standard drama, edited by Epes Sargent. [vol. IV] no. XXV)
I. Title.
A 34-2239
Rochester. Univ. Library for Library of Congress PR1243.M68 no. 25 [a39b1]

NK 0209857 NRU WaS MiU NN IU MH DLC PU ViU

34 Knowles, James Sheridan, 1784-1862.
Virginius: a tragedy, in five acts. London, Davidson [1848]?
70 p., 1 l. 18°. [Cumberland (J.) British theatre, v. 6]

NK 0209858 DLC

Knowles, James Sheridan, 1784–1862.
... Virginius; a tragedy in five acts. By James Sheridan Knowles. With the stage business, cast of characters, costumes, relative positions, &c. as performed by Mr. Forrest, Mr. Macready, and other eminent tragedians. New York, J. Douglas, 1848.
iv, 5-72 p. 18cm. (Modern standard drama, edited by Epes Sargent. [vol. IV] no. XXV)

NK 0209859 ViU

Knowles, James Sheridan. 1784-1862.
Virginius. A tragedy in five acts . . . New York. French. [185-?] 72 pp. [French's Standard drama. No. 25.] 19 cm., in 6s.

NK 0209860 MB NIC NBuG MiU

[KNOWLES, James Sheridan] 1784-1862
Virginius. N.Y. [cop. 1860].
pp.72. Port of Edwin. Forrest. (FORREST, Edwin, Edwin, Edition of Shakspearian and other plays, etc.,8).

NK 0209861 MH

An K762 883v Rare Books Col
KNOWLES, JAMES SHERIDAN, 1784-1862.
... Virginius. By James Sheridan Knowles... London: J. Dicks, 313, Strand; and all booksellers. New York: Samuel French & son, 122, Nassau Street-sole agents [1883?] cover title, 23p. 1 illus. 18cm. in envelope in folder 23cm. (Dicks' standard plays. no.246)
Title vignette.
In double columns.
Advertisements: inside front cover, [2]p. at end.
1. Virginia, daughter of Virginius - Drama. I. Title.

NK 0209862 TxU InU

Rare PR 4859 K5V8 1891
Knowles, James Sheridan, 1784-1862.
Virginius: a tragedy in five acts. With the stage business, cast of characters, costumes, relative positions, &c. As performed by Mr. Forrest, Mr. Macready, and other eminent tragedians. New York, London, S. French [1891?]
72 p. 18cm. (French's standard drama. [vol. 4] no. 25)
Prologue written by J. H. Reynolds, Epilogue written by Barry Cornwall.

NK 0209863 NIC IU

VOLUME 300

Knowles, James Sheridan, 1784-1862.
Virginius, a tragedy by James Sheridan Knowles; edited with notes by Calvin S. Brown ... New York, A. S. Barnes and company, 1898.
3 p.l., 3-92 p. 17½cm.
"From the editor's 'Later English drama'."
On cover: The later English drama. Brown.

1. Virginia, daughter of Virginius—Drama. I. Brown, Calvin Smith, 1866- ed. II. Title.

NK 0209864 ViU OCU OrP OCl

PR 4859 K5V5 1914
Knowles, James Sheridan, 1784-1862.
Virginius; a tragedy. Edited with notes by Calvin S. Brown. New York, A. S. Barnes, 1914.
371 p.

Notes taken from the editor's Later English drama.

I. Title.

NK 0209865 PPT OrP

KNOWLES, JAMES SHERIDAN, 1784-1862.
Virginius; a tragedy in five acts as performed at the Theatre Royal, Covent Garden, by James Sheridan Knowles. (In: Moses, M.J., editor. Representative British dramas, Victorian and modern. Boston, 1931. 21½cm. p.9-47.)

614629A. 1. Drama, English. I. Title.

NK 0209866 NN OO OCl OEac

Lilly PR 4859 .K5 W54 1834
KNOWLES, JAMES SHERIDAN, 1784-1862
Das Weib, oder: Thron und Hütte. Drama in fünf Acten. Nach dem Englischen des James Sheridan Knowles für das deutsche Theatre bearbeitet von Wilhelm Gerhard. Leipzig, Baumgärtner's Buchhandlung, 1834.
vi, 114 p. 22 cm.

First German edition.
Bound in cloth-backed boards, with printed paper label on spine.

NK 0209867 InU

919.8 K13a 1926
Kane, Elisha Kent, 1820-1857.
Adrift in the Arctic ice pack, from the history of the first U. S. Grinnell expedition in search of Sir John Franklin, by Elisha Kent Kane, M.D. Ed. by Horace Kephart. New York, Macmillan, 1926 [c1915]
402p. incl.front. (double map) illus. 20cm.
"The following pages comprise chapters XX to XLVI of Dr. Kane's work 'The U. S. Grinnell expedition in search of Sir John Franklin: a personal narrative' (London and New York, 1854) omitting nothing but some scientific observations."--Introd.

NK 0209868 IU

Knowles, James Sheridan, 1784-1862
The wife, a tale of Mantua, a play in five acts. London, Lacy, n.d.
64p. (In French's standard drama. The acting edition, v. 33.)

NK 0209869 OCIW

PR4889 .K5W6 18— Austrian
Knowles, James Sheridan, 1784-1862.
The wife. [n.p. 18--]
102 p. 24 cm.
Caption title; title page wanting.

NK 0209870 ICU

KNOWLES, James Sheridan, 1784-1862.
The wife; a tale of Mantua. [London, T.H. Lacy, 18- .]

pp.64.
On cover:-Lacey's Anglo-American edition of standard , 1.
Two copies are bound together. One is cut for acting.

NK 0209871 MH CLSU IU

PR 4859 .K5 W7 18--
Knowles, James Sheridan, 1784-1862.
... The wife: a tale of Mantua. A play, in five acts, by James Sheridan Knowles. With the stage directions, and corrected as played at the Park theatre [by] J.B.Addis, prompter. New York, S.French & son; London, S.French [18--]
iv, [5]-68 p. 19cm. (French's standard drama. no.V)

NK 0209872 MiU CSt PU IaU MWA

Knowles, James Sheridan, 1784-1862.
. . . The wife; a tale of Mantua. A play in five acts, by James Sheridan Knowles . . . New York: T. H. French[, 18—?] iv, 6-68 p. 12°. (French's standard drama. no. 5.)

1. Drama, English. 2. Title. December 17, 1926
N. Y. P. L.

NK 0209873 NN

KNOWLES, James Sheridan, 1784-1862.
The wife, a tale of Mantua; a play in five acts. [New York, J.Perry, etc., etc., 18-]

pp.64.

On cover:-Lacy's Anglo-American edition of standard plays, 1.
Two copies are bound together , one cut for acting.

NK 0209874 MH

KNOWLES, James Sheridan, 1784-1862.
The wife, or The gather's grave; a tale of Mantua. A play in five acts. Philadelphia, Turner & son, [18-].

pp.69.
At head of title:-Turner's American stage.

NK 0209875 MH

Knowles, James Sheridan, 1784-1862.
The wife; a tale of Mantua. n.p. [1833]
1 p.l., 179-248 p. 16°.
T.-p. wanting.
Prompter's copy, interleaved. Ms. notes.

NK 0209876 NN

Knowles, James Sheridan, 1784-1862.
The wife: a tale of Mantua. A play, in five acts. By James Sheridan Knowles ... London, E. Moxon, 1833.
5 p. l., 120 p. 20½cm.
Epilogue, by Charles Lamb.

I. Title. 15-16672

Library of Congress PR4859.K5W5

NK 0209877 DLC InU CtY PU-F WU NjP NN

KNOWLES, JAMES SHERIDAN, 1784-1862.
The wife: a tale of Mantua. A play in five acts. By James Sheridan Knowles. London, E. Moxon, 1833.
5 p.l., 120 p. 8°.

Promptbook.
Interleaved, with ms. notes.

1.Drama, English. 2. Drama--Promptbooks and typescripts. i. Subs for NCO p.v.393

NK 0209878 NN

Lilly Library PR 4859 .K5 W5 1833
KNOWLES, JAMES SHERIDAN, 1784-1862
The wife: a tale of Mantua. A play, in five acts. By James Sheridan Knowles ... Second edition. London, E. Moxon, 1833.
5 p.l., 120 p. 21 cm.

NK 0209879 InU OU PU-F MH

TS 2740 172
Knowles, James Sheridan, 1784-1862.
The wife: a tale of Mantua. A play, in five acts. By James Sheridan Knowles ... Second edition.
London:Edward Moxon, Dover street.1833.
5p.l.,120p. 21cm.
Prompt copy, interleaved, with ms. directions throughout, and ms. cast of characters including Nantz.
Inscribed: To Frederick Coleman Nantz. Thomas B. Shaw. 1837.

NK 0209880 MH

Lilly Library PR 4859 .K5 W5 1833a
KNOWLES, JAMES SHERIDAN, 1784-1862
The wife: a tale of Mantua. A play, in five acts. By James Sheridan Knowles ... Third edition. London, E. Moxon, 1833.
5 p.l., 120 p. 21 cm.

NK 0209881 InU PU

Lilly PR 4084 .L 3
KNOWLES, JAMES SHERIDAN, 1784-1862
The wife: a tale of Mantua. A play, in five acts. By James Sheridan Knowles ... Fourth edition. London, E. Moxon, 1833.
5 p.l., 120 p. 21 cm.

Bound with The Lady of Lyons, by B. Disraeli. London, 1839.

NK 0209882 InU CU MH

Lilly Library PR 4859 .K5 W5 1833c
KNOWLES, JAMES SHERIDAN, 1784-1862
The wife: a tale of Mantua. A play, in five acts. By James Sheridan Knowles ... Fifth edition. London, E. Moxon, 1833.
5 p.l., 120 p. 19 cm.

NK 0209883 InU MH

VOLUME 300

Lilly Library PR 4859 .K5 W5 1833d KNOWLES, JAMES SHERIDAN, 1784-1862
The wife: a tale of Mantua. A play, in five acts. By James Sheridan Knowles ... Sixth edition. London, E. Moxon, 1833.
5 p.ℓ., 120 p. 22 cm.

One leaf publisher's advts. precedes title page.
Bound in quarter red morocco; uncut.

NK 0209884 InU IU NcU MnU NjP MH

---

822 K76h 1848 Knowles, James Sheridan, 1784-1862.
The wife, a tale of Mantua. A play in five acts. New York, E. B. Clayton ₍1833?₎
72p. 15cm.

Bound with the author's The hunchback. New York, 1848.

NK 0209885 IU MH

Knowles, James Sheridan, 1784-1862.
The wife: a tale of Mantua. A play in five acts. New York, E.B. Clayton [pref. 1833]
vi, 7-72 p. nar. 24°. (Clayton's edition)
Prompter's copy, marginal notes.

NK 0209886 NN

PR4889 .K5W6 1833 Knowles, James Sheridan, 1784-1862.
The wife: a tale of Mantua. A play, in five acts ... Philadelphia, Carey, Lea & Blanchard, 1833.
144 p.

NK 0209887 ICU

Lilly Library PR 4859 .K5 W5 1836 KNOWLES, JAMES SHERIDAN, 1784-1862
The wife: a tale of Mantua. A play, in five acts. By James Sheridan Knowles ... Seventh edition. London, E. Moxon, 1836.
4 p.ℓ., 72 p. 20.5 cm.

NK 0209888 InU NN MH IaU TxU PU CtY WaU MoU

KNOWLES, James Sheridan, 1784-1862.
The wife; a tale of Mantua; A play in five acts. nNew York, M. Douglas, [184-?]

pp.60.
At head of title:-Modern standard drama, Edited by Epes Sargent, 5.

Imperfect:- lacks are after p.60.

NK 0209889 MH

KNOWLES, James Sheridan, 1784-1862.
The wife; a tale of Mantua; A play in five acts. New York, T.H. French, etc., etc., [184-?]

pp.68.
At head of title:-French's standard drama, 5.
This copy is cut for acting.

NK 0209890 MH CSmH

Knowles, James Sheridan, 1784-1862.
The wife; a tale of Mantua. A play in five acts. New-York, W.Taylor & co. [184-?]

68 p. 19 cm.
At head of title:- Modern standard drama. Edited by Epes Sargent, 5.

NK 0209891 MH CSt NN RPB PSt CtHT-W

₍Knowles, James Sheridan₎ 1784-1862.
The wife: a tale of Mantua. ₍n.p., 1842?₎

₍307₎-395 p. 15cm. ₍A Collection of plays. v. 6, no. 5₎

Caption title.

NK 0209892 MnU

Knowles, James Sheridan, 1784-1862.
The wife: a tale of Mantua. A play, in five acts.
New York. Taylor. 1845. 68 pp. [Modern standard drama. No. 5.] 12°.

NK 0209893 MB

Knowles, James Sheridan, 1784-1862.
... The wife: a tale of Mantua; a play in five acts. By James Sheridan Knowles. With the stage directions marked and corrected as played at the Park theatre, by J. B. Addis, prompter. New York, W. Taylor; Baltimore and Washington, D. C., Taylor, Wilde, & co., 1846.
1 p. l., ₍5₎-68 p. 19ᶜᵐ. (Modern standard drama, edited by Epes Sargent. ₍vol. I₎ no. v)

I. Title.

A 34—2221

Rochester. Univ. Library for Library of Congress PR1243.M68 no. 5 ₍a40b1₎

NK 0209894 NRU NcD IU OCl MH

Knowles, James Sheridan, 1784-1862.
The wife; a tale of Mantua. A play in five acts. By James Sheridan Knowles...marked and corrected as played at the Park Theatre, by J.B. Addis, prompter. New York: J. Douglas, 1847.
iv p., 1 l., (1)6-68 p. 12°. (Modern standard drama. no. 5.)

In verse.
In: NCO p. v. 394, no. 5.

1. Drama (English). 2. Title. 3. Series.
N. Y. P. L. November 29, 1915.

NK 0209895 NN MH PPL

Knowles, James Sheridan, 1784-1862.
The wife; or, The father's grave: a tale of Mantua: a play in five acts. By James Sheridan Knowles. ₍n. p., 185-?₎ 69 p. 15cm.

Prompt-book of Wm. J. Le Moyne and J. R. Pitman. Interleaved, with ms. notes, ground plans etc.
With cast of characters.
Imperfect: t.-p. missing; title from label on cover.

1. Drama, English. 2. Prompt-books.
N. Y. P. L. December 27, 1944

NK 0209896 NN

Knowles, James Sheridan, 1784-1862.
... The wife: a tale of Mantua; a play in five acts. By James Sheridan Knowles. With the stage directions marked and corrected as played at the Park theatre, by J. B. Addis, prompter. New York, W. Taylor; & co., ₍185-?₎

iv, ₍5₎-68 p. 18ᶜᵐ. (Modern standard drama, edited by Epes Sargent. ₍vol. I₎ no. v)

NK 0209897 ViU

[Knowles, James Sheridan] 1784-1862.
The wife: a tale of Mantua. [Drama]
[London, 186-?]
68 p. 12°.
T.-p. missing.
Prompter's copy, interleaved with Ms. notes.

NK 0209898 NN

PR 1245 N53+ v.3 Knowles, James Sheridan, 1784-1862.
The wife: a tale of Mantus. A play, in five acts.

(In The New York drama. New York c1877. 26cm. v. 3. p. 193-213)

NK 0209899 NIC

An K762 883w Rare Books Col KNOWLES, JAMES SHERIDAN, 1784-1862.
... The wife. By James S. Knowles ... London: J. Dicks, 313, Strand; and all booksellers [1883?] cover title, 22p. 1 illus. 18cm. in envelope in folder 23cm. (Dicks' standard plays. no.288)
Title vignette.
In double columns.
Advertisements: inside front cover, [2]p. at end.

I. Title.

NK 0209900 TxU InU

---

822 K76w 189- Knowles, James Sheridan, 1784-1862.
... The wife: a tale of Mantua. A play, in five acts ... With the stage directions, and corrected as played at the Park theatre ... New York, S. French; [etc., etc., 189-?]
68p. (French's standard drama. no.V)

NK 0209901 IU MB MH

Rare PR 4859 K5 W6 1891 Knowles, James Sheridan, 1784-1862.
The Wife, a tale of Mantua. A play in five acts. With the stage directions, and corrected as played at the Park Theatre, J. B. Addis, prompter. New York, T. H. French; London, S. French ₍1891?₎
68 p. 19cm. (French's standard drama. no. 5)

With autograph: Wm. Kittredge.
Ms. copies of the parts of Antonio and Lorenzo la id in.

NK 0209902 NIC

Knowles, James Sheridan, 1784-1862, supposed author.
The wife, or women as they are; a domestic drama. London, 1835.
see under title

Lilly Library PR 4859 .K5 W59 KNOWLES, JAMES SHERIDAN, 1784-1862
William Tell: a play, in five acts, by James Sheridan Knowles ... Printed from the acting copy, with remarks ... As now performed at the Theatres Royal, London ... London, J. Cumberland₍n. d.₎
86 p. incl. front. 14.5 cm. (Cumberland's British Theatre, no. 154)
Issue with "Camden New Town" in imprint.

NK 0209904 InU MH

VOLUME 300

Knowles, James Sheridan, 1784–1862.
William Tell: a play, in five acts, by James Sheridan Knowles ... Printed from the acting copy, with remarks, biographical and critical, by D.—G. ... As performed at the Theatres Royal ... London, Davidson [n. d.]
85, [1] p. incl. front. 15cm. (Cumberland's British theatre. London, ca. 1825–55. v. 22 [no. 7])
Remarks by George Daniel, editor of the series.
Without the music (by Bishop, adapted from Rossini)
Reissue of Cumberland's earlier edition.
1. Tell, Wilhelm—Drama. I. Bishop, Sir Henry Rowley, 1786–1855. II. Title.
Library of Congress PR1243.C8 vol. 22 21-14532

NK 0209905 DLC OCl CtY

TS 2741.51
Knowles, James Sheridan, 1784-1862
William Tell. [2d ed. Glasgow? 18'
91 p.
Caption title
Dedication dated 1825

NK 0209906 MH

[Knowles, James Sheridan] 1784-1862.
[William Tell: a play in five acts] [London? 18--]
1 p.l., 95-196 p. 16°.
Title-page missing.
Prompter's copy. Ms. copy.

NK 0209907 NN

Knowles, James Sheridan, 1784-1862.
William Tell: a play ... London, Music Publishing Co. [18--]
1 p.l., 5-86 p. 1 pl. nar. 24° bd. as 4°.
Prompter's copy: interleaved with Ms. notes

NK 0209908 NN

KNOWLES, James Sheridan, 1784-1862.
William Tell; a play, in five acts. Philadelphia, Weikel and Bunn, etc., [18-?]
24°. pp. 88.

NK 0209909 MH

[Knowles, James Sheridan,] 1784–1862.
William Tell. [New York? 182–?] 89 p. 24°.
Caption-title.
An historical play in 5 acts.
Imperfect: title-page, p. 3-4 and p. 89 wanting.
1. Drama (English). 2. Title.
N. Y. P. L. June 16, 1919.

NK 0209910 NN

Knowles, James Sheridan, 1784-1862.
William Tell; a play in five acts. Campe's ed. Nurnberg, Campe [182- ?]
88 p.

NK 0209911 MH

Knowles, James Sheridan, 1784–1862.
William Tell: a play, in five acts. By James Sheridar Knowles, esq. First performed at the Theatre royal Drury lane, May 11, 1825. London, T. Dolby [1825?]
2 p. l., 83 p. 21½cm.
Illustration of act 3, scene 3, inserted.
1. Tell, Wilhelm. I. Title. 15-16673
Library of Congress PR4859.K5W55

NK 0209912 DLC InU CoU WU NN CtY CSmH MB

In
K763
1
Knowles, James Sheridan, 1784-1862.
William Tell; a play in five acts, as performed at the London and New York theatres. New York, E.M. Murden, 1825.
87 p. 16 cm.

NK 0209913 CtY MH

822
K76w
1833
Knowles, James Sheridan, 1784-1862.
William Tell: a play, in five acts. First performed at the Theatre Royal, Drury Lane, May 11, 1825. 2d.ed. London, J. Cumberland, 1826.
91p. 22cm.
Bound with the author's The wife. London, 1833.

NK 0209914 IU InU

Knowles, James Sheridan, 1784-1862.
William Tell: a play, in five acts...[and in verse] printed from the acting copy, with remarks, biographical and critical, by D.-G. [i. e., G. Daniel]...as performed at the Theatres Royal, London. Embellished with a fine engraving, by Mr. Bonner, from a drawing taken in the theatre, by R. Cruikshank. London: G. H. Davidson [1828]. 1 p.l., (1)6-86 p., 1 pl. 24°. (Cumberland's British theatre. v. 22.)
Bound with his: The Love-chase; a comedy... London, 1840. 24°.
1. Drama (English). 2. Daniel, George. 3. Bonner, George William, engraver. 4. Cruikshank, Robert, illustrator. 5. Title.
N. Y. P. L. May 18, 1914.

NK 0209915 NN CSt

KNOWLES, James Sheridan, 1784-1862.
William Tell; a play, in five acts. Philadelphia, C. Neal, 1828.
24°. pp. 89.
This copy is cut for acting.

NK 0209916 MH CSmH

Knowles, James Sheridan, 1784-1862.
William Tell; a play, in five acts, by James Sheridan Knowles... Printed from the acting copy, with remarks, biographical & critical... London, J. Cumberland [1829]
86p. (In Cumberland's British theatre, v.22)

NK 0209917 MiU InU OCU OO

Knowles, James Sheridan, 1784-1862.
...William Tell; a play, in five acts. By James Sheridan Knowles...Printed from the acting copy, (Cumberland's edition,) with remarks, biographical and critical, by D-G. To which are added, a description of the costume, -cast of the characters -entrances and exits -relative positions of the performers on the stage -and the whole stage business, as now performed at the London, New-York, & Philadelphia theatres. New-York: Owen Phelan, [183-]
85,[1] pl 14 cm.
Bound with: Buc stone, John. Luke the laborer... Baltimore, 1838.
1. Drama. I.Title 2.Tell, William. II. Bishop, Sir Henry Rowley, 1786-1855 III. Daniel, George, 1789-1864.

NK 0209918 MiU-C CtY NN

Rare
PR
4859
K5
W7
1830
Knowles, James Sheridan, 1784-1862.
William Tell: a play in five acts. Printed from the acting copy, with remarks, biographical and critical, by D.-G. ... As performed at the Theatres Royal, London... Engraving by Mr. Bonner. London, J. Cumberland [1830?]
86 p. 16cm. [Cumberland's British theatre. v. 22, no. 7]
Interleaved, with ms. additions; size of leaf 19cm.
With autograph: J. Moore

NK 0209919 NIC

RA822.7
K73w
1835
Knowles, James Sheridan, 1784-1826.
William Tell: a play, in five acts, by James Sheridan Knowles ... Embellished with a fine engraving, by Mr. Bonner, from a drawing taken in the theatre, by Mr. R. Cruikshank. London: John Cumberland [1835?]
86p.front.14cm.
I. Cruikshank, Isaac Robert, 1789-1856, illus. (RA cat only) II. Title.
mr

NK 0209920 OC

Knowles, James Sheridan, 1784–1862.
...William Tell. A play in three acts. By James Sheridan Knowles... with the stage business, cast of characters, costumes, relative positions, &c. New York: S. French & Son[, 184–?]. v, 8–50 p. 12°. (French's standard drama. no. 39.)
1. Drama, English. 2. Title.
N. Y. P. L. May 13, 1925

NK 0209921 NN MB MWA DFo OCl MH

Knowles, James Sheridan, 1784–1862.
... William Tell; a play in three acts. By James Sheridan Knowles. As acted by Mr. Forrest, with the stage business, cast of characters, costumes, relative positions, &c. New York and Baltimore, W. Taylor & co.; Boston, Redding and co.; [etc., etc., 1846?]
v, [1], [7]–50 p. 19cm. (Modern standard drama, edited by Epes Sargent. [vol. v] no. xxxix)
A re-arranged version in three acts with the "under-plot" entierly omitted. *cf.* Editorial introd.
I. Title.
A 34—2253
Richester. Univ. Library for Library of Congress PR1243.M68 no. 39 [a40b1]

NK 0209922 NRU NN MH IU ViU

KNOWLES, James Sheridan, 1784-1862.
William Tell; a play in three acts. As acted by Mr. Forrest. New York, J. Douglas, 1848.
pp. 50.
"Modern standard drama, 39."
Lacks paper cover.

NK 0209923 MH MB NIC

VOLUME 300

822
K76w
1833
Knowles, James Sheridan, 1784-1862.
William Tell. An historical play, in three acts. As arr. by Thomas Hailes Lacy. London, T. H. Lacy [1850?]
51p. 20cm.

Bound with the author's The wife. London, 1833.
"First performed at the Theatre Royal Drury Lane ... May 11, 1825."

NK 0209924 IU CtY

Knowles, James Sheridan, 1784-1862.
William Tell; a play in three acts, as acted by Mr.Forrest. New-York, W.Taylor & co. [186-?]
50 p. 19 cm.
"Modern standard drama, 39."

NK 0209925 MH

Knowles, James Sheridan, 1784-1862
...William Tell. A play in three acts... New York, French [1876?]
50p. D. (French's standard drama. no.XXXIX)

NK 0209926 IaU

An
K762
883w2
Rare
Books
Col
KNOWLES, JAMES SHERIDAN, 1784-1862.
... William Tell. By Sheridan Knowles ... London: J. Dicks, 313, Strand; and all booksellers. New York: Samuel French & son, 122, Nassau Street-sole agents [1883?] cover title, 29p. 1 illus. 18cm. in envelope in folder 23cm. (Dicks' standard plays. no.238)
Title vignette.
In double columns.
Without the music (by Bishop, adapted from Rossini)
Advertisements: inside front cover, [2]p. at end.

NK 0209927 TxU IU

Lilly
Library
PR 4859
.K5 W69
KNOWLES,JAMES SHERIDAN,1784-1862
Woman's wit, or, Love's disguises. A play, in five acts. By James Sheridan. Knowles. [London,J. Dicks,n. d.]
26 p . 1 illus. 18.5 cm. (Dicks' Standard plays, no. 302)

Copy 1 in blue; copy 2 in pink printed paper wrappers.

NK 0209928 InU

Knowles, James Sheridan, 1784-1862.
Woman's wit; or, Love's disguises. A play, in five acts. By James Sheridan Knowles ... Boston, H. P. Nichols & co. [1838]
63 p. $21\frac{1}{2}$cm.

1. Title. 1-22792

Library of Congress PR4859.K5A78

NK 0209929 DLC NN

Lilly
Library
PR 4859
.K5 W7
KNOWLES,JAMES SHERIDAN,1784-1862
Woman's wit; or, Love's disguises. A play, in five acts. By James Sheridan Knowles ... London, E. Moxon, 1838.
4 p.ℓ., 120 p. 21.5 cm.

First edition.
Copy 1 in half purple morocco; copy 2 in drab paper wrappers, uncut; copy 3, in quarter red morocco, is author's inscribed presentation copy.

ViU IU
NK 0209930 InU NNC TxU CSmH CtY MH IaU MnU OU WU

KNOWLES, James Sheridan, 1784-1862.
Woman's wit, or Love's disguises; a play, in five acts. New York, J.& H. G. Langley, etc., etc., 1838.

pp.124.
Two copies are boundtogether,one cut for acting.

NK 0209931 MH ICU CSmH

KNOWLES, James Sheridan, 1784-1862.
Woman's wit, or Love's disguises; a play, in five acts. Philadelphia, etc., Turner & Fisher, [dedication, 1838]

24°. pp.82. Front.
At head of title:Turner's dramatic library)
"1st American from the 1st London ed."
Two copies are bound together. One is cut for acting.

NK 0209932 MH CSmH NN PKsL

Lilly
Library
PR 4859
.K5 D31
KNOWLES, JAMES SHERIDAN, 1784-1862
The wrecker's daughter. A play, in five acts. By James Sheridan Knowles. [London, J. Dicks, n. d.]
22 p. 1 illus. 18.5 cm. (Dicks' Standard plays, no. 313)

In yellow printed paper wrappers.

NK 0209933 InU

Knowles, James Sheridan, 1784-1862.
...The wrecker's daughter. A play, in five acts. By James Sheridan Knowles... Embellished with a beautiful engraving. Philadelphia: F. Turner [etc., etc., 183-?] 63 p. front. 14½cm. (Turner's dramatic library.)

1. Drama, English. I. Title.
N. Y. P. L. March 3 1941

NK 0209934 NN MH CtY

KNOWLES, James Sheridan, 1784-1862.
The wrecker's daughter; a play, in five acts. 2d ed. Philadelphia, etc., Turner & Fisher, [183-]

24°. pp. 71. Front.
Turner's dramatic library.
Cover: Turner's dramatic library of acting plays, vol. iv, no.26. New York, Turner's Fisher.

NK 0209935 MH

KNOWLES, James Sheridan, 1784-1862.
The wrecker's daugher; a play.
Philadelphia, F. Turner, etc., etc., [1836]

pp.63+. Front.

Cover:-Turner's dramatic library of acting plays, vol iv. no. 26.

NK 0209936 MH

Lilly
Library
PR 4859
.K5 D32
1837
KNOWLES,JAMES SHERIDAN,1784-1862
The wrecker's daughter. A play in five acts. By James Sheridan Knowles ... New-York, P. Menard, 1837.
62 p. 14.5 cm.

First American edition.
An adaptation of his The daughter.
Bound in quarter red morocco.

I. Knowles,James Sheridan,1784-1862--The daughter.

NK 0209937 InU MB MH OC

TF
238
.C4
K73
Knowles,Sir James Thomas,1831-1908,comp.
The Channel Tunnel and public opinion. London, K.Paul,Trench, 1883.
viii,136 p. 25 cm.

1.Tunnels--English Channel. I.Title.

NK 0209938 MiU

Knowles, *Sir* James Thomas, 1831-1908, *comp.*
King Arthur and his knights, compiled and arranged by Sir James Knowles ... (J. T. K.) with illustrations by Louis Rhead ... New York and London, Harper & brothers [°1923]
xiv p., 1 l., 383 p. incl. illus., plates. col. front. 23½cm.
"New and ninth edition."
"Merely a word-for-word reprint of my early effort to popularise the Arthur legends. It is little else than an abridgment of Sir Thomas Malory's version ... with a few additions from Geoffrey of Monmouth and other sources—and an endeavour to arrange the many tales into a more or less consecutive story."—Pref.
1. Arthur, King. I. Malory, Sir Thomas, 15th cent. Le morte d'Arthur. II. Rhead, Louis. 1857-1926, illus. III. Title.
24—2022
Library of Congress PN685.K5 1923

NK 0209939 DLC McU MB OrP Or PWcS NN PPPH-I MH

K[nowles] J[ames] T[homas] 1831-1908.
The legends of King Arthur and his Knights of the Round Table. Compiled and arranged by J.T.K. London, Strahan and Co., 1868.
xvi, 234 p. 16°.

NK 0209940 NN

Knowles, James Thomas. 1831-1908.
Legends of King Arthur and his Knights of the Round table. [3 ed. *Anon.*] London, 1868. 16°.
1218

NK 0209941 MdBP MA

PN685
K5
1869
Knowles, Sir James Thomas, 1831-1908, comp.
The legends of King Arthur and his knights of the Round table; comp. and arranged by James Knowles (J. T. K.) [4th ed.] London, Strahan, 1869.
xvi, 234 p.

1. Arthur, King. I. Malory, Sir Thomas, 15th cent/Le morte d'Arthur. II. Title.

NK 0209942 CU

VOLUME 300

KNOWLES, James Thomas, 1831-1908.
The legends of King Arthur and his knights of the Round Table. Lond. Routledge. 1880. Illus. Sm. 8°.

NK 0209943 MB

Knowles, James Thomas, 1831-1908.
The legends of King Arthur and his Knights of the Round Table. London. Warne & Co. 1895. 8°.

Δ1026 — T.r. — Arthur, King.

NK 0209944 MB

Knowles, Sir James Thomas, 1831-1908, *comp.*
The legends of King Arthur and his knights; comp. and arranged by James Knowles (J. T. K.) ... 8th ed. London and New York, Warne and co., 1895.
xi, 308 p. 20½cm.
First published 1862 under the initials "J. T. K."
"Merely a word-for-word reprint of my early effort to popularise the Arthur legends. It is little else than an abridgment of Sir Thomas Malory's version ... with a few additions from Geoffrey of Monmouth and other sources—and an endeavour to arrange the many tales into a more or less consecutive story."—Pref.
1. Arthur, King. I. Malory, Sir Thomas, 15th cent. Le morte d'Arthur. II. Title.
14-20085
Library of Congress PN685.K5

NK 0209945 DLC MB GU OCl PPL NN OCl FTaSU FMU MsSM

Knowles, Sir James, Thomas, 1831-1908.
The legends of King Arthur and his knights. Compiled and arranged by Sir James Knowles ... Illustrated by Lancelot Speed. [9th ed.] London and New York, F. Warne and co. [1912]
xx, 308 p. col. front., plates (part col.) 22cm.

1. Arthur, King. I. Title.
A 14-187
Title from New Haven Libr. Printed by L. C

NK 0209946 CtNhN NBuC IdU MdBP PP MB

---

ar W 18133
Knowles, Sir James, Thomas, 1831-1908.
The legends of King Arthur and his knights. Illustrated by Lancelot Speed. [10th ed.] London and New York, F. Warne [1921]
xv, 308 p. illus. 21cm.

1. Arthur, King.

NK 0209947 NIC

Knowles, Sir James Thomas, 1831-1908.
The legends of King Arthur and his knights. Compiled and arranged by Sir James Knowles... 12th ed. London, and N.Y., F. Warne and co., c1930.
308p. (The Chandos classics)

NK 0209948 OO

Knowles, Sir James Thomas, 1831-1908, ed.

The Nineteenth century and after, a monthly review ... v. 1- Mar. 1877- London. H. S. King & co. [etc.] 1877-[19

LIBS-J PN 685 .K5 1866
Knowles, Sir James Thomas, 1831-1908, comp.
The story of King Arthur and his knights of the round table. Compiled and arranged by J. T. K. 2. ed., rev. London, F. Warne, 1866.
260 p. illus.

Abridged from Sir Thomas Malory's Morte d'Athur with a few additions

from Geoffrey of Monmouth and other sources.

#Arthur, King.
(A) Malory, Sir Thomas, 15th cent. Le morte d'Arthur.

(A) The story of King Arthur and his knights of the round table.

NK 0209952 MoU

Knowles (Jerome, Jr.) and Associates, *Northeast Harbor, Me.*
Residential cost manual: basic house approach. Northeast Harbor, Me. [1954]
unpaged. illus. 29 cm.

1. Building—Estimates. 2. Dwellings. 3. Real property—Valuation. I. Title.
TH435.K5 692.5 54-25930 ‡

NK 0209953 DLC MB NN

Knowles, John.
The little tin god, a comedy in three acts. London, S. French [1947]
111 p. 19 cm. (French's acting edition, no. 282)

I. Title.
PR6021.N48L5 822.91 49-25213*

NK 0209954 DLC

KNOWLES, JOHN.
Social credit and Christian ideals, by the Reverend John Knowles... London [Printed by G.Stevens & Co., 1935]
77 p. 18½cm. (Vedette series.)

Advertising matter, p. 73-77.

872242A. 1. Credit, Social. 2. Sociology, Christian.

NK 0209955 NN CaBViP

BR83 .733
Knowles, John, of London.
Correspondence between Mr. John Knowles and the Charity Commissioners, regarding the Grammar School at Giggleswick. [London, Bradbury and Evans, Printers, 1863]
16 p. 21 cm.

I. Gt. Brit. Board of Charity commissioners. II. Title.

NK 0209956 MB

Knowles, John, schoolmaster, ed.

PE1146 .A73 1826
Ashton, of Liverpool.
The new expositor, containing tables of words from one to seven syllables, inclusive, accented and divided according to the most approved method of pronunciation, to which are added, tables of synonymous words, vulgar anglicisms, corrected, remarkable events, discoveries, and inventions, chronologically arranged, names of men of learning and genius, geographical, arithmetical, and other useful tables, originally compiled by Ashton and Clegg. Rev., corr. and improved, by J. Knowles. 39th ed., newly stereotyped and considerably enl. London, Printed for G. Cowie, 1826.

---

*EC65 K7625 668a
Knowles, John, fl.1646-1668.
An answer to Mr. Ferguson's book, intituled, Justification onely upon a satisfaction. Wherein he is friendly reprov'd, fully silenc'd, and clearly instructed. Whereunto is added, a compendium, or brief discourse concerning the ends & intents of Christ's death and passion, consider'd as a ransom. By John Knowls ...
[London] Printed for J.J.and sold by P.P. and W.C.[1668?]
224p. 15.5cm.
Pages 119,122 misnumbered 115,118.
"Errata": p.224.

NK 0209958 MH NNUT-Mc

Knowles, John, fl.1646-1668.

A modest plea for private mens preaching. Or An answer to a booke intituled, Private men no pulpit-men; composed by Master Giles Workman ... London, Printed in the yeare 1648.
36 p. 19cm.

NK 0209959 CLU-C

623.9 K73
Knowles,John,1781-1841.
An appendix,containing the principles & practice of constructing ships,as invented & introduced by Sir Robert Seppings...By John Knowles...[London, W.Clowes, 1882]
2 p.ℓ.,62 p. plans (1 double,fold.), fold.tables. 28½ x 21½ cm.

NK 0209960 MiU

VM 158 K73 1822
Knowles, John, 1781-1841.
The elements and practice of naval architecture; or, A treatise on ship-building, theoretical and practical, on the best principles established in Great Britain... 3d ed., with an appendix, containing th principles ... introduced by Sir Robert Seppings. By John Knowles. London, W. Simpkin and R. Marshall, 1822.
2 p. l., [iii]-xvi, 438 p., 1 l., 27 (i. e. 28), [1], lviii double p., lix-lxxv, [1] p., 2 l., 62 p. front., 15 pl. (part fold.) tab. 29 c
1. Ship- building. 2. Naval architecture. I. Seppings, Sir Robert, 1767-18

NK 0209961 DSI PPF DN DP NN

---

*EC8 K7625 821i
Knowles, John, 1781-1841.
An inquiry into the means which have been taken to preserve the British navy, from the earliest period to the present time, particularly from that species of decay, now denominated dry-rot. By John Knowles ...
London:Printed and sold by Winchester and Varnham,61,Strand.1821.
xv,[1],viii,164p. 26cm.,in case 27cm.
Full straight-grained blue morocco, with broad gilt border of acorns on covers; blue

watered silk doublures & fly-leaves; gilt edges; lettered in gilt on front cover "To His Imperial Majesty Alexander, emperor of all the Russias, and king of Poland. This work is humbly, and respectfully, presented by the author"; in cloth case.
Imperfect: p.[i-ii] (half-title) wanting.

NK 0209963 MH MdBP NN DN PPF PPL MH-A

Knowles, John, 1781-1841, ed.

Fuseli, Henry, 1741-1825.
Lectures on painting, delivered at the Royal academy, by Henry Fuseli ... London, H. Colburn and R. Bentley, 1830.

VOLUME 300

Knowles, John, 1781-1841.
The life and writings of Henry Fuseli ...
see under Fuseli, Henry, 1741-1825.

Knowles, John, 1781-1841.
—— Recherches sur les moyens employés dans la marine anglaise pour la conservation des bois et des vaisseaux, depuis les temps les plus reculés jusqu' à ce jour, et particulièrement pour les garantir de la maladie connue sous le nom de pourriture sèche. Traduit par ordre de s. exc. le ministre de la marine. Paris. 1825. 8°. pp. xvi, 146+.

NK 0209966 MH-A

Knowles, John Alder, 1881-
Essays in the history of the York school of glass-painting, by John A. Knowles, F. S. A.; illustrated with sketches and photographs by the author. London, Society for promoting Christian knowledge; New York, The Macmillan company, 1936.
xv, 268 p. illus., LXIII pl. (part col.; incl. front., facsims.) 25 x 18½ cm.

1. Glass painting and staining—York, Eng. I. Title: York school of glass-painting.

37-13397

Library of Congress NK5344.Y6K6
[3] 748

NK 0209967 DLC ViU PSt WaU CLU N CU KU NcU WU OCl OClMA CSmH NCorniC NN

Knowles, John Alder, 1881-
Henry Gyles, glass-painter of York, by John A. Knowles. [Oxford, Eng.: Walpole Soc., 1923.] [47-]72 p. illus., plates, port. 4°.
Caption-title.
Repr.: Walpole Soc., London. The eleventh volume of the Walpole Soc. 1923.

1. Gyles, Henry, 1640?-1709. 2. Glass, Stained and painted.
N. Y. P. L. May 25, 1926

NK 0209968 NN NIC MB

TP845
G54
Knowles, John Alder, 1881-
Mediaeval processes of glass manufacture.
(In: Glass, v. 4, no. 7,8,9, July, Aug., Sept. 1927. illus. 28 cm. p. 303-9; 343-5, 349, 359; 391, 395-399)

9369. 1. Manufacture of glass--Hist. I. Title.

NK 0209969 NCorniC

N
12
W21++
v.17
Knowles, John Alder, 1881-
William Peckitt, glass-painter.
(In Walpole Society, London. The volume of the Walpole Society. London. 32cm. v. 17 (1929) p. [45]-59. [7] plates)

1. Peckitt, William, 1731-1795.
2. Glass painting and staining--England.

NK 0209970 NIC

NK5344
.Y6K7
KNOWLES, JOHN ALDER, 1881-
...The York glass-painters [London, n.pub. 1927], 16p. (York minster historical tracts, no.21)

Cover-title.

NK 0209971 InU

Knowles, John Courtland.
The problem of the Far East.
[7] p. 27 cm.
Typewritten mss.
Commencement oration, 1907.

NK 0209972 RPB

Knowles, John Halliley.
The vikings' farewell; chorus for men's voices words by A.R. Loftus-Tottenham. Vocal score. New York, G. Schirmer, n.d.
20 p. (G. Schirmer's collection of oratorios and cantatas)
Pl. no. 15114.
Piano accompaniment. TTBB.

NK 0209973 OCl

BV85
K55
Knowles, John Harris, 1832-1908
A day-book for Lent; being scripture, thought, prayer and promise, from Ash Wednesday to Easter, a daily help for busy people, by Canon Knowles ... New York, James Pott & company, 1898 [c1893]
58 p. 17.8 cm.

1. Lent. I. Title

NK 0209974 CSmH

Knowles, John Harris, 1832-1908
A flight in spring, in the car Lucania from New York to the Pacific coast and back, during April and May, 1898, as told by the Rev. J. Harris Knowles. New York [J. J. Little & co.] 1898.
x, 204 p. front. (port.) 19½ cm.
Seven hundred and fifty copies privately printed for Frederick Humphreys, M. D. No. 750.

1. U. S.—Descr. & trav.

98—1406

Library of Congress E168.K73
[a44b1]

NK 0209975 DLC OrU ICN MiU

Knowles, John Harris, 1832-1908.
From summer land to summer; a journey from Thomasville, Georgia, to New York, during April and May, 1899 ... with illustrations from photographs by ... F. L. Humphreys and ... L. Schumacher. New York [J. J. Little & co.] 1899.
x, 186 p. illus. 12°

Subject entries: Southern states—Descr. & trav.

Dec. 21, 99-168

Library of Congress, no. F211.K73. Copyright.

NK 0209976 DLC PPYH GU-De NcD MH

Knowles, John Harris, 1832-1908, *ed.*
Not changed but glorified, and other verses, ed., with a preface, by Canon Knowles. 4th ed. New York, J. Pott and company, 1900.
3 p. l., 5-38 p. col. front. 19 cm.

1. Consolation—Poetry. 2. Death—Poetry. I. Title.

25-15311

Library of Congress PN6110.D4K5 1900

NK 0209977 DLC IEG ViU OO

Knowles, John Harris, 1832-1908.
To England and back; a winter vacation, by Canon Knowles ... Chicago, A. C. McClurg and co., 1892.
231 p. front. (port.) 16 cm.
Originally published in the Living church.

1. England—Descr. & trav.—1801-1900. I. Title.

DA625.K73 3—1727

NK 0209978 DLC PP PPL PPLT OCl WaWW

[Knowles, John Power] 1808-1887.
... Banks, banking and kindred subjects ... [Providence, 1857]
2 v. 24 cm.
Cover-title.
Several of the articles are signed: A looker on.
Clippings from the Providence journal and Providence daily post, 1857.

NK 0209979 RPB

[Knowles, John Power] 1808-1887.
... Defense of Wayland's "Limits of human responsibility." [Providence, 1839]
[7] p. 24 cm.
Cover-title.
Articles signed: Civis.
Clippings from the Providence journal, 1839.

NK 0209980 RPB

[Knowles, John Power] 1808-1887.
The General assembly not guilty; or, The court vs. the assembly.
Caption-title, 7 p. O.
From the Providence post.
Signed: Quilibet.
Contains autograph letter from author.

NK 0209981 RPB

Knowles, John Power, 1808-1887.
Inaugural address of John P. Knowles ... as chairman of the United brothers' society of Brown university, September, 1835. [Providence 1835?]
cover-title, [19] p. 22 cm.
Manuscript.

NK 0209982 RPB

Knowles, John Power, 1808-1887.
... Inaugural address ... before the United brothers' society of Brown university, September, 1835. St. Paul, Minn., 1936.
cover-title, 19 numb. l. 22 cm.
Manuscript transcription by John Power Knowles, junior, class of 1880, in 1936.
With Knowles, John Power. Inaugural address ... 1835.

NK 0209983 RPB

Knowles, John Power, 1808-1887.
"Opinion in admiralty case of Childs vs. Gladding." n.p., n.d.
[2] p. 24 cm.
Newspaper clippings.

NK 0209984 RPB

[Knowles, John Power] 1808-1887.
... Political contributions to newspapers, 1839. [Providence, 1839]
[8] p. 24 cm.
Cover-title.
Some of the articles have signature: Kappa.
Newspaper clippings.

NK 0209985 RPB

VOLUME 300

Law

Knowles, John Power, 1808-1887, reporter.

Rhode Island. *Supreme court.*
... Reports of cases argued and determined in the Supreme court of Rhode Island ... v. 1-
[March 1828-
Providence [etc.] 1847-19

[Knowles, John Power] 1808-1887.
Review of Whittier's poems. [Providence, 1838?]
[4] p. 24 cm.
Cover-title.
Articles signed: Philo-Neutral.
Newspaper clippings.

NK 0209987 RPB

[Knowles, John Power] 1808-1887.
To the members of the General assembly, to convene in Newport, June 23, 1856. [Newport, 1856?]
4 p. 24 cm.
Caption-title.
Signed: One of the bar.
An article concerning the R.I. judiciary system.

NK 0209988 RPB

Knowles, John Stanley.
The philosophy of a commoner, by John Stanley Knowles, A. B. Los Angeles, Calif., Wetzel publishing company, inc., 1928.
324, [2] p. front. (port.) 20½cm.
"References": [2] p. at end.

1. Philosophy. I. Title.
Library of Congress BD21.K6 29-6878

NK 0209989 DLC

Knowles, Joseph, 1869-
Alone in the wilderness, by Joseph Knowles; illustrated from drawings on birch bark, made by the author in the woods with burnt sticks from his fires, together with photographs taken before and after his experiences. Boston, Small, Maynard & company [°1913]
7 p. l., 295 p. front., plates, ports. 20½cm.
Narrative of the author's experience in living "the life of a primitive man for two months in the wilderness of northern Maine".

1. Camping. 2. Outdoor life. 3. Maine—Descr. & trav. I. Title.
14-1961
Library of Congress SK601.K6

MB NN PPA LU MeB ICRL
NK 0210001 DLC Or ICJ MiU OOxM OCl OO PPAN ViU

Knowles, Joseph, 1869-
Alone in the wilderness; illustrated from drawings on birch bark, made by the author in the woods with burnt sticks from his fires ... Tor.Copp[c1913].
Front.plates,ports.O.

NK 0210002 CaBViP

Knowles, Joseph, 1869-
Alone in the wilderness, by Joseph Knowles; illustrated from drawings on birch bark, made by the author in the woods with burnt sticks from his fires, together with photographs taken before and after his experiences. London, Longmans, 1914.
7 p.l., 295 p. front., plates, ports. 20.5 cm
Narrative of the author's experience in living "the life of a primitive man for two months in the wilderness of northern Maine."
1. Camping. 2. Outdoor life. 3. Maine - Descr Descr. & trav. I. Title.

NK 0210003 CU

Knowles, Joseph A.
Fethard: its abbey, etc. ... by Rev. J. A. Knowles... Dublin, J. Duffy and co., 1903. xv, 167 p. illus. 18cm.

320663B. 1. Fethard, Ire.—Hist. 2. Fethard abbey.
N. Y. P. L.

NK 0210004 NN FU CtY IU PV ICU

Knowles, Joseph A
St. Brigid, patroness of Ireland. Dublin, Printed by Browne and Nolan, 1907.
xiv, 292 p. illus.

1. Brigid, Saint, of Ireland, ca.453-ca.524.

NK 0210005 WaU NN MB PV OrU CMenSP

Knowles, Joseph B
Notes on the law and incidents of tenures in England, by Joseph B. Knowles, advised by H. B. Durley Grazebrook. London, Estates Gazette, 1912.
261 p. 22cm.

On spine: Law of tenures.

1. Land tenure - Gt. Brit. I. Grazebrook, H. B. Durley. II. Title. III. Title: Law of tenures.

NK 0210006 GU-L

Knowles, Joseph H., ed.

Pearl of days ...

New York, W. B. Ketcham, 18

Knowles, Mrs. Joseph H.
See
Knowles, Ellin J. (Toy), 1835-1929.

Knowles, Josephine Pitcairn.
The upholstered cage. London: Hodder and Stoughton [1912]. xxxvi, 420 p. 12°.

1. Girls. 2. Woman.—Occupations.
N. Y. P. L. May 28, 1913.

NK 0210009 NN MB

Knowles, Josephine Pitcairn.
The upholstered cage, by Josephine Pitcairn Knowles. London [etc.] Hodder and Stoughton [1913]
1 p. l., xxxvi, 420 p. 20cm.
Considers the problem of the unmarried daughter, the sheltered woman of no vocation who lives with her parents in the home signified by the "upholstered cage."

1. Woman—Social and moral questions. 2. Woman—England. I. Title.
A 13-1201
Title from Chicago Pub. Libr. Printed by L. C.

NK 0210010 CU MiU ICJ

KNOWLES, Joshua.
A common alphabet for Indian languages, or 53 alphabetic letters for 20,000 syllabic symbols. Eastbourne, W.H.Christian, 1913.

21 cm. pp.26,(1).

NK 0210011 MH

Knowles, J[oshua]
Oriental Braille ... One alphabet for the blind for all oriental languages. By the Rev. J. Knowles ... and L. Garthwaite ... London, The British and foreign Bible society, 1902.
59 p. 21cm.
Title also in Braille.
3-25911

NK 0210012 DLC

Knowles, Joshua.
Our duty to India and Indian illiterates. Romanic letters for Indian languages. By Rev. J. Knowles. London, Christian literature society for India, 1910.
1 p. l., 66 p. illus. 20½cm.

1. Transliteration—Oriental languages. 2. India—Languages. I. Title. II. Title: Illiterates, Indian.
20-141
Library of Congress P226.K6

NK 0210013 DLC CtY

Knowles, Josiah Nickerson, 1830-1896.
The Crusoes of Pitcairn's island, being an account of the wreck of the "Wild Wave" of Boston on Oeno island in the Pacific, and the subsequent adventures of her master and crew on Pitcairn's island, as related in the diary of Captain Josiah Nickerson Knowles of Brewster ... [Providence] Priv. print. for H. S. Hoyt and J. K. Hoyt, jr., 1938.
[21] p. front. 27½ x 21½cm.
Photoprinted.
"Edition of one hundred copies."
1. Wild Wave (Clipper-ship) 2. Pitcairn island. I. Title.
38-16109
Library of Congress G530.K62
—— Copy 2.
Copyright A 117824 [5] 910.4

NK 0210014 DLC MB MH

PC 5327 F518 Knowles, Juan.
La lingüística; disquisición sobre la aplicación de la Ley de Grimm y la metátesis en la derivación de las voces portuguesas, aplicable a la lengua castellana o a cualquier otro idioma. Buenos Aires, La Facultad, 1924.
33 p. 20 cm. (Estudios de filología. Primera serie)
Caption title: El nuevo gran diccionario de la lengua portuguesa y el diccionario de Cándido de Figueiredo.

1. Figueiredo, Cándido de, 1846-1925. Novo dicionário da língua portuguesa. 2. Portuguese language -- dictionaries. I. Title: El nuevo gran diccionario de la lengua portuguesa y el diccionario de Cándido de Figueiredo.

NK 0210016 NSyU

Knowles, Kenneth Guy Jack Charles.
Strikes—a study in industrial conflict, with special reference to British experience between 1911 and 1947. Oxford, B. Blackwell, 1952.
xiv, 330 p. diagrs., tables. 25 cm. (Oxford University Institute of Statistics. Monographs, 3)
Bibliographical footnotes.

1. Strikes and lockouts. 2. Strikes and lockouts—Gt. Brit. (Series: Oxford. University. Institute of statistics. Monograph no. 3)
HD5307.K6 1952a 331.892942 A 52—8995
Minnesota. Univ. Libr. for Library of Congress [a57g1]†

DNLM ViU DCU MB MH PPT DLC PU-L MU CU DS MiU
NK 0210017 MnU MU CU DS MiU CaBVaU DLC TxU NN NIC

Knowles, Kenneth Guy Jack Charles.
Strikes; a study in industrial conflict, with special reference to British experience between 1911 and 1947. New York, Philosophical Library, 1952.
xiv, 330 p. diagrs. 26 cm.
Bibliographical footnotes.

1. Strikes and lockouts. 2. Strikes and lockouts—Gt. Brit.
HD5307.K6 1952 331.892942 53-6015

NK 0210018 DLC FU OU TxU OClJC PPLas PSC NN OOxM

VOLUME 300

Knowles, L.C.A.
see Knowles, Mrs. Lilian Charlotte Anne (Tomm) 1870-1926.

Knowles, Laura Thornton, 1862–
Southern recipes tested by myself, by Laura T. Knowles. New York, George H. Doran company [°1913]
8 p. l., 161 p. 19½cm.

1. Cookery, American—Southern states. I. Title.
13–23394
Library of Congress TX715.K7

NK 0210020 DLC MU ViU NN ICJ

Knowles, *Sir* Lees, *bart.*, 1857–1928.
The British in Capri, 1806–1808, by Sir Lees Knowles, baronet ... London, John Lane; New York, John Lane company, 1918.
330 p. incl. front., illus., plan, geneal. tables. plates, ports. (part col.) double map. 23cm.
CONTENTS.—Introduction.—Sir Sidney Smith, 1764–1840.—Joachim Murat.—Sir Richard Church.—The Neapolitan and French accounts of the capture of Capri, by General Pietro Colletta and Colonel Francis Maceroni.—Attack on the island of Capri.—Journal of occurrences during the enemy's attack on the island of Capri.—Papers presented to the House of commons relating to the capture of the isle of Capri by the French forces.—Major John Hamill.
1. Capri—Hist. 2. Naples (Kingdom)—Hist. I. Title.
18–18862
Library of Congress DG975.C2K6

NK 0210021 DLC NIC NcD MiU OU OC1W PU NN MB

Knowles, Sir Lees, Bart., 1857–1928.
LF2819 A day with Corps-students in Germany. London, Simpson, Marshall, Hamilton, Kent [1913]
K5 55 p. plates(part col.) 26cm.
Includes music for "Old Heidelberg" and "Lied des Trompeters von Säckingen."

1.Heidelberg. Universität - Students. I.Title.

NK 0210022 CSt CU MH TU

Knowles, Sir Lees, bart., 1857–1928.
A day with Korps-students in Germany. Heidelberg, Groos, 1908.
16p.

NK 0210023 OC1W

179.7
K762d
1911 KNOWLES, Sir LEES, bart., 1857–1928.
A day with korps-students in Germany, being an account of some Heidelberg duels, by Sir Lees Knowles ... With four illustrations. 2d ed. Heidelberg, K. Groos Nachfolger, H. Kieser [c1911]
20p. illus. 18½cm.

1. Dueling - Germany. 2. Students - Germany. I. Title.
6-W-3

NK 0210024 TxU

Knowles, Sir Lees, Baronet. 1857–1928.
The development of British colonial policy during the nineteenth and twentieth centuries.
(In Co-operative Wholesale Societies Limited. Annual for 1908. Pp. 242–269. Manchester. 1908.)

H9257 — Great Britain. Colonies.

NK 0210025 MB

Knowles, *Sir* Lees, *bart.*, 1857–1928.
Fun, fact, and extract, by Sir Lees Knowles. London, The St. Catherine press, 1921.
3 p. l., 245 p., 2 l. 18cm.
"A medley of general information and amusement."

1. Anecdotes. I. Title.
22–16928
Library of Congress PN6261.K5

NK 0210026 DLC NN

Knowles, *Sir* Lees, *bart.*, 1857–1928.
A gift of Napoleon; being a sequel to Letters of Captain Engelbert Lutyens, orderly officer at Longwood, Saint Helena, Feb. 1820 to Nov. 1823, ed. by Sir Lees Knowles ... London, John Lane; New York, John Lane company, 1921.
2 p. l., iii–vii p., 2 l., 63 p. front. (port. group) pl., facsims. 25½cm.
"Limited to 250 copies: 105."
On Napoleon's presentation of Coxe's Life of Marlborough to the officers of the 20th regiment, and the consequent removal from duty at Longwood of Captain Engelbert Lutyens.
CONTENTS.—A gift of Napoleon.—Inscription of the gift.—Correspondence.—Marchand and St. Denis.—Marlbrough s'en va-t-en guerre.—Marshal Soult.
1. Napoléon I—Captivity, 1815–1821. 2. Lutyens, Engelbert, 1784–1830. I. Title.
21–16244
Library of Congress DC203.9.K7

NK 0210027 DLC NN

Knowles, *Sir* Lees, *bart.*, 1857–1928.
"Irish impressions," by Sir Lees Knowles, bart. ... London and Bolton, Tillotson & son, ltd. [1918]
20 p. 21½cm.
"Reprinted from the 'Saturday review'."

1. Ireland—Hist.—Sinn Fein rebellion, 1916. 2. Ireland—Descr. & trav. 3. Irish question. I. Title.
45–49582
Library of Congress DA962.K6

NK 0210028 DLC NN MH

DA962
.K6 Knowles, Sir Lees, bart., 1857–1928.
"Irish impressions"; reprinted from "The Saturday Review" with a foreword by the Editor. 2d. ed. London, Tillotson [1919?]
20p. 22cm.

1. Ireland--History--Sinn Fein Rebellion, 1916. I. Title.

NK 0210029 MB

Knowles, Sir Lees, art. 1857–

Lutyens, Engelbert, 1784–1830.
Letters of Captain Engelbert Lutyens, orderly officer at Longwood, Saint Helena: Feb. 1820 to Nov.: 1823: ed. by Sir Lees Knowles ... London, John Lane; New York, John Lane company, 1915.

Knowles, *Sir* Lees, *bart.*, 1857–1928.
Minden and the seven years' war. By Sir Lees Knowles, baronet ... London, Simpkin, Marshall, Hamilton, Kent & co., ltd. [1914]
4 p. l., 113 p., 1 l. front., pl., ports., double map. 25cm.
Bibliography: p. 104–105.

1. Minden, Ger.—Hist. 2. Seven years' war, 1756–1763. I. Title.
DD901.M58K6 47–36704

NK 0210031 DLC CU NN

KNOWLES, Sir LEES, bart., 1857–1928.
Minden and the Seven years' war. London, Simpkin, Marshall, Hamilton, Kent [1914] 113 p. illus.,ports.,maps. 26cm.

Film reproduction. Negative.
Bibliography, p. 104–105.

1. Seven years' war, 1756–1763. 2. Minden, Battle of, 1759.

NK 0210032 NN

Knowles, Sir Lees, bart., 1857–1928.

Greenwood, Harry, 1847– *ed.*
Real property statutes, comprising those passed during the years 1874–1884 inclusive; consolidated with the earlier statutes thereby amended. With copious notes. By Harry Greenwood ... 2d ed. by the author, assisted by Lees Knowles ... London, Stevens and sons, 1884.

Knowles, Sir Lees, bart., 1857–1928.

Gt. Brit. *Parliament. House of commons. Select committee on plumbers' registration bill.*
Report from the Select committee on the plumbers' registration bill; together with the proceedings of the Committee, minutes of evidence, appendix, and index. Ordered, by the House of commons, to be printed, 8 April 1892. London, Printed for H. M. Stationery off., by Eyre and Spottiswoode [1892]

Knowles, Sir Lees, bart., 1857–1928.
The taking of Capri 1806–1808 ...
see under Farace, Antonio.

Knowles, Sir Lees, bart., 1857–1928.

Knowles, Robert, 1790–1813.
The war in the Peninsula; some letters of Lieutenant Robert Knowles, of the 7th, or Royal, fusiliers, a Lancashire officer. Arranged and annotated by his great-great-nephew Sir Lees Knowles, baronet ... July 25th, 1913. Bolton, Tillotson & son, ltd, 1913.

Knowles, Leonard, 1901–
Linage; how to make money from news, a guide for young journalists and beginners, by Leonard Knowles. London: Sir I. Pitman & Sons, Ltd., 1936. 135 p. 19cm.

850094A. 1. Journalism—Reporting. I. Title.
N. Y. P. L.

NK 0210037 NN NNC TxU

Knowles, Lester.
In business with a 1250 multilith; a beginners' manual of offset lithography. [Colton? Calif., 1955]
195 p. illus. 22 cm.

1. Offset printing. I. Title.
Z252.5.O5K5 655.32 55–42647 ‡

NK 0210038 DLC MB PGloS

Knowles, Lester.
Weird and comic experiences with the insane, by Lester Knowles ... Highland, Calif., Harlem press [°1932]
193 p. front. (port.) illus. 18cm.

1. Insane, Criminal and dangerous. 2. Insane—Care and treatment. I. Title.
32–17462
Library of Congress RC606.K6
Copyright A 52840 [3] 362.2

NK 0210039 DLC

Knowles, Levi, 1813-1898.
In memory of Levi Knowles. Philadelphia
see under title

VOLUME 300

Knowles, Lilian Charlotte Anne (Tomn) 1870-1926.
The economic development of the British overseas empire, by L. C. A. Knowles ... London, G. Routledge & sons, ltd., 1924-
v. fronts. (v. 2: port.) fold. maps. 22½ cm. (*Half-title:* Studies in economics and political science ... no. 76, 103 in the series of monographs by writers connected with the London School of economics and political science)
Vols. 2- : By the late L. C. A. Knowles ... and C. M. Knowles. Bibliography: v. 2, p. 589-599; v. 3, p. 343-346.
1. Gt. Brit.—Colonies. 2. Gt. Brit.—Colonies—Econ. condit. 3. Tropics. 4. Canada—Econ. condit. 5. Africa, South—Econ. condit. I. Knowles, Charles Matthew. II. Title.
HC246.K5 24—28124

TU CaBVa CaBVaU
OOxM PBm NjN ICJ OrU TU IdPI ICJ OrPR CaBViP OC1W
NK 0210041 DLC DS GU-L OCU OU PU MH NcD MtU MiU

Knowles, Lilian Charlotte Anne (Tomn) 1870-1926.
Economic development in the nineteenth century; France, Germany, Russia, and the United States, by the late L. C. A. Knowles ... London, G. Routledge & sons, ltd., 1932.
viii, 368 p. 22cm. (*Half-title:* Studies in economics and political science ... No. 109 in the series of monographs by writers connected with the London school of economics and political science)
Companion volume to the author's The industrial and commercial revolutions in Great Britain during the nineteenth century, published 1921. *cf.* Pref.
Bibliography: p. 351-354.
1. Economic conditions. 2. Europe — Econ. condit. 3. U. S. — Econ. condit. 4. Commercial policy. I. Title.
Library of Congress HC53.K6 [a44k1] 32—17460 330.903

IdPI CaBVa OrPR DAU
NN ICJ DL PPD PBm PU CU Wa KMK OrU CaBVaU FTaSU MtU
NK 0210042 DLC IdU OrU OCU OU OC1 OC1W OO MiU MB

Knowles, *Mrs.* Lilian Charlotte Anne (Tomn) 1870-1926.
Economic development in the nineteenth century; France, Germany, Russia, and the United States, by the late L. C. A. Knowles ... London, G. Routledge & sons, ltd., 1936.
viii, 368 p. 22cm. (*Half-title:* Studies in economics and political science ... no. 109 in the series of monographs by writers connected with the London school of economics and political science)
"Reprinted 1936"
Companion volume to the author's The industrial and commercial revolutions in Great Britain during the nineteenth century, published 1921. *cf.* Pref.
Bibliography: p. 351-354.

NK 0210043 ViU

Knowles, Lilian Charlotte Anne (Tomn) 1870-1926.
Economic development in the nineteenth century: France, Germany, Russia, and the United States. London, Routledge [1948]
viii, 368 p. (Studies in economics and political science, 109)

NK 0210044 MH

Knowles, Lilian Charlotte Anne (Tomn) 1870-1926.
The economic development of the British overseas empire, by L. C. A. Knowles..: v. 1- New York: A. & C. Boni, 1925- v. front., maps. 8°. (Studies in economics and political science. no. 76.)
Contents: v. 1. The empire as a whole. The British tropics.
1. Economic history—Gt. Br.—Colonies. 2. Ser.
N. Y. P. L.

NK 0210045 NN OO MH OrSaW

9330
942A58 Knowles, Lilian Charlotte Anne (Tomn) 1870-1926.
The economic development of the British overseas empire. 2d ed. rev. London, G. Routledge 1928-1936.
3 v. illus., front., port. (v.2) maps. 22cm. (Half-title: Studies in economics and political science... nos. 76, 103, and 110 in the series of Monographs by writers connected with the London School of Economics and Political Science)
Vol. 2 and 3: By the late L.C.A.

Continued in next column

Continued from preceding column

Knowles... and C. M. Knowles.
Bibliography: v. 2, p. 589-599; v. 3, p. 343-346.
1. Gt. Brit.—Colonies. 2. Gt. Brit.—Colonies—Econ. condit. 3. Tropics. 4. Canada—Econ. condit. 5. Africa, South—Econ. condit. I. Knowles, Charles Matthew II. Title. III. Series.

NK 0210047 MB OC1 ViU MiU

Knowles, Lilian Charlotte Anne (Tomn) 1870-1926.
The industrial and commercial revolutions in Great Britain during the nineteenth century, by L. C. A. Knowles ... London, G. Routledge & sons, ltd.; New York, E. P. Dutton & co., 1921.
xii, 420 p. 19 cm. (*Half-title:* Studies in economics and political science ... no. 61 in the series of monographs by writers connected with the London school of economics and political science)
Pages [413]-420, advertising matter.
"Some books for further reference": p. [393]-403.
1. Gt. Brit.—Econ. condit.—1918- 2. Labor and laboring classes—Gt. Brit. 3. Machinery in industry. 4. Gt. Brit.—Economic policy. 5. Industry and state—Gt. Brit. I. Title.
HC255.K6 21—3907

ICJ ICU NjP
NK 0210048 DLC MtU WaS PU NcD PBa PU DAU ICJ OrU

KNOWLES, LILIAN CHARLOTTE ANNE (TOMN), 1870-1926.
The industrial and commercial revolutions in Great Britain during the nineteenth century. London, G. Routledge: New York, E.P. Dutton, 1921. xii, 420 p. (Studies in economics and political science, no. 61)
Film reproduction. Negative.
Bibliography, p. [393]- 403.
(Continued)
1. Economic history--Gt. Br., 1760- . 2. Commerce--Gt. Br., 19th cent. 3. Industries--Gt. Br. 4. Transportation--Gt. Br. I. Series.

NK 0210050 NN

330.942 Knowles, Lillian Charlotte Anne (Tomn), 1870-
K7621 1926.
1922 The industrial and commercial revolutions in Great Britain during the nineteenth century. 2d rev. ed. London, G. Routledge, New York, E. P. Dutton, 1922.
xii, 420p. 23cm. (Studies in economics and political science, no. 61)
Bibliography: p. [393]-403.

NK 0210051 IU OC1 CaBVaU

Knowles, Lilian Charlotte Anne (Tomn) 1870-1926.
Nc95
G55 The industrial and commercial revolutions
921Kc in Great Britain during the nineteenth century. 3d rev. ed. London, G. Routledge; New York, E.P. Dutton, 1924.
xii, 416 p. illus. 22 cm. (Studies in economics and political science, no. 61)

NK 0210052 CtY MiU OC1W ViU PKsL

Knowles, Lilian Charlotte Anne (Tomn) 1870-1926.
The industrial and commercial revolutions in Great Britain during the nineteenth century, by L. C. A. Knowles ... 4th (rev.) ed., eighth thousand. London, G. Routledge & sons, ltd.; New York, E. P. Dutton & co., 1926.
xii, 416 p. 22½ cm. (*Half-title:* Studies in economics and political science ... no. 61 in the series of monographs by writers connected with the London school of economics and political science)
"Some books for further reference": p. [393]-403.
1. Gt. Brit.—Econ. condit. 2. Labor and laboring classes—Gt. Brit. 3. Machinery in industry. 4. Gt. Brit.—Economic policy. 5. Industry and state—Gt. Brit. I. Title.
HC255.K6 1926 330.942 26—22386

IdPI PU OrPR NcU
NK 0210053 DLC GU PHC PSC PU AU NIC WaU MB MtU IdU

KNOWLES, [Mrs]. L[ilian] C[harlotte] A[nne] (Tomn)] 1870-1926.
The industrial and commercial revolutions in Great Britain during the nineteenth century 11th thousand. London, G.Routledge & Sons, Ltd., etc., etc., 1927.
Half-title: Studies in economics and political science.

NK 0210054 MH CaBVa

Knowles, *Mrs.* Lilian Charlotte Anne (Tomn) 1870-1926.
The industrial and commercial revolutions in Great Britain during the nineteenth century, by L. C. A. Knowles ... London, G. Routledge & sons, ltd.; New York, E. P. Dutton & co., 1930.
xii, 416 p. 22½ cm. (*Half-title:* Studies in economics and political science ... no. 61 in the series of monographs by writers connected with the London school of economics and political science)
"Reprinted October, 1930."

NK 0210055 ViU CaBVaU

Knowles, Lilian Charlotte Anne (Tomn) 1870-1926.
The industrial and commercial revolutions in Great Britain during the nineteenth century... London, Routledge, 1933.
416 p. 22 cm. (Studies in economics and political science, ed.by the director of the London school of economics and political science. no.61)
4th ed.
"Some books for further reference": p. [393]-403.

NK 0210056 NjP WaTC OCU ODW OU OC1W OO MiU OC1U

Knowles, *Mrs.* Lilian Charlotte Anne (Tomn) 1870-1926.
The industrial and commercial revolutions in Great Britain during the nineteenth century, by L. C. A. Knowles ... London, G. Routledge & sons, ltd.; New York, E. P. Dutton & co., 1937.
xii, 416 p. 22½cm. (*Half-title:* Studies in economics and political science ... no. 61 in the series of monographs by writers connected with the London school of economics and political science)
"Some books for further reference": p. [393]-403.
"Reprinted February, 1937."

NK 0210057 ViU

Knowles, Lilian Charlotte Anne (Tomn), 1870-1926.
The industrial and commercial revolutions in Great Britain during the nineteenth century... 4th (rev.) ed.: London, G. Routledge & sons, ltd.; New York, E.P. Dutton & co., 1941.
416p. (Studies in economics and political science... no. 61 in the series of monographs by writers connected with the London school of economics and political science)

NK 0210058 OC1

Knowles, Lillian Charlotte Anne (Tomn) 1870-1926.
HC255 The industrial and commercial revolutions in
K73 Great Britain during the nineteenth century. London, G. Routledge; New York, E.P. Dutton [1947]
xii, 416 p. 19cm. (Studies in economics and political science, no.61)
First published 1921.
Bibliography: p. [393]-403.
1. Gt.Brit. - Econ. condit. - 1918-1945. 2. Labor and laboring classes - Gt. Brit. 3. Machinery in industry. 4. Gt. Brit. - Economic policy. 5. Industry and state - Gt. Brit. I. Title.

NK 0210059 CSt-H PU

Knowles, Mrs. Lilian Charlotte Anne (Tomn) 1870-1926, ed.
Deploige, Simon, 1868-1927.
The referendum in Switzerland, by Simon Deploige ... with a letter on the referendum in Belgium by M. J. van den Heuvel ... tr. into English by C. P. Trevelyan ... ed. with notes, introduction, and appendices by Lilian Tomn ... London, New York [etc.] Longmans, Green, and co., 1898.

VOLUME 300

811
K762t
Knowles, Louise J
Thoughts in metre. By Louise J. Knowles. Milwaukee, Wis., Cramer, Aikens & Cramer, 1889.
69p.

NK 0210061 IU RPB NBuG

Knowles, Lucia M.
If ye love me; a topical arrangement of Christ's commandments. Boston, L. C. Page & co., 1900.
65 p. 12°. (The day's work series)

Library of Congress Copyright Oct. 11, 1900-68

NK 0210062 DLC

Knowles, M.
History of Wicken, by M. Knowles. London, E. Stock, 1902.
viii, 156 p. incl. front., pl. 21cm.

Subject entries: Wicken, Eng. (Cambridgeshire)—Hist. 2-30491

Library of Congress, no. DA690.W596K7.

NK 0210063 DLC IU MB

Knowles, M.B.
Education. Moral education of the first consequence. To make good citizens the duty and province of the teacher. Denver, 1898.
30 p. 23 cm.

NK 0210064 RPB

HC103
K56
Knowles, M B
The slave of the rings and The road to freedom, and other subjects. Denver, Colo., [Merchants Pub. Co.] 1896.
243 p. ports. 17cm.

1. U.S. - Econ. condit. I. Title. II. Title: The road to freedom.

NK 0210065 CoU

TD1949
K763
KNOWLES, M B 1921-
Synthesis of 5-pyridyl substituted hydantoins. Austin, Tex., 1949.
86 numb. l., 2l. diagr. 29cm.

Thesis (Ph.D.) - University of Texas, 1949.
Vita.
Bibliography: numb. l. 85-86.

595029, cop.1
595030, cop.2
1. Hydantoins. I. Title.

NK 0210066 TxU

[Knowles, Mabel Winifred] 1875-
Angela goes to school, by May Wynne [pseud.] Cleveland, New York, The World syndicate publishing company [c1929]
253 p. front. 19½cm.

I. Title.

Library of Congress PZ7.K763An 29-20016 Revised

NK 0210067 DLC

Knowles, Mabel Winifred, 1875-
A blot on the escutcheon, by May Wynne [pseud] New York, R.F.Fenno & co. [190-]

NK 0210068 MH

[Knowles, Mabel Winifred] 1875-
The claim that won, by May Wynne [pseud.] ... London, Everett & co., ltd. [c1912]
302 p., 1 l. 19½cm.

I. Title. 12-23761 Revised 2

Library of Congress PZ3.K7635Cl

NK 0210069 DLC

[Knowles, Mabel Winifred] 1875-
An English girl in Serbia; the story of a great adventure, [by] May Wynne [pseud.] ... London: Collins' Clear-type Press [1916]. 215 p. incl. col'd front., col'd pl. (part mounted.) 4°.

1. European war, 1914- —Fiction. 2. Juvenile literature.—Fiction (English). 3. Title.
N. Y. P. L.

NK 0210070 NN

[Knowles, Mabel Winifred] 1875-
For Charles the Rover; a romance, by May Wynne [pseud.] ... New York: R. F. Fenno & co. [1911] 324 p. 19½cm.

157479B. 1. Fiction, English. 2. Charles Edward Louis Philip Casimir Stuart, called the Young Pretender, 1720-1788—Fiction. I. Title.
N. Y. P. L.

NK 0210071 NN

Knowles, Mabel Winifred, 1875-
For church and chieftain. By May Wynne [pseud.].
London. Mills & Boon, Ltd. [1909.] (5), 314 pp. 19½ cm., in 8s.
A romance of the Geraldine rebellion in Ireland, 1579.

L2091 — T.r. — Ireland. Hist. Fict. Elizabeth, 1558-1603.

NK 0210072 MB

[Knowles, Mabel Winifred] 1875-
The Gipsy count, by May Wynne [pseud.] ... New York, The John McBride co., 1909.
322 p. col. front. 19½cm.

I. Title. 9-10082 Revised 2

Library of Congress PZ3.K7635G

NK 0210073 DLC

[Knowles, Mabel Winifred] 1875-
Gwennola, by May Wynne [pseud.] ... London, A. Rivers, ltd. [1926]
288 p. 19½cm.

I. Title. 26-17471 Revised

Library of Congress PZ3.K7635Gw

NK 0210074 DLC

[Knowles, Mabel Winifred] 1875-
Henry of Navarre; a romance of August, 1572. New York and London, G. P. Putnam's sons, 1908.
vi p., 1 l., 346 p. front. 19½cm.

1. Henri IV, king of France, 1553-1610—Fiction. 2. St. Bartholomew's day, Massacre of, 1572—Fiction. I. Title.
8-30614 Revised 2

Library of Congress PZ3.K7635H

NK 0210075 DLC NN PPL OCl

Knowles, Mabel Winifred, 1875-
Henry of Navarre; a romance; from the play "Henry of Navarre" by William Devereaux; frontis. by H.R. Brook. Popular edition. London, Greening & co., 1909.
319p.

NK 0210076 OClUr

823.912
K73H
Knowles, Mabel Winifred, 1875-
"Hey for cavaliers!" a romance, by May Wynne [pseud.] London, Greening, 1912.
313 p. 19 cm.

NK 0210077 NcD

Knowles, Mabel Winifred, 1875-
A king's masquerade: a romance. By May Wynne [pseud.].
— London. Greening & Co., Ltd. 1910. 320 pp. 18½ cm., in 8s.
A tale of the youth of James V., of Scotland, 1528.

K9942 — T.r. — Scotland. Hist. Fict. James V., 1513-1542.

NK 0210078 MB

[Knowles, Mabel Winifred] 1875-
Little Sallie Mandy's Christmas present, by May Wynne [pseud.] with illustrations from original drawings by Bess Goe Willis. Philadelphia, Henry Altemus company [c1929]
60 p., 1 l. incl. col. front., col. illus. 14½cm. [Altemus' wee books for wee folks]

I. Title. 29-6443 Revised

Library of Congress PZ7.K763Li

NK 0210079 DLC

[Knowles, Mabel Winifred] 1875-
The masked rider, by May Wynne [pseud.] illustrations and decorations by Peggy Paver Beck. Chicago, New York, Laidlaw brothers, 1931.
4 p. l., 256 p. illus., pl. 20cm.

I. Title. 31-30513 Revised

Library of Congress PZ7.K763Mas

NK 0210080 DLC PPAp

Knowles, Mabel Winifred, 1875-
Mistress Cynthia. By May Wynne [pseud.].
— London. Greening & Co. Limited. 1910. 320 pp. 17½ cm.
A fictitious story of the Jacobite plots with France and Spain, 1739.

L870 — T.r. — Jacobites. — Great Britain. Hist. Fict. George II., 1727-1760.

NK 0210081 MB

[Knowles, Mabel Winifred] 1875-
... Patient Pat joins the circus, by May Wynne [pseud.] with illustrations from original drawings by Bess Goe Willis. Philadelphia, Henry Altemus company [c1931]
60 p., 1 l. incl. col. front., col. illus. 14½cm. (Altemus' wee books for wee folks)

I. Title. 31-24074 Revised

Library of Congress PZ10.3.K761Pat

NK 0210082 DLC

VOLUME 300

[Knowles, Mabel Winifred] 1875–
... Peter Rabbit and the big black crows, by May Wynne [pseud.] with illustrations by Bess Goe Willis. Philadelphia, Henry Altemus company [c1931]
58 p., 1 l. incl. col. front., col. illus. 14cm. (Altemus' Peter Rabbit series)
Illustrated lining-papers in colors.

I. Title.
Library of Congress PZ10.3.K761Pe 32-665 Revised

NK 0210083 DLC

Knowles, Mabel Winifred, 1875–
The Peter Rabbit playtime story book, with illustrations from original drawings by Bess Goe Willis. Philadelphia, Henry Altemus company [c1931]

[Knowles, Mabel Winifred] 1875–
A prince of intrigue, a romance of Mazeppa, by May Wynne [pseud.] ... London, Jarrolds, limited [1920]
3 p. l., 9-251, [1] p. 19½cm.

I. Title.
Library of Congress PZ3.K7635Pr 20-12602 Revised

NK 0210085 DLC

[Knowles, Mabel Winifred] 1875–
Robin Hood to the rescue, by May Wynne [pseud.] 56p. il. Exeter, A. Wheaton & co. [1927]

Cover-title.

NK 0210086 OCl

Knowles, Mabel Winifred, 1875–
Ronald Lindsay. [A novel.] By May Wynn [pseud.].
— London. Long. [1905.] 310 pp. 19 cm., in 8s.
The scene is laid in Scotland, at the time of the Rebellion of 1689.

K3593 — T.r. — Scotland. Hist. Fict. Rebellion of 1689.

NK 0210087 MB

[Knowles, Mabel Winifred] 1875–
The terror of the moor, by May Wynne [pseud.] ... London, A. Rivers, ltd. [1928]
2 p. l., 7-287 p. 19½cm.

I. Title.
Library of Congress PZ3.K7635Te 28-18584 Revised

NK 0210088 DLC

[Knowles, Mabel Winifred] 1875–
The "Veiled lady", a romance, by May Wynne [pseud.] and Draycot M. Dell ... London, Jarrolds, limited [1918]
viii, 286 p. 19cm.

I. Dell, Draycot Montagu, 1888– joint author. II. Title.
Library of Congress PZ3.K7635Ve 19-922 Revised

NK 0210089 DLC

Knowles, Malcolm Shepherd, 1913–
How to develop better leaders, by Malcolm and Hulda Knowles. New York, Association Press [1955]
64 p. illus. 20 cm. (A Leadership library book)

1. Leadership. I. Knowles, Hulda, joint author. II. Title.
BF637.L4K57 374.24 55—9113 ‡

ViU IaU CSt MiU KyWAT KyLxCB OrCS OrP Wa WaS WaTC WaT PPEB OOxM OClW LU MsSM OO PHC PCC OU MsU CaBVaU CaBVa
NK 0210090 DLC MU NN FMU MB NIC IU PPD CU PPPL PP

Knowles, Malcolm Shepherd, 1913–
Informal adult education; a guide for administrators, leaders, and teachers. With a foreword by Harry A. Overstreet. New York, Association Press, 1950.
xvi, 272 p. illus. 24 cm.
Bibliography: p. 253-258.

1. Education of adults. I. Title.
LC5215.K6 374 50-8886

WaS OrPS OrU WaT Or Wa WaTC
CaBVaU DI PHC MB ViU ICU NNC TU MB NcU CaBVa OrP
NK 0210091 DLC KyWAT MB KEmT ViU MU PPLT FMU PPT PP

LC 5215 K73I 1950 Knowles, Malcolm Shepherd, 1913-
Informal adult education; a guide for administrators, leaders, and teachers. With a foreword by Harry A. Overstreet. New York, Association Press, 1951 [c1950]
xvi, 272 p. illus. 23 1/2 cm.

Includes bibliography.

1. Education, Continuing. I. Title. [1. Adult education]

NK 0210092 WU-M NcGU

---

374 K763t Knowles, Malcolm Shepherd, 1913–
Teaching adults in informal courses. New York, Association Press [c1954]
71p. 22cm.

"A two-chapter excerpt from the author's ... Informal adult education."

1. Education of adults. I. Knowles, Malcolm S. Informal adult education. II. Title.

NK 0210093 TxU

Wason Film 1608 Knowles, Margaret Isabel.
The expansion of British influence in the Malay Peninsula, 1867-1885; a study in Nineteenth Century imperialism. Madison, 1935.
251, 6 l. map.

Thesis--University of Wisconsin.
Microfilm (negative) Madison, University of Wisconsin Library, 1967. 1 reel. 35mm.
1. British in Malaya. I. Title.

NK 0210094 NIC

Knowles, Maria.
History of Wicken
see Knowles, M

PR 6021 K757c Knowles, Marion Miller
A Christmas bouquet, by Marion Miller Knowles. [Malvern, Australia, H. Mullin, printer, 1914]
44 p.

Poems.
Author's autographed presentation copy.

NK 0210096 CLU

Iq K763 912 Knowles, Marion (Miller)
Corinne of Corrall's Bluff. Melbourne, W. P. Linehan, 1912.
197p. port. 19cm.

NK 0210097 CtY

Knowles, Marion Miller.
Fronds from the Blacks' spur, by Marion Miller Knowles... Melbourne [etc.] G. Robertson and co. [18—?] viii, 184 p. illus. 19cm.
Poems.

NK 0210098 NN

---

821 K763f Knowles, Marion Miller.
Fronds from the blacks' spur. Melbourne, G. Robertson [1911]
viii, 184p. illus., port. 19cm.

Poems.

NK 0210099 TxU WU

Knowles, Marion (Miller)
Love, luck and lavender, original poems. 2d ed. [Malvern, H. Mullin, n.d.]
49p. 22cm.

NK 0210100 IEN

Ib55 tl K763 Knowles, Marion (Miller)
Roses on the window sill; original poems. Melbourne, Varley, Printers, 1913.
44p. 19cm.
Pamphlet

NK 0210101 CtY MnU

821.9 K73se Knowles, Marion (Miller)
Selected poems. 1st ed. Melbourne, Arrow, 1935.
xiii, 330p. port. 19cm.

NK 0210102 IEN

Iq K763 900 [Knowles, Marion (Miller)]
Shamrock and wattle bloom; a series of short tales and sketches, by Marion Miller. Melbourne, Edgerton & Moore, 1900.
208p. 19cm.

NK 0210103 CtY

PR 6021 .N48 S6 Knowles, Marion Miller
Songs from the hills. 4th ed. Melbourne, E. A. Vidler [n. d.]
204 p. 19 cm.

NK 0210104 WU

W821.99 K73s Knowles, Marion (Miller)
Songs from the hills by Marion Miller. London, Melville, Mullen & Slade, 1898.
204p. 20cm.

NK 0210105 NcU

VOLUME 300

Knowles, Mark, 1882- joint author.

Van Den Branden, Felicien, 1907-
Plastering skill and practice ₍by₎ Felicien Van Den Branden ₍and₎ Mark Knowles. Chicago, American Technical Society, 1953.

Knowles, Mary Henrietta (Davis) 1846-1926.
... Grammaire de la conversation; direct method in French, by Mary H. Knowles ... and Berthe Des Combes Favard ... Boston, New York ₍etc.₎ D. C. Heath & co. ₍°1916₎
cixiii, 171 p. 18½ᶜᵐ. (Heath's Modern language series)

1. French language—Conversation and phrase books. 2. French language—Grammar—1870– I. Favard, Berthe Des Combes, joint author.
Library of Congress PC2121.K5 16-12920 Revised

NK 0210107 DLC OrSaW PU OCl MH NN ViU

Knowles, Mary Henrietta (Davis) 1846-1926.
Perfect French possible; some essential and adequate helps to French pronunciation and rhythm, by Mary H. Knowles ... and Berthe Des Combes Favard ... Boston, D. C. Heath & co., 1910.
x, 52 p. 19ᶜᵐ.

1. French language—Pronunciation. I. Favard, Berthe Des Combes, joint author. II. Title.
Library of Congress PC2137.K57 10-20793 Revised

MB MH
NK 0210108 DLC CU MoU ViU CaBVaU PSC PU PP OO OOxM

Knowles, Mary Henrietta (Davis) 1846-1926.
Perfect French possible, some essential and adequate helps to French pronunciation and rhythm, by Mary H. Knowles ... and Berthe Des Combes Favard ... Boston, New York ₍etc.₎ D. C. Heath & co. ₍°1910₎
x, 45 p. 18ᶜᵐ.

1. French language—Pronunciation. I. Favard, Berthe Des Combes, joint author. II. Title.
Library of Congress PC2137.K57 1910 a 43-29543

NK 0210109 DLC

Knowles, Mary Henrietta (Davis) 1846-1926.
Perfect French possible, some essential and adequate helps to French pronunciation and rhythm, by Mrs. M.H. Knowles and B.D. Favard.
Bost., Heath, 1912.
52 p.

NK 0210110 PU

Knowles, Mary Henrietta (Davis) 1846-1926.
... Perfect French pronunciation, a system of applied phonetics with drill in rhythmic French, by Mary H. Knowles ... and Berthe Des Combes Favard ... Boston, New York ₍etc.₎ D. C. Heath and company ₍°1924₎
vi p., 1 l., 72 p. illus. 19ᶜᵐ. (Heath's modern language series)

1. French language—Pronunciation. I. Favard, Berthe Des Combes, joint author.
Library of Congress PC2137.K58 24-12311

NK 0210111 DLC FTaSU OrP OCl OClU CtY PU PJB MB

Knowles, Mary Henrietta (Davis) 1846-1926.
Some essential and adequate helps to French pronunciation and rhythm, by Mary H. Knowles ... and Berthe Des Combes Favard ... ₍Chicago?₎ 1907.
2 p. l., 9-28 p. 20ᶜᵐ.

1. French language—Pronunciation. I. Favard, Berthe Des Combes, joint author.
Library of Congress PC2137.K6 7-23627 Revised 2

NK 0210112 DLC OCl

Knowles, Mary (Morris) 1733-1807.
A brief account of the vision and death of the late Lord Lyttleton; to which is added, an Anecdote of Lord Kaimes, and the melancholy end of a profligate young man. Stanford ₍N. Y.₎ Printed and sold by Daniel Lawrence. 1804. 12 p. 15½cm.

32099B. 1. Lyttelton, George Lyttelton, 1st baron, 1709-1773. 2. Apparitions, ghosts, etc.—Gt. Br. 3. Kames, Henry Home, lord, 1696-1782.
N. Y. P. L.

NK 0210113 NN RPB

[Knowles, Mary (Morris)] 1733-1807.
A brief account of the vision and death of the late Lord Lyttleton; to which is added, An anecdote of Lord Kaimes. Philadelphia: Printed and sold by Joseph Rakestraw, no. 190, North Third street. 1807.
12 x 19.5 cm. 12 p.

Preface signed "B. F." According to the preface, the account was "printed from the original in the handwriting of Mary Knowles . . . " and first appeared in the American Daily Advertiser about 1803. Mary Knowles wrote the account down for William Savery.

NK 0210115 OCHP PPL

₍Knowles, Mary (Morris)₎ 1733-1807.
Compendium of a controversy on water-baptism. London, Printed by C. Stower 1805.
7 p. 22ᶜᵐ.

NK 0210116 NjPT

---

*EC75 J6371 805d

Knowles, Mary (Morris) 1733-1807.
Dialogue between Mrs. Knowles and Dr. Johnson. London:Printed by C.Stower,Charles street, Hatton Garden.1805.
1p.l.,8p. 22.5cm.
First published in the Gentleman's magazine, June, 1791.

NK 0210117 MH OCU NjP

---

*EC75 K7631 791p

[Knowles, Mary (Morris) 1733-1807]
The Pope's journey to the other worlds, to seek advice and assistance against the National assembly of France.
London:Printed for J.Ridgway,no.1,York street, St.James's square.M.DCC.XCI.
8°. 3p.l.,[5]-33p. 21.5cm.
In verse.
Inscribed (partly cropped): from the Author Mary Knowles to F. S.

NK 0210118 MH

Knowles, Mary (Morris) 1733-1807.
Verses... n. p., n. d.
caption title ₍1₎ p. 20½cm.

NK 0210119 PHC

Knowles, Matilda.
Gathering jewels, 1887
see under Knowles, James, 1811-1886.

QK589 .K6

Knowles, Matilda Cullen, 1865-
Lichens of Ireland. Dublin, Hodges, Figgis; London, Williams & Norgate, 1929.
179-434 p. 28 cm. (Proceedings of the Royal Irish Academy. Section B, v.38, no.12)

Cover title.

1. Lichenes - Ireland. i. s.

NK 0210121 NNBG ICJ OCU MiU

QK 589 .K74

Knowles,Matilda Cullen, 1865-
... The maritime and marine lichens of Howth. By Matilda C.Knowles. Communicated by R.Lloyd Praeger. ... London, Pub.by the Royal Dublin society; ₍etc., etc.₎ 1913.
cover-title,79-143 p. pl.III-IX,fold. map. 26ᶜᵐ. (The scientific proceedings of the Royal Dublin society. v.XIV (n.s.) no.6,August,1913)
Bibliography: ₍ ₎-142.
1.Lichens - Ireland - Howth I.Title.

NK 0210122 MiU PU-B

Knowles, Matilda Cullen, 1865- joint author

Farran, G P.
... Results of a biological survey of Blacksod Bay, co. Mayo, comp. by G. P. Farran, with notes on the lichenes by M. C. Knowles and on the Tunicata by R. Hartmeyer ... London, H. M. Stationery off., Printed by Browne and Nolan, ltd., Dublin, 1915.

Knowles, May Wynne
see Knowles, Mabel Winifred, 1875-

275.2 K76

Knowles, Merle.
Progress report of neighborhood group work among 4-H club girls in Glade School Community, Jones County, December, 1949. [n.p., 1949?]
7 l.

1. 4-H clubs.

NK 0210125 DNAL

Knowles, Michael Clive
see **Knowles, David,** *Father,* 1896-

Knowles, Michael David, *Father*
see **Knowles, David,** *Father,* 1896-

Knowles, Morris, 1869-
...Cantonment construction, by Morris Knowles... ₍Pittsburgh?, 1918.₎ p. 192-225. illus., plates. 8°.
Repr.: Engineers' Soc. of Western Pa. Proc. v. 34. 1918.

1. Military training camps.
N. Y. P. L.

NK 0210128 NN

VOLUME 300

628.1 Knowles, Morris, 1869-
K76d Description of experimental filter plant at Pittsburgh and results of experiments. [Pittsburgh, 1900]
p.148-88 illus.

Reprinted from Journal of the New England water works association, vol.XV., no.2.

NK 0210129 IU OU

Knowles, Morris, 1869-
Engineering problems of regional planning, by Morris Knowles... [Boston?] National Conference on City Planning [192-?]. 24 p. 8°.

1. Regional planning. 2. National Conference on City Planning.
N. Y. P. L.

NK 0210130 NN

Knowles, Morris, 1869-
Fair average prices in cost of reproduction and the trend of prices after the war. By Morris Knowles ... before New Jersey utilities association, Atlantic City, May 31, 1919 ... [Philadelphia, Automatic printing & stationery co.] ©1919.
cover-title, 15 p. diagrs. 23cm.

1. Public utilities—Valuation 2. Prices. I. Title.
Library of Congress HD2765.K7 19-12151

NK 0210131 DLC

Knowles, Morris, 1869-
Industrial housing; with discussion of accompanying activities; such as town planning—street systems—development of utility services—and related engineering and construction features. By Morris Knowles ... 1st ed. New York [etc.] McGraw-Hill book company, inc., 1920.
xxv, 408 p. illus. (incl. plans) 24cm.
Bibliography: p. 388-393.

1. Labor and laboring classes—Dwellings. 2. Housing. 3. Cities and towns—Planning. I. Title.
Library of Congress HD7287.K6 20-16847

DL OC1 MU NcRS WaS CaBVaU PBm PU PP
NK 0210132 DLC OOxM ODW OU MH MiHM MB TU ViU NN ICU

Knowles, Morris, 1869-
Pittsburgh. *Filtration commission.*
Report of the Filtration commission of the city of Pittsburgh, Pennsylvania, January, 1899. [Pittsburgh? 1899?]

Knowles, Morris, 1869-
Report upon metropolitan water and sewerage systems, to the Essex border utilities commission, Ontario, Canada, by Morris Knowles, consulting engineer. Windsor, Ont., The Record printing company, limited, 1917.
108 p. illus., fold. plans, fold. tables, fold. diagrs. 23cm.

1. Water-supply—Ontario—Essex Co. 2. Sewerage—Ontario—Essex Co. I. Ontario. Essex border utilities commission. II. Title: Metropolitan water and sewerage systems, Report upon.
Library of Congress TD27.E8K 19-9400

NK 0210134 DLC

Knowles (Morris) inc.
Abstracts of reports upon several phases of a city plan for greater Wheeling. Wheeling Improvement association, Wheeling, W. Va., 1920. Pittsburgh,[1920]
37 p. illus. (part. fold.) plans (part fold.) tables. 29 cm.
Cover title.
1. Cities and towns - Planning - Wheeling, W. Va.

NK 0210135 NcU

Knowles (Morris) inc.
A city plan for the city of Hopewell, Virginia, 1929[-1930] ... Pittsburgh, Cleveland, M. Knowles, incorporated [1930?]
1 v. maps (part fold.) tables (part fold.) diagrs. 28½cm.
Reproduced from type-written copy.
Each part has special t.-p. and table of contents.
CONTENTS.—Growth and development of Hopewell.—Thoroughfares and the street system.—Transportation; rail, water and air.—Parks, playgrounds and schools.—A five-year improvement program.—Proposed zoning ordinance.—Legislative considerations.

1. Cities and towns—Planning. 2. Hopewell, Va.—Public works. I. Hopewell, Va. Ordinances, etc. II. Title.
Library of Congress NA9127.H6K6 42-30681

NK 0210136 DLC

KNOWLES (MORRIS) INC.
Preliminary report and program for city planning at Canton, Ohio. The City Planning Commission, December 1924. Morris Knowles, Incorporated... [Pittsburgh? 1924] 43 p. incl. chart, tables. 22½cm.

815712A. 1. Cities—Plans—U.S.—O.—Canton. I. Canton, O. City Planning Commission.

NK 0210137 NN ICU

Knowles (Morris) inc.
Preliminary report to the City planning commission of the city of Easton, Pennsylvania, 1948. [Easton, 1948] 7 f. 36cm.
Report made by Morris Knowles, inc., at the request of the commission.

I. Easton, Pa. City planning commission.
N. Y. P. L.

NK 0210138 NN

710.1 Knowles (Morris) inc.
K76e A progress report on the comprehensive general plan for Erie, Pa. [Erie, Pa., City Planning Commission [1955?]
40p. illus., col.maps. 29cm.

1. Cities and towns--Planning--Erie, Pa. I. Erie, Pa.--City Planning Commission.

NK 0210139 IU

Knowles (Morris) inc.
Report upon a thoroughfare plan for the city of Canton, Ohio. The City Planning Commission, December, 1926. Morris Knowles, Incorporated... [Pittsburgh? 1927?] 80 p. charts, plans, tables. 28cm.
Reproduced from typewritten copy; cover printed.

718617A. 1. Traffic—U. S.—O.—Canton, 1926. 2. Canton, O.—Streets. I. Canton, O. City Planning Commission.
N. Y. P. L.

NK 0210140 NN OC1

Knowles (Morris) inc.
Report upon certain phases of a city plan for the city of High Point, N. C., July, 1928 ... Morris Knowles, incorporated, engineers ... [High Point, N. C., Printed by Barber-Hall printing co., 1929]
83 p. incl. illus., plans (part fold.) diagrs. 31 x 23½cm.
Submitted to the City planning commission.
CONTENTS.—Proposed thoroughfare and railroad grade elimination plan.—Proposed park and school plan.

1. Cities and towns—Planning. 2. High Point, N. C.—Public works. I. High Point, N. C. City planning commission.
Library of Congress NA9127.H45K6 31-16531
[2] 917.56

NK 0210141 DLC NN

Knowles (Morris) inc.
Street and road map, Pittsburgh metropolitan district. Pittsburgh, Municipal Planning Association, ©1921.
12 maps 66 x 99 cm.
Scale ca. 1:12,000.
Blueprint.
In upper margins: Citizens Committee on City Plan of Pittsburgh.

1. Pittsburgh—Maps. 2. Cities and towns—Planning—Pittsburgh—Maps. I. Citizens Committee on City Plan of Pittsburgh. II. Title.
G3824s.P6 12.K6 Map 67-345

NK 0210142 DLC

Knowles (Morris) inc.
Street map, Pittsburgh. Pittsburgh, Municipal Planning Association, ©1921.
20 maps 66 x 96 cm.
Scale ca. 1:4,800.
Blueprint.
In upper margins: Citizens Committee on City Plan of Pittsburgh.

1. Pittsburgh—Maps. 2. Cities and towns—Planning—Pittsburgh—Maps. I. Citizens Committee on City Plan of Pittsburgh. II. Title.
G3824s.P6 4.K6 Map 67-360

NK 0210143 DLC

Knowles (Morris) inc.
Topographical map, Pittsburgh. Pittsburgh, Municipal Planning Association, ©1921.
20 maps 68 x 98 cm.
Scale 1:4,800.
Blueprint.
Relief shown by contours.
In upper margins: Citizens Committee on City Plan of Pittsburgh.

1. Pittsburgh—Maps, Topographic. 2. Cities and towns—Planning—Pittsburgh—Maps. I. Citizens Committee on City Plan of Pittsburgh. II. Title.
G3824s.P6C1 4.K61 Map 67-359

NK 0210144 DLC

Knowles, Nathaniel, 1899-
The torture of captives by the Indians of eastern North America ... [by] Nathaniel Knowles ... Philadelphia, 1940.
1 p. l., p. 151-225. 25½cm.
Thesis (PH. D.)—University of Pennsylvania, 1939.
"Reprint from Proc. Amer. philosophical society, vol. 82, no. 2, 1940."
Bibliography: p. 220-225.

1. Torture. 2. Indians of North America—Captivities.
Library of Congress E85.K67 40-11990
Univ. of Pennsylvania Libr 970.6899

NK 0210145 PU MtU GU NcU PHC PPTU PU OC1 NNC ViU DLC

Knowles, Neale S.
Outlines in home economics, one-half year course
see under Iowa. Dept. of Public Instruction.

Knowles, Neale S., and others.
Planning and serving meals [by] Neale S. Knowles, Louise H. Campbell, Mabel C. Bentley... [Ames, Ia.: Ia. State College of Agriculture and Mechanic Arts, 1916.] 32 p., 1 col'd pl. illus., tables. 8°. (Iowa State College of Agriculture and Mechanic Arts. Home economics bull. no. 1.)
Caption-title.
Plate printed on both sides.

1. Cookery (American). 2. Campbell, Louise Hathaway, jt. au. 3. Bentley, Mabel C., jt. au. 4. Title.
N. Y. P. L.

NK 0210147 NN

VOLUME 300

Knowles, Neale S.
... Principles of domestic science, applied to preparation of food. By Neale S. Knowles. Harrisburg, C. E. Aughinbaugh, printer to the state of Pennsylvania, 1909.
42 p. front., plates. 23½cm. (Commonwealth of Pennsylvania. Department of agriculture. Bulletin no. 188)

1. Cookery. 2. Domestic economy.
Agr 10-1760
Library, U. S. Dept. of Agriculture 2P38B no. 188

NK 0210148 DNAL MiU OCl NN

Knowles, Norman.
Tables showing the production of slubbing, intermediate, and roving frames; also of mules, ring and flyer throstles. By Norman Knowles... Manchester [etc.] J. Heywood, 1885. 77 p. 8 x 15cm.

1. Yarn—Tables, calculations, etc.
N. Y. P. L.

NK 0210149 NN

Knowles, Paulden Ford, 1916-
A study of Bromus mollis L. and its hybrids with other Bromus species, by Paulden Ford Knowles ... [Berkeley, Calif., 1943]
3 p.l., 123 numb. l. incl. mounted plates, fold. map, tables. 29 cm.
Thesis (Ph.D.) - Univ. of California, Feb. 194:
"Literature list": p. 117-123.
1. Hybridization, Vegetable. 2. Brome-grass.

NK 0210150 CU

Knowles, R. J.

Tonkin, A S
The law and special taxation of private companies in New Zealand. Part I. The law of private companies, by A. S. Tonkin ... Part II. Special taxation of proprietary companies, by R. J. Knowles ... Wellington, N. Z. [etc.] [Butterworth & co., ltd. (Aus.); etc., etc.] 1945.

Knowles, Reginald L., illus.

Parr, Harriet, 1828-1900.
Legends from fairy land, narrating the history of Prince Glee & Princess Trill, the cruel persecutions & condign punishment of Aunt Spite, the adventures of the great Tuflongbo, & the story of the blackcap in the giant's well; by Holme Lee [pseud.] With illustrations by Reginald L. Knowles & Horace J. Knowles, & an introduction by Effie H. Freemantle. London, Chatto & Windus; Philadelphia, J. B. Lippincott co., 1908.

KNOWLES, Richard.
Phonetic tendency in Romance languages.
Thesis, [Harvard University, 1931].

Typewritten. 4°. ff.(1), VI, 103.
"Bibliography", ff. III-VI.

NK 0210153 MH

Knowles, Richard, 1550?-1610.
see Knolles, Richard, 1550?-1610.

Knowles, Richard Brinsley, 1820-1882.
Ashburnham manuscriptes ...
see under Gt. Brit. Parliament. House of Commons.

KNOWLES, Richard Brinsley, 1820-1882.
The life of James Sheridan Knowles. Privately printed for James McHenry. London, [Chiswick press], 1872.

2 vol. f°. Extra-illustrated.
"25 copies printed."
Extended to 2 folio volumes by the insertion of portraits, play-bills, etc.,

NK 0210156 MH CtY

Knowles, Richard Brinsley, 1820-1882.
The life of James Sheridan Knowles, by his son, Richard Brinsley Knowles. London, Priv. print. for James M'Henry, 1872.
xi, 177 p. 33cm.
"Revised and edited by Francis Harvey."
"List of works written and edited by James Sheridan Knowles": p. [v]-ix;
"Books relating to James Sheridan Knowles": p. ix-xi.
"Only twenty-five copies."

1. Knowles, James Sheridan, 1784-1862. 2. Knowles, James Sheridan, 1784-1862—Bibl. I. Harvey, Francis, 1830-1899, ed.
25-24741
Library of Congress PR4859.K5Z65

NK 0210157 DLC InU TxHU PBL OU NjP NcU

Knowles, Richard Brinsley, 1820-1882.
The maiden aunt; a comedy, by Richard Brinsley Knowles. London: E. Moxon, 1845. 62 p. 16°
Mutilated: front edges of leaves torn and stained.

1. Drama (English). 2. Title.
N. Y. P. L.

NK 0210158 NN PP InU MiU NIC CSmH MH

Knowles, Richard Brinsley, 1820-1882.
The Maiden Aunt; a story. New York, 1849.

NK 0210159 PPL

Knowles, Richard Brinsley, 1820-1882.
The manuscripts of Colonel Towneley, at Towneley hall, Burnley.
(*In* Gt. Brit. Historical manuscripts commission. Fourth report. London, 1874. 32cm. Appendix, p. 406-416)
"Colonel Towneley's collection ... contains ... [a manuscript] which contributes a valuable addition to the life of ... [Edmund Spenser]"— p. 406.
—— —— Supplementary note to Colonel Towneley's manuscripts.
(*In* Gt. Brit. Historical manuscripts commission. Fourth report. London, 1874. 32cm. Appendix, p. 613-614)
Signed: R. B. Knowles.
1. Spenser, Edmund, 1552?-1599. I. Towneley, Charles, 1803-1876.
A C 40-594
ALA-Coop. cataloging com. for Library of Congress [DA25.M1 vol. 4]
[3] (942.0061)

NK 0210160 DLC

Knowles, Richard Brinsley, 1820-1882.
Gt. Brit. *Historical manuscripts commission.*
The manuscripts of the Earl of Ashburnham. [London, Printed by G. E. Eyre and W. Spottiswoode for H. M. Stationery off., 1881]

[Knowles, Richard Brinsley] 1820-1882.
The manuscripts of the Earl of Ashburnham.
(*In* Gt. Brit. Historical manuscripts commission. Eighth report. London, 1881. 32cm. Appendix, pt. III, p. [1]-110)
"Mr. [R. B.] Knowles' ... report."—8th rept., p. [vii]

I. Ashburnham, Bertram Ashburnham, 5th earl of, 1840-1913.
A 42-5246
ALA-Coop. cataloging com. for Library of Congress [DA25.M1 vol. 8]
[3] (942.0061)

NK 0210162 DLC

Knowles, Richard Brinsley, 1820-1882.
The manuscripts of the Most Honourable the Marquis of Bute, at Eccleston square.
(*In* Gt. Brit. Historical manuscripts commission. Third report. London, 1872. 32cm. Appendix, p. 202-209)
Signed: R. B. Knowles.

I. Bute, John Patrick Crichton-Stuart, 3d marquis of, 1847-1900.
A C 39-2295
ALA-Coop. cataloging comm. for Library of Congress [DA25.M1 vol. 3]
[4] (942.0061)

NK 0210163 DLC

Knowles, Richard Brinsley, 1820-1882.
The manuscripts of the Right Honourable the Earl of Denbigh at Newnham Paddox.
(*In* Gt. Brit. Historical manuscripts commission. Fourth, sixth-eighth report. London, 1874-81. 32cm. 4th rept., app., p. 254-276; 6th rept., app., p. 277-287; 7th rept., app., p. 196-232; 8th rept., app., pt. I, p. 552-572)
Signed: R. B. Knowles.
Title varies: pt. 1, The manuscripts of the Right Honourable the Earl of Denbigh at Newnham Paddox; pt. 2, The Earl of Denbigh's manuscripts. (Second report.); pt. 3, The Earl of Denbigh's manuscripts. (Third report.); pt. 4, The manuscripts of the Earl of Denbigh. (Concluding notice.)
Part 5, prepared by Mrs. S. C. Lomas, published separately as an unnumbered report of the Gt. Brit. Historical manuscripts commission.
I. Denbigh, Rudolph William Basil Feilding, 8th earl of, 1823-1892.
ALA-Coop. cataloging com. for Library of Congress A C 40-671
[DA25.M1 vol. 4, 6-8]
[2] (942.0061)

NK 0210164 DLC

Knowles, Richard Brinsley, 1820-1882
The story of a family. By the author of the Maiden Aunt, R. B. Knowles. Boston, 1850.

NK 0210165 PPL

Knowles, Richard Brinsley, 1820-1882.
The use of sunshine. By the author of the Maiden Aunt, R. B. Knowles. New York, 1852.

NK 0210166 PPL

Knowles, Richard E
Victor-Émile Michelet, poète ésotérique. Préf. de Gaston Bachelard. Paris, J. Vrin, 1954.
xii, 308 p. port. 20 cm. (Essais d'art et de philosophie)
Bibliography: p. 285-305.

1. Michelet, Victor Émile, 1861-1938.
A 55-925
Illinois. Univ. Library for Library of Congress [1]

NK 0210167 IU CaBVaU MiU CtY NNC MH ViU IaU NN

Knowles, Richard George, 1858- , and R. Morton.
...Baseball, by R. G. Knowles and Richard Morton... London: G. Routledge & Sons, Ltd., 1896. 132 p. diagrs., front., illus., plates, ports. 12°. (The "oval" series of games. v. 8.)

22542A. 1. Baseball. 2. Morton, Richard, jt. au. 3. Series.
N. Y. P. L.

NK 0210168 NN MiD

Knowles, Richard George, 1858-
R. G. Knowles' Knowledge of the world and its ways. Being a collection of stories told by R. G. Knowles ... and chronicled by Richard Morton. Together with a biographical sketch and a critical appreciation by Richard Morton. London, Francis, Day, & Hunter; New York, T. B. Harms & co. [1894]
105 p. 19cm.

I. Morton, Richard. II. Title: Knowledge of the world and its ways.
12-14074
Library of Congress PN6161.K7

NK 0210169 DLC

VOLUME 300

828
K733m Knowles, Richard George, 1858-
A modern Columbus, by R.G.Knowles. His voyages. His travels. His discoveries... London, T.W.Laurie [n.d,]
xii,301,[1] p.incl.front.(port.) plates. 22½ cm.
Reminiscences.

NK 0210170 MiU

Knowles, Richard George, 1858-
A modern Columbus, by R. G. Knowles; his voyages, his travels, his discoveries ... London, T. W. Laurie, ltd. [1915]
xii, 301, [1] p., 1 l. incl. front. (port.) plates. 22½cm.
An autobiography.

1. Actors—Correspondence, reminiscences, etc. I. Title.

18-1390

Library of Congress PN2598.K75A3

NK 0210171 DLC ViU CtY NN

Knowles, Richard George, 1858-
Of stories—just a few, by R. G. Knowles. New York, London [etc.] M. Witmark & sons [1904]
4 p. l., 178 p. front. (port.) illus. 20cm.

4-8884

NK 0210172 DLC

Knowles, Richard Mark
see Knowles, Mark, 1882-

F
4055
.467
KNOWLES, ROBERT, 1790-1813.
The war in the Peninsula; some letters of Lieut. Robert Knowles, a Bolton officer. Arranged by his great-great-nephew Sir Lees Knowles, bart.... Bolton-le-Moors, Lancashire, 1909.
69p.

"Reprinted from the Bolton 'Journal and guardian'."

NK 0210174 ICN

Knowles, Robert, 1790-1813.
The war in the Peninsula; some letters of Lieutenant Robert Knowles, of the 7th, or Royal, fusiliers, a Lancashire officer. Arranged and annotated by his great-great-nephew Sir Lees Knowles, baronet ... July 25th, 1913. Bolton, Tillotson & son, ltd, 1913.
92 p. incl. geneal. tab. front., pl., 3 maps (2 fold.) 21cm.

1. Peninsular war, 1807-1814—Personal narratives. I. Knowles, Sir Lees, 1st bart., 1857- ed. II. Title.

14-14231

Library of Congress DC232.K6

NK 0210175 DLC CaBVaU

W 1
CA207
1933
Suppl.
KNOWLES, Robert, 1883-
The Calcutta School of Tropical Medicine, 1920-1933; an essay-review. Alipore, Bengal, Bengal Govt. Press, 1934.
168, xlvii p. (Supplement to the Annual report of the school for 1933)
1. Calcutta. School of Tropical Medicine Series: Calcutta. School of Tropical Medicine. Annual report ... 1933, suppl.

NK 0210176 DNLM IU

Knowles, Robert, 1883-
An introduction to medical protozoology, with chapters on the spirochætes and on laboratory methods. By Robert Knowles ... Calcutta, Thacker, Spink & co., 1928.
xii, 887 p. illus., xiv (i. e. 15) pl. (part col., 1 fold.) diagrs. 25cm.
"References" at end of each chapter in part II.
"References to literature": p. [771]-862.

1. Protozoa, Pathogenic. I. Title: Medical protozoology.

Agr 28-1540

Library, U. S. Dept. of Agriculture 436K76

NK 0210177 DNAL NcD CU MiU OU PPC PU-Z

QX
50
K73i
1944
KNOWLES, Robert, 1883-
Introduction to medical protozoology. 2d ed., rev. and abridged by B. M. Das Gupta. Calcutta, Dhur, 1944.
xviii, 323 p. illus., port.
1. Protozoa - Pathogenic
I. Das Gupta, Biraj Mohan, 1889-

NK 0210178 DNLM CU

WC
750
K73m
1927
KNOWLES, Robert, 1883-
Malaria, its investigation and control with special reference to Indian conditions, by Robert Knowles and Ronald Senior-White. Calcutta, Thacker, Spink, 1927.
vi, 220 p. illus.
1. Malaria 2. Malaria - India
I. Senior-White, Ronald

NK 0210179 DNLM CU ICU PPC IU-M

Knowles, Robert, 1883-
... Puzzles and fallacies in the examination of stained films in the tropics, by Lieut.-Col. R. Knowles ... Lieut.-Col. Hugh W. Acton ... and Assistant-Surgeon B. M. Das Gupta ... Calcutta, Pub. for the Indian research fund association by Thacker, Spink & co. [1929]
1 p. l., 35, [7] p. VII pl. (part col.) 25 cm. (Indian medical research memoirs. no. 13. June, 1929)
"References": p. 30-35.

1. Blood—Examination. I. Acton, Hugh William, joint author. II. Das Gupta, B. M., joint author. III. Title.

A 33-375

Princeton Univ. Libr. for Library of Congress [a57d½]

NK 0210180 NjP MiU

Knowles, Robert, 1883-
... Studies in avian spirochaetosis. Parts I & II. By Lieut.-Colonel R. Knowles ... Assist. Surgeon B. M. Das Gupta ... and B. C. Basu ... Calcutta, Pub. for the Indian research fund association by Thacker, Spink & co., ltd. [1932]
2 p. l., 113 p. incl. tables, diagr. 11 pl. on 9 l. 25cm. (Indian medical research memoirs ... no. 22, February, 1932)
"References": p. 103-113.
CONTENTS.—pt. I. Review of the previous literature, 1891 to 1930.—pt. II. Report of the Spirochaetosis transmission inquiry under the Indian research fund association, at the Calcutta school of tropical medicine, 1927 to 1931.
1. Poultry—Diseases. 2. Blood—Parasites. I. Das Gupta, Biraj Mohan, 1889- joint author. II. Basu, B. C., joint author.

A 33-816

Title from Princeton Univ. Printed by L. C.

NK 0210181 NjP PPC NNC

Knowles, Robert, 1883-
... Studies in the parasitology of malaria. By Lieut.-Colonel R. Knowles ... and R. Senior White ... assisted by Assistant Surgeon B. M. Das Gupta ... Calcutta, Pub. for the Indian research fund association by Thacker, Spink & co. [1930]
xii, 436 p. col. pl., XII maps (part fold.) tables (1 fold.) diagrs. 25cm. (Indian medical research memoirs; supplementary series to the Indian journal of medical research. Memoir no. 18, December, 1930)
Label mounted on cover: Constituting Appendix C of the Annual report for 1930 of the Calcutta school of tropical medicine and hygiene.
"References": p. 404-436.
1. Malarial fever. I. Senior-White, Ronald, joint author. II. Das Gupta, Biraj Mohan, 1889- III. Indian research fund association.

A 33-335 Revised †

Princeton univ. Library for Library of Congress R111.I 55 no. 18 [a37c1]† (610.72) 614.53

NK 0210182 NjP MiU PU-Z DLC

Knowles, Robert Edward, 1868-
The attic guest. N.Y., Revell, 1903.
202 p.

NK 0210183 PPCCH

Knowles, Robert Edward, 1868-
The attic guest; a novel, by Robert E. Knowles ... New York, Chicago [etc.] F. H. Revell company [c1909]
3 p. l., 9-402 p. 20cm. $1.20

9-26805

Library of Congress PZ3.K764At

NK 0210184 DLC OU CaOTP CaBVaU TxU OC1 OC1W

Knowles, Robert Edward, 1868-
The dawn at Shanty Bay, by Robert E. Knowles. [Chicago, New York, etc.] F. H. Revell company [c1907]
156 p. incl. col. front., illus. 21cm.
Decorated by Griselda Marshall McClure.

I. Title.

7-39193

Library of Congress PZ3.K764Da

NK 0210185 DLC TxU NN CaBVaU

Knowles, Robert Edward, 1868-
The handicap; a novel of pioneer days, by Robert E. Knowles ... New York, Chicago [etc.] Fleming H. Revell company [c1910]
2 p. l., 7-386 p. 19½cm. $1.20

10-24901

Library of Congress PZ3.K764H

NK 0210186 DLC TxU OU WaS CaBVa CaBVaU

Knowles, Robert Edward, 1868-
St. Cuthbert's; a novel [by] Robert E. Knowles. New York, Chicago [etc.] F. H. Revell company [c1905]
339 p. 20cm.

I. Title.

5-32322

Library of Congress PZ3.K764S

MH ViU NcD TxU TNJ OU
NK 0210187 DLC CaBVaU WaS PPGi PPL OC1W OC1 MiU

PR 6021
N529 S2
1909
Knowles, Robert Edward, 1868-
St. Cuthbert's; a novel [by] Robert E. Knowles. New York, Grosset & Dunlap [1909, c1905]
339 p. 20 cm.

"Special limited edition."

NK 0210188 OU PP

Knowles, Robert Edward, 1868-
The singer of the Kootenay; a tale of to-day, by Robert E. Knowles ... New York, Chicago [etc.] Fleming H. Revell company [c1911]
2 p. l., 7-368 p. 19½cm. $1.25

I. Title.

11-26610

Library of Congress PZ3.K764Si

PPGi MH WaU
NK 0210189 DLC WaSp Or CaBVaU CaBViPA CaBVa ViU

VOLUME 300

Knowles, Robert Edward, 1868–
The undertow; a tale of both sides of the sea [by] Robert E. Knowles ... New York, Chicago [etc.] F. H. Revell company [c1906]
403 p. 20cm.

I. Title.
6—38396
Library of Congress PZ3.K764Un

NK 0210190 DLC OU NcU TxU CaBVaU CaBVa PPL PPGi

Knowles, Robert Edward, 1868–
The undertow. Toronto, McClelland and Stewart limited [c1935]

NK 0210191 CaBVaU

Knowles, Robert Edward, 1868–
The web of time, by Robert E. Knowles ... New York, Chicago [etc.] F. H. Revell company [c1908]
415 p. 20½cm.

I. Title.
8-31462
Library of Congress PZ3.K764W

NK 0210192 DLC WaU TxU CaBVaU OCl OClW MH

TK7 .G4 no.67 1951
Knowles, Robert W
Precision bridges for instrument transformer testing, by R. W. Knowles and N. T. Kohlhardt. Pittsfield, Mass., Apparatus Dept., General Electric [Co.] 1951.
[4] p. illus. 28cm. (General Electric [Co.] Pittsfield Laboratory. Apparatus Dept. Contributions, no. 67)
Cover title.
"Reprinted from General electric review, Nov. 1951, pp. 14-17".
Bibliography: p. [4]
1. Electric transformers—Testing. I. Kohlhardt, Norman T jt. author. II. Title. III. Title: Instrument transformer testing. IV. Ser.

NK 0210193 ViU

Knowles, Rollin Henry
An encyclopedia-dictionary and reference handbook of the ophthalmic sciences. Designed to give, in complete and accurate statement, and in the readiest form for popular use, the orthography, pronunciation, meaning and etymology of all the words and terms used in the ophthalmic science. By R. H. Knowles, M. D. New York, The Jewelers' circular publishing co., 1903.
3 p. l., 491, [1] p. illus., diagrs. 26cm.
3-15481

NK 0210194 DLC DNLM ICJ NNC ViU PPJ

Knowles, Rollin Henry.
Eye defects; how to detect and correct them. By R. H. Knowles ... New York, Spencer optical mfg. co. [c1898]
96 p. illus., diagrs. 23½ cm.

1. Eye—Examination. 2. Eyeglasses. I. Spencer optical co., firm, New York.
RE981.K73 7—14344

NK 0210195 DLC DNLM

Knowles, Ruth, 1899–
A boon book of poems, by Ruth Knowles. Indiana, Pa., Printing house of Park [c1931]
30 p. 24½cm.

I. Title. [Full name: Ruth Loretta Rosecrans Knowles]
31-21730
Library of Congress PS3521.N76B6 1931
Copyright A 38042 [2] 811.5

NK 0210196 DLC

BV4501 .T7
Knowles, Ruth Gawthrop (Moore) 1879– comp.
Tomkins, Floyd Williams, 1850–1932.
Sunshine on life's way; being selections from the writings of the Rev. Floyd W. Tomkins ... collected by Mrs. Winthrop Curtis Knowles. New York, E. P. Dutton & company, 1913.

Knowles, Ruth (Sheldon) 1915–
Hubbin' it; the life of Bob Wills, by Ruth Sheldon ... [Kingsport, Tenn., Kingsport press, inc., 1938]
vii, 147 p. front., ports. 21 cm.
Frontispiece (portrait) laid in.
Music: p. 145–147.

1. Wills, James Robert, 1905– I. Title.
ML422.W6K6 927.8 38–15348 rev

NK 0210198 DLC Wa OrU TxU

PR 4859 .K58 D68
KNOWLES,S
Done Brown! Manchester, J. Brook & Co. [etc.,etc.] n. d.
[297]-310 p. 18 cm. (Laughable Dialogues, no. 22)

NK 0210199 InU

Knowles, S.
The gospel in Gonda: being a narrative of events in connection with the preaching of the gospel in the Trans-Gha'gra' country. By the Rev. S. Knowles ... With an introduction by the Rev. J. W. Waugh, D. D. Lucknow, Printed at the Methodist publishing house, 1889.
x, 248 p. 19cm.
5-42807

NK 0210200 DLC CtY-D CU

Knowles, Sarah Elizabeth Mary
see
Bolton, *Mrs.* **Sarah (Knowles) 1841–1916.**

Knowles, Sheridan
SEE
Knowles, James Sheridan

Knowles, Susanne.
Birth of Venus, and other poems by Susanne Knowles. London, Macmillan & co. ltd, 1945.
vi, 33, [1] p. 19cm.

I. Title.
45-6859
Library of Congress PR6021.N49B5
[3] 821.91

NK 0210203 DLC FMU

Maryland BT 980 .K5
Knowles, Thomas
Satan's devices exposed, in four sermons ... Annapolis, Published by George Shaw & co.,1812.
1 v. (various pagings) 14 cm.

1. Devil. I. Title.

NK 0210204 MdU

---

*EC7 C5797 751ec
Knowles, Thomas, 1723-1802.
An answer to An essay on spirit [by Robert Clayton]: wherein it is shewn, that the author's interpretation of Scripture is imperfect: and his representation of the opinions of the antient Fathers, unfair. By Thomas Knowles ...
London:Printed for C.Bathurst,at the Cross-Keys in Fleetstreet.MDCCLIII. (Price eighteen-pence.
8°. 120p. 20.5cm.
No.3 in a volume bound for Thomas Hollis with his emblem stamped in gilt on front & back covers.

NK 0210205 MH

231.4 K73e
Knowles, Thomas, 1723-1802.
The existence and attributes of God not demonstrable à priori; in answer to the arguments of the learned Dr. Clarke, and his followers... Cambridge, Printed by J. Bentham, 1746.
95p. 20cm.

With this is bound the author's The scripture-doctrine of the excellence and attributes of God. Cambridge, 1750.

NK 0210206 IEN MWA CBPac

Knowles, Thomas, 1723-1802, ed.
Hervey, John Hervey, *baron,* 1696–1743.
Letters between Lord Hervey and Dr. Middleton concerning the Roman Senate. Pub. from the original manuscripts, by Thomas Knowles. London, Printed for W. Strahan [etc.] 1778.

Mhc9 K763 P3
Knowles, Thomas, 1723-1802
The passion; or, A descriptive and critical narrative of the incidents, as they occurred, on each day of the week in which Christ's sufferings are commemorated, with reflexions calculated for religious improvement. London, Printed for L.Davis,1780.
213p. 17cm.

NK 0210208 CtY

Knowles, Thomas, 1723-1802.
Primitive Christianity; or, Testimonies from the writers of the first four centuries; to prove that Jesus Christ was worshipped, as God, from the beginning of the Christian Church. London, L. Davis, 1789.
viii, 124 p. 21 cm.
1. Church history - Primitive and early church.

NK 0210209 MdBP MH-AH

231.4 K73e
Knowles, Thomas, 1723-1802.
The scripture-doctrine of the excellence and attributes of God.... To which is prefixed a pref., in answer to a late pamphlet, entitled, Some thoughts concerning the argument à priori... Cambridge, Printed by J. Bentham, 1750.
xxxiv,[10],369p. [With his The existence and attributes of God. Cambridge, 1746]

NK 0210210 IEN

VOLUME 300

W 4 L66 1772 K.1 KNOWLES, Thomas, d. 1786
Tentamen medicum inaugurale de vita sedentaria ... Lugduni Batavorum, Apud Theodorum Haak, 1772.
32 p. 24 cm.
Diss. - Leyden.

NK 0210211 DNLM

823 K764b Knowles, Vernon, 1899-
Beads of coloured days; a study in behaviour. London, W. Gardner, Darton [1926]
vii, 358p. 19cm.
A novel.

NK 0210212 TxU

PR 6021 .N5 B9 Knowles, Vernon, 1899-
Bypaths. Adelaide, G. Hassell, 1921.
15 p. 19 cm. (in binder, 22)

NK 0210213 WU TxU

Knowles, Vernon, 1899-
The experience of poetry, by Vernon Knowles. London, G. Newnes limited [1935]
128 p. 18cm.
Contents.—The fear of poetry.—From the beginning.—The man himself.—Give sorrow words.—Sermons in stones.—Scanty plot of ground.—Behind the veil.—A tale to tell.—The present adventure.
1. Poetry. I. Title.
A 37-175
Ohio. State univ. Library for Library of Congress PN1075.K73 [2]

NK 0210214 OU LU NN WaSpG

823 K764h Knowles, Vernon, 1899-
Here and otherwhere. London, R. Holden [1926]
ix, 257p. illus. 21cm.
Short stories.

NK 0210215 TxU ICarbS

Knowles, Vernon, 1899-
The ladder, by Vernon Knowles. Frontispiece drawing by Eric Bailey. London, Mandrake press, 1929. 98 p. front. 16cm. (Mandrake booklets.)

NK 0210216 NN ICN ICarbS MH

Knowles, Vernon, 1899-
Love is my enemy. London, Hammond, Hammond [1947]
55 p. 21 cm.
Poems.
I. Title.
A 49-2652*
New York. Public Libr for Library of Congress [1]

NK 0210217 NN MH

Knowles, Vernon, 1899-
Poems, by Vernon Knowles. London, W. Gardner, Darton & co. ltd. [1925]
viii, 56 p. 21cm. 6/-
25-23082
Library of Congress PR6021.N5P6 1925

NK 0210218 DLC TxU

Knowles, Vernon, 1899-
Prince Jonathan; a dramatic lyric, by Vernon Knowles. London: Simpkin, Marshall, Ltd., 1935. 49 p. 22½cm.
790348A. N. Y. P. L. 1. Poetry, English. I. Title.

NK 0210219 NN CtY

821 K764r Knowles, Vernon, 1899-
The ripening years. London, R. Holden [1927]
32p. 21cm.
Poems.

NK 0210220 TxU

821 K764s Knowles, Vernon, 1899-
Songs and preludes. Adelaide, Publishers Limited, printers, 1917.
38p. 19cm.

NK 0210221 TxU

PR 6021 N5 S7 1924 Knowles, Vernon, 1899-
The street of queer houses and other stories. Illus. by William Saphier. New York, Boullion-Biggs [1924]
156 p. illus.

NK 0210222 NSyU

Knowles, Vernon,
The street of queer houses and other tales, by Vernon Knowles. London: W. Gardner, Darton & Co., Ltd.[, 1925.] vii, 225 p. incl. plates. 8°.
Contents: The street of queer houses. The weeping god. A matter of characterization. The house of yesterdays. The three gods. The pendant. The author who entered his ms. The mask. The man who was troubled by his shadow. The book of the thousand answers. The idealist. The broken statue. The house that took revenge. The Elizabethan gown. Honeymoon cottage.
226571A. N. Y. P. L. 1. Fiction, English. 2. Title.

NK 0210223 NN

823.91 K73t Knowles, Vernon, 1899-
Two and two make five. London, Newnes [1935]
255p.
Short stories.

NK 0210224 ICarbS

Knowles, Vincent Devereux.
Evidence in brief; a clear and concise statement of the principles of evidence. London, E. Wilson, 1905.
154 p. 19 cm.
1. Evidence (Law)—Gt. Brit.
58-51867 ‡

NK 0210225 DLC ICRL

KNOWLES, V[incent] Devereux.
Evidence in Brief. 2d ed. London, 1910.
xxiv+154 p.

NK 0210226 MH-L

Knowles, Vincent Devereux.
Evidence in brief; a clear and concise statement of the principles of evidence, by V. Devereux Knowles ... 3d ed. London, E. Wilson, 1913.
xxviii, 154 p. 19cm.
1. Evidence (Law)
22-15283

NK 0210227 DLC

Knowles, Vincent Devereux.
Knowles's Evidence in brief; a clear and concise statement of the principles of evidence, by Albert Lieck ... and Sophie Lieck ... 4th ed. London, Sir I. Pitman & sons, ltd., 1933.
xxvi, 158 p. 19cm.
Bibliography: p. 147-148.
1. Evidence (Law)—Gt. Brit. I. Lieck, Albert Henry, ed. II. Lieck, Sophie, joint ed.
35-21316
Library of Congress [2] 347.940942

NK 0210228 DLC GU-L

Knowles, Vincent Devereux.
The science of the sword, by V. Devereux Knowles... Singapore [etc.] Kelly & Walsh [1935] 111 p. illus. 26cm.
The book contains reproductions of some plates from Angelo's "Ecole des Armes" dated 1765.—cf. Preface.
2. ed.
Author's autographed presentation copy.
246170B. N. Y. P. L. 1. Fencing.

NK 0210229 NN

Knowles, W.
Naughty Clara. Song [with accompaniment for pianoforte]. Words by Hunter. Music by Knowles.
Boston. White, Smith & Co. [186-?] 5 pp. 35½ cm.
Appended is: Naughty Clara. Ladies' version, which may be sung to the same music. Written by Hunter.
L5195 — Double main card. — Knowles, W. (M1) — Hunter, ——. (M2) — T.r. (1) — Songs. With music. (1)

NK 0210230 MB

F863 .6 K58 Knowles, W H , appellant.
(James H. Yeates, respondent)
Contested election for the office of Sheriff of Plumas County. Creed Haymond and John D. Goodwin, of counsel for respondent.
No. 858 in the Supreme Court of the State of California.
Contents.
[1] Brief for respondent. Sacramento, 1866. (30 p.)
[2] Petition for rehearing. Sacramento, 1866. (45 p.)
1. Plumas Co., Calif. Sheriff's Dept. - Contested elections. I. Yeates, James H , respondent. II. Haymond, Creed, 1836-1893. III. Goodwin, John D . IV. California. Supreme Court.

NK 0210231 CU-B

Knowles, W. J.
Prehistoric stone implements from the river Bann and Lough Neagh. (Royal Irish Academy. Proc. Dublin, 1912. 8°. v. 30, section C., p. 195-222, 8 pl.)
1. Stone implements, Gt. Br.: Ireland.
N. Y. P. L.

NK 0210232 NN

VOLUME 300

Knowles, W J.
Second report on the prehistoric remains from the sandhills of the coast of Ireland. By W. J. Knowles ... A paper read before the Royal Irish academy, January 12, 1891; and reprinted from the "Proceedings," 3rd ser., vol. I., no. 5. ‹Fifty copies only reprinted ...› Dublin, Printed at the University press, by Ponsonby and Weldrick, 1891.
cover-title, 612-625 p. XXII-XXIV pl. 22cm.

1. Ireland—Antiq.

Library of Congress GN806.I6K7 5-2321†

NK 0210233 DLC

Knowles, Walter.
Calculating scale. A substitute for the slide rule. By W. Knowles, B.A. .... London, E. & F. N. Spon; New York, Spon & Chamberlain, 1903.
29, [3] p. 16x13cm.
[3] p. left blank for "Notes".

NK 0210234 ICJ MH PPSteph

N.J.-Y BX8481 .O63K
Knowles, Wilbur Stoddard, -1944.
A century of Methodism in Orange, New Jersey. Prepared by Wilbur Stoddard Knowles and issued by the authority and with the approval of the Centennial Committee, November, nineteen thirty. ‹Orange, N.J., 1930›
24p. illus. (incl. ports.) 23½cm.
NjR

1. Orange, N.J. United Methodist Church.

NK 0210235 DAS NjR

IM 8 64h
Knowles, William.
A half century of interaction between scientific management and industrial government. ‹Madison› 1948.
Microfilm copy (negative) made by Dane County Title Co. for the Library, University of Wisconsin.
Collation of the original: 359l.
Thesis—University of Wisconsin.
Bibliography: leaves 352-359.

NK 0210236 IU

[Knowles, William]
A short account of the last hours of Mr. and Mrs. James Knowles. [By William Knowles; with a poem, In memoriam, by George F. Sargent. New York, 1887]
16 p. 24°.
One of 2000 copies printed.

NK 0210237 NN

Knowles, William, poet.
Poems, by William Knowles. Indianapolis, Carlon & Hollenbeck, 1881.
viii, 101 p. incl. front. 22cm.
"Contributed poems": p. ‹87›-101.

Library of Congress PS2197.K3 28-1988
Copyright 1881: 19989

NK 0210238 DLC OClWHi

Knowles, William, reporter. FOR OTHER EDITIONS SEE MAIN ENTRY
Gordon, John, *d.* 1845, *defendant.*
The trial of John Gordon and William Gordon, charged with the murder of Amasa Sprague, before the Supreme court of Rhode Island, March term, 1844: with all the incidental questions raised in the trial carefully preserved—the testimony of the witnesses nearly verbatim—and the arguments of counsel and a correct plat of all the localities described in the testimony, prepared expressly for this report. Reported by Edward C. Larned and William Knowles. Providence: Printed at the office of the Daily transcript. March, 1844. ‹2d ed.› Providence, S. S. Rider, 1884.

Mhc9 K764 Se5
Knowles, William, fl.1662
A serious call to obstinate sinners: or, A sounding trumpet to the unconverted. Laying forth the danger of living in sin ... By William Knowles B. in P. ... London, Printed for Fr. Coles, on Saffron Hill in Vine-street near Hattonsgarden. 1677.
1p.l., 19, [3]p. 14cm.
Signatures: A8B4.
Imperfect: p. 3-4 mutilated.

NK 0210240 CtY

[Knowles, William] 1816-1885.
Coroners and coroners' juries. [Providence, 1883]
6, [1] p. 25 cm.
Caption-title.
Signed: An old coroner.

NK 0210241 RPB

Knowles, William, 1816-1885.
Incomprehensible God; a discourse by Walter Stackpole [pseud.] Providence, 1884.
23 cm.
Clippings inserted in pam. no. 32A.

NK 0210242 RPB

1901 KN9492a
Knowles, William Armour
The ages [Wainwright, Alta., 1924?]
11, [1] l. 23 cm.

Typewritten.
In verse.
Author's autographed copy.

1. Canadian poetry. I. Title.

NK 0210243 RPB

Knowles, William Clark, 1840-
By gone days in Ponsett-Haddam, Middlesex County, Connecticut; a story by Rev. William C. Knowles ... New York, Priv. print., 1914.
3 p. l., 3-65 p., 1 l. 2 fold. maps (incl. front.) 23½cm.

1. Ponsett, Conn.—Hist. I. Title.

Library of Congress F104.P78K7 15-19301

NK 0210244 DLC OClWHi NN

LIBS-J BJ 1661 .K596
Knowles, William E C
Leonard Barton, the blind boy, and other stories, by William E. C. Knowles. New York, Phinney, Blakeman & Mason [18--?]
62 p. illus. (The casket of juveniles, 1)

#Youth--Conduct of life.
(A) Leonard Barton, the blind boy.

NK 0210245 MoU OO NBuG

Knowles, William Franklin.
... Changes in farming in the fruit and vegetable areas of south Jersey, by W. F. Knowles ... ‹New Brunswick, 1939›
20 numb l., incl. tables. 28 x 21½cm.
Caption title.
At head of title: Extension service, New Jersey state college of agriculture and Agricultural experiment station, Rutgers university, New Brunswick, N. J. New Jersey land use planning committee meeting, New Brunswick, N. J., March 16, 1939.
Reproduced from type-written copy.

1. Farms—New Jersey. 2. Agriculture—New Jersey—Stat. I. Rutgers university, New Brunswick, N. J. Extension service in agriculture and home economics. II. New Jersey land use planning committee.

Library of Congress HD1775.N5K6 44-33002
‹2› 338.1

NK 0210246 DLC

Knowles, William H
Personnel management, a human relations approach. New York, American Book Co. ‹1955›
488 p. illus. 22 cm.

1. Personnel management.

HF5549.K6 658.3 55—2025 ‡

Or OrPS WaS DI OrCS OrU
OCU OCl TxU ViU NN DS PU-W NcGU OClW IdPI OrLgE Wa
NK 0210247 DLC CoU KEmT CtY TU MU MiU NcRS PV OU

Knowles, William Henry.
Corstopitum: report on the excavations in 1910
see under Forster, Robert Henry, 1867-1923.

Knowles, William Henry, illus.
Vestiges of Old Newcastle and Gateshead, 1890
see under Boyle, John Robert, 1853-1907.

Knowles, William J.
Features of inauguration of the Franklin statue in Boston, September 17th, 1856. [Poem.]
Boston. The Author. 1856. 12 pp. 18½ cm.
A portrait of Franklin is inserted.

N576 — Franklin, Benjamin, 1706-1790. Statues.

NK 0210250 MB RPB NNC MH PHi DS

Knowles, William J.
Poetical expression of the Gospels. By William J. Knowles. Boston, The author, 1858.
96 p. incl. front., illus. 17cm.

1. Bible. N. T. Gospels—History of Biblical events—Poetry. 2. Bible—History of Biblical events—Poetry—N. T. Gospels. I. Title.

Library of Congress BS2557.K6 36-32736
——— Copy 2. 19cm.
Copyright ‹2› [226] 811.39

NK 0210251 DLC PHi OO MB RPB PU

Knowles, William J.
Poetical expression of the Gospels.
Boston. The Author.
8s.
Bound in the original paper covers.
[2d edition.] 1859.

H3011 — T.r. — Bible. N. T. Gospels. Paraphrases. English.

NK 0210252 MB RPB

VOLUME 300

Knowles, William Muiry, 1875-
Bakery talks. By W. M. Knowles ("Semper eadem.") London: The Baker and Confectioner, Ltd.[, 1920.] 76 p. 12°.

387081A. 1. Bread making.
N. Y. P. L.

NK 0210253 NN

Knowles, William Pitcairn.
Dutch pottery and porcelain, by W. Pitcairn Knowles. London, G. Newnes, limited; New York, C. Scribner's sons [1904]
xv, [1], 122 p., 1 l. 65 pl. (part col.) incl. front. 23cm. (*Half-title: Newnes' library of the applied arts*)
Appendix: A. The Delft potteries.—B. The members of the guild of St. Luke.

1. Pottery, Dutch. 2. Pottery—Marks. I. Title.

5-4249
Library of Congress NK4107.K7 [29f1]

NK 0210254 DLC CLSU NcD MB Or OrU WaS ICJ OCl OClW OOxM OO NN WaU PPPM

Knowles, William Pitcairn.
Dutch pottery and procelain. Lond., c1905.

NK 0210255 PP OU OClMA

Knowles, William Pitcairn.
Dutch pottery and porcelain, by W. Pitcairn Knowles. London, B. T. Batsford; New York, C. Scribner's sons [1913]
xv, [1], 122 p., 1 l. 65 pl. (part col.) incl. front. 23cm. (*Half-title: Batsford's Collector's library*)
Appendix A: The Delft potteries, p. 71-72. Appendix B: The members of the guild of St. Luke, p. 73-111.

1. Pottery, Dutch. 2. Pottery—Marks. I. Title.

A 14-416
The Booklist for Library of Congress [NK4107.K]

NK 0210256 IU MdBWA NcRS OrP OrU Wa WaT CU MH CSt OCU OO OU OClMA

Knowles, William Plenderleith.
Jim McWhirter, by W. P. Knowles. London, The C. W. Daniel company [1933]
282 p. 19cm.
Music: p. 177.

I. Title.

34-1056
Library of Congress PR6021.N53J5 1933
Copyright A ad int. 18499 [2] 828.91

NK 0210257 DLC

Knowles, William Standish, 1917-
A preliminary investigation of the constituents of *Astragalus wootoni*. β-substituted-$\Delta^{\alpha,\beta}$-butenolides of the naphthalene, indene and norcholane series ... by William Standish Knowles. New York city, 1942.
2 p. l., 18 p. 25½cm.
Thesis (PH. D.)—Columbia university, 1942.
Vita.
"References": p. 9, 15, 18.

1. Butenolides. 2. Astragalus.

A 43-1772
Columbia univ. Libraries for Library of Congress QD305.A6K6 [2]†

NK 0210258 NNC CU DLC

Knowles, Mrs. Winthrop Curtis
see Knowles, Ruth Gawthrop (Moore) 1879-

Knowles-Foster, Frances G.
Jehanne of the golden lips, by Frances G. Knowles-Foster. New York, J. Lane company, 1910.
3 p. l., 311 p. 19cm.

A 10-2240
Title from Chicago Pub. Libr. Printed by L. C.

NK 0210260 ICU PJA PPAp PU PPL NN

Knowles-Foster, Frances G.
The written law, by Frances G. Knowles-Foster ... London, Mills & Boon, limited [1912]
xi, 356 p. incl. front. plates. 20cm. 6/-

I. Title.

12-6562
Library of Congress PZ3.K768W

NK 0210261 DLC

Knowles-Williams, Gweneth
The Shakespearian conception of comedy. Pretoria, 1954.
2 v. (308 l.)

Thesis, Pretoria.
Bibliography: v. 2, l. 301-308.

1. Shakespeare, William, 1564-1616. Comedies

NK 0210262 NNC

Knowles & Buckstone's plays
see under Knowles, James Sheridan, 1784-1862.

Knowles & Maxim, *firm, publishers.*
... Real pen-work. Self-instructor in penmanship ... Pittsfield, Mass., Knowles & Maxim [1881]
2 p. l., [10] p., 1 l., [10] p., 8 l. incl. illus. (partly col.) plates (partly col.) 28½ x 39½cm.
Illus. t.-p. Added t.-p., engr.

1. Penmanship.

11-26390
Library of Congress Z43.K71

NK 0210264 DLC ICN NN MH

Knowles & Maxim, *firm, publishers.*
Real pen work. Self-instructor in penmanship ... Pittsfield, Mass., Knowles & Maxim [1882]
41 l., [8] p. incl. illus. (partly col.) plates. 23 x 29½cm.

1. Penmanship.

11-26391
Library of Congress Z43.K72

NK 0210265 DLC

Knowles & Maxim, *firm, publishers.*
Real pen work. Self-instructor in penmanship ... Pittsfield, Mass., and St. Catharine's, Ontario, Knowles & Maxim [1884]
42 l., [9] p. incl. illus. (partly col.) plates. 23 x 28½cm.
Cover-title: Golden gems of penmanship, and self instructor.

1. Penmanship.

11-26392
Library of Congress Z43.K722

NK 0210266 DLC ICN

Wing
fZW
883
.K 759

KNOWLES & MAXIM, firm, publishers.
Real pen work. Self-instructor in penmanship. Detroit, Mich., A.W. Knowles & Co. [1885?]
[50] l. incl. illus. (part col.) 22x28cm.

"Copyrighted 1881, by Knowles & Maxim."

NK 0210267 ICN

CS71
.K7296
1940

The Knowles family.
St. Paul, Minn., L. F. Knowles [19
v. 28½ cm.

CS71.K7296 1940 57-34193

NK 0210268 DLC ICN MnHi

Knowles Steam Pump Works.
Circular steam pumping machinery.
N.Y. n.d.
8 p.

NK 0210269 PPF

KNOWLES STEAM PUMP WORKS.
Illustrated catalogue of Knowles improved fire pumps. Boston, etc., [1890]
pp.19. Illustr.

NK 0210270 MH

Knowles steam pump works.
Illustrated catalogue, 1895. Bacon patent air lift pump. Knowles steam pump works, New York ... London [etc.] [New York, Press of E. A. Fiske & co., °1895]
35, [1] p. illus. 18½ x 14½cm.

1. Pumping machinery—Catalogs.

CA 7-3025 Unrev'd
Library of Congress TJ908.K732

NK 0210271 DLC

Knowles Steam Pump Works
Illustrated price list of Knowles steam pumping machinery. N.Y. n.d.
32 p.

NK 0210272 PPF

Knowles steam pump works
Mining pumps. N.Y. 1887.
62 p.

NK 0210273 PPF

VOLUME 300

Knowles Steam Pump Works.
Palmer Special Sinking pump. N.Y. 1895.
4 p.

NK 0210274 PPF

Knowles Steam Pump Works
Patent condenser; steam pumps and engines.
Circular. n.p. n.d.
6 p.

NK 0210275 PPF

Knowles steam pump works.
Revised illustrated catalogue. Knowles steam pump works. New York, Boston ... [etc.] [New York? °18
v. illus., fold. plates. 17 x 13½–26cm.
Title varies: 1874, Illustrated price list of Knowles patent steam pumps. 1881, Descriptive catalogue of Knowles steam pump works. 1885– , Revised illustrated catalogue.

1. Pumping machinery—Catalogs.
CA 6—2315 Unrev'd
Library of Congress TJ908.K73 1892

NK 0210276 DLC DSI MH PPF

Knowles steam pump works.
Special catalogue of electric power pumps, manufactured by the Knowles steam pump works ... New York ... London ... [etc.] [New York? 1896]
44 p. illus. 19 x 15cm.

1. Pumping machinery—Catalogs.
CA 7-5568 Unrev'd
Library of Congress TJ910.K7 1896

NK 0210277 DLC

Knowles steam pump works.
Special illustrated catalogue of Knowles new mining pumps. New York, Boston, Knowles steam pump works [18
v. illus., pl. 23cm.

1. Mine pumps.
CA 6—2316 Unrev'd
Library of Congress TN325.K7

NK 0210278 DLC

Knowles Steam Pump Works.
[Steam pumps; a collection of catalogues. New York, 1896–1904.] 6 pams. in 1 v. illus. (incl. plans), tables. 12°.

368080A. 1. Pumps, Steam—Catalogues.
N. Y. P. L.

NK 0210279 NN

628.1 Knowles steam pump works.
K76w Water supply and pumping machinery, by Knowles steam pump works, engineers. Boston, Mass. and New York, N.Y., U.S.A. Boston, 1890.
65p. incl.tables. XXVIIA(i.e.28)pl.(part fold.)
Plates I-IX are included in the paging.

1. Water supply machinery. 2. Pumping machinery.

NK 0210280 IU WaS

Knowles, Vose and Co.
For New York, the steamboat President ...
Providence, 1836.
38 x 30 cm.
Poster.

NK 0210281 RPB

Knowling, Mrs. Harold
SEE
Buchanan, Merial, 1886-

Knowling, Meriel Buchanan
see
Buchanan, Meriel, 1886-

Knowling, Richard John, 1851-1919
The Acts of the Apostles. [Commentary.]
(In Bible. New Testament. Greek. The Expositor's Greek Testament. Vol. 2, pp. 1-554. London. 1900.)

G1935 — Bible. N. T. Acts. Commentaries.

NK 0210284 DLC MB

Knowling, Richard John, 1851-1919, ed.
The Epistle of St. James... London [1904]
see under Bible. N. T. James. English. 1904.

Also with dates 1910 and 1922, with the name of Knowling underscored in the title.

Knowling, Richard John, 1851-1919, ed.

Bible. *N. T. Greek. 1897.*
The expositor's Greek Testament; edited by the Rev. W. Robertson Nicoll ... London, Hodder and Stoughton, 1897–1910.

BS Knowling, Richard John, 1851-1919.
2360 Literary criticism and the New Testament.
.K73 Published under the direction of the Tract Committee. London, Society for Promoting Christian Knowledge, 1907.
vi, 101 p. 19cm.
Manchester Cathedral lectures, 1907.
Bibliographical footnotes.

1. Bible. N. T. - Criticism, interpretation, etc. I. Title.

NK 0210287 DCU PBm PHC

Knowling, Richard John, 1851-1919.
... Literary criticism and the New Testament... 2d ed., rev. London, Society for promoting Christian knowledge, 1910.
vi, 101 p. 19cm. (Manchester cathedral lectures. 1907)
"Published under the direction of the Tract committee."
Bibliographical footnotes.

NK 0210288 NjPT MH-AH

BT230 Knowling, Richard John, 1815-1919
K5 Messianic interpretation and other studies by R.J.Knowling. London, S.P.C.K., 1910.
181p. 20cm.
Errata tipped in: p.7.

1. Jesus Christ - Messiahship. 2. Bible. N.T. - Criticism, interpretation, etc. I. Title.

NK 0210289 IaU IEG CLamB PPPD

BT317 Knowling, Richard John, 1851-1919
K6 Our Lord's virgin birth and the criticism of today. Published under the direction of the Tract Committee. London, Society for Promoting Christian Knowledge, 1903.
95 p. 19 cm.

1. Virgin birth. I. Society for Promoting Christian Knowledge, London. Tract Committee. II. Title.

NK 0210290 MeB OO

Knowling, Richard John, 1851-1919.
Our Lord's virgin birth and the criticism of to-day. By R. J. Knowling... Reprint. Published under the direction of the Tract Committee. London: Society for Promoting Christian Knowledge, 1904. 95 p. 19cm.
"The following papers appeared in the Churchman, in the earlier part of 1903." — p. 3.

529463A. 1. Jesus Christ—Virgin birth. I. Society for Promoting Christian Knowledge, London. Tract Committee.
N. Y. P. L.

NK 0210291 NN PPPD NNUT ICU MH MBrZ

Knowling, Richard John, 1851-1919.
Our Lord's virgin birth and the criticism of to-day. By R. J. Knowling ... Third issue. Published under the direction of the Tract committee. London [etc.] Society for promoting Christian knowledge; New York, E. S. Gorham, 1907.
100 p. 18½cm.
"The following papers appeared in the Churchman, in the earlier part of 1903."—p. [3]

1. Virgin birth. I. Society for promoting Christian knowledge, London. Tract committee. II. Title.
39-407
Library of Congress BT317.K6 1907

NK 0210292 DLC IEG ViU

Knowling, Richard John, 1851-1919.
The testimony of St. Paul to Christ viewed in some of its aspects, by R. J. Knowling ... New York, C. Scribner's sons, 1905.
viii, 533 p. 23½ cm.
On verso of half-title: Boyle lectures, 1903-5.
"Recent literature": p. 496-528.
CONTENTS.—1st ser. 1903: The documents.—2d ser. 1904: St. Paul's testimony in relation to the Gospels.—3d ser. 1905: St. Paul's testimony in relation to the life of the church.
1. Paul, Saint, apostle. 2. Bible. N. T. Gospels—Evidences, authority, etc. 3. Church history—Primitive and early church. I. Boyle lectures, 1903-1905.
BS2651.K6 6—11301

NK 0210293 DLC MB NIC NcD PPT OClW NNUT MH CtY IaU

BS Knowling, Richard John, 1851-1919.
2651 The testimony of St. Paul to Christ viewed in
K73 some of its aspects. 2d ed. London, Hodder and Stoughton, 1906.
viii, 533 p. 23 cm.

1. Paul, Saint, Apostle. 2. Bible. N. T. Gospels - Evidences, authority, etc. 3. Church history - Primitive early church.

NK 0210294 DCU OO NjNbS

Knowling, Richard John, 1851-1919.
The testimony of St. Paul to Christ viewed in some of its aspects...[3rd ed.] London, [etc.] Hodder and Stoughton, [1911].

NK 0210295 OCl PPWe

VOLUME 300

Knowling, Richard John, 1851-1919.
The witness of the epistles. A study in modern criticism, by the Rev. R. J. Knowling ... London and New York, Longmans, Green & co., 1892.
xii, 451 p. 23cm.

1. Bible. N. T. Epistles of Paul. 2. Jesus Christ. 3. Paul, Saint, apostle.

MiU OO PPL PCC PHC NcWilA
NK 0210296 MiU NjPT IaU CtY-D NjNbS CtY MB MH ICU

Knowls, John.
See
Knowles, John, fl. 1646-1668.

Knowlson, Arthur, joint author.
Muller, Julius Washington, 1867-
Deep sea fishing grounds, Fire Island to Barnegat; wrecks, fishing banks, reefs, by Julius W. Muller and Arthur Knowlson; charts drawn especially for this book by Julius W. Muller ... Brooklyn, N. Y., Knowlson & Muller, °1915.

Knowlson, Arthur.
FOR OTHER EDITIONS SEE MAIN ENTRY
Muller, Julius Washington, 1867-
Fishing around New York; where to find them, how to rig, how to catch them; chart of hooks showing exact sizes to use, etc., by J. W. Muller; Arthur Knowlson, collaborator. Rev. 1932. Brooklyn, N. Y., F. Weidner printing & pub. co., inc., °1932.

Knowlson, John C.
The complete cattle-doctor: a treatise on the diseases of horned cattle and calves. Written in plain language, which those who can read may easily understand. The whole being the result of seventy years extensive practice of the author, John C. Knowlson ... New-York, Wilson and company, Brother Jonathan press, 1845.
64 p. 22cm. (*On cover:* Brother Jonathan monthly library, no. 16)
Caption and running title: The complete cow-doctor.

1. Cattle—Diseases. I. Title. II. Title: The complete cow-doctor.

22-15247

Library of Congress SF961.K5

NK 0210300 DLC OC1WHi

Knowlson (John C.) The complete cattle doctor. A treatise on the diseases of horned cattle and calves. 64 pp. 8°. *New York, Wilson & Co.*, 1847.

NK 0210301 DNLM Vi

Knowlson (J[ohn] C.) The complete cow-leech, or cattle-doctor; being a treatise on the disorders of horned cattle, with the complete farrier, or horse-doctor. x (2 l.), 120 pp., 1 pl. 8°. *London, Longman* [*and others*, 1819].

NK 0210302 DNLM DNAL

Knowlson, John C
The complete farrier or, Horse doctor; a guide for the treatment of horses in all diseases to which that noble animal is liable... 29th American ed. N.Y., Dick and Fitzgerald, n.d.
64p.

Bound with Rarey, J.S. Tamin, or, Breaking the horse.

NK 0210303 OU

Knowlson, John C.
The complete farrier, or horse-doctor ... Philadelphia, T. B. Peterson [18-?]
vi, 7-64 p. 8°.

NK 0210304 NN

Knowlson, John C.
——. The complete farrier, or horse-doctor; being the art of farriery made plain and easy; explaining the nature of the disorders to which a horse is subject, and the best methods of preventing or curing them, [etc.]. 127 pp., 2 l. 8°. *Otley, T. F. Bristow*, 1820.
Bound with the preceding.

NK 0210305 DNLM

R
674
.467
KNOWLSON, JOHN C.
The complete farrier, or horse-doctor. A treatise on the diseases of horses... New-York, Wilson and co., 1846.
64p. 22cm.

Cover-title: Knowlson's Complete farrier...

NK 0210306 ICN TxCM

Knowlson, John C
The complete farrier, or horse doctor. A treatise on the diseases of horses: written in plain language, which those who can read may easily understand. The whole being the result of seventy years extensive practive of the author. N.Y., Wilson, 1848.
64p. O.

NK 0210307 OO

Knowlson, John C.
——. The complete farrier, or horse-doctor; a treatise on the disease of horses. 64 pp. 8°. *New York, Wilson & Co.*, 1849.

NK 0210308 DNLM InU

Knowlson, John C
Knowlson's complete farrier, or horse doctor. Cincinnati and St. Louis, Stratton and Barnard, 1850.
64p.

NK 0210309 OC1WHi

Knowlson, John C.
The complete farrier,...
Phila., 1851

SF951
.K73

NK 0210310 DLC

Knowlson, John C.
The complete farrier: or, Horse doctor, a guide for the treatment of diseases of horses: to which are added valuable hints for choosing a horse, and directions for the training; the whole being the result of fifty years' extensive practice. By John C. Knowlson. New York: J. G. Wells [etc., etc.] 1859. 64 p. illus. 22½cm.

1. Horse—Diseases. I. Title.
N. Y. P. L.

NK 0210311 NN

SF
961
.K5
1834
Knowlson, John C
The Yorkshire cattle-doctor & farrier; a treatise on the diseases of horned cattle, calves, and horses. The twenty-sixth thousand, rev. and corr. London, W. Walker [1834]
272 p. illus. 22 cm.

"Second edition."

1. Cattle - Diseases. 2. Horses - Diseases I. Title.

NK 0210312 WU DNAL PU-V OrCS DNLM

Knowlson, Joseph S.
England's need in education, a suggested remedy, by Joseph S. Knowlson ... London, A. C. Fifield, 1911.
2 p. l., 7-187 p. diagr. 19½cm.

1. Elementary education—Gt. Brit. 2. Education.

E 11-1216

Library, U. S. Bur. of Education LA633.K76

NK 0210313 DHEW ICJ

Knowlson, Thomas Sharper, 1867-
The art of success, by T. Sharper Knowlson ... New York and London, F. Warne and co., 1902.
xi, 163 p. 19cm.

1. Success. I. Title.

Library of Congress BJ1611.K7 2—26498

NK 0210314 DLC ICJ OC1 OC1W MH

Knowlson, Thomas Sharper, 1867-
The art of success, by T. Sharper Knowlson ... London and New York, F. Warne and co., 1908.
xi, 163 p. 18cm.

1. Success. I. Title.

E 14-1009

Library, U. S. Bur. of Education HF5386.K74

NK 0210315 DHEW

Knowlson, Thomas Sharper. 1867-
The art of success.
— London. Warne & Co. 1909. ix, 174 pp. 18 cm., in 8s.

H3232 — Success in life. — T.r.

NK 0210316 MB PU

Knowlson, Thomas Sharper, 1867-
The art of sympathy, by T. Sharper Knowlson ... London and New York, F. Warne and co., 1910.
iii-x, 206 p. 18cm.

1. Sympathy.

12-34867

Library of Congress BJ1533.S9K5

NK 0210317 DLC ICJ NN

BF441
.K65
Knowlson, Thomas Sharper, 1867-
The art of thinking. London and New York, F. Warne, 1899.
viii, 139 p.

1. Thought and thinking.

NK 0210318 ICU WaS OC1

VOLUME 300

Knowlson, Thomas Sharper, 1867–
The art of thinking. viii,139 p. D. London: F. Warne & Co., 1900.

NK 0210319 ICJ ICRL PPL

Knowlson, Thomas Sharper, 1867–
The art of thinking, by T. Sharper Knowlson ... London and New York, F. Warne and co., 1901.
viii, 139 p. 18cm.
Title in red and black.

1. Thought and thinking.
W 10–144
Washington, D. C. Public library for Library of Congress [BF455.K

NK 0210320 DWP

Knowlton, Thomas Sharper, 1867–
The art of thinking... London and New York, Warne, [1901?]
153p.
"Rev. edition"

NK 0210321 OO OC1W

Knowlson, Thomas Sharper, 1867–
The art of thinking, by T. Sharper Knowlson ... London and New York, F. Warne and co., 1905.
viii, 189 p. 18cm.
Title in red and black.

NK 0210322 ViU

154.7 K73a 1906 Knowlson, Thomas Sharper, 1867–
The art of thinking...rev. and enl. London, Warne, 1906.
153p. D.
"An additional list of books for thinkers": p.147-153.
Philos.

NK 0210323 IaU

Knowlson, T[homas] Sharper, 1867–
The art of thinking. London: Frederick Warne and Co. [1913?] x, 153 p. 12°.
List of books, p. 147-153.

1. Intellect. 2. Title.
N. Y. P. L.

NK 0210324 NN

Knowlson, Thomas Sharper, 1867–
The art of thinking, by T. Sharper Knowlson ... [Rev. ed.] London, T. W. Laurie ltd. [1917?]
x, 153 p. 17½cm.

1. Thought and thinking.
E 18–1148
Library, U. S. Bur. of Education BF131.K7

NK 0210325 DHEW ICJ ICRL

Knowlson, Thomas Sharper, 1867–
The art of thinking, by T. Sharper Knowlson ... New York, Thomas Y. Crowell company [c1921]
ix, 165 p. 19cm.
First issued in 1899. A new chapter has been added, entitled "Some defects of present day thinking". cf. Pref.
"An additional list of books for thinkers": p. [161]-165.

1. Thought and thinking. I. Title.
Library of Congress BF455.K6 1921 21–20063

NK 0210326 DLC Or ICRL MiU OCU ODW OU

Knowlson, Thomas Sharper, 1867–
Business! practical hints for master and man; by T. Sharper Knowlson ... London and New York, F. Warne and co., 1909.
x, 202, [1] p. 17½cm.

1. Business.
W 10–88
Washington, D. C. Public Library

NK 0210327 DWP OC1 ICJ

Knowlson, T[homas] Sharper, 1867–
Business! Practical hints for master and man. London, F. Warne & Co. [1910]
x, 202 p., 1 l. 12°.

NK 0210328 NN

Knowlson, Thomas Sharper, 1867–
Business psychology; a system of mental training for commercial life, by T. Sharper Knowlson ... Libertyville, Ill., Sheldon university press, 1912.
215 p. 22cm.

1. Business. 2. Success. I. Title.
19–3546
Library of Congress HF5386.K65

NK 0210329 DLC OWoC ViU LU ICJ ICU MB

Knowlson, Thomas Sharper, 1867–
The century student's manual, by T. Sharper Knowlson ... London and New York, F. Warne and co., 1910.
vii, 197 p. 18cm.
"Appendix ... A list of encyclopædias, dictionaries and other works of general reference selected by T. Sharper Knowlson" (16 p.) in pocket of cover.

1. Education. 2. Books and reading. 3. Reference books—Bibl.
11–25950
Library of Congress LC31.K6

NK 0210330 DLC OC1 ICJ MB

Knowlson, Thomas Sharper, 1867–
Conklin's The way to think and how to remember, by T. Sharper Knowlson and Eustace H. Miles, ... To which is added Loisette's system of memory culture. Edited by Prof. Geo. W. Conklin, ... Chicago, Ill., G. W. Ogilvie & Co., c1904.
175 p. 14x6½cm.

NK 0210331 ICJ DLC

Knowlson, Thomas Sharper, 1867–
Creating new ideas, showing how, when and where. By T. Sharper Knowlson ... London, Thorsons publishers ltd [1945]
147, v. p. illus., diagr. 19cm. ["Life my teacher" books]
Bibliographical foot-notes.

1. Psychology, Applied. I. Title.
45–10333
Library of Congress BF636.K59
[3] 150.13

NK 0210332 DLC

Knowlson, Thomas Sharper, 1867–
The education of the will, a popular study; by T. Sharper Knowlson ... Philadelphia, J. B. Lippincott company; London, T. W. Laurie [1909]
4 p. l., 210 p. 19cm.

1. Mind and body. 2. Will.
W 9–192
Washington, D. C. Public Library

NK 0210333 DWP PBa MiU OC1 ICJ NN PPSteph

Knowlson, Thomas Sharper, 1867–
The education of the will; a popular study. Philadelphia, J.B.Lippincott co., etc., etc., [191-?]

NK 0210334 MH

Knowlson, Thomas Sharper, 1867–
The education of the will; a popular study, by T. Sharper Knowlson ... London, T. W. Laurie [1913]
4 p. l., 210 p. 19 cm.

1. Will.
E 13–1653
U. S. Office of Education. Library for Library of Congress [a48b½]

NK 0210335 DHEW PSC NN

Knowlson, Thomas Sharper, 1867–
How to become efficient; an introductory study of first principles, by T. Sharper Knowlson ... London, T. W. Laurie ltd. [1913]
2 p. l., [vii]-ix, [10]-144 p. 18cm.

1. Success. I. Title.
E 14–271
Library, U. S. Bur. of Education HF5386.K76

NK 0210336 DHEW MiU ICJ

Knowlson, Thomas Sharper, 1867–
How to study English literature; with an appendix on fine passages in prose and poetry selected by Prof. Dowden, Thomas Hardy, George Meredith and many others; by T. Sharper Knowlson. London, G. Richards, 1901.
2 p. l., vii-xii, 155, [1] p. 19½cm. (Half-title: The "How to" series. [IX])

1. English literature—Study and teaching.
3–6995 Revised
Library of Congress PR33.K5

NK 0210337 DLC MiU MH

Knowlson, T[homas] Sharper, 1867–
Leo Tolstoy; a biographical and critical study, by T. Sharper Knowlson ... London and New York, F. Warne & co., 1904.
190 p. front. (port.) 19½cm.
Bibliography: p. 178-190.

1. Tolstoi, Liov Nikolaevich, graf, 1828–
4–22907

NK 0210338 DLC GEU CU InU CSt TNJ NIC MiU OC1W OC1 PPL NN

Knowlson, T[homas] Sharper, 1867–
Logic for the million; edited by T. Sharper Knowlson. London: T. Werner Laurie [19—?]. 4 p.l., 248(3) p. 12°.

1. Logic.
N. Y. P. L.

NK 0210339 NN FMU

Knowlson, Thomas Sharper, 1867–
Money-making by short-story writing.
London. Neuman & Castarede. [1905.] 156 pp. Sm. 8°.
This work is based on Charles Raymond Barrett's book, entitled, Short story writing [2553-35].

F7447 — Barrett, Charles Raymond. — Short story. — Authorship. — T.r.

NK 0210340 MB

VOLUME 300

Knowlson, Thomas Sharper, 1867–
Originality; a popular study of the creative mind, by T. Sharper Knowlson ("Thomas Sharnol") ... London, T. W. Laurie ltd., 1917.
xvi, 303, [1] p. 23cm.

1. Genius. I. Title.

Library of Congress BF412.K6 18—11176

NK 0210341 DLC ViU OU PPPL ICJ NN MiU

Knowlson, Thomas Sharper, 1867–
Originality; a popular study of the creative mind, by T. Sharper Knowlson ("Thomas Sharnol")... Philadelphia: J. B. Lippincott Co., 1918. xvi, 303(1) p. 8°.
Printed in Great Britain.

1. Originality. 2. Genius. 3. Thought. 4. Title: Creative mind. 5. Title: Mind, Creative.
N. Y. P. L.

NK 0210342 NN NIC CtY-M ICarbS OKentU PPL PU OCl OCU MB MH CtY IdU Or WaS WaSpG WaT

Knowlson, Thomas Sharper, 1867-
Originality; a popular study of the creative mind, by T. Sharper Knowlson ("Thomas Sharnol") ... London, Laurie, 1919.
303 p.

NK 0210343 NcRS

Knowlson, Thomas Sharper, 1867–
Originality; a popular study of the creative mind, by T. Sharper Knowlson ("Thomas Sharnol") ... London, T. W. Laurie ltd., 1920.
xvi, 303, [1] p. 23cm.

NK 0210344 CU CtY CtY-M NjP

Knowlson, Thomas Sharper, 1867-
The origins of popular supersitions and customs. By T. Sharper Knowlson. N.Y., J. Pott & co., n.d.
242 p. D.

NK 0210345 NcD PPRCl

Knowlson, T[homas] Sharper, 1867–
The origins of popular superstitions and customs. London: T. Werner Laurie [190–?]. x, 242 p. 12°.

1. Manners and customs. 2. Superstition. 3. Fasts and feasts. 4. Days (anal.). 5. Marriage (anal.). 6. Title.
N. Y. P. L.

NK 0210346 NN

Knowlson, Thomas Sharper, 1867–
The origins of popular superstitions and customs; by T. Sharper Knowlson ... London, T. W. Laurie [1910]
x, 242 p. 19 cm.
Title within green border.
"Based on Brand's Popular antiquities, the first edition published in 1841, supplemented by the results of later investigations."—Pref.
Contents. — Introduction. — Superstition and customs relating to days and seasons.—Marriage superstitions and customs.—Divination and omens.—Miscellaneous superstitions and customs.

1. Superstition. 2. Manners and customs. I. Brand, John, 1744–1806. Observations on the popular antiquities of Great Britain. II. Title.

[GR65.K] W 10—323
Washington, D. C. Pub. Library for Library of Congress [65r37b½]

NK 0210347 DWP OrP WaSp Or OKentU ODW PU-Mu FMU OCl OLak DSI ICJ

Knowlson, Thomas Sharper, 1867–
The origins of popular superstitions and customs, by T. Sharper Knowlson ... New York, J. Pott & co.; [etc., etc., 1910]
x, 242 p. 19½cm.
"... Based on Brand's Popular antiquities, the edition published in 1841, supplemented by the results of later investigation."—Pref.
Contents.—Introduction.—Superstitions and customs relating to days and seasons. — Marriage superstitions and customs. — Divination and omens.—Miscellaneous superstitions and customs.

I. Brand, John, 1744-1806. Observations on the popular antiquities of Great Britain.

11-6440

NK 0210348 DLC Or PPL MB

398.3
K73o
Knowlson, Thomas Sharper, 1867-
The origins of popular superstitions and customs. London, T.W.Laurie, 1930.
x,242p. 22cm.
"First printed 1910."
"Based on Brand's Popular antiquities, the edition published in 1841, supplemented by the results of later investigation."

1.Superstition. 2.Manners and customs. I.Brand, John, 1744-1806. Observations on the popular antiquities of Great Britain. II.Title.

NK 0210349 CLSU MH OLak OCl NcD NcU IU

Knowlson, Thomas Sharper, 1867–
The origins of popular superstitions and customs, by T. Sharper Knowlson ... New impression. London, T. W. Laurie, ltd., 1934.
x, 242 p. 22cm.
"First printed 1910 ... Reprinted 1934."
"Based on Brand's Popular antiquities, the edition published in 1841, supplemented by the results of later investigation."—Pref.
Contents. — Introduction. — Superstitions and customs relating to days and seasons.—Marriage superstitions and customs.—Divination and omens.—Miscellaneous superstitions and customs.

1. Superstition. 2. Manners and customs. I. Brand, John, 1744–1806. Observations on the popular antiquities of Great Britain. II. Title.

Library of Congress GR65.K5 1934 35—7406
[a38d1] 390

NK 0210350 DLC TNJ NcU PSC OClW ViU

398.3
K73o
Knowlson, Thomas Sharper, 1867-
The origins of popular superstitions and customs. London, T. Werner Laurie [1940]
x,242p. 20cm.

First published 1910.
"Based on Brand's Popular antiquities... 1841, supplemented by the results of later investigation."

1. Superstition. 2. Manners and customs.

NK 0210351 NcU FU

Knowlson, Thomas Sharper, 1867–
Put on your thinking cap, by T. Sharper Knowlson. <First series> London, Thorsons [1944]
256 p. 19cm. ["Life my teacher" books]

I. Title.

Library of Congress PN6331.K59 44-8136
[3] 828.91

NK 0210352 DLC FTaSU MsSM

Knowlson, Thomas Sharper, 1867–
The secret of concentration, by T. S. Knowlson ... With a foreword by S. Parkes Cadman ... New York and London, Harper & brothers, 1931.
xi p., 1 l., 235 p. diagrs. 20cm.
"First edition."

1. Attention. I. Title. II. Title: Concentration, The secret of.

Library of Congress BF321.K6 31-24506
——— Copy 2.
Copyright A 42382 [3] 154

NK 0210353 DLC DNW NN PPPCPh PPTU OEac OClU MB

Knowlson, Thomas Sharper, 1867-
The secret of concentration, by T. S. Knowlson ... With a foreword by S. Parkes Cadman ... New York and London, Harper & brothers [c1931]
xi p., 1 l., 235 p. diagrs. 20 cm.
"Third edition."
1. Attention. I. Title. II. Title: Concentration, The secret of.

NK 0210354 NcRS

Knowlson, Thomas Sharper, 1867–
Selling your ability, by T. S. Knowlson. New York, London, G. P. Putnam's sons, 1933.
xii, 297 p. incl. diagrs., forms. 22½cm.

1. Applications for positions. I. Title.

Library of Congress HF5383.K6 33—1999
——— Copy 2.
Copyright A 58814 [a39m1] 331.1152

NK 0210355 DLC OrCS WaS OrP OrPR MiU OU OCl OClh MB NN

Knowlson, Thomas Sharper, 1867–
Selling your ability, by T. Sharper Knowlson. London, Thorsons [1944]
176 p. incl. forms, diagrs. 22cm.

1. Applications for positions. I. Title.

Library of Congress HF5383.K6 1944 44-13090
[3] 331.115

NK 0210356 DLC

Knowlson, Thomas Sharper, 1867-
Selling your ability. [2.ed.] London, Thorsons [1946] 176 p. illus. 22cm.

1. Applications for positions. I. Title.

NK 0210357 NN

Knowlson, Thomas Sharper, 1867–
Think for yourself; letters on the formation of a personal creed, by T. Sharper Knowlson ... London, T. W. Laurie ltd. [1934]
224 p. 22cm.
"Questions and problems" at end of each letter.
Suggested reading: p. 191-200.

1. Thought and thinking. I. Title.

Library of Congress BF455.K63 35-3911
[3] [159.9556] 153.6

NK 0210358 DLC OO

Knowlson, Thomas Sharper, 1867–
A thought book on the Socratic method, ed. by T. Sharper Knowlson. London, T. W. Laurie, ltd. [1920]
viii, 199, [1] p. 22½cm.

I. Title.

Library of Congress PN6331.K6 21-6123

NK 0210359 DLC PSC TxU

Knowlson, Thomas Sharper, 1867– , editor.
A thought book on the Socratic method; edited by T. Sharper Knowlson. Philadelphia: J. B. Lippincott Co. [1920?] viii, 199 p. 8°.

3246A. 1. Quotations. 2. Mental discipline.
N. Y. P. L.

NK 0210360 NN OCU

VOLUME 300

KNOWLSON, THOMAS SHARPER, 1867–
What does Robert Burns mean to you? By T.S. Knowlson. [New York? 1929.] 17 p. 24°.

Cover-title.
"An address given at the meeting of the Robert Burns Memorial Assoc., in Central Park, New York City, Saturday June 29th, 1929."

584638A. 1. Burns, Robert, 1759–1796.

NK 0210361 NN

Knowlson, Thomas Sharper, 1867–

Ennever, William Joseph, 1869– FOR OTHER EDITIONS SEE MAIN ENTRY
Your mind, and how to use it; a self-instruction course, showing how to develop the powers of mind and memory for the achievement of success in life, business, professional and social, by W. J. Ennever ... associate editor, T. Sharper Knowlson ... London, Thorsons ltd; [New York] Doubleday, Doran & co. [1942]

Knowlton,
Fruits of philosophy
see Knowlton, Charles, 1800–1850.

Knowlton, Ada M.
Pleasant words, containing a choice selection of original poems. By Ada M. Knowlton ... [v. 1– Victory, N. Y., Messenger company, 1875–
v. 15cm.

I. Title.

Library of Congress PS2197.K32 28–2181

NK 0210364 DLC

Knowlton, Alonzo J., joint author.
Dodge's Geography of New England
see under
Allen, Lyman R

Knowlton, Anna Colby.
Diabetic cook book, by Anna Colby Knowlton. Englewood, N. J., A. C. Knowlton, 1912.
118 p. 19cm. $2.00

1. Cookery for the sick. 2. Diabetes. I. Title.

Library of Congress RC909.K8 12-27833

NK 0210366 DLC NN ICJ

Knowlton, Annie I.
Good-bye, Old South, good-bye! By Annie I. Knowlton. Illustrated by Charles W. Hall. [Worcester, Mass., Bullard art publishing company, 1887]
6 l. incl. col. illus., facsim. 26cm.
Illustrated by hand in water-colors; illustrated cover.
In verse.

1. Worcester, Mass. First church—Poetry. I. Hall, Charles W., illus. II. Title.

Library of Congress PS2197.K34 28-6621

NK 0210367 DLC

[Knowlton, Annie I.] comp.
Love's litany. Worcester, Mass., n.d.
22 p. 14 cm.

NK 0210368 RPB

[**Knowlton, Annie I**
My lover's love. Worcester, Mass., Bullard art publishing company [1887]
5 l. 18 x 16cm.

I. Title.

Library of Congress PS2197.K35 28–2182
Copyright 1887: 26291

NK 0210369 DLC

Knowlton, Annie (Rogers).
Why, Jessica! A comedy in one act, by Annie Rogers Knowlton. Boston, W. H. Baker & co., 1918. 24 p. 19cm. (Baker's edition of plays.)

1. Drama, American. I. Title.
N. Y. P. L.

NK 0210370 NN CtY WaU RP MH RPB

Knowlton, Ansel Alphonso, 1876–
Laboratory manual in physics, by A. A. Knowlton ... and Marcus O'Day ... 1st ed. New York [etc.] McGraw-Hill book company, inc., 1930.
xi, 127 p. illus., diagrs. 23½cm. $1.25

1. Physics—Laboratory manuals. I. O'Day, Marcus Driver, 1897– joint author.

Library of Congress QC37.K6 30–12878
Copyright A 23249 [5] 530.7

NK 0210371 DLC OrPR MtBuM MB OClU OClW ViU NcD CU

Knowlton, Ansel Alphonso, 1876–
Laboratory manual in physics, by A. A. Knowlton ... and Marcus O'Day ... 2d ed. New York and London, McGraw-Hill book company, inc., 1935.
xi, 137 p. illus., diagrs. 34cm.
"The order of topics has been changed to agree with that in the second edition of 'Physics for college students' and all page and chapter references have been corrected to refer to that edition."—Pref. to 2d ed.

1. Physics—Laboratory manuals. I. O'Day, Marcus Driver, 1897– joint author.

Library of Congress QC37.K6 1935 35–20931
——— Copy 2.
Copyright A 85725 [2] 530.72

NK 0210372 DLC NN WaTC OrU-D

Knowlton, Ansel Alphonso, 1876–
Physics for college students; an introduction to the study of the physical sciences, by A. A. Knowlton ... 1st ed. New York [etc.] McGraw-Hill book company, inc., 1928.
xix, 641 p. illus., col. pl., diagrs. 23½cm.
"References" at end of some of the chapters.

1. Physics.

Library of Congress QC21.K58 1928 28—10495

OrU-D DAL MH
ODW OCU OClU MiU OClh OClW WaU NIC CU KEmT PPF ViU
NK 0210373 DLC CaBVaU OrSaW OrPR PSC PBm PU OU

Knowlton, Ansel Alphonso, 1876–
Physics for college students; an introduction to the study of the physical sciences, by A. A. Knowlton ... 2d ed. New York and London, McGraw-Hill book company, inc., 1935.
xxi, 623 p. illus., col. pl., diagrs. 23½cm.
"References" at end of some of the chapters.

1. Physics.

Library of Congress QC21.K58 1935 35–5336
——— Copy 2.
Copyright A 81260 [5] 530

PU-Sc OCl
NK 0210374 DLC NcD CU WaS OrU-D OrPR Or OrP PWcS

Knowlton, Ansel Alphonso, 1876–
... Preparation and properties of the Heusler alloys ... [New York] 1911.
1 p. l., p. [54]–68. illus. 24cm.
Thesis (PH. D.)—University of Chicago.
"Reprinted from the Physical review, vol. XXXII., no. 1, January, 1911."

1. Magnetism. 2. Alloys.

Library of Congress QC761.K7 11-32507

NK 0210375 DLC NIC NcD NN MtBC PPAmP ICJ

Knowlton, Archer Eben, 1886–
Electric power metering; a textbook of practical fundamentals, by Archer E. Knowlton ... 1st ed. New York and London, McGraw-Hill book company, inc., 1934.
ix, 340 p. illus., diagrs. 23½cm.
Bibliography at end of chapter VI.

1. Electric meters. I. Title.

Library of Congress TK301.K57 34–39679
——— Copy 2.
Copyright A 77260 [5] 621.37

MB PV PPD PPF ViU OrP WaT IdU WaS Or OrCS
NK 0210376 DLC NcRS NN NcD CU MiU OClW OU OCl MiHM

Knowlton, Archer Eben, 1886– ed.

TK151 .S8

Standard handbook for electrical engineers. [1st]– ed. New York, McGraw-Hill, 1908–

Knowlton, Ben S.
The expert's assistant. A compendium giving rules for the certain direction of all kinds of errors in posting, etc. ... [By] Ben S. Knowlton. St. Paul, Minn, Pioneer press company, 1890.
v, 117 p. 23cm.

1. Bookkeeping.

Library of Congress HF5659.K7 6-33004†

NK 0210378 DLC

Knowlton, Mrs. Bernice Bettman, joint comp.

Knowlton, William Augustus, 1838–1933.
Life, letters and speeches of Dr. William Augustus Knowlton, compiled by Marion Wilcox and Bernice B. Knowlton ... Cleveland, O., The Gates press, 1938.

Knowlton, Charles, 1800–1850.
Address of Dr. Charles Knowlton, before the friends of mental liberty, at Greenfield, Mass., and, Constitution of the United Liberals of Franklin County, Mass. Boston: J. P. Mendum, 1845. 23 p. 16°.

1. Speech.—Liberty of, U. S. 2. United Liberals of Franklin County (Mass.).
N. Y. P. L.

NK 0210380 NN

VOLUME 300

Knowlton, Charles, 1800-1850.
Elements of modern materialism: inculcating the idea of a future state, in which all will be more happy, under whatever circumstances they may be placed than if they experienced no misery in this life. By Charles Knowlton ... Adams, Mass., Printed for the author, by A. Oakey, 1829.
viii, [9]-448 p. 21½cm.

1. Materialism.

10-28616†

Library of Congress B921.K53E4 1829

NK 0210381 GHi NBuG DNLM MB NCH IaDmD DLC MiU-C NcU IaU NNNAM MH-AH VtU MWA NcU

Knowlton, Charles, 1800-1850.
Fruits of philosophy [by] Knowlton. [London? 187-?]
cover-title, [3]-47, [1] p. 17½cm.

1. Birth control. 2. Malthusianism. I. Title.

CA 28-556 Unrev'd

Library of Congress HB875.K72 1870 a

NK 0210382 DLC NBuG MA MB OU NIC

Knowlton, Charles, 1800-1850.
Fruits of philosophy, an essay on the population question. 2d new ed., with notes. London, Freethought Pub. Co. [187-?]
56 p. 19 cm.

1. Birth control. 2. Malthusianism. I. Title.

HB875.K72 1870b 49-36564*

NK 0210383 DLC CaBVaU ICU DNLM MH NN RPB WU MdBJ

Knowlton, Charles, 1800-1850.
Fruits of philosophy. An essay on the population question. By Charles Knowlton, M.D. ... 2d new ed., with notes. Seventieth thousand. London, Freethought publishing company [1877]
vi, [2], [9]-56 p. 18cm.
Listed by Roorbach as having been published by the author in 1839. According to The twentieth century biog. dict. of notable Americans, first published in 1833.
"Publishers' preface" signed: Charles Bradlaugh, Annie Besant.
1. Birth control. I. Bradlaugh, Charles, 1833-1891, ed. II. Besant, Mrs. Annie (Wood) 1847- ed.

NK 0210384 MiU IaU ICU MH-BA IU MBCo

HB875 K56 1877
[Knowlton, Charles] 1800-1850.
Fruits of philosophy, an essay on the population question, by Charles Bradlaugh and Mrs. Annie Besant. 3d new ed., with notes. London, Publishing Co. [1877?]
58 p.

Cover title.

1. Birth control. 2. Malthusianism. I. Bradlaugh, Charles, 1833-1891. II. Besant, Annie (Wood) 1847-1933. III. Title.

NK 0210385 CU

HQ 56 K76 1878
KNOWLTON, Charles, 1800-1850
Fruits of philosophy. An essay on the population question. By Charles Knowlton, M.D., New York. New edition. Chicago, Printed for the proprietors by W. H. M. Smythe [ca. 1878]
32 p. 18 1/2 cm.

Bound in original dark green cloth, front cover lettered in gilt.

NK 0210386 MBCo

Knowlton, Charles, 1800-1850.
Fruits of philosophy; an essay on the population question. New ed., with notes. London, Freethought Pub. Co. [1879?]

NK 0210387 MH

HQ 56 K76 1886
KNOWLTON, Charles, 1800-1850
Fruits of philosophy. An essay on the population question. By Charles Knowlton, M.D. ... Newcastle-on-Tyne, W. Robinson, bookseller, 1886.
47, [1] p. 18 cm.

In original tan printed wrappers.

NK 0210388 MBCo

HQ 56 K76 1889
KNOWLTON, Charles, 1800-1850
Fruits of philosophy. An essay on the population question. By Charles Knowlton, M.D. ... Newcastle-on-Tyne, J. B. Barnes, 1889.
47, [1] p. 18 1/2 cm.

Unbound.

NK 0210389 MBCo

RG136 890K
Knowlton, Charles, 1800-1850.
Fruits of philosophy. An essay on the population question. [Edited by Annie Besant and Charles Bradlaugh] Second new edition. London, Freethought, [1890?]
56p. 18cm.

1. Conception - Prevention. 2. Birth control. I. Besant, Annie Wood, 1847-1933, ed. II. Bradlaugh, Charles, 1833-189. jt. ed. III. Title.

NK 0210390 CtY-M

HB 875 K72
Knowlton, Charles, 1800-1850
Fruits of philosophy; an essay on the population question. New ed., with notes and appendix. London, R. Forder, 1894.
57p. 18cm.
Cover title.

1. Birth control 2. Malthusianism I. Title

NK 0210391 WU

Knowlton, Charles, 1800-1850.
Fruits of philosophy, a treatise on the population question, by Charles Bradlaugh and Mrs. Annie Besant, Chicago, The Stein Co., n.d. YA 27179
94p. 18cm.

NK 0210392 DLC

Knowlton, Charles, 1800-1850.
Fruits of philosophy; a treatise on the population question [edited] by Charles Bradlaugh and Annie Besant. [2. new ed. New York] International pub. co. [n. d.] 58 p. 19cm.

1. Birth control. 2. Population. I. Besant, Annie (Wood), 1847-1933, ed. II. Bradlaugh, Charles, 1833-1891, ed. III. Title.

NK 0210393 NN NcD

[**Knowlton, Charles**] 1800-1850.
Fruits of philosophy. A treatise on the population question. [Ed.] by Charles Bradlaugh and Mrs. Anne Besant. [Chicago, G. E. Wilson, 18—]
20, [2] p. 22½cm.

1. Birth control. 2. Malthusianism. I. Bradlaugh, Charles, 1833-1891, ed. II. Besant, Mrs. Annie (Wood) 1847-1933, ed. III. Title.

6-7888

Library of Congress HB875.K72 1870

NK 0210394 DLC DNLM MH

Knowlton, Charles, 1800-1850.
Fruits of philosophy. A treatise on the population question. [2d new ed. Chicago, Published] by Charles Bradlaugh and Anne Besant; Garden City Pub. Co. [187-?]
22p. 22cm.

1. Birth control. 2. Sex manuals. I. Bradlaugh, Charles, 1833-1891. II. Besant, Annie (Wood) 1847-1933.

NK 0210395 NcD-MC DNLM

KNOWLTON, CHARLES, 1800-1850.
Fruits of philosophy. A treatise on the population question. [Edited] by Charles Bradlaugh and Mrs Annie Besant. [2. new ed.] [Chicago] [International pub. co.] [188-?] vi, 58 p. 12°.

Microfiche (neg.) 2 sheets. 11 x 15cm. (NYPL FSN 13,163)

Draper Collection.

1. Birth control 2. Population. I. Bradlaugh, Charles, 1833-1891, ed. II. Besant, Annie (Wood) 1847-1933. ed.

NK 0210396 NN

Knowlton, Charles, 1800-1850.
Fruits of philosophy; a treatise on the population question. San Francisco: The Reader's Library, 1891. 87 p. 12°.

1. Generation. 2. Besant, Annie, jt. au. N. Y. P. L.

N. Y. PUBLIC LIBRARY

NK 0210397 NN

Knowlton, Charles, 1800-1850.
Fruits of philosophy; a treatise on the population question, by Charles Bradlaugh and Mrs. Annie Besant. Chicago: The Wilson pub. co. [1897] 87 p. 18½cm. (Wilson's library of fiction. v. 4, no. 3.)

1. Birth control. 2. Population. I. Besant, Annie (Wood), 1847-1933, jt. au. II. Title. N. Y. P. L.

NK 0210398 NN

Knowlton, Charles, 1800-1850.
Fruits of philosophy, or The private companion of young married people. 2d ed. London, J. Watson [18-]

40 p. 16 cm.
"Reprinted from the American ed."

NK 0210399 MH CtY

KNOWLTON, Charles, 1800-1850.
Fruits of philosophy, or The private compani of young married people. 2d ed., with additions. Boston, 1833.

sq. 48o.

NK 0210400 MH

VOLUME 300

HQ 56 K76 1834
KNOWLTON, Charles, 1800-1850
Fruits of philosophy: or, the private companion of young married people. By Charles Knowlton, M.D. ... Reprinted from the American edition. Second edition. London, J. Watson [ca. 1834]
vi, [7]-40 p. 16 cm.

Manuscript notes.
Disbound.

1. Sex instruction. 2. Conception--Prevention.

NK 0210401 MBCo

Knowlton, Charles, 1800-1850.
Fruits of philosophy; or, The private companion of young married people ... 3d ed., with additions. Boston, 1834.
190p. 8cm.

1. Sex manuals. 2. Books, Miniature. I. Title. II. Title: The private companion of young married people.

NK 0210402 NcD-MC

HQ 56 K76 1839
KNOWLTON, Charles, 1800-1850
Fruits of philosophy, or the private companion of adult people. By Charles Knowlton, M.D. ... Fourth edition, with additions ... Philadelphia, F.P. Rogers, printer, 1839.
vi, [7]-128 p. 11 1/2 cm.

FOR FURTHER DETAILS SEE MAIN CARD.

NK 0210403 MBCo NNNAM

HQ 56 K76 1841
KNOWLTON, Charles, 1800-1850
Fruits of philosophy: or, the private companion of young married couples. By Charles Knowlton, M.D. ... London, James Watson [1841?]
40 p. 17 1/2 cm.

Autograph of Aurelis B. Wakefield.
Unbound.

A. Ex libris: Wakefield, Aurelis B.

NK 0210404 MBCo

Knowlton, Charles, 1800-50
Fruits of philosophy, or The private companion of young married people. Reprinted from the American ed. L, Watson, 1853

NK 0210405 MH

HQ 56 K76 1877
KNOWLTON, Charles, 1800-1850
Fruits of philosophy, or the private companion of adult people. By Charles Knowlton, M.D. ... Tenth edition, with additions. Boston, Published by subscription, 1877.
128 p. 11 1/2 cm.

Bound in contemporary green cloth, spine stamped and lettered in gilt.

NK 0210406 MBCo

Knowlton, Charles, 1800-1850.
Fruits of philosophy, or the private companion of adult people, by Charles Knowlton, M. D., edited with an introductory notice by Norman E. Himes ... with Medical emendations by Robert Latou Dickinson ... Mount Vernon [N. Y.] Peter Pauper press, 1937.
3 p. l., v-xv p., 1 l., 107 p., 1 l. 24cm. [Medical aspects of human fertility series, issued by the National committee on maternal health]
"Four hundred and fifty copies of this book have been printed."

1. Birth control. 2. Malthusianism. I. Himes, Norman Edwin, 1899- ed. II. Dickinson, Robert Latou, 1861- III. Title.

38-4628

Library of Congress HB875.K72 1937
——— Copy 2.
Copyright A 111673 [5] 612.63

NK 0210407 DLC IU MBCo CU NcD PPC OO NcD MiU-C

Knowlton, Dr. Charles (1800-1850)
History of the recent excitement in Ashfield. Ashfield, 1804.
24 p. 8°

NK 0210408 MWA

Knowlton, Charles, 1800-1850.
A history of the recent excitement in Ashfield... by Dr. Knowlton. Part 1. [Ashfield, Mass., 1834.] 24 p. 8°.

Caption-title.
Probably no more published.

NK 0210409 NN NcD MH

Knowlton, Charles, 1800-1850.
Speech of Dr. Charles Knowlton, in support of materialism, against the argument of Origen Bacheler, the great Goliah, and champion of the cross, 1836. Philadelphia, Printed for the society of "Free enquirers," 1838.
16 p. 21 cm. [With Robinson, John. The savage. 1838]
1. Materialism.

NK 0210410 CU PHi

Knowlton, Charles, 1800-1850.
Two remarkable lectures delivered in Boston, by Dr. C. Knowlton, on the day of his leaving the jail at East Cambridge, March 31, 1833, where he had been imprisoned, for publishing a book. Boston, A. Kneeland, 1833.
33 p. 21½cm.

1. Mind and body.

Library of Congress BF171.K7 1-1886 Revised

NK 0210411 DLC TxU NN MB MBCo

MIC-1 BF 171 .K7 Govt. Doc. Rm.
Knowlton, Charles, 1800-1850.
Two remarkable lectures delivered in Boston, by Dr. C. Knowlton, on the day of his leaving the jail at East Cambridge, March 31, 1833, where he had been imprisoned, for publishing a book. Boston, A. Kneeland, 1833.
33 p. 22 cm.
Microfilm copy.

1. Mind and body.

NK 0210412 NBuU MB

Knowlton, Charles, 1800-1850.
Vruchten der philosophie. Verhandeling over de bevolkingskwestie en de sexueele moraal, door Charles Knowlton, ... Uit het Engelsch door Dr. X. Naar het honderd zeventigste duizendtal, der tweede met aanteekeningen verrijkte Uitgaaf. Vierde geheel herzien en verbeterde druk [met afbeeldingen en vermeerderd met Aphorismen van E. Douwes-Dekker, jr.]. Rotterdam, J. H. H. Rothmeijer, 1880.
62 p. illus. 20½cm.

NK 0210413 ICJ

Knowlton, Charles B.
The art of writing, practical and ornamental. Illustrated by a series of practical copies embracing every variety of style. By Charles B. Knowlton. Buffalo, N. Y., C. B. Knowlton, ©1871.
4 numb. l., [3]-12 p., 13-36 numb. l. incl. plates. 14½ x 24 cm.
Engraved, except numb. leaf 4 and pages [3]-12.
Numbered leaves printed on one side only.
Cover-title: Gems of pen art.

1. Calligraphy.

Z43.K73 11—26393

NK 0210414 DLC

741.26 K73
Knowlton, Charles B.
Gems of pen art, by C.B. Knowlton. Buffalo, Chirographical Pub. Co., [n.d.]
36p. 14cm.

1. Penmanship. 2. Pen drawing. I. Title. II. Title: Pen art. III. Buffalo author. III. Buffalo imp.

NK 0210415 NBuHi

Knowlton, Charles B.
Gems of pen art, by Charles B. Knowlton ... Buffalo, Chirographical publishing company, ©1872.
4 numb. l., 12 p., 13-36 numb. l. incl. plates. 14½ x 24cm.
The numbered leaves are engraved.
Issued in 1871 under title: The art of writing.

1. Penmanship. I. Title.

CA 21-219 Unrev'd

Library of Congress Z43.K73 1872

NK 0210416 DLC

Knowlton, Charles B.
Knowlton's copy book, practical penmanship, embracing business and ladies' styles ... By C. B. Knowlton ... Buffalo, N. Y., C. B. Knowlton [1866]
1 p. l., xii p., 25 pl. 11½ x 22cm.
Engr. t.-p.
Cover-title: Writing.

1. Penmanship.

11-26394

Library of Congress Z43.K73C

NK 0210417 DLC NN

Knowlton, Charles B.
Practical lessons in book-keeping.

NK 0210418 DLC

Knowlton, Charles B.
Practical lessons in penmanship, by Charles B. Knowlton ... Buffalo, Chirographical publishing company [1872]
48 p. incl. 2 pl. vi pl. 23½cm.
Engr. t.-p.

1. Penmanship.

11-26395

Library of Congress Z43.K73P

NK 0210419 DLC NN

Knowlton, Charles S
Post offices of Orange County, California, past and present. [Placentia, Calif.] Printed by Placentia Courier [1947]
16 p. 22 cm.

1. Postal service—U. S.—Orange Co., Calif.

HE6376.A1C35 383.49494 48-18986*

NK 0210420 DLC C

Knowlton, Clarence H., joint author.

Chadwick, *Mrs.* **Mara Louise Pratt-.**
America's story for America's children, by Mara L. Pratt. Rev. ed. ... Boston, New York [etc.] D. C. Heath and company [1929-

VOLUME 300

Knowlton, Clarence Hinckley, 1876–
The asters of the Massachusetts South Shore.
= [Hingham, Mass.?] South Shore Nature Club. 1931. 10 pp. 23½ cm.
The title is on the cover.

D21 — Aster. The plant.

NK 0210422 MB NBuG

QK125 .K55 Knowlton, Clarence Hinckley, 1876–
Flora of Rocky Woods Reservation, Medfield, Massachusetts. [Boston, 1950]
11 p. 23 cm.

Cover title.

1. Botany - Massachusetts - Rocky Woods Reservation. 2. Rocky Woods Reservation, Medfield, Mass. i.t.

NK 0210423 NNBG DNAL

QK941 .M4 7 Knowlton, Clarence Hinckley, 1876–
Plant societies of south-eastern Massachusetts. Hingham, Mass., South Shore Nature Club, 1949.
10 p. 23 cm.

Cover title.

1. Phytosociology - Massachusetts. i.t.

NK 0210424 NNBG DNAL

Knowlton, Clarence Hinckley, 1876–
Trees of the Massachusetts South shore (Quincy to Duxbury, and inland)... n.p., South shore nature club, 1933.

13 p.

NK 0210425 MH

F 805 S75K5828 Knowlton, Clark S
Recommendations for the solution of land tenure problems among the Spanish American [sic. N.p., n.d.]
7 l. 28cm.

1. Spanish Americans in New Mexico. 2. Right of property - New Mexico. I. Title.

NK 0210426 CoU

MICROFILM F7155 **Knowlton, Clark S**
Spatial and social mobility of the Syrians and Lebanese in the city of São Paulo, Brasil. 1955.
viii, 340 l. illus.

Thesis, Vanderbilt University.
Bibliography: l. 333-342.
Microfilm (positive) Ann Arbor, Mich., University Microfilms, 1955. 1 reel. (Publication no. 13754)

NK 0210427 NNC WU

Knowlton, Clover Gates.
Opportunities for vocational education available in the community of Worcester to the early adolescent ... [by] Clover Gates Knowlton ... [Hyannis? Mass.] °1940.
4 p. l., 66 (i. e. 67) numb. l. 29 x 23cm.
Thesis (ED. M.)—State teachers college, Hyannis, Mass.
Type-written (carbon copy)

1. Vocational education—Massachusetts—Worcester.
42-5509
Library of Congress LC1046.5.W6K5

NK 0210428 DLC

Knowlton, Daniel Chauncey, 1876–
Age of discovery and trade expansion [1487–1670. By] Daniel C. Knowlton [and] T. Walter Wallbank. Chicago, A. J. Nystrom [1955]
col. map 87 x 120 cm. (Knowlton-Wallbank world history maps. Map no. K. W. 12)
Scale 1 : 34,848,000; 550 miles to the inch.

1. Discovery (in geography)—Maps. 2. World maps. I. Wallbank, Thomas Walter, 1901– joint author. II. Nystrom (A. J.) and Company, Chicago. III. Title.

G3201.S5 1955.K5 Map 56–325

NK 0210429 DLC FU

Knowlton, Daniel Chauncey, 1876–
Alexander's empire, 323 B. C. [By] Daniel C. Knowlton [and] T. Walter Wallbank. Chicago, A. J. Nystrom [1955]
col. map 87 x 120 cm. (Knowlton-Wallbank world history maps. Map no. K.W.4)
Scale 1 : 4,435,200; 70 miles to the inch.
Insets: Growth of Macedonia, 359 B. C.–334 B. C. [ca. 1 : 2,800,000]—Kingdoms of Alexander's successors about 200 B. C. [ca. 1 : 9,600,000]—Greek federations about 230 B. C. [ca. 1 : 2,800,000]

1. Near East—Historical geography—Maps. I. Wallbank, Thomas Walter, 1901– joint author. II. Nystrom (A. J.) and Company, Chicago. III. Title.

G7421.S2 1955.K5 Map 56–320

NK 0210430 DLC FU

H83 .S75 Knowlton, Daniel Chauncey, 1876– joint author.

Steinberg, Samuel, 1899–
The American way in community life [by] Samuel Steinberg [and] Daniel C. Knowlton. Boston, D. C. Heath [1948]

Knowlton, Daniel Chauncey, 1876–
... Beginnings of our nation, by Daniel C. Knowlton ... and Charles M. Gill ... New York, Cincinnati [etc.] American book company [°1935]
xii, 513 p. incl. col. front., illus. 19½cm. (The westward march of man)
Published 1934 under title: When we were colonies.
Includes bibliographies.
Illustrated lining-papers.

1. U. S.—Hist.—Colonial period. I. Gill, Charles Mark, 1870– joint author. II. Title.
35-18258
Library of Congress D21.W52 1935 vol. 3
Copyright A 85432 [5] (909) 973.2

NK 0210432 DLC OrLgE OClh PPStarr

Knowlton, Daniel Chauncey, 1876–
The bicentennial pageant of George Washington. Teachers' manual
see under George Washington Memorial Association.

Knowlton, Daniel Chauncey, 1876–
Christian Europe and the Crusades. [By] Daniel C. Knowlton [and] T. Walter Wallbank. Chicago, A. J. Nystrom [1955]
col. map 87 x 120 cm. (Knowlton-Wallbank world history maps. Map no. K. W. 9)
Scale 1 : 4,752,000; 75 miles to the inch.
"The map shows the extent of Christianity and the political divisions at the time of the First Crusade [1096]."

1. Europe—Historical geography—Maps. 2. Near East—Historical geography—Maps. 3. Crusades—Maps. I. Wallbank, Thomas Walter, 1901– joint author. II. Nystrom (A. J.) and Company, Chicago. III. Title.

G5701.S33 1955.K5 Map 56–324

NK 0210434 DLC

Knowlton, Daniel Chauncey, 1876–
A course in ancient history, by Daniel C. Knowlton, for the Columbia university home study courses. [New York, Columbia university press, 1929.
1 v.

Prepared for Columbia university extension teaching.

1. History, Ancient - Outlines, syllabi, et I. Columbia university. Extension teaching Home study.

NK 0210435 NNC

Knowlton, Daniel Chauncey, 1876–
A course in English history, by Daniel C. Knowlton, for the Columbia university home study courses. [New York] Department of university extension, 1927.
[66] p.

1. Gt. Brit. - History - Outlines, syllabi, etc. I. Columbia university. Extension teaching. Home study.

NK 0210436 NNC

Knowlton, Daniel Chauncey, 1876–
Cradles of world civilization: Centers of early civilization; Egyptian, Old Babylonian and Aegean. By Daniel C. Knowlton and T. Walter Wallbank. Chicago, A. J. Nystrom [1955]
col. map 86 x 120 cm. (Knowlton-Wallbank world history maps. Map no. K. W. 1)
Scale 1 : 4,435,200; 70 miles to the inch.
Insets: Ancient China.—Ancient India.

1. Geography, Ancient—Maps. I. Wallbank, Thomas Walter, 1901– joint author. II. Nystrom (A. J.) and Company, Chicago.

G3201.S2 1955.K5 Map 55–1076

NK 0210437 DLC

Knowlton, Daniel Chauncey, 1876–

Kimball, Reginald Stevens.
Current-events instruction; a textbook of principles and plans, by Reginald Stevens Kimball ... with chapters by Paul Klapper ... Daniel C. Knowlton ... Roy W. Hatch ... Leonard O. Packard ... Boston, New York [etc.] Houghton Mifflin company [°1929]

Knowlton, Daniel Chauncey, 1876–
Decline of Western colonialism in Asia, 1954 [by] Daniel C. Knowlton [and] T. Walter Wallbank. Chicago, A. J. Nystrom [1954]
col. map 87 x 120 cm. (Knowlton-Wallbank world history maps. Map no. K. W. 27)
Scale 1 : 8,870,400; 140 miles to the inch.

1. Asia—Politics—Maps. 2. Asia—Historical geography—Maps. I. Wallbank, Thomas Walter, 1901– joint author. II. Nystrom (A. J.) and Company, Chicago. III. Title.

G7401.F3 1954.K5 Map 54–630

NK 0210439 DLC

VOLUME 300

Knowlton, Daniel Chauncey, 1876–
... The development of our nation, by Daniel C. Knowlton ... and Mary Harden ... New York, Cincinnati [etc.] American book company [°1934]
ix, [349]–658, [xiii]–xli p. col. front., illus. (incl. ports., maps, facsims.) col. pl., diagrs. 20½cm. (The westward march of man)
Also published as part two of "Since we became a nation", 1934.
Includes bibliographies.
1. U. S.—Hist. I. Harden, Mary, joint author. II. Title.
Library of Congress D21.W52 36-6015
——— Copy 2. E178.1.K653
[3] (909) 973

NK 0210440 DLC PPAp

Knowlton, Daniel Chauncey, 1876–
Empires of the Near East. [By] Daniel C. Knowlton [and] T. Walter Wallbank. Chicago, A. J. Nystrom [1955]
4 col. maps on sheet 97 x 128 cm. (Knowlton-Wallbank world history maps. Map no. K. W. 2)
Scale 1 : 9,504,000; 150 miles to the inch.
CONTENTS.—Egyptian and Hittite Empires, about 1450 B. C.—Assyrian Empire, about 660 B. C.—Lydian, Median, and Babylonian Empires, about 550 B. C.—Persian Empire, about 500 B. C.
1. Near East—Historical geography—Maps. I. Wallbank, Thomas Walter, 1901– joint author. II. Nystrom (A. J.) and Company, Chicago.
G7421.S2 1955.K52 Map 56–371

NK 0210441 DLC FU

Knowlton, Daniel Chauncey, 1876 –
Essentials in modern European history, by Daniel C. Knowlton ... and Samuel B. Howe ... New York, Chicago, Longmans, Green and co., 1917.
x, 437 p. illus., maps (1 double) 20½cm. (*On verso of t.-p.:* Essentials in European history series) $1.50
"General bibliography": p. [411]–416.
1. Europe—Hist.—1789–1900. I. Howe, Samuel Burnett, joint author.
Library of Congress D359.K7 17—14802
Copyright A 462713 [a25e1]

NK 0210442 DLC NIC WaE WaS OCl MH NN MB PPAp

Knowlton, Daniel Chauncey, 1876–
Essentials in modern European history, by Daniel C.Knowlton, and Samuel B.Howe. New ed. New York, etc., Longmans, Green and co., 1918.

NK 0210443 MH PU

Knowlton, Daniel Chauncey, 1876–
Europe after the Congress of Vienna, 1815. [By] Daniel C. Knowlton [and] T. Walter Wallbank. Chicago, A. J. Nystrom [1955]
col. map 87 x 120 cm. (Knowlton-Wallbank world history maps. Map no. K. W. 16)
Scale 1 : 4,752,000; 75 miles to the inch.
Inset: Revolutionary Europe, 1820–1848.
1. Europe—Historical geography—Maps. I. Wallbank, Thomas Walter, 1901– joint author. II. Nystrom (A. J.) and Company, Chicago.
G5701.S6 1955.K5 Map 56–326

NK 0210444 DLC FU

Knowlton, Daniel Chauncey, 1876–
Europe at the outbreak of World War II; annexations of Hitler and Mussolini to Sept. 1, 1939. [By] Daniel C. Knowlton [and] T. Walter Wallbank. Chicago, A. J. Nystrom [1953]
col. map 87 x 120 cm. (Knowlton-Wallbank world history maps. Map no. K. W. 23)
Scale 1 : 5,322,240; 84 miles to the inch.
1. Europe—Maps. I. Wallbank, Thomas Walter, 1901– joint author. II. Nystrom (A. J.) and Company, Chicago.
G5700 1939.K5 Map 54–68

NK 0210445 DLC

Knowlton, Daniel Chauncey, 1876–
Europe in 1953 [by] Daniel C. Knowlton [and] T. Walter Wallbank. Chicago, A. J. Nystrom [1953]
col. map 87 x 120 cm. (Knowlton-Wallbank world history maps. Map no. K. W. 28)
Scale 1 : 5,322,240; 84 miles to the inch.
"Boundaries are 1953 de facto boundaries, pending approval of peace treaties."
1. Europe—Maps. I. Wallbank, Thomas Walter, 1901– joint author. II. Nystrom (A. J.) and Company, Chicago.
G5700 1953.K5 Map 54–66

NK 0210446 DLC

Knowlton, Daniel Chauncey, 1876–
Expansion of Islam, 622–750. [By] Daniel C. Knowlton [and] T. Walter Wallbank. Chicago, A. J. Nystrom [1955]
col. map 87 x 120 cm. (Knowlton-Wallbank world history maps. Map no. K. W. 8)
Scale 1 : 7,096,320; 112 miles to the inch.
Inset: Eastern Roman Empire and western Asia on the eve of the Mohammedan conquests [1 : 13,305,600; 210 miles to the inch.
1. Mediterranean region — Historical geography — Maps. 2. Near East—Historical geography—Maps. I. Wallbank, Thomas Walter, 1901– joint author. II. Nystrom (A. J.) and Company, Chicago. III. Title.
G3201.S3 1955.K4 Map 56–271 rev 2

NK 0210447 DLC

Knowlton, Daniel Chauncey, 1876–
History and government of New Jersey,... New York, Chicago, c1918

F134
.K73

NK 0210448 DLC

Knowlton, Daniel Chauncey, 1876–
History and the other social studies in the junior high school, by Daniel C. Knowlton ... New York, Chicago [etc.] C. Scribner's sons [°1926]
iv p., 2 l., 210 p. front., illus., plates, diagrs. 19½cm.
"Bibliographical note" at end of each chapter.
1. History — Study and teaching. 2. Social sciences — Study and teaching.
Library of Congress LB1641.K6 26—13637

WaSp
OEac OCl OClJC PPTU PU PP ViU MB PV NcD NcRS MiEM
NK 0210449 DLC CaBVaU OrSaW Or MtU WaTC MiU OU OCU

Knowlton, Daniel Chauncey, 1876–
A home study course in civil government: History HD, prepared by Daniel C. Knowlton. New York, Columbia university press, 1930.
39 l.
At head of title: Columbia university in the city of New York. University extension, Home study.
1. Political science - Outlines, syllabi, etc. I. Columbia university. Extension teaching. Home study.

NK 0210450 NNG DLC

Knowlton, Daniel Chauncey, 1876–
Illustrated topics for ancient history, arranged by Daniel C. Knowlton, PH. D. Philadelphia, Pa., McKinley publishing company, °1913.
[116] p. illus. (incl. maps, plans) 28½cm. $0.65
Loose leaves in binder.
1. History, Ancient—Outlines, syllabi, etc. I. Title.
Library of Congress D59.K6 14—2014

NK 0210451 DLC Or

Knowlton, Daniel Chauncey, 1876–
Illustrated topics for ancient history, arranged by Daniel C. Knowlton, PH.D. Philadelphia, Pa., McKinley pub. co., c1913. rev. ed.1922.
[116]p.

NK 0210452 OO PU

Knowlton, Daniel Chauncey, 1876–
Illustrated topics for medieval and modern history, arranged by Daniel C. Knowlton... Philadelphia, McKinley pub. co., c1922.
[156] p. illus. maps. Q.
Loose leaves in binder.

NK 0210453 OO

Knowlton, Daniel Chauncey, 1876–
Industrialization of the world. [By] Daniel C. Knowlton [and] T. Walter Wallbank. Chicago, A. J. Nystrom [1955]
col. map 89 x 120 cm. (Knowlton-Wallbank world history maps. Map no. K. W. 18)
Scale 1 : 34,214,400; 540 miles to the inch.
Inset: Expansion of the Industrial Revolution. [2 maps: United States, ca. 1 : 9,720,000, and Europe, ca. 1 : 15,000,000)
1. Industry—Maps. 2. World maps. I. Wallbank, Thomas Walter, 1901– joint author. II. Nystrom (A. J.) and Company, Chicago. III. Title.
G3201.M1 1955.K5 Map 55–874

NK 0210454 DLC

Knowlton, Daniel Chauncey, 1876– ed.

Crawford, William Harris, 1772–1834.
... The journal of William H. Crawford, edited by Daniel Chauncey Knowlton. Northampton, Mass., Department of history of Smith college [1925]

Knowlton, Daniel Chauncey, 1876–
The Knowlton work-book in American history, by Daniel C. Knowlton ... New York, London, The Century co. [°1930]
vii, 323 p., 10 l. incl. illus., maps. 24½cm. $1.00
Leaves of graph sheets (10 at end)
1. U. S.—Hist.—Outlines, syllabi, etc. 2. U. S.—Hist.—Examinations, questions, etc. I. Title.
Library of Congress E178.2.K73 30-28201
——— Copy 2.
Copyright A 29390 [5] 973

NK 0210456 DLC PPTU

Knowlton, Daniel Chauncey, 1876 –
Making history graphic; types of students' work in history, by Daniel C. Knowlton ... with a foreword by Otis W. Caldwell ... New York, Chicago [etc.] C. Scribner's sons [°1925]
v p., 2 l., ix–xi, 154 p. illus. (part col., incl. maps) diagrs. 21cm.
1. History—Study and teaching. I. Title.
Library of Congress D16.3.K6 25—11560

CaBVaU
ODW OU OOxM PU PWcS MB NN WaTC MtU OrPR Or CaBVa
NK 0210457 DLC NcD NcRS NcGU CoU PRosC OCl OClJC

Knowlton, Daniel Chauncey, 1876–
... The making of our nation, by Daniel C. Knowlton and Mary Harden ... New York, Cincinnati [etc.] American book company [°1934]
x, 351, xiv–xlii p. col. front., illus. (incl. ports., maps, facsims.) col. pl., diagrs. 20½cm. (The westward march of man)
Also published as part one of "Since we became a nation", 1934.
Includes bibliographies.
1. U. S.—Hist. I. Harden, Mary, joint author. II. Title.
Library of Congress D21.W52 36-6016
——— Copy 2. E178.1.K652
[3] (909) 973

NK 0210458 DLC

VOLUME 300

Knowlton, Daniel Chauncey, 1876–
The Mediterranean world, 550–500 B. C. ₍By₎ Daniel C. Knowlton ₍and₎ T. Walter Wallbank. Chicago, A. J. Nystrom ₍1955₎
col. map 87 x 120 cm. (Knowlton-Wallbank world history maps. Map no. K.W.3)
Scale 1 : 4,752,000 ; 75 miles to the inch.
1. Mediterranean region—Historical geography—Maps. I. Wallbank, Thomas Walter, 1901– joint author. II. Nystrom (A. J.) and Company, Chicago.
G6531.S2 1955.K5 Map 56–321

NK 0210459 DLC

Knowlton, Daniel Chauncey, 1876–
Migrations of the peoples in the fifth century. ₍By₎ Daniel C. Knowlton ₍and₎ T. Walter Wallbank. Chicago, A. J. Nystrom ₍1955₎
col. map 87 x 120 cm. (Knowlton-Wallbank world history maps. Map no. K. W. 7)
Scale 1 : 4,752,000 ; 75 miles to the inch.
Inset: Germanic settlements within the Roman Empire. Scale ₍1 : 14,256,000₎ 225 miles to the inch.
1. Europe—Historical geography—Maps. I. Wallbank, Thomas Walter, 1901– joint author. II. Nystrom (A. J.) and Company, Chicago. III. Title.
G5701.S2 1955.K5 Map 56–323

NK 0210460 DLC FU

Knowlton, Daniel Chauncey, 1876–
Minimum realia for the social studies ₍by₎ Daniel C. Knowlton.
(*In* National education association of the United States. Addresses and proceedings, 1933. p. 786–788)
1. Visual instruction. ₍1. Visual education₎ 2. Social sciences—₍Study and₎ teaching. I. Title.
E 34–235
Library, U. S. Office of Education L13.N212 1933
Library of Congress [L13.N4 1933]

NK 0210461 DHEW

Knowlton, Daniel Chauncey, 1876–
Motion pictures in history teaching; a study of the Chronicles of America photoplays, as an aid in seventh grade instruction, by Daniel C. Knowlton, PH. D., and J. Warren Tilton, PH. D. ₍New Haven₎ Pub. for the Dept. of education, Yale university by the Yale university press, 1929.
x p., 1 l., 182 p., 1 l. front., illus. (maps) plates. 24ᶜᵐ.
"Books used in preparing the set of readings": p. ₍167₎–168; "Bibliography of references": 1 leaf at end.
1. Moving-pictures in education. 2. U. S.—Hist.—Study and teaching. 3. History—Study and teaching. I. Tilton, John Warren, 1891– joint author. II. Yale university. Dept. of education. III. Title. IV. Title: The Chronicles of America photoplays.
Library of Congress LB1044.K6 30–1277

OrP KEmT WaTC OrCS CaBVaU
OU OC1W OC1 MiU OO CLSU ViU MH FMU NcD ScU NIC Or
NK 0210462 DLC AAP OrU CoU NN PPPM PU-Penn PPGi

Knowlton, Daniel Chauncey, 1876–
Napoleonic empire, 1812. By Daniel C. Knowlton and T. Walter Wallbank. Chicago, A. J. Nystrom ₍1955₎
col. map 87 x 120 cm. (Knowlton-Wallbank world history maps. Map no. K. W. 15)
Scale 1 : 4,752,000 ; 75 miles to the inch.
1. Europe—Historical geography—Maps. 2. France—Historical geography—Maps. I. Wallbank, Thomas Walter, 1901– joint author. II. Nystrom, (A. J.) and Company, Chicago.
G5701.S6 1955.K49 Map 55–1077

NK 0210463 DLC

Knowlton, Daniel Chauncey, 1876– joint ed.
FOR OTHER EDITIONS SEE MAIN ENTRY
Larned, Josephus Nelson, 1836–1913.
The new Larned History for ready reference, reading and research; the actual words of the world's best historians, biographers and specialists; a complete system of history for all uses, extending to all countries and subjects and representing the better and newer literature of history, based on the work of the late J. N. Larned, A. M., now completely rev., enl. and brought up to date; Donald E. Smith, PH. D., editor-in-chief, Charles Seymour, PH. D., Augustus H. Shearer, PH. D., Daniel C. Knowlton, PH. D., associate editors ... Springfield, Mass., C. A. Nichols publishing company ₍1928?₎

Knowlton, Daniel Chauncey, 1876–
... Our America past and present, by Daniel C. Knowlton ... and Mary Harden ... New York, Cincinnati ₍etc.₎ American book company ₍°1938₎
1 p. l., vii, 787, ix–lii p. col. front., illus., col. plates, diagrs. 21ᶜᵐ. (The westward march of man)
Maps on lining-papers.
Published in 1934 and 1936 under title: Since we became a nation; also published separately in 1934 in two parts: The development of our nation and The making of our nation.
Includes bibliographies.
1. U. S.—Hist. I. Harden, Mary, joint author. II. Title.
38–11317
Library of Congress E178.1.K654
——— Copy 2.
Copyright A 117381 ₍5₎ 973

NK 0210465 DLC PP Wa OCU

Knowlton, Daniel Chauncey, 1876–
... Our America past and present, by Daniel C. Knowlton ... and Mary Harden ... New York, Cincinnati ₍etc.₎ American book company ₍°1939₎
1 p. l., vii, 787, ix–lii p. col. front., illus. (incl. ports., maps, plans, facsims.) col. plates, diagrs. 20½ᶜᵐ. (The westward march of man)
Maps on lining-papers.
Published in 1934 and 1936 under title: Since we became a nation; also published separately in 1934 in two parts: The development of our nation and The making of our nation.
Includes bibliographies.
1. U. S.—Hist. I. Harden, Mary, joint author. II. Title.
39–24388
Library of Congress E178.1.K654 1939
——— Copy 2.
Copyright A 132372 ₍2₎ 973

NK 0210466 DLC

Knowlton, Daniel Chauncey, 1876–
... Our America, past and present, by Daniel C. Knowlton ... and Mary Harden ... New York, Cincinnati ₍etc.₎ American book company ₍°1941₎
1 p. l., vii, 787, ix–lii p. incl. illus., plates, tables, diagrs. col. front., col. plates. 21ᶜᵐ. (The westward march of man)
Maps on lining-papers.
Published in 1934 and 1936 under title: Since we became a nation; also published separately in 1934 in two parts: The development of our nation and The making of our nation.
Includes bibliographies.
1. U. S.—Hist. I. Harden, Mary, joint author. II. Title.
41–21430
Library of Congress E178.1.K654 1941
₍a44d1₎ (909) 973

NK 0210467 DLC WaS

Knowlton, Daniel Chauncey, 1876–
... Our America, past and present, by Daniel C. Knowlton ... and Mary Harden ... New York, Cincinnati ₍etc.₎ American book company ₍1942₎
1 p. l., vii, 787, ix–lii p. incl. illus., plates, tables, diagrs. col. front., col. plates. 21ᶜᵐ. (The Westward march of man)
Published in 1934 and 1936 under title: Since we became a nation; also published separately in 1934 in two parts: The development of our nation and The making of our nation.
Bibliography at end of each chapter except one. "Reading references": p. ix–xiii.
1. U. S.—Hist. I. Harden, Mary, joint author. II. Title.
42–19926
Library of Congress E178.1.K654 1942
₍2₎ 973

NK 0210468 DLC

Knowlton, Daniel Chauncey, 1876–
... Our America, past and present, by Daniel C. Knowlton ... and Mary Harden ... New York, Cincinnati ₍etc.₎ American book company ₍1944₎
1 p. l., vii, 806, ix–lii p. incl. illus., plates, diagrs. col. front., col. plates. 21ᶜᵐ. (The Westward march of man)
Published in 1934 and 1936 under title: Since we became a nation; also published in 1934 in two separate parts: The development of our nation and The making of our nation.
Bibliography at end of each chapter except one. "Reading references": p. ix–xiii.
1. U. S.—Hist. I. Harden, Mary, joint author. II. Title.
44–3506
Library of Congress E178.1.K654 1944
₍3₎ 973

NK 0210469 DLC PPAp

Knowlton, Daniel Chauncey, 1876–
... Our America past and present, by Daniel C. Knowlton ... and Mary Harden ... New York, Cincinnati ₍etc.₎ American book company ₍1945₎
1 p. l., vii, 810, ix–lii p. incl. illus., plates, diagrs. col. front., col. plates. 21ᶜᵐ. (The Westward march of man)
Published in 1934 and 1936 under title: Since we became a nation; also published in 1934 in two separate parts: The development of our nation and The making of our nation.
Bibliography at end of each chapter except one. "Reading references": p. ix–xiii.
1. U. S.—Hist. I. Harden, Mary, joint author. II. Title.
45–7719
Library of Congress E178.1.K654 1945
₍4₎ 973

NK 0210470 DLC

E178
.1
.K654
1946
Knowlton, Daniel Chauncey, 1876–
... Our America, past and present, by Daniel C. Knowlton ... and Mary Harden ... New York, Cincinnati ₍etc.₎ American book company ₍1946₎
1 p. l., vii, 810, ix–lii p. illus. (incl. ports., maps) diagrs. 21ᶜᵐ. (The Westward march of man)
Published in 1934, 1936 and 1939 under title: Since we became a nation; also published in 1934 in two separate parts: The development of our nation and The making of our nation.
"Reading references": p. ix–xiii.
1. U. S.—Hist. I. Harden, Mary, joint author. II. Title.
46–20687
Library of Congress E178.1.K654 1946
₍2₎ 973

NK 0210471 DLC

Knowlton, Daniel Chauncey, 1876–
... Our beginnings in the past, a first book in history, by Daniel C. Knowlton ... and Armand J. Gerson ... New York, Cincinnati ₍etc.₎ American book company ₍°1933₎
xi, ₍1₎, 242 p. incl. col. front., illus., maps. 19½ᶜᵐ. (The westward march of man)
1. History, Ancient — Juvenile literature. 2. Civilization — Hist. — Juvenile literature. I. Gerson, Armand Jacques, 1881– joint author. II. Title.
33–23334
Library of Congress D21.W52 vol. 1
Copyright A 63541 ₍3₎ (909) 930

OU OO OC1 PPAp
NK 0210472 DLC OrMonO OrLgE Or WaSp OrP PWcS OEac

Knowlton, Daniel Chauncey, 1876–
... Our past in western Europe; a second book in history, by Daniel C. Knowlton ... and Mary A. Wheeler ... New York, Cincinnati ₍etc.₎ American book company ₍°1933₎
xiii, ₍1₎, 346 p. incl. col. front., illus. 19ᶜᵐ. (The westward march of man)
1. Europe—History, Juvenile. 2. America—Disc. & explor.—Juvenile literature. I. Wheeler, Mary Alexandria, joint author. II. Title.
33–30264
Library of Congress D21.W52 vol. 2
Copyright A 66257 ₍5₎ (909) 940

OU OC1
NK 0210473 DLC OrLgE OrMonO Or WaSp PWcS PPTU PU

Knowlton, Daniel Chauncey, 1876–
... Our past in western Europe, by Daniel C. Knowlton ... and Mary A. Wheeler ... New York, Cincinnati ₍etc.₎ American book company ₍°1935₎
xiii, ₍1₎, 272 p. incl. col. front., illus. (incl. maps) 19½ᶜᵐ. (The westward march of man)
Maps on lining-papers.
1. Europe—History, Juvenile. 2. America—Disc. & explor.—Juvenile literature. I. Wheeler, Mary Alexandria, joint author. II. Title.
35–8089
Library of Congress D21.W52 1935 vol. 2
——— Copy 2. D103.K6 1935
Copyright A 83144 ₍3₎ (909) 940

NK 0210474 DLC OC1h

VOLUME 300

Knowlton, Daniel Chauncey, 1876–
Reference map of the Roman world. ₍By₎ Daniel C. Knowlton ₍and₎ T. Walter Wallbank. Chicago, A. J. Nystrom ₍1955₎
col. map 87 x 120 cm. (Knowlton-Wallbank world history maps. Map no. K. W. 5)
Scale 1 : 4,752,000 ; 75 miles to the inch.
Inset: Cultural divisions of the Roman Empire. Scale ₍1 : 13,-305,600₎ 210 miles to the inch.
1. Rome—Description, geography—Maps. I. Wallbank, Thomas Walter, 1901– joint author. II. Nystrom (A. J.) and Company, Chicago. III. Title: Roman world.
G6700 300.K5 Map 56–322

NK 0210475 DLC FU

Knowlton, Daniel Chauncey, 1876–
Russian and Japanese expansion in the Far East; extent of empires in Far East at time of Japanese attack on Pearl Harbor, Dec. 7, 1941. ₍By₎ Daniel C. Knowlton ₍and₎ T. Walter Wallbank. Chicago, A. J. Nystrom ₍1954₎
col. map 87 x 120 cm. (Knowlton-Wallbank world history maps. Map no. K. W. 24)
Scale 1 : 8,870,400 ; 140 miles to the inch.
1. East (Far East)—Politics—Maps. 2. East (Far East)—Historical geography—Maps. I. Wallbank, Thomas Walter, 1901– joint author. II. Nystrom (A. J.) and Company, Chicago. III. Title.
G7801.F3 1941.K5 Map 54–629

NK 0210476 DLC

Knowlton, Daniel Chauncey, 1876–
... Since we became a nation, by Daniel C. Knowlton ... and Mary Harden ... New York, Cincinnati ₍etc.₎ American book company ₍°1934₎
x, 655, xi–li p. col. front., illus., col. plates, diagrs. 21cm. (The westward march of man)
Includes bibliographies.
1. U. S.—Hist. I. Harden, Mary, joint author. II. Title.
34–19479
Library of Congress D21.W52 vol. 4
——— Copy 2. E178.1.K65
Copyright A 74025 ₍5₎ (909) 973

NK 0210477 DLC OrMonO OrLgE Or PBa PPTU OU OLak ODW

Knowlton, Daniel Chauncey, 1876–
... Since we became a nation, by Daniel C. Knowlton ... and Mary Harden ... New York, Cincinnati ₍etc.₎ American book company ₍°1936₎
x, 655, xi–xlviii p. col. front., illus., col. plates, diagrs. 21cm. (The westward march of man)
Maps on lining-papers.
Also published separately in two parts "The making of our nation" and "The development of our nation", 1934.
Includes bibliographies.
1. U. S.—Hist. I. Harden, Mary, joint author. II. Title.
36–11558
Library of Congress D21.W52 1935
——— Copy 2. E178.1.K65 1936
Copyright A 94666 ₍5₎ (909) 973

NK 0210478 DLC ICRL OClh

Knowlton, Daniel Chauncey, 1876–
... Since we became a nation, by Daniel C. Knowlton ... and Mary Harden ... New York, Cincinnati ₍etc.₎ American book company ₍°1939₎
x, 655, xi–xlviii p. col. front., illus., col. plates, diagrs. 21cm. (The westward march of man)
Maps on lining-papers.
Also published separately in two parts "The making of our nation" and "The development of our nation", 1934.
Includes bibliographies.
1. U. S.—Hist. I. Harden, Mary, joint author. II. Title.
39–2779
Library of Congress D21.W52 1939 vol. 4
——— Copy 2. E178.1.K65 1939
Copyright A 125460 ₍5₎ (909) 973

NK 0210479 DLC PPAp

Knowlton, Daniel Chauncey, 1876–
Spread of Christianity to the end of the fourth century. ₍By₎ Daniel C. Knowlton ₍and₎ T. Walter Wallbank. Chicago, A. J. Nystrom ₍1955₎
col. map 87 x 120 cm. (Knowlton-Wallbank world history maps. Map no. K. W. 6)
Scale 1 : 4,752,000 ; 75 miles to the inch.
Inset: Palestine in the time of Christ ₍ca. 1 : 1,000,000₎
1. Geography—Historical—Maps. 2. Bible—Geography—Maps. 3. Ecclesiastical geography—Maps. I. Wallbank, Thomas Walter, 1901– joint author. II. Title.
G3201.S2 1955.K52 Map 55–1107

NK 0210480 DLC FU

DA32
.K73

Knowlton, D[aniel] C[hauncey], 1876-
Studies in English history, prepared for use in the Ithaca high school by D. C. Knowlton... [Ithaca] Ithaca high school, 1903.

NK 0210481 DLC

Knowlton, D₍aniel₎ C₍hauncey₎ 1876 –
Studies in English history, prepared for the use of high schools and academies, by D. C. Knowlton ... Rev. ed. ₍Ithaca, N. Y.₎ Ithaca high school, 1906.
71 p. 23½cm.
Interleaved.
Bibliography: p. ₍5₎–13.
1. Gt. Brit.—Hist.—Outlines, syllabi, etc.
6–40555
Library of Congress DA32.7.K7 (Copyright A 158368)

NK 0210482 DLC

E178
.2
.K74
Knowlton, Daniel Chauncey, 1876–
Study guide for American history ... [by] Daniel C. Knowlton ... Newtonville, Mass., The Jennings publishing company [c1936
v. 23cm.
Cover-title.
1. U. S.--Hist.--Outlines, syllabi, etc. I. Title.

NK 0210483 DLC

D209
.K55
Knowlton, Daniel Chauncey, 1876–
Study guide for modern history ... an aid to a quick grasp of the subject and source of a comprehensive review [by] Daniel C. Knowlton ... Newtonville, Mass., The Jennings publishing company [c1935-
v. 23cm.
Cover-title.
1. History, Modern--Outlines, syllabi, etc. I. Title.

NK 0210484 DLC

Knowlton, Daniel Chauncey, 1876– joint author.

Webster, Hutton, 1875–
A teacher's manual accompanying the Webster-Knowlton-Hazen European history maps, by Hutton Webster ... Daniel C. Knowlton ... Charles Downer Hazen ... Chicago, Ill., A. J. Nystrom & co. ₍°1924₎

FOR OTHER EDITIONS SEE MAIN ENTRY

767
A734b
Knowlton, Daniel Chauncey, 1876-
Teachers' manual especially prepared for use with The Bicentennial pageant of George Washington ... New York, George Washington memorial association, inc., c1932.
30 p.
Partial contents.- Analysis of the etchings: 1. Historical content. 2. Problems of reconstruction. 3. Teaching values.

NK 0210486 MiDA

IT
E178.1
1936
.K6T
Knowlton, Daniel Chauncey, 1876–
Teachers' manual for Since we became a nation ₍by₎ Daniel C. Knowlton... New York, Cincinnati ₍etc.₎ American book company ₍°1936₎
47p. 19cm.
"Reading references for the teacher": p.46-47.
1.U.S. - Hist. - Study and teaching.
New York Univ.Wash.Sq.

NK 0210487 NNU-W

Knowlton, Daniel Chauncey, 1876–
U. S. S. R. in 1955. By Daniel C. Knowlton and T. Walter Wallbank. Chicago, A. J. Nystrom ₍1955₎
col. map 87 x 120 cm. (Knowlton-Wallbank world history maps. Map no. K. W. 29)
Scale 1 : 7,236,800 ; 130 miles to the inch.
Also entitled: Russia in 1955.
1. Russia—Maps. I. Wallbank, Thomas Walter, 1901– joint author. II. Nystrom (A. J.) and Company, Chicago.
G7000 1955.K5 Map 55–1069

NK 0210488 DLC

Knowlton, Daniel Chauncey, 1876–
The use of the photoplay in the teaching of history.
(*In* National education association of the United States. Addresses and proceedings, 1928. p. 951–955)
1. Moving-pictures in education. 2. History—₍Study and₎ teaching.
E 31–233
Library, U. S. Office of Education L13.N212 1928
₍2₎

NK 0210489 DHEW OU

Knowlton, Daniel Chauncey, 1876–
... When we were colonies, by Daniel C. Knowlton ... and Charles M. Gill ... New York, Cincinnati ₍etc.₎ American book company ₍1934₎
xii, 370 p. incl. col. front., illus. 19½ cm. (The Westward march of man)
Includes bibliographies.
——Teachers' manual for When we were colonies ₍by₎ Charles M. Gill ... New York, Cincinnati ₍etc.₎ American book company ₍°1936₎
32 p. 19 cm.
E188.K672
1. U. S.—Hist.—Colonial period. I. Gill, Charles Mark, 1870– II. Title.
D21.W52 vol. 3 973.2 34–7014 rev
——— Copy 2. E188.K67

NK 0210490 DLC OU PPT Or OrLgE OrMonO WaSp

Knowlton, Daniel Chauncey, 1876–
The world after the First World War, 1924. By Daniel C. Knowlton and T. Walter Wallbank. Chicago, A. J. Nystrom ₍1955₎
col. map 86 x 119 cm. (Knowlton-Wallbank world history maps. Map no. K. W. 22)
Scale 1 : 34,214,400 ; 540 miles to the inch.
1. World maps. I. Wallbank, Thomas Walter, 1901– joint author. II. Nystrom (A. J.) and Company, Chicago.
G3200 1924.K5 Map 55–1068

NK 0210491 DLC

VOLUME 300

Knowlton, Daniel Chauncey, 1876–
The world in 1914 ₍by₎ Daniel C. Knowlton ₍and₎ T. Walter Wallbank. Chicago, A. J. Nystrom ₍1954₎
col. map 87 x 120 cm. (Knowlton-Wallbank world history maps. Map no. K. W. 19)
Scale 1 : 34,214,400 ; 540 miles to the inch.
Inset, 85 miles to the inch : Central Europe in 1914.
1. World maps. 2. Geography, Historical—Maps. I. Wallbank, Thomas Walter, 1901– joint author. II. Nystrom (A. J.) and Company, Chicago. III. Title.
G3200 1914.K5 Map 54–628
NK 0210492 DLC

Knowlton, Daniel Chauncey, 1876–
World War II in Europe and northern Africa ₍by₎ Daniel C. Knowlton ₍and₎ T. Walter Wallbank. Chicago, A. J. Nystrom ₍1953₎
col. map 87 x 120 cm. (Knowlton-Wallbank world history maps. Map no. K. W. 25)
Scale 1 : 5,322,240 ; 84 miles to the inch.
Inset : Partition of Poland, 1939.
1. World War, 1939–1945—Maps. 2. Europe—Maps. I. Wallbank, Thomas Walter, 1901– joint author. II. Nystrom (A. J.) and Company, Chicago. III. Title.
G3201.S7 1953.K5 Map 54–67
NK 0210493 DLC

Knowlton, Daniel Chauncey, 1876–
World War II in the Pacific ₍by₎ Daniel C. Knowlton ₍and₎ T. Walter Wallbank. Chicago, A. J. Nystrom ₍1954₎
col. map 87 x 120 cm. (Knowlton-Wallbank world history maps. Map no. K. W. 26)
Scale 1 : 14,889,600 ; 235 miles to the inch.
1. World War, 1939–1945—Maps. 2. Pacific area—Maps. I. Wallbank, Thomas Walter, 1901– joint author. II. Nystrom (A. J.) and Company, Chicago. III. Title.
G9231.S7 1954.K5 Map 54–685
NK 0210494 DLC

Knowlton, Daniel Stimson, 1861-
A calendar for Americans
see under title

Knowlton, Daniel Stimson, 1861-
A calendar of the Constitution of the United States
see under title

Knowlton, Daniel Stimson, 1861-
Franklin calendar, A, for 1928. Compiled by Daniel S. Knowlton. = [Boston. United Shoe Machinery Corporation.] 1928. 1 v. Illus. Portraits. Vignettes. 13 cm.
The cover title is used.
N5525 — Almanacs. — Franklin, Ben｣, 1706–1790. — United Shoe Machinery Corporation, Beverly, Mass. Pubs. — ｣owlton, Daniel Stimson, compiler and editor, 1861–
NK 0210497 MB LNHT

Knowlton, Daniel Stimson, 1861– ed.
Thomson, Henry Czar Merwin, 1863–
In the early eighties and since with Yale '83, by Henry C. M. Thomson; with Reminiscences various and sundry, by one and another, edited by Daniel S. Knowlton ... ₍Boston₎ Priv. print. by subscription, 1923.

Knowlton, Daniel Stimson, 1861-
A Lincoln calendar for the year 1920
see under title

Knowlton, Daniel Stimson, 1861- comp.
A Pilgrim calendar for the year 1921
see under title

₍**Knowlton, Daniel Stimson**₎ 1861–
A primer of boots & shoes; being certain information calculated for the instruction of children, young or old. Prepared by D••••• S•••••• K•••••••• ... ₍Cambridge, Mass., The Riverside press₎ 1914.
24 p. 18cm.
1. Boots and shoes. I. Title.
Library of Congress HD9787.A2K6 14–13182 Revised
NK 0210501 DLC NN OU MB

Knowlton, Daniel Stimson, 1861-
Washington calendar for the year 1922
see under title

Knowlton, David Hunter, ed.
The Age; ₍a monthly magazine of literature and art for home and school₎ v. 1; Jan.–Dec. 1882. ₍Farmington, Me., Knowlton, McLeary & co., 1882₎

₍**Knowlton, David Hunter**₎
Plant study for children. Farmington, Me., D. H. Knowlton & comp'y, °1882.
cover-title, 20 forms. 17cm.
1. Botany—Analysis blanks. 5–26696†
Library of Congress QK57.K7
NK 0210504 DLC

₍**Knowlton, David Hunter**₎ *comp.*
Speeches for little people. A collection of standard poetry and prose for the youngest ... Farmington, Me., D. H. Knowlton & co., 1891.
viii, ₍9₎–128 p. 18cm.
1. Readers and speakers—1870– I. Title.
Library of Congress PN4271.K4 13–6660
NK 0210505 DLC

Knowlton, David M., joint author.
Knowlton, Ebenezer.
The champion speller containing two thousand test words ... By E. & D. M. Knowlton. San Francisco, A. Roman & co., 1875.

Knowlton, Dexter A ,1812-1876.
A sketch of the life of D.A. Knowlton, written by himself. ₍Brooklyn?, N.Y.,ca.1866₎
13p. 29cm.
Typed carbon copy ms.
Caption title.
NK 0210507 IHi

Knowlton, Don, 1892–
Advertising for banks, by Don Knowlton ... with collaboration of the Financial advertisers association, and an introduction by Francis H. Sisson ... New York, Chicago ₍etc.₎ Rand, McNally & company ₍°1932₎
xix, 533 p. illus. 22cm.
1. Advertising—Banks and banking. I. Financial advertisers association. II. Title.
Library of Congress HF6161.B2K6 32–25265
——— Copy 2.
Copyright A 54989 ₍5₎ 659.1
NK 0210508 DLC MB NN OKentU OCl OClW OU PP PSt

Knowlton, Don, 1892–
Brick house stories, by Don Knowlton. Cleveland, O., The Gates press, 1936.
8 p. l., 112 p. front., plates. 25cm.
"Of this edition 85 copies have been privately printed."
"All the stories in this book are stories about when I used to live at the Brick house when I was a little boy."—Pref.
I. Title. 36–9561
Library of Congress PZ7.K768Br
——— Copy 2.
Copyright A 92858 ₍3₎
NK 0210509 DLC OClW OCl

KNOWLTON, DON, 1892 –
Cooperation in public relations. New York: Savings Bank Division, Amer. Bankers' Assoc., 1931. 11 p. 8°.
587352A. 1. Banks and banking—Methods. I. American Bankers' Association. Savings Bank Division.
N. Y. P. L. March 31, 1932
NK 0210510 NN PU

Knowlton, Don, 1892–
Profit and loss, by Don Knowlton. New York ₍etc.₎ Hill & Knowlton ₍1944₎ 16 p. 22cm.
1. Corporations—Finance—U. S. 2. World war, 1939– nomic aspects—U. S.
N. Y. P. L. May 23, 1945
NK 0210511 NN

Knowlton, Don, 1892 –
These bankers, by Don Knowlton; illustrated by Arthur De Bebian. New York, The Bankers publishing company, 1927.
3 p. l., 9–80 p. illus. 18cm.
I. Title. 27–24858
Library of Congress PS3521.N77T5 1927
NK 0210512 DLC LU OCl OClFRB

Knowlton, Dorothy Gillespie, 1903–
San Francisco suite, for the piano. Cincinnati, Willis Music Co. ₍1948₎
7 v. 30 cm.
CONTENTS.—Cable car.—Flower stand.—Chinese New Year.—Fisherman's Wharf.—Telegraph Hill.—Market Street.—Golden Gate sunset.
1. Suites (Piano) I. Title.
M24.K75S3 49–15435*
NK 0210513 DLC

Knowlton, E , supposed author.
Sustaining the Christian ministry
see under Freewill Baptist Printing Establishment.

VOLUME 300

*F612 Knowlton, E.A., company, Rochester, Minn
C59R6 Nature's beauty spots in and near
1931k Rochester, Minnesota. ₍Rochester,Minn.. E.A.Knowlton company, 1931₎
cover-title,₍22₎ p. illus. 28cm.

"This booklet is a collection of a few views, a preliminary edition, seeking to determine if a larger one is needed or wanted."

NK 0210515 MnHi

Knowlton, Miss E T
Poems for children, by Miss G. ₍!₎ T. Knowlton. Cincinnati, G. L. Weed, 1849.
72 p.

Name corrected in pencil on title-page.

NK 0210516 NNC RPB

Knowlton, Ebenezer.
The champion speller containing two thousand test words ... By E. & D. M. Knowlton. San Francisco, A. Roman & co., 1875.
24 p. 14½cm.
On cover: Third thousand.—Revised.

1. Spellers. I. Knowlton, David M., joint author.
CA 11-2081 Unrev'd
Library of Congress PE1146.K7

NK 0210517 DLC

Knowlton, Ebenezer.
... Southwestern California. Written expressly for "The Resources of California", by Prof. Knowlton ... The great Colorado desert problem!
(*In* **The Resources of California. San Francisco, 1873. 66½ x 48cm. v. 2, no. 11, p. 1-2**)

1. California, Southern—Descr. & trav. I. Title.
Rc-867
Library of Congress F866.R37 vol. 2, no. 11

NK 0210518 DLC

Knowlton, Edgar.
Electrical machinery
see under International Correspondence Schools, Scranton, Pa.

KNOWLTON, Edgar Colby.
Natura as an allegorical figure. Thesis, Harvard University,1918.

Typewritten, 4o. ff.iii,(4). 251, vi,vii,72. "Bibliography", appendix, B. ff. vii.
HU 90.1263

NK 0210520 MH

Knowlton, Edgar Colby, joint author.
Hanford, James Holly, 1882-
The Nelson handbook of English, by James Holly Hanford ... Malcolm McLeod ... Edgar C. Knowlton ... New York, T. Nelson and sons, 1931.

PR Knowlton, Edgar Colby.
5869 The novelty of Wordsworth's Michael as a
M6 pastoral.
K73 (In Modern Language Association of America. Publications. Baltimore. 24cm. v. 35 (1920) p. 432-446)
Healey 1392.

1. Wordsworth, William, 1770-1850. Michael. I. Modern Language Association of America. Publications. v. 35, no. 4.

NK 0210522 NIC

Knowlton, Edgar Colby.
An outline of world literature from Homer to the present day, by Edgar C. Knowlton ... New York, T. Nelson & sons, 1929.
vi p., 1 l., 391 p. 19cm. (*Half-title:* Nelson's English series)
"Suggestions for further reading": p. 369-380.

1. Literature—Outlines, syllabi, etc. 2. Literature—Bio-bibl. I. Title.
29-1872
Library of Congress PN524.K6

MB PPL PSC PP
OrSaW OrPR MtBC OrP OEac OClCC ODW OCl OO OClh ViU
NK 0210523 DLC MoU NcD OrMonO Or OrLgE OrAshS WaS

PN524 Knowlton, Edgar Colby.
.K6 An outline of world literature from Homer to the present day, by Edgar C. Knowlton. New York, T. Nelson & sons, 1937 ₑc1929ₑ
vi, 391 p. 19 cm. (Half-title: Nelson's English series)
"Suggestions for further reading": p. 369-380.

1. Literature--Outlines, syllabi, etc. 2. Literature--Bio-bibl. I. Title.

NK 0210524 AAP MH OrSaW PBa

Knowlton, Edgar Colby.
Syllabus: Comparative literature, 1927-28. Deleware, O., Ohio Wesleyan service department, c1927.
136 l.

"This syllabus for English 379-380 is for comparative literature in Europe from Homer to the present day."

1. Literature - Outlines, syllabi, etc.

NK 0210525 NNC DLC

Knowlton, Edgar Colby, jr.
Ada Negri: Il Posto dei vecchi.

Honors thesis - Harvard university, 1941.

NK 0210526 MH

₍Knowlton, Edward Rogers₎
Beach patrol, by Kerk Rogers ₍*pseud.*₎ ... New York, M. S. Mill co., inc. ₍1943₎
276 p. 21cm.

I. Title.
43-13079
Library of Congress PZ3.K7686Be

NK 0210527 DLC WaS WaE OEac OCl PP

₍Knowlton, Edward Rogers₎
... Too many yesterdays. New York, M. S. Mill co., inc. ₍1942₎
315 p. 21cm.
Author's pseud., Kerk Rogers, at head of title.

I. Title.
42-16181 Revised
Library of Congress PZ3.K7686To

NK 0210528 DLC PP

₍Knowlton, Edward Rogers₎
... With intent to destroy. New York, M. S. Mill co., inc ₍1944₎
251 p. 21cm.
Author's pseud., Kerk Rogers, at head of title.

I. Title.
44-47198
Library of Congress PZ3.K7686Wi

NK 0210529 DLC NcD PPDrop

---

q784.3 Knowlton, Edwin G
Sh37 Down by the sea, a bass song ... Boston, H.
v.7 Tolman & co.; Chicago, Root & Cady; [etc., etc.]
no.52 c1859.
5p.

[Sheet music printed in Chicago prior to 1871. v.7, no.52]
Plate no.: 3689.

NK 0210530 IU

---

q784.3 Knowlton, Edwin G
Sh37 ... Gentle laughing May; song and chorus written
v.1 and composed by Edwin G. Knowlton. Chicago,
no.4 H. M. Higgins, c1860.
5p.

₍Sheet music printed in Chicago prior to 1871. v.1,no.4₎

NK 0210531 IU

Knowlton, Effie F., joint author.
Kelly, Daniel James.
A practicable school health program, by Daniel J. Kelly ... and Effie F. Knowlton ... ₍New York, Metropolitan life insurance company press, 1930₎

F Knowlton, Elizabeth
2270.2 The Arhuaco Indians, twenty years after.
I5K76 [n.p., 1944?]
263-266 p.

Caption title.
"Reprinted from American anthropologist, vol.46, no.2, April-June 1944."

1. Ijca Indians. I. Title.

NK 0210533 CLU

Knowlton, Elizabeth.
The Naked mountain, by Elizabeth Knowlton. New York, London, G. P. Putnam's sons, 1933.
7 p. l., 3-335 p. front., plates, ports., map. 24cm.
Plate facing p. 104 accompanied by guard sheet with diagram of Rakiot route.
"Story of the German American Himalaya expedition to Nanga Parbat."—Foreword.
"Rand Herron": p. ₍299₎-310.

1. Deutsch-amerikanische Himalaya expedition, 1932. 2. Nanga Parbat. 3. Himalaya mountains—Descr. & trav. 4. Herron, Elbridge Rand, 1902-1932. I. Title.
Library of Congress DS485.H6K6 33—33044
——— Copy 2.
Copyright A 66978 ₍a38g2₎ 915.46

OCl OClh OO MB NN Or CaBVa OrPR WaT WaE
NK 0210534 DLC WaSp OrP WaU CU PP PPGi OLak OEac

Knowlton, Elizabeth
The naked mountain. N.Y. Junior literary guild and Putnam, 1934, c1933.
333 p.

NK 0210535 PP PPStarr

VOLUME 300

Knowlton, Evelyn Hope (Puffer) 1905–
Pepperell's progress; history of a cotton textile company, 1844–1945. Cambridge, Harvard Univ. Press, 1948.
xxix, 511 p. illus., ports., maps, facsims. 23 cm. (Harvard studies in business history, 13)
"Notes and references": p. [473]–493.

1. Pepperell Manufacturing Company. I. Title. (Series)
HD9879.P42K6 677.21065 49–7354*

MtU OrP OrPS MiEM
ViU MH DNAL OC1JC IdU OrCS WaSpG WaTC WaWW CaBVaU
NK 0210536 DLC MoU C OU PU CoU MdBP ICJ ICU TxU MB

Knowlton, Fanny Snow
... The costume box; text by Margaret Knowlton Wilcox, music by Fanny Snow Knowlton. Boston, Oliver Ditson co., [c1929]
55p.
At head of title-page: A musical play for girls.

NK 0210537 OC1 PPTU

Knowlton, Fanny Snow
Hawthorn and lavender; a song-cycle for women's voices, with piano accompaniment; the words selected from the poems of Wm. E. Henley... Cleveland, Rogers, c1903.
47p.

NK 0210538 OC1 OrU

Knowlton, Fanny Snow
... The mermaid, cantata for women's voices, soprano, solo and chorus. Words by Tennyson... Cleveland, The Eastman co. [c1909]
31p.

NK 0210539 OC1

Knowlton, Fanny Snow, *comp.*
Nature songs for children. By Fanny Snow Knowlton ... Springfield, Mass., New York [etc.] Milton Bradley company, 1898.
111 p. 27½cm.
With music.

1. Children's songs. I. Title.
12–34997
Library of Congress M1997.K73

NK 0210540 DLC PBa OEac OCU OC1

Knowlton, Fanny Snow, comp.
Nature songs for children. Springfield, Mass., etc., Milton Bradley co. 1906.

NK 0210541 MH PPPL

Knowlton, Fanny Snow, *comp.*
Nature songs for children. By Fanny Snow Knowlton ... Springfield, Mass., New York [etc.] Milton Bradley company, 1917.
108, [2] p. 27cm.
With music.

NK 0210542 CU

Knowlton, Fanny Snow, compiler.
Songs of other days. I. Puritan days. II. Revolutionary days. III. Ante-bellum days. An illustrative historical concert, compiled and arranged by Fanny Snow Knowlton. Boston: O. Ditson Co. [cop. 1922.] Publ. pl. no. 74343. 98 p. illus. 4°.
Contains directions for stage settings, costumes, etc., and words and music of the songs with piano acc.

JUILLIARD FOUNDATION FUND.
1. Pageants, U. S. 2. Folk songs (English). 3. Songs (American). 4. Title.
N. Y. P. L. October 21, 1924

NK 0210543 NN WaT OrP MB CoD OO OC1 PP RPB Mi

Knowlton, Frank Hall, 1860–1926. An account of the progress in botany for the years 1887, 1888. Washington. 1890. 8°. pp. [24].
"From the Smithsonian report for 1888," pp. 475–496.

NK 0210544 MH-A OC1W

Knowlton, Frank Hall, 1860–1926.
Additions to the flora of Washington and vicinity, from April 1, 1884, to April 1, 1886.
[Washington, 1886.] 106–132 pp. 8°.
Reprinted from the Proceedings of the Biological society of Washington, vol. 3.
5825.10.3

NK 0210545 MB OO MH-A

Knowlton, Frank Hall, 1860–1926.
Annotated list of the fossil plants of the Bozeman, Montana, coal field, with table of distribution, and description of new species. By F. H. Knowlton ... [Washington, Govt. print. off., 1893]
1 p. l., p. 43–66. pl. v–vi. 24½cm.
Extract from Bulletin no. 105, U. S. Geological survey.

1. Paleobotany—Montana. 2. Paleobotany—Carboniferous.
11–23648
Library of Congress QE919.K73

NK 0210546 DLC NjP OO OC1W PPAmP MH-A

Knowlton, Frank Hall, 1860–1926.
... Birds of the world; a popular account, by Frank H. Knowlton ... with a chapter on the anatomy of birds, by Frederic A. Lucas; the whole ed. by Robert Ridgway ... with 16 colored plates and 236 illustrations. New York, H. Holt and company, 1909.
xiii, 873 p. illus., plates (16 col., incl. front.) 26cm. (American nature series. Group 1. Natural history)

1. Birds. I. Ridgway, Robert, 1850–1929, ed. II. Lucas, Frederic Augustus, 1852–1929.
9–7956
Library of Congress QL673.K7

IdB OrPR WaSp WaS OrCS OrU IdU ICF-A
MiU DN ViU DI-GS ICJ MB NN PPL PPAN PP MnU-A OrP
NK 0210547 DLC CaBVaU GU CU LU TU OU OO OC1 OC1W

Knowlton, Frank Hall, 1860-1926.

Diller, Joseph Silas, 1850–1928.
... The Bohemia mining region of western Oregon, with notes on the Blue river mining region and on the structure and age of the Cascade range, by J. S. Diller; accompanied by a report on the fossil plants associated with the lavas of the Cascade range, by F. H. Knowlton ... Washington, Govt. print. off., 1900.

Knowlton, Frank Hall, 1860-1926.

Smithsonian institution.
Botany.
(*In* Smithsonian institution. Annual report, 1880–83. Washington, 1881–84. 23½cm. 1880, p. 313–329; 1881, p. 391–408; 1882, p. 551–

Knowlton, Frank Hall, 1860–1926.
Botany for 1887 and 1888. By F. H. Knowlton ...
(*In* Smithsonian institution. Annual report. 1888. Washington, 1890. 23½cm. p. 475–496)

1. Botany—Hist.
S 15–677
Library of Congress Q11.S66 1888
Library, Smithsonian Institution

NK 0210550 DLC

Knowlton, Frank Hall, 1860–1926.
... A catalogue of the Cretaceous and Tertiary plants of North America, by Frank Hall Knowlton. Washington, Govt. print. off., 1898.
247 p. 23½cm. (U. S. Geological survey. Bulletin no. 152)
Bibliography: p. 13–23.

1. Paleobotany—North America. 2. Paleobotany—Cretaceous. 3. Paleobotany—Tertiary.
G S 5–713
U. S. Geol. survey. Library for Library of Congress 042.690(200) K77 [QE75.B9 no. 152]

ODW OU OC1 OO DLC ViU
NK 0210551 DI-GS NNBG NjP WaWW WaS PU PPAN PPL MiU

Knowlton, Frank Hall, 1860–1926.
... A catalogue of the Mesozoic and Cenozoic plants of North America, by F. H. Knowlton. Washington, Govt. print. off., 1919.
815 p. fold. tab. 23 cm. (U. S. Geological survey. Bulletin 696)
At head of title: Department of the interior.
——— Copy 2. QE935.K6
——— Supplement to Catalogue of Mesozoic and Cenozoic plants of North America, 1919–37, by Robert Smith La Motte. Washington, U. S. Govt. print. off., 1944.
ii, 330 p. 23 cm. (U. S. Geological survey. Bulletin no. 924)

At head of title: United States Dept. of the interior, Harold L. Ickes, secretary. Geological survey, W. E. Wrather, director.
"Errors and omissions in Bulletin 696": p. 325–330.
Bibliography: p. 7–64.
QE75.B9 no. 924
——— Copy 2. QE935.K6 Suppl.

1. Paleobotany — Mesozoic. 2. Paleobotany — Cenozoic. 3. Paleobotany—North America. I. La Motte, Robert Smith, 1895– II. Title.
QE75.B9 no. 696 561.197 G S 20–83
U. S. Geol. Survey. Libr. for Library of Congress [a55r45m1]†

PU PBa PPAN MtBC WaWW ViU DLC
NK 0210553 DI-GS NBuG ICJ OO MB MiU OU OC1 ODW OCU

QE702 K56 **Knowlton, Frank Hall, 1860-1926.**
Collected papers. [1890-1930]
1 v. of pamphlets. illus.
Binder's title.
Table of contents in volume.

NK 0210554 CU

Knowlton, Frank Hall, 1860–1926.
Contributions to the geology and paleontology of San Juan County, New Mexico. 4. Flora of the Fruitland and Kirtland formations. (In United States. Geological Survey. Shorter contributions to general geology, 1916. Professional paper 98. Pp. 327–353. Washington. 1916.)
Cretaceous fossils.

L1711 — San Juan County, N. M. and paleon. — Cretaceous fossils. — Paleobotany.

NK 0210555 MB PPAN

Knowlton, Frank Hall, 1860-1926.

Ward, Lester Frank, 1841–1913.
... The Cretaceous formation of the Black hills as indicated by the fossil plants, by Lester F. Ward, with the collaboration of Walter P. Jenney, Wm. M. Fontaine, and F. H. Knowlton. Extract from the Nineteenth annual report of the [U. S. Geological] survey, 1897–98. Part II—Papers chiefly of a theoretic nature. Washington, Govt. print. off., 1899.

VOLUME 300

Knowlton, Frank Hall, 1860–1926.
Description of a collection of Kootanie plants from the Great Falls coal field of Montana, by F. H. Knowlton.
(*In* Smithsonian institution. Smithsonian miscellaneous collections. Washington, 1908. 24½ cm. vol. L. (Quarterly issue, vol. IV) p. 105–128. pl. XI–XIV)
Publication 1715.
Originally published June 27, 1907.
1. Paleobotany—Carboniferous. 2. Paleobotany—Montana. I. Title: Kootanie plants.
Q11.S7 vol. 50 16—11635

NK 0210557 DLC ViU NBuU OC1W OCU OC1 MtHi WaS CaBVaU

Knowlton, F[rank] H[all] 1860–1926.
... Description of fossil woods and lignites from Arkansas, by F. H. Knowlton ... [Little Rock, 1891]
249–267 p. illus. 23cm.
Caption title.
From the Annual report of the Geological survey of Arkansas for 1889, vol. II.
1. Paleobotany—Arkansas. 2. Lignite.
Library, U. S. Geol. survey G S 6–1144

NK 0210558 DI-GS OC1MN MtBuM PPAmP

Knowlton, Frank Hall, 1860–1926.
Description of a new fossil fern of the genus *Gleichenia* from the Upper Cretaceous of Wyoming. By Frank H. Knowlton ...
(*In* U. S. National museum. Proceedings. Washington, 1913. 23½cm. v. 45, p. 555–558. pl. 44)
1. Gleichenia. 2. Paleobotany—Wyoming.
Library of Congress Q11.U55 vol. 45 14—4151

NK 0210559 DLC CaBVaU WaS MiU OC1 OC1MN OU OO PPAN

Knowlton, Frank Hall, 1860–1926.
Description of new fossil liverwort from the Fort Union beds of Montana. By Frank Hall Knowlton.
(*In* U. S. National museum. Proceedings. Washington, 1909. 23½ cm. v. 35, p. 157–159. pl. XXV)
Issued November 9, 1908.
1. Hepaticae—Montana. 2. Paleobotany—Montana.
[Q11.U55 vol. 35] S 34—235
Smithsonian Institution. Library for Library of Congress [a56e½]

NK 0210560 DSI CaBVaU MiU OU NjP NN PPAN

Knowlton, Frank Hall, 1860–1926.
——— Description of a new fossil species of Chara [C. Stantoni. Bloomington, Ind. 1893]. 8°. Illustr.
"From *Botanical gazette*," 1893, xviii, 141–142.

NK 0210561 MH-A OC1W

Knowlton, Frank Hall, 1860–1926
——— Description of a new fossil species of the genus Chara [C. compressa. Crawfordsville, Ind. 1888]. 8°. Illustr.
"From the *Botanical gazette*," 1888, xiii, 156–157.

NK 0210562 MH-A

Knowlton, Frank Hall, 1860–1926
——— Description of a new problematical plant [Paleohillia arkansana] from the lower cretaceous of Arkansas. [New York. 1895.] 8°. Illustr.
"Reprinted from the *Bulletin of the Torrey botanical club*," 1895, xxii, 387–390.

NK 0210563 MH-A

Knowlton, Frank Hall, 1860–1926.
Description of a problematic organism from the Devonian. n.p. [1889]

NK 0210564 NjP

Knowlton, Frank Hall. A Description of a supposed new species of fossil wood [Pityoxylon Pealei n. sp.] from Montana. [New York. 1896.] 8°. Plate.
"Reprinted from the *Bulletin of the Torrey botanical club*," 1896, xxiii, 250–252.

NK 0210565 MH-A

Knowlton, Frank Hall, 1860–1926.
Description of two new fossil figs from Wyoming and Montana. 1911.
4p. pamp.

NK 0210566 MtHi

Knowlton, Frank Hall, 1860–1926.
Description of two new species of fossil coniferous wood from Iowa and Montana. By F. H. Knowlton ...
(*In* U. S. National museum. Proceedings. Washington, 1889. 23½cm. v. 11, 1888, p. 5–8. pl. II–III)
Issued November 8, 1888.
1. Trees, Fossil. 2. Paleobotany—U. S.
Library, Smithsonian Institution S 33–72
Library of Congress [Q11.U55 vol. 11]

NK 0210567 DSI MH-A OU

Knowlton, Frank Hall, 1860–1926.
Description of two species of *Palmoxylon*—one new—from Louisiana. By F. H. Knowlton ...
(*In* U. S. National museum. Proceedings. Washington, 1889. 23½cm. v. 11, 1888, p. 89–91. pl. XXX)
Issued November 8, 1888.
1. Paleobotany.
Library, Smithsonian Institution S 33–85
Library of Congress [Q11.U55 vol. 11]

NK 0210568 DSI OU NjP MH-A

Knowlton, Frank Hall, 1860–1926.
Descriptions of fossil plants from the Mesozoic and Cenozoic of North America. I. By F. H. Knowlton ...
(*In* Smithsonian institution. Smithsonian miscellaneous collections. Washington, 1910. 24½cm. vol. LII (Quarterly issue, vol. V) p. 489–496. pl. LXIII–LXIV)
Publication 1884.
CONTENTS.—1. Two new fossil chain-ferns (*Woodwardia*) from Oregon and Wyoming.—2. A new name for *Davallia tenuifolia* Swartz, as identified by Dawson, and *Asplenium tenerum* Lesquereux.
1. Ferns, Fossil. 2. Paleobotany—Mesozoic. 3. Paleobotany—Cenozoic. 4. Paleobotany—North America.
Library of Congress Q11.S7 vol. 52 16—12725

NK 0210569 OCU DLC MoU NBuU WaS CaBVaU MiU OC1W OU OCI

Knowlton, Frank Hall, 1860–1926.
... Directions for collecting recent and fossil plants, by F. H. Knowlton ... Part B of Bulletin of the United States National museum, no. 39. Washington, Govt. print. off., 1891.
46 p. illus. 24½ cm.
At head of title: Smithsonian institution. United States National museum.
1. Plants—Collection and preservation.
Library of Congress Q11.U6 5—26686

NK 0210570 ICJ MB NN PHC MdBP PP PU OrP WaS CaBVaU ViU MoU DLC MdBP DNLM MiU OC1 OCU OC1MN OO MH-A

Knowlton, Frank Hall, 1860–1926.
Turner, Henry Ward, 1857–
... The Esmeralda formation, a fresh-water lake deposit in Nevada, by H. W. Turner; with a description of the fossil plants, by F. H. Knowlton, and of a fossil fish, by F. A. Lucas ... Washington, Govt. print. off., 1900.

Knowlton, Frank Hall, 1860–1926, ed.
Lesquereux, Leo, 1806–1889.
... The flora of the Dakota group, a posthumous work, by Leo Lesquereux. Ed. by F. H. Knowlton. Washington, Govt. print. off., 1891.

Knowlton, Frank Hall, 1860–1926.
... The flora of the Denver and associated formations of Colorado, by Frank Hall Knowlton. A posthumous work, edited by Edward Wilber Berry. Washington, U. S. Govt. print. off., 1930.
2 p. l., 142 p. incl. 59 pl. 29cm. (U. S. Geological survey. Professional paper 155)
At head of title: United States Department of the interior.
Bibliographical foot-notes.
1. Paleobotany—Colorado. 2. Paleontology—Cretaceous. 3. Paleontology—Tertiary. I. Berry, Edward Wilber, 1875– II. Title.
G S 30—137
U. S. Geol. survey. Library (200) B no. 155
——— Copy 2. QE75.P9 no. 155
for Library of Congress QE924.K68
[a43m1]

NK 0210573 OC1 ODW PU PPL PPAN MB DLC InU NNBG DI-GS CaBVaU OrU OrCS WaWW OU MiU OO

Knowlton, Frank Hall, 1860–1926.
The flora of the Fox Hills sandstone. Plates.
(In United States. Geological Survey. Shorter contributions to general geology, 1916. Professional paper 98. Pp. 85–93. Washington. 1916.)
Cretaceous fossils collected in Colorado.
K9088 — Colorado. Geol. and paleon. Cretaceous fossils. — Fox Hill sandstone. — Paleobotany.

NK 0210574 MB MiU OU PPAN MdBJ

Knowlton, Frank Hall, 1860–1926.
Flora of the Fruitland and Kirtland formations.. (In United States. Geological survey. Shorter contributions to general geology. 1916, 1917. Contributions to the geology and paleontology of San Juan county, New Mexico. pt. 4, p. 327–353) In United States Geological survey professional paper 98.

NK 0210575 OU

Knowlton, Frank Hall, 1860–1926.
Flora of the Latah formation of Spokane, Washington, and Coeur d'Alene, Idaho. By F. H. Knowlton.
(*In* United States. Geological Survey. Shorter contributions to general geology, 1925. Professional paper 140 — A. Pp. 17–81. Plates. Washington. 1926.)
D6952 — Idaho. Geol. & paleon. — Washington, State. Geol. & paleon. — Coeur d'Alene Mountains. — Latah formation. — Paleobotany.

NK 0210576 MB OU PPAN

Knowlton, Frank Hall, 1860–1926.
... Flora of the Montana formation, by Frank Hall Knowlton. Washington, Govt. print. off., 1900.
ix, 118, xi p., 1 l. xix pl. 23½cm. (U. S. Geological survey. Bulletin no. 163)
1. Paleobotany—Cretaceous. 2. Paleobotany—U. S. I. Title.
G S 5—720
U. S. Geol. survey. Library QE75.B9 no. 163
for Library of Congress
——— Copy 2. QE924.K7

NK 0210577 PU DLC PP PPAN DI-GS WaS WaWW MtHi MiU OU ODW OC1 OO ICJ

VOLUME 300

Knowlton, Frank Hall, 1860–1926.
A fossil flora from the frontier formation of southwestern Wyoming, by F. H. Knowlton. Washington: Gov. Prtg. Off., 1917. ii, 73–107 p., 7 pl. 4°. (United States. Geological Survey. Professional paper 108-F.)
Shorter contributions to general geology, 1917.

1. Palaeontology (Botanical), U. S.: Wyoming. 2. Series.
N. Y. P. L. April 11, 1918.

NK 0210578 NN OU MB PPAN

Knowlton, Frank Hall, 1860-1926.
—— The fossil flora of the Bozeman coal field; abstract. [Washington. 1892]–93. 8°.
"Proceedings of the Biological society of Washington," 1892–93, vii, 153–154.

NK 0210579 MH-A

Knowlton, Frank Hall, 1860–1926.
... Fossil flora of the John Day basin, Oregon, by Frank Hall Knowlton. Washington, Govt. print. off., 1902.
153, iii p. xvii pl. 23½cm. (U. S. Geological survey. Bulletin no. 204)
Subject series: C, Systematic geology and paleontology, 58.

1. Paleobotany—Oregon. G S 5—744
U. S. Geol. survey. Library for Library of Congress [QE75.B9 no. 204]

NK 0210580 DI-GS NBuU NNBG WaS WaWW OrPR MiU OU PP ODW OC1 PU PPAN

Knowlton, Frank Hall, 1860–1926.
Fossil flora of the Yellowstone national park, by Frank Hall Knowlton ... Washington, Gov't print. off., 1899.
1 p. l., 651–882 p. 45 pl. 31½ x 24½cm.
"Extract from 'Geology of the Yellowstone national park,' Monograph xxxii of the United States Geological survey, part ii, chapter xiv."

1. Paleobotany—Yellowstone national park.
Library, U. S. Geol. survey G S 7–1011

NK 0210581 DI-GS OO PU-B NNBG MB

Knowlton, Frank Hall, 1860–1926.
Fossil forests of the Yellowstone national park. Department of the interior. Office of the secretary. [Washington, Govt. print. off.] 1914.
31 p. incl. illus., map, diagr. 23½cm.
By F. H. Knowlton, United States Geological survey.

1. Petrified forests. 2. Paleobotany—Yellowstone national park. I. Title.
Library of Congress QE991.K6 14—30651

NK 0210582 DLC CU TU CU-B MtHi PPAmP MiU OU PPAN NIC DNW NN

[**Knowlton, Frank Hall**] 1860–1926.
... Fossil forests of the Yellowstone national park. Washington, Govt. print. off., 1921.
30 p. illus., chart. 23cm.
At head of title: Department of the interior. Albert B. Fall, secretary. National park service. Stephen T. Mather, director.
"Publications on Yellowstone national park": p. 30.

1. Petrified forests. 2. Paleobotany—Yellowstone national park. I. U. S. National park service. II. Title.
Library of Congress QE991.K6 1921 21–26368

NK 0210583 DLC MtBC NNBG

[**Knowlton, Frank Hall**] 1860–1926.
... Fossil forests of the Yellowstone national park. Washington, U. S. Govt. print. off., 1928.
30 p. illus., map. 23½cm.
At head of title: United States Department of the interior. Hubert Work, secretary. National park service. Stephen T. Mather, director.
"By F. H. Knowlton, United States Geological survey."—p. 3.
"The national parks at a glance": p. 2.
"Publications on Yellowstone national park": p. 30.

1. Petrified forests. 2. Paleobotany—Yellowstone national park. I. U. S. National park service. II. Title.
Library of Congress QE991.K6 1928 28–26410

NK 0210584 DLC CU-B DI MH-A

Knowlton, Frank Hall, 1860-1926.
—— A fossil nut pine from Idaho. [New York. 1901.] 8°. Illustr.
"Reprinted from Torreya," 1901, i, 113–114.

NK 0210585 MH-A

Knowlton, Frank Hall, 1860-1926.
—— Fossil plants as an aid to geology. Chicago. [1894.] 8°.
"Reprinted from the Journal of geology," 1894, ii, 365–382.

NK 0210586 MH-A NjP

Knowlton, F[rank] H[all] 1860-1926.
Fossil plants associated with the lavas of the Cascade range. (In Diller, J[oseph] S... The Bohemia mining region of western Oregon... Washington, 1900.

6
4433

NK 0210587 DLC MB

Knowlton, Frank Hall, 1860–1926.
Fossil plants from Kukak Bay. Plates.
(In Harriman Alaska Expedition. Alaska. Vol. 4, pp. 149–162. New York, 1904.)

F3603 — Kukak Bay, Alaska. — Paleobotany.

NK 0210588 MB OO PPAN DI-GS MH-A

Knowlton, Frank Hall, 1860–1926.
Fossil plants from the tertiary lake beds of south-central Colorado.
(In United States. Geological Survey. Shorter contributions to general geology, 1922. Professional paper 131. Pp. 183–197. Plates. Table. Washington. 1923.)
Public Library, February 5, 1924.
M7880 — Colorado. Geol. and paleon. — Paleobotany.

NK 0210589 MB CU-B OU

Knowlton, Frank Hall, 1860–1926.
Fossil plants of the Esmeralda formation. Plate.
(In Turner. The Esmeralda formation. Pp. 209–222. Washington, 1900.)

E8320 — Paleobotany.

NK 0210590 MB

Knowlton, Frank Hall, 1860–1926.
Fossil plants of the Judith River beds. Plates.
(In Stanton and Hatcher. Geology and paleontology of the Judith River beds. Pp. 129–168. Washington. 1905.)

G102 — Paleobotany.

NK 0210591 MB OO

KNOWLTON, Frank Hall, 1860–1926.
The fossil plants of the Payette formation. Plates.
(In United States. Geological survey. 18th annual report, part pp. 721–744. Washington, 1898.)

NK 0210592 MB

Knowlton, Frank Hall, 1860–1926.
... Fossil wood and lignite of the Potomac formation, by Frank Hall Knowlton. Washington, Govt. print. off., 1889.
72 p. vii pl. 23½cm. (U. S. Geological survey. Bulletin no. 56)

1. Lignite. 2. Paleobotany—Cretaceous. 3. Paleobotany—U. S. G S 5—640
U. S. Geol. survey. Library for Library of Congress 690(220) K77 [QE75.B9 no. 56]

NK 0210593 DI-GS NBuU WaS WaWW MiU OO OC1 ODW OC1W MdBP MH ICJ NjP PU

Knowlton, Frank Hall, 1860-1926.

Stanton, Timothy William, 1860–
... Geology and paleontology of the Judith river beds, by T. W. Stanton and J. B. Hatcher; with a chapter on the fossil plants by F. H. Knowlton. Washington, Govt. print. off., 1905.

Knowlton, Frank Hall, 1860-1926, joint author.

QE75 .P9 no. 101

Lee, Willis Thomas, 1864–1926.
... Geology and paleontology of the Raton Mesa and other regions in Colorado and New Mexico, papers by Willis T. Lee and F. H. Knowlton. Washington, Govt. print. off., 1917.

Knowlton, Frank Hall, 1860-1926.

Shaler, Nathaniel Southgate, 1841–1906.
... Geology of the Richmond basin, Virginia, by Nathaniel Southgate Shaler and Jay Backus Woodworth ... Washington, Govt. print. off., 1899.

Knowlton, Frank Hall, 1860-1926, joint author.

Hague, Arnold, 1840–1917.
... Geology of the Yellowstone national park. Part ii. Descriptive geology, petrography and paleontology, by Arnold Hague, J. P. Iddings, W. H. Weed and C. D. Walcott, G. H. Girty, T. W. Stanton, and F. H. Knowlton. Washington, Govt. print. off., 1899.

Knowlton, Frank Hall, 1860-1926.

Harriman Alaska expedition, 1899.
Harriman Alaska expedition, with cooperation of Washington academy of sciences. Alaska ... New York, Doubleday, Page & co., 1901–

Knowlton, Frank Hall, 1860–1926.
... The Jurassic flora of cape Lisburne, Alaska, by F. H. Knowlton ... Washington, Govt. print. off., 1914.
1 p. l., p. 39–64. plates. 29½cm. (U. S. Geological survey. Professional paper, 85—D)
Part D of professional paper 85, "Contributions to general geology, 1913."
Published January 28, 1914.
1. Paleobotany—Jurassic. 2. Paleobotany—Alaska — Cape Lisburne. I. Title.
G S 14—156
U. S. Geol. survey. Library for Library of Congress (200) B no. 85—D QE75.P9 no. 85—D
——— Copy 2. QE923.K7

NK 0210599 DI-GS KEmT OrCS OrU MiU OU ODW OC1 PP DLC ICJ MB NN MdBJ MiHM

VOLUME 300

Knowlton, Frank Hall, 1860-1926.

Weed, Walter Harvey, 1862–
... The Laramie and the overlying Livingston formation in Montana, by Walter Harvey Weed, with report on flora, by Frank Hall Knowlton. Washington, Govt. print. off., 1893.

Knowlton, Frank Hall, 1860–1926.
... The Laramie flora of the Denver basin, with a review of the Laramie problem, by F. H. Knowlton. Washington, Govt. print. off., 1922.
iv, 175 p. xxviii pl., tables. 29 cm. (U. S. Geological survey. Professional paper 130)
At head of title: Department of the interior.

1. Paleobotany. 2. Geology, Stratigraphic—Cretaceous. I. Title.
QE75.P9 no. 130 G S 22-387
——— Copy 2. QE924.K73
U. S. Geol. Survey. Libr. for Library of Congress [a59m1]†

PP PPAN MH-A WaWW OrCS OrU CaBVaU DLC
NK 0210601 DI-GS OU NNBG CU OO OCU ODW MiU OC1W ICJ

Knowlton, Frank Hall, 1860-1926.
——— Lesquereux's flora of the Dakota group; a reply.. [Bloomington, Ind. 1893.] 8°.
"From Botanical gazette," 1893, xviii, 37-39.

NK 0210602 MH-A

Knowlton, Frank Hall, 1860-1926, ed.

Lesquereux, Leo, 1806–1889.
List of fossil plants collected by Mr. I. C. Russell, at Black creek, near Gadsden, Ala., with descriptions of several new species. By Leo Lesquereux, Columbus, Ohio. ⟨Compiled and prepared for publication by F. H. Knowlton ...⟩

Knowlton, Frank Hall, 1860–1926.
List of plants collected by Mr. Charles L. McKay at Nushagak, Alaska, in 1881, for the United States National museum. By Frank H. Knowlton.
(*In* U. S. National museum. Proceedings. Washington, 1886. 23½cm. v. 8, 1885, p. 213–221)
Issued July 24, 1886.

1. Plants. 2. Botany—Alaska. I. McKay, Charles L.
S 32-543
Library, Smithsonian Institution
Library of Congress [Q11.U55 vol. 8]

NK 0210604 DSI MB OU MH-A OC1W

Knowlton, Frank Hall, 1860-1926, comp.

Lesquereux, Leo, 1806–1889.
List of recently identified fossil plants belonging to the United States National museum, with descriptions of several new species. By Leo Lesquereux, Columbus, Ohio. ⟨Compiled and prepared for publication by F. H. Knowlton.⟩

Knowlton, Frank Hall, 1860–1926.
A lower Jurassic flora from the upper Matanuska valley, Alaska. By F. H. Knowlton ...
(*In* U. S. National museum. Proceedings. Washington, 1917. 23½cm. v. 51, p. 451–460. pl. 79–82)

1. Paleobotany—Jurassic. 2. Paleobotany—Alaska.
17—23848
Library of Congress Q11.U55 vol. 51
——— Copy 2. Q11.U55 vol. 51 2d set

NK 0210606 DLC CaBVaU WaS MiU OC1MN OU OC1 OO PPAN

Knowlton, Frank Hall, 1860-1926.

Lindgren, Waldemar, 1860–
... The mining districts of the Idaho basin and the Boise ridge, Idaho, by Waldemar Lindgren. With a report on the fossil plants of the Payette formation, by Frank Hall Knowlton ... Washington, Govt. print. off., 1898.

Knowlton, Frank Hall, 1860-1926.
——— A new fossil hepatic [Preissites Wardii] from the lower Yellowstone in Montana. [New York. 1894.] 8°. pp. [2]. Plate.
"Reprinted from the *Bulletin of the Torrey botanical club*," 1894, xxi,

NK 0210608 MH-A

Knowlton, Frank Hall, 1860–1926.
New species of fossil wood (*Araucarioxylon arizonicum*) from Arizona and New Mexico. By F. H. Knowlton ...
(*In* U. S. National museum. Proceedings. Washington, 1889. 23½cm. v. 11, 1888, p. 1–4. pl. 1)
Issued November 8, 1888.

1. Trees, Fossil. 2. Paleobotany—U. S. I. Title.
S 33-71
Library, Smithsonian Institution
Library of Congress [Q11.U55 vol. 11]

NK 0210609 DSI NjP OU MH-A

Knowlton, Frank Hall, 1860-1926.

Hobbs, William Herbert, 1864–
... The Newark system of Pomperaug Valley, Connecticut, by William Herbert Hobbs, with a report on fossil wood, by F. H. Knowlton ... Washington, Govt. print. off., 1901.

Knowlton, Frank Hall, 1860-1926.
——— The nomenclature question. Some inconsistencies in plant nomenclature. [Madison, Wis. 1896.] 8°.
"From the *Botanical gazette*," 1896, xxi, 82-85.

NK 0210611 MH-A

Knowlton, Frank Hall, 1860–1926.
... Notes on a few fossil plants from the Fort Union group of Montana, with a description of one new species. By F. H. Knowlton ... Washington, Govt. print. off., 1893.
cover-title, 33–36 p. II pl. 25½cm.
From the Proceedings of the United States National museum. vol. xvi, p. 33–36.

1. Paleobotany—Montana.
9-15540
Library of Congress QE937.M9K6

NK 0210612 DLC OU CaBVaU OC1 MiU DSI PCM NjP MH-A

Knowlton, Frank Hall, 1860-1926, joint author.
Fontaine, William Morris, 1835–1913.
Notes on Triassic plants from New Mexico. By Wm. M. Fontaine and F. H. Knowlton.

[**Knowlton, Frank Hall**] 1860–1926.
... Obituary notice of Charles Christopher Parry, read before the Philosophical society of Washington October 15, 1892. Washington, The Society, 1895.
cover-title, p. 497–499. 24½cm.
Signed: F. H. Knowlton.
At head of title: Philosophical society of Washington. Bulletin, vol. xii, pp. 497–500.

1. Parry, Charles Christopher, 1823–1890. I. Philosophical society of Washington, Washington, D. C.
27-9708
Library of Congress QK31.P35K6

NK 0210614 DLC MH-A

Knowlton, Frank Hall, 1860-1926, ed.
The Plant world; a monthly journal of general botany ... v. 1–22; Oct. 1897–Dec. 1919. Binghamton, N. Y., W. N. Clute & co.; [etc., etc.] 1897–1919.

Knowlton, Frank Hall, 1860–1926.
Plants of the past; a popular account of fossil plants, by Frank Hall Knowlton ... with 90 illustrations. Princeton, Princeton university press, 1927.
xix, 275 p. front., illus. 24 cm.
Bibliography: p. 271–272.

1. Paleobotany. I. Title.
QE905.K6 27—11191

NcD NcRS MH-G ViU NjP TU WaU MiU ICJ MB OC1W
MtU MtBC OrPR IdU-SB WaS Or CaBVaU CaBVa OC1 OCU OU
NK 0210616 DLC FU CU KEmT CoU NIC NNBG CaBViP IdU

Knowlton, Frank Hall, 1860-1926, ed.

Lesquereux, Leo, 1806–1889.
List of fossil plants collected by Mr. I. C. Russell, at Black creek, near Gadsden, Ala., with descriptions of several new species. By Leo Lesquereux, Columbus, Ohio. ⟨Compiled and prepared for publication by F. H. Knowlton ...⟩
(*In* U. S. National museum. Proceedings. Washington, 1889 23½cm. v. 11, 1888, p. 83–87. pl. xxix)

Knowlton, Frank Hall, 1860–1926.
The relations of paleobotany to geology. By Dr. F. H. Knowlton ...
(*In* Smithsonian institution. Annual report, 1912. Washington, 1913. 23½cm. p. 353–358)
"Reprinted ... from the American naturalist, vol. 46, April, 1912."

1. Paleobotany. 2. Geology.
13—25683
Library of Congress Q11.S66 1912

NK 0210618 DLC WaS MiU OCU OU OC1 OO ICJ MH-A

Knowlton, Frank Hall, 1860–1926.
... Remarks on the fossil turtles accredited to the Judith River formation, by F. H. Knowlton ... Baltimore, Md., Williams & Wilkins company [1911]
cover-title, p. 51–65. 26cm. (Proceedings of the Washington academy of sciences. vol. xiii, no. 3)

1. Turtles, Fossil. I. Title: Judith River formation.
12-24670
Library of Congress Q11.W3 vol. 13, no. 3
——— Copy 2. QE862.C5K5

NK 0210619 DLC MiU OO OC1MN MB

Knowlton, Frank Hall, 1860-1926.

Dall, William Healey, 1845–1927.
... Report on coal and lignite of Alaska, by William Healey Dall ... Washington, Govt. print. off., 1896.

Knowlton, Frank Hall, 1860-1926.
Report on some fossil wood from the Richmond basin, Virginia. Plate.
(In United States. Geological Survey. 19th annual report, part 2, pp. 516-519. Washington, 1899.)

June 19,
*D5903 — Wood (fossil).

NK 0210621 MB

VOLUME 300

Knowlton, Frank Hall, 1860–1926.
A review of the fossil flora of Alaska, with descriptions of new species. By F. H. Knowlton.
(*In* U. S. National museum. Proceedings. Washington, 1895. 23½cm. v. 17, 1894, p. 207–240. pl. IX)
Issued August 2, 1894.

1. Paleobotany—Alaska.

S 33-400
Library, Smithsonian Institution
Library of Congress [Q11.U55 vol. 17]

NK 0210622 DSI MH-A NjP CaBVaU OCl OU

Knowlton, Frank Hall, 1860–1926.
A review of the fossil plants in the United States national museum from the Florissant lake beds at Florissant, Colorado, with descriptions of new species and list of type-specimens. By F. H. Knowlton ...
(*In* U. S. National museum. Proceedings. Washington, 1917. 23½ cm. v. 51, p. 241–297. pl. 12–27)

1. Paleobotany—Colorado. 2. Paleobotany—Miocene.
Q11.U55 vol. 51 17—23841
——— Copy 2. Q11.U55 vol. 51 2d set

CaBVaU
NK 0210623 DLC MiU OClMN OU OCl OO NN MH-A WaS

Knowlton, Frank Hall, 1860–1926.
Revision of the flora of the Green River formation, with descriptions of new species.
(*In* United States. Geological Survey. Shorter contributions to general geology, 1922. Professional paper 131. Pp. 133–182. Plates. Washington. 1923.)

M7877 — Wyoming. Geol. and paleon.— Paleobotany.— Green River formation.

NK 0210624 MB InU OU

Knowlton, Frank Hall, 1860–1926.
A revision of the genus *Araucarioxylon* of Kraus, with compiled descriptions and partial synonymy of the species. By F. H. Knowlton ...
(*In* U. S. National museum. Proceedings. Washington, 1890. 23½cm. v. 12, 1889, p. 601–617)
Issued May 22, 1890.

1. Trees, Fossil. 2. Paleobotany.

S 33-177
Library, Smithsonian Institution
Library of Congress [Q11.U55 vol. 12]

NK 0210625 DSI CaBVaU NjP OU OClW

Knowlton, Frank Hall, 1860-1926.
Ward, Lester Frank, 1841–1913.
... Status of the Mesozoic floras of the United States. First paper: The older Mesozoic, by Lester F. Ward, with the collaboration of Wm. M. Fontaine, Atreus Wanner, and F. H. Knowlton. Extract from the Twentieth annual report of the ⌊U. S. Geological⌋ survey, 1898–99. Part II—General geology and paleontology. Washington, Govt. print. off., 1900.

NK 0210633 OrCS

Knowlton, Frank Hall, 1860–1926
... The stratigraphic relations and paleontology of the "Hell Creek beds", "Ceratops beds" and equivalents, and their reference to the Fort Union formation, by F. H. Knowlton. Baltimore, Md., Washington academy of sciences, 1909.
cover-title, p. 179–238. 26cm. (Proceedings of the Washington academy of sciences. vol. XI, no. 3)

1. Geology—The West. 2. Geology, Stratigraphic—Cretaceous. 3. Geology, Stratigraphic—Eocene.
10—31684
Library of Congress Q11.W3 vol. 11
——— Copy 2. QE80.K6

NK 0210627 DLC NNBG OCU OO OClMN MB ICJ

Knowlton, Frank Hall, 1860-1926.
——— The tertiary floras of the Yellowstone national park. [New Haven. 1896.] 8°.
"From the *American journal of science*," 1896, ii, 51–58.

NK 0210628 MH-A

Knowlton, Frank Hall, 1860-1926.
Lindgren, Waldemar, 1860–
... The Tertiary gravels of the Sierra Nevada of California, by Waldemar Lindgren. Washington, Govt. print. off., 1911.

Knowlton, Frank Hall, 1860-1926.
Reeside, John Bernard, 1889– ed.
... Upper Cretaceous and Tertiary formations of the western part of the San Juan basin, Colorado and New Mexico, by John B. Reeside, jr., and Flora of the Animas formation, by F. H. Knowlton. Washington, Govt. print. off., 1924.

Knowlton, Frank Lester, 1894–1940.
... Building plans and bill of materials for O. A. C. 400-hen laying house, by Frank L. Knowlton. Corvallis, Ore., 1923.
1 sheet. illus., plans. 45 x 30cm fold. to 23cm. (Oregon. Agricultural experiment station. Station circular 51)
Printed on both sides.

1. Poultry. 2. Farm buildings. ⌊1, 2. Poultry houses⌋ I. Title.
A 24-93
Title from Oregon Agr. College. Printed by L. C.

NK 0210631 OrCS

Knowlton, Frank Lester, 1894–1940.
... Chick brooding and rearing, by Frank L. Knowlton. Corvallis, Or., Oregon state system of higher education, Federal cooperative extension service, Oregon state college, 1937.
cover-title, 15, ⌊1⌋ p. incl. illus., tables. 23cm. (⌊Oregon state agricultural college. Federal cooperative extension service⌋ Extension bulletin 497)
"Cooperative extension work in agriculture and home economics, Wm. A. Schoenfeld, director."

1. Poultry. I. Title.
A 37-227
Oreg. st. agr. coll. Library S537.O7A5 no. 497
for Library of Congress ⌊2⌋

NK 0210632 OrCS OrCA

Knowlton, Frank Lester, 1894–1940.
Chick brooding and rearing, by Frank L. Knowlton. Corvallis, Oregon state system of higher education, Federal cooperative extension service, Oregon state college, 1940.
20 p. incl. illus., tables. 23cm. (⌊Oregon. State agricultural college. Federal cooperative extension service⌋ Extension bulletin 549)
Cooperative extension work in agriculture and home economics, Wm. A. Schoenfeld, director.

1. Poultry. I. Title.
A 41-248
Oreg. st. agr. coll. Library S537.O7A5 no. 549
for Library of Congress [S537.O7A5 no. 549]
⌊2⌋ (630.717)

Knowlton, Frank Lester, 1894–1940.
Congenital loco in chicks ⌊by Frank L. Knowlton⌋ Corvallis, Ore., 1929.
15 p. illus., tables. 23cm. (Oregon. Agricultural experiment station, Corvallis. Station bulletin 253)
"Literature cited": p. 15.

1. Poultry—Diseases. I. Title. II. Title: Loco in chicks, Congenital.
A 29-832
[S105.E2 no. 253]
Title from Oreg. Agr. College. Printed by L. C.

NK 0210634 OrCS OrPR OrU

Knowlton, Frank Lester, 1894–1940, joint author.
⌊Scudder, Henry Desborough⌋ 1881–
... Cost and efficiency in commercial egg production in Oregon. Corvallis, Agricultural experiment station, Oregon state agricultural college, 1931.

Knowlton, Frank Lester, 1894–1940, joint author.
⌊Burrier, Arnold Stewart⌋ 1902–
... Cost of producing turkey hatching eggs in Oregon. Corvallis, Agricultural experiment station, Oregon state agricultural college, 1934.

Knowlton, Frank Lester, 1894–1940.
... Force-molting of white leghorn hens, by Frank L. Knowlton. Corvallis, Agricultural experiment station, Oregon state agricultural college, 1936.
cover-title, 8 p. incl. tables. 23cm. (Oregon. Agricultural experiment station. Station circular 119)

1. Poultry. 2. Leghorns (Poultry) I. Title.
A 36-1070
Oreg. st. agr. coll. Library S105.E3 no. 119
for Library of Congress ⌊2⌋

NK 0210637 OrCS

Knowlton, Frank Lester, 1894–1940.
... O. A. C. portable poultry fence, by Frank L. Knowlton. Corvallis, Ore., 1926.
1 sheet. illus., plans. 31 x 23cm. fold. to 23cm. (Oregon. Agricultural experiment station, Corvallis. Station circular 69)
Printed on both sides.

1. Fences. 2. Poultry. I. Title.
A 26-106
Title from Oregon Agric. College. Printed by L. C.

NK 0210638 OrCS

Knowlton, Frank Lester, 1894–1940.
... O. S. C. brooder houses, by Frank L. Knowlton. Corvallis, Or., Oregon state system of higher education, Federal cooperative extension service, Oregon state college, 1938.
cover-title, 16 p. incl. plans (1 double) illus. 23cm. (Oregon state agricultural college. Federal cooperative extension service. Extension bulletin 511)
"Cooperative extension work in agriculture and home economics, Wm. A. Schoenfeld, director."
"Oregon state ... college and United States Department of agriculture cooperating."

1. Farm buildings. 2. Poultry. ⌊1, 2. Poultry houses⌋ I. Title.
A 38-1048
Oreg. st. agr. coll. Library S537.O7A5
for Library of Congress ⌊2⌋

NK 0210639 OrCS

Knowlton, Frank Lester, 1894–1940.
... Open air range house, by Frank L. Knowlton. Corvallis, Ore., 1924.
1 sheet. illus., plans. 45 x 30 cm. fold. to 23 cm. (Oregon. Agricultural experiment station, Corvallis. Station circular 54)
Printed on both sides.

1. Poultry. 2. Farm buildings. ⌊1, 2. Poultry houses⌋ I. Title.
A 24—274
Oregon. State College. Library
for Library of Congress ⌊a51c1⌋

NK 0210640 OrCS

Knowlton, Frank Lester, 1894–1940, jt. author
Lunn, Alfred Gunn, 1883–
... Oregon experiment station trap-nest, by Alfred G. Lunn and Frank L. Knowlton. Corvallis, Ore., 1923.

VOLUME 300

[Knowlton, Frank Lester] 1894-1940.
... Poultry housing. Corvallis, Or., Oregon state agricultural college, Extension service, 1935.
46, [2] p. illus., plans. 23cm. (Oregon state agricultural college. Extension service. Extension bulletin 480)
Caption title: By F. L. Knowlton, H. E. Cosby [and] F. E. Price. "Cooperative extension work in agriculture and home economics, Wm. A. Schoenfeld, director."
1. Farm buildings. 2. Poultry. [1. 2. Poultry houses] I. Cosby, Hubert Elmer, joint author. II. Price, Frederick Earl, 1898- joint author. III. Title.
A 35-1891
Title from Oreg. Agr. College. Printed by L. C.

NK 0210642 OrCS OEac

Knowlton, Miss G T
see Knowlton, Miss E T

Knowlton, George Clinton, 1906- joint author.

Tuttle, Waid Wright, 1893-
An introduction to experimental human physiology, by W. W. Tuttle ... and G. Clinton Knowlton ... St. Louis, The C. V. Mosby company, 1939.

Knowlton, George Clinton, 1906-
The respiratory metabolism of atrophic muscle, by G. Clinton Knowlton ... [Baltimore, 1934]
[1], 200-208 p. 25cm.
Thesis (PH. D.)—University of Iowa, 1934.
By G. C. Knowlton and H. M. Hines.
"Reprinted from the American journal of physiology, vol. 109, no. 2, August, 1934."
"References": p. 208.
1. Atrophy, Muscular. 2. Respiration. 3. Metabolism. I. Hines, Harry Matlock, 1898- joint author.
35-1311 Revised
Library of Congress QP321.K5 1934
Univ. of Iowa Libr. [r41d2] 612.7465

NK 0210645 IaU DLC

Knowlton, George Clinton, 1906- joint author

QM23 .F72 1950

Francis, Carl C 1901-
Textbook of anatomy and physiology, by Carl C. Francis [and] G. Clinton Knowlton. 2d ed. St. Louis, Mosby, 1950.

Knowlton, George Clinton, 1906- joint author.

Francis, Carl C 1901-
Textbook of anatomy and physiology for nurses, by Carl C. Francis ... G. Clinton Knowlton ... [and] W. W. Tuttle ... With 338 text illustrations and 39 color plates. St. Louis, The C. V. Mosby company, 1943.

Knowlton, George Franklin, joint author.
Aerial spraying
see under
Lieberman, Frank V 1911-

Knowlton, George Franklin.
The digestive tract of *Longistigma caryae* (Harris) by George F. Knowlton ... [Columbus, O., 1925]
[1], 244-252 p. illus. 20cm. (*On cover:* Ohio state university. Contributions from the Department of zoology and entomology. no. 82)
"Reprinted from the Ohio journal of science, vol. XXV, no. 5, September, 1925."
1. Digestive organs—Insects. 2. Longistigma caryae.
27-27023
Library of Congress QL1.O33 no. 82

NK 0210649 DLC PU OU OCU MiU

---

422 K76

Knowlton, George Franklin.
Insect food of Uta stansburiana stansburiana in the Timpie area of Utah. [n.p.] 1948.
197-198 p.
1. Lizards. Food. 2. Ura stansburiana stansburiana. I. Title.

NK 0210650 DNAL

422.12 K76

Knowlton, George Franklin.
100 years of professional entomology in the U.S.A. [Salt Lake City? 1954]
7 l.
1. Entomology, Economic. U.S. Addresses, essays, lectures.

NK 0210651 DNAL

Knowlton, George Franklin,
Studies on the beet leafhopper in northern Utah... [Columbus, The Ohio state university, 1932. 3 p. 2-200 numb. l. Thesis (PH.D.)- The Ohio state university.

NK 0210652 OU

595.7 K76u

Knowlton, George Franklin.
... Utah insects ... contribution from the Department of entomology, Utah agricultural experiment station. Logan, Utah, 1939-40.
6pt. in 1v. ([Utah. Agricultural college, Logan. Agricultural experiment station] Mimeograph series 200 (Technical))
Parts 1, 4, and 6 by G. F. Knowlton and F. C. Harmston; pt.5 by G. F. Knowlton, F. C. Harmston, and G. S. Stains.
1. Insects--Utah. I Harmston, Fred C., joint author. II. Stains, G. S., joint author.

NK 0210653 IU

Knowlton, George Henry, *comp.*
Errata and addenda to Dr. Stocking's History and genealogy of the Knowltons of England and America, together with a complete index to both books and a supplement with copies of old wills, administration records, etc. With the approval of Rev. Charles Henry Wright Stocking, D. D., comp. for the Knowlton association of America, by George Henry Knowlton ... Boston, The Everett press company, 1903.
3 p. l., 234 p. ports. 24½cm.
1. Knowlton family. I. Stocking, Charles Henry Wright, 1835- History and genealogy of the Knowltons. II. Knowlton association of America.
Library of Congress CS71.K73 1903 5-14809

NK 0210654 DLC ICN PHi OClWHi MB MWA

Knowlton, Harold Eugene, 1919-
The development of a waste treatment method for a styrene aqueous waste ... 1950.
136 numb. l.
Thesis (Ph. D.) - Ohio state university, 1950.

NK 0210655 OU

Knowlton, Harry Bass, 1889-
Heat treatment, uses and properties of steel, by H. B. Knowlton ... Cleveland, O., American society for steel treating, 1929.
5 p. l., 437 p. illus., diagrs. 23½cm.
1. Steel. I. Title.
29-24061
Library of Congress TS320.K6

IU MB MiHM PHC
NK 0210656 DLC ICRL WaS OClW OU OCl OCU PSC ICJ

Knowlton, Harry Edward, 1890-
Changes in technology and labor requirements in crop production: potatoes, by Harry E. Knowlton, Robert B. Elwood and Eugene G. McKibben ... Philadelphia, Pa., 1938.
xiii, 134 p. incl. front., illus. (incl. map) tables, diagrs. 25½cm. (*Half-title:* National research project on reemployment opportunities and recent changes in industrial techniques ... Studies of changing techniques and employment in agriculture ... [Report no. A-4])
Series title in part also on t.-p.
Photoprinted.
Issued also in Changes in technology and labor requirements in crop production: vegetables, potatoes, sugar beets (National research project on reemployment opportunities and recent changes in industrial techniques) (1937-39)
Bibliographical foot-notes.
1. Potatoes. 2. Agricultural laborers—U. S. 3. Agricultural machinery. I. Elwood, Robert B., joint author. II. McKibben, Eugene George, 1895- joint author. III. Title.
A 41-4355
Catholic univ. of America. Library
for Library of Congress S441.N3 no. A-4

NK 0210658 DCU DLC NN PPT DAU

Knowlton, Harry Edward, 1890- joint author.

Schilletter, Julian Claude, 1901-
Changes in technology and labor requirements in crop production: vegetables, by J. C. Schilletter, Robert B. Elwood and Harry E. Knowlton. Work projects administration, National research project ... Philadelphia, Pa., 1939.

Knowlton, Harry Edward, 1890-
Studies in pollen with special reference to longevity ... by Harry E. Knowlton ... [Ithaca, 1922]
1 p. l., p. 747-798. 22cm.
Thesis (PH. D.)—Cornell university, 1920.
"Published as Cornell univ. agr. expt. station Memoir 52: 747-798, January, 1922."
Bibliography: p. 789-798.
1. Pollen.
22-23534 Revised
Library of Congress QK658.K6
Cornell Univ. Libr. [r41c2]

NK 0210660 NIC NN MH-A MiU OU DLC

Knowlton, Harry Edward, 1890- A study of the hardiness of the fruit buds of the peach. By H. E. Knowlton and M. J. Dorsey. [Morgantown. 1927.] 8°. pp. 28. 2 plates. (West Virginia — Agricultural experiment station. Bulletin, 211.)
"Literature cited," pp. 27-28.

NK 0210661 MH-A DAS

Knowlton, Harry Neil, 1889-
How to build a box...by Captain H. N. Knowlton... Boston: Safepack Mills [cop. 1919]. 26 p., 1 l. diagrs., illus. 2°.
1. Boxes.—Manufacture.
N. Y. P. L.

NK 0210662 NN

Knowlton, Harry Neil, 1889-

Martin, Charles Carroll, 1875-
Export packing; a guide to the methods employed by successful shippers, by C. C. Martin; with chapters by D. T. Abercrombie ... H. N. Knowlton ... [and] M. C. Fitz Gerald ... New York city, Boston [etc.] American exporter, The Johnston export publishing co. [c1921]

Knowlton, Helen
Suggestions for the health of children. Ithaca, 1916.
p. 67-76.

NK 0210664 DL OrU Or

VOLUME 300

Knowlton, Helen Gingrich.
Hearthstones. Philadelphia, Dorrance [°1955]
55 p. 20 cm. (Contemporary poets of Dorrance, 466)

I. Title.
PS3521.N777H4 811.5 54-12867 ‡

NK 0210665 DLC C

Knowlton, Helen Mary, 1832-1918.
Art-life of William Morris Hunt, by Helen M. Knowlton With illustrations from his works. Boston, Little, Brown and company, 1899.
xii, 219 p. incl. front. plates, ports. 21 cm.

1. Hunt, William Morris, 1824-1879.
ND237.H9K5 99—5670

NK 0210666 DLC ViU MoU MiU NBuU OClJC MWA PSC TxU MB NN OOxM OCl OO WaS OClW

Knowlton, Helen Mary, 1832-1918.
Art-life of William Morris Hunt. With illus. from his works. Boston, Little, Brown, 1900.
xii, 219 p. plates, ports.

NK 0210667 MH-FA MB NcD

Knowlton, Helen Mary, 1832-1918.
Hints for pupils in drawing and painting. By Helen M. Knowlton. With illustrations from charcoal drawings, by William M. Hunt. Boston, Houghton, Osgood and company, 1879.
32 p. front., plates. 18cm.

1. Drawing. 2. Painting. I. Hunt, William Morris, 1824-1879.
9—22659
Library of Congress NC715.K7

NK 0210668 DLC CU PBm PPL

Knowlton, Helen Mary, 1832-1918.
Hints for pupils in drawing and painting. By Helen M. Knowlton. With illustrations from charcoal drawings, by William M. Hunt. Boston, Houghton, Osgood and company, 1880.
32 p. front., plates. 18cm.
First pub. in 1879.

1. Drawing. 2. Painting. I. Hunt, William Morris, 1824-1879.
9—22660
Library of Congress NC715.K72

NK 0210669 DLC OCl PU

Knowlton, Helen Mary, 1832-1918.
Hints for pupils in drawing and painting ... With illustrations from charcoal drawings, by William M. Hunt. Boston, Houghton, Mifflin and company, 1882.
32 p.

NK 0210670 MiEM

Knowlton, Helen Mary, 1832-1918.
Hints for pupils in drawing and painting. By Helen M. Knowlton. With illustrations from charcoal drawings by William M. Hunt. Boston, Houghton, Mifflin and company, 1883.
32 p. pl. 18cm.

1. Drawing. 2. Painting. I. Hunt, William Morris, 1824-1879.
18-4967
Library of Congress NC715.K72 1883

NK 0210671 DLC

Knowlton, Helen Mary, 1832-1918.
Hints for pupils in drawing and painting. By Helen M. Knowlton. With frontispiece from charcoal drawing. Boston and New York, Houghton, Mifflin and company, 1887.
32 p. pl. 18cm.

NK 0210672 ViU

Knowlton, Helen Mary, 1832-1918, comp.
Hunt, William Morris, 1824-1879. FOR OTHER EDITIONS SEE MAIN ENTRY
W. M. Hunt's talks on art. Boston, Houghton, Mifflin and company, 1881.

Knowlton, Helen Mary, 1832-1918.
William Morris Hunt, artist: the life story of one of America's greatest painters — his paintings and lectures on art a great influence.
= [Boston? 1913?] (11) pp. Illus. Portraits. Plates. 34½ cm.

L6423 — Hunt, William Morris, 1824-1879.

NK 0210674 MB MWA OClMA

Knowlton, Hosea Morrill, 1847-1902.
Address [on John Marshall]. Portrait.
(In Dickinson. John Marshall: the tribute of Massachusetts. Pp. 3-12. Boston, 1901.)

NK 0210675 MB

Knowlton, Hosea Morrill, 1847-1902.
The Grand Army of the Republic. An address... at Edgartown, Mass., May 30, 1889.- Cottage City. Martha's Vineyard Herald. 1889.
16p.

NK 0210676 OClWHi

Knowlton, Hosea Morrill, 1847-1902.
Hosea Morrill Knowlton; tribute...
see under Bar of the County of Bristol, Mass.

Knowlton, Hosea Morrill, 1847-1902.
Massachusetts. *Committee on corporation laws.*
... Report of the Committee on corporation laws, created by acts of 1902, chapter 335. January, 1903. Boston, Wright & Potter printing co., state printers, 1903.

973.7
K766
Knowlton, Hosea Morrill, 1847-1902.
The tragedy of the rebellion, an address delivered before William Logan Rodman Post, no. 1, Robert G. Shaw Post, no. 146, and R. A. Peirce Post, no. 190, of the Grand Army of the republic, at Liberty hall, New Bedford, Mass., May 30, 1890. New Bedford, Mercury pub. co., printers, 1890.
22 p. 23cm.

NK 0210679 NNC

LC1011
K5
Knowlton, Hosea Morrill, 1847-1902
A trained mind; an address delivered before the Alumni Association of the New Bedford High School, February 29, 1884, by Hosea M. Knowlton. New Bedford [Mass.] Mercury Publishing Company, printers, 1884.
12 p. 23 cm.

1. Education - Addresses, essays, lectures. I. Title.

NK 0210680 MeB

332.14
K76i
Knowlton, Hugh.
Investment banking phases of the federal Securities act and Securities exchange act. [New York, The New York state society of certified public accountants, 1934]
p.29-50. (The New York state society of certified public accountants. Bulletin, July, 1934)

Caption title.

NK 0210681 IU

Knowlton, Hugh, 1893-
Air transportation in the United States, its growth as a business, by Hugh Knowlton. Chicago, Ill., The University of Chicago press [1941]
vii, 72 p. incl. tables, diagrs. 21cm.

1. Aeronautics, Commercial—U. S. I. Title.
42-3587
Library of Congress TL521.K6
[30] 387.70973

NK 0210682 DLC CoU CU NIC NcD CaBViP OrCS MtU OrP WaS OU OClCC OClW OCl OO OrU PSC PWcT PPTU WaSpG

Knowlton, Isaac Case.
Annals of Calais, Maine, and St. Stephen, New Brunswick; including the village of Milltown, Me., and the present town of Milltown, N. B., by the Rev. I. C. Knowlton. Calais, J. A. Sears, printer, 1875.
208 p. 18cm.

1. Calais, Me.—Hist. 2. St. Stephen, N. B.—Hist. 3. Milltown, N. B.—Hist.
1—8945
Library of Congress F29.C15K7

NK 0210683 DLC MeB NIC MnHi MU CaNSWA CtY PHi PPL MeWC OClWHi OCl MWA MH NN Nh

Knowlton, Isaac Case, 1819-1894.
Through the shadows. By Rev. I. C. Knowlton ... Boston, Universalist publishing house, 1885.
2 p. l., [iii]-v p., 1 l., [9]-210 p. 18cm.

1. Universalism. 2. Future punishment—Controversial literature. I. Title.
41-41814
Library of Congress BX9941.K73

NK 0210684 DLC CtY MH-AH

Knowlton Mrs. Isabella Marion (Shaw)
Frost, *Mrs.* **Josephine C.**
Ancestors of Amyntas Shaw and his wife Lucy Tufts Williams, showing Mayflower lines never before published from Myles Standish, John Alden, William Mullines and Thomas Rogers, comp. for their daughter Isabella M. Knowlton by Josephine C. Frost (Mrs. Samuel Knapp Frost) ... [New York?] 1920.

Knowlton, J.
A compilation of rules and definitions on the philiology of language. Partly original and partly selected from different authors. By J. Knowlton. Lynn: J. F. Kimball, 1851. 28 p. 4. ed. 24°.

1. English language.—Grammar.
N. Y. P. L. November 20, 1922.

NK 0210686 NN

Knowlton, J.M.
Beauty: a poem. Sing-Sing, N.Y., 1848.
15 p. nar. D.

NK 0210687 RPB

VOLUME 300

Knowlton, J. M.
The prize of life: a poem. Sing-Sing, N.Y., 1850.
12 p. nar. D.

NK 0210688 RPB

Knowlton, J M, agriculturist.
Our hardy grapes; what to plant; how to plant, train, and manage them. By J. M. Knowlton ... New York, Coutant & Baker, 1863.
iv, [5]-96 p. illus. 18cm.
p. 81-96, advertising matter.

1. Viticulture—U. S.

11-30269

Library of Congress SB389.K73

NK 0210689 DLC

Knowlton, James Albert.
Dislaleo; a volume containing upwards of a hundred poems written upon various occasions, by James Albert Knowlton. Greentown, Ind., The Gem printing company [1928]
2 p. l., 7-143 p. 19cm.

I. Title.

29-17095

Library of Congress PS3521.N78D5 1928

NK 0210690 DLC

Knowlton, James Albert.
Halen and Wendaline, seven stories in one, by James Albert Knowlton. [Greentown, Ind., The Gem printing co., °1930]
1 p. l., [5]-162 p. 19cm.
In verse.

I. Title.

Library of Congress PS3521.N78H3 1930 31-10198
Copyright A 36561 [2] 811.5

NK 0210691 DLC ViU

Knowlton, James Albert.
Leeden's league; or, The voyagers' quest, by James Albert Knowlton. The endeavors of resolute men, who through a hundred trials are led onward by an unseen hand to a desired goal, are herein related ... Tipton, Ind., J. O. Lee [1923]
1 p. l., 5-425 p. 19cm.

I. Title.

23-7730

Library of Congress PZ3.K769Le

NK 0210692 DLC

Knowlton, James Albert.

Origin. By J. A. Knowlton with illustrations by C. I. Marston and Ray G. Bullock. Boston, The Eastern Publishing Company, 1900.
1 p. l., iii-vi, 7-339 p. plates. 20½cm.
Original green cloth, pictorial spine, silver lettering.
Wright III, 3184.

I. Title.

NK 0210693 ViU CtY

FILM Knowlton, James Albert.
Origin ... Boston, Eastern Publishing Co., 1900.
339 p. illus. (Wright American fiction, v.III, 1876-1900, no.3184, Research Publications Microfilm, Reel K-20)

NK 0210694 NcD CU

Knowlton, J[ames] A[lbert]
The span of sight, a collection of poems. Franklin, Ind., 1898.
95 p. 15 cm.

NK 0210695 RPB

Knowlton, Jay F, 1886–
... Knives, how to make them in the school forge shop [by] Jay F. Knowlton ... Milwaukee, Wis., The Bruce publishing co. [1928]
cover-title, 3-38 p. illus., diagrs. 19½cm. (Industrial-arts brochures. no. 9)

1. Knives. 2. Forging.

A 29-115 Revised

Title from Detroit Pub. Libr.
Library of Congress TT215.K6
[r32c2] 682

NK 0210696 MiD OrP OCl NN OEac

Knowlton, Jerome Cyril, 1850-1916.
Anson on contracts. [Chicago, Callaghan and company, '1908?]
245 p. 23cm.

NK 0210697 MiU-L

Knowlton, Jerome Cyril, 1850-1916.
Cases on criminal law, by Jerome C. Knowlton ... assisted by John W. Dwyer ... Chicago, Callaghan & company, 1902.
xi, 397 p. 24cm.

1. Criminal law. I. Dwyer, John William, joint author.

2-26328

NK 0210698 DLC IdU WaU-L NBuU-L FU PU-L OClW ViU-L

Knowlton, Jerome Cyril, 1850-1916.
Lectures on criminal law, by Prof. Jerome C. Knowlton ... Notes reported by Theo. F. Lake. University of Michigan, law class of 1901. Ann Arbor, 1898.
1 p.l., 91 numb. l. 27.5 cm.
Reproduced from typewritten copy.
——— Questions. [n.p., 1898?]
11 numb. l. 27.5 cm. (In Michigan. University. Law school. Law lectures, first year. [Ann Arbor, Mich. 1898-99])
1. Criminal law. I. Michigan. University. Law school. Class of 1901. II. Lake, Theodor

Franklin. III. Title.

NK 0210700 MiU-H

Knowlton, Jerome Cyril, 1850-1916.
Lectures on Jewish institutions, including the trial of Jesus from a lawyer's point of view, by Prof. J. C. Knowlton. Delivered to the students of the University of Michigan. Ann Arbor, 1894.
69 l. 28 cm.
Leaves variously numbered.
(In U. of M. law lectures. Ann Arbor, Mich., [1894-1902] vol. 3. [1894-1900])
1. Michigan. University. Law school. II. Title. III. Title: The trial of Jesus.

NK 0210701 MiU-H

Knowlton, Jerome Cyril, 1850-1916.
Lectures on Jewish institutions [including the trial of Jesus from a lawyer's point of view] by Professor J.C. Knowlton ... Ann Arbor [D.A. Edwards] 1894 [-1895]
6 pts. in 1 v. 27.5 cm.
Mimeographed.
Delivered to the students of the University of Michigan.
Contents. - I. The civil institutions of the Jews in the time of Christ. - II. The people and the state. -III.-IV. - The school and the synagogue. Parties in Judea. - V. Jurisprudence of the Jews.

Continued in next column

Continued from preceding column

VI. A study in Jewish jurisprudence. The trial of Jesus.
1. Jews - Political and social conditions. 2. Jews - Law. I. Title: Jewish institutions.

NK 0210703 MiU-H

KNOWLTON, J[erome] Cyril, 1850-1916.
Lectures on Jewish institutions, including the trial of Jesus from a lawyer's point of view, delivered to the students of the university of Michigan. Ann Arbor, [1909?]

(Multigraphed)

NK 0210704 MH-L OCH

Knowlton, Jerome Cyril, 1850-1916.
Lectures on Jewish institutions, including the trial of Jesus from a lawyer's point of view. By Prof. J.C. Knowlton ... Ann Arbor, Mich., C. E. Barthell, 1923.
1 p.l., 64 numb.l. 28cm.
Mimeographed.
"Delivered to the students of the University of Michigan."

1. Jews—Political and social conditions. 2. Jews—Law. 3. Jesus Christ—Trial.

NK 0210705 MiU-L

Knowlton, Jerome Cyril, 1850-1916.
Lecutres on quasi-contracts, by Jerome C. Knowlton ... Notes taken by A. E. Boynton. University of Michigan. Law class of 1900. Ann Arbor, Mich., Edwards bros., 1898.
1 p.l., 12 numb. l. 27.5 cm.
Reproduced from typewritten copy.
(In Michigan. University. Law school. Law lectures, first year. [Ann Arbor, Mich., 1898-99])
1. Boynton, Albert Eugene. II. Michigan. University. Law school. Class of 1900. III. Title.

NK 0210706 MiU-H

Knowlton, Jerome Cyril, 1850-1916.
Lectures on railway law, delivered by J. C. Knowlton ... to Class of 1900, Department of law, University of Michigan. Reported by A. E. Boynton. Ann Arbor, Mich., Edwards bros. [1909]
39 numb. l. 28 cm.
(In U. of M. law lectures. Ann Arbor, Mich., [1894-1902] vol. 1 [1898-1902]
1. Railways, - Law. I. Boynton, Albert Eugene. II. Michigan. University Law school. Class of 1900. III. Title.

NK 0210707 MiU-H

Knowlton, Jerome Cyril, 1850-1916.
Outline of contracts. [Ann Arbor? 1899?]
13 numb. l. 27.5 cm.
Caption title.
Reproduced from typewritten copy.
(In Michigan. University. Law school. Law lectures, first year. [Ann Arbor, Mich., 1898-99])
1. Contracts.

NK 0210708 MiU-H

Knowlton, Jerome Cyril, 1850-1916, ed.
Anson, *Sir* William Reynell, *bart.*, 1843-1914.
Principles of the English law of contract and of agency in its relation to contract, by Sir William R. Anson, bart. ... 2d American from 4th London ed. Edited and annotated by Jerome C. Knowlton ... Chicago, Callaghan and company, 1887.

VOLUME 300

Knowlton, Jerome Cyril, 1850-1916. ed.

FOR OTHER EDITIONS SEE MAIN ENTRY

Anson, *Sir* **William Reynell,** *bart.*, 1843-1914.

Principles of the law of contracts; based on the original text of Sir William R. Anson, bart. ... as edited by Jerome C. Knowlton ... revised and edited, with American notes, by Charles Joseph Turck ... 1939 ed. by Thomas H. Patterson ... Chicago, Callaghan and company, 1939.

Knowlton, Jerome Cyril, 1850-1916.

Walsh, Charles Clinton, 1867–

... Questions and answers on Blackstone, designed for use of law students, whether in office, law or correspondence schools; placing in the hands of the student work actually required by the leading law schools; containing questions with the answers which would be required for admission to the bar of any state and by any law school in the United States. By C. C. Walsh. Chicago, Callaghan & company [190-?]

Knowlton, Jerome Cyril, 1850-1916.

Walsh, Charles Clinton, 1867–

... Questions and answers on contracts, designed for use of law students, whether in office, law or correspondence schools; placing in the hands of the student work actually required by the leading law schools; containing questions with the answers which would be required for admission to the bar of any state and by any law school in the United States. By C. C. Walsh. Chicago, Callaghan & company [190-?]

Knowlton, Jerome Cyril, 1850-1916.

Thomas McIntyre Cooley... [No imprint.] cover-title, 16 p.

Reprinted from Michiganlaw review, v. 5, no. March 1907.

NK 0210713 MiU

Knowlton, Jerome Cyril, 1850-1916.

The trial of Jesus a study in Jewish jurisprudence... Washington, [c1900]
26p.

YA 23465

NK 0210714 DLC DNC

Knowlton, Joan A joint author.

A syllabus of Baroque art in Europe

see under

Knowlton, John Howard Barnes.

Knowlton, Joan A joint author.

A syllabus of later XVIII century art

see under

Knowlton, John Howard Barnes.

LD3907 .G7 1951 .K6 Knowlton, John Howard Barnes, 1914-

The graphic art of Gustave Doré.
v,249p. plates.

Thesis (Ph. D.) - N. Y. U., Graduate School, 1951.

Bibliography: p.[227]-244.

NK 0210717 NNU-W

ARCH LIBRARY 709.03 K767 Knowlton, John Howard Barnes.

A syllabus of baroque art in Europe [by] John H.B.Knowlton and Joan A. Knowlton. [Iowa City?] Department of Art, State University of Iowa, c1952.

1 v. (various pagings) 28 cm.

NK 0210718 KyU

N5305 K46 Art Knowlton, John Howard Barnes

A syllabus of later XVIII century art and XIX century painting, by John H.B. Knowlton and Joan A. Knowlton. [Iowa City] State University of Iowa, Dept. of Art, 1952.
146p. 28cm.

1. Art - Outlines, syllabi, etc. 2. Art - Hist. - 17th and 18th cent. 3. Painting - Hist. - 19th cent. I. Knowlton, Joan A jt. author.

NK 0210719 IaU

Knowlton, John K[imball] 1850–

Knowlton's framing & estimate book ... [Chelmsford? Mass.] 1903.

75 p. illus. 16½cm. 3-22919

NK 0210720 DLC

[**Knowlton, John Stocker Coffin**]

Carl's tour in Main street ... [4th ed.] Worcester, Mass., Sanford and Davis, 1889.

2 p. l., 246 p. front. 19½cm.

By J. S. C. Knowlton and Clarendon Wheelock. First published in the Worcester palladium in 1855 and reprinted in that paper, 1857-1858, and again in 1874. *cf.* Note.

1. Worcester, Mass. — Streets — Main street. 2. Worcester, Mass.— Descr. I. Wheelock, Clarendon, joint author. II. Rice, Franklin Pierce, 1852– III. Title.

14-10177

Library of Congress F74.W9K7

NK 0210721 DLC MWA MU MH

[Knowlton, John Stocker Coffin] 1798-1871.

...[Our speech ... [Worcester, Mass., 1848]

12 p. 20 cm. (Palladium extra. Worcester, October 18, 1848)

Caption-title.

"From the Worcester Palladium of September 27, 1848."

In double columns.

1. Campaign literature, 1848—Democratic—Massachusetts. I. Title. II. Worcester Palladium. Extra.

NK 0210722 CSmH

Knowlton, John Wellington, 1907- joint author.

Rossini, Frederick Dominic, 1899–

... Calorimetric determination of the heats of combustion of ethylene and propylene, by Frederick D. Rossini and John W. Knowlton ...

(R P 1024, *in* U. S. National bureau of standards. Journal of research of the National bureau of standards. Washington, U. S. Govt. print. off., 1937. 23½cm. September, 1937, v. 19, no. 3, p. 249-262 incl. tables, diagrs.)

Knowlton, John Wellington, 1907- joint author.

Rossini, Frederick Dominic, 1899–

... Heat and free energy of formation of deuterium oxide, by Frederick D. Rossini, John W. Knowlton, and Herrick L. Johnston ...

(R P 1287, *in* U. S. National bureau of standards. Journal of research of the National bureau of standards. Washington, U. S. Govt. print. off., 1940. 23½cm. April, 1940, v. 24, no. 4, p. 369-388 incl. 1 illus., tables)

Knowlton, John Wellington, 1907–

The heat of combustion of cyanogen, by John Wellington Knowlton ... [College Park, Md.] 1941.

1 p. l., iv, 34 (*i. e.* 42) numb. l. incl. tables (part fold.) 28½ x 23cm.

Thesis (PH. D.)—University of Maryland, 1941.
Type-written (carbon copy)
Tables are extra numbered leaves.
"References": leaves 33-34.

1. Cyanogen. 2. Combustion. 3. Thermochemistry. I. Title.

A 41-4294

Maryland. Univ. Library for Library of Congress QD181.C15K6

NK 0210725 MdU DLC

Knowlton, John Wellington, 1907- joint author.

FOR OTHER EDITIONS SEE MAIN ENTRY

Rossini, Frederick Dominic, 1899–

... Heats of combustion and of formation of the normal olefin (alkene-1) hydrocarbons in the gaseous state, by Frederick D. Rossini and John W. Knowlton ...

(R P 1028, *in* U. S. National bureau of standards. Journal of research of the National bureau of standards. Washington, U. S. Govt. print. off., 1937. 23½cm. September, 1937, v. 19, no. 3, p. 339-345 incl. tables, diagrs.)

QD516 .K57 Knowlton, John Wellington,1907-

...Heats of combustion of letranelhylmethane and 2-methylbutane...
[Wash.,1939]
p.415-424 23 1/2 cm.

([U.S.] Bureau of standards. Research paper no. Part of Journal of research of the National bureau of standards, 19

NK 0210727 DLC

Knowlton, John Wellington, 1907–

... Heats of combustion of tetramethylmethane and 2-methylbutane, by John W. Knowlton and Frederick D. Rossini ...

(R P 1193, *in* U. S. National bureau of standards. Journal of research of the National bureau of standards. Washington, U. S. Govt. print. off., 1939. 23½cm. April, 1939, v. 22, no. 4, p. 415-424 incl. tables, diagrs.)

Running title: Tetramethylmethane and 2-methylbutane.
"References": p. 424.

1. Thermochemistry. 2. Combustion. 3. Tetramethylmethane. 4. Methylbutane. I. Rossini, Frederick Dominic, 1899– joint author. II. Title.

39-26499

Library of Congress QC1.U52 vol. 22, no. 4
——— Copy 2. T1.U42 vol. 22, no. 4
[4] (506.173) 547.21

NK 0210728 DLC OU

Knowlton, John Wellington, 1907–

... Method and apparatus for the rapid conversion of deuterium oxide into deuterium, by John W. Knowlton and Frederick D. Rossini ...

(R P 1050, *in* U. S. National bureau of standards. Journal of research of the National bureau of standards. Washington, U. S. Govt. print. off., 1937. 23½cm. December, 1937, v. 19, no. 6, p. 605-612 incl. 1 illus., tab.)

Running title: Conversion of deuterium oxide into deuterium.
"References": p. 612.

1. Deuterium oxide. 2. Deuterium. I. Rossini, Frederick Dominic, 1899– joint author. II. Title. III. Title: Conversion of deuterium oxide into deuterium.

37-29069

Library of Congress QC1.U52 vol. 19, no. 6
——— Copy 2. T1.U42 vol. 19, no. 6
[8] (506.173) 546.11

NK 0210729 DLC OU

Knowlton, Joseph.

A new system of book-keeping by single entry, particularly calculated for mechanics and retail dealers. Boston, J.H.Eastburn, 1828.

NK 0210730 MH

KNOWLTON, Joseph.

A short but comprehensive grammar, designed for the use of schools. 2d ed. with alterations and improvements. Salen, printed by Foote & Brown, 1832.

24°.pp.84.

NK 0210731 MH NNC ICU

VOLUME 300

Knowlton, Josephine (Gibson) 1885–
The innocent cause. 1st ed. [Washington, Pub. by Caslon Press] 1948.
274 p. front. 24 cm.

I. Title.

PZ3.K7695 In 48-8066*

NK 0210732 DLC

Knowlton, Josephine (Gibson) 1885–
My turtles, by Josephine Gibson Knowlton ... 1st ed. ... [Washington, Printed by Caslon press] 1943.
1 p. l., [1], x-xxxvii, 39-222 p. incl. plates, facsim. col. front., mounted port. 24cm.
"Limited edition of three hundred copies. This is number 99."

1. Turtles. I. Title.

Library of Congress QL666.C5K6 43-9692
[3] 598.13

NK 0210733 DLC KAS NN OClW PSt

Knowlton, Josephine (Gibson) 1885–
Roma, by Josephine Gibson Knowlton. [New Haven, Priv. print. °1929]
[27] p. front., pl. 22½cm.
"500 copies ... the Yale university press ... November 1929."
The story of an Italian sparrow.

1. Sparrows. 2. Birds—Legends and stories. I. Title.

Library of Congress QL795.B57K5 30-2922

NK 0210734 DLC ViU MnU MeB NcD KyU

Knowlton, Josephine (Gibson) 1885–
Roma. Privately printed. [2d printing.]
— [New Haven, Yale University Press. 1930.] (27) pp. Portrait. Plate. 22 cm.
Roma was an Italian pet sparrow.

N8828 — Sparrows. — Roma. Title.

NK 0210735 MB

Knowlton, Julius W.

Stevens, Henry S.
Address delivered at the dedication of monument of the 14th Conn. vols. at Gettysburg, Penn., July 3d, 1884, by Comrade H. S. Stevens; with a description of the monument, &c. Also, an account of the trip of the 14th C. V. to Gettysburg, July 1-3, '84, by Comrade J. W. Knowlton ... Middletown, Conn., Pelton & King, printers, 1884.

Knowlton, Kathryn, 1899–
... A study of certain metabolic effects of testosterone propionate in eunuchoids and in normal men and women ... by Kathryn Knowlton ... [Los Angeles, 1940]
1 p. l., 135-153, 20 p. illus., diagrs. 25½cm.
Thesis (PH. D.)—University of Chicago, 1939.
Without thesis note.
"Private edition, distributed by the University of Chicago libraries, Chicago, Illinois."
"Reprinted from Endocrinology, vol. 23, no. 2, August 1938, vol. 26, no. 1, January 1940."
"References": p. 152-153, 20.
1. Metabolism. 2. Testosterone propionate. 3. Hormones. I. Title: Eunuchoids.

Library of Congress QP951.K6 1940 41-88
Univ. of Chicago Libr.
——— Copy 2. [2] 615.36

NK 0210737 DLC

Knowlton, Kent, 1872–

Bigelow, Melville Madison, 1846-1921.
The law of fraudulent conveyances, by Melville Madison Bigelow ... with editorial notes, by Kent Knowlton ... Boston, Little, Brown and company, 1911.

Knowlton, Lawrence Gane, 1901–
Some experiments on iron ... by Lawrence Gane Knowlton ... [Ithaca, N. Y., 1928]
1 p. l., p. [1572]-1595. 26½cm.
Thesis (PH. D.)—Cornell university, 1927.
"Reprinted from the Journal of physical chemistry, vol. 32 ... (1928)."

1. Iron.

Library of Congress QD181.F4K6 1927 30-24509
[2] 546.72

NK 0210739 DLC NIC OU MH

Knowlton, M. D., co.
... Catalog.
Rochester, N. Y.
1 v. front., illus. 23½cm.
Only latest issue in Library is kept on shelf.

1. Paper box machinery.

Library of Congress TS1200.K6 CA 22-506 Unrev'd

NK 0210740 DLC WaS OCl

811
K767o
Knowlton, Mabel Angeline.
Ocean souvenirs. [poems] Drawings by Norma Madge Lyon. [Eugene, Ore., c1939]
[1l]p. illus. 15cm.

NK 0210741 OrU

Knowlton, Marcus Perrin.
Legislation and judicial decision in their relation to each other and to the law. Address . . . at the Yale Law School, June 24, 1901.
= New Haven. Ryder. 1901. (1), 16 pp. 8°.
Reprinted from the Yale Law Journal, December, 1901 [*5662.33.11].

F3837 — Yale College. Law school. Addresses. — Legislation. — Judgment.

NK 0210742 MB MH

Knowlton, Miles Justin, 1825-1874.

PL1976
.M6
1876
Morrison, William T 1834 *or* 5-1869.
An Anglo-Chinese vocabulary of the Ningpo dialect. By Rev. W. T. Morrison ... Rev. and enl. Shanghai, American Presbyterian mission press, 1876.

Knowlton, Miles Justin, 1825-1874.
China as a mission field; a premium tract. By Rev. M.J. Knowlton, missionary to China. Philadelphia, Bible and Publication Society [1870?]
32p. 19cm.
"No. 113. Premium offered by Rev. I.J. Roberts, late missionary to China."
Includes "What China is" from China and the Chinese, by J.L. Nevius.
1. Missions. China. I. Title.

NK 0210744 NcWsW MSaE RPB

Knowlton, Miles Justin, 1825-1874.
The foreign missionary; his field and his work. By Rev. M. J. Knowlton ... Philadelphia, Bible and publication society, 1872.
x, [1]-228 p. 20cm.
"This book embodies the results of about eighteen years of personal experience and observation in the foreign mission field."—Pref.

1. Missions, Foreign. I. Title.

Library of Congress BV2060.K57 33-7480
266

NK 0210745 DLC NjNbS CtY PCC PPTU

Knowlton, Miles Justin, 1825-1874.
Lecture on ancient Christian missions in China ... n.p., n.d.
22.5 cm.

NK 0210746 CtY-AO

Knowlton, Miles Justin, 1825-1874.
The rivers of China ... [n.p., 1869]
12 p. 22.5 cm.

NK 0210747 CtY

Knowlton, Millard, 1875–
... Syphilis and infant deaths, by Millard Knowlton .. regional consultant, United States Public health service ... Washington, Govt. print. off., 1921.
10 p. diagrs. 23½cm.
Reprint no. 696 from the Public health reports, v. 36, no. 38, September 23, 1921 (p. 2305-2312)

1. Syphilis. 2. Infants—Mortality. I. U. S. Public health service. Public health reports. Reprint 696.

Library of Congress RC201.K7 21-27506

NK 0210748 DLC CaBVaU MiU OClW

Knowlton, Miner, 1804-1870.
... Instructions and regulations for the militia and volunteers of the United States. Comprehending the exercises and movements of the infantry of the line, light infantry, and riflemen. As established by authority for the government of the regular army. Together with Manual for non-commissioned officers of the infantry and rifles—U. S. army. By Captain Alfred Sully ... Prepared and arranged from Cooper's tactics, Scott's tactics, Gilham's manual, Hardee's tactics, and other authorities, by Captain Miner Knowlton ... Philadelphia, C. Desilver, 1861.
[324] p. illus. (incl. music) diagrs. 20cm.
Incomplete? Parts I and IV-VI only, with separate paging.
Part V: Manual for non-commissioned officers ... by A. Sully.

1. U. S.—Army—Infantry—Drill and tactics. 2. U. S.—Militia—Handbooks. I. Sully, Alfred, 1821-1879.

Library of Congress UD160.K7 20-3935†

NK 0210750 DLC PHi PPL OOC PU PP

Knowlton, Miner, 1804-1870.
Lands belonging to the U. States at West Point. West Point, 1839. 68 p. 4°. (United States. Military Acad. at West Point.)
Mimeographed.

1. Land (Public), U. S.: N. Y.: West Point. 2. West Point, N. Y.—History. 3. Off. au.
N. Y. P. L.

NK 0210751 NN NBu

Uxq71
K839m
[Knowlton, Miner] 1804-1870.
Military pyrotechny, for the use of the cadets of the U.S. military academy, West Point ... [n.p.]1839.
1p.l.,40p. 24pl. 33cm.
Lithographed by George Aspinwall.
Attributed also to James Duncan Zebina Kinsley. cf. U.S. Military academy. The centennial of the United States military academy, v.1,p.463.

NK 0210752 CtY DLC ICJ

4UF
325
Knowlton, Miner, 1804-1870.
Notes on gunpowder, percussion, powder, cannon and projectiles. [ ] Litho.by G. Aspinwall, 1841.
75 p.

NK 0210753 DLC-P4 NWM CtY

VOLUME 300

Knowlton, Miner Rockwell, 1847-

Knowlton association of America.
Prospectus and year book containing the history, constitution, by-laws, list of officers and members of the Knowlton association of America from its organization, with an account of the first and second reunions. Comp. and ed. by William Herrick Griffith ... published under the auspices of Miner Rockwell Knowlton ... and William Herrick Griffith ... and presented by them to association members. Albany, N. Y., S. H. Wentworth, printer, 1897.

Knowlton, Murray.
The cruise of a tuna clipper; a narrative of San Diego's fishing industry, based upon the account of a boy rich in the traditions of the sea who shipped aboard the Conte Bianco and sailed south across the equator to the far-away Galapagos islands, written by Murray Knowlton; illustrated by Aloys Bohnen. [San Diego, Calif.] Pub. and printed by the city schools of San Diego, 1937.
4 p. l., 177 p. illus., plates. 20½cm.
Maps on lining-papers.
"This book was prepared under the direction of the San Diego city schools curriculum project, Works progress administration, official project 65-3-1994 ... and presented to the San Diego city schools by the Board of education."—Verso of 2d prelim. leaf.
1. Fishing—Juvenile literature. 2. Tuna fish. I. San Diego, Calif. Board of education. II. Title.
37-8934
Library of Congress SH351.T8K6
——— Copy 2.
Copyright A 104915 [3] 639.2758

NK 0210756 DLC

Knowlton, Murray.
San Diego harbor; a survey of San Diego harbor, its ships, piers, dredges, planes, and people, written by Murray Knowlton, illustrated by George Rhone. [San Diego] The City schools of San Diego, California, 1938.
4 p. l., 124 p. plates. 20½ x 16cm.
"Prepared under the direction of the San Diego city schools curriculum project, Works progress administration ... and presented to the San Diego city schools by the Board of education."—Verso of 2d prelim. leaf.
1. San Diego, Calif.—Harbor. I. San Diego, Calif. Board of education. II. U. S. Work projects administration.
43-40493
Library of Congress TC225.S16K6
[2] 387.1

NK 0210757 DLC CU-S

Knowlton, Norman P
Mitotic time determined by x-rays, by Norman P. Knowlton, Jr. [and] William R. Widner. Oak Ridge, Tenn., Technical Information Branch, Oak Ridge Extension AEC, 1949.
19 p., tables, diagrs. 27cm.
At head of title: United States Atomic Energy Commission. AECU-366 (LADC-683)
1. Karyokinesis—Measurement. 2. X-rays—Physiological effect. I. Widner, William R jt. author. II. Title. III. Ser.

NK 0210758 ViU

Knowlton, Norman P
The value of blood counts in individuals exposed to ionizing radiation, by Norman P. Knowlton, Jr. Oak Ridge, Tenn., Technical Information Branch, Oak Ridge Extension AEC, 1949.
24 p., tables, diagrs. 27cm.
At head of title: United States Atomic Energy Commission. AECU-397 (LADC-682)
1. Radiation—Physiological effect. I. Title. II. Ser.

NK 0210759 ViU

Knowlton, Philip Arnold, 1887-
First lessons in geography, by Philip A. Knowlton. [New York] The Macmillan company, °1924.
vi, 257 p. incl. col. front., illus. (part col.) 24cm.
1. Geography—Text-books—1870-
24-8643
Library of Congress G126.K6
[a26e2]

PWcT
NK 0210760 DLC OrP CU OCU OEac OClh OLak OU ODW OCl

Knowlton, Philip Arnold, 1887-
First lessons in geography. Rev. ed. By Philip A. Knowlton ... [New York, The Macmillan company, 1929.
vi, 271 p. incl. col. front., illus. (part col.) 23cm.
1. Geography—Text-books—1870-
29-11424
Library of Congress G126.K6 1929

NK 0210761 DLC

Knowlton, Philip Arnold, 1887-
Introduction to world geography, by Philip A. Knowlton ... [New York] The Macmillan company, °1927.
iv, 298 p. illus. (part col., incl. maps) 26cm.
"Suggestions for outside reading": p. 288.
1. Geography—Text-books—1870-
27-18787
Library of Congress G127.K6

PU-Penn
NK 0210762 DLC OrMonO OCU OClh OU OOxM OCl PPTU

Knowlton, Philip Arnold, 1887-
Introduction to world geography. Rev. ed. By Philip A. Knowlton ... [New York, The Macmillan company] 1932.
iv, 298 p. illus. (part col.; incl. maps) diagrs. 26cm.
"Published August, 1927 ... Revised edition published July, 1932."
"Suggestions for outside reading": p. 288.
1. Geography—Text-books—1870-
33-10002
Library of Congress G127.K6 1932
Copyright A 53316 [3] 910

NK 0210763 DLC

Knowlton, Philip Arnold, 1887-
Introductory geography ... prepared especially for use in grade four-A[-B] in New York city, by Philip A. Knowlton ... and C. C. Van Liew ... New York, The Macmillan company, 1929.
2 v. fronts., illus., col. plates, maps. 26cm.
"Books to read": v. 1, p. 117; duplicated in v. 2, p. 139.
1. Geography—Text-books—1870- I. Van Liew, Charles Cecil, 1862- joint author.
29-9346
Library of Congress G126.K63

NK 0210764 DLC

HD2984 .P7 1953 Knowlton, Philip Arnold, 1887-
FOR OTHER EDITIONS SEE MAIN ENTRY
Profit-Sharing Research Foundation.
Profit sharing in practice; report on visits to profit-sharing establishments, 1951-1952, by P. A. Knowlton, director of research. Rev. [Long Island City, N. Y.] °1953.

Knowlton, Philip Arnold, 1887-
Profit sharing patterns; a comparative analysis of the formulas and results of the plans of 300 companies with 730,000 employees. Evanston, Ill., Profit Sharing Research Foundation, 1954.
144 p. illus. 29 cm.
1. Profit-sharing—U. S. I. Profit-Sharing Research Foundation. II. Title.
HD2984.K55 658.324 55-2257 ‡
Library of Congress [5615]

OrCS OrU WaT NcU CoU NIC IdB OrP
TxU AU WaS WaTC WaWW FTaSU WaSpG WaU-L GU NIC Wa
IU NcD MiD MH NcC PU-W AAP TU ViU OOxM PP LU OClW
NK 0210766 DLC CaBVaU Wa NBuU OCU OU PSC IEN MB

Knowlton, Philip Arnold, joint author.
FOR OTHER EDITIONS SEE MAIN ENTRY
Yoakam, Gerald Alan, 1887-
Reading to learn; introductory book, by Gerald A. Yoakam, William C. Bagley and Philip A. Knowlton; with drawings by H. H. Gilmore. New York, The Macmillan company, 1938.

Knowlton, Philip Arnold, joint author.

Yoakam, Gerald Alan, 1887-
Reading to learn ... a work-type informational reader, by Gerald A. Yoakam, William C. Bagley and Philip A. Knowlton; with drawings by George M. Richards. New York, The Macmillan company, 1935.

LB1044 .R39 Knowlton, Philip Arnold, 1887-
A **Report** to educators on teaching films survey, conducted by Harcourt Brace and Company [and others. New York, Harper, 1948]

HD 2984 .K76 Knowlton,Philip Arnold,1887-
Studies in profit sharing: 1.Discontinued plans 2.Plan changes. [Long Island City,N.Y.] Profit-Sharing Research Foundation, c1952,'53.
32 p. illus. 28 cm.
1.Profit-sharing--U.S. I.Profit-Sharing Research Foundation.

LU MoU OCU
NK 0210770 MiU IU ViU TxU OU MiD NBuG DCU NIC N NN

Knowlton, Philip E.
FOR OTHER EDITIONS SEE MAIN ENTRY
Addams, George Stanton, 1869-
A treatise on practice and procedure in the probate courts of Ohio, including the law of wills and administration of estates with forms and journal entries, by George S. Addams ... and Grover C. Hosford ... 3d ed. by Cloys P. McClelland ... Cincinnati, The W. H. Anderson company [°1941]

BJ 1471 .K73 Knowlton, Pitt G
Origin and nature of conscience; an exposition and criticism of the empirical-evolution theory of the origin of conscience with constructive conclusions. [Oberlin, Ohio, News Press, 1896]
150 p. 24 cm.
Diss. — Leipzig.
Binder's title: Ethical problems: Conscience.
1. Conscience.

NK 0210772 DCU MH ODW ICRL NjP CtY OO OU

Law Knowlton, Robert E., joint ed.

Keedy, Edwin Roulette, 1880- ed.
Cases and statutes on administration of the criminal law, selected and arr. by Edwin R. Keedy and Robert E. Knowlton. [Rev. ed.] Indianapolis, Bobbs-Merrill [1955]

Knowlton, Robert James, 1931-
The disamortization and nationalization of ecclesiastical property in Mexico, 1856-1910.
vi, 709 l. illus.
Thesis -State University of Iowa, 1963
Microfilm, positive.

NK 0210774 MH

VOLUME 300

Knowlton, Thomas Anson.
The economic theory of George Bernard Shaw, by Thomas Anson Knowlton. Orono, Me., Printed at the University press, 1936.
v, 82 p. 23 cm. (*On cover:* University of Maine studies. Second series, no. 39)
The Maine bulletin. Vol. XXXIX, no. 4.
Bibliography: p. 76-80.
1. Shaw, George Bernard, 1856-1950. I. Title.
PR5368.E4K6 928.2 36-28415
NK 0210775 DLC MtU OrCS WaSpG PU ViU OCU OO OU OOxM ODW PBm NIC FMU MoU MB ViU

Knowlton, Sarah, plaintiff.
Testimony of Asa B. Foster and copies of contracts (therein referred to) given in cause Dame Sarah Knowlton vs Asa B. Foster and Bradley Barlow, garnishee, in Superior court, Montreal. [Montreal, 1880] 63 p. 21½cm.
Cover-title.
1. No subject. I. Foster, Asa B , 1852?- , defendant. II. Barlow, Bradley, defendant.
N. Y. P. L.
NK 0210776 NN

Knowlton, W. T.
Discussion of some details of design and construction of sanitary sewers. Read before the Engineers and Architects Association, April, 1906. [Los Angeles?] 1906. 8 p. 8°.
1. Sewers.—Construction.
N. Y. P. L.
NK 0210777 NN

Knowlton, Wallace Miles, joint author.
Channing, Walter, 1849-
A case of metastatic adrenal tumors in the left midfrontal and ascending frontal convolutions. By Walter Channing, M. D., and Wallace M. Knowlton, M. D. [Baltimore? 1903?]

Knowlton, William Augustus, 1838-1933.
Life, letters and speeches of Dr. William Augustus Knowlton, compiled by Marion Wilcox and Bernice B. Knowlton ... Cleveland, O., The Gates press, 1938.
2 v. fronts., ports. 24½cm.
Paged continuously.
"First edition."
I. Wilcox, Marion, comp. II. Knowlton, Mrs. Bernice Bettman, joint comp. III. Title.
Library of Congress R154.K393A4 39-8520
——— Copy 2.
Copyright A 126651 [2] 926.1
NK 0210779 DLC OCl NcD

Knowlton, William H.
Akron, O. *Charters.*
The charter and revised ordinances of the city of Akron, Ohio, including all ordinances of a general nature in force August 15, 1927, with appendix containing gas franchise and motor bus and street railway franchise. Revised, codified and rearranged by Henry M. Hagelbarger and William H. Knowlton, director of law and assistant, the city of Akron, Ohio. Published by authority of the Council of the city of Akron, Ohio. [Akron, Printed in U. S. A. by the Ben Franklin printing co., 1927.

Knowlton, William Smith, 1839-
Auld land syne.
(In Davison, Charles, - Semi-centennial address ... Foxcroft, 1892- 20 cm. p. 31-35)
NK 0210781 RPB

811.49
K72M
Knowlton, William Smith, 1839-
Modern classics and other poems ... Augusta, Me, Kennebec Journal press, 1912.
65 p. illus. 19½cm.
NK 0210782 NcD RPB MeWaC

Knowlton, William Smith, 1839-
The old schoolmaster; or, Forty-five years with the girls and boys, by William Smith Knowlton. Augusta, Me., Burleigh & Flynt, printers, 1905.
269 p. front. (port.) plates. 21½cm.
1. Maine—Soc. life & cust. 2. Education—Maine. I. Title.
Library of Congress F25.K73 5-24236
NK 0210783 DLC MeB MB

Knowlton, William Smith, 1839-
Sangerville, centennial poem ...
Augusta, Me., n.d.
24 p. 19 cm.
NK 0210784 RPB

Knowlton, Willie H.
Progressive simple interest treatise: in which the latest modern improvements, and such older principles as have been well established by practical tests, are harmonized ... By Willie H. Knowlton. Victory, Cayuga co., N. Y., Messenger company, 1875.
22 p. 15cm.
1. Interest and usury—Tables, etc.
Library of Congress HG1628.K7 7-13391†
NK 0210785 DLC

Knowlton, Winthrop, 1930-
American foreign policy and the separation of parties; an examination of the problem of bipartisanship, 1918-1952
Honors thesis - Harvard, 1953
1. U.S. - Foreign policy
NK 0210786 MH

Knowlton, N.J. Presbyterian Church.
Records of the first English and German Presbyterian congregation in Knowlton, Warren County, N. J., 1766-1804. Copied and translated from the original records in German. Newark, N. J., 1918. 39 l. f°.
Typewritten.
1. Knowlton, N. J.—Churches (Presbyterian). 2. Knowlton, N. J.—Genealogy.
N. Y. P. L.
NK 0210787 NN MB

Knowlton, Quebec. Brome County Historical society
see Brome County historical society, Knowlton, Quebec.

Knowlton association of America.
Knowlton, George Henry, *comp.*
Errata and addenda to Dr. Stocking's History and genealogy of the Knowltons of England and America, together with a complete index to both books and a supplement with copies of old wills, administration records, etc. With the approval of Rev. Charles Henry Wright Stocking, D. D., comp. for the Knowlton association of America, by George Henry Knowlton ... Boston, The Everett press company, 1903.

Knowlton association of America.
Prospectus and year book containing the history, constitution, by-laws, list of officers and members of the Knowlton association of America from its organization, with an account of the first and second reunions. Comp. and ed. by William Herrick Griffith ... published under the auspices of Miner Rockwell Knowlton ... and William Herrick Griffith ... and presented by them to association members. Albany, N. Y., S. H. Wentworth, printer, 1897.
88 p. 22½cm.
1. Knowlton family. I. Griffith, William Herrick, 1866- ed. II. Knowlton, Miner Rockwell, 1847- III. Title.
15-2147
Library of Congress CS71.K73 1897 a
NK 0210790 DLC MB Nh MWA

R676
K769r
Knowlton Brothers, Watertown, N. Y.
Ravenna; a background for things of beauty. [Watertown, N. Y., n.d.]
1 v. (unpaged, chiefly illus.) 14 plates.
On cover: A gift from the art and romance of old Italy.
Caption title: Ravenna covers.
1. Paper - Sample books 2. Printing - Specimens I. T: Ravenna covers.
NK 0210791 MiD

*
Z247
.K56
1923
Knowlton Bros., Watertown, N. Y.
Ravenna; a background for things of beauty. [Utica, N. Y., Moser & Cotins, 1923?]
unpaged. illus. 32cm.
1. Paper—Sample books. I. Title.
NK 0210792 ViU

Z676
fK769
Knowlton Brothers, Watertown, New York.
Ravenna; a background for things of beauty. [Watertown, 1927]
2 double leaves, 14 double plates. 32cm.
On cover: A gift from the art and romance of old Italy.
A paper sample book, with designs by various typographers.
NK 0210793 MnU

Known but to God ...
see under [Walsh, Paul P

Known signatures
see under [Armstrong, Terence Ian Fytton] 1912-

Known to none, Author of.
Conquered, the story of a contest
see under title

Ip
K769
871
Known to none. A village romance... London, Smith, Elder & Co., 1871.
2 p.l., 297, [1] p. 20 cm.
NK 0210797 CtY

VOLUME 300

The KNOWN saying in the New Testament, That a Kingdom divided | can't stand, is very seasonable at this juncture, by all Protestants | to be seriously considered: And if ever Vnity (if not in Worship, | yet in Love and Affections) will be necessary, it must certainly be | Now; . . .
Without t.p. 19.4x15.5cm. 14p.
Not identified. Words above taken from p. 1.

NK 0210798 NNUT-Mc

Knowne laws. A short examination of the counsells and actions of those that have withdrawne the King from the government and protection of his people. London, 1643.
1 p. l., 6 p. 19cm.
Signature: A⁴.

1. Gt. Brit.—Constitutional law. 2. Gt. Brit.—Hist.—Civil war, 1642–1649—Pamphlets.
40-24944
Library of Congress DA412.1643.K5

MnU NNUT-Mc CtY ICN MH CSmH DFo
NK 0210799 DLC MoU MnU CU-A ICU WU OU InU CLU-C PU

Knowsley, Hall, Lancashire.
A catalogue of the library at Knowsley Hall
see under Derby, Edward Henry Stanley, 15th earl of, 1826-1893.

W 6 P3 KNOWSON, Georges.
Cours d'harmonie physiologique. L'équilibre de l'organisme, source de santé physique et morale par une vie saine et rationnelle ... Fontainbleau [1954]
33 l.
1. Hygiene

NK 0210801 DNLM

[Knox.]
The lion of the tribe of Judah. By a friend of the Jews. Fredericksburg, Va.: J. White, 1871. 21 p. 8°.
Contains autograph note of author.

1. Jesus Christ.—Messiahship. 2. Title.
N. Y. P. L. June 11, 1913.

NK 0210802 NN

Knox, Dr.
see Knox, Robert, 1791-1862.

Knox, Mr., of Bristol
see Knox, Thomas, of Bristol.

Knox, Adeline (Trafton) 1845–
An American girl abroad. By Adeline Trafton. Illustrated by Miss L. B. Humphrey. Boston, Lee & Shepard, 1872.
245 p. front., pl. 17½ cm.

1. Europe—Descr. & trav.—1800-1918. I. Title.
3—11017
Library of Congress D919.K74

OCl PU PPL PP NN MH ViU
NK 0210805 DLC OKentU TxU MeB ViU TU CtY OO OU OEac

FILM 4274 PR v.2 reel K7 Knox, Adeline (Trafton) 1845–
An American girl abroad. By Adeline Trafton. Illustrated by Miss L. B. Humphrey. Boston, Lee and Shepard, 1872.
245 p. illus. (Wright American fiction, v.II, 1851-1875, no.1496, Research Publications Microfilm, Reel K-7)

1. Europe - Descr. & trav. - Guide-books. I. Title. II.x. Trafton, Adeline.

NK 0210806 PSt CU

Ed 869Kb [Knox], Mrs. Adeline (Trafton) 1845–
An American girl abroad. By Adeline Trafton. Illustrated by Miss L.B.Humphrey. Boston, Lee and Shepard; New York, Lee, Shepard and Dillingham, 1873.
245p. front., plates. 17½cm.

NK 0210807 CtY

[KNOX], Mrs. Adeline (Trafton), 1845–
An American girl abroad. Illustrated by Miss L.B.Humphrey. Boston, Lee and Shepard, etc., etc., 1874.

Front.

NK 0210808 MH

Knox, *Mrs.* Adeline (Trafton) 1845–
An American girl abroad. By Adeline Trafton. Illustrated by Miss L. B. Humphrey. Boston, Lee and Shepard, 1900.
245 p. front., plates. 18cm. [The girlhood series]

1. Europe—Descr. & trav. I. Title.
Library of Congress D919.K743 0-645 Revised

NK 0210810 DLC PPFr

Knox, *Mrs.* Adeline (Trafton) 1845–
Dorothy's experience. By Adeline Trafton ... Boston, Lee and Shepard; New York, C. T. Dillingham [1890]
211 p. 16½cm.

I. Title.
7—14191
Library of Congress PZ3.K77D

NK 0210811 DLC MB OCl PPL NN

FILM Knox, *Mrs.* Adeline (Trafton) 1845–
Dorothy's experience. By Adeline Trafton ... Boston, Lee and Shepard; New York, C. T. Dillingham [1890]
211 p. 16½cm.
(Wright American Fiction, v. III, 1876-1900, no. 3186, Research Publications, Inc. Microfilm, Reel K-20)

NK 0210812 NcD CU

Knox, *Mrs.* Adeline (Trafton) 1845–
His inheritance. By Adeline Trafton ... Boston, Lee and Shepard; New York, C. T. Dillingham, 1878.
1 p. l., 5-428 p. 19½cm.

I. Title.
8—30859
Library of Congress PZ3.K77H

NK 0210813 DLC PPL MB ICN ViU NcD

FILM Knox, *Mrs.* Adeline (Trafton) 1845–
His inheritance. By Adeline Trafton ... Boston, Lee and Shepard; New York, C. T. Dillingham, 1878.
1 p. l., 5-428 p. 19½cm.

(Wright American Fiction, v. III, 1876-1900, no. 3187, Research Publications, Inc. Microfilm, Reel K-20)

NK 0210814 NcD CU

---

* PS646 .F53 .K669A5 1874 Knox, Adeline (Trafton) 1845–
Katherine Earle. Illustrated. Boston: Lee and Shepard; New York: Lee, Shepard and Dillingham, 1874.
2 p. l., 5-325, [7] p. front. 20cm.
Publisher's advertisements: [7] p. at end.
Wright II, 1497.

NK 0210815 ViU OU NNC IU ICU NN CSmH

FILM 4274 PR v.2 reel K7 Knox, Adeline (Trafton) 1845–
Katherine Earle. By Miss Adeline Trafton... Boston, Lee and Shepard, 1874.
325 p. illus. (Wright American fiction, v.II, 1851-1875, no.1497, Research Publications Microfilm, Reel K-7)

NK 0210816 CU

Ix K77 874K Knox, Adeline (Trafton) 1845–
Katherine Earle, by Adeline Trafton. Boston, Lee and Shepard, 1875.
325 p. plates. 20 cm.

NK 0210817 CtY

Knox, *Mrs.* Adeline (Trafton) 1845–
Katherine Earle, by Adeline Trafton ... Boston, Lee and Shepard, 1902.
1 p. l., 325 p. front., pl. 19cm. (American girl's series [v. 3])
2-22404

NK 0210818 DLC

KNOX, ALEXANDER.
The closing door. [New York, MCA management, 1949?] 73, 55 l. 29cm.

Typescript.
Produced at the Empire theatre, N.Y., 1 December, 1949.

1. Drama, American. I. Title.

NK 0210819 NN

Knox, Alexander
The closing door [a play in two acts. New York] Theatre Arts, 1950, c1949.
p. 62-88. illus.

NK 0210820 MiD

Knox, Alexander.
Old master; a comedy, by Alexander Knox ... London, Constable & co ltd [1940]
5 p. l., 128, [1] p. 19cm.
"First published 1940."

I. Title.
A 42-1102
New York. Public library for Library of Congress [2]

NK 0210821 NN OU RPB OCl

VOLUME 300

Knox, Alexander, M. D.
An enquiry into the actual state of our knowledge of cholera, with practical directions regarding its prevention and treatment. By Alexander Knox ... Dublin, J. McGlashan; [etc., etc.] 1849.
vi p., 1 l., 266 p. 17½cm.
"Chronological bibliography of cholera": p. [247]-260.

1. Cholera, Asiatic.
35-36463
Library of Congress RC126.K68

NK 0210822 DLC

DA990 .D7K7 **Knox, Alexander,** *M. D.*
A history of the county of Down, from the most remote period to the present day; including an account of its early colonization, ecclesiastical, civil, and military polity, geography, topography, antiquities and natural history ... By Alexander Knox, M. D. ... Dublin, Hodges, Foster & co., 1875.
viii, 724 p. front., illus. 22½cm.

1. Down, Ire. (County)

NK 0210823 ICU KU OCl CSmH MH ICN ViLxW

Knox, Alexander, *M. D.*
The Irish watering places, their climate, scenery, and accommodations; including analyses of the principal mineral springs, by Dr. R. Kane, and remarks on the various forms of disease to which they are adapted; together with directions for the regimen of invalids ... By Alexander Knox ... Dublin, W. Curry, jun. and co.; [etc., etc.] 1845.
viii, 336 p. front. 20cm.

1. Health resorts, watering places, etc.—Ireland.
4—2272
Library of Congress RA855.5.K74

NK 0210824 DLC FU PV NcD-MC NN

Knox, Alexander, novelist.
Bride of quietness, by Alexander Knox. London, Macmillan and co., limited, 1933.
2 p. l., 302 p. 19½cm.

I. Title.
33-11374
Library of Congress PZ3.K7712Br

NK 0210825 DLC NcU

Knox, Alexander, novelist.
Bride of quietness, by Alexander Knox. New York, The Macmillan company, 1933.
3 p. l., 302 p. 19½cm.

I. Title.
33-20823
Library of Congress PZ3.K7712Br 2

NK 0210826 DLC OU OrU ViU

BY517.01 .K74c [Knox, Alexander] 1757-1831.
Candid animadversions on Mr. Henry Moore's Reply, by the author of "Considerations on a separation of the Methodists from the Established Church." Bristol, Printed by Bulgin and Rosser, 1794.
36 p. 19cm.
"Reasons against separation from the Church of England, copied from the Works of the Rev. John Wesley": p. 33-36.

NK 0210827 IEG

BY517.01 .K74co [Knox, Alexander] 1757-1831.
Considerations on a separation of the Methodists from the Established Church; addressed to such of them as are friendly to that measure, and particularly to those in the city of Bristol, by a member of the Established Church. Bristol, Printed by Bulgin and Rosser, 1794.
36 p. 17cm.

1. Methodist Church in Gt. Brit.--Relations--Church of England. I. Title.

NK 0210828 IEG TxU

Knox, Alexander, 1757-1831.
The doctrine of the sacraments, as exhibited in several treatises first published in the remains of Alexander Knox.
London,1838.
1 v. 12°

NK 0210829 PPPrHi PPLT

[**Knox, Alexander**] 1757-1831.
Essays on the political circumstances of Ireland, written during the administration of Earl Camden, with an appendix, containing thoughts on the will of the people. And a postscript now first published. By a gentleman of the north of Ireland. Dublin, Printed by Graisberry & Campbell, 1798.
xviii, 284 p. 21½cm.

1. Ireland—Pol. & govt.—1760-1820. 2. United Irishmen. I. Title.
35-36546
Library of Congress DA948.5.K5 1798

NK 0210830 DLC IaU IEN ICN ICU PHC MH

Knox, Alexander, 1757-1831.
Essays on the political circumstances of Ireland, written during the administration of Earl Camden; with an appendix, containing thoughts on the will of the people ... By Alexander Knox, esq. London, Printed for the author by J. Plymsell, 1799.
xviii, 240 p., 1 l. 22cm.

1. Ireland—Pol. & govt.—1791-1800. 2. United Irishmen.
8-14143†
Library of Congress DA948.5.K5

NK 0210831 DLC NN CtY InU NcD UU IU MB

Rare DA 948 .5 K74 Knox, Alexander, 1757-1831.
Essays on the political circumstances of Ireland, written during the administration of Earl Camden; with an appendix, containing thoughts on the will of the people ... and a postscript, now first published. 2d ed. Dublin, J. Milliken, 1799.
xviii,234 p. 22cm.

1. Ireland--Pol. & govt.--1791-1800. 2. United Irish men.

NK 0210832 NIC

BX 5148 K58 Knox, Alexander, 1757-1831.
The grace of sacraments; being treatises on baptism and the eucharist, by Alexander Knox (1757-1831); ed., with a preface by William Dalrymple Maclagan. London, etc., Longmans, Green, and Co., 1905.
xxxv, 275p. 20cm.

1. Sacraments - Church of England. I. Title.

NK 0210833 NRCR NcD RP

[**Knox, Alexander**] 1757-1831.
An inquiry, on grounds of scripture and reason, into the use and import of the eucharistic symbols. Dublin, Printed by R. Beere & co., 1824.
3 p. l., 93 p. 19cm.

1. Lord's supper. I. Title.
21-12054
Library of Congress BV825.K7

NK 0210834 DLC NN

Knox, Alexander, 1757-1831.
Southey, Robert, 1774-1843. FOR OTHER EDITIONS SEE MAIN ENTRY
The life of Wesley; and rise and progress of Methodism. By Robert Southey ... With notes by the late Samuel Taylor Coleridge, esq., and remarks on the life and character of John Wesley, by the late Alexander Knox, esq. Edited by the Rev. Charles Cuthbert Southey ... 2d American ed., with notes, etc., by the Rev. Daniel Curry ... New York, Harper & brothers, 1874.

Knox, Alexander, 1757-1831.
Remains. London, J.Duncan and J.Cochran 1834. 2 vols. front.(port.) 22cm.

1. Religion.

NK 0210836 MWelC CaBVaU PHC PPL-R

Knox, Alexander, 1757-1831.
Remains of Alexander Knox ... London, J. Duncan and J. Cochran, 1834-37.
4 v. front. (port.) 22 cm.
Edited by J.J. Hornby.
Vol. 3-4 pub. by J. Duncan.
I. Hornby, James J ed.

NK 0210837 CU PPStC PPPD

BX5037 .K74 **KNOX,ALEXANDER,1757-1831.**
Remains of Alexander Knox ... 2d ed. ... London,J.Duncan[etc.]1836-
v. front.(port.) 22cm.
Edited by James J.Hornby.

1.Theology--19th and 20th cent.

NK 0210838 ICU IU CtY IEG CU CtY-D

BR85 .K6 **Knox, Alexander,**1757-1831.
Remains. 3d ed.
London, Duncan and Malcolm,1844.
4 v.

NK 0210839 DLC NjR PPLT MdBP MH IEG

BY80 .W18 1802 Knox, Alexander, 1757-1831.
Remarks, on An expostulatory address to the members of the Methodist society, by the Rev. J. Walker, in a letter to that gentleman. Dublin, Printed by Graisberry & Campbell, 1802.
62 p. 17 cm.
Bound with Walker, John. An expostulatory address... Dublin, 1802.

NK 0210840 IEG

VOLUME 300

230.7
W181eYk
1803 **Knox, Alexander, 1757-1831.**
Remarks on an expostulatory address to the members of the Methodist Society, by the Rev. J. Walker, in a letter to that gentleman. 2d ed. Dublin, Printed by Graisberry & Campbell, 1803.
62 p. 20cm.
1. Walker, John, 1768-1833. An expostulatory address to the members of the Methodist Society in Ireland. 2. Methodism.

NK 0210841 FU

BV825
.K74
1843
in:
SWTS
Knox, Alexander, 1757-1831.
A treatise on the use and import of the Eucharistic symbols. With a prefatory letter and a postscript, by the author; and an appendix, extracted from Bishop Jeremy Taylor. Baltimore, Joseph Robinson, 1843.
165p. 15cm.
1. Lord's Supper. I. Title. II. Taylor, Jeremy, bp. of Down and Conner, 1613-1667. The real presence and spiritual, of Christ in the blessed sacrament.

NK 0210842 IEG MdU

Knox, Alexander, 1849-1912.
The climate of the continent of Africa, by Alexander Knox ... Cambridge, The University press, 1911.
xii, (2), 552 p. 13 maps, diagr. 24cm.
12 maps in pocket.
1. Africa—Climate.
A 12-887
Title from Cincinnati Pub. Libr. Printed by L. C.

NK 0210843 OCU MiEM CU CLU CtY PPAN DNLM OOxM MiU DAS ICJ NN MB

Knox, Alexander, 1849-1912.
Differential calculus for beginners. With a selection of easy examples. By Alexander Knox ... London, Macmillan and co., 1884.
viii, [9]-112 p. col.front., diagrs. 15cm.
Caption title: On certain infinitesimals, limits, and differential co-efficients.
1. Calculus, Differential.

NK 0210844 MiU MeB MiEM DAU RPB MH NN MiHM PPTU

Knox, Alexander, 1849-1912.
... Glossary of geographical and topographical terms and of words of frequent occurrence in the composition of such terms and of place-names, by Alexander Knox ... London, E. Stanford, 1904.
xl, 432 p. 20 cm. (*Half-title:* Stanford's compendium of geography and travel (supplementary volume))
Series title also at head of t.-p.
1. Geography—Dictionaries. 2. Names, Geographical.
G103.K72 5—4475

NK 0210845 DLC CaBVaU OrU OrP PP NcD PU PHC ICJ ViU OO OC1 OC1W OU OCU NIC NcD NN PPD

Knox, Alexander, 1849-1912.
Gt. Brit. *War office. Intelligence division.*
... A guide to recent large scale maps, including both surveys and compilations; together with a list of some large sheet atlases, forming a supplement to "Notes on the government surveys of the principal countries of the world" (1882). Prepared in the Intelligence division, War office, by Alexander Knox ... London, Printed for H. M. Stationery off., by Harrison and sons, 1899.

Knox, Alexander, 1849-1912.
Gt. Brit. *War office.*
... Notes on the geology of the continent of Africa. With an introduction and bibliography. Compiled in the Department of the general staff, War office, by Alexander Knox ... London, Printed for H. M. Stationery off., by Harrison and sons, 1905.

Knox, Alexander, 1849-1912. comp.
FOR OTHER EDITIONS SEE MAIN ENTRY
Gt. Brit. *War office.*
... Rules for the transliteration of place-names occurring on foreign maps. Comp. in the Topographical section, General staff, by Alexander Knox, B. A., map curator. 1906. London, H. M. Stationery off. [printed by Harrison & sons] reprinted, 1919.

Knox, Alexander A.
The new playground; or, Wanderings in Algeria, by Alexander A. Knox ... London, C. K. Paul & co., 1881.
viii, 482 p. 20cm.
1. Algeria—Descr. & trav. I. Title.
5—9819
Library of Congress DT279.K74

NK 0210849 DLC OCU PP PPL TxU CU

DT
279
E83
Knox, Alexander A.
The new playground; or, Wanderings in Algeria. 2d. ed. Lond., Paul, 1883.
viii, 482.p.

NK 0210850 PU NN

W 6
P3
KNOX, Alexander Campbell White
First aid competitions and casualty make-up. 1st ed. London, St. John Ambulance Assn., 1952.
55 p.
1. First aid - Study & teaching

NK 0210851 DNLM

Knox, Alfred Dillwyn.
The first Greek anthologist, with notes on some choliambic fragments, by A. D. Knox. Cambridge, University press, 1923.
xiv, 37 p. 19½cm.
According to a conjecture of the author, the anthologist is Cercidas.
1. Greek poetry—Collections. 2. Cercidas. I. Title.

NK 0210852 MiU OCU CtY PBm NN MH MiU MB IU NjP NIC

Knox, Alfred Dillwyn, ed. and tr.
FOR OTHER EDITIONS SEE MAIN ENTRY
Herondas.
Herodes, Cercidas and the Greek choliambic poets (except Callimachus and Babrius) edited and translated by A. D. Knox ... London, W. Heinemann, ltd.; New York, G. P. Putnam's sons, 1929.

Knox, Alfred Dillwyn,
Herondas.
... The Mimes and fragments, with notes by Walter Headlam ... edited by A. D. Knox ... Cambridge, The University press, 1922.

Knox, *Sir* Alfred William Fortescue, 1870–
With the Russian army, 1914-1917, being chiefly extracts from the diary of a military attaché, by Major-General Sir Alfred Knox ... with 58 illustrations chiefly from photographs taken by the author and 19 maps London, Hutchinson & co., 1921.
2 v. fronts., plates, ports., maps (part fold.; in pockets) 23½cm.
Paged continuously.
1. European war, 1914-1918—Campaigns—Eastern. 2. European war, 1914-1918—Russia. 3. Russia—Hist.—Revolution, 1917- I. Title.
22—1222
Library of Congress D550.K6

NK 0210855 DLC NcD TU CSf PP ICJ NN MB

Knox, *Sir* Alfred William Fortescue, 1870–
With the Russian army, 1914-1917, being chiefly extracts from the diary of a military attaché, by Major-General Sir Alfred Knox ... with 58 illustrations, chiefly from photographs taken by the author, and 19 maps ... New York, E. P. Dutton and company, 1921.
2 v. fronts., plates, ports., maps (part fold.; in pockets) 23½cm.
Paged continuously.
"Printed in Great Britain."
1. European war, 1914-1918—Campaigns—Eastern. 2. European war, 1914-1918—Russia. 3. Russia—Hist.—Revolution, 1917- I. Title.
22—20507
Library of Congress D550.K6

NK 0210856 DLC IdU OC1 NjN

D
550
.K74
1921a
Knox, Sir Alfred William Fortescue, 1870-
With the Russian army, 1914-1917; being chiefly extracts from the diary of a military attaché. London, Hutchinson, 1921.
2 v. illus.
Paged continuously.
Photocopy. Ann Arbor, Mich., University Microfilms, 1970. 2 v.(double leaves)
1. European War, 1914-1918--Campaigns--Eastern. 2. Russia--Hist.--Revolution, 1917-1921. I. Title.

NK 0210857 MiU

Knox, Alice, ed.
Dempster, Charlotte Louisa Hawkins, 1835-1913.
The manners of my time, by C. L. Hawkins Dempster ... London, G. Richards ltd., 1920.

Knox, Alice Adelaide.
The induction, development, and heritability of fasciations. By Alice Adelaide Knox.
(*In* Carnegie institution, Washington, D. C. Publications. Washington, D. C., 1908. 25½cm. no. 98 (pt. 2) 20 p. illus., v pl.)
"Literature cited": p. 17.
1. Abnormalities (Plants)
9—35054
Library of Congress QK882.C3

NK 0210859 DLC WaWW OrPR NcD CU MdBP OCU OC1MN OC1 OU MiU PU-B Wa OrSaW I ICJ

Knox, Alice Adelaide.
... The stem of Ibervillea Sonorae. 1907. p. 329-344. [Contributions from the department of botany of Columbia university, no. 235)
"Reprinted from Bulletin of the Torrey botanical club, vol. 34, 1907."

NK 0210860 CU

Knox, Alice Vance.
General practice and X-rays; a handbook for the general practitioner and student, by Alice Vance Knox ... with chapters on the production of X-rays and instrumentation by Robert Knox ... containing 32 page plates and 56 diagrams in the text. London, A. & C. Black, ltd., 1921.
xiv, 214 p. illus., xxxii pl. (incl. front.) 19cm. (Edinburgh medical series. General editor: John D. Comrie)
1. Radiography. 2. X-rays. I. Knox, Robert, 1868–
S G 21—68
U. S. Surg.-gen. off. Libr. for Library of Congress [a41d1]

NK 0210861 DNLM ICJ PPC

VOLUME 300

BV
1539
K56 Knox, Alice W
The infant Sunday school, by Alice W. Knox and Charles E. Knox. With an appendix by J. H. Vincent. New York, Carlton & Lanahan, etc. [1870]
166 p. 17 cm.

1. Religious education of children. 2. Sunday-schools. I. Knox, Charles Eugene, 1833-1900, joint author. II. Vincent, J. H. III. Title.

NK 0210862 NRCR OCl NBuG

Knox, Alice Williams, 1905–
Influence of pregnancy on infection of mice with the Columbia SK virus of murine poliomyelitis. Ann Arbor, University Microfilms, 1951.
([University Microfilms, Ann Arbor, Mich.] Publication no. 2829)
Microfilm copy of typescript. Positive.
Collation of the original: 95, R 10 l. diagrs., tables.
Thesis—Columbia University.
Abstracted in Microfilm abstracts, v. 11 (1951) no. 4, p. 1056–1057.
Bibliography: leaves [R 1]–R 10.
1. Pregnancy. 2. Poliomyelitis.
Microfilm AC–1 no. 2829 Mic A 51–566

Michigan. Univ. Libr.
for Library of Congress [1]†

NK 0210863 MiU NNC DLC

Knox, Allan

Maxton, John Purdon, *ed.*
Regional types of British agriculture, by fifteen authors. Edited by J. P. Maxton ... London, G. Allen & Unwin ltd. [1936]

Knox, Andrew Gibson, 1923-
Conductivity of electrolytes in methanol. Philadelphia, 1950.
64, xv numb. l. 29 cm.
Thesis (Ph.D.) - University of Pennsylvania, 1950.
Typewritten.
Vita.
Bibliography: l. [63]-64.

NK 0210865 PU

Knox, Ann.
Featured on Broadway, by Ann Knox ... New York, London, The Century co. [©1930]
4 p. l., 3–333 p. 19½ᶜᵐ. $2.50
"First printing."

I. Title.
Library of Congress PZ3.K7713Fl 30–24841

NK 0210866 DLC MH

Knox, Ann.
Flowerdown, by Ann Knox. New York & London, The Century co. [1928]
2 p. l., 3–334 p. 19½ᶜᵐ. $2.50

I. Title.
Library of Congress PZ3.K7713Fl 28–22463

NK 0210867 DLC

---

*
PR6021
.N545G7 Knox, Ann
1926
The green bough [poems] London, J. Cape, 1926.
62 p. 20cm.
Inscribed: "To Pamela. With best love from Mary Tabor. Christmas 1926. These verses have been written by my young cousin — Her first effort."

NK 0210868 ViU

Knox, Ann.
Sons and daughters, a novel by Ann Knox. London, Hutchinson & co., ltd. [1932]
287 p. 19½ᶜᵐ.

I. Title.
Library of Congress PZ3.K7713So 33–981
[3]

NK 0210869 DLC

Knox, Ann.
Vallejo Kitty, by Ann Knox ... New York & London, The Century co. [©1929]
3 p. l., 3–321 p. 19½ᶜᵐ. $2.50

I. Title.
Library of Congress PZ3.K7713Val 29–17218

NK 0210870 DLC OU

Knox, Arthur Edward.
Autumns on the Spey. By A. E. Knox ... With four illustrations by Wolf. London, J. Van Voorst, 1872.
4 p. l., 171 p. col. front., col. plates. 19½ᶜᵐ.

1. Hunting—Scotland. 2. Spey River. I. Title.
12–32491
Library of Congress SK189.K72

NK 0210871 DLC CaBVaU CtY CU FMU NIC MdBP OClW

Uzn71
850k Knox, Arthur Edward
Game birds and wild fowl: their friends and their foes ... London, J. Van Voorst, 1850.
x, 264p. front., plates. 20cm.

NK 0210872 CtY CSmH MH CtMW NN CU CaBVaU

Knox, Arthur Edward.
Ornithological rambles in Sussex; with a systematic catalogue of the birds of that county, and remarks on their local distribution. By A. E. Knox. London, J. Van Voorst, 1849.
vi, 250 p. plates. 20 cm.

NK 0210873 LU CU

Knox, A[rthur] E[dward]
Ornithological rambles in Sussex; with a systematic catalogue of the birds of that county, and remarks on their local distribution. By A. E. Knox ... 3d ed. London, J. Van Voorst, 1855.
xii, 260 p. 4 pl. (incl. front.) 18½ᶜᵐ.
Illustrations by J. Wolf.

1. Birds—England—Sussex.
Library of Congress QL676.K74 5–23860

NK 0210874 DLC ICU ICF-A

Knox, Avon
p1951
K74
A85h He knew the Master, a religious play in three acts. Boston, Baker's Plays [c1954]
38 p. diagr. 19 cm.
Harris Collection

NK 0210875 RPB NN

D
760
.A9
K74 Knox, B M
Brief historical notes on Ayrshire Yeomanry (Earl of Carrick's Own), 152 Field Regiment, R.A., 1939-45. Ayr, Stephen & Pollock [1946]
80 p. illus.

1. Gt. Brit. Army. Ayrshire (Earl of Carrick's Own) Yeomanry. 2. World War, 1939-1945--Regimental histories--Gt. Brit.--Ayrshire (Earl of Carrick's Own) Yeomanry.

NK 0210876 MiU

Knox, Betty.
Over here from over there, a pictorial record: 25 years of Anglo-American comradeship in arms and peace, in 118 authentic photos. By Betty Knox. London, Alliance press limited [1944]
[83] p. illus. (incl. ports., facsims.) 21ᶜᵐ.

1. U. S.—Relations (general) with Gt. Brit. 2. Gt. Brit.—Relations (general) with U. S. 3. World war, 1939–1945—U. S. I. Title.
45–8924
Library of Congress E183.8.G7K68
[3] 940.5373

NK 0210877 DLC

Knox, Brownlow William, 1806–1873, *appellant.*
... Between Brownlow William Knox, appellant, and Frederick Gye, respondent ... [London, Printed by G. and J. W. Taylor, 1871?]
48 p., 2 l., 19 p., 3 l., 413 p., 1 l. 27 x 21ᶜᵐ.
Involving the Royal Italian opera, Covent Garden. Contains Appellants' case, Respondents' case, and Joint appendix, each with half-title and separate paging; no general title. Several pages in the appendix are canceled in red ink, and pages 27–40, 47–76, 209–262 removed, as "consisting of matter not in evidence on this appeal."
At head of title: In the House of lords. Upon appeal from the High court of chancery.
I. Gye, Frederick, 1810–1878, respondent. II. Gt. Brit. Court of chancery.
10–19165

NK 0210878 DLC

Knox, C V S
Design details of the Goodyear model K airship. [New York, Aeronautical digest publishing corporation, c1945]
[21] p. illus., diagrs.

1. Air-ships. I. Goodyear aircraft corporation, Akron, O.

NK 0210879 NNC

KB
El
Un
O
K77a Knox, Carl Stapleton, 1917-
A study of the deterrents operating in second class city high schools in Kansas which inhibit curriculum revision. [Lawrence, Kan.] 1955.
xii, 285 l. diagrs., tables. 28cm.

Thesis (Ed.D.)--University of Kansas, 1955.
Typewritten.
Abstract: l.276-285.
Bibliography: l.272-275.

1. Education, Secondary. Curricula. 2. Education. Kansas. Curricula. I. Title.

NK 0210880 KU

FILM
371.1
K77i Knox, Carl Warner, 1916-
An investigation of the job satisfaction of graduates of the University of Illinois now engaged in school teaching and administration. Ann Arbor, University Microfilms [1953]

([University Microfilms, Ann Arbor, Mich.] Publication no. 5980)

Microfilm copy of typescript. Positive.
Collation of the original: vii, 161 l. form (in pocket)

Thesis--University of Illinois.
Vita.
Bibliography: leaves 132-140.

NK 0210882 IU

VOLUME 300

Knox, Carleton Everett.
Ad astra per aspera. Emporia, Kan., 1915.
unpaged. 18cm. (Worth while series)

Cover title.
Text within ornamental borders.

NK 0210883 KU

Knox, Carleton Everett.
Brotherhood, from Day dreams, by Carleton Everett Knox ... [Kansas City, Mo., Walkenhorst printing co., °1917]
[30] p. 12 x 16cm. (Worth while series)

I. Title.
Library of Congress PS3521.N8B7 1917 17-21731

NK 0210884 DLC

Knox, Carleton Everett.
... Day dreams, a collection done in verse by one who loves his fellow men [by] Carleton Everett Knox. Kansas City, Mo., C. E. Knox, °1916.
40 p. 19½cm. (Worth while series)

I. Title.
Library of Congress PS3521.N8D3 1916 17-25885

NK 0210885 DLC

KNOX, CARLETON EVERETT.
Heart's desire, by Carleton Everett Knox... First edition. [Kansas City, Mo., cop. 1928.] 15 l. 12x16cm. (His: Worth while series.)

686076A. 1. Poetry, American. I. Title.

NK 0210886 NN

Knox, Carleton Everett.
The human touch, by Carleton Everett Knox. Kansas City, Mo., The Knox art co. [°1922]
121 p. 19½cm.
Poems.

I. Title.
Library of Congress PS3521.N8H8 1922 22-21584

NK 0210887 DLC

Knox, Carleton Everett.
Kansas land, from Day dreams, by Carleton Everett Knox ... [Kansas City, Mo., Walkenhorst printing co., °1917]
[30] p. 12 x 16cm. (Worth while series)

I. Title.
Library of Congress PS3521.N8K3 1917 17-21732

NK 0210888 DLC

Knox, Carleton Everett.
Love's fancies, from Day dreams, by Carleton Everett Knox ... [Kansas City, Mo., Walkenhorst printing co., °1917]
[30] p. 12 x 16cm. (Worth while series)

I. Title.
Library of Congress PS3521.N8L6 1917 17-21733

NK 0210889 DLC

Knox, Carleton Everett.
Select verse for home and school, comp. especially for use in schools from the writings of Carleton Everett Knox. Kansas City, Mo., The Knox art company [°1919]
36 p. 18cm. $0.35

I. Title. 19-16013
Library of Congress PS3521.N8A6 1919

NK 0210890 DLC

KNOX, CARLETON EVERETT.
The span of life, by Carleton Everett Knox. [Kansas City, Mo.: The Knox Art Co., cop. 1920] 4 l. 14½cm.

Cover-title.

814188A. 1. Poetry, American. I. Title.

NK 0210891 NN

KNOX, CARLETON EVERETT.
Success is yours, by Carleton Everett Knox... Second edition... Kansas City, Mo., 1928. 15 l. 14½cm.

681357A. 1. Poetry, American. I. Title.

NK 0210892 NN

KNOX, CARLETON EVERETT.
Yours truly, Junior Brown, by Carleton Everett Knox... [Kansas City, Mo., cop. 1917.] 16 l. 11½x15cm. (His: Worth while series.)

686076A. 1. Poetry, American. I. Title.

NK 0210893 NN

Knox, Cecilia M 1905-
Principles of pediatrics and pediatric nursing, by Cecilia M. Knox ... Philadelphia, F. A. Davis company, 1945.
x, 527 p. illus., col. plates, diagrs. 22½ cm.
Includes bibliographies.

1. Children—Diseases. 2. Nurses and nursing. S G 45—137
U. S. Army Medical Libr. for Library of Congress RJ45.K64 [a48i1]† 618.92

NK 0210894 DNLM ICRL DLC OU OC1W ViU MiDP

Knox, Cecilia M 1905-
Principles of pediatrics and pediatric nursing ... Rev. ed. Philadelphia, Davis, 1947.
x, 527 p. illus. (part col.) 22cm.

1. Children—Diseases. [1. Children—Care and hygiene] 2. Nurses and nursing. [2. Nursing, Pediatric]
RJ45.K64 1947 618.92 Med 47-1427
© 31Mar47; F. A. Davis company, Philadelphia; A11931.

U. S. Army medical library for Library of Congress [WY159K74p 1947] [6]†

NK 0210895 DNLM DLC

Knox, Charles.
The daily doesn't, by Charles Knox. (In: Nicholson, K. Revues. New York, 1926. 12°. p. [93-100.])

274580A. 1. Drama, American. 2. Title. January 12, 1927
N. Y. P. L.

NK 0210896 NN OC1 MH

Knox, Charles, joint author.

Nicholson, Kenyon.
Here's to your health! An adventure of a medicine man, in three acts, by Kenyon Nicholson and Charles Knox ... New York, S. French; London, S. French, ltd., °1927.

Knox, Charles B., gelatine co., inc., Johnstown, N. Y.
Knox, Rose (Markward) 1857-
Mrs. Knox's meatless main dishes and leftover hints. [Johnstown, N. Y., Charles B. Knox gelatine co., inc., 1942]

[Knox, Charles B., gelatine co., inc., Johnstown, N. Y.]
Studies of edible gelatine in the dietary... [Albany, N. Y., Argus co., c1923]
2 pts. in 1 v. illus., diagrs.

Contents.--[pt. 1] The value of gelatine in infant and child feeding.--pt. 2. The value of gelatine in digestion, stomach disorders, intestinal putrefaction, the diet of convalescents, scurvy, tuberculosis, the feeding of nauseating foods; with re- cipes for general uses.

NK 0210899 NNC PPC PPD

Knox, Charles Cook.
Principles of real estate appraising, by Charles C. Knox .. Youngstown, O., R. C. Knox, °1924.
75 p. 24½ cm.

1. Real property—Tables, etc. I. Title: Real estate appraising.
HD1387.K5 24-14492 rev

NK 0210900 DLC MB

Knox, Charles Edwin, 1871-
Description of the elevator equipment and the electric installation in the Woolworth Building, New York City, by Charles E. Knox. [New York? 1913?] p. 95-112. diagrs., illus., plan, pl. 8°.
Cover-title.
Repr.: New York Electrical Soc. New series, 1913, no. 6.

1. New York City.—Buildings (Office): Woolworth Building.
2. Building fittings. April 3, 1922.
N. Y. P. L.

NK 0210901 NN

Knox, Charles Edwin, 1871-
Electric light wiring, by C. E. Knox ... New York, McGraw publishing company, 1907.
v, 219 p. illus., diagrs. (part fold.) 24½cm.

1. Electric lighting—Wiring.
Library of Congress TK4255.K7 7-18292

NK 0210902 DLC CU MiU OCU OU PPD NjP ICJ MB NN PPStef

Knox, Charles Edwin, 1871-

American school of correspondence, *Chicago.*
Electric wiring and lighting ... Part I—Electric wiring, by Charles E. Knox ... Part II—Electric lighting, by George E. Shaad ... Chicago, American school of correspondence, 1913.

Knox, Charles Eugene, 1833-1900.

Bloomfield theological seminary, *Bloomfield, N. J.*
Addresses at the inauguration of Rev. Charles E. Knox, as president and professor of homiletics, church government and pastoral theology, and Rev. George C. Seibert, PH. D., as professor of Biblical exegesis and theology, in the German theological school, of Newark, N. J. New York, A. D. Randolph & company [1874?]

VOLUME 300

Knox, Charles Eugene, 1833–1900.
David the king; with a study on the location of the Psalms in the order of David's life. By the Rev. Charles E. Knox ... New York, A. D. F. Randolph & co. [c1875]
vi, 461, iii p. maps (1 fold.) 19½cm.

1. David, king of Israel. 2. Bible. O. T. Psalms—Criticism, interpretation, etc. 3. Bible—Criticism, interpretation, etc.—O. T. Psalms.

Library of Congress BS580.D3K6 31-23046
Copyright 1875: 13158 221.92

NK 0210905 DLC IEG CSaT OO OCH MB

BV1561 .K64 Knox, Charles Eugene, 1833-1900.
...Graduated Sunday-school text-books.
New York,1866-

NK 0210906 DLC

Knox, Charles Eugene, 1833–1900.
Love to the end, a book for the communion Sabbath. By the Rev. Charles E. Knox. Philadelphia, Presbyterian publication committee; New York, A. D. F. Randolph [c1865]
v, 7-58 p., 1 l. 18½cm.

1. Lord's supper. I. Presbyterian church in the U. S. A. Publication committee. II. Title.

35-37078
Library of Congress BT420.K7 232.957

NK 0210907 DLC PPPrHi

Knox, Charles E[ugene], 1833-1900.
Origin and annals of the "Old church on the green;" the First Presbyterian church of Bloomfield; being a historical sermon prepared by . . . C. E. Knox, covering . . the period 1668–1896, with explanatory and reminiscent notes. Bloomfield, S. M. Hulin, 1901.
83 pp. front., illus., pl., port. 8°.

1-21800—M 1 Aug. 1

NK 0210908 NjP CSmH OClWHi PHi

17 1701a Knox, Charles Eugene, 1833-1900.
Outline of the Saviour's life: doctrine and incidents from St. John. The third year of the graduated sunday-school-text-book. New York, A.D.F. Randolph, 1865.
130 p. 1 map. 16°.

NK 0210909 DLC

Knox, Charles Eugene, 1833-1900.
Outline of the Saviour's life. Doctrine and incidents from St. John. N.Y., Randolph, 1866. 130p. (Graduated S.S. Text books 3d year)

NK 0210910 OO

Knox, Charles Eugene, 1833-1900
Outline of the Saviour's life, doctrine and incidents from St. John; the third year of the graduated Sunday-school text-books. N.Y., Randolph, 1867.
130 p.

NK 0210911 PPPrHi

17 B.83 Knox, Charles Eugene, 1833-1900.
Outline of the saviour's life: incidents and instructions from Luke. The second year of the graduated sunday-school text-books. New York, A.D.F. Randolph, 1864.
v., 87 p. 1 map. 16°.

NK 0210912 DLC

17 Knox, Charles Eugene, 1833-1900.
Psalms, songs, prayers, prophecies. New York, 1868.
16°.

NK 0210913 DLC

Knox, Charles Eugene, 1833-1900.
A sermon delivered in the Reformed Dutch Church, Utica, on the occasion of the death of Mrs. John F. Seymour, Sept. 9, 1860 ...
Utica, 1860.
19 p. 23 cm.

NK 0210914 CtY

Knox, Charles Eugene, 1833–1900.
Sermons and addresses of Our Saviour. The fourth year of the graduated Sunday-school text-books. By Charles E. Knox ... New York, A. D. F. Randolph, 1866.
iv, [3]-188 p. 17½cm.
Title vignette.

1. Sunday-schools—Question-books. 2. Jesus Christ—Words. I. Title.

35-28544
Library of Congress BT307.K6 232.9

NK 0210915 DLC

Knox, Charles Eugene, 1833-1900.

The sixtieth anniversary of the marriage of John J. and Sarah Ann Knox, October 7th, 1873 ... New York, Printed by E. O. Jenkins [1873]

Knox, Charles Eugene, 1833-1900.
Sketch of the life of Captain John J. Knox Williams... who fell in defence of his country at the Battle of Chapin farm, September 29-30, 1864. (In the Sixtieth anniversary of the marriage of John J. and Sarah Ann Knox, October 7, 1873... N.Y. [1873?] p. 45-107)

NK 0210917 OClWHi

Knox, Charles Eugene, 1833-1900.
A year with St. Paul; or, Fifty-two lessons for the Sundays of the year. N.Y., Randolph [c1862]
349 p. front. (map), maps. D.

NK 0210918 NcD

Knox, Charles Eugene, 1833–1900.
A year with St. Paul; or, Fifty-two lessons for the Sundays of the year. By Charles E. Knox. New York, A. D. F. Randolph, 1863.
viii, 319, 104 p. front., illus. (incl. maps, plans) 19½cm.
"Questions" at end of each chapter are paged consecutively (104 p.)

1. Paul, Saint, apostle—Study. I. Title.

39-11835
Library of Congress BS2507.K6 1863
[2] [922.1] 225.92

NK 0210919 DLC CtY PPL NN OO ICU PPWe NjNbS

Knox, Charles Eugene, 1833-1900.
A year with St. Paul; or, Fifty-two lessons for the Sundays of the year. N.Y., 1864.

NK 0210920 ODW

Knox, Charles Eugene, 1833-1900.
A year with St. Paul; or, Fifty-two lessons for the Sundays of the year. New York, A.D.F. Randolph, 1865.
iv, 2 l., 349 (1) p., 1 l. 12°.

NK 0210921 NN

Knox, Charles Eugene, 1833-1900.
A year with St. Paul; or, Fifty-two lessons for the Sundays of the year, by Charles E. Knox. New York, A.D.F. Randolph & co., 1869.
iv, [4], 349, 104 p. front. (map), illus. 17 cm.
Questions at end of each lesson paged separately.
1. Paul, Saint, apostle.

NK 0210922 CU OU OO

Knox, Charles Eugene, 1833–1900.
A year with St. Paul; or, Fifty-two lessons, for the Sundays of the year. By Charles E. Knox. New and rev. ed. New York, A. D. F. Randolph & company, 1877.
iv, [4], 349, 104 p. front., illus. (incl. maps, plans) 18cm.
"Questions" at end of each chapter are paged consecutively (104 p.)

1. Paul, Saint, apostle—Study. I. Title.

39-11836
Library of Congress BS2507.K6 1877
Copyright 1877: 7432 [2] [922.1] 225.92

NK 0210923 DLC NN

KNOX, Charles H.
Address delivered at the commencement of the Normal College of the city of New York, June 21, 1894. New York, Hall of the Board of Education, 1894.
pp.16.

NK 0210924 MH

*M1 .M6 no.246 Knox, Charles H composer.
Give back my heart, I gave it to you; words and music by Charles H. Knox. Minneapolis, c1943.
score (5 p.) 31 cm.

NK 0210925 MnHi

*M 1 .M6 no.270 **Knox, Charles H composer.**
You lit a candle in my heart. Words & music by Charles H. Knox. Minneapolis, 1943.
5 p. 31 cm.

1. Music--Minnesota. I. Title.

NK 0210926 MnHi

Knox, Charles Henry, d. 1855.
The defensive position of England.... London, Saunders & Otley, 1852.
viii, 90 p. 8°.

NK 0210927 NN

Knox, Charles Henry, d. 1855, tr.

Goethe, Johann Wolfgang von, 1749–1832.
Faust, a tragedy. By J. W. von Goethe. Tr. by Captain Knox ... London, J. Ollivier, 1847.

VOLUME 300

Knox, Charles Henry, *d.* 1855.
Harry Mowbray, by Captain Knox ... London, J. Ollivier, 1843.
1 p. l., 384 p. front., plates. 22cm.
Music: p. 84-[85]; 372-375.

I. Title.

Library of Congress PZ3.K7713Har 42-27125
[2]

NK 0210929 DLC NN NdU PPiU CtY NcU MH

Knox, Charles Henry, d.1855
The rittmeister's budget; a strange medley.
3 v. London,Saunders and Otley,1842.

Contents:
v.1. Legends of the Black Forest.- Legends of the Neckar.- Legends of the Rhine and its left bank.
v.2. Legends of the Moselle.
v.3. Legends of the Rhine from Cologne to Mayence.

NK 0210930 OCl

KNOX, CHARLES HENRY, d. 1855.
The spirit of the polka; being an historical and analytical disquisition on the prevailing epidemic, its origin and mission. By Captain Knox. London, J. Ollivier, 1845. 86 p. 18cm.

Includes music.

1. Polka.

NK 0210931 NN

Knox, Charles Henry, d. 1855
Traditions of the Rhine. [2],iv,282p.
London, J. Ollivier, 1840.

NK 0210932 OCl

Knox, Charles Henry, d. 1855.
Traditions of western Germany. The Black Forest, the Neckar, the Odenwald, the Taunus, the Rhine, and the Moselle ... London, Saunders and Otley, 1841.
3 v. 20 cm.
Contents.- 1. The Black Forest and its neighbourhood. 2. The Moselle and its archbishops. #. The Rhine and its legends.

NK 0210933 RPB

Knox, Charles Webster, 1896- joint author.

Marsden, Stanley J 1897-
The breeding of turkeys [by] Stanley J. Marsden ... Charles W. Knox ...
(*In* U. S. Dept. of agriculture. Yearbook of agriculture, 1937, p. 1350-1366. illus. (incl. map) 23cm. Washington, 1937)

Knox, Charles Webster, 1896-
... Correlation studies of egg production and possible genetic interpretations. By Charles W. Knox ... Morley A. Jull ... and Joseph P. Quinn ...
(*In* U. S. Dept. of agriculture. Journal of agricultural research. v. 50, no. 7, April 1, 1935, p. 573-589. 23cm. Washington, 1935)
Contribution from Bureau of animal industry (A—165)
Published July 1, 1935.
"Literature cited": p. 588-589.

1. Eggs—Production. I. Jull, Morley Allan, 1885- joint author. II. Quinn, Joseph Patrick, 1889- joint author.

Library, U. S. Dept. of Library of Congress Agriculture 1Ag84J vol. 50, no. 7 [S21.A75 vol. 50, no. 7] Agr 35-445

NK 0210935 DNAL OU OCl

Mann Microfilm QP 187 V48
Knox, Charles Webster, 1896-
The genetics of plumage color in poultry. [Ames, Iowa] 1927.

Filmed as seventh item on film with Venzke, W. G. The embryological development and physiology of the endocrine organs of the common fowl (Gallus domesticus).
Microfilm copy of typescript. Made in 1955 by Iowa State College of Agriculture and Mechanic Arts. Negative.
Collation of the original: 51 l. tables.
Thesis - Iowa State College of Agriculture and Mechanic Arts.
Bibliography: leaves 48-51.

NK 0210936 NIC

[**Knox, Charles Webster**] 1896-
Selecting breeding stock for broiler production ... [Washington, U. S. Govt. print. off., 1943]
8 p. illus. 23 cm. (U. S. Dept. of agriculture. Leaflet no. 233)
"By Charles W. Knox ... and Clement D. Gordon."—p. 3.
Contribution from Bureau of animal industry.

1. Poultry breeding. [1. Poultry—Breeding] 2. [Broilers (Poultry)] I. Gordon, Clement Davis, 1909- joint author. II. Title. III. Title: Broiler production.

SF487.K578 636.5081 Agr 43-119
U. S. Dept. of Agr. Libr. for Library of Congress 1Ag84L no. 233 [a62g½]†

NK 0210937 DNAL DLC WaWW

Knox, Charles Webster, 1896-
... Studies on the genetics of plumage color in poultry by C. W. Knox ... [Ames, Ia., 1927]
cover-title, 1 p. l., p. [107]-131. 22cm.
Thesis (PH. D.)—Iowa state college of agriculture and mechanic arts, 1927.
At head of title: Iowa state college of agriculture and mechanic arts. Doctoral thesis no. 63.
"Paper no. 12 from Iowa state college Poultry husbandry department."
"Reprinted from Technical research bulletin 105 of the Iowa agricultural experiment station, Ames, Iowa, December, 1926."
"Literature cited": p. 130-131.
1. Poultry. 2. Heredity. 3. Feathers. 4. Color of birds.

Library of Congress SF487.K58 1927 28-19452
Iowa State College of Agriculture and Mechanic Arts Libr.

NK 0210938 IaAS DLC

Knox, Clarke, 1879-
Office and factory manual for fruit and vegetable canners, by C. Knox. San Francisco, Calif., 1924.
719 p. 24 cm.

1. Fruit, Canned. 2. Vegetables, Canned. I. Title.

TX603.K5 24—8088

NK 0210939 DLC ICJ C

Knox, Cleone, *pseud.*
see
King-Hall, Magdalen, 1904-

KNOX, Clinton Everett.
French interests and policy in the Ottoman Empire, 1887-1905.

Typewritten. 28 x 21 cm. Tables, and map.
Thesis, Ph. D.- Harvard University, 1940.

NK 0210941 MH

070.34 K77v
Knox, Clyde H
The value of a newspaper now--1941. An address delivered by Clyde H. Knox of Kansas City, Mo., at the Young editors club luncheon of the Kansas press association, at Topeka, Kansas, January 24, 1941. [Kansas City, Mo.?, 1941]
[4]p.

1. Newspapers--Valuation. I. Title.

NK 0210942 IU MnU

Knox, Collie, 1899-
Atlantic battle, by Collie Knox, with a foreword by Admiral Sir Percy Noble ... London, Methuen & co., ltd. [1941]
vii, 108, [1] p. front., plates. 19cm.
"First published in 1941."

1. European war, 1939- —Naval operations. 2. Merchant marine—Gt. Brit. 3. Convoy. I. Title.

Library of Congress D771.K56 1941 41-28044
[3] 940.545

NK 0210943 DLC CtY FMU DS

PN 5123 .K5 A3 1938b
Knox, Collie, 1899-
Collie Knox again. With 9 pictures.
London, Chapman and Hall [1938]
196,[1]p. illus.

Autobiography.

NK 0210944 ScU

---

824 K774
Knox, Collie, 1899-
Draw up your chair. London, Chapman and Hall [1939]
236p. port. 19cm.

Essays.

1. Conduct of life. I. Title.

NK 0210945 TxU

Knox, Collie, 1899-
For ever England, an anthology compiled by Collie Knox. London, Toronto [etc.] Cassell and company ltd. [1943]
244 p. 22cm.
Prose and poetry.
"First edition, December 1943. Second edition, December 1943."

1. English literature (Selections: Extracts, etc.) 2. Gt. Brit.—Descr. & trav. I. Title.

A 44-1716
Harvard univ. Library for Library of Congress [3]

NK 0210946 MH InU

Knox, Collie, 1899- *comp.*
For ever England, an anthology compiled by Collie Knox. London, Toronto [etc.] Cassell and company ltd. [1944]
244 p. 22cm.
Verse and prose.
"First edition, December 1943 ... Third edition, June 1944."

1. English literature (Selections: Extracts, etc.) 2. Gt. Brit.—Descr. & trav. I. Title.

Library of Congress ° PR1111.H5K6 1944 45-343
[3] 820.82

NK 0210947 DLC

Knox, Collie, 1899-
Heroes all, by Collie Knox. London, Hodder & Stoughton limited [1941]
319 p. 19½cm.
"First printed February, 1941."

1. European war, 1939- —Gt. Brit. 2. Heroes. I. Title.

Library of Congress D744.K55 1941 41-7926
[2] 940.5342

NK 0210948 DLC

VOLUME 300

Knox, Collie, 1899–
It had to be me. London, Methuen ⌊1947⌋
xii, 244 p. plates, ports. 22 cm.
Reminiscences.
Sequel to It might have been you.

I. Title.
PN5123.K5A35 920.5 48-17458*

NK 0210949 DLC OKentU

Knox, Collie, 1899–
It might have been you ⌊by⌋ Collie Knox; with fifteen plates. London, Chapman & Hall ltd. ⌊1938⌋
vii, 427 p. front., plates, ports. 22cm.
Autobiography.
"First published, 1938."

I. Title.
39-373
Library of Congress PN5123.K5A3 1938
Copyright A ad int. 24499 ⌊3⌋ 920.5

NK 0210950 DLC

Knox, Collie, 1899–
People of quality. London, Macdonald ⌊1947⌋
254 p. ports. 23 cm.

1. Gt. Brit.—Biog. I. Title.
DA585.A1K6 920.042 47-28667*

NK 0210951 DLC CaBViP CaBVaU DS FMU NcU

Knox, Collie, 1899–
The un-beaten track, by Collie Knox, with foreword by the Rt. Hon. Lord Leathers ... With 9 half-tone illustrations. London, Toronto ⌊etc.⌋ Cassell and company ltd. ⌊1944⌋
199 p. front., illus. (map) plates. 19½cm.
"First published 1944."

1. Great western railway (Gt. Brit.) 2. World war, 1939– Transportation. I. Title.
45-2956
Library of Congress HE3020.G8K6
⌊4⌋ 385

NK 0210952 DLC CtY

Knox, Collie, 1899–
Voices of British radio, original portraits and personal stories. ⌊London, D. Waddington Publications, 1948?⌋
110 p. ports. (part col.) 28 cm. (Personality portraits)
Cover title.

1. Radio—Biog. I. Title. (Series)
TK6545.A1K57 927.914 49-16572*‡

NK 0210953 DLC

Knox, Collie, 1899–
We live and we learn. London, W. H. Allen, 1951.
192 p. 19 cm.

I. Title.
PN5123.K5A38 824.91 52-30749 ‡

NK 0210954 DLC

Knox, Cyril St. George.
Humorous verses. Ilfracombe, Devon, A.H.Stockwell, 1950.
23 p.

NK 0210955 MH

Wing
fZ
40583
.467
KNOX, D., & CO., Fredericksburg, O.
Specimens of wood type manufactured by D.Knox & co., Fredericksburg, Ohio, 1858. Dubuque, Gilmore & Corr,1858.
143 numb.leaves. 32½cm.

NK 0210956 ICN

Knox, D B *comp.*
Children's funny sayings; an amusing book for everybody, collected by D. B. Knox. London, T. F. Unwin ltd. ⌊1925⌋
3 p. l., 9-206 p. 19cm.
"Second impression."

1. Children—Anecdotes and sayings. 2. English wit and humor. I. Title.
26-4332
Library of Congress PN6328.C5K6

NK 0210957 DLC OKentU

Knox, D B *comp.*
Everybody's anecdotes, collected by D. B. Knox ... for use by speakers, writers, broadcasters and conversers. London, T. F. Unwin ltd. ⌊1928⌋
256 p. 19cm.

1. Anecdotes. I. Title.
39-4611
Library of Congress PN6261.K53
⌊2⌋ 808.8

NK 0210958 DLC NN

Knox, D B , ed.
Laugh and grow fat; seven hundred humorous stories collected by D. B. Knox... For use by speakers, writers, broadcasters & conversers. [London] J. Clarke & co. [1938] vii,9-191 p. 20cm.

1. Wit and humor, English—Collections. I. Title.

NK 0210959 NN

Knox, D B *comp.*
More quotable anecdotes as collected by D. B. Knox. London, T. F. Unwin ltd. ⌊1926⌋
219, ⌊1⌋ p. 19½cm.
"First published in 1926."

1. Anecdotes. 2. English wit and humor. I. Title.
Library of Congress PN6261.K55 26-14422

NK 0210960 DLC OCl

BV
4225
.K77
Knox, D B. comp.
New illustrations for pulpit and platform, compiled by D. B. Knox. London, J. Clarke & co., limited ⌊n.d.⌋
256 p. 19½cm.

NK 0210961 DNC

Knox, D B *comp.*
Quotable anecdotes for various occasions as collected by D. B. Knox. London, T. F. Unwin ltd. ⌊1924⌋
223, ⌊1⌋ p. 19½cm.
Second impression.

1. Anecdotes. I. Title.
24—11036
Library of Congress PN6261.K54 1924

NK 0210962 DLC Or NcC CaBVa PPGi NN OCl OOxM

Knox, D. B.
Quotable anecdotes for various occasions, as collected by D. B. Knox. New York: E. P. Dutton and Co., 1924. 223 p. 12°

1. Anecdotes. 2. Wit and humor. 3. Title.
N. Y. P. L. August 29, 1924

NK 0210963 NN WaS MH OKentU OCl OClh

Knox, D B comp.
Quotable anecdotes for various occasions as collected by D. B. Knox. London, T. F. Unwin, ltd. [1925]
223, [1] p. 19.5 cm.
"Seventh impression, 1925."

NK 0210964 CtY

Knox, D. B., comp.
Quotable anecdotes for various occasions;as collected by D.B. Knox. London, T. F. Unwin ltd., 1928.
223 p.

NK 0210965 PU

Knox, D. B.
Quotable anecdotes for various occasions; as collected by D. B. Knox. London: Ernest Benn, Ltd., 1931⌊, 1924–31⌋. 128 p. 12°.

1. Anecdotes. 2. Wit and humor. 3. Title.
N. Y. P. L. September 12, 1934

NK 0210966 NN Mb

TL671
.5
.B677
1943
Knox, Dale I., joint author.
Brown, Frank Shenkel.
Aircraft sheetmetal assembly. Goodyear, Training division ... Prepared by F. S. Brown. ⌊Akron, O., 1943⌋

15
9408
Knox, David,& sons machinery co.
Catalogue and price list of shoe and leather machinery, cutters and dies. [Lynn, Mass., 1895]
152 p. sq. 18°.

NK 0210968 DLC

Knox, David Hepburn.
Dr. Johnson in Scotland.
(*In* Royal Philosophical Society of Glasgow, Scotland. Proceedings. Vol. 52, pp. 46–57. Glasgow. 1924.)
Refers to Johnson's visit to Scotland in 1773.

D4700 — Johnson, Samuel, LL.D., 1709–1784. — Scotland. Geog.

NK 0210969 MB

Knox, Dorothea Heness
see
Martin, Dorothea (Knox)

Knox, Dudley Wright, 1877–
American naval participation in the great war. n.p. 1928.

NK 0210971 DN

VOLUME 300

Div. of Maps

Knox, Dudley Wright, 1877-

Esnauts et Rapilly, *Paris.*
Carte de la partie de la Virginie ou l'armée combinée de France & des États-Unis de l'Amérique a fait prisonniere l'armée anglaise commandée par Lord Cornwallis le 19 oct.bre 1781, avec le plan de l'attaque d'York-town & de Glocester. Levée et dessinée sur les lieux par ordre des officiers gen.x de l'armée française & américaine. Paris, Esnauts et Rapilly [1781; Washington, D. C., Naval historical foundation, 1945.

Knox, Dudley Wright, 1877-
The eclipse of American sea power, by Capt. Dudley W. Knox ... New York city, American army & navy journal, inc. [c1922]
x p., 1 l., 140 p. fold. maps. 19½cm.
"Presents the American version of the Conference [on the limitation of armament,"—p. vi.

1. Washington, D. C. Conference on the limitation of armament, 1921-1922. 2. U. S.—Navy. I. Title. II. Title: American sea power, The eclipse of.

Library of Congress JX1974.5.K6 23-1114

NK 0210973 DLC MH OKentU NcU DN ICJ NN DN-Ob

Knox, Dudley Wright, 1877-
The founders of the American Navy. By Dudley Knox, Captain, U.S. Navy. n.p., n.d.
caption-title, 2 p. 35 1/3 cm.
Mimeo.

NK 0210974 PHi

Knox, Dudley Wright, 1877-
A history of the United States Navy, by Dudley W. Knox ... with an introduction by William L. Rodgers ... New York, G. P. Putnam's sons, 1936.
xvii p., 1 l., 481 p. front., illus. (incl. maps) plates, diagrs. 24 cm.
"Principal references" at end of each chapter.

1. U. S.—History, Naval. 2. U. S. Navy—Hist.

E182.K77 [353.7] 359.0973 36—18870

PU PHC
WaTC WaWW MB DSI DS NN MB GU OLak OCU MiU ViU DN
NK 0210975 DLC OO OCl WaS CaBVa MtBuM WaSp WaSpG

Knox, Dudley Wright, 1877-
A history of the United States Navy, with a foreword by Chester W. Nimitz and an introd. by William L. Rodgers. Rev. ed. New York, G. P. Putnam's Sons [1948]
xxiii, 704 p. illus., maps. 25 cm.
On spine: New enlarged edition through World War II.
Includes bibliographies.

1. U. S.—History, Naval. 2. U. S. Navy—Hist.

E182.K77 1948 359 48—2547*

ViU OCl DS ICU TU MB OrP FU CaBVaU OrLgE OrP WaT
NK 0210976 DLC FMU KU ScCleA NcU GU OClW OU MiU

Knox, Dudley Wright, 1877-
Naval essays. Annapolis, n.d.

NK 0210977 DN

Knox, Dudley Wright, 1877-
The naval genius of George Washington, by Dudley W. Knox ... with a foreword by Admiral Hilary P. Jones ... Boston, Printed by the Riverside press for Houghton Mifflin company, 1932.
6 p. l., 3-137, [1] p. front., plates, ports., maps. 25 cm.
Each plate accompanied by guard sheet with descriptive letterpress.
"Five hundred and fifty numbered copies of this book, of which five hundred are for sale, were printed ... in January, 1932. This is number 509."
"List of sources": p. [129]-[132]
1. Washington, George, pres. U. S., 1732-1799. 2. U. S.—Hist.—Revolution—Naval operations. I. Title.

E312.25.K67 [973.35] 923.173 32—4494

NN OCl LU MH OCl OU ODW OEac ViU NcD PPL ICJ PU DN
NK 0210978 DLC CaBVaU OrSaW OrCS OrU WaS WaTC MB

Knox, Dudley Wright, 1877-
The naval genius of George Washington; with a foreword by Hilary P. Jones. Boston, Houghton Mifflin Co. [1942]
137 p. illus., ports., maps. 24cm.
Bibliography: p. [129-132]

1. Washington, George, pres. U. S., 1732-1799. 2. U. S.—Hist.—Revolution—Naval operations. I. Title.

NK 0210979 ViU

Knox, Dudley Wright, 1877-

Meyers, William H b. 1815.
Naval sketches of the war in California; reproducing twenty-eight drawings made in 1846-47, by William H. Meyers ... descriptive text by Capt. Dudley W. Knox ... introduction by Franklin D. Roosevelt. New York, Random house, 1939.

E591 .U58

Knox, Dudley Wright, 1877-

U. S. *Navy dept.*
... Official records of the Union and Confederate navies in the war of the rebellion ... ser. I, v. 1-27; ser. II, v. 1-3. Washington, Govt. print. off., 1894-1922.

Knox, E. V.
See
Knox, Edmund George Valpy, 1881-

Knox, Edmund Arbuthnott, bp. of Manchester, 1847-1937.
Ryle, John Charles, *bp. of Liverpool,* 1816-1900.
... Bishops Latimer and Ridley, their lives and times, their writings and martyrdom. By John Charles Ryle ... With a foreword by the Right Rev. E. A. Knox ... London, C. J. Thynne & Jarvis, ltd., 1925.

[Knox, Edmund Arbuthnott] bp. of Manchester, 1847-
Does the ornaments rubric necessarily refer to the eucharistic vestments? An open letter to his Grace the Lord Archbishop of Canterbury, from the Lord Bishop of Manchester. London, New York [etc.] Longmans, Green, and co., 1913
Cover title, 32 p. 22 1-2 cm.

NK 0210984 NNG MdBJ PP

BT 265 K53

Knox, Edmund Arbuthnott, Bp. of Manchester, 1847-1937.
The glad tidings of reconciliation, by E. A. Knox. London, Longmans, Green, 1916.
235 p. 20 cm.

1. Reconciliation. I. Title.

NK 0210985 NRCR InAndC-T

Knox, Edmund Arbuthnott, *bp. of Manchester,* 1847-1937.
John Bunyan in relation to his times, by Edmund Arbuthnott Knox ... London, New York [etc.] Longmans, Green and co., 1928.
x, 116 p. 19½cm.

1. Bunyan, John, 1628-1688. 2. Church and state in Gt. Brit.

Library of Congress PR3331.K6 29—1342

PP MB NN WaU
NK 0210986 DLC WaS NcD TxU MBrZ MiU OCl OClW NRCR

Knox, Edmund Arbuthnott, bp. of Manchester, 1847-1937.
A letter to His Grace the Lord Archbishop of Canterbury, from the Right Rev. E. A. Knox...on the occasion of the presentation of a memorial against changes in the communion office and alternative communion services. Followed by a verbatim report of the speeches made on that occasion (November 27th, 1924). London [etc.] Longmans, Green & co., 1925. 31 p. 21½cm.

133381B. 1. Lord's Supper— Administration. June 16, 1942
N. Y. P. L.

NK 0210987 NN

YA 26407

Knox, Edmund Arbuthnott, Bp. of Manchester, 1847-
A message of Christ to an age of unrest and other Blackpool mission addresses. By the Right Revd. E.A. Knox, D.D. Lord Bishop of Manchester. Longmans, Green and co. New York, Calcutta, 1913
vi, 52 p. 16 cm.

NK 0210988 DLC

Knox, Edmund Arbuthnott, *bp. of Manchester,* 1847-
On what authority? A review of the foundations of Christian faith, by the Right Revd. Edmund Arbuthnott Knox ... London, New York [etc.] Longmans, Green and co., 1922.
2 p. l., [vii]-xi, 284 p. 19cm. $2.50

I. Title

Library of Congress BT1101.K655 22-23732

NK 0210989 DLC PPPD NN MB

Knox, Edmund Arbuthnott, *bp. of Coventry,* 1847-
Pastors and teachers; six lectures on pastoral theology, delivered in the Divinity school, Cambridge, in the year 1902, by the Right Rev. Edmund Arbuthnott Knox ... with an introduction by the Right Rev. Charles Gore ... London, New York and Bombay, Longmans, Green, and co., 1902.
xix, 300 p. 19½cm.
The appendix contains the following catechisms: 1. Luther's. 2. Church of England. 3. Heidelberg. 4. The shorter catechism. 5. Russian catechism. 6. The penny catechism of the Roman church. 7. Catechism of the Free evangelical church.
3-427

NK 0210990 DLC NcD PPPD MB

Knox, Edmund Arbuthnott, *bp. of Manchester,* 1847-
Reminiscences of an octogenarian, 1847-1934, by the Right Revd. Edmund Arbuthnott Knox ... With 24 illustrations. 2d impression. London, Hutchinson & co., ltd. [1935]
336 p. front., plates, ports. 24cm.

I. Title. 35-14413

Library of Congress BX5199.K55A3 1935 a
[2] 922.342

NK 0210991 DLC PPL IEG KU NN PHC

Knox, Edmund Arbuthnott, *bp. of Manchester,* 1847-
Robert Leighton, archbishop of Glasgow; a study of his life, times & writings, by the Right Rev. E. A. Knox ... with forewords by John Buchan ... and the Rev. Professor Archibald Main ... London, J. Clarke & co., limited [1930]
xviii, 19-280 p. illus. (map) plates, 2 port. (incl. front.) facsim. 23cm.

1. Leighton, Robert, abp. of Glasgow, 1611-1684. 2. Church and state in Scotland. 3. Scotland—Church history.

Library of Congress BX5395.L4K6 31-6068
[3] 922.341

NK 0210992 DLC CtY-D TU IEG NN ICN MH CtY

VOLUME 300

Knox, Edmund Arbuthnott, bp. of Manchester, 1847-
Sacrifice or sacrament? Which is the teaching of the Anglican communion office? By the Right Rev. E.A.Knox ... London, New York[etc.]Longmans, Green and co., 1914.
xii, 210 p. 20cm.
Bibliographical footnotes.

NK 0210993 ViAlTh CtY PPPD PU IMunS MH MiU

BX5149 .C5K74 1915
Knox, Edmund Arbuthnott, Bp. of Manchester, 1847-
Sacrifice or sacrament? Which is the teaching of the Anglican communion office? Reissue. London, Longmans, Green, 1915.
xii, 210p. 20cm.
in: SWTS

1. Lord's Supper--Anglican Communion. 2. Lord's Supper--Sacrifice. I. Title.

NK 0210994 IEG

Knox, Edmund Arbuthnott, *bp. of Manchester*, 1847-
The tractarian movement, 1833-1845; a study of the Oxford movement as a phase of the religious revival in western Europe in the second quarter of the nineteenth century. By the Right Rev. E. A. Knox ... London, New York, Putnam, 1933.
xix, 410 p. 22cm.
Bibliography: p. 398-403.

1. Oxford movement. I. Title.

Library of Congress BX5100.K6 35-19916
[2] 283.42

NK 0210995 DLC GU CSt ICU MiU OO PHC IEN NN

BX 5100 K6 1934
Knox, Edmund Arbuthnott, Bp. of Manchester, 1847-1937.
The Tractarian movement, 1833-1845; a study of the Oxford movement as a phase of the religious revival in western Europe in the second quarter of the nineteenth century. [2d ed.] London, New York, Putnam [1934]
xix, 418 p. 19 cm.
"First published 1933."
Bibliography: p. 401-408.

1. Oxford movement. I. Title.

NK 0210996 Vi PPPD NcD

BX5145 .A63K73 1927
Knox, Edmund Arbuthnott, Bp. of Manchester, 1847-
The unscriptural character of the alternative consecration prayer; a reply to the Rt. Rev. R.G. Parsons. 2d ed., containing notes by the Bishop of Middleton and comments thereon by Bishop Knox. London, Longmans, Green, 1927.
63p. 18cm.
SWTS

1. Church of England. Book of Common Prayer--Communion service. 2. Lord's Supper--Anglican Communion. I. Parsons, Richard Godfrey, 1882-1948. II. Title.

NK 0210997 IEG

HG 942 D5
Knox, Edmund F Vesey.
The Irish land question as affected by the appreciation of gold. Dublin, M.H. Gill, 1892.
7 p. 21 cm.

Bound with: Dick, G.H. The depression of trade. 1886.

1. Land tenure--Ireland. 2. Currency question--Gt. Brit. 3. Bimetallism. I. Title.

NK 0210998 LU NcD CtY RPB

Knox, Edmund George Valpy, 1881-
Awful occasions, by "Evoe" (E.V. Knox). London, Methuen & co., ltd. [1927]

"The greater part of the contents of this book has previously appeared in the pages of "Punch".

NK 0210999 OCl

821.91 K74b
Knox, Edmund George Valpy, 1881-
Blue feathers, by E. V. Knox (Evoe) Illus. by G. L. Stampa. London, Chatto & Windus [1929]
x, 147p. illus. 20cm.

NK 0211000 ICarbS MH

Knox, Edmund George Valpy, 1881-
Bluebells... N.Y., The Laugh club. [193-?]
151p.

Printed in Great Britain.

NK 0211001 OU

Knox, Edmund George Valpy, 1881-
Bluebells, by E. V. Knox ... New York, R. M. McBride & company [1934]
1 p. l., v-viii, 151, [1] p. 17½cm.
Printed in Great Britain.
Sketches reprinted from the author's "Awful occasions", "Slight irritations", "This other Eden", and other collections.

I. Title.

Library of Congress PR6021.N56A6 1934 34-35156
[3] 827.91

NK 0211002 DLC MiU OrStbM PPA NN

Knox, Edmund George Valpy, 1881-
The brazen lyre, by E. V. Knox. London, Smith, Elder & co., 1911.
vii, [1], 126, [1] p. 19cm.

I. Title.

A 13-286

Title from Enoch Pratt Free Libr. Printed by L. C.

NK 0211003 MdBE CoU WaSpG NN

Knox, Edmund George Valpy, 1881-
... E. V. Knox ('Evoe') London, Methuen & co., ltd. [1934]
viii, 151, [1] p. 17cm. (Methuen's library of humour, edited by E. V. Knox)

Library of Congress PR6021.N56A6 1934 a 35-2556
[3] 827.91

NK 0211004 DLC PHC

Knox, Edmund George Valpy, 1881-
Fiction as she is wrote, by E. V. Knox ("Evoe" of Punch) With 20 illustrations by George Morrow. London, Methuen & co., ltd. [1923]
xi, 148 p. front., plates. 17½cm.
"All the sketches ... have previously appeared in ... Punch."—Author's note.
"First published in 1923."

1. Parodies. I. Morrow, George, 1869- illus. II. Title.

Library of Congress PN6231.P3K5 24—19789

NK 0211005 DLC IdU CaOTP NcU

Knox, E[dmund George] V[alpy] 1881- 827-K
Fiction as she is wrote [by] Evoe; with illustrations by George Morrow. New York: The Dial Press Inc., 1924. 148 p. pl. 16°.

Too late; or, Edward Ferguson. The secret of Proome. Gently does it. The hidden hand. The amazing precincts; or, Queer scenes from clerical life. Pash, paint and Peppercastor. Little Red Riding Hood. December flame. Me; or, The strange episode of the reincarnated Greek. Blindworms. The ice-bound trail. Desert love; or, A brace of sheiks.

1. Wit and humor. 2. Title.
N. Y. P. L. November 28, 1924

NK 0211006 NN PU OCl MiU IU

Knox, Edmund George Valpy, 1881-
Folly calling, by E. V. Knox ('Evoe'). Illustrated by P. M. London, Methuen & co., ltd. [1932]
vi p., 1 l., 108 p., 1 l. illus. 17½cm.
"Most of the verses which appear in these pages have been previously printed in Punch."

I. Title.

A 35-673

Title from Brown Univ. PR6021.N56F6 Printed by L. C.

NK 0211007 RPB

Knox, Edmund George Valpy, 1881-

Shepard, Ernest Howard.
Fun & fantasy, a book of drawings by Ernest H. Shepard with an introduction by A. A. Milne. London, Methuen & co. ltd. [1927]

Knox, E[dmund George] V[alpy] 1881-
Gorgeous times, by Evoe. London: Methuen & Co., Ltd.[, 1926.] 144 p. 16°.

Contents: The Skelton dinner. The crush. The old friend. The invalids. Solitude. The illness of Clare. Le soleil. The wireless fiend. The inn. The cottage. The rock-garden. The heart of England. The wife in the car. How to live long. On being fit. Discipline. A talk with Mussolini. The back benchers. The great strike.

NK 0211009 NN

Knox, Edmund George Valpy, 1881-
Here's misery! A book of burlesques, by E. V. Knox (Evoe). With sixteen illustrations by Eric Fraser. London: Methuen & Co., Ltd.[, 1931.] xi, 143 p. incl. front. illus. [2. ed.] 12°.

575346A. 1. Wit and humor, English. I. Fraser, Eric, illustrator. I. Title.
N. Y. P. L. May 6, 1932

NK 0211010 NN

Knox, Edmund George Valpy, *1881-* 45594.408
An hour from Victoria, and some other excursions. [Essays.]
— London. George Allen & Unwin Ltd. [1924.] 156, (1) pp. 17 cm., in 8s.

NK 0211011 MB CaBVaU OCl PSC

Knox, Edmund George Valpy, 1881- *comp.*
Humorous verse, an anthology chosen by E. V. Knox. London, Chatto and Windus [1931]
xix, 267, [1] p. 17½cm. (*Half-title:* The Phoenix library. [no. 77])
"First published 1931."

NK 0211012 WaU

VOLUME 300

Knox, Edmund George Valpy, 1881- *comp.*
Humorous verse, an anthology chosen by E. V. Knox. London, Chatto and Windus [1932]
xix, 267, [1] p. 17½cm. (*Half-title:* The Phoenix library. [no. 77])
"First published 1931, reprinted 1932."

1. English wit and humor. 2. English poetry—20th cent. I. Title.

Library of Congress PR1195.H8K6 1932 32-15498
[2] [821.08] 827.08

NK 0211013 DLC MB

Knox, Edmund George Valpy, 1881- *comp.*
Humorous verse; an anthology. London, Chatto & Windus, 1950.
xix, 267 p. 19 cm. (The Phoenix anthologies, no. 5)

1. English wit and humor. 2. English poetry—20th cent. I. Title. (Series)
PR1195.H8K6 1950 827.082 52-19252

NK 0211014 DLC IdPI MH TU LU MiU IU

Knox, Edmund George Valpy, 1881-
I'll tell the world! A guide to the greatness of England, mainly intended for American use, by E. V. Knox ('Evoe') illustrated by George Morrow. London, Chatto & Windus [1927]
xi, 142 p. incl. plates. 19cm.
"Most of the contents of this book have been published in Punch in a rather different form."

1. Gt. Brit.—History, Comic, satirical, etc. I. Title.

Library of Congress DA33.K5 28-1579

NK 0211015 DLC NcU

Knox, Edmund George Valpy, 1881-
I'll tell the world! A guide to the greatness of England, mainly intended for American use, by Evoe (E. V. Knox) illustrated by George Morrow. Garden City, N. Y., Doubleday, Doran & company, inc., 1928.
xi, 147 p. incl. plates. 20cm.
"Most of the contents of this book have been published in Punch in a rather different form."

1. Gt. Brit.—History, Comic, satirical, etc. I. Title.
Library of Congress DA33.K5 1928 28-9853

NK 0211016 DLC WaS ICRL WaU OU OCl MB NN PU

PR 6021 .N56 I 8
Knox, Fdmund George Valpy, 1881-
It occurs to me. London, Methuen [1926]
vi,147p.

NK 0211017 ScU

B825K771 S7 1920
Knox, Edmund George Valpy, 1881-
A little loot. London, Allen & Unwin [1920]
133 p. 17cm.

NK 0211018 NNC NjP MH NcU

Knox, Edmund George Valpy, 1881-
The mechanism of satire. Cambridge [Eng.] University Press, 1951.
31 p. 19 cm. (The Leslie Stephen lecture, 1951)
Cover title.

1. Satire. I. Title. (Series)
A 52-982

Yale Univ. Library for Library of Congress [3]

TxU CU NIC IEN
NK 0211019 CtY CaBVaU IdPI MtU OrPS OrU MH NNU-W

Knox, Edmund George Valpy, 1881- *ed.*
Mr. Punch on the links, edited by E. V. Knox ('Evoe') including 32 illustrations. New York, Rae D. Henkle co., inc., 1929.
x p., 1 l., 147 p. incl. front., plates. 23cm.

1. Golf. I. Title.
Library of Congress GV967.K6 29-16462

NK 0211020 DLC OCl

Knox, Edmund George Valpy, 1881- comp.

Chesterton, Gilbert Keith, 1874-
On running after one's hat and other whimsies, by G. K. Chesterton; selected by E. V. Knox ... New York, R. M. McBride & company, 1933.

Knox, Edmund George Valpy, 1881-
"Parodies regained", by Evoe (E. V. Knox of "Punch".) Illustrated by Geo. Morrow. London, Methuen & co., ltd. [1921]
x, 114 p., 1 l. incl. front., illus., plates. 17½cm.
Title vignette; full page illustrations.
"All the verses ... have previously appeared in ... Punch."—Pref.

1. Parodies. I. Morrow, George, 1869- illus. II. Title.

Library of Congress PN6110.P3K6 22-6348

NK 0211022 DLC ICU CLSU NjP

Knox, Edmund George Valpy, 1881-

Leacock, Stephen Butler, 1869-
The perfect salesman, by Stephen Leacock; edited by E. V Knox. New York, R. M. McBride & company [c1934]

Knox, Edmund George Valpy, 1881-
Poems of impudence, by Evoe (E. V. Knox) illustrated by Arthur Watts. London, T. F. Unwin ltd. [1926]
128 p. incl. plates. front. 19cm.
"Most of these verses have appeared in Punch."

I. Title.

Library of Congress PR6021.N56P6 1926 27-2998

NK 0211024 DLC WaSp

Knox, Edmund George Valpy, 1881-
Poems of impudence, by Evoe (E. V. Knox) illustrated by Arthur Watts. Garden City, N. Y., Doubleday, Page & company, 1927.
vi p., 1 l., 121 p. incl. plates. 20cm.
"Most of these verses have appeared in Punch."

I. Title.
Library of Congress PR6021.N56P6 1927 27-7989

NK 0211025 DLC MB FMU NN OCl

Knox, E[dmund George] V[alpy], 1881-
Quaint specimens. Lond.Methuen[1925]
vi,185p.S.

NK 0211026 CaBViP

Knox, Edmund George Valpy, 1881-
Slight irritations, by E. V. Knox ('Evoe') London, Methuen & co. ltd. [1931]
v, 163, [1] p., 1 l. 17½cm.
Essays.

I. Title.

Library of Congress PR6021.N56S6 1931 32-30393
[2] 824.91

NK 0211027 DLC

Knox, Edmund George Valpy, *1881-* 4579.309
These liberties. [Parodies.] By E. V. Knox ("Evoe" of Punch). — London. Methuen & Co., Ltd. [1923.] viii, 151, (1) pp. 17 cm., in 8s.

M6641 — T.r. — Wit and humor. English. — Parodies and burlesques.

NK 0211028 MB OU CaBVaU MH IU

Knox, Edmund George Valpy, 1881-
Things that annoy me, by E. V. Knox ('Evoe') London, Methuen & co. ltd. [1930]
vi p., 1 l., 184 p., 1 l. 17½cm.
Short essays, most of which have appeared in Punch.
"First published in 1930."

I. Title.

Library of Congress PR6021.N56T4 1930 32-12190
[2] 827.91

NK 0211029 DLC CaBVaU CtY MB

Knox, Edmund George Valpy, 1881-
This other Eden, by E. V. Knox ('Evoe') London, Methuen & co. ltd. [1929]
v, [1], 153, [1] p. 17½cm.
Sketches, most of which have appeared in Punch.

I. Title.
Library of Congress PR6021.N56T5 1929 30-14610
[2] 827.91

NK 0211030 DLC CtY NN

823.91 K742w
Knox, Edmund George Valpy, 1881-
Wonderful outings, by E. V. Knox ("Evoe") London, Methuen [1928]
vii, 151p. 18cm.

NK 0211031 ICarbS CtY

Knox, Edward M 1842-1916.
Catalogue of the private gallery of valuable paintings belonging to Mr. Edward M. Knox, to be sold at unrestricted public sale at Mendelssohn hall ... [January 26th, 1906] The sale will be conducted by Thomas E. Kirby, of the American art association, managers. New York [Press of J. J. Little & co.] 1906.
[155] p. 23cm.

1. Paintings—Private collections. I. American art association, New York.

Library of Congress N5220.K6 6-14446

NK 0211032 DLC

VOLUME 300

Knox, Edward M 1842-1916.
The story of the hat, by Edward M. Knox. New York, The Bell publishing company, °1900.
cover-title, 147 p. illus. 14cm.

1. Hats.
Mar. 15, 1900-59
Library of Congress TS2185.K74 Copyright

NK 0211033 DLC MB

Knox, Edward P
Jr31 A plea for a man-made mountain, by Edward
01 P.Knox. Toms River, N.J., New Jersey courier, inc., 1936.
"Limited edition."

NK 0211034 CtY

KNOX, Edward Prentiss.
The man with the nose, a comedy for boys in two acts. Boston, W.H.Baker & Co., [cop.1910].
pp.19.

NK 0211035 MH PU DLC RPB

561
K771s
Geol
Lib'y
Knox, Elizabeth M
The spores of Lycopodium, Phylloglosum, Selaginella and Isoetes and their value in the study of microfossils of the Paleozoic age. Edinburgh [Printed for the Botanical Society by Neill] 1950.
1p.l., 209-257p. plates. (Transactions and proceedings of the Botanical Society of Edinburgh, v.35, pt.3, 1949-50)
1. Paleobotany - Paleozoic. I. Title. II. Series: Botanical Society of Edinburgh. Transactions and proceedings, v.35, pt.3.

NK 0211036 TxU

Knox, Ellen Mary, 1858-
Bible lessons for schools. Exodus. London, Macmillan, 1907.
214p. S.

NK 0211037 OO OC1W PPPD

Knox, Ellen Mary, 1858-
Bible lessons for schools: Genesis. London, Macmillan, 1907.
171 p. S.

NK 0211038 OC1W

KNOX, ELLEN MARY, 1858-
Bible lessons for schools: The Acts of the Apostles, by E. M. Knox... London: Macmillan and co., ltd., 1908. xii, 401 p. maps, plan. 18cm.

120369B. 1. Bible. N.T. Acts. I. Title.

NK 0211039 NN CaNSWA OO ODW

Knox, Ellen Mary, 1858-
Canadian education and the war, by E. M. Knox... [Toronto: Ontario Press, Ltd., 1915.] 15(1) p. nar. 16°.

1. European war, 1914- . 2. Education, Canada. 3. Title.
N. Y. P. L. June 2, 1916.

NK 0211040 NN

KNOX, ELLEN MARY, 1858-
The girl of the new day, by E. M. Knox... Toronto: McClelland & Stewart [1919] viii, 241 p. 21cm.

983255A. 1. Woman—Occupations—Canada. I. Title.

NK 0211041 NN OO CaOTU CaBVaU

Knox, Ellis Gilbert, 1928-
The bases of rigidity in fragipans. [Ithaca, N.Y.,] 1954.
72 l. illus. 29cm.
Thesis (Ph.D.)--Cornell Univ., Sept. 1954.

NK 0211042 NIC

Knox, Ellis Gilbert, 1928-
Jefferson County soils and soil map. Ithaca, N. Y., New York State College of Agriculture, 1952.
sheet. col. map. 72 x 56 cm. fold. to 36 x 28 cm.
Text, with tables and illus. on recto numbered as 4 pages. Col. map on verso, scale ca. 1: 175,000, has title: Soil association map of Jefferson County, New York, 1952.

1. Soils—New York (State)—Jefferson Co.—Maps. I. Cornell University. New York State College of Agriculture.
G3803.J4 1952.K5 Map 55-740

NK 0211043 DLC

Knox, Emeline L.
Gems from the field of thought, or A glimpse into mute life. By Miss Emeline L. Knox. Utica, N. Y., T. J. Griffiths, printer, 1891.
vii, [9]-117 p. 18½cm.
Poems by a deaf mute.

I. Title. II. Title: A glimpse into mute life.
28-2183
Library of Congress PS2197.K37

NK 0211044 DLC

Knox, Emma (Hackett) 1849-
The story of the old homestead (the Smith-Hackett homestead) by Emma Hackett Knox. [Rahway, N. J.] Priv. print. [The Quinn & Boden company, inc.] 1937.
vii, 284 p. illus. (maps) plates, ports., facsims. 23½ cm.
"The old homestead is in the central part of Salem county, New Jersey."—Pref.
CONTENTS.—pt. I. Brief sketch of English history. A brief biography of George Fox. A brief biography of John Fenwick.—pt. II. The owners and the families that have lived on the old homestead: the Smith and Hackett ancestors.—pt. III. A tribute, by Charles F. Hackett. Brief sketch of the Hackett family by Elizabeth Hackett Emmel. A genealogical table of the descendants of Joseph and Rebecca Smith Hackett by Elizabeth Hackett Emmel and Emma Hackett Knox.

1. Hackett family. 2. Smith family. I. *Emmel, Elizabeth (Hackett) 1854-1935. II. Hackett, Charles Ford, 1853-1926. III. Title. IV. Title: The old homestead, The story of.
Full name: Emma Ellen (Hackett) Knox.
CS71.H119 1937 37-37570

NK 0211046 DLC PHi

QY
K74a
1909
KNOX, Ernest Blake
Aids to microscopic diagnosis; bacterial and parasitic diseases. London, Baillière, Tindall and Cox, 1909.
viii, 156 p. (The Students' aids series)

NK 0211047 DNLM

Knox, Ernest Blake.
Buller's campaign with the Natal field force of 1900, by E. Blake Knox ... London, R. B. Johnson, 1902.
xx, 336 p. 16 pl. (incl. front., port.) 7 maps (part fold.) 23cm.
Appendix I: Note on the medical aspects of the Natal campaign, first published by the author in more technical form in the Medical press and circular, Aug. 28, 1901.

1. South African war, 1899-1902. I. Title.
3-1903
Library of Congress DT930.K74
[a19e1]

NK 0211048 DLC NN ICJ ICN PPL TxU IEN

UH
K74m
1911
KNOX, Ernest Blake
Military sanitation and hygiene. London, Baillière, Tindall and Cox, 1911.
xii, 346 p. illus.

NK 0211049 DNLM PPC

Knox, Errol Galbraith, 1889- ed.

Who's who in the commonwealth of Australia, by Fred Johns ... Sydney, Australia, Angus & Robertson, ltd., 1922-

---

Knox, Esther Melbourne.
The flags of dawn, by Esther Melbourne Knox, illustrated by Marie A. Lawson. Boston, Little, Brown and company, 1944.
5 p. l., [3]-298 p. incl. front., plates. 20cm.
"First edition."

1. Gt. Brit.—Hist.—John, 1199-1216—Fiction. I. Lawson, Marie (Abrams) illus. II. Title.
44-2812
Library of Congress PZ7.K771F1

NK 0211051 DLC Wa Or OC1 PP

Knox, Esther Melbourne.
Swift flies the falcon; a story of the first crusade; illustrated by Ruth King. N. Y., Junior literary guild and Winston, 1939.
245 p. illus. O.
Bibliography p. 245.

NK 0211052 PP

Knox, Esther Melbourne.
Swift flies the falcon; a story of the first crusade, by Esther Melbourne Knox; illustrated by Ruth King. Philadelphia, Chicago [etc.] The John C. Winston company [°1939]
vii, 245 p., 1 l. illus. 23cm.
Illustrated lining-papers.
"First edition."
Bibliography: p. 245.

1. Crusades—First, 1096-1099—Fiction. I. Title.
39-9648
Library of Congress PZ7.K771Sw

OC1h
NK 0211053 DLC WaSp OrP WaS Or CaBVaU OO OEac OC1

Knox, Estrid (Ott)
...Bimbi reiser jorden rundt; oversatt av Gunvor Fossum. 2. oppl. Oslo, H. Aschehoug & co., 1945.
192 p. illus. 19cm. (Aschehougs utvalgte for piker. nr. 9)
"Illustrert av Marie Hjuler."

NK 0211054 NN

VOLUME 300

Knox, Estrid (Ott).
...I Guds Billede. København: Jespersen og Pios Forlag, 1930. 206 p. 8°.

496402A. 1. Fiction, Danish. I. Title.
N. Y. P. L. October 29, 1930

NK 0211055 NN

KNOX, ESTRID (OTT).
Mit den finnischen Lottas. Vom Heldentum der Frau, mit einem Vorwort von Oberst i. Gst Sarasin. 9. Aufl. [Zürich] Schweizer Spiegel Verlag [1940] 118 p. illus., port. 22cm.

"Aus dem Dänischen übersetzt."

1. Finno-Russian war, 1939-1940--Medical and sanitary affairs. 2. Förening-gen Lotta Svärd.

NK 0211056 NN

Knox, Ethel Louise. Ballads of Paul Bunyan.

M1549
.8
.S85B3 **Strong, May Agnes.**

Ballads of Paul Bunyan, choral cycle for mixed voices and narrator; ballads by Ethel Louise Knox, music by May A. Strong. Philadelphia, Theodore Presser co., °1943.

Knox, Eunice.
An Indian swimming pageant. New York, 1933.
6 l. 28 cm.
Mimeograph copy.
Cover title.

NK 0211058 RPB

Knox, Fitzhugh, 1867–
Genealogy of the Fitzhugh, Knox, Gordon, Selden, Horner, Brown, Baylor, (King) Carter, Edmonds, Digges, Page, Tayloe and allied families, compiled by Fitzhugh Knox. Atlanta, Ga. [Printed by Foote & Davies co.] 1932.

2 p. l., 3-44 p. illus. (incl. ports., facsim., coat of arms) fold. geneal. tab. $28\frac{1}{2}$cm.

Title from cover.
"This is a limited edition of 1000 copies."
Traces the descent of the author through each family.

1. Fitzhugh family. 2. Knox family. 32-13131

Library of Congress CS71.F567 1932

NK 0211059 OClWHi DLC

Knox, Florence Clay.
Butterflies and balsam; a one-act play for women, adapted for stage or drawing room, by Florence Clay Knox... New York [etc.] Longmans, Green and co. [1948] 20 p. 19cm.

1. Drama, American. I. Title.
N. Y. P. L. October 26, 1950

NK 0211060 NN RPB MiD

Knox, Florence Clay.
A face at the window; a play for Christmas in one act, by Florence Clay Knox ... staged by Nathaniel Edward Reeid ... New York, N. Y., Chicago, Ill. [etc.] Longmans, Green and co. [°1939]

3 p. l., 3-41 p. diagr. $18\frac{1}{2}$cm. (*On cover: Longmans' play series*)

"First edition."

1. Christmas plays. I. Reeid, Nathaniel Edward. II. Title.
40-2924
Library of Congress PN6120.C5K597
——— Copy 2.
Copyright D pub. 67425 [3] 812.5

NK 0211061 DLC OCl

Knox, Florence Clay.
For distinguished service; a duologue for two women, by Florence Clay Knox. (In: Johnson, T., editor. Miniature plays for stage or study. Boston[, cop. 1930]. 12°. p. 82-96.)

Caption-title.
In one act.

526892A. 1. Drama, American. I. Title.
N. Y. P. L. June 17, 1931

NK 0211062 NN OCl

Knox, Florence Clay.
Many happy returns of the day; a comedy in one act, by Florence Clay Knox... New York: Longmans, Green and Co., 1929. 29 p. 12°. (Longmans' play ser.)

465863A. 1. Drama, American. 2. Title.
N. Y. P. L. March 18, 1930

NK 0211063 NN MiD DLC OCl RPB Or

Knox, Florence Clay
The matrimonial fog; a comedy in one act.
Boston, Baker, 1918.
19 p. (Baker's acting plays)

NK 0211064 NNC Or IU CtY NN RPB MH

Knox, Florence Conner.
Foothill lyrics, by Florence Conner Knox. Salem, Or. Statesman publishing co. [1945]

3 p. l., [5]-76 p. front. (port.) 22cm.

45-6071
Library of Congress PS3521.N814F6
[3] 811.5

NK 0211065 DLC OrU Or

Knox, Florence Conner.
Woman, and other poems by Florence Conner Knox. [Portland, Or., Kilham stationery & printing co., °1945]

93 p. incl. front. (port.) $22\frac{1}{2}$cm.

Errata slip inserted.

I. Title. 46-14099
Library of Congress PS3521.N814W6
[2] 811.5

NK 0211066 DLC OrU Or

Knox, Francis.
Restrictive practices in the building industry, by Frank Knox and Jossleyn Hennessy. London, Institute of Economic Affairs, 1906.

v, 64 p. tables. 22 cm. (Institute of Economic Affairs, London. Research monographs, no. 1) 7/6 B 66-6817

1. Construction industry—Law and legislation—Great Britain. 2 Restraint of trade—Great Britain. 3. Trade-unions—Building trades—Great Britain. I. Hennessy, Jossleyn, joint author. II. Title. III. Series.

338.826900942 66-71299

NK 0211067 DLC

Knox, Francis, pseud.
Harry's work
see Pennypacker, Morton, 1872-

Knox, Frank
see
Knox, Franklin, 1874-

Knox, Frank Albert.
Canada - world trader. [Ottawa, Cloutier]1944.
19p.illus.D. (Canadian affairs, vol. 1, no.5)

NK 0211070 CaBViP

Knox, Frank Albert.

HC106
.3
.M25 **Marshall, Herbert, 1887–**

Canadian-American industry; a study in international investment, by Herbert Marshall ... Frank A. Southard, jr. ... [and] Kenneth W. Taylor ... with an excursus on the Canadian balance of payments by Frank A. Knox ... New Haven, Yale university press; Toronto, The Ryerson press, for the Carnegie endowment for international peace, Division of economics and history, 1936.

KNOX, Frank Albert.
Canadian capital movements and the Canadian Balance of international payments, 1900-1934; The Canadian balance of payments. (In Marshall & others. Canadian-American industry. c1936. p.296-324)

NK 0211072 WaWW

HD9695 Knox, Frank Albert
C22K5 The Canadian electrical manufacturing industry: an economic
Documents analysis by F.A. Know in association with C.L. Barber and D.W.
Dept. Slater, for the Canadian Electrical Manufacturers Association.
[Toronto, 1955?]
v, 91 p. tables.

1. Electric industries - Canada.

NK 0211073 CU OCl NN ICU CaOTU CaBViP CaBVa CaBVaU

Knox, Frank Albert.
Dominion monetary policy, 1929–1934. A study prepared for the Royal commission on dominion-provincial relations, by F. A. Knox. Ottawa, 1939.

1 p. l., iv numb. l., 3 l., 93 numb. l. incl. tables. diagrs. 35cm.

Reproduced from type-written copy.
Issued also in French.

1. Currency question—Canada. I. Canada. Royal commission on dominion-provincial relations. II. Title.
40-30859
Library of Congress HG654.K6
[3] 332.40971

OrU NcD
NK 0211074 DLC OrPR CaBVa DS OCl PU ViU NIC CaBVaU

Knox, Frank Albert.
Excursus; Capital movements and the Canadian balance of international payments, 1900–1934.
(*In* Marshall, Herbert, and others. Canadian-American industry ... Pp. 296–324. New Haven. 1936.)

E2033 — Credit. — Canada. Fin. — Mercantilism.

NK 0211075 MB

Knox, Frank Albert.
Politique monétaire du Canada, 1929–1934. Étude préparée pour la Commission royale des relations entre le dominion et les provinces par F. A. Knox. Ottawa, 1939.

1 p. l., iv, ii numb. l., 1 l., 98 numb. l. incl. tables. diagrs. 35cm.

Reproduced from type-written copy.
Issued also in English.

1. Currency question—Canada. I. Canada. Royal commission on dominion-provincial relations. II. Title.
40-21281
Library of Congress HG654.K62
[2] 332.40971

NK 0211076 DLC

VOLUME 300

Knox, Frank M
Design and control of business forms. New York, McGraw-Hill, 1952.
219 p. illus. 29 cm. (NOMA series in office management)

1. Business—Forms, blanks, etc. I. Title.
HF5371.K6 651 51—12570 ‡

NK 0211077 DLC DNAL CU MiU DNLM OkU TU CaBVa MB TxU NN PBL PCtvL PPBMR CaBVaU OrCS OrU WaS IdPI MtU WaT WaTC MtBC OrP Or OrSaW

Knox, Frank M
The how and why of pay roll records with employment and pay roll forms that work. An original research project by the Frank M. Knox Co., inc., on the control and standardization of printed material for efficient business management. Tulsa, Ross-Martin Co., 1946.
134 p. forms. 29 cm.

1. Wages—U. S. 2. Business—Forms, blanks, etc. 3. Employment management.
HD4932.F6K5 658.32 48-25088*

NK 0211078 DLC OCl TxU

[Knox, Frank M., company]
The Knox standard guide to planned printing. An abridged edition of the Knox plan for printing control. [New York, Frank M. Knox company, inc., c1940.
1 v. illus., tables, diagrs. 29½cm.

Loose-leaf.
Reproduced from type-written copy.

1. Printing, Practical.

NK 0211079 NNC

Knox, Frank M., company.
... Standard production data. [New York] Frank M. Knox company [c1936]
1 v. tables, diagrs. (part fold.) 29cm.

At head of title: The Knox plan for printing control (Advertising and promotional printing) Manual number five.
Loose-leaf.
"This copy, no. 46."

1. Printing, Practical.

NK 0211080 NNC

Knox, Franklin, 1874-1944.
...Address of Frank Knox of Illinois at the dinner of the Economic club of New York, Hotel Astor, New York city, Tuesday evening, March 24, James P. Warburg presiding... [New York, 1936] broadside. 63½ x 45½cm.
At head of title: Release morning papers, Wednesday, March 25...
Comprises text of the address and a summary.

35110B. 1. United States—Politics, 1933– 2. Economic history—U. S., 1933–
N. Y. P. L. October 8, 1941

NK 0211081 NN

Knox, Franklin, 1874–
The brotherhood of courage [by] Frank Knox. An address delivered before the War congress of American industry, December 2, 1942. [New York, The National association of manufacturers, 1943]
14 p. 22cm.

1. World war, 1939– —U. S. 2. World war, 1939– —Addresses, sermons, etc. I. National association of manufacturers of the United States of America. II. Title.
[Full name: William Franklin Knox]
43-1907
Library of Congress D769.1.K6
[3] 940.5373

NK 0211082 DLC

Knox, Franklin, 1874-1944.
The complete address by the Honorable Frank Knox...to the English-speaking union, Chicago, December 6, 1943. Also brief extracts: from the farewell statement of the Honorable Henry L. Stimson...and from the June addresses and Oct. 7 broadcast of General-of-army Eisenhower... [Norfolk, Va., 1945] 21 p. 23cm.

1. World war, 1939–1945—Peace. I. Stimson, Henry Lewis, 1867– II. Eisenhower, Dwight David, 1890– . III. Glasgow, Arthur Graham, 1865–
N. Y. P. L. January 23, 1948

NK 0211083 NN Vi NNC

Knox, Franklin, 1874-1944.
Front page editorials of 1933
see under Chicago Daily News.

Knox, Franklin, 1874– 1944.
Labor under dictatorships and democracies; a series of editorials reprinted from the Chicago daily news and an address before the Chicago association of commerce, July 21, 1937, by Frank Knox. [Chicago, The Chicago daily news, inc., °1937]
2 p. l., 7-73 p. 24cm.

1. Labor and laboring classes—Europe. I. Title.
[Full name: William Franklin Knox]
37-19137
Library of Congress HD8376.K55
——— Copy 2.
Copyright A 109111 [3] 331.04

NK 0211085 DLC OrU CU TxU PPTU OCl ICJ

Knox, Franklin, 1874-1944.
The meaning of Munich, being a series of three editorials as published in the Chicago daily news in autumn 1938 [n. p., Priv. print., 1938?]
17 p. 16 cm.
"Three hundred copies printed ... Number 1."

1. World politics—Addresses, essays, lectures. 2. Munich Four-Power Agreement, 1938. I. Title.
Full name: William Franklin Knox.
D450.K55 940.504 51-52273

NK 0211086 DLC NN

Knox, Franklin, 1874–
The price of a managed economy; a series of editorials reprinted from the Chicago daily news and an address before the Commercial club of Chicago, June 15, 1934, by Frank Knox. [Chicago, The Chicago daily news, inc., °1934]
[40] p. 27½cm.

1. Industry and state. 2. Economic policy. I. Title.
[Full name: William Franklin Knox]
35-18358
Library of Congress HD3611.K55
[2] 330.1

NK 0211087 DLC OClJC IU NcD

Knox, Franklin, 1874-
The testing of the American ideal. Address... to the Los Angeles County Republican assembly... July 25, 1935. n. p. [1935]
20 p.

NK 0211088 MiD-B

Knox, Franklin, 1874–
The United States navy in national defense, by Frank Knox. Washington, D. C., American council on public affairs [°1941]
1 p. l., 40 p. 21cm.

1. U. S.—Navy. I. American council on public affairs. II. Title.
[Full name: William Franklin Knox]
41-15177
Library of Congress VA58.K55
[10] 359.0973

NK 0211089 DLC OU OLak CtY

Knox, Franklin, 1874-1944.
"We planned it that way", by Frank Knox. New York, Toronto, Longmans, Green and co., 1938.
viii p., 1 l., 82 p. 19½ cm.
"First printed August 1938; reprinted twice August 1938."

1. U. S.—Economic policy. 2. U. S.—Pol. & govt.—1933-1945. I. Title.
[Full name: William Franklin Knox]
38—30187
Library of Congress HC106.3.K58 1938b
[a50f1] 330.973

NK 0211090 DLC NcD Or PP OCl OClW OClh NN MH OrU WHi

Knox, Frederick John.
Account of the gigantic whale, or rorqual, the skeleton of which is now exhibiting in the great rooms of the Royal Institution, Princes Street. *Edinburgh: J. Carfrae & Son*, 1835. 15 pp. 8°.
In: *C p. v. 1172.

NK 0211091 NN DNLM

Knox, Frederick John.
——— Account of the whale; now exhibiting in the Trades' Hall, Glasgow. 4 pp., 1 pl. 8°. [s. p. 1835. [P., v. 1534.]

NK 0211092 DNLM

Knox, Frederick John.
The anatomist's instructor, and museum companion: being practical directions for the formation and subsequent management of anatomical museums. By Frederick John Knox ... Edinburgh, A. and C. Black; London, Longman, Rees, Orme, Brown, Green & Longman, 1836.
xii, 152 p. front., illus. 18cm.
"Errata" slip mounted on p. 152.

1. Anatomical specimens--Collection and preservation.

NK 0211093 MiU CaBVaU KyU DNLM PPPH

Knox, Frederick John.
The Anatomist's Instructor ... Edinb., 1854. 16°.

NK 0211094 CtY

Knox (Frederick John)
Catalogue of anatomical preparations illustrative of the whale, particularly the Great Northern Rorqual (*Balæna maximus borealis*), now exhibiting in the Pavilion, North College Street. *Edinburgh; Neill & Co.*, 1838. 39 pp. 8°.
In: *C. p. v. 1049.

NK 0211095 NN

Knox, *Sir* Geoffrey George, 1884–
The last peace and the next, by Sir Geoffrey Knox ... London, New York [etc.] Hutchinson & co. ltd. [1943]
87, [1] p. 18cm.

1. European war, 1914-1918—Peace. 2. World war, 1939– —Peace. 3. Germany—Hist.—1918– I. Title.
43-17857
Library of Congress D816.K57
[5] 940.5

NK 0211096 DLC DS

Knox, George.
Cases argued and determined in the Supreme Court of New South Wales
see under New South Wales. Supreme Court.

VOLUME 300

Knox, George.
The speech of the Honourable George Knox, representative in Parliament for the University of Dublin, in the House of commons, February 17, 1800, on the subject of an incorporate union of Great Britain and Ireland. London, Printed for J. Debrett, 1800.
20 p. 21.5 cm. [Binder's title: British tracts 9]

NK 0211098 CtY

Knox, George, F. R. S.
Experiments and observations on the Newry-pitch-stone and its products and on the formation of pumice. Lond., n.p., 1822.
26 p.

NK 0211099 PU

Knox, George, F. R. S.
On bitumen in stones... Lond., n.p. 1823.
12 p.

NK 0211100 PU

622.78 K77c Knox, George, professor.
Coal washing; the latest development in the hydraulic classification of coal and minerals, by Prof. George Knox and Further improvements on the 'Draper' washer, by John Marriott Draper. Papers read before the South Wales institute of engineers at Cardiff, November 29th, 1918, and January 31st, 1919. Cardiff [Eng.] 1919.

cover-title, 43p. illus., tables, diagrs.

"Paper reprinted from the 'Proceeding of the South Wales institute of engineers' vol.XXXIV., no.3, and vol.XXXV, no.1."

NK 0211102 IU

Knox, George, professor.
Mining subsidence. (In: International Congress of Geologists, XII. Ottawa, 1913. Compte-rendu. Ottawa, 1914. 4°. p. 797-806.)

1. Mines, etc.
N. Y. P. L. January 11, 1917.

NK 0211103 NN

Knox, George Albert, 1918-
Kenneth Burke as literary theorist and critic. Ann Arbor, University Microfilms [1953]
([University Microfilms, Ann Arbor, Mich.] Publication 6417)
Microfilm copy (positive) of typescript.
Collation of the original: 1 v. (various pagings)
Thesis—University of Washington.
Abstracted in Dissertation abstracts, v. 13 (1953) no. 6, p. 1195.
Vita.
Includes bibliography.

1. Burke, Kenneth, 1897-
Microfilm AC-1 no. 6417 Mic A 53-2044

Washington. Univ. for Library of Congress Seattle. Library [1]†

NK 0211104 WaU OU NcD NN CU GU DLC

Knox, George Edward
The criminal law of the Bengal presidency ... Calcutta, Thacker, Spink & co., 1873.
2 v.

1. Criminal law - Bengal. 2. Criminal procedure - Bengal. I. Bengal. Laws, statutes, etc.

NK 0211105 NNC

KNOX, Sir G[eorge] E[dward].
Digest of Civil Procedure in British India. Allahabad, 1877.

2 vol. 8vo.

NK 0211106 MH-L

WBC K74a 1836 KNOX, George Frederick
The art of cupping; being a brief history of the operation, from its origin to the present time; its utility; minute rules for its performance; a list of the diseases in which it is most beneficial; and a description of the various instruments employed; &c. London [1836?]
68 p.

NK 0211107 DNLM MBCo KyU

Knox, George H. 1871- ed.
Leadership.
Des Moines, Ia., Personal help publishing co. [19

Knox, George H 1871-
... Leadership, by George H. Knox ... Des Moines, Ia., Personal help publishing company, 1909.
2 p. l., 13-311 p. front. (port.) 20 cm. (Personal help library)

1. Success. 2. Salesmen and salesmanship. I. Title.
HF5386.K7 9—15408

NK 0211109 DLC ICJ ICRL

Knox, George H 1871-
Leadership. Des Moines, Iowa, Personal help publishing co., 1911.

"Personal help library."

NK 0211110 MH

Knox, George H 1871- 3589a.165
Leadership.
— Des Moines. Personal Help Publishing Co. 1912. 311 pp. Portrait. [Personal help library.] 19 cm., in 8s.
Lectures to young men on success in life.

H8741 — Young men, Lectures to. — T.r. — S.r. — Success.

NK 0211111 MB OOxM

Knox, George H. 1871-
Personal help school of achievement, lesson I. by George H. Knox...
Des Moines, [c 1905].

BJ1611 .K75

NK 0211112 DLC

Knox, George H 1871-
... Ready money, by George H. Knox ... Des Moines, Ia., Personal help publishing company, 1905.
2 p. l., 13-317 p. front. (port.) 19½cm. (Personal help library)

1. Success. I. Title.

Library of Congress BJ1611.K8 5—5448

ICarbS NIC
NK 0211113 DLC MtBC Or OrU-M MiU OO OCl NjP LU

Knox, George H 1871-
... Ready money, by George H. Knox ... Des Moines Ia., Personal help publishing company, 1906.
2 p. l., 13-317 p. front. (port.) 19½cm. (Personal help library)

NK 0211114 DLC ICRL OO ViU ICJ

Knox, George H 1871-
Ready money. Des Moines, Iowa, Personal help publishing co., 1908.

At head of title: Personal help library.

NK 0211115 MH

Knox, George H 1871- 3589a.167
Ready money.
— Des Moines. Personal Help Publishing Co. 1911. 317 pp. Portraits. Facsimiles. [Personal help library.] 19 cm., in 8s.
Advice to young men on the elements of success.
The second part of the book consists of extracts from famous speeches.

H8743 — Young men, Lectures to. — T.r. — Success. — S.r.

NK 0211116 MB OOxM MH

Knox, George H 1871- comp.
... Thoughts that inspire ... Arranged and comp. by George H. Knox ... Des Moines, Ia., Personal help publishing company, 1905.
2 v. fronts. (ports.) 20cm. (Personal help library)

1. Maxims. I. Title.

Library of Congress PN6331.K5 5—20761

NK 0211117 DLC MtBC Wa WaS Or MiU OOxM

Knox, George H 1871- comp.
... Thoughts that inspire ... Arranged and comp. by George H. Knox ... Des Moines, Ia., Personal help publishing company, 1907-1912.
2 v. fronts. (ports.) 20cm. (Personal help library)

NK 0211118 ICJ ICRL MB ODW

Knox, George H. 1871-
What are you cut out for?... Des Moines, Personal help pub. co., c1904.
3 p.

NK 0211119 OU

Knox, George Platt.
How should the school system contribute to an intelligent choice of vocation on the part of the pupil? [Problems relating to child welfare, D]
(In National education association of the United States. Journal of proceedings and addresses, 1912. p. 417-425)

1. Vocational guidance.

E 13-756

Library, U. S. Bur. of Education

NK 0211120 DHEW OO OU

VOLUME 300

Knox, George W.
National and municipal governments, by George W. Knox ... [Niagara Falls, °1927]
1 p. l., 22 p. 23cm.

1. Municipal government—U. S. 2. Municipal government. I. Title.

Library of Congress JS345.1927.K6 27-11686

NK 0211121 DLC

Knox, George Willard.
Light, vision and lenses; an introductory text-book of geometrical, physiological and ophthalmic optics, by G. W. Knox and V. J. Ellerbrock. [Columbus? Ohio, 1949 [i. e. 1950]
xvi, 350 p. illus. (part col.) 23 cm.

1. Optics, Physiological. 2. Spectacles. I. Ellerbrock, Vincent J., joint author. II. Title.

RE951.K6 617.75 50-4854

NK 0211122 DLC DNLM

Knox, George Willard
The relation of dynamic factors to flicker and fusion. [Columbus] The Ohio state university, 1940.
9 p. l., 245, [1] numb. l.

Thesis (Ph.D.)-Ohio state university.

NK 0211123 OU

Knox, George William, 1853-1912.
The Baccalaureate sermon preached before the candidates for degrees in Columbia University. [n.p., 1905].
10p. YA 9541

NK 0211124 DLC NN NjP

Knox, George William, 1853-1912.
The Christian point of view; three addresses by George William Knox, Arthur Cushman McGiffert, Francis Brown ... New York, C. Scribner's sons, 1902.

Knox, George William, 1853-1912.
A comment upon Shushi's philosophy. By George Wm. Knox ...
(*In* Asiatic society of Japan. Transactions. Yokohama, 1893. 23cm. v. 20, pt. 1, p. 148-154)

1. Chu, Hsi, 1130-1200.

Chicago. Univ. Library for Library of Congress AS552.A83 vol. 20 [AS552.Y8 vol. 20] [4] A C 38-3556 (068.52)

NK 0211126 ICU NcD OU DLC

Knox, George William, 1853-1912.
... The development of religion in Japan, by George William Knox ... New York and London, G. P. Putnam's sons, 1907.
xxi, 204 p. 21cm. (American lectures on the history of religions. Sixth series—1905-1906)
"Sources": p. xv-xvii.

7-6732

OrCS WU
OU OCl PU OOxM ViU PPTU PHC NN MB CaBVaU NBuU CoU
NK 0211127 DLC NcD OrU-M OrP WaS MtU CU MiU OO ODI

Knox, George William, 1853-1912.
The direct and fundamental proofs of the Christian religion; an essay in comparative apologetics, based upon the Nathaniel William Taylor lectures for 1903 given before the Divinity school of Yale university, by George William Knox ... New York, C. Scribner's sons, 1903.
viii p., 1 l., 196 p. 19½cm.

1. Apologetics—20th cent. I. Title: Christian religion.

Library of Congress BT1101.K7 3-22943

MB NN NNUT ViU NRCR PU
NK 0211128 DLC NIC NcD NcU MH-AH NjNbS OO OClW ODW

Knox, George William, 1853-1912.
The direct and fundamental proofs of the christian religion: an essay in comparative apologetics based upon the Nathaniel William Taylor Lectures for 1903 given before the Divinity School of Yale University. N.Y., Scribner's, 1910, [c1903]
viii, 196p. 19cm.

NK 0211129 PPPrHi OrSaW

Knox, George William, 1853-1912.
The gospel of Jesus the son of God, an interpretation for the modern man, by George William Knox ... Boston and New York, Houghton Mifflin company, 1909.
xix, [1], 118, [2] p. 17½cm. (*Half-title:* Modern religious problems, ed. by A. W. Vernon)

1. Christianity—20th cent. I. Title.

Library of Congress BR121.K7 9-28489

MB CU TxDaM NcD NcRS OCl
NK 0211130 DLC WaTC OrP NjNbS PPLT PHC NRCR OO OClW

Knox, George William, 1853-
Imperial Japan; the country & its people, by George William Knox. London, G. Newnes, limited, 1905.
xi, 294 p., 1 l. col. front., plates. 22½cm.
"I have used in this volume, chapters VII., IX., and X., portions of my translations from Japanese books which have been printed in the Transactions of the Asiatic society of Japan, and, chapter VIII., in the Independent."

1. Japan.

Library of Congress DS821.K67 5-36150

NK 0211131 DLC CaBVaU WU NcD CU CtY DNW NjP MB NN

Knox, George William, 1853-1912.
Japanese life in town and country, by George William Knox ... New York and London, G. P. Putnam's sons, 1904.
xii p., 1 l., 275 p. front., 18 pl., fold. map. 19cm. (*Half-title:* Our Asiatic neighbours)

1. Japan—Soc. life & cust.

Library of Congress DS821.K68 4-29700

PCC PPL OrPR CaBVaU Wa
ViU OCU OCIW ODW MiU OO OCIW DN NjP ICJ NN MB PU
NK 0211132 DLC NcD NNC CU LU GU HU-EWC WaSp Or OrP

Knox, George William, 1853-1912.
Japanese life in town and country. New York, etc., G.P.Putnam's sons, 1905.

NK 0211133 MH OCl OEac

Knox, George William, 1853-
Japanese life in town and country. N.Y., 1906.

NK 0211134 NjP

Knox, George William, 1853-1912.
Japanese life in town and country. New York: G. P. Putnam's Sons, 1908. xii(i), 275 p., 1 folded map, 19 pl. 12°. (Our Asiatic neighbours.)

1. Japan.—History. 2. Japan.—Religion. 3. Japan.—Social life and customs. 4. Series.
N. Y. P. L. March 29, 1911.

NK 0211135 NN CSt

Wason DS821 K74 1909 Knox, George William, 1853-1912.
Japanese life in town and country. New York, Young People's Missionary Movement of the United States and Canada, 1909 [c1904]
xii, 275 p. illus. 18cm. (Our Asiatic neighbors)

Mission study reference library no. 15. Japan.
1. Japan--Social life & cust. I. Title.

NK 0211136 NIC

Knox, George William, 1853-1912.
A Japanese philosopher
see under Muro, Kyuso, 1658-1734.

Knox, George William, 1853-1912.
The mystery of life ... Tokyo, 1890.
1 p.l., iv, 174 p. 20 cm.
Leaf of "errata" pasted in at end.

NK 0211138 CtY

Knox, George William, 1853-1912.
The new theology the fulfulling of the old. Address ... before the Associated Alumni of Union Theological Sem'y, in New York, May 18th, 1897. New York, Treasury Magazine Press, 1897.

NK 0211139 PPPrHi

Knox, George William, 1853-1912.
The relation of the church at home to the church abroad. An address, by Rev. George William Knox ... read at the third annual meeting of the Quaker Hill conference, September the fourth, nineteen hundred and one. Quaker Hill, N. Y., The Quaker Hill conference association, 1903.
13 p. 19½ x 12cm. (*On cover:* Quaker Hill series, v)

1. Missions.

Library of Congress BV2070.K6 8-5806 Revised

NK 0211140 DLC NN

Knox, George William, 1853-
The spirit of the Orient, by George William Knox. New York, T. Y. Crowell & co. [1906]
xvi, [2], 311, [1] p. front., 29 pl. 20½cm.
"Reprinted by permission from 'The Chautauquan' for September, October and November, 1905."
CONTENTS.—Introductory: America and the East.—The American point of view.—The Asiatic point of view.—India, its people and customs.—India, its spirit and problems.—China, its people and customs.—China, its spirit and problems.—Japan, its people and customs.—Japan, its spirit and problems.—The new world.—Bibliography (p. [309]-[312])

1. The East. I. Title.

Library of Congress DS518.K5 6-34855

OO NN NcD LU OkU NcU OKentU MH OrU OCl WaS
NK 0211141 DLC OrP PPL NRCR MB MiU OCIW ODW OCl

VOLUME 300

Knox, George William, 1853-1912, tr.

Arai, Hakuseki, 1657–1725.
... A translation of the "Hyō-chū-ori," &c., by Dr. G. W. Knox.
(In Asiatic society of Japan. Transactions. [Yokohama, etc., 1902] 23cm. v. 30, pt. 2, p. [1]–xii, [89]–238)

Knox, Gertrude Leverich.
The lost locket
see under Forman, Mrs. R R

784.3 K77r
Knox, Gertrude Leverich.
Rockin' time. Words and music by Gertrude Leverich Knox. Arranged for 3 female voices by W. Rhys-Herbert. [New York] J. Fischer & bro., c1908.
4p.

Caption title.

1. Negro songs. I. Rhys-Herbert, W. II. Title.

NK 0211144 IU

Knox, Gertrude Leverich.
A rose dream, a fairy operetta for young people
see under Forman, Mrs. R.R.

Knox, Gilbert.
Curiosity rewarded; a dialogue between Gilbert Knox [pseud.] and the curious public. Ottawa, The Graphic publishers [c1926]

cover-title, 12 p. 19cm.

"A souvenir of the triennial meeting, Canadian women's press club, with the compliments of the Graphic publishers, Ottawa. Toronto, Ontario, June 22nd to 25th, 1926."

NK 0211146 CaBVaU

Knox, Gilbert.
The kinder bees. London, Lovat Dickson & Thompson [1935]
4p.l.,11-315,[1]p. 20cm.

NK 0211147 TxU CaBVaU CaBVa

Knox, Gilbert.
The land of afternoon, a satire by Gilbert Knox [pseud.] Ottawa, The Graphic publishers [c1924]
4 p. l., 11-352 p. 20cm.

1. Canada—Fiction. I. Title.

NK 0211148 CaOKQ CaBVa CU

Knox, Gilbert.
The land of afternoon; a satire, by Gilbert Knox. Ottawa, The Graphic publishers [1925]
4 p. l., 11-352 p. 20cm.

I. Title.

Library of Congress PZ3.K7724La 26-7275

NK 0211149 DLC CtY CaBVaU NN

Knox, Gordon Daniell.
All about electricity; a book for boys, by Gordon D. Knox ... New York, Funk and Wagnalls company [1914]
xx, 356 p. col. front., illus., plates. 21½cm.

1. Electricity—Juvenile literature. 2. Electric engineering—Juvenile literature. I. Title.

21-16419

Library of Congress TK148.K6

NK 0211150 DLC TxU OClh NN

Knox, Gordon Daniell. 620-K
All about engineering; a book for boys on the great civil and mechanical engineering wonders of the world; with illustrations from photographs. London: Cassell and Co., Ltd. [19—?] iii-366 p., 3 diagr., 32 pl. (2 col'd). 8°.

1. Title. 2. Engineering.
N. Y. P. L. June 29, 1914.

NK 0211151 NN

Knox, Gordon Daniell.
All about engineering; a book for boys on the great civil and mechanical engineering wonders of the world, by Gordon D. Knox, with two colour plates and many illustrations from photographs. London, New York [etc.] Cassell and company, ltd. [1913]
xvi, 366 p. incl. col. front. plates (1 col.) 21½cm.

1. Engineering.

Library of Congress TA19.K5 14—30428

NK 0211152 DLC OEac PU-Sc

Knox, Gordon Daniell, joint author.

Wignall, T C.
Atoms, by T. C. Wignall and G. D. Knox. London, Mills & Boon, limited [1923]

Knox, Gordon Daniell.
... Engineering, by Gordon D. Knox ... London & Edinburgh, T. C. & E. C. Jack, 1915.
xi, 275, [1] p. col. front., illus., 16 pl. 21cm. (Half-title: "Romance of reality" series, ed. by E. Hawks)

1. Engineering.

A 16-672

Title from City Library, Springfield, Mass. Printed by L. C.

NK 0211154 MS OCl NN

Knox, Gordon Daniell.
.... Engineering. By Gordon D. Knox, ... New York, F. A. Stokes Company, [1915].
xi, 275, [1] p. col. front., 23 illus., 16 pl. 21cm. (Half-title: "Romance of reality" series.)
Series title also at head of t.-p.
Printed in Great Britain.

NK 0211155 ICJ Or MH

Knox, Gordon Daniell, tr.

Coquelle, P 1858–
Napoleon & England, 1803–1813; a study from unprinted documents by P. Coquelle; tr. from the French, by Gordon D. Knox ... With an introduction by J. Holland Rose ... London, G. Bell and sons, 1904.

Knox, Gordon Daniell.
The spirit of the soil; or, An account of nitrogen fixation in the soil by bacteria and of the production of auximones in bacterized peat. By Gordon D. Knox ... with a foreword by Professor W. B. Bottomley ... London, Constable and company ltd., 1915.
xiii, 242 p. front., plates. 19cm.
"List of papers by Professor William Beecroft Bottomley, M. A., dealing with bacterial fixation of nitrogen and the effect of soluble humates in the soil": p. 239.
1. Nitrification. [1. Nitrogen—Fixation] 2. Peat. I. Bottomley, William Beecroft, 1853–1922. II. Title.

Agr 16-343 Revised

Library, U. S. Dept. of Agriculture 56K77

NK 0211157 DNAL PP PU-B ICJ

Knox, Gordon D[aniell]. 631-K
The spirit of the soil; or, An account of nitrogen fixation in the soil by bacteria and of the production of auximones in bacterized peat; with a foreword by W. B. Bottomley. New York: Frederick A. Stokes Co. [pref. 1915.] 242 p. pl. 12°.

List of papers, p. 239.

1. Soils. 2. Title.
N. Y. P. L. August 30, 1916.

NK 0211158 NN

Knox, Gordon Daniell.
The spirit of the soil; or an account of nitrogen fixation in the soil by bacteria and of the production of auximones in bacterized peat. With a foreword by W. B. Bottomley. London, Constable, 1916.
xiii, 242 p. front., plates. 19 cm.

"List of papers by Professor William Beecroft Bottomley, M. A., dealing with bacterial fixation of nitrogen and the effect of soluble humates in the soil" p. 239.

NK 0211159 NIC

Knox, Gordon Daniell.
The spirit of the soil; or, An account of nitrogen fixation in the soil by bacteria and of the production of auximones in bacterized peat, by Gordon D. Knox ... with a foreword by Professor W. B. Bottomley ... 2d impression. London, Constable and company ltd., 1916.
xiii, 242 p. front., plates. 19cm.
"List of papers by Professor William Beecroft Bottomley, M. A., dealing with bacterial fixation of nitrogen and the effect of soluble humates in the soil": p. 239.

1. Nitrification. 2. Peat. I. Title.

17-110

Library of Congress S651.K7

NK 0211160 DLC NIC C PHC CtY MB

S651 .K7 1916
Knox, Gordon Daniell.
The spirit of the soil; or, An account of nitrogen fixation in the soil by bacteria and of the production of auximones in bacterized peat; with a foreword by W. B. Bottomley. New York, F. A. Stokes Co. [1916]
xiii, 242 p. plates. 19cm.
"List of papers by ... William Beecroft Bottomley ... dealing with bacterial fixation of nitrogen and the effect of soluble humates in the soil": p.239.
1. Nitrification. 2. Peat. I. Title.

NK 0211161 ViU

Knox, H. C., joint author.

Comings, W R
Lessons in language & composition, by W. R. Comings ... and H. C. Knox ... Medina, O., 1882.

VOLUME 300

D526.2 K74
Knox, H J
Soldier cartoons of the American Forces in Germany. [Coblenz, Krabbensche Buchdruckerei, 1919?]
50 p. of illus. 17x30cm.

1.European War, 1914-1918 - Humor, caricatures, etc. I. Title.

NK 0211163 CSt-H

Knox, Harry, 1867-
The law of copyright in designs: with the statutes, rules, forms and international convention. By Harry Knox ... and Jesse W. Hind ... London, Reeves and Turner, 1899.
xvi, 247, [1] p. 2 illus. 25cm.

1. Copyright—Designs. 2. Copyright—Gt. Brit. I. Hind, Jesse William, 1886- joint author. II. Gt. Brit. Laws, statutes, etc.

Library of Congress Z654.K71 4—31990
[a40b1] -655.62

NK 0211164 DLC OU ICJ

Knox, Harry P
A study of blackboard visibility. Thesis, 1938.
40pp.

NK 0211165 OCIW

Knox, Helen, 1885-
Mrs. Percy V. Pennybacker; an appreciation, by Helen Knox ... New York, Chicago [etc.] Fleming H. Revell company [°1916]
192 p. front., plates, ports. 19½cm. $1.00

1. Pennybacker, Mrs. Anna J. (Hardwicke) 1861-
Library of Congress CT275.P56K7 16-15464

NK 0211166 DLC ViU OCIW NN

HG179 .F5 1950
Knox, Helen, 1885- joint author.

Finke, Mary Berkeley.
Moneywise; the intelligent woman's guide to everyday finance [by] Mary Berkeley Finke and Helen Knox. New York, Putnam [1950]

Knox, Helen M
An abstract of German grammar. Ithaca, N.Y., Andrus & Church, 1908.

NK 0211168 MH

Knox, Henry, 1641?-1716.
A catalogue of most excellent and curious new books; to be sold by way of auction; upon Munday the 23 day of June 1701...Edinburgh, Printed in the year, 1701.

NK 0211169 DFo

Knox, Henry, 1750-1806.
Works by this author printed in America before 1801 are available in this library in the Readex Microprint edition of Early American Imprints published by the American Antiquarian Society.
This collection is arranged according to the numbers in Charles Evans' American Bibliography.

NK 0211170 DLC

Knox, Henry, 1750-1806.

Historical records survey. *Massachusetts.*
A calendar of the General Henry Knox papers, Chamberlain collection, Boston public library. Prepared by the Historical records survey, Division of women's and professional projects, Works progress administration. Boston, Mass., The Historical records survey, 1939.

E83 .794 .W3
Knox, Henry, 1750-1806.

Wayne, Anthony, 1745-1796.
Campaign into the wilderness; the Wayne-Knox-Pickering-McHenry correspondence. Edited by Richard C. Knopf. Columbus, Anthony Wayne Parkway Board, Ohio State Museum, 1955.

Knox, Henry, 1750-1806.
A catalogue of books, imported and to be sold by Henry Knox, at the London book-store, a little southward of the town-house, in Cornhill. Boston, 1773. 40 p. 4°.

1. Bibliography—Catalogues, Booksellers'.
N. Y. P. L. April 22, 1927

NK 0211173 NN MH MB

---

*pAB7 K7794 799f
Knox, Henry, 1750-1806.
For sale, lots or tracts of land of any size, as may best suit the purchasers, from 100 acres to 1000 acres, and upwards. The lands hereby offered for sale, are within the rich tract of country between the river Kennebeck, and the bay and river of Penobscot, called the Muscongus, or Waldo Patent, and which comprehends the Muscongus, and St. George's Rivers ... June 15, 1799.
[Boston?1799]
broadside. 53x31.5cm.
Not in Evans or Ford.

NK 0211174 MH MB PPRF

Knox, Henry, 1750-1806.
Henry Knox and the London Book-store in Boston, 1771-1774
see under title

E172 .A35 vol. 56
Knox, Henry, 1750-1806.

Adams, John, *Pres. U. S.,* 1735-1826.
John Adams, Knox, and Washington.
(*In* **American Antiquarian Society, Worcester, Mass. Proceedings. Worcester, 1947. 25 cm. v. 56, p. [207]-238)**

Knox, Henry B.
A Sermon preached ... at the Inauguration of the Hadleigh Rifle Corps, July 25th, 1860. Hadleigh, 1860.
8 p. 16°. [In v. 736, College Pamphlets]

NK 0211177 CtY

Knox, Henry B.
A Sermon preached in Hadleigh Church, Sep. 19th, 1847.... Hadleigh [1847?]
15 p. 8°. [In v. 736, College Pamphlets]

NK 0211178 CtY

Knox, Henry Macdonald, 1916-
Two hundred and fifty years of Scottish education, 1696-1946. Edinburgh, Oliver and Boyd [1953]
258 p. 23 cm.

1. Education—Scotland—Hist. I. Title.

LA651.K56 370.941 53-4363 ‡

MdBJ NcD TU IaU CtY ICU MH NN CaBVaU CaBVa
NK 0211179 DLC KEmT MH GU AU N TxU MB CoU WaS MtU

---

*HJ 518 .K6
Knox, Henry Martyn, 1830-1904.
The Office of Public Examiner, a Minnesota notion; an address before the American Bankers' Association, at Pittsburgh, Pa., October 12, 1887. New York, Bankers' Pub. Association, 1887.
7 p. 23 cm.

Cover title.

1. Minnesota. Office of Public Examiner. I. Title.

NK 0211180 MnHi

Knox, Herman Warren, 1881- ed.

Who's who in New York (city and state) ... 1st- ed.; 1904-
New York city, Who's who publications, inc. [1904]-

Knox, Horatio B.
... The destruction of the Gaspee, by Horatio B. Knox ... [Providence] Department of education, state of Rhode Island, 1908.
15, [1] p. 23½cm. (Rhode Island educational circulars. Historical series—III)

1. Gaspee (Schooner) 2. Rhode Island—Hist.—Revolution.

Library of Congress F76.R32 no. 3 9—2374
——— Copy 2 E215.6.K74

NK 0211182 DLC CU MB MiU OO OCl MWA RPJCB NN

HD 9529 T6U5
Knox, Howard A
Development of the American tin plate industry. Reprinted with permission of Iron age. Pittsburgh, Carnegie-Illinois Steel Corporation, United States Steel [1947?]
49 p. illus. (part col.) 24cm.

1. Tin plate. I. Carnegie-Illinois Steel Corporation.

NK 0211183 CoU

W 6 P3
KNOX, Howard Andrew, 1885-
Alien mental defectives; a collection of papers descriptive of the tests and methods employed by the United States Public Health Service, Ellis Island, N. Y. Chicago, Stoelting [1914?]
[33] p. illus.

NK 0211184 DNLM NIC PBm OCIW

VOLUME 300

Knox, Howard Vicenté.
The evolution of truth, and other essays, by Howard V. Knox... London: Constable & Co., Ltd., 1930. vi, 180 p. 8°.
Reprinted from various sources.
Bibliographical footnotes.
Contents: Green's refutation of empiricism. Mr. Bradley's 'Absolute criterion.' Pragmatism: the evolution of truth. What is pragmatism?, by J. B. Pratt. (A review.) The philosophy of William James. Has Green answered Locke? The letters of William James. Is determinism rational?
487991A. 1. Philosophy—Essays and misc. N. Y. P. L. August 14, 1930
NK 0211185 NN CU ICU MH PSC

Knox, Howard Vicenté.
The evolution of truth, and other essays, by Howard V. Knox ... New York, R. R. Smith inc. [1930]
vi p., 1 l., 180 p. 22cm.
Printed in Great Britain.
"First American edition 1930."
CONTENTS.—Green's refutation of empiricism.—Mr. Bradley's 'absolute criterion'.—Pragmatism: the evolution of truth.—What is pragmatism? by J. B. Pratt (a review)—The philosophy of William James.—Has Green answered Locke?—The letters of William James.—Is determinism rational?
1. Philosophy—Addresses, essays, lectures. 2. Truth. I. Title.
30-31394
Library of Congress B29.K6
[3] 192.04
NK 0211186 DLC NcD OC1U OO OU MH

Knox, Howard Vicenté.
Gt. Brit. *Historical manuscripts commission.*
The manuscripts of Captain H. V. Knox.
(*In its* Report on manuscripts in various collections. London, 1909. 25cm. v. 6, p. [81]-296, [440]-449)

Knox, Howard Vicenté.
The philosophy of William James. London: Constable & Co., Ltd., 1914. x, 112 p., 1 port. 12°. (Philosophies: ancient and modern.)
Bibliography, p. ix-x.
1. James, William, 1842-1910. N. Y. P. L. September 16, 1914.
NK 0211188 NN OO OCU OOxM MH PHC PPPD PU IaU

Knox, Howard Vicenté.
The philosophy of William James, by Howard V. Knox. New York, Dodge publishing company, 1914.
x, 112 p. front. (port.) 17½cm. (*Half-title:* Philosophies: ancient and modern)
"Chronological list of William James's works": p. ix. "Some books, etc., on James": p. x.
1. James, William, 1842-1910.
A 15-2361 Revised
Title from Illinois Univ. Printed by L. C.
NK 0211189 IU OU ViU CSaT PBm PWcS MB NN

Knox, Howard Vicenté.
The will to be free; a critique of deterministic theory and a vindication of real alternatives in human purpose, by Howard V. Knox ... with preface by L. P. Jacks ... and J. A. Stewart ... London, Constable and company ltd., 1928.
xvi, 237 p. 22½cm.
1. Free will and determinism. I. Title.
29-10770
Library of Congress BF621.K6
NcD MH NN
NK 0211190 DLC CaBVaU CU-I NIC CtY OClW OCl OO PSC

Knox, Howard Vicenté.
The will to be free; a critique of deterministic theory and a vindication of real alternatives in human purpose, by Howard V. Knox...with preface by L. P. Jacks...and J. A. Stewart... New York: E. P. Dutton and Co., Inc. [, 1929?] xvi, 237 p. 22½cm.
574307A. 1. Will—Liberty. N. Y. P. L. March 7, 1933
NK 0211191 NN ICarbS OU CU OKentU OrPR MB MH PHC

Knox, Hubert Thomas.
The history of the county of Mayo to the close of the sixteenth century, by Hubert Thomas Knox ... Dublin, Hodges, Figgis & co., ltd., 1908.
xvii, 451 p. incl. geneal. tables. front., port., maps (3 fold.) 25½cm.
1. Mayo, Ire. (County)—Hist.
9-22571
Library of Congress DA990.M3K6
NK 0211192 DLC CaOTP TxU CtY NN MB

Knox, Hubert Thomas.
Notes on the early history of the dioceses of Tuam, Killala, and Achonry. Dublin: Hodges, Figgis & Co., Ltd., 1904. xvi, 410 p., 1 map. 8°.
1. Church history, Gt. Br.: Ireland. N. Y. P. L. November 17, 1913.
NK 0211193 NN TxU WaU ICN MH

Knox, Hugh, *d.* 1790.
Works by this author printed in America before 1801 are available in this library in the Readex Microprint edition of Early American Imprints published by the American Antiquarian Society.
This collection is arranged according to the numbers in Charles Evans' American Bibliography.
NK 0211194 DLC

Knox, Hugh, *d.* 1790.
The dignity and importance of the gospel ministry, displayed in a sermon, preached by the Revd. Hugh Knox, A. M. on the day of his ordination, before the Presbytery of New-York ... New-York: Printed and Sold by Hugh Gaine, at the Printing-Office, between the Fly and Meal-Markets, 1755.
1 p. l., ii, 24 p. 20½cm.
I. Title.
24-8987
BV4009.K6
NK 0211195 DLC CtHi MHi MWiW-C NjP RPJCB

Knox, Hugh, d. 1790.
Discourse delivered on the 6th of September 1772... St. Croix, 1772.
NK 0211196 RPJCB

WW20 K74 D
Knox, Hugh, 1733-1790.
Discourses on the truth of revealed religion and other important subjects. By Hugh Knox ... London: Printed for Thomas Cadell, 1768.
2v. 18cm.
NK 0211197 NNUT DLC NjNbS CtY NjP NN

Knox, Hugh, *d.* 1790.
The duty and importance of waiting for our great chang[e] A discourse, delivered on the third day of the year 1768, in t[he] church of Saba. St. Christopher, 1768.
32 p. 23 cm.
Half-title and running title: A New Year's discourse.
1. Presbyterian Church—Sermons. I. Title.
BX9178.K6D8 47-42729*
NK 0211198 DLC PPPrHi

Knox, Hugh, d. 1790.
A form of renewing covenant with God, at the Lord's table. By Hugh Knox, D.D. in St. Croix. [New-Ipswich, N. H. Published for S. Payson, D.D. Simeon Ide. printer. 1815]
12 p. 18 cm. Uncut.
Caption-title.
1. Lord's supper. I. Title.
NK 0211199 CSmH

*AC7 K7727 D820f
Knox, Hugh, d.1790.
A form of renewing covenant with God, at the Lord's table. By Hugh Knox, D.D. in St. Croix. Brunswick[Me.]:Printed by Joseph Griffin. 1820.
12p. 21.5cm.
Caption title; imprint on p.12.
Taken from essays 5 & 8 of his The moral and religious miscellany.
NK 0211200 MH MeWC

Knox, Hugh, ca. 1733-1790.
A letter to the Rev. Mr. Jacob Green, of New Jersey, pointing out some difficulties in the Calvinistick scheme of divinity, respecting free will, divine decrees, particular redemption, &c. and requesting a solution of them. By Hugh Knox... London: Printed for G. Keith, J. Johnson... [1770]. 101 p. 8°.
1. Calvinism. N. Y. P. L. January 15, 1929
NK 0211201 NN NjP

Knox, Hugh, *d.* 1790.
A letter to the Rev. Mr. Jacob Green, of New-Jersey, pointing out some difficulties in the Calvinistic scheme of divinity, respecting free will, divine decrees, particular redemption, &c., and requesting a solution of them. By Hugh Knox ... New-York: Printed by T. and J. Swords, no. 160 Pearl-street. 1809.
2 p. l., 54 p. 22½cm.
1. Calvinism—Controversial literature. I. Green, Jacob, 1722-1790.
45-34008
Library of Congress BX9424.K6
NK 0211202 DLC NjPT CtY PPPrHi NN

Knox, Hugh, *d.* 1790.
The moral and religious miscellany; or, Sixty-one aphoretical essays on some of the most important Christian doctrines and virtues. New-York, Printed by Hodge and Shober, 1775.
360 p. 20 cm.
1. Presbyterian Church—Addresses, essays, lectures. 2. Theology, Doctrinal—Addresses, essays, lectures. 3. Virtue. I. Title.
BX8915.K58 1775 51-49547
MiU-C MdBJ-G
NK 0211203 DLC MeWC NcD PHi MWA MH ICN RPJCB NN

VOLUME 300

Knox, Hugh, *d.* 1790.
The moral and religious miscellany; or, Sixty-one aphoretical essays, on some of the most important Christian doctrines and virtues. By Hugh Knox ... Hartford: Reprinted by Hudson and Goodwin. M.DCC.XC.
viii, [9]-352 p. 20½ cm.

1. Presbyterian church—Addresses, essays, lectures. 2. Theology, Doctrinal—Addresses, essays, lectures. 3. Virtues. I. Title.
BX8915.K58 1790 46-41576

NK 0211204 DLC RPJCB MoU MnU CtY NNUT CSmH MWA IU NN WaS KyU

Knox, Hugh, d. 1790.
The moral and religious miscellany: or, sixty-one aphoretical essays, on some of the most important Christian doctrines and virtues... Gettysburg, Pa. Robert Harper, 1807.
432p.

NK 0211205 OClWHi PSt PHi NcU NcD

*
BX8915
.K58
1808
Knox, Hugh, d. 1790.
The moral and religious miscellany; or, Sixty-one aphoretical essays, on some of the most important Christian doctrines and virtues. Harrisburgh—Printed and sold by John Wyeth. 1808.
2 v. 18cm.
1. Presbyterian Church—Addresses, essays, lectures. 2. Theology, Doctrinal—Addresses, essays, lectures. 3. Virtue. I. Title.

NK 0211206 ViU InU PMA DGU ViU OrPR MA CSmH OOxM PSt NNUT DLC NWM

Knox, Hugh, *d.* 1790.
Select sermons on interesting subjects. Glasgow, Printed by R. & A. Foulis, 1776.
2 v. 17 cm.

1. Presbyterian Church—Sermons.
BX9178.K6S4 61-57118 ‡

NK 0211207 DLC NjP

[Knox, *Mrs.* Isa (Craig)] 1831-1903.
The Burns festival. Prize poem recited at the Crystal palace. January 25, 1859. London, Bradbury and Evans, 1859.
7 p. 25½cm.

1. Burns (Robert) in fiction, drama, poetry, etc. I. Title.
Library of Congress PR4335.K6 2—20502

NK 0211208 DLC

[Knox, Isa (Craig),] 1831–
Deepdale vicarage. By the author of "Mark Warren," etc., etc. London: Cassell, Petter, Galpin & Co. [1876?] vii, 405 p. front. 12°.
"This story originally appeared in an early volume of the Quiver."

12741A. 1. Fiction (English). 2. Title.
N. Y. P. L. August 23, 1921.

NK 0211209 NN

Rare Book Room
Ip
K772
864
Knox, Isa (Craig), 1831-1903.
Duchess Agnes, etc. By Isa Craig. London, Alexander Strahan, 1864.
iv,228p. 17cm.
Contents. - Duchess Agnes, a drama. - Odes and idylls. - Songs and sketches. - Found dead. - Pleasant place.
In manuscript on t.-p.: "Mrs Lewes [i.e., George Eliot] with the writer's kind regards".

NK 0211210 CtY

Knox, Isa (Craig) 1831-1903.
Duchess Agnes, etc., by Isa Craig. 2d ed. London, A.Strahan, 1865.
iv,228p. 17cm.

NK 0211211 CtY OCl NN PSt

Knox, Isa Craig, 1831-1903.
The essence of slavery
see under Kemble, Frances Anne, 1809-1893.

823.8
K74e
Knox, Mrs. Isa (Craig) 1831-1903.
Esther West; a story. London, New York, Cassell, Petter, and Galpin [1870]
369p.

NK 0211213 ICarbS NN

[Knox, Isa (Craig),] 1831-1903.
The half-sisters. By the author of "Deepdale vicarage," "Mark Warren," etc., etc. London: Cassell, Petter, Galpin & Co. [1876?] vii, 406 p. front., plates. 12°.
"This story originally appeared in an early volume of the Quiver."

12762A. 1. Fiction (English). 2. Title.
N. Y. P. L. August 23, 1921.

NK 0211214 NN

[Knox, Isa (Craig),] 1831-1903.
Hold fast by your Sundays! By the author of "Deepdale vicarage". New illustrated ed. ... London, Lord's day observance society [n.d.]
124p. illus. 19cm.

NK 0211215 NNUT

[KNOX, ISA (CRAIG)] 1831-1903.
In duty bound. By the author of "Mark Warren"...&c., &c. ... New York: Harper & bros., 1870. 121 p. 23½cm.

113844B. 1. Fiction, Scottish. I. Title.

NK 0211216 NN MH OCl MB

Knox, Isa Craig, 1831-1903.
In duty bound. By the author of "Mark Warren." [anon.] New York, Beadle & Adams, 1884.
32 p. 4°. [Waverley library. v. 9. no. 233]

NK 0211217 DLC

Knox, Isa Craig, 1831-
The little folks' history of England. By Isa Craig-Knox. With illustrations by R. E. Galindo. 8th ed. London, New York, (etc.) Cassell, Petter, Galpin & co., (1871?)
vii, (1) 284 p. incl. front., illus. 17 cm.
On cover: Young folks' history of England.

NK 0211218 DHEW

Knox, Isa (Craig) 1831–
The little folks' history of England. By Isa Craig-Knox. With illustrations by R. E. Galindo and others. 10th ed. New York, London [etc.] Cassell & company, limited [°1885]
x, 284 p. front., illus., pl. 18½cm.

Subject entries: Gt. Brit.—Hist.—Compends.
2-16276
Library of Congress, no. DA32.K74.

NK 0211219 DLC MB

Knox, *Mrs.* Isa(Craig) 1831—. Poems. 12 p.
(Miles, A. H.. Poets ... of the century, v. 7, p. 465.)

NK 0211220 MdBP

Ap
K7724p
1856
Stark
Lib'y
Knox, Isa (Craig) 1831-1903.
Poems by Isa [pseud.] Edinburgh and London, W. Blackwood and Sons, 1856.
x (i.e. xi),[1],172,[2],16p. 16cm.
Page xi numbered x.
Advertisements: [2],16p. at end.
With autograph of S. Maxton.

I. Title. A.F.: Maxton, S.

NK 0211221 TxU

821.08
K74P
Knox, Isa (Craig) 1831-1903, comp.
Poems: an offering to Lancashire. London, E. Faithfull, 1863.
62 p. 19 cm.

1. English poetry (Collections)

NK 0211222 NcD CaBVaU MH NjP MB IU FTaSU

Knox, Isa (Craig) 1831-1903.
Spring songs.
2 p. (Fraser's Mag. v. 61, 1860, p. 501)

NK 0211223 MdBP

DA32
.K74
Knox, Mrs. Isa (Craig) 1831-1903.
The young folks' history of England. By Isa Craig-Knox. With illustrations by R. E. Galindo. Boston, Lee & Shepard; New York, Lee, Shepard, & Dillingham [1876]
vii, [1] 280 p. incl. front., illus. 15 1/2cm.

1. Gt. Brit.—History, Juvenile. I. Title.

NK 0211224 MB

Knox, Israel, 1904–
The aesthetic theories of Kant, Hegel, and Schopenhauer, by Israel Knox ... New York, Columbia university press, 1936.
xi, 219, [1] p. 21½ cm.
Thesis (PH. D.)—Columbia university, 1936.
Vita.
Published also without thesis note.
Bibliography: p. [193]-207.

1. Kant, Immanuel, 1724-1804. 2. Hegel, Georg Wilhelm Friedrich, 1770-1831. 3. Schopenhauer, Arthur, 1788-1860. 4. Esthetics. I. Title.
B2799.E7K6 1936 701 37—4671

NK 0211225 DLC IdPI ViU ScU FMU

VOLUME 300

Knox, Israel, 1904–
The aesthetic theories of Kant, Hegel, and Schopenhauer, by Israel Knox. New York, Columbia university press, 1936.
xi, 219 p. 22½ cm.
Issued also as thesis (PH. D.) Columbia university.
Bibliography: p. [193]–207.

1. Kant, Immanuel, 1724–1804. 2. Hegel, Georg Wilhelm Friedrich, 1770–1831. 3. Schopenhauer, Arthur, 1788–1860. 4. Aesthetics. I. Title.
B2799.E7K6 1936a 701 36–21333

NcD GU NcU MiU
NK 0211226 DLC OrCS OO OClW OCU OU PSC PBm OrPR

Knox, J.
Port Sunlight works continuation school. An address given to the Joint industrial council of the soap & candle trades at Birmingham... March, 1920, by J. Knox, M.A. (Port Sunlight, Printed by Lever brothers, limited, 1920)
22 p. 18½ cm.

NK 0211227 DL

Knox, J.R., tr.

Boisseau, François Gabriel, 1791–1836.
Physiological pyretology; or, A treatise on fevers: according to the principles of the new medical doctrine. By F. G. Boisseau ... 1st American, from the 4th French ed. Tr. by J. R. Knox, M. D. Philadelphia, Carey & Lea, 1832.

Knox, Jackson.
...Captain Clew, the fighting detective; or, Against terrible odds. A romance of the wolves of New York. By Jackson Knox, "Old Hawk." New York: Beadle & Adams, 1892. 31 p. illus. f°. (Beadle's dime library. no. 740.)
Caption-title.

NK 0211229 NN

Knox, Jackson.
...The hurricane detective; or, Through thick and thin. A romance of the toils and meshes of the great city. By Jackson Knox, "Old Hawk." New York: Beadle & Adams, 1892. 32 p. illus. f°. (Beadle's dime library. no. 732.)
Caption-title.

NK 0211230 NN

Knox, Jacqueline Lloyd.
Bittersweets; a book of verse, by Jacqueline Lloyd Knox. [Philadelphia] Dorrance & co., inc. [1938]
50 p. 19½cm.

I. Title.
38-33362
Library of Congress PS3521.N82B5 1938
——— Copy 2.
Copyright A 123192 [2] 811.5

NK 0211231 DLC

Knox, James.
Appeal of James Knox to the Board of trustees of the College of the city of New York, from the action of the Executive committee, discharging him from the position of tutor in the college. New York, Evening post steam presses, 1876.
76 p. 26cm.

I. New York. City college. Board of trustees.
E 10-338 Revised
U. S. Off. of educ. Library for Library of Congress LD3818.K77 [r41b2]

NK 0211232 DHEW NN

Knox, James
Cubical calculator, giving the cubic capacity of jute and cotton bales, tea and oil in cases, also, goat skins, both casks and bales. Thacker, 1919.

NK 0211233 OrP

265.3
K77 **Knox, James.**
De necessitudine Deiparam inter et eucharistiam. Romae, Officium Libri Catholici, 1949.
xix, 262 p. 25 cm.
"Appendix. De manuscripto Michaelis Cosentini De gloriosa Virgine Sanctissimi Sacramenti nuncupata": p. [221]-254.
Bibliography.
1. Eucharist. 2. Mary, Virgin—Theology. 3. Michele da Cosenza, Father, 17th cent.

NK 0211234 MoSU-D DCU IMunS

DA
880
T38
K56
1831
Knox, James, cartographer.
The topography of the basin of the Tay; intended as a companion to the map of the basin of the Tay... Edinburgh, J. Anderson [etc.] 1831.
xii, 226, 22 p. illus. 20 cm.

1. Tay River, Scotland. I. Title.

NK 0211235 CaBVaU

Knox, James, Rev.
A token of affectionate remembrance: being a farewell discourse ... in Norwalk, (Conn.) ... Philadelphia, 1839.
iv, [5]-59 p. 12.5 cm.

NK 0211236 CtY

Knox (JAMES) 1807-1869.
On commercial training, with suggestions as to its place in college and school instruction. *Edinburgh: Sutherland & Knox,* 1858. 19 pp. 8°.
In: *C. p. v. 669.

NK 0211237 NN

Knox, James, 1807–1876.
Nebraska and Kansas. Speech of Hon. James Knox, of Illinois, in the House of representatives, May 19, 1854. [Washington, Printed at the Congressional globe office, 1854]
8 p. illus. 23½cm.
Caption title.

1. Kansas-Nebraska bill.
10-31652
Library of Congress E433.K72

NK 0211238 DLC

DA
890
A28
K74
Knox, Sir James, 1862-
Airdrie, a historical sketch. Airdrie, Baird & Hamilton, 1921.
178 p. illus.
"Compiled in response to a request by the Burgh of Airdrie Centenary Committee on the occasion of the hundredth anniversary of the erection of Airdrie into a Burgh of Barony."

1. Airdrie, Scot.--Hist. I. Title.

NK 0211239 MiU

Knox, James, 1862-
Airdrie bards, past and present. Issued by the Airdrie Burns club. Airdrie [Scotland] Baird & Hamilton, 1930.
viii, 349 p. 22 cm.

NK 0211240 MH

Knox, Sir James, 1862-
The triumph of thrift: the story of the savings bank of Airdrie, instituted 1835, by James Knox ... Airdrie [Scot.] Baird & Hamilton, ltd., 1927.
xvi, 366 p. front., plates, facsims., tab.

NK 0211241 MH-BA CLU

Knox, James, 1909–
Sunday's children. Decorations by David Hendrickson. Boston, Houghton Mifflin, 1955.
186 p. illus. 22 cm.
Autobiographical.

I. Title.
Full name: James Hervey Orr Knox.
PZ4.K75Su 55-8875 ‡

OEac PP WaU KyU KyLE
NK 0211242 DLC CaBVa OrP Wa WaE WaS WaT CU LU OOxM

Knox, James Carter. No. 2 in **M.158.17
Be merciful after Thy power. [Anthem. Accomp. for organ.] Boston. Schmidt & Co. 1883. 7 pp. L. 8°.

E2768 — Church music. Anthems, &c.

NK 0211243 MB

KNOX, James Carter.
Benedic Anima Mea. Anthem. n.p., n.d.

NK 0211244 MH

Knox, James Carter. No. 1 in **M.158.17
Benedictus, in C. [Accomp. for organ.] Boston. Schmidt & Co. 1884. 7 pp. L. 8°.

E2768 — Church music. Anthems, &c.

NK 0211245 MB

KNOX, James Carter.
Blessed be the man that provideth. B., 1881
f°.
(Sacred music for church and home.)

NK 0211246 MH

KNOX, James Carter
Give alms of thy goods. B., [c1881].
f°. pp.6.
(Sacred music for church and home.)

NK 0211247 MH

VOLUME 300

Knox, James Carter.
Henry Augustus Coit, first rector of Saint Paul's school, Concord, New Hampshire, by James Carter Knox ... New York [etc.] Longmans, Green, and co., 1915.
4 p. l., 3-149, [1] p. 2 port. (incl. front.) facsim. 19½cm. $1.00

1. Coit, Henry Augustus, 1830-1895.
Library of Congress LD7501.C8S32 15-20411

NK 0211248 DLC IaU ICRL PU PPL OU OC1W ICJ NN MB

Knox, James Carter.
Hymns and responses, by James C. Knox ... 2d ed. Boston, A. P. Schmidt & co., °1883.
2 p. l., 3-21 p. 22cm.
With music.

1. Hymns, English.
Library of Congress M2121.K6H9 1883 45-41414

NK 0211249 DLC

KNOX, JAMES Carter.
Twenty hymns, by James C. Knox... Boston: The A.P. Schmidt Co., cop. 1919. 25 p. 22cm.
English words; music for 4 voices.

1. Hymns.

NK 0211250 NN

Knox, James Hall Mason, 1872-
Baby welfare (by) J.H. Mason Knox... Chicago, American medical association, n.d.)
16 p. illus. 20 1/2 cm. (American medical association. Council on health and public instruction. Public health series)
Caption title.

NK 0211251 DL OO

Knox, James Hall Mason, 1872-
The beginning and development of child hygiene in Baltimore and Maryland. [Baltimore, Maryland State Dept. of Health] 1948.
36 p. 22 cm.
Cover title: Child hygiene in Baltimore and Maryland.
Bibliographical footnotes.

1. Children—Care and hygiene. 2. Infants—Mortality. 3. Child welfare—Maryland. I. Maryland. Bureau of Child Hygiene. II. Title.
RA609.K78 618.92 A 49-10563*
Enoch Pratt Free Libr.

NK 0211252 MdBE DLC

Knox, James Hall Mason, 1872-

White House conference on child health and protection. *Sect. I: Medical service. Committee on medical care for children.*
Child health centers: a survey; report of the Subcommittee on health centers, J. H. Mason Knox, jr., chairman, Lillian Laser Strauss, vice-chairman, White House conference on child health and protection. New York, London, The Century Co. [°1932]

Knox, James Hall Mason, 1872-
Talks to mothers about their babies, by Dr. J. H. Mason Knox ... Bureau of child hygiene, Maryland State department of health, Baltimore. [Baltimore, The Sun book & job printing off., inc.] 1923.
85, [2] p. 23cm.
"Reprinted from the Baltimore Sun."

1. Infants—Care and hygiene. I. Title.
E 23-442
Library, U. S. Bur. of Education RJ61.K64

NK 0211254 DHEW CU OC1 OC1W

Knox, James Hall Mason, 1872-

Maryland. *Bureau of child hygiene.*
Where Maryland stands in child health. By Dr. J. H. Mason Knox, jr., chief. Bureau of child hygiene, Maryland State department of health. Baltimore, 1924.

Knox, James Hall Mason, d. 1903.
Christ's presence in affliction. A sermon preached in the First Pres. Ch., Germantown, Pa., June 19, 1859. Philadelphia, Ashmead, 1859.

NK 0211256 PPPrHi

Knox, James Hall Mason, d. 1903.
Discourse commemorative of the Rev. David X. Junkin, D.D. ... delivered ... June 20, 1880. Bristol, Pa., 1880.

NK 0211257 PPPrHi

Knox, James Hall Mason, d. 1903.
A discourse commemorative of the Rev. George Junkin ... by the Rev. James H. Mason Knox ... delivered in the West Spruce Street Presbyterian Church, Philadelphia ... June 28, 1868. Philadelphia, Printed by A. Martien, 1868.
45 p. 24cm.

1. Junkin, George, 1790-1868.

NK 0211258 NNC

Knox, James Hall Mason, d. 1903.
Discourse occasioned by the decease of Robert Hobart Smith, Delivered Sept. 5, 1858 ... Philadelphia, 1858.

NK 0211259 PPPrHi PHi

Knox, James Hall Mason, d. 1903.
Discourses at the inauguration [of J.H.M. Knox] as president of Lafayette college, Easton, Pa., June 24th, 1884
see under Lafayette College, Easton, Pa.

Knox, James Hall Mason, d. 1903.
Historical data concerning the Presbyterian church at Bristol, Bucks Co., Pa. 1845-1882. Manuscripts.

NK 0211261 PPPrHi

Knox, James Samuel, 1872-1945.
Business efficiency, by James Samuel Knox... Cleveland, 1918. 295 p. front. (port.) 8°.

81649A. 1. Salesmanship and salesmen.
N. Y. P. L. April 25, 1923.

NK 0211262 NN ICRL

Knox, James Samuel, 1872-1945.
A modern course in salesmanship, by James S. Knox and John Knox. [1st ed.] Oak Park, Ill., Knox Business Book Co., 1951.
xvii, 579 p. illus. 21 cm.
"A successor to ... [the authors'] ten pamphlet course entitled Salesmanship and business engineering."

1. Salesmen and salesmanship. I. Knox, John Jay, joint author.
HF5438.K568 658.85 51-10727

NK 0211263 DLC WaS Wa PP

Knox, James Samuel, 1872-
Personal efficiency, by James Samuel Knox, A. M. Cleveland, O., The Knox business book co., 1919.
4p. l., 254 p. front. (port.) illus., plates, diagrs. 20½cm.

1. Success. I. Title. II. Title. Efficiency. Personal.
Library of Congress HF5386.K75 19-19467

NK 0211264 DLC ICRL PP OC1ND OC1 ICJ

HF
5386 Knox, James Samuel, 1872-1945.
K75 Personal efficiency, by James Samuel Knox.
1919a School ed. New York, Gregg [°1919]
254 p. illus., diagrs. 21 cm.

1. Success. I. Title.

NK 0211265 LU

Knox, James Samuel, 1872-
Personal efficiency. Cleveland, O., Knox business book co., 1920.
254p.

NK 0211266 OC1W CU

Knox, James Samuel, 1872-
Personality in action, by James Samuel Knox ... and Mrs. Alice H. Horner ... and Mrs. Ruth Wade Ray ... Oak Park (Chicago) Ill., The Knox business book company [°1940]
viii, [2], 404 p. 21cm.

1. Personality. 2. Efficiency, Industrial. I. Horner, Mrs. Alice H., joint author. II. Ray, Mrs. Ruth Wade, joint author. III. Title.
Library of Congress BF698.K6 40-33857
——— Copy 2.
Copyright [3] 170

NK 0211267 DLC MtBC OC1 OEac OLak PP

Knox, James Samuel, 1872-1945.
Personality in action, by James S. Knox and Alice H. Horner and Ruth Wade Ray. Oak Park, Ill., Knox Business Book Co., 1948.
viii, 404 p. diagrs. 21 cm.

1. Success. 2. Personality. I. Horner, Alice H. II. Ray, Ruth Wade. III. Title.
BF637.S8K6 1948 170 49-660*

NK 0211268 DLC

VOLUME 300

Knox, James Samuel, 1872–1945.
Personality in action, by James S. Knox, Alice H. Horner, and Ruth Wade Ray. Oak Park, Ill., Knox Business Book Co., 1953.
367 p. illus. 21 cm.

1. Success. 2. Personality. I. Title.
BF637.S8K6 1953 *179 170 54–189 ‡

NK 0211269 DLC TU

Knox, James Samuel, 1872–1945.
Salesmanship and business efficiency, by James Samuel Knox ... [Red Wing, Minn., Red Wing printing co.] 1912.
231 p. 20½cm. $1.50
"With the exception of lessons one and three, which are new, every lesson in this book has been taken out of the four volumes of our regular salesmanship course."—Introd.

1. Salesmen and salesmanship.
Library of Congress HF5438.K57 12—17228

NK 0211270 DLC WaS OCl ICJ

Knox, James Samuel, 1872–
Salesmanship and business efficiency, by James Samuel Knox. Cleveland, O., 1915.
295 p. front. (port.) chart. 20½cm. $1.75

1. Salesmen and salesmanship. I. Title.
Library of Congress HF5438.K57 1915 15—13857

NK 0211271 DLC NN CU OU OLak OCl

Knox, James Samuel, 1872–
Salesmanship and business efficiency, by James Samuel Knox. Cleveland, O., 1916.
295 p. front. (port.) chart. 20½cm. $1.75

NK 0211272 DLC PP NN ViU

Knox, James Samuel, 1872–
Salesmanship and business efficiency, by James Samuel Knox ... [Akron, O., Superior printing co.] 1917.
348 p. front. (port.) 20½ cm.

1. Salesmen and salesmanship. I. Title.
Library of Congress HF5438.K57 1917 17—5443

NK 0211273 DLC NcD

Knox, James Samuel, 1872–
Salesmanship and business efficiency, by James Samuel Knox ... Cleveland, O., 1917.
438 p. front. (port.) 20½ cm.

NK 0211274 OkU

Knox, James Samuel, 1872– 658 R706
Salesmanship and business efficiency, by James Samuel Knox, A.M. Cleveland, Ohio, [The Knox School of Salesmanship and Business Efficiency], 1918.
[4], 295, [1] p. front. (port.). illus. 20cm.

NK 0211275 ICJ

Knox, James Samuel, 1872–
Salesmanship and business efficencey...
[Red Wing, Minn., Red Wing printing co., 1918.
295p.

NK 0211276 OOxM

Knox, James Samuel, 1872–
Salesmanship and business efficiency. Cleveland, Knox business book co., 1920.
295p. front (port)

NK 0211277 OCl MH

Knox, James Samuel 1872–
Salesmanship and business efficiency.
Cleveland, Knox business book co., 1921.
348p.

NK 0211278 OCl CU

Knox, James Samuel, 1872–
Salesmanship and business efficiency, by James Samuel Knox ... Cleveland, O., Knox business book company, 1922.
406 p. incl. illus., charts. front. (port.) 20½cm.
"Revised edition."

1. Salesmen and salesmanship. I. Title.
Library of Congress HF5438.K57 22—12001

NK 0211279 DLC PPD OClW OCl ICJ

Knox, James Samuel, 1872–
Salesmanship and business efficiency...
N.Y., Chicago [etc.] The Gregg pub. co., [c1922]
406p.
"Revised ed."
School ed.

NK 0211280 MiU MH PPTU PPAp

Knox, James Samuel, 1872–
Salesmanship and business efficiency. Cleveland: Knox Business Book Co., 1923. 406 p. charts, illus., port., tables. [rev. ed.] 12°.

1. Salesmanship. 2. Efficiency (Industrial).
N. Y. P. L. April 22, 1925

NK 0211281 NN

HF5438 K57 1925 **Knox, James Samuel,** 1872–
Salesmanship and business efficiency.
Oak Park, Ill., Knox Business Book Co., 1925.
406 p. illus., port. 20cm.
1. Salesmen and salesmanship. I. Title.

NK 0211282 CoU

Knox, James Samuel, 1872–
Salesmanship and business efficiency (School ed.) by James Samuel Knox ... New York, Chicago [etc.] The Gregg publishing company [c1926]
378 p. incl. pl., diagrs. 20½cm.
"Suggestive reading list": p. 357–358.

1. Salesmen and salesmanship. I. Title.
Library of Congress HF5438.K57 1926 a 26—15165

NK 0211283 DLC MH PP

Knox, James Samuel, 1872–
Salesmanship and business efficiency, by James Samuel Knox. Oak Park, Ill., The Knox business book company, 1926.
2 p. l., 368 p. illus., port. 20cm.

1. Salesmen and salesmanship. I. Title.
Library of Congress HF5438.K57 1926 26–15163

NK 0211284 DLC CU NN OCX ViU OU

Knox, James Samuel, 1872–
Salesmanship and business efficiency, by James Samuel Knox ... Oak Park, Ill., The Knox business book company [c1936]
9 p. l., [17]–382 p. illus., diagrs. 20½cm.

1. Salesmen and salesmanship. I. Title.
Library of Congress HF5438.K57 1936 36–8172
——— Copy 2.
Copyright A 92187 [3] 658.8

NK 0211285 DLC

Knox, James Samuel, 1872–
Salesmanship and business efficiency, by James Samuel Knox ... Oak Park, Ill., The Knox business book company [c1937]
9 p. l., [17]–414 p. illus., diagrs. 20½cm.
"Suggestive reading list": p. 395–396.

1. Salesmen and salesmanship. I. Title.
Library of Congress HF5438.K57 1937 37–17195
——— Copy 2.
Copyright A 107979 [2] 658.8

NK 0211286 DLC

Knox, James Samuel, 1872–
Salesmanship and business efficiency, by James Samuel Knox ... Oak Park, Ill., The Knox business book company, 1946.
10 p. l., 19–414 p. illus., diagrs. 20½cm.
"Suggestive reading list": p. 395–396.

1. Salesmen and salesmanship.
Library of Congress HF5438.K57 1946 46–21485
[3] 658.8

NK 0211287 DLC

Knox, James Samuel, 1872–
Salesmanship and business efficiency. Oak Park, Ill., Knox business book co., 1947 [c1946]
414 p., illus.

Bibliography: p. 395–396.

NK 0211288 MiD

Knox, James Samuel, 1872–
Salesmanship and business efficiency. Rev. and enl. ed. Oak Park, Ill., Knox Business Book Co., 1949.
xv, 463 p. illus. 21 cm.

1. Salesmen and salesmanship.
HF5438.K57 1949 658.8 50–3431

NK 0211289 DLC

Knox, James Samuel, 1872–1945.
Salesmanship and business efficiency. Rev. and enl. ed. by John Knox. Oak Park, Ill., Knox Business Book Co., 1950.
463 p. illus. 21 cm.

NK 0211290 LU OCl

VOLUME 300

Knox, James Samuel, 1872-1945.
Salesmanship and business efficiency. Rev. and enl. ed. by John Knox. Oak Park, Ill., Knox Business Book Co., 1951.
463 p. illus. 21 cm.

1. Salesmen and salesmanship.
HF5438.K57 1951 658.8 51-7841 ‡

NK 0211291 DLC CaBVa WaS

Knox, James Samuel, 1872-1945.
Salesmanship and business efficiency, by James S. Knox and John Knox. Oak Park, Ill., Knox Business Book Co., 1953.
463 p. illus. 21 cm.

1. Salesmen and salesmanship. I. Knox, John Jay. II. Title.
HF5438.K57 1953 658.8 54-15399 ‡

NK 0211292 DLC PP MiD OEac

Knox, James Samuel.
Salesmanship and personal efficiency, by James Samuel Knox ... [Akron, O., Superior printing co.] 1917.
2 p. l., 438 p. front., illus., ports. 20½cm. $2.75
Chapter XIII, The science of judging men, by Dr. Edwin Morrell: p. 300-430.

1. Salesmen and salesmanship. 2. Physiognomy. I. Morrell, Edwin. II. Title.
Library of Congress HF5438.K58 17-20758

NK 0211293 DLC MiD OCl MiU

Knox, James Samuel, 1872- 658 R706
Salesmanship and personal efficiency, by James Samuel Knox ... [Akron, O., Superior printing co.] 1918.
2 p. l., 295 p. front., illus., ports. 20½cm. $2.75

NK 0211294 ICJ

658.89 Knox, James Samuel, 1872-
K77sa Salesmanship and personal efficiency. Cleveland, Knox Business Book Co., 1919 [c1917]
348 p. illus., ports. 20 cm.

1. Salesmen and salesmanship. I. Title.

NK 0211295 LU MiD

Knox, James Samuel, 1872-
The science and art of selling. New York, etc., Gregg Publishing co. [c.1912]

NK 0211296 MH

Knox, James Samuel, 1872-
The science and art of selling, by James Samuel Knox ... Cleveland, O., Knox business book company, 1921.
6 p. l., 380 p. incl. illus., diagrs. front. (port.) 20½cm.

1. Salesmen and salesmanship. I. Title.
Library of Congress HF5438.K59 21-14201

NK 0211297 DLC WaS NcD OCl ICJ

Knox, James Samuel, 1872-
The science of applied salesmanship ... By James Samuel Knox ... Des Moines, Ia., Knox school of applied salesmanship, 1911.
4 v. fronts. (ports.) 23½cm.

1. Salesmen and salesmanship.
Library of Congress HF5438.K6 11-16795 Revised

NK 0211298 DLC ICJ

Knox, James Samuel, 1872-
The science of applied salesmanship...
Cleveland, Author, 1917-1919.
13 v. in 1.

On cover: The Knox school of applied salesmanship.

NK 0211299 OCl

Knox, James Samuel, 1872-
Subscription book salesmanship, by J. S. Knox. Oak Park, Ill., The Knox business book company [c1926]
1 p.l., 68 p. 20cm.
"Revised edition."
With his Salesmanship and business efficiency. Oak Park, Ill., 1926.

1. Salesmen and salesmanship. 2. Booksellers and bookselling—Colportage, subscription trade, etc. I. Title.

NK 0211300 ViU

Knox, James Samuel, 1872-
Teacher's manual to accompany The science and art of selling...
New York, Boston, [c 1923]

HF5438
.K593

NK 0211301 DLC DHEW

BR83
.426 Knox, James Spenser, 1789-1862.
Mysteries compared, or the phraseology of the New Testament illustrated through the terms in use among the ancients explanatory of the worship and course of instruction pursued in the heathen temples. Dublin, W. Curry, Jun., 1842.
37 p. 20 cm.

NK 0211302 MB

Knox, James Spencer, 1789-1862.
The thoughtful year. Dublin, 1844.

NK 0211303 PPL

QM33
K77
Knox, James Suydam, 1840-1892.
Physicians' anatomical aid; a manikin of superimposed diagramatic plates, designed to assist in surgery, diagnoses and general practice. Constructed under the supervision of J. Suydam Knox ... D. W. Graham ... [and] J. E. Owens ... Chicago, Published by the Western publishing house, c1888.
1 v. col. plates. 38½ x 56cm.

Date on cover: January 15, 1889.

NK 0211304 NNC PPC KU-M CtY CtY-MHi

Knox, James William, 1919-
The Ol' Double Trouble. Pittsburgh, R. T. Lewis Co. [1949]
56 p. illus., ports., maps (on lining-papers) 23 cm.

1. LST 491 (Ship) 2. World War, 1939-1945—Naval operations, American.
D774.L25K6 940.545 49-15253*

NK 0211305 DLC

Knox, Janet.
The shepherd of Bethlehem, a one-act Christmas play, by Janet Knox. Chicago, T. S. Denison & company [c1928]
34 p. 18cm. (*On cover:* Denison's Christmas plays)

1. Christmas plays. I. Title.
Library of Congress PN6120.C5K6 CA 36-1062 Unrev'd
Copyright D 85063 [2] 812.5

NK 0211306 DLC

Knox, Janet, pseud.
Patty and Jo
see McKechnie, Jean Lyttleton, 1925-

Knox, Janette Hill.
Justa Hamlin's vocation, by Janette Hill Knox. New York, London [etc.] The Abbey press [1902]
4, 238 p. 20½cm. 2-19676

NK 0211308 DLC NN

Knox, Jaxon, 1882-
It will be all right on the night; play in one act, by Jaxon Knox... New York: S. French, 1926. 21 p. 12°. (French's internat. copyrighted ed. of the works of the best authors. no. 543.)

1. Amateur theatricals. 2. Title.
N. Y. P. L. November 10, 1926

NK 0211309 NN CaBVaU MiD PPYH RPB OCl OrCS

Knox, Jaxon, 1882- joint author.
Clark, A Mortimer, 1881-
Progress in English, by A. Mortimer Clark ... and Jaxon Knox ... Garden City, N. Y., Doubleday, Doran & company, inc. [c1931]

Knox, Jean Lindsay.
A key to brotherhood, poems by Jean Lindsay Knox. New York, The Paebar publishing company [c1932]
[24] p. 23cm.

I. Title.
Library of Congress PS3521.N83K4 1932 32-19054
——— Copy 2.
Copyright A 54173 [2] 811.5

NK 0211311 DLC

VOLUME 300

Knox, Jessie A *ed.*
Plays with a purpose, a group of short sketches for presentation by home economics students, edited by Jessie A. Knox. New York, Lakeside publishing co., 1930.
141 p. 21cm.

1. Domestic economy—Juvenile literature. I. Title.

Library of Congress TX148.K6 30-12517
Copyright A 22291 [3] 640

NK 0211312 DLC CLSU KEmT PPPL OO OLak OEac OClh OCl

Knox, Jessie A., ed.

Practical home economics. v. 22, no. 1-4, Jan.-Apr. 1927; v. 5, no. 5-12, v. 6- May 1927-
[New York, Lakeside publishing company, etc., etc., 1927-

Knox, *Mrs.* **Jessie Juliet (Daily)**
In the house of the Tiger, by Jessie Juliet Knox ... Cincinnati, Jennings and Graham; New York, Eaton and Mains [c1911]
255 p. front. (port.) plates. 18½cm. $1.25

1. Chinese in San Francisco. I. Title.

Library of Congress F869.S3K74 11-28337 Revised

NK 0211314 DLC NIC OO MiU ICJ

Knox, *Mrs.* **Jessie Juliet (Daily)**
Little Almond Blossoms, a book of Chinese stories for children, by Jessie Juliet Knox; with illustrations from photographs of Chinese children in California. Boston, Little, Brown, and company, 1904.
5 p. l., 246 p., 1 l. front., 14 pl. 20cm.

I. Title.

Library of Congress PZ7.K773L 4-27987 Revised

NK 0211315 DLC

Knox, Joe.
Little Benders. [1st ed.] Philadelphia, Lippincott [1952]
255 p. 21 cm.

I. Title.

PZ3.K7738Li 52-9533 ‡

NcD WaE WaS WaT
NK 0211316 DLC OrP Or IdB MtU FTaSU OU OOxM TxU NN

Knox, John.
The great mistake, by John Knox. Washington, D. C., National foundation press, inc. [c1930]
176 p. illus. (facsims.) 23½ cm.

1. Hoover, Herbert Clark, pres. U. S., 1874-1964. I. Title.

E802.K74 923.173 30—28495

OU OCl MWA MB ViU PPLas NBuHi MdBP OkU FTaSU
NK 0211317 DLC OC FU PV PP DS AAP TxU NcD ICarbS

Knox, John.
The great mistake, by John Knox. Washington, D. C., National foundation press, inc. [1931]
176 p. illus. (facsims.) 23½cm.

NK 0211318 ViU OrU

E KNOX, JOHN.
5 The great mistake; can Herbert Hoover explain
.H 7684 his past?... Revised edition. Baltimore,Md., Grace press,inc.[c1932]
212p. 21cm.

NK 0211319 ICN WaSp KEmT

Knox, John.
Word-change puzzles, by John Knox. Chicago, New York, Laird and Lee, 1927.
143 p. illus. 19½cm.

1. Puzzles. I. Title.

Library of Congress GV1507.W8K6 27-18533

NK 0211320 DLC

[Knox, John] of Edinburgh.
Remarks on the late proceedings of the Synod of Glasgow and Ayr in Dr. M'Gill's cause, in a letter to a friend ... Edinburgh, 1790.
15 p.

NK 0211321 NjP

Knox, John, pseud.
Crumbs from the land o' cakes
see Carter, Peter, 1825-1900.

Knox, John, pseud.
... Emigrant-drengen. [København] S. Hasselbalch, 1928.
163 p. 20cm.

I. Title.

Library of Congress PT8175.K57E5 1928 30-17126

NK 0211323 DLC NN

Knox, *Rev.* **John,** *L. M., pseud.*
A sermon for the times ... Preached in aid of the "Jacobins of Maryland". By Rev. John Knox, L. M. Baltimore, Printed for the author, 1864.
8 p. 20½cm.
"A hit at Mr. Blair and the Maryland conservatives."—Sabin, Bibl. amer., v. 9, p. 530.

1. Maryland—Pol. & govt.—Civil war. I. Title.

Library of Congress F185.K74 22-9852

NK 0211324 DLC NIC NcD MdU PHi OClWHi PPL MB

Knox (John), *the younger, pseud.*
The first blast of the trumpet against the monstrous usurpation of church-patrons in Scotland. *Edinburgh: Waugh & Innes,* 1833. 2 p.l., iv, 5-44 pp. 8°.
In: **ZWGF** p. v. 21.

NK 0211325 NN

Knox, John, 1505-1572.
Works by this author printed in America before 1801 are available in this library in the Readex Microprint edition of Early American Imprints published by the American Antiquarian Society.
This collection is arranged according to the numbers in Charles Evans' American Bibliography.

NK 0211326 DLC

Knox, John, 1505-1572.
The works of John Knox; collected and edited by David Laing. v. 1- Edinburgh: Printed for the Wodrow soc., 1846-
v. facsims., port. 22cm. [Wodrow society, Edinburgh. Publications, no. 10]
Each v. has added special t.-p.
Vol. 1-2 comprise the 4 books of his History of the Reformation in Scotland and the 5th book forming a sequel to it, with appendices, glossary and index of persons and places.

1. Theology—Collected works. 2. Reformation—Gt. Br.—Scotland. I. Laing, David, 1793-1878, ed. II. Bannatyne club, Edinburgh. III. Ser.
N. Y. P. L. *Card revised* September 12, 1941

OCl OCU ICN IaDuU-S PPPrHi DLC PPT MiU PU MH PPWe
NK 0211327 NN NRCR CtY KStMC IEN CU MdBP IU PHC ICU

Knox, John, 1505-1572.
The works of John Knox. Edinburgh, Printed for the Bannatyne Club, 1846.

NK 0211328 NN

BR385
K74 Knox, John, 1505-1572.
L18 The works of John Knox, collected and edited by David Laing. Edinburgh, Printed for the Woodrow society, 1846-1848.
6 v. 23 cm.
v.3, 4, 6 are reprint editions.

1. Scotland--Church history. 2. Reformation--Scotland. I. Laing, David, 1793-1898, ed.

NK 0211328-1 PPiPT

Knox, John, 1505-1572.
The works of John Knox; collected and edited by David Laing ... Edinburgh: J. Thin, 1895. 6 v. facsims., illus., pl., ports. 23cm. [Wodrow society, Edinburgh. Publications, no. 10]
Vol. 1-2 comprise the 4 books of his History of the Reformation in Scotland and the 5th book forming a sequel to it, with appendices, glossary, and index of persons and places; originally issued 1846-64.

1. Theology—Collected works. 2. Reformation—Gt. Br.—Scotland. I. Laing, David, 1793-1878, ed. II. Ser.
N. Y. P. L. *Card revised* September 2, 1941

NK 0211329 NN KyLxCB OOxM OCl CU WaU MiEM

STC Knox, John, 1505-1572.
15059 An admonition or warning that the faithful Christiãs in London, Newcastel, Barwycke & others, may auoide Gods vengeaũce ...
Colophon: From Wittonburge by Nicholas Dorcastor, 1554.
A-E8. (A1, probably blank, lacking) 8vo.
Also published in 1554 with the title: A godly letter sent too the fayethfull in London ...
Possibly Heber-D. Laing-Britwell Court-Harmsworth copy.

NK 0211330 DFo

FILM
Knox,John,1505-1572.
An admonition or vvarning that the faithful Chiistiãs in London,Newcastel Barwycke & others,may auoide Gods vengeaũce,both in thys life and in the life to come. Compyled by ... John Knokes ... [Antwerp? 1554]
Colophon: From Wittonburge by Nicholas Dorcaster ... M.D.liiii.the.viii.of May ...
University microfilms no.16213 (carton 640)
Short-title catalogue no.15059.
Microfilm

NK 0211331 MiU CaBVaU

VOLUME 300

Ag K773 560a Rare Books Col
Knox, John, 1505-1572.
An answer to a great nomber of blasphemous cauillations written by an Anabaptist, and aduersarie to Gods eternal predestination. And confvted by Iohn Knox ... Wherein the author so discouereth the craft and falshode of that sect, that the godly knowing that error, may be confirmed in the trueth by the euident Worde of God ... [Geneva] Printed by Iohn Crespin, 1560.
455p. 16cm.
Signatures: A-Ee[8] Ff[4] (last leaf unsigned)
1. Predestination. Sp.: DeGolyer Collection.

NcWsW
NK 0211332 TxU NcD DFo NNUT ICN MWA MH NNUT-Mc

FILM
Knox, John, 1505-1572.
An answer to a great nomber of blasphemous cauillations written by an Anabaptist, and aduersarie to Gods eternal predestination. And confvted by Iohn Knox ... ₍Geneva₎ Printed by Iohn Crespin. M.D.LX.
University microfilms no.14949 (case 43, carton 253)
Short-title catalogue no.15060.

1. Predestination. 2. Election (Theology)

NK 0211333 MiU

Knox, John, 1505-1572.
An Ansvver To A Great Nvmber Of Blasphemovs Cavillations Written By An Anabaptist, and aduersarie to ... Predestination. And confuted by Iohn Knox... London: Imprinted for Thomas Charde, 1591. 443 p. 15cm. (8°.)
STC 15061.
First published at Geneva, 1560.
A reply to "The confutation of the errors of the careles by necessitie", including part of the text. — *cf. pref.*
Imperfect: upper edges cropped.

1. Predestination. 2. Anabaptists. I. The confutation of the errors of the careles by necessitie.
N. Y. P. L. *Card revised* August 30, 1943

NK 0211334 NN ViHarEM DFo ICU CSmH MH PWW

FILM
Knox, John, 1505-1572.
An ansvver to a great nvmber of blasphemovs cavillations written by an Anabaptist, and aduersarie to Gods eternall predestination. And confuted by Iohn Knox ... Imprinted at London for Thomas Charde. 1591.
University microfilms no.14950 (case 43, carton 253)
Short-title catalogue no.15061.

1. Predestination. 2. Election (Theology)

NK 0211335 MiU CaBVaU CtY

STC 15062
Knox, John, 1505-1572.
An answer to a letter of a Iesuit named Tyrie ... Imprentit at Sanctandrois be Robert Lekpreuik, 1572.
A-E[8], F[4], ₍G₎[1]. (Gathering D misbound: 1, 2, 4, 3, 6, 5, 7, 8) 8vo.
Outer margins trimmed, affecting text.
Contains a letter written to his mother-in-law, Elizabeth Bowes, in 1554.
Wm. Herbert-Geo. Chalmers-Britwell Court-Harmsworth copy.

NK 0211336 DFo

FILM
Knox, John, 1505-1572.
An answer to a letter of a Iesvit named Tyrie, be Iohne Knox ... Imprentit at Sanct Androis be Robert Lekpreuik ... 1572.
University microfilms no.16214 (case 79, carton 473)
Short-title catalogue no.15062.

1. Tyrie, James, 1543-1597.

NK 0211337 MiU

Mhc5 K774 Ap4
Knox, John, 1505-1572.
The appellation of Iohn Knoxe from the cruell and most iniust sentence pronounced against him by the false bishoppes and clergie of Scotland, with his supplication and exhortation to the nobilitie, estates, and cõmunaltie of the same realme. Printed at Geneva [by J.Pullain and A.Rebul?] 1558.
80numb.ℓ. 14cm.
"An admonition to England and Scotland to call them to repentance, written by Antoni Gilby": ℓ.59 verso ℓ.77 recto; "Psalme of David XCIIII, turned into metre, by w.Kethe": ℓ.78 verso - ℓ.80 recto.

NK 0211339 CtY DFo MWiW-C ICN NjPT

FILM
Knox, John, 1505-1572.
The appellation of Iohn Knoxe from the cruell and most iniust sentence pronounced against him by the false bishoppes and clergie of Scotland, with his supplication and exhortation to the nobilitie, estates, and cõmunaltie of the same realme. Printed at Geneva ₍by J.Pullain and A.Rebul?₎ M.D.LVIII.
"An admonition to England and Scotland to call them to repentance, written by Antoni Gilby": verso of leaf 59-recto of leaf 77.
"Psalme of David XCIIII, turned in to metre, by W.Kethe": verso of leaf 78-recto of leaf 80.
University microfilms no.16215 (case 79, carton 473)
Short-title catalogue no.15063.
I. Gilby, Anthony, d.1585. An admonition to England and Scotland. II. Bible. O.T. Psalms XCIV. III. Kethe, William, d.1608?

NK 0211340 MiU CaBVaU

Knox, John, 1505-1572.
The appellation of John Knox from the cruell and most unjust sentence pronounced against him, by the false bishops and clergie of Scotland; with his supplication and exhortation to the nobility, states and communalty of the same realme. Edinb'g, Fleming, 1732.
33 p.

NK 0211341 PHi

Knox, John, 1505-1572.
Appreciations by United Original Seceders
see under United Original Secession Church (1842-1956)

Knox, John, 1505-1572.
The book of common order, commonly called John Knox's liturgy
see under Church of Scotland. Book of Common Order.

Knox, John, 1505-1572.
A confession & declaratiõ of praiers. Rome [London, H. Singleton] 1554. 8vo.
First Edition
STC 15073 pt.2

NK 0211344 MWiW-C

STC 15066
Knox, John, 1505-1572.
The copie of a letter sent to ... ladye Mary dowagire, regent of Scotland ... in the yeare, 1556. Here is also a notable sermon ... wherin is ... proved that the masse is ... abhominable before God and idolatrye ... ₍n.p., 1556?₎
A-H[8]. 16mo.
Possibly Britwell Court-J.L. Clawson-Harmsworth copy.

NK 0211345 DFo

FILM
Knox, John, 1505-1572.
The copie of a letter, sent to the Ladye Mary dowagire, regent of Scotland, by John Knox in ... 1556. Here is also a notable sermon, made by ... John Knox, wherin is euydentlye proued that the masse is and alwayes hath ben abhominable before God and idolatrye ... ₍Geneva?₎ 1556.
"Here is briefly declared ... what opinion we Christians haue of the Lordes Supper": ₍6₎ p.at end.
University microfilms no.16218 (case 74, carton 442)
Short-title catalogue no.15066.
1. Mary, queen consort of James V, king of Scotland, 1515-1560. 2. Mass. 3. Lord's Supper.

NK 0211346 MiU

Case C 657 .467
KNOX, JOHN, 1505-1572.
The copie of a lettre deliuered to the Ladie Marie, regent of Scotland.. in the yeare of our Lord 1556, and nowe augmented and explaned by the author, in the yeare... 1558. Geneva, Printed b I.Poullain, and A.Rebul, 1558.
28 ℓ. 13cm.
Device of A.Reboul on t.-p. Initials.
STC 15067.

NK 0211347 ICN MWiW-C

FILM
Knox, John, 1505-1572.
The copie of a lettre deliuered to the Ladie Marie, Regent of Scotland, in the yeare of Our Lord 1556, and nowe augm.and explaned, in the yeare of Our Lord 1558. Geneva, Printed by I.Poullain, and A.Rebul, 1558.
Short-title catalogue no.15067 (carton 964)

1. Mary, Queen consort of James V, King of Scotland, 1515-1560.

NK 0211348 MiU CaBVaU

FILM
Knox, John, 1505-1572.
The copie of an epistle sent by Iohn Knox ... vnto the inhabitants of Newcastle, & Barwike. In the end wherof is added a briefe exhortation to England for the spedie imbrasing of Christes Gospel hertofore suppressed & banished ... At Geneva. M. D. LIX.
"A brief exhortation" has special t.p.
"The names of the martyrs": p.109-126.
University microfilms no.16216 (case 74, carton 442)
Short-title catalogue no.15064.
1. Reformed church—Doctrinal and controversial works.

NK 0211349 MiU CaBVaU

Knox, John, 1505-1572, supposed author.
Copy of a roll of parchment, which was found in a corner of one of the vaults of the cathedral
see under title

Case C 657 .468
KNOX, JOHN, 1505-1572.
A faythfull admonition made...vnto the professours of Gods truthe in England, wherby thou mayest learne howe God wyll haue his churche exercised with troubles, and how he defendeth it in the same... ₍Kalykow(i.e. Zürich? C. Froschauer?)1554₎
₍125₎p. 13cm.
Signatures : A[4], B-H[8], I[4] (I 4, blank? wanting)
STC 15069.
Bound by F. Bedford. Armorial bookplate: Ie. V. Rensse-

NK 0211351 ICN DFo CtY CSmH MWiW-C

VOLUME 300

FILM
Knox, John, 1505-1572.
A faythfull admonition made by Iohn Knox, vnto the professours of Gods truthe in England, wher by thou mayest learne howe God wyll haue his churche exercised with troubles, and how he defendeth it in the same ... ₍Zürich? C. Froschauer? 1554₎
Colophon: Jmprynted at Kalykow ... 1554.
"The epistle of a banyshed manne out of Leycester Shire" precedes text.
University microfilms no.14951 (case 43, carton 253)
Short-title catalogue no.15069.
1. Gt. Brit.—Pol.& govt.—1553-1558. I. Title.

NK 0211352 MiU CaBVaU

STC 15070
₍Knox, John₎ 1505-1572.
The first blast of the trumpet against the monstruous regiment of women .. ₍Geneva, J. Crespin₎ 1558.
A-G[8]. 8vo.

NK 0211353 DFo CSmH MWiW-C

Knox, John, 1505-1572.
The first blast of the trvmpet against the monstrvovs regiment of women ... ₍Geneva, J. Crespin₎ M.D.LVIII.
University microfilms no.14952 (case 43, carton 253)
Short-title catalogue no.15070.
Microfilm.

1. Woman—Social and moral questions. I. Title.

NK 0211354 MiU CaBVaU

Knox, John, Scottish Reformer. 1505-1572. **H.95.113
The first blast of the trumpet against the monstruous regimen of women. Added, the contents of the Second blast, and A letter to the people of Edinburgh, 1571.
Edinburgh. Pr. by T. Lumisden and J. Robertson. 1733. (2), 30 pp. Sm. 4°.
Questions the right of women to govern and is especially directed against Queen Mary of England.

F9011 — T.r. — Women.

NK 0211355 MB

Knox, John, 1505-1572.
The first blast of the trumpet against the monstrous regimen of women. By Mr. John Knox, minister of the gospel at Edinburgh. To which is added, the contents of the second blast, and a letter from John Knox to the people of Edinburgh, anno 1571... Edinburgh: Printed: and Philadelphia: Re-printed by Andrew Steuart, 1766. 64 p. 12°. (In: Buchanan, George, 1506-1582. De jure regni apud Scotos...)

1. Woman in public offices. 2. Queens. January 8, 1915.
N. Y. P. L.

NK 0211356 NN TxDaM NPV MH-L MiU-C PHi CtY P

Knox, John, 1505-1572.
... The first blast of the trumpet against the monstrous regiment of women. 1558. Ed. by Edward Arber ... London ₍The editor₎ 1878.
xviii, 62 p. 20cm. (*Half-title: The English scholar's library etc. no. 2*)
At head of t.-p.: The English scholar's library of old and modern works.
With reproduction of t.-p. of original (1558) ed.
Bibliography: p. [vii]-viii.
Appendix: John Knox's apological defence of his First blast &c. to Queen Elizabeth.

1. Woman—Social and moral questions. 2. Queens. I. Arber, Edward, ed.
12-17012
Library of Congress PR1121.A7 no. 2

CLU NIC NcD
NK 0211357 DLC MtU OrU OO OClW MiU PP PHC PPL GU

LX46 K74f
Knox, John, 1505-1572.
The first blast of the trumpet against the monstrous regiment of women, 1558. Edited by Edward Arber. Westminster ₍London₎ A. Constable, 1895.
xviii, 62 p. 21 cm. (The English scholar's library of old and modern works, no. 2)

With reproduction of t.p. of original (1558) ed.

Appendix: John Knox's apologetical defence of his First blast &c. to Queen Elizabeth.
Bibliography: p. ₍vii₎-viii.

1. Woman - Social and moral questions. 2. Kings and rulers. I. Arber, Edward, 1836-1912, ed. II. Series.

NK 0211359 CtY-D IaU TU WaU PBm MiU

Knox, John, 1505-1572.
'The first blast of the trumpet against the monstrous regiment of women.' [Extract.] 1558.
(In Dearmer. Religious pamphlets. p. 80-83. N.Y., 1898)

NK 0211360 MB

STC 15071
₍Knox, John₎ 1505-1572.
The first₍-thirde₎ booke of the history of the reformation of religioun within the realme of Scotland./ ₍T. Vautrollier, 1587₎

B-2M[8]. 8vo.
No more perfect copy is known as the work was seized at the press and suppressed by Abp. Whitgift. The title is taken from the MS of 1566 from which this edition was printed.
Running title: The historie of the Church of Scotland.
Duke of Hamilton -Harmsworth copy.

NK 0211361 DFo MH CSmH

Knox, John, 1505-1572.
₍The first booke of the history of the Reformation of religioun within the realme of Scotland ... London, T. Vautrollier, 1587₎
Imperfect; title supplied from Brit.mus. Catalogue; missing parts of text in manuscript from 1644 edition.
Running title: The historie of the Chvrch of Scotland.
University microfilms no.14953 (case 43, carton 253)
Short-title catalogue no.15071.
Microfilm.
1. Reformation—Scotland. 2. Scotland—Church history. I. Title: The historie of the Church of Scotland.
II. Title.

NK 0211362 MiU CaBVaU

FILM
Knox, John, 1505-1572.
A fort for the afflicted ... Written ... by Iohn Knoxe ... Imprinted at London ... by Thomas Dawson, 1580.
"To the religious reader" signed: Abraham Flemming.
University microfilms no.16221 (carton 555)
Short-title catalogue no.15072.

1. Bible. O.T. Psalms VI—Criticism, interpretation etc. I. Title.

NK 0211363 MiU CaBVaU

Knox, John, 1505-1572.

Geneva. English church. *Liturgy and ritual.*
John Knox's Genevan service book, 1556. The liturgical portions of the Genevan service book used by John Knox while a minister of the English congregation of Marian exiles at Geneva, 1556-1559, by William D. Maxwell ... with a foreword by Prof. James Mackinnon ... Edinburgh, London, Oliver and Boyd, 1931.

₍**Knox, John**₎ 1505-1572.
George Wishart, scholar, saint, reformer, martyr ... St. Andrews, Printed for the University by W. C. Henderson & son, ltd., University press, 1946.
27 p. plates, ports., plan. 22cm.
"A St. Mary's college book."
On cover: 1546 1st March 1946.
"Reprinted from Knox's History (Laing) vol. I., pp. 125-171."—p. 5.

1. Wishart, George, 1513?-1546.
A 47-3718
Harvard univ. Library for Library of Congress ₍2₎

NK 0211365 MH CtY PU CtY-D MB NNU-W NNC

Knox, John, 1505-1572.
Das Glaubensbekenntniss der schottischen Kirche.--Knox an seine geliebten Brüder, das Volk von Schottland.
(In Brandes, F. John Knox. 1862)

NK 0211366 NIC

Rare Book Room Mhc5 K774 G6
Knox, John, 1505-1572.
A godly letter sent too the fayethfull in London / Newcastell / Barwyke / and to all other within the realme off Englande / that loue the cõminge of oure Lorde Jesus by Jhon Knox ... Imprinted in Rome, before the Castell of S. Aungel / at the signe of Sainct Peter. [i.e. London, Printed by Hugh Singleton] In the moneth of July / in the yeare of our Lord. 1554.
[55]p. 14cm.

Signatures: A-C[8]D[4].
Singleton's device at end.
A second part appeared in the same year, with title: A confession & declaratiõ of praiers.
Imperfect: a few side-notes mutilated and restored.

NK 0211368 CtY DFo CSmH MWiW-C

FILM
Knox, John, 1505-1572.
A godly letter sent too the fayethfull in London, Newcastell, Barwyke and to all other within the realme off Englande, that loue the cõminge of Oure Lorde Jesus by Jhon Knox ... Jmprinted in Rome ₍i.e. London, H. Singleton₎ ... 1554.
In 2 parts; pt.2 has title: A confession & declaratiõ of praiers added thervnto by Jhon Knox ... Jmprinted in Rome ... 1554.
University microfilms no.14954 (case 43, carton 254)
Short-title catalogue no.15073.
1. Mass. 2. Prayer. I. Title.

NK 0211369 MiU CaBVaU

STC 15074
Knox, John, 1505-1572.
Heir followeth the coppie of the ressoning which was betuix the Abbote of Crosraguell and John Knox ... concerning the masse ... Imprinted at Edinburgh by Robert Lekpreuik, 1563.
Colophon.
☞[4], +[4], ☞[4], A-H[4]. 4to.
The abbot of Crosraguel was Quintin Kennedy.
Pembroke library-Harmsworth copy.

NK 0211370 DFo

Knox, John, 1505-1572.
Heir followeth the coppie of the ressoning which was betuix the Abbote of Crosreguell and John Knox, in Mayboill concerning the masse, in the yeare of God, a thousand five hundreth thre scoir and two yeares... Edinburgh, R. Lekpreuik, 1563 ₍Edinburgh, G. Ramsay, 1812₎
facsim.: ₍12₎, 32 l. 24cm.

"Reprinted... from an original copy in the Auchinleck library."
I Kennedy, Quintin, 1520-1564

NK 0211371 NjPT

VOLUME 300

[Knox, John] 1505-1572.
[The historie of the Chvrch of Scotland]
see his The first booke of the history of the Chvrch of Scotland.

KNOX, John, 1505-1572.
The history of the reformation in Scotland. Edin., 1846-48.

2 vol. Port. and fac-sims. (In his Works, 1846, etc., I., II.
Forms no.10 of the Publications of the Wodrow society.

NK 0211373 MH

Knox, John, 1505-1572.
History of the Reformation in Scotland. Edited by William Croft Dickinson. London, New York, Nelson [1949]
2 v. 25 cm.
Bibliography: v. 2, p. 343-350.

1. Reformation—Scotland.

BR385.K6 1949 274.1 50-12368

NK 0211374 MH MiD MiU GU OCU PPT IU CaBVaU CaBVa OrPR DLC WaS Wa Vi DFo NNC CtY-D ICU TxU MB

Knox, John, 1505-1572.
John Knox's History of the Reformation in Scotland; ed. by William Croft Dickinson. New York, Philosophical library [1950]
2 v. geneal. tables.

"Bibliographical note": v. 1, p. lxxxviii-cix.
"A note on authorities": v. 2, p. 343-350.

NK 0211375 MsU KMK KEmT NNC Or MtU OrSaW WaTC TU KEmT ICMcC

D 543 .467 KNOX, JOHN, 1505-1572.
The history of the reformation of religion in Scotland...to which are appended, several other pieces of his writing; including the first book of discipline, complete, and his Dispute with the Abbot of Crossraguel, not given with any former edition; with a memoir, historical introduction, and notes, by William M'Gavin... Glasgow, Blackie, Fullarton & co., 1831.
lxxi, 581p.

Contents.—Introduction.—Life of John Knox.—Ceremonial at laying the foundation stone of Knox's monument at Glasgow.—Knox's general preface.—History of the reformation of religion in Scotland.—Letter delivered to the Lady Mary, regent of Scotland, from John Knox.—The appellation of John Knox from the sentence pronounced against him by bishops and clergy.—Letter to the commonalty of Scotland.—Admonition to the professors of the truth in England in 1554.—The first blast against the regimen of women.—Letter to the people of Edinburgh.—Sermon delivered in 1565.—First book of discipline.—Oration against reforming preachers, by Quentin Kennedy.—Reasoning concerning the mass between Quentin Kennedy and John Knox in Maybole.

NK 0211378 ICN MH DLC-P4 PPL MeB PPPrHi

Knox, John, 1505-1572.
The history of the reformation of religion in Scotland, to which are appended several other pieces of his writing; including the first book of discipline, complete, and his dispute with the Abbot of Crossraguel... With a memoir, historical introduction and notes; by W. M'Gavin. Glasgow, Blackie & son, 1832.
3 p.l., lxxi, 581pp., 1pl., 3 port.

2. ed.

NK 0211379 NNUT CtY

Knox, John, 1505-1572.
The history of the reformation of religion in Scotland, to which are appended several other pieces of his writing; including The first book of discipline, complete, and his dispute with the Abbot of Crossraguel... With a memoir, historical introduction and notes; by W. M'Gavin. Glasgow, Blackie & son, 1841.
3 p.l., lxxi, 581 pp., 1 pl., 3 port. 8°

3. ed.

NK 0211380 NN

Knox, John, 1505-1572.
History of the Reformation of religion in Scotland ... With a memoir, Historical introduction and notes by William M'Gavin. 4th ed. Glasgow, Blackiem, 1844.
652 p.

NK 0211381 PU

BR 385 K7 1905 Knox, John 1505-1572.
The history of the reformation of religion in Scotland; with which are included Knox's Confession and The book of discipline. A twentieth century edition, revised and edited by Cuthbert Lennox. New York, Chicago[etc.] Fleming H. Revell co., [1905].
xvi, 432p. front.(port.) 22cm.
1.Reformation - Scotland. 2.Scotland - Church history. I.Lennox, Cuthbert, ed.

NK 0211382 PPPrHi TxDaM IEN TxU IMunS NNUT CBPac OCl MeB NjPT WU Mi CSf

---

Rare BR 385 K74++ 1732 Knox, John, 1505-1572.
The historie of the Reformatioun of religioun within the realm of Scotland. Conteining the manner and be quhat [sic] persons the lycht of Chrystis evangell has bein manifested unto this realme, after that horribill and universal defectioun from the treuth, whiche has come by the means of that romane Antichryst. Together with the life of Iohn Knoxe, the author, and several curious pieces wrote by him, particularly that most rare and scarce one intitled, The first blast of the trumpet against the monstruous regiment of women, and a large index and glossary. Taken from the original ms. in the University Library of Glasgow, and compared with other ancient copies. Edinburgh, Printed by R. Fleming, 1732.
lvi, 488 p. 31cm.

"The life of the author": p. i-lvi.
"The first blast of the trumpet against ... women": p. 468-486.
1. Reformation--Scotland. 2. Scotland--Church hist. 3. Woman--Social and moral questions. I. Knox, John, 1505-1572. The first blast of the trumpet...

NK 0211385 NIC NPV NjPT CLSU ViU MH ODW PPPrHi NNUT

---

*Adams 181 .4 Knox, John, 1505-1572.
The history of the reformation of religion within the realm of Scotland; together with the life of the author and several curious pieces wrote by him. Added, I. An admonition to England and Scotland to call them to repentance, written by Antoni Gilby. II. The first and second books of discipline. Glasgow: Printed, and sold by J. Galbraith and Company. MDCCLXI.
558 p. port. 24cm.
1. Reformation—Scotland. 2. Scotland—Church history. I. Gilby, Anthony, d. 1585. II. Church of Scotland. General Assembly. III. Title.

NK 0211386 MB PPiPT

Knox, John, reformer, 1505-72.
The history of the reformation of religion within the realm of Scotland. Containing the manner, and by what persons, the light of Christ's gospel has been manifested unto this realm... Together with the life of the author, and several curious pieces wrote by him, viz., I. His appellation from the...sentence pronounced against him, by the false bishops and clergy of Scotland... II. His faithful admonition to the true professors of the gospel of Christ within the kingdom of England. III. His letter to Queen Mary. IV. His Exhortation to England... V. The first blast of the trumpet against the monstrous regiment of women. VI. A sermon, on Isaiah xxvi. 13. &c. By J. Knox. To which is added, I. An admonition to England and Scotland...written by Antoni Gilby. II. The first and second books of discipline... III. The form of process in the Judicatories of the Church of Scotland, with relation to scandals and censures. IV. A large alphabetical index to this history, and the other pieces. Edinburgh: H. Inglis, 1790.
2 p.l., lx, (1)62-572 p., 1 port. sq. 4°.

1. Reformation, Gt. Br.: Scotland. 2. Gilby, Anthony.
N. Y. P. L. July 8, 1913.

NK 0211388 NN NjP

BR385 .K6 1898 Knox, John, 1505-1572.
The history of the reformation of religion within the realm of Scotland. Edited for popular use by C. J. Guthrie. London, A. & C. Black, 1898.
xxvi, 364 p. illus. 21cm.
Bibliographical footnotes.
1. Reformation—Scotland. 2. Scotland—Church history. I. Guthrie, Charles John Guthrie, Lord, 1849-1920, ed. II. Title.

NK 0211389 NNC MB CLSU ICarbS PP MH PPL PPPD OU MBr-Z

BR385 .K7 Knox, John, 1505-1572.
The history of the reformation of religion within the realm of Scotland, written by John Knox. Ed. for popular use by C. J. Guthrie, Q. C. With notes, summary, glossary, index, and fifty-six illustrations. 2d ed. London, A. and C. Black, 1899.
xxvi, 364 p. incl. front., illus., ports., facsim. 21cm.

1. Reformation—Scotland. 1. Scotland—Church history.

NK 0211390 ICU PPTU

Knox, John, 1505-1572.
The historie of the reformatioun of religioun within the realm of Scotland by John Knox; a selection edited by Ralph S. Walker. [Edinburgh] Pub. for the Saltire society by Oliver and Boyd ltd., 1940.
72 p. 19cm. (*Half-title:* The Scottish classics)
"Knox's principal works": p. 14.

1. Reformation—Scotland. 2. Scotland—Church history. I. Walker, Ralph Spence, 1904- ed. II. Title.

A 41-3187

Illinois. Univ. Library for Library of Congress [2]

NK 0211391 OClW ICarbS ICN IU OrU NNC CLSU NIC NN MH ICU OCl

VOLUME 300

Knox, John, 1505–1572.
The historie of the reformation of the Church of Scotland; containing five books: together with some treatises conducing to the history... London, G. Thomason and O. Pullen, 1664.
460, 122 p. 30cm.

Edited, with a life of Knox and a preface, by David Buchanan.—*cf. Dictionary of national biography.*

"The appellation of John Knox, from the...sentence pronounced against him," "To his beloved brethren the commonalty of Scotland," "A faithfull admonition... to the true professors of the Gospel of Christ within the kingdom of England, 1554," "The copie of a letter delivered to Queen Mary, regent of Scotland," and "A sermon ⌊August 19, 1565⌋" 122 p. at end.

1. Reformation—Gt. Br.—Scotland. . Buchanan, David, 1595?–1652? ed.
N. Y. P. L. *Card revised* August 8, 1945

TxDaM-P IU
MiU RPB NcD CaBVaU CSmH ICN ICU DLC NNUT NN NIC CSt
NK 0211393 NN NcU MH OCl DFo PPL IU MiU CU CLU-C

D 543 .4665 KNOX, JOHN, 1505-1572.
The history of the reformation of the church of Scotland... To which is added, The life of the author, and several...pieces written by him, viz. I. his appeal from the...unjust sentence pronounced against him... II. his...admonition to the true professors of the Gospel of Christ... III. his letter to Queen Mary... IV. his exhortation to England for the...embracing of Christ's Gospel. V. The first blast of the trumpet against the monstrous regiment of women. VI. A sermon on Isaiah XXVI, 13, &c.... Paisley,D. Gardner,1791.
v. 21cm.

NK 0211394 ICN MH-AH NcD ICMcC

Knox, John, 1505-1572.
On justification
see under Balnaves, Henry, d. 1579.

Knox, John, 1505-1572.

... **Prefaces** and prologues to famous books, with introductions, notes and illustrations. New York, P. F. Collier & son ⌊°1910⌋

Mhc5 K774 1845 Knox, John, 1505-1572.
Select practical writings. Issued by the Committee of the General Assembly of the Free Church of Scotland, for the Publication of the Works of Scottish Reformers and Divines. Edinburgh,1845.
352p. 19cm.

NK 0211397 CtY NN NjR MeWC PPPrHi PU

STC 20642.5 Knox, John, 1505-1572.
A sermon preached by John Knox minister of Christ Iesus in the publique audience of the church of Edenbrough, within the realme of Scotland, vpon Sonday, the 19. of August 1565. For the which the said Iohn Knoxe was inhibite preaching for a season ... To this is adioyned an exhortation vnto all the faythfull within the sayde realme, for the reliefe of suche as faythfully trauayle in the preaching of Gods worde. Written by the same Iohn Knoxe, at the commaundement of the ministerie aforesayd.

[London]Imprinted[by H.Denham?].Anno.1566.
24°. 7p.ℓ.,2-49,11 numb.ℓ. 13cm.
STC 15075.
No.4 in a volume of tracts.

NK 0211399 MH MWiW-C DFo

FILM Knox,John,1505-1572.
A sermon preached by John Knox in the publique audience of the Church of Edenbrough, within the realme of Scotland,vpon Sonday, the.19.of August.1565. For the which the said Iohn Knoxe was inhibite preaching for a season. To this is adioyned an exhortation vnto all the faythfull within the sayde realme,for the reliefe of suche as faythfully trauayle in the preaching of Gods Worde. ⌊Edinburgh?⌋ 1566.
Short-title catalogue no.15075 (carton 964)

NK 0211400 MiU CaBVa

Knox, John, 1505-1572.
The source and bounds of kingly power.
(In Fish, Henry Clay. History and repository of pulpit eloquence. v. 2, p. 207-228)

NK 0211401 RPB

Knox, John, 1505-1572.
Writings of Rev. John Knox.
Phila., n.d.
2d American ed. 12°

NK 0211402 NNUT

Knox, John, 1505-1572.
Writings of the Rev. John Knox ... 1st American ed. Philadelphia, Presbyterian board of publication ⌊18—⌋
vi, iii-iv, 5-456 p. front. (port.) 19½cm.
(On cover: British reformers ⌊9⌋)

I. Presbyterian church in the U. S. A. Board of publication. II. Ser.

NK 0211403 ViU PHi

Knox, John, 1505-1572.

Writings of the Rev. John Knox ... London, Printed for the Religious tract society ⌊1830?⌋
xxiv, 456 p. front. (port.) 19½cm. (On cover: British reformers ⌊no.9⌋)

CBBD
NK 0211404 NcD PPWe ViU MH CtY WaWW OO MeWC MiEM NIC

Knox, John, 1505-1572.
Writings of the Rev. John Knox...1st American ed. Philadelphia, Presbyterian board of publication, 1842.
vi, ⌊iii⌋-iv, 5-24,456 p. front. (port.) 20cm. (*In* British reformers 1842-43. v. 9)

NK 0211405 MiU PPLT ViU

⌊**Knox, John**⌋ 1720-1790.
Address to the right honourable and honourable directors of the British society, for extending the fisheries and improving the sea coasts of the kingdom. ⌊London? 1787⌋
1 p. l., 18 p. 22cm.
Signed: John Knox. London, May 1, 1787.

1. Fisheries—Scotland. 2. British society for extending the fisheries, and improving the sea coasts of this kingdom. I. Title.
44-20812
Library of Congress SH259.K56
⌊2⌋ 639.22

NK 0211406 DLC

[Knox, John] 1720-1790, pub.
A complete collection of the most remarkable voyages, selected from the writers of all nations ...
see under title

Knox, John, 1720-1790.
A discourse on the expediency of establishing fishing stations, or small towns, in the Highlands of Scotland and the Hebride islands ... London, Sold by J.Walter ⌊etc.⌋ 1786.
2 p.ℓ., 43 p. tables. 20 cm.

NK 0211408 MH-BA CtY

Knox, John, 1720-1790.

Extracts from the publications of Mr. Knox, Dr. Anderson, Mr. Pennant and Dr. Johnson; relative to the northern and north-western coasts of Great Britain. London, Printed by C. Macrae, 1787.

Knox, John, 1720-1790, supposed author.

Guthrie, William, 1708-1770.
A geographical, historical, and commercial grammar; exhibiting the present state of the world ... By William Guthrie, esq. The astronomical part by James Ferguson, F. R. S. ... The 24th ed., studiously revised and carefully corrected. London, C. and J. Rivington; ⌊etc., etc.⌋ 1827.

⌊**Knox, John**⌋ 1720-1790, *pub.*
A new collection of voyages, discoveries and travels: containing whatever is worthy of notice, in Europe, Asia, Africa and America ... The whole consisting of such English and foreign authors as are in most esteem ... London, J. Knox, 1767.
7 v. plates (part fold.) fold. maps, fold. plans, tables. 21½cm.

1. Voyages and travels. I. Title.
6-3068
Library of Congress G160.K75

NIC NcD TU PBL TxU CSt DSI MB NN CU-B
NK 0211411 DLC WaS OC RPJCB OClW OCl ViU MiU-C PPL

Knox, John, 1720-1790. FOR OTHER EDITIONS SEE MAIN ENTRY

Guthrie, William, 1708-1770.
A new geographical, historical, and commercial grammar; and present state of the several kingdoms of the world ... By William Guthrie, esq. The astronomical part by James Ferguson, F. R. S. To which have been added the late discoveries of Dr. Herschell, and other eminent astronomers. Illustrated with a correct set of maps, engraved from the most recent observations and draughts of geographical travellers ... The 15th ed., cor., and considerably enl. London, Printed for C. Dilly ⌊etc.⌋ 1795-

---

Knox, John, 1720-1790, supposed author.

Guthrie, William, 1708-1770. FOR OTHER EDITIONS SEE MAIN ENTRY
A new system of modern geography: or, A geographical, historical, and commercial grammar; and present state of the several nations of the world ... By William Guthrie. The astronomical parts corrected by Dr. Rittenhouse ... 1st American ed., cor., improved, and greatly enl. Philadelphia, M. Carey, 1794-95.

Knox, John, 1720-1790.
Observations on the northern fisheries. With a discourse on the expediency of establishing fishing stations, or small towns, in the Highlands of Scotland, and the Hebride islands. To which is added, the last report from the committee appointed by the House of commons, to enquire into the state of the British fisheries. By John Knox ... London, Printed for J. Walter ⌊etc.⌋ 1786.
iv, 158 p. 22cm.

1. Fisheries—Scotland.
A 18-1446
Harvard univ. Library for Library of Congress ⌊a40b1⌋

NK 0211414 MH CSt MH-BA

VOLUME 300

*G160
.E75
v.7
[Knox, John] 1720-1790, pub.
A short view of the naval transactions of Britain: beginning with the reign of Queen Elizabeth, and ending with the Peace of Versailles in 1762.
(In [Knox, John] pub. A collection of voyages, discoveries and travels. London, 1767. 21 1/2cm. p. 193-528)

1. Gt. Brit.—Navy—Hist. 2. Gt. Brit.—History, Naval.

NK 0211416 MB

Knox, John, 1720-1790.
A tour through the highlands of Scotland, and the Hebride Isles, in MDCCLXXXVI. By John Knox. London, Printed for J. Walter ₍etc.₎; ₍etc., etc.₎ 1787.
clxxii, 276, 103, ₍5₎ p. 21cm.
The tour, in the interest of "the proposed society for extending the fisheries and improving the sea-coasts of the kingdom" was begun June 29, 1786. The present work covers the first part only, from Oban to Cape Wrath. The promised continuation seems to have remained unpublished.
Book-plate: William Winter.
In manuscript on t.-p.: William Winter 1897.
1. Fisheries--Scotland. 2. Scotland--Econ. condit

NK 0211417 MiU PPL PP OClW ICN NN NjP TxU NNC ICU TU MH

Knox, John, 1720-1790, supposed author.

Guthrie, William, 1708-1770.
A universal geography: or, A view of the present state of the known world ... Originally compiled by William Guthrie, esq., the astronomical part by James Ferguson ... Accompanied with twenty-one correct maps. 3d American ed., with extensive additions and alterations, by several American editors ... Philadelphia: Published by Benjamin Warner, No. 171, High Street. Also for sale at his store in Richmond, (Va.) and by Wm. P. Bason, Charleston, (S. C.) 1820.

Knox, John, 1720-1790.
A view of the British empire, more especially Scotland; with some proposals for the improvement of that country, the extension of its fisheries, and the relief of the people. By John Knox. London, Printed for J. Walter ₍etc.₎ 1784.
1 p. l., lxx, 113, ₍1₎ p. 22cm.

1. Scotland—Economic conditions. 2. Fisheries—Scotland. 3. Herring-fisheries.
A 18-1447
Title from Harvard Univ. Printed by L. C.

NK 0211419 MH RPJCB MH-BA CtY PHi WaU

Knox, John, 1720-1790.
A view of the British empire, more especially Scotland; with some proposals for the improvement of that country, the extension of its fisheries, and the relief of the people. By John Knox ... 3d ed., greatly enl. London, Printed for J. Walter; ₍etc., etc.₎ 1785.
2 v. 21cm.

1. Scotland—Economic conditions. 2. Fisheries—Scotland. 3. Herring-fisheries.
A 18-1448
Title from Harvard Univ. Printed by L. C.

NK 0211419-1 MH PMA MH-BA CU NjP NNC MB

Knox, John, 1720-1790.
A view of the British Empire, more especially Scotland; with some proposals for the improvement of that country, the extension of its fisheries, and the relief of the people. 4th ed. London, J. Walter, 1789.
xl, 670 p. 21 cm.
1. Scotland. Economic conditions. 2. Fisheries. Scotland. 2. Herring-fisheries. I. Title.

NK 0211419-2 NcD PP NN CtY NNC

Knox, John, 1720-1790.
Voyage dans les montagnes de l'Écosse et dans les isles Hébrides, fait en 1786... Tr. de l'anglois... A Paris, Chez Defer de Maisonneuve ₍etc., etc.₎ 1790.
2 v. 21 cm.
A report to the members of the British society for extending the fisheries and improving the sea coast of the kingdom.

NK 0211419-3 NjP IU MH

Knox, *Capt.* **John,** *d.* 1778.
... The battle of Quebec. From Captain John Knox's "Historical journal of the campaigns in North America for the years 1757, 1758, 1759, and 1760". ₍Boston, Directors of the Old South work, 1896₎
16 p. 20cm. (Old South leaflets. ₍General series. v. 3₎ no. 73)
Caption title.
Extract from Parkman's "Montcalm and Wolfe" (p. 12-15)

1. Quebec campaign, 1759. I. Title.
Library of Congress E173.O44 vol. 3 20—20740

NK 0211419-4 DLC OrPR ViU WaS NcU MiU OO ODW OU OCU OCl ViU MB PSC PHi PPL

DD411
.A5
1774
Knox, Capt. John, d. 1778.

The Annual register of world events.
A complete history of the late war, or, Annual register, of its rise, progress, and events, in Europe, Asia, Africa, and America ... With ... additions ... taken from Capt. John Knox's Historical journal of the war in America. 6th ed ... Dublin, J. Exshaw, 1774.

Knox, *Capt.* **John,** *d.* 1778.
An historical journal of the campaigns in North-America, for the years 1757, 1758, 1759, and 1760: containing the most remarkable occurrences of that period; particularly the two sieges of Quebec, &c. &c., the orders of the admirals and general officers; descriptions of the countries where the author has served, with their forts and garrisons; their climates, soil, produce; and a regular diary of the weather. As also several manifesto's, a mandate of the late bishop of Canada; the French orders and disposition for the defence of the colony, &c. &c. &c. By Captain John Knox ... London, Printed for the author; and sold by W. Johnston ₍etc.₎ 1769.
2 v. fronts. (ports.) fold. maps. 27½ cm.

1. U. S.—Hist.—French and Indian war, 1755-1763.
E199.K74 2—12669

NK 0211419-5 DLC PHi MB NN MiU-C CSmH CtY MdAN ViW ViU PBL RPJCB InU FTaSU CaOTU MWA PBL MdBP N NBuHi NIC CaBVaU

Knox, *Capt.* **John,** *d.* 1778.
An historical journal of the campaigns in North America for the years 1757, 1758, 1759, and 1760, by Captain John Knox; ed. with introduction, appendix and index by Arthur G. Doughty ... Toronto, The Champlain society, 1914-16.
3 v. plates, ports., maps (part fold.) plans (part fold.) facsims. 25 cm. (*Half-title:* The publications of the Champlain society. VIII-X)
Series note also on added t.-p.
Includes reproduction of t.-p. of original edition, London, 1769.
Vol. 3 has title: Appendix to an historical journal ...
No. L16 of 520 copies printed.
PARTIAL CONTENTS OF APPENDIX.—Journal of Major-General Jeffery Amherst and Colonel William Amherst, 1758-1760.—Two letters from a French officer ₍Thomas Pichon₎ of the garrison at Louisbourg.—Lists of British and French officers killed and wounded at Louisbourg and Quebec, 1758-1760.—Private diary kept by Sir William Johnson at Niagara and Oswego, 1759.—The cartel regarding exchange of prisoners, 1759.—₍James₎ Murray's journal ₍May 18-Sept. 17, 1760₎—Documents relating to an engagement between French and English ships in Baie des Chaleurs in 1760.—List of works consulted.—General index.
1. U. S.—Hist.—French and Indian war, 1755-1763. 2. U. S.—Hist.—French and Indian war, 1755-1763—Registers, lists, etc. 3. U. S.—Hist.—French and Indian war, 1755-1763—Bibl. I. Doughty, Sir Arthur George, 1860-1936, ed. II. Amherst, Jeffery Amherst, 1st baron, 1717-1797. III. Amherst, William, 1732-1781. IV. Johnson, Sir William, bart., 1715-1774. V. Murray, James, d. 1794.
Library of Congress E199.K76 14—18944

NK 0211419-6 DLC WaS WaSp MH MB ICN ICJ OO OCl OCU MiU OClWHi CaBVaU NcD MiU-C ViU PPL PPAmP CaOTU OkU CaNSWA NcU NcD RPJCB MU FMU MoU N CU AAP

Knox, John, 1790-1858.
The church glorious; a discourse delivered on the occasion of the opening, for divine worship, the building erected by the consistory of the Reformed Dutch Church of the City of New-York, on the corner of Fourth street and Lafayette place, May 9, 1839. By the Rev. John Knox... New-York: R. Carter, 1839. 38 p. 22½cm.
"Address, delivered by the Rev. Dr. Knox, Nov. 9, 1836, when the corner-stone of the church in La Fayette place was laid," p. ₍33₎-36.

863585A. 1. New York (City)—Churches, Reformed Church in America—Middle Dutch.
N. Y. P. L. December 31, 1936

NK 0211419-7 NN MWA MB PPPrHi DLC NjNbS

Knox, John, 1790-1858.
Comfort in sorrow. A discourse occasioned by the death of Mrs. Marianne F. M'Elroy... Delivered... Nov. 27, 1836. New York: R. Carter, 1836. 11 p. 8°.
In: ZIZ p. v. 7, no. 14.

1. M'Elroy, Marianne F. 2. Sermons (Funeral).
N. Y. P. L. July 24, 1911.

NK 0211420 NN PPPrHi DLC

Knox, John, 1790-1858.
The death of the aged pious--a blessing. A sermon, occasioned by the death of the Rev. Gerardus A. Kuypers, D.D. preached in the Middle Dutch church, June 7, 1833. By the Rev. John Knox ... New-York, G. F. Hopkins & son, printers ... 1833.
23 p. 21 1/2 cm.

1. Kuypers, Gerardus Arense, 1766-1833. I. Title.

NK 0211421 CSmH NN PHi NjNbS PPPrHi ICN NjP

Knox, John, 1790-1858.
The good and faithful servant. A discourse, delivered in the Reformed Dutch Church on Lafayette Place... 1849, on the occasion of the death of the Rev. William Cahoone. New-York: J. Moffet, 1849. 21 p. 8°.

1. Cahoone, Rev. William.
N. Y. P. L. December 2, 1912.

NK 0211422 NN NjNbS RPB PPPrHi

Knox, John, 1790-1858.
Memorial of the Rev. John Knox, D. D.
see under title

Knox, John, 1790-1858.
Parental responsibility and parental solicitude; two discourses, delivered in the Middle Dutch church, by John Knox, D.D., senior pastor of the Collegiate Reformed Dutch church, in the city of New York. New York: Printed by H. R. Piercy, 7 Theatre Alley. 1834.
34 p. 20.5cm.
The second discourse, Parental solicitude, has separate half-title at p. ₍19₎

NK 0211424 MiU-C PPPrHi RPB

Knox, John, 1790-1858.
Preparation for death: a sermon on the occasion of the death of Lt. Col. Alexander Ramsay Thompson, of the U. S. army, who was killed in battle with the Indians at Okee-cho-bee, Florida, December 25, 1837, delivered in the Middle Dutch church, February 11, 1838. By the Rev. John Knox ... New-York, Printed by W. Osborn, 1838.
27 p. fold. front. 23cm.

1. Thompson, Alexander Ramsay, 1793-1837.
17-19959
Library of Congress E83.835.T46

NK 0211425 DLC FTaSU PPPrHi PHi NjNbS NWM OClWHi

VOLUME 300

Knox, John, 1790-1858.
A sermon occasioned by the death of Rev. Gerardus A. Kuypers
see his The death of the aged pious.

Knox, John, 1867- *ed.*
Uddrag af Retsplejeloven til brug ved underretterne, ved J. Knox og S. Grundtvig. København, I kommission hos G. E. C. Gad [1919]
3 p. l., 5-43 p. 22cm.
Cover-title: Underretsproceduren.
CONTENTS.—Borgerlige sager.—Straffesager.

1. Civil procedure — Denmark. 2. Criminal procedure — Denmark. I. *Grundtvig, Stener, 1860- joint ed. II. Denmark. Laws, statutes, etc. III. Title. IV. Title: Underretsproceduren.
[*Full name:* John Eduard Lemmich Knox]
36-34924
Library of Congress [2] [347.909489] 349.489079

NK 0211427 DLC

Knox, John, 1898-
Gt. Brit. *Geological survey.*
... The economic geology of the Fife coalfields ... Edinburgh. H. M. Stationery off., 1931-

---

Knox, John, 1900-
Chapters in a life of Paul. New York, Abingdon-Cokesbury Press [1950]
168 p. 24 cm.

1. Paul, Saint, apostle.
BS2505.K56 [922.1] 225.92 50-5882
[12]

OrPR WaWW MoU InU FTaSU KyWAT
PP ViU ICU MB WaS OrSaW WaT WaTC IdPI MtU IdU Or OrCS
NK 0211429 DLC TU KxLxCB OKentU OCU OCl OOxM PLFM

Knox, John, 1900-
Chapters in a life of Paul. London, A. and C. Black, 1954.
168p. 24cm.

1. Paul, Saint, apostle. I. Title.

NK 0211429-1 KAS CLSU CaBVaU

Knox, John, 1900-
Christ the Lord; the meaning of Jesus in the early church, by John Knox. Chicago, New York, Willett, Clark & company, 1945.
xi p., 1 l., 146 p. 20½cm. (*Half-title:* The Ayer lectures of the Colgate-Rochester divinity school, Rochester, N. Y.)
"A bibliography": p. 134-139.

1. Jesus Christ—Person and offices.
45-11302
Library of Congress BT205.K5
[3] 232

PSt MB FU KyWAT MsSM NcGU NcD IndAndC-T
NK 0211429-2 DLC WaTC WaS MB OrSaW OCl PPPD PP NRCR

BR115 .R2K7 Knox, John, 1900-
... The Christian church and race ... New York, Federal council of the Churches of Christ in America [1945]
24 p. (Pamphlet library on the church and minority peoples)

1. Race problems.

NK 0211429-3 ICU

BT 734.2 K7 Knox, John, 1900-
The Christian church and race. New York, The Commission on the Church and Minority Peoples of the Federal Council of the Churches of Christ in America [1954]
24 p. 22cm. (Pamphlet library on the church and minority peoples)

Photocopy.

1. Church and race problems. I. Title.

NK 0211429-4 CBPac

Knox, John, 1900-
Criticism and faith. New York, Abingdon-Cokesbury Press [1952]
128 p. 20 cm.

1. Bible—Criticism, interpretation, etc. 2. Bible—Evidences, authority, etc. I. Title.
BS520.K6 220.7 52-8843 ‡

PPWe ODW OCH OrPR NIC KyU KyLxT KyLxCB OrU WaS WaTC
NK 0211429-5 DLC OrP Or PSt OCl PP PBL PU MB PPEB

Knox, John, 1900-
Criticism and faith. London, Hodder and Stoughton [1953]
126 p. 20 cm.

1. Bible—Criticism, interpretation, etc. 2. Bible—Evidences, authority, etc. I. Title.
BS520.K6 1953 220.7 54-28864 ‡

NK 0211429-6 DLC MB TxFTC

Knox, John, 1900-
The early church and the coming great church. New York, Abingdon Press [1955]
160 p. 21 cm. (Hoover lectures [1955])

1. Church history—Primitive and early church. 2. Christian union. I. Title.
BR165.K63 270.1 55-6765 ‡

Or LU OO PP PCC MB NcD OOxM PPWe PPPD PBL PPT WaTC
NK 0211429-7 DLC MH-AH NIC NNC PSt CaBVa MBtS WaS

Knox, John, 1900-
The fourth Gospel and the later Epistles. New York, Abingdon-Cokesbury Press [°1945]
157 p. 19 cm. (A Guide for Bible readers)

1. Bible. N. T. John—Study—Text-books. 2. Bible. N. T. Epistles—Study—Text-books. I. Title. (Series)
BS2616.K6 225.5 48-10445*

NK 0211429-8 DLC OrSaW MoU NcD NjPT ICU OCl

Knox, John, 1900-
"He whom a dream hath possessed"; some aspects of the art of religious living, by John Knox ... New York, R. Long & R. R. Smith, inc., 1932.
viii p., 2 l., 3-121 p. 19½cm.
"The title and, in part, the structure of this small volume are derived from 'He whom a dream hath possessed' by Shaemas O'Sheel."—p. vii.

1. Christian life. I. O'Sheel, Shaemas, 1886- He whom a dream hath possessed. II. Title.
32-5569
Library of Congress BV4501.K6
——— Copy 2.
Copyright A 47640 [2] 248

NK 0211429-9 DLC NRCR NcD PPLT ViU

Knox, John, 1900-
The man Christ Jesus, by John Knox. Chicago, New York, Willett, Clark & company, 1941.
100 p. 19cm.

1. Jesus Christ—Character. 2. Jesus Christ—Humanity. I. Title.
41-51780
Library of Congress BT304.K55
[10] 232.9

CaBVa MtBC OO OCl OOxM OClW PHC PP
NK 0211430 DLC Or KyU KyLxT NcD NcC NIC NRCR

Knox, John, 1900-
The man, Christ Jesus. New York, Harper & Brothers [1941]
100 p.

NK 0211430-1 MH-AH OrPR

Knox, John, 1900-
The man Christ Jesus, by ... Chicago, N.Y., Willett, Clark & company, 1942.
100 p. 19 cm.

NK 0211431 PPTU PPWe NcGU NcRS NcC

Knox, John, 1900-
Marcion and the New Testament, an essay in the early history of the canon, by John Knox ... Chicago, Ill., The University of Chicago press [1942]
ix, 195 p. 20cm.
"Bibliography of modern works cited": p. 183-190.

1. Marcion, of Sinope, 2d cent. 2. Bible. N. T.—Canon. 3. Bible—Canon—N. T.
42-25863
Library of Congress BS2320.K55
[4] 225.1

OU ViU PPLT PPT WaU NcD MoU KyWAT DDO
NK 0211432 DLC OrP OrU WaS MH-AH NRCR OCl OClW OO

Knox, John, 1900-
On the meaning of Christ. New York, C. Scribner's Sons, 1947.
xvi, 117 p. 20 cm. (William Belden Noble lectures, Harvard Univ., 1947)

1. Jesus Christ—Significance. 2. Church. I. Title. II. Series.
BT205.K53 232 47-6933*

KyLxCB NcGU
NK 0211433 DLC OrP WaS CtY MH ICU NcD MB KyU NBuU

Knox, John, 1900-
On the meaning of Christ. New York, C. Scribner's Sons, 1955.
xvi, 117 p. 20 cm. (William Belden Noble lectures, Harvard Univ., 1947)

NK 0211434 OClW OrPR

Knox, John, 1900-
... Philemon among the letters of Paul; a new view of its place and importance ... by John Knox. Chicago, Ill., The University of Chicago press, 1935.
ix, 57 p., 1 l. 23cm.
Thesis (PH. D.)—University of Chicago, 1935.
Published also without thesis note.

1. Bible. N. T. Philemon—Criticism, interpretation, etc. 2. Bible—Criticism, interpretation, etc.—N. T. Philemon. I. Title.
36-8952
Library of Congress BS2765.K6 1935
Univ. of Chicago Libr.
——— Copy 2. [2] 227.86

NK 0211435 ICU OCU NjPT NIC NcD OO MiU MBrZ DLC

VOLUME 300

Knox, John, 1900–
Philemon among the letters of Paul; a new view of its place and importance, by John Knox. Chicago, Ill., The University of Chicago press [1935]
ix, 57 p., 1 l. 23½cm.
Issued also as thesis (PH. D.) University of Chicago.

1. Bible. N. T. Philemon—Criticism, interpretation, etc. 2. Bible—Criticism, interpretation, etc.—N. T. Philemon. I. Title.
36-8933
Library of Congress BS2765.K6 1935 a
—— Copy 2.
Copyright A 92520 [2] 227.86

NK 0211436 DLC

Knox, John, 1900– *ed.*
Religion and the present crisis, edited by John Knox. Chicago, Ill., The University of Chicago press [1942]
xi, 165 p. 21cm. (*Half-title:* [Chicago. University] Charles R. Walgreen foundation lectures)
Bibliographical references included in preface.
CONTENTS.—Christianity refinding itself, by E. C. Colwell.—Building a better democracy, by E. E. Aubrey.—Re-examining pacifism, by John Knox.—Maintaining fellowship across lines of conflict, by C. T. Holman.—Achieving personal stability, by H. N. Wieman.—Anticipating the post-war mind, by C. W. Gilkey.—Preparing for durable peace, by J. T. McNeill.—Educating for a new world-order, by W. C. Bower.—Redeeming culture through crisis, by Wilhelm Pauck.
1. U. S.—Church history. 2. Civilization, Christian. I. Title.
42-10793
Library of Congress BR516.K63
[8] 261

OC1 Wa OU OC1CC OO OEac PPT PPLT
NK 0211437 DLC OrP OrU WaS NRCR KEmT MsU NcD NcGU

F2646
.E42
Knox, John, 1904-

Eichner, Erich.
A cidade maravilhosa, Rio de Janeiro, e seus arredores. The marvellous city. Documentário fotográfico organizado por Erich Eichner; síntese histórica de John Knox, com as traduções em inglês francês e alemão. Rio de Janeiro, Kosmos [194–?]

F2515
.E4
Knox, John, 1904-

Eichner, Erich.
Gente e terra do Brasil. Documentário fotográfico organizado por Erich Eichner, síntese histórica e econômica de John Knox, pref. de Carlos Rizzini; com as traduções em inglês, francês e espanhol. [Rio de Janeiro] Livraria Kosmos [1946?]

[**Knox, John Armoy**] 1851–1906.
All about the Klondike gold mines. New York, The Miners' News Pub. Co. [1897]
59 p. map. 23 cm.
By J. A. Knox and J. G. Pratt.

1. Klondike gold fields. I. Pratt, J. G., joint author. II. Title.
F931.K74 1-15768 rev*

NK 0211440 DLC NN NNC

KNOX, J[ohn] Armoy, 1851-1906.
A comic opera in three acts, entitled The false prophet! written by J. Armoy Knox and Charles M. Snyder. [New York?], 1887.

pp.58. Illustr.
Interleaved.

NK 0211441 MH

Knox, John Armoy, 1851–1906.
A [devil] of a trip; or, The log of the yacht Champlain. As kept by J. Armoy Knox ... and illus. by Thos. Worth. [c1888] London, Texas Siftings Pub. Co.
128 p. illus. 23½cm. (*On cover:* The unique series, no. 1)
Title represented in the form of a rebus.

NK 0211442 N

Knox, John Armoy, 1851–1906.
A [devil] of a trip; or, The log of the yacht Champlain. As kept by J. Armoy Knox ... and illus. by Thos. Worth. New York, National literary bureau [c1888]
128 p. illus. 23½cm. (*On cover:* The unique series, no. 1)
Title represented in the form of a rebus.

Library of Congress PZ3.K774D 7-14192†

NK 0211443 DLC TxU CaBVaU

Knox, John Armoy, 1851-1906.
Harley's wife. [1884]
see under Roach, James Connor.

Knox, John Armoy, 1851-1906, joint author.
Sweet, Alexander Edwin, 1841–1901.
Humoristische reise durch Texas von Galveston bis zum Rio Grande, von Alexander E. Sweet und J. Armoy Knox. Aus dem englischen, von Reinhold Teuscher ... Mit 167 illustrationen im text und 10 holzschnitttafeln. Jena, H. Costenoble, 1884.

Knox, John Armoy, 1851-1906.
McFadden's spirits. [1884]
see under Roach, J.C.

Knox, John Armoy, 1851-1906, joint author.
Sweet, Alexander Edwin, 1841–1901. FOR OTHER EDITIONS SEE MAIN ENTRY
On a Mexican mustang, through Texas, from the Gulf to the Rio Grande. By Alex E. Sweet and J. Armory Knox ... Hartford, Conn., S. S. Scranton & company, 1883.

PN6161
.S855
Knox, John Armoy, 1851-1906, joint author.

Sweet, Alexander Edwin, 1841–1901.
Sketches from "Texas siftings." By Sweet and Knox. Illustrated by W. H. Caskie. New York, Texas siftings publishing company, 1882.

G
827
.467
KNOX, JOHN ARMOY, 1851-1906.
Texas siftings afloat. Or The log of the yacht Champlain. As kept by J.Armoy Knox and illustrated by Thos. Worth. London,Texas siftings publishing company,ltd.[1888]
126p. 24cm.

Published in the United States under title: The devil of a trip.
Account of a trip from lake Champlain, through the Richelieu river into the Saint Lawrence, down to the Saguenay, then out into the Gulf of Saint Lawrence, around Nova Scotia, and to New York.

NK 0211449 ICN

Knox, John Armoy, 1851-1906, joint author.
Sweet, Alexander Edwin, 1841–1901.
Three dozen good stories from Texas siftings. Comprising sketches by Alex. Sweet and J. Armoy Knox. With nearly 100 illustrations by Thomas Worth and other artists ... New York, Chicago, J. S. Ogilvie and company, 1887.

HB172
.L85
Knox, John B., joint author.

Loomis, H B
How did we get this way? Contributed by H. B. Loomis and John B. Knox ... New York, N. Y., William B. Dana company [1943]

Knox, John Ballenger.
The people of Tennessee; a study of population trends. Prepared for the Bureau for Sociological Research, with the assistance of Jerry W. Combs, Jr. [and others] With an introd. by William E. Cole. Knoxville, University of Tennessee Press, 1949.
xvi, 191 p. illus., maps. 24 cm.
Bibliography: p. [178]–187.

1. Tennessee—Population. I. Tennessee. University. Bureau of Sociological Research. II. Title.
HB3525.T2K5 312 49-48571*

AU OOxM ODW NcD MtU
NK 0211452 DLC IdU WaS WaSp ViU ICU MB DNAL TxU

Knox, John Ballenger.
The sociology of industrial relations; an introduction to industrial sociology. New York, Random House [1955]
348 p. illus. 24 cm.

1. Industrial relations. I. Title.
HD6971.K6 331 55-7642 ‡

FMU TxU C ViU MB NcRS PV CaBViP
OU NN CU IU PBL AU KMK NIC CaBVaU PPLas PPD MsSM
NK 0211453 DLC OrU TU PBm PPT OOxM NcD OC1W OC1

976.1
K773a
Knox, John Barnett, 1857-1935.
Address on his installation as President of the Constitutional Convention of Alabama, May 22, 1901. Montgomery, Ala., Brown Print. Co., 1901.
16p. 23cm. (State of Alabama Constitutional Convention, 1901. Document no.2)

"Printed by order of Convention."

1. Alabama - Pol. & govt. - 1865- I. Alabama. Constitutional Convention, 1901. Sp.: Littlefield Fund.

NK 0211454 TxU NjP

973.7
K773a
Knox, John Barnett, 1857-1935.
Address to the students of the University of Alabama, delivered June 3d, 1903, at Clark's Hall, University, Ala. Commencement term 1902-'03. Anniston, Ala., G.H. Norwood, printer, 1903.
32p. 23cm.

Cover title.

1. U.S. - Hist. - Civil War - Addresses, sermons, etc. I. Alabama. University. Sp.: Littlefield Fund.

NK 0211455 TxU

E382
.K5
Knox, John Barnett, 1857-
Andrew Jackson. Delivered before State Bar Association of Tennessee, at Nashville, June 11, 1914. [Nashville? 1914?]
cover-title, 43 p. 25 cm.

At head of title: Soldier, patriot, statesman.

1. Jackson, Andrew, Pres. U.S., 1767-1845.
I. Bar Association of Tennessee.

NK 0211456 T MH

VOLUME 300

Knox, John Barnett, 1857-
... The expansion of the United States, by John B. Knox. [Anniston? Ala., 1916]
12 p. 23½cm.
Caption title.

1. U. S.—Territorial expansion.
22-9820
Library of Congress E768.K74

NK 0211457 DLC

---

*
E340
.C15K5 Knox, John Barnett, 1857-
1911
John C. Calhoun, his services to his country and his place in history. Revised and reprinted from the Montgomery Advertiser, May 14, 1911. Anniston, Ala., Norwood Print, [1911?]
41 p. 22cm.
Letter signed by the author laid in.

1. Calhoun, John Caldwell, 1782-1850.

NK 0211458 ViU AU

JK
1929 Knox, John Barnett, 1857-1935.
A2 Justice to the South, by John B. Knox. Anniston [Ala.]
K74 Norwood Print [1901?]
22 p. 27 cm.
Title from original paper cover.

1. Negroes - Politics and suffrage. 2. Suffrage - Southern States. 3. Southern States - Pol. & govt. - 1865- I. Title.

NK 0211459 Vi NN PU

Knox, John Barnett, 1857-1935.
The Rhea letter; a little letter which made a heap of history. The authority of General Jackson to invade Florida during the war with the Seminole Indians, as disclosed in the Rhea letter
Anniston, Ala., 1917

NK 0211460 GEU

Knox, John B[arnett], 1857-
Soldier, patriot, statesman
see his Andrew Jackson.

Knox, John Clark, 1881-
Comments on Labor courts
see under Kirshbaum, Louis, ed.

Knox, John Clark, 1881-
The courts and the trade associations
see under Bank of America, New York.

Knox, John Clark, 1881-
A judge comes of age, by John C. Knox ... New York, C. Scribner's sons, 1940.
6 p. l., 353 p. front. (port.) illus. 22 cm.

1. Lawyers—New York (State)—Correspondence, reminiscences, etc. I. Title.
——— Copy 2. JK1519.K6A3
40-33160

WaU-L KyLx NcU OrU
OLak OCl h ViU-L IdU-L OrP IdU WaT WaSp WaS Or FU
NK 0211464 DLC PU-L NBuU-L ViU NcD CU-AL PP OCl

Knox, John Clark, 1881-
A judge comes of age... N.Y., Scribner, 1941.
353p.

NK 0211465 OU NcC NcRS

Knox, John Clark, 1881-
Labor-capital and the public, by Judge John C. Knox... Respectability for sale, by Louis Kirshbaum. [New York: L. Kirshbaum] 1940. 20 p. 18½cm.

1. Courts, Industrial—U. S. 2. Trade unions—U. S. I. Kirshbaum, Louis. II. Title. III. Title: Respectability for sale.
N. Y. P. L. January 14, 1941

NK 0211466 NN MH

Knox, John Clark, 1881-
Lectures on legal topics ... 1925-1926, by J. Gilmer Korner, jr., Philip J. McCook, John C. Knox ... [and others] New York, The Macmillan company, 1929.

Knox, John Clark, 1881-
Order in the court, by John C. Knox ... New York, C. Scribner's sons, 1943.
4 p. l., 341 p. 21½cm.

1. Judges—New York (State)—Correspondence, reminiscences, etc. I. Title.
43-7352

WaS WaT
WaU-L PP PU-L OEac OU OCl ViU-L MiHM CaBViP Or OrP
NK 0211468 DLC NBuU-L NIC NcD NcU FU IdU-L CaBVaU

Knox, John Colvin, 1817-1880.

Pennsylvania. *Laws, statutes, etc.*
The Penal code of Pennsylvania, by Isaac H. Shields ... Philadelphia, R. Welsh & co., 1883-94.

Knox, John Colvin, 1817-1880.

Law

Pennsylvania. *Commissioners to revise the Penal code.*
Report of the commissioners appointed to revise the Penal code of the commonwealth of Pennsylvania, January 4, 1860. ⟨Printed by order of the House of representatives⟩ Harrisburg, A. B. Hamilton, state printer, 1860.

Knox, John Crawford.
French, English and Italian antique furniture...
see under Feuchtwanger, Austin J.

25.3 Knox, John D.
2355a Paths to wealth. Printed for the author. New York, Phillips & Hurst, 1883.
538 p. 13 pl. 12°.

NK 0211472 DLC

Knox, John D.
Paths to wealth. New York, Phillips & Hunt, 1884.
538 p. illus.
1. Business. 2. Success.

NK 0211473 KMK

Knox, *Mrs.* John D.
When sorrow comes, a collection of comforting thoughts for those who mourn, by Mrs. John D. Knox. Eskridge, Kan., 1931.
32 p. 24cm.
Verse and prose.

I. Title.
31-19557
Library of Congress BV4900.K5
Copyright A 37794 [2] 820.8

NK 0211474 DLC

Western Americana
Zc39
878kn
Knox (John D.) & Company.
Knox's investor's guide, Topeka, Kansas ... Topeka, Geo. W. Martin, Kansas Publishing House, 1878.
[cover-title, 16 p. illus. 23 cm.

1. Kansas - Econ. condit. 2. Topeka, Kan. 3. Mortgages - Kansas. 4. Real property - Kansas - Hist.

NK 0211475 CtY

Knox (John D.) & Co.
Knox's investor's guide, Topeka, Kansas. Real estate mortgage loans, county, township, and school district bonds. Read and circulate. Jan. 1. 1883. *Kansas City: Ramsay, Millett & Hudson*, 1883. 32 pp. 8°.

NK 0211476 NN RPB

Knox (John D.) & Company.
Knox's investors' guide, Topeka, Kansas. Real estate mortgage loans, Sept. 1, 1885. Topeka, 1885.
26 p. illus. 8°.

NK 0211477 MB

Knox, John Eduard Lemmich
see Knox, John, 1867-

Knox, John Harvey, joint author.

Snapp, Roscoe Raymond.
... Summer rations for fattening steers, by Roscoe R. Snapp and John H. Knox ... Urbana, Ill. [University of Illinois] 1929.

Knox, John Jay, joint author.

HF5438
.K568

Knox, James Samuel, 1872-1945.
A modern course in salesmanship, by James S. Knox and John Knox. [1st ed.] Oak Park, Ill., Knox Business Book Co., 1951.

Knox, John Jay, 1791-1876.
The sixtieth anniversary of the marriage of John J. and Sarah Ann Knox
see under title

VOLUME 300

Knox, John Jay, 1828–1892.
...Address, by Ex-comptroller Knox, of New York. Chicago: C. H. Blakely & Co., 1890. 13 p. 8°.
At head of title: Meeting of the Chicago Bankers Club.

1. Money, U. S.
N. Y. P. L. June 23, 1922.

NK 0211482 NN

Knox, John Jay, 1828–1892.
Address of the Hon. John Jay Knox <comptroller of the currency,> before the Merchants' association of Boston, November 27, 1880 ... New York [1880]
cover-title, 8 p. 23 cm.
Reprinted from the Banker's magazine and Statistical register, 1880–81, v. 35, p. 544–551, where it appears under the title: Comptroller Knox's address at Boston.

1. National banks (U. S.) 2. Banks and banking—U. S.
HG2557.K6 1—3460
——— Copy 3. [Knox, J. J. Reports and addresses, v. 3, no. 2] HG2416.K7 vol. 3, no. 2
Library of Congress [a51c½]

NK 0211483 DLC NIC OC1FRB OC1WHi C

Knox, John Jay, 1828–1892.
... The Chamber of commerce of New York, upon free silver coinage. Address of John Jay Knox. Also "Three pecks to a bushel," from the Journal of commerce. [New York, 1891]
7 p. 23cm.
Caption title.
Reprinted from the Banker's magazine, Feb., 1891.

1. Silver question.
CA 8–2454 Unrev'd
Library of Congress HG556.K72

NK 0211484 DLC CU C OC1WHi ViU-L MdBP NN MH

Knox, John Jay, 1828–1892.
Continuance of the national banking system. Address of the Hon. John Jay Knox, comptroller of the currency, at the annual convention of the American bankers' association, at Louisville, Kentucky, October 10th, 1883. New York, The Bankers' publishing association, 1883.
8 p. 23cm.
[Knox, J. J. Reports and addresses. v. 3, no. 8]

1. Banks and banking—U. S. I. American bankers' association.
10–2730
Library of Congress HG2416.K7

NK 0211485 DLC

Knox, John Jay, 1828–1892.
... The distribution of the surplus money of the United States among the states. <Abstract.> [Washington? 1884?]
p. 103–106. 23cm. [Knox, J. J. Reports and addresses. v. 3, no. 10]
Caption title.
From the Bulletin of the Philosophical society of Washington, 1884. vol. VI, p. 103–106.

1. Finance—U. S. 2. Currency question—U. S.
10–9200
Library of Congress HG2416.K7

NK 0211486 DLC

Knox, John Jay, 1828–1892.
Dry bank statistics. Address of the Hon. John Jay Knox, comptroller of the currency, at the annual convention of the American bankers' association, at Niagara Falls, August 11th, 1881. 1st ed. New York, The Bankers' publishing association, 1881.
cover-title, 16 p. 23cm.

1. Banks and banking—U. S. I. American bankers' association.
24–31230
Library of Congress HG2557.K66 1881

NK 0211487 DLC

Knox, John Jay, 1828–1892.
Dry bank statistics. Address of the Hon. John Jay Knox, comptroller of the currency, at the annual convention of the American bankers' association, at Niagara Falls, August 11th, 1881. 2d ed. New York, The Bankers' publishing association, 1881.
cover-title, 16 p. 23cm.

1. Banks and banking—U. S. I. American bankers association.
CA 8–1153 Unrev'd
Library of Congress HG2557.K66
——— Copy 2. [Knox, J. J. Reports and addresses, v. 3, no. 3]
Library of Congress HG2416.K7

NK 0211488 DLC

Knox, John Jay, 1828–1892.
Fifth report of the American bankers' association upon bank taxation. Extracted from the official report of the ... annual convention ... at Saratoga, August 6th, 7th, and 8th, 1879. Address of Hon. John Jay Knox ... New York, Bankers' publishing association, 1879.
14 p. 22½ cm.

1. Banks and banking—U. S.—Taxation. I. American bankers' association.
HG1768.U5A6 5✓ 6–24595

NK 0211489 DLC OC1WHi

Knox, John Jay, 1828–1892.
A history of banking in the United States. c1892.
218 p.

Paging irregular
From Rhodes journal, 1892.

NK 0211490 OC1

Knox, John Jay, 1828–1892.
A history of banking in the United States, by ... John Jay Knox ... assisted by a corps of financial writers in the various states; the entire work ... revised and brought up to date by Bradford Rhodes ... and Elmer H. Youngman ... New York, B. Rhodes & company, 1900.
1 p. l., xxii, 880 p. front., illus. (facsims.) ports. 24cm.
Each portrait accompanied by guard sheet with descriptive letterpress.
1. Banks and banking—U. S.—Hist. I. Rhodes, Bradford, 1845–1924, ed. II. Youngman, Elmer Haskell, 1861– joint ed.
0–2538 Revised
Library of Congress HG2461.K6

MiU OC1JC OU OO MWA PP PPL ICJ I Nh
NK 0211491 DLC WaS CoU DAU CU FTaSU NBuHi PPD PU

Knox, John Jay, 1828–1892.
A history of banking in the United States, by the late John Jay Knox ... assisted by a corps of financial writers in the various states; the entire work ... revised and brought up to date by Bradford Rhodes ... and Elmer H. Youngman ... New York, B. Rhodes & company, 1903.
2 p. l., [iii]–xxii, 880 p. incl. tables. front., ports. 25cm.
Portraits accompanied by guard sheets with descriptive letterpress.

1. Banks and banking—U. S.—Hist. I. Rhodes, Bradford, 1845–1924, ed. II. Youngman, Elmer H., joint ed.
8—3255
Library of Congress HG2461.K62

NjP PPFRB IdPI ViU
NK 0211492 DLC ScU IdU MtU OrP MiU OCU OC1 OOxM

HG551 .K7
Knox, John Jay, 1828-1892.
Interview before the Committee on Coinage, Weights and Measures of the House of Representatives upon the Coinage act of 1873 and the silver question, Saturday, February 21, 1891. Washington, Govt. Print. Off., 1891.
21 p. 23cm.

Cover title.

NK 0211493 MnHi CU

KNOX, JOHN JAY, 1828-1892.
Interview of John Jay Knox, before the Committee on coinage, weights, and measures of the House of Representatives, upon the Coinage act of 1873, and the silver question, Saturday, February 21, 1891. Washington, Govt. print. off., 1891. 21 p. 23cm.

Film reproduction. Negative.
1. Money--U.S., 1879-1896.

NK 0211494 NN

Knox, John Jay, 1828–1892.
... Lectures on banking, by Jno. Jay Knox. [New York? 1881?]
6 p., 1 l. 23cm.
[Knox, J. J. Reports and addresses. v. 3, no. 5]
Caption title.
At head of title: <From Rhodes' journal of banking, December, 1881.>
Pub. under title: History of banks and banking. v. 36, p. 445–449.

1. Banks and banking—U. S.
10–2731
Library of Congress HG2416.K7

NK 0211495 DLC

Knox, John Jay, 1828–1892.
The national banking system. Resumption and the silver question. Address of the Hon. John Jay Knox, comptroller of the currency, at the annual convention of the American bankers' association, at Saratoga, August 7th, 1879. New York, The Bankers' publishing association, 1879.
14 p. 23½cm.

1. National banks—U. S. 2. Currency question—U. S.
CA 8–1150 Unrev'd
Library of Congress HG2557.K75
——— Copy 2. HG2416.K7 vol. 3

NK 0211496 DLC CtY NcD PPFRB NN PPTU

Knox, John Jay, 1828–1892.
New York as the great banking center. Address of Hon. John Jay Knox, at the annual dinner of the New York Chamber of commerce, May, 1882. [New York, 1882]
8 p. 23cm.
Also published in the Banker's magazine, 1881–1882. v. 36, p. 921–925.

1. Banks and banking—New York (City)
CA 8—1133 Unrev'd
Library of Congress HG2613.N53K7
——— Copy 2. [Knox, J. J. Reports and addresses, v. 3, no. 6] HG2416.K7

NK 0211497 DLC

KNOX, JOHN JAY, 1828-1892.
New York as the great banking center; address of John Jay Knox, at the annual dinner of the New York Chamber of commerce, May, 1882. [New York, 1882] 8 p. 23cm.

Film reproduction. Positive.
Also published in the Banker's magazine, 1881-1882, v.36, p. 921-925.
1. Banks and banking--U.S.-- N.Y.--New York.

NK 0211498 NN

HG608 .A4 1890
Knox, John Jay, 1828–1892.
U. S. *Congress. House. Committee on Banking and Currency.*
A permanent national bank circulation; an interview between the Committee on Banking and Currency, House of Representatives, and John Jay Knox, president of the National Bank of the Republic, New York City, on the 16th day of January, 1890. Washington, Govt. Print. Off., 1890.

VOLUME 300

Knox, John Jay, 1828-1892.

U. S. *Congress. House. Committee on banking and currency.*

Remarks of John Jay Knox, comptroller of the currency, before the Committee on banking and currency, House of representatives, on the substitute for a bill to retire the circulating-notes of the national banks, and for other purposes. Printed by request of the committee. February 19, 1878. Washington, Govt. print. off., 1878.

NK 0211501 ... see below

Knox, John Jay, 1828-1892.
Report in relation to a revision of the laws on the mint and coinage of the United States, 1870. n.t.p.
8°

NK 0211501 MnHi PP

Knox, John Jay, 1828–1892.

Reports and addresses of Comptroller Knox. Coinage and banking. [Washington, New York, 1873–83]

24 v. in 3. 23cm.

Binder's title.

CONTENTS.—v. 1, no. 1, 3-6. Annual report of the comptroller of the currency. [11th-15th] 1873-1877. no. 2. ... National-bank circulation. Letter from the secretary of the Treasury.—v. 2, no. 1. Remarks of John Jay Knox ... before the Committee on banking and currency, House of representatives ... February 19, 1878. no. 2-4. Annual report of the comptroller of the currency. [16th-18th] 1878-1880. no. 5. Refunding of the national debt. Notes of an interview between the Finance committee of the Senate and the secretary of the Treasury, the comptroller of the currency, and the treasurer of the United States. no. 6-7. ... Annual report of the commissioner of the Freedman's savings and trust company. 1882-1883.—v. 3, no. 1. The national banking system. Resumption and the silver question. Address of the Hon. John Jay Knox ... no. 2. ... Address of the Hon. John Jay Knox ... before the Merchants' association of Boston. no. 3. Address of the Hon. John Jay Knox before the American bankers' association, on the 11th August, 1881, upon dry bank statistics. no. 4, 7, 9. Annual report of the comptroller of the currency. [19th-21st] 1881-1883. no. 5. ... Lectures on banking, by Jno. Jay Knox. no. 6. New York as the great banking center. Address of Hon. John Jay Knox. no. 8. Continuance of the national banking system. Address of the Hon. John Jay Knox. no. 10. ... The distribution of the surplus money of the United States among the states. ‹Abstract.› no. 11. ... National bank circulation. Interview with the Hon. John Jay Knox ... and William B. Greene (by the Senate Committee on finance)

1. Banks and banking—U. S.—Addresses, essays, lectures.

CA 10-4707 Unrev'd

Library of Congress HG2416.K7

NK 0211503 DLC NCH

Knox, John Jay, 1828-1892.
Resumption and the banks. Extracts from the address of Hon. J. J. Knox, August 7th, 1879. [1879]
8 p. 8°.
n.t.-p.

NK 0211504 MB

Knox, John Jay, 1828-1892.

U. S. *Treasury dept.*

Salary tables of the Treasury department, for every month and quarter of the year. Tables calculated and prepared by John Jay Knox, disbursing clerk. Printed by order of the secretary of the Treasury. Washington, Gov't print. off., 1865.

Knox, John Jay, 1828–1892.

The surplus and the public debt. Address of the Hon. John Jay Knox ... at the annual convention of the American bankers' association, at Pittsburgh, Pennsylvania, October 12th, 1887 ... New York, Bankers publishing association, 1887.

20 p. 23cm.

"Reprinted from the Official report of the Association."

1. Debts, Public—U. S.

8-36071

Library of Congress HJ8112.K7

NK 0211506 DLC OO OFH NN

Knox, John Jay, 1828–1892.

United States notes; a history of the various issues of paper money by the government of the United States, by John Jay Knox, with an appendix containing the recent decision of the Supreme court of the United States and the dissenting opinion upon the legal tender question. New York, C. Scribner's sons, 1884.

xii, 247 p. facsims. (incl. front.) 23½cm.

1. Paper money—U. S. 2. Finance—U. S.—Hist.

6—26812

Library of Congress HG601.K73

NK 0211507 DLC NcU KMK KEmT FMU MdBP PPB OrPR MWA MH MB PHC OU OCl OClFRB OClWHi OO DN MnHi MdBP OFH DS OrCS

Knox, John Jay, 1828–1892.

United States notes; a history of the various issues of paper money by the government of the United States, by John Jay Knox ... with an appendix containing the recent decision of the Supreme court of the United States and the dissenting opinion upon the legal tender question. 2d ed. rev. London, T. F. Unwin, 1885.

xii, 247 p. facsims. (incl. front.) 23½cm.

1. Paper money—U. S. 2. Finance—U. S. Hist.

6—26813

Library of Congress HG601.K74

NK 0211508 DLC MiU OCU PV NjP OU PKsL

Knox, John Jay, 1828–1892.

United States notes; a history of the various issues of paper money by the government of the United States, by John Jay Knox ... with an appendix containing the recent decision of the Supreme court of the United States and the dissenting opinion upon the legal tender question. 2d ed. rev. New York, C. Scribner's sons, 1885.

xii, 247 p. facsims. (incl. front.) 23½cm.

1. Paper money—U. S. 2. Finance—U. S.—Hist.

13-19186

Library of Congress HG601.K748

NK 0211509 DLC CU MWA I

Knox, John Jay, 1828-1892.
United States notes; a history of the various issues of paper money by the government of the United States. With an appendix containing the recent decision of the Supreme Court of the United States and the dissenting opinion upon the legal tender question. New York: C. Scribner's Sons, 1888. xii, 247 p. 3. ed. 12°.

1. Money (Paper), U. S.
N. Y. P. L. January 22, 1914

NK 0211510 NN CoU TU IU MWA OClW DL MtU OrP CU ViU NjN NjP

Knox, John Jay, 1828-1892. 332.0973 O400

United States notes. A history of the various issues of paper money by the Government of the United States. With an appendix containing the recent decision of the Supreme Court of the United States and the dissenting opinion upon the legal tender question. Third edition revised. xii,247 p. il. D. New York: C. Scribner's Sons, 1894.

NK 0211511 ICJ

Knox, John Jay, 1828–1892.

United States notes; a history of the various issues of paper money by the government of the United States, by John Jay Knox ... with an appendix containing the recent decision of the Supreme court of the United States and the dissenting opinion upon the legal tender question. 3d ed. rev. New York, C. Scribner's sons, 1899.

xii, 247 p. 19cm.

1. Paper money—U. S. 2. Finance—U. S.—Hist.

4—3827

Library of Congress HG601.K75

[a4511] 332.53

NK 0211512 DLC IdU PSC OCl OOxM ODW NjP

Knox, John Knox.

... Geology of the serpentine belt coleraine sheet, Thetford-Black Lake mining district, Quebec ... by John Knox Knox. Chicago, Ill., 1918.

73 p. incl. plates. fold. map. 24cm.

Thesis (PH. D.)—University of Chicago, 1917.
Private edition, distributed by the University of Chicago libraries.
Bibliography: p. 10.

1. Geology—Quebec (Province)

19-12686

Library of Congress QE193.K7
Univ. of Chicago Libr. [2]

NK 0211513 ICU DLC NIC PPAmP MiU NjP

Knox, John P.

A historical account of St. Thomas, W. I., with its rise and progress in commerce; missions and churches; climate and its adaptation to invalids; geological structure; natural history, and botany; and incidental notices of St. Croix and St. Johns; slave insurrections in these islands; emancipation and present condition of laboring classes. By John P. Knox ... New York, C. Scribner, 1852.

xii, [13]-271 p. front., fold. map. 18½cm.

1. St. Thomas, Virgin islands of the United States. 2. West Indies, Danish—Descr. & trav.

2—14208

Library of Congress F2105.K74

NK 0211514 DLC MU OU NcU TxU OCU OCl OFH OClWHi MiU MdBP MH-A MnU CU-B DN ICJ NN NjP MWA PPAN PHi NjNbS MH-BA MChB

D 2851585 .46

KNOX, JOHN P., Rev.
Anniversary discourse of a twenty-five years' pastorate, preached March 28, 1880, by the pastor, Rev. John P. Knox. Published by request. New York, Prall, 1880.
32p.

Half-title: Memorial of Presbyterian church, Newtown, L.I., from the year 1652 to 1880.

NK 0211515 ICN NB NBHi NNQ PPPrHi NjNbS

Knox, John P., Rev.
Brief history of the Prot. Reformed Dutch Church, Nassaw, N.Y.
Albany, 1841.
31 p. 8°

NK 0211516 MWA CtY NjNbS

Knox, John P., Rev.
Brief outline of the life and character of Mrs. Aletta Knox.
N.Y., 1854.
136 p. 12°

NK 0211517 MWA

Knox, John Samuel, 1884–

The old chimney, and other rhymes, by John Samuel Knox. Siloam Springs, Ark., Bar D press, 1940.

96 p. incl. front. (port.) 1 illus. 19½cm.

I. Title.

40-6153

Library of Congress PS3521.N835O55 1940

——— Copy 2.

Copyright A 139070 [2] 811.5

NK 0211518 DLC NcD

VOLUME 300

Knox, Joseph, 1877- 3979.237
Elementary chemical theory and calculations.
— London. Gurney & Jackson. 1912. vii, 102, (2) pp. 18½ cm., in 8s.
Contains many problems and solutions.

K280 — Chemical arithmetic. — Problems and examples. Colls.

NK 0211519 MB

Knox, Joseph, 1877- 541.9 S001
Elementary chemical theory and calculations, by Joseph Knox, 149849 .... London, Gurney and Jackson, 1920.
vii, 102, [2] p. incl. 1 illus., tables. 19cm.
On cover: Second edition.

NK 0211520 ICJ

Knox, Joseph, 1877-
Elementary chemical theory and calculations, by Joseph Knox ... London [etc.] Gurney and Jackson [1932]
vii, 138 p., 1 l. 1 illus. 19cm.
"Third edition, 1932."

1. Chemistry, Physical and theoretical. 2. Chemistry—Problems, exercises, etc. I. Title.

Library of Congress QD453.K55 1932 33-15222
[3] 541

NK 0211521 DLC OCU

Knox, Joseph, 1877-
Elementary chemical theory and calculations ... 4th ed. London, 1942.
138 p.

NK 0211522 PSt

Knox, Joseph, 1877-
The fixation of atmospheric nitrogen, by Joseph Knox ... London, Gurney & Jackson, 1914.
vii, 112 p. illus. 19cm. (*Half-title:* Chemical monographs ... no. IV)
Bibliography: p. 105-110.

1. Nitrogen.

Library of Congress TP245.N8K5 14-14783

NK 0211523 DLC CaBVaU PPF ICJ NN NjP

661.65 K74f
Knox, Joseph, 1877-
The fixation of atmospheric nitrogen, by Joseph Knox. New York, Van Nostrand, 1914.
vii, 112p. illus. 19cm. (Half-title: Chemical monographs ... no. IV)
Bibliography: p. 105-110.

1. Nitrogen. I. Chemical monographs, no.4.

MB
NK 0211524 TxDaM WaTC OrPR DCU OU MiU KMK CU PSC PHC

Knox, Joseph, 1877-
The fixation of atmospheric nitrogen, by Joseph Knox ... 2d ed. London, Gurney & Jackson, 1921.
vii, 124 p. diagrs. 19cm. (*Half-title:* Chemical monographs, ed. by A. C. Cumming ... No. IV)
Bibliography: p. 115-121.

1. Nitrification. [1. Nitrogen—Fixation]

U. S. Dept. of agr. Library for Library of Congress 309K77 [TP245.N] Agr 22—538

NK 0211525 DNAL NcRS OrP

Knox, Joseph, 1877-
The fixation of atmospheric nitrogen, by Joseph Knox ... 2d ed. New York, D. Van Nostrand company, 1921.
vii, 124 p. diagrs. 19cm. (*Half-title:* Chemical monographs ... no. IV)
Printed in Great Britain.
Bibliography: p. 115-121.

1. Nitrogen.

Library of Congress TP245.N8K5 1921 22-11259

NK 0211526 DLC MtBC NIC CU OC1 OC1W MiU NN ICJ MiHM

Knox, Joseph, 1877-
Physico-chemical calculations, by Joseph Knox ... London, Methuen & co., ltd. [1912]
viii, 188 p. 19cm.

1. Chemistry, Physical and theoretical. 2. Chemistry—Problems, exercises, etc.

Stanford univ. Library for Library of Congress [a37g1] A 12-1069

NK 0211527 CSt WaS NcD ODW OOxM NN

Knox, Joseph, 1877- 508 27
Physico-chemical calculations, by Joseph Knox, ... New York, D. Van Nostrand Company, 1912.
viii, 188 p. 19cm. (*On cover:* Text-books of science.)

NK 0211528 ICJ DBS NIC NNC

Knox, Joseph, 1877-
Physico-chemical calculations. 2d ed. London, 1916.
188 p.

NK 0211529 PHC

Knox, Joseph, 1877-
Physico-chemical calculations, by Joseph Knox ... New York, D. Van Nostrand Company, 1916.
viii, 1888 p. 19 cm. (On cover: Text-books of science)

NK 0211530 CU NcU

Knox, Joseph, 1877-
Physico-chemical calculations, by Joseph Knox... 3d ed. London, Methuen & co., ltd. [1919]
viii, 188 p. 19cm. (On cover: Text-books of science)
"This collection...is based on Abegg and Sackur's 'Physikalisch-chemische rechen-aufgaben' (Sammlung Göschen [455])"—Pref.

1. Chemistry, Physical and theoretical. 2. Chemistry—Problems, exercises, etc. I. Abegg, Richard Wilhelm Heinrich, 1869-1910. Physikalisch-chemische rechenaufgaben. II. Sackur, Otto, 1880-1914, joint author. Physikalisch-chemische rechenaufgaben. III. Title. IV. Ser.

NK 0211531 ViU DNAL MiU CU

Knox, Joseph, 1877-
Physico-chemical calculations... London, Methuen, [1920] 4th ed.

NK 0211532 OO PPHa

QD457 .K73
Knox, Joseph, 1877-
Physico-chemical calculations. 5th ed. with logarithmic tables. London, Methuen [1924]
viii, 194 p. (Text-books of science)
Second imprint on mounted label: New York, D. Van Nostrand.
"This collection ... is based on Abegg and Sackur's 'Physikalisch-chemische Rechen-aufgaben' (Sammlung Göschen [445])"—Pref.
1. Chemistry, Physical and theoretical. 2. Chemistry—Problems, exercises, etc.

NK 0211533 ICU MiU OClUr

Knox, Joseph, 1877-
Physico-chemical calculations... 9th ed. London, Methuen, [1931]
188p.

NK 0211534 OCU

Knox, Joseph, 1877-
Physico-chemical calculations, by ... 10th ed. London, 1934.
194 p.

NK 0211535 PPD

Knox, Joseph, 1877-
Physico-chemical calculations, by Joseph Knox ... 11th ed. London, Methuen & co. ltd. [1936]
viii, 194 p. 19cm. (*On cover:* Text-books of science)
"This collection ... is based on Abegg and Sackur's 'Physikalisch-chemische rechen-aufgaben' (Sammlung Göschen [445])"—Pref.

1. Chemistry, Physical and theoretical. 2. Chemistry—Problems, exercises, etc. I. Abegg, Richard Wilhelm Heinrich, 1869-1910. Physikalisch-chemische rechenaufgaben. II. Sackur, Otto, 1880-1914, joint author. Physikalisch-chemische rechenaufgaben. III. Title.

Library of Congress QD453.K57 1936 38-254
[3] 541

NK 0211536 DLC

Knox, Joseph, 1877-
Physico-chemical calculations... London, Methuen, [1944]
194p.

NK 0211537 OU

Knox, Joseph, 1877- joint author.

Japp, Francis Robert, 1848-
Researches in organic chemistry carried out in the University of Aberdeen, by Francis Robert Japp ... and William Maitland ... Joseph Knox ... James Wood ... Aberdeen, Printed for the University, 1905.

Yb71 851k
Knox, Joseph Alexander
[Autograph album of Joseph A.Knox, containing the autographs of his classmates and friends]
22½cm.

NK 0211539 CtY

VOLUME 300

Knox, Julie LeClerc, 1870–
The Dufour saga, 1796–1942; the story of the eight Dufours who came from Switzerland and founded Vevay, Switzerland county, Indiana, by Julie LeClerc Knox ... Crawfordsville, Ind., Howell-Goodwin printing company [1942]
166, [1] p. pl. 22½cm.

1. Dufour family.
42-23919
Library of Congress CS71.D86 1942

NK 0211540 DLC NN

Knox, Julie Le Clerc, 1870–
Some interesting pioneer homesteads in and around Vevay, Indiana. [2d ed. Vevay? 1948]
58 p. illus., port. 16 cm.
Cover title.

1. Vevay, Ind.—Historic houses, etc. I. Title.
F534.V4K5 1948 977.2125 49-145*

NK 0211541 DLC NN MiD

Knox, Katharine (McCook)
The portraits of the Adams-Clement collection and their painters. [Washington] Smithsonian Institution, 1951.
16 l. 29 cm.

1. Portraits, American. 2. Portrait-painters, American. I. Title.
ND1311.K55 56-31541 ‡

NK 0211542 DLC DSI

Knox, Katharine (McCook)
The Sharples, their portraits of George Washington and his contemporaries; a diary and an account of the life and work of James Sharples and his family in England and America, by Katharine McCook Knox. New Haven, Yale university press; London, H. Milford, Oxford university press, 1930.
xvi, 133 p. incl. front., illus., ports., facsims. 28½cm.
"The diary and letters of Ellen Sharples ... are freely quoted in these pages."—p. [3]

1. Sharples, James, 1750?–1811. 2. Sharples family. 3. Washington, George, pres. U. S.—Portraits. 4. Portrait painting—U. S. I. Sharples, Mrs. Ellen (Wallace) 1769–1849. II. Title.
31—621
Library of Congress ND497.S45K6
[a45o1] 927.5

NK 0211543 OClWHi OClMA OClW OU OCl MB ViU PHi PBm DLC DI NcC NcD RPJCB NcU WaS OrP PU MWA

*E312 U43 v.3 p.288-293
Knox, Mrs. Katharine (McCook)
Washington and his associates; an exhibition of portraits, by Katharine McCook Knox ...
(In United States. George Washington bicentennial commission. History of the George Washington bicentennial celebration. Washington, D. C., 1932. 31½cm. v. 3, p. 288-293 incl. front., ports.)
"... reprinted from the June, 1932, issue 'The American magazine of art'".

NK 0211544 NBuG

PZ8 .K773 Co
Knox, Kathleen.
Cornertown chronicles: new legends of old lore. By Kathleen Knox ... London, Griffith and Farran; New York, E. P. Dutton and co., 1880.
256 p. front., illus., plates. 18 1/2cm.
T.-p. illustrated.

NK 0211545 MB

KNOX, Kathleen.
English lessons for schoolroom use. London, G.Bell and Sons, 1882.

19 cm.

NK 0211546 MH

Knox, Kathleen.
Fairy gifts, or A wallet of wonders. Illustrations by Kate Greenaway. London, Griffith and Farran, etc. etc., [18–].
pp. (3), 124. 4 plates and other illus.

NK 0211547 MH MB

PZ8 .K773 Fai
Knox, Kathleen.
Fairy gifts; or, A wallet of wonders. By Kathleen Knox ... Illustrations by Kate Greenaway. London, Griffith and Farran; New York, E. P. Dutton & co. [1882]
128 p. incl. front., illus. 16 1/2cm.
Illustrated t.-p.; initials.

1. Fairy tales. I. Title. II. Title: A wallet of wonders.

NK 0211548 MB

Knox, Kathleen.
Father Time's story book. For the little ones. With illustrations by H. W. Petherick. New York: E. P. Dutton & Co. [187-?] 2 p.l., [iii]-iv, 192 p., 4 pl. 16°.

1. Juvenile literature.—Fiction (American). 2. Petherick, Horace William, illus.
N. Y. P. L. December 13, 1911.

NK 0211549 NN DLC

Knox, Kathleen. 1467.1
Lily of the valley. A story for little boys and girls.
London. Ward & Co. 1876. Colored illus. 16°.

NK 0211550 MB

Knox, Kathleen. 1467.2
Meadowleigh. A holiday history.
London. Ward & Co. 1876. Colored illus. 16°.

NK 0211551 MB

PZ 7 .K756
Knox, Kathleen.
Queen Dora: the life and lessons of a little girl. New York, Pott, Young [18--]
255 p. illus.

NK 0211552 MiU

Knox, Kathleen. 82.3
Queen Dora: the life and lessons of a little girl.
London. Griffith & Farran. 1879. Illus. Sm. 8°.

Δ1027 — T.r.

NK 0211553 MB

Knox, Kathleen. *Q.57.18
Seven birthdays; or, the children of fortune. A fairy chronicle. Illustrations by K. Greenaway.
— London. Griffith & Farran. 1876. (1), 223 pp. Plates. Vignettes. 17 cm., in 8s.

M4097 — T.r. — Greenaway, Kate, illus., 1846-1901. — Fairy tales.

NK 0211554 MB

Knox, Kathleen.
Seven birthdays, or The children of fortune; a fairy chronicle. Illustrations by K. Greenaway. New York, Polt, Young & Co., [1879]
Plates and vignettes.

NK 0211555 MH

Knox, Kathleen. 1789.29
Wildflower Win. The journal of a little girl.
London. Ward & Co. 1876. Illus. Sm. 8°.

NK 0211556 MB

Knox, Kenneth Leith, 1920–
The effect of fluid velocity on the rate of growth of single crystals. New York, 1948.
v, 48 p. illus., tables. 24 cm.
Thesis—Columbia University.
Vita.
Bibliography: p. 47.

1. Crystallization. 2. Crystallography.
QD921.K66 548.5 A 50-6310
Columbia Univ. for Library of Congress Libraries [1]†

NK 0211557 NNC DLC

KNOX LAURA.
Was it Providence? A short romance, by Laura Knox. Indianapolis, Ind.: The Ironclad Age, 1894. 24 p. 17cm.
Cover-title.

700659A. 1. Fiction, American. I. Title.
cwa

NK 0211558 NN

KNOX, Lawrence Howland.
[Bicyclic structures prohibiting the Walden inversion. Replacement reactions in 1-substituted 1-acocamphanes.]

Typewritten. 28 x 21 cm ff.(5),87.
Thesis, Ph.D.- Harvard University, 1940.

NK 0211559 MH

[Knox, Leah]
Christmas customs in other lands.
Phila. and N.Y. Ruttle, Shaw & Wetherill, 1937.

31 p.

NK 0211560 PSC PPPL

Knox, Linda.
Garment pattern by simple methods, for upper primary and lower secondary classes... Sydney [etc] W. Brooks & co [1945?] 48 p. illus. 18cm.

1. Dressmaking—Patterns.

NK 0211561 NN

VOLUME 300

 Knox, Linda.
Textile study for the consumer. Sydney, Brooks [1946?]
64 p. (Textile series)

NK 0211562 DNAL

Knox, Lizzie A.
An interior view of our county asylum for the insane, situated on Camden street, Newark, N. J., together with the presentment of the grand jury regarding the same. Newark: published in the interest of humanity, 1884. 44 p. 8°.

Ford collection.

1. Insane.—Asylums, U. S.: Newark.
N. Y. P. L. May 7, 1912.

NK 0211563 NN

Knox, Loren H B.
I enter myself, by Loren H. B. Knox. Boston, The Four seas company [°1929]
56 p. 19½cm.
Poems.

I. Title.

Library of Congress PS3521.N84 I 2 1929 29-30297

NK 0211564 DLC

Knox, Loren H B.
The prisoned poet, and other poems by Loren H. B. Knox. London, The Merton press ltd. [°1923]
3 p. l., 55 p. 19cm.

I. Title.

Library of Congress PS3521.N84P7 1923 24-12593

NK 0211565 DLC CtY

Knox, Loren H. B.
To Alvin York.
In-his-The prisoned poet, and other poems. London, n. d. 19 cm. p. 4-6.

NK 0211566 RPB

Knox, Loren Laertes, 1811-1901.
Address delivered at the opening of the East Maine conference seminary, Bucksport, Aug. 20, 1851. Bangor, 1851.
16 p. 22 cm.

NK 0211567 RPB

KNOX, Loren Laertes, 1811-1901.
Duty-death-destiny: a funeral discourse for Rev. D. H. Mansfield, in Bangor, June 26th. Bangor, 1855.
pp. 16.

NK 0211568 MH CtY RPB

Knox, Loren Laertes, 1811–1901.
Evangelical rationalism: or, A consideration of truths practically related to man's probation. By Loren L. Knox, D. D. Cincinnati, Hitchcock and Walden; New York, Nelson & Phillips, 1879.
250 p. 17½cm.
A refutation of the doctrine of probation after death.

1. Theology, Doctrinal. 2. Probation after death. 3. Reward (Theology) I. Title.

40-15262

Library of Congress BT78.K7
Copyright 1879: 921 [2] 230

NK 0211569 DLC NjNbS ODW OO

 Knox, Loren Laertes, 1811-1901.
Money matters, explained to the young... New York, 1852.
132p.

NK 0211570 DLC

Knox, Lou.
Red river valley. Modern arrangement and new lyrics by Lou Knox. New York, Leeds music corp. [c1944]
First line: Please come back to the Red river valley.

Printed for the Music Division
1. U. S.—Red river valley. I. Song index (2).
N. Y. P. L. April 18, 1947

NK 0211571 NN

KNOX, *Mrs.* LUCY (FLUCKER). [Wife of Henry Knox.] Montpelier, Dec. 14, 1800. To Samuel Thatcher. A. L. S.
3 p.

NK 0211572 TKL

Knox, Mrs. Lucy (Flucker).
. Dec. 26, 1800. To Samuel Thatcher. A. L. S.
1 p.

NK 0211573 TKL

Knox, Mrs. Lucy (Flucker).

——. Boston, Oct. 8, 1811. To Samuel Thatcher, Warren. A. L. S. 2 p.

NK 0211574 TKL

Knox, *Hon. Mrs.* Lucy (Spring-Rice) 1845–1884.
Sonnets and other poems. By the Hon. Mrs. O. N. Knox. London [Priv. print. by R. Barrett and sons] 1872.
iv p., 1 l., 52 p. 19cm.

I. Title.

17-17108

Library of Congress PR4859.K57 1872

NK 0211575 DLC MdBP

Knox, Mable Davey.
Chevy takes off. New York, Exposition Press [1950]
128 p. 22 cm.

1. U. S.—Descr. & trav.—1940– I. Title.

E169.K7 917.3 50-12453

NK 0211576 DLC TxU

Knox, Marcus.
The silent Baltic; or, Detained near Kiel, by Marcus Knox ... London, Academy architecture [1914?]
64 p. 18½cm.

1. European war, 1914– —Personal narratives. I. Title.

15-4774

Library of Congress D640.K7

NK 0211577 DLC NcU NN

Knox, Margaret, 1866–
Lütkenhaus, *Mrs.* Anna May (Irwin) 1874– *ed.*
New plays for school children, edited by Anna M. Lütkenhaus ... with an introduction by Margaret Knox ... New York, London, The Century co. [°1929]

Knox, Margaret, 1866–
Our children's neglected inheritance.
(*In* National education association of the United States. Addresses and proceedings, 1924. p. 150-157)

1. Religious education—U. S. I. Title.

E 26-357

Library, U. S. Bur. of Education

NK 0211579 DHEW OO OU

Knox, Margaret, 1866 -
The principal's point of view of the selection of children for special classes.
(*In* National education association of the United States. Journal of proceedings and addresses, 1916. p. 877-879)

[1. Backward children] [2. Abnormal children—Education] 1, 2. Children, Abnormal and backward.

E 17-965

Library, U. S. Bur. of Education

NK 0211580 DHEW OU OO

Knox, Margaret, 1866–
The rainy day book for boys and girls, by Margaret Knox ... and Anna M. Lütkenhaus ... New York & London, The Century co. [°1924]
ix p., 3 l., 3-242 p. front., plates. 19½cm. $1.75

I. Lütkenhaus, Mrs. Anna May (Irwin) 1874– joint author. II. Title.

24—23646

Library of Congress GV1201.K6

NK 0211581 DLC NN PPPL OLak

Knox, Margaret, 1866– joint ed.
Lütkenhaus, *Mrs.* Anna May (Irwin) 1874– *ed.*
Story and play readers, ed. by Anna M. Lütkenhaus ... in collaboration with Margaret Knox ... New York, The Century co., 1917.

VOLUME 300

Knox, Marguerite.
Key to Plane geometry by John C. Stone, A. M., and James F. Millis, A. M., prepared under the direction of the authors by Marguerite Knox ... Chicago, New York [etc.] B. H. Sanborn & co. [c1917]
1 p. l., 111 p. diagrs. 19½cm.

1. Geometry, Plane. I. Stone, John Charles, 1867– Plane geometry. II. Millis, James Franklin, 1875–

Library of Congress QA455.S732 17-8220

NK 0211583 DLC

Knox, Marguerite.
Key to Plane geometry by John C. Stone, A. M., and James F. Millis, A. M., prepared under the direction of the authors, by Marguerite Knox ... Chicago, New York [etc.] B. H. Sanborn & co. [c1917]
1 p. l., 190 p. diagrs. 19½cm.
"Key to Solid geometry" with special t.-p.: p. [113]-190.

1. Geometry, Plane. 2. Geometry, Solid. I. Stone, John Charles, 1867– Plane geometry. II. Stone, John Charles, 1867– Solid geometry. III. Millis, James Franklin, 1875–

Library of Congress QA455.S732 1917 a 17-29871

NK 0211584 DLC OCX

M
287.643
C591M Knox, Martin van Buren, 1841-1912.
A historical sketch of the Methodist Episcopal church in Claremont, N.H. Claremont, N.H., Claremont manufacturing co., 1882.
49p. 23cm.

1. Methodist church in New Hampshire.

NK 0211585 TxDaM MWA OClWHi Nh NhDo

Knox, Martin Van Buren, 1841-1912.
History of the St. James Methodist Episcopal Church, Manchester, N. H. 1881–1892.
= Manchester, N. H. Printed at "Le fidèle messager." 1892. 24, (1) pp. Plate. 8°.

F8249 — Manchester, N. H. Churches. St. James Methodist Episcopal Church.

NK 0211586 MB

Knox, Martin Van Buren, 1841–1912.
The religious life of the Anglo-Saxon race, by M. V. B. Knox ... Boston, Sherman, French & company, 1913.
5 p. l., 536 p. 21½cm.

1. Anglo-Saxon race. 2. Gt. Brit.—Church history. 3. U. S.—Church history. I. Title.

Library of Congress BR743.K7 13-10277

NK 0211587 DLC WaS CSaT ICU MB CU OCl

Knox, Martin Van Buren, 1841-1912. 2398.171
Schroon Lake: the Indian legend of its name. A poem. With illustrations from paintings by Frances Luella Way.
= Wahpeton, N. D. The Author. 1901. (35) pp. Plates. 24°, obl.

F8431 — Schroon Lake. — Way, Frances Luella, illus.

NK 0211588 MB

Knox, Martin Van Buren, 1841-1912.
A winter in India and Malaysia among the Methodist missions, by Rev. M. V. B. Knox ... With an introduction by Bishop John F. Hurst. New York, Hunt & Eaton; Cincinnati, Cranston & Stowe, 1891.
306 p. front. 19cm.

1. India — Descr. & trav. 2. Methodist Episcopal church — Missions. 3. Missions—India.

Library of Congress DS413.K74 4—29881

NK 0211589 DLC NjNbS OrU NIC ODW Nh

Knox, Martin Van Buren, 1841-1912.
A winter in India and Malaysia, among the Methodist missions,....N.Y. 1892.
306 p.

NK 0211590 PU PPPD

Knox, Mertice MacCrea (Buck) 1875-
Handicrafts for the handicapped
see under Hall, Herbert James, 1870-1923.

Knox, Mertice MacCrea (Buck) 1875-
Work for the deformed; what is being done to give crippled children a chance to become useful members of society. 4°. *New York*, 1907.
Cutting from: Craftsman, N. Y., 1907, xii, 193-204, 3 pl.

NK 0211592 DNLM

RM735
.H3 **Knox, Mertice MacCrea (Buck) 1875-** joint author.
Hall, Herbert James, 1870-1923.
The work of our hands; a study of occupations for invalids, by Herbert J. Hall, M. D., and Mertice M. C. Buck. New York, Moffat, Yard & company, 1915.

Knox, Millard Fillmore.
Only the optomist [!] wins; what Congress can do to employ all the unemployed in the United States of America. By M. F. Knox ... Seattle, Wash., Press of Mechanics publishing company, c1915.
1 p. l., 7-145 p. front. (port.) 19½cm. $0.50

1. Currency question—U. S. 2. Social problems—Miscellanea. I. Title.

Library of Congress HG538.K7 15-8038

NK 0211594 DLC IEN

Knox, Ned.
So may you find the year; a book of verse for and about children, together with the child's relationship to the legal holidays, commemorative and festive days, of the national year, by Ned Knox. Boston, The Christopher publishing house [c1937]
x p., 1 l., 13-96 p. 20½cm.

I. Title.

Library of Congress PZ8.3.K76So 37-22495

NK 0211595 DLC

Knox, Mrs. Nelly Lloyd
see
Heath, Mrs. Nelly Lloyd Knox.

Knox, Newton B.
HC95
.U5
1949 **U. S.** *Bureau of the Census.*
The industrial censuses of the American Nations, by Newton B. Knox, consultant, international statistics, Bureau of the Census, with appendix tables prepared by Maria Antonieta Lois. Washington, U. S. Govt. Print. Off., 1949.

Knox, *Hon. Mrs.* O N.
see
Knox, *Hon. Mrs.* Lucy (Spring-Rice) 1845-1884.

Knox, Olive Elsie.
Black Falcon; illustrated by Clarence Tillenius. New York, Bouregy & Curl [1955]
192 p. illus. 21 cm.

1. Tanner, John, 1780?-1847—Fiction. I. Title.

PZ7.K774Bl 55-14471 ‡
Library of Congress [2]

NK 0211599 DLC WaSp CaBViPA

Knox, Olive Elsie.
By paddle and saddle, by Olive Elsie Knox. Toronto, The Macmillan company of Canada limited, 1943.
ix p., 1 l., 270 p. 20½cm.

1. Simpson, Sir George, 1792?-1860—Fiction. I. Title.

Library of Congress PZ7.K774By 44-4515

NK 0211600 DLC IEdS CaBVaU CaBVa

819.3
K775b **Knox, Olive Elsie.**
By paddle and saddle, by Olive Elsie Knox. Toronto, The Macmillan company of Canada limited, 1945 [c1943]
ix p., 1 l., 270 p. 20½cm.

NK 0211601 TxU CaOTU

Knox, Olive Elsie.
How we hear. Sewing seams with steel. By Olive E. Knox, B. A. Toronto, The Macmillan company of Canada limited, 1945.
4 p. l., 63 p. 17½cm. (*On cover:* Macmillan radio plays. Book no. 3)

1. Hearing. 2. Welding. 3. Radio plays. I. Title. II. Title: Sewing seams with steel.

QP461.K55 612.85 Med 47-1245

NK 0211602 DLC CaBVaU

VOLUME 300

819.3
K775l Knox, Olive Elsie.
Little Giant (Miss-top-ashish) the story of Henry Kelsey. Illustrated by Clarence Tillenius. Toronto, Ryerson Press [1951]
196p. illus.,map (on lining-papers) 21cm.

1. Kelsey, Henry, ca. 1670-ca. 1724 - Fiction. I. Title.

NK 0211603 TxU CaOTU

Knox, Olive Elsie.
Little Giant (Miss-top-ashish) the story of Henry Kelsey. Illustrated by Clarence Tillenius. New York, Bouregy & Curl [1954]
186 p. illus. 21 cm.

1. Kelsey, Henry, ca. 1670–ca. 1724—Fiction. I. Title.

PZ7.K774Li 54-13187 ‡

NK 0211604 DLC Or PPGi CaBViPA

Knox, Olive Elsie.
Penicillin. Fresh water from the sea. By Olive E. Knox, B. A. Toronto, The Macmillan company of Canada limited, 1945.
3 p. l., 61 p. 18 cm. (*On cover:* Macmillan radio plays. Book no. 1)

1. Penicillin. 2. Sea-water, Distillation of. 3. Radio plays. I. Title. II. Title: Fresh water from the sea.

RS165.P38K55 615.3292411 Med 47-1900

NK 0211605 DLC CaBVaU

819.3
K775r **Knox, Olive Elsie.**
Red River shadows. Toronto, MacMillan, 1948.
viii, 303p. 22cm.

CaBVa
NK 0211606 TxU CaBVaU CaBViPA MH AkU NN KyU MtU

Knox, Olive Elsie.
Wheels and friction. Sulfa drugs. By Olive E. Knox, B. A. Toronto, The Macmillan company of Canada limited, 1945.
3 p. l., 54 p. 17½cm. (*On cover:* Macmillan radio plays. Book no. 2)

1. Wheels. 2. Friction. 3. Sulphonamides. 4. Radio plays. I. Title. II. Title: Sulfa drugs.

TJ181.5.K5 792 47-3718

NK 0211607 DLC CaBVaU

Knox, Owen A.
Oklahoma story--1940. With a note by Carey McWilliams. [Washington, National Federation for Constitutional Liberties, 1940]
15 p.

1. Civil rights - Oklahoma. 2. Communism - Oklahoma.

NK 0211608 NNC MiEM NN MH NcD

KNOX, PATRICIA.
Do you know Johannesburg? By Patricia Knox and Thelma Gutsche. [Vereeniging, Unie-Volkspers, 1947]
113 p. illus. 26cm.

—— Selective index [compiled by] Johannesburg public library [Johannesburg] 1957. 6 l. 24cm.

Inserted in above.
1. JOHANNESBURG--DESCR. I. Gutsche, Thelma, joint author II. Johannesburg. Public library.

NK 0211609 NN

Knox, Patrick.
Poems. Aberdeen, G. King, 1827.
pp. 123 +.

NK 0211610 MH

Knox, Paul J.
I don't care if I never wake up. Words and music by Paul J. Knox. Chicago, W. Rossiter, c1899.
First line: There's a certain yellow coon.

1. Laziness. 2. Negroes. I. Song index (2).
N. Y. P. L. February 23, 1951

NK 0211611 NN

Knox, Peter.
Programme of law studies, containing a full course of study for the law student. By Peter Knox. Rockford, Ill., Register book and job printing house, 1868.
21 p. 22cm.

1. Law—Study and teaching. I. Title.

32-2072

NK 0211612 DLC

Knox, Peter Edmund, 1923- joint author.
HC605
.H8 **Hutton, Geoffrey William,** 1909-
Searchlight on Australia, by Geoffrey Hutton and Peter Knox. Melbourne, F. W. Cheshire [1948]

382.0973
K77a Knox, Philander Chase, 1853-1921.
Address before the Chicago Association of Commerce at Chicago, February 15, 1911. [Chicago? 1911?]
37p. 23cm.

1. U.S.--Comm.--Canada. 2. Canada--Comm.--U.S. 3. Reciprocity.

NK 0211614 IU

Knox, Philander Chase, 1853-1921.
Address of Hon. Philander C. Knox before the American society for judicial settlement of international disputes. Cincinnati, Ohio, November 8, 1911. [Baltimore? 1911]
41 p. 23cm.

1. U. S.—For. rel. 2. Arbitration, International.

22-12812

Library of Congress JX1961.U6K6

NK 0211615 DLC PHi NN

Knox, Philander Chase, 1853-1921.
Address of Hon. Philander C. Knox before the Chicago association of commerce at Chicago, February 15, 1911. [n. p., 1911]
37 p. 23cm.
Caption title: Reciprocity with Canada.

1. U. S.—Comm.—Canada. 2. Canada—Comm.—U. S. 3. Reciprocity.

16-16790

Library of Congress HF1732.C2K72

NK 0211616 DLC PHi

Knox, Philander Chase, 1853-1921.
Address of Hon. Philander C. Knox, Memorial hall, Columbus, Ohio, November 2, 1910. [n. p., 1910]
49 p. 23cm.

1. Campaign literature, 1910—Republican—Ohio.

22-16512

Library of Congress JK2357.1910.K5

NK 0211617 DLC

Knox, Philander Chase, 1853-1921.
Address of Hon. Philander C. Knox, Music hall, Cincinnati, Ohio, November 5, 1910. [n. p., 1910?]
1 p. l., 53 p. 23cm.

1. Campaign literature, 1910—Republican—Ohio.

22-16511

Library of Congress JK2357.1910.K6

NK 0211618 DLC

Knox, Philander Chase, 1853-1921.
Address of Hon. Philander Chase Knox, at a mass meeting held under the auspices of the Union league, at the Academy of music, Philadelphia, October 20, 1908. [n. p., 1908?]
59 p. 22½cm.

1. Campaign literature, 1908—Republican.

10-13674

Library of Congress JK2357.1908.K5

NK 0211619 DLC WaU-L

Knox, Philander Chase, 1853-1921.
Address of Hon. Philander Chase Knox at a patriotic mass meeting in Exposition music hall, Pittsburgh, Pa., March 31st, 1917. [Philadelphia, Allen, Lane & Scott, printers, 1917]
1 p. l., 16 p. 23cm.

1. U. S.—For. rel.—Germany. 2. Germany—For. rel.—U. S. 3. European war, 1914- —Naval operations—Submarine.

17-21848

Library of Congress D619.K7

NK 0211620 DLC

Knox, Philander Chase, 1853-1921.
Address of Hon. Philander Chase Knox at the dedication of the monument erected to the memory of Major-General Edward Braddock in Braddock memorial park, Fayette County, Pennsylvania, October 15th, 1913. [n. p., 1913?]
23 p. 23½cm.

1. Braddock, Edward, 1695?-1755. 2. Braddock's campaign, 1755.

22-13246

Library of Congress E199.B795

NK 0211621 DLC PHi

VOLUME 300

Knox, Philander Chase, 1853–1921.
Address of Senator Philander Chase Knox, at Pittsburgh, Pa., Friday, October 30th, 1908. ⌈n. p., 1908?⌉
58 p. 23cm.

1. Campaign literature, 1908—Republican.
10-13673
Library of Congress JK2341.A7 1908 a

NK 0211622 DLC

Knox, Philander Chase, 1853–1921.
Address of the Honorable Philander C. Knox, secretary of state, at the centenary celebration of the state of Louisiana at New Orleans, April 30, 1912. ⌈n. p., 1912⌉
30 p. 23cm.

1. Louisiana. 2. Louisiana purchase.
16-23270
Library of Congress F369.K74

NK 0211623 DLC

Knox, Philander Chase, 1853–1921.
⌈Addresses⌉

NK 0211624 ICJ

Knox, Philander Chase, 1853–1921.
Addresses of Philander C. Knox, United States senator from Pennsylvania during the presidential campaign of 1904. ⌈Philadelphia? 1904?⌉
2 p. l., ⌈3⌉-48, 39, 15 p. 25½cm.

1. U. S.—Pol. & govt.—1904.
9-26181
Library of Congress JK2357.1904.K6

NK 0211625 DLC

Knox, Philander Chase, 1853–1921.
... The altar of our nationality. Address of Hon. Philander C. Knox delivered at Independence square, Philadelphia, July fourth, 1921 ... Washington, Govt. print. off., 1921.
6 p. 23cm. (⌈U. S.⌉ 67th Cong., 1st sess. Senate. Doc. 44)
Presented by Mr. Moses. Ordered printed July 5, 1921.

1. Fourth of July orations. I. Title.
21-26700
Library of Congress E286.P54 1921

NK 0211626 DLC OO MiU

Knox, Philander Chase, 1853–1921.
U. S. *Dept. of state.*
... Battleships for Argentine Republic. Message from the President of the United States, transmitting answer of the secretary of state to Senate resolution of February 27, 1911, relative to the construction of battleships for Argentine Republic ... ⌈Washington, Govt. print. off., 1911⌉

Knox, Philander Chase, 1853–1921.
The commerce clause of the Constitution and the trusts. An address delivered by Philander C. Knox ... before the Chamber of commerce, Pittsburg, Pa., on October 14, 1902. Washington, Govt. print. off., 1902.
1 p. l., 42 p. 24½cm.

1. Trusts, Industrial—U. S. 2. Interstate commerce.
10-10033
Library of Congress HD2795.K7

NK 0211628 DLC PPB NjP OO NN

Knox, Philander Chase, 1853–1921.
The Department of state; address of Hon. Philander C. Knox before the National civic federation. New York, N. Y., December 11, 1911. ⌈New York? 1911⌉
53 p. 23cm.

1. U. S. Dept. of state. I. Title.
22-12813
Library of Congress JK853.K6

NK 0211629 DLC PHi NN

Knox, Philander Chase, 1853–1921.
The development of the federal power to regulate commerce. Address of Senator Philander C. Knox to the graduating classes of the Law school of Yale university, on June 24, 1907. ⌈New Haven, 1907?⌉
20 p. 23cm.

1. Interstate commerce. 2. U. S.—Commercial policy.
10-12198
Library of Congress HF1455.K7

NK 0211630 DLC OClWHi

Knox, Philander Chase, 1853–1921.
U. S. *Congress. House. Committee on foreign affairs.*
Diplomatic and consular appropriation bill ... Statement of Hon. Philander C. Knox, secretary of state, accompanied by Mr. S. Y. Smith, chief of the diplomatic bureau, and Mr. Wilbur J. Carr, director of the consular service, Department of state ... ⌈Washington, Govt. print. off., 1911⌉

Knox, Philander Chase, 1853–1921.
Sanguily y Garritt, Manuel, 1849–
Discursos pronunciados por los señores Manuel Sanguily ... y Philander C. Knox ... en el banquete que el honorable presidente de la república ofreció al último de los citados señores en la Secretaría de gobernación la noche del 11 de abril de 1912. Habana, Impr. "El Fígaro," 1912.

Knox, Philander Chase, 1853–1921.
The future of commerce. Address of Senator Philander C. Knox, before the Chamber of commerce of Pittsburgh ... Wednesday, February 12th, 1908. ⌈Pittsburg, 1908?⌉
40 p. 24½cm.

1. Inland navigation—U. S. 2. U. S.—Commercial policy.
10-12197
Library of Congress HE393.K7

NK 0211633 DLC Or NcD NN

Knox, Philander Chase, 1853–1921.
The future of commerce; address of Senator Philander C. Knox before the Chamber of commerce of Pittsburgh, Pittsburgh, Pennsylvania, Wednesday, February 12th, 1908. ⌈Washington? 1908?⌉
40 p. 23½cm.
Favoring improvement of harbors and inland waterways.

1. Inland navigation—U. S. 2. U. S.—Commercial policy.
10-33643
Library of Congress HE393.Z7K72

NK 0211634 DLC

Knox, Philander Chase, 1853–1921.
... The future of commerce. Address of Senator Philander C. Knox before the Chamber of commerce of Pittsburg ... February 12, 1908 ... Washington, Gov't print. off., 1908.
16 p. 23cm. (⌈U. S.⌉ 60th Cong., 1st sess. Senate. Doc. 277)
Referred to the Committee on commerce and ordered printed, Feb. 14, 1908.
Favoring improvement of harbors and inland waterways.

1. Inland navigation—U. S. 2. U. S.—Commercial policy. I. U. S. 60th Cong., 1st sess., 1907–1908. Senate.
8-35141
Library of Congress HE393.Z7K7

NK 0211635 DLC PPB OO MiU

Knox, Philander Chase, 1853–1921.
In opposition to the resolution reported from the Committee on privileges and elections "that Reed Smoot is not entitled to a seat as a senator of the United States from the state of Utah." Speech of Hon. Philander C. Knox, of Pennsylvania, in the Senate of the United States, Thursday, February 14, 1907. Washington, Govt. print. off., 1907.
1 p. l., 30 p. 24cm.

1. Smoot, Reed, 1862– 2. Mormons and Mormonism.
CA 10-3926 Unrev'd
Library of Congress JK1189.59th.U8K6

NK 0211636 DLC

Knox, Philander Chase, 1853–1921.
In the Circuit Court of the U.S. For the district of Minnesota
see under U.S. Dept. of Justice.

Knox, Philander Chase, 1853–1921.
U. S. *Dept. of justice.*
Instruction to United States commissioners. Not applicable to officials in Alaska, Porto Rico, or the Philippine Islands. April 1, 1904 ... Washington, Govt. print off., 1904.

Knox, Philander Chase, 1853–1921.
... International unity, by Philander C. Knox ... New York city, American association for international conciliation, 1910.
13 p., 1 l. 19½cm. (International conciliation, pub. monthly by the American association for international conciliation ... no. 28)
⌊Address delivered before the Pennsylvania society of New York, December 1909.

1. International cooperation. I. Title.
13-9614
Library of Congress JX1907.A8 no. 28
— Copy 2. ⌈a24f1⌉

NK 0211639 DLC CaBVaU OrPR WaS WaU-L DAU DS PPLT PHC PCC OClWHi OO OU MiU OCl MB PPTU

VOLUME 300

Knox, Philander Chase, 1853-1921.

U. S. *Dept. of state.*

... Lands on Magdalena Bay. Message from the President of the United States transmitting in response to Senate resolution of May 16, 1912, copies of correspondence relative to the American syndicate interested in lands on Magdalena Bay ... Washington [Govt. print. off.] 1912.

Knox, Philander Chase, 1853-1921.

... The law of labor and trade. Address by P. C. Knox ... before the annual meeting of the Pennsylvania bar association. Held at Cresson, Pa., June 30th, 1897. [n. p., 1897]

1 p. l., 25 p. 24cm.

1. Labor laws and legislation. 2. Restraint of trade. I. Title.

24-17412

Library of Congress HD7834.K6

NK 0211641 DLC PHi

Knox, Philander Chase, 1853-1921.

U. S. *Congress. Senate. Committee on the judiciary.*

Liability of common carriers to employees. Hearings [Feb. 20, 1908] before a subcommittee of the Committee on the judiciary, United States Senate, on the bill (S. 3080) relating to the liability of common carriers engaged in commerce to which the regulative power of Congress extends under the Constitution of the United States ... Washington, Govt. print. off., 1908.

Knox, Philander Chase, 1853-1921.

U. S. *Congress. Senate. Committee on military affairs.*

... Maj. Gen. Enoch H. Crowder ... Report. <To accompany S. 2867.> ... [Washington, Govt. print. off., 1919]

Knox, Philander Chase, 1853-1921.

Memorial address by Hon. Philander C. Knox on the battlefield of Gettysburg, May 30, 1908. [n. p., 1908]

22 p. 23½ cm.

1. Gettysburg, Battle of, 1863.

9-14740

Library of Congress E475.53.K74

NK 0211644 DLC ViU WaU-L

Knox, Philander Chase, 1853-1921.

The Monroe doctrine and some incidental obligations in the zone of the Caribbean; address of Hon. Philander C. Knox, before the New York state bar association, New York, N. Y., January 19, 1912. [New York? 1912?]

55 p. 22cm.

1. Monroe doctrine. 2. U. S.—For. rel.—Spanish America. 3. Spanish America—For. rel.—U. S.

16-11093

Library of Congress JX1425.K6

NK 0211645 DLC DPU DS OClWHi

Knox, Philander Chase, 1853-1921.

U. S. *Dept. of state.*

Outline of the organization and work of the Department of state. Prepared by direction of the secretary of state. Washington, 1911.

Knox, Philander Chase, 1853-1921.

Panama canal. Speech of Hon. P. C. Knox, of Pennsylvania, in the Senate of the United States, Tuesday, June 19, 1906. Washington, 1906.

21 p. 23cm.

1. Panama canal—Construction.

CA 10-2458 Unrev'd

Library of Congress TC774.K7

NK 0211647 DLC

Knox, Philander Chase, 1853-1921

The Panama canal and the commerce of the Caribbean. Address of the Honorable Philander C. Knox, secretary of state, at the annual banquet of the California development board in San Francisco, California, May 7, 1912. [n. p., 1912?]

43 p. 23cm.

1. Panama canal. 2. U. S.—Comm.—South America. 3. South America—Comm.—U. S.

17-7730

Library of Congress TC774.K73

NK 0211648 DLC CU-B PHi DPU

Knox, Philander Chase, 1853-1921.

[The pending arbitration treaties] address of Hon. Philander C. Knox before the American society for judicial settlement of international disputes, Cincinnati, O., November 8, 1911. [No imprint] 41 p.

NK 0211649 MiEM

Knox, Philander Chase, 1853-1921.

... The pending arbitration treaties. Address of Hon. Philander C. Knox before the American society of judicial settlement of international disputes, Cincinnati, Ohio, November 8, 1911 ... Washington [Govt. print. off.] 1912.

12 p. 24½cm. ([U. S.] 62d Cong., 2d sess. Senate. Doc. 298)

Presented by Mr. Bailey. Ordered printed February 8, 1912.

1. U. S.—For. rel.—Gt. Brit. 2. U. S.—For. rel.—France. 3. Arbitration, International. I. Title.

12-35167

Library of Congress JX1961.A3K6

NK 0211650 DLC DNW OO MiU

Knox, Philander Chase, 1853-1921.

Pennsylvania—New England; their relation to the most effective principle of federation embodied in the American constitution; an address by Senator Philander C. Knox, at a banquet of the New England Society of Pennsylvania, December 23, 1907 at Philadelphia. Washington, D. C., Press of the Law reporter printing company [1907?]

14 p. 23cm.

A criticism of Dr. Hannis Taylor's claim that Pelatiah Webster was the original designer of the Constitution.

1. U. S.—Constitutional history. 2. Webster, Pelatiah, 1725-1795.

10-19286

Library of Congress JK119.K6

NK 0211651 DLC

Knox, Philander Chase, 1853-1921.

The people, the railroads and the national authority; address of Hon. Philander C. Knox before the Lincoln club, Kalamazoo, Michigan, Tuesday, February 11th, 1908. [Washington? 1908?]

26 p. 23cm.

1. Railroads and state—U. S.

10-33660

Library of Congress HE2757.1908.K74

NK 0211652 DLC Or PPB NN

Knox, Philander Chase, 1853-1921.

... The people, the railroads and the national authority; an address delivered before the Civic forum ... New York city, April 22, 1908, by Philander C. Knox ... with portrait. New York, The Civic forum, 1908.

14 p. port. 18½cm. (Civic forum addresses, vol. I, no. 8)

1. Railroads and state—U. S.

8-30511

Library of Congress H31.C52 vol. 1, no. 8

NK 0211653 DLC NN

---

536 Knox, Philander Chase, 1853-1921.

President Venustiano Carranza. Correct statements made by Senator Knox, of Pennsylvania in the Senate. Mexican Embassy, Wash., D. C., [1917]

NK 0211654 DPU

Knox, Philander Chase, 1853-1921.

Public and official utterances of Philander Chase Knox, secretary of state, on the occasion of the special embassy to Japan, September, 1912. Washington, Govt. print. off., 1912.

13 p. 23cm.

A mission to pay a tribute of respect to the memory of the late Emperor; to manifest the appreciation of the American people of the wonderful achievements under His Majesty's benign reign; and to express the sympathetic American interest in the new Japan.

1. Mutsuhito, emperor of Japan, 1852-1912. 2. Japan—Econ. condit. I. U. S. Dept. of state. II. Title.

14-30937

Library of Congress DS849.U6K6

NK 0211655 DLC

Knox, Philander Chase, 1853-1921.

Railroad rate regulation. Speech of Hon. Philander C. Knox, of Pennsylvania, in the United States Senate, Wednesday, March 28, 1906. Washington, Govt. print. off., 1906.

1 p. l., 56 p. 24cm.

1. Railroads—U. S.—Rates.

9-30557†

Library of Congress HE1843.A7K72

NK 0211656 DLC PPB MH CSmH

Knox, Philander Chase, 1853-1921.

The reasonableness and lawfulness of the general features of the President's rate regulation policy. Address by Senator Philander C. Knox, at banquet of Pittsburgh, Chamber of commerce, November 3, 1905. [Pittsburg, 1905?]

8 p. 28cm.

1. Railroads—U. S.—Rates. 2. Railroads and state—U. S.

10-12195

Library of Congress HE1843.K7

NK 0211657 DLC NcD NN MiU

KNOX, PHILANDER CHASE, 1853-1921.

The reasonableness and lawfulness of the general features of the president's rate regulation policy. Address at banquet of Pittsburgh Chamber of Commerce, November 3, 1905. [Pittsburgh, 1905] 8 p. 27cm.

Microfiche (neg.) 1 sheet. 11 x 15cm. (NYPL FSN 14,479)

1. Railways--Rates--U.S. I. Pittsburgh Chamber of Commerce.

NK 0211658 NN

VOLUME 300

Knox, Philander Chase, 1853-1921.
... Reciprocity with Canada—address of Hon. Philander C. Knox. [Washington, Govt. print. off., 1911]
9 p. 23cm. ([U. S.] 61st Cong., 3d sess. House. Doc. 1418)
Ordered to be printed March 3, 1911.
Address before the Chicago association of commerce, February 15, 1911.

1. U. S.—Comm.—Canada. 2. Canada—Comm.—U. S. 3. Reciprocity. I. U. S. 61st Cong., 3d sess., 1910-1911. House. II. Title.
11—35269
Library of Congress HF1732.C2K7

NK 0211659 DLC NN OO MiU

Knox, Philander Chase, 1853-1921.
U. S. *Dept. of state.*
... Relations between United States and Republic of Colombia. Message from the President of the United States, transmitting report by the secretary of state on the subject of relations between the United States and the Republic of Colombia. [Washington, Govt. print. off., 1913]

Knox, Philander Chase, 1853-1921.
Remarks of Senator Philander C. Knox, at a dinner given to the Pennsylvania delegation in Congress, by Hon. Joseph C. Sibley, December 4, 1907. [Washington, 1907?]
7 p. 22cm.
10-13670
Library of Congress JK2341.A7 1907

NK 0211661 DLC NN MiU

KNOX, PHILANDER CHASE, 1853-1921.
Remarks... at a dinner given to the Pennsylvania delegation in Congress by Hon. Joseph C. Sibley, December 4. 1907. [n.p., 1907] 7 p 22cm.

Film reproduction. Negative.

1. Republican party.

NK 0211662 NN

Knox, Philander Chase, 1853-1921.
U. S. *Dept. of justice.* FOR OTHER EDITIONS SEE MAIN ENTRY
... Reply of the attorney-general dated January 3, 1903, to a communication dated December 20, 1902, from the Hon. George F. Hoar, chairman of the Committee on the judiciary, United States Senate. Sherman antitrust law, and list of decisions relating thereto. Also an address delivered by Attorney-General Philander C. Knox on the commerce clause of the Constitution and the trust, at Pittsburg, Pa., October 14 1902 Washington, Govt. print. off.. 1903.

Knox, Philander Chase, 1853-1921.
U. S. *Dept. of state.*
... Slavery in Peru. Message from the President of the United States, transmitting report of the secretary of state, with accompanying papers, concerning the alleged existence of slavery in Peru ... Washington, Govt. print. off., 1913.

Knox, Philander Chase, 1853-1921.
Speech ... and in the Senate ... June 17, 1919, on Senate Res. no. 76, requesting the Peace conference to provide that the U. S. may reserve the question of entering the league of nations,proposed... until the subject is further considered. Govt., 1919.
44 p.

NK 0211665 Or

Roosevelt
Knox, Philander Chase, 1853-1921.
Speech at a mass meeting in the Academy of music, Philadelphia, held under the auspices of the Manufacturers club of Philadelphia, Saturday evening, October first, 1904. n.p. [1904]
48 p. 26 cm.

NK 0211666 MH

Knox, Philander Chase, 1853-1921.
Speech at Pittsburg, Pennsylvania, November 5th, 1904. [Pittsburg? 1904]
15 p. 28 cm.

1. Campaign literature, 1904—Republican.
E758.K55 48-34893*

NK 0211667 DLC MH

Knox, Philander Chase, 1853-1921.
Speech at the Union League Club, New York, October 20th, 1904. [New York? 1904]
39 p. 28 cm.

1. U. S.—Economic policy. 2. Industry and state—U. S.
HC106.K728 48-34186*

NK 0211668 DLC

Knox, Philander Chase, 1853-1921.
Speech in the Senate, August 29, 1919. In Old Colony trust company, Boston
The treaty of Versailles, American opinion. Boston, Mass., Old Colony trust company c1919. p. 35-67.

NK 0211669 OCl

Knox, Philander Chase, 1853-1921.
Speech of Hon. Philander C. Knox, of Pennsylvania, in the Senate of the United States, on the Brownsville resolutions, Wednesday, January 16, 1907. Washington, 1907.
8 p. 23cm.

1. Brownsville, Tex.—Riot, 1906.
CA 10-2007 Unrev'd
Library of Congress UB323.A4 1907 a

NK 0211670 DLC

Knox, Philander Chase, 1853-1921.
Speech of Hon. Philander Chase Knox in the United States Senate, December 18, 1918, on resolution introduced by Mr. Knox favoring the separation of the consideration of the revision of the laws of the sea and the establishment of a League of Nations from the questions involved in making peace with the Central Empires. Washington, Govt. print. off. 1918. 28 p. 23 cm.

NK 0211671 DNW

JX1975 .K6
Knox, Philander Chase, 1853-1921.
Speech of Hon. Philander Chase Knox in the United States Senate, March 1, 1919. Constitution of league of nations. Washington, Govt. print. office, 1919.
40 p. 23 cm.

NK 0211672 DLC DNW Or

Knox, Philander Chase, 1853-1921.
Speech of Senator Philander C. Knox, of Pennsylvania, at Philadelphia, Pa., October 29th, 1906. [Philadelphia? 1906?]
cover-title, 8 p. 29½cm.

1. Campaign literature, 1906—Republican. 2. Pennsylvania—Pol. & govt.
10—13672
Library of Congress JK2357.1906.K5

NK 0211673 DLC

Knox, Philander Chase, 1853-1921.
Speech of Senator Philander C. Knox of Pennsylvania, at Pittsburgh, Pennsylvania, October 27th, 1906. [Pittsburg? 1906?]
1 p. l., 34 p. 28cm.

1. Campaign literature, 1906—Republican. 2. Pennsylvania—Pol. & govt.
10-13671
Library of Congress JK2341.A7 1906 a

NK 0211674 DLC

Knox, Philander Chase, 1853-1921. FOR OTHER EDITIONS SEE MAIN ENTRY
Speeches incident to the visit of Philander Chase Knox, secretary of state of the United States of America, to the countries of the Caribbean. February 23 to April 17, 1912. Washington, Govt. print. off., 1913.

Knox, Philander Chase, 1853-1921.
The spirit and purpose of American diplomacy; address by Hon. Philander C. Knox at the commencement exercises of the University of Pennsylvania at Philadelphia, Pa., June 15, 1910. [n. p., 1910?]
57 p. 22½cm.

1. U. S.—For. rel. I. Title.
16-3825
Library of Congress JX1407.K6

NK 0211676 DLC WHi DS PU PHi DPU OCU

1207
Knox, Hon. Philander Chase, 1853-1921.
El spiritu y los fines de la diplomacia Americana. 1910.
33 p.
Typewritten.

NK 0211677 DPU

Knox, Philander Chase, 1853-1921.
U. S. *59th Cong., 1st sess., 1905-1906. Senate.*
... State statutes regarding review of orders of state railroad commissions, etc. ... Provisions in the statutes of the several states with regard to review of orders of state railroad commissions, or defense against the enforcement of such orders. [Washington, Gov't print. off., 1906]

VOLUME 300

Knox, Philander Chase, 1853-1921.
Canada. *Dept. of finance.*
Tariff relations between the United States and the Dominion of Canada. Correspondence and statements 1911. Ottawa, Government printing bureau, 1911

Knox, Philander Chase, 1853-1921.
U. S. *Congress. Senate. Committee on the judiciary.*
... To regulate interstate commerce in intoxicating liquors, etc. ... Report. <To accompany S. 6576.> [Washington, Gov't print. off., 1908]

Knox, Philander Chase, 1853-1921.
Treaty of Versailles; speech of Hon. Philander Chase Knox of Pennsylvania delivered in the Senate of the United States, Friday, August 29, 1919. Washington [Govt. print. off.] 1919.
36 p. 23cm.

1. Versailles, Treaty of, June 28, 1919 (Germany)
43-36001
Library of Congress D643.A7K58
[2]

NK 0211681 DLC CSt-H PPFML

Knox, Philander Chase, 1853-1921.
The true relation of the United States to the League of nations. Speech of Hon. Philander C. Knox, ... Thursday, November 6, 1919. [Washington, Govt. print. off., 1919.]
4 p.

YA 5000 (Congressional speeches, by author)
J 17

NK 0211682 DLC

Knox, Philander Chase, 1853-1921.
The visit to Costa Rica of His Excellency the secretary of state of the United States of America
see under Costa Rica. La Gaceta.

Knox, R. G., and Wade **Toole.**
The brood sow.
[Toronto.] 1923. 16 pp. Illus. Plans. Tables. [Ontario, Province. Department of Agriculture. Bulletin 301.] 23½ cm.

D3487 — S.r.c. — Jt. auth. — Swine.

NK 0211684 MB

Knox, R. G.
Selection, care and management of the boar.
Toronto. 1924. 13 pp. Illus. Plans. Tables. [Ontario, Province. Department of Agriculture. Bulletin 307.] 23½ cm.

D3533 — S.r.c. — Swine.

NK 0211685 MB

Knox, R S
Shakespeare today... c1935.

NK 0211686 MiU

Knox, Raymond Collyer, 1876-1952.
Nichols, Robert Hastings, 1873-
... Courses in the history of the Christian church ... by Robert Hastings Nichols ... under supervision of Rev. Raymond C. Knox ... for the Columbia university Home study courses. New York, Columbia university, 1923-

---

Knox, Raymond Collyer, 1876-1952.
In lumine tuo, by Raymond C. Knox ... New York, Columbia university press, 1931.
x, 201, [1] p., 1 l. 19½cm.

"The addresses contained in this book were delivered at various times in the daily service held in Saint Paul's chapel, Columbia university."—Foreword.

1. Sermons, American. I. Title.
31-14961
Library of Congress BX5937.K65 I 6
——— Copy 2.
Copyright A 38282 [3] [252.03] 232.9

NK 0211688 DLC MH-AH MB OO OU ViU

COLUMBIANA
CK4
K7733 Knox, Raymond Collyer, 1876-1952.
The kingdom of values. [Baccalaureate sermon delivered in St. Paul's Chapel, on Sunday, June 3, 1934. [1934]
[283]-286 p. 26cm.

From Columbia University quarterly, September 1934.

NK 0211689 NNC

Knox, Raymond Collyer, 1876-1952.
Knowing the Bible, by Raymond C. Knox ... New York, The Macmillan company, 1927.
xv p., 1 l., 19-277 p. illus., maps (1 double) diagr. 21cm.
"Selected bibliography": p. 265-274.

1. Bible—Hist. 2. Bible—Study. I. Title.
27-1863
Library of Congress BS475.K6

MB NjNbS PP PPDrop PHC OCl OO ViU DAU MB NN
NK 0211690 DLC OrPR NcD InAndC-T Or WaWW OrSaW PPLT

Knox, Raymond Collyer, 1876-1952.
Knowing the Bible,....N.Y. 1929.
277 p.

NK 0211691 PSC MBrZ

Knox, Raymond Collyer, 1876-1952.
Knowing the Bible, by Raymond C. Knox... New York, The Macmillan company, 1931.
19-277 p.

"Reprinted August, 1927."

NK 0211692 OOxM PPPD MiU

Knox, Raymond Collyer, 1876-1952.
Knowing the Bible, by Raymond C. Knox ... Rev. ed. New York, The Macmillan company, 1936.
3 p. l., v-xv p., 1 l., 19-281 p. illus., maps (1 double) diagr. 20½cm.
Includes bibliographies.

1. Bible—Introductions. 2. Bible—Study. I. Title.
36-19210
Library of Congress BS475.K6 1936
——— Copy 2.
Copyright A 98204 [2] 220

NK 0211693 DLC MU WaTC OrP PCC PPT OO OCl

Knox, Raymond Collyer, 1876-1952.
Knowing the Bible. Rev.ed. NY, Macmillan, 1949
xv, 281 p. illus.

NK 0211694 MH

CK4
K7734 Knox, Raymond Collyer, 1876-1952.
Life's highest reward. Baccalaureate sermon delivered at St. Paul's Chapel, Sunday, 1 June, 1930. [1930]
[328]-334 p. 26cm.

"Reprinted from the Columbia University quarterly, September, 1930, vol. XXII, no. 3."

NK 0211695 NNC

CK4
K7735 Knox, Raymond Collyer, 1876-1952.
The preservation of life. Baccalaureate sermon delivered in St Paul's Chapel, Columbia University, Sunday, 29 May, 1932. [1932]
[357]-363 p. 26cm.

From Columbia University quarterly, September, 1932.

NK 0211696 NNC

Knox, Raymond Collyer, 1876-1952.
Religion and the American dream, by Raymond C. Knox ... with an introduction by Nicholas Murray Butler. New York, Columbia university press, 1934.
xii p., 2 l., [3]-155 p., 1 l. 22½cm.
"Notes": p. [145]-150.

1. Sociology, Christian. 2. Religious education. I. Title.
34-17637
Library of Congress BR115.S6K6
——— Copy 2.
Copyright A 72798 [3] 261

MsSM PHC PSC OO OU OCl OCU MB ViU
NK 0211697 DLC GU PPPrHi NcD OrStbM WaS OrCS OrU NIC

Knox, Raymond Collyer, 1876-1952.
Report of Raymond C. Knox ... on significant religious conditions and movements in Europe, 1932-33. [New York, 1933?]
22 p. 23½cm.

NK 0211698 NNC

Knox, Raymond Collyer, 1876-1952, ed.
The Review of religion. v. 1- Nov. 1936-
New York, Columbia university press [1936-

CK4
K773 Knox, Raymond Collyer, 1876-1952.
The tidings of the mind. Baccalaureate sermon delivered in St. Paul's Chapel, Columbia University, Sunday, 31 May, 1931. [1931]
[294]-301 p. 26cm.

"Reprinted from the Columbia University quarterly, September 1931, vol. XXIII, no 3."

NK 0211700 NNC

VOLUME 300

Knox, Reuben, 1850–1930.
The law of chattel mortgages in New Jersey, including the conditional sales act, by Reuben Knox ... Newark, N. J., Soney & Sage, 1918.
iii, 214 p. 24cm. $3.50

1. Chattel mortgages—New Jersey. 2. Sales, Conditional. 18-3574
Library of Congress

NK 0211701 DLC

Knox, Reuben, 1850–1930, *comp.*
The law of married women in New Jersey, by Reuben Knox ... Plainfield, N. J., New Jersey law journal publishing co., 1912.
561 p. 24 cm.

1. Married women—New Jersey. I. New Jersey. Laws, statutes, etc.
12—13884

NK 0211702 DLC NcD PPB PPHirL

Knox, Reuben, 1850–1930
The law of real property mortgages in New Jersey, by Reuben Knox ... Newark, N. J., Soney & Sage, 1918.
vii, 557 p. 23½cm. $6.50

1. Mortgages—New Jersey. 18-3380
Library of Congress

NK 0211703 DLC PPB

Law

Knox, Richard C., ed.

Taylor's forms of legal papers, with instructions for drawing legal instruments. Copyright ... by Richard C. Knox. [Chicago, ©1898.

Knox, Richard F., complainant.
In the Circuit Court of the United States, for the ninth judicial circuit. In and for the District of California. Richard F. Knox and Joseph Osborn, complainants, vs. The Quicksilver Mining Company, defendant. San Francisco, Pacific Coast Law Printing and Publishing Co., 1880–
v.

Contents.- v.1. Testimony. v.2. Pleadings and exhibits.

NK 0211705 CU CSmH

Knox, Robert, of Scarborough.
Descriptions, geological, topographical, and antiquarian in eastern Yorkshire, between the rivers Humber and Tees. — London. The Author. 1855. xiv, 209 pp. Plates. Maps. 8°.

F3254 — Yorkshire, England. Descr.

NK 0211706 MB MdBP MH

DS489
K74

Knox, Robert, 1640?–1720.
An account of the captivity of Capt. Robert Knox, and other Englishmen, in the island of Ceylon; and of the captain's miraculous escape, and return to England, in September 1680; after a detention on the island of nine teen years and a half. Written by himself, and first printed in 1681. To which is prefixed, a sketch of the geography, civil and natural history, commerce, &c. of Ceylon, brought down to the year 1815. London, Printed for J. Hatchard, 1818.
324 p. 17cm.
1.Ceylon. 2.Knox, Robert, 1640?–1720

NK 0211707 CSt CU MiU TU

Knox, Robert, 1640?–1720.
An account of the captivity and escape of Captain Robert Knox; an English gentleman, who was treacherously detained, nearly twenty years, in the kingdom of Kandy, in the interior of the island of Ceylon; by Rajah Singha, then native sovereign of the Kandian dominions. Originally published by Captain Knox, in the year 1681, and dedicated to the Court of directors of the honorable East India company. And now re-published with an introductory preface, and notes, by W. M. Harvard ... London, Sold by T. Blanshard [etc.] 1821.
1 p. l., xii, iii, 152p. front. 19cm.
1. Knox, Robert, 1640?-1720. I. Harvard, W. M.

NK 0211708 CtW

DS489
.5
K6
1908

Knox, Robert, 1640?-1720.
Account of the captivity of Capt. Robert Knox, and other Englishmen, in the island of Ceylon; and of the Captain's miraculous escape, and return to England, in September, 1680; after detention on the island of nineteen years and a half. Written by himself, and first printed in 1681. London, Printed for J. Hatchard, 1818; [Colombo, Reprinted by A.M. & J. Ferguson, 1908]
6,[5]-182 p.

NK 0211709 CU MH

Rare Book Room
Is94
t1
v.4

[Knox, Robert] 1640?-1720.
The captive in Ceylon. Revised by the Committee of publication. Philadelphia, American Sunday school union[18--?]
16p.incl.front.,1 illus. 10½cm.
([American Sunday-school union. Tracts] no.89, II. series)
Based on Knox's An historical relation of the island Ceylon.
Pamphlet

NK 0211710 CtY

Knox, Robert, 1640?-1720.
The captive in Ceylon. Rev. by the Committee of Publication of the American Sunday-School Union. Philadelphia [184-?]
16 p. front. 11cm. (The Child's Library, v. 6, [no. 5])

I. American Sunday-School Union. II. Ser.

NK 0211711 ViU

Knox, Robert, 1640?–1720.
Ceylanische reise-beschreibung; oder, Historische erzehlung von der in Ost-Indien gelegenen insel Ceylon ... in englischer sprache heraus gegeben durch Robertum Knox ... Benebenst unterschiedl. zu erklärung der sachen dienlichen kupfferstücken; und absonderlich, woran es sonst bissher noch gemangelt, einer neuen und richtigen land-charte über diese insel: wie auch einer vorrede des herrn Hookii. Jetzo ins hochteutsche mit fleiss übersetzt, und mit einem vollständigen register versehen. Leipzig, J. F. Gleditsch, 1689.
38 p. l., 411, [41] p. front., plates, fold. map. 21½ x 17½cm.
1. Ceylon.
DS489.K743 47-34588

NK 0211712 DLC IU MiU CtY CU

Knox, Robert, 1640?–1720.
T'eyland Ceylon in sijn binnenste, of't koningrijck Candy geopent. Vertaeld door S. de Vries. Utrecht, W. Broedelet, 1692. sm. 4°. pp. (14), 291 +. Map and plates.
Running-title: — Historische beschrijvingh van 't eyland Ceylon.

Ceylon||Au: Historische|AcS 232893

NK 0211713 MH

Knox, Robert, 1640?–1720.
An historical account of the island of Ceilon in the East-Indies: written by Robert Knox, a captive there near twenty years. Improved with all necessary additions taken out of the History of Capt. John Ribeyro, a Portuguese, who has also written about said island. (*In* Harris, John, 1667?–1719. Navigantium atque itinerantium bibliotheca. London, 1705. 40cm. vol. II, p. 450–484)

1. Ceylon.

5-13886†
Library of Congress G160.H27

NK 0211714 DLC MnHi

Knox, Robert, 1640?–1720.
An historical relation of Ceylon, together with somewhat concerning severall remarkeable passages of my life that hath hapned since my deliverance out of my captivity, by Robert Knox, a captive there near twenty years. Glasgow, J. MacLehose and sons, 1911.
lxvii, [1], 459, [1] p. front. (port.) 21 pl. (1 fold.) fold. map. 23cm.
T.-p. in red and black.
Reprint, including facsimile of t.-p. of original edition, London, 1681. Ed. by James Ryan. Includes "the issue for the first time of the autobiography of Knox."
1. Ceylon—Descr. & trav. 2. Ceylon—Soc. life & cust. 3. Knox, Robert, 1640?–1720. I. Ryan, James.
A 11-2206
Title from Lynn, Mass., Pub. Libr. Printed by L. C.

PP PU-Mus NN OCl OCU MiU MB IU
NK 0211715 MLy NIC CU InU FMU WaS OrU NjNbT NcU CtY

Knox, Robert, 1640?–1720.
An historical relation of the island Ceylon, in the East-Indies: together, with an account of the detaining in captivity the author and divers other Englishmen now living there, and of the author's miraculous escape. Illustrated with figures, and a map of the island. By Robert Knox ... London, Printed by R. Chiswell, 1681.
12 p. l., 189 p. front. (port.) plates, fold. map. 32½cm.
Preface signed: Robert Hooke.

1. Ceylon.
15-12033
Library of Congress DS489.K74

MiU CSmH NN MdBP
NK 0211716 DLC PPL MnU ViU NjP CLU-C NcD NcU CtY PHi

Knox, Robert, 1640?-1700.
An historical relation of the island of Ceylon in the East Indies. Together with an account of the detaining in captivity the author, and divers other Englishmen now living there; and of the author's miraculous escape. London, J.Mawman, 1817.

NK 0211717 MH

Knox, Robert 1640?-1720.
An historical relation of the island of Ceylon; with an account of the captivity of divers Englishmen, and of the author's escape... London, 1727.

NK 0211718 PPL

Knox, Robert, 1640?-1720.

[**Fellowes, Robert**]
The history of Ceylon, from the earliest period to the year MDCCCXV; with characteristic details of the religion, laws, & manners of the people and a collection of their moral maxims & ancient proverbs. By Philalethes, A. M. Oxon. [*pseud.*] To which is subjoined, Robert Knox's Historical relation of the island, with an account of his captivity during a period of near twenty years ... London, J. Mawman, 1817.

VOLUME 300

Knox, Robert, 1640?-1720.
Nineteen years' captivity in the kingdom of Conde Uda in the highlands of Ceylon, 1660-79; together with his singular deliverance. [From his Historical relation.] London, 1681; repr. 1877. 8°. (Arber, E., *Eng. garner*, v. 1.) 2117

NK 0211720 MdBP OU MiU

Knox, Captain Robert, 1640?-1720
Nineteen years' captivity in the Kingdom of Conde Uda in the highlands of Ceylon, . . . between March 1660 & October 1679: together with his singular deliverance from that strange and pagan land.
(In An English garner. Voyages and travels. Vol. 2, pp. 295-429. New York. [1903.])

F1296 — Ceylon. Geog.

NK 0211721 MB NN I

Knox, Robert, 1640?-1720.
Précis historique de la captivité...
Percival, Robert.
Voyage à l'île de Ceylon, fait dans les années 1797 à 1800; contenant l'histoire, la géographie et la description des mœurs des habitans, ainsi que celle des productions naturelles du pays; par Robert Percival ... Suivi de la relation d'une ambassade envoyée, en 1800, au roi de Candy; orné de plusieurs planches, et d'une carte de l'île de Ceylan ... Tr. de l'anglais par P. F. Henry ... Paris, Dentu, an XI. (1803)

Knox, Robert, 1640?-1720.
Relation ou voyage de l'isle de Ceylan, dans les Indes Orientales. Contenant une description exacte de cette isle, la forme de son gouvernement, de commerce, les mœurs, les coûtumes, & la religion de ses habitans: avec un recit de la captivité de l'auteur & de divers autres Anglois, & de sa delivrance après vingt années d'esclavage. Par Robert Knox. Traduit de l'anglois. Enrichi de figures avec la carte de l'isle ... À Amsterdam, Chez P. Marret, 1693.
2 v. in 1. front., plates (part fold.) fold. map. 16½cm.
Preface signed: Robert Hooke.
1. Ceylon—Description and travel. 2. Ceylon—Social life and customs.
G S 34-378
Libr., U. S. Geol. Surv., Geo. F. Kunz Collection K590(649) K77

NK 0211723 DI-GS TU WU IaU CLU MiU MH-A NjP NN

Knox, Robert, 1640?-1720.
Robert Knox in the Kandyan Kingdom; selected and edited by E. F. C. Ludowyk. With 4 photographs by Lionel Wendt. [London] Oxford University Press [1948]
xxvi, 175 p. illus., map (on lining paper) 19 cm.
"Abridgement of Robert Knox's An historical relation of Ceylon and of some parts of his Autobiography."
1. Ceylon—Descr. & trav.
DS489.K747 915.48 50-56631

NK 0211724 DLC NSyU CU-B MH IU ICU NcD ViU WaU

KNOX, [Robert], 1791-1862
Account of the dissection of a young rorqual with a few observations on the anatomy of the foetal mysticetus. By Dr. Knox. [Edinburgh, 1834.]
12 p. 20 1/2 cm.
No t.p.

NK 0211725 MH

Knox, Robert, 1791-1862, ed.
Fau, Julien.
The anatomy of the external forms of man, intended for the use of artists, painters and sculptors. By Doctor J. Fau. Atlas containing twenty-eight drawings from nature; lithographed by M. Leveillé, pupil of M. Jacob. Ed. with additions by Robert Knox ... London, Bailliere, Tindall, and Cox [1868]

Knox, Robert, 1791-1862.
Engravings of the Ligaments, copied from the original works of the Caldanis ...
see under Caldani, Leopoldo Marco Antonio, 1725-1813.

KNOX, ROBERT, 1791-1862.
WB 25952
Fish and fishing in the lone glens of Scotland. With a history of the propagation, growth and metamorphoses of the salmon... London, G. Routledge & co., 1854.
144p. illus.
1. Fishing - Scotland.

NK 0211728 CtY CU NjP ICN MH NN PP NIC NBuG CaBVaU

Knox, Robert, 1791-1862.
Great artists and great anatomists; a biographical and philosophical study. By R. Knox ... London, J. Van Voorst, 1852.
xii, 213, [1] p. 19½cm.
CONTENTS.—George Cuvier.—Etienne Geoffroy (St. Hilaire)—Leonardo da Vinci.—Michael Angelo.—Raphael.
1. *Cuvier, Georges, baron, 1769-1832. 2. Geoffroy Saint-Hilaire, Étienne, 1772-1844. 3. Leonardo da Vinci, 1452-1519. 4. Buonarroti, Michel Angelo, 1475-1564. 5. Raffaele Sanzio, 1483-1520. I. Title.
11—7127
Library of Congress N6922.K7

NK 0211729 DLC CtY PPAFA PPPH PP MdBP OU ICU NN

Knox, Robert, 1791-1862, supposed author.
The greatest of our social evils
see under [Richelot, Gustave Antoine] 1806-1893.

Knox, Robert, 1791-1862.
——. Letter to the lord provost and town-council of Edinburgh. 8 pp. 8°. [Edinburgh, 1837.]

NK 0211730 DNLM PPC NN

Knox, Robert, 1791-1862.
Man: his structure and physiology; popularly explained and demonstrated. By R. Knox... London [etc.] H. Bailliere, 1857. lxiii, 172 p. illus. 20cm.
286074. 1. Physiology. N. Y. P. L.
Card revised April 2, 1945

NK 0211731 NN PPPH MH NNC

QT 104 K74M 1858
Knox, Robert, 1791-1862.
Man: his structure and physiology, popularly explained and demonstrated. 2d ed. with an appendix. London, Bailliere, 1858.
lxiii, 179 p. illus. (part fold., part col.) 19 1/2 cm.
1. Anatomy. 2. Physiology.

NK 0211732 WU-M CtY MiU

Knox, Robert, 1791-1862.
A manual of artistic anatomy, for the use of sculptors, painters, and amateurs, by Robert Knox ... London, H. Renshaw, 1852.
1 p. l., [v]-xxv p., 1 l., 175 p. illus. 18cm.
1. Anatomy, Artistic.
11-20669
Library of Congress NC760.K74

NK 0211733 DLC NN ICJ PPPM PPC DNLM

KNOX, Robert, 1791-1862.
A manual of human anatomy: descriptive, practical and general. London, Renshaw, 1853.
xxiii, 672 pp. Illus. 17 cm.

NK 0211734 MBCo PPC MdBP

Knox, Robert, 1791-1862, tr.
Milne-Edwards, Henri, 1800-1885.
A manual of zoology. By M. Milne Edwards. Tr. from the last French edition by R. Knox ... 2d ed., with many additional observations, and illustrated by 572 highly-finished wood engravings. Ed. by C. Carter Blake ... London, H. Renshaw, 1863.

Hist. 19th c.
QL 45 G762E 1828
Knox, Robert, 1791-1862.
Notice respecting the presence of a rudimentary spur in the female Echidna of New Holland. [Edinburgh, 1826?]
3 p. 21 1/2 cm. EDINBURGH COLLECTION
"Read before the Wernerian Natural History Society, 27th May 1826."
"From the Edinburgh new philosophical journal."
Author's presentation copy to the Plinian Society of Edinburgh.
Bound with Grant, R. E., An essay on the study of the animal kingdom, 1828.
1. Insectivora. I. Title. [1. Insectivora]

NK 0211736 WU-M

Knox, Robert, 1791-1862.
——. Observations and cases illustrative of the pathology and treatment of necrosis. 12 pp. 8°. [Edinburgh, 1821.] [Also, in: P., v. 664.]

NK 0211737 DNLM

QL 45 G762E 1828
Knox, Robert, 1791-1862.
Observations on the anatomi[c]al structure of the cassowary of New Holland (Casuarius Novae Hollandiae, Cuv.). [Edinburgh, 1823?]
9 p. 1 plate. 21 1/2 cm. EDINBURGH COLLECTION
"Read before the Wernerian Natural History Society, 26th April 1823."
"Extracted from the Edinburgh philosophical journal."
Bound with Grant, R. E., An essay on the study of the animal kingdom, London, 1828.
1. Birds. I. Title.
[1. Cassowaries.]

NK 0211738 WU-M

Knox (R[obert]) [1791-1862]. Observations on the anatomy of a human fœtus, presenting several remarkable congenital deformities. 6 pp., 1 pl. 8°. [Edinburgh, 1826.] [P., v. 1829.]
Repr. from: Edinb. J. M. Sc., 1826, I.

NK 0211739 DNLM

VOLUME 300

Hist.
19th c
QL
45
G762E
1828

Knox, Robert, 1791-1862.
Observations on the anatomy of the duck-billed animal of New South Wales, the Ornithorynchus paradoxus of naturalists. [Edinburgh, n.d.] EDINBURGH COLLECTION
47 p. i, vi-v plates. 21 1/2 cm.
"From the Memoirs of the Wernerian Natural History Society."
Bound with Grant, R. E., An essay on the study of the animal kingdom, 1828.
1. Mammals. I. Title. [1. Platypus.]

NK 0211740 WU-M

KNOX, Robert, 1791-1862.
Observations on the natural history of the salmon, herring and vendace. Edinburgh, printed by Neill & company. 1833.
4°. pp. 60. Plate.
"From the Transactions of the Royal Society of Edinburgh, vol. xii."

NK 0211741 MH

Knox, Robert, 1791-1862.
——. Observations on the regeneration of bone in cases of necrosis and caries, being a supplement to a memoir on the same subject inserted in the Edinburgh Medical and Surgical Journal for Jan'y, 1822. 8 pp., 2 pl. 8°. [Edinburgh, 1822.] [Also, in: P., v. 664.]

NK 0211742 DNLM

Knox, Robert, 1791-1862.
Observations upon a "Report by the select committee on salmon fisheries, Scotland: together with the minutes of evidence, appendix, and index." 30th June, 1836. By Robert Knox ... Edinburgh, A. & C. Black, 1837.
26 p. 22cm.
1. Fisheries—Scotland. 2. Salmon-fisheries.
A 18-1449
Title from Harvard Univ. Printed by L. C.

NK 0211743 MH

QL
45
G762E
1828

Knox, Robert, 1791-1862.
On the mode of growth, reproduction, and structure of the poison-fangs in serpents. [Edinburgh, n.d.] EDINBURGH COLLECTION
15 p. plate. 21 1/2 cm.
"From the Memoirs of the Wernian Natural History Society."
Author's presentation copy to the Plinian Society of Edinburgh.
Bound with Grant, R. E., An essay on the study of the animal kingdom, 1828.
1. Snakes. I Title. [1. Snakes]

NK 0211744 WU-M

QL
45
G762E
1828

Knox, Robert, 1791-1862.
On the wombat of Flinders. [Edinburgh, 1826?] EDINBURGH COLLECTION
8 p. 21 1/2 cm.
"Read before the Wernerian Society 14th January 1826."
"From the Edin. new phil. journal."
Author's presentation copy to the Plinian Society of Edinburgh.
Bound with Grant, R. E., An essay on the study of the animal kingdom, 1828.
1. Marsupia- lia. I. Title. [1. Wombats.]

NK 0211745 WU-M

Knox, Robert, 1791-1862.
Plates of the arteries of the human body; after Tiedemann ...
see under Tiedemann, Friedrich, 1781-1861.

WE
K72p
1825

KNOX, Robert, 1791-1862.
A probationary essay, on the causes and treatment of lateral curvature of the human spine ... Edinburgh, Neill, 1825.
52 p.

NK 0211747 DNLM PPC WU-M

Knox (Robert) [1791-1862]. *Quædam de viribus stimulantium et narcoticorum in corpore sano continens. 3 p. l., 29 pp. 8°. Edinburgi, 1814.

NK 0211748 DNLM

Knox, Robert, 1791-1862.
The races of men: a fragment. By Robert Knox ... London, H. Renshaw, 1850.
1 p. l., [v]-viii, 479, [1] p. illus. 15cm.
1. Ethnology.
5-29904
Library of Congress GN310.K7

NK 0211749 DLC InU PPT CtY PPC PPL TNF MdBP ICJ DSI

Knox, Robert, 1791-1862.
The races of men: a fragment. By Robert Knox ... Philadelphia, Lea & Blanchard, 1850.
323 p. 20cm.
1. Ethnology. 2. Race.
43-40248
Library of Congress GN310.K7 1850 a

MU KU-M
NK 0211750 DLC CtY PPWa PPL OClWHi NN MH ViW NIC

Knox, Robert, 1791-1862.
The races of men: a philosophical enquiry into the influence of race over the destinies of nations. By Robert Knox ... 2d ed., with supplementary chapters ... London, H. Renshaw, 1862.
viii, 600 p. illus. 18½cm.
1. Ethnology. 2. Race. I. Title.
17-15406
Library of Congress GN310.K7 1862

OCl MB
NK 0211751 DLC ICU DNLM ViU CtY PPAN MdBP MiU ODW

Knox, Robert, 1791-1862.
——. Second letter to the lord provost and town-council of Edinburgh. 9 pp. 8°. [Edinburgh, 1837.]

NK 0211752 DNLM PPCI

Knox, Robert, 1791-1862, tr. and ed.

Cloquet, Hippolyte, 1787-1840.
A system of human anatomy: translated from the 4th ed. of the French of H. Cloquet ... with notes and a corrected nomenclature, by Robert Knox ... Edinburgh, Maclachlan and Stewart, 1828.

RK53
T73

Knox, Robert, 1815-1883.
Church and state. The duty of the Presbyterian Church of Ireland in these eventful times. London, Hamilton, Adams, 1868.
16p.
Bound with Trimmor, Rev. Dr., pseud. A rational and scriptural vindication...of American slavery. Belfast, 1861.

1. Church and state in Ireland - Addresses, essays, lectures. 2. Presbyterian Church of Ireland - Addresses, essays, lectures. I. Title. II. Title: The duty of the Presbyterian Church of Ireland in these eventful times.

NK 0211755 CSaT PPPrHi NN

Knox, Robert, 1815-1883.
Conflicts of the clergy in the Presbyterian Church: their cause, consequences and cure. 3rd ed. Belfast, Mayne, 1852.
(pam.)

NK 0211756 PPPrHi

178
K74c
LIMITED CIRCULATION

Knox, Robert, 1815-1883.
The crime & curse of Britain. [Belfast, Alex Mayne for the Presbytery of Belfast, 1871?]
12 p. 20cm.
Title from caption, imprint from colophon.
"A report on Intemperance and the Liquor Traffic, submitted to the Presbytery of Belfast, on the 7th November, 1871."
Disbound. Sprinkled edges.

1. Temperance and religion. 2. Alcoholism. 3. Liquor problem. 4. Presbyterian Church in Ireland. I. Title.

NK 0211758 FU

BR759
.A1P13
no. 16
in:
SWTS

Knox, Robert, 1815-1883.
The crisis. Plain truths and stern facts for earnest men. 12th thousand. London, Hamilton, Adams; Edinburgh, Andrew Elliot; Belfast, Mayne, Aitchison, 1868.
16p. 21cm. (Pamphlets [no. 16])
1. Church of Ireland--Establishment and disestablishment. I. Title.

NK 0211759 IEG CSaT FU MB

△
BR83
.810

Knox, Robert, 1815-1883.
Intolerance of the Irish church; a Presbyterian minister threatened with legal pains and penalties for having conducted divine service in consecrated ground. [Belfast, Printed by A. Mayne, 1868]
8 p. 22 cm.

NK 0211760 MB

VOLUME 300

RK53
T73
Knox, Robert, 1815-1883.
Ireland under the new church act. Plain truths and stern facts for earnest men, no. 2. Dublin, Moffatt, 1869.
16p.

Bound with Trimmer, Rev. Dr., pseud. A rationaland scriptural vindication...of American slavery. Belfast, 1861.

1. Church and state in Ireland - Addresses, essays, lectures. I. Title.

NK 0211761 CSaT

268
K74l
Knox, Robert, 1815-1883.
The lambs of the flock; or, the Necessity and practicability of extending the sabbath-school system. A sermon delivered in the First Presbyterian Church, Saintfield, on the 27th of August, 1848. Being the anniversary of the sabbath-schools of that district. [Four lines] Belfast, William M'Comb, 1848.
25 p. . 17cm.

Sermon on John XXI.15.
Disbound. Sprinkled red edges.

1. Presbyterian Church in Ireland. 2. Presbyterian Church - Sermons. 3. Sermons, English. 4. Religious education - Ireland. 5. Sunday-schools. I. Title.

NK 0211763 MB

Knox, Robert, 1815-1883.
The Ulster Revival; an Address to Sabbath Schools. Philadelphia, Presb. Board of Publ.
55 p. 12°.

NK 0211764 CtY

Knox, Robert, 1868-1928.
Radiography and radio-therapeutics, by Robert Knox ... [2d ed.] New York, The Macmillan company; London, A. & C. Black, ltd., 1917-18.
2 v. front., illus., plates (1 col.) 25½cm. (*Half-title:* The Edinburgh medical series)

Paged continuously.
Printed in Great Britain.
"A short list of some important books on radiology": v. 1, p. iv at end.

CONTENTS.—pt. I. Radiography.—pt. II. Radio-therapeutics.

1. Radiography.

18—9527

Library of Congress RC78.K6 1917

PP MiU ICJ WaU
NK 0211765 DLC ICJ OrU-D OrU-M DNLM ICRL PU-D PPT

KNOX, Robert, 1868-1928.
Radiography and radio-therapeutics. New York MacMillian, 1918,19.

2v. Illus. Plates. (The Edinburgh Medical Series.) 24 1/2 cm.
Contents:-Radiography.2 Radio-therapeutics.
Pt.1 belongs to the 3rd ed.; Pt.2, to 2d ed.

NK 0211766 MBCo

WN
100
qK74r
KNOX, Robert, 1868-1928.
Radiography and radio-therapeutics. [3d ed.] London, Black, 1919-
v. illus. (Edinburgh medical series)
Series

NK 0211767 DNLM ViU OClW MiU

Knox, Robert, 1868-1928.
Radiography and radio-therapeutics. [3d ed.] New York, Macmillan, 1919.
2v. illus.

NK 0211768 ICRL MH PU-D PU-P PPC

WN
100
qK74r
KNOX, Robert, 1868-1928.
Radiography and radio-therapeutics. [4th ed.] London, Black, 1923-
v. illus. (Edinburgh medical series)
Series

NK 0211769 DNLM PPC MiU OClW CaBVaU

WI
700
qK74r
1920
KNOX, Robert, 1868-1928.
Radiography in the examination of the liver, gall bladder, and bile ducts. London, Heinemann [1920?]
64 p.
Reprinted from Archives of radiology and electrotherapy, July, August, September, and October 1919.

NK 0211770 DNLM KU-M OU OClW-H CaBVaU

Knox, Robert, 1868-1928.
Radiography, X-ray therapeutics by Robert Knox... with 78 plates, 337 hundred and 37 illustrations in the text and a frontispiece in colour. London, A. & C. Black, ltd., 1917.
2 vols.
xxi. 406 p. col. front., illus., LXIV pl. 26cm. (Edinburgh medical series)
"Glossary": p. 387-390.
21 Oct. 1930
1. Radiography. 2. Radiotherapy. 3. X-rays.

NK 0211771 DAL DNLM

Knox, Robert, 1868–1928.
Radiography, X-ray therapeutics and radium therapy, by Robert Knox ... with sixty-four plates, two hundred and forty-six illustrations in the text and a frontispiece in colour. London, A. & C. Black, ltd., 1915.
xxi, 406 p. col. front., illus., LXIV pl. 26cm. (Edinburgh medical series)

"Glossary": p. 387-390.

1. Radiography. 2. Radiotherapy. 3. X-rays.

S G 17—58

U. S. Surg.-gen. off. Librar.
for Library of Congress [a42e1]

NK 0211772 DNLM OrU-M PPC ICJ

Knox, Robert, 1868–1928.
Radiography, X-ray therapeutics and radium therapy, by Robert Knox ... with sixty-four plates, two hundred and fortv-six illustrations in the text and a frontispiece in colour. New York, Macmillan, 1915.
xxi, 406 p. col. front., illus., LXIV pl. 26 cm. (Edinburgh medical series)

"Glossary": p. 387-390.

NK 0211773 DSI IU OCU OOxM ICJ PHC PPJef OClW-H

Knox, Robert, 1868-1928.
Radiography X-ray therapeutics and radium therapy. New York, Macmillan, 1916.
406p. illus.

NK 0211774 ICRL DNLM

Knox, Robert, 1868-1928.
Radiography, X-ray therapeutics and radium therapy,...with 64 plates, 200 and forty-six illus. in the test.
2 ed. N.Y. 1917-18

390 p.

NK 0211775 PPC

Knox, Robert, 1868–1928.
A text-book of X-ray therapeutics, by Robert Knox ... completed and edited by Walter M. Levitt ... London, A. & C. Black, ltd., 1932.
xii, 250 p. illus., XI pl. (incl. col. front.) on 9 l., diagrs. 26cm. (*Half-title:* The Edinburgh medical series)
"First edition published in 1915 as part II of Radiography and radio-therapeutics [*i. e.* Radiography, X-ray therapeutics and radium therapy] ... This (fourth) edition, enlarged but with radium therapy omitted, published 1932."
On cover: Fourth edition edited by Walter M. Levitt.
Bibliography: p. 237-242.
1. X-rays—Therapeutic use. I. Levitt, Walter Montague, 1900- II. Title: X-ray therapeutics.

35-19267

Library of Congress RM847.K6 1932
[2] 615.84

NK 0211776 DLC ICU MiU

Knox, Robert Baker, 1917-
Some cultural aspects of the Quinquenarios of Pedro Gutiérrez de Santa Clara. Ann Arbor, University Microfilms, 1952.
([University Microfilms, Ann Arbor, Mich.] Publication no. 3520)
Microfilm copy of typescript. Positive.
Collation of the original: ii, 166 l.
Thesis—University of Michigan.
Abstracted in Dissertation abstracts, v. 12 (1952) no. 2, p. 188.
Bibliography: leaves 163-166.

1. Gutiérrez de Santa Clara, Pedro, fl. 1544-1603. Los cinco libros llamados Quinquenarios.

Mic A 53-45

Michigan. Univ. Lib..
for Library of Congress [1]

NK 0211777 MiU

Knox, Robert C.
Self-analysis and world achievement, by Robert C. Knox ... [n. p., 1920]
1 l., 40 p. 16cm.

1. Mental suggestion. I. Title.

21-19949

Library of Congress BF645.K7

NK 0211778 DLC

Knox, Robert J., defendant.
Alfaro, Francisco.
Cuestiones constitucionales. Alegaciones que como defensor del abogado americano Roberto J. Knox, presenta á la Suprema corte de justicia de la nacion el Lic. Francisco Alfaro, pidiendo la revocación de la sentencia pronunciada por el Juzgado 1° de distrito de esta capital, en el juicio de amparo, promovido por el mismo Knox, contra actos del juez 2.° de lo criminal, que lo condenó como responsable del delito de estafa. Mexico, Tip. "El Libro diario", 1893.

Knox, Robert Seward.
High level planning in the United States regarding Germany, 1941-46. Washington, 1949.
167 l. 29 cm.
Thesis (M. A.)—Georgetown University.

1. U. S.—For. rel.—Germany. 2. Reconstruction (1939-)—Germany. 3. World War, 1939-1945—Congresses, conferences, etc. I. Title.

D829.G3K58 52-28266 ‡

NK 0211780 DLC

VOLUME 300

Knox, Robert Walter, 1897-

U. S. *Coast and geodetic survey.*
... Terrestrial magnetism. Magnetic declination in Texas in 1927, by W. N. McFarland and Robert W. Knox ... Washington, U. S. Govt. print. off., 1928.

Knox, Ronald Arbuthnott, 1888- ed.
... Aenid. Bks. VII to IX
see under Vergilius Maro, Publius.

Knox,Ronald Arbuthnott, 1888-1957.
The Acts of the Apostles;St.Paul's letters to the churches. New York,Sheed & Ward, 1954. 322p. (Knox,R.A. A new Testament Commentary,v.2)

Bible-New Testament-Acts
Bible-New Testament-Epistles
Title

NK 0211783 NjN

Knox, Ronald Arbuthnott, 1888- tr.
All my life love
see under
Day, Michael, ed.

Knox, Ronald Arbuthnott, 1888-
...Anglican cobwebs, by the Rev. Ronald Knox... London: Sheed and Ward[, 1928]. 59 p. 12°. (The Twelvepenny ser. [no.] 5.)

388039A. 1. Anglican Churches—Roman intercommunion. 2. Ser.
N. Y. P. L. December 18, 1928

NK 0211785 NN CaBVaU

Knox, Ronald Arbuthnott, 1888-
Barchester pilgrimage, by Ronald A. Knox. London, Sheed & Ward, 1935.
ix, [1], 278 p. incl. map, geneal. tables. 20½cm.
Written in the style of Anthony Trollope, being the story of Barchester down to the present day.

I. Trollope, Anthony, 1815-1882. II. Title.
Library of Congress PZ3.K776Bar 36-3535

OrPR CtY PRosC PPL ICU PBm NjP OO OLak OClJC NN
NK 0211786 DLC IEN NBuC NIC IaU MiU IEG LU WaSpG

AC-L Knox, Ronald Arbuthnott, 1888-1957.
W357L Barchester pilgrimage, by Ronald A. Knox.
K776b London, Sheed & Ward, 1936.
xi,[1],278p. incl. map, geneal. tables. 19½cm.
"First published October, 1935. Second edition March, 1936."
Written in the style of Anthony Trollope, being the story of Barchester down to the present day.
Bookplate of Evelyn Waugh.
I. Trollope, Anthony, 1815-1882. II. Title.

NK 0211787 TxU

Knox, Ronald Arbuthnott, 1888-
Barchester pilgrimage, by Ronald A. Knox. New York, Sheed & Ward, inc., 1936.
xi, [1], 278 p. incl. map, geneal. tables. 20cm.
Written in the style of Anthony Trollope, being the story of Barchester down to the present day.

I. Trollope, Anthony, 1815-1882. II. Title. 38-24915
Library of Congress PZ3.K776Bar 3

NK 0211788 DLC PPA PPT PV OCl OCU OClh

Knox, Ronald Arbuthnott, 1888-
The belief of Catholics [by] R. A. Knox. [London] E. Benn, limited, 1927.
2 p. l., 3-254 p. 19cm. [What I believe series]

1. Catholic church—Doctrinal and controversial works—Catholic authors. I. Title.
Library of Congress BX1751.K68 1927 a 27-24400

OClStM
NK 0211789 DLC C-V KyLxCB MB PPWe OClW OCX OO MH

Knox, Ronald Arbuthnott, 1888-
The belief of Catholics [by] R. A. Knox. New York and London, Harper & brothers [°1927]
2 p. l., 3-254 p. 19½cm. [What I believe series]

1. Catholic church—Doctrinal and controversial works—Catholic authors. I. Title. 27-24401
Library of Congress BX1751.K68 1927
Copy 2.

NcRS NjNbS PV PP PU CU MB CU NN
NK 0211790 DLC NcC Or MB WaSpG IdU OrStbM CaBVaU

Knox, Ronald Arbuthnott, 1888-1957.
The belief of Catholics, by R. A. Knox. London, Sheed & Ward, 1939.
254 p. 18cm. (Unicorn books)

NK 0211791 FMU OCl OClJC LLafS

Knox, Ronald Arbuthnott, 1888-
The belief of Catholics [by] R. A. Knox. New York, Sheed & Ward, 1940.
2 p. l., 3-254 p. 18½cm. [Catholic masterpieces. no. 8]

1. Catholic church — Doctrinal and controversial works — Catholic authors. I. Title.
Library of Congress BX1751.K68 1940 40-31209
——— Copy 2. [2] 282

NK 0211792 DLC KAS ViU PP

Knox, Ronald Arbuthnott, 1888-
The belief of Catholics. [4th ed.] London, New York, Sheed and Ward [1953]
ix, 214 p. 21 cm.

1. Catholic Church—Doctrinal and controversial works—Catholic authors. I. Title.
[BX1751.K] A 55-1977 rev
Cornell Univ. Library for Library of Congress [r55c2]

NK 0211793 NIC WaS OO OCl PPLT MB MiU

Knox, Ronald Arbuthnott, 1888- *ed.*
The best detective stories of the year 1928, edited by Father Ronald Knox and H. Harrington, with an introduction by Father Ronald Knox. London, Faber & Faber limited [1929]
xxiii p., 1 l., 27-486 p. 19½cm.
American edition (H. Liveright) has title: The best English detective stories of 1928.

1. Detective stories. 2. Short stories, English. I. Harrington, Henry, joint ed. II. Title.
Library of Congress PZ1.K775Bd 30-8798

NK 0211794 DLC PPL MH

823.08 Knox, Ronald Arbuthnott, 1888- ed.
K 776 B Best detective stories; 1st ser. Ed. by
ser.1 Father Ronald Knox and H. Harrington. With an introduction by Father Ronald Knox. London, Faber and Faber limited [1935]
xxiii p., 1 l., 27-486 p. 19cm.
First pub. in 1929 as The best detective stories of the year 1928; "reprinted in this new edition September, 1933 ... and January, 1935."
American edition (H. Liveright) has title: The best English detective stories of 1928.

NK 0211795 OO

Knox, Ronald Arbuthnott, 1888- ed.
The Best English detective stories of
New York, H. Liveright, 1929-

Knox, Ronald Arbuthnott, 1888-1957, tr.
The birth of the Lord Jesus Christ, according to the Gospels of Saint Matthew and Saint Luke. [Saint Paul, Minn., 1952]
see under Bible. N. T. Matthew. English. Selections. 1952. Knox.

AC-L Knox, Ronald Arbuthnott, 1888-1957.
W357L The body in the silo, by Ronald A. Knox.
K776bo [London] Hodder & Stoughton [1933]
317p. illus. 19cm.
Cock Robin mystery.
Formerly published under the title: Settled out of court.
From the library of Evelyn Waugh.

NK 0211798 TxU MH

Knox, Ronald Arbuthnott, 1888-
A book of acrostics, by Ronald Knox. London, Methuen & co., ltd. [1924]
vii, 136 p. 17cm.

1. Acrostics. I. Title.
Library of Congress PN6371.K6 25-3334

NK 0211799 DLC CtY IEN CaBVaU

Knox, Ronald Arbuthnott, 1888-1957, tr.
The book of Psalms in Latin and English...
New York, 1948
see under Bible. O.T. Psalms. English. 1948. Knox.

VOLUME 300

WA 27953 Knox, Ronald Arbuthnott, 1888-1957.
Bread or stone; four conferences on impetrative prayer. London, Society of SS. Peter and Paul, 1915.
55 p. illus. 18 cm.

1. Prayer. I. Title (1)

NK 0211801 CtY NjR

Knox, Ronald Arbuthnott, 1888–
Broadcast minds, by Ronald Knox ... London, Sheed & Ward, 1932.
xv, 280 p. 19½cm.
Essays.

1. Christianity—Evidences. 2. Philosophy and religion. 3. Religion and science—1900– 4. Rationalism. I. Title.
Library of Congress BT1101.K72 33—19
——— Copy 2.
Copyright A ad int. 17073 [39d1] 239

NN MB PV PPCCH OC1JC
NK 0211802 DLC WaSpG OrStbM NN TU MiU WaWW TxU CtY

AC-L K776br 1933 Knox, Ronald Arbuthnott, 1888-
Broadcast minds. New York, Sheed & Ward, 1933.
xv, 280p. 19cm.

Essays.
With dust jacket.

NK 0211803 TxU

Knox, Ronald Arbuthnott, 1888–
Caliban in Grub street, by Ronald A. Knox. London, Sheed & Ward, 1930.
xii, 221, [1] p. 20½ cm.

1. Religion. 2. Religion in literature. I. Title.
PR6021.N6C3 1930 210 30—14542

PRosC FU ICU MiU
NK 0211804 DLC FU TxU WaSpG IEG KMK InU OClStM OCX

Knox, Ronald Arbuthnott, 1888–
Caliban in Grub street, by Ronald A. Knox ... New York, E. P. Dutton and co., inc. [c1930]
xii p., 1 l., 221, [1] p. 19½cm.

1. Religion. 2. Religion in literature. I. Title.
Library of Congress PR6021.N6C3 1930 a 30—20191
——— Copy 2.
Copyright A 25593 [39g1] 201

NK 0211805 DLC OrStbM MB TxU MeB PV PU MB OCU OCX

PR 6021 N6 C3 1930 **Knox, Ronald Arbuthnott, 1888-1957.**
Caliban in Grub street, by Ronald A. Knox. London, Sheed & Ward, 1931.
xii, 221, [1] p. 20 cm.
First published in 1930.

NK 0211806 NBuC

BR 1700 K6 Knox, Ronald Arbuthnott, 1888-1957.
Captive flames; a collection of panegyrics, by Ronald Knox. London, Burns, Oates, 1940.
149p. 19cm.

1. Christian biography I. Title

NK 0211807 WU PPLT CtY

Knox, Ronald Arbuthnott, 1888–
Captive flames; a collection of panegyrics by the Right Reverend Monsignor Ronald Knox. London, Burns, Oates [1941]
vi p., 1 l., 149 p. 19cm.
"First printed October 1940; second impression January 1941."

1. Christian biography. I. Title.
Library of Congress BR1700.K6 1941 a 41-24697
[2] 922.2

NK 0211808 DLC PPCCH

Knox, Ronald Arbuthnott, 1888–
Captive flames; a collection of panegyrics by the Right Reverend Monsignor Ronald Knox. [New York, Spiritual book associates, c1941]
1 p. l., v–vi, [2], 149 p. 19½cm.
"May, 1941, selection of the Spiritual book associates, with the permission of Burns Oates, London."
With this is bound, as issued: Johnson, V. C. Our guiding star. New York, c1941.

1. Christian biography. I. Title.
Library of Congress BR1700.K6 41-12707
[3] 922.2

NK 0211809 DLC OClND

Knox, Ronald Arbuthnott, 1888-
Catholicism, the religion of moderation and common sense, by Rev. Ronald Knox... Brooklyn, N.Y., International Catholic truth society [n.d.]
24 p., 17cm.

Pages [15]-24, advertising matter.

NK 0211810 NjPT

BX 1756 .K74 1914 Knox,Ronald Arbuthnott,1888-
The Church in bondage. London, The Society of SS.Peter & Paul, 1914.
80 p. 23 cm.

NK 0211811 MiU

Hd9 K776 A1 1914 Knox, Ronald Arbuthnott, 1888-1957.
The Church in bondage, by R.A. Hilary Knox. London, Society of SS. Peter & Paul, 1914.
88 p. 24 cm.

NK 0211812 CtY

Knox, Ronald Arbuthnott, 1888–
The church on earth, by the Reverend R. A. Knox, M. A. London, Burns, Oates & Washbourne, ltd. [1929]
v, 90 p. 16½ cm. (*Half-title:* The Treasury of the faith series: xx)

1. Catholic church. I. Title.
BX1751.K69 29—8137

NK 0211813 DLC OrStbM OCX

Knox, Ronald Arbuthnott, 1888–
The church on earth, by the Reverend R. A. Knox, M. A.; introduction by Rt. Rev. Msgr. James H. Ryan ... New York, The Macmillan company, 1929.
4 p. l., 90 p. 17cm. (*Half-title:* The treasury of the faith series: 20)

1. Catholic church. I. Title.
Library of Congress BX1751.K69 1929 a 29-12636

NK 0211814 DLC PV PPCCH OCX OClND

Knox, Ronald Arbuthnott, 1888–
A commentary on the Gospels. New York, Sheed & Ward, 1952–56.
3 v. 22 cm.
"Meant to be read in conjunction with the Knox New Testament."
Vols. 2–3 have title: A New Testament commentary for English readers.
Vol. 1 published in London in 1953 under title: A New Testament commentary for English readers.

1. Bible. N. T.—Commentaries. I. Title. II. Title: A New Testament commentary for English readers.
BS2341.K6 225.7 52–10614 rev 2 ‡

OO OCH WaSpG PIm OClND PRosC MB MBtS
NK 0211815 DLC Or NBuT OrStbM FTaSU Wa NRCR IU WaS

Knox, Ronald Arbuthnott, 1888–
The Creed in slow motion. [Sermons] London, Sheed & Ward, 1949.
x, 238 p. 21 cm.

1. Apostles' Creed. I. Title.
BT993.K6 1949 238.1 49–4443*

NK 0211816 DLC ICU TxU CU

Knox, Ronald Arbuthnott, 1888–
The Creed in slow motion. [Sermons] New York, Sheed & Ward, 1949.
x, 238 p. 21 cm.

1. Apostles' Creed. I. Title.
BT993.K6 1949a 238.1 49–6285*

NIC NjPT OClJC CMenSP PPC MB OWorP
NK 0211817 DLC WaSpG OrStbM CaBVa NcD CoU FU OCl InNd

Knox, Ronald Arbuthnott, 1888- ed.

BS392 .K5 **Bible.** *Dutch. Selections. 1946.*
De H. Schrift. Verkorte en omgeschikte uitg. Door Ronald Knox, in het Nederlandsch uitg. en ingeleid door A. Decoene en Fr. de Hovre. Brussel, De Kinkhoren [1946]

Knox, Ronald Arbuthnott, 1888–
Difficulties; being a correspondence about the Catholic religion between Ronald Knox and Arnold Lunn. London, Eyre & Spottiswoode, ltd., 1932.
x p., 1 l., 278, [1] p. 22½cm.

1. Catholic church—Doctrinal and controversial works. I. Lunn, Arnold Henry Moore, 1888– II. Title.
Library of Congress BX1779.K6 32-11671
Copyright A ad int. 16252 [2] 230.2

NK 0211819 DLC WaWW PPPD MnSST

VOLUME 300

BX 1779 .K74 1952 Knox, Ronald Arbuthnott, 1888-
Difficulties; being a correspondence about the Catholic religion between Ronald Knox and Arnold Lunn. A new edition with two additional letters in conclusion. London, Eyre & Spottiswoode, 1952.
xi, 274 p. 22 cm.
First edition, 1932.

1. Catholic Church--Doctrinal and controversial works. I. Lunn, Arnold Henry Moore, 1888- II. Title.

IMunS
NK 0211820 MiU TxU MH NNC NcD InU PP CaBVaU PPiPT

4B-468 Knox, Ronald Arbuthnott, 1888-
Dios y el 'atomo. [Traducción de Gustavo Weigel y R. Tejeda Lawrence. Santiago de Chile] Zig-zag [1948]
220 p. (Biblioteca de cultura)

NK 0211821 DLC-P4

Knox, Ronald Arbuthnott, 1888-
Double cross purposes, by Ronald A. Knox. London, Hodder & Stoughton, limited [1937]
314 p. incl. pl., map. 19½cm.

I. Title.
37-17346
Library of Congress PZ3.K776Do

NK 0211822 DLC WU CaBVaU MnU

Knox, Ronald Arbuthnott, 1888-
Enthusiasm; a chapter in the history of religion, with special reference to the XVII and XVIII centuries. New York, Oxford University Press, 1950.
viii, 622 p. 21 cm.
Bibliography: p. [592]-595.

1. Enthusiasm. 2. Church history—17th cent. 3. Church history—18th cent.
BR112.K5 271.6 50-10375

ViU IaU PV MBtS PPDrop MiU FMU KyWAT
IdU IdPS CaBVaU WaSpG WaS OrU OrPR Or ICU TU MH NN
NK 0211823 DLC CaBVa MB TxU OrSaW OrCS OrStbM MoSU

Knox, Ronald Arbuthnott, 1888-1957.

BX2003 .A4 1946 **Bible.** *N. T. Epistles and Gospels, Liturgical. English. 1946. Knox.*
The Epistles and Gospels for Sundays and holydays; translation and commentary by Ronald Knox. New York, Sheed & Ward, 1946.

Knox, Ronald Arbuthnott, 1888-
Essays in satire, by Ronald A. Knox. London, Sheed and Ward [1928]
3 p. l., ix-xi p., 1 l., 15-287 p. 19cm.
"First published October, 1928; second impression December, 1928."
CONTENTS.—Introduction: on humour and satire.—Reunion all around.—Absolute and Abitofhell.—A new cure for religion.—The new sin.—Studies in the literature of Sherlock Holmes.—A ramble in Barsetshire.—The identity of the pseudo-Bunyan.—The authorship of "In memoriam".—Materials for a Boswellian problem.—Jottings from a psycho-analyst's note-book.—A forgotten interlude.

1. Satire, English. I. Title.
29-8687
Library of Congress PR6021.N6E7 1928 a

CtY NjNbS PPL PHC OCX MiU
NK 0211825 DLC WU CaOTP TxU CaBVaU WaU NcU ScU ICU

Knox, Ronald Arbuthnott, 1888-
Essays in Satire. London, 1929.

NK 0211826 OClStbM

---

824 K776e 1930 Knox, Ronald Arbuthnott, 1888-
Essays in satire, by Ronald A. Knox. London, Sheed and Ward [1930]
3 p. l., ix-xi p., 1 l., 15-287p.

First published 1928; cheap ed. 1930.

Contents.- Introduction: on humour and satire.- Reunion all around.- Absolute and Abitofhell.- A new cure for religion.- The new sin.- Studies in the literature of Sherlock Holmes.- A ramble in Barsetshire.-

Contents cont'd.- The identity of the pseudo-Bunyan.- The authorship of "In memoriam."- Materials for a Boswellian problem.- Jottings from a psycho-analyst's note-book.- A forgotten interlude.

1. Satire, English. I. Title.

NK 0211828 TxFTC

Knox, Ronald Arbuthnott, 1888-
Essays in satire, by Ronald A. Knox. New York, E. P. Dutton & co., inc. [°1930]
3 p. l., ix-xi p., 1 l., 15-287 p. 19½cm.
CONTENTS.—Introduction: on humour and satire.—Reunion all round.—Absolute and Abitofhell.—A new cure for religion.—The new sin.—Studies in the literature of Sherlock Holmes.—A ramble in Barsetshire.—The identity of the pseudo-Bunyan.—The authorship of "In memoriam".—Materials for a Boswellian problem.—Jottings from a psycho-analyst's note-book.—A forgotten interlude.

1. Satire, English. I. Title.
30-7434
Library of Congress PR6021.N6E7 1930

LU PPLas PU PV OCX OU OCl ViU MB NN
NK 0211829 DLC Or IU WaSpG OrStbM NNC CoU OKentU

Knox, Ronald Arbuthnott, 1888-1957.
Essays in satire. London, New York, Sheed and Ward [1954]
192 p. 20 cm.

NK 0211830 CaBVaU IdPI ICarbS

---

827 K776e 1954r **Knox, Ronald Arbuthnott, 1888-**
Essays in satire, by Ronald A. Knox. London and New York, Sheed and Ward [1955]
ix, 11-192p. 19cm.
"This edition [published] 1954. Reprinted 1955."

1. Satire, English. I. Title.

NK 0211831 TxU MB MiU InU MH NN OCU

AC-L W357L K776ess Knox, Ronald Arbuthnott, 1888-1957.
The essentials of spiritual unity, by Ronald Knox. London, Catholic Truth Society, 1918.
36p. 19cm.
Publisher's advertisements ([2]p.) bound in at end and printed on paper wrappers.
From the library of Evelyn Waugh.

NK 0211832 TxU

Knox, Ronald Arbuthnot, 1888-
The footsteps at the lock. London, Methuen [1928]
160 p. 20cm.

NK 0211833 FU CoU DGU WU CaBVaU

Knox, Ronald Arbuthnot, 1888-
The footsteps at the lock, by Ronald A. Knox. London, Methuen & co., ltd. [1929]
19.5 cm.
"First published ... 1928; second and cheaper edition, 1929."
Map on lining paper.

NK 0211834 CtY

Knox, Ronald Arbuthnott, 1888-
The footsteps at the lock. 4th ed. London, Methuen & co., ltd. [1933]
viii, 248 p. 19 cm.

NK 0211835 MH

PR 6021 N6F6 1936 Knox, Ronald Arbuthnott, 1888-1957.
The footsteps at the lock. [5th ed.]
London, Methuen [1936]
viii, 248 p. 18cm.

NK 0211836 CoU

PR6021 N6F6 1950 Knox, Ronald Arbuthnott, 1888-1957.
The footsteps at the lock. [5th ed.]
London, Methuen [1950]
160 p. 19cm.

NK 0211837 CoU KMK ICarbS NBC MiU ICU InStme

Knox, Ronald Arbuthnott, 1888-1957.
God and the atom, by Ronald Knox ... London, Sheed & Ward, 1945.
vii, 9-143 p. 19 cm.
"First published 1945."

1. Apologetics—20th cent. 2. Atomic power. I. Title.
[BT1101.K] A 46-4331
Harvard Univ. Library for Library of Congress [a60d½]

NK 0211838 MH TxU CU ICU CaBVaU

Knox, Ronald Arbuthnott, 1888-
God and the atom, by R. A. Knox ... [New York] Sheed & Ward, 1945.
6 p. l., 3-166 p. 19½cm.

1. Apologetics—20th cent. 2. Atomic power. I. Title.
46-762
Library of Congress * BT1101.K73
[25] 239

OCl ND OCl
OrP OrStbM MBtS TNJ-R WU FTaSU MiDP PHC PV PP MB
NK 0211839 DLC WaSp PPC WaS OrLgE Nc-SC WaSpG NcD

VOLUME 300

Knox, Ronald Arbuthnott, 1888-1957.
The Gospel in slow motion. New York, Sheed & Ward, 1950.
x, 182 p. 21 cm.

1. Catholic Church—Sermons. 2. Sermons, English. I. Title.
BX1756.K68G6 252.02 50—10287

NK 0211839-1 DLC KAS MBtS OrStbM WaSpG ScCleA

Knox, Ronald Arbuthnott, 1888-1957, tr.
A harmony of the Gospels in the Knox translation
see under Bible. N.T. Gospels. English. Harmonies. 1944. Knox. (also: 1945?)

PR 10 U8 K5 1935 H4
Knox, Ronald Arbuthnott, 1888-1957.
Heaven and Charing Cross; sermons on the Holy Eucharist. London, Burns, Oates & Washbourne [1935]
90 p. 19 cm.

1. Lord's Supper - Sermons. I. Title.

NK 0211839-2 CaBVaU CtY MBtS IMunS PRosC

Knox, Ronald Arbuthnott, 1888–
Heaven and Charing cross; sermons on the holy eucharist, by Rev. Ronald A. Knox ... New York, E. P. Dutton & co., inc. [°1936]
vi, 90 p. 19½cm.
"First edition."

1. Lord's supper—Sermons. 2. Catholic church—Sermons. 3. Sermons, English. I. Title.
36-5076
Library of Congress BX2215.K6
——— Copy 2.
Copyright A 91404 [3] 265.3

NK 0211839-3 DLC OWorP WaSpG OrStbM PLatS MB NcD

PR 10 U8 K5 1952
Knox, Ronald Arbuthnott, 1888-1957.
The hidden stream; a further collection of Oxford conferences. London, Burns, Oates, 1952.
ix, 220 p. 23 cm.

1. Catholic Church - Apologetic works. I. Title.

NK 0211839-4 CaBVaU DGU PU TxU

Mza751 K776
Knox, Ronald Arbuthnott, 1888-1957.
The hidden stream; a further collection of Oxford conferences. London, Burns [&] Oates [1953]
ix, 220 p. 22 cm.

1. Catholic Church - Doctrinal and controversial works - Catholic authors - 20th cent. I. Title (1)

NK 0211839-5 CtY MdBJ IEG

Knox, Ronald Arbuthnott, 1888–
The hidden stream. New York, Sheed & Ward, 1953.
248 p. 21 cm.

1. Catholic Church—Apologetic works. I. Title.
BX1751.K692 239 53—5196 ‡

FU WaU MoU NIC
PPLas MiU ScCleA MB OrStbM OrP NBuT MBtS NbU WaSpG
NK 0112839-6 DLC Or OrCS PV PPCCH OClW PRosC PWcS

Knox, Ronald Arbuthnott, 1888-1957, tr.
The Holy Bible
see under Bible. English. 1944-50. Knox. Also with dates 1948-49. 1950? 1954. 1955.

Knox, Ronald Arbuthnott, 1888-1957, ed. and tr.
The Holy Bible; an abridgement and rearrangement. London, Sheed and Ward, 1936
see under Bible. English. Selections. 1936. Douai. Also with date 1937.

Knox, Ronald Arbuthnott, 1888-1957, ed. and tr.
Holy Week
see under Catholic Church. Liturgy and ritual. Holy Week offices. English & Latin.

AC-L W357L K776ho
Knox, Ronald Arbuthnott, 1888-1957.
An hour at the front [by Ronald Knox. London, Society of SS. Peter & Paul, 1914]
[32]p. 13cm.
"Second impression making 20,000 copies."
From the library of Evelyn Waugh.
Title vignette.
Head pieces.

NK 0211840 TxU

Knox, Ronald Arbuthnott, 1888–
In soft garments, a collection of Oxford conferences, by the Right Reverend Monsignor Ronald Knox ... London, Burns, Oates, 1942.
ix, 188 p. 19cm.
Lectures delivered during the years 1926 to 1938 when the author was chaplain at Oxford. *cf.* Pref.

1. Catholic church—Apologetic works. I. Title.
42-50449
Library of Congress BX1751.K693
[2] 230.2

NK 0211841 DLC CtY WaSpG

Knox, Ronald Arbuthnott, 1888–
In soft garments; a collection of Oxford conferences. [2d ed.] London, Burns, Oates [1953]
214 p. 23 cm.

1. Catholic Church—Apologetic works. I. Title.
BX1751.K693 1953 230.2 54-30704 ‡

NK 0211842 DLC TxU PP MB ScCleA

Knox, Ronald Arbuthnott, 1888–
In soft garments; a collection of Oxford conferences. [2d ed.] New York, Sheed & Ward [1953]
214 p. 22 cm.

1. Catholic Church—Apologetic works. I. Title.
[BX1751] 230.2 56-3335 ‡
Printed for A. B. P. by Library of Congress [3]

NK 0211843 OrStbM OrP Wa NIC MBtS MiU PP MB OCl

---

*EC9 K7766 910j
Knox, Ronald Arbuthnott, 1888-1957.
Juxta salices, by R. A. Knox ...
Oxford, Alden & co.ltd., Bocardo press. London: Simpkin, Marshall, Hamilton, Kent & co.ltd. 1910.
xp., 2l., [3]-88p. 19cm.
Original dark blue cloth.

NK 0211844 MH TxU WU CtY

LF509 .K74 1939
Knox, Ronald Arbuthnott, 1888-1957.
Let dons delight; being variations on a theme in an Oxford common-room. London, Sheed & Ward, 1939.
vii, 280p. 20cm.

1. Oxford. University--Intellectual life. 2. Religious thought--Gt. Brit. I. Title.

NK 0211845 IEG OU OClW PBm MiU PPCCH CaQMM

Knox, Ronald Arbuthnott, 1888–
Let dons delight; being variations on a theme in an Oxford common-room, by Ronald A. Knox ... New York, Sheed & Ward, 1939.
vii, 280 p. 20½cm.
"Printed in Great Britain."

1. Oxford. University—Intellectual life. 2. Religious thought—Gt. Brit. I. Title.
39-15154
Library of Congress LF509.K6
[4] 378.42

NBuC MB NN
NK 0211846 DLC IaU MBtS WaSpG WaU Or ICU DGU FU

Knox, Ronald Arbuthnott, 1888–
Let dons delight; being variations on a theme in an Oxford common-room, by Ronald A. Knox ... London, Sheed & Ward, 1941.
vii, 280 p. 20.5 cm. (The Ark library)
"Printed in Great Britain."
1. Oxford. University - Intellectual life. 2. Religious thought - Gt. Brit. 3. Oxford. University. I. Ser.

NK 0211847 CtY

Mnd9 K776 M3
Knox, Ronald Arbuthnot, 1888-1957.
The Mass in slow motion. London, Sheed & Ward, 1948.
xix, 139 p. 21 cm.

1. Mass. I. Title (1)

NK 0211848 CtY TxU

VOLUME 300

Knox, Ronald Arbuthnott, 1888–
The Mass in slow motion. [Sermons] New York, Sheed & Ward, 1948.
xix, 139 p. 21 cm.

1. Mass—Sermons. 2. Catholic Church—Sermons. 3. Sermons, English. I. Title.
BX2230.K55 265.3 48-8400*‡

NK 0211849 DLC NBuT MiU ScCleA OClW MB TxU NjPT MiU FU CaBVaU OrPS IU KMK WaSpG OrStbM CaBVa

Knox, Ronald Arbuthnott, 1888-
The Mass in slow motion; [sermons] London, Sheed & Ward, 1950.
xix, 139 p. 21 cm.

NK 0211850 PU

Knox, Ronald Arbuthnott, 1888-
Meditations on the Psalms ... New York, 1919
see under Bible. O.T. Psalms. English. 1919.

Knox, Ronald Arbuthnott, 1888–
Memories of the future, being memoirs of the years 1915–1972, written in the year of grace 1988, by Opal, lady Porstock; ed. by Ronald A. Knox. 3d ed. London, Methuen & co., ltd. [1923]
xv, 244 p. 19½cm.
A satire.

I. Title.
Library of Congress PR6021.N6M4 1923 23-9978

NK 0211851 DLC WaTC OrStbM NN OCX OO OCl PP PRosC PV NN IU IaU NcD PSt

Knox, Ronald Arbuthnott, 1888– 1957.
Memories of the future; being memories of the years 1915–1972, written in the year of grace 1988 by Opal, Lady Porstock; edited by Ronald A. Knox. London, Methuen & Co., Ltd. [1923.]
xv. 244 p. 3. ed. 19cm.
Film reproduction.

1. Satire, English. I. Title.

NK 0211852 NN

Knox, Ronald Arbuthnott, 1888–
Memories of the future, being memoirs of the years 1915–1972, written in the year of grace 1988, by Opal, lady Porstock; ed. by Ronald A. Knox. **New York, George H. Doran Co. [1923]**
xv, 244 p. 19½cm.
A satire.

NK 0211853 ViU NNC MH CtY NSyU MBtS PSt NcD ViU PU CLSU

PR6021 .N6M5 1923 Knox, Ronald Arbuthnott, 1888-1957.
Memories of the future; being, Memoirs of the years 1915-1972, written in the year of grace 1988, by Opal, Lady Porstock. Edited by Ronald A. Knox. Toronto, McClelland & Stewart [1923]
xv, 244 p.

NK 0211854 ICU

Knox, Ronald Arbuthnott, 1888-1957.
Miracles. New York, Paulist Press [1928].
32 p. 19 cm. ([Pamphlets, v.68])

NK 0211855 PLatS OCl

Knox, Ronald Arbuthnott, 1888- ed. and tr.
The Miracles of King Henry VI.
The miracles of King Henry VI, being an account and translation of twenty-three miracles taken from the manuscript in the British museum (Royal 13 c. viii) with introductions by Father Ronald Knox ... and Shane Leslie ... Cambridge [Eng.] The University press, 1923.

Knox, Ronald Arbuthnott, 1888–
The mystery of the kingdom and other sermons, by the Rev. Ronald Knox, M. A. London, Sheed & Ward [1928]
vii, 180, [1] p. 19cm.

I. Title.
Library of Congress BX1756.K7M9 29-24853

NK 0211857 DLC WaSpG WU PRosC OClJC OCX

Knox, Ronald Arbuthnott, 1888–
The mystery of the kingdom and other sermons, by Mgr. Ronald Knox, M. A. London, Sheed & Ward, 1937.
vii, 180, [1] p. 19½cm.
"Cheap edition, February 1937."
"The sermons were delivered at the Carmelites' church in Kensington ... [and] at St. Charles', Ogle street."—p. vi.

1. Jesus Christ—Parables—Sermons. 2. Catholic church—Sermons. 3. Sermons, English. I. Title.
Library of Congress BT375.K6 1937 37-33147
[3] 226.8

NK 0211858 DLC OrStbM

Knox, Ronald Arbuthnott, 1888-
The mystery of the kingdom and other sermons... London, Sheed & Ward, 1952.
vii, 180 p., 19cm.

NK 0211859 NjPT

Knox, Ronald Arbuthnott, 1888–
Nazi and Nazarene, by Ronald Knox. London, Macmillan and co., ltd., 1940.
32 p. 18½cm. (*On cover:* Macmillan war pamphlets, no. 5)

1. Catholic church in Germany. 2. Church and state in Germany—1933– 3. Germany—Religion—1933– 4. National socialism. I. Title.
Library of Congress BX1536.K65 41-14397
[5] 261.70943

NK 0211860 DLC OrCS OrU CaBViP MsU CaBVaU DS OOxM OU OO NNC

Knox, Ronald Arbuthnott, 1888-1957, tr.
The New Testament ...
see under Bible. N.T. English. 1944. Knox. (also 1945, 1946, 1947, 1948, 1949?, 1950, 1951, 1953, 1954)

Knox, Ronald Arbuthnott, 1888–1957.
A New Testament commentary for English readers. London, Burns, Oates and Washbourne [1953–56]
3 v. 22 cm.
"Meant to be read in conjunction with the Knox version of the New Testament."
Vol. 1 published in New York in 1952 under title: A commentary on the Gospels.
CONTENTS.—v. 1. The Gospels.—v. 2. The Acts of the Apostles. St. Paul's letters to the churches.—v. 3. The later Epistles. The Apocalypse.

1. Bible. N. T.—Commentaries. I. Title.
BS2341.K62 225.7 54-34236 rev

NK 0211862 DLC WaSpG CaBVaU CaBVa CU NcD MH ICU PPPD PRosC OU PPLT LU MiU TxU PPWe CLSU PPLT

BS 2341 .K71 Knox, Ronald Arbuthnott, 1888-
A New Testament commentary for English readers. New York Sheed & Ward, 1953-
v. 22 cm.
Contents. --
v.2. The Acts of the Apostles; St. Paul's Letters to the Churches (Romans - 2 Thessalonicans)

1. Bible. N. T. - Commentaries.

NK 0211863 DCU PPCCH PP NjPT

BS2341 .K62 1954 Knox, Ronald Arbuthnott, 1888-1957.
A New Testament commentary for English readers. New York, Sheed & Ward, 1954.
v. 21 cm.
"Meant to be read in conjunction with the Knox New Testament."
Contents-v. 1. The Gospels.-v. 2. The Acts of the Apostles. St. Paul's letters to the churches.-v. 3. The later Epistles. The Apocalypse.
1. Bible. N. T. Commentaries. I. Title.
BS2341.K62 1954

NK 0211864 MB

BX 1754 K58 1953 Knox, Ronald Arbuthnott, 1888-1957.
Off the record. London and New York [1953]
176p. 21cm.

1. Catholic Church - Doctrinal and controversial works, Popular I. Title

NK 0211865 WU CaBVaU ICU IEG

Knox, Ronald Arbuthnott, 1888–
Off the record. New York, Sheed and Ward, 1954.
176 p. 21 cm.

1. Catholic Church—Doctrinal and controversial works, Popular. I. Title.
BX1754.K58 282 54-6138 ‡

NK 0211866 DLC OrStbM Or WaSpG WaU PPLas MB NN PRosC PIm PP OCl

BS455 .K5
Knox, Ronald Arbuthnott, 1888–
On Englishing the Bible. London, Burns, Oates, 1949.
101 p. 19 cm.

1. Bible—Versions. I. Title.
A 50-6469
North Carolina. Univ. Library for Library of Congress [1]

NK 0211867 NcU PBm OrU WaSpG NjPT CU MB TU ICN TxU NcD DLC WaS CLSU LU CtY CaBVaU

VOLUME 300

Knox, Ronald Arbuthnott, 1888–
On getting there, by Ronald A. Knox. London, Methuen & co. ltd. [1929]
viii, 226 p., 1 l. 17½cm.
Essays, reprinted with two exceptions from the Evening standard.

I. Title.

Library of Congress PR6021.N6O57 1929 29-20837

NK 0211868 DLC CtY TU TxU IEG NcU CaBVaU

Knox, Ronald Arbuthnott, 1888–
An open-air pulpit, by Father Ronald Knox. London, Constable and co. ltd., 1926.
3 p. l., 5-186 p., 1 l. 19½cm. 6/

I. Title.

Library of Congress PR6021.N6O6 1926 27-7622

NK 0211869 DLC CtY TxU

Knox, Ronald Arbuthnott, 1888–
Other eyes than ours, by Ronald A. Knox ... London, Methuen & co., ltd. [1926]
vii, 246 p., 1 l. 19½cm.

I. Title.

Library of Congress PZ3.K776Ot 26-11065

NK 0211870 DLC

AC-L W357L K776pa
Knox, Ronald Arbuthnott, 1888-1957.
Patrick Shaw-Stewart, by Ronald Knox. Glasgow, Melbourne [etc.] W. Collins sons & co., ltd., 1920.
2p.ℓ.,205,[1]p. front.(port.) 20cm.
Publisher's advertisements ([14]p.) bound in at end.
Bookplate of Evelyn Waugh.

I. Shaw-Stewart, Patrick Houston, 1888-1917.

NK 0211871 TxU IEG MH WaU IU CtY

AC-L W357L K776pra
Knox, Ronald Arbuthnott, 1888-1957.
Prayer. I. The prayer of petition and the prayer of acts. [n.p., 1939?]
14p. 22½cm.
Caption title.
Removed from a whole number of The clergy review, v.16, June 1939[?]
From the library of Evelyn Waugh.

I. Title: The prayer of petition and the prayer of acts.

NK 0211872 TxU

AC-L W357L K776pr
Knox, Ronald Arbuthnott, 1888-1957.
Prayer. II. The prayer of acts and the prayer of stupidity. [n.p., 1939?]
16p. 21½cm.
Caption title.
Reprinted from The clergy review, v.17, July 1939 [?]
Autograph note by Evelyn Waugh, p.7.
From the library of Evelyn Waugh.

NK 0211873 TxU

AC-L W357L K776pro
Knox, Ronald Arbuthnott, 1888-1957.
Proposed New English version of the scriptures. [n.p., 1940?]
9p. 21cm.
Caption title.
Autograph note on p.[1] by Evelyn Waugh: "Circulated to the hierarchy before Low Week, 1940."
From the library of Evelyn Waugh.

NK 0211874 TxU

AC-L W357L K776prov
Knox, Ronald Arbuthnott, 1888-1957.
Proving God: a new apologetic, by R.A. Knox. With a pref. by Evelyn Waugh. London, The Month [195-?]
52p. 22cm.
Rebound in green cloth over original wrappers with armorial crest of Evelyn Waugh stamped in gold on front cover.
Bookplate of Evelyn Waugh.

I. Waugh, Evelyn, 1903-1966. II. Title.

NK 0211875 TxU KAS OrStbM

Knox, Ronald Arbuthnott, 1888-1957, tr.
The Psalms, a new translation
see under Bible. O. T. Psalms. English. 1947. Knox. (also 1955)

879.8 09 K74
Knox,Ronald Arbuthnott,1888-
Remigium alarum ... Scripsit Ronaldus Arbuthnott Knox ... Oxonii, B.H Blackwell, 1910.
7 p. 19½ cm. ([Oxford. University.] Chancellor's prize: Latin verse. 1910)

NK 0211877 MiU CtY MdBJ MH PU IU

PR 10 U8 K5 1955
Knox, Ronald Arbuthnott, 1888-1957.
A retreat for lay people. London, Sheed and Ward, 1955.
x, 246 p. 21 cm.

1. Devotional exercises. I. Title.

NK 0211878 CaBVaU TxU

Knox, Ronald Arbuthnott, 1888–
A retreat for lay people. New York, Sheed and Ward, 1955.
258 p. 21 cm.

1. Meditations. 2. Retreats. I. Title.

BX2182.K58 *242.3 269 55—7477 ‡

NK 0211879 PIm OClUr WaS OrP Wa PP PV PPPD PRosC MB DCU NcD OCl ScCleA DLC MoU MiU CaBVa OrStbM MBtS WaSpG

PR 10 U8 K5 1946 R4
Knox, Ronald Arbuthnott, 1888-1957.
A retreat for priests. London, Sheed & Ward, 1946.
v, 185 p. 21 cm.

1. Devotional exercises. I. Title.

NK 0211880 CaBVaU TxU MoU

Knox, Ronald Arbuthnott, 1888–
Retreat for priests, by Ronald Knox. New York, Sheed and Ward, 1946.
3 p. l., 186 p. 22cm.

1. Meditations. 2. Clergy—Religious life. 3. Retreats. I. Title.
BX2182.K6 250 47-1565

NK 0211881 DLC WaSpG PPLas MBtS OrStbM

Mhd9 K776 R42
[Knox, Ronald Arbuthnott, 1888-1957]
Reunion all round; or, Jael's hammer laid aside, and the milk of human kindness beaten up into butter and serv'd in a lordly dish; being a plea for the inclusion within the Church of England of all Mahometans, Jews, Buddhists, Brahmins, Papists, and atheists, submitted to the consideration of the British publick by ... the authour of "Absolute and Abitofhell." London, Printed by Charles Jacobi, for Samuel Gurney; Sold by the Society of SS. Peter and Paul, 1914.

32 p. illus. 24 cm.

Cover title: Reunion all round; a particularly private & confidential letter to everybody.

I. Title(1) II. Title: Jael's hammer laid aside (1)

NK 0211883 CtY NjP MH TxU WaSpG

BX 1756 .K742 R5
Knox,Ronald Arbuthnott,1888-
The rich young man; a fantasy. London, Sheed and Ward [1928]
[32] p. 21 cm.

NK 0211884 MiU CtY CaBVaU OClJC PLatS

Knox, Ronald Arbuthnot, 1888-
Robert Browning, Pippa passes ...
see under Browning, Robert, 1812-1889.

Knox, Ronald Arbuthnott, 1888–
St. Paul's gospel. London, Catholic Truth Society [1950]
54 p. 19 cm.

1. Bible. N. T. Epistles of Paul—Theology. 2. Paul, Saint, apostle. I. Title.
BS2651.K63 1950 227 51-17277

NK 0211886 DLC MBtS DGU

Knox, Ronald Arbuthnott, 1888–
St. Paul's gospel. New York, Sheed & Ward, 1950.
72 p. 20 cm.

1. Bible. N. T. Epistles of Paul—Theology. 2. Paul, Saint, apostle. I. Title.
BS2651.K63 1950a 227 51-1963

NK 0211887 MiU MB DLC OKentU WaSpG OrStbM OWorP MBtS

---

227 K74s 1953
Knox, Ronald Arbuthnott, 1888-
St.Paul's gospel. London and New York, Sheed and Ward [1953]
103p. 19cm.

Continued in next column

VOLUME 300

Continued from preceding column

1.Bible. N.T. Epistles of Paul - Theology. 2.Paul, Saint, apostle. I.Title.

NK 0211888 CLSU OCH PPLT

AC-L W357L K776s [Knox, Ronald Arbuthnott, 1888-1957.] St. Wulstan; being the substance of a sermon preached in St. Wulstan's Church, Fleetwood, January 19th, 1947. [Preston [Eng.] T. Snape, 1947?] 15p. illus. 18cm.

From the library of Evelyn Waugh.

NK 0211889 TxU

Knox, Ronald Arbuthnott, 1888–
Sanctions: a frivolity, by Ronald A. Knox ... London, Methuen & co., ltd. [1924]
v, [1], 265, [1] p. 19½cm.

I. Title.
Library of Congress PZ3.K776Sa 24—12437

NK 0211890 DLC CaBVaU CtY MB PV OClJC

KNOX, RONALD ARBUTHNOTT, 1888-
Sanctions: a frivolity, by Ronald A.Knox. London: Sheed & Ward, 1932. v, 265 p. [2. ed.] 19½cm. (The Ark library.)

601830A. 1. Fiction, English. I. Title.

NK 0211891 NN OCX

AC-L K776sa 1933 Knox, Ronald Arbuthnott, 1888-
Sanctions: a frivolity. London & New York, Sheed & Ward, 1933.
v, 265p. 19cm.

With dust jacket.

NK 0211892 TxU MB PRosC

Knox, Ronald Arbuthnott, 1888–
A selection from the occasional sermons of the Right Reverend Monsignor Ronald Arbuthnott Knox ... Edited by Evelyn Waugh. London, Dropmore Press, 1949.
102 p. 28 cm.

1. Catholic Church—Sermons. 2. Sermons, American.
BX1756.K68S4 252.02 49-54559*

NK 0211893 DLC MH NN NNC NBuC TxU

252.02 K74sc Knox, Ronald Arbuthnott, 1888-1957.
A sermon preached on the feast of S. Charles, K.M. 1912, at S. Cuthbert's Church, Philbeach Gardens, S.W. Sussex, Society of King Charles the Martyr [1912?]
11 p.
At head of title: Society of King Charles the Martyr.

NK 0211894 TxDaM-P

Knox, Ronald Arbuthnott, 1888–
Settled out of court, by Ronald A. Knox. New York, E. P. Dutton & co., inc. [°1934]
317 p. incl. pl. 19½cm.
Illustrated t.-p.
"First edition."

I. Title.
Library of Congress PZ3.K776Se 34-7023

NK 0211895 DLC CaBVaU PPL

PR6021 .N885 1906 Modern Poetry Knox, Ronald Arbuthnott, 1888-1957.
Signa severa. Eton «Eng.» Spottiswoode, 1906.
vii, 63 p.
Verses.

NK 0211896 ICU CtY CaBVaU

FOR OTHER EDITIONS SEE MAIN ENTRY

Knox, Ronald Arbuthnott, 1888-
Six against Scotland yard, in which Margery Allingham, Anthony Berkeley, Freeman Wills Crofts, Father Ronald Knox, Dorothy L. Sayers, Russell Thorndike commit the crime of murder which ex-Superintendent Cornish, C. I. D., is called upon to solve. Garden City, N. Y., The Sun dial press, inc. [1937]

Knox, Ronald Arbuthnott, 1888–
Some loose stones; being a consideration of certain tendencies in modern theology illustrated by reference to the book called "Foundations," by R. A. Knox. London, New York [etc.] Longmans, Green, and co., 1913.
xxiv, 233 p. 20cm.

NK 0211898 CLSU NcD PLatS CaBVaU

Knox, Ronald Arbuthnott, 1888–
Some loose stones; being a consideration of certain tendencies in modern theology illustrated by reference to the book called "Foundations," by R. A. Knox ... 2d impression. London, New York [etc.] Longmans, Green, and co., 1913.
xxiv, 233 p. 20cm.

1. Foundations; a statement of Christian belief. 2. Modernist-fundamentalist controversy. I. Title.
Library of Congress BT78.F67K55 14-5984 Revised

PV OCX OCl
NK 0211899 DLC ICRL WaSpG NN TxU PPEB OKentU

Knox, Ronald Arbuthnott, 1888-
Some loose stones; being a consideration of certain tendencies in modern theology illustrated by reference to the book called "Foundations." by R. A. Knox... 3d. impression. London, New York, «etc.» Longmans, Green, and co., 1914.
233 p.

NK 0211900 MiU PPWe PPPD

BT78 .F65K5 1915 in: SWTS Knox, Ronald Arbuthnott, 1888-
Some loose stones; being a consideration of certain tendencies in modern theology illustrated by reference to the book called "Foundations". New ed....London, Longmans, Green, and Co., 1915.
xxviii, 247p. 20cm.

1. Foundations; a statement of Christian belief. 2. Modernist-fundamentalist controversy. I. Title.

NK 0211901 IEG OCX PV

Knox, Ronald Arbuthnott, 1888–
A spiritual Aeneid, by R. A. Knox ... London, New York [etc.] Longmans, Green and co., 1918.
4 p. l., 263, [1] p. 22½cm.
"A religious autobiography."—Pref.

I. Title.
Library of Congress BX4705.K6A3 18-15072

OClW PV NN IU
NK 0211902 DLC TxU MU KMK PRosC MiU OCX OCl OO

Knox, Ronald Arbuthnott, 1888–
A spiritual Aeneid, by R. A. Knox ... London, New York [etc.] Longmans, Green and co., 1919.
4 p. l., 263, [1] p. 22½cm.
"A religious autobiography."—Pref.
2d impression.

NK 0211903 CU PPCCH PV NcU

Knox, Ronald Arbuthnott, 1888–
A spiritual Aeneid. Westminster, Md., Newman Press, 1948.
263 p. 22 cm.

I. Title.
[BX4705.K6A] A 50-4887
Catholic Univ. of America. Library for Library of Congress [5]

ViU
NK 0211904 DCU CU MBtS OClJC MB OClND WaSpG OrStbM

PZ 3 K776 St Knox, Ronald Arbuthnott, 1888-1957
Still dead [by] Ronald A. Knox. [London] Hodder & Stoughton [1934]
320p. 20cm.

NK 0211905 WU NN CaBVaU CaOTP

Knox, Ronald Arbuthnott, 1888–
Still dead [by] Ronald A. Knox. New York, E. P. Dutton & co., inc. [°1934]
4 p. l., 11-320 p. 1 illus. 19½cm.
Illustrated t.-p.
"First edition."

I. Title.
Library of Congress PZ3.K776St 34-32402
[5]

NK 0211906 DLC OEac MB

Knox, Ronald Arbuthnott, 1888-
Still dead. [London] Hodder and Stoughton [1935]
320 p. 19 cm.

NK 0211907 MH

Knox, Ronald Arbuthnott, 1888-
Still dead «by» Ronald A. Knox. London, Pan Books«1952»
187p. 18cm.
"First published 1934..."

NK 0211908 KAS